WORLD LIST
of
UNIVERSITIES

and

other Institutions of
Higher Education

Twentieth Edition

INTERNATIONAL ASSOCIATION OF UNIVERSITIES
ASSOCIATION INTERNATIONALE DES UNIVERSITÉS
1, rue Miollis, 75732 Paris Cedex 15

STOCKTON

Prepared by the International Universities Bureau

Director: F. Eberhard

Edited by: Ann C.M. Taylor

Published biennially.
Twentieth Edition 1995 published
in the United States and Canada by
STOCKTON PRESS
345 Park Avenue South, 10th Floor, New York, NY 10010–1707

The Library of Congress has catalogued this serial publication as follows:

Library of Congress Cataloging-in-publication Data

World list of universities.
  Paris. International Association of Universities.
    v. 24 cm
Biennial.
  English

  1. Universities and colleges – Directories. I. International Association of Universities. II. Title:
  L900.157   378   79-645502
  ISBN 1-56159-109-2   MARC-S

Twentieth Edition 1995 published in the United Kingdom by
MACMILLAN PUBLISHERS LTD
Distributed by Macmillan Direct
Brunel Road, Houndmills, Basingstoke, Hants RG21 6XS

British Library Cataloguing in Publication Data

World list of universities and other institutions of higher education. – 20th ed.–
  1995
  1. Universities and colleges – Directories
  378'.0025   L900

Macmillan ISBN 0-333-54011-5
IAU ISBN   92-9002-159-4
ISSN   0084-1889

Typeset by BPC Whitefriars, Tunbridge Wells

Printed and bound in Great Britain by The Bath Press, Avon

TABLE OF CONTENTS
TABLE DE MATIÈRES

FOREWORD

The *World List of Universities and Other Institutions of Higher Education* is long established as an invaluable information tool for all those concerned with higher education in its international context. It is one of the standard reference works produced, together with the International Handbook of Universities, by the International Association of Universities. Whereas the Handbook contains comprehensive information on over 5,500 university level institutions, the World List is a concise directory, including, in addition to universities, other institutions offering terminal degrees after three to four years of higher education. The data is maintained at, and periodically updated by, the IAU/Unesco Information Centre on Higher Education, established at the International Universities Bureau.

The Twentieth Edition of the *World List* includes more than 11,000 entries, covering 178 countries. In addition, information is given on major National Academic Bodies directly concerned with higher education. The presentation of the new Edition of the *World List* has been modified and enhanced to facilitate reference. The institution entries are more clearly arranged, spelling out in full the main Divisions of Study and adding, where available, the names of the Academic Head, the Chief Administrative Officer and the Director of International Relations. The extensive descriptive information contained in previous editions of the *World List* on national and international organizations in higher education has not been retained in order to remain consistent with the directory style; this information will find a more appropriate place in the *Handbook*.

The listing of institutions is based on information made available from authoritative national sources. It reflects the classifications prevailing in the respective country and does not imply any judgement of the International Association of Universities. Every effort has been made to ensure that the information published is complete and accurate, and the International Universities Bureau is grateful to the government departments and central academic bodies who have provided the data. For those entries for which recent information has not been received in time for publication, material contained in the Nineteenth Edition has been retained. Any corrections and additions will be welcomed for inclusion in the next Edition.

AVANT-PROPOS

La *World List of Universities and Other Institutions of Higher Education* constitue depuis de nombreuses années un précieux outil d'information pour ceux qui s'intéressent à l'enseignement supérieur dans son contexte international. Elle constitue, avec l'*International Handbook of Universities*, l'un des ouvrages de référence produits par l'Association internationale des Universités. Alors que le *Handbook* fournit des informations détaillées sur plus de 5.500 établissements de niveau universitaire, la *World List* est un répertoire concis qui comprend, outre les universités, les autres établissements offrant des diplômes terminaux conférés après trois à quatre années d'études supérieures. Le Centre AIU/Unesco d'Information sur l'Enseignement supérieur est responsable, au sein du Bureau international des Universités, de la collecte et la mise à jour des données.

La Vingtième Edition de la *World List* comprend plus de 11.000 établissements dans 178 pays. Elle comprend également des données sur les principaux organismes nationaux d'enseignement supérieur. La présentation de la nouvelle édition de la *World List* a été modifiée et améliorée afin d'en faciliter la consultation. Les établissements qui y figurent sont classés plus clairement avec le nom complet des principales divisions d'études. Les noms des Chefs d'Etablissement, des Directeurs de l'Administration et des Directeurs des Relations internationales sont donnés dans la mesure de la disponibilité de l'information. L'information exhaustive contenue dans les éditions précédentes de la *World List* sur les organisations nationales et internationales de l'enseignement supérieur a été supprimée afin de garder le style "répertoire" de l'ouvrage. Ces informations trouveront une place plus appropriée dans le *Handbook*.

La liste des établissements est basée sur des renseignements fournis par les organismes nationaux compétents d'enseignement supérieur. Elle reflète la classification reconnue dans le pays concerné et ne reflète nullement jugement de l'Association internationale des Universités. Le plus grand soin a été apporté afin d'assurer aux informations publiées dans cet ouvrage le maximum d'exactitude et le Bureau international des Universités remercie vivement les nombreux services gouvernementaux et les organismes universitaires nationaux qui ont bien voulu fournir les données. Pour les établissements pour lesquels aucune information récente n'a été communiquée à temps pour la publication celle contenue dans la Dix-neuvième Edition a été retenue. Toute communication visant des corrections ou des modifications sera prise en consideration pour la prochaine edition.

EXPLANATORY NOTE

The *World List of Universities and Other Institutions of Higher Education* has been designed to serve as a concise directory to facilitate cooperation and exchange throughout the world of higher education. The terms "university" and "institution of higher education" carry, in different systems, varying connotations. The listing contained in the *World List* follows the offical classifications used by the competent national academic and education bodies in the respective countries.

Information is classified under chapter headings for 178 countries and territories.

(a) *Universities*

The entries comprise all institutions, whether or not they bear the name "University", whose degrees are considered to be of university level in the country concerned.

(b) *Other Institutions of Higher Education*

This category lists all other institutions offering terminal degrees after three to four years of higher education.

(c) *National Academic Bodies*

Country chapters also list, where available, information on national university organizations, rectors' conferences, higher education councils, etc. Government agencies in charge of higher education and National Commissions for Unesco are also included.

The classification following national standards has been adopted for reasons of practical convenience and constitutes in no way an "assessment" by the International Association of Universities. It should be noted that neither independent schools and faculties of theology, nor military academies or similar institutions are included.

For each institution the name in English, except when, for practical reasons the national language has been retained, the postal and telecommunication details, the names of the Academic Head, the Administrative Officer, and the Director of International Relations, as well as a listing of the Main Divisions of Study by Faculties, Colleges, Schools, Departments, Institutes, etc., and the date of foundation are given. The information follows denominations used in the country. Thus, a Faculty of Medicine, for example, may or may not include dentistry, pharmacy or nursing; a Faculty of Philosophy covering the humanities may or may not include the social sciences. More detailed information may be found in the *International Handbook of Universities* for the institutions listed there. As for the date of the institution's foundation, in a number of cases, two or more dates are given – the first being that of the original foundation and the subsequent dates those on which major changes took place (e.g. a college founded in 1917 and accorded full university status in 1936).

The designations employed in this volume and the presentation of the material essentially follow United Nations practice and do not imply any expression of opinion on the part of the International Association of Universities concerning the legal status of any country, or of its authorities, or concerning the delimitations of the Frontiers of any country or territory.

Institutions marked with an asterisk (*) are members of the International Association of Universities.

NOTE EXPLICATIVE

La *World List of Universities and Other Institutions of Higher Education* a été conçue comme un répertoire concis servant à faciliter la coopération et les échanges dans le monde de l'enseignement supérieur. Les termes "université" et "établissement d'enseignement supérieur" ont un sens différent selon les systèmes. La *World List* suit les classifications officielles utilisées par les organismes éducatifs et universitaires nationaux compétents des différents pays.

Les informations sont classées par chapitre et couvrent 178 pays et territoires.

(a) *Universités*

Les entrées comprennent tous les établissements, qu'ils portent ou non le nom d'"Université", dont les diplômes sont considérés de niveau universitaire dans le pays concerné.

(b) *Autres Etablissements d'Enseignement supérieur*

Cette catégorie répertorie tous les autres établissements offrant des diplômes terminaux après trois ou quatre années d'études supérieures.

(c) *Organismes universitaires nationaux*

Les chapitres des pays offrent également, lorsqu'elles sont disponibles, des informations sur les organisations universitaires nationales, les conférences de recteurs, les conseils d'enseignement supérieur, etc. Les organismes gouvernementaux responsables de l'enseignement supérieur et les Commissions nationales de l'Unesco sont également incluses.

La classification selon les normes nationales a été adoptée pour la commodité des utilisateurs et ne doit nullement être considérée comme une tentative d'"évaluation" de la part de l'Association internationale des Universités. Il convient de noter que les écoles indépendantes, les facultés de théologie, les académies militaires et autres établissements de ce type ne sont pas inclus.

On trouve pour chaque établissement son nom en anglais, à l'exception des cas ou, pour des raisons pratiques, le nom dans la langue du pays a été retenu, les coordonnées postales et de télécommunications, le nom du Chef de l'Etablissement, de l'Administrateur, et du Directeur des Relations internationales, ainsi que les principales divisions d'études par faculté, collège, école, département, institut, etc. et la date de fondation. Les renseignements suivent les dénominations utilisées par le pays. C'est ainsi qu'une faculté de médecine peut ou non comprendre une section d'odontologie, de pharmacie ou une école d'infirmières; une faculté de philosophie qui englobe les sciences humaines peut ou non enseigner les sciences sociales. On trouvera à ce sujet des informations plus complètes dans *l'International Handbook of Universities* pour les établissements y figurant. En ce qui concerne la date de fondation de l'établissement, dans certains cas, au moins deux dates sont données - la première correspondant à la date de première fondation et les autres aux principaux changements survenus (par exemple un collège fondé en 1917 et auquel il a été conféré le statut d'université en 1936).

Les désignations employées dans le présent ouvrage et la présentation des màtieres dans l'ensemble se conforment aux usages des Nations Unies et ne traduisent aucune prise de position de l'Association internationale des Universités quant au statut juridique des pays ou de leurs autorités, ni quant à la délimitation des frontières des pays ou territoires.

Les établissements marqués d'un astérisque (*) sont Membres de l'Association internationale des Universités.

ABBREVIATIONS

	ENGLISH	FRENCH
A	Academy	Académie
B	Board(s)	Conseil(s)
C	College	Collège
Ce	Centre	Centre
D	Department	Département
Div	Division	Division
F	Faculty	Faculté
I	Institute	Institut
IPAG	Institute of Preparatory Administrative Studies	Institut de Préparation à l'Administration générale
IUP	Professional University Institute	Institut universitaire professionalisé
IUT	University Institute of Technology	Institut universitaire de Technologie
L	Laboratory	Laboratoire
P	Programme	Programme
S	School	Ecole
Sect	Section	Section
U	University	Université
Ut	Unit	Unité

OFFICERS OF THE INTERNATIONAL ASSOCIATION OF UNIVERSITIES

Administrative Board 1995–20000
(Elected at 10th General Conference in New Dehli)

President
Wataru Mori — *Former President, University of Tokyo, Japan*

Vlce-Presidents
Flavio Fava de Moraes — *Rector, University of São Paulo, Brazil*
Hans van Ginkel — *Rector, University of Utrecht, Netherlands*

Honorary Presidents

Walter Kamba	President 1990–1995, Zimbabwe
Justin Thorens	President 1985–1990, Switzerland
Guillermo Soberón	President 1980–1985, Mexico
Blagovest Sendov	Acting President 1984, Bulgaria
Martin Meyerson	Acting President 1983 & 1985, USA
Roger Gaudry	President 1975–1980, Canada
Constantine K Zurayk	President 1965–1970, Lebanon

BOARD MEMBERS

Thomas Bartlett	*Chancellor, State University New York, USA*
Paolo Blasi	*Rector, University of Florence, Italy*
Michel Falise	*Recteur Emérite, Université catholique de Lille, France*
Luis Garita Bonilla	*Rector, Universidad de Costa Rica*
Henrik Toft Jensen	*Rector, Roskilde University, Denmark*
Triloki Nath Kapoor	*Vice-Chancellor, Panjab University, India*
Boleslaw Mazurkiewicz	*Former Rector, Technical University of Gdansk, Poland*
Hassan Mekouar	*Recteur, Université Mohammed I, Morocco*
Guoguang Mu	*President, Nankai University, People's Republic of China*
Hanna Nasir	*President, Birzeit University, Palestine*
Daniel Ona-Ondo	*Recteur, Université Omar Bongo, Gabon*
Avelino José Porto	*Rector, Universidad de Belgrano, Argentina*
Robert Prichard	*President, University of Toronto, Canada*
Stuart Saunders	*Vice-Chancellor, University of Cape Town, South Africa*
Abdul Majid Sheikh Hussein	*President, AlBaath University, Syria*
Trevor Smith	*Vice-Chancellor, University of Ulster, UK*
Charas Suwanwela	*President, Chulalongkorn University, Thailand*
Ludmila Verbitskaja	*Rector, Saint-Petersburg University, Saint-Petersburg, Russian Federation*

DEPUTY BOARD MEMBERS

Günal Akbay, *Rector, Ankara University, Turkey*; Abdullah Al-Kobaisi, *Former President, University of Qatar*; William Allaway, *Director Emeritus, Education Abroad Programme, University of California, Santa Barbara, US*; John Belcher, *Pro-Rector, University of Westminster, UK*; Michael Daxner, *President, Carl Von Ossietzky University of Oldenburg, Germany*; Hashim Mohamed El Hadi, *Vice-Chancellor, University of Khartoum, Sudan*; Paul Fogelberg, *Vice-Rector, University of Helsinki, Finland*; Fawzi A. Gharaibeh, *President, University of Jordan*; Madappa Madaiah, *Vice-Chancellor, University of Mysore, India*; Gamal Eldin Mokhtar, *President, Arab Academy for Science and Technology, Egypt*; Ahmadou L. Ndiaye, *Recteur, Université de Saint-Louis, Sénégal*; Agripino Nuñez, *Rector, Universidad Católica 'Madre y Maestra', Dominican Republic*; Keiji Otani, *President, Sophia University, Japan*; Michael Stathapoulos, *Former Rector, University of Athens, Greece*, Heinrich Stremitzer, *Former Rector, Vienna University of Economics and Business Administration, Austria*; Julio Terán Dutari, *Rector, Pontificia Universidad Católica del Ecuador*; Luc Weber, *Recteur, Université de Genève, Switzerland*; Brian Wilson, *Vice-Chancellor, University of Queensland, Australia*; Gheorghe Zgura, *Rector, Technical University of Bucharest, Romania*; Lauro Ribas Zimmer, *Rector, Universidade Estácio de Sá, Rio de Janeiro, Brazil*.

SECRETARY-GENERAL

Franz Eberhard, *Director, International Universities Bureau*

IAU at a Glance

The International Association of Universities (IAU), founded in 1950, is a worldwide organization with member institutions in over 120 countries, which, cooperates with a vast network of international, regional and national bodies. Its permanent Secretariat, the International Universities Bureau, is located at Unesco, Paris, and provides a wide variety of services to Member Institutions and to the international higher education community at large.

Activities and Services

- Forum for Cooperation, Exchange and Debate
- Representation of University Interests
- IAU/Unesco Information Centre on Higher Education
- International Information Networks
- Comparative studies, higher education policy research
- Meetings and seminars
- Promotion of academic mobility
- Credential evaluation
- Consultancy and advice
- Clearinghouse functions

Publications

- International Handbook of Universities
- World List of Universities and Other Institutions of Higher Education
- Issues in Higher Education (monographs)
- Higher Education Policy (quarterly)
- IAU Newsletter (bimonthly)
- Papers and Reports

L'AIU en Bref

L'Association internationale des Universitiés (AIU), fondée en 1950, est une organisation mondiale qui comprend des membres dans quelque 120 pays et coopère avec un vaste réseau d'organisations internationales, régionales et nationales. Son Secretariat, le Bureau international des Universités est situé à l'Unesco, à Paris, et offre de nombreux services à ses Etablissements membres et à la communauté universitaire internationale dans son ensemble.

Activites et services

- Forum de coopération, d'échanges et de débats
- Représentation des intérets des universités
- Centre AIU/Unesco d'information sur l'Enseignement supérieur
- Réseaux internationaux d'information
- Etudes comparées et recherches sur les politiques d'enseignement supérieur
- Réunions et séminaires
- Mobilité académique
- Reconnaissance de diplômes
- Conseil

Publications

- International Handbook of Universities
- World List of Universities and Other Institutions of Higher Education
- Issues in Higher Education (monographies)
- Higher Education Policy (trimestriel)
- Nouvelles de l'AIU (bimestriel)
- Documents et rapports

Headquarters

Unesco House
1, rue Miollis
F-75732 Paris Cedex 15, France
Telephone: +33 1 -45-68-25-45
Fax: +33 1-47-34-76-05
E-mail: iau@unesco.org
Telex: 270602

President

Dr. Wataru Mori, Former President, University of Tokyo

Secretary-General

Dr. Franz Eberhard, Director, International Universities Bureau

WORLD LIST
of
UNIVERSITIES

and

other Institutions of
Higher Education

AFGHANISTAN

UNIVERSITIES

Balkh University
Mazar-i-Sharif
Founded: 1988
F: Engineering; Literature; Agriculture; Economics.

Herat University
Herat
Founded: 1988
F: Literature; Fine Arts; Economics.

Kabul State Medical Institute
Kabul
Founded: 1932, 1980
F: Medicine; Curative Medicine; Stomatology; Medicine (Herat); Medicine (Herat); Medicine (Nangarhar).

Kabul University
[Pohantoon-e-Kabul]
Aliabad, Kabul
Tel: +93 40341-3
President: Tahair Enayat (1990-)
Administrative Pro-Rector: Naim Ashrafi
Founded: 1932, 1945
Agriculture; Education; Economics; Fine Arts; Geosciences; Law and Political Science; Literature and Languages; Pharmacy; Natural Sciences; Natural Sciences; Social Sciences; Journalism; Veterinary Medicine; Engineering.

University of Islamic Studies Kabul
Kabul
Founded: 1988

Kandhar University
Kandhar
Founded: 1988
F: Agriculture.

University of Nangarhar
Jalalabad
Founded: 1963
F: Medicine; Agriculture; Engineering; Education.

NATIONAL ACADEMIC BODIES

Ministry of Education
P.O. Box 717, Kabul
Tel: +93(873) 32076
Fax: +93(873) 150-5152
Minister: Maulawi Jalilullah Maulawizada

Afghan National Commission for Unesco
Ministry of Education, P.O. Box 717, Kabul
Tel: +93(873) 21751
Fax: +93(973) 281
Telex: 23157 natcomaf
Chairman: Maulawi Jalilullah Maulawizada, Minister of Education
Seċretary-General: Mohammad Ishaq

ALBANIA

UNIVERSITIES

'Aleksandër Xhuvani' University of Elbasan
Elbasan
Tel: +355(545) 2782
Founded: 1971

'Eqerem Çabej' University of Gjirokstra
Gjirokastra
Tel: +355 757
Founded: 1971

Polytechnic University of Korçë
Korçë
Tel: +355(82) 42230
Fax: +355(82) 42230
Rector: Dhimitraq Skende
Founded: 1971
F: Agriculture; Economics; Education.

'Luigj Gurakuqi' University of Shkodër
Shkodër
Founded: 1957, 1991
F: Natural Sciences; Social Sciences and Teaching.

Agricultural University of Tiranë
Kamzë, Tiranë
Tel: +355(42) 28201
Fax: +355(42) 27969
Founded: 1971
F: Agronomy; Veterinary Science; Forestry; Agricultural Economics.

Polytechnic University of Tiranë
Tiranë
Engineering.

University of Tiranë
Prof. Petit Radovicka, Tiranë
Tel: +355(42) 28258
Fax: +355(42) 28258
Telex: 211
Founded: 1957
F: Mechanical and Electrical Engineering; Construction Engineering; Geology and Mining; Natural Sciences; Medicine; Economics; Political Science and Law; History and Philology.
I: Folklore.

OTHER INSTITUTIONS

Academy of Fine Arts Tiranë
Tiranë
Tel: +355(42) 22384
Founded: 1966
Fine Arts.

Higher Institute of Physical Education 'Vojo Kushi'
Tiranë
Physical Education.

NATIONAL ACADEMIC BODIES

Ministry of Education
Rue Kongresi i Permetit, Tiranë
Tel: +355(42) 6307
Fax: +355(42) 32002
Minister: Xhezair Teliti

Albanian National Commission for Unesco
Ministry of Foreign Affairs (Unesco), Tiranë
Tel: +355(42) 34657
Fax: +355(42) 32970
Telex: 2164 mpj ab
President: Yili Vejsiu
Secretary-General: Rudolf Marku

ALGERIA

UNIVERSITIES

*University of Algiers
[Université d'Alger]
2, rue Diddouche Mourad, Alger
Tel: +213(2) 64-69-70
Fax: +213(2) 63-53-03
Telex: 66529 unial dz
Recteur: O. Sakhri
Founded: 1859, 1909
I: Medical Sciences; Arabic Language and Literature; Law and Administration; Economics; Social Sciences and Psychology; Foreign Languages; Library Science and Documentation; Political Science; Education; Speech Therapy; Archaeology; History; Philosophy; Translation and Interpretation.

*University of Science and Technology 'Houari Boumediène' Algiers
[Université des Sciences et de la Technologie Houari Boumediène]
B.P.9, Dar El Beida, Eldjazair, Alger
Tel: +213(2) 75-12-85
Fax: +213(2) 13-76-43-11
Telex: 64343 dz usta
Recteur: Salah Djebaili (1989-)
Founded: 1974
I: Natural Sciences; Chemistry; Physics; Mathematics; Earth Sciences; Electronics; Chemical Engineering; Mechanical Engineering; Computer Sciences; Civil Engineering; Higher Technical Studies.

University of Annaba
[Université d'Annaba]
Route El-Hadjar, Annaba
Tel: +213(8) 83-34-29
Telex: 81847 uarto dz
Founded: 1971, 1975
I: Computer Sciences; Mines and Metallurgy; Civil Engineering; Electrotechnology; Natural Sciences; Economics; Foreign Languages; Arabic Language and Literature; Social Sciences; Law; Exact Sciences.

University Centre of Batna
[Centre Universitaire de Batna]
Batna
I: Law and Administrative Sciences; Arabic Language and Literature; Biological Sciences; Exact Sciences and Technology; Economics; Foreign Languages.

University of Constantine
[Université de Constantine]
Ain-El-Bey, Constantine
Tel: +213(4) 69-73-85
Telex: 92436 unczl dz
Recteur: Ali Benslitane
Founded: 1961, 1969
I: Biological Sciences; Economics; Medical Sciences; Physical Education and Sport; Arabic Language and Literature; Construction Engineering; Foreign Languages; Social Sciences; Education and Psychology; Law and Administrative Sciences; Earth Sciences; Architecture and Town Planning; Exact Sciences; History; Veterinary Medicine; Food Technology; Physics; Chemistry.

University Centre of Mostaganem
[Centre Universitaire de Mostaganem]
Mostaganem
I: Biological Sciences; Exact Sciences; Physics.

University of Oran
[Université d'Oran]
Rue du Colonel Lofti, Es Senia, Oran
Recteur: Mohamed Abbou (1993-)
Founded: 1961, 1966
I: Economics; Medical Sciences; Arabic Language and Literature; Foreign Languages; Social Sciences; Mathematics; Physics; Chemistry; Earth Sciences; Biological Sciences; Exact Sciences; History; Demography; Law and Administrative Sciences.

University of Science and Technology of Oran
[Université des Sciences et de la Technologie d'Oran]
B.P.1505, El M'Naouer, Oran
Tel: +213 34-19-63
Telex: 22701
Founded: 1975
I: Electronics; Electrotechnology.

*University Ferhat Abbas, Sétif
[Université Ferhat Abbas]
Sétif
Tel: +213 90-36-40
Telex: 86077 unset dz
Recteur: Djafer Benachour (1993-)
Founded: 1978, 1985
I: Electronics; Industrial Chemistry; Mechanical Engineering; Computer Sciences; Economics; Medical Sciences; Architecture; Modern Languages; Physics.
Ce: Lifelong Education.

University Centre of Sidi-Bel-Abbès
[Centre Universitaire de Sidi-Bel-Abbès]
Sidi-Bel-Abbès
I: Biological Sciences; Exact Sciences; Physics.

University Centre of Tiaret
[Centre Universitaire de Tiaret]
Tiaret (Tagdempt)
I: Exact Sciences; Biological Sciences.

University Centre of Tizi-Ouzou
[Centre Universitaire de Tizi-Ouzou]
Hasnaoua, Tizi-Ouzou
Tel: +213 40-56-51
Telex: 76079 unive dz
Founded: 1977
I: Economics; Law and Administrative Sciences; Arabic Literature; Agriculture; Technology; Electrical Engineering; Computer Sciences.
C: Research and Development.

University Centre of Tlemcen
[Centre Universitaire de Tlemcen]
Boulevard Pasteur, P.O. Box 94, Tlemcen
Tel: +213(7) 20-09-22
Fax: +213(7) 20-41-89
Telex: uv.tlm/ 18971 uv. tlm
Rector: Zoubir Chaouche-Ramdane
Secretary-General: Mourad Benkalfat
Founded: 1974, 1989
I: Economics; Law; Arabic Language and Literature; Biological Sciences; Exact Sciences; Civil and Mechanical Engineering; Hydraulics; Forestry; Medical Sciences; Foreign Languages; Popular Cultures.

OTHER INSTITUTIONS

Ecole nationale vétérinaire
Avenue Pasteur, El-Harrach, Alger
Tel: +213 766-781
Veterinary Medicine.

Ecole normale supérieure
Kouba, Alger
Teacher Training.

Ecole normale supérieure d'Enseignement polytechnique
Es Senia, Oran
Founded: 1970

Ecole polytechnique d'Architecture et d'Urbanisme
El Harrach, Alger
Founded: 1970
Architecture and Town Planning.

Institut de Telécommunications d'Oran
Oran
Telecommunications.

Institut national agronomique
El Harrach, Alger
Tel: +213 761-987
Telex: 54802 ina dz
Founded: 1966
Agriculture.

NATIONAL ACADEMIC BODIES

Ministry of Higher Education and Scientific Research
[Ministère de l'Enseignement supérieur et de la Recherche scientifique]
II, Chemin Doudou Mokhtar, Ben-Aknoun, Alger
Tel: +213(2) 79-00-37
Fax: +213(2) 78-31-97
Ministre: Boubakeu Benbouzid

Algerian National Commission for Unesco and Alesco
[Commission nationale algérienne pour l'Unesco et l'Alecso]
B.P. 65K, El Mouradia, Alger
Tel: +213(2) 59-08-49
Fax: +213(2) 60-73-48
Telex: 66547
Président: Amar Sakhri, Minister of Education
Secrétaire général: Mohamed Amara

ANGOLA

UNIVERSITIES

*University Agostinho Neto
[Universidade Agostinho Neto]
Avenida 4 de Fevereiro 7, Caixa postal 815-C, Luanda
Tel: +244(2) 37132
Telex: 3076 univela an
Reitor: José Luis Guerra Marques
Founded: 1962, 1968, 1976, 1985
F: Science; Agriculture; Law; Economics; Engineering; Medicine.
I: Education (Lubango); Correspondence Courses (Education).

NATIONAL ACADEMIC BODIES

Ministry of Education
[Ministério da Educação]
C.P. 1451, Luanda
Tel: +244(2) 323-326
Fax: +244(2) 321-592
Minister: Manuel João Bernardo

Angolan National Commission for Unesco
[Commission nationale angolaise pour l'Unesco]
Ministère de l'Education, C.P. 1451, Luanda
Tel: +244(2) 337-010
Chairman: Manual João Bernardo, Minister of
Education
Permanent Secretary: Manuel Teodoro Quata

ARGENTINA

UNIVERSITIES AND TECHNICAL UNIVERSITIES

PUBLIC INSTITUTIONS

National University Central Buenos Aires Province
[Universidad Nacional del Centro de la Provincia de Buenos Aires]
Gral. Pinto 399, 7000 Tandil (Buenos Aires)
Tel: +54(293) 22062-3
Rector: Carlos Albert Nicolini
Secretario de Administración: José Luis Bianchini
Founded: 1964, 1974
F: Exact Sciences; Veterinary Science;
Economics; Humanities; Engineering (Olavarría);
Agriculture (Azul).

*University of Buenos Aires
[Universidad de Buenos Aires]
Calle Viamonte 430/444, Buenos Aires
Tel: +54(1) 312-04-69
Fax: +54(1) 311-05-16
Telex: 18649
Rector: Oscar J. Shuberoff (1994-97)
Secretario General: Gustavo López
International Relations: Lautaro García Batallán
Founded: 1821
F: Exact and Natural Sciences; Social Sciences;
Philosophy and Letters; Engineering; Medicine;
Dentistry; Law and Social Science; Pharmacy and
Biochemistry.

National University of Catamarca
[Universidad Nacional de Catamarca]
esqviv 612, 4700 San Fernando del Valle de
Catamarca
Tel: +54(833) 250-89
Rector: Julio Salerno
Founded: 1972
F: Agriculture; Applied Sciences and
Technology; Economics and Administration; Exact
and Natural Sciences; Humanities; Health
Sciences.
I: Education.
S: Nursing.

National University of Comahue
[Universidad Nacional del Comahue]
Buenos Aires 1400, 8300 Neuquén
Tel: +54 235-96
Fax: +54 236-09
Telex: 84266 uncnq ar
Rector: Pablo Bohoslavsky
Secretario de Hacienda: Eduardo Mutchinik
Founded: 1965, 1971
F: Economics and Administration; Engineering;
Tourism; Humanities; Education; Social Services;
Agriculture.
S: Biology; Languages.
I: Marine Biology.

National University of Córdoba
[Universidad Nacional de Córdoba]
Obispo Trejo Sanabria 242, 5000 Córdoba
Tel: +54(51) 69-49-05
Telex: 51822 bucor
Rector: Francisco Delich
Secretario Administrativo: Armando J. Gutiérrez
Founded: 1613, 1621, 1621, 1854
F: Architecture and Town Planning; Agriculture;
Economics; Exact, Physical and Natural Sciences;
Medicine; Chemistry; Law and Social Sciences;
Philosophy and Humanities; Mathematics,
Astronomy, and Physics; Dentistry.
S: Languages.

National University of the North-East Corrientes
[Universidad Nacional del Nordeste]
Calle 25 de Mayo 868, 3400 Corrientes
Tel: +54(783) 250-60
Rector: Federico Kaenel
Secretario General Administrativo: Jorge
Guillermo Odriozola
Founded: 1956
F: Agriculture; Veterinary Science; Law and
Social and Political Sciences; Exact and Natural
Sciences and Surveying; Humanities
(Resistencia); Economics (Resistencia); Medicine;
Architecture and Town Planning (Resistencia);
Engineering (Resistencia); Natural Resources
(Formosa); Industrial Engineering (Presidente
Roque Sáenz Peña); Dentistry.

National University of Cuyo
[Universidad Nacional de Cuyo]
Parque General San Martín, 5500 Mendoza
Tel: +54(61) 25-32-19
Fax: +54(61) 38-01-50
Telex: 55267 mendoz ar
Rector: Armando Bertranov
Secretaria Administrativa: María Alícia
Fernández de Caloiro
Founded: 1939
F: Agriculture; Economics; Medicine; Political
and Social Sciences; Philosophy and Letters;
Petroleum and Industrial Engineering.
I: Physics (San Carlos de Bariloche).
S: Dentistry; Music; Plastic Arts; Industrial
Design; Drama; Education.

National University of Entre Ríos
[Universidad Nacional de Entre Ríos]
Galarza 617, 3260 Concepción del Uruguay (Entre Ríos)
Tel: +54(442) 255-73
Fax: +54(442) 255-73
Rector: Cesar Gotfried
Director General de Administración: Pedro Sandoval
Founded: 1973
F: Education (Paraná); Agriculture (Paraná); Engineering; Food Technology (Concordia); Economics (Paraná); Administration (Concordia); Social Service (Paraná); Health Sciences; Bromatology.

National University of Formosa
[Universidad Nacional de Formosa]
Brandsen 1082,B3600, Formosa
Tel: +54(717) 304-89
Rector: Roberto Juan Acosta
Secretario General de Administración: Fernando Miño
Founded: 1989

National University of General San Martin
[Universidad Nacional de General San Martín]
Calle 91 (ex-San Lorenzo) 3391, 1650 Buenos Aires, San Martín
Tel: +54(1) 767-56-73
Rector: Daniel Malcom

National University of General Sarmiento
[Universidad Nacional de General Sarmiento]
Buenos Aires
Tel: +54 805-08-38
Rector: Roberto Noel Domeq
Secretaria: Francisca Castel

National University of Jujuy
[Universidad Nacional de Jujuy]
Avenida Bolivia 2335, 4600 San Salvador de Jujuy
Tel: +54(882) 256-17
Fax: +54(882) 286-01
Rector: Jorge Augusto Vanmessen
Founded: 1973, 1974
F: Agriculture; Engineering; Economics; Humanities and Social Sciences.
D: Extension.

National University of La Matanza
[Universidad Nacional de La Matanza]
Florencio Varela 1903, 1754 San Justo (Buenos Aires)
Tel: +54(1) 651-37-49
Rector: Ernesto Cartier
Founded: 1989

National University of La Pampa
[Universidad Nacional de La Pampa]
9 de Julio 149, 6300 Santa Rosa (La Pampa)
Tel: +54(954) 231-09
Fax: +54(254) 334-08
Telex: 83132 ulpam
Rector: Carlos Arenzo
Secretario Administrativo: Jorge Dlouky
Founded: 1958, 1973
F: Humanities; Economics; Exact and Natural Sciences; Agriculture; Veterinary Science.
I: Labour Studies.

National University of La Patagonia 'San Juan Bosco'
[Universidad Nacional de La Patagonia 'San Juan Bosco']
25 de Mayo 427, 9000 Comodoro Rivadavia (Chubut)
Tel: +54(967) 233-93
Fax: +54(967) 344-42
Telex: 86022
Rector: Arturo Canero
Secretario Administrativo: Hector Baztan
Founded: 1980
F: Engineering; Economics; Humanities; Engineering.
Ce: Forestry Research.
L: Micropaleontology; Chemical Engineering; Aquaculture.

National University of La Plata
[Universidad Nacional de La Plata]
Calle 7,776, 1900 La Plata (Buenos Aires)
Tel: +54(21) 21-55-01
Fax: +54(21) 25-69-67
Telex: 31151 Bulapar
Rector: Luis Julian Lima
Secretario (Económicos Financieros): Ruben Torres
Founded: 1890, 1906
F: Agriculture; Engineering; Humanities and Education; Law and Social Sciences; Veterinary Science; Exact Sciences; Medicine; Natural Sciences; Economics; Architecture and Town Planning; Dentistry; Astronomic Sciences and Geophysics; Fine Arts.
S: Social Work; Journalism and Social Communication.

National University of La Rioja
[Universidad Nacional de La Rioja]
Avenida Ortíz de Ocampo 1700, 5300 La Rioja
Tel: +54(822) 260-69
Rector: Enrique Daniel Tello Roldan
Founded: 1960, 1972
D: Basic Studies; Health Sciences; Social Sciences; Applied Sciences.
I: Provincial Studies; Arid Zones Research; Anthropology.
D: Extension.

National University of the Litoral
[Universidad Nacional del Litoral]
Boulevard Pellegrini, 2750 Santa Fe
Tel: +54(42) 344-61
Fax: +54(42) 55-24-68
Telex: 34688
Rector: Hugo Guillermo Storero
Founded: 1899, 1919
F: Economics; Chemical Engineering; Law and Social Sciences; Biochemistry.
I: Music.
S: Food Technology (Reconquista, Gálvez); Education; Agriculture and Veterinary Science (Esperanza); Health Sciences.

National University of Lomas de Zamora
[Universidad Nacional de Lomas de Zamora]
Camino de Cintara Km 2, Casilla de Correo 95, 1832 Lomas de Zamora (Buenos Aires)
Tel: +54(1) 244-81-14
Fax: +54(1) 292-42-45
Telex: 22067 calom-ar
Rector: Carlos Mario Clerc
Director General de Servicios Administrativos: Aldo Oscar Codesido
Founded: 1972
F: Economics; Social Sciences; Engineering and Agriculture; Law; Mechanical and Industrial Engineering.

*National University of Luján
[Universidad Nacional de Luján]
Ruta 5 km. 70, 6700 Luján (Buenos Aires)
Tel: +54(323) 231-71
Fax: +54(323) 257-95
Rector: Juan Carlos Busnelli
Secretario Coordinación Administrativa: Alberto Gabriel Cascallares
Founded: 1972
D: Science and Technology; Social Studies; Education.

National University of Mar del Plata
[Universidad Nacional de Mar del Plata]
Boulevard Juan Bautista Alberdi 2695, 7600 Mar del Plata (Buenos Aires)
Tel: +54(23) 396-76
Fax: +54(23) 241-97
Telex: 39036 unrec ar
Rector: Jorge Domingo Petrillo (1994-)
Secretario Asuntos Económicos Financieros: Jorge Ruben Castro
Founded: 1961, 1975
F: Humanities; Law; Architecture and Town Planning; Agriculture (Balcarce); Economics and Social Sciences; Engineering; Exact and Natural Sciences.
S: Health Sciences.
C: Psychology.
I: Biological Research; Political Science and Hispanoamerican Integration; Economic Research; Materials Science and Technology Research (INTEMA).

Ce: Hispanoamerican Letters; Coastal Geology; Regional Computer.
D: Vocational Orientation.

National University of Misiones
[Universidad Nacional de Misiones]
Campus Universitario, Ruta 12 km 7 1/2, Estafeta postal Miguel Lanus, 3304 Posadas (Misiones)
Tel: +54(752) 809-16
Fax: +54(752) 805-29
Rector: Ricardo Roberto Biazzi
Secretaría General Académica: María Luisa Teresa Morchio de Passalacqua
Founded: 1973
F: Humanities and Social Sciences; Exact and Natural Sciences, and Chemistry; Economics; Engineering; Forestry.
I: Aesthetic Studies.
S: Nursing.

National University of Quilmes
[Universidad Nacional de Quilmes]
Roque Saenz Peña 180, 1876 Bernal (Buenos Aires)
Tel: +54 259-30-90
Rector: Julio Villar
Founded: 1989

National University of Río Cuarto
[Universidad Nacional de Río Cuarto]
Campus Universitario, Enlace 6 y 36-km. 603, 5800 Río Cuarto (Córdoba)
Tel: +54 246-16
Fax: +54 459-80
Telex: 54572-cunrc-ar
Rector: Alberto Cantero Gutiérrez
Secretario Economico: Carlos Omar Dominguez
Founded: 1971
F: Agriculture and Veterinary Science; Engineering; Exact and Natural Sciences, Physics, and Chemistry; Economics; Humanities.
S: Nursing.

National University of Rosario
[Universidad Nacional de Rosario]
Córdoba 1814, 2000 Rosario (Santa Fe)
Tel: +54(41) 25-70-60
Fax: +54(41) 25-94-64
Rector: Jan Carlos Millet
Secretario Administrativo: Jorge Luis Rasines
Founded: 1968
F: Medical Sciences; Dentistry; Biochemistry and Pharmacy; Economics; Agriculture; Law; Political Science and International Relations; Exact Sciences and Engineering; Architecture, Planning and Design; Humanities and Arts; Veterinary Science (Casilda).
I: Music.
S: Plastic Arts; Psychology.
D: Extension.

National University of Salta
[Universidad Nacional de Salta]
Buenos Aires 177, 4400 Salta
Tel: +54(87) 31-13-71
Fax: +54(87) 31-16-11
Telex: 65121 unsat ar
Rector: Rafael Marcelo Rivero
Secretaria: Sonia Alvarez de Trogliero
Founded: 1972
F: Exact Sciences; Technology; Natural Sciences; Humanities; Health Sciences; Economics, Law, and Social Sciences.
I: Industrial Chemistry (Research); Solar Energy Research; Mineral Research; Regional Development.

National University of San Juan
[Universidad Nacional de San Juan]
José Ignacio de la Roza 391, 5400 San Juan
Tel: +54(64) 21-45-36
Fax: +54(64) 21-45-86
Telex: 59100 unsja-ar
Rector: Julio Abel del Bono
Secretaria Administrativa Financiera: César Aguirre
Founded: 1973
F: Engineering; Exact, Physical and Natural Sciences; Philosophy, Humanities and Arts; Social Sciences; Architecture.
S: Industrial Engineering; Commerce.

National University of San Luis
[Universidad Nacional de San Luis]
Ejercito de Los Andes 950, 5700 San Luis
Tel: +54(653) 268-88
Fax: +54(653) 209-27
Telex: 58125 unsl ar
Rector: Alberto Puchmuller
Secretaría Hacienda, Administración: Hugo Alberto Saitua
Founded: 1973
F: Engineering and Business Administration; Mathematics, and Physical and Natural Sciences; Chemistry, Biochemistry, and Pharmacy; Education.
I: Applied Mathematics (IMASL); Research in Technologic Chemistry (INTEQUI).

National University of Santiago del Estero
[Universidad Nacional de Santiago del Estero]
Avenida Belgrano 1912, 4200 Santiago del Estero
Tel: +54(85) 22-25-95
Fax: +54(85) 22-25-95
Telex: 64120 unset-ar
Rector: Huberto Herrera
Founded: 1973
F: Basic Sciences; Humanities; Natural Resources; Hydrology; Exact Sciences and Technology; Area of Health Sciences.
I: Wood Technology; Entomology.
Ce: Rural Education.

National University of the South Bahia
[Universidad Nacional del Sur]
Avenida Colón 80, 8000 Bahía Blanca (Buenos Aires)
Tel: +54(91) 249-86
Fax: +54(91) 320-53
Telex: 81712 dujor ar
Rector: Carlos Enrique Mayer
Founded: 1948, 1956
D: Agriculture; Economics; Electrical Engineering; Chemistry and Chemical Engineering; Humanities; Administration; Biology; Engineering; Geography; Geology; Mathematics; Physics.
I: Oceanography; Biochemical Research.
Ce: Semi-Arid Zone Renewable Natural Resource.

*National University of Tucumán
[Universidad Nacional de Tucumán]
Ayacucho 491, 4000 San Miguel de Tucumán
Tel: +54(81) 31-07-05
Fax: +54(81) 31-14-62
Telex: 60-143 butuc-ar
Rector: César Atilio Catalan (1990-94)
Secretario Administrativo: Jorge Antonio Bascary
Founded: 1912, 1921
F: Agriculture and Animal Husbandry; Architecture and Town Planning; Biochemistry, Chemistry, and Pharmacy; Economics; Exact Sciences and Technology; Natural Sciences; Law and Social Sciences; Philosophy and Letters; Medicine; Dentistry; Arts.
S: Nursing; Physical Education.

Federal University of Patagonia Austral
[Universidad Federal de la Patagonia Austral]
Mariano Moreno 39-piso 1, 9400 Santa Cruz, Río Gallegos
Tel: +54(966) 235-05
Rector: Carlos Pérez Rasetti

Institute of Military Studies
[Instituto de Enseñanza Superior del Ejército]
Avenida Luis Maria Campos 230, 1425 Buenos Aires
Tel: +54(1) 773-24-05
Rector: Raúl Oscar Racana
Military Studies.

University Institute of Aeronautics Cordóba
[Instituto Universitario Aeronáutico]
Avenida Fuerza Aérea Km. 6 1/2, 5000 Córdoba
Tel: +54(51) 60-39-58
Rector: Raul Juan Carlos Camussi
Founded: 1971
Aeronautical Engineering.

University Institute of Naval and Maritime Studies
[Instituto Universitario de Estudios Navales y Marítimos]
Comodoro Py 2055-piso 4, 1104 Buenos Aires
Tel: +54(1) 312-50-01
Rector: Jorge Enrico

University Institute of Police Studies Buenos Aires
[Instituto Universitario de la Policia Federal]
Rosario 532, 1424 Buenos Aires
Tel: +54(1) 99-24-26
Rector: Horacio Alberto Rojas
Founded: 1977
Police Studies.

PRIVATE INSTITUTIONS

University of Aconcagua
[Universidad del Aconcagua]
Catamarca 147, 5500 Mendoza,
Tel: +54(61) 24-12-57
Rector: Osvaldo Caballero
Director de Contabilidad: Oscar Edmundo Lamattina
Founded: 1964
F: Social Sciences and Administration; Economics; Psychology.
D: Postgraduate Studies.

*University of Belgrano
[Universidad de Belgrano]
Zabala 1851, 1426 Buenos Aires
Tel: +54(1) 786-22-37
Fax: +54(1) 775-46-31
Telex: 18658
Rector: Avelino José Porto (1964-)
Secretario General: Eustaquio Castro
Founded: 1964
F: Law and Social Sciences; Architecture; Economics; Humanities; Agriculture; Technology; Engineering; Graduate Studies; Distance Studies.
S: Economics and International Business.

Argentine University of Business Administration Buenos Aires
[Universidad Argentina de la Empresa]
Lima 761, 1073 Buenos Aires
Tel: +54(1) 381-38-50
Rector: César Marzagalli
Director Administrativo: Oscar García
Founded: 1957, 1963
F: Administrative Studies; Agriculture; Economics; Law and Social Sciences; Engineering.
I: Economics; Computer Sciences.
Ce: Vocational Orientation.

Argentine University 'John F. Kennedy' Buenos Aires
[Universidad Argentina 'John F. Kennedy']
Calle Bartolomé Mitre 1411, 1037 Buenos Aires
Tel: +54(1) 476-43-38
Fax: +54(1) 467
Rector: Miguel Herrera Figueroa
Secretario Consejo Académico: Mario Coscio
Founded: 1961, 1964

D: Chemistry; Biology; Psychology; Clinical Psychology; Literature; Mathematics; Construction Engineering; Planning and Development; Political Science; Public Relations; History; Sociology; Computer Science; Systems Design; Computing Technologies; Education; Social Service; Demography and Tourism; Law; Work Studies; Economics; Business; Arts; Communication; Anthropology; Philosophy.

Austral University - Buenos Aires
[Universidad Austral - Buenos Aires]
Avenida Juan de Garay 125, 1063 Buenos Aires
Tel: +54(1) 361-59-46
Fax: +54(1) 361-13-29
Rector: José Luis Gómez López Egea
Secretario Académico: Carlos Pujadas
Founded: 1991
F: Information Sciences; Engineering; Business Administration.
S: Business and Corporate Management.
I: Law and Social Sciences; Safety and Risk Evaluation; Social Development.

Buenos Aires Technology Institute
[Instituto Tecnológico de Buenos Aires]
Avenida Eduardo Madero 351, 1106 Buenos Aires
Tel: +54(1) 342-77-48
Rector: Ernesto Manuel Ruiz
Secretario Administrativo: Roberto José Bellili
Founded: 1960
D: Marine and Mechanical Engineering; Mathematics, Physics and Chemistry; Electronics; Computer Sciences; Industrial Engineering; Oceanography; Extension.

Centre for the Exact Sciences Buenos Aires
[Centro de Altos Estudios en Ciencias Exactas]
Avenida de Mayo 1396, 1085 Buenos Aires
Tel: +54(1) 381-65-20
Rector: Jorge Eduardo Bosch
Founded: 1967
Exact Sciences.

*Palermo University Buenos Aires
[Universidad de Palermo]
Mario Bravo 1302, 1175 Buenos Aires
Tel: +54(1) 963-15-60
Fax: +54(1) 963-15-60
E-Mail: undalb.edu.ar
Rector: Ricardo H. Popovsky (1986-)
Secretary-General: J. C. Lavignolle
Founded: 1990
S: Managerial and Economics Sciences; Art and Design; Law; Social Sciences; Science and Technology.
Ce: Japan Studies; Management Research; University Quality Managerial; Educational Sciences (Advanced).

*Pontifical Catholic University of Argentina Buenos Aires
[Pontificia Universidad Católica Argentina 'Santa María de Los Buenos Aires']
Juncal 1912, 1116 Buenos Aires
Tel: +54(1) 812-33-89
Rector: Mgr Guillermo Pedro Blanco
Founded: 1958, 1960
F: Theology; Philosophy and Letters; Humanities and Education (Mendoza); Law and Political Science; Law and Social Science (Rosario); Social Science and Economics; Physical and Mathematical Sciences, and Engineering; Agriculture; Economics (Paraná); Arts and Music.
I: Culture and University Extension; Integrated Studies; Health Sciences; Extension.
S: Social Communications.
C: Education (Paraná).

*Salvador University Buenos Aires
[Universidad del Salvador]
Viamonte 1856, 1056 Buenos Aires
Tel: +54(1) 42-96-30
Fax: +54(1) 812-46-25
Telex: 18691 eiras ar
Rector: Juan Alejandro Tobias (1991-94)
Secretario General: Pablo Gabriel Varela
Founded: 1944, 1956
F: Law; Education and Communication Sciences; Social Sciences; Medicine; Philosophy; Philosophy (San Miguel); Theology (San Miguel); History and Letters; Psychology; Psychopedagogy; Economics; Administration.
S: Oriental Studies; Scenic Art; Chemistry.
I: Latin American for Medical Research.

University of Business and Social Sciences-Buenos Aires
[Universidad de Ciencias Empresariales y Sociales - Buenos Aires]
Paraguay 1345, 1057 Buenos Aires
Tel: +54(1) 811-02-28
Rector: Horacío O'Donnell
Business and Social Sciences.

University of the Cinema-Buenos Aires
[Universidad del Cine - Buenos Aires]
Pasaje Giufra 330, 1063 Buenos Aires
Tel: +54(1) 362-04-50
Rector: Manuel Antin
Cinema Studies.

University Institute of Biomedical Sciences-Buenos Aires
[Instituto Universitario de Ciencias Biomedicas - Buenos Aires]
Solis 453, 1078 Buenos Aires
Tel: +54(1) 383-11-10
Fax: +54(1) 381-03-23
Rector: Ricardo Horacío Puchel
Biomedical Sciences.

University Institute of Health Science-Buenos Aires
[Instituto Universitario de Ciencias de la Salud - Buenos Aires]
Larrea 770, 1030 Buenos Aires
Tel: +54(1) 961-27-41
Fax: +54(1) 54-01-962-2490
Rector: Hector Barcelo
Health Sciences.

University Maimónides Buenos Aires
[Universidad Maimónides]
Talcahuano 456, 1013 Buenos Aires
Tel: +54(1) 382-46-03
Fax: +54(1) 814-43-84
Rector: Lino Marcos Budiño (1991-95)
Founded: 1990
F: Medicine; Dentistry; Humanities; Oriental Studies.
I: Research.

University of the Merchant Navy Buenos Aires
[Universidad de la Marina Mercante]
Billinghurst 376, 1174 Buenos Aires
Tel: +54(1) 87-11-30
Rector: Eduardo Alberto Simmons
Founded: 1968
F: Engineering; Administration and Economics.

University of the Fraternity 'Santo Tomas de Aquino' Buenos Aires
[Universidad de las Fraternidades y Agrupaciones 'Santo Tomas de Aquino' (F.A.S.T.A.)]
Gascón 3145, 7600 Buenos Aires, Mar del Plata
Tel: +54(23) 268-89
Rector: Juan Carlos Catalano

University of Social Studies Buenos Aires
[Universidad del Museo Social Argentino]
Avenida Corrientes 1723, 1042 Buenos Aires
Tel: +54(1) 40-69-24
Rector: Guillermo Garbarini Islas
Protesorero: Hector Henz
Founded: 1956
F: Political Science, Law, and Economics; Social Service; Information Sciences; Therapeutic Sciences.
S: Choral Studies.

University of Torcuato di Tella - Buenos Aires
[Universidad Torcuato di Tella]
11 de septiembre 2139, 1428 Buenos Aires
Tel: 54(1) 781-50-13
Rector: Gerardo della Paolera

9

University of Concepción del Uruguay
[Universidad de Concepción del Uruguay]
8 de Junio 522, 3260 Concepción del Uruguay
(Entre Ríos)
Tel: +54(442) 277-21
Fax: +54(422) 227-21
Rector: Jorge Alberto Diaz Velez
Founded: 1969
F: Economics; Highway Engineering,
Architecture, and Town Planning.

*Catholic University of Córdoba
[Universidad Católica de Córdoba]
Trejo 323, 5000 Córdoba
Tel: +54(51) 23-83-89
Fax: +54(51) 24-13-02
Rector: Miguel A. Moreno, S.J. (1991-93)
Secretario Académico: Juan Sardo
Founded: 1956, 1959
F: Architecture; Agriculture; Economics and
Administration; Political Science and
International Relations; Chemistry; Law and
Social Sciences; Philosophy and Humanities;
Engineering; Medicine.
I: Administration Sciences; Reality Research
and Political Analysis.

University Blas Pascal Córdoba
[Universidad Blas Pascal]
Lima 363, 5000 Córdoba
Tel: +54(51) 24-37-83
Rector: Alberto Osvaldo Lorenzatti
Founded: 1990

Catholic University of Cuyo
[Universidad Católica de Cuyo]
Avenida José de la Roxa 1516, Oeste, 5400
Rivadavia (San Juan)
Tel: +54(64) 23-02-91
Rector: Pedro Luis Maria Martin
Founded: 1959
F: Food Technology; Economics; Law and Social
Sciences; Philosophy and Humanities; Business
Administration and Tourism (Mendoza); Social
Service (San Luis).
S: Nursing.

Adventist University of La Plata
[Universidad Adventista del Plata]
25 de Mayo 99, 3103 Villa Libertador San Martín
(Entre Ríos)
Tel: +54(43) 99-92-98
Rector: Carlos Morales
Director Asuntos Económicos: Roberto Mato
Founded: 1990

Catholic University of La Plata
[Universidad Católica de La Plata]
Calle 13 No. 1227, 1900 La Plata (Buenos Aires)
Tel: +54(21) 412-91
Rector: Cayetano Licciardo
Administrador General: Jorge Benzrihen
Founded: 1964
F: Architecture; Applied Mathematics;
Economics; Law; Social Sciences; Education.

University of Notarial Studies La Plata
[Universidad Notarial Argentina]
Calle 51, No. 435, 1900 La Plata (Buenos Aires)
Tel: +54(21) 21-05-52
Rector: Nestor Pérez Lozano
Founded: 1962
Notarial Studies.

University School of Theology Mar del Plata
[Escuela Universitaria de Teología]
Pasaje Catedral 1750, 7600 Mar del Plata
(Buenos Aires)
Tel: +54(23) 286-33
Rector: Carlos Humberto Malfa
Founded: 1958
Theology.

University Champagnat - Mendoza
[Universidad Champagnat]
San Martín 866, 5501 Mendoza, Godoy Cruz
Tel: +54(61) 22-77-92
Rector: Francisco Lucena Carrillo

University 'Juan Agustín Maza' Mendoza
[Universidad 'Juan Agustín Maza']
Avenida de Acceso Este 2245, 5519 San José-
Guaymallen-Mendoza
Tel: +54(61) 26-10-36
Rector: Roberto Manuel de Rossetti
Founded: 1960
F: Physical and Mathematical Sciences;
Pharmacy and Biochemistry; Engineering;
Journalism; Oenology and Horticulture (Rodeo
del Medio).
S: Nutrition.

University of Mendoza
[Universidad de Mendoza]
Avenida Boulogne sur Mer 665, 5500 Mendoza
Tel: +54(61) 24-70-17
Fax: +54(61) 31-11-00
Telex: 18660 delphi ar
Rector: Juan Carlos Menghini (1993-)
Secretario Administrativo: Juan Carlos Pereira
Founded: 1959
F: Law and Social Sciences; Architecture and
Town Planning; Engineering.
Ce: Higher Studies.
I: Public Law; Private Law; High Frequencies;
Digital Techniques; Informatics; Special
Microwave Applications.

University of Morón
[Universidad de Morón]
Cabildo 134, 1708 Morón (Buenos Aires)
Tel: +54(1) 629-24-04
Fax: (1)+54 627-85-51
Rector: Omar Lima Quintana
Secretario de Asuntos Administrativos: Miguel
Angel Galán
Founded: 1960
F: Law and Social Sciences; Engineering; Exact
and Natural Sciences, and Chemistry;
Architecture; Economics; Agriculture; Philosophy

and Letters; Tourism; Computer Sciences and Communication.
S: Social Service.

Catholic University of Salta
[Universidad Católica de Salta]
Casilla de Correo 18, 4428 Campo Castañares (Salta)
Tel: +54(87) 21-90-00
Rector: Patricio Colombo Murua
Founded: 1963
F: Arts and Science; Economics and Administration; Engineering; Law.
S: Social Service.
D: Extension.

University of the North 'Santo Tomás de Aquino' San Miguel de Tucumán
[Universidad del Norte 'Santo Tomás de Aquino']
9 de Julio 165, 4000 San Miguel de Tucumán
Tel: +54(81) 22-88-05
Fax: +54(81) 31-03-25
Rector: Héctor Luis Partridge
Secretario General: Francisco José Torres Nieto
Founded: 1956, 1965
F: Humanities; Economics and Administrative Studies; Law and Social Sciences; Industrial Engineering; Philosophy; Anthropology and Psychology; Theology.
I: Social Work 'Juan XXIII'.
I: History.

Catholic University of Santa Fe
[Universidad Católica de Santa Fe]
Echagüe 7151, 3000 Santa Fe
Tel: +54(42) 614-33
Rector: José María Passeggi
Founded: 1957, 1960
F: Philosophy; Law; Economics; History; Letters; Architecture; Education; Soil Science.

University of the Latinamerican Educational Centre Santa Fe
[Universidad del Centro Educativo Latinoamericano]
Avenida Pellegrini 1352, 2000 Santa Fe, Rosario
Rector: Rogelio Panton
Delegado Organizador: Juan Ciliberto

Catholic University of Santiago del Estero
[Universidad Católica de Santiago del Estero]
Avenida Alsina y Nuñez del Prado, Campo Universitario, 4200 Santiago del Estero
Tel: +54(85) 21-38-20
Rector: Jorge Luis Feijoo
Founded: 1960, 1969
F: Law and Political and Social Sciences; Economics; Education.
D: Applied Mathematics; Extension.

San Andres University Victoria
[Universidad San Andres]
Vito Dumas 284 esq. Arias, 1644 Victoria (Buenos Aires)
Tel: +54(1) 742-26-09
Fax: +54(1) 746-26-47
E-Mail: udesa.eud.ar
Rector: Francisco Fernando von Wuthenau (1989-)
Secretario General: Adrian E. Orti
Founded: 1990
D: Humanities; Economics; Business Administration.

NATIONAL ACADEMIC BODIES

Ministry of Culture and Education
[Ministerio de Cultura y Educación]
Buenos Aires
Tel: +54(1) 423-461
Minister: Jorge Rodríguez

Council of Rectors of Argentine National Universities
[Consejo de Rectores de Universidades Nacionales de Argentina]
Avenida Eduardo Madero 235, Buenos Aires
Founded: 1977

Centre for Educational Information
[Centro Nacional de Información Educativa]
Paraguay 1657, piso 18, 1062 Buenos Aires
Tel: +54(1) 25753
Fax: +54(1) 331-1134
Director: Laureano García Elorrio

Argentine National Commission for Unesco
[Comisión Nacional Argentina para la Unesco]
Pissurno 935, piso 1, off. 116, 1020 Buenos Aires
Tel: +54(1)812-9121
Fax: +54(1) 814-3792
Presidente: Jorge Rodríguez, Minister of Culture and Education
Secretario Permanente: Franciso José Piñón

ARMENIA
UNIVERSITIES

American University of Armenia
[Hayastani Americian Hamalsaran]
Marshal Bagramian St. 40, 375019 Yerevan
Tel: +7885(2) 273-239
Fax: +7885(2) 151-048
President: Mihran Agbabian (1990-)
Director: Michael Kouchakchian
International Relations: Gayane Haroutunian
Founded: 1990
F: Earthquake Engineering; Industrial Engineering; Business and Management; Political Sciences.

State Engineering University of Armenia

[Hayastani Petakan Chartaragitakan Hamalsaran]
Terian St. 105, 375009 Yerevan
Tel: +7885(2) 560-132
Fax: +7885(2) 561-581
President: Yuri L.Sargissian (1989-94)
International Relations: Levon S.Hopsepian
Founded: 1991
*F: Electrical Engineering; Power Engineering;
Mechanical-Machine Building Engineering;
Technical Cybernetics; Computer Engineering;
Radio Engineering; Mining and Metallurgy;
Professional Level Improvement of Industrial
Specialists; Foreign Economic Affairs.
S: Foreign Students; Graduate.
Ce: Computer; Research.*

*Yerevan State University

[Yerevani Petakan Hamalsaran]
Alex Manoogian 1, 375049 Yerevan
Tel: +7885(2) 550-612
Fax: +7885(2) 151-087
Telex: 243388 himn 8u
Rector: Radick Martirossian (1993-1994)
Vice-Rector (Administration): M.R. Buniatian
International Relations: Pro-Rector, Rafael
Kh.Matevossian
Founded: 1919
*F: Mathematics; Mechanics; Mathematical
Cybernetics Automatic Analysis; Information and
Computer Mathematics; Physics; Radiophysics;
Chemistry; Biology; Geology; Geography;
Economics; Philology; Russian Philology;
Romanic and Germanic Philology; Oriental
Studies; History; Philosophy, Psychology and
Sociology; Law; Foreign Students (Preparatory).*

OTHER INSTITUTIONS

Armenian State Institute of Physical Culture

[Haikakan Petakan Fizikakan Kulturayi Institut]
Alex Manoogian St. 11, 375070 Yerevan
Tel: +7885(2) 556-281
Rector: Hrachik G. Topalian (1976-94)
Founded: 1945
Physical Education.

Haikakan Giukhatntesakan Institut

Terian St. 74, 375009 Yerevan
Tel: +7885(2) 581-164
Rector: Mikhail A. Giulkhasian (1978-94)
Founded: 1930
*Agronomy; Agricultural Economics; Agricultural
Mechanization and Electrification;
Hydroclimatization.*

Haikakan Petakan Fizikakan Kulturayi Institut

Alex Manoogian St. 11, 375070 Yerevan
Tel: +7885(2) 556-281
Rector: Hrachik G. Topalian (1976-94)
Founded: 1945
Physical Education.

Haikakan Petakan Mankavarzhakan Institut

Khanjian St. 10, 375005 Yerevan
Tel: +7885(2) 522-604
Rector: Ashot S. Paremouzian (1989-94)
International Relations: Levon Gevorkian
Founded: 1922
Pedagogy.

Yerevani Anasnabuzhakan Anasnabutsakan Institut

Nalbandian St. 128, 375200 Yerevan
Tel: +7885(2) 521-232
Rector: Mher S. Melkonian
Founded: 1928
*Animal Husbandry; Veterinary; Technology of
Milk Products.*

Yerevani Chartarapeta-Shinararakan

Terian St. 105, 375009 Yerevan
Tel: +7885(2) 582-937
Fax: +7885(2) 565-984
Rector: Ares G. Beglarian (1989-94)
International Relations: Vardges H. Yedoyan
Founded: 1989
*Architecture and Urban Design; Structural
Technology; Industrial and Civil Construction;
Structural Engineering; Traffic Structures.*

Yerevani Gekharvestatarakan Institut

Isahakian St. 36, 375009 Yerevan
Tel: +7885(2) 560-726
Rector: Vahagn A. Mkrtchian (1974-94)
International Relations: Romella M. Grikorian
Founded: 1944
Arts; Theatre.

Yerevani Otar Lezouneri Petakan Mankavarshakan Institut

H. Emin St. 123, 375093 Yerevan
Tel: +7885(2) 253-772
Rector: Ivetta N.Arakelian (1989-94)
Founded: 1962
*Foreign Languages (English, French, German,
Russian).*

Yerevani Petakan Bzhshkakan Institut

Koryun St. 2, 375025 Yerevan
Tel: +7885(2) 581-802
Fax: +7885(2) 565-481
Rector: Vilen P. Hakopian (1987-94)
International Relations: Samvel Mairapetian
Founded: 1932
*General Medicine; Sanitation and Hygiene;
Stomatology; Pharmacology; Pediatry.*

Yerevani Petakan Conservatoria

Sauat-Nova St. 1A, 375009 Yerevan
Tel: +7885(2) 581-164
Rector: Tigran Mansourian (1993-94)
Founded: 1923
Music.

Yerevani Zhokhovrdakan Tntesoutian Institut
Abovian St.52, 375025 Yerevan
Tel: +7885(2) 521-720
Rector: Grikor E. Kirakossian (1993-94)
Founded: 1975
General Economics; Management and Foreign Economic Relations; Marketing and Science of Commodities; Engineering-Economics; Finance.

NATIONAL ACADEMIC BODIES

Ministry of Higher Education and Science
Movses Khorenatsi, 13, 375010 Yerevan
Tel: +7885(2) 520-632
Fax: +7885(2) 564-110
Minister: V. Gnouni

Armenian National Commission for Unesco
Baghramian Avenue, 10, 375019 Yerevan
Tel: +7885(2) 588-886
Fax: +7885(2) 588-816
Telex: 243313 diana su
Chairman: Vahan Papazian, Minister and Foreign affairs
Secretary-General: Violetta Aghababia

AUSTRALIA

UNIVERSITIES AND INSTITUTES OF TECHNOLOGY

PUBLIC INSTITUTIONS

University of Adelaide
South Australia 5001
Tel: +61(8) 228-5333
Fax: +61(8) 224-0464
Telex: univad AA89141
Cable: univad adelaide
Vice-Chancellor: G. Brown (1994-2000)
Registrar: F.J. O'Neill
Founded: 1874
F: Agricultural and Natural Resource Sciences; Architecture and Urban Design; Arts; Dentistry; Economics and Commerce; Engineering; Law; Mathematical and Computer Sciences; Medicine; Performing Arts; Science.
Ce: Australian Studies; Asian Studies; Petroleum Geology and Geophysics; Women's Studies Research; Teletraffic Research; Cooperative Research (Tissue Growth, Basin Analysis, Soil and Land Management, Materials Welding, Sensor, Viticulture).

Ut: Road Accident Research.
Conservatorium: Music.

*Australian National University
Canberra, A.C.T. 0200
Tel: +61(6) 249-5111
Fax: +61(6) 249-5571
Vice-Chancellor: Deane Terrell (1994-2000)
Pro-Vice-Chancellor (Planning and Administration): P.A. Selth
Founded: 1946
F: Arts; Asian Studies; Economics and Commerce; Law; Engineering and Information Technology; Science.
I: Arts; Advanced Studies.
S: Mathematical Sciences; Medical Research; Art; Music.
Research S and Ut: Biological Sciences; Chemistry; Earth Sciences; Pacific and Asian Studies; Physical Sciences and Engineering; Social Sciences; Information Sciences and Engineering; NH and MRC Social Psychiatry.
Ce: Information Science Research; Visual Sciences; Epidemiology and Population Health; Humanities Research; Resource and Environmental Studies; Continuing Education.
Mount Stromlo and Siding Springs Observatory.

CANBERRA INSTITUTE OF THE ARTS
GPO Box 804, Canberra, A.C.T. 2601
Tel: +61(6) 249-5701
Fax: +61(6) 249-5705

University of Ballarat
P.O. Box 663, Ballarat, Victoria 3353
Tel: +61(53) 279-000
Fax: +61(53) 279-545
Vice-Chancellor: D.W. James (1994-)
Academic Registrar: M. Mary Hickey
International Relations: K.G. Hawkins
Founded: 1990
F: Arts, Education and Humanities; Business and Information Management; Engineering and Science; Life Sciences.

University of Canberra
P.O. Box 1, Belconnen, A.C.T. 2616
Tel: +61(1) 201-5111
Fax: +61(1) 201-5999
E-Mail: australian and academic and research network (AARNET)
Vice-Chancellor: D.A. Aitkin (1991-98)
Deputy Vice-Chancellor (Administration): J. Grant
Founded: 1967, 1989
F: Applied Science; Communication; Education; Environmental Design; Information Sciences and Engineering; Management.
Ce: Applied Ecology Research; Corporate Law Research; Communication and Information Research; Public Sector Management Research; Water Research; Professional Education; Australian Regolith Studies.

Central Queensland University
Rockhampton, Queensland 4702
Tel: +61(79) 30-9777
Fax: +61(79) 36-1361
Vice-Chancellor: G.V.H. Wilson (1991-)
Registrar: K.G. Window
Founded: 1967, 1990
F: Applied Sciences; Arts; Business; Education;
Engineering; Health Sciences.
Ce: Capricornia Aboriginal and Islander Tertiary
Education.
D: Distance and Continuing Education.

*Charles Sturt University
The Grange, Panorama Avenue, Bathurst, New
South Wales 2795
Tel: +61(63) 384-200
Fax: +61(63) 384-833
Vice-Chancellor: C.D. Blake (1990-)
Secretary: P.G. Hodgson
Founded: 1989
F: Arts; Commerce; Health Studies; Science and
Agriculture; Teacher Education.
Ce: Conservation Farming; Image Analysis;
Rural Social Research; Parks, Recreation and
Heritage; Grape and Wine Research.
Graduate S: Police Management.

Curtin University of Technology
G.P.O. Box U1987, Perth, Western Australia 6001
Tel: +61(9) 351-2255
Fax: +61(9) 351-2255
Telex: AA92983
Cable: curtin university perth
Vice-Chancellor: John Maloney (1988-)
Executive Director (Finance and Property
Division): Peter Walton
International Relations: John Walsh
Founded: 1967, 1987
D: Engineering and Science; Arts, Education
and Social Sciences; Business and
Administration; Health Sciences; Research and
Development.
I: Agriculture.
S: Mines.

Muresk Institute of Agriculture
Northam, Western Australia 6401
Tel: +61(96) 224-530
Fax: +61(96) 221-709
Director: Murray Hawkins (1991-)
Manager: Ibrahim El-Wardani
Founded: 1926
Agriculture.

WESTERN AUSTRALIAN SCHOOL OF MINES
PO Box 597, Kalgoorlie, Western Australia 6430
Tel: +61(90) 805-000
Fax: +61(90) 805-100
Director: David Spottiswood (1991-)
Administrator: J.M. Murphy
Founded: 1903
D: Mineral Exploration and Mining Geology;
Minerals Engineering and Extractive Metallurgy;
Mining Engineering and Mine Surveying.

*Deakin University
Geelong, Victoria
Tel: +61(52) 271-100
Fax: +61(52) 272-001
E-Mail: dianeeakin.edu.au
Telex: duniv aa35625
Vice-Chancellor: John A. Hay (1992-)
Secretary: Russell H. Elliott
Founded: 1974, 1993
F: Arts; Education; Health and Behavioural
Sciences; Management; Science and Technology.
I: Arts; Distance Education; Koorie Education;
Nursing Research; Taxation and Policy Research.
Ce: Studies in Literary Education; Australian
Studies; Management Services; Aquatic Science;
Applied Social Research; Technology
Management; National Systems Management;
Health Options, Research and Development;
Psychology Research; Public Policy Research
and Development; Women's Research; Arabic
and Middle Eastern Studies; Asian Business;
Biological and Chemical Research; Molecular
Structure and Function; Regional Studies;
Education and Change.

BURWOOD CAMPUS
221 Burwood Highway, Burwood, Victoria 3125
Tel: +61(3) 244-6100

GEELONG CAMPUS
Pigdons Road, Waurn Ponds, Geelong, Victoria
3217
Tel: +61(52) 27-1100

RUSDEN CAMPUS
662 Blackburn Road, Clayton, Victoria 3168
Tel: +61(3) 244-7100

TOORAK CAMPUS
336 Glenferrie Road, Malvern, Victoria 3144
Tel: +61(3) 244-5100

WARRNAMBOOL CAMPUS
Sherwood Park, Princes Highway, Warrnambool,
Victoria 3280
Tel: +61(55) 63-3100

*Edith Cowan University
Pearson Street, Churchlands, Western Australia
6018
Tel: +61(9) 273-8333
Fax: +61(9) 273-8661
E-Mail: postman.cowan.edu.au
Vice-Chancellor: Roy Lourens (1993-)
Executive Director (Administration): Warren Snell
International Relations: Stephen Hunter
Founded: 1990
F: Arts; Business; Education; Health and Human
Sciences; Science, Technology and Engineering.
A: Performing Arts (Western Australian).

BUNBURY INSTITUTE OF ADVANCED EDUCATION
Robertson Drive, Bunbury (Western Australia)
6230
Advanced Education.

CHURCHLANDS CAMPUS
Pearson St, Churchlands (Western Australia) 6018
Tel: +61(9) 383-0333

CLAREMONT CAMPUS
Goldsworthy Rd, Claremont (Western Australia) 6010

JOONDALUP CAMPUS
Joondalup Drive, Joondalup (Western Australia) 6027

MOUNT LAWLEY CAMPUS
2 Bradford St, Mount Lawley (Western Australia) 6050
Tel: +61(9) 370-6111

EXTERNAL STUDIES CAMPUS
P.O. Box 830, Claremont (Western Australia) 6010

The Flinders University of South Australia
G.P.O. Box 2100, Adelaide, South Australia 5001
Tel: +61(8) 201-3911
Fax: +61(8) 201-3000
Vice-Chancellor: J.F. Lovering (1987-)
Director of Administration and Registrar: V. Massaro
Founded: 1963, 1966
F: Education, Humanities, Law and Theology; Health Sciences; Science and Engineering; Social Sciences.
I: Labour Studies (National).
Ce: CSIRO/Flinders Joint Research in Information Technology; Electronic Structure of Materials; Education and Training in Addiction (National); Neuroscience.
National Tidal Facilities.

*Griffith University
Nathan, Queensland 4111
Tel: +61(7) 875-7111
Fax: +61(7) 875-7965
Telex: AA40362
Vice-Chancellor: L.R. Webb (1985-)
Pro-Vice-Chancellor (Administration): A.C. Mc Andrew
International Relations: J. Conroy
Founded: 1971
F: Asian and International Studies; Environmental Sciences; Commerce and Administration; Education; Health and Behavioural Sciences; Humanities; Science and Technology.
L: Business and Hotel Management; Education and the Arts; Nursing and Health Sciences; Engineering and Applied Science.
I: Women's Research and Policy; Software Quality Research; Cultural Policy Studies; Applied Environmental Research; Law, Ethics and Public Affairs (National); Queensland Pharmaceutical Research.
Ce: Allied for Open Learning; Asian Spatial Information and Analysis Network; Applied Linguistics and Languages; Australian Public Sector Management; Catchment and In-Stream Research; Leisure Research; Research on Employment and Work; Strategic Change and Development; Strategic Human Services; Technology Management; Study of Australia-Asia Relations; Asian Languages and Studies (Key); Language Testing and Curriculum; Queensland Studies; Rotary District 9600 for Cardiavascular Research; Science Policy Research.
Ut: European Comparative Studies; Land Conservation Research; Neuropsychology; Study of Religious Change and Consciousness; Waste Management Research.

GOLD COAST UNIVERSITY COLLEGE
PMB 50, Gold Coast Mail Centre, Queensland 4217
Tel: +61(75) 94-8800
Fax: +61(75) 94-8777
Pro-Vice Chancellor and Director: M.G. Irving (1991-)
Administrator: J. Hucks
International Relations: J. Conroy
D: Business and Hotel Management; Education and the Arts; Nursing and Health Sciences; Engineering and Applied Sciences.
Ce: Applied Education; Tourism and Hotel Management Research; Ecotourism Research (International); Research and Information for Australian Agricultural Cooperatives.

GRAVATT CAMPUS
Queensland 4111
Tel: +61(7) 875-7111
Fax: +61(7) 875-5910
Vice-Chancellor: L.R. Webb (1984-)
International Relations: J. Conroy
Ce: Crime Policy and Public Safety; Deafness Studies and Research; Multimedia Research and Development; Education Management; Skill Formation Research and Development.
I: Learning in Mathematics and Language; Motor Learning and Graphic Communication.

QUEENSLAND COLLEGE OF ART
P.O. Box 84, Morningside, Queensland 4170
Tel: +61(7) 395-9170
Fax: +61(7) 395-6739
Provost and Director: I. Howard (1993-)
Administrator: L. Shorter
International Relations: J. Conroy
Ce: Design Excellence.

QUEENSLAND CONSERVATORIUM OF MUSIC
P.O. Box 28, Albert Street, Brisbane, Queensland 4002
Tel: +61(7) 875-6333
Fax: +61(7) 875-6262
Provost and Director (Acting): Janet Delpratt (1993-)
Registrar: I. Wallace
International Relations: J. Conroy

James Cook University of North Queensland
Townsville, Queensland 4811
Tel: +61(77) 814-111
Fax: +61(77) 796-371
Vice-Chancellor: R.M. Golding (1986-)
Pro-Vice-Chancellor (Administration) and
Registrar: K.S. Lester
International Relations: D. Petersen
Founded: 1961, 1970
F: Arts; Commerce and Economics; Education;
Engineering; Law; Science.
S: North Queensland Clinical; Behavioural
Sciences; Biological Sciences; Education;
Commerce; Tropical Veterinary Science and
Agriculture (Graduate).
Ce: Tropical Health and Medicine; Tropical
Freshwater Research; Tropical Marine Studies;
Aboriginal and Torres Strait Islander
Participation, Research and Development; Rural
Education Research and Development; Anton
Breinl for Tropical Health and Medicine; Applied
Economic Research and Analysis; Interactive
Multimedia; Women's Studies; Melanesian
Studies; Multidisciplinary Studies of Back Pain
(National); Remote Sensing; Southeast Asian
Studies; Study of Teacher Development;
Economic Geology (National Key).
Ut: Economic Geology Research; ICU Sugar -
Advanced Technology; Material Culture.
I: Tropical Architecture; Tropical Natural
Resources.
Board: Environmental Studies.

*La Trobe University
Melbourne 3083, Victoria
Tel: +61(3) 479-2000
Fax: +61(3) 471-0093
E-Mail: vcatrobe.edu.au
Telex: AA33143
Vice-Chancellor and Principal: M.J. Osborne
Founded: 1964
F: Economics, Education and Social Sciences;
Health Sciences; Humanities; Science and
Technology.

ALBURY-WODONGA CAMPUS
Bundoora, Victoria 3083
Tel: +61(60) 55-600

LA TROBE UNIVERSITY, BENDIGO
P.O. Box 199, Bendigo, Victoria 3550
Tel: +61(54) 447-222
Fax: +61(54) 447-777

Macquarie University
Sydney, New South Wales 2109
Tel: +61(2) 850-7111
Fax: +61(2) 850-7433
Vice-Chancellor: Dianne Yerbury (1987-)
Registrar and Vice-Principal: B.J. Spencer
Founded: 1964
I: Early Childhood; Asia Pacific Research.
S: Behavioural Sciences; Biological Sciences;
Chemistry; Earth Sciences; Economic and
Financial Studies; Education; English and

Linguistics; History, Philosophy and Politics; Law;
Mathematics, Physics, Computing, Electronics;
Modern Languages; Management (Graduate);
Environment (Graduate).
Ce: Ancient History Documentary Research;
Egyptology; Commonwealth Special Research for
Lasers and Applications; Dictionary Research;
Joint CSIRO - Macquarie University for Advanced
Systems Engineering; Learning for Numeracy
Skills; Mineral and Energy Economics; English
Language Teaching and Research (National); HIV
Social Research, Macquarie University AIDS
Research Unit (Nationaln); Post-Colonial
Literatures and Language Research; Speech,
Hearing and Language Research; Analytical
Biotechnology; Applied Social Research;
Australian Mineral Exploration Technologies;
Chinese Political Economy; Chiropractic;
Comparative Genocide Studies; Conflict
Resolution; Ecostratigraphy and Paleobiology;
Japanese Economic Studies; Language in Social
Life; Number Theory Research; Petrology and
Lithospheric Studies; Research into Special
Education and Rehabilitation; Slavonic and East
European Studies; Studies in Money, Banking
and Finance; Climactic Impacts.

*Royal Melbourne Institute of Technology (RMIT)
G.P.O. Box 2476V, Melbourne 3001, Victoria
Tel: +61(3) 662-0611
Fax: +61(3) 663-2764
E-Mail: beanland@rmit.edu.au
Vice-Chancellor: David G. Beanland
Administration Registrar: John M. Hartwell
International Relations: Tony Adamo
Founded: 1887, 1934, 1960, 1992
F: Applied Science; Social Sciences and
Communications; Art and Design; Biomedical and
Health Sciences; Business; Education;
Engineering; Environmental Design and
Construction; Nursing.
Sectors: Technical and Further Education.

*University of Melbourne
Grattan Street, Parkville, Victoria 3052
Tel: +61(3) 344-4000
Fax: +61(3) 344-5104
Telex: unimelb AA35185
Cable: unimelb, parkville, victoria
Vice-Chancellor and Principal: D.G. Penington
(1988-)
Registrar and Deputy Principal: J.B. Potter
International Relations: C.B. Schedvin
Founded: 1853
F: Agriculture and Forestry; Architecture and
Planning; Arts; Economics and Commerce;
Engineering; Law; Medicine, Dentistry and Health
Sciences; Music; Science; Veterinary Science.
I: Applied Economic and Social Research;
Education; Judicial Administration; National
Vision Research.
S: Management.

C: Arts (Victorian); Agriculture and Horticulture (Victorian).
Ce: Asian Business; Asian Law; Australian; Comparative Constitutional Studies; Geographic Information Systems and Modelling; Study of Higher Education; Social Biology Resources; Statistical Consulting.

HAWTHORN INSTITUTE OF EDUCATION
442 Auburn Road, Hawthorn, Victoria 3122
Tel: +61(3) 810-3322
Fax: +61(3) 810-3188
E-Mail: briwil@erebus.hie.unimelb.eov.au
Director: J.M. Hearn (1987-)
Associate Director: B. Williamson
International Relations: Associate Director, Commercial Unit, D. Mitchel
Ce: Studies in Adult and Vocational Development; Continuing Education and Training; Human Resources Development.

VICTORIAN COLLEGE OF THE ARTS
234 St. Kilda Road, Melbourne, Victoria 3004
Tel: +61(3) 685-9300
Fax: +61(3) 682-1841
Director: C. Gregory (1989-)
International Relations: C. Gregory
Founded: 1981
S: Art; Dance; Drama; Film and Television; Music.

*Monash University
Wellington Road, Clayton, Victoria 3168
Tel: +61(3) 905-4000
Fax: +61(3) 905-4007
Telex: monash aa32691
Vice-Chancellor and President: M.I. Logan (1987-92)
General Manager: P.B. Wade
Founded: 1958
F: Arts; Business and Economics; Computing and Information Technology; Education (Clayton and Frankston Campuses); Engineering; Law; Medicine; Science.
C: Pharmacy (Victorian).

CAULFIELD CAMPUS
911 Dandenong Road, Caulfield East, Victoria 3145
Tel: +61(3) 903 2000
Fax: +61(3) 2400

GIPPSLAND CAMPUS
Switchback Road, Churchill, Victoria 3842
Tel: +61(51) 22 6200
Fax: +61(51) 22 6300

PENINSULA CAMPUS
McMahons Road, Frankston, Victoria 3199
Tel: +61(3) 904 4000
Fax: +61(3) 904 4190

VICTORIAN COLLEGE OF PHARMACY
381 Royal Parade, Parkville, Victoria 3052
Tel: +61(3) 903 9000
Fax: +61(3) 903 9581
Pharmacy.

Murdoch University
South Street, Murdoch, Western Australia 6150
Tel: +61(9) 360-6000
Fax: +61(9) 360-2507
E-Mail: user@csuvaxl.csu.murdoch.edu.au
Telex: mulib AA92711
Vice-Chancellor: P.J. Boyce (1985-)
Registrar: R. MacWilliam
International Relations: L.R. Davidson
Founded: 1973
S: Biological and Environmental Sciences; Economics and Commerce; Education; Humanities; Law; Mathematical and Physical Sciences; Social Sciences; Veterinary Studies.
I: Environmental Science; Molecular Genetics and Animal Disease; Research into Safety and Transport.
Ce: Asia Research on Social, Political and Economic Change; Co-operative Research in Hydrometallorgy (A.J. Parker); Research in Culture and Communications; Mathematics, Science and Technology Education; Western Australian Labour Market Research; State Agricultural Biotechnology; Research on Women.
Ut: Social Programme Evalutation; Computer and Network Services; Murdoch University Energy Research; Aboriginal Education.

University of New England
Armidale, New South Wales 2351
Tel: +61(67) 733-333
Fax: +61(67) 733-122
E-Mail: bruce.thom.edu.au
Telex: 166050
Vice-Chancellor: Bruce G.Thom (1994-)
Registrar: R. Davis
International Relations: Terry Cavanagh
Founded: 1938, 1954
F: Arts; Economic Studies; Education, Nursing and Professional Studies; Sciences.

*The University of New South Wales
Sydney, New South Wales 2052
Tel: +61(2) 385-1000
Fax: +61(2) 385-2000
E-Mail: records.admin@unsw.edu.au
Telex: AA26054
Cable: unitech, sydney
Vice-Chancellor and Principal: J.R. Niland (1992-94)
Registrar and Deputy Principal: C. Condous
International Relations: M.C. Schroder
Founded: 1949, 1958
F: Applied Sciences; Built Environment; Biological and Behavioural Sciences; Commerce and Economics; Engineering; Law; Medicine; Professional Studies; Science; Arts and Social Sciences.
S: Management (Graduate).
C: Fine Arts.
Board of Studies: Science and Mathematics; Taxation.
I: Administration; Languages.

Ce: Liberal and General Studies; Aboriginal Law; Marine Science; Human Rights; Industrial Relations Research; Kingsford Legal; Japanese Economic and Management Studies; National Drug and Alcohol Research; HIV Epidemiology and Clinical Research; Social Policy Research.

The University of Newcastle
Callaghan, Newcastle, New South Wales 2308
Tel: +61(49) 21-5000
Fax: +61(49) 21-6922
Vice-Chancellor: R.J. Mortley
Secretary: G. Cheong
International Relations: Assistant Vice-Chancellor, I. Graham
Founded: 1951, 1965
F: Architecture; Art and Design; Arts and Social Science; Economics and Commerce; Education; Engineering; Law; Medicine and Health Sciences; Music; Nursing; Science and Mathematics.

Northern Territory University
P.O. Box 40146, Casuarina, Northern Territory 0811
Tel: (89) 466-666
Fax: (89) 270-612
E-Mail: pricedärwin.ntu.edu.au
Telex: ntuni AA85235
Vice-Chancellor: M.E. Nairn (1989-)
Registrar: D.M. Price
International Relations: Director, External Relations, Keith Solomon
Founded: 1989
F: Arts; Business; Education; Law; Science.
I: Technical and Further Education.
S: Construction and Engineering Trades; Commerce, Tourism, Hospitality; Technology; Vehicle and Electrical Trades; Vocational and Access Studies.
Ce: Aboriginal and Islander Studies; Development Management; Energy Studies; Social Research; Southeast Asian Studies; Studies of Language in Education; Teaching and Learning in Diverse Educational Context.

*The University of Queensland
St. Lucia, Brisbane, Queensland 4072
Tel: +61(7) 365-1111
Fax: +61(7) 365-1199
E-Mail: b.wilson@mailbox.uq.oz.au
Telex: univqld AA40315
Vice-Chancellor: Brian G. Wilson (1879-95)
Secretary and Registrar: D. Porter
International Relations: Pro-Vice-Chancellor, External Affairs, A.G. Rix
Founded: 1910
F: Agricultural Science; Architecture and Planning; Arts; Commerce and Economics; Dentistry; Education; Engineering; Law; Medicine; Music; Science; Social Work; Veterinary Science.
I: Modern Languages.
Ce: Language Teaching and Research; Australian Studies; Drug Design and Development; Information Technology Research;

Molecular Biology and Biotechnology; Microscopy and Microanalysis.
Groups: Biological Sciences; Health Sciences; Humanities; Physical Sciences and Engineering; Social Sciences Group.

*UNIVERSITY OF QUEENSLAND GATTON COLLEGE
Lawes QLD 4343
Tel: +61(74) 601-111
Fax: +61(74) 601-499
Telex: unvqldaa40315
Director: H.R. Lovell (1991-94)
Registrar: Gay Westmore
Founded: 1897, 1990
F: Applied Science; Business.

*University of Southern Queensland
Toowoomba, Queensland 4350
Tel: +61(76) 312-100
Fax: +61(76) 361-762
Vice-Chancellor: R.B. Leal (1992-94)
Registrar: Alan Finch
International Relations: Geoff Edmondson
Founded: 1967, 1990
F: Commerce; Sciences; Arts; Education; Engineering and Surveying; Business.

*Queensland University of Technology
G.P.O. 2434, Brisbane, Queensland 4001
Tel: +61(7) 864-2111
Fax: +61(7) 864-1510
Telex: AA44699
Vice-Chancellor: R.D. Gibson
Registrar: B.S. Waters
Founded: 1965, 1989
F: Arts; Built Environment and Engineering; Business (Gardens Point); Health (Kelvin Grove); Information Technology (Gardens Point); Law (Gardens Point); Science (Gardens Point); Teacher Education (Carseldine); Teacher Education (Kelvin Grove).
Ce: Aboriginal and Torres Strait Islander.

CARSELDINE CAMPUS
Tel: +61(7) 283 6222
Fax: +61(7) 864 4999
S: Humanities; Social Sciences.

KEDRON PARK CAMPUS
Tel: +61(7) 357 7077
Fax: +61(7) 864 4499
Vice-President: R.D. Gibson

KELVIN GROVE CAMPUS
Tel: +61(7) 352 8111
Fax: +61(7) 864 3998
Vice-Chancellor: R.D. Gibson
Registrar: B.S. Waters
Founded: 1989
F: Education.
S: Arts; Human Movement Studies; Nursing; Optometry; Public Health.

*University of South Australia
GPO Box 2471, Adelaide, South Australia 5001
Tel: +61(8) 302-6611
Fax: +61(8) 302-2466
Telex: iteca AA 82565
Vice-Chancellor: David Robinson (1992-)
Registrar: Liz Watson
International Relations: Robert Koenne
Founded: 1991
F: Aboriginal and Islander Studies; Applied Science and Technology; Art, Architecture and Design; Business and Management; Education; Engineering; Health and Biomedical Sciences; Humanities and Social Sciences; Nursing.

Southern Cross University
PO Box 157, Lismore, New South Wales 2480
Tel: +61(66) 203600
Fax: +61(66) 221300
E-Mail: vice-chancellor@scu.edu.au
Vice-Chancellor: Bavvy Conynghaw (1994-)
Director of Administration: Malcolm Marshall
International Relations: Pro-Vice-Chancellor (Academic), Zbys Klich
Founded: 1994
F: Arts; Business Computing; Education and Work training; Health Sciences; Law and Criminal Justice; Resource Science Management.

Sunshine Coast University College
Nambour, Queensland 4560
Tel: +61(71) 41-6244
Fax: +61(71) 41-7769
Founded: 1994

*Swinburne University of Technology
P.O. Box 218, Hawthorn, Victoria 3122
Tel: +61(3) 214-8911
Fax: +61(3) 214-5454
E-Mail: jgw@stan.xx.swin.oz.au
Vice-Chancellor: J.G. Wallace (1986-)
Deputy Vice-Chancellor: F.G. Bannon
International Relations: Pro-Vice-Chancellor, L. Kilmartin
Founded: 1908
D: Business Humanities and Social Sciences (Schools); Social Sciences and Arts; Business and Information Systems; Engineering and Industrial Sciences.
Ce: Applied Colloid Science; Applied Neurosciences; Business Development and Training; Engineering Technology; Housing and Planning; Industrial Democracy; Psychological Services; Women's Studies; Systems Methodologies; Scientific Instrumentation Training (National); New Media Arts and Technologies (National); For Women (National); Korean Studies (National).

*University of Sydney
Sydney, New South Wales 2006
Tel: +61(2) 692-2222
Fax: +61(2) 692-456 (Vice-Chancellor); +61(2) 692-4607 (Registrar)
Cable: univsyd, sydney
Vice-Chancellor and Principal: D. McNicol
Registrar and Deputy Principal: S. Chapinan
International Relations: Deputy Principal (External Relations), L. Plelan
Founded: 1850
F: Agriculture; Architecture; Dentistry; Economics; Education; Engineering; Law; Medicine; Science; Veterinary Science; Nursing; Arts.
C: Arts.
Conservatorium: Music.

CUMBERLAND COLLEGE
PO Box 170, Lidcombe, New South Wales 2141
Tel: +61(2) 646 6444
Fax: +61(2) 646 4853
Director: J. Kinneak

GRADUATE SCHOOL OF BUSINESS
Tel: +61(2) 550-8637
Fax: +61(2) 550-8603
Director: M. Welles (1986-)
Business.

INSTITUTE OF NURSING STUDIES
88 Mallett Street, Campterdown, New South Wales 2050
Tel: +61(2) 517 0222
Fax: +61(2) 517 0208
Principal: L. Russell (1991-)
Nursing.

NSW CONSERVATORIUM OF MUSIC
Macquarie Street, Sydney, New South Wales 2000
Tel: +61(2) 230 1222
Fax: +61(2) 230 1296
Director: J. Hopkins
Music.

ORANGE AGRICULTURAL COLLEGE
Leeds Parade, Orange, New South Wales 2800
Tel: +61(63) 63 5555
Fax: +61(63) 63 5590
E-Mail: orange@oac.usqd.edu.au
Principal: John Chudleigw (1990-94)
Registrar: Jennifer Hector
Founded: 1973
Agriculture.

SYDNEY COLLEGE OF THE ARTS
266 Glebe Point Road, Glebe, New South Wales 2037
Tel: +61(2) 692 0266
Fax: +61(2) 692 9235
Director: R. Dunn
Arts.

*University of Technology Sydney

P.O. Box 123, Broadway, Sydney, New South
Wales 2007
Tel: +61(2) 330-1990
Fax: +61(2) 330-1551
E-Mail: @ uts.edu. au./u queries to: university
secretary, uts.edu au.
Telex: untas AA75004
Vice-Chancellor and President: R.D. Guthrie
(1986-)
Executive Director, University Administration:
Robyn Kemmis
International Relations: Peter Inman
Founded: 1965, 1988
F: Design, Architecture and Building; Business;
Social Sciences; Education; Engineering; Law
and Legal Practice; Sciences; Mathematical and
Computing Sciences; Nursing.
S: Adult Education; Physical Sciences;
Accounting; Management; Architecture;
Biological and Biomedical Sciences; Building
Studies; Computing Sciences; Design; Adult
Vocational Education; Civil Engineering;
Electrical Engineering; Mechanical Engineering;
Engineering (Graduate); Adult and Language
Education; Teacher Education; Humanities;
Finance and Economics; Business (Graduate);
Law; Legal Practice (College of Law); Leisure
and Tourism Studies; Information Studies;
Marketing; Mathematical Sciences; Nursing
Therapeutics; Nursing Health Studies; Legal
Practice.
C: Environmental Toxicology; Graduate Nursing
Studies; Local Government Education and
Research; Groundwater Management (National).

KURING-GAI CAMPUS
Eton Road, Lindfield, New South Wales 2070
Tel: +61(2) 330 1990
Fax: +61(2) 330 5549
E-Mail: uts.edu.au
Telex: untas aa75004
Vice-Chancellor and President: R.D. Guthrie
(1986-)
Executive Director, University Administration:
Robyn Kemmis
International Relations: Peter Inman
F: Business and Social Sciences; Nursing
Education.

*University of Tasmania

Hobart Campus, Churchill Avenue, G.P.O. Box
252C, Hobart, Tasmania 7001
Tel: +61(2) 202-101
Fax: +61(2) 202-186
Vice-Chancellor and Principal: Alan D. Gilbert
(1991-)
Deputy Principal and Registrar: Chris Chapman
International Relations: Deputy Principal,
Property, Development and University Services,
Bob Cleary
Founded: 1890, 1991

F: Humanities and Social Sciences; Education;
Engineering and Surveying; Science; Business;
Design; Visual and Performing Arts; Nursing.
F: Law; Medicine and Pharmacy.
S: Art.
I: Antarctic and Southern Ocean Studies.
Ce: Regional Economic Analysis; Population
Health Research (Menzies).
Div: Forestry and Cooperative Research Centre
for Temperate Hardwood Forestry (CSIRO).
Conservatorium: Music.

LAUNCESTON CAMPUS
PO Box 1214, Launceston, Tasmania 7250
Tel: +61(2) 243-201
Fax: +61(2) 243-6304
F: Humanities and Social Science; Education;
Engineering and Surveying; Science; Busines;
Design; Visual and Performing Arts; Nursing.
Ce: Performing Arts.

Victoria University of Technology

PO Box 11428 mmc, Melbourne, Victoria 3000
Tel: +61(3) 688-4000
Fax: +61(3) 689-4069
Vice-Chancellor: Jarlath Ronayne (1991-)
Deputy Vice-Chancellor: Eric Lund
International Relations: Director of External
Affairs, Michael Halls
Founded: 1990
F: Arts; Business; Engineering; Human
Development; Science.
D: Technical and Further Education.
Ce: Environmental Safety and Risk Engineering;
Strategic Economic Research; Rehabilitation,
Exercise and Sport Sciences; Asia-Pacific
Studies; Bioprocessing and Food Technology.

The University of Western Australia

Nedlands, Western Australia 6009
Tel: +61(9) 380-38381
Fax: +61(9) 382-4071
Telex: 92992
Cable: uniwest perth
Vice-Chancellor: Fay Gale (1989-96)
Registrar: M.R. Orr
International Relations: D. Nesdale
Founded: 1911, 1990
F: Agriculture; Arts; Engineering and
Mathematical Sciences; Economics, Commerce,
Education and Law; Medicine; Science.
Ce: Aboriginal Programmes; Asian Studies;
Linguistics; Rural Education Research;
Microscopy and Microanalysis; Water Research;
Co-operative Research for Legumes in
Mediterranean Agriculture; Crystallography;
Indian Ocean for Peace Studies; Advanced
Mineral and Materials Processing (Research).

University of Western Sydney

Office of the Vice-Chancellor, P.O. Box 1000, St. Mary's, New South Wales 2760
Tel: +61(2) 833-1222
Fax: +61(2) 678-1804
E-Mail: n.thompson@uws.edu.au
Vice-Chancellor: Brian W. Smith (1989-)
Secretary: Norman Thompson
International Relations: Christine Brierley
Founded: 1989

University of Western Sydney, Hawkesbury

Bourke Street, Richmond, New South Wales 2753
Tel: +61(45) 701-333
Fax: +61(45) 783-979
E-Mail: n.burnett@uws.edu.au
Deputy Vice-Chancellor and Chief Executive Officer: John Clark (1993-)
Registrar: Noel Burnett
Founded: 1891, 1989
F: Agriculture and Horticulture; Science and Technology; Health, Humanities and Social Ecology; Management.

University of Western Sydney, Macarthur

P.O. Box 555, Campbelltown, New South Wales 2560
Tel: +61(46) 203-100
Fax: +61(46) 281-298
E-Mail: k.jenningsúws.edu.au
Deputy Vice-Chancellor and Chief Executive Officer: David Campbell Barr (1989-)
Registrar: Keith Jennings
Founded: 1975, 1983, 1989
F: Law; Arts and Social Sciences; Business and Technology; Education; Health.
Ce: Innovation and International Trade; Language Export Research; Health Services Research.
I: Gambling Research.

University of Western Sydney, Nepean

PO Box 10, Kingswood, New South Wales 2747
Tel: +61(47) 36-0222
Fax: +61(47) 36-0714
E-Mail: g.stlawrence@nepean.uws.edu.au
Deputy Vice-Chancellor: Jillian Maling (1989-)
Manager, Academic and Administrative Services: Garry St. Lawrence
International Relations: Vivienne Porter
Founded: 1973, 1989
F: Commerce; Education; Health Studies; Humanities and Social Sciences; Science and Technology; Visual and Performing Arts.
D: Continuing Education West.
Ce: Communication, Health and Education Research (CHER); Women's Research (Focus on Women in the community, as well as academic issues); Electrochemichal Research and Analytical Technology.

*University of Wollongong

Northfields Avenue, Wollongong, New South Wales 2522
Tel: +61(42) 213-555
Fax: +61(42) 213-477
E-Mail: k.mckinnon@uow.edu.au
Telex: 29022
Cable: uniofwol
Vice-Chancellor and Principal: G.R. Sutton (1995-)
Vice-Principal: K.E. Baumber
International Relations: Vice-Principal (International), J.W. Langridge
Founded: 1961, 1975
F: Arts; Commerce; Education; Engineering; Law; Health and Behavioural Sciences; Informatics; Science; Arts.

PRIVATE INSTITUTIONS

Australian Catholic University

P.O. Box 968, North Sydney, New South Wales 2059
Tel: +61(2) 739-2900
Fax: +61(2) 739-2905
Vice-Chancellor: P.J. Drake (1991-)
Secretary: R.G. Doyle
Founded: 1991
F: Arts and Science; Education (primary and secondary); Health Sciences.
S: Business.

McAULEY CAMPUS, QUEENSLAND
Everton Park, PO Box 247, Queensland 4053
Tel: +61(7) 855-7100
Fax: +61(7) 855-7105
Director (Acting): P. Meere (1994-)
Director of Administration: V. Bourke
Founded: 1991
F: Arts and Sciences; Education; Health Sciences.
S: Business.

N.S.W. CAMPUSES
N.S.W. Secretariat, 179 Albert Road, Strathfield 2135
Tel: +61(2) 739-2100
Fax: +61(2) 739-2232
Principal: M. Dynan (1991-)
Director of Administration: P. Haggerty
Founded: 1991
F: Arts and Sciences; Education; Health Sciences.
S: Business.

SIGNADOU CAMPUS
PO Box 256, Dickson, ACT 2602
Tel: +61(6) 209-1100
Fax: +61(6) 209-1105
Principal: R. Lewins, O.P. (1991-)
Deputy Principal: R. Storrier
Founded: 1991
F: Arts and Sciences; Education.

VICTORIA CAMPUSES
PO Box 146, East Melbourne, Victoria 3002
Tel: +61(3) 563-3723
Fax: +61(3) 563-3725
Principal: B. Daffey (1991-)
Director of Administration: G. Easton
Founded: 1991
F: Arts and Sciences; Education; Health
Sciences.
S: Business.

Bond University
Gold Coast, Queensland 4229
Tel: +61(75) 951-111
Fax: +61(75) 951-140
Executive Chancellor: H. Messel (1993-)
Dean: C.J. Madden
International Relations: L. Holyman
Founded: 1989
S: Business; Humanities and Social Sciences;
Information and Computing Sciences; Law.
Ce: Language.

University of Notre Dame Australia
P.O. Box 1295, Freemantle, Western Australia
6160
Tel: +61(9) 430-0500
Fax: +61(9) 430-6031
Vice-Chancellor: P. Tannock
Registrar: K.D. O'Sullivan
Founded: 1992

OTHER INSTITUTIONS

PUBLIC INSTITUTIONS

Australian Maritime College
PO Box 986, Lauceston, Tasmania 7250
Tel: +61(3) 260711
Fax: +61(3) 260717
Principal: R.F. Short (1992-)
Director, Corporate Services: M. Hall
International Relations: Manager, Asia-Pacific
Maritime Centre, J. Hawkins
Founded: 1978
F: Maritime Transport and Engineering;
Fisheries and Marine Environment.

Avondale College
Freemans Drive, PO Box 19, Cooranbong, New
South Wales 2265
Tel: +61(49) 771-107
Fax: +61(49) 772-578
Principal: G.A. Madigan (1991-)
Registrar: D. Cooke
Founded: 1989
D: Art, Design and Technology; Business
Studies; Education; Humanities; Mathematics and
Computing; Music; Nursing; Science; Theology.

Marcus Oldham Farm Management College
Pigdon Road, Waurn Ponds, Victoria 3216
Tel: +61(52) 433-533
Fax: +61(52) 44-1263
Deputy Principal: C. Hacking
International Relations: C. Hacking
Founded: 1961
Farm Management.

NATIONAL ACADEMIC BODIES

Department of Employment, Education and Training
16-18 Mort Street, GPO Box 9880, Canberra, ACT
2601
Tel: +61(6) 240-8111
Fax: +61(6) 240-9783
Telex: aa62616
Secretary: D. Volker (1993-)
International Relations: R. Peacock
Founded: 1987

Australian Vice-Chancellors' Committee (AVCC)
1-5 Geils Court, GPO Box 1142, Deakin, ACT 2600
Tel: +61(6) 285-8200
Fax: +61(6) 285-8211
E-Mail: f.s.hambley@avcc.edu.au
President: D. McNicol (1994-95)
Executive Director: F.S. Hambly
Founded: 1920

National Office of Overseas Skills Recognition (NOOSR)
PO Box 1407, Canberra City, ACT 2601
Tel: +61(6) 276-7644
Fax: +61(6) 276-7566
Telex: aa62612
Assistant Secretary: J. Ledgar
Founded: 1986

Higher Education Research and Development Society of Australasia Incorporated
c/o Professional Development Centre, University
of New South Wales, Kensington, New South
Wales 2033
Tel: +61(2) 697-4937
Fax: +61(2) 662-8730
Telex: via aa26054
Cable: vua ubutech, sydney
President: David Boud
Honorary Secretary: Alan Prosser
Founded: 1972

Australian National Commission for Unesco
UN Social Section, Department of Foreign Affairs
and Trade, Administrative Building, Parkes Way,
Parkes, ACT 2600
Tel: +61(6) 261-2896
Fax: +61(6) 261-3424
Cable: unesco canberra
Chairman: K. Wiltshire (1993-)
Secretary: Andrew Todd
International Relations: K. Wiltshire
Founded: 1946

AUSTRIA

UNIVERSITIES

College of Music and Dramatic Art Graz
[Hochschule für Musik und darstellende Kunst in
Graz]
Leonhardstrasse 15, 8010 Graz
Tel: +43(316) 389-0
Fax: +43(316) 325-04
Rektor: Otto Kolleritsch (1991-95)
Rektoratsdirektor: Hermann Becke
International Relations: Petra Ernst-Kúhr
Founded: 1816, 1963, 1970
*D: Music and Dramatic Art (including Music
Ethnology, Jazz Research, Electronic Music, and
Music Aesthetics and Evaluation Research);
Composition, Music Theory, Conducting;
Keyboard Instruments; String Instruments; Wind
and Percussion Instruments; Music Education;
Church Music; Voice and Stage Design; Jazz;
Performing Art.*
*I: Music Ethnology; Music Aesthetics and
Evaluation Research; Performance Practice; Jazz
Research; Electronic Music.*

*Karl Franzens University of Graz
[Karl-Franzens-Universität Graz]
Universitätsplatz 3, 8010 Graz
Tel: +43(316) 380
Fax: +43(316) 384-750
Telex: 031 1662 ubgrz
Rektor: Helmut Konrad
Universitätsdirector: Michael Suppanz
Founded: 1585, 1782, 1827
*Catholic Theology; Law; Social Sciences and
Economics; Medicine; Human Sciences; Natural
Sciences.*
C: Data Processing.
I: Fundamental History Research.

Technical University of Graz
[Technische Universität Graz]
Rechbauerstrasse 12, 8010 Graz
Tel: +43(316) 873-0
Fax: +43(316) 827-679
Telex: 311221
Rektor: Josef W. Woł.niz (1991-93)
Universitätsdirektor: Fritz Auer
International Relations: Maria Edlinger.
Founded: 1811, 1865, 1955

*F: Architecture; Constructional Engineering;
Mechanical Engineering; Electrical Engineering;
Technical-Natural Sciences.*
C: Computer and Information Services.
*I: Electron Microscopy and Fine Structure
Research; Alternative Energy and Biomass
Research.*

University of Innsbruck
[Leopold-Franzens Universität Innsbruck]
Innrain 52, 6020 Innsbruck
Tel: +43(512) 507-0
Rector: Hans Moser
Universitätsdirektor: Friedrich Luhan
International Relations: Mathias Schennach
Founded: 1669
*F: Catholic Theology; Law; Social Sciences and
Economics; Medicine; Human Sciences; Natural
Sciences; Civil Engineering and Architecture.*
*I: Alpine Research (Obergurgl/Ötztal);
Interpretation; America; Electron Microscopy;
Physical Education.*

University of Klagenfurt
[Universität Klagenfurt]
Universitätsstrasse 65, 9021 Klagenfurt
Tel: +43(463) 2700-0
Fax: +43(463) 2700-100
Rektor: Willibald Dórfler
Universitätsdirektor: Arnulf Longin
International Relations: Barbara Gluyas-Friehs
Founded: 1970, 1975
D: Computer Sciences.
*I: Teaching of Contemporary History; Teaching
of Geography; Teaching of History; Teaching of
Mathematics; Teaching of Anglo-American
Studies; Teaching of Germanic Languages and
Literature; Teaching of Romance Philology;
Teaching of Slavic Studies; Teaching of
Educational Economics and Sociology; Teaching
of Curriculum Research and Organizational
Development in Education; Psychology;
Philosophy and Group Dynamics; General and
Applied Linguistic; Educational Technology and
Media; Interuniversity Research for Distance
Education; Interuniversity Research for
Technology Media Didactics and Engineering
Education; Comparative Literature; Law; Further
Education.*
S: Business and Economics.

University of Mining and Metallurgy Leoben
[Montanuniversität Leoben]
Franz-Josef-Strasse 18, 8700 Leoben
Tel: +43(3842) 402-0
Fax: +43(3842) 402-308
Telex: 033322 mhbleo
Rektor: Albert T. Oberhofer
Universittsdirektor: Adalbert Neuburg
International Relations: Albert F. Oberhofer
Founded: 1840, 1904, 1975

Mining Engineering; Mine Surveying; Metallurgy;
Petroleum Engineering; Refractories and
Ceramics Engineering; Mining and Metallurgy
Machinery; Plastics Technology; Materials
Sciences; Mining Geology.

Johannes Kepler University Linz
[Johannes Kepler Universität Linz]
Altenberger Strasse 69, 4040 Linz-Auhof
Tel: +43(732) 2468-0
Fax: +43(732) 2468-10
Telex: 2-2323 unili a
Rektor: Johannes Hengstschläger (1991-95)
ProrektorUniversitätsdirektor: Peter Weiss:
Othmar Köckinger
International Relations: Edith Zakel
Founded: 1962, 1975
F: Law; Social Sciences and Economics;
Technology and Natural Sciences.
Research I: Law; Micro Processor Technology;
Optoelectronics; Social Planning; Symbolic
Computation; Knowledge Processing; European
Law; Health Care and Health Systems.
I: Interdisciplinary for Development
Co-operation.

University of Art and Industrial Design Linz
[Hochschule für künstlerische und industrielle
Gestaltung in Linz]
Hauptplatz 8, 4010 Linz
Tel: +43(732) 785-173
Fax: +43(732) 783-508
Rektor: Wolfgang Stifter (1992-96)
Rektoratsdirektor (Chief Administrator): Robert
Klug
Founded: 1947, 1973
D: Aesthetic Education; Environmental Design;
Applied Graphic Arts.

Academy of Music and the Performing Arts 'Mozarteum' Salzburg
[Hochschule für Musik und darstellende Kunst
'Mozarteum' in Salzburg]
Mirabellplatz 1, 5020 Salzburg
Tel: +43(662) 75534-0
Rector: Wolfgang Roscher
Executive Director: Annemarie
Lassacher-Sandmeier
International Relations: Andrea Matschl
Founded: 1841, 1914, 1953, 1970
Music and Fine Arts.

University of Salzburg
[Universität Salzburg]
Residenzplatz 1, 5010 Salzburg
Tel: +43(662) 8044-0
Rektor: Edgar Morscher
Universitatsdirektor: Raimund Spruzina
International Relations: Markus Bayer
Founded: 1617, 1962
F: Theology; Law; Philosophy; Natural Sciences.
Ce: International Research.
I: Interuniversity Research for Distance
Education.

Academy of Fine Arts Vienna
[Akademie der bildenden Künste in Wien]
Schillerplatz 3, 1010 Wien
Tel: +43(1) 58816
Fax: +43(1) 587-7977
Rektor: Carl Pruscha
International Relations: Christa Sichrovsky
Founded: 1696
Fine Arts.

College of Music and Dramatic Art Vienna
[Hochschule für Musik und darstellende Kunst in
Wien]
Lothringerstrasse 18, 1030 Wien
Tel: +43(1) 58806
Rector: Michael Frischenschlager
Executive Director: Elizabeth Freismüth
International Relations: Isabel Olade-Schmid
Founded: 1817, 1920, 1970
Music and Dramatic Art.

University of Agriculture Vienna
[Universität für Bodenkultur Wien]
Gregor Mendelstrasse 33, 1180 Wien
Tel: +43(1) 342-500
Fax: +43(1) 369-1659
Cable: bodenkultur A-1180
Rektor: Manfried Welan
Universitätsdirektor: Ilona Glzer
International Relations: Irene Múller
Founded: 1872, 1975
D: Agriculture; Forestry and Wood Technology;
Cultivation and Water Technology; Food and
Fermentation Technology; Landscape Ecology
and Design.

University of Applied Arts Vienna
[Hochschule für angewandte Kunst in Wien]
Oskar-Kokoschka-Platz 2, 1010 Wien
Tel: +43(1) 7133
Fax: +43(1) 71133-2858
Rektor: Oswald Oberhuber
Universitätsdirektor: Heinz Adamek
Founded: 1867, 1948, 1970
F: Architecture; Fine Arts; Plastic Arts and
Design; Visual Communication; Art and Art
Education.

University of Technology Vienna
[Technische Universität Wien]
Karlsplatz 13, 1040 Wien
Tel: +43(1) 58801
Telex: 131.000 tvfwa
Rektor: Peter Skalicky
Universitätsdirektor: Ernst Schranz
Founded: 1815, 1872
F: Land Development and Architecture; Civil
Engineering; Mechanical Engineering; Electrical
Engineering; Natural Sciences.

*University of Vienna
[Universität Wien]
Dr. Karl Lueger-Ring 1, 1010 Wien
Tel: +43(1) 401-03
Fax: +43(1) 402-3800
E-Mail: alfred.ebenbauer@univie.ac.at
Telex: 115619
Rektor: Alfred Ebenbauer
Universitätsdirektor: Franz Skacel
Founded: 1365, 1377, 1384, 1850
F: Catholic Theology; Protestant Theology; Law; Social Sciences and Economics; Medicine; Basic and General Sciences; Human Sciences; Mathematics and Natural Sciences.

*Vienna University of Economics and Business Administration
[Wirtschaftsuniversität Wien]
Augasse 2-6, 1090 Wien
Tel: +43(1) 340-525
Fax: +43(1) 340-525
E-Mail: EARN/BITNET: wupost@awiwuw11
Telex: 111-127 wuw a
Rektor: Fritz Scheuch (1991-)
Universitätsdirektor: Hans Dieter Libowitzky
Founded: 1898, 1919, 1975
D: Business Administration; Economics; Law; Human Sciences.

Vienna University of Veterinary Medicine
[Veterinärmedizinische Universität Wien]
Linke Bahngasse 11, 1030 Wien
Tel: +43(1) 711-55-211
Fax: +43(1) 711-55-205
Rektor: Ehmar Bamberg (1991-95)
Universitätsdirektor: Herbert Maska
Founded: 1896, 1908, 1920, 1975
Veterinary Medicine.

NATIONAL ACADEMIC BODIES

Ministry of Science and Research
[Bundesministerium für Wissenschaft und Forschung]
Minoritenplatz 5, 1010 Wien
Tel: +43(1) 53120-0
Fax: +43(1) 53150-5155
Telex: 111157 bmfwf a
Minister for Science and Research: Erhard Busek
Founded: 1970

Austrian Science Foundation
[Fonds zur Förderung der wissenschaftlichen Forschung (FWF)]
Weyringergasse 35, 1040 Wien
Tel: +43(1) 505-6740
Fax: +43(1) 505-6739
President: Helmut Rauch
Secretary-General: Eva Glück
Founded: 1968

Standing Conference of Austrian Rectors
[Österreichische Rektorenkonferenz (ÖRK)]
Liechtensteinstrasse 22a, 1090 Wien
Tel: +43(1) 310-56560
Fax: +43(1) 310-5656-22
Chairman: Johannes Hengstschläger
Secretary-General: Andrea Henzl Suess

Union of Austrian Learned Societies/ Association des Sociétés scientifiques autrichienne
[Verband der wissenschaftlichen Gesellschaf ten österreichs (VWGÖ)]
Lindengasse 37, 1070 Wien
Tel: (222) 93 21 66
Fax: (222) 52 62 054
President: Hans Hoyer
Secretary-General: Rainer Zitta
Founded: 1949

Austrian National Commission for Unesco
Mentergasse 11, 1070 Wien
Tel: +43(1) 523-6421
Fax: +43(1) 5261-30120
Cable: unescokom wien
President: Gerald Mader
Secretary-General: Harald Gardos

AZERBAIJAN

UNIVERSITIES

Azerbaijan Industrial University
[Azerbajdžanskij Industrial'nyj Universitet]
Pr. Lenina 20, 307061 Baku
Tel: +994(12) 93-83-85
F: Geology and Prospecting; Chemical Engineering; Petroleum Production; Mechanical Engineering; Energetics; Automation of Production Processing; Engineering Economics.
D: Evening Studies; Correspondence Courses.
I: Branch (Sumgaita).

Azerbaijan University of Arts
[Azerbajdžanskij Gosudarstvennyj Universitet Iskusstv]
Ul. Karganova 13, 370000 Baku
Dramatic Art; Fine Arts.

*Bakin University
[Bakinskij Gosudarstvennyj Universitet]
Ul. P. Lumumby 23, 370073 Baku
Rektor: A.A. Bakir-Zade
Founded: 1920
F: History; Philology; Journalism; Oriental Studies; Library Science; Law; Economics; Mathematics and Applied Mathematics; Physics; Chemistry; Biology; Geology and Geography; Correspondence Courses.
D: Evening Studies.

Occidental University Baku
Baku
Rektor: Gussein Bagirov
Founded: 1991, 1993
Politology; Management; Sociology of Management.

OTHER INSTITUTIONS

Azerbajdžanskaja Gosudarstvennaja Konservatorija
Ul. G. Dimitrova 98, 370014 Baku
Music.

Azerbajdžanskij Gosudarstvennyj Medicinskij Institut
Ul. Bakihanova 23, 370022 Baku 22
Medicine.

Azerbajdžanskij Sel'skohozjajstvennyj Institut
Ul. Azizbekova 262, 374700 Kirovabad
Tel: +994 2-10-64
Agriculture.

Bakinskij Gosudarstveenyj Ekonomiceskij Institut
Ul. Kommanisticeskaja 6, 370000 Baku
Economics.

Bakinskij Inzenerno-Stroitel'nyj Institut
Ul. Krylova 13, 370073 Baku
Tel: +994(12) 38-33-96
Civil Engineering.

Kirovabadskij Tehnologiceskij Institut
Prosp. Kiraz., Kirovabad
Technology.

NATIONAL ACADEMIC BODIES

Ministry of Education
Government House, 377016 Baku
Tel: +994(12) 937-266
Fax: +994(12) 937-773
Minister: Fridoun Djalilov

Azerbaijan National Commission for Unesco
Ministry of Foreign Affairs, Ganjilar Meidany 3, 37060 Baku
Tel: +994(12) 925-606
Fax: +994(12) 651-038
Chairman: Hassan Hasanov, Minister of Foreign Affairs

BAHAMAS

OTHER INSTITUTIONS

College of The Bahamas
Poinciana Drive and Thompson Boulevard, P.O. Box N4912, Nassau, N.P.
Tel: +809 323-8550
Fax: +809 326-7834
E-Mail: neil e, sealey
President: Keva M. Bethel (1982-)
Registrar: Roger G. Brown
Founded: 1974
Div: Business and Administrative Studies; Humanities; Library; Natural Sciences; Nursing Allied Health Services; Social Sciences; Teacher Education; Technology.
Ce: Continuing Education and Extensive Services.

NATIONAL ACADEMIC BODIES

Ministry of Education
P.O. Box, 3913/14 Nassau
Minister: Cornelius A. Smith

Bahamas National Commission for Unesco
Ministry of Education, P.O. Box N3913/14, Nassar
Tel: +809 322-8140
Fax: +809 322-8491
Chairman: Cornelius A. Smith, Minister of Education
Secretary-General: Elma I. Gassaway

BAHRAIN

UNIVERSITIES

*Arabian Gulf University
P.O. Box 26671, Manama
Tel: +973 440-044
Fax: +973 440-002
Telex: 73119 agu bn
President: Abdullah M. Al-Refai
General Director: Riyadh Yousuf Hamza
Founded: 1980
C: Medicine and Medical Sciences; Education; Applied Sciences.

*University of Bahrain
P.O. Box 32038, Manama
Tel: +973 449-266
Fax: +973 440-033
Telex: 9552 bn
President: Ibrahim J. Al Hashemi (1991-)
Vice-President (Administration): Samir Fakhro
International Relations: Nazar Al Baharna
Founded: 1987

C: Engineering; Science; Arts (Sukhair); Business and Management (Sukhair); Education (Sukhair).
Ce: English Language.

OTHER INSTITUTIONS

College of Health Sciences
Salmenia Medical Centre, PO Box 12, Manama
Telex: 8511 health bn
Founded: 1976
Health Sciences.

Hotel and Catering Training Centre
PO Box 22088, Muharraq
Tel: +973 32-019
Telex: htc muharraq
Founded: 1975
Hotel and Catering Training.

NATIONAL ACADEMIC BODIES

Ministry of Education
PO Box 43, Manama
Tel: +973 680-071
Fax: +973 680-161
Telex: 9090 tarbia bn
Minister: Ali Mohammed Fakhro

Bahrain National Commission for Unesco
Ministry of Education, PO Box 43, Manama
Tel: +973 258-400
Fax: +973 272-252
Telex: 9094 tarbia bn
Chairman: Ali Mohammed Fakhro, Minister of Education
Secretary-General: Rashid Mohammed Sulaybikh

BANGLADESH

UNIVERSITIES

Bangladesh Agricultural University
Mymensingh 2202
Tel: +880(91) 43-33
Cable: agrivarsity, mymensingh, bangladesh
Vice-Chancellor: S.M. Farouk (1993-)
Registrar: A.H. Khan
Founded: 1961, 1972
F: Agricultural Economics and Rural Sociology; Agricultural Engineering and Technology; Agriculture; Animal Husbandry; Veterinary Sciences; Fisheries.
Committee: Advanced Studies and Research.
I: Research System.
Ce: Extension.

Bangladesh University of Engineering and Technology
Ramna, Dhaka 1000
Tel: +880(2) 500252
Fax: +880(2) 863026
Cable: engineering university, dhaka
Vice-Chancellor: M. Shahjahan
Registrar: Abu Taher
Founded: 1961
F: Architecture and Planning; Civil Engineering; Electrical and Electronic Engineering; Engineering; Mechanical Engineering.
I: Appropriate Technology; Flood Control and Drainage Research.

University Chittagong
University Post Office, Chittagong
Tel: +880(31) 210131-9
Cable: chittagong university, chittagong, bangladesh
Vice-Chancellor: A.M. Serajuddin
Registrar: A. Rashid
Founded: 1966
F: Arts; Commerce; Education; Law; Medicine; Sciences; Social Sciences.
I: Forestry; Marine Science.

BANGABANDHU LAW COLLEGE
Chittagong
Tel: +880(31) 210-130
Law.

BANGLADESH COLLEGE OF FINE ARTS
University P.O., Chittagong
Tel: +880(31) 210-130
Fine Arts.

CHITTAGONG LAW COLLEGE
University P.O., Chittagong
Tel: +880(31) 210-130
Law.

CHITTAGONG MEDICAL COLLEGE
University P.O., Chittagong
Tel: +880(31) 210-130
Medicine.

GOVERNMENT COLLEGE OF FINE ARTS
University P.O., Chittagong
Fine Arts.

SYLHET LAW COLLEGE
University P.O., Chittagong
Tel: +880(31) 210-130
Law.

SYLHET OSMANI MEDICAL COLLEGE
University P.O., Chittagong
Tel: +880(31) 210-130
Medicine.

TEACHER TRAINING COLLEGE
University P.O., Chittagong
Tel: +880(31) 210-130
Teacher Training.

TEACHER TRAINING COLLEGE
Comilla
Teacher Training.

TEACHER TRAINING COLLEGE
Feni
Teacher Training.

*University of Dhaka
Ramna, Dhaka 1000
Tel: +880(2) 505161
Fax: +880(2) 865583
Cable: Dhaka University, BD
Vice-Chancellor: Emajuddin Ahamed
Registrar: A.Z. Sikder
Founded: 1921
*F: Arts; Biological Sciences; Commerce;
Education; Law; Medicine; Postgraduate Medical
Science and Research; Science; Social Sciences.*
Bureau: Economic Research.
*I: Business Administration; Education and
Research; Fine Arts; Modern Languages;
Nutrition and Food Science; Social Welfare and
Research Ce.; Statistical Research and Training;
Cardiovascular Diseases; Child Health; Diseases
of the Chest and Hospital; Postgraduate Medicine
and Research; Ophthalmology and Hospital;
Preventive and Social Medicine; Disabled
(Rehabilitation).*
*C: Medicine; Leather Technology; Homeopathic
Medical; Bangladesh Medical; Medicine;
Medicine (Mymensing); Sher-i-Bangla Medical
(Barisal); Home Economics; Nursing; Physical
Education; Textile Technology; Dental; Sir
Salinullah Medical; Technical Teacher Training;
Teacher Training; Teacher Training
(Mymensingh); Teacher Training (for Women)
(Mymensingh).*

BANGLADESH HOMEOPATHIC MEDICAL COLLEGE
Ramna, Dhaka 1000
Tel: +880(2) 500-010
Cable: dhaka university, bangladesh
Homeopathic Medicine.

BANGLADESH INSTITUTE OF CHILD HEALTH
Ramna, Dhaka 1000
Tel: +880(2) 500-010
Cable: dhaka university, bangladesh
Child Health.

BANGLADESH INSTITUTE OF RESEARCH AND REABILITATION IN
DIABETES, ENDOCRYNE AND METABOLIC DISORDERS
Ramna, Dhaka 1000
Tel: +880(2) 500-010
Cable: dhaka university, bangladesh
*Diabetes, Endocryne and Metabolic Disorders
Research.*

COLLEGE OF HOME ECONOMICS
Ramna, Dhaka 1000
Tel: +880(2) 500-010
Cable: dhaka university, bangladesh
Home Economics.

COLLEGE OF LEATHER TECHNOLOGY
Ramna, Dhaka 1000
Tel: +880(2) 500-010
Cable: dhaka university, bangladesh
Leather Technology.

COLLEGE OF NURSING
Ramna, Dhaka 1000
Tel: +880(2) 500-010
Cable: dhaka university, bangladesh
Nursing.

COLLEGE OF PHYSICAL EDUCATION
Ramna, Dhaka 1000
Tel: +880(2) 500-010
Cable: dhaka university, bangladesh
Physical Education.

COLLEGE OF TEXTILE TECHNOLOGY
Ramna, Dhaka 1000
Tel: +880(2) 500-010
Cable: dhaka university, bangladesh
Textile Technology.

DHAKA DENTAL COLLEGE
Ramna, Dhaka 1000
Tel: +880(2) 500-010
Cable: dhaka university, bangladesh
Dentistry.

DHAKA MEDICAL COLLEGE
Ramna, Dhaka 1000
Tel: +880(2) 500-010
Cable: dhaka university, bangladesh
Medicine.

INSTITUTE OF DISEASES OF THE CHEST AND HOSPITAL
Ramna, Dhaka 1000
Tel: +880(2) 500-010
Cable: dhaka university, bangladesh
Diseases of the Chest.

INSTITUTE OF POSTGRADUATE MEDICINE AND RESEARCH
Ramna, Dhaka 1000
Tel: +880(2) 500-010
Cable: dhaka university, bangladesh
Medicine and Research.

MYMENSINGH MEDICAL COLLEGE
Mymensingh
Medicine.

NATIONAL INSTITUTE OF OPHTHALMOLOGY
Ramna, Dhaka 1000
Tel: +880(2) 500-010
Cable: dhaka university, bangladesh
Ophthalmology.

REHABILITATION INSTITUTE AND HOSPITAL FOR THE DISABLED
Ramna, Dhaka 1000
Tel: +880(2) 500-010
Cable: dhaka university, bangladesh
Rehabilitation Studies.

SHER-E-BANGLA MEDICAL COLLEGE
Barisal
Medicine.

SIR SALIMULLAH MEDICAL COLLEGE
Ramna, Dhaka 1000
Tel: +880(2) 500-010
Cable: dhaka university, bangladesh
Medicine.

TEACHER TRAINING COLLEGE
Mymensingh
Teacher Training.

TECHNICAL TEACHER TRAINING COLLEGE
Ramna, Dhaka 1000
Tel: +880(2) 500-010
Cable: dhaka university, bangladesh
Teacher Training (Technical).

Jahangirnagar University
Savar, Dhaka
Tel: +880(2) 400-185
Cable: university, savar, haka
Vice-Chancellor: K.S. Ahmed
Registrar: M. Ali
Founded: 1970, 1972
F: Arts and Humanities; Mathematical and Physical Sciences; Social Sciences.
I: Life Sciences; Computer and Information Technology.

University of Khulna
Khulna, Khulna 9100
Tel: +880(41) 21393
Fax: +880(41) 20313
Vice-Chancellor: Md. G.A. Fakir (1993-)
Registrar: S.M. Abu Bakar
Founded: 1987
F: Science Engineering Technology; Architecture; Urban and Rural Planning; Management Business Administration.

Islamic University Kushtia
Kushtia
Tel: +880 46-00
Fax: +880 813-144 (Attention: Islamic University)
Cable: islamic university, kushtia
Vice-Chancellor: Muhammad Abdul Hamid
Registrar: Md. Abdul Quasem
Founded: 1979
F: Humanities and Social Sciences; Theology and Islamic Studies.

*University of Rajshahi
P.O. Rajshahi University, Rajshahi
Tel: +880(721) 6041
Cable: university, rajshahi
Vice-Chancellor: Anisur Rahman
Registrar: M.O. Faruk
Founded: 1953
F: Arts; Commerce; Education; Engineering; Law; Life and Earth Sciences; Medicine; Science; Social Sciences.
I: Bangladesh Studies; Biological Science.

Shahjalal University of Science and Technology
East Subidbazar, Sylhet 3100
Tel: +880(821) 4306
Telex: sust. sylhet (821) 5257
Vice-Chancellor: Sadruddin Ahmed Chawdhury
Registrar: Mohammed Habibur Rahman
Founded: 1987
S: Physical Sciences; Management and Business Administration; Agricultural Mineral Sciences.
F: Applied Sciences and Technology; Social Sciences; Life Sciences.

NATIONAL ACADEMIC BODIES

Ministry of Education
Bangladesh Bureau of Education, Information and Statistics, I Sonargaon Road (Palashi-Nilkhet), Dhaka 1205
Tel: +880(2) 415-172
Fax: +880(2) 863-420
Minister: Jamirrudin Sircar

Association of Universities of Bangladesh
Dhaka
Chairman: S.M. Farouk, Vice-Chancellor, Bangladesh Agricultural University

Bangladesh National Commission for Unesco
Ministry of Education, 1 Asian Highway (Palashi-Nilkhet), Dhaka 1205
Tel: +880(2) 508-432
Telex: 632294 bncu bg
Cable: unesconat dhaka
Chairman: Jamirrudin Sircar, Minister of Education
Secretary-General: Md. Irshadul Haq

BARBADOS

UNIVERSITIES

University of the West Indies, Cave Hill Campus
P.O. Box 64, Bridgetown
Tel: +1809 425-1310
Fax: +1809 425-1327
Telex: 2257 univados
F: Law; Arts and General Studies; Social Sciences; Natural Sciences.
S: Lifelong Studies.
I: Social and Economic Research; Caribbean Law.

Ce: *Mangagement; Development Studies; Forestry.*

NATIONAL ACADEMIC BODIES

Ministry of Education
Jemmott's Lane, Bridgetown
Tel: +1809 427-3272
Minister: Tyrone Estwick

Barbados National Commission for Unesco
Ministry of Education, Jemmott's Lane,
Bridgetown
Tel: +1809 427-3272 (ext. 266)
Fax: +1809 436-2411
Cable: mined barbados
Chairman: Tyrone Estwick, Minster of Education
Secretary: Guildford Bruce Alleyne

BELARUS

UNIVERSITIES

Academy of Physical Culture and Sports of the Republic Belarus
Masherov Avenue 105, 220600 Minsk
Tel: +7(0172) 50-63-43
Fax: +7(0172) 50-80-08
Rector: V. Sokolov
Physical Education.

Belarus Academy of Arts
F. Skorina Avenue 81, 220600 Minsk
Tel: +7(0172) 32-15-42
Fax: +7(0172) 32-20-41
Rector: V. Sharangovich
F: *Theatre; Arts; Industrial Arts.*

Belarus Academy of Music
Internationalnaya St. 30, 220030 Minsk
Tel: +7(0172) 27-49-42
Fax: +7(0172) 26-19-96
Rector: M. Kozinests
Music.

Belarus Agricultural Academy
Mogilev District, 213410 Gorky
Tel: +7(02233) 2-15-45
Fax: +7(02233) 2-15-87
Rector: S. Nazarov
F: *Agronomy; Zoology Engineering; Mechanization of Agruculture; Water Resources Amelioration; Land Development; Economics; Accountances.*

Belarus Agriculture-Technical University
F. Skorina Avenue 99, 220608 Minsk
Tel: +7(0172) 64-61-91
Fax: +7(0172) 64-41-16
Rector: L. Gerasimovich
F: *Mechanization of Agriculture; Electrification.*

Belarus State Pedagogical University
Sovelskaya St. 18, 220809 Minsk
Tel: +7(0172) 26-40-20
Fax: +7(0172) 26-40-24
Rector: L. Tikhonov
F: *Mathematics; Physics; Nature Study; History; Belorussian Philology and Culture; Russian Philology; Pre-school Education; Pedagogics and Methods of Elementary Study; Music Pedagogy; Defectology.*

Belarus State Polytechnical Academy
F. Skorina Avenue 65, 220027 Minsk
Tel: +7(0172) 32-40-55
Fax: +7(0172) 25-21-93
Rector: M. Demtchuk
F: *Machine Building; Mechanics and Technology; Energetics; Energy Construction; Civil Construction; Road Construction; Architecture; Cyber and Cybertechnical Systems; Tool Construction.*

Belarus State Technological University
Sverdlov St.m 13, 220630 Minsk
Tel: +7(0172) 26-02-78
Fax: +7(0172) 26-10-75
Rector: I. Zharsky
F: *Forest; Wood Industry Technology; Technology of Organic Matter; Chemical Technology.*

*Belarus State University
F. Skorina Avenue 4, 220080 Minsk
Tel: +7(0172) 20-75-38
Fax: +7(0172) 26-59-40
Rektor: F. Kaputsky
F: *Biology; Physics; Geography; Chemistry; Mechanics and Mathematics; History; Radiophysics and Electronics; Journalistics; Philology; Philosophy; Economy and Law; Applied Mathematics and Information.*

Belarus State University of Economics
Partisan Avenue, 26, 220072 Minsk
Tel: +7(0172) 49-40-32
Fax: +7(0172) 49-51-06
Rector: R. Karseko
F: *Management; International Economic Relations; Economics and Finance; Banking; Economic Accountances; Accountances and Statistics; Commerce.*

Belarus State University of Transport
Kirov St. 34, 246653 Gomel
Tel: +7(0232) 52-57-18
Fax: +7(0232) 55-41-96
Rector: P. Gruntov
F: *Transport Engineering and Management.*

Belarus University of Informatics and Radioelectronics
P. Brovka St. 6, 220600 Minsk
Tel: +7(0172) 32-32-35
Fax: +7(0172) 31-09-14
Rector: V. Ilyin
F: Construction Technology; Automation and Electronics; Radiotechnics and Electronics; Computer Technics; Electrocommunication.

Brest Pedagogical Institute
Boulevard of Cosmonauts 21, Brest 224665
Tel: +7(01622) 3-01-41
Fax: +7(01622) 3-00-96
Rector: V. Stepanovich
F: Physical Culture; Philology; Pedagogies; Pre-school Education; History; Physics and Mathematics; Nature Studies.

Brest Polytechnical Institute
Moskovskaja St. 267, 220017 Brest
Tel: +7(01622) 42-74-57
Fax: +7(01622) 42-74-57
Rector: L. Korshun
F: Electronics and Mechanics; Civil Engineering; Water Supply and Hydroamelioration.

Gomel Institute for Co-operation
October Avenue 52A, 246029 Gomel'
Tel: +7(0232) 48-17-07
Fax: +7(0232) 47-80-68
Rector: N. Pisarenko
F: Commerce; Accountances and Finance; Economics and Management.

Gomel Polytechnical Institute
October Avenue 48, 246746 Gomel
Tel: +7(0232) 48-16-00
Fax: +7(0232) 47-91-65
Rector: A. Shaginyan
F: Machine Building; Automation and Electronics; Mechanics and Technology.

Gomel State Medical Institute
Langer St. 5, 240600 Gomel
Tel: +7(0232) 53-10-62
Fax: +7(0232) 53-98-31
Rector: U. Bondazhevsky
F: Medicine.

Gomel State University
Sovetskaya St. 104, 246699 Gomel'
Tel: +7(0232) 56-31-13
Fax: +7(0232) 57-81-11
Rector: L. Shemetkov
F: History and Law; Philology; Mathematics; Biology; Economy; Physics; Geology and Geography.

Grodno Agricultural Institute
Tereshkova St. 28, 230600 Grodno
Tel: +7(0232) 47-01-68
Fax: +7(0232) 47-14-97
Rector: Ye. Vitun
F: Agronomy; Plant Protection; Zoology Engineering.

Grodno State Medical Institute
Gorky St. 80, 230015 Grodno
Tel: +7(0152) 33-53-41
Fax: +7(0152) 33-53-41
Rector: D. Malakov
Medicine.

Grodno State Univerity
Ozheshko St., 22, 230023 Grodno
Tel: +7(0152) 47-01-73
Fax: +7(0152) 44-84-61
Telex: 194203 kvant
Rector: Alexander V. Bodakov (1973-)
F: History; Byelorussian Philology and Culture; Mathematics; Law; Physics; Engineering; Belorussian Philology and Culture; Biology; Pedagogics and Elementary Study (primary level); Physical Culture.

Minsk State Linguistic University
Zakharov St. 21, 220034 Minsk
Tel: +7(0172) 33-32-35
Fax: +7(0172) 36-75-04
Rector: V. Makarov
F: English; French; German; Spanish; Language; Interpretation.

Minsk State Medical Institute
Dzerzhinsky Avenue 83, 220116 Minsk
Tel: +7(0172) 71-94-24
Fax: +7(0172) 72-61-97
Rector: A. Kubarko
F: Medicine; Dentisry.

Minsk University of Culture
Rabkorovskaya St. 17, 220001 Minsk
Tel: +7(0172) 25-51-54
Fax: +7(0172) 26-20-96
Rector: Ya. Grigorovich
F: Arts; Culture; Library and Information Systems.

Mogilev Machine Building Institute
Lenin St. 70, 212005 Mogilev
Tel: +7(0222) 23-61-00
Fax: +7(0222) 25-80-91
Rector: V. Hodyrev
Machine Building.

Mogilev State Pedagogical Institute
Cosmonauts St. 1, 212028 Mogilev
Tel: +7(0222) 26-31-17
Rector: Ye. Kudryashov
F: Philology; Biology; Physics and Mathematics; History; Pedagogies; Pre-school Care; Physical Training.

Mogilev Technological Institute
Schmidt Avenue 3, 212027 Mogilev
Tel: +7(0222) 44-03-63
Rector: A. Grichenko
Technical Studies.

Mozyr State Pedagogical Institute
Students' St. 28, 247760 Mozyr
Tel: +7(02351) 2-15-85
Fax: +7(02351) 2-54-26
Rector: V. Dudarenko
*F: Physics and Mathematics; Philology;
Engineering Pedagogy; General Technical
Studies and Physics; Pedagogics and Methods of
Elementary Education.*

Polotsk State Pedagogical Institute
Blohina St. 29, 211440 Novopolotsk
Tel: +7(02144) 5-20-12
Fax: +7(02144) 5-42-63
Rector: E. Babenko
*F: Foreign Languages; Finance and Economics;
Machine Building; Radiotechniques; Technology;
Construction; Sanitary Engineering.*

Vitebsk State Medical Institute
Frunze Avenue 27, 210602 Vitebsk
Tel: +7(0212) 4-17-65
Rector: M. Sachok
Medicine.

Vitebsk State Pedagogical Institute
Moscowsky Avenue, 33, 210036 Vetebsk
Tel: +7(0212) 5-41-05
Rector: V. Vinogradov
*F: Philology; Belarus Languages and Literature;
Mathematics and Physics; Biology; Graphic Arts;
Pedagogics (elementary level); Physical Training.*

Vitebsk Technological Institute of Light Industry
Moscow Avenue 72, 210028 Vitebsk
Tel: +7(0212) 5-50-26
Fax: +7(0212) 5-80-74
Rector: I. Bashmetov
*F: Mechanics and Technology; Economics and
Technology; Design and Technology.*

Vitebsk Veterinary Institute
1st Dovator St. 7/11, 210619 Vitebsk
Tel: +7(0212) 37-02-81
Fax: +7(0212) 37-02-84
Rector: M. Zhakov
Zoology; Veterinary Medicine.

NATIONAL ACADEMIC BODIES

Ministry of Education
Sovetskaya St. 9, 220010 Minsk
Tel: +7(0172) 27-47-36
Fax: +7(0172) 20-80-57
Minister: Victor Anatoljevitch Gaicenok

National Commission of Belarus for Unesco
Bul' Lenin 19, 220030 Minsk
Tel: +7(0172) 27-34-02
Fax: +7(0172) 27-45-21
Telex: 252193 kvark
Cable: unescocom minsk
Chairman: M.P. Kravtchenko
Secretary-General: Natalia I. Jilevitch

BELGIUM

UNIVERSITIES

Luxembourg University Foundation Arlon
[Fondation Universitaire Luxembourgeoise]
Avenue de Longwy, 185, 6700 Arlon
Tel: +32(63) 21-58-11
Fax: +32(63) 21-58-00
Directeur: Louis de Backer (1991-95)
Directeur administratif: Louis Hanin
Founded: 1971, 1983
D. of Environmental Sciences.

Catholic University of Brussels
[Katholieke Universiteit Brussel]
Vrijheidslaan 17, 1080 Brussel
Tel: +32(2) 412-42-11
Fax: +32(2) 412-42-00
Rector: Frank Gotzen (1992-)
Head, Administrative Services: Jan de Leemheer
International Relations: Tine Verhelst
Founded: 1969
*F: Law; Philosophy and Letters; Economic,
Political and Social Sciences; Social and Political
Sciences.*
D: Philosophy; Germanic Philology; History.

*Free University of Brussels
[Université Libre de Bruxelles]
Avenue Franklin D. Roosevelt 50, 1050 Bruxelles
Tel: +32(2) 650-21-11
Fax: +32(2) 650-36-30
Telex: unilib 230-69
Recteur: Françoise Thys-Clément (1992-)
Secrétaire général: Christian Dejean
Founded: 1834
*F: Philosophy and Letters; Law; Sciences;
Psychology and Education; Medicine; Applied
Sciences; Social, Political, and Economic
Sciences.*
*I: Pharmacy; Physical Education; Statistics;
Labour; European Studies; Oriental Languages
and Civilizations; Religious Studies and of
Secularity; Phonetics; Sociology; Philosophy;
Higher Studies of Belgium.*
*S: Public Health; Nursing (annexed to the
University); Criminology.*
Ce: Computer.

*Free University of Brussels
[Vrije Universiteit Brussel]
Campus Oefenplein Pleinlaan 2, 1050 Brussel
Tel: +32(2) 64-21-11
Fax: +32(2) 16-41-22-82
Telex: 61.051 vubco-b
Rector: Robert Dejaegere (1990-94)
Algemeen Directeur: Lee Peeters
International Relations: Mieke Gijsemans
Founded: 1834, 1970
*F: Philosophy and Letters; Law; Science;
Medicine and Pharmacy; Applied Sciences;*

Social, Political, and Economic Sciences;
Psychology and Education.
I: Physical Education.

*University Faculties Saint-Louis Brussels
[Facultés Universitaires Saint-Louis]
Boulevard du Jardin Botanique 43, 1000
Bruxelles
Tel: +32(2) 211-78-11
Fax: +32(2) 211-79-97
Recteur: Michel van de Kerchove
Founded: 1858, 1969, 1974
F: Philosophy and Letters; Law; Economic,
Political, and Social Sciences; S. of Philosophical
and Religious Studies; Interdisciplinary Sem. of
Law.
Ce: Sociological Studies; Economic Research.

Faculty of Agricultural Sciences of Gembloux
[Faculté des Sciences agronomiques de
Gembloux]
Passage des Déportés 2, 5030 Gembloux
Tel: +32(81) 62-22-64
Fax: +32(81) 61-45-44
Telex: 59482
Recteur: C. Deroanne (1988-96)
Directeur administratif: B. Cuvelier
Founded: 1860, 1920, 1947, 1965
Agriculture.

State University of Ghent
[Rijksuniversiteit te Gent]
Sint-Pietersnieuwstraat 25, 9000 Gent
Tel: +32(9) 264-31-11
Fax: +32(9) 264-31-11
E-Mail: jacques.willem@rug.ac.be
Telex: 12754
Rector: J. Willems (1993-)
Vice-Rector: E. Vermeersch
Founded: 1816
*F; Philosophy and Letters; Law; Science;
Medicine; Applied Sciences; Economics;
Veterinary Medicine; Psychology and Education;
Agriculture; Pharmacy; Polical and Social
Sciences.*
S: Management; Criminology.
D: Teacher Training.

*Catholic University of Leuven
[Katholieke Universiteit Leuven]
Naamsestraat 22, 3000 Leuven
Tel: +32(16) 28-37-11
Fax: +32(16) 28-41-96
Telex: 25715
Rector: Roger Dillemans (1985-)
Administrator: Karel Tavernier
Founded: 1425, 1517, 1834, 1970
F: Theology; Philosophy; Canon Law; Law;
Economics and Applied Economics; Social
Sciences.
Inter-U, Inter-F, Ce. and I: Teacher Education;
Catholic Documentation and Research; Christian
Ethics; China-Europe; Labour Studies; Micro-

Electronics; Language; Central and Easteuropean
Studies.

*State University of Liège
[Université de Liège]
7, place du 20 août, 4000 Liège
Tel: +32(41) 66-21-11
Fax: +32(41) 66-57-08 (Rectorat)
Telex: 41397 univlg
Recteur: Arthur Bodson (1989-94)
Administrateur: René Grosjean
Founded: 1816, 1835, 1959
F: Philosophy and Letters; Law; Science;
Medicine; Veterinary Medicine; Applied Sciences;
Psychology and Educational Science; Economics,
Business, Administration, and Social Science.
S: Criminology.

*Catholic University of Louvain
[Université Catholique de Louvain]
Place de l'Université 1, 1348 Louvain-la-Neuve
Tel: +32(10) 47-21-11
Fax: +32(10) 47-29-99
Telex: 59516
Recteur: Pierre Macq (1991-)
Administrateur général: Jean Moulart
International Relations: Aime François
Founded: 1425, 1834, 1970
F: Theology and Canon Law; Law; Economic,
Political, and Social Sciences; Medicine;
Philosophy and Letters; Psychology and
Education; Science; Applied Sciences;
Agriculture; Open F. for Adult Education
Teachers; Open F. for Economics and Social
Sciences.
I: Philosophy; Modern Languages; Logography;
International I. for Cellular and Molecular
Pathology.
Ce: Theatre Studies; Operations Research and
Econometrics; Operations Research and
Econometrics.

Catholic University Faculty of Mons
[Faculté Universitaire Catholique de Mons]
Chaussée de Binche 151, 7000 Mons
Tel: +32(65) 32-32-11
Fax: +32(65) 31-56-91
Rector: Jean Lhoas (1981-)
Founded: 1896, 1921, 1934, 1965
I: Applied Economics; Political Science and
Public Administration; Lifelong Education
(INUFOP); Economic Analysis; Financial
Management; Marketing; Computer Sciences and
Quantitative Management; Languages; Applied
Mathematics; SMB and Information Systems;
Audit Evaluation and Accountancy; Human
Sciences; Administrative and Political Sciences.
Ce: Research on the Economic Efficiency of
Retailing (CREER); Audio-visual.

BELGIUM

*Polytechnical Faculty of Mons
[Faculté polytechnique de Mons]
9, Rue de Houdain, 7000 Mons
Tel: +32(65) 37-41-11
Fax: +32(65) 37-42-00
Telex: 57851 fpmons
Recteur: C. Bouquegneau (1986-96)
Administrateur: C. Bouquegneau
Founded: 1837, 1921
F: Applied Sciences.
Ce: High Technology Research and Development.

*University of Mons-Hainaut
[Université de Mons-Hainaut]
Place du Parc, 20, 7000 Mons
Tel: +32(65) 37-31-11
Fax: +32(65) 37-30-54
Telex: 57764 ue Mons-B
Recteur: Albert Landercy (1993-)
Administrateur: José Quenon
Founded: 1899, 1899, 1920, 1965, 1971
F: Science; Economic and Social Sciences; Medicine; Psychology and Education.
S: Translation and Interpretation.

*University Faculties Notre-Dame de la Paix Namur
[Facultés Universitaires Notre-Dame de la Paix]
61, Rue de Bruxelles, 5000 Namur
Tel: +32(81) 72-41-11
Fax: +32(81) 72-40-03
Telex: 59222 facnamb
Recteur: Maurice Gilbert, S.J. (1993-)
Secrétaire général: Raymond Paquay
Founded: 1831, 1929, 1971
F: Philosophy and Letters; Law; Economics and Social Sciences; Science; Medicine.
I: Computer Sciences; Studies in Solid Interface (ISIS).
S: Modern Languages.
Ce: Third Age (UTAN); Lifelong Education; Medico-Psychology; Technological; Technology Assessment (CITA) (InterUniversity).
Research: Informatics and Law; Law and Social Security; Regional Law.
D: Education and Technology.
Ut: Electronic Microscopy.
L: Nuclear Reaction (LARN).

OTHER UNIVERSITY INSTITUTIONS

Antwerp Municipal College of Industrial Engineering
[Stedelijke industriële hogeschool Antwerpen]
Paardenmarkt 94, 2000 Antwerpen
Tel: +32(3) 231-50-36
Fax: +32(3) 231-86-70
Algemeen Directeur: I. de Mets (1982-)
Secretaris: I. de Mets
Founded: 1977, 1982
Industrial, Engineering, and Construction.

Catholic College of Industrial Engineering Antwerp
[Katholieke industriële hogeschool Antwerpen]
Salesianenlaan 30, 2660 Hoboken
Tel: +32(3) 828-16-40
Fax: +32(3) 828-57-49
E-Mail: bastenie@kiha.be
Rector: Alfred Popelier
International Relations: Jos Kuppens
Founded: 1960, 1977
D: Electro-Mechanics; Electrical Engineering; Electronics; Biochemistry; Industrial Chemistry; Industrial and Chemical Chemistry.

Catholic Flemish Institute of Higher Education Antwerp
[Katholieke Vlaamse Hogeschool]
J. De Bomstraat 11, 2018 Antwerpen
Tel: +32(3) 225-06-40
Fax: +32(3) 231-30-60
Directeur: Rik Van Leuven
Beheerder-Scretaris: Bob Dalying
International Relations: Miet Kestelijn
Founded: 1919
D: Psychology; Speech Therapy; Translators and Interpreters.
Research Ce.: Terminology and Lexicography; Educational Software; Science of Translation.

Henry van de Velde Institute Antwerp, Higher Institute for Architectural Sciences and Product Development
[Henry van de Velde-Instituut, Antwerpen, Hoger Instituut voor Architectuurwestenschappen en Produktontwikkeling]
Mutsaetstraat 31, 2000 Antwerpen
Tel: +32(3) 231-70-84
Fax: +32(3) 226-04-11
Director: Walter Toubhans (1989-)
Secretary-Administrator: Huguette Mees
Founded: 1663, 1885, 1992
D: Architecture; Product Development; Interior Design; Conservation of Historic Buildings; Urban Development and Town Planning; Architectural Drawing.

College of Business Administration and Economics Antwerp
[Handelschogeschool Antwerpen]
Korte Nieuwstraat 33, 2000 Antwerpen
Tel: (3) 32-74-52
Founded: 1925, 1969
Business Administration and Economics.

Higher Institute of Translators and Interpreters Antwerp

[Hoger instituut voor vertalers en tolken van het Gemeenschapsonderwijs]
Schildersstraat 41, 2000 Antwerpen
Tel: +32(3) 238-98-33
Fax: +32(3) 248-19-07
E-Mail: (3) 248-1934
Directeur: J. Soenen
Secretaris: F. Crauwels
Founded: 1961
Translation and Interpretation.

Prince Leopold Institute of Tropical Medicine Antwerp

[Prins Leopold Instituut voor Tropische Geneeskunde]
Nationalestraat 155, 2000 Antwerpen
Tel: +32(3) 247-66-66
Fax: +32(3) 216-14-31
Telex: 31648 tropic b
Cable: metropical antwerpen
Directeur: Luc Eyckmans (1976-)
Vast Secretaaris: Marc Van Boven
International Relations: L. Colyckmans
Founded: 1931, 1960
Public Health; Tropical Biomedical Sciences; Tropical Veterinary Production; Tropical Medicine; Medical and Veterinary Mycology and in Epidemiology.
Research D: *Parasitology; Community Health; Infection and Immunity; Animal Health and Production; Clinical Research.*

Nautical College Antwerpen

[Hogere Zeevaartschool Antwerpen]
Noordkasteel-605 6, 2030 Antwerpen
Tel: +32(3) 231-62-48
Fax: +32(3) 225-06-39
Directeur: Roger Smet (1989-95)
Deputy Administrator: Anne Courbois
F: Maritime Studies.

State University Centre of Antwerp

[Universitair Centrum Antwerpen]
Groenenborgerlaan 171, 2020 Antwerpen
Tel: +32(3) 218-02-11
Fax: +32(3) 218-02-17
Rector: W. Decleir
Beheerder (Administrator): B. Heijnen
Founded: 1965
F: Science; Applied Economics; Medical Sciences.
I: Developing Countries; Translation and Interpretation.
Open University.

University Faculty 'Sint-Ignatius' of Antwerp

[Universitaire Faculteiten Sint-Ignatius te Antwerpen]
Prinssttraat 13, 2000 Antwerpen
Tel: +32(3) 220-41-11
Fax: +32(3) 220-44-20
Telex: 33599 ufsia b
Rector: J. Van Houtte
Secretaris generaal: R. Van der Goten
International Relations: H.A. Fivez
Founded: 1852, 1965
F: Arts; Law; Political and Social Sciences; Applied Economics.
S: Management (IPO).
Ce.: Business Administration (CBA); Applied Linguistics (Interfaculties); Mexican Studies; Law (Research); Continuing Education/Continuing Adult Education (IDEA).
P: European Studies.
D: Philosophy and Religious Studies (Research); History (Research); Languages and Literature (Research); Sociology and Social Policy (Research); Socio-Economic Research (Research); Third World Studies (Research); Business Economics (Research).
Open U.

University Institute of Antwerp

[Universitaire Instelling Antwerpen]
Universitetsplein 1, 2610 Antwerpen-Wilrijk
Tel: +32(3) 820-20-20
Fax: +32(3) 820-22-49
Telex: 33646
Rector: Freddy Adams (1983-95)
Vaste Secretaris: Lode Lambeets
Founded: 1971
F: Science; Law and Political and Social Sciences; Philosophy and Letters; Medicine and Pharmacy.
D: Mathematics and Computer Sciences; Physics; Chemistry; Biochemistry; Biology; Medicine; Pharmacy; Romance Philology; Germanic Philology; Law; Political and Social Sciences; Education.
Interdisciplinary P: Occupational Health; Environmental Sciences.
I: Materials Science.
Open U.

State Institute of Industrial Engineering Arlon

[Institut supérieur industriel de la Communauté française]
Chemin de Weyler 2, 6700 Arlon
Tel: +32(63) 22-05-17
Fax: +32(63) 22-08-90
Directeur: Pierre Winandy
Administrateur-Secrétaire: Marcel Thomas
Founded: 1977
Industrial Engineering.

Business School for Commerce and Administration Brussels

[Bestuurs-en Handelswestenschappen]
Trierstraat 84, 1040 Brussel
Tel: +32(2) 230-12-60
Fax: +32(2) 230-99-90
Algemeen Directeur: Herman J. Vermeylen
(1991-)
Hoofd v/d Administratie: Gerk Fabre
Founded: 1938, 1948
National, European and International Business Administration; Commerce, Economics, Public and Private Finance; Marketing Management; Public Administration.

Catholic Institute of Commercial Studies Brussels

[Institut catholique de hautes Études commerciales]
2 boulevard Brand Whitlock, 1150 Bruxelles
Tel: +32(2) 739-37-11
Fax: +32(2) 738-38-03
Directeur: Pierre Dupriez
Founded: 1931, 1954
D: International Commerce; Financial Administration; Marketing Studies; Computer Sciences; Control and Revision; Human Resources; Public Administration; Commerce; Language Commission.
S: Fiscal Studies.
Ce: Marketing Research; Lifelong Education; Management.

Central School of 'Arts et Métiers' Brussels

[École Centrale des Arts et Métiers (ECAM)]
Rue du Tir 14, 1060 Bruxelles
Tel: (2) 539-38-10
Fax: (2) 539-11-63
Directeur: Gaston Decornet (1975-)
Secrétaire général: A. Huylenbroeck
Founded: 1989, 1977
Ut: Mechanical Engineering; Electrical Engineering; Electronics; Automation and Robotics; Civil Engineering; Mathematics; Computer Sciences; Technology; Human, Social, and Economic Studies; Chemistry and Physics.

College of Economics 'Sint Aloysius' Brussels

[Economische Hogeschool Sint-Aloysius]
Stormstraat 2, 1000 Brussel
Tel: +32(2) 210-12-11
Fax: +32(2) 217-64-64
Directeur: Dirk de Ceulaer
International Relations: Romain Eeckhout
Founded: 1925

College of Industrial Engineering Brussels

[Industriële Hogeschool]
Nijverheidskaai 170, 1070 Brussel
Tel: +32(2) 520-18-10
Fax: +32(2) 520-71-23
Directeur: W. Martens
Beheerder: J. de Maeyer
Founded: 1977
D: Mechanical Engineering; Electrical Engineering; Mathematics and Physics; Electronics.

College for Translation and Interpretation Brussels

[Erasmushogeschool Brussel]
Trierstraat 84, 1040 Brussel
Tel: +32(2) 230-12-60
Fax: (2) 230-99-90
Algemeen Directeur: Herman J. Vermeylen
(1978-)
Secretaris: Martine Mallefroy
International Relations: Chantal Delmotte
Founded: 1958, 1964
Translation and Interpretation; Terminology and Terminography; Social and Business Communication, Intercultural Relations; European Law Terminology.

Flemish College of Economics Brussels

[Vlaamse economische hogeschool Brussel]
336 Koningsstraat, 1210 Brussel
Tel: +32(2) 221-12-11
Fax: +32(2) 219-78-79
President: S.F. Vandenhoeck (1969-)
Hoofd v/d Administratie: W. Grijseels
International Relations: Gigrid Greytens
Founded: 1968
Commerce and Business Administration; Translation and Interpretation; Lifelong Education.

Institute of Architecture of the French Community-'La Cambre' Brussels

[Institut supérieur d'Architecture de la Communauté française-La Cambre]
Place Flagey 19, 1050 Bruxelles
Tel: +32(2) 640-96-96
Fax: +32(2) 647-46-55
Directeur: Marcel Pesleux
Founded: 1926
Industrial Design; Applied and Monumental Arts; Cinematographic Technology.

Institute of Architecture 'Saint-Luc' Brussels

[Institut supérieur d'Architecture Saint-Luc Bruxelles]
57, rue d'Irlande, 1060 Bruxelles
Tel: +32(2) 537-34-19
Fax: +32(2) 537-00-63
Directeur: Willy Serneels
Founded: 1904, 1977
Architecture.

Institute of Architecture Victor Horta Brussels
[Institut supérieur d'Architecture intercommunal Victor Horta (I.S.A.I)]
ULB Campus de la Plaine, boulevard du Triomphe, C.P. 248, 1050 Bruxelles
Tel: +32(2) 650-50-95
Fax: +32(2) 650-50-93
Director: Adrien Cools
Founded: 1763, 1977, 1984, 1986
Architecture.

Institute of Commerce 'Saint-Louis' Brussels
[Institut supérieur de Commerce Saint-Louis]
Rue du Marais, 113, 1000 Bruxelles
Tel: +32(2) 219-27-03
Fax: +32(2) 217-11-65
Directeur: J. Vanbesien
Founded: 1925, 1934
Commerce (Day and Evening courses).

Institute of the French Community for Translation and Interpretation Brussels
[Institut supérieur de la Communauté française de Traducteurs et Interprètes]
Rue Joseph Hazard, 34, 1180 Bruxelles
Tel: +32(2) 345-98-70
Fax: +32(2) 346-21-34
Directeur: Georges Guislain
Founded: 1958, 1970
Translation and Interpretation.

Institute of Industrial Engineering of the French Community Brussels
[Institut supérieur industriel de la Communauté française]
Rue Royale, 150, 1000 Bruxelles
Tel: +32(2) 2174-45-40
Fax: +32(2) 217-46-40
Directeur: Léonard Hocks
Founded: 1956, 1977
Sec: Nuclear Science; Electrical and Electonic Engineering; Mechanical Engineering; Chemical Engineering.

Cooremans Institute Brussels
[Institut Cooremans]
Place Anneessens 11, 1000 Bruxelles
Tel: +32 512-54-91
Fax: +32 511-24-67
Directeur: Roger Van Damme (1978-)
Chef de travaux: Jacqueline Reumont
Founded: 1971
F: Commerce; Administration; Translation and Interpretation.

Open Institute Marie Haps Brussels
[Institut Libre Marie Haps]
Rue d'Arlon 11, 1040 Bruxelles
Tel: +32(2) 511-92-92
Fax: +32(2) 511-98-37
Directeur: Bernard Devlamminck (1991-)
Secrétaire générale: Brigitte Quoilin-Claude
Founded: 1919, 1963
Translation and Interpretation.

Meurice Institute (ISI) Brussels
[Institut Meurice (ISI)]
Avenue Emile Gryzon 1, 1070 Bruxelles
Tel: +32(2) 526-73-00
Fax: +32(2) 526-73-01
Directeur: Patrick Dysseler
President: P. Boucher
Founded: 1954
Sec: Industrial Bio-Engineering; Aliphatic Nitril Hydrogenation Catalysis Mechanism; Organic and Polymer Chemistry; Food Sciences and Technology; Analytical Chemistry; Computer Techniques; Fermentation (Brussels); Biochemistry-Microbiology; Sonochemistry-Microbiology; Natural Substances.

Protestant University Faculty of Brussels
[Universitaire protestante theologische faculteit Brussel/Faculté de Théologie protestante Bruxelles]
Bollandistenstraat 40, 1040 Brussel

Institute of Higher Studies in Social Communication Brussels
[Institut des hautes Etudes des Communications sociales (IHECS)]
rue de l'Etuve 58-60, 1000 Bruxelles
Tel: +32(2) 512-90-93
Fax: +32(2) 512-38-97
Director: Freddy Laurent
Socio-Cultural Studies and Lifelong Education; Publicity; Press and Information; Public Relations.

Provincial Institute of Architecture Diepenbeek
[Provinciaal Hoger Architectuurinstituut]
Universitaire campus, Gebouw E, 3590 Diepenbeek
Tel: +32(11) 26-90-11
Fax: +32(11) 26-90-19
Directeur: E. Vangeel
Assistant Directeur: P. Bongaerts
International Relations: Head, Academic Studies, H.P. Froyen
Founded: 1955, 1970
Architecture; Interior Design; Traffic Analysis and Planning.

Catholic College of Industrial Engineering Ghent
[Katholieke industriële hogeschool Oost-Vlaanderen]
Gebr. Desmetsrraat 1, 9000 Gent
Tel: +32(9) 223-60-01
Fax: +32(9) 225-62-69
Directeur: L. Haerens
International Relations: H. Lauwereys
Founded: 1977
Industrial Engineering.

Advanced Institute of Architecture 'Sint-Lucas' Ghent
[Hoger Architectuurinstituut Sint-Lucas]
Zwartezustersstraat 34, 9000 Gent
Tel: +32(9) 225-42-90
Fax: +32(91) 223-46-36
Directeur: Walter Steenhoudt
Beheerder-Secretaris: André Foucart
International Relations: Erasmus-programme, Freddy de Guchteneere
Founded: 1862
Architecture; Conservation and Restoration; Urbanism.

Provincial College for Translation and Interpretation Ghent
[Provinciale hogeschool voor vertalers en tolken]
Brusselsepoortstraat 93, 9000 Gent
Tel: +32(9) 223-94-51
Fax: +32(9) 223-97-05
Directeur: Daul Van Hauwermeiren (1987-)
Executive Director: Toni De Wispelaere
International Relations: Peirre Bonnarens
Founded: 1937, 1952
Translation and Interpretation; Terminology; Business Administration and Communications; Japanese Studies.

State Polytechnic B.M.E. Ghent
[Industriële hogeschool van het Gemeenschapsonderwijs - B.M.E.]
Schoonmeersstraat 52, 9000 Gent
Tel: +32(9) 221-38-31
Fax: +32(9) 221-19-37
Rector: Gilbert Bartholomees (1994-)
Deputy Directeur: Gilbert Bartholomees
International Relations: Alfred de Wit
Founded: 1827, 1977, 1989
Ut: General Subjects; Natural Sciences; Electro-Mechanics; Electric Energy-Technics; Automation; Electronics; Civil Engineering.
S: Graduate.

Technical University-CTL Ghent
[Industriële hogeschool van het Gemeenschapsonderwijs-C.T.L. Gent]
Voskenslaan 270, 9000 Gent
Tel: +32(9) 221-80-11
Fax: +32(9) 221-68-68
Directeur: G. Aelterman (1989-)

Beheerder Secretaris: H. De Kuyper
International Relations: Hoofd van Studiebureau, L. Hertveldt
Founded: 1977
Industrial Engineering; Technical Research.

Hainaut Province Institute of Industrial Engineering Charleroi
[Institut supérieur industriel de la Province de Hainaut]
Boulevard Solvay 31, 600 Charleroi
Tel: +32(71) 32-23-19
Fax: +32(71) 30-19-07
Directeur: Georges Sand
Industrial Engineering; Agriculture.

Evangelical Theological Faculty Heverlee/Leuven
[Evangelische theologische faculteit Heverlee/Leuven]
St. Jansbergsteenweg 97, 3030 Heverlee/Leuven
Tel: +32(16) 20-08-95
Fax: +32(16) 20-09-43
Academisch Directeur/Decaan: Gie Vleugels
Administratief Directeur: Jef De Vriese
International Relations: Jan Verbruggen
Founded: 1919, 1983
Theology.

Institute of Industrial Engineering of the French Community Huy-Gembloux-Verviers (Huy)
[Institut supérieur industriel de la Communauté française de Huy-Gembloux-Verviers (Huy)]
Rue St.-Victor 3, 4500 Huy
Tel: +32(85) 21-48-26
Fax: +32(85) 21-15-41
Directeur: Francis Delanaye
Secrétaire générale: Mme Dussart
Industrial Engineering; Textile (Verviers).

Kempen Catholic Higher School of Industrial Engineering Geel
[Katholieke industriële hogeschool der Kempen]
Technische Schoolstraat 52, 2440 Geel
Tel: +32(14) 58-55-75
Fax: +32(14) 58-48-59
President: Martens Paul (1972-)
Beheerder: Maurice Vaes
International Relations: Herman Van Looy
Founded: 1959
Industrial Engineering; Agriculture Engineering.

Provincial College of Industrial Engineering Kortrijk
[Provinciale industriële hogeschool]
Graaf Karel de Goedelaan 5, 8500 Kortrijk
Tel: +32(56) 21-54-65
Fax: +32(56) 21-04-13
Directeur: Geerard Verplancke (1977-)
Beheerder-Secretaris: A.M. Debevere
International Relations: Hoofd van Studiebureau, Jean-Pierre De Paepe
Founded: 1957, 1977
Industrial Engineering.

Groep T College of Industrial Engineering Leuven

[Industriële Hogeschool Groep T Leuven]
Campus Blauwput, Vuurkruisenlaan 4, 3000
Leuven
Tel: +32(16) 23-08-50
Fax: +32(16) 22-83-43
Founded: 1960, 1970, 1977, 1980
*D: Mathematics; Physics; Chemistry; Materials
Science; Electromechanical Engineering;
Chemical and Biochemical Engineering;
Economics-Management; Communication-
Languages; Information Technology.*

Institute of Architecture 'Lambert Lombard' Liège

[Institut supérieur d'Architecture intercommunal
Lambert Lombard (ISAI)]
Rue Saint-Gilles 33, 4000 Liège
Tel: +32(41) 22-31-67
Fax: +32(41) 23-13-05
Directeur: Y. Clossen
Founded: 1835
Architecture.

Institute of Architecture 'St.-Luc' of Wallonie Liège

[Institut supérieur d'Architecture St.-Luc de
Wallonie]
Rue Ste. Marie 30, 4000 Liège
Tel: +32(41) 23-38-10
Fax: +32(41) 23-72-82
Directeur: André Verhulst
Founded: 1880, 1977
Architecture; Architecture (Tournai).

Institute of Industrial Engineering 'Gramme' Liège

[Institut Gramme Liège (Institut supérieur
industriel)]
Quai de Condroz, 28, 4031 Liège (Angleur)
Tel: +32(41) 43-07-26
Fax: +32(41) 43-30-28
Directeur: Jules Dubois (1977-)
Directeur adjoint: M. Clotuche
Founded: 1906
Industrial Engineering.

Institute of Industrial Engineering Liège

[Institut supérieur industriel liégeois]
Quai Gloesener 6, 4020 Liège
Tel: +32(41) 41-13-85
Fax: +32(41) 42-01-17
Directeur: Paul Merchier
Founded: 1977
*Ut: Biochemistry, Biotechnology and
Environment; Chemistry; Civil Engineering;
Electrical Engineering; Electronics; Mechanical
Engineering; Computer Sciences; Automation;
Socio-economics; Physics; Mathematics; Design.*

School of Commercial Studies Liège

[École des Hautes Études commerciales (HEC
Liège)]
Rue Louvrex 21, 4000 Liège
Tel: +32(41) 32-72-11
Fax: +32(41) 32-72-40
Directeur: Marcel Aldenhoff (1968-)
Chef du Bureau d'Etudes: Christiane
Henneghien-Orban
Founded: 1898, 1934
*D: Management and Quantitative Methods;
Marketing; Computer Sciences; Languages;
Economics; Law; Human Resources;
Management; Applied Sciences.*

Limburg Catholic Institute of Industrial Engineering

[Katholieke industriële hogeschool voor Limburg]
Universitaire Campus, 3610 Diepenbeek
Tel: +32(11) 22-21-42
Fax: +32(11) 24-30-83
E-Mail: @kihl.be
Directeur: Robert Bollen (1976-)
Deputy Directeur: Jos Merckx
International Relations: Head, Study Department,
Willy Indeherberge
Founded: 1977
*Chemical Engineering; Electro-Mechanical
Engineering; Electrical Engineering.*

Limburg Community Educational College of Industrial Engineering Hasselt

[Industriële hogeschool van het
Gemeenschapsonderwijs-Limburg]
Maastrichterstraat 100, 3500 Hasselt
Tel: +32(11) 22-14-77
Fax: +32(11) 23-18-07
Directeur: J. Vanhees
Beheerder-Secretaris: H. Piryns
Founded: 1977
Industrial Engineering.

Limburg University Centre

[Limburgs Universitair Centrum]
Universitaire Campus, 3590 Diepenbeek
Tel: +32(11) 26-81-11
Fax: +32(11) 26-81-99
E-Mail: lucearnõiluco1
Telex: 39948 luc b
Rector: Henri Martenshaegen (1988-95)
Vast Secretaris: Willy Goetstouwers
Founded: 1971
*F: Medical Sciences and Dentistry; Applied
Economics; Sciences; Applied Economics.
D: Managerial Economics; Economics-Law;
Basic Medical Sciences; Man-Society-
Communication; Chemistry-Biology-Geology;
Mathematics-Physics-Informatics.
I: Material Research.
Open U.*

Malines Municipal College of Industrial Engineering Mechelen

[Stedelijke industriële hogeschool Mechelen]
Leopoldstraat 42, 2800 Mechelen
Tel: +32(15) 41-22-11
Fax: +32(15) 41-22-21
Directeur: Guido Pardon
Beheerder-Secretaris: Dirk Teugels
Founded: 1977, 1982
D: Chemistry; Electronics; Electrical Engineering.

Hainaut Catholic Institute of Industrial Engineering Mons

[Institut supérieur industriel catholique du Hainaut]
Avenue de l'Hôpital, 22, 7000 Mons
Tel: +32(65) 31-73-67
Fax: +32(65) 35-28-16
Directeur: André Lhost (1985-2001)
Founded: 1977
D: Chemical Engineering and Biochemistry; Electro-mechanical Engineering; Electrical Engineering and Electronics.
Ce: Computer Sciences; Computer Sciences and Applied Mathematics.

Institute of Architecture of the City of Mons

[Institut supérieur d'Architecture intercommunal de la Ville de Mons (ISAI)]
Rue d'Havre, 88, 7000 Mons
Tel: +32(65) 31-46-20
Fax: +32(65) 36-46-61
Directeur: A. Godart
Architecture.

School of International Interpretation Mons

[École d'Interprètes internationaux de l'Université de Mons-Hainaut]
Avenue du Champ de Mars, 7000 Mons
Tel: +32(65) 37-36-01
Fax: +32(65) 37-30-54
Directeur: Marcel Voisin
Founded: 1962, 1965
International Interpretation; American Studies; Irish Studies.

State Institute of Industrial Engineering Mons

[Institut supérieur industriel de la Communauté française]
Avenue V. Maistriau 8, Bte. A., 7000 Mons
Tel: +32(65) 33-81-54
Fax: +32(65) 31-30-51
Cable: Isiem Mons
Directeur: Paul Robert
Founded: 1959, 1977
S: Industrial Engineering; Construction Engineering; Electrical Engineering; Electronics; Automation, Radio and Television.

West Flanders Catholic College of Industrial Engineering Ostende

[Katholieke industriële hogeschool West-Vlaanderen]
Zeedijk 101, 8400 Oostende
Tel: +32(59) 50-89-96
Fax: +32(59) 70-42-15
Rector: G. Manderyck
Executive: E. Degroote
International Relations: E. Degroote
Founded: 1948
D: Chemistry and Biochemistry; Electronics; Electro-Mechanical Engineering; Industrial Engineering.
I: Technology.

Institute of Architecture 'St.-Luc' of Wallonia Ramegnies-Chin

[Institut supérieur d'Architecture St.-Luc de Wallonie]
Chaussée de Tournai 50, 7520 Ramegnies-Chin
Tel: +32(69) 22-72-02
Architecture.

Catholic College of Industrial Enginering 'De Nayer-Mechelen' Sint-Katelyne-Waver

[Katholieke industriële hogeschool De Nayer-Mechelen]
Jan De Nayerlaan 5, 2560 Sint-Katelyne-Waver
Tel: +32(15) 31-69-44
Fax: +32(15) 31-74-53
Directeur: W. Asselman (1991-)
Beheerder-Secretaris: P. Liekens
International Relations: G. Golens
Founded: 1922
S: Chemistry; Electronics; Electro-Mechanics; Construction Engineering; Electro-Mechanics (Graduate).

Institute of Industrial Engineering of the French Community Huy-Gembloux-Verviers (Verviers)

[Institut supérieur industriel de la Communauté française de Huy-Gembloux-Verviers (Verviers)]
rue du Séroule 8, 4800 Verviers
Tel: +32(87) 22-30-40
Industrial Engineering.

Luxembourg Catholic Institute of Industrial Engineering Virton

[Institut supérieur industriel catholique du Luxembourg]
Arts et Métiers, Rue de Pierrard 112, 6760 Virton
Tel: +32(63) 57-63-27
Fax: +32(63) 57-67-62
Directeur: André Petitjean
Founded: 1900, 1977
Ut: Mathematics and Science; Mechanical Engineering Construction; Mechanical Engineering Fabrications; Human Sciences and Business Administration; Thermic and Fluid Engineering; Electrical and Electronic Engineering; Informatics and Automatics; Research Ce. (CRISIP).

NATIONAL ACADEMIC BODIES

Ministry of Education, Research and Training
[Ministère de l'Education, de la Recherche et de la Formation]
Direction générale de l'Enseignement supérieur et de la Recherche scientifique, Cité Administrative de l'Etat, Quartier Arcades-D 6è étage, boulevard Pachéco 19 bte 0, 1010 Bruxelles (Visitors: rue Royale 204, 1010 Bruxelles)
Tel: +32(2) 210-55-11
Fax: +32(2) 210-55-17
Telex: 64556 edunat b
Directeur général: André Philippart

Ministry for the Flemish Community
[Ministerie van de Vlaamse Gemeenschap]
Département Onderwijs Administratie Hoger Onderwijs en Wetenschappelijk Onderzoek, Koningstraat 136, 1000 Brussel
Tel: +32(2) 211-42-11
Directeur-generaal: L. Van Buyten
International Relations: D. De Schrijver

Flemish Interuniversity Council
[Vlaamse Interuniversitaire Rand (VL.-I.R.)]
Egmonstraat 5, 1050 Brussel
Tel: +32(2) 512-9110
Fax: +32(2) 512-29-96
Chairman: R. Dillemns
Director-General: Jozef Van der Perre
Founded: 1976

Foundation Francqui
[Fondation Francqui]
Rue d'Egmont 11, 1050 Bruxelles
Tel: +32(2) 511-81-00
Fax: +32(2) 513-64-11
Chairman: Jacques Groothaert
Administrator: Luc Eyckmans
Founded: 1932

Interuniversity Council of the French Community
[Conseil Interuniversitaire de la Communauté Française (C.I.U.F.)]
Rue d'Egmont 5, 1050 Bruxelles
Tel: +32(2) 504-92-90
Fax: +32(2) 502-27-68
Chairman: Pierre Macq
Permanent Secretary: Etienne Loeckx
Founded: 1980

The National Fund for Scientific Research
[Fonds national de la Recherche scientifique/ National Fonds voor Wetenschappelijk Onderzoek]
Rue Egmont 5, 1050 Bruxelles
Tel: +32(2) 512-91-10
Fax: +32(2) 512-58-90
Secrétaire générale: M.J. Simoen

University Foundation
[Fondation universitaire/Universitaire Stichting]
Rue d'Egmont 11, 1050 Bruxelles
Tel: +32(2) 511-81-00
Fax: +32(2) 513-64-11
Chairman: Gilbert De Landsheere
Administrator: Louis Baeck
Founded: 1920

Belgian National Commission for Unesco
[Commission nationale belge pour l'Unesco]
Ministère des Affaires étrangères, Rue Quatre Bras 2, 1000 Bruxelles
Tel: +32(2) 516-84-57
Fax: +32(2) 513-91-48
Telex: 21376
Cable: belext bruxelles
Secrétaire général: Georges Henri Dumont
Founded: 1922

BELIZE

OTHER INSTITUTIONS

Belize College of Agriculture
Central Farm, Cayo District
Tel: +501(92) 2640
Principal: Hugh O'Brien (1994-)
Secretary: Noemi August
Founded: 1977

Belize School of Nursing
Princess Margaret Drive, P.O. Box 615, Belize City
Fax: +501(2) 30830
Principal Tutor: Patricia A. Beet (1993-94)
Principal Nursing Officer: Julia Castillo
Founded: 1963

Belize Teachers' College
P.O. Box 579, Princess Margaret Drive, Belize City
Tel: +501(2) 44413/02
Fax: +501(2) 33941
Principal: Cynthia Thompson (1989-)
Founded: 1965

Belize Technical College Sixth Form
P.O. Box 366, Freetown Road, Belize City
Tel: +501(2) 44896
Fax: +501(2) 33577
Principal: Cecil E. Reneau (1992-)
Registrar: Douglas Morrison
International Relations: Cecil E. Reneau
Founded: 1952
D: Building and Civil Engineering; Business Studies; Electrical and Mechanical Engineering; Education and Life Science; Science.

Corozal Community College
Corozal Town, Corozal District
Tel: +501(4) 22541
Chairman, Board of Governors: Paulino Montalvo (1988-)
Principal/Dean: Carlos O. Castillo
Founded: 1978
D: *English; Spanish; Science; Mathematics; Social Studies; Business; Physical Education.*

Stanncreek Ecumenical College
P.O. Box 84, Dangriga Town, Stanncreek District
Tel: +501(5) 22654
Fax: +501(5) 3247
Principal: Phyllis Cayetano (1992-)
Vice-Principal: Marina Woodye
Founded: 1986
D: *Business; Science; Arts.*

University College of Belize
P.O. Box 990, Princess Margaret Drive, Belize City
Tel: +501(2) 32733
Fax: +501(2) 30255
President: Angel E. Cal (1990-)
Secretary: Alvaro Rosado
International Relations: Mustafa Toure
Founded: 1986
D: *Adult and Continuing Education; Business Administration; Education.*

NATIONAL ACADEMIC BODIES

Ministry of Education
Ministry of Education, Belmopan
Tel: +501(8) 22324
Fax: +501(8) 23389

Belize National Commission for Unesco
Ministry of Education, Belmopan
Tel: +501(8) 22329
Fax: +501(8) 23389
Telex: 102 foreign belize
President: Santos Mahung
Secretary-General: Lewis G. Belisle, Jr

BENIN

UNIVERSITIES

*National University of Bénin
[Université nationale du Bénin]
B.P. 526, Cotonou
Tel: +229 36-00-74
Telex: 5010
Recteur: Gratien Jean Zanouvi (1994-)
Secrétaire général: Roger N'tia
Founded: 1970, 1976
F: *Letters, Arts and Human Sciences; Law, Economics and Political Science; Science and Technology; Agriculture; Health Sciences.*

C: *Polytechnic.*
S: *Teacher Training (secondary level).*
I: *Economics (National); Sports and Physical Education (National); Advanced Biological Studies; Public Health (Regional); Mathematics and Physical Sciences.*
Ce: *Administration (National).*

CENTRE BÉNINOIS DE LANGUES ÉTRANGÈRES
Cotonou
Foreign Languages.

CENTRE RÉGIONAL DE DÉVELOPPEMENT SANITAIRE
Cotonou
Sanitary Development.

COLLÈGE POLYTECHNIQUE UNIVERSITAIRE
B.P. 2009, Abomey-Calavi

ECOLE NATIONALE D'ADMINISTRATION
Abomey-Calavi
Tel: +229 36-01-43
Administration.

ECOLE NORMALE INTÉGRÉE
Teacher Training.

ECOLE NORMALE INTÉGRÉE
Parakou
Teacher Training.

ECOLE NORMALE INTÉGRÉE
Natitingou
Teacher Training.

ECOLE NORMALE SUPÉRIEURE
Teacher Training.

INSTITUT DE MATHÉMATIQUES ET DE SCIENCES PHYSIQUES
Porto-Novo
Mathematics and Physical Sciences.

INSTITUT NATIONAL D'ECONOMIE
Cotonou
Economics.

INSTITUT NATIONAL D'ENSEIGNEMENT D'EDUCATION PHYSIQUE ET SPORTIVE
B.P. 169, Porto-Novo
Physical Education and Sports.

NATIONAL ACADEMIC BODIES

Ministry of National Education
[Ministère de l'Education nationale]
B.P. 520, Cotonou
Tel: +229 30-19-91
Fax: +229 30-18-48
Ministre: Karim L. Dramane

Benin National Commission for Unesco
[Commission nationale béninoise pour l'Unesco]
B.P. 520, Porto-Novo
Tel: +229 21-25-30
Fax: +229 21-25-30
Cable: commission unesco porto-novo
Président: Karim L. Dramane, Minister of Education
Secrétaire général: Ayouba Babio

BHUTAN

OTHER INSTITUTIONS

Sherubtse Degree College
Kanglung
Cable: Tashigang
Principal: Zangley Dukpa
Founded: 1983
Arts; Sciences; Commerce.

NATIONAL ACADEMIC BODIES

Ministry of Social Services
Department of Education, Thimphu
Tel: +975 22912
Fax: +975 22578
Minister: Tashi Tobgyel
Director-General: Thinley Gyamtsho

Bhutan National Commission for Unesco
Ministry of Social Services, Thimphu
Tel: +975 22912
Fax: +975 22578
President: Tashi Tobgyel, Minister of Social
Services
Secretary-General: Thinley Gyamtsho

BOLIVIA

UNIVERSITIES AND TECHNICAL UNIVERSITIES

Technical University of Beni 'Mcal. José Ballivian'-Trinidad-Beni
[Universidad Técnica del Beni 'Mcal. José Ballivian'-Trinidad-Beni]
Calle Sucre, Casilla Postal 38, Trinidad-Beni
Tel: +591(46) 21590
Fax: +591(46) 21590
Rector: Hernán Melgar Justiniano
Secretario General: Vidal Chávez
Founded: 1967
F: Animal Husbandry; Agriculture; Forestry (Riberalta); Economics.

University of San Simón-Cochabamba
[Universidad Mayor de San Simón-Cochabamba]
Avenida Oquendo y Sucre, Casilla Postal 992, Cochabamba
Tel: +591(42) 25512
Fax: +591(42) 32545
Telex: 636 3 umssbv
Rector: Tonchi Marinkovic Uzqueda
Secretario General: Eddy Delgadillo
Founded: 1832, 1930
F: Agriculture and Stockbreeding; Architecture; Biochemistry and Pharmacy; Dentistry; Economics and Sociology; Humanities and Education; Law and Political Sciences; Medicine; Sciences and Technology.
S: Agriculture.

Catholic University Boliviana
[Universidad Católica Boliviana]
c. 14 de Septiembre 4807, Obrajes, Casilla Postal 4805, La Paz
Tel: +591(2) 783148
Fax: +591(2) 786707
Rector: Luis Antonio Boza Fernández (1989-93)
Secretaria Académica: Elizabeth Alvarez R.
Founded: 1966
Business Administration; Economics; Psychology; Social Communication; Social Communication (Cochambamba); Religious Sciences; Religious Sciences (Cochambamba); Public Relations; Tourism; Law; Agro-Industrial Studies (Compues); Philosophy; Psychopedagogy (Santa Cruz).

National University of the 20th Century-Llallagua
[Universidad Nacional Siglo XX-Llallagua]
Llallagua, Casilla Postal 8721 LP, Llallagua-Potosí
Tel: +591(56) 52222
Fax: +591(56) 52222
Rector: Edgar Lima Torrez
Secretario General: Héctor Rioja
Founded: 1984
Mining Engineering; Metallurgical Engineering; Agriculture and Stockraising; Agriculture and Stockraising (Santa Cruz); Agriculture and Stockraising (Campesina); Technics; Nursing; Nursing (Campesina); Nursing (Cochabanba); Communication Science.

University of San Andrés-La Paz
[Universidad Mayor de San Andrés-La Paz]
Avenida Villazón 1995, Casilla Postal 6042, La Paz (Murillo)
Tel: +591(2) 359490
Fax: +591(2) 359491
Telex: 343 8 umsabv
Rector: Antonio Saavedra Muñoz
Secretaria General: Wilma Amusquivar
Founded: 1831, 1972
F: Medicine; Pharmacy and Biochemistry; Dentistry; Pure and Natural Sciences; Engineering; Agriculture; Geology; Architecture and Arts; Technology; Social Sciences; Law and Political Science; Humanities and Education; Economics and Finance.

Technical University of Oruro-Oruro
[Universidad Técnica de Oruro-Oruro]
Avenida 6 de Octubre 1209, Casilla Posta 49, Oruro
Tel: +591(52) 50100
Fax: +591(52) 42215
Rector: Pablo Zubieta
Secretario General: Javier Rojas
Founded: 1892, 1937
F: Economics and Finance; Engineering; Law and Political and Social Sciences; Agriculture and Stockraising; Technical Studies; Architecture and Town Planning.

Autonomous University Tomás Frías-Potosí

[Universidad Autónoma Tomás Frías-Potosí]
Avenida del Maestro, Casilla Postal 36, Potosí
Tel: +591(62) 27300
Fax: +591(62) 26663
Rector: Abdón Sosa Yañez
Secretario General: Carlos Araníbar
Founded: 1892, 1931
*F: Law, and Political and Social Sciences;
Engineering; Economics, Finance and
Administration; Arts; Agriculture and Animal
Husbandry; Science; Mining Engineering;
Polytechnic; Geology Engineering; Accountancy
(Ciudad de Tupiza); Mechanical Engineering
(Ciudad de Uyuni).*

Autonomous University Gabriel René Moreno-Santa Cruz

[Universidad Autónoma Gabriel René Moreno-Santa Cruz]
Plaza 24 de Septiembre, Casilla postal 702, Santa
Cruz de la Sierra
Tel: +591(3) 365533
Fax: +591(3) 342160
Rector: Silverio Márquez T.
Secretario General: Mauricio Peña
Founded: 1880, 1911
*F: Law and Social Sciences; Economics and
Finance; Exact Sciences and Technology;
Agriculture; Veterinary Science and Animal
Husbandry; Polytechnic; Technology
(Vallegrande).*

University of San Francisco Xavier-Sucre

[Universidad Mayor de San Francisco
Xavier-Sucre]
Junín esq. Estudiantes 692, Casilla 212,
Sucre-Chuquisaca
Tel: +591(64) 23245
Fax: +591(64) 32205
Rector: Enrique Azurduy
Secretario General: Jaime Villalta
Founded: 1624, 1930
*F: Health Sciences; Law and Political and Social
Sciences; Economics, Finance and
Administration; Technology; Humanities;
Agriculture, Stockraising, and Forestry.
I: Polytechnic.*

Juan Misael Saracho University-Tarija

[Universidad Juan Misael Saracho-Tarija]
Avenida Las Américas 0149, Casilla Postal 51,
Tarija
Tel: +317(66) 43110
Fax: +317(66) 43403
Rector: Juan Cuevas Aguilera
Secretaria General: Hilda Mercado Guzman
Founded: 1886, 1946

*F: Social Science; Economics and Finance;
Dentistry; Agriculture and Forestry; Sciences and
Technology; Accountancy (Bermejo); Agriculture
(Yacuiba); Animal Husbandry (Villamontes);
Polytechnic; Technology (Vallegrande).*

OTHER INSTITUTIONS

Colegio Nacional de Comercio
Tarija City
Commerce.

Colegio Nacional de Comercio 'Felipe Leonor Rivera'
Santa Cruz
Commerce.

Conservatorio Nacional de Música
Avenida 6 de Agosto 2092, La Paz
Founded: 1908
Music.

Escuela Industrial Superior de la Nación 'Pelawo Domengo Murilla'
La Paz
Founded: 1942
Industrial Studies.

Escuela Nacional de Enfermería
Calle 16 de Julio 83, Obrajes, La Paz
Nursing.

Escuela Normal Especializada Técnica
La Paz
Teacher Training (Technical).

Escuela Normal Integra 'Enrique Finot'
Avenida Ejército esq. Aba Barba, Santa Cruz
Founded: 1956
Teacher Training.

Escuela Normal Integra 'Mariscal Sucre'
Sucre
Teacher Training.

Escuela Normal Integrada Católica
Cochabamba
Founded: 1949
Teacher Training.

Escuela Normal Superior 'Simón Bolívar'
Villa IV Centenario, La Paz
Founded: 1917
Teacher Training.

Escuela Superior de Bellas Artes
Calle Rosendo Gutiérrez 323, La Paz
Founded: 1928
Fine Arts.

Instituto Comercial Superior de la Nación
Calle Campero 94, La Paz
Founded: 1944
Commerce.

Instituto Comercial Superior de la Nación 'Federico Alvarez Plate'
Ayacucho 6737, Cochabamba City
Commerce.

Instituto Nacional de Comercio
Oruro City
Commerce.

Instituto Normal Superior de Educación Física
Calle Juande Vargas 311, La Paz
Physical Education.

Instituto Superior de Comercio
Trinidad City
Commerce.

Instituto Superior de Educación
La Paz
Education.

Instituto Superior de Educación Rural
Tarija
Rural Education.

NATIONAL ACADEMIC BODIES

Ministry of Education and Culture
[Ministerio de Educación y Cultura]
Avenida Arce 2408, La Paz
Tel: +591(2) 37-32-63
Minister: Enrique Ipiña Melgar

Executive Committee of the Bolivian Universities
[Comité Ejecutivo de la Universidad Boliviana (C.E.U.B.)]
Avenida Arce 2606, Casilla Postal 4722, La Paz
Tel: +591(2) 379967
Fax: (2) 379967
Secretario Ejecutivo: Mario Ríos Aráoz
Founded: 1982

Bolivian National Commission for Unesco
[Comisión Nacional Boliviana para la Unesco]
Ministerio de Educación y Cultura, Avenida Arce 2408, La Paz
Tel: +591(2) 373269
Fax: +591(2) 378756
Telex: 3286
Presidente: Enrique Ipiña Melgar, Minister of Education
Secretario Permanente: Félix Guillermo Alarcón Eguino

BOSNIA AND HERZEGOVINA

UNIVERSITIES

University of Banja Luka
[Univerzitet 'Djuro Pucar Stari' u Banjaluci]
Trg palih boraca br. 2, 78 000 Banjaluka
Tel: +387(78) 35018
Founded: 1975

F: Law; Economics; Electrical Engineering; Mechanical Engineering; Technology; Medicine.
S: Mechanical Engineering.
I: History; Economics; Work Protection; Materials Technology; Scientific Research Work; Professional Electronics; Machine Tool Factory Development; Agriculture; Economics and Development Entreprise.
A: Pedagogical.

University of Mostar
[Univerzitet u Mostaru]
Put za Glavicu 10, 88000 Mostar
Tel: +387(88) 22-124
Fax: +387(88) 22-179
Rector: Zdenko Kordić
International Relations: Željko Šuman
Founded: 1977
F: Economics; Law; Mechanical Engineering; Civil Engineering.
A: Pedagogy.
I: Agriculture.

University of Sarajevo
[Univerzitet u Sarajevu]
Obala Vojvode Stepe 7-11, 71 000 Sarajevo
Tel: +387(71) 214-320
Rector: Jusuf Mulic
Founded: 1949
F: Architecture and Town Planning; Economics; Electrical Engineering; Political Science; Physical Education; Pharmacy; Philosophy; Civil Engineering; Mechanical Engineering; Mechanical Engineering (Zenica); Medicine; Metallurgy (Zenica); Agriculture; Law; Science; Transport Engineering; Dentistry; Forestry; Veterinary Medicine.
A: Fine Arts; Drama; Music.
S: Education; Nursing; Economics and Commerce; Management; Social Work.
I: Biology; Architecture; Computer Sciences; Economics; Oriental Research; Thermo-and Nuclear Techniques; Welding; Electroenergetic; Work Protection; Ergonomics.

University of Tuzla
[Univerzitet u Tuzli]
Rudarska 71, 75 000 Tuzla
Tel: +387(75) 34-650
Rektor: Ibro Pašić
Founded: 1976
F: Chemical Technology; Mining and Geology; Medicine; Electrical Engineering; Economics.
C: Education.
I: Chemical Engineering; Coal Research and Carbochemistry; Mining Research; Work and Environmental Protection Research; Economics.
Ce: Data Processing.

NATIONAL ACADEMIC BODIES

Ministry of Education
Sarajevo

National Commission of Bosnia and Herzegovina for Unesco
Sarajevo
Tel: +387(71) 144-6327
Fax: +387(71) 151-6210
Chairman: Sreben Dizdar
Secretary-General: Husein Panjeta

BOTSWANA

UNIVERSITIES

*University of Botswana
Private Bag 0022, Gaborone
Tel: +267(31-35-37) 351-151
Fax: +267(31-35-37) 356-591
Telex: 2429 bd
Cable: university, gaborone
Vice-Chancellor: T. Tlou
Registrar (Acting): D.O. Mokgautsi
International Relations: Deputy Vice-Chancellor, M.J. Melamu
Founded: 1976, 1982
F: Education; Engineering; Humanities; Science; Social Sciences.
I: Development Research and Documentation (National).
Ce: Continuing Education.

BOTSWANA COLLEGE OF AGRICULTURE
P/Bag 0027, Gaborone
Tel: +267(31-35-37) 352-381
Fax: +267(31-35-37) 314-253
Telex: 2429bd
Principal: E.J. Kemsley (1991-)
Registrar: M.M. Motsete
Founded: 1991
D: Agricultural Economics Education and Extension; Agricultural Engineering and Land Planning; Animal Science and Production; Basic Sciences; Crop Science and Production.
Ce: Inservice and Continuing Education.

Botswana Polytechnic
P/Bag 005, Gabarone
Tel: +267(31-35-37) 352305
Fax: +267(31-35-37) 352-309
Principal: G.A.J. Kerton

NATIONAL ACADEMIC BODIES

Ministry of Education
Gabarone
Tel: +267(31-35-37) 360-0400
Fax: +267(31-35-37) 360-0458
Cable: thuto bd
Minister: Raymond Matlapeng Ridwell Molomo

Botswana National Commission for Unesco
Ministry of Education, Gabarone
Tel: +267(31-35-37) 360-0439
Telex: 2944 thuto bd
Cable: unesco thuto botswana
President: Raymond Matlapeng Ridwell Molomo, Minister of Education
Secretary: L.G. Mothusi

BRAZIL

UNIVERSITIES

PUBLIC INSTITUTIONS

Federal University of Acre
[Universidade Federal do Acre]
Avenida Getúlio Vargas 654, 69915-900 Rio Branco (Acre)
Tel: +55(68) 226-1422
Fax: +55(68) 226-1162
Telex: 69-2532
Reitor: Lauro Julião de Sousa Sobrinho
Founded: 1971
F: Law; Economics; Letters.
I: Human Science and Letters.

Federal University of Alagoas
[Universidade Federal de Alagoas]
Br 101 Norte Km 14 Campus A.C., Simóes Tabuleiro do Martins, 57072-340 Maceió (Alagoas)
Tel: +55(82) 322-2269
Fax: +55(82)322-2345
Telex: 822307
Reitor: Fernando Cardoso Gama
Founded: 1961
Ce: Exact and Natural Sciences; Technology; Biology; Health Sciences; Human Sciences, Letters and Arts; Applied Social Sciences; Agriculture; Education.

Federal University of Amapa
[Universidade Federal do Amapa]
Avenida Juscelino Kubitschek, 68900 Macapa (Amapa)
Tel: +55(96) 222-3585

University of Amazonas
[Fundação Universidade do Amazonas]
Estrada do Contorno, 3000 Aleixo, 69077-000 Manaus (Amazonas)
Tel: +55(92) 237-6060
Fax: (92) 237-8345
Telex: 92-2554
Reitor: Nelson Abrahim Fraiji
Diretor: Carlos Eduardo de Souza Gonçalves
Founded: 1962
F: Education; Technology; Health Sciences; Agriculture; Social Studies; Law.
I: Exact Sciences; Tropical Diseases; Human Sciences and Letters; Exact Sciences; Biological Sciences; Human Sciences and Letters; Biological Sciences.

Ce: Environmental Sciences; Environmental Sciences.

Bahia Southwest State University
[Universidade Estadual Suddeste da Bahia]
Estrada do Bem-Querer, Km. 4, 45100 Vitória da Conquista (Bahia)
Tel: +55(73) 422-1143
Founded: 1980
C: Teacher Training; Nursing and Midwifery (Jequié); Teacher Training (Jequié).
S: Business Administration; Agriculture; Animal Husbandry (Itapetinga).

Federal University of Bahia
[Universidade Federal da Bahia]
Rua Augusto Viana s/n, 40140 Salvador (Bahia)
Tel: +55(71) 245-2811
Fax: +55(71) 245-9002
Telex: (71) 1978
Founded: 1575
F: Architecture; Communication; Dentistry; Medicine; Philosophy and Human Sciences; Pharmacy; Economics; Education; Law.
I: Biology; Earth Sciences; Letters; Mathematics; Physics; Health Sciences; Chemistry.
S: Administration; Agriculture; Nursing; Veterinary Medicine; Music; Dance; Theatre; Dietetics; Fine Arts; Library Science; Polytechnic.
Ce: Afro-Oriental Studies; Bahian Studies; Interdisciplinary Studies for Public Services.

State University of Bahia
[Universidade do Estado da Bahia]
Estrada das Barreiras s/n, Cabula, 40110-060 Salvador (Bahia)
Tel: +55(71) 245-2811
Fax: +55(71) 245-2460
Reitor: Luis Felipe Peret Serpa (1989-93)

Regional University of Blumenau
[Universidade Regional de Blumenau]
Rua Antonio da Veiga 140, 89012-900 Blumenau (Santa Catarina)
Tel: +55(473) 22-8288
Fax: +55(473) 22-8818
Telex: 47-3302
Reitor: Celso Mário Zípf (1990-94)
Founded: 1968
Ce: Applied Social Sciences; Human Sciences, Letters and Arts; Exact and Natural Sciences; Technology; Education.

University of Brasília
[Fundação Universidade de Brasília]
Campus Universitário, Asa Norte, 70910-900 Brasília, D.F.
Tel: +55(61) 348-2022
Fax: +55(61) 272-0003
Telex: (61) 2730
Cable: unibras
Reitor: João Claudio Todorov
Founded: 1961

F: Applied Social Studies; Communication; Health Sciences; Technology.
I: Human Sciences; Exact Sciences; Biological Sciences; Psychology; Letters; Performing and Visual Arts; Geosciences; Architecture and Urbanism.
D: Anthropology; Molecular Biology and Structure of Proteins; Botany; Physiological Sciences.

*State University of Campinas
[Universidade Estadual de Campinas]
Cidade Universitária 'Zeferino Vaz', Caixa Postal 1170, 13081-970 Campinas (São Paulo)
Tel: +55(192) 39-7766
Fax: +55(192) 394-717
E-Mail: jr.martins@ccvax.unicamp.br
Telex: 019 1150
Reitor: José Martins Filho (1994-98)
Secretário Geral: Irineu Ribeiro dos Santos
Founded: 1966
I: Biology; Fine Arts; Economics; Language Studies; Geosciences; Mathematics, Statistics and Computer Science; Chemistry; Philosophy and Humanities; 'Gleb Wataghin' I. of Physics.
S: Mechanical Engineering; Food Engineering; Civil Engineering.
S: Electrical Engineering; Physical Education; Dentistry; Medical Sciences; Education; Agricultural Engineering; Chemical Engineering.

Regional University of Carari
[Universidade Regional do Cariri]
Rua Coronel Antonio Luiz, Pimenta, 6310000 Crato (Ceará)
Tel: +55(85) 521-0160
Fax: +55(85) 521-0049
Telex: 89-1168

State University of Ceará
[Universidade Estadual do Ceará]
Paranjana, 1700, Campus do Itaperi, 60740-000 Fortaleza (Ceará)
Tel: +55(85) 292-4499
Fax: +55(85) 292-4299
Telex: 852295
Reitor: Paulo de Melo Jorge Filho (1992-96)
Secretaria: Maria Rejane Assumpão Auto
Founded: 1977
Ce: Applied Social Studies; Human Sciences; Science and Technology; Health Services; Humanities; Veterinary Science; Education (Limoeiro do Norte, Iguatu, Crateús, Itapipoca).

Federal University of Ceará
[Universidade Federal do Ceará]
Avenida da Universidade 2853 Benfica, 60020-181 Fortaleza (Ceará)
Tel: +55(85) 281-4333
Fax: +55(85) 243-4746
Telex: (85) 1077
Reitor: Antônio de Albuquerque Sousa Filho
Founded: 1955
F: Home Economics; Food Technology; Human Nutrition.

Federal University of Espírito Santo

[Universidade Federal do Espírito Santo]
Campus 'Dr. Alaor de Queiroz Araújo', Avenida
Fernando Ferrari s/n, 29060-900 Vitória (Espírito
Santo)
Tel: +55(27) 335-2222
Fax: +55(27) 335-2244
Telex: 27-2330
Reitor: Roberto da Cunha Penedo
Founded: 1954
Ce: Arts; Law and Economics; Lifelong
Education; Computer; Biomedical Studies;
Physical Education and Sport; Education; General
Studies; Technology; Agriculture.
I: Dental Medicine; Technology.
D: Brazilian Studies.

State University of Feira de Santana

[Universidade Estadual de Feira de Santana]
Km 3, BR-116, Campus Universitário, 44031-460
Feira de Santana (Bahia)
Tel: +55(75) 224-1521
Fax: +55(75) 224-2284
Telex: 75-2403
Reitor: Josué da Silva Mello (1991-95)
Founded: 1970
D: Letters and Arts; Health Sciences; Biology;
Exact Sciences; Education; Civil Engineering;
Human Sciences and Philosophy.

*Federal University of Fluminense

[Universidade Federal Fluminense]
Rua Miguel de Frias 9, Icaraí, 24220-000 Niterói
(Rio de Janeiro)
Tel: +55(21) 717-8080
Fax: +55(21) 717-4553
Telex: 21-32076 uvfl
Reitor: Manoel Pereira Leite de Almeida
Chefe de GabineteA.A.I. International Assistant:
Liulcede Carvalho Melo Cabral: Luiz Antonio L.
Coelho
Founded: 1960, 1965
F: Dentistry; Veterinary Science; Pharmacy;
Nutrition.
I: Earth Sciences; Human Sciences and
Philosophy; Languages and Literature;
Mathematics; Biomedical; Physics; Medicine.
Ce: Applied Social Studies; General Studies;
Medical Science; Technology; Economics and
Administration; Law; Chemistry; Biology; Arts
and Social Communication; Veterinary
Experimental (Ibagua); Education; Law.
S: Industrial Metallurgical Engineering (Volta
Redonda); Nursing; Engineering; Architecture and
Town Planning; Social Service.
D: Social Service (Campos); Rodolpho Albino
University L.
C: Nilo Peçanha Agricultural; Ildefonso Bastos
Borges Technical-Agricultural.
Ut: José Veríssimo Advanced (Oriximiná, Pará).

Federal University of Goiás

[Universidade Federal de Goiás]
Rodovia Goiânia Neropolis, 12, Caixa Postal 131,
74001-970 Goiânia (Goiás)
Tel: +55(62) 205-1000
Fax: +55(62) 205-1327
Telex: 62-2206
Reitor: Ary Monteiro do Espirito Santo
Chefe de Gabinete: Zezuca Pereira Da Silva
Founded: 1960
F: Dentistry; Medicine; Nursing and Nutrition;
Pharmacy and Biochemistry; Education; Law.
S: Agriculture; Veterinary Medicine;
Engineering.
I: Arts; Biology; Mathematics and Physics;
Tropical Pathology and Public Health; Chemistry
and Earth Sciences; Human Sciences and
Letters; Extension D.

Federal University of Juiz de Fora

[Universidade Federal de Juiz de Fora]
Rua Benjamin Constant 790, Caixa postal 656,
36015-400 Juiz de Fora (Minas Gerais)
Tel: +55(32) 215-5966
Fax: +55(32) 215-6382
Reitor: Renê Gonçalves de Matos
Founded: 1960
F: Law; Medicine; Economics; Education;
Dentistry; Engineering; Pharmacy and
Biochemistry.
I: Biological and Earth Sciences; Human
Sciences and Letters; Exact Sciences.

State University of Londrina

[Universidade Estadual de Londrina]
Campus Universitário, 86055-900 Londrina
(Paraná)
Tel: +55(433) 221-2000 (ext. 421)
Fax: +55(433) 276-932
E-Mail: BITNET: eloářfuel
Telex: 43-2256
Reitor: Jackson Proença Testa
Chefe de Gabinete: Darli Antonio Soares
Founded: 1971
Ce: Biological Sciences; Human Sciences and
Letters; Exact Sciences; Applied Social Studies;
Health Sciences; Education, Communication
Studies, and Arts; Agriculture; Technology and
Town Planning; Physical Education and Sports;
Language L.; Nucleus of Environmental Studies;
Nucleus of Economic and Social Research;
Nucleus of Afro-Asian Studies.

Federal University of Maranhão

[Universidade Federal do Maranhão]
Largo dos Amoles 351, 65000 São Luís
(Maranhão)
Tel: +55(98) 225-0865
Telex: 98-2214
Reitor: Jerônimo Pinheiro
Secretário Geral: Maria Da Graça Buhatem
Medeiros
Founded: 1966

Ce: Technology; Health Sciences; Physical Education, and Nursing; Basic Studies; Social Sciences.

State University of Maranhão
[Universidade Estadual do Maranhão]
Campus Universitário Paulo VI, 65020 São Luis (Maranhão)
Tel: +55(98) 221-5433
Fax: +55(98) 221-5285
Reitor: Aldy Mello de Araújo (1991-95)
Founded: 1972
F: Administration; Agriculture; Engineering; Veterinary Medicine; Education.

State University of Maringá
[Fundação Universidade Estadual de Maringá]
Avenida Colombo 3690, 87020-900 Maringá (Paraná)
Tel: +55(44) 226-2727
Fax: +55(44) 222-2754
Telex: 44-2198
Reitor: Décio Sperandio
Founded: 1970
Ce: Human Sciences, Letters, and Arts; Exact Sciences; Technology; Biology and Health Sciences; Economics and Social Sciences; Education.
I: Japanese; Languages.

Federal University of Mato Grosso
[Universidade Federal de Mato Grosso]
Avenida Fernando Corrêa da Costa s/n, 78060-900 Cuiabá (Mato Grosso)
Tel: +55(65) 315-5511
Fax: +55(65) 361-1119
Telex: 65-2371
Reitor: Luzia Guimaraes
Founded: 1970
Ce: Letters and Human Sciences; Exact Sciences and Technology; Social Sciences; Agriculture; Biological and Health Sciences.

Federal University of Mato Grosso do Sul
[Universidade Federal de Mato Grosso do Sul]
Campus Universitária 649, 79070-900 Campo Grande (Mato Grosso do Sul)
Tel: +55(67) 787-3311
Fax: +55(67) 787-1081
Telex: 67-2331
Reitor: Celso Vitório Pierezan
Founded: 1963, 1970, 1979
Ce: Biological and Health Sciences; Exact Sciences and Technology; Human and Social Sciences.
D: Science, Geography, History, and Letters (Aquidauana); Administration, Accountancy, Biology, Geography, History, Letters, Mathematics, Education, and Psychology (Corumbá); Agriculture, Accountancy, Geography, History, Letters, Mathematics, and Education (Dourados); Geography, History, Letters, Biology, Mathematics, and Education (Três Lagoas).

*Federal University of Minas Gerais
[Universidade Federal de Minas Gerais]
Avenida Antônio Carlos, 31270-900 Belo Horizonte (Minas Gerais)
Tel: +55(31) 448-1000
Fax: +55(31) 491-1056
Telex: 31-2305
Reitor: Tomaz Aroldo da Mota Santos
International Relations: Dirceu B. Greco
Founded: 1927
I: Biology; Exact Sciences and Physics; Geosciencies.
F: Economics; Law; Education; Pharmacy and Biochemistry; Philosophy and Humanities; Letters; Medicine; Dentistry; Schools; Architecture; Engineering; Veterinary Medicine; Music; Fine Arts; Library Science; Nursing.

State University of Montes Claros
[Universidade Estadual de Montes Claros]
Rua Cel Celestino 75, 39400 Montes Claros
Tel: +55(38) 221-0014

Federal University of Ouro Prêto
[Universidade Federal de Ouro Prêto]
Rua Diogo de Vasconcelos 122, 35400-000 Ouro Prêto (Minas Gerais)
Tel: +55(31) 551-1100
Fax: +55(31) 551-1689
Telex: 31-2954
Reitor: Renato Godinho Navarro
Founded: 1969
I: Social and Human Sciences; Arts and Culture; Biological and Exact Sciences.
S: Mines; Pharmacy.

Federal University of Pará
[Universidade Federal do Pará]
Rua Augusto Correa, 66075-110 Belém (Pará)
Tel: +55(91) 229-2088
Fax: +55(91) 229-9677
Telex: 91-1013
Reitor: Marcos Ximenes Ponte
Founded: 1957
Ce: Exact and Natural Sciences; Biological Sciences; Philosophy and Human Sciences; Letters and Arts; Biomedical Sciences; Technology; Socio-economic Studies; Education.

Federal University of Paraíba
[Universidade Federal de Paraíba]
Campus Universitário, 580590-900 João Pessôa (Paraíba)
Tel: +55(83) 224-7200
Fax: +55(83) 225-1901
Telex: 83-2187
Reitor: Neroaldo Pontes de Azevedo
Founded: 1955
Ce: Human Sciences, Letters and Arts; Applied Social Sciences; Education; Health Sciences; Technology; Exact and Natural Sciences;

Humanities (Campina Grande); Science and Technology (Campina Grande); Biology and Health Sciences (Campina Grande); Agriculture (Areia); Agricultural Technology (Bananeiras); Education (Cajazeiras); Law (Sousa); Rural Health and Technology.

State University of Paraíba
[Universidade Estadual da Paraíba]
Avenida Marechal Floriano Peixoto 718, 58015 - 280 Campino Grande (Paraíba)
Tel: +55(83) 341-3300
Fax: +55 341-4509
Telex: 832331
Reitor: Itan Pereira da Silva (1988-92)
Founded: 1987

Federal University of Paraná
[Universidade Federal do Paraná]
Rua XV de Novembro 1299, 80060-000 Curitiba (Paraná)
Tel: +55(41) 362-3038
Fax: +55(41) 264-2243
E-Mail: fariaﬁufpr
Telex: (41) 5100
Cable: 362-3038
Reitor: José Henrique de Farias
Vice-Reitor: Mário Portugal Pederneiras
Ce: Health Sciences; Humanities, Arts and Languages; Education; Technology; Agrarian Sciences; Exact Sciences; Biological Sciences; Applied Sciences; Marine Biology; Hydraulics and Hydrology; Civil Engineering Studies; Exploratory Geology; Physics for Special Materials; Biochemistry; Regional History; Bone Marrow Transplantation Studies; Sociology for Industrial Development; Management and Use of the Soil; Micropropagation of Cultures; Management of Planned and Native Forests; Environment and Development; Veterinary Medicine and Animal Husbandry; Research and Food Processing.

Federal University of Pelotas
[Universidade Federal de Pelotas]
Campus Universitário, 96100-010 Pelotas (Rio Grande do Sul)
Tel: +55(532) 21-2033
Fax: +55(532) 21-5023
Telex: (532) 302
Reitor: Antônio César Gonçalves Borges
Founded: 1883, 1969
F: Veterinary Medicine; Education; Home Economics; Law; Medicine; Agriculture; Dentistry; Architecture; Nursing and Obstetrics; Agricultural Engineering; Meteorology; Nutrition.
I: Human Sciences; Biological Sciences; Physics and Mathematics; Chemistry and Earth Sciences; Letters and Arts; Sociology and Political Science.
S: Physical Education.
Conservatory of Music.
Ce: Biotechnology.

Federal Rural University of Pernambuco
[Universidade Federal Rural de Pernambuco]
Rua Don Manoel de Medeiros s/n, 52171-900 Recife (Pernambuco)
Tel: +55(81) 441-4577
Fax: +55(81) 441-4697
Telex: 81-1195
Reitor: Manoel Francisco De Moraes Cavalcanti
Founded: 1912, 1947
D: Physics and Mathematics; Chemistry; Biology; Morphology and Animal Physiology; Letters and Human Sciences; Agriculture; Rural Technology; Veterinary Medicine; Animal Husbandry; Fishery; Education; Home Economics.

Federal University of Pernambuco
[Universidade Federal de Pernambuco]
Avenida Professor Moraes Rego, Cidade Universitária, 50670-901 Recife (Pernambuco)
Tel: +55(81) 271-8000
Fax: +55(81) 232-8029
Telex: 81-1267
Reitor: Éfrem de Aguiar Maranhão
Founded: 1946, 1965
F: Law; Ce. for Arts and Communication.
Ce: Exact and Natural Sciences; Biology; Philosophy and Human Sciences; Education; Social Sciences; Health Sciences; Technology.

Federal University of Piauí
[Universidade Federal do Piauí]
Campus Universitaria, 64049-550 Teresina (Piauí)
Tel: +55(86) 232-1322
Fax: +55(86) 232-2812
Telex: 86-2271
Reitor: Charles Carvalho C. da Silveira
Founded: 1971
Ce: Health Sciences; Natural Sciences; Human Sciences and Letters; Education; Agricultural Sciences; Technology.

State University of Piauí
[Universidade Estadual do Piauí]
Rua João Cabral s/n, Pirajá, 64000 Teresina (Piauí)
Tel: +55(86) 223-5757
Fax: +55(86) 223-2433
D: Education; Letters and Arts; Biological Science and Physical Education; Natural and Physical Science; Administration and Computer Science.

State University of Ponta Grossa
[Universidade Estadual de Ponta Grossa]
Praça Santos Andrade s/n, 84010-330 Ponta Grossa (Paraná)
Tel: +55(422) 25-21-21
Fax: +55(422) 23-77-08
Telex: 422-242
Reitor: Roberto Frederico Merhy (1991-95)
Founded: 1969

D: *Languages; Mathematics and Statistics; Physics; Geosciences; Physical Education; General Biology; History; Social Service; Teaching Methods and Techniques; Education; Accountancy; Communication; Economics; Business Administration; Law; Dentistry; Pharmaceutical Sciences; Data Processing; Engineering; Agronomy; Chemistry; Clinical and Toxicological Analysis.*

University of Rio Grande
[Universidade do Rio Grande]
Rua Eng. Alfredo Huch 475, 96201-900 Rio Grande (Rio Grande do Sul)
Tel: +55(532) 32-3300
Fax: +55(532) 32-3346
Telex: 53-2373
Reitor: Carlos Rodolfo Brandão Hartmann
Founded: 1969
D: *Biology and Morphology; Law; Medicine; Midwifery and Infant Nursing; Physiology and Pharmacy; Pathology; Library Science and History; Earth Sciences; Economics; Oceanography; Mathematics; Education; Letters and Arts; Chemistry; Materials and Construction; Physics; Surgery.*

Federal University of Rio Grande do Norte
[Universidade Federal do Rio Grande do Norte]
Campus Universitário, Lagoa Nova Km 7, BR 101, 59072-970 Natal (Rio Grande do Norte)
Tel: +55(84) 231-1266
Fax: +55(84) 231-4467
E-Mail: aguiar at brufrn bitnet
Telex: 2296
Reitor: Geraldo dos Santos Queiroz
Pró-Reitora Acadêmica: Dione Violeta de Medeiros
Founded: 1958
Ce: *Exact Sciences; Humanities, Letters, and Arts; Technology; Applied Social Sciences; Biosciences; Women Studies and Research; Food and Drug Research; Data Processing; Health Sciences; Brazilian Problems Studies.*
I: *Marine Biology; Anthropology.*
S: *Home Economics; Music; Agronomic (Jundiai).*

Regional University of Rio Grande do Norte
[Fundação Universidade Regional do Rio Grande do Norte (FURRN)]
Rua Quintino Bocaiúva, s/n, Praça Miguel Faustino, 59600 Mossoró (Rio Grande do Norte)
Tel: +55(84) 321-1833
Fax: (84) 317-4323
Telex: 84-3211 urrn
Reitor: Maria Das Neves Gurgel De Oliveira Castro
Founded: 1968
F: *Education; Social Work; Economics Sciences.*
S: *Nursing; Physical Education.*
I: *Mathematics and Natural Sciences; Science and Humanities; Arts and Languages.*

Federal University of Rio Grande do Sul
[Universidade Federal do Rio Grande do Sul]
Avenida Paulo Gama 110, 90046-000 Pôrto Alegre (Rio Grande do Sul)
Tel: +55(51) 228-1633
Fax: +55(51) 227-2295
Telex: 51-1055
Reitor: Hélgio H.C. Trindade
Founded: 1934, 1965
F: *Agriculture; Education; Veterinary Science; Dentistry; Medicine; Pharmacy; Law; Economics; Library Science and Journalism; Architecture.*
I: *Arts; Biology; Mathematics; Food Technology; Philosophy and Human Sciences; Physics; Earth Sciences; Letters; Hydrology Research; Chemistry; Informatics.*
S: *Nursing; Engineering; Physical Education.*
Observatory.

*Federal University of Rio de Janeiro
[Universidade Federal do Rio de Janeiro]
Avenida Brigadeiro Trompowski s/n, 21945-970 Rio de Janeiro (Rio de Janeiro)
Tel: +55(21) 290-2112
Fax: +55(21) 260-7903
E-Mail: cos 99214@ufrj.bitnet
Telex: 21-22924
Reitor: Paulo Alcantara Gomes
Secretario: Ivan Rodrigues da Silva
Founded: 1920, 1961
I: *Physics; Child Care and Education; Mathematics; Chemistry; Philosophy and Social Science; Psychology; Industrial Economics; Biological and Health Sciences; Microbiology; Biology; Nutrition; Biophysics; Geoscience; Urban and Region Research and Planning; Gynaecology; Neurology; Psychiatry.*
F: *Architecture and Town Planning; Letters; Education; Law; Pharmacy; Medicine; Dentistry; Economics.*
S: *Fine Arts; Music; Communication; Social Service; Nursing; Physical Education and Sports; Engineering; Chemistry.*
Ce: *Mathematics and Natural Sciences; Letters and Arts; Philosophy and Human Sciences; Legal and Economic Sciences.*

*State University of Rio de Janeiro
[Universidade do Estado do Rio de Janeiro]
Rua São Francisco Xavier 524, Maracanã, 20559-900 Rio de Janeiro (Rio de Janeiro)
Tel: +55(21) 284-8322
Fax: +55(21) 284-5033
Telex: 21 39065
Reitor: Hésio de Albuquerque Cordeiro (1992-96)
Founded: 1961
F: *Administration and Finance; Social Service; Education; Engineering; Law; Economics.*
I: *Human Sciences; Social Medicine; Criminology; Economic, Social and Political Studies; Mathematics and Statistics; Physics; Chemistry; Earth Sciences; Design and Applied Arts; Philosophy and Letters; Psychology and Social Communication.*

Ce: Biomedical Studies; Technology; Science; Education and Human Sciences.

University of Rio de Janeiro
[Universidade do Rio de Janeiro]
Avenida Pasteur, 296, 22295-900 Rio de Janeiro
(Rio de Janeiro)
Tel: +55(21) 295-5737
Fax: +55(21) 541-8394
Telex: 21-701
Reitor: Sérgio Luiz Magarão (1992-96)
Pró-Reitor Administrativo: Affonso Fernando Maia
Founded: 1969
Ce: Biological and Health Sciences; Arts and Languages; Humanities; Technological Sciences.

Federal University of Rondônia
[Universidade Federal de Rondônia]
Avenida Presidente Dutra 2965, 78900-500 Pôrto Velho (Rondônia)
Tel: +55(69) 216-8500
Fax: +55(69) 216-8506
Telex: 69-2152
Reitor: Francisco Aparecido Ferreira
Founded: 1982
F: Economics; Accountancy; Administration.

Federal University of Roraima
[Universidade Federal de Roraima]
Campus do Paricarana s/n, Jardim Floresta, 69300 Boa Vista (Roraima)
Tel: +55(95) 224-7461
Telex: 922093
Founded: 1988

*Federal University of Santa Catarina
[Universidade Federal de Santa Catarina]
Campus Universitário 'Trindade', 88040-900 Florianópolis (Santa Catarina)
Tel: +55(482) 31-9449
Fax: +55(482) 34-4069
E-Mail: BITNET: listservřlncc
Telex: 0482240
Reitor: Antônio Diomario Queiroz
Founded: 1968
Ce: Mathematics, Physics, and Chemistry; Biology; Arts and Communication; Human Sciences; Law; Agriculture and Animal Husbandry; Technology; Socio-economic Studies; Health Sciences; Education; Physical Education.

*Santa Catarina State University
[Universidade do Estado de Santa Catarina]
Madre Benvenuta 499, 88035-000 Florianópolis (Santa Catarina)
Tel: +55(482) 34-2000
Fax: +55(482) 34-6000
E-Mail: udesc 07řufsc.bitnet; Internet: udesc 07@ibm.ufsc.br
Telex: 482485
Reitor: Raimundo Zumblick
Vice-Reitor Administrativo: Marcilio Fortes de Barros
Founded: 1965

F: Education; Engineering; Agriculture and Veterinary Medicine.
S: Physical Education; Administration; Arts.
I: Engineering Foundation (FITEJ) (Joinville Technological); Administration and Management (ITAG) (Technical).
Ce: Educational Studies and Research (CEPE).
U: Extension (FIEPE-CAV).

Federal University of Santa Maria
[Universidade Federal de Santa Maria]
Cidade Universitária Km 9, 97111-970 Santa Maria (Rio Grande do Sul)
Tel: +55(55) 226-1616
Fax: +55(55) 226-1975
Telex: 55-2230
Reitor: Odilon Antônio Marcuzzo do Canto
Chefe de Gabinete: António Carlos Machado
Founded: 1961
Ce: Natural and Exact Sciences; Technology; Health Sciences; Rural Sciences; Social and Human Sciences; Arts and Letters; Education; Physical Education.

*Federal University of São Carlos
[Universidade Federal de São Carlos]
Rodovia Washington Luiz, Km. 235, 13565-905 São Carlos (São Paulo)
Tel: +55(162) 74-8111
Fax: +55(162) 71-2081
Telex: 16-2369
Reitor: Newton Lima Neto
Founded: 1960, 1968
Ce: Education and Human Sciences; Science and Technology; Health Sciences and Biology.

*State University Paulista 'Julio de Mesquita Filho' Sâo Paulo
[Universidade Estadual Paulista 'Julio de Mesquita Filho']
Praça de Sé 108, 01001-900 São Paulo (São Paulo)
Tel: +55(11) 32-7171
Fax: +55(11) 36-1870
Telex: 11-19001
Reitor: Arthur R. de Macedo
Secretário Geral: Darvin Beig
Founded: 1976
F: Dentistry (Araçatuba); Technology; Pharmaceutical Sciences (Araraquara); Veterinary Medicine and Animal Husbandry; Textile Technology; Technology (Baixada Santista); Sciences; Engineering and Technology; Arts, Architecture and Communication; Engineering (Ilha Solteira); Dentistry; Technology (Sorocaba); Philosophy and Sciences; Sciences and Technology; Agrarian and Veterinary Sciences; Engineeering (Guratinguetá); Medicine; Agricultural Sciences; Dentistry (Araraquara); Science and Letters.
I: Chemistry; Sciences and Letters; Bio-Sciences; Bio-Sciences (Rio Claro); Bio-Sciences, Letters and Exact Sciences (São José do Rio Prêto); Geo-Sciences and Exact Sciences;

Theoretical Physics; History, Law and Social
Service (Franca); Arts; Meteorologic Research.

*University of São Paulo
[Universidade de São Paulo]
Campus 'Armando De Salles Oliveira', Cidade
Universitária-Butantã, P.O. Box 8191, 05508-900
São Paulo
Tel: +55(11) 212-6200
Fax: +55(11) 815-5665
Telex: 1180902 uspo br
Reitor: Flavio Fava de Moraes
Secretária Geral: Lor Cury
Founded: 1943
F: Pharmaceutical Sciences; Medicine;
Education; Odontology (Bauru); Medicine
(Ribeirão Preto); Odontology (Ribeirão Preto);
Veterinary Medicine and Animal Husbandry;
Philosophy, Science, and Letters (Ribeirão
Preto); Odontology; Public Health; Philosophy,
Letters, and Human Sciences; Architecture and
Urbanism; Pharmaceutical Sciences (Ribeirão
Preto); Law; Economics and Administration.
S: Engineering (São Carlos); Communications
and Arts; Physical Education; Nursing;
Polytechnic.
I: Electrotechnical Engineering and Power;
Astronomical and Geophysical; Biosciences;
Brazilian Studies; Physics; Advanced Studies;
Biomedical Sciences; Geosciences; Mathematical
Sciences (São Carlos); Physics and Chemistry
(São Carlos); Mathematics and Statistics;
Psychology; Chemistry; Oceanography; Nursing
S. (Ribeirão Preto).
C: 'Luiz De Queiroz' Agricultural (Piracicaba).
Ce: Marine Biology; Nuclear Power in
Agriculture.

*Federal University of Sergipe
[Universidade Federal de Sergipe]
Campus Universitário, 49100-000 São Cristovão
(Sergipe)
Tel: +55(79) 241-2848
Fax: +55(79) 241-3995
E-Mail: řufse.bitnet
Telex: 79-2189
Reitor: Luiz Hermínio de Aguiar Oliveira (1993-)
Founded: 1968
Ce: Exact Sciences and Technology; Biological
and Health Sciences; Applied Social Sciences;
Education and Humanities.

University of Taubaté
[Universidade de Taubaté]
Rua 4 de Marco 432, 12020-270 Taubaté (São
Paulo)
Tel: +55(122) 32-7555
Fax: +55(122) 32-7660
Telex: 12-2251
Reitor: Milton de Freitas Chagas
Founded: 1976
F: Social Service; Philosophy, Science, and
Letters; Economics and Administration; Law.
S: Physical Education; Engineering.

University of Tocantins
[Universidade de Tocantins]
Rua Hozana Cavalcante 155, Setor Santa
Filomena, 77650 Miracema do Tocantins
(Tocantins)
Founded: 1991

Federal University of Uberlândia
[Universidade Federal de Uberlândia]
Avenida Engenheiro Diniz 1178, 38401-136
Uberlândia (Minas Gerais)
Tel: +55(34) 235-0355
Fax: +55(34) 234-8022
Telex: 34-3264
Reitor: Nestor Barbosa de Andrade
Founded: 1969
Ce: Biomedical Sciences; Exact Sciences and
Technology; Human Sciences and Arts.
S: Physical Education.

University of Vale do Itajaí
[Universidade do Vale do Itajaí]
Rua Uruguai 458, 88302-202 Itajaí (Santa
Catarina)
Tel: +55(473) 263-0211
Fax: +55(473) 44-5334
Telex: 471113
Reitor: Edison Villela (1990-)
Founded: 1989
F: Administration, Economics and Accountancy;
Law and Social Sciences; Tourism and Hotel
Administration; Nursing and Midwifery;
Philosophy, Science and Letters; Dentistry;
Psychology.

Federal University of Viçosa
[Universidade Federal de Viçosa]
Avenida Peter Henry Rolfs, s/n, 36570-000 Viçosa
(Minas Gerais)
Tel: +55(31) 899-2101
Fax: +55(31) 899-2203
Telex: 31-1587
Reitor: Antônio Lima Bandeira
Founded: 1927, 1969
Ce: Exact Sciences and Technology; Biological
and Health Sciences; Humanities, Letters and
Arts; Agriculture; Research, Experimentation and
Extension (Minas Tringle); Grain Storage
Training.

PRIVATE INSTITUTIONS

*University of Alfenas
[Universidad de Alfenas]
Campus Universitária, Rodovia MG 179 Km.0,
37130 - 000 Alfenas (Minas Gerais)
Tel: +55(35) 922-2000
Fax: +55(35) 921-4403
Telex: (35) 2168
Reitor: Edson Antônio Velano
Founded: 1979, 1988
F: Law; Medicine; Chemical and Pharmaceutical
Sciences.

I: Exact and Biological Sciences; Veterinary Medicine; Arts and Technology; Social and Human Sciences; Agriculture; Dentistry.
Ce: Data Processing.

University of the Sacred Heart Bauru
[Universidade do Sagrado Coração]
Rua Irmã Arminda 10-50, Caixa Postal 511, 17001 Bauru (São Paulo)
Tel: +55(14) 232-2311
Reitora: Ir. Jacinta Turolo Garcia (1988-)
Secretária Geral: Gesiane Monteiro Branco Folkis
Founded: 1953, 1986
D: Social Sciences; Education; Nursing; Nutrition and Pharmacy; Letters and Arts; Psychology.
Ce: Exact and Natural Sciences; Research and Postgraduate Studies; Biological Sciences.

*Saint Francis University Bragança Paulista
[Universidade São Francisco]
Avenida Francisco de Assis 218, 12900-000 Bragança Paulista (São Paulo)
Tel: +55(11) 404-1500
Fax: +55(11) 404-1825
Telex: 11-79949
Reitor: Constâncio Nogara, O.F.M. (1989-95)
Secretário Geral: Silvia Silvani Sgubin de Almeida
Founded: 1967, 1985
F: Law; Pharmacy; Medical Sciences; Philosophy, Science and Literature; Human Sciences; Economics and Administration; Odontology; Engineering; Education and Social Sciences; Business and Administration; Juridical Sciences; Administrative and Exact Sciences.
I: Anthropology (Franciscan).
Ce: Regional History Study; Franciscan History Study.

University of Região da Campanha
[Universidade da Região da Campanha]
Avenida Tupy Silveira 2099, 96400-110 Bagé (Rio Grande do Sul)
Tel: +55(532) 42-2244
Fax: +55(532) 42-2898
Reitor: Morvan Meirelles Ferrugem

*Pontifical Catholic University of Campinas
[Pontifícia Universidade Católica de Campinas]
Rodovio D. Pedro I, Km. 112, 13089-500 Campinas (São Paulo)
Tel: +55(192) 52-0899
Fax: +55(192) 53-4281
Telex: 19-1806
Reitor: Gilberto Luiz Moraes Selber (1994)
Founded: 1941, 1955, 1957, 1972
F: Nursing; Dentistry; Social Service; Physical Education; Law; Education.
I: Informatics; Arts and Communication; Biology.
C: Commerce.

*Lutheran University of Brazil Canoas
[Universidade Luterana do Brasil]
101, Rua Miguel Tostes, Caixa Postal 124, 92420-280 Canoas (Rio Grande do Sul)
Tel: +55(51) 477-4000
Fax: +55(51) 477-1313
Telex: (52) 3167 cels br
Reitor: Ruben E. Becker
Founded: 1972, 1989
C: Economic and Juridical Sciences; Technology; Health Sciences; Education, Sciences, and Literature; Natural and Exact Sciences.

University of Caxias do Sul
[Universidade de Caxias do Sul]
Rua Francisco Getúlio Vargas 1130, 95070-560 Caxias do Sul (Rio Grande do Sul)
Tel: +55(54) 222-4133
Fax: +55(54) 222-8223
Telex: 54-3734
Reitor: Ruy Pauletti
Founded: 1967
Ce: Biological and Health Sciences; Philosophy and Education; Applied Social Studies; Exact Sciences and Technology; Human Sciences and Arts.
I: Biotechnology; Administration and Technology.
S: Hotel Administration.

University of Cruz Alta
[Universidade de Cruz Alta]
Parida Benito s/n, 98100 Cruz Alta (Rio Grande do Sul)
Tel: +55(55) 322-1660

University of Fortaleza
[Universidade de Fortaleza]
Avenida Washington Soares 1321, 60811-341 Fortaleza (Ceará)
Tel: +55(85) 273-2833
Fax: +55(85) 273-1667
Telex: 85-37
Reitor: Antônio Colaço Martins
Secretário Geral: Epitácio Quezado Cruz
Founded: 1971
Ce: Technology; Administration; Health Sciences; Human Sciences.

Catholic University of Goiás
[Universidade Católica de Goiás]
Praça Universitária, 1440, 74605-010 Goiânia (Goiás)
Tel: +55(62) 227-1188
Fax: +55(62) 224-3617
Telex: 62-1276
Reitor: Clélia Brandão Alvarenga Craveiro
Secretario Geral: Rosival Barbosa Lagares
Founded: 1959
Ce: Human Sciences; Scientific Technology.
D: Business; Architecture; Biological and Biomedical Sciences; Accounting; Economics; Education; Nursing; Engineering; Philosophy and

Theology; History, Geography and Social Sciences; Legal Sciences; Business; Architesture; Biological and Biomedical Sciences; Economics.
I: Pre-History and Anthropology; Sub-humid Tropic.
Ce: Biological Research and Study; Youth Village Research and Study.

University of Guarulhos
[Universidade de Guarulhos]
Praça Tereza Cristina 1, 07023-070 Guarulhos (São Paulo)
Tel: +55(11) 209-3688
Fax: +55(11) 940-1133
Reitor: Antönio Veronezi
Assessor da Reitoria: Danilo de Mello
Founded: 1970, 1982
Ce: Biological and Health Sciences; Exact Sciences and Technology; Communication Sciences, Letters, and Arts; Human and Social Sciences.

University of Ijuí
[Universidade de Ijuí]
C.P. 560, Rua São Francisco 501, Bairro São Geraldo, 98700-000 Ijuí (Rio Grande do Sul)
Tel: +55(55) 332-6100
Fax: +55(55) 332-3717
Telex: 2210
Reitor: Walter Frantz
Secretário Académico: Tania Maria Lucchese
Founded: 1957, 1985
Ce: Health Sciences; Education; Socio-Economic Studies.
I: Science, Technology and Health; Philosophy and Social Sciences; Exact and Natural Sciences.

University of Itauna
[Universidade de Itauna]
Avenida Dona Cota 397, 35680-033 Itauna (Minas Gerais)
Tel: +55(37) 241-1080
Fax: +55(37) 241-3719
Telex: 11-54535
Reitor: Marcos G. de Cerqueira Lima

University of Marilía
[Universidade de Marilía]
Avenida Fignyo Muzzy Filho 1001, 17500 Marilía (São Paulo)
Tel: +55(11) 469-5333
Fax: +55(11) 469-2490
Telex: 11-54535

Pontifical Catholic University of Minas Gerais
[Pontifícia Universidade Católica de Minas Gerais]
Avenida Dom José Gaspar 500, 30552-970 Belo Horizonte (Minas Gerais)
Tel: +55(31) 319-1144
Fax: +55(31) 319-1225
Telex: 31-3339
Reitor: Geraldo Magela Teixeira
Founded: 1958, 1983

Ce: Human Sciences; Technology; Biological and Health Sciences; Social Sciences.

University Braz Cubas Mogi das Cruzes
[Universidad Braz Cubas]
Rua Francisco Rodrigues Rilho 1233, Mogilar, 08773-380 Mogi das Cruzes (São Paulo)
Tel: +55(11) 469-6444
Fax: +55(11) 469-7737
Reitor: Mauricio Chermann
Founded: 1984
F: Law; Economics; Engineering; Philosophy, Social Sciences and Letters; Architecture and Town Planning.
I: Social Communication.

*University of Mogi das Cruzes
[Universidade de Mogi das Cruzes]
Avenida Dr. Cândido Xavier de Almeida Souza, 200, 08780-911 Mogi das Cruzes (São Paulo)
Tel: +55(11) 469-5333
Fax: +55(11) 468-3844
Telex: 54535
Reitor: Maria da Conceição Bernardo Silva
Secretário Geral: Rubens Guilhemat
Founded: 1964
F: Accounting and Economics; Biological Sciences-Medical Science; Business Administration; Pharmacy and Biochemistry; Computer Sciences; Architecture and Town Planning; Medicine; Communication Studies; Engineering; Dentistry; Physical Education; Education; Economics; Law.
Ce: Human Sciences; Biomedical Sciences; Exact Sciences and Technology; Sports Sciences.
C: Philosophy and Social Science; Letters and Fine Arts; Biological Sciences; Psychology; Science; Nursing; Nutrition; Phonaudiology; Physiotherapy.

Pontifical Catholic University of Paraná
[Pontifícia Universidade Católica do Paraná (PUC-PR)]
Rua Imaculada Conceição 1155, Prado Velho, 80215-030 Curitiba (Paraná)
Tel: +55(41) 322-1515
Fax: +55(41) 225-4373
Telex: 4135085 puc-p
Reitor: Euro Brandão
Vice-Reitor Administrativo: Aramis Demeterco
Founded: 1959
Ce: Theology and Human Sciences; Law and Social Sciences; Exact Sciences and Technology; Biology and Health Sciences.
I: Environmental Sanitation; Technology; Physical Therapy; Psychology (Paranaense); Phonaudiology (Paranaense).
D: Biology.

University of Passo Fundo
[Universidade de Passo Fundo]
Campus Universitário, 99052-630 Passo Fundo
(Rio Grande do Sul)
Tel: +55(54) 311-1324
Fax: +55(54) 311-1307
Telex: 54-5394
Reitor: Elydo Alcides Guareschi
Vice-Reitor: Ilmo Santos
Founded: 1968
F: Education; Law; Economics; Medicine;
Dentistry; Agriculture; Physical Education;
Engineering.
I: Exact and Earth Sciences; Philosophy and
Human Sciences; Fine Arts; Biology.

*Catholic University of Pelotas
[Universidade Católica de Pelotas]
Rua Felix da Cunha 412, 96010-900 Pelotas (Rio
Grande do Sul)
Tel: +55(532) 25-3455
Fax: +55(532) 25-3105
Telex: 53-2454
Reitor: Jandir João Zanotelli
Founded: 1960
Ce: Human Sciences; Exact Sciences and
Technology; Biological and Health Sciences.
I: Social Planning and Business Administration;
Sea and Inland Water Research.

Catholic University of Pernambuco
[Universidade Católica de Pernambuco]
Rua do Principe 526, 50050-900 Recife
(Pernambuco)
Tel: +55(81) 216-4000
Fax: +55(81) 231-1842
Telex: 81-2776
Reitor: Theodoro Paulo Severino Peters, S.J.
Founded: 1951, 1973
Ce: Social Sciences; Theology and Human
Sciences; Science and Technology.
D: History; Education; Psychology; Law;
Sociology; Chemistry; Physics.

University of Pernambuco
[Universidade de Pernambuco]
Avenida Agamenon Magalhaes s/n, Santo
Amaro, 50040-010 Recife (Pernambuco)
Tel: +55(81) 421-3111
Fax: +55(81) 224-4623
Telex: 81-2310
Reitor: Julio Fernando Pessoa Correia

Catholic University of Petrópolis
[Universidade Católica de Petrópolis]
Rua Benjamin Constant 213, Caixa Postal 90944,
25610-130 Petrópolis (Rio de Janeiro)
Tel: +55(242) 42-5062
Fax: +55(242) 42-7747
Telex: 21-31637
Reitor: Maria da Glória Rangel Sampaio
Fernandes (1991-95)
Vice-Reitor: Getúlio Chehab
Founded: 1954

I: Exact and Natural Sciences; Theology,
Philosophy, and Human Sciences; Arts and
Communication.
F: Law; Education; Economics, Accountancy,
and Administration.
S: Rehabilitation; Engineering.
Ce: Theoretical Physics; Informatics.

*Methodist University of Piracicaba
[Universidade Metódista de Piracicaba]
Rua Rangel Pestana 762, 13400-901 Piracicaba
(São Paulo)
Tel: +55+55(194) 33-5011
Fax: +55(194) 22-8204
Telex: 19-1914 umep-br
Reitor: Almir de Souza Maia
Secretary-General: Irene de Carvalho Macêdo
Jardim
Founded: 1975, 1981
S: Applied Sciences; Biological and Health
Sciences; Liberal Arts; Technology; Philosophy
and Theology.
C: Exact Sciences.

University 'Oeste Paulista' of Presidente Prudente
[Universidade do Oeste Paulista]
Rua José Bongiovani 700, Cidade Universitária,
19050-680 Presidente Prudente (São Paulo)
Tel: +55(182) 21-0666
Fax: +55(182) 21-0200
Telex: 182-529
Reitor: Clóvis Othoniel Dantas Carapeba
Founded: 1987
F: Health Sciences; Dentistry; Pharmacy and
Biochemistry; Medicine; Veterinary Medicine;
Animal Husbandry and Agriculture; Civil
Engineering; Computer Sciences; Law,
Administration, and Accountancy; Science,
Letters, and Education.

Candido Mendes University Conglomerate Rio de Janeiro
[Conjunto Universitario Candido Mendes
(Sociedad Brasileira de Instrução) Rio de
Janeiro]
Praça XV de Novembro 101, Centro, 20010 Rio de
Janeiro (Rio de Janeiro)
Tel: +55(21) 222-6201
Presidente: Candido Mendes
Founded: 1981
F: Political Science and Economics (2); Law (2);
Law, Economics, Administration, Accountancy,
and Education; Economics, Administration, and
Accountancy (Campos); Business Administration
(Friburgo).

Gama Filho University Rio de Janeiro
[Universidade Gama Filho]
Rua Manoel Vitorino 625, Piedade, 20748 -900 Rio
de Janeiro (Rio de Janeiro)
Tel: +55(21) 269-7272
Fax: +55(21) 289-8394
Reitor: Sergio de Moraes Dias (1984-94)
Founded: 1972

Ce: *Biology and Health Sciences; Exact Sciences and Technology; Social Sciences; Human Sciences; Business Administration; Economics; Acounting; Social Work; Social Commmunication; History; Law; Biology; Medicine; Dentistry; Nutrition; Nursing; Engineering; Architecture; Physical Education; Education; Psychology; Geology; Chemistry; Representation and Analyses of Form; Geography; Letters and Arts.*
I: *Research Gonzaga Da Gama Filho.*

*Pontifical Catholic University of Rio de Janeiro

[Pontifícia Universidade Católica do Rio de Janeiro]
Rua Marquês de São Vicente 225, 22453-900 Rio de Janeiro (Rio de Janeiro)
Tel: +55(21) 529-9922
Fax: +55(21) 274-4197
Telex: 21-31048
Reitor: Laércio Dias de Moura, S.J. (1982-)
Registro: Rute Boluda Valero
Founded: 1941, 1947
Ce: *Studies in Telecommunication (CETUC); Theology and Human Sciences; Language Foreign Students-The Rio Datacentre (RDC); Social Sciences; Science and Technological Studies; Health Sciences.*
I: *Applied Psychology; Technological; International Relations.*

University 'Estacio da Sa' Rio de Janeiro

[Universidade Estacio da Sa]
Rua do Bispo 83, Rio Comprido, 20261-060 Rio de Janeiro (Rio de Janeiro)
Tel: +55(21) 503-7000
Fax: +55(21) 606-1870
Telex: 213-4243
Reitor: Lauro Ribas Zimmer

*University Santa Úrsula Rio de Janeiro

[Universidade de Santa Úrsula]
Rua Fernando Ferrari 75, 22231-040 Rio de Janeiro (Rio de Janeiro)
Tel: +55(21) 552-5542
Fax: +55(21) 551-6446
Telex: 34929
Reitora: Maria do Carmo Bettencourt de Faria
Founded: 1938, 1975
Ce: *Theology and Philosophy; Human and Social Sciences; Education; Biology and Nutrition; Library Science and Literature; Exact Sciences and Technology; Architecture and Arts.*
D: *Applied Psychology; Administrative Sciences; Psychology; Social Studies; Accounting Sciences; Juridical Sciences; General and Plant Biology; Animal Biology; Nutrition and Food Technology; Civil Engineering; Mechanical Engineering; Electrical Engineering; Chemistry; Physics; Mathematics; Analysis and Form Representation; Architecture; Aesthetics and History of the Arts; Theology; Philosophy; Psychology and Education;*

Educational Planning and Administration; Linguistics and Philology; Library Science.
I: *Economic Science and Government.*

University of Ribeirão Prêto

[Universidade de Ribeirão Prêto]
Avenida Costabile Romano 2201, 14095 Ribeirão Prêto (São Paulo)
Tel: +55(16) 627-3300
Telex: 16-6036 asen
Founded: 1971
F: *Human Sciences; Art; Exact Sciences; Education; Health Sciences.*

*Pontifical Catholic University of Rio Grande do Sul

[Pontifícia Universidade Católica do Rio Grande do Sul]
Avenida Ipiranga 6681, Caixa postal 1429, 90620-900 Pôrto Alegre (Rio Grande do Sul)
Tel: +55(51) 339-1511
Fax: +55(51) 339-1564
Telex: 51-3349
Reitor: Irmão Norberto Francisco Rauch (1990-)
Chefe de Gabinete: Eurico Saldanha De Lemos
Founded: 1931, 1948, 1950
I: *Mathematics; Geriatrics; Informatics; Physics; Chemistry; Theology and Religious Sciences; Biology; Letters and Arts; Philosophy and Human Sciences; Psychology.*
S: *Education; Social Service; Communications Media; Law; Political Science and Economics; Dentistry; Medicine.*
S: *Polytechnic; Animal Husbandry, Veterinary Medicine and Agriculture (Campus II); Accountancy and Business Administration (Campus II); Philosophy, Science and Letters (Campus II); Law (Campus II Uruguaiana).*

Catholic University of Salvador

[Universidade Católica de Salvador]
Praça 2 de Julio 7, 40080-121 Salvador (Bahia)
Tel: +55(71) 3365244
Fax: +55(71) 336-0853
Reitor: José Carlos Almeida da Silva
Founded: 1961
I: *Exact and Natural Sciences; Philosophy; Letters; Music; Theology.*
F: *Education; Nursing; Economics; Law.*
S: *Engineering; Social Service; Business Administration.*

University of South Santa Catarina

[Universidade do Sul de Santa Caterina (UNISUL)]
Avenida José Acacio Moreira 787, 88704-900 Tubarão (Santa Catarina)
Tel: +55(486) 22-5222
Fax: +55(486) 22-5222
Telex: 0484 562 uvsl
Reitor: Silvestre Heerdt
Chefe de Gabinete: Joaquim de Sá Faraco
Founded: 1964, 1989

I: Administration; Computer Sciences; Science; Accountancy; Economics; Social Service; Geography; History; Law; Education; Nursing and Midwifery; Civil Engineering; Philosophy; Letters; Psychology; Chemical Engineering; Education; Biological and Health Sciences; Human Sciences; Arts and Letters; Technological Sciences; Applied and Social Sciences; Juridical Sciences; Exact Sciences.

Catholic University of Santos
[Universidade Católica de Santos]
Rua Euclides da Cunha 241, 11065-101 Santos (São Paulo)
Tel: +55(132) 37-3435
Fax: +55(132) 37-2149
Telex: 13-1978
Reitor: bFrancisco Prado de Oliveira Ribeiro
Founded: 1954
F: Administration; Architecture; Science; Biology; Accountancy; Economics; Law; Nursing; Social Studies; Philosophy; Geography, History and Letters; Applied Mathematics; Education.

University 'Santa Cecília dos Bandeirantes' Santos
[Universidade Santa Cecília dos Bandeirantes]
Rua Oswaldo Cruz 250, 11045-907 Santos (São Paulo)
Tel: +55(132) 34-4925
Fax: +55(132) 34-5297
Reitor: Milton Teixeira
Founded: 1961, 1969, 1986
F: Plastic Arts; Science and Technology; Civil Engineering; Industrial Engineering; Physical Education; Commerce and Administration; Education and Human Sciences; Dentistry.
Ce: Computer.
D: Extension.

Sinos Valley University São Leopoldo
[Universidade do Vale do Rio dos Sinos]
Avenida Unisinos 950, 93020-000 São Leopoldo (Rio Grande do Sul)
Tel: +551(51) 592-0333
Fax: +55(51) 592-1035
Telex: 524076 savs
Reitor: Aloysio Bohnen (1990-)
Registrar: José Marculano
Founded: 1954, 1969, 1970
Ce: Humanistic Studies; Communication Studies; Health Sciences; Health Sciences; Technological Studies; Documentation and Research; Law Studies; Economic Sciences; Exact Sciences; Technological Studies.
I: Research; Planarian Research.

Mackenzie University São Paulo
[Universidade Mackenzie]
Rua Maria Antonia 403, Higienópolis, 01222 São Paulo (São Paulo)
Tel: +55(11) 256-6611
Fax: +55(11) 256-9280
Cable: collemack
Reitor: Aurora Catharina Giora Albanese
Secretário Geral: Nelson Callegari
Founded: 1870, 1952, 1961
F: Architecture and Town Planning; Exact and Experimental Sciences; Technology; Communication and Arts; Letters and Education; Law; Engineering; Economics, Accountancy and Administration.
I: Technology.

Paulista University São Paulo
[Universidade Paulista]
Avenida Paulista, 900, 04026-002 São Paulo
Tel: +55(11) 578-6455
Fax: +55(11) 275-1541
Reitor: João Carlos de Genio
Founded: 1972, 1988
I: Human Sciences; Health Sciences; Engineering; Social Sciences and Administration.
Ce: Research in Psychology and Education.
D: Extension.

*Pontifical Catholic University of São Paulo
[Pontifícia Universidade Católica de São Paulo]
984 Rua Monte Alegre, Perdizes, 05014-901 São Paulo (São Paulo)
Tel: +55(11) 263-0211
Fax: +55(11) 62-4920
Telex: (11) 82462 fspo br
Reitor: António Carlos Caruso Ronca (1994-)
Vice-Reitor Academico: Fernando José de Almeida
Founded: 1946, 1947
Ce: Human Sciences; Education; Research Resources and Information in Reading; Law, Economics and Business Administration; Mathematics, Physics and Technology; Biomedical Sciences.
I: Special Studies; Portuguese Studies.
D: Education and Recuperation of Communication Disorders.

University Camilo Castelo Branco São Paulo
[Universidad Camilo Castelo Branco]
Rua Carolina Fonseca 584, Itaquera, 08230 São Paulo (São Paulo)
Tel: +55(11) 205-0099
Founded: 1972

University São Judas Tadeu São Paulo
[Universidade São Judas Tadeu]
Rua Taquari 546, 31660 São Paulo (São Paulo)
Tel: +55(11) 948-1677
Founded: 1971, 1989
F: Letters, Arts, Communication and Education; Biology and Health Sciences; Exact Sciences and Technology; Human Sciences.

University of Uberaba
[Universidade de Uberaba]
Avenida Guilherme Ferreira 217, 38010 Uberaba
(Minas Gerais)
Tel: +55(34) 332-3322
Telex: 48-4562
Founded: 1965

OTHER INSTITUTIONS

PUBLIC INSTITUTIONS

Centro de Educação Técnica da Utramig
Avenida Afonsa Peña 3400, 30130 Belo Horizonte,
MG
Tel: +55(31) 221-3677
Founded: 1975
Education; Technology.

Centro Federal de Educação Tecnologica da Bahia
Via Universitária, 43700 Simoes Filho, BA
Tel: +55(71) 396-8400
Telex: 71-2335 cetf br
Founded: 1976
Technology.

Centro de Ensino Superior do Vale do São Francisco
Avenida Colonel Trapia 202, 56440 Belém do São
Francisco PE
Tel: +55(81) 936-1248
Founded: 1975
Education; Social Sciences.

Centro de Tecnologia da Industria e Construção
Avenida Tarcy Vargas 1200, 69050 Manaus, AM
Tel: +55(92) 236-2826
Founded: 1974
Engineering; Computer Sciences.

Centro Federal de Educação Tecnologica de Minas Gerais
Avenida Amazonas 30410 Gamaleira, Belo
Horizonte, MG
Tel: +55(31) 332-8400
Telex: 31-3863 cf br
Founded: 1959
Education; Electric Engineering.

Centro Federal de Educação Tecnologica do Maranho
Avenida Getúlio Vargas 4, 65000 São Luis, MA
Tel: +55(98) 1640
Telex: 98-2214
Founded: 1991

Centro Federal de Educação Tecnologica do Paraná
Avenida 7 de Setembro 3165 Centro, 80230
Curitiba, PR
Tel: +55(41) 224-5333
Telex: 41-5562 cfet br
Founded: 1978
Technology.

Centro Federal de Educação Tecnologica do Rio de Janeiro
Avenida Maracaña 229 Sao Cristovão, 20271 Rio
de Janeiro, RJ
Tel: +55(21) 248-9873
Founded: 1978
Engineering.

Centro Integrado de Ensino Superior da FUOC
Campus Universitário 2125, 89600 Joasaba SC
Tel: +55(495) 220-288
Founded: 1968

Centro Integrado de Ensino Superior de Concordia
Rua Lauro Mueller 21, 89700 Concordia, SC
Tel: +55(499) 440-850
Founded: 1976

Centro Universitário de Caceres
Rua General Osorio 362, 78200 Caceres, MT
Tel: +55(65) 221-1776
Founded: 1984

Escola de Artes Plásticas
Avenida Amazonas 6252, 3000 Belo Horizonte,
MG
Tel: +55(31) 332-0007
Founded: 1964
Plastic Arts.

Escola de Biblioteconomia e Documentação de São Carlos
Rua São Sebastiao, 13560 São Carlos, SP
Tel: +55(162) 721-308
Founded: 1959
Library Science and Documentation.

Escola de Ciências Médicas de Alagoas
Avenida Siqueira Campos 2095, 57010 Maceió,
AL
Tel: +55(82) 221-3093
Medicine.

Escola de Educação Física de São Carlos
Rua Sao Sebiastiao 2828, 13560 São Carlos, SP
Tel: +55(162) 721-308
Physical Education.

Escola de Enfermagen
Rua Teresina 495, 69057 Manaus, AM
Tel: +55(92) 234-4897
Founded: 1951
Nursing.

Escola de Enfermagen Magalhaes Barata
Avenida José Bonifáo 1289, 66000 Belém, PA
Tel: +55(91) 229-0236
Founded: 1949
Nursing.

Escola de Engenheria de Piracicaba
Avenida Mons. Martinho Salgot 560, 13400
Piracicaba, SP
Tel: +55(19) 421-4892
Founded: 1968
Engineering.

Escola de Farmácia e Odontologia de Alfenas
Rua Gabriel Monteiro da Silva, 37130 Alfenas, MG
Tel: +55(35) 921-1011
Telex: 35-2105 efoa br
Founded: 1914
Medicine.

Escola de Música de Belo Horizonte
Rua Riacpuelo 1351, 30750 Belo Horizonte, MG
Tel: +55(31) 464-8303
Founded: 1964
Music.

Escola de Música do Espírito Santo
Avenida Princesa Isabel 610, 29010 Vitoría, ES
Tel: +55(27) 222-0195
Founded: 1971
Music.

Escola de Música e Belas Artes do Paraná
Rua Emiliano Perneta 179, 80010 Curitiba, PR
Tel: +55(41) 223-1129
Founded: 1951
Music and Fine Arts.

Escola Federal de Engenharia de Itajubá
Rua Colonel Renno 7, 37500 Itajubá, MG
Tel: +55(35) 622-1966
Telex: 35-4274 efei br
Founded: 1913
Engineering.

Escola Nacional de Ciencias Estatísticas
Rua André Cavalcanti 106, 20231 Rio de Janeiro, RJ
Tel: +55(21) 224-7677
Founded: 1961
Statistics.

Escola Paulista de Medicina
Rue Botucatu 740, 04023 Sao Paulo, SP
Tel: +55(11) 572-6033
Telex: 11-36977
Founded: 1956
Medicine.

Escola Politécnica de Pernambuco
Praça do Internacional, 507509 Recife, PE
Tel: +55(81) 227-2855
Founded: 1912

Escola Superior de Agricultura de Lavras
Campus Universitário, 37200 Lavras, MG
Tel: +55(35) 821-3700
Telex: 35-3007 esag br
Founded: 1908
Agriculture.

Escola Superior de Agricultura e Ciências de Machado
Avenida Cr. Aihayde Pereira de Souza s/n, 37750 Machado, MG
Tel: +55(35) 931-1866
Founded: 1974
Agriculture.

Escola Superior de Ciências Agrarias de Rio Verde
Campus Universitário, Rio Verde, GO
Tel: +55(62) 627-0796
Agriculture.

Escola Superior de Ciências Contábeis e Administrativas
Rua Pascoal Meller, Campus Universitário, 88800 Criciuma, SC
Tel: +55(484) 381-411
Founded: 1975
Accountancy and Administrative Sciences.

Escola Superior de Ciências Humanas de Rio Verde
Campus Universitário s/n, 75900 Rio Verde, GO
Tel: +55(62) 621-1839
Founded: 1984
Human Sciences.

Escola Superior de Educação Física de Avare
Praça Altino Arantes 163, 18700 Avare, SP
Tel: +55(147) 221-133
Founded: 1973
Physical Education.

Escola Superior de Educação Física de Cruzeiro
Rua Dr. José R.A. Sobrinho 191, 12700 Cruzeiro, SP
Tel: +55(12) 544-1865
Founded: 1970
Physical Education.

Escola Superior de Educação Física de Goiás
Avenida Anhanguera 1420, 74000 Goiania, GO
Tel: +55(62) 261-1443
Founded: 1967
Physical Education.

Escola Superior de Educação Física de Jundiaí
Rua Rodrigo Soares de Oliveira s/n, 13200 Jundiaí, SP
Tel: +55(11) 434-7600
Founded: 1974
Physical Education.

Escola Superior de Educação Física de Mossoro
Dionisto Filgeuira 383, 59600 Mossoro, RN
Tel: +55(84) 321-4994
Telex: 84-3211
Founded: 1973
Physical Education.

Escola Superior de Educação Física de Recife
Campus Universitário da FESP s/n, 50000 Recife, PE
Tel: +55(81) 421-2224
Founded: 1953
Physical Education.

Escola Superior de Educação Física do Pará
Avenida 1 de Dezembro 817, 66240 Belém, PA
Tel: +55(91) 226-0436
Founded: 1970
Physical Education.

Faculdade de Administração de Mineiros
Rua 22 Esquima Com. Avenida 21, 75830 Mineiros, GO
Tel: +55 661-1970
Founded: 1986
Administration.

Faculdade de Administração e de Ciências Contábeis de Arapongas
a das Garcas 290, 86700 Arapongas, PR
Tel: +55(432) 523-730
Founded: 1980
Administration; Accountancy.

Faculdade de Administração e Economia de São João da Boa Vista
Avenida Dr. Oscar Piraja Martins 15, 13870 São João da Boa Vista, SP
Tel: +55(196) 233-022
Founded: 1965
Administration; Economics.

Faculdade de Agronomia Luiz Meneghel
Rodovia Br. 369, Km-54-Saida P/Andira, 86360 Bandirantes, PR
Tel: +55(43) 742-1123
Cable: agrofal
Founded: 1970
Agriculture.

Faculdade de Artes do Paraná
Rua Almirante Barroso 78, 80510 Curitiba, PR
Tel: +55(41) 223-7490
Founded: 1967
Arts.

Faculdade de Ciências Administrativas de Poços de Caldas
Avenida Padre Francisco Cletos Cox s/n, 37700 Poços de Caldas, MG
Tel: +55(35) 714-1001
Founded: 1973
Administration.

Faculdade de Ciências Agrarias de Araripina
Avenida Florentino Alves Batista s/n, Campus Universitário, 56280 Araripina, PE
Tel: +55(81) 931-1435
Founded: 1986
Agriculture.

Faculdade de Ciências Agrarias de Itumbiara
Rua Caldas Novas 320, 76100 Itumbiara, GO
Tel: +55(62) 431-3609
Founded: 1985
Agriculture.

Faculdade de Ciências Agrarias do Pará
Avenida Perimetral s/n, 66050 Belém, PA
Tel: +55(91) 226-0436
Telex: 91-1892 fagp br
Founded: 1945
Agriculture.

Faculdade de Ciências Biológicas de Araras
Avenida Cr. Maximiliano Barutto s/n 1, 13600 Araras, SP
Tel: +55(195) 411-411
Founded: 1974
Biological Sciences.

Faculdade de Ciências Contábeis de Curitibanos
Avenida Leoberto Leal, 89520 Curitibanos, SC
Tel: +55(482) 451-649
Founded: 1976
Accountancy.

Faculdade de Ciências Contábeis de Sobral
Avenida da Universidade, 62100 Sobral, CE
Tel: +55(85) 611-2213
Founded: 1970
Accountancy.

Faculdade de Ciências da Administração de Garanhuns
Rue Ernesto Dourado 390, 55300 Garanhuns, PE
Tel: +55(81) 761-1596
Founded: 1977
Administration.

Faculdade de Ciências de Administração de Limoeiro
Avenida Jeronimo Heraclio, 55700 Centro Limoeiro, PE
Tel: +55(81) 628-1397
Founded: 1976
Administration.

Faculdade de Ciências de Administração de Pernambuco
Avenida Abdias de Carvalho s/n, 50000 Recife, PE
Tel: +55(81) 228-5644
Founded: 1956
Administration.

Faculdade de Ciências de Administração de Petrolina
Campus Universitário, 56300 Petrolina, PE
Tel: +55(81) 961-0494
Founded: 1984
Administration.

Faculdade de Ciências e Letras de Avare
Praça Altino Arantes 163, 18700 Avare, SP
Tel: +55(147) 221-133
Founded: 1969
Sciences and Letters.

Faculdade de Ciências e Letras de Bragança Paulista
Avenida Francisco S. Lucchesi Filho 770, 12900 Bragança Paulista, SP
Tel: +55(11) 433-3525
Founded: 1968
Sciences and Letters.

Faculdade de Ciências e Letras de Campo Mourão
Avenida Comendador N. Marcondes 1972, 87300 Campo Mourão, PR
Tel: +55(44) 823-1880
Founded: 1974
Sciences and Letters.

Faculdade de Ciências e Letras de Fernandópolis
Avenida Teotonio Vilela s/n, 15600 Fernandópolis, SP
Tel: +55(174) 424-475
Founded: 1983
Sciences and Letters.

Faculdade de Ciências e Letras de Mafra
Avenida Presidente Nereu Ramos 1071, 89300 Mafra, SC
Tel: +55(476) 420-059
Founded: 1973
Sciences and Letters.

Faculdade de Ciências e Letras de Matão
Rua Cesario Mota 644, 15990 Matão, SP
Tel: +55(16) 282-1226
Founded: 1971
Sciences and Letters.

Faculdade de Ciências Econômicas de Anápolis
Avenida Juscelino Kubitschek 146, 77100 Anápolis, GO
Tel: +55(62) 324-3962
Founded: 1973
Economic Sciences.

Faculdade de Ciências Econômicas de Mossoro
BR 110 km 48 s/n, Campus Central, 59600 Mossoro, RN
Tel: +55(84) 321-4994
Telex: 84-3211
Founded: 1968
Economics.

Faculdade de Ciências Econômicas e Administrativas de Franca
Avenida Major Nicacio 2433, 14400 Franca, SP
Tel: +55(16) 722-4104
Founded: 1951
Economics; Administration.

Faculdade de Ciências Econômicas e Administrativas de Osasco
Rua Projetada, 06010 Osasco, SP
Tel: +55(11) 703-2955
Founded: 1965
Economic and Administrative Sciences.

Faculdade de Ciências Humanas Arnaldo Busato
Rua de Faculdade 2550, 85900 Toledo, PR
Tel: +55(452) 523-535
Founded: 1980
Human Sciences.

Faculdade de Ciências Humanas de Francisco Beltrão
Rua Maringa 1200, 85600 Francisco Beltrão, PR
Tel: +55(46) 523-3740
Founded: 1975
Human Sciences.

Faculdade de Ciências Humanas de Marechal Candido Rondon
Rua Costa e Silva s/n, 85960 Marechal Candido Rondon, PR
Tel: +55(452) 543-216
Human Sciences.

Faculdade de Ciências Humanas do Cabo
Rua do Campo, 54500 Cabo, PE
Tel: +55(81) 521-0400
Founded: 1980
Human Sciences.

Faculdade de Ciências Médicas de Pernambuco
Rua Arnobio Marques, 50040 Recife, PE
Tel: +55(81) 231-0785
Founded: 1951
Medicine.

Faculdade de Ciências Sociais Aplicadas de Foz do Iguaçu
Rua Silvino dal Bo, 85890 Foz do Iguaçu, PR
Tel: +55(455) 732-290
Founded: 1979
Applied Social Sciences.

Faculdade de Ciências Socio-Economicas de Joinville
Campus Universitário s/n, 89200 Joinville, SC
Tel: +55(474) 253-200
Founded: 1971
Socio-Economic Sciences.

Faculdade de Direito de Cachoeíro de Itapemirim
Rua Mario Imperial 56, 29300 Cachoeíro de Itapemirim, ES
Tel: +55(27) 522-0128
Founded: 1966
Law.

Faculdade de Direito de Conselheiro Lafaiete
Praça Barao de Queluz 11, 36400 Conselheiro Lafaiete, MG
Tel: +55(31) 721-1069
Founded: 1970
Law.

Faculdade de Direito de Franca
Avenida Major Niçacio 2377, 14400 Franca, SP
Tel: +55(16) 724-4500
Founded: 1961
Law.

Faculdade de Direito São Bernardo do Campo
Rua Java 425, 09750 São Bernardo do Campo, SP
Tel: +55(11) 458-0222
Founded: 1965
Law.

Faculdade de Educação, Ciências e Letras de Cascavel
Rua Carlos Gomes 2569, Campus Universitário, 85800 Cascavel, PR
Tel: +55(435) 234-981
Telex: 451-091
Founded: 1972 ˋ
Education, Sciences and Letters.

Faculdade de Educação, Ciências e Letras de Ilmosa Saad Fayad
Rua Ferroviara o Esq., Rua 2 s/n Nordeste, 73800 Formosa, GO
Tel: +55(61) 631-1187
Founded: 1986
Education, Sciences and Letters.

Faculdade de Educação, Ciências e Letras de Ipora
Avenida El. de Agosto s/n qd 01 Esq. c/r 2, 76540 Ipora, GO
Tel: +55(62) 674-1152
Founded: 1989
Education, Sciences and Letters.

Faculdade de Educação, Ciências e Letras de Irati
Rua Cel Pires 826, 84500 Irati, PR
Tel: +55(424) 221-381
Founded: 1975
Education, Sciences and Letters.

Faculdade de Educação, Ciências e Letras de Itapuranga
Praça Joao Nunes Prdigao 80, 76650 Itapuranga, GO
Tel: +55(62) 745-1112
Founded: 1990
Education, Sciences and Letters.

Faculdade de Educação, Ciências e Letras de Morrinhos
Rua 14 625 qd 01 Esq. c/r 2, 75650 Morrinhos, GO
Tel: +55(62) 421-2329
Founded: 1988
Education, Sciences and Letters.

Faculdade de Educação, Ciências e Letras de Porangatu
Rua 25 s/n qd 01 Esq. c/r 2, 76550 Porangatu, GO
Tel: +55(61) 771-1033
Founded: 1985
Education, Sciences and Letters.

Faculdade de Educação, Ciências e Letras de Quirinopolis
Avenida Com. Pedro I 135, 76260 Quirinopolis, GO
Tel: +55(62) 651-2151
Founded: 1990
Education, Sciences and Letters.

Faculdade de Educação de Candinhas
Rua Roberto Elhke 86, 89460 Candinhas, SC
Tel: +55(476) 220-436
Founded: 1986
Education.

Faculdade de Educação de Itaberaí
Rua Presidente Costa e Silva 212, 24800 Itaberaí, RJ
Tel: +55 735-1014
Founded: 1979
Education.

Faculdade de Educação de Mossoro
Praça Miguel Faustino, 59600 Mossoro, RN
Tel: +55(84) 321-4994
Telex: 84-3211
Founded: 1973
Education.

Faculdade de Educação de Sobral
Avenida da Universidade, 62100 Sobral, CE
Tel: +55(85) 611-2213
Education.

Faculdade de Educação e Ciências Humanas
Avenida Tanceirantes 1140, 76170 Anicuns, GO
Tel: +55(62) 544-1379
Founded: 1985
Education and Human Sciences.

Faculdade de Educação Física da Alta Araraquarense
Rua Oito 854, 15775 Santa Fe do Sul, SP
Tel: +55(176) 312-921
Founded: 1972
Physical Education.

Faculdade de Enfermagen e Obstetrícia de Adamantina
Rua 9 de Julho 730, 17800 Adamantina, SP
Tel: +55(189) 213-345
Founded: 1985
Nursing and Midwifery.

Faculdade de Enfermagem e Obstetrícia de Fernandópolis
Avenida Teotonio Vilela, 15600 Fernandópolis, SP
Tel: +55(174) 424-475
Founded: 1983
Nursing and Midwifery.

Faculdade de Enfermagem e Obstetrícia de Passos
Rua Juca Stockler 1130, 37900 Passos, MG
Tel: +55(35) 521-2714
Founded: 1981
Nursing and Midwifery.

Faculdade de Enfermagem e Obstetrícia de Sobral
Avenida da Universidade, 62100 Sobral, CE
Tel: +55(85) 611-1827
Founded: 1975
Nursing School.

Faculdade de Enfermagem 'Nossa Senhora das Graças'
Rua Arnobio Marques, 50040 Recife, PE
Tel: +55(81) 421-2776
Founded: 1949
Nursing.

Faculdade de Engenharia Civil de Passos
Avenida Juca Stockler, 37900 Passos, MG
Tel: +55(35) 521-714
Founded: 1976
Engineering.

Faculdade de Engenharia de Poços de Caldas
Avenida Pe. Francis Cletus Cox s/n, 37700 Poços de Caldas, MG
Tel: +55(35) 714-1001
Founded: 1986
Engineering.

Faculdade de Farmacia e Bioquímica do Espiríto Santo
Avenida Cleto Nunes 133, 29020 Vitória, SP
Tel: +55(27) 322-1088
Founded: 1975
Pharmacy and Biochemistry.

Faculdade de Filosofia, Ciências e Letras de Adamantina
Rua Nove de Julho 730, 17800 Adamantina, SP
Tel: +55(189) 211-176
Founded: 1972
Philosophy, Sciences and Letters.

Faculdade de Filosofia, Ciências e Letras de Alegre
Rua Belo Amorim 100, 29500 Alegre, ES
Tel: +55(27) 552-1412
Founded: 1973
Letters and Philosophy.

Faculdade de Filosofia, Ciências e Letras de Araxa
Avenida Amazonas, 38180 Araxa, MG
Tel: +55(34) 661-1920
Founded: 1973
Philosophy, Sciences and Letters.

Faculdade de Filosofia, Ciências e Letras de Boa Esperança
Rua Marechal Floriano Peixoto, 37170 Boa Esperança, MG
Tel: +55(35) 962-1223
Founded: 1977
Philosophy, Sciences and Letters.

Faculdade de Filosofia, Ciências e Letras de Catanduva
Rua Maranhao, 15800 Catanduva, SP
Tel: +55(175) 222-323
Founded: 1967
Philosophy, Sciences and Letters.

Faculdade de Filosofia, Ciências e Letras de Itumbiara
Avenida de Furnas, 76100 Itumbiara, GO
Tel: +55(62) 431-609
Founded: 1979
Philosophy, Sciences and Letters.

Faculdade de Filosofia, Ciências e Letras de Joinville
Campus Universitário, 89200 Joinville, SC
Tel: +55(474) 253-200
Founded: 1972
Philosophy, Sciences and Letters.

Faculdade de Filosofia, Ciências e Letras de Mandaguari
Estrada Sao Pedro km 01, 86970 Mandaguari, PR
Tel: +(44) 233-1356
Founded: 1966
Philosophy, Sciences and Letters.

Faculdade de Filosofia, Ciências e Letras de Patos de Minas
Rua Major Gote s/n, 38700 Patos de Minas, MG
Tel: +55(34) 821-3742
Founded: 1970
Letters and Philosophy.

Faculdade de Filosofia, Ciências e Letras de Patrocínio
Rua Artur Botelho 403, 38740 Patrocíno
Tel: +55(34) 831-3737
Founded: 1974
Letters and Philosophy.

Faculdade de Filosofia, Ciências e Letras de Penápolis
Campus Universitário, 16300 Penápolis, SP
Tel: +55(186) 522-315
Founded: 1967
Philosophy, Sciences and Letters.

Faculdade de Filosofia, Ciências e Letras de Poços de Caldas
Avenida Padre Francis Cletus Cox, 37700 Poços de Caldas, MG
Tel: +55(34) 714-1001
Founded: 1966
Philosophy, Sciences and Letters.

Faculdade de Filosofia, Ciências e Letras de Prof. José A. Vieira
Pca. Olecarido 25, 37750 Machado, MG
Tel: +55(35) 931-1866
Founded: 1968
Philosophy, Sciences and Letters.

Faculdade de Filosofia, Ciências e Letras de São José do Rio Pardo
Avenida Dep. Eduardo Vicente Nasser 1020, 13720 São José do Rio Pardo, SP
Tel: +55(19) 661-1704
Founded: 1966
Philosophy, Sciences and Letters.

Faculdade de Filosofia, Ciências e Letras de São Manuel
Rua Quintino Bocaiuva s/n, 18650 São Manuel, SP
Tel: +55(149) 413-766
Founded: 1988
Philosophy, Sciences and Letters.

Faculdade de Filosofia de Rio Verde
Rua Senador Martins Borges 269, 75900 Rio Verde, GO
Tel: +55(62) 621-1839
Founded: 1975
Philosophy.

Faculdade de Filosofia Dom José de Sobral
Avenida Universidade s/n, 62100 Sobral, CE
Tel: +55(85) 611-2213
Founded: 1961
Philosophy.

Faculdade de Filosofia e Ciências Humanas de Goiatuba
Rua Piaui 460, 75600 Goiatuba, GO
Tel: +55(62) 425-1560
Founded: 1989
Philosophy and Human Sciences.

Faculdade de Filosofia e Ciências Humanas de Gurupi
Avenida Alameda Madrid 2190, 77400 Gurupi, TO
Tel: +55(62) 851-2091
Founded: 1985
Philosophy and Human Sciences.

Faculdade de Fisiotérapia de Patrocinio
Rua Artur Botelho s/n, 38740 Patrocinio, MG
Tel: +55(34) 831-3737
Founded: 1974
Physiotherapy.

Faculdade de Formaçao de Professores de Araripina
Rua 11 de Setembro 163, 56280 Araripina, PE
Tel: +55(81) 931-1001
Founded: 1979
Teacher Training.

Faculdade de Formaçao de Professores de Arcoverde
Rua Gumercindo Cavalcante s/n, 56500 Arcoverde, PE
Tel: +55(81) 821-0574
Founded: 1984
Teacher Training.

Faculdade de Formação de Professores de Garanhuns
Rua Cap Pedro Rodrigues 105, 55300 Garanhuns, PE
Tel: +55(81) 761-1343
Founded: 1966
Teacher Training.

Faculdade de Formação de Professores de Goiana
Rua Poco do Rei s/n, 55900 Goiana, PR
Tel: +55(81) 626-0517
Founded: 1979
Teacher Training.

Faculdade de Formação de Professores de Nazare da Mata
Rua Professor Americo Brandao 43, 55800 Nazare da Mata, PE
Tel: +55(81) 633-1141
Founded: 1966
Teacher Training.

Faculdade de Formação de Professores de Petrolina
Petrolina s/n br 203 Km. 2, 56300 Petrolina, PE
Tel: +55(81) 961-2033
Founded: 1969
Teacher Training.

Faculdade de Formação de Professores Grau de Serra Talhada
Avenida Afonso Magalhaes, 56900 Serra Talhada, PE
Tel: +55(81) 831-1090
Founded: 1983
Teacher Training.

Faculdade de Medicina de Jundiaí
Rua Francisco Telles 250, 13200 Jundiaí, SP
Tel: +55(11) 437-5726
Founded: 1969
Medicine.

Faculdade de Medicina do Triangulo Mineiro
Praça Manuel Terra s/n, 38100 Uberaba, MG
Tel: +55(34) 312-7722
Telex: 34-3206
Founded: 1954
Medicine.

Faculdade de Odontologia de Nova Friburgo
Rua Sylvio H. Braune 22, 28625 Nova Friburgo, RJ
Tel: +55(245) 222-916
Founded: 1971
Odontology.

Faculdade de Odontologia de Pernambuco
Avenida Gal Newton Cavalcanti 146, 54750 Recife, PE
Tel: +55(822) 271-0186
Founded: 1960
Odontology.

Faculdade de Tecnologia de São Paulo
Praça Cel. Fernando Prestes 30, 01124 São Paulo, SP
Tel: +55(11) 229-5847
Founded: 1970
Technology.

Faculdade de Tecnologia de Sobral
Avenida da Universidade s/n, 62100 Sobral, CE
Tel: +55(85) 611-2213
Founded: 1978
Technology.

Faculdade de Tecnologia de Sorocaba
Avenida Eng. Carlo Reinaldo Mendes, 18013 Sorocaba, SP
Tel: +55(152) 326-881
Technology.

Faculdade Estadual de Ciências Econômicas de Apucarana
Rodovia do Café BR 376, 86800 Apucarana, PR
Tel: +55(434) 227-400
Founded: 1960
Economic Sciences.

Faculdade Estadual de Direito do Norte Pioneiro
Avenida Manoel Ribas 711, 86400 Jacarèzinho, PR
Tel: +55(437) 220-862
Founded: 1968
Law.

Faculdade Estadual de Educação do Para
Rua Professor Nelson Ribeiro 156, 66000 Belem, PA
Tel: +55(91) 226-2023
Founded: 1986
Education.

Faculdade Estadual de Educação Física de Jacarèzinho
Avenida Getúlio Vargas 2, 86400 Jacarèzinho, PR
Tel: +55(437) 220-498
Founded: 1972
Physical Education.

Faculdade Estadual de Filosofia, Ciências e Letras de Cornélio Procópio
Rua Portugal 340, 86300 Cornélio Procópio, PR
Tel: +55(435) 232-922
Founded: 1960
Philosophy, Sciences and Letters.

Faculdade Estadual de Filosofia, Ciências e Letras de Guarapuava
Presidente Zacarias 875 Santa Cruz, 85100 Guarapuava, PR
Tel: +55(42) 723-1869
Founded: 1970
Philosophy, Sciences and Letters.

Faculdade Estadual de Filosofia, Ciências e Letras de Jacarèzinho
Rua Padre Melo 1200, 86400 Jacarèzinho, PR
Tel: +55(437) 220-643
Founded: 1960
Philosophy, Sciences and Letters.

Faculdade Estadual de Filosofia, Ciências e Letras de Paranáguá
Rua Commendor Correa Junior 81, 83200 Paranáguá, PR
Tel: +55(41) 422-6911
Founded: 1960
Philosophy, Sciences and Letters.

Faculdade Estadual de Filosofia, Ciências e Letras de União da Vitória
Praça Colonel Amazonas s/n, Caixa postal 234, 84600 União da Vitória, PR
Tel: +55(425) 224-433
Founded: 1960
Philosophy, Sciences and Letters.

Faculdade Estadual de Filosofia, Ciências e Letras Paranavaí
Avenida Gabriel Esperidião s/n, 87700 Paranavai, PR
Tel: +55(44) 422-0943
Founded: 1966
Philosophy, Sciences and Letters.

Faculdade Estadual de Medicina do Pará
Trav. 14 de Abril 1462, 66000 Belém, PA
Tel: +55(91) 229-2548
Founded: 1971
Medicine.

Faculdade Federal de Ciências Médicas de Porto Alêgre
Rua Prof. Sarmento Leite 245, 90050 Porto Alêgre, RS
Tel: +55(51) 224-8615
Founded: 1961
Medicine.

Faculdade Federal de Odontologia de Diamantina
Rua da Glória 187, 39100 Diamantina, MG
Tel: +55(38) 931-1024
Telex: 38-7044
Founded: 1945
Odontology.

Faculdade Municipal de Administração e Ciências Econômicas de União da Vitória
Avenida Bento Munhoz da Rocha Neto 3856, União da Vitória, PR
Tel: +55(4) 522-1837
Founded: 1975
Administration and Economics.

Faculdades Reunidas de Administração, Ciências Contábeis, e Ciências Econômicas de Palmas
Rua Dr. Bernardo Ribeiro Viana 903, 84670 Palmas, PR
Tel: +55(462) 623-388
Founded: 1980
Administration, Accountancy and Economics.

Instituto de Ciências Humanas de Mossoro
BR 110 km 48 Campus Central, 59600 Mossoro, RN
Tel: +55(84) 321-4994
Founded: 1976
Human Sciences.

Instituto de Educação de Minas Gerais
Rua Pernambuco s/n, 30130 Belo Horizonte, MG
Tel: +55(31) 222-9637
Founded: 1974
Education.

Instituto de Ensino Superior de Mococa
Praça Madre Cabrini 87, Vila Mariano, 13730 Mococa, SP
Tel: +55(196) 550-340
Founded: 1972
Education.

Instituto de Letras e Artes de Mossoro
BR 110 km 48 s/n Campus Central, 59600 Mossoro, RN
Tel: +55(84) 321-4994
Telex: 84-3211
Founded: 1972
Letters and Fine Arts.

Instituto Militar de Engenharia
Praça Cen. Tiburcio 80, 22290 Rio de Janeiro, RJ
Tel: +55(21) 295-3232
Founded: 1928
Engineering.

Instituto Municipal de Ensino Superior de São Caetano do Sul
Avenida Goiás 3400, Barcelona, 80140 São Caetano do Sul, SP
Tel: +55(11) 453-1577
Founded: 1968

Instituto Rio Branco
Esplanade dos Ministerios, 70170 Brasília, DF
Tel: +55(61) 211-6184
Telex: 61-311
Founded: 1945
International Relations.

Instituto Superior, Ciências e Letras Artes Tres Coracões
Avenida Castelo Branco 82, 37410 Tres Coracões, MG
Tel: +55(35) 231-2046
Founded: 1967
Sciences, Letters and Fine Arts.

Instituto Superior de Ciências Exactas e Naturais de Mossoro
BR 110 km 48 s/n Campus Central, 56900 Mossoro, RN
Tel: +55(84) 321-4994
Founded: 1976
Exact and Natural Sciences.

Instituto Superior de Educação do Para
Avenida Almirante Barroso s/n, 66000 Belem, PA
Tel: +55(91) 226-2023
Founded: 1991
Education.

Instituto Tecnólogico de Aeronáutica
Praça Mar. Eduardo Gomes, 12225 Sao José dos Campos, SP
Tel: +55(12) 341-2444
Founded: 1950
Aeronautics.

PRIVATE INSTITUTIONS

Associação de Ensino de Botucatu
Avenida Leonardo Vilas Boas 351, 18600 Botucatu, SP
Tel: +55(149) 224-343
Founded: 1963

Centro Artistico-Musical de Santos
Rua Dr. Egydio Martins 181, 11030 Santos, SP
Tel: +55(132) 361-735
Founded: 1964
Music.

Centro de Ensino Superior
Estrada Chapeco Sao Carlos Km. 7, 89800 Chapeco, SC
Tel: +55(49) 722-5033
Founded: 1972

Centro de Ensino Superior de Catalão
Avenida Presidente Medici s/n, 75700 Catalão, GO
Tel: +55(62) 441-3899
Founded: 1985
Administration; Law; Education.

Centro de Ensino Superior de Jaragua do Sul
Avenida dos Immigrantes, 89250 Jaragua do Sul, SC
Tel: +55(473) 720-983

Centro de Ensino Superior de Jataí
Rua Santos Dumont E. M. Rondon, 76300 Jataí, GO
Tel: +55(62) 631-3547
Founded: 1985
Administration; Law.

Centro de Ensino Superior de Juiz de Fora
Rua Halfeld 1179, 36015 Juiz de Fora, MG
Tel: +55(32) 211-0255
Founded: 1972
D: Arts; Social Sciences; Education; Literature; Psychology.

Centro de Ensino Superior de Sant'Ana do Livramento
Avenida Daltro Filho 1537, 97570 Sant'Ana do Livramento, RS
Tel: +55(55) 242-3055
Founded: 1981

Centro de Ensino Superior de São Carlos
13560 Sao Carlos, SP
Tel: +55(162) 711-255
Founded: 1972
Economics; Law (ocial Sciences); Education.

Centro de Ensino Superior de Valença
Rua Sargento Victor Hugo 161, 27600 Valença, RJ
Tel: +55(244) 521-888
Founded: 1968
F: Economics; Letters and Philosophy; Law; Social Sciences; Medicine.

Centro de Ensino Superior do Para-Belem
Avenida Nazare 630, 66040 Belem, PA
Tel: +55(91) 222-5808
Founded: 1985
Medicine; Technology.

Centro de Ensino Superior do Vale do Paraiba
BR 343 Km. 4, 6400 Teresina, PI
Tel: +55(86) 232-5079
Founded: 1985
Economics.

Centro de Ensino Superior Plinio Mendes dos Santos
Rua Ceará 333, 79050 Campo Grande, MT
Tel: +55(67) 382-7660
Founded: 1976
Administration and Commerce; Sciences; Education.

Centro de Ensino Unificado de Brasília
EQN 707/ 907 Conjunto C., 70740 Brasília, DF
Tel: +55(61) 272-1252
Founded: 1968
Economics and Administration; Letters and Philosophy; Law; Education; Social Sciences.

Centro de Estudos de Comportamento Humano
Avenida Joaquim Nabuco 1023, 69000 Manaus, AM
Tel: +55(92) 234-0610
Founded: 1985
Behavioural Studies.

Centro de Estudos Superiores do Carmo
Rua Egydio Martins 181, 11030 Santos, sSP
Tel: +55(132) 361-735
Mathematics and Natural Sciences; Education; Communication and Social Studies.

Centro de Estudos Superiores de Londrina
Rua Juscelino Kubitschek 1260, 86020 Londrina, PR
Tel: +55(432) 242-075
Founded: 1972
Architecture; Siences; Biology; Social Sciences; Education; Psychology; Nursing.

Centro de Estudos Superiores de Maceió
Rua Conego Machado, 57055 Maceió
Tel: +55(82) 221-3296
Founded: 1974
Economics; Psychology; Letters and Philosophy.

Centro de Estudios Superiores do Medio Amazonas
Travessa Francisco Correia 34, 68100 Santarem, PA
Tel: +55(91) 522-8933
Founded: 1990
Biology; Nursing.

Centro de Formação de Professores de Disciplinas Especializadas
Avenida Cussy de Almeida 187, 16015 Araçatuba, SP
Tel: +55(18) 623-1188
Founded: 1976
Education; Administrative Sciences; Economics; Law.

Centro Integrado de Ensino de Brechim
Avenida sete de Setembro 1621, 99700 Brechim, RS
Tel: +55(54) 321-1922
Founded: 1976

Centro Integrado de Ensino de Santo Angelo
Rua Universidades das Missoes 393, Campus Universitario, 98800 Santo Angelo, RS
Tel: +55(55) 312-1599
Founded: 1969

Centro Integrado de Ensino Frederico Westphalen
Rua Assis Brasil 709, 98400 Frederico Westphalen, RS
Tel: +55(55) 344-1168
Founded: 1974

Centro Integrado de Ensino Superior
Rua Itororo 800, 89500 Caçador, SC
Tel: +55(496) 620-544
Founded: 1977

Centro Integrado de Ensino Superior
Rua 10 de Marco s/n, 89560 Videira, SC
Tel: +55(495) 331-422
Founded: 1973

Centro Integrado de Ensino Superior de Alegrete
Praça Getúlio Vargas, 97540 Alegrete, RS
Tel: +55(55) 422-1105
Administrative Sciences; Social Sciences; Education; Letters and Philosophy; Economics.

Centro Integrado de Ensino Superior do Amazonas
Rua Djalma Batista 1151, 69050 Manaus, AM
Tel: +55(92)-236-3434
Founded: 1986
Economics.

Centro Superior de Ciências Sociais de Vila Velha
Rua Sete de Setembro 70, Centro, 92010 Vila Velha, ES
Tel: +55(27) 229-1644
Founded: 1976
Social Sciences.

Centro Tecnológica de Educação Superior do Oeste Paranaense
Rua Bolivia s/n, Esquina Venezue, 85920 Assis Chateaubriand, PR
Founded: 1990
Education.

Conjunto Universitário Candido Mendes (Sociedade Brasileira de Instruçao)
Praça XV de Novembro 101, Centro, 20010 Rio de Janeiro, RJ
Tel: +55(21) 231-0648
Founded: 1902
Political Sciences and Economics; Law.

Conservatório Brasileiro de Música
Avenida Graça Aranha 57, 20030 Rio de Janeiro, RJ
Tel: +55(21) 240-6131
Founded: 1936
Music.

Conservatório Dramático e Musical de São Paulo
Rua Conselheiro Crispiniano 352, 01037 São Paulo, SP
Tel: 55(11) 223-9231
Founded: 1939
Music.

Conservatório de Música de Niterói
Rua Sao Pedro 96, 24020 Niterói, RJ
Tel: 55(21) 719-2330
Founded: 1965
Music.

Escola de Administração de Empresas de São Paulo
Avenida Nove de Julho 2029, 01313 São Paulo, SP
Tel: +55(11) 284-2311
Telex: 11-3756363
Founded: 1954
Business Administration.

Escola de Biblioteconomia
Avenida Dr. Arnaldo de Senna, 37290 Formigá, MG
Tel: +55(37) 321-2997
Founded: 1968
Library Sciences.

Escola de Ciências Contábeis
Fazenda Tres Poços s/n, 27180 Volta Redonda, RJ
Tel: +55(24) 342-6400
Founded: 1974
Accountancy.

Escola de Ciências Médicas de Volta Redonda
Fazenda Tres Poços-est, Pinheiral/Volta Redonda, 27180 Volta Redonda, RJ
Tel: +55(24) 342-6400
Founded: 1974
Medicine.

Escola de Educação Física de Assis
Avenida Doctor Doria 204, 19800 Assis, SP
Tel: +55(18) 322-2552
Founded: 1970
Physical Education.

Escola de Educação Física de Bauru
Praça 9 de Julho 1-51, 17050 Bauru, SP
Tel: +55(142) 342-955
Founded: 1953
Physical Education.

Escola de Educação Física de Volta Redonda
Rua Vinte e Oito 619, 27263 Volta Redonda, RJ
Tel: +55(24) 342-6400
Founded: 1971
Physical Education.

Escola de Enfermagen Matias Alb. Coelho
Campus Universitario s/n, Jardin Fragoso, 53000 Olinda, PE
Tel: +55(81) 429-0795
Founded: 1986
Nursing.

Escola de Enfermagem Santa Emilia de Rodat
Praça Caldas Brandao s/n, 58023 João Pessoa, PB
Tel: +55(83) 221-2925
Founded: 1959
Nursing.

Escola de Enfermagen Souza Marques
Avenida Ernant Cardoso 335 Campus, 21310 Rio
de Janeiro, RJ
Tel: +55(21) 390-6365
Founded: 1985
Nursing.

Escola de Enfermagem Wenceslau Braz
Avenida Cesário Alvim 472, 37500 Itajubá, MG
Tel: +55(35) 622-0930
Founded: 1954
Nursing.

Escola de Engenharia de Agrimensura
Avenida Joana Angelica 1381 Casa, 40050
Salvador, BA
Tel: +55(71) 241-6922
Founded: 1934
Agriculture.

Escola de Engenharia de Lins
Avenida Nicolau Zarvos 1925, 16400 Lins, SP
Tel: +55(145) 222-300
Founded: 1964
Engineering.

Escola de Engenharia de Vassouras
Avenida Expedicionario, Oswaldo de Almeida
Ramos 280, 27700 Vassouras, RJ
Tel: +55(244) 711-595
Founded: 1984
Engineering.

Escola de Engenharia de Volta Redonda
Estrada Volta Redonda Pinheiral s/n, 27180 Volta
Redonda, RJ
Tel: +55(24) 342-6400
Founded: 1970
Engineering; Computer Sciences.

Escola de Engenharia Industrial de São José dos Campos
Avenida Barao do Rio Branco 882, 12240 São
José dos Campos, SP
Tel: +55(123) 219-144
Founded: 1968
Engineering.

Escola de Engenharia Kennedy
Rua José Dias Vieira 46, 31510 Belo Horizonte,
MG
Tel: +55(31) 447-1761
Founded: 1964
Engineering.

Escola de Engenharia Mauá
Estrada das Lagrimas 2035, 09580 São Caetano
do Sul, SP
Tel: +55(11) 442-1900
Founded: 1962
Engineering.

Escola de Medicina de Santa Casa de Misericorda de Vitória
Avenida N. Sra da Penha s/n, Caixa postal 36,
29045 Vitória, ES
Tel: +55(27) 227-3033
Founded: 1968
Medicine.

Escola de Medicina e Saúde Pública
Rua Frei Henrique 08, 40050 Salvador, BA
Tel: +55(71) 243-2723
Founded: 1953
Medicine.

Escola de Medicina Souza Marquêz
Rua do Catete 6, 22220 Rio de Janeiro, RJ
Tel: +55(21) 231-2134
Founded: 1970
Medicine.

Escola de Odontologia de Volta Redonda
Rua Luiz A. Pereira 76, 27285 Volta Redonda, RJ
Tel: +55(24) 342-6400
Founded: 1970
Odontology.

Escola de Sociologia e Politica de São Paulo
Rua General Jardim 522, Vila Buarque, 01223
São Paulo, SP
Tel: 55(11) 256-1552
Founded: 1946
Sociology and Politics.

Escola Guignard
Avenida Alfonso Pena, 30130 Belo Horizonte, MG
Tel: +55(31) 226-8511
Founded: 1983
Fine Arts.

Escola Superior de Administração de Negócios
Avenida Humberto de Alencar, Castelo Branco
3740, 09850 São Bernardo do Campo, SP
Tel: +55(11) 419-5833
Founded: 1972
Business Administration.

Escola Superior de Administração de Negócios
Rua Sao Joaqim 180, 01508 São Paulo, SP
Tel: +55(11) 278-0955
Founded: 1961
Business Administration.

Escola Superior de Agrimensura de Minas Gerais
Rua Aquilles Lobo 524, 30150 Belo Horizonte, MG
Tel: +55(31) 224-6494
Founded: 1974
Agriculture.

Escola Superior de Agronomia de Paraguaçu Paulista
Rua Prof. Jayme Monteiro, 19700 Paraguaçu, Paulista, SP
Tel: +55(183) 611-953
Founded: 1974
Agriculture.

Escola Superior de Artes Santa Marcelina
Rua Dr. Costa Leite 548, 18600 Botucatu, SP
Tel: +55(14) 922-0577
Founded: 1974
Fine Arts.

Escola Superior de Ciências Contábeis e Administrativas de Ituiutaba
Avenida Geraldo Alves Tavares 1980, 38300 Ituiutaba, MG
Tel: +55(34) 261-2838
Founded: 1970
Business Administration.

Escola Superior de Educação Física da Alta Paulista
Rua Mandaguaris 274, 17600 Tupá, SP
Tel: +55(144) 421-218
Founded: 1970
Physical Education.

Escola Superior de Educação Física de Muzambinho
Rua Cinah s/n, 37890 Muzambinho, MG
Tel: +55(35) 571-1155
Founded: 1975
Physical Education.

Escola Superior de Educação Física de São Caetano do Sul
Rua Amazonas 2031, 09540 São Caetano do Sul, SP
Tel: +55(11) 441-3233
Founded: 1971
Physical Education.

Escola Superior de Educação Física e Desportos de Catanduva
Avenida Paulo de Faria s/n, 15800 Catanduva, SP
Tel: +55(175) 227-656
Founded: 1973
Physical Education.

Escola Superior de Educação Física e Técnicas Desportivas de Andradina
Rua Amazonas 571, 16900 Andradina, SP
Tel: +55(186) 234-088
Founded: 1973
Physical Education.

Escola Superior de Educação Física e Técnicas Desportivas de Araçatuba
Rua Mato Grosso 1141, 16100 Arçatuba, SP
Tel: +55(186) 234-088
Founded: 1971
Physical Education.

Escola Superior de Enfermagen e Obstetrícia de Vassouras
Rua Dr. Joaquim Teixeira, Leite 53, Predio, 27700 Vassouras, RJ
Tel: +55(244) 711-595
Founded: 1988
Nursing.

Escola Superior de Ensino
Estrada Caetano Monteiro 857, 24320 Niteroi, RJ
Tel: +55(21) 616-3311
Founded: 1985
Health Sciences.

Escola Superior de Estatística da Bahia
Avenida Joana Angelica 51, 40050 Salvador, BA
Tel: +55(71) 241-3430
Founded: 1966
Statistics.

Escola Superior de Estudios Empresariais e Informática
Avenida Sete de Setembro 3060, 80230 Curitiba, PR
Tel: +55(41) 225-1143
Founded: 1990
Business Administration; Computer Sciences.

Escola Superior de Estudios Sociais
Rua Padre Gattone 112, 88350 Brusque, SC
Tel: +55(473) 553-234
Founded: 1973

Escola Superior de Propaganda e Marketing
Rua Cr. Alvaro Alvim 123, 04018 São Paulo, SP
Tel: +55(11) 572-2408
Founded: 1978
Publicity and Marketing.

Escola Superior de Relaçaes Públicas
Avenida Conselheiro Rosa e Silva 891, 52050 Recife, PE
Tel: +55(81) 222-5802
Founded: 1973
Public Relations.

Escola Superior de Secretariar do Pernambuco
Rua Co. Paissandu 632, 52010 Recife, PE
Tel: +55(81) 231-3807
Founded: 1985
Secretarial Studies.

Escola Superior de Tecnologia de Críciuma
Rua Pascoel Meller, 88000 Críciuma, SC
Tel: +55(484) 381-411
Founded: 1975
Engineering.

Faculdade Adventista de Educação
Est Itapecerica da Serra Km-23, 05835 São Paulo, SP
Tel: +55(11) 511-4011
Founded: 1973
Education.

Faculdade Adventista de Enfermagem
Est Itapeceria da Serra Km-23, 05835 São Paulo, SP
Tel: +55(11) 511-4011
Founded: 1968
Nursing.

Faculdade Alvorada de Informática e Processamento de Dados
SGAN-Quadra 916 Conjunto
Tel: +55(61) 273-6181
Founded: 1988
Computer Sciences.

Faculdade Anchieta
Avenida Rudge 400, 01133 São Paulo, SP
Tel: +55(11) 825-7088
Founded: 1954

Faculdade Anglo-Americano da Amazonia
Rua Marques de Monte Alegre 1/400 Km., 69000 Manaus, AM
Tel: +55(23) 642-42
Founded: 1989

Faculdade Anglo-Americana do Rio de Janeiro
Avenida das Americanas 2063, 22600 Rio de Janeiro, RJ
Tel: +55(21) 439-1365
Founded: 1989
Computer Sciences.

Faculdade Anhanguera de Ciências Humanas
Rua Piragibe Leite 456, Cidade Jardim, 74000 Goiânia, GO
Tel: +55(62) 287-2288
Founded: 1977
Human Sciences.

Faculdade Anhembi Morumbi
Rua Casa do Ator 90, 04546 São Paulo, SP
Tel: +55(11) 533-0588
Founded: 1972
Administration; Secretarial Studies.

Faculdade Auxilium de Filosofia, Ciências e Letras
Rua Nicolau Zarvos 754, 16400 Lins, SP
Tel: +55(145) 222-733
Founded: 1959
Philosophy Sciences and Letters.

Faculdades Associadas Ipiranga
Avenida Pazare 993, 04263 São Paulo, SP
Tel: +55(11) 274-8555
Founded: 1971
Letters and Philosophy; Economics; Education.

Faculdade Bethencourt da Silva
Rua Frederico Silva 86, 20230 Rio de Janeiro, RJ
Tel: +55(21) 224-5814
Founded: 1981
Education.

Faculdade Brasileira de Ciências Jurídicas
Praça de República 50, 20211 Rio de Janeiro, RJ
Tel: +55(21) 231-1965
Founded: 1952
Law.

Faculdade Brasileira de Recursos Humanos
Avenida Santo Amaro 4039, 04555 São Paulo, SP
Tel: +55(11) 535-0188
Founded: 1985
Human Resources.

Faculdade Camaquense de Ciências Contábeis e Administrativas
Rua Alvaro Macedo 105, 96180 Camaqua, RS
Tel: +55(51) 671-1640
Founded: 1974
Accountancy; Administration.

Faculdade Capixaba de Informática
Rua Anselmo Serrat 199, 29040 Vitoria, ES
Tel: +55(27) 222-7531
Founded: 1990
Computer Sciences.

Faculdade Carioca de Informática
Rua Marques de Olinda 31, 22251 Rio de Janeiro, RJ
Tel: +55(21) 551-8448
Founded: 1990
Computer Sciences.

Faculdade Católica de Administração e Economia
Rua 24 de Maio 135, 8000 Curitiba, PR
Tel: +55(41) 233-4222
Founded: 1959
Administration; Economics.

Faculdade Católica de Ciências Econômicas da Bahia
Avenida Joana Angelica, 40050 Nazare, BA
Tel: +55(71) 243-5832
Economics.

Faculdade Cuiabana de Educação e Letras
Rua Guilherme Hann 43, 78000 Cuiaba, MT
Tel: +55(65) 322-4063
Founded: 1988
Education.

Faculdade da Ilha
Rua Prof. Hilariao da Rocha 809, 21910 Rio de Janeiro, RJ
Tel: +55(21) 396-1965
Administration.

Faculdade de Administração Champagnat
Rua Professor Estevao Pinto 400, Serra, 30210 Belo Horizonte, MG
Tel: +55(31) 223-4998
Founded: 1974
Administration.

Faculdade de Administração, Ciências Contábeis e Econômicas de Teresopolis
Avenida Albert Torres 111, 25960 Teresopolis, RJ
Tel: +55(21) 742-3152
Founded: 1975
Administration; Accountancy; Economics.

Faculdade de Administração da Fundação Armando Alvares Penteado
Rua Alagoas 903, 01242 São Paulo, SP
Tel: +55(11) 826-4233
Founded: 1977
Administration.

Faculdade de Administração da Guanabara
Rua General Severino 159 Botafogo, 22290 Rio de Janeiro, RJ
Tel: +55(21) 295-3099
Founded: 1977
Administration.

Faculdade de Administração de Assis
Avenida Dr. Doria 204, 19800 Assis, SP
Tel: +55(18) 322-2552
Founded: 1970
Administration.

Faculdade de Administração de Capivari
Rua Barao do Rio Branco 374, 13360 Capivari, SP
Tel: +55(194) 911-694
Founded: 1972
Administration.

Faculdade de Administração de Empresas Amador Aguiar
Rua Narcisco Sturlini 883, 06010 Osasco, SP
Tel: +55(11) 701-6000
Founded: 1972
Business Administration.

Faculdade de Administração de Empresas de Araçatuba
Rua Mato Grosso, 16100 Araçatuba, SP
Tel: +55(186) 235-128
Founded: 1969
Business Administration.

Faculdade de Administração de Empresas de Catanduva
Rua do Seminario 281, 15800 Catanduva, SP
Tel: +55(175) 222-405
Founded: 1972
Business Administration.

Faculdade de Administração de Empresas de Governador Valadares
Rua José de Tassis s/n, Vila Bretas, 35030 Governador Valadares, MG
Tel: +55(33) 221-3066
Founded: 1975
Business Administration.

Faculdade de Administração de Empresas de Jahú
Rua Tenente Navarro 642, 17200 Jahú, SP
Tel: +55(146) 223-435
Founded: 1972
Business Administration.

Faculdade de Administração de Empresas de João Pessoa
BR 230 Km. 22, 58000 João Pessoa, PB
Tel: +55(83) 231-1418
Founded: 1973
Business Administration.

Faculdade de Administração de Empresas de Santos
Rua Armando de S. Oliveira 150, 11050 Santos, SP
Tel: +55(132) 351-311
Founded: 1969
Business Administration.

Faculdade de Administração de Empressas do Alto Vale de Itajaí
Rua Dr. Guilherme Gemballa 13, 89160 Rio do Sul, SC
Tel: +55(478) 220-988
Founded: 1967
Business Administration.

Faculdade de Administração de Lavras
Praça Dr. Augusto Silva 616, 37800 Lavras, MG
Tel: +55(35) 821-3298
Founded: 1990
Administration.

Faculdade de Adminstração de Nova Andradina
Rua Artur da Costa e silva 999, 79750 Nova Andradina, MS
Founded: 1988
Administration.

Faculdade de Administração de Pinhal
Avenida Hélio Vergueiro Leite s/n, 13990 Espirito Santo do Pinhal, SP
Tel: +55(19) 651-8604
Founded: 1976
Administration.

Faculdade de Administração de Santa Marta
Rua Dr. Olavo Gomes Pinto 61, 37170 São Lourenco, MG
Tel: +55(35) 821-2230
Administration.

Faculdade de Administração e Ciências Contábeis
Rua Ibiracu s/n, 29900 Linhares, ES
Tel: +55(27) 264-2339
Founded: 1988
Administration; Accountancy.

Faculdade de Administração e Ciências Contábeis Campos Salles
Rua Nossa Senhora da Lapa 284, 05072 São Paulo, SP
Tel: +55(11) 260-6477
Founded: 1973
Administration; Accountancy.

Faculdade de Administração e Ciências Contábeis Luzwell
Avenida Chibaras 74, 04076 São Paulo, SP
Tel: +55(11) 549-1611
Founded: 1972
Administration.

Faculdade de Administração e Ciências Contábeis Nove de Julho
Rua Diamatina 302, 02117 São Paulo, SP
Tel: +55(11) 939-898
Founded: 1985
Administration; Accountancy.

Faculdade de Administração e Ciências Contábeis Tibiriça
Largo São Bento s/n, 01029 São Paulo, SP
Tel: +55(11) 375-485
Founded: 1972
Administration; Accountancy.

Faculdade de Administração e Informática
Avenida Antônio de Cassata 472, 37640 Santa Rita do Sapucai, MG
Tel: +55(35) 631-1219
Founded: 1971
Administrative Sciences; Computer Sciences.

Faculdade de Administração Hospitalar
Avenida Duquesa de Goias 735, 05686 São Paulo, SP
Tel: +55(11) 531-1620
Founded: 1973
Hospital Administration.

Faculdade de Administração Rural de Colatina
Rua Fioravante Rossi 2930, 29700 Colatina, ES
Founded: 1990
Rural Administration.

Faculdade de Administração São José
Rua Marechal Soares Andrea 90, 21710 Rio de Janeiro, RJ
Tel: +55(21) 331-3695
Founded: 1980
Administration.

Faculdade de Administração Tres de Maio
Avenida Avai 370, 98910 Tres de Maio, RS
Tel: +55(55) 531-1161
Founded: 1970
Administration.

Faculdade de Agronomia de Ituverava
Rua Flausino B. Sandoval 1259, 14500 Ituverava, SP
Tel: +55(16) 729-3410
Founded: 1987
Agriculture.

Faculdade de Agronomia e Zootecnica Manoel Carlos Gonçalves
Avenida Helio Vergueiro Leite s/n, 13990 Espírito Santo do Pinhal, SP
Tel: +55(19) 651-3579
Founded: 1968
Agriculture.

Faculdade de Arquitetura de Barra do Pirai
Rodovia Benjamin Ielpo, 27100 Barra do Pirai, RJ
Tel: +55(244) 421-523
Architecture.

Faculdade de Arquitetura e Urbanismo
Rua do Paissandu 632 Boa Vista, 52010 Recife, PE
Tel: +55(81) 225-0549
Founded: 1987
Architecture and Town Planning.

Faculdade de Artes Alcantara Machado
Avenida Libertade 899, 01508 São Paulo, SP
Tel: +55(11) 270-2433
Founded: 1972
Fine Arts.

Faculdade de Artes da Fundação Brasileira de Teatro
SDS Bloco C Ed. FBT, 70300 Brasília, DF
Tel: +55(61) 226-0188
Founded: 1980
Fine Arts.

Faculdade de Artes Plásticas
Rua Alagoas 903, 01242 São Paulo, SP
Tel: +55(11) 549-7122
Founded: 1972
Plastic Arts.

Faculdade de Belas Artes de São Paulo
Rua Alvarim Alvim 76 2 Pavimenic, 04018 São Paulo, SP
Tel: +55(11) 549-7122
Founded: 1941
Fine Arts.

Faculdade de Biblioteconomia e Documentação
Rua General Jardim 522, 01223 São Paulo, SP
Tel: +55(11) 258-8899
Founded: 1940
Library Sciences.

Faculdade de Biologia e Psicologia Maria Theresa
Rua Visconde do Rio Branco 869, 24020 Niterói, RJ
Tel: +55(21) 719-0660
Founded: 1975
Health Sciences.

Faculdade de Ciências Administrativas, Contábeis e Econômicas de Umuarama
Praça Mascarenhas de Moraes s/n, 87500 Umuarama, PR
Tel: +55(446) 226-566
Founded: 1980
Administration; Accountancy; Economics.

Faculdade de Ciências Administrativas de Canoinhas
Rua Robert Ehlke s/n, 89460 Canoinhas, SC
Tel: +55(476) 220-436
Founded: 1973
Administration.

Faculdade de Ciências Administrativas de Curvelo
Rua Joao Pessoa 88, 35790 Curvelo, MG
Tel: +55(38) 721-3945
Founded: 1991
Administration.

Faculdade de Ciências Administrativas de Ponta Pora
Rua Tiracentes 349, 79900 Ponta Pora, MS
Tel: +55(67) 431-1002
Founded: 1989
Administration.

Faculdade de Ciências Administrativas e Contábeis de Atibaia
Avenida de 9 de Julho 298, 12940 Atibaia, SP
Tel: +55(11) 484-4140
Founded: 1971
Administration; Accountancy.

Faculdade de Ciências Administrativas e Contábeis do Vale do Ribeira
Rua Sao Francisco Xavier 165, 11900 Registro, SP
Tel: +55(138) 212-411
Founded: 1985
Administration; Accountancy.

Faculdade de Ciências Administrativas e Comercio Exterior Positivo
Avenida Nossa Senhora Aparecida 174, 80420 Curitiba, PR
Tel: +55(41) 342-2728
Founded: 1975
Administration; Foreign Commerce.

Faculdade de Ciências Administrativas e Contábeis Paulo Eiro
Rua Barao de Cotegipe 111, 04721 São Paulo, SP
Tel: +55(11) 523-8522
Founded: 1972
Administration; Accountancy.

Faculdade de Ciências Administrativas e Contábeis Tabajara
Avenida Jandira 455, 04080 São Paulo, SP
Tel: +55(11) 240-2988
Founded: 1976
Administration; Accountancy.

Faculdade de Ciências Administrativas, Economicas e Contábeis de Guaxupe
Avenida Cona Floriana 463, 37800 Guxupe, MG
Tel: +55(35) 551-1267
Founded: 1988
Administration; Economics; Accountancy.

Faculdade de Ciências Agrarias de Rondonopolis
Rondonopolis, MT
Agriculture.

Faculdade de Ciências Aplicadas Sagrado Coração
Avenida Sao Mateus s/n 3 Andar, 29900 Linpares, ES
Tel: +55(27) 264-0309
Founded: 1985
Applied Sciences.

Faculdade de Ciências Aplicadas São José dos Campos
Avenida Barao do Rio Branco 882, 12240 São José dos Campos, SP
Tel: 55(123) 219-144
Telex: 123-3452
Founded: 1987
Applied Sciences.

Faculdade de Ciências Biologicas da Saúde Dr. Bezerra Menezes
Rua Tobias de Macedo Junior 333, 82000 Curitiba, PR
Tel: +55(41) 335-1717
Founded: 1989
Health Sciences.

Faculdade de Ciências Contábeis
Rua 20, 383, 14780 Barretos, SP
Tel: +55(173) 225-733
Founded: 1987
Accountancy.

Faculdade de Ciências Contábeis
Rua Anselmo Serrat 199 Bloco 1, 29040 Vitoria, ES
Tel: +55(27) 222-5665
Founded: 1976
Accountancy.

Faculdade de Ciências Contábeis, Administrativas e Econômicas do ICNPF
Rua Goitacazes 1762, 30190 Belo Horizonte, MG
Tel: +55(31) 275-1922
Founded: 1972
Accountancy; Administration; Economics.

Faculdade de Ciências Contábeis e Atuariais Alta Noreste
Avenida Cussy Almeida 187, 16015 Araçatuba, SP
Tel: +55(186) 231-188
Founded: 1974
Accountancy and Actuarial Sciences.

Faculdade de Ciências Contábeis da Fund. Visconde Cairo
Rua Salete 50, 40115 Salvador, BA
Tel: +55(71) 241-4861
Founded: 1966
Accountancy.

Faculdade de Ciências Contábeis de Araçatuba
Rua Mato Grosso, 16100 Araçatuba, SP
Tel: +55(186) 235-128
Founded: 1975
Accountancy.

Faculdade de Ciências Contábeis de Caratinga
Rua Joao Pinheiro 286, 35300 Caratinga, MG
Tel: +55(33) 321-3377
Founded: 1972
Accountancy.

Faculdade de Ciências Contábeis de Itapetininga
Avenida Joao Barth s/n, 18200 Itapetininga, SP
Tel: +55(152) 710-503
Founded: 1966
Accountancy.

Faculdade de Ciências Contábeis de Jequie
Rua Padre Albino Freire, 43200 Jequie, BA
Tel: +55(73) 525-1593
Founded: 1989
Accountancy.

Faculdade de Ciências Contábeis de Lucélia
Avenida Internacional 3000, 17780 Lucélia, SP
Tel: +55(189) 511-289
Founded: 1972
Accountancy.

Faculdade de Ciências Contábeis de Ponte Nova
Rua dos Vereadores 177, 35430 Ponte Nova, MG
Tel: +55(31) 881-2580
Founded: 1978
Accountancy.

Faculdade de Ciências Contábeis de Rio Claro
Rua Nove 15, 13500 Rio Claro, SP
Tel: +55(195) 342-887
Founded: 1972
Accountancy.

Faculdade de Ciências Contábeis e Administrativas
Rua Cristiano Osorio 10, 13870 São João da Boa Vista, SP
Tel: +55(196) 233-121
Founded: 1973
Accountancy; Administration.

Faculdade de Ciências Contábeis e Administrativas de Barra do Garcas
Rua Walapitis 33, 78600 Barra do Garcas, MT
Tel: +55(65) 446-2148
Founded: 1990
Accountancy; Administration.

Faculdade de Ciências Contábeis e Administrativas de Empresas
Avenida Ernani Cardoso 345, 21310 Rio de Janeiro, RJ
Tel: +55(21) 390-6365
Founded: 1971
Accountancy; Business Administration.

Faculdade de Ciências Contábeis e Administrativas Cruizeiro do Sul
Avenida Dr. Ussiel Cirilo, 08060 São Paulo, SP
Tel: +55(11) 297-1777
Founded: 1972
Accountancy; Administration.

Faculdade de Ciências Contábeis e Administrativas de Avare
Praça Padare Tavares 46, 18700 Avare, SP
Tel: +55(147) 221-677
Founded: 1975
Accountancy; Administration.

Faculdade de Ciências Contábeis e Administrativas de Lins
Rua Dom Bosco 265, 16400 Lins, SP
Tel: +55(145) 224-733
Founded: 1972
Accountancy; Administration.

Faculdade de Ciências Contábeis e Administrativas de Marília
Avenida Hygino Muzzy Filho 529, 17500 Marília, SP
Tel: +55(144) 330-833
Founded: 1970
Accountancy; Administration.

Faculdade de Ciências Contábeis e Administrativas de Rolandia
Rua Dom Pedro 11, 400, 86600 Rolandia, PR
Tel: +55(432) 561-813
Founded: 1974
Accountancy; Administration.

Faculdade de Ciências Contábeis e Administrativas de Santa Rosa
Rua Santos Dumont 820, 98900 Santa Rosa, RS
Tel: +55(55) 512-1659
Founded: 1976
Accountancy and Administrative Sciences.

Faculdade de Ciências Contábeis e Administrativas de Sorocaba
Avenida Gen. Osorio 215, 18165 Sorocaba, SP
Tel: +55(152) 323-062
Founded: 1968
Accountancy; Administration.

Faculdade de Ciências Contábeis e Administrativas de Tangara da Serra
Rocovia MT 358, Km. 07 1097, 358 Km.-7, 78300 Tangara da Serra, MT
Tel: +55(65) 726-1739
Founded: 1990
Accountancy; Administration.

Faculdade de Ciências Contábeis e Administrativas de Taquara
Rua Julio de Castilhos 2084, 95600 Taquara, RS
Tel: +55 642-1256
Accountancy; Administration.

Faculdade de Ciências Contábeis e Administrativas de Votuporanga
Rua Pernambuco 1624, 5500 Votuporanga, SP
Tel: +55(174) 223-700
Founded: 1973
Accountancy; Administration.

Faculdade de Ciências Contábeis e Administrativas 'Machado Sobrinho'
Rua Pedro Celeste s/n, 36030 Juiz de Pora, MG
Tel: +55(32) 234-1436
Founded: 1969
Accountancy; Administration.

Faculdade de Ciências Contábeis e Administrativas 'Moraes Júnior'
Rua Recente Feijo 63, 20060 Rio de Janeiro, RJ
Tel: +55(21) 221-8334
Founded: 1970
Accountancy; Administration.

Faculdade de Ciências Contábeis e Administrativas São Judas Tadeu
Rua Don Diego de Souza, 100-Bloc AB, 91350 Pôrto Alegre, RS
Tel: +55(51) 240-7888
Founded: 1970
Accountancy; Administration.

Faculdade de Ciências Contábeis e Administrativas São Paulo Apostolo
Rua José Bonifacio 140, 20771 Rio de Janeiro, RJ
Tel: +55(21) 249-2266
Founded: 1974
Accountancy; Administration.

Faculdade de Ciências Contábeis e Administrativas Tupa
Rua Cherentes 36, 17600 Tupa, SP
Tel: +55(144) 422-620
Founded: 1970
Accountancy; Administration.

Faculdade de Ciências Contábeis e Administrativas Varzea Grande
Avenida Com. Orlando Chaves 2655, 78150 Varzea Grande, MT
Tel: +55(65) 381- 3736
Founded: 1989
Accountancy; Administration.

Faculdade de Ciências Contábeis e Economicas de São Luis
Parque Urbano Santos 561, 65020 São Luis, MA
Founded: 1990
Accountancy; Economics.

Faculdade de Ciências da Saúde Barao de Maua
Rua Ramos de Azevedo, 4090 Ribeirao Prêto, SP
Tel: +55(16) 625-4935
Health Sciences.

Faculdade de Ciências da Sáude de Joinville
Rua Sao José 490, Centro, SC
Tel: +55(474) 228-577
Founded: 1986
Health Sciences.

Faculdade de Ciências da Sáude de Nova Iguaçu
Avenida Abilio Augusto Tavora 2134, Bloco B, 26260 Nova Iguaçu, RJ
Tel: +55(21) 767-8605
Founded: 1976
Health Sciences.

Faculdade de Ciências da Saúde de Umurama
Praça Mascarenhas de Moraes s/n, 87500 Umurama, PR
Tel: +55(446) 226-566
Founded: 1989
Health Sciences.

Faculdade de Ciências da Saúde e Sociais
Rua Correa Dutra 126, 22210 Rio de Janeiro, RJ
Tel: +55(21) 285-552-8090
Founded: 1981
Health Sciences.

Faculdade de Ciências da Saúde São Camilo
Avenida Nazare 1501, 04263 São Paulo, SP
Tel: +55(11) 272-4760
Founded: 1975
Health Sciences.

Faculdade de Ciências de Barretos
Avenida Prof. Roberto Frade Monte, 14780 Barretos, SP
Tel: +55(173) 226-411
Founded: 1974
Sciences.

Faculdade de Ciências de Computação Cristo Rei
Praça Prei Elias Zulian 216, 84045 Ponta Grossa, PR
Tel: +55(422) 249-322
Founded: 1990
Computer Sciences.

Faculdade de Ciências e Artes Aplicadas de Londrina
Avenida Paris 675, 86020 Londrina, PR
Tel: +55(43) 226-2874
Founded: 1985
Arts and Design.

Faculdade de Ciências e Educação de Criciuma
Rua Pascoal Meller s/n, Campus Universitario, 88800 Criciuma, SC
Tel: +55(484) 381-411
Founded: 1975
Sciences and Education.

Faculdade de Ciências e Informática
Rua Cruz Machado 555, 80410 Curitiba, PR
Tel: +55(41) 224-9352
Founded: 1988
Sciences and Computer Sciences.

Faculdade de Ciências e Letras da Alta Sorocabana
Praça Raul Farquim s/n, 9030 President Prudente, SP
Tel: +55(182) 334-744
Founded: 1972
Sciences and Letters.

Faculdade de Ciências e Letras de Araras
Rua Quadra H., 13600 Araras, SP
Tel: +55(195) 413-047
Founded: 1974
Sciences and Letters.

Faculdade de Ciências e Letras Cruzeiro do Sul
Avenida Dr. Ussiel Cirilo, 08060 São Paulo, SP
Tel: +55(11) 297-1777
Sciences and Letters.

Faculdade de Ciências e Letras de Osorio
Rua Lobo da Costa 1042, 95520 Osorio, RS
Tel: +55(51) 663-1763
Founded: 1981
Sciences and Letters.

Faculdade de Ciências e Letras de Ribeirão Pires
Rua Comendador Joao Ugliengo 12, 09400 Ribeirão Pires, SP
Tel: +55(11) 459-2066
Founded: 1973
Sciences and Letters.

Faculdade de Ciências e Pedagogia de Lages
Avenida Castelo Branco, 88500 Lages, SC
Tel: +55(49) 222-1022
Founded: 1970
Sciences and Education.

Faculdade de Ciências Econômicas, Administrativas e Contábeis de Belo Horizonte
Rua Coere 200, 30310 Belo Horizonte, MG
Tel: +55(31) 227-1388
Founded: 1966
Economicis; Administration; Accountancy.

Faculdade de Ciências Econômicas, Administrativas e Contábeis de São Sebastião do Paraíso
Avenida Wenceslau Braz 1018, 37950 São Sebastião do Paraíso, MG
Tel: +55(35) 531-199
Founded: 1970
Economics; Administration; Accountancy.

Faculdade de Ciências Econômicas, Contábeis, Administrativas, Jurídicas e Sociais de Lages
Avenida Castelo Branco 170, 88500 Lages, SC
Tel: +55(49) 222-1022
Founded: 1971
Economics; Accountancy; Administration; Law; Social Sciences.

Faculdade de Ciências Econômicas, Contábeis, e Administração de Emprêsas Padre Anchieta
Avenida Dr. Andoniro Ladeira 94, 13200 Jundiaí, SP
Tel: +55(11) 434-8444
Founded: 1966
Accountancy; Business Administration; Economics.

Faculdade de Ciências Econômicas, Contábeis e Administrativas de Barbacena
Rua Monsenhor José Augusto 203, Alto da Fabrica, 36200 Barbacena, MG
Tel: +55(32) 331-3182
Founded: 1966
Economics; Accountancy; Administration.

Faculdade de Ciências Econômicas, Contábeis e Administrativas de Varginha
Rua Cantaduvas 173, 37100 Varginha, MG
Tel: +55(35) 221-2808
Founded: 1970
Economics; Accountancy; Administration.

Faculdade de Ciências Econômicas, Contábeis e Administrativas de Visconde do Rio Branco
Avenida Ruy Bouchardet s/n, 36520 Visconde do Rio Branco, MG
Tel: +55(32) 551-1600
Founded: 1972
Economics; Accountancy; Administration.

Faculdade de Ciências Econômicas, Contábeis e Administrativas 'Prof. de Placido e Silva'
Praça Senador Correia, 80420 Curitiba, PR
Tel: +55(41) 233-8423
Founded: 1974
Economics; Accountancy; Administration.

Faculdade de Ciências Econômicas da Região dos Vinhedos
Alameda Joao dal Sasso 800, 95700 Bento Gonçalves, RS
Tel: +55(54) 252-1188
Founded: 1974
Economics.

Faculdade de Ciências Econômicas de Arçatuba
Rua Mato Grosso 1141, 16100 Arçatuba, SP
Tel: +55(18) 623-8098
Telex: 900
Founded: 1990
Economics.

Faculdade de Ciências Econômicas de Bauru
Praça 9 de Julho, 17100 Bauru, SP
Tel: +55(142) 349-955
Founded: 1961
Economics.

Faculdade de Ciências Econômicas de Divinópolis
Praça do Mercado 191, 35500 Divinópolis, MG
Tel: +55(37) 221-5921
Founded: 1969
Economics.

Faculdade de Ciências Econômicas de Itauna
·Avenida Governador Magalhes Pinto, 35680 Itauna, M
Tel: +55(37) 241-9255
Founded: 1975
Economics.

Faculdade de Ciências Econômicas de Patos
Rua Antenor Navarro, 58700 Patos, PB
Tel: +55(83) 421-2819
Economics.

Faculdade de Ciências Econômicas de Sao Paulo
Avenida da Libertade, 01502 São Paulo, SP
Tel: +55(11) 277-0122
Founded: 1949
Economics.

Faculdade de Ciências Econômicas do Alto Taquari
Rua Joao Tallini, 95900 Lajeado, RS
Tel: +55(51) 714-2166
Founded: 1969
Economics.

Faculdade de Ciências Economicas do Esprito Santos
Rua Fioravante Rossi 2930, 29700 Colatina, ES
Founded: 1970
Economics.

Faculdade de Ciências Econômicas do Sul de Minas
Avenida Presidente Tancredo, de Almeida Neves, 19030 Itajubá, MG
Tel: +55(35) 622-1200
Founded: 1966
Economics.

Faculdade de Ciências Econômicas do Triângulo Mineiro
Avenida Apranto de Azevedo 1530, 38001 Uberaba, MG
Tel: +55(34) 332-4043
Founded: 1965
Economics.

Faculdade de Ciências Econômicas Dom Bosco
Estrada Resenda Riachuelo, 27500 Resende, RJ
Tel: +55(24) 354-1140
Founded: 1968
Economics.

Faculdade de Ciências Econômicas e Administrativas de Guaratinguetá
Avenida Pedro de Toledo 195, 12500 Guaratinguetá, SP
Tel: +55(12) 522-2911
Founded: 1973
Economics; Administration.

Faculdade de Ciências Econômicas e Administrativas de Guaratinguetá
Praça Raul Furquim s/n, 19030 Presidente Prudente, SP
Tel: +55(182) 334-744
Founded: 1970
Economics; Administration.

Faculdade de Ciências Econômicas e Administrativas de Santo André
Avenida Principe de Gales 821, 09060 Santo André, SP
Tel: +55(11) 449-3093
Founded: 1954
Economics; Administration.

Faculdade de Ciências Econômicas e Contábeis Candido Rondon
Rua Pimenta Bueno 544, 78000 Cuiaba, MT
Tel: +55(65) 322-9413
Founded: 1989
Economics; Accountancy.

Faculdade de Ciências Exactas e Humanas Santos Dumont
Rua Cel. Manuel F. de Souza 200, 08060 SPaulo, SP
Tel: +55(11) 297-1794
Founded: 1988
Human Sciences.

Faculdade de Ciências Exactas e Tecnológicas
Rua Coitacazes 1762, 30190 Belo Horizonte, MG
Tel: +55(31) 275-1922
Founded: 1989
Exact Sciences and Technology.

Faculdade de Ciências Gerenciais da Una
Rua Aimores 1451, 30140 Belo Horizonte, MG
Tel: +55(31) 226-5677
Founded: 1965
Management.

Faculdade de Ciências Humanas da Fumec
Rua Cobri 200, 30310 Belo Horizonte, MG
Tel: +55(31) 221-7451
Founded: 1971
Human Sciences.

Faculdade de Ciências Humanas de Aracruz
Rua Prof. Berilio Basilio Santibo, 29190 Aracruz, ES
Tel: +55(27) 256-1102
Founded: 1990
Human Sciences.

Faculdade de Ciências Humanas de Curvelo
Raimunda de Souza Marques, 35790 Curvelo, MG
Tel: +55(38) 721-1835
Human Sciences.

Faculdade de Ciências Humanas de Itabira
Rua Dr. Sizenando de Barros 90, 35900 Itabira, MG
Tel: +55(31) 831-3770
Founded: 1981
Human Sciences.

Faculdade de Ciências Humanas de Ivaipora
Avenida Minas Gerais 651, 86870 Ivaipora, PR
Tel: +55(434) 721-414
Founded: 1989
Human Sciences.

Faculdade de Ciências Humanas de Olinda
Largo da Misericordia s/n, 53000 Olinda, PE
Tel: +55(81) 429-4046
Founded: 1973
Human Sciences.

Faculdade de Ciências Humanas de Para de Minas
Rua Ricardo Marinho 110, 35660 Para de Minas, MG
Tel: +55(37) 231-1308
Founded: 1969
Human Sciences.

Faculdade de Ciências Humanas de Pedro Leopoldo
Rua Teofilo Calazans de Barrosioo, 33600 Pedro Leopoldo, MG
Tel: +55(31) 661-2111
Founded: 1969
Human Sciences.

Faculdade de Ciências Humanas de Pernambuco
Avenida Joao de Barros 561, 50050 Recife, PE
Tel: +55(81) 221-4423
Founded: 1988
Human Sciences.

Faculdade de Ciências Humanas de Veracruz
Rua Pacre Antonio Ribeiro Pint 142, 29000 Vitoria, ES
Tel: +55(27) 227-5874
Founded: 1990
Human Sciences.

Faculdade de Ciências Humanas do Sul Paulista
Rua Prof. Rivadavia Marques Júnior 338, 18400 Itapeva, SP
Tel: +55(15) 522-0605
Founded: 1976
Human Sciences.

Faculdade de Ciências Humanas do Vale do Rio Grande
Avenida Covern Dr. Ademar, Pereira de 1200, 15400 Olimpia, SP
Tel: +55(17) 281-3077
Founded: 1990
Human Sciences.

Faculdade de Ciências Humanas e Letras de Rondonia
Rua Cuque de Caxias 2454, CCL a Ferreira, 78900 Pôrto Velho, RO
Tel: +55(69) 223-2233
Founded: 1988
Human Sciences; Letters.

Faculdade de Ciências Humanas e Sociais de Curitiba
Rua Tobias de Macedo Júnior 333, Bairro de Santo Ignacio, 82000 Curitiba, PR
Tel: +55(41) 335-1717
Founded: 1975
Human Sciences; Social Sciences.

Faculdade de Ciências Humanas e Sociais Padre Humberto
Rua Maj. Porphirio Henriques 41, 28300 Itaperuna, RJ, 28300 Itaperuna, RJ
Tel: +55(249) 220-610
Founded: 1987
Human Sciences; Social Sciences.

Faculdade de Ciências Humanas Esuda
Rua Almeida Cunha 100, 50150 Recife, PE
Tel: +55(81) 222-6586
Founded: 1974
Human Sciences.

Faculdade de Ciências Jurídicas e Administrativas de Rondonopolis
Avenida Ari Coelho 829, 78700 Rondonopolis, MT
Tel: +55(65) 421-1340
Founded: 1988
Law; Administration.

Faculdade de Ciências Jurídicas e Administrativas de São Luis
Parque Urbano Santos 561, 65020 São Luis, MA
Founded: 1990
Law; Administration.

Faculdade de Ciências Jurídicas e Sociais
João Luiz Ribeiro de Morais, 58000 JoPessoa,
PB
Tel: +55(83) 231-1418
Founded: 1973
Law; Social Sciences.

Faculdade de Ciências Jurídicas e Sociais de Barbacena
Rua Monsenhor José Augusto 203, 36200
Barbacena, MG
Tel: +55(32) 331-3182
Founded: 1974
Law; Social Sciences.

Faculdade de Ciências Jurídicas e Sociais Vianna Junior
Avenida dos Andradas 415, 36025 Juiz de Fora,
MG
Tel: +55(32) 212-2940
Founded: 1970
Law; Social Sciences.

Faculdade de Ciências Médicas de Minas Gerais
Alameda Ezequiel Dias 275, 30130 Belo
Horizonte, MG
Tel: +55(31) 222-9066
Founded: 1951
Medicine.

Faculdade de Ciências Médicas de 'Santa Casa de São Paulo'
Rua Dr. Cesário Motta Júnior 112, 01221 São
Paulo, SP
Tel: +55(11) 220-7288
Founded: 1968
Medicine.

Faculdade de Ciências Médicas de Santos
Rua Oswaldo Cruz, 11045 Santos, SP
Tel: +55(132) 351-148
Founded: 1967
Medicine.

Faculdade de Ciências Médicas 'Dr. José António Garcia Coutinho'
Avenida Alfredo Custodio de Paula 320, 37550
Pouso Alegre, MG
Tel: +55(35) 421-3504
Founded: 1968
Medicine.

Faculdade de Ciências Médicas e Paramédicas Fluminense
Rua Pracinha Wallace Paes Leme 1338, 26525
Nilopolis, RJ
Tel: +55(21) 791-0559
Founded: 1986
Health Sciences.

Faculdade de Ciências Políticas e Econômicas do Rio de Janeiro
Rua da Assembleia 10, 20011 Rio de Janeiro, RJ
Tel: +55(21) 224-8622
Founded: 1919
Political Science; Economics.

Faculdade de Comunicação FAAP
Rua Alagoas 903 Pacaembu, 02142 São Paulo, SP
Tel: +55(11) 826-4233
Founded: 1972
Communication.

Faculdade de Comunicação Social 'Casper Libero'
Avenida Paulista 900, 01310 São Paulo, SP
Tel: +55(11) 287-4322
Founded: 1947
Communication.

Faculdade de Danca de Londrina
Avenida Paris 675, 86100 Londrina, PR
Tel: +55(43) 226-2874
Founded: 1989
Dance.

Faculdade de Desenho de Tatui
Rua Prof. Oracy Gomes 665, 18270 Tatui, SP
Tel: +55(152) 510-460
Founded: 1987
Design.

Faculdade de Desenho Industrial de Maua
Rua Alonso Vasconcelos Pacecho, Vila Vitória,
09310 Maua, SP
Tel: +55(11) 416-2166
Founded: 1975
Industrial Design.

Faculdade de Direito da Alta Paulista
Rua Mandaguaris 1010, 17600 Tupa, SP
Tel: +55(144) 421-862
Founded: 1970
Law.

Faculdade de Direito de Anápolis
Avenida Universitária, 77100 Anápolis, GO
Tel: +55(62) 324-4680
Founded: 1969
Law.

Faculdade de Direito de Araçatuba
Rua Mato Grosso 1146, 16100 Araçatuba, SP
Tel: +55(186) 234-088
Founded: 1971
Law.

Faculdade de Direito de Bauru
Praça 9 de Julho 1-51, 17100 Bauru, SP
Tel: +55(142) 342-955
Founded: 1952
Law.

Faculdade de Direito de Campos
Rua Tenente Colonel Cardoso 349, 28100
Campos, RJ
Tel: +55(247) 233-250
Founded: 1960
Law.

Faculdade de Direito de Colatina
Rua Pioravante Rossi 2930, 29700 Colatina, ES
Tel: +55(27) 722-0533
Founded: 1972
Law.

Faculdade de Direito de Curitiba
Rua Emiliano Perneta 268, 80000 Curitiba, PR
Tel: +55(41) 223-2986
Founded: 1951
Law.

Faculdade de Direito de Itaúna
Rua Sao Sebastiao 676, 35680 Itaúna, MG
Tel: +55(37) 241-2788
Founded: 1973
Law.

Faculdade de Direito de Itú
Avenida Tiradentes s/n, 13300 Itú, SP
Tel: +55(11) 409-1114
Founded: 1973
Law.

Faculdade de Direito de Joinville
Rua Sao José 490, 89200 Joinville, SC
Tel: +55(474) 228-577
Founded: 1980
Law.

Faculdade de Direito de Marília
Avenida Hygino Muzzy Filho 529, 17500 Marília,
SP
Tel: +55(144) 330-833
Founded: 1970
Law.

Faculdade de Direito de Nova Iguaçu
Avenida Abilio Augusto Tavora 2134, 26260 Nova
Iguaçu, RJ
Tel: +55(21) 767-7176
Founded: 1974
Law.

Faculdade de Direito de Olinda
Rua de São Bento 200, 53000 Olinda, PE
Tel: +55(81) 429-1300
Founded: 1971
Law.

Faculdade de Direito de Osasco
Rua Narciso Sturlini 883, 06010 Osasco, SP
Tel: +55(11) 701-6000
Founded: 1969
Law.

Faculdade de Direito de Pinhal
Avenida Helio Vergueiro Leite s/n, 13990 Espírito
Santo do Pinhal, SP
Tel: +55(19) 651-3604
Founded: 1966
Law.

Faculdade de Direito de Presidente Prudente
Praça Raul Furquim s/n, 19100 Presidente
Prudente, SP
Tel: +55(182) 334-744
Founded: 1961
Law.

Faculdade de Direito de Santo Angelo
Rua João A. Rodrigues 471, 98800 Santo Angelo,
RS
Tel: +(55) 312-1477
Founded: 1963
Law.

Faculdade de Direito de São Carlos
Rua Dr. Marino da Costa Terra, 13560 São
Carlos, SP
Tel: +55(162) 717-222
Founded: 1968
Law.

Faculdade de Direito de Sete Lagoas
Avenida Marechal Castelo Branco, 35700 Sete
Lagoas, MG
Tel: +55(31) 921-2022
Founded: 1974
Law.

Faculdade de Direito de Sorocaba
Rua Dra. Ursulina L. Torres 123, 18100 Sorocaba,
SP
Tel: +55(152) 322-975
Founded: 1957
Law.

Faculdade de Direito de Teófilo Otôni
Rua Frei Dimas 111, 39800 Teófilo Otôni, MG
Tel: +55(33) 521-2745
Founded: 1976
Law.

Faculdade de Direito de Umuarama
Praça Mascarenhas de Moraes s/n, 87500
Umuarama, PR
Tel: +55(446) 226-566
Founded: 1980
Law.

Faculdade de Direito de Varginha
Rua José Gonçalves Pereira, 37100 Varginha,
MG
Tel: +55(35) 221-1900
Founded: 1966
Law.

Faculdade de Direito do Oeste de Minas
Rua Minas Gerais 900, 35500 Divinópolis, MG
Tel: +55(37) 221-5975
Founded: 1966
Law.

Faculdade de Direito do Sul de Minas
Avenida Jo-o Beraldo 430, 37550 Pouso Alegre,
MG
Tel: +55(35) 421-1339
Founded: 1959
Law.

Faculdade de Direito do Vale do Rio Doce
Rua Artur Bernardes, 35100 Governador
Valadares, MG
Tel: +55(33) 271-2004
Founded: 1969
Law.

Faculdade de Direito Padre Anchieta
Rua Bom Jesus de Pirapora 140, 13200 Jundiaí,
SP
Tel: +55(11) 434-8444
Founded: 1969
Law.

Faculdade de Direito Prof. Milton Campos
Rua Milton Campos 202, Villa da Serra, 34000
Belo Horizonte, MG
Tel: +55(31) 286-1677
Founded: 1975
Law.

Faculdade de Direito São João Boa Vista
Rua General Osorio 433, 13870 São João Boa
Vista, SP
Tel: +55(196) 233-012
Founded: 1966
Law.

**Faculdade de Economia da Fundacão
Armando Alvares Penteado**
Rua Alagoas 903 Picaembu, 01242 São Paulo, SP
Tel: +55(11) 826-4233
Founded: 1977
Economics.

**Faculdade de Economia e Finanças do Rio
de Janeiro**
Praça da República 62, 20211 Rio de Janeiro, RJ
Tel: +55(21) 231-1965
Founded: 1916
Economics; Finance.

**Faculdade de Economia, Finanças e
Administrativas de São Paulo**
Rua Altinopolis 147, 02334 São Paulo, SP
Tel: +55(11) 267-6244
Founded: 1943
Economics; Finance; Administration.

Faculdade de Economia 'São Luís'
Rua Haddock Lobo 400, 01414 São Paulo, SP
Tel: +55(11) 257-3022
Founded: 1948
Economics.

Faculdade de Educacão
Campus do Ipe, 58000 João Pessoa, PB
Tel: +55(83) 231-1418
Founded: 1980
Education.

**Faculdade de Educacão'Antonio A. Reis
Neves'**
Rua 20, 383, 14780 Barretos, SP
Tel: +55(173) 225-733
Founded: 1973
Education.

**Faculdade de Educacão Artistica de Santa
Rosa**
Rua Santos Dumont 820, 98900 Santa Rosa, RS
Tel: +55(55) 512-1747
Founded: 1989
Arts.

Faculdade de Educacão Campos Salles
Rua Nossa Senhora da Lapa 284, 05072 São
Paulo, SP
Tel: +55(11) 260-6477
Founded: 1971
Education.

**Faculdade de Educacão, Ciências e Artes
'Dom Bosco'**
Rua Agosto Chiesa 679, 15150 Monte Aprazivel,
SP
Tel: +55(172) 751-736
Founded: 1973
Education; Sciences; Arts.

**Faculdade de Educacão, Ciências e Letras
do Alto Taquari**
Estrada Lajeado Arroio do Meio Km, Vila Jardim,
95900 Lajeado, RS
Tel: (51) 714-2166
Founded: 1969
Education; Sciences; Letters.

**Faculdade de Educação, Ciências e Letras
'Don Domenico'**
Rua Dr. Arthur Costa Filho 20, 11410 Guaruja, SP
Tel: +55(13) 286-6457
Founded: 1973
Education; Sciences; Letters.

**Faculdade de Educação, Ciências e Letras
da Regiao dos Vinhedos**
Alameda João Dal Gasso 800, 95600 Bento
Gonçalves, RS
Tel: +55(54) 252-1188
Founded: 1970
Education; Sciences; Letters.

**Faculdade de Educacão, Ciências e Letras
'Olavio Bilac'**
Avenida Lusitania 169, 21011 Rio de Janeiro, RJ
Tel: +55(21) 260-5552
Founded: 1974
Education; Sciences; Letters.

**Faculdade de Educação, Ciências e Letras
de Ponta Pora**
Avenida Presidente Vargas 725, 79900 Ponto
Pora, MS
Tel: +55(67) 431-2107
Founded: 1987
Education; Sciences; Letters.

**Faculdade de Educação, Ciências e Letras
Positivo**
Avenida N. S. Aparecida 174, 80320 Curitiba, PR
Tel: +55(41) 342-2728
Founded: 1988
Education; Sciences; Letters.

Faculdade de Educação, Ciências e Letras Urubupunga
Avenida Cel. Jonas Alves de Mello 1660, 15370
Pereira Barreto, SP
Tel: +55(18) 761-1933
Founded: 1973
Education; Sciences; Letters.

Faculdade de Educação da Bahia
Rua da Mangueira, 40000 Salvador, BA
Tel: +55(71) 243-8826
Founded: 1967
Education.

Faculdade de Educação de Assis
Avenida Doctor Doria, 19800 Assis, SP
Tel: +55(18) 322-2552
Founded: 1970
Education.

Faculdade de Educação de Cacoal
Rua Cos. Esportes 1038, 78935 Cacoal, RO
Tel: +55(69) 441-4503
Founded: 1987
Education.

Faculdade de Educação de Caraguatatuba
Avenida Frei Pacifico Wagner s/n, 11760
Caraguatatuba, SP
Tel: +55(124) 222-666
Founded: 1988
Education.

Faculdade de Educação de Guaratinguetá
Avenida Pédro de Toledo 195, 12500
Guaratinguetá, SP
Tel: +55(12) 522-2911
Founded: 1974
Education.

Faculdade de Educação de Ivaipora
Avenida Minas Gerais 651, 86170 Ivaipora, PR
Tel: +55(434) 721-414
Founded: 1987
Education.

Faculdade de Educação de João Monlevade
Rua Tiete 100, 35930 João Monlevade, MG
Tel: +55(31) 851-4784
Founded: 1972
Education.

Faculdade de Educação de Joinville
Rua Sao José 490, 89200 Joinville, SC
Tel: +55(474) 253-200
Founded: 1973
Education.

Faculdade de Educação de Lavras
Praça Dr. Augusto Silva 616, 37200 Lavras, MG
Tel: +55(35) 821-3298
Education.

Faculdade de Educação de Taquara
Rua Julio de Castilhos 2084, 95000 Taquara, RS
Tel: +55(51) 642-1256
Founded: 1970
Education.

Faculdade de Educação e Ciências Pinheirense
Rua Cardeal Arcoverde 1097 Pinheiros, 05407
São Paulo, SP
Tel: +55(11) 813-6570
Founded: 1974
Education and Sciences.

Faculdade de Educação Física
BR 230 Km. 22 Campus Universitario, 58100 João
Pessoa, PB
Tel: +55(83) 231-1418
Founded: 1973
Physical Education.

Faculdade de Educação Física de Barra Bonita
Rua Joao Gerin 275, 17340 Barra Bonita, SP
Tel: +55(146) 410-300
Founded: 1972
Physical Education.

Faculdade de Educação Física de Lins
Rua Dom Bosco 265, 16400 Lins, SP
Tel: +55(145) 224-733
Founded: 1972
Physical Education.

Faculdade de Educação Física de Santo André
Travesse Cisplatina 20, 09000 Santo André, SP
Tel: +55(11) 449-0700
Founded: 1970
Physical Education.

Faculdade de Educação Física de Sorocaba
Rua da Penha 680, 18100 Sorocaba, SP
Tel: +55(152) 320-684
Founded: 1971
Physical Education.

Faculdade de Educação Física do Norte do Paraná
Avenida Paris 675, 36020 Londrina, PR
Tel: +55(43) 226-2864
Founded: 1973
Physical Education.

Faculdade de Educação Física e Desporto 'Maria Thereza'
Rua Visconde do Rio Branco 869, 24020 Niteroi,
RJ
Tel: +55(21) 719-0660
Founded: 1989
Physical Education.

Faculdade de Educação Física Montenegro
Avenida São Vicente de Paula 462, 45745
Ibicaraí, BA
Tel: +55(73) 242-1125
Founded: 1989
Physical Education.

Faculdade de Educação Osorio Campos
Rua Prof. Alfredo G. Filgueiras, 28500 Nilopolis,
RJ
Tel: +55(21) 791-945
Founded: 1974
Education.

Faculdade de Educação Padre Anchieta
Rua Bom. Jesus Pirapora 140, 13100 Jundíai, SP
Tel: +55(11) 434-8444
Telex: 11-79844 eac
Founded: 1968
Education.

Faculdade de Educação Paulo Eiro
Rua Barao de Cotegite 111, 04121 São Paulo, SP
Tel: +55(11) 523-8522
Founded: 1990
Education.

Faculdade de Educação São Luis
Rua Floriano Peixoto 873, 14870 Jaboticabal, SP
Tel: +55(16) 322-0530
Founded: 1972
Education.

Faculdade de Educação Tecnica Nilopolis
Rua Prof. Alfredo Ilgueiras 537, 26500 Nilopolis,
RJ
Tel: +55(21) 761-4440
Education.

Faculdade de Educação 'Thereza Pôrto Marques'
Rua São Sebastio 25, 12300 Jacarei, SP
Tel: +55(123) 518-569
Founded: 1988
Education.

Faculdade de Enfermagen e Obstetrícia de Jahú
Rua Tenente Navarro 642, 17200 Jahú, SP
Tel: +55(146) 223-343
Founded: 1985
Nursing and Midwifery.

Faculdade de Enfermagem e Obstetrícia 'Dom Domenico'
Rua Dr. Arthur Costa Filho 20, 11410 Guaruja, SP
Tel: +55(132) 866-457
Nursing and Midwifery.

Faculdade de Enfermagen Hospitaleiro 'Albert Einstein'
Avenida Albert Einstein 627 Morumbi, 15652 São
Paulo, SP
Tel: +55(11) 845-1233
Founded: 1989
Nursing.

Faculdade de Enfermagem 'Luiza Marillac'
Rua Dr. Satamini 245, 20270 Rio de Janeiro, RJ
Tel: +55(21) 264-9350
Founded: 1942
Nursing.

Faculdade de Enfermagem 'Nossa Senhora Medianeira'
Avenida Presidente Vargas 2377, 97101 Santa
Maria, RS
Tel: +55(55) 221-1726
Founded: 1955
Nursing.

Faculdade de Enfermagem 'São José'
Avenida Nazare, 04263 São Paulo, SP
Tel: +55(11) 272-4760
Founded: 1959
Nursing.

Faculdade de Engenharia Civil de Araraquara
Avenida Brasil 782, 14800 Araraquara, SP
Tel: +55(62) 222-4281
Founded: 1969
Civil Engineering.

Faculdade de Engenharia Civil de Nova Iguaçu
Rua Anita 152, 26260 Nova Iguaçu, RJ
Tel: +55(244) 421-243
Founded: 1973
Civil Engineering.

Faculdade de Engenharia Civil de Itajuba
Avenida Dr. Antonio Braga Filho 687, 37500
Itajuba, MG
Tel: +55(35) 622-0844
Founded: 1973
Engineering.

Faculdade de Engenharia da Fumec
Rua Cobre, 30000 Belo Horizonte, MG
Tel: +55(31) 221-2800
Founded: 1971
Engineering.

Faculdade de Engenharia da Fundação 'Armando Alvares Penteado'
Rua Alagoas 903, 01242 Sao Paulo, SP
Tel: +55(11) 665-918
Founded: 1967
Engineering.

Faculdade de Engenharia de Agrimensura de Araraquara
Avenida Brasil 782, 14800 Araraquara, SP
Tel: +55(16) 222-4281
Founded: 1966
Engineering.

Faculdade de Engenharia de Agrimensura de Pirassununga
Avenida dos Academicos 1, 13630 Pirassununga,
SP
Tel: +55(195) 613-845
Engineering.

Faculdade de Engenharia de Barra Pirai
Rod Benjamin Telpo Km. 11, Campus
Universitario, 27100 Barra do Pirai, RJ
Tel: +55(244) 421-243
Founded: 1973
Engineering.

Faculdade de Engenharia de Barretos
Avenida Prof. Roberto Frade Monte 389, Campus
Universitario, 14780 Barretos, SP
Tel: +55(173) 226-411
Founded: 1966
Engineering.

Faculdade de Engenharia de Itaúna
Rua Santana 676, 35680 Itaúna, MG
Tel: +55(37) 241-2289
Founded: 1978
Engineering.

Faculdade de Engenharia de São José do Rio Preto
Avenida Bady Bassitt 3777, 15035 São José do
Rio Preto, SP
Tel: +55(172) 321-622
Founded: 1976
Engineering.

Faculdade de Engenharia de Sorocaba
Rodovia Sen. José Ermirio de Moraes, Km. 1.5,
18100 Sorocaba, SP
Tel: +55(15) 232-9717
Founded: 1976
Engineering.

Faculdade de Engenharia de Varginha
Avenida Benjamin Constant 78, 38100 Varginha,
MG
Tel: +55(35) 221-3823
Founded: 1979
Engineering.

Faculdade de Engenharia Industrial
Avenida Humberto de Alencar, Castelo Branco
3972, 09700 São Bernardo do Campo, SP
Tel: +55(11) 419-0200
Founded: 1946
Engineering.

Faculdade de Engenharia Química de Lorena
Rodovia Lorena/Itajuba, 12600 Lorena, SP
Tel: +55(125) 523-922
Telex: 61-25579
Founded: 1971
Chemical Engineering.

Faculdade de Engenharia São Paulo
Rua Arabe, 04042 São Paulo, SP
Tel: +55(11) 881-1022
Founded: 1975
Engineering.

Faculdade de Engenharia Souza Marquês
Avenida Ernani Cardoso 335, 21310 Rio de
Janeiro, RJ
Tel: +55(21) 390-6365
Founded: 1972
Engineering.

Faculdade de Estudos Sociais Aplicados de Aracajú
Rua Estancia 362, 49000 Aracajú, SP
Tel: +55(79) 222-2202
Founded: 1979
Social Studies.

Faculdade de Estudos Sociais de Varzea Grande
Avenida Com. Orlando Chaves 2655, 28150
Varzea Grande, MT
Tel: +55(65) 381-3736
Founded: 1991
Social Studies.

Faculdade de Filosofia 'Bernardo Sayão'
Avenida Universitária Km-3, 77100 Anápolis, GO
Tel: +55(62) 324-4680
Founded: 1961
Philosophy.

Faculdade de Filosofia, Ciências e Letras Barao de Mauá
Rua Ramos de Azevedo 423, 14100 Ribeirao
Prêto, SP
Tel: +55(16) 625-4935
Founded: 1968
Philosophy, Sciences and Letters.

Faculdade de Filosofia, Ciências e Letras Carlos Queiroz
Avenida Cel Clementino Gonçalves 1651, 8900
Santa Cruz do Rio Pardo, SP
Tel: +55(143) 721-173
Founded: 1971
Philosophy, Sciences and Letters.

Faculdade de Filosofia, Ciências e Letras de Araçatuba
Rua Mato Grosso 1141, 6100 Araçatuba, SP
Tel: +55(186) 234-088
Founded: 1966
Philosophy, Siences and Letters.

Faculdade de Filosofia, Ciências e Letras de Araguari
Avenida Minas Gerais 1889, 38440 Araguari, MG
Tel: +55(34) 241-3900
Founded: 1968
Philosophy, Sciences and Letters.

Faculdade de Filosofia, Ciências e Letras de Arapongas
Rua des Garças 290, 86700 Arapongas, PR
Tel: +55(43) 252-1016
Founded: 1968
Philosophy, Sciences and Letters.

Faculdade de Filosofia, Ciências e Letras de Barra do Piraí
Rodovia Benjamin Ielpo Km. 11, 27100 Barra do
Piraí, RJ
Tel: +55(24) 442-1243
Founded: 1972
Philosophy, Sciences and Letters.

Faculdade de Filosofia, Ciências e Letras de Bebedouro
Rua Prof. Orlando F. de Carvalho 325, 14700
Bebedouro, SP
Tel: +55(173) 421-100
Founded: 1970
Philosophy, Sciences and Letters.

Faculdade de Filosofia, Ciências e Letras de Belo Horizonte
Avenida Antonio Carlos 521, 31210 Belo
Horizonte, MG
Tel: +55(31) 442-6955
Founded: 1964
Philosophy, Sciences and Letters.

Faculdade de Filosofia, Ciências e Letras de Caratinga
Avenida São José 49, 35300 Caratinga, MG
Tel: +55(33) 321-2930
Founded: 1975
Philosophy, Sciences and Letters.

Faculdade de Filosofia, Ciências e Letras de Caruarú
Rua Azevedo Coutinho, 55100 Caruarú, PE
Tel: +55(81) 721-2611
Founded: 1969
Philosophy, Sciences and Letters.

Faculdade de Filosofia, Ciências e Letras de Congonhas
Praça Santo Afonso 90 Basilica, 36404
Congonhas, MG
Tel: +55(31) 731-1541
Founded: 1987
Philosophy, Sciences and Letters.

Faculdade de Filosofia, Ciências e Letras de Diamantina
Travessa Mercedes Murao 77, 39100 Diamantina,
MG
Tel: +55(38) 931-1922
Founded: 1968
Philosophy, Sciences and Letters.

Faculdade de Filosofia, Ciências e Letras de Duque de Caxias
Avenida Presidente Kennedy 9422, 25045 Duque
de Caxias, RJ
Tel: +55(21) 771-3669
Founded: 1972
Philosophy, Sciences and Letters.

Faculdade de Filosofia, Ciências e Letras de Formiga
Avenida Dr. Arnaldo de Senna, 37290 Formiga,
MG
Tel: +55(37) 321-2997
Founded: 1967
Philosophy, Sciences and Letters.

Faculdade de Filosofia, Ciências e Letras de Guarulhos
Rua Barao de Mauá 600, 07000 Guarulhos, SP
Tel: +55(11) 209-3533
Founded: 1971
Philosophy, Sciences and Letters.

Faculdade de Filosofia, Ciências e Letras de Guaxupe
Avenida D. Floriana s/n, 37800 Guaxupe, MG
Tel: +55(35) 551-1267
Founded: 1969
Philosophy, Sciences and Letters.

Faculdade de Filosofia, Ciências e Letras de Itajubá
Avenida Dr. Antonio Braga Filho 687, 37500
Itajubá, MG
Tel: +55(35) 622-0844
Founded: 1965
Philosophy, Sciences and Letters.

Faculdade de Filosofia, Ciências e Letras de Itapetininga
Avenida Joao Barth s/n, 18200 Itapetininga, SP
Tel: +55(15) 271-0503
Founded: 1968
Philosophy, Sciences and Letters.

Faculdade de Filosofia, Ciências e Letras de Itararé
Rua Joao Batista Veiga 1725, 18460 Itararé, SP
Tel: +55(155) 321-330
Founded: 1973
Philosophy, Sciences and Letters.

Faculdade de Filosofia, Ciências e Letras de Itaúna
Rua Prof. Francisco Santiago 275, 35610 Itaúna,
MG
Tel: +55(37) 241-2921
Founded: 1975
Philosophy, Sciences and Letters.

Faculdade de Filosofia, Ciências e Letras de Ituverava
Rua Cel. Flausino Barbosa Sandoval 1259, 14500
Ituverava, SP
Tel: +55(16) 729-2326
Founded: 1971
Philosophy, Sciences and Letters.

Faculdade de Filosofia, Ciências e Letras de Jahú
Rua Tenente Navarro 642, 17200 Jahú, SP
Tel: +55(146) 223-435
Founded: 1966
Philosophy, Sciences and Letters.

Faculdade de Filosofia, Ciências e Letras de Jales
Avenida Francisco Jales 1891, 15700 Jales, SP
Tel: +55(176) 321-620
Founded: 1970
Philosophy, Sciences and Letters.

Faculdade de Filosofia, Ciências e Letras de Macae
Rua Tenente Rui Lopes Ribeiro 200, 28700
Macae, RJ
Tel: +55(247) 621-457
Founded: 1973
Philosophy, Sciences and Letters.

Faculdade de Filosofia, Ciências e Letras de Manhuaçu
Avenida Marcionilia Breder Sather 01, 36900 Manhuaçu, MG
Tel: +55(33) 331-1898
Founded: 1989
Philosophy, Sciences and Letters.

Faculdade de Filosofia, Ciências e Letras de Nova Iguaçu
Avenida Abilio Augusto Tavora 2134, 26000 Nova Iguaçu, RJ
Tel: +55(21) 767-7221
Philosophy, Sciences and Letters.

Faculdade de Filosofia, Ciências e Letras de Ouro Fino
Rodovia MG 290 Km. 59 Ouro Fino, 37570 Ouro Fino, MG
Tel: +55(35) 441-1426
Founded: 1972
Philosophy, Sciences and Letters.

Faculdade de Filosofia, Ciências e Letras de Palmas
Rua Dr. Bernardo Ribeiro Viana 903, 84670 Palmas, PR
Tel: +55(462) 623-388
Founded: 1968
Philosophy, Sciences and Letters.

Faculdade de Filosofia, Ciências e Letras de Patos
Rua Horacio Nobrega, 58700 Patos, PB
Tel: +55(83) 421-2606
Founded: 1970
Philosophy, Sciences and Letters.

Faculdade de Filosofia, Ciências e Letras de Pirajú
Rua Joao Hailer 408, 18800 Pirajú, SP
Tel: +55(143) 512-078
Founded: 1975
Philosophy, Sciences and Letters.

Faculdade de Filosofia, Ciências e Letras de Presidente Wenceslau
Avenida Carlos Platzeck, 19400 Presidente Wenceslau, SP
Tel: +55(182) 712-373
Philosophy, Sciences and Letters.

Faculdade de Filosofia, Ciências e Letras de Registro
Rua São Francisco Xavier 165, 11900 Registro, SP
Tel: +55(138) 212-411
Founded: 1972
Philosophy, Sciences and Letters.

Faculdade de Filosofia, Ciências e Letras de Santiago
Vinte de Setembro 2410, 97700 Santiago, RS
Tel: +55(55) 251-1715
Founded: 1975
Philosophy, Sciences and Letters.

Faculdade de Filosofia, Ciências e Letras de Santo André
Avenida Principe de Gales 821, 09060 Santo André, SP
Tel: +55(11) 449-3158
Founded: 1966
Philosophy, Sciences and Letters.

Faculdade de Filosofia, Ciências e Letras de São Caetano do Sul
Rua Amazonas, 95040 São Caetano do Sul, SP
Tel: +55(11) 441-3233
Philosophy, Sciences and Letters.

Faculdade de Filosofia, Ciências e Letras de São João da Boa Vista
Rua Cristiano o Orio 10, 13870 São Joao da Boa Vista, SP
Tel: +55(196) 233-266
Founded: 1971
Philosophy, Sciences and Letters.

Faculdade de Filosofia, Ciências e Letras de Sete Lagoas
Avenida Marechal Castelo Branco, 35700 Sete Lagoas, MG
Tel: +55(31) 921-2010
Philosophy, Sciences and Letters.

Faculdade de Filosofia, Ciências e Letras de Sorocaba
Avenida General Osório 35, 18060 Sorocaba, SP
Tel: +55(152) 327-153
Founded: 1952
Philosophy, Sciences and Letters.

Faculdade de Filosofia, Ciências e Letras de Tatui
Rua Prof. Cracy Gomes, 18270 Tatui, SP
Tel: +55(152) 510-460
Founded: 1971
Philosophy, Sciences and Letters.

Faculdade de Filosofia, Ciências e Letras de Tangara da Serra
Avenida Brasil 1248, 78830 Tangara da Serra, MT
Tel: +55(65) 726-1101
Founded: 1989
Philosophy, Sciences and Letters.

Faculdade de Filosofia, Ciências e Letras de Teofilo Otoni
Rua Prei Dimas 111, 39800 Teofilo Otoni, MG
Tel: +55(33) 521-2745
Founded: 1966
Philosophy, Sciences and Letters.

Faculdade de Filosofia, Ciências e Letras de Ubá
Praça São Januario 276, 36500 Ubá, MG
Tel: +55(32) 532-4657
Founded: 1970
Philosophy, Sciences and Letters.

Faculdade de Filosofia, Ciências e Letras de Umuarama
Praça Mascarenhas de Moraes 29, 87500
Umuarama, PR
Tel: +55(446) 226-566
Founded: 1972
Philosophy, Sciences and Letters.

Faculdade de Filosofia, Ciências e Letras de Varginha
Rua Maria B. Resende 78, 37100 Varginha, MG
Tel: +55(35) 221-5165
Founded: 1966
Philosophy, Sciences and Letters.

Faculdade de Filosofia, Ciências e Letras de Vassouras
Avenida Exp. Oswaldo de A. Ramos, 27700
Vassouras, RJ
Tel: +55(244) 711-595
Founded: 1971
Philosophy, Sciences and Letter.

Faculdade de Filosofia, Ciências e Letras de Volta Redonda
Rua Gov. Luiz Monterra 81, 27293 Volta Redonda, RJ
Tel: +55(24) 342-4530
Founded: 1971
Philosophy, Sciences and Letters.

Faculdade de Filosofia, Ciências e Letras do Alto São Francisco
Avenida Formiga, 35595 Luz, MG
Tel: +55(37) 421-1494.
Founded: 1979
Philosophy, Sciences and Letters.

Faculdade de Filosofia, Ciências e Letras Dom Bosco
Estrada Resende/Riachuelo Km-1, 27500
Resende, RJ
Tel: +55(24) 354-1140
Founded: 1973
Philosophy, Sciences and Letters.

Faculdade de Filosofia, Ciências e Letras Dom Bosco
Rua Santa Rosa 536, 98900 Santa Rosa, RS
Tel: +55(24) 354-1140
Founded: 1973
Philosophy, Sciences and Letters.

Faculdade de Filosofia, Ciências e Letras Eugenio Pacelli
Rua Joaquim Roberto Duarte 470, 37550 Pouso
Alegre, MG
Tel: +55(35) 421-1736
Founded: 1972
Philosophy, Sciences and Letters.

Faculdade de Filosofia, Ciências e Letras 'Gonçalves Dias'
Parque Urbano Santos 561, 65020 Sao Luis, MA
Founded: 1990
Philosophy, Sciences and Letters.

Faculdade de Filosofia, Ciências e Letras Imaculada Conceição
Rua Andradas 1614, 97100 Santa María, RS
Tel: +55(55) 221-2792
Founded: 1957
Philosophy, Sciences and Letters.

Faculdade de Filosofia, Ciências e Letras Madre Gertrudes de Sao José
Avenida Monte Castelo 03, 29300 Cachoeiro do
Itapemirim, ES
Tel: +55(27) 522-5036
Founded: 1967
Philosophy, Sciences and Letters.

Faculdade de Filosofia, Ciências e Letras Mater Divinae Gratiae
Rua Monsenhor J. Augusto 203, 36200
Barbacena, MG
Tel: +55(32) 331-3182
Founded: 1966
Philosophy, Sciences and Letters.

Faculdade de Filosofia, Ciências e Letras Ministro Tarso Dutra
Avenida Alcides Chacon Couto 395, 1790-0
Dracena, SP
Tel: +55(18) 821-1191
Founded: 1969
Philosophy, Sciences and Letters.

Faculdade de Filosofia, Ciências e Letras Nossa Senhora do Patrocinio
Rua Madre Maria Basília 965, 13300 Itú, SP
Tel: +55(11) 482-2547
Founded: 1958
Philosophy, Sciences and Letters.

Faculdade de Filosofia, Ciências e Letras Nove de Julho
Rua Diamantina 302, 02117 São Paulo, SP
Tel: +55 939-898
Founded: 1985
Philosophy, Sciences and Letters.

Faculdade de Filosofia, Ciências e Letras 'Prof. Carlos Pasquale'
Rua Oriente 123, 03016 São Paulo, SP
Tel: +55(11) 229-8960
Founded: 1972
Philosophy, Sciences and Letters.

Faculdade de Filosofia, Ciências e Letras 'Prof. Nair Fortes Abu-Merhy'
Avenida 18 de Julho 210, 36660 Além Paraíba, MG
Tel: +55(32) 462-2951
Founded: 1983
Philosophy, Sciences and Letters.

Faculdade de Filosofia, Ciências e Letras Santa Cruz do Rio Pardo
Avenida Joaquim de Souza Campos 80, 13900
Santa Cruz do Rio Pardo, SP
Tel: +55(143) 721-754
Founded: 1972
Philosophy, Sciences and Letters.

Faculdade de Filosofia, Ciências e Letras Santa Marcelina
Rua do Bomfim, 36880 Muriae, MG
Tel: +55(32) 721-1026
Founded: 1961
Philosophy, Sciences and Letters.

Faculdade de Filosofia, Ciências e Letras São Bernardo do Campo
Rua Americo Brasiliense 449, 09715 São Bernardo do Campos, SP
Tel: +55(11) 443-3277
Founded: 1971
Philosophy, Sciences and Letters.

Faculdade de Filosofia, Ciências e Letras São Borja
Avenida Presidente Tancredo Neves 210, Campus Universitario, 97670 Sao Borja, RS
Tel: +55(55) 431-1687
Founded: 1974
Philosophy, Sciences and Letters.

Faculdade de Filosofia, Ciências e Letras Souza Marques
Avenida Ernant Cardoso 335-345, 21310 Rio de Janeiro, RJ
Tel: +55(21) 390-6365
Founded: 1968
Philosophy, Sciences and Letters.

Faculdade de Filosofia, Ciências e Letras Tangara da Serra
Avenida Brasil 1248, 78830 Tangara da Serra, MT
Tel: +55(65) 726-2650
Founded: 1990
Philosophy, Sciences and Letters.

Faculdade de Filosofia, Ciências e Letras Tibirica
Largo Sao Bento, 01405 São Paulo, SP
Tel: +55(11) 887-8531
Philosophy, Sciences and Letters.

Faculdade de Filosofia, Ciências e Letras Tuiuti
Rua Marcelino Champagnat 505, 80430 Curitiba, PR
Tel: +55(41) 335-3131
Founded: 1973
Philosophy, Sciences and Letters.

Faculdade de Filosofia de Campo Grande
Estrada da Caroba 685 Campo Grande, 23085 Rio de Janeiro, RJ
Tel: +55(21) 394-1230
Founded: 1966
Philosophy.

Faculdade de Filosofia de Itaperuna
Rua Major Porphiro Henriques 41, Itaperuna, RJ
Tel: +55(249) 220-610
Founded: 1968
Philosophy.

Faculdade de Filosofia do Recife
Avenida Conde da Boa Vista 921, 50000 Recife, PE
Tel: +55(81) 231-0621
Founded: 1943
Philosophy.

Faculdade de Filosofia do Vale do São Patricio
Praça Alvaro de Melo Rua 21, 76700 Ceres, GO
Tel: +55(62) 721-1318
Founded: 1976
Philosophy.

Faculdade de Filosofia 'Nossa Senhora da Imaculada Conceição'
Avenida Sen. Salcado Filho 7427, 94400 Viamo, RS
Tel: +55(51) 285-1177
Founded: 1957
Philosophy.

Faculdade de Filosofia Nossa Senhora do Sion
Rua Padre Nattuzzi, 37400 Campanha, MG
Tel: +55(35) 261-1187
Founded: 1975
Philosophy.

Faculdade de Filosofia Santa Dorotéia
Rua Monsenhor Miranda 86, 28600 Nova Friburgo, RJ
Tel: +55(245) 222-900
Founded: 1967
Philosophy.

Faculdade de Fisiotérapia de São Caetano do Sul
Rua Amazonas 2031, 09540 São Caetano do Sul, SP
Tel: +55(11) 441-3233
Founded: 1987
Physiotherapy.

Faculdade de Fisiotérapia Don Domenico
Rua Arthur da Costa Filho 20, 11410 Guaruja, SP
Tel: +55(13) 286-6457
Founded: 1984
Physiotheraphy.

Faculdade de Formação de Professores de Arapiraca
Rua Governador Luiz Cavalcante s/n, Alto do Cruzeiro, 57300 Arapiraca, AL
Tel: +55(82) 521-3786
Founded: 1971
Teacher Training.

Faculdade de Formação de Professores de Penedo
Rua 15 de Novembro s/n Terceiro Andar, 57200 Penedo, AL
Tel: +55(82) 551-2694
Founded: 1972
Teacher Training.

Faculdade de Formação de Professores de Vitória de Santo Antônio
Lot Sao Vicente Ferrer s/n Caja, 55600 Vitória de Santo Antônio, PE
Tel: +55(81) 523-1020
Founded: 1976
Teacher Training.

Faculdade de Formação de Professores e Especialistas em Educação
Rua Julio de Castilho, 96180 Camaqua, RS
Tel: +55(51) 671-1640
Founded: 1972
Teacher Training.

Faculdade de Formação de Professores do Instituto Americano de Lins
Rua Tenente Florencio Puppo Neto 200, Jardim Americano, Lins, SP
Tel: +55(14) 522-2223
Founded: 1970
Teacher Training.

Faculdade de Formação de Professores Sao Judas Tadeu
Rua Dom Diego de Souza 100, Cristo Redentor, 01350 Pôrto Alegre, RS
Tel: +55(51) 240-8888
Founded: 1978
Teacher Training.

Faculdade de Humanidades 'Pedro II'
Rua Pirauba s/n, 20940 Sao Cristovão, RJ
Tel: +55(21) 580-6426
Founded: 1969
Human Sciences.

Faculdade de Informática Cruzeiro do Sul
Avenida Cr. Ussiel Cirilo 225 Villa Jacci, 08060 São Paulo, SP
Tel: +55(11) 297-1777
Founded: 1985
Computer Sciences.

Faculdade de Informática de Lins
Avenida Nicolau Zarvos 1925, 6400 Lins, SP
Tel: +55(145) 222-300
Founded: 1987
Computer Sciences.

Faculdade de Informática de Londrina
Avenida Paris 675 J-Piza, 86020 Londrina, PR
Tel: +55(43) 226-2874
Founded: 1989
Computer Sciences.

Faculdade de Informática de Osasco
Rua Narciso Sturlini 883, 06010 Osasco, SP
Tel: +55(11) 701-6000
Founded: 1986
Computer Sciences.

Faculdade de Informática de Rio de Janeiro
Rua Barão de Mesquita 426, 20510 Rio de Janeiro, RJ
Tel: +55(23) 571-6160
Founded: 1988
Computer Sciences.

Faculdade de Informática do Paraná
Avenida Paris 675, 86020 Londrina, PR
Tel: +55(43) 226-2874
Founded: 1989
Computer Sciences.

Faculdade de Informática Maria Thereza
Rua Visconde do Rio Branco 869, 24020 Niteroi, RJ
Tel: +55(21) 719-0660
Founded: 1989
Computer Sciences.

Faculdade de Letras e Educaçde Vacaria
Avenida Presidente Kennedy 2020, Vila Militar, 95200 Vacaria, RS
Tel: +55(54) 231-2055
Founded: 1974
Letters and Education.

Faculdade de Medicina de Barbacena
Plaça Antonio Carlos s/n, 36200 Barbacena, MG
Tel: +55(32) 331-3296
Founded: 1976
Medicine.

Faculdade de Medicina de Campos
Rua Alberto Torres 217, 28100 Campos, RJ
Tel: +55(247) 226-788
Founded: 1967
Medicine.

Faculdade de Medicina de Catanduva
Avenida Sao Vicente de Paula, 15800 Catanduva, SP
Tel: +55(175) 223-280
Founded: 1969
Medicine.

Faculdade de Medicina de Itajubá
Rua Cel. Reno Júnior 368, 37500 Itajubá, MG
Tel: +55(35) 622-1100
Telex: 35-4256
Founded: 1968
Medicine.

Faculdade de Medicina de Marília
Avenida Monte Carmelo, 17500 Marília, SP
Tel: +55(144) 331-744
Founded: 1967
Medicine.

Faculdade de Medicina de Petrópolis
Rua Machado Fagundes 326, 25710 Petrópolis, RJ
Tel: +55(24) 242-7017
Founded: 1967
Medicine.

Faculdade de Medicina de Teresópolis
Avenida Alberto Torres 111, 25950 Teresópolis, RJ
Tel: +55(21) 742-3152
Founded: 1970
Medicine.

Faculdade de Medicina de Vassouras
Rua Dr. Joaquin Teixeira Leite 53, 27700
Vassouras, RJ
Tel: +55(244) 711-595
Founded: 1969
Medicine.

Faculdade de Medicina do ABC
Avenida Principe de Gales, 09000 Santo André,
SP
Tel: +55(11) 449-3071
Founded: 1969
Medicine.

Faculdade de Medicina Veterinaria 'Prof. Antonio Sec. de São José'
Avenida Pelio Vergueiro Leite 1 Centro, 13990
Espirito Santo Pinhal, SP
Tel: +55(19) 651-3629
Founded: 1987
Veterinary Medicine.

Faculdade de Medicina Veterinaria 'Otavio Bastos'
Rua General Osorio 433 Centro, 13990 São Paulo,
SP
Tel: +55(196) 233-833
Founded: 1987
Veterinary Medicine.

Faculdade de Música 'Carlos Gomes'
Rua Almeida Torres 264, 01530 São Paulo, SP
Tel: +55(11) 278-1162
Founded: 1963
Music.

Faculdade de Música Palestrina
Rua Gen. Vitorino 305, 90020 Pôrto Alegre, RS
Tel: +55(51) 227-3316
Founded: 1968
Music.

Faculdade de Música Santa Cecilia
Praça Barao do Rio Branco 59, 12400
Pindamonhangaba, SP
Tel: +55(122) 425-755
Founded: 1975
Music.

Faculdade de Música Santa Marcelina
Rua Dr. Costa Leite 548, 18600 Botucatu, SP
Tel: +55(14) 922-0577
Founded: 1962
Music.

Faculdade de Nutrição Don Domenico
Rua Dr. Arthur da Costa Filho 20, 11410 Guaruja,
SP
Tel: +55(13) 286-2617
Founded: 1984
Nutrition.

Faculdade de Nutrição e Fondaudiologia
Rua Dr. Lauro de Oliveira 71, 90410 Pôrto Alegre,
RS
Tel: +55(512) 317-720
Founded: 1977
Nutrition and Phonology.

Faculdade de Odontologia de Barretos
Avenida Prof. Roberto Frade Monte 389, 14700
Barretos, SP
Tel: +55(173) 226-411
Founded: 1984
Odontology.

Faculdade de Odontologia de Campos
Avenida Visc. de Alvarenga 143, 28100 Campos,
RJ
Tel: +55(247) 230-616
Founded: 1972
Odontology.

Faculdade de Odontologia de Caruaru
Avenida Portugal 385, 55100 Caruaru, PE
Tel: +55(81) 721-0258
Founded: 1959
Odontology.

Faculdade de Odontologia de Itaúna
Rua Zeze Lima, 35680 Itaúna, MG
Tel: +55(37) 241-3711
Founded: 1975
Odontology.

Faculdade de Odontologia de Lins
Rua Tenente Florencia Pupo Neto 200, 16400
Lins, SP
Tel: +55(14) 522-5088
Founded: 1954
Odontology.

Faculdade de Odontologia do Norte Paraná
Avenida Paris 675 J-Piza, 86020 Londrina, PR
Tel: +55(43) 226-2874
Founded: 1989
Odontology.

Faculdade de Odontologia do Planalto Central
SPIS QI 7 Conj. 10 Bloco E-F s/n, Lago Sul, 71600
Brasília, DF
Tel: +55(61) 248-5100
Founded: 1987
Odontology.

Faculdade de Odontologia João Prudente
Avenida Universitária Km-3, 77100 Anápolis, GO
Tel: +55(62) 324-4680
Founded: 1971
Odontology.

Faculdade de Psicologia de Joinville
Rua Sao José 490, 89200 Joinville, SC
Tel: +55(474) 228-577
Founded: 1985
Psychology.

Faculdade de Psicologia Padre Anchieta
Rua Edm. Jesus de Pirapora 140, 13200 Jundiai,
SP
Tel: +55(11) 434-8444
Founded: 1988
Psychology.

Faculdade de Reabilitação da ASCE
Rua Uaruma 80 Higienopolis, 21050 Rio de
Janeiro, RJ
Tel: +55(21) 260-1550
Founded: 1976
Physical Therapy.

**Faculdade de Reabilitação do Norte do
Paraná**
Avenida Paris 675, 86020 Londrina, PR
Tel: +55(43) 226-2874
Founded: 1987
Physical Therapy.

Faculdade de Reabilitaçỏo Planalto Central
SHIS QI 7 Conj. 10 Bloco E-F s/n, Lago Sul, 71600
Brasília, DF
Tel: +55(61) 248-5100
Founded: 1990
Physical Therapy.

Faculdade de Reabilitação Tuiuti
Rua Marcelino Champagnat, 804030 Curitiba, PR
Tel: +55(41) 335-3131
Founded: 1981
Physical Therapy.

Faculdade de Serviço Social de Bauru
Praça 9 de Julho 1-51, 17100 Bauru, SP
Tel: +55(142) 342-955
Founded: 1964
Social Work.

Faculdade de Serviço Social de Lins
Rua Dom Lucio 165, 16400 Lins, SP
Tel: +55(145) 222-300
Founded: 1958
Social Work.

Faculdade de Serviço Social de Piracicaba
Avenida Independencia 3000, 13400 Piracicaba,
SP
Tel: +55(194) 222-332
Founded: 1963
Social Work.

**Faculdade de Serviço Social de President
Prudente**
Praça Raul Furquim s/n, 19030 President
Prudente, SP
Tel: +55(182) 334-744
Founded: 1986
Social Work.

Faculdade de Tecnologia da FAAP
Rua Alagoas 903, 01242 São Paulo, SP
Tel: +55(11) 826-4233
Founded: 1972
Technology.

Faculdade de Tecnologia de Rio Claro
Rua Nove 1864, 13500 Santa Cruz, SP
Tel: +55(195) 346-320
Founded: 1981
Technology.

**Faculdade de Tecnologia em
Processamento de Dados**
Rua 20, 383, 14780 Barretos, SP
Tel: +55(173) 225-733
Founded: 1981

**Faculdade de Tecnologia em
Processamento de Dados Arçatuba**
Praça Joao Pessoa 330, 16010 Arçatuba, SP
Tel: +55(18) 623-6014
Founded: 1990
Technology.

**Faculdade de Tecnologia em
Processamento de Dados de Pinhal**
Avenida Pelio Vergueiro Leite 1, Bloco E, 13990
Espirito Santo do Pinhal, SP
Tel: +55(196) 514-418
Founded: 1988
Computer Sciences.

Faculdade de Tecnologia Padre Anchieta
Rua Edm. Jesus de Pirapora 140, 13200 Jundiai,
SP
Tel: +55(11) 434-8444
Founded: 1989
Technology.

Faculdade de Turismo da Bahia
Rua la Mangueira 32, 40040 Salvador, BA
Tel: +55(71) 243-8826
Founded: 1981
Tourism.

Faculdade de Zootécnia de Uberaba
Rua Dom Luiz Santana 115, 38100 Uberaba, MG
Tel: +55(34) 333-1188
Founded: 1975
Zoology.

Faculdade do Clube Naútico Mogiano
Rua Caec Diogo Oliver 758, 08750 Mogi das
Cruzes, SP
Tel: +55(11) 469-6613
Founded: 1972
Physical Education.

Faculdade Dom Bosco de Educação Física
Avenida 3 Sul, 702, 70310 Brasília, DF
Tel: +55(61) 223-2650
Founded: 1976
Physical Education.

**Faculdade Espírito Santense de
Administração**
Rua Anselmo Serrat 199, 29040 Vitória, ES
Tel: +55(27) 222-5344
Founded: 1976

**Faculdade Evangélica de Medicina do
Paraná**
Rua Princesa Isabel 1580, 80000 Curitibá, PR
Tel: +55(41) 223-2633
Founded: 1969
Medicine.

Faculdade Ibero-Americana de Letras e Ciências Humanas
Avenida Brigadeiro Luis Antonio 871, 01317 São Paulo, SP
Tel: +55(11) 370-071
Founded: 1971
Letters and Human Sciences.

Faculdade Integrada do Nordeste de Minas
Avenida Olecario Maciel 1136, 38600 Paracatu, MG
Tel: +55(61) 671-3668
Founded: 1987
Education; Social Sciences.

Faculdade Itu
Rua Joao Vicente 1215, 21331 Rio de Janeiro, RJ
Tel: +55(21) 390-8909
Founded: 1986

Faculdade Leonardo da Vinci
Avenida Irai 1718, 04082 São Paulo, SP
Tel: +55(11) 573-5544
Computer Sciences.

Faculdade Marcelo Tupinamba
Rua Vergueiro, 04010 São Paulo, SP
Tel: +55(12) 549-6899
Founded: 1974
Music.

Faculdade Maria Augusta Ribeiro Daher
Rua Santa Rosa 168, 12300 Jacarei, SP
Tel: +55(12) 351-4425
Founded: 1987
Administration.

Faculdade Mozarteum de São Paulo
Rua Nava dos Portugueses, 02462 São Paulo, SP
Tel: +55(11) 950-0788
Founded: 1973
Fine Arts.

Faculdade Niteroiense de Educação, Letras e Turismo
Rua Visconde de Rio Branco 123, 24020 Niterói, RJ
Tel: +55(21) 717-0513
Founded: 1975
Education; Letters; Tourism.

Faculdade Niteroiense de Formação de Professores
Rua Visconde do Rio Branco 123, 24020 Niterói, RJ
Tel: +55(21) 717-0513
Founded: 1972
Teacher Training.

Faculdade Niteroiense de Medecina Veterinaria
Rua Visconde do Rio Branco 123, 24030 Niteroi, RJ
Tel: +55(21) 717-0513
Founded: 1990
Veterinary Medicine.

Faculdade Olindense de Ciências Contabeis e Administrativas
Rua do Bonfim 37, 53000 Olinda, PE
Tel: +55(81) 429-2486
Founded: 1972
Accountancy; Administration.

Faculdade Olindense de Formação de Professores
Campus Universitario Funeso s/n Fragoso, 53000 Olinda, PE
Tel: +55(81) 429-0957
Founded: 1973
Teacher Training.

Faculdade para Executivos
Avenida Junqueira Aires, 59000 Natal, RN
Tel: +55(84) 217-5851
Founded: 1981
Executive Training.

Faculdade Paulista de Administração
Avenida Rudge 315, 01133 São Paulo, SP
Founded: 1988
Administration.

Faculdade Paulista de Ciências, Letras e Educação
Avenida Rudge 315, 01133 São Paulo, SP
Tel: +55(115) 425-888
Founded: 1971
Sciences; Letters; Education.

Faculdade Paulista de Serviço Social de São Caetano do Sul
Avenida Paraíso 600, 09500 São Caetano do Sul, SP
Tel: +55(11) 743-6422
Founded: 1972
Social Work.

Faculdade Paulista de Serviço Social
Rua Lopes Chaves 273, 01154 São Paulo, SP
Tel: +55(11) 660-246
Founded: 1940
Social Work.

Faculdade Paulistana de Ciências e Letras
Rua Madre Cabrini 38, 04020 São Paulo, SP
Tel: +55(11) 549-3033
Founded: 1972
Sciences; Letters.

Faculdade Pinheiro Guimaraes
Rua Silveira Martius 151, 22221 Rio de Janeiro, RJ
Tel: +55(21) 285-7995
Founded: 1968

Faculdade Pôrto-Alegrense de Ciências Contábeis e Administrativas
Avenida Mandel Elias 2001, 91300 Pôrto Alegre, RS
Tel: +55(512) 343-533
Founded: 1971
Accountancy; Administration.

Faculdade Pôrto-Alegrense de Educação, Ciências e Letras
Avenida Elias Mandel, 91300 Pôrto Alegre, RS
Tel: +55(512) 344-522
Founded: 1968
Education, Sciences and Letters.

Faculdade Regional de Medicina de São José do Rio Prêto
Avenida Brigadeiro Faria Lima 5416, 15090 São José do Rio Prêto, SP
Tel: +55(172) 325-733
Founded: 1968
Medicine.

Faculdade Renato Cozzolino
Avenida Automovel Club Km. 61/62, 25395 Magé, RJ
Tel: +55(21) 739-1940
Founded: 1988
Letters and Mathematics.

Faculdade Riopretense de Ciências e Letras
Rua Ipiranga 3460, 15100 São José do Rio Prêto, SP
Tel: +55(172) 321-655
Founded: 1972
Sciences and Letters.

Faculdade Riopretense de Communicação Social
Rua Eduardo Nielsen 960, 19030 São José do Rio Preto, SP
Tel: +55(17) 233-7910
Founded: 1990
Social Communication.

Faculdade Riopretense de Servico Social
Rua Eduardo Nielsen 960, 15030 São José de Boa Vista, SP
Tel: +55(17) 233-7910
Founded: 1990
Social Work.

Faculdade Rui Barbosa de Administração de Empressa
Rua Francisco Rosa 422, 48910 Salvador, BA
Tel: +55(71) 240-5056
Founded: 1990
Business Administration.

Faculdade Rui Barbosa de Tecnologia e Processamento de Dados
Rua Francisco Rosa 422, 49000 Salvador, BA
Tel: +55(71) 240-5056
Founded: 1990
Computer Sciences.

Faculdade Sagres de Ciências Contábeis e Atuariais
Rua Gabriel dos Santos 30, 07231 São Paulo
Accountancy; Actuarial Sciences.

Faculdade Salesiana de Educação Física
Rua Santa Rosa, 98900 Santa Rosa, RS
Tel: +55 512-1683
Founded: 1981
Physical Education.

Faculdade Salesiana de Filosofia, Ciências e Letras
Rua Dom Bosco 284, Caixa postal 29, 12600 Lorena, SP
Tel: +55(12) 552-2033
Founded: 1952
Philosophy; Sciences; Letters.

Faculdade Salesiana de Tecnologia
13100 Campinas, SP
Tel: +55(19) 241-2188
Founded: 1986
Technology.

Faculdade Salvador de Ciências Contábeis
Avenida Cardeal da Silva 132, 40220 Salvador, BA
Tel: +55(71) 235-2068
Founded: 1990
Accountancy.

Faculdade Salvador de Comunicação Social
Avenida Cardeal da Silva 132, 40220 Salvador, BA
Tel: +55(71) 235-2068
Founded: 1990
Social Communication.

Faculdade Salvador de Processamento de Dados
Avenida Cardeal da Silva 132, 40220 Salvador, BA
Tel: 55(71) 235-2068
Founded: 1979
Computer Sciences.

Faculdade São Camilo de Aministração Hospitalar
Rua Barao do Bananal 1111, 05021 São Paulo, SP
Tel: +55(11) 864-2199
Founded: 1985
Hospital Administration.

Faculdade Unificad para o Ensino das Ciências
Avenida Floriano Peixoto 296, 59020 Natal, RN
Tel: +55(84) 222-2314
Founded: 1981
Sciences.

Faculdade Versalhes de Pedagogia e Letras
Rua Cr. Murici 706, 80020 Curitiba, PR
Tel: +55(41) 225-1668
Founded: 1989
Education; Letters.

Faculdades da Zona Leste de São Paulo
Rua Cesario Galero 448, 03071 São Paulo, SP
Tel: +55(11) 941-3499
Founded: 1972
Law and Administration.

Faculdades de Barra Mansa
Rua Vereador P. de Carvalho 267, 27400 Barra
Mansa, RJ
Tel: +55(24) 322-0222
Founded: 1966
Law and Economics.

Faculdades Integradas Alcantara Machado
Praça Tres Coraçoes 300, 05608 São Paulo, SP
Tel: +55(11) 270-2433
Founded: 1972
Social Sciences.

Faculdades Integradas Anglo-Americano
Rua General Severiano 159, 22290 Rio de
Janeiro, RJ
Tel: +55(213) 258-173
Founded: 1977

Faculdades Integradas Augusto Motta
Avenida Paris 72, 21041 Rio de Janeiro, RJ
Tel: +55(21) 280-3636
Founded: 1974
Social Sciences.

Faculdades Integradas Bennett
Rua Marques de Abrantes 55, 22230 Rio de
Janeiro, RJ
Tel: +55(21) 245-8000
Founded: 1971
Law and Economics.

Faculdades Integradas Castelo Branco
Avenida Santa Cruz 1631 Realengo, 21710 Rio de
Janeiro, RJ
Tel: +55(21) 331-1207
Founded: 1973
Social Sciences.

Faculdades Integradas Católicas de Brasília
Areas Complementares, 72000 Taguatinga, DF
Tel: +55(61) 356-2000
Founded: 1974
Philosophy; Social Sciences.

Faculdades Integradas da Upis
SEP Sul EQ 712/912 Modulo A 712, 70361
Brasília, DF
Tel: +55(61) 242-7718
Founded: 1973
Sciences.

Faculdades Integrades de Barra do Garcas
Rua Walapilis 33, 78600 Barra do Carcas, MT
Tel: +55(65) 446-1601
Founded: 1989
Administration; Education.

Faculdades Integradas de Cassilandia
Rua Martiniano José de Moura 470, 79540
Cassilándia, MS
Tel: +55(67) 596-1413
Founded: 1988
Education.

Faculdades Integradas de Cruzeiro
Rua Dom Bosco 35 Centro, 12700 Cruzeiro, SP
Tel: +55(125) 441-603
Founded: 1972
Administration.

Faculdades Integrades de Cuiaba
Avenida Beira Rio 397, 78090 Cuiaba, MT
Tel: +55(65) 321-4488
Founded: 1988
Health Sciences; Law.

Faculdades Integradas de Diamantino
Rodovia Riberto Campos Km. 1, 78400
Diamantina, MT
Tel: +55(65) 736-1176
Founded: 1989
Administration.

Faculdades Integradas de Dourados
Rua Balbima de Matos 2121, 79800 Dourados, MS
Tel: +55(67) 421-3121
Founded: 1976
Law; Administration.

Faculdades Integradas de Fatima do Sul
Rua Tenente Antonio Joao 1410, 79700 Fatima do
Sul, MS
Tel: +55(67) 467-1307
Founded: 1980
Accountancy.

Faculdades Integradas de Guarulhos
Rua Ir. Soion Fernandes 155, 07070 Guarulhos,
SP
Tel: +55(11) 209-3233
Founded: 1971
Accountancy.

Faculdades Integradas de Jacarepagua
Laceira da Freguesia 196, 22760 Rio de Janeiro,
RJ
Tel: +55(21) 392-6646
Founded: 1976
Computer Sciences.

Faculdades Integradas de Jaciara
Rua Juruce 1231, 78820 Jaciara, MT
Tel: +55(65) 461-1377
Founded: 1989
Accountancy.

Faculdades Integradas de Maringa
Avenida Cuedner 1610, 87060 Maringa, PR
Tel: +55(442) 236-360
Founded: 1990

Faculdades Integradas de Navirai
Rua Laurentino Pires de Arruda 28, 79950
Navirai, MS
Tel: +55(67) 461-2089
Founded: 1988
Geography.

Faculdades Integradas de Ourinhos
Rua Arlindo Luz 800, 19900 Ourinhos, SP
Tel: +55(14) 322-2033
Founded: 1970
Business Administration.

Faculdades Integradas de Santa Cruz do Sul
Rua Cel. Oscar J. Jost 1551, 96800 Santa Cruz do Sul, RS
Tel: +55(51) 713-1011
Founded: 1964
Accountancy; Law.

Faculdades Integradas de São Gonçalo
Rua Lambari 10 Trindade, 24400 São Gonçalo, RJ
Tel: +55(21) 701-0505
Founded: 1976
Sciences.

Faculdades Integradas de São José dos Campos
Praça Candido Dias Castejon, 12200 São José dos Campos, SP
Tel: +55(123) 222-355

Faculdades Integradas de Vilhena
Rua Joscelino Kubitschek 245, 78950 Vilhena, RO
Tel: +55(69) 321-2822
Founded: 1989

Faculdades Integradas do Instituto Ritter dos Reis
Rua Santos Dumont 888, 92120 Canoas, RS
Tel: +55(51) 272-3187
Founded: 1971

Faculdades Integradas do Triangulo
Rua Barau de Camarcos 695, 38400 Uberlandia, MG
Tel: +55(34) 236-4066
Founded: 1972
Health Sciences; Sciences; Social Sciences.

Faculdades Integradas Hebraico Brasileira Renascença
Rua Prates 790, 01121 São Paulo, SP
Tel: +55(11) 2286450
Founded: 1973

Faculdades Integradas Helio Alonso
Rua Muniz Barreto 51, 22251 Rio de Janeiro, RJ
Tel: +55(21) 551-5448
Founded: 1972
Tourism; Public Relations.

Faculdades Integradas Ibirapuera
Avenida Irai, 04082 São Paulo, SP
Tel: +55(11) 533-2022
Founded: 1971
Sciences.

Faculdades Integradas Moacyr Sreder Bastos
Rua Engenheiro Trindade 229, 23000 Rio de Janeiro, RJ
Tel: +55(21) 394-1787
Founded: 1971
Economics; Administration.

Faculdades Integradas Ploanalto Central
Rua Americano do Brasil 156, 77200 Luziania, GO
Tel: +55(61) 621-3144
Founded: 1990
Law and Administration.

Faculdades Integradas Riopretense
Rua Yvette Gabriel Atique 45, 15025 São José do Rio Preto, SP
Tel: +55(172) 325-355
Founded: 1971
Business Administration; Law.

Faculdades Integradas Rui Barbosa
Rua Rodrigues Alves 932 Centro, 16900 Adradina, SP
Tel: +55(187) 223-492
Founded: 1966
Social Sciences and Economics.

Faculdades Integradas Santana
Rua Voluntarios do Patria 257, 02011 São Paulo, SP
Tel: +55(11) 298-8000
Founded: 1970
Economics and Administration.

Faculdades Intgerades Senador Flaquer Santo Andre
Rua Senador Flaquer 456, 09010 Santo Andre, SP
Tel: +55(11) 449-8899
Founded: 1969
Administration.

Faculdades Integradas Silva e Souza
Rua Uranos 733 Ramos, 21060 Rio de Janeiro, RJ
Tel: +55(21) 260-6422
Founded: 1981
Architecture.

Faculdades Integradas Teresa D'Avila
Avenida Peixoto de Castro, 12600 Lorena, SP
Tel: +55(125) 522-888
Founded: 1968
Home Economics; Librarian Studies.

Faculdades Integradas Teresa D'Avila
Rua Siqueira Campos 483, 09015 Santo André, P
Tel: +55(11) 449-7477
Founded: 1969

Faculdades Integradas Tiradentes
Rua Lagarto 264, 49000 Aracajú, SP
Tel: +55(79) 221-1778
Founded: 1972
Economics and Administrative Sciences; Law; Social Sciences.

Faculdades Integradas Vale do Rio Doce
Rua Moreira Sales 695, 35730 Governador Valadales, MG
Tel: +55(332) 213-182
Founded: 1968

Faculdades Integradas Veiga de Almeida
Rua Ibituruna 108, 20771 Rio de Janeiro, RJ
Tel: +55(21) 264-6172
Founded: 1972
Letters and Human Sciences.

Faculdades Matogrissen de Ciências Contábeis e Administrativas Cuiaba
Rua Guilherme Hahn 43, 78000 Cuiabá, MT
Tel: +55(65) 321-9794
Founded: 1990
Accountancy.

Faculdades Metodistas Integradas Izabela Hendrix
Rua Bahia 2020, 30060 Belo Horizonte, MG
Tel: +55(31) 344-0977
Founded: 1936
Sciences; Education; Social Sciences.

Faculdades Metropolitanas Unidas
Rua Tagua 150, 01508 São Paulo, SP
Tel: +55(11) 270-2433
Telex: 21-930
Founded: 1968

Faculdades Oswaldo Cruz
Rua Brigadeiro Galvao 540, Barra Funda, São Paulo, SP
Tel: +55(11) 825-4266
Founded: 1966
Sciences.

Faculdades Reunidas Nuño Lisboa
Avenida Ministro Edgard Romero 807, 21361 Rio de Janeiro, RJ
Tel: +55(21) 391-1743
Founded: 1971
Mathematics and Engineering.

Faculdades Santo Amaro
Rua Prof. Eneas de Siqueira Neto 340, Campus Universitario, 04829 Sao Paulo, SP
Tel: +55(11) 520-9611
Founded: 1970
Tourism.

Faculdades São Judas Tadeu
Rua Clarimundo de Melo 79, 20740 Rio de Janeiro, SP
Tel: +55(21) 289-8749
Founded: 1974
Education.

Faculdades São Marcos
Avenida Nazare 900, 04262 São Paulo, SP
Tel: +55(11) 274-5711
Founded: 1972
Sciences, Philosophy and Letters; Administration.

Faculdades Unidas Católicas de Mato Grosso
Avenida Mato Grosso, 79019 Campo Grande, MG
Fax: +55(67) 382-4261
Telex: 67-2575
Founded: 1961
Economics and Accounting; Law.

Faculdades Unidas do Centro Norte
Rua Projetada
Tel: +55(67) 292-1314
Founded: 1989
Administration and Education.

Faculdades Unidas Grande Rio
Rua Marques de Herval 1160, 25000 Duque de Caxia, RJ
Tel: +55(21) 771-4251
Founded: 1972
Health Sciences.

Federaçao das Escolas Superiores de Ilheus e Itabuna
Rodovia Ilheus-Itabuna Km. 16, 45660 Ilheus, BA
Tel: +55(73) 231-8118
Founded: 1974
Economics.

Federação das Faculdades, Ciências e Letras Jandaia do Sul
Rua P. Joao Barbieri s/n, 86000 Jandaia do Sul, PR
Tel: +55(43) 432-1113
Founded: 1973

Federação das Faculdades Isoladas de Araraquara
Rua Voluntarios da Patria 1309 Centro, 14800 Araraquara, SP
Tel: +55(16) 222-0499
Founded: 1972
Economics.

Federação de Escolas Faculdades Integradas Simosen
Rua Ibitiuva 151, 21710 Rio de Janeiro, RJ
Tel: +55(21) 331-3022
Founded: 1971
Administration and Economics.

Federação de Escolas Superiores do ABC
Rua do Sacramento 230, 09735 São Bernardo do Campo, SP
Tel: +55(11) 457-3733
Founded: 1971
Administration.

Federação de Estabelecimentos de Ensino Superior em Novo Hamburgo
Rua Maurício Cardoso 510, 93510 Novo
Hamburgo, RS
Tel: +55(512) 933-144
Founded: 1970
Health Sciences.

Instituto de Ciências Exactas de Americana
Rua Dom Bosco 100, 13470 Americano, SP
Tel: +55(194) 603-367
Founded: 1984
Engineering.

Instituto de Ciências Exactas
Avenida 45 SQD Quadra 910, 32 Bloco D, 70390
Brasília, DF
Tel: +55(61) 243-8011
Founded: 1989
Exact Sciences.

Instituto de Ciências Sociais
SEPS 704, 904 704 Blatotes, 70390 Brasília, DF
Tel: +55(61) 321-3838
Founded: 1968
Social Sciences.

Instituto de Ciências Sociais de Americana
Rua Dom Bosco 100, 13470 Americana, SP
Tel: +55(194) 603-367
Founded: 1972
Social Sciences.

Instituto de Ciências Sociais do Paraná
Rua General Carneiro 216, 80000 Curitiba, PR
Tel: +55(41) 264-3311
Founded: 1969
Social Sciences.

Instituto de Ciências Sociais e Aplicadas
Avenida V-5 Quadra 910, SGA SUL 32, Bloco D,
70390 Brasilía, DF
Tel: +55(61) 243-8011
Founded: 1981
Social Sciences.

Instituto de Ciências Sociais e Aplicadas de Rondonopolis
Avenida Ari Coelho 829, 78700 Rondonopolis, MT
Tel: +55(65) 421-1340
Founded: 1989
Social and Applied Sciences.

Instituto de Ensino Superior e Pesquisa
Campus Universitário, 35500 Divinopolis, MG
Tel: +55(37) 221-2799
Founded: 1966
Social Sciences.

Instituto de Ensino Superior Santo André
Rua Delfim Moreira 40 Centro, 09000 Santo
André, SP
Tel: +55(11) 449-9962
Founded: 1972
Accountancy; Computer Sciences.

Instituto de Psicologia
BR 230 Km. 22 Blocos E/F, 58000 João Pessoa,
PB
Tel: +55(83) 231-1418
Founded: 1972
Psychology.

Instituto Metódista Bennet
Rua Marques de Abrantes 55, Massengo, 22230
Rio de Janeiro, RJ
Tel: +55(21) 245-8000

Instituto Nacional de Telecomunicaçães
Avenida João de Camargo 510, 37540 Santa Rita
do Sapucai, MG
Tel: +55(35) 631-1788
Founded: 1965
Telecommunications.

Instituto Paraibanas de Educação
Campus do Ipe BR/230 Km. 22, Agua Feia, 58065
João Pessoa, PB
Tel: +55(83) 231-1418
Fax: +55(83) 231-1130
Law; Social Sciences.

Instituto Santareno de Ensino Superior
Avenida Mendonca Furtado 1050, 68100
Santarem, PA
Tel: +55(91) 522-5088
Founded: 1985
Administration.

Instituto Superior de Ciências Aplicadas
Via 147 Limeira Piracicaba, 13480 Limeira, SP
Tel: +55(19) 441-5367
Founded: 1970
Administration.

Instituto Superior de Ciências e Artes Humanas de Lavras
Rua Padre José Poggel 506, 37200 Lavras, MG
Tel: +55(35) 821-2230
Founded: 1968
Sciences.

Instituto Superior de Ensino e Pesquisa de Ituiutaba
Avenida Rio Grande, Rua Bahia, 38300 Ituiutaba,
MG
Tel: +55(34) 261-3344
Founded: 1970
Agriculture; Sciences; Engineering.

Instituto Superior de Estudos Sociais Clovis Bevilacqua
Avenida Lusitania 169, 21011 Rio de Janeiro, RJ
Tel: +55(21) 260-5552
Founded: 1972
Social Sciences.

Instituto Superior de Hotelaria e Turismo
Rua São Vicente 245, 01222 São Paulo, SP
Tel: +55(11) 366-569
Telex: 11-25732
Founded: 1989
Tourism.

Instituto Unificado de Ensino Superior Objetivo
Avenida Emilia Tavares 1993, 74610 Goiania, GO
Tel: +55(62) 285-2233
Founded: 1988
Pharmacy; Computer Sciences.

Uniao das Faculdades Francanas
Anel Viario, 14400 Franca, SP
Tel: +55(16) 722-1444
Founded: 1972
Architecture; Sciences.

Unidas Escolares de Instituição Moura Lacerda
Rua Padre Euclides 995, Campos Elisios, 214085
Ribeirao Prêto, SP
Tel: +55(16) 636-1010
Founded: 1931
Economic Sciences; Philosophy, Letters and Sciences.

Unidas Integradas de Ensino Superior do Vale do Jacui
Rua Major Ouriques 2284, 96500 Cachoeira do Sul, RS
Tel: +55(51) 722-4318
Founded: 1970
Administration.

NATIONAL ACADEMIC BODIES

Ministry of Education and Sports
[Ministerio de Educação e dos Desporto]
Esplanade dos Ministerios-Bloc'L', Brasília, DF
Tel: +55(61) 225-6515
Fax: +55(61) 224-3618
Minister: Murilio de Avellar Hingel

Council of Brazilian University Rectors
[Conselho de Reitores das Universidades Brasileiras (CRUB)]
SEP/Norte Quadra-516 Lote-09, 70770 Brasília
Tel: +55(61) 272-2960
Fax: +55(61) 274-4621
Telex: (61)1972
President: Eduardo José Pereira Coelho
Secretary-General: Maria Helena Alves García
Founded: 1966

Coordination Office for the Development of Higher Education Personnel
[Coordenação do Aperfeiçoamento de Pessoal de Nivel Superior (CAPES)]
Ministério de Educação, Anexo 1, 70070 Brasília, DF
Tel: +55(61) 321-3200
Telex: 2018
Founded: 1951

Brazilian Institute for Education, Science and Culture (Unesco)
[Instituto Brasileiro de Educação, Ciências e Cultura (Unesco)]
Palácio Itamarati, 196 Avenida Marechal Floriano, 20080 Rio de Janeiro, RJ
Tel: +55(21) 516-2458
Fax: +55(21) 55-6897
Telex: 2121761 ibecc rio de Janeiro
Chairman: José Pelucio Ferreira
Executive Secretary: Joaquim Caetano Gentil Netto

BRUNEI DARUSSALAM

UNIVERSITIES

University of Brunei Darussalam
Gadong, Bandar Seri Begawan 3186
Tel: +673(2) 427-001
Fax: +673(2) 427-003
Telex: unibrun bu 2725
Cable: universiti, brunei
Vice-Chancellor: Dato Abu Bakar bin Haji Apong (1991-)
Registrar and Secretary: Janin Erih
Founded: 1985
F: Arts and Social Sciences; Education; Management and Administration Studies; Sciences; Islamic Studies.
A: Brunei Studies.

NATIONAL ACADEMIC BODIES

Ministry of Education
Bandar Seri Begawan 1170
Tel: +673(2) 44233
Fax: +673(2) 40250
Cable: miedu brunei

BULGARIA

UNIVERSITIES AND OTHER UNIVERSITY INSTITUTIONS

American University in Bulgaria
[Amerikanski Universitet]
2700 Blagoevgrad
Tel: +359(73) 20968
Fax: +359(73) 20603
E-Mail: watkins@aubg.bg
President: Julia M. Watkins (1993-)
Dean (Academic Affairs): Hugh Fullerton
Founded: 1991
Applied Economics; Business Administration; Computer Science; English; History; Journalism - Mass Communication; Political Science - International Relations.

Bulgarian State Conservatory

[Balgarska Darzhavna Conservatoria]
11 Klement Gotvald Blvd., 1505 Sofia
Tel: +359(2) 442-079
Fax: +359(2) 463-677
Founded: 1921
Music.

Burgas Free University

[Burgas Svobodan Universitet]
101 Alexandrovska Str., 8000 Burgas
Tel: +359(56) 22152
Fax: +359(56) 29567
Rector: Evgeny Viktorov Golovinsky (1993-94)
Vice-Rector: Alexander Vahram Kizirian
Founded: 1991
*F: Law; Business; Agronomy; Education;
Applied Mathematics and Informatics; Technical
(English-Bulgarian Technical C.).
Ce: Humanitarian.*

EUROPEAN COLLEGE OF BUSINESS AND TECHNOLOGY
19 Hristo Botev Str., Veliko Tarnovo
Tel: +359(62) 24028
Fax: +359(62) 23958
Technology.

Higher Agricultural Institute

[Vissh Selskostopanski Institut]
12 D. Mendleev Str., 4000 Plovdiv
Tel: +359(32) 23498
Fax: +359(32) 233-157
Telex: 04405
Rector: Dimitar Braykov (1991-)
Executive Director: Petar Torozov
International Relations: Vassil Garnevski
Founded: 1945
*F: Agronomy; Horticulture; Plant Protection;
Tropical and Subtropical Agriculture;
Agrobusiness.
C: Agriculture.*

Higher Economic Institute

[Vissh Ikonomiceski Institut]
Studentski grad 'hristo Botev', 1100 Sofia
Tel: +359(2) 629-313
Fax: +359(2) 689-029
Telex: 22040
Founded: 1920
Economics.

Higher Forest-Technical Institute

[Vissh Lesotehniceski Institut]
10 Kliment Ohridski Str., 1156 Sofia
Tel: +359(2) 622-830
Fax: +359(2) 680-335
Founded: 1925
Forestry.

Higher Financial-Economic Institute 'D.D. Tsenov'

[Vissh Finansovo-Stopanski Institut 'D.D. Tsenov']
2 Emil Chakarov Str., 5250 Svishtov
Tel: +359(631) 25407
Fax: +359(631) 23472
Telex: 66684
Rector: Atanas Damyanov (1991-95)
Vice-Rector: Ivan Spiridonov
International Relations: Vice-Rector, Nicola Yankov
Founded: 1936
*F: Finance; Accountancy; Business Management
and Marketing; Business (Lovech); Corporate
Economics; Free.
S: Business Management.
C: Business (Lovech, Lom).*

Higher Institute of Animal Production and Veterinary Medicine

[Vissh Institut po Zootehnika i Veterinarna Meditsina]
Studentsko gradche, 6000 Stara Zagora
Tel: +359(42) 39024
Fax: +359(42) 34102
Cable: 88465
Rector: Simeon Simeonov (1993-)
International Relations: Svetoslav Tzolov
Founded: 1922
Animal Production and Veterinary Medicine.

Higher Institute of Architecture and Construction

[Vissh Institut po arkitectura i stoitelstvo]
1 Hristo Smirnenski Blvd., 1421 Sofia
Tel: +359(2) 666-770
Fax: +359(2) 656-809
Telex: 23574
Founded: 1942
Architecture and Construction.

Higher Institute of Chemical Engineering

[Vissh Himiko-Tehnologiceski Institut]
8 Kliment Ohridski Str., 1156 Sofia
Tel: +359(2) 623-111
Fax: +359(2) 685-488
Founded: 1945
Chemical Engineering.

Higher Institute of Chemical Technology 'A. Zlatarov'

[Vissh Himiko Tvehnologiceski Institut 'Prof. Dr. A. Zlatarov']
Prof. Jakimov Str., 8010 Bourgas
Tel: +359(56) 660-119
Fax: +359(56) 686-141
Telex: 83689
Rector: Nikolay Ralev (1993-94)
Director: Stoyko Tankov
International Relations: Vice-Rector, Tanev
Founded: 1963
*F: Organic Chemical Technology; Inorganic
Chemical Technology; Management; Pedagogy;
Free.*

Higher Institute of Drama 'Krastyu Sarafov'
[Vissh Institut za Teatralno Izkustvo 'Krastyu Sarafov']
108-A Rakovsky Str., 1000 Sofia
Tel: +359(2) 879-862
Fax: +359(2) 897-389
Rector: Hristo Roukov (1994-98)
Executive Director: Ivan Alexandrov
International Relations: Snejina Tankovska
Founded: 1948
Theatre; Cinema.

Higher Institute of Education 'Neophit Rilski'
[Vissh Pedagogiceski Institut 'Neophit Rilski']
66 Alexi Velichkov Str., 2700 Blagoevgrad
Tel: +359(73) 20629
Fax: +359(73) 29325
Founded: 1983
Education.

Higher Institute for Fine and Applied Arts 'Nikolai Pavlovich'
[Vissh Institut za Isobrazitelni Izkustvo 'Nikolai Pavlovich']
1 Sipka Str., 1000 Sofia
Tel: +359(2) 881-702
Fax: +359(2) 873-328
Rector: Ognyan Avramov Shoshev (1994-97)
Assistent Rector: Makedonka Yanakieva Rudolf
International Relations: Deputy Rector, Nikolai Georgiev Alexiev
Founded: 1896
F: Fine Arts; Applied Arts.

Higher Institute of Food, Wine and Tobacco Industries
[Vissh Institut po Hranitelna i Vkusova Promislenost]
26 Lenin Blvd., 4000 Plovdiv
Tel: +359(32) 441-811
Fax: +359(32) 440-102
Founded: 1948
Food, Wine and Tobacco Industries.

Higher Institute of Medicine
[Vissh Meditsinski Institut]
1 Kliment Ohridski Str., 5800 Pleven
Tel: +359(64) 29105
Fax: +359(64) 29153
Telex: 34590
Rector: Kuncho Ignatov (1991-)
Executive Director: Ilia Petrov
International Relations: Alexander Alexiev
Founded: 1974
Medicine.

Higher Institute of Medicine 'Iv.P. Pavlov'
[Vissh Medicinski Institut 'Iv.P. Pavlov']
15A Vassil Aprilov Str., 4000 Plovdiv
Tel: +359(32) 444-000
Fax: +359(32) 442-194
Telex: 044440
Founded: 1945
Medicine.

Higher Institute of Medicine
[Vissh Medicinski Institut]
15 Dimitar Nestorov Blvd., 1431 Sofia
Tel: +359(2) 517-282
Founded: 1918
Medicine.

Higher Institute of Medicine
[Vissh Medicinski Institut]
11 Armeiska Str., 6000 Stara Zagora
Tel: +359(42) 48064
Fax: +359(42) 47000
Founded: 1982
Medicine.

Higher Institute of Medicine
[Vissh Meditsinski Institut]
55 Marin Drinov Str., 9010 Varna
Tel: +359(52) 225-022
Fax: +359(52) 222-584
Telex: 77464 med fac bg
Rector: Dimitar Kamburov (1990-)
Executive Director: Hristo Petrov
Founded: 1961
F: Health Management.
S: Medicine.

Higher Institute of National Economy
[Vissh Institut za Narodno Stopanstvo]
77 Kniaz Borisi Blvd., 9002 Varna
Tel: +359(52) 213-511
Fax: +359(52) 235-680
Telex: 77382
Rector: Kaliyu Donev
Executive Director: Statko Ivanov
International Relations: Dimitar Radilov
Founded: 1920
F: Business Administration; World Economy; Accountancy and Finance; Management; Law.

Higher Institute of Sports
[Vissh Institut za Fiziceska Kultura]
Gurguliat Str., 1000 Sofia
Tel: 359(2) 879-620
Fax: +359(2) 883-064
Founded: 1942
Physical Education and Sports.

Higher Machine-Electrotechnical Institute
[Vissh Massinno-elektrotehniceski Institut]
4 Hadji Dimitar Str., 5300 Gabrovo
Tel: +359(66) 20511
Fax: +359(66) 24856
Founded: 1964
Machine-Electrotechnical Engineering.

Higher Machine-Electrotechnical Institute
[Vissh Massinno-Elektrotehniceski Institut]
Obshtina Studentska, 1756 Sofia
Tel: +359(2) 877-870
Fax: +359(2) 683-215
Telex: 22575
Founded: 1945
Machine-Electrotechnical Engineering.

PLOVDIV BRANCH
[FILIAL PLOVDIV]
61 Sankt Peterburg Blvd., 4000 Plovdiv
Tel: +359(32) 262-197
Fax: +359(32) 233-256
Telex: 22575
Founded: 1945
Machine-Electrotechnical Engineering.

Higher Machine-Electrotechnical Institute
[Vissh Mashinno-Elektrotehniceski Institut, Varna]
Studentska Str., 9010 Varna
Tel: +359(52) 881-811
Fax: +359(52) 871-910
E-Mail: recvmi@ac.tu-varna.bg
Telex: 77401 mei vn
Rector: Assen Nedev
Registrar: Hristo Patev
Founded: 1962
*F: Machine Technologies; Mechanical
Engineering; Shipbuilding; Electrical Engineering;
Electronics; Computer Science and Automatics;
Ecology and Environmental Protection; Law.*

Higher Pedagogical Institute of Music
[Vissh Musikalno-Pedagogicheski Institut]
2 Samodumov Str., 4025 Plovdiv
Tel: +359(32) 228-311
Fax: +359(32) 231-668
Rector: Ivan Spassov
Secretary-General: Nicola Lautliev
International Relations: Ivan Spassov
Founded: 1971
Music.

Higher Pedagogical Institute 'Konstantin Preslavsky'
[Vissh Pedagogicheski Institut 'Konstantin
Preslavski']
9700 Shoumen
Tel: +359(54) 63151
Fax: +359(54) 63171
E-Mail: rector@uni-shoumen.bg
Telex: 73421
Rector: Vladimir Shkodrov (1991-94)
Administrative Director: Mihail Mihailov
International Relations: Valentina Stoeva
Founded: 1971
*F: Bulgarian Philology, History and Theology;
Russian Philology; Modern Languages;
Mathematics and Computer Science; Physics;
Chemistry; Chemistry; Biology; Preschool and
Special Education; Primary Education; Arts
Education.
S: Open.
Ce: Postgraduate Teacher Training.
I: Higher Teaching Qualification (Varna).*

Higher Technical School 'A. Kanchev'-Rousse
[Vissh Tehnitchesko Uchilishte 'Angel
Kanchev'-Rousse]
8 Studentska Str., 7017 Rousse
Tel: +359(82) 451-092
Fax: +359(82) 451-092
Telex: 62462
Rector: Boris Tomov (1993-)
Principal Secretary: Valery Guegov
International Relations: Todorka Todorova
Founded: 1954
*F: Mechnical and Manufacturing Engineering;
Agricultural Machinery; Autotransport; Electrical
and Electronic Engineering; Free-Access;
Business and Management; Law.
Ce: Mathematics.*

Institute of Foreign Students
[Institut za Chzhdestranni Studenti]
27 Kosta Lultchev Str., 1111 Sofia
Tel: +359(2) 723-481
Fax: +359(2) 723-877
Rector: Georgi D. Neykov
Studies for Foreign Students.

Plovdiv University
[Plovdivski universitet 'Paissii Hilendarski']
24 Tsar Assen Str., 4000 Plovdiv
Tel: +359(32) 225-385
Fax: +359(32) 238-607
Telex: 44251
Rector: Nikola Petkov Balabanov (1989-93)
Administration Officer: Jordan Ganchev Bakalov
Founded: 1961, 1972
*F: Chemistry; Biology; Mathematics; Physics;
Philology and Education; Public Professions.*

Sofia University 'St. Kliment Ohridski'
[Sofiiski universitet 'Sv. Kliment Ohridski']
15 Tzar Osvoboditel Blv., 1000, ofia
Tel: +359(2) 801-176
Fax: +359(1) 463-589
Telex: 23296
Rector: Ivan Lalov
Founded: 1888, 1904, 1944
*F: Philosophy; History; Slavonic Philology;
Western Philology; Mathematics and Theoretical
Mechanics; Physics; Chemistry; Biology; Geology
and Geography; Law; Journalism; Social
Professions.*

*University of Mining and Geology
Dărvénitza, Sofia 1156
Tel: +359(2) 62-581
Fax: +359(2) 62-1042
Rector: Tsvetan Tsekov
*F: Geological Prospecting; Mining
Electromechanics; Mining Technology;
Humanities; European.*

*Veliko Tarnovo University
[Veliko Tarnovski Universitet]
2 Teodosi Tarnovski Str., 5003 Veliko Tarnovo
Tel: +359(62) 20070
Fax: +359(62) 28023
Telex: 66769
Rector: Vladimir Popov (1991-95)
University Manager: Oleg Bozanov
International Relations: Vice-Rector, Nikolay Kolev
Founded: 1962, 1971
F: History; Philology; Fine Arts; Education; Law; Theology; Mathematics and Computer Science; Public Health; Management.

NATIONAL ACADEMIC BODIES

Ministry of Science and Education
[Ministerstvo na naukata i obrazovanieto]
blvd. Stamboliiski 18, 1000 Sofia
Tel: +359(2) 84-81
Fax: +359(2) 871-289
Telex: 23255
International Relations: Jordan Stoychkov

Legalization Commission
[Legalizatzionna Komisia]
blvd. Maria Louisa 22, Sofia
Tel: +359(2) 83-861
Telex: 23255
President: Zlati Zlatanov (1949-)

Higher Attestation Commission
[Vissha Atestatzionna Komisia]
Bulgaria blvd. 1, 1463 Sofia
Tel: +359(2) 51-501

National Commission of the Republic of Bulgaria for Unesco
[Natzionalna Komisia za Unesco]
blvd. Al. Jendov 2, 1113 Sofia
Tel: +359(2) 722-691
Fax: +359(2) 736-289
Cable: bulunesco sofia
President: Todor Tchurov, Deputy Minister of Foreign Affairs
Secretary-General: Hristo Georgiev

BURKINA FASO

UNIVERSITIES

*University of Ougadougou
[Université de Ouagadougou]
03 B.P. 7021, Ouagadougou
Tel: +226 30-70-64
Fax: +226 30-72-42
Recteur: Alfred S. Traore (1990-)
Secrétaire général: Pascal Toé
Founded: 1965, 1969, 1974

F: Languages, Letters, Arts, and Human and Social Sciences (FLASHS); Sciences and Techniques (FAST); Law and Political Sciences (FDSP); Economics and Management (FASEG); Health Sciences (FSS); Sciences of Education (INSE).
I: Rural Development; Technology.
S: Computer Sciences (ESI).
Ce: Economics and Social Research.

HIGHER INSTITUTE OF LANGUAGES, LETTERS AND ARTS
[INSTITUT SUPÉRIEUR DES LANGUES, DES LETTRES ET DES ARTS]
Ouagadougou
Tel: 30-73-18
Founded: 1965
Languages, Letters and Arts.

INSTITUTE OF CHEMISTRY
[INSTITUT DE CHIMIE]
Ouagadougou
Tel: +226 30-88-52
Founded: 1985
Chemistry.

INSTITUTE OF EDUCATION
[INSTITUT DES SCIENCES DE L'EDUCATION]
Ouagadougou
Tel: +226 33-34-62
Founded: 1985
Education.

INSTITUTE OF HUMAN AND SOCIAL SCIENCES
[INSTITUT DES SCIENCES HUMAINES ET SOCIALES]
Ouagagougou
Tel: +221 30-73-18
Founded: 1965
Human and Social Sciences.

INSTITUTE OF MATHEMATICS AND PHYSICS
[INSTITUT DE MATHÉMATIQUES ET DE PHYSIQUE]
Ouagadougou
Tel: +226 33-20-41
Founded: 1975
Mathematics and Physics.

INSTITUTE OF NATURE SCIENCES
[INSTITUT DES SCIENCES DE LA NATURE]
Ouagadougou
Tel: +226 30-70-20
Founded: 1980
Nature Sciences.

INSTITUTE OF RURAL DEVELOPMENT
[INSTITUT DE DÉVELOPPEMENT RURAL]
Ouagadougou
Tel: +226 30-71-59
Founded: 1973
Rural Development.

SCHOOL OF ECONOMICS
[ECOLE SUPÉRIEURE DES SCIENCES ÉCONOMIQUES]
Ouagadougou
Tel: +221 30-73-69
Founded: 1975
Economics.

SCHOOL OF HEALTH SCIENCES
[ECOLE SUPÉRIEURE DES SCIENCES DE LA SANTÉ]
Ouagadougou
Tel: +226 30-75-43
Founded: 1980
Health Sciences.

SCHOOL OF LAW
[ECOLE SUPÉRIEURE DE DROIT]
Ouagadougou
Tel: +226 33-23-86
Founded: 1975
Law.

UNIVERSITY INSTITUTE OF TECHNOLOGY
[INSTITUT UNIVERSITAIRE DE TECHNOLOGIE]
Ouagadougou
Tel: +226 33-23-49
Founded: 1970
Technology.

OTHER INSTITUTIONS

Ecole nationale d'Administration et de Magistrature
B.P. 7013, Ouagadougou
Tel: +226 30-66-09
Administration and Magistracy.

Ecole inter-Etats d'Ingénieurs de l'Equipement rural
B.P. 2023, Ouagadougou
Rural Engineering.

Ecole inter-Etats des Techniciens supérieurs de l'Hydraulique et de l'Equipment rural
B.P. 594, Kamboinse-Ouagadougou
Hydrology and Rural Engineering.

Institut national des Sports
B.P. 7035, Ouagadougou
Physical Education and Sports.

Institut pédagogique
B.P. 7043, Ouagadougou
Founded: 1965
Teacher Training.

NATIONAL ACADEMIC BODIES

Ministry of Secondary and Higher Education and Scientific Research
[Ministère des Enseignements secondaire, supérieur et la Recherche scientifique]
B.P 7046, Ouagadougou
Tel: +226 30-77-56
Ministre: Mélégué Maurice Traore

National Commission for the Equivalence of Diplomas
[Commission nationale des Equivalences, des Titres et des Diplômes]
B.P. 7021, Ouagadougou
Tel: +226 30-24-62

Burkina Faso National Commission for Unesco
[Commission nationale burkinabé pour l'Unesco]
Boîte postale 7046, Ouagadougou 03
Tel: +226 30-72-15
Fax: +226 31-56-14
Telex: 5555 secgouv
Président: Mélégué Maurice Traore, Ministre d'Education
Secrétaire général: Moussa Ernest Ouedraogo

BURUNDI

UNIVERSITIES

*University of Burundi
[Université du Burundi]
B.P. 1550, Bujumbura
Tel: +257 222059
Fax: +257 223288
Telex: 5161
Recteur: Pascal-Firmin Ndimira
Founded: 1960, 1964, 1977
Law; Letters and Human Sciences; Sciences; Agronomical Sciences; Psychology and Sciences of Education; Medicine; Applied Sciences; Economical and Administrative Sciences.
I: Applied Pedagogy; Physical Education and Sports; Technical Studies (Higher); Agriculture (Higher); Commerce (Higher).

NATIONAL ACADEMIC BODIES

Ministry of Higher Education and Research
[Ministère de l'Enseignement supérieur et de la Recherche scientifique]
B.P. 1990, Bujumbura
Tel: +257 228477
Telex: 5202.mesrs bdi
Directeur général: Evariste Nzeyimana

Burundi National Commission for Unesco
[Commission nationale du Burundi pour l'Unesco]
Ministère de l'Enseignement supérieur, et de la Recherche scientifique, B.P. 1990
Tel: +257 224517
Fax: +257 228477
Telex: 5202.mesrs bdi
Directeur: Thomas Ndikumana

CAMBODIA

UNIVERSITIES

University of Fine Arts Phnôm Penh
[Université des Beaux-Arts]
Boulevard U.R.S.S., Phnôm Penh
Tel: +855(2) 3125
Founded: 1965
*F: Choreography; Plastic Arts; Music;
Archaeology; Architecture and Town Planning.*

University of Phnôm Penh
[Sakâl Vityalay Phnôm Penh]
133 Moha Vithei Preah Bat Norodam, Phnôm
Penh
Tel: +855(2) 3572
Cable: uniphnompenh
Rector: Simsamreth Var
Founded: 1960, 1970
*F: Law and Economics; Medicine and
Paramedical Studies; Pharmacy; Letters and
Human Sciences; Science; Education; Commerce;
Dentistry.*
I: Modern Languages.
S: Education.

OTHER INSTITUTIONS

Ecole supérieure des Cadres de Gestion de l'Education
Moha Vithei Tou Samut, Phnôm-Penh
Tel: +855(2) 3179
Founded: 1985
Educational Management.

Faculté mixte de Médecine, de Pharmacie et d'Odonto-Stomatologie
Moha Vithei Achar Mean, Phnôm-Penh
Tel: +855(2) 5273
Founded: 1979
Medicine, Pharmacy, and Stomatology.

Institut de Sciences économiques
Moha Vithei Achar Mean, Phnôm-Penh
Tel: +855(2) 4171
Founded: 1984
Economics.

Institut technique agricole
Khum Dangko Srok Danko, Phnôm-Penh
Founded: 1984
Agriculture.

Institut technique d'Amitié kampucheo-soviétique
Moha Vithei Sahapheap Soviet, Phnôm-Penh 1981
Tel: +855 259-79

NATIONAL ACADEMIC BODIES

Ministry of National Education and Fine Arts
[Ministère de l'Education nationale et des
Beaux-Arts]
Phnôm-Penh
Ministre: Ung Huot

Cambodia National Commission for Unesco
[Commission Nationale du Cambodge pour
l'Unesco]
c/o Unesco Office, B.P. 29, Phnôm-Penh
Tel: +855(2) 326-299
Fax: +855(2) 326-163

CAMEROON

UNIVERSITIES

University of Buéa
[Centre Universitaire de Buéa]
P.O. Box 63, Buéa, South-West Province
Tel: +237 32-21-34
Fax: +237 32-22-72
Telex: 5155 kn
Vice-chancelier: Dorothy Limunga Njeuma
Secrétaire général: Kashim I. Tala
Founded: 1977, 1992
*Advanced S: Translations and Interpreters
(ASTI).*

University of Douala
[Université de Douala]
B.P. 2071, Douala
Tel: +237 42-62-19
Telex: 6140 kn
Recteur: Stanislas Meloné
Secrétaire général: Bruno Bekolo Ebé
Founded: 1977
S: Economics and Commerce; Teacher Training.

SCHOOL OF TECHNICAL TEACHER TRAINING
[ECOLE NORMALE SUPÉRIEURE DE L'ENSEIGNEMENT
TECHNIQUE]
B.P. 1872, Douala
Tel: +237 42 66 09
Founded: 1979
Teacher Training (Technical).

HIGHER SCHOOL OF ECONOMICS AND COMMERCE
[ECOLE SUPÉRIEURE DES SCIENCES ÉCONOMIQUES ET
COMMERCIALES]
B.P. 1971, Douala
Tel: +237 42 52 98
Founded: 1979
Economics and Commerce.

University of Dschang
[Université de Dschang]
Dschang
Telex: 7013 kn
Recteur: Eno Belinga (1993-)
Founded: 1977
Agriculture.

NATIONAL INSTITUTE OF RURAL DEVELOPMENT
[INSTITUT NATIONAL DE DÉVELOPPEMENT RURAL]
Yaoundé
Founded: 1988
Rural Development.

*University of Ngaoundéré
[Université de Ngaoundéré]
B.P. 454, Ngaoundéré
Tel: +237 25-12-45
Fax: +237 25-25-73
Telex: 7645 kn
Recteur: Jean Messi
Secrétaire général: François-Xavier Etoa
Founded: 1977, 1982, 1993
F: Letters and Human Sciences; Law and Political Science; Economics and Management; Science; Education.
S: Agro-Industrial Sciences; Geology and Mining Exploration; Veterinary Medicine; Chemical Engineering and Mineral Studies.
I: Technology (IUT).

HIGHER SCHOOL OF AGRO-FOOD TECHNOLOGIES
[ECOLE NATIONALE SUPÉRIEURE DES INDUSTRIES AGRO-ALIMENTAIRES DU CAMEROUN]
B.P. 454, Ngaoundéré
Founded: 1982
Agro-Food Technologies.

*University of Yaoundé
[Université de Yaoundé]
B.P. 337, Yaoundé
Tel: +237 22-07-44
Telex: 8384 u y kn
Chancelier: Laurent Esso
Vice-Chancelier: Jacob Nguh Lifangi
Founded: 1962
F: Law and Economics; Sciences; Letters and Human Sciences.
S: Education; Journalism; Polytechnical.
I: International Relations.
Ce: Health Sciences.

UNIVERSITY CENTRE OF HEALTH SCIENCES
[CENTRE UNIVERSITAIRE DES SCIENCES DE LA SANTÉ]
B.P. 337, Yaoundé
Founded: 1969
Health Sciences.

POLYTECHNIC SCHOOL
[ECOLE NATIONALE SUPÉRIEURE POLYTECHNIQUE]
B.P. 738, Yaoundé
Tel: +237 22 21 05
Founded: 1971
Engineering.

TEACHER TRAINING SCHOOL
[ECOLE NORMALE SUPÉRIEURE]
B.P. 47, Yaoundé
Tel: +237 22 09 13
Founded: 1961
Teacher Training.

HIGHER SCHOOL OF INFORMATION SCIENCES
[ECOLE SUPÉRIEURE DES SCIENCES ET TECHNIQUES DE L'INFORMATION]
B.P. 1328, Yaoundé
Founded: 1970
Information Sciences.

INSTITUTE OF INTERNATIONAL RELATIONS
[INSTITUT DES RELATIONS INTERNATIONALES]
B.P. 1637, Yaoundé
Founded: 1972
International Relations.

OTHER INSTITUTIONS

Centre national d'Administration et de Magistrature
B.P. 128, Yaoundé
Tel: +237 22-24-31
Administration; Magistracy.

Ecole nationale de l'Administration et de la Magistrature
B.P. 1180, Yaoundé
Tel: +237 22-37-54
Founded: 1959
Administration; Magistracy.

Ecole nationale des Assistants Sociales
Yaoundé
Social Work.

Ecole nationale supérieure de Police
B.P. 148, Yaoundé
Tel: +237 22-42-60
Police Training.

Ecole nationale supérieure des Travaux publics
B.P. 510, Yaoundé
Founded: 1982
Public Works.

Ecole supérieure des Postes et Télécommunications
B.P. 1186, Yaoundé
Tel: +237 22-37-00
Post and Telecommunications.

Faculté de Théologie Protestante de Yaoundé
Yaoundé
Theology (Protestant).

Institut de Formation et de Recherche démographiques
B.P. 1556, Yaoundé
Tel: +237 22-24-71
Founded: 1972
Demographic Training and Research.

Institut des Techniques administratives et financières
B.P. 23-11-40, Yaoundé
Tel: +237 2013
Finance; Administration.

Institut International des Assurances
B.P. 1575, Yaoundé
Insurance Studies.

Institut National de la Jeunesse et des Sports
B.P. 1016, Yaoundé
Founded: 1961
Physical Education.

Institut Panafricain de développement
B.P. 4078, Douala
Tel: +237 42-37-70
Panafrican Development.

Institut sous-régional de Statistiques et d'Economie appliquée
Yaoundé
Founded: 1961
Statistics and Economics.

NATIONAL ACADEMIC BODIES

Ministry of National Education
[Ministère de l'Education nationale]
B.P. 1600, Yaoundé
Tel: +237 23-40-50
Fax: +237 23-08-55
Telex: 8418 mesres kn
Ministre: Robert Mbella Mbappe

Cameroon National Commission for Unesco
[Commission nationale de la République du Cameroun pour l'Unesco]
Ministère de l'Education nationale, B.P. 1600, Yaoundé
Tel: +237 22-49-96
Telex: mineduc 8551 kn yaoundé
Président: Robert Mbella Mbappe, Minister of Education

CANADA

UNIVERSITIES

Acadia University
P.O. Box 1269, Wolfville, Nova Scotia B0P 1X0
Tel: +1(902) 542-2201
Fax: +1(902) 542-7224
Cable: acadia university, wolfville, nova scotia
President and Vice-Chancellor: Kelvin K. Ogilvie (1993-)
Registrar and Secretary, Senate: David Green
Founded: 1838, 1891
F: Arts; Commerce; Management and Education; Pure and Applied Sciences; Theology.

University of Alberta
University Campus NW, Edmonton, Alberta T6G 2E1
Tel: +1(403) 492-3111
Telex: 037-2979 uofa edm
Cable: university, edmonton, alberta T6G 2E5
President and Vice-Chancellor: Paul Davenport
Associate Vice-President and Registrar: Brian Silzer
International Relations: Wilfred Allan
Founded: 1906

F: Agriculture, Forestry and Home Economics; Arts; Business; Dentistry; Education; Engineering; Law; Extension; Saint-Jean (Arts, Education, and Science); Graduate Studies and Research; Home Economics; Medicine; Nursing; Pharmacy and Pharmaceutical Sciences; Physical Education and Recreation; Rehabilitation Medicine; Science.
S: Native Studies; Library and Information Studies.

Athabasca University
Box 10,000, Athabasca, Alberta T0G OBO
Tel: +1(403) 675-6111
Fax: +1(403) 675-6477
Telex: 037-41755
President: Terrence Morrison
Registrar: Alex Reed
International Relations: Barbara Spronk
Founded: 1970
F: Administrative Studies; Arts; Science.
Ce: Distance Education.

Augustana University College
4901-46 Avenue, Camrose, Alberta T4V 2R3
Tel: +1(403) 679-1100
Fax: +1(403) 679-1129
Cable: camrose lutheran university college
President: Glen Johnson (1992-97)
Registrar: Raymond Blacklock
International Relations: Leroy Johnson
Founded: 1910, 1985, 1991
Div: Biology and Chemistry; Fine Arts; Humanities; Physical Education; Physical and Mathematical Sciences; Social Sciences.

Bishop's University
Lennoxville, Québec J1M 1Z7
Tel: +1(819) 822-9600
Fax: +1(819) 822-9661
Cable: bishop's university, lennoxville
President and Vice-Chancellor: Hugh Scott
Registrar and Secretary-General: Ann Montgomery
International Relations: Secretary, Corporation and Senate, Elizabeth A. Towers
Founded: 1843
Div: Business Administration; Humanities.
D: Natural Sciences and Mathematics; Social Sciences.

Brandon University
70-18 Street, Brandon, Manitoba R7A 6A9
Tel: +1(204) 728-9520
Fax: +1(204) 726-4573
Telex: 07502721
Cable: brandon university
President and Vice-Chancellor: C. Dennis
Registrar and Secretary, Senate: Tom Mitchell
International Relations: Director, International Development Projects, P.G. Halamandaris
Founded: 1899
F: Arts; Education; Sciences; Music; General Studies.

Brescia College
1285 Western Road, London, Ontario N6G 1H2
Tel: +1(519) 432-8353
Fax: +1(519) 679-6489
Telex: 111
Principal: Sister Dolores Kuntz
Registrar: Marion Hawkins
Founded: 1919
English; Home Economics; Languages; Social Sciences.

British Columbia Open University
4355 Mathissi Place, Burnaby, British Columbia
V5G 4S8
Tel: +1(604) 431-3100
Fax: +1(604) 431-3333
Telex: 04-357674
President: Glen Farrell
Registrar: Susan Haglund
Founded: 1988
P: Academic Studies (Humanities, Social Sciences, Mathematics); Administrative and Applied Studies.

*The University of British Columbia
2329 West Mall, Suite 100, Vancouver, British Columbia V6T 1Z1
Tel: +1(604) 822-2211
Telex: 045-1233
Cable: greypoint
President and Vice-Chancellor: David W. Strangway
Registrar and Director, Student Services: Richard i40Spencer
International Relations: Larry R. Sproul
Founded: 1908, 1980
F: Agriculture Sciences; Applied Science; Arts; Commerce and Business Administration; Dentistry; Education; Forestry; Graduate Studies; Medicine; Pharmaceutical Sciences; Science; Law.
S: Audiology and Speech Sciences; Rehabilitation Sciences; Nursing; Music; Library, Archival and Information Studies; Architecture; Community and Regional Planning; Family and Nutritional Sciences; Human Kinetics; Social Work.
Ce: Transportation Studies; Human Settlements; Continuing Education.
I: Sustainable Development Research (SDRI); Asian Research.

Brock University
500 Glenridge Avenue, Saint Catharines, Ontario L2S 3A1
Tel: +1(905) 688-5550
President and Vice-Chancellor: Terrence White (1993-97)
Registrar: Louis Ariano
International Relations: Associate Vice-President (Academic), Ralph D. Morris
Founded: 1962
F: Business; Education; Humanities; Mathematics and Sciences; Physical Education and Recreation; Social Science.

*The University of Calgary
2500 University Drive N.W., Calgary, Alberta T2N 1N4
Tel: +1(403) 220-5110
Fax: +1(403) 282-7298
Telex: 03-821545
Cable: university, calgary
President and Vice-Chancellor: Murray Fraser
Registrar: Gary Krivy
International Relations: Executive Director, International Centre, William Warden
Founded: 1945, 1966
F: Education; Engineering; Environmental Design; Fine Arts; General Studies; Graduate Studies; Humanities; Law; Management; Medicine; Nursing; Physical Education; Science; Social Sciences; Social Work; Continuing Education.

Campion College
3737 Wascana Parkway, Suite 100, Regina, Saskatchewan S4S 0A2
Tel: +1(306) 359-1251
President: Joseph Schner
Registrar: Loretta Leibel
Founded: 1917
Psychology; English; Film and Video; French; Humanities and Religious Studies; Philosophy.

University College of Cape Breton
P.O. Box 5300, Station A, Sydney, Nova Scotia B1P 6L2
Tel: +1(902) 562-0119
President: Jacquelyn Thayer Scott (1993-98)
Registrar: Burkhard Strelke
International Relations: Director, Centre for International Studies, Brian Tennyson
Founded: 1974, 1982
F: Arts and Science; Business; Student Services; Technology and Trades.
S: Science and Technology; Applied Arts and Development Studies; Arts and Social Sciences.

Carleton University
125 Colonel By Drive, Ottawa, Ontario K1S 5B6
Tel: +1(613) 788-7400
Telex: 054-4232
Cable: carleton university, Ottawa
President and Vice-Chancellor: Robin Farquhar
Vice-President (Academic) and Registrar: L.A. Copley
International Relations: D.R.F. Taylor
Founded: 1942, 1952, 1957
F: Arts; Engineering; Graduate Studies and Research; Science; Social Sciences; Architecture; Business; Canadian Studies; Computer Science; Industrial Design; International Affairs; Public Administration; Social Work; Journalism and Communication; Comparative Literary Studies.
S: International Affairs (Norman Paterson).
I: Studies in Art and Culture; Central/East European and Russian-Area Studies; Interdisciplinary Studies.

Concordia College
7128 Ada Boulevard NW, Edmonton, Alberta T5B 4E4
Tel: +1(403) 479-8481
Fax: +1(403) 474-1933
President (Acting): Richard W. Kraemer
Registrar: Judy D. Kruse
Founded: 1921, 1987
Div: Humanities; Religious Studies; Science; Education and Social Sciences.

*Concordia University
1455 de Maisonneuve Boulevard West, Montreal, Quebec H3G 1M8
Tel: +1(514) 848-2424
Fax: +1(514) 848-3494
Cable: concordia university, montreal, quebec
Rector and Vice-Chancellor (Acting): Charles Bertrand (1994-)
Registrar: Bruce Smart
International Relations: Director, Centre for International Academic Cooperation, Bruce Mabley
Founded: 1974
F: Arts and Science; Commerce and Administration; Engineering and Computer Science; Graduate Studies; Fine Arts.
S: Community and Public Affairs.

Dalhousie University
1236 Henry Street, Halifax, Nova Scotia B3H 3J5
Tel: +1(902) 494-2211
Fax: +1(902) 494-2139
Telex: 019-21863
Cable: dalhousie university, halifax, nova scotia B3H 3J5
President and Vice-Chancellor: Howard C. Clark
Registrar: Gudrun Curri
International Relations: Barry Lesser
Founded: 1818, 1988
F: Arts and Social Sciences; Dentistry; Graduate Studies; Health Professions; Management; Medicine; Science; Law.
S: Business Administration; Education; Human Communication Disorders; Library and Information Studies; Nursing; Occupational Therapy; Physiotherapy; Recreation, Physical and Health Education; Resource and Environmental Studies; Maritime Social Work; Dental Hygiene; Health Services Administration; Public Administration; Pharmacy.

Dominican College of Philosophy and Theology
[Collège dominicaine de Philosophie et de Théologie]
96 avenue Empress, Ottawa (Ontario) K1R 7G3
Tel: +1(613) 233-5696
Cable: dominican college of philosophy and theology, ottawa, ontario
President and Regent of Studies: Michel Gourgues, O.P.

Secretary of Studies and Registrar: Marie-Thérèse Nadeau, cnd
Founded: 1909, 1967
I: Pastoral Theology; Philosophy; Theology.

University of Guelph
50 Stone Road East, Guelph, Ontario N1G 2W1
Tel: +1(519) 824-4120
Fax: +1(519) 767-1350
Cable: university of guelph, guelph ontario
President and Vice-Chancellor: Mordechai Rozanski (1993-98)
Registrar: Arnold Holmes
International Relations: Jim C.M. Shute
Founded: 1964
C: Arts; Biological Science; Family and Consumer Studies; Physical and Engineering Science; Social Science; Graduate Studies; Agriculture (Ontario); Veterinary (Ontario).
S: Hotel and Food Administration; Human Biology; Rural Planning and Development; Continuing Education; Engineering; Environmental Sciences; Landscape Architecture.

Huron College
1349 Western Road, London, Ontario N6G 1H3
Tel: +1(519) 438-7224
Fax: +1(519) 438-3938
Telex: 064-7134
Principal: Charles J. Jago
Registrar: Eugene Carson
Founded: 1863
F: Arts and Social Science; Theology.
D: Economics; English; French; History; Philosophy; Politics; Psychology.

King's College
266 Epworth Avenue, London, Ontario N6A 2M3
Tel: +1(519) 433-3491
Fax: +1(519) 433-2227
Telex: 064-7134
Principal: Philip Mueller
Registrar: Marilyn Mason
Founded: 1955
D: Economics Business and Mathematics; History and Political Science; Modern Languages; Philosophy and Religious Studies; Psychology; Sociology; Social Work.

The King's University College
9125-50 Street, Edmonton, Alberta T6B 2H3
Tel: +1(403) 465-3500
Fax: +1(403) 465-3534
President: Henk W.H. Van Andel
Registrar and Director of Admission: Tom Dolhanti
Founded: 1979
Div: Natural Sciences; Social Sciences; Humanities.

University of King's College
6350 Coburg Road, Halifax, Nova Scotia B3H 2A1
Tel: +1(902) 423-3357
Cable: king's college, halifax, nova scotia
President and Vice-Chancellor: Colin J. Starnes
(1993-)
Registrar: Patricia M. Robertson
Founded: 1789, 1802, 1923
C: Arts and Science.
F: Arts and Social Sciences; Science.
S: Journalism.
P: Foundation Year; Contemporary Studies.

Lakehead University
855 Oliver Road, Thunder Day, Ontario P7B 5E1
Tel: +1(807) 343-8110
Fax: +1(807) 343-8023
Telex: 073-4594
Cable: lakehead university, thunder bay, ontario
President and Vice-Chancellor: Robert G.
Rosehart
Registrar: Pentti A. Paularinne
International Relations: Director, Office of
Research and Graduate Studies, Connie Nelson
Founded: 1946, 1956, 1965
F: Arts and Science; Professional Studies.
S: Business Administration; Engineering;
Forestry; Nursing; Outdoor Recreation:; Physical
Education and Athletics; Education.

Laurentian University of Sudbury
[Université Laurentienne de Sudbury]
935 Ramsay Lake Road, Sudbury, Ontario P3E
2C6
Tel: +1(705) 675-1151
Fax: +1(705) 675-4812
Telex: 067-7569
Cable: laurentian university, sudbury, ontario
President/Recteur: Ross Paul
Registrar/Secrétaire général: Jack Porter
International Relations: Frank Smith
Founded: 1960
F: Humanities; Professional Schools; Science
and Engineering; Social Science.
S: Commerce and Administration; Education;
Engineering; Human Movement; Nursing; Social
Work; Sports Administration; Translators and
Interpreters.

*Laval University
[Université Laval]
Case Postal 2208, Succulsale Terminus, Québec,
Québec G1K 7P4
Tel: +1(418) 656-2131
Telex: 051-31621
Cable: regunlaval quebec
Recteur: Michel Gervais
Registraire: Pierre Allard
International Relations: Jacques Parent
Founded: 1663, 1971, 1991
F: Architecture and Development; Agriculture
and Food Technology; Arts; Education; Forestry
and Geodesy; Law; Letters; Medicine;
Philosophy; Administration and Engineering;
Social Sciences; Theology; Graduate Studies.

The University of Lethbridge
4401 University Drive West, Lethbridge, Alberta
T1K 3M4
Tel: +1(403) 329-2111
President and Vice-Chanellor: Howard E. Tennant
Registrar: Fred Rosmanitz
International Relations: Keith McCurdy
Founded: 1967
F: Arts and Science; Education; Management;
Student Affairs.
S: Fine Arts; Nursing.

Luther College
3737 Wascana Parkway, Regina, Saskatchewan
S4S 0A2
Tel: +1(306) 585-5333
Fax: +1(306) 585-5267
President: Donald King
Registrar: Mary Jesse
Founded: 1913
Biology; English; French; Geography; History;
Mathematics; Philosophy; Psychology; Religious
Studies; Sociology.

McMaster University
280 Main Street West, Suite 20, Hamilton, Ontario
L8S 4L8
Tel: +1(905) 525-9140
Fax: +1(905) 527-0100
Telex: 061-8347
Cable: mcmaster university, hamilton
President and Vice-Chancellor: Geraldine A.
Kenney-Wallace
Vice-President (Administration): Suson Porter
International Relations: Gary Warner
Founded: 1887
F: Business; Engineering; Health Sciences;
Humanities; Science; Social Sciences.
S: Graduate Studies; Social Work; Nursing.
Ce: Continuing Education; Arthritic Diseases;
Electrophotonic Materials and Devices; Flexible
Manufacturing; Health Economics and Policy
Analyses; International Health; Peace Studies;
Religion and Aging; Mission and Evangelism
Research (McMaster); Aging and Health
Education; Instructional Development;
Management of Technology and Innovation.
I: Materials Research; Energy Studies; Energy
Studies; Molecular Biology and Biotechnology;
Materials Research; Polymer Production
Technology.
P: Arts and Science (separate degree).
L: Communication Research (CRL).

The University of Manitoba
350 Chancellor Mathesson Road, Winnipeg,
Manitoba R3T 2N2
Tel: +1(204) 474-8880
Fax: +1(204) 269-4629
Cable: university of manitoba, winnipeg, canada
President and Vice-Chancellor: Arnold Naimark
(1981-)
Vice-Chancellor (Administration): T.G. Falconer
International Relations: W.F.W. Neville
Founded: 1877

Faculties: Arts; Architecture; Agriculture and Food Sciences; Dentistry; Engineering; Education; Graduate Studies; Human Ecology; Law; Management; Medicine; Pharmacy; Physical Education and Recreation; Science; Social Work; Continuring Education; Nursing.
Schools: Music; Medical Rehabilitation; Agriculture; Art.

University of Moncton
[Université de Moncton]
Centre universitaire de Moncton, 165, avenue Massey, Moncton, New Brunswick E1A 3E9
Tel: +1(506) 858-4000
Fax: +1(506) 858-4379
Telex: 014-353
Recteur: M. Jean-Bernard Robichaud
Sécretaire général: Gilles Long
International Relations: Dean, Faculty of Research and Graduate Studies, Christophe Jankowski
Founded: 1864, 1963
F: Administration; Arts; Lifelong Education; Research and Graduate Studies; Sciences and Engineering; Social Sciences; Education.
S: Law; Nursing; Nutrition and Family Studies; Engineering; Physical Education and Leisure Studies; Social Services; Forestry.

Memorial University of Newfoundland
P.O. Box 4200, Station C, St John's, Newfoundland A1C 5S7
Tel: +1(709) 737-8000
Fax: +1(709) 737-4569
Telex: 027-4101
President and Vice-Chancellor: Arthur W. May
Registrar: Glenn W. Collins
International Relations: Tony Williamson
Founded: 1925, 1949
F: Arts; Business Administration; Education; Engineering and Applied Science; Medicine; Science.
S: Graduate Studies; General and Continuing Studies; Music; Nursing; Pharmacy; Physical Education and Athletics; Social Work.
P: Fine Arts.
Ce: Cold Ocean Resources Engineering; Earth Resources Research; Development Support Communications (Don Snowden); International Reference for Avian Haematozoa; Ocean Science.
U: Maritime History Archive/Maritime Studies Research.
I: Social and Economic Research; Fisheries and Marine.

Polytechnic School of Montreal
[Ecole polytechnique de Montréal]
Case postal 6079, Succursale A, Montréal, Succursale Centre Ville, Québec H3C 3A7
Tel: +1(514) 340-4711
Telex: 05-24146
Directeur: André Bazergui
Registraire: Claude Brissette
International Relations: Yvon Gervais
Founded: 1873
D: Chemical Engineering; Civil Engineering; Electrical Engineering and Computer Engineering; Industrial Engineering; Mechanical Engineering; Mineral Engineering; Physics; Applied Mathematics; Metallurgy and Materials Engineering.

School of Higher Commercial Studies, Montreal
[Ecole des hautes études commercials]
5255, avenue Decelles, Montréal, Québec H3T 1V6
Tel: +1(514) 340-6000
Fax: +1(514) 340-6411
Directeur: Jean Guertin
Secrétaire général: J.-Denis Duquette
Founded: 1907
Commerce.

*University of Montreal
[Université de Montréal]
Case postal 6128, Succursale Centre Ville, Montréal, Québec H3C 3J7
Tel: +1(514) 343-2098
Fax: +1(514) 343-5976
Cable: université de montréal (québec), canada
Recteur: René Simard (1993-)
Secrétaire général: Michel Lespérance
International Relations: Jean-Louis Fortin
Founded: 1876, 1919
F: Arts and Sciences; Continuing Education; Dental Medicine; Education Sciences; Environment Design; Graduate Studies; Law; Medicine; Music; Nursing; Pharmacy; Theology; Veterinary Medicine; Optometry.
S: Architecture; Psycho-Education; Social Work; Town Planning; Speech Pathology and Audiology; Landscape Architecture; Industrial Design; Library and Information Sciences; Criminology; Industrial Relations.
D: Physical Education.
Ce: Mass Spectrometry (Regional); Biomedical Engineering; Animal Reproduction (CRRA); Comparative Criminology (CICC) (International); Inter-University for Discourse Analysis and Text Sociocriticism (CIADEST); East Asian Studies (CETASE); Research and Development in Economics (CRDE); Interuniversity Research on Toxicology (CIRTOX); Research in Mathematics (CRM); Neurological Sciences Research (CRSN); Public Law Research (CRDP); Research on Transportation (CRT); Inter-University Research

in High Performance Computer Architecture and VLSI (GRIAO).
I: Research in Plant Biology (IRBV); Mathematical Sciences (ISM); Research in the History of Architecture.
L: High Field NMR Regional; Challenging Needs and Learning; Nuclear Physics.
Observatories: Mount Mégantic Astronomical.

Mount Allison University
Sackville, New Brunswick E0A 3C0
Fax: +1(506) 364-2216
Cable: mount allison, sackville, new brunswick
President and Vice-Chancellor: Ian D.C. Newbould
Registrar: Leonard A. Owen
International Relations: Dean, Social Science, Peter Ennals
Founded: 1839, 1858, 1886
F: Arts; Science; Social Science.

Mount Saint Vincent University
166 Bedford Highway, Suite 1, Halifax, Nova Scotia B3M 2J6
Tel: +1(902) 457-6788
Fax: +1(902) 445-3960
Cable: mount saint vincent university, halifax, nova scotia
President and Vice-Chancellor: Elizabeth Parr-Johnston
Registrar: Diane Morris
International Relations: Director of Research, David Furrow
Founded: 1925, 1966
F: Human and Professional Development; Humanities and Sciences.

University of New Brunswick
P.O. Box 4400, Station A, Fredericton, New Brunswick E3B 5A3
Tel: +1(506) 453-4666
Fax: +1(506) 453-4599
Telex: 014-46202
Cable: unb fredericton
President: Robin L. Armstrong
Registrar: Deanne Dennison (Fredericton); Barry Beckett (Saint John)
International Relations: Christina Paponnet-Cantat
Founded: 1785, 1828
F: Administration; Arts (Saint John); Computer Science; Education; Engineering; Forestry; Graduate Studies and Research; Law; Nursing; Physical Education and Recreation; Science; Science, Applied Science and Engineering (Saint John).
D: Business (Saint John); Humanities and Languages (Saint John); Mathematics,

Engineering and Computer Science (Saint John); Sciences (Saint John); Social Science (Saint John).

Nipissing University
100 College Drive, Box 5002, North Bay, Ontario P1B 8L7
Tel: +1(705) 474-3450
Fax: +1(705) 474-1947
President and Vice-Chancellor: Denis Lawrence (1990-95)
Registrar: Denis Lawrence
International Relations: David Marshall
Founded: 1967
F: Education; Arts and Science.
S: Business and Economics.

Nova Scotia Agricultural College
P.O. Box 550, Station Main, Truro, Nova Scotia B2N 5E3
Tel: +1(902) 893-6600
Cable: nova scotia agricultural college, truro, nova scotia
Principal: Leslie E. Haley (1989-)
Registrar: Tom Dolhanty
International Relations: Director, Centre for International Development, Dale Ells
Founded: 1905
D: Agricultural Engineering; Animal Science; Biology; Chemistry and Soil Science; Economics and Business Management; Humanities; Mathematics and Physics; Plant Science.

Nova Scotia College of Art and Design
5163 Duke Street, Halifax, Nova Scotia B3J 3J6
Tel: +1(902) 422-7381
Fax: +1(902) 425-2420
President: Ian Christie Clark
Registrar: Stephanie Smith
Founded: 1887, 1969
Div; Art Education; Art History; Craft; Design; Foundation; Studio; Graduate Studies (Craft, Design, Studio).

Technical University of Nova Scotia
P.O. Box 1000, Station Central RPO, Halifax, Nova Scotia B3J 2X4
Tel: +1(902) 420-7500
Fax: +1(902) 420-7551
Telex: (tuns) 019-21566
Cable: tuns, halifax, nova scotia
President and Vice-Chancellor: Edward Rhodes
Registrar: Kent Hurley
International Relations: Director, Research Services, Robert Eagle
Founded: 1907, 1980
F: Architecture; Engineering.
S: Computer Science.
Ce: Energy Studies.

The Ontario Institute for Studies in Education
252 Bloor Street West, Suite 1, Toronto, Ontario
M5S 1V6
Tel: +1(416) 923-6641
Fax: +1(416) 926-4725
E-Mail: oise.on.ca
Telex: 06217720
Cable: Oisetor
Director and Secretary, Board of Governors:
Arthur M. Kruger (1992-97)
Registrar: Patricia Buitenhaus
International Relations: Comparative,
International and Development Education Centre,
Joseph. P. Farrell
Founded: 1965
D: *Adult Education; Applied Psychology;
Curriculum; Educational Administration; History
and Philosophy of Education; Instruction and
Special Education; Measurement, Evaluation and
Computer Application; Sociology in Education.*
Ce: *Applied Cognitive Science; Comparative,
International and Development Education;
Franco-Ontarian Studies/Recherches en
Education Franco-Ontarienne; Modern Language;
Women's Studies for Education.*

*Université d'Ottawa/University of Ottawa
Case postal 450, Succursale A, Ottawa, Ontario
K1N 6N5
Tel: +1(613) 564-3311
Fax: +1(613) 564-5829
E-Mail: @acadvm.1.uottawa.ca
Cable: university of ottawa, canada
Recteur et vice-chancelier/Rector and Vice-
Chancellor: Marcel Hamelin (1990-97)
Registraire/Registrar: George H. von Schoenberg
International Relations: Serge Monnette
Founded: 1848, 1866, 1965
F: *Administration; Arts; Education; Engineering;
Health Science; Civil Law; Common Law;
Medicine; Science; Social Sciences.*
S: *Graduate Studies; Human Kinetics; Nursing;
Psychology; Social Services; Translation and
Interpretation.*
Ce: *Trade Policy and Law (Canadian); Research
on French Canadian Culture; Electrochemical
Science and Technology; Human Rights Research
and Education; International Water Engineering;
Ottawa-Carleton for Communications Research.*
I: *Industrial Membrane Research; Biotechnology
Research; Mental Health Research;
Neuromuscular Research; Research on the
Environment and the Economy; Bridge
Engineering (Ottawa-Carleton);
Telecommunications Research of Ontario; Eye
(Ottawa General Hospital); Heart (Ottawa Civic
Hospital); Medical Engineering.*

University of Prince Edward Island
550 University Avenue, Charlottetown, Prince
Edward Island C1A 4P3
Tel: +1(902) 566-0439
Fax: +1(902) 566-0420
Cable: upei, charlottetown, p.e.i.
President and Vice-Chancellor: C.W.J. Eliot
Registrar and University Secretary: John De
Grace
International Relations: Department of Religious
Studies, David Morrison
Founded: 1969
F: *Arts; Business Administration; Education;
Science; Veterinary Medicine; Nursing.*

*University of Quebec
[Université du Québec]
2857, boulevard Laurier, Saint-Foy (Québec) G1V
2M3
Tel: +1(418) 657-3551
Fax: +1(418) 657-2132
Telex: 051 31623
Cable: université du québec, saint-foy, québec
Président: Claude Hamel (1993-98)
Secrétaire général: Pierre Nadeau
International Relations: Fernand Caron
Founded: 1968

Institute 'Armand Frappier', University of Quebec
[Institut Armand-Frappier]
531 boulevard des Prairies, C.P. 100, Succursale
LDR, Ville de Laval, Québec H7N 4Z3
Tel: +1(514) 687-5010
Fax: +1(514) 687-5010, ext.: 501
Telex: 055-62171
Cable: instfrap-val
Directeur général: Claude Pichette
Registraire: Nicole Paquet
International Relations: Directeur Scientifique,
Michel Trudel
Founded: 1938, 1972
Research Ce: *Application of Science to
Nutrition; Applied Microbiology; Immunology;
Virology; Applied Sciences and Food Technology.*

National Institute of Scientific Research, University of Quebec
[Institut national de la Recherche scientifique]
2635, boulevord Hochelaga, Suite 640, C.P. 7500,
Sainte-Foy (Québec) G1V 4C7
Tel: +1(418) 654-2500
Fax: +1(418) 654-2525
Directeur général: Alain Soucy
Registraire: Réal Pelland
International Relations: Responsable des
services à la recherche, Magella Cantin
Founded: 1969
Research Ce: *Energy and Materials; Geo-
resources; Health; Oceanography;
Telecommunications; Urbanization.*
D: *Water.*

National School of Public Administration, University of Quebec
[Ecole nationale (d')Administration publique]
945 rue Wolfe, Sainte-Foy (Québec) G1V 3J9
Tel: +1(418) 657-2485
Fax: +1(418) 657-2620
Directeur général: Pierre de Celles
Registraire: Jean-Marc Alain
International Relations: Direction, Affaires
extérieures, Serge Raymond
Founded: 1969
Public Administration (postgraduate).

School of Higher Technology, University of Quebec
[Ecole de Technologie supérieure]
4750, avenue Henri-Julien, Montréal, Québec H2T
2C8
Tel: +1(514) 289-8800
Fax: +1(514) 289-8950
Directeur général: Robert L. Papineau
Registraire: Anne Beaulieu
International Relations: Fernand Caron
Founded: 1974
*D: Automated Production Engineering;
Construction Engineering and Management;
Electrical Engineering; Mechanical Engineering.*

Tele University, University of Quebec
[Télé Université]
2635 boulevard Hochelaga, 7e étage, Québec
(Québec) G1V 4V9
Tel: +1(418) 652-2262
Fax: +1(418) 657-2094
Directeur général: Jean-Guy Béliveau
Registraire: Guy Savoie
International Relations: M. Pierre Patry
Founded: 1972
*D: General Studies; Computer Science Applied
to Education; Development; Multidisciplinary
Studies; Scientific and Technological Culture;
Social Sciences.*

University of Quebec Abitibi-Temiscamingue
[Université du Québec en Abitibi-Témiscamingue]
42 Monseigneur-Rhéaume est, C.P. 700, Rouyn,
Québec J9X 5E4
Tel: +1(819) 762-0971
Fax: +1(819) 797-4727
Recteur: Jules Arseneault
Registraire: Norman Murphy
International Relations: André Gbodossou
Founded: 1983
*D: Administrative Sciences and Accountancy;
Applied Sciences; Educational Sciences; Human
Behaviour Sciences; Social and Health Sciences.*

University of Quebec at Chicoutimi
[Université du Québec à Chicoutimi]
555, boulevard de l'Université Est, Chicoutimi,
Québec G7H 2B1
Tel: +1(418) 545-5011
Fax: +1(418) 545-5012
Recteur: Martin Côté (1994-)
Registraire: Renée Gagnon
International Relations: Doyen des études
avancées et de la recherche, Jayanta Guha
Founded: 1969
*D: Applied Sciences; Arts and Letters; Basic
Sciences; Economic and Administration Sciences;
Educational Sciences; Human Sciences; Religious
Sciences.*

University of Quebec at Hull
[Université du Québec à Hull]
C.P. 1250, Succursale B, Hull (Québec) J8X 3X7
Tel: +1(819) 595-3900
Fax: +1(819) 595-3924
Recteur: Francis Whyte
Registraire: Richard Bérubé
International Relations: Doyen des études
avancées et de la recherche, Jean-Georges
Lengellé
Founded: 1970, 1981
*D: Accountancy; Administrative Sciences; Arts
and Sciences; Computer Science; Educational
Sciences; Human Sciences.*

*University of Quebec at Montreal
[Université du Québec à Montréal]
C.P. 8888, Succursale, Centre Ville, Montréal
(Québec) H3C 3P8
Tel: +1(514) 987-3000
Fax: +1(514) 987-3095
Telex: 051-31623
Recteur: Claude Corbo
Registraire: Ygal Leibu
International Relations: Jean-Pierre Lemasson
Founded: 1969
*D: Accountancy; Administration; Art History;
Biological Sciences; Chemistry; Communication;
Dance; Design; Drama; Earth Sciences;
Economics; Education; Fine Arts; Geography;
History; Law; Linguistics; Literary Studies;
Mathematics and Computer Science; Music;
Philosophy; Physical Education; Physics; Political
Science; Psychology; Religious Studies;
Sexology; Social Work; Sociology; Urban Studies
and Tourism.
I: Environmental Sciences.*

University of Quebec at Rimouski
[Université du Québec à Rimouski]
Case postal 3300, Succursale Bureau-chef,
Rimouski (Québec) G5L 3A1
Tel: +1(418) 723-1984
Fax: +1(418) 724-1525
Recteur: Marc-André Dionne
Registraire: Raymond Côté
International Relations: Doyen des études
avancées dt de la recherche, Pierre Couture
Founded: 1969, 1973

D: Biology and Health Sciences; Economics and Management; Educational Sciences; Human Sciences; Letters; Mathematics and Computer Sciences; Oceanography; Religious Sciences and Ethics.

University of Quebec at Trois-Rivières

[Université du Québec à Trois-Rivières]
C.P. 500, Succursale Bureau-chef, Trois-Rivières (Québec) G9A 5H7
Tel: +1(819) 376-5011
Fax: +1(819) 376-5012
Recteur: Jacques A. Plamondon (1994-)
Registraire: René Côté
International Relations: Bureau de liaison Université-Milieu, André Quirion
Founded: 1969
D: Accountancy; Administration and Economics; Arts; Chemistry-Biology; Educational Sciences; Engineering; French; Health Sciences; Human Sciences; Leisure Sciences; Mathematics and Computer Sciences; Modern Languages; Philosophy; Physical Education; Physics; Psychology; Theology.

*Queen's University at Kingston

99 University Avenue, Kingston, Ontario K7L 3N6
Tel: +1(613) 545-2000
Fax: +1(613) 545-6300
Telex: dial new york city +1(00) 961000 user code ale 6741
Cable: queen's university, kingston, ontario
Principal and Vice-Chancellor: William C. Leggett (1994-)
Registrar: Alison Morgan
International Relations: A.R. Tony Eastham
Founded: 1841
F: Applied Science; Arts and Science; Education; Law; Medicine; Women.
S: Graduate Studies and Research; Nursing; Business; Physical and Health Education; Rehabilitation Therapy; Industrial Relations; Public Administration; Urban and Regional Planning.
Ce: International Relations; Resource Studies; Industrial Relations; International Relations.
I: Intergovernmental Relations.

Redeemer College

777 Highway 53 East, Ancaster, Ontario L9K 1J4
Tel: +1(905) 648-2131
Fax: +1(905) 648-2134
President: Justin Cooper (1994-)
Registrar: Marian Ryks-Szele Kouzky
Founded: 1976
D: Business; Education; General Arts; General Science; Religion and Theology; Psychology; Sociology; French; Philosophy; History; Political Science; Physical Education.
Ce: Advanced Studies in Faith and Science (Pascal).

*The University of Regina

3737 Wascana Parkway, Suite 100, Regina, Saskatchewan S4S 0A2
Tel: +1(306) 585-4111
Fax: +1(306) 585-5255
Telex: 961-000
Cable: university Regina
President and Vice-Chancellor: Donald O. Wells (1990-98)
Registrar and Director of Student Services: Gail Meehan
International Relations: Associate Vice-President (Research), Nick Cercone
Founded: 1961, 1974
F: Administration; Arts; Education; Engineering; Fine Arts; Graduate Studies and Research; Physical Activity Studies; Science; Social Work; University Extension.
S: Journalism and Communications; Human Justice.
Research Ce: Canadian Plains.
Research Ut/I: Energy; Regina Water.

Ryerson Polytechnic University

350 Victoria Street, Toronto, Ontario M5B 2K3
Tel: +1(416) 979-5000
President: Terence W. Grier
Registrar: Keith C. Alnwick
International Relations: Sam Mikhil
Founded: 1948, 1963
F: Applied Arts; Arts; Business; Community Services; Continuing Education; Engineering and Applied Science.

Saint-Anne University

[Université Sainte-Anne]
Pointe-de-l'Eglise (Nouelle-Écosse) B0W 1M0
Tel: +1(902) 769-2114
Fax: +1(902) 767-2930
Recteur: Harley d'Entremont
Registraire: Murielle Comeau
International Relations: Vice-recteur, Affaires extérieures, Leger Comeau
Founded: 1890, 1977
F: Arts and Sciences.
D: Education (Teaching of French and in French, elementary and secondary levels); Science; Humanities; French Studies; English Studies; Business; French Immersion (French as second language).
Ce: Arabian Studies; Youth Literature.
Research Ce: Small Enterprises (Jodray).

University College of Saint-Boniface

[Collège universitaire de Saint-Boniface]
200, avenue de la Cathédrale, Saint Boniface, Manitoba R2H 0H7
Tel: +1(204) 233-0210
Telex: cn/cp
Recteur: Paul Ruest
Registraire: Marlene L. Cormier
International Relations: Fernand Girard
Founded: 1818
F: Arts and Science; Education.

S: Technical and Professional Studies; Continuing Education.

St. Francis Xavier University

P.O. Box 5000, Station Main, Antigonish, Nova Scotia B2G 1C0
Tel: +1(902) 863-3300
Fax: +1(902) 867-5153
Cable: university, antigonish, nova scotia
President and Vice-Chancellor: David J. Lawless
Registrar: Bernard V. Liengme
International Relations: A.A. MacDonald
Founded: 1853, 1866
F: Arts; Science.
I: Coady International.
S: Continuing Education and Summer; Extension.

The University of St. Jerome's College

81 Waterloo University Campus, Waterloo, Ontario N2L 3G3
Tel: +1(519) 884-8110
Fax: +1(519) 884-5759
President: Douglas Letson
Registrar: Dana Woito
Founded: 1865
D: English; History; Italian and French; Mathematics; Philosophy; Psychology; Religious Studies; Sociology.

St. John's College

400 Dysart Road, The University of Manitoba Campus, Winnipeg, Manitoba R3T 2M5
Tel: +1(204) 474-853
Warden and Vice-Chancellor: M.R. McLean
Registrar: T.E.K. shirtliff
Founded: 1866

Saint Mary's University

Halifax, Nova Scotia B3H 3C3
Tel: +1(902) 420-5400
Fax: +1(902) 420-5566
Cable: saint mary's university, halifax, nova scotia
President: Kenneth L. Ozmon
Registrar: Elizabeth A. Chard
International Relations: Denis Leclaire
Founded: 1802, 1841
F: Arts; Commerce; Education; Science.
Div: Engineering.

University of St. Michael's College

81 Saint Mary Street, Toronto, Ontario M5S 1J4
Tel: +1(416) 926-1300
Fax: +1(416) 926-7276
President and Vice-Chancellor: Richard M.H. Alway
Registrar: Robert T. O'Halloran, C.S.B.
Founded: 1852, 1958
F: Theology.
D: Classics; English; French; German; Philosophy; Religious Studies.

Saint Paul's College

430 Dysart Road, Winnipeg, Manitoba R3T 2M6
Tel: +1(204) 474-8575
Fax: +1(204) 269-6629
Telex: 07-587721
Rector: R.A. Lebrun
Registrar: I. Sexton
Founded: 1926
Arts and Sciences.

Saint Paul University

223, Main Street, Ottawa (Ontario) K1S 1C4
Tel: +1(613) 236-1393
Fax: +1(613) 782-3005
Cable: saint paul university, ottawa, ontario
Recteur: Dale Schlitt (1994-)
Secretaire général et Registraire: Eugène Marcotte
Founded: 1848, 1965
F: Canon Law; Theology.
I: Mission Studies:; Pastoral Studies; Social Communications.
Ce: Research in Canadian History and Religion; Techno-Ethics.

Saskatchewan Indian Federated College

Regina Campus, 3737 Wascana Parkway, Suite 100, Regina, Saskatchewan S4S 0A2
Tel: +1(306) 584-8333
Fax: +1(306) 584-0955
President: Eber Hampton
International Relations: Ronald Hoenes
Founded: 1976
S: Business and Public Administration; Indian Social Work; Indian Studies.
D: English; Indian Communications Arts; Indian Education; Indian Fine Art; Indian Health Studies and Science; Indian Languages, Literatures and Linguistics.

St. Thomas University

P.O. Box 4569, Station A, Fredericton, New Brunswick E3B 5G3
Tel: +1(506) 452-7700
Telex: 014-46202
President and Vice-Chancellor: Daniel W. O'Brien
Registrar: Lawrence Batt
International Relations: Vice-President (Academic), Roger Barnsley
Founded: 1910
D: Anthropology; Economics; Education; English; History; Philosophy; Political Science; Psychology; Religious Studies; Romance Languages; Social Work; Sociology.

St. Thomas More College

1437 College Drive, Saskatoon, Saskatchewan S7N 0W6
Tel: +1(306) 966-8900
Fax: +1(304) 966-8904
President: John Thompson
International Relations: Professor of History, D.L. Farmer
Founded: 1936

D: *Biblical Literature and Religious Studies; Economics; English; French; History; Philosophy; Political Studies; Psychology; Sociology.*

University of Saskatchewan
Saskatoon, Saskatchewan S7N 0W0
Tel: +1(306) 244-4343
Fax: +1(306) 966-8670
Telex: 0742659
Cable: university of saskatchewan canada
President and Vice-Chancellor: J.W.G. Ivany
Registrar: Ken M. Smith
Founded: 1907
C: *Agriculture; Arts and Science; Commerce; Dentistry; Education; Engineering; Graduate Studies; Law; Medicine; Nursing; Pharmacy; Physical Education; Veterinary Medicine.*
S: *Agriculture; Physical Therapy.*

University of Sherbrooke
[Université de Sherbrooke]
2500 boulevard Université, Sherbrooke (Québec) J1K 2R1
Tel: +1(819) 821-7000
Telex: bibuniv shb 05-836149
Cable: university, sherbrooke, p.q.
Recteur: Pierre Reid (1993-97)
Registraire: Jacques Carbonneau
International Relations: Directeur, bureau de la recherche, Jacques Oliva Bélair
Founded: 1954, 1957
F: *Administration; Applied Sciences; Education; Law; Letters and Human Sciences; Medicine; Physical Education and Sports; Science; Theology.*
S: *Music.*

Simon Fraser University
8888 Barnet Highway, Burnaby, British Columbia V5A 1S6
Tel: +1(604) 291-3111
Telex: 043-54614
Cable: burmount
President and Vice-Chancellor: John O. Stubbs (1993-)
Registrar: W. Ronald Heath
International Relations: Gregg Macdonald
Founded: 1963
F: *Applied Sciences; Arts; Business Administration; Education; Science; Continuing Studies; Graduate Studies.*
S: *Contemporary Arts.*

University of Sudbury/Université de Sudbury
935 Ramsey Lake Road, Sudbury, Ontario P3E 2C6
Tel: +1(705) 673-5661
Fax: +1(705) 673-4912
Recteur: Jacques Monet, S.J.
Founded: 1913
D: *Folklore; Native Studies; Philosophy; Religious Studies.*

University of Toronto
King's College Circle, Toronto, Ontario M5S 1A1
Tel: +1(416) 978-2011
Fax: +1(416) 978-8182
Telex: 06-218915 ut eng tor
Cable: university of toronto, ontario, canada
President: J. Robert S. Prichard
Assistant Vice-President (Planning), Registrar: Daniel Lang
International Relations: Malia Cioni
Founded: 1827, 1849, 1890
F: *Applied Science and Engineering; Arts and Science; Dentistry; Education; Forestry; Law; Library and Information Science; Management; Medicine; Music; Nursing; Pharmacy; Social Work.*
S: *Architecture and Landscape Architecture; Physical and Health Education; Graduate Studies; Continuing Studies.*
Ce: *Criminology; Industrial Relations; Medieval Studies; Study of Religion; Russian and East European Studies; International Studies; Comparative Literature; Nuclear Engineering; South Asian Studies; Studies of Aging; Study of Drama; Urban and Community Studies.*
I: *Biomedical Engineering; History and Philosophy of Science and Technology; Canadian for Theoretical Astrophysics; Aerospace Studies; Environmental Studies.*
Observatory: *David Dunlap.*

Trent University
P.O. Box 4800, Station Main, Peterborough, Ontario K9J 7B8
Tel: +1(705) 748-1011
Fax: +1(705) 748-1246
Telex: 06-962824
Cable: trent university
President and Vice-Chancellor: Leonard Conolly (1994-99)
Registrar: Alan P. Saxby
International Relations: Karanja Njoroge
Founded: 1963
F: *Arts and Science; Research and Graduate Studies.*

University of Trinity College
6 Hoskin Avenue, Toronto, Ontario M5S 1H8
Tel: +1(416) 978-2522
Fax: +1(416) 978-2797
Cable: trinity college, toronto
Provost and Vice-Chancellor: Robert H. Painter
Registrar: Bruce W. Bowden
Founded: 1851, 1904
F: *Arts; Divinity.*

Trinity Western University
7600 Glover Road, Langley, British Columbia V3A 6H4
Tel: +1(604) 888-7511
Fax: +1(604) 888-5336
President: R. Neil Snider (1974-)
Registrar: R. Orville Lyttle

International Relations: Vice-President (Academic Affairs), Donald M. Page
Founded: 1962, 1985
F: *Business and Economics; Natural and Applied Science; Social Sciences and Education; Arts and Religious Studies; Teacher Education; Graduate Affairs.*
D: *Fine Arts and Drama; Physical Education and Recreation; Religious Studies; Chemistry; Life and Earth Sciences; Mathematical Sciences; Psychology; Sociology and Anthroplogy; Communications and Linguistics; English and Modern Language; Music; Philosophy; Geography; History/Political Sciences; Biology; Nursing.*
I: *Aviation.*

University of Victoria
P.O. Box 1700, Station Comml Servcnt, Victoria, British Columbia V8W 2Y2
Tel: +1(604) 721-7211
Fax: +1(604) 721-8653
President and Vice-Chancellor: David F. Strong
University Secretary and Registrar: Sheila Sheldon-Collyer
International Relations: Associate Vice-President (Academic), John A. Schofield
Founded: 1903, 1963
F: *Arts and Science (Humanities); Arts and Science (Science); Arts and Science (Social Sciences); Education; Engineering; Fine Arts; Graduate Studies; Human and Social Development; Law.*
S: *Business; Child and Youth Care; Music; Nursing; Physical Education.*

University of Waterloo
200 University Avenue West, Waterloo, Ontario N2L 3G1
Tel: +1(519) 885-1211
Fax: +1(519) 888-4521
E-Mail: userid@watdcs.uwaterloo.ca
Telex: 069-55259
Cable: university of waterloo, waterloo, ontario
President and Vice-Chancellor: James Downey
Registrar: C. Trevor Boyes
International Relations: Pauline O'Neill
Founded: 1957, 1959
F: *Applied Health Sciences; Arts; Engineering; Environmental Studies; Mathematics; Science.*
S: *Accountancy; Architecture; Optometry; Urban and Regional Planning.*

The University of Western Ontario
1151 Richmond Street, London, Ontario N6A 3K7
Tel: +1(519) 679-2111
Telex: 0647134
Cable: western, london, canada
President and Vice-Chancellor: Paul Davenport (1994-)
Registrar: Gordon J. Smiley
International Relations: Frederick J. Keenan
Founded: 1878, 1923

F: *Applied Health Sciences; Arts; Dentistry; Education; Engineering; Graduate Studies; Journalism; Kinesiology; Law; Medicine; Music; Nursing; Part-time and Continuing Education; Science; Social Science.*
S: *Journalism (Graduate); Business Administration; Library and Information Science.*

Victoria University Toronto
73 Queen's Park Crescent, Toronto, Ontario M5S 1K7
Tel: +1(416) 585-4524
Fax: +1(416) 585-4584
Cable: vicollege, toronto
President and Vice-Chancellor: Roseanne Runte (1994-)
Registrar: Kenneth R. Thompson
Founded: 1836, 1841, 1892
F: *Arts and Science; Theology (Emmaunuel College).*

Wilfrid Laurier University
75 University Avenue West, Waterloo, Ontario N2L 3C5
Tel: +1(519) 884-1970
President and Vice-Chancellor: Lorna R. Marsden
Registrar: Peter L. Tron
International Relations: Dean, Faculty of Social Work, Frank Turner
Founded: 1911, 1959, 1973
F: *Arts and Science; Graduate Studies; Music; Business and Economics; Social Work.*

*University of Windsor
401 Sunset Avenue, Windsor, Ontario N9B 3P4
Tel: +1(519) 253-4232
Fax: +1(519) 973-7050
E-Mail: netnorth
Cable: university of windsor, windsor, ontario
President and Vice-Chancellor: Ronald W. Ianni
Registrar: Francis L. Smith
International Relations: R. Julian Cattaneo
Founded: 1857, 1956
F: *Arts; Business Administration; Education; Engineering; Graduate Studies and Research; Human Kinetics; Law; Science; Social Science; Continuing Education.*
S: *Music; Nursing; Social Work; Visual Arts; Dramatic Art; Computer Science; Humanities.*
Research Ut: *Social Science.*

University of Winnipeg
515 Portage Avenue, Winnipeg, Manitoba R3B 2E9
Tel: +1(204) 786-7811
President and Vice-Chancellor: Marsha P. Hanen
Secretary: Roger A. Kingsley
International Relations: Associate Vice-President (Academic), Herbert Mays
Founded: 1871, 1938, 1967
F: *Arts and Science; Theology; Collegiate.*

*York University

4700 Keele Street, North York, Ontario M3J 1P3
Tel: +1(416) 736-2100
Fax: +1(416) 736-5700
Telex: 065-24736
Cable: yorkuniv toronto
President: Susan Mann (1992-97)
Associate Vice-President (Registrar): Gene Denzel
International Relations: Director, York International, H. Ian Macdonald
Founded: 1959
F: *Administrative Studies; Arts; Education; Environmental Studies; Fine Arts; Graduate Studies.*
S: *Law (Osgoode Hall); Pure and Applied Science.*
C: *Atkinson.*
Ce: *Feminist Research; Jewish Studies; Refugee Studies; Research on Latin America and the Caribbean; Canadian Studies (Robarts); Health Studies; Asia Pacific Studies; Atmospheric Chemistry; International and Strategic Studies; Research in Earth and Space Sciences; Public Law and Public Policy; Research on Work and Society; Study of Computers in Education.*
I: *Social Research.*
Research P: *La Marsh on Violence and Conflict Resolution.*

NATIONAL ACADEMIC BODIES

Association of Universities and Colleges of Canada (AUCC)/Association des Universités et Collèges du Canada (AUCC)

350 Albert Street, Suite 600, Ottawa, Ontario K1R 1B1
Tel: +1(613) 563-1236
Fax: +1(613) 563-9745
Chairman: Michel Gervais (1993-95)
President: Claude Lajeunesse
International Relations: Eva Egron-Polak
Founded: 1911

Association of Atlantic Universities (A.A.U.)/ Association des Universités de l'Atlantique

5657 Spring Garden Road, Suite 403, Halifax, Nova Scotia B3J 3R4
Tel: +1(902) 425-4230
Fax: +1(902) 425-4233
E-Mail: ammack@ac.dal.Ca (Net north)
Chair: Elizabeth Parr Johnston (1994-97)
Executive Director: Anne-Marie MacKinnon
International Relations: Anne-Parie Mackinnon
Founded: 1964

Canadian Bureau for International Education (CBIE)/Bureau canadien de l'Education internationale (BCEI)

220 Laurier Avenue West, Suite 1100, Ottawa, Ontario K1P 5Z9
Tel: +1(613) 237-4820
Fax: +1(613) 237-1073
E-Mail: jholmes@ccs.carleton.ca
Telex: 053-3255
Chair, Board of Directors: Robin Farquhar (1993-95)
President: James W. Fox
Founded: 1966

Canadian International Development Agency(CIDA)/Agence canadienne de développement international (ACDI)

Place du Centre, 200 Promenade du Portage, Hull, Quebec K1A OG4
Tel: +1(819) 997-5456
Fax: +1(819) 953-5469
Telex: 053-4140 cida hull
President: Huguette Labelle (1993-)
Founded: 1968

Canadian Society for the Study of Higher Education (CSSHE)/La Société canadienne pour l'étude de l'énseignement supérieur (SCEES)

350 Albert Street, Suite 320, Ottawa, Ontario K1R 1B1
Tel: +1(613) 563-1236 Ext. 270
Fax: +1(613) 563-7739
E-Mail: kclements@aucc.ca
President: Alice Boberg
Executive Secretary: Kenneth Clements
International Relations: Kenneth Clements
Founded: 1970

Conference of Rectors and Principals of Quebec Universities (CREPUQ)/Conférence des recteurs et des principaux des universités du Québec

C.P. 952, Succursale Place du Parc, bureau 1200, 300, rue Léo-Parizeau, Montréal (Québec) H2W 2N1
Tel: +1(514) 288-8524
Fax: +1(514) 288-0554
Président: Claude Hamel (1993-95)
Directeur général: Jacques Bordeleau
International Relations: Chargée de recherche, Johanne Néron
Founded: 1967

Council of Ontario Universities (COU)/ Conseil des universités de l'Ontario

444 Yonge Street, Suite 203, Toronto, Ontario M5B 2H4
Tel: +1(416) 979-2165
Fax: +1(416) 979-8635
Chairman: David Smith
President: Peter George
International Relations: Peter George
Founded: 1962

International Development Research Centre (IDRC)/Centre de recherches pour le développement international (CRDI)
P.O. Box 8500, Ottawa, Ontario K1G 3H9
Tel: +1(613) 236-6163
Fax: +1(613) 238-7230
Secretary and General Counsel: Robert Auger
President: Keith Bezanson
Founded: 1970

Statistics Canada
Ottawa, Ontario K1A 0T6
Tel: +1(613) 951-8285
Fax: +1(613) 951-9040
Chief, Postsecondary Education Section: Douglas Lynd
Founded: 1919

Canadian Commission for Unesco/ Commission canadienne pour l'Unesco
350 Albert Street, P.O. Box 1047, Ottawa, Ontario K1P 5V8
Tel: +1(613) 546-4325
Fax: +1(613) 566-4405
President: Roseann Runte
Secretary-General: Vivian F. Launay
International Relations: Information Officer, Terry O'Grady
Founded: 1957

CENTRAL AFRICAN REPUBLIC

UNIVERSITIES

*University of Bangui
[Université de Bangui]
Avenue des Martyrs, B.P. 1450, Bangui
Tel: +236(61) 20-00
Recteur: Nali Mamadou
Secrétaire général: Maurice Saragba
Founded: 1969
F: Law and Economics; Letters and Humanities; Science and Technology; Health Sciences.
S: Education.
I: Business Administration; Rural Development; Applied Linguistics.
D: Research in Science Education; Mathematics and Computer Sciences.

NATIONAL ACADEMIC BODIES

Ministry of National and Higher Education
[Ministère de l'Education nationale et de l'Enseignement supérieur]
B.P. 1583, Bangui
Tel: +236(61) 43-00
Telex: mineduc 5333 rc bangui
Ministre: Etienne Goyemide

Central African National Commission for Unesco
[Commission nationale centrafricaine pour l'Unesco]
B.P. 1583, Bangui
Tel: +236(61) 43-00
Fax: +236(61) 35-61
Telex: mineduc 5333 rc bangui
Président: Etienne Goyemide
Secrétaire général: Abel Koulaninga

CHAD

UNIVERSITIES

University of N'Djaména
[Université du N'Djaména]
B.P. 1117, N'Djaména
Tel: +235(51) 4444
Fax: +235(51) 4033
Telex: 5369 kd
Recteur: Tom Erdimi (1991-)
Secrétaire-général: Zozabe Issaya
Founded: 1971
F: Letters, Modern Languages, and Human Sciences; Law, Economics, and Business Administration; Exact and Applied Sciences; Health Sciences.
I: Stockraising; Human Sciences Research.

HIGHER INSTITUTE FOR EDUCATION
[INSTITUT NATIONAL DES SCIENCES DE L'EDUCATION]
B.P. 473, N'Djaména
Tel: +235(51) 4487
Fax: +235(51) 4550
Directeur: Helou Djarma (1991-94)
Directeur d'Etudes: Beasngar Tchanglayé
Education.

OTHER INSTITUTIONS

Centre National d'Appui à la Recherche
B.P. 1228, N'Djaména
Tel: +235(51) 2435
Fax: +235(51) 5884
Directeur: Abakar Adoum Haggar
Founded: 1988
Research.

Ecole nationale d'Administration et de Magistrature
B.P. 758, N'Djaména
Tel: +235(51) 4097
Fax: +235(51) 4356
Directeur: Mangaral Banté
Founded: 1963
Finance; Diplomatic Studies; Technical Studies; Administration.

Ecole nationale des Travaux publics
N'Djaména
Tel: +235(51) 4971
Fax: +235(51) 3709
Telex: 5222 kd
Founded: 1965
Public Works.

Institut de Recherches du Coton et des Textiles
route de Farcha, B.P. 764, N'Djaména
Tel: +235(51) 2751
Fax: +235(51) 3228
Directeur: Pareal Alladoumnaué Nadingar (1946-)
Founded: 1932
Cotton and Textile Research.

NATIONAL ACADEMIC BODIES

Ministry of National Education
[Ministère de l'Education nationale]
B.P. 731, N'Djaména
Tel: +235(51) 4476
Fax: +235(51) 4581
Ministre: Mahamat Ahmat Al-Habo

Chad National Commission for Unesco
[Commission nationale tchadienne pour l'Unesco]
Ministère de l'Education nationale, B.P. 731, N'Djaména
Tel: +235(51) 4671
Fax: +235(51) 6330
Cable: unesco ndjamena
Président: Dange Laobele
Secrétaire-général: Khalil Alio

CHILE

UNIVERSITIES AND TECHNICAL UNIVERSITIES

PUBLIC INSTITUTIONS

Catholic University of the North, Antofagasta
[Universidad Católica del Norte]
Avenida Angamos 0610, Apartado postal 23, Antofagasta
Tel: +56(83) 222-040
Fax: +56(83) 241-724
Telex: 225097
Cable: Udelnorte
Rector: Juan Music Tomicic
Founded: 1956
F: Architecture; Science; Economics and Administration; Education; Marine Sciences; Engineering.
D: Extension.

University of Antofagasta
[Universidad de Antofagasta]
Antonio Angamos 601, Antofagasta
Tel: +56(83) 247-804
Fax: +56(83) 247-786
Rector: Jaime Godoy Jorquera
Founded: 1981
F: Engineering; Education and Humanities; Health Sciences.
I: Oceanography Research; Anthropological Research.

*University of Atacama
[Universidad de Atacama]
Avenida Copyapu 435, Copiapó
Tel: +56(52) 212-005
Fax: +56(52) 212-662
Rector: Mario Maturana Claro
Secretario General: Alejandro Alvarez Davies
Founded: 1957, 1981
F: Engineering; Humanities and Education.
S: Technology.
I: Scientific and Technological Research; Postgraduate Studies; Mining and Water Legislation; Mining Technical Assistants.

University of Bío Bío
[Universidad del Bío Bío]
Casilla 5-C, Avenida Collao 1202, Concepción
Tel: +56(41) 314-364
Fax: +56(41) 313-897
Telex: 343135 concepción
Rector: Roberto Goycoolea Infante (1992-)
Vice-Rector (Academic): Hilario Hernández Gurruchaga
Founded: 1988
F: Architecture, Construction, and Design (Concepción and Chillán); Business Management; Education; Engineering; Natural Resources; Sciences.
S: Architecture; Construction; Design.
D: Auditing and Administration; Information Systems; Arts and Letters (Chillón); Education (Chillón); History and Geography (Chillón); Electrical Engineering; Industrial Engineering; Forestry; Mechanical Engineering; Agro-Industry and Environmental Science (Chillón); Nutrition (Chillón); Physics; School of Nursing (Chillón); Mathematics; Chemistry; Mathematics and Physics (Chillón).

Catholic University of Chile
[Pontificia Universidad Católica de Chile]
Alameda 340, Casilla 114-D, Santiago
Tel: +56(2) 222-4516
Fax: +56(2) 222-5515
Telex: 240395 pucva cl
Cable: Alameda 340
Rector: Juan de Dios Vial Correa (1985-)
Founded: 1888
F: Agriculture; Architecture and Fine Arts; Biology; Economics and Administration; Physics; History, Geography, and Political Science; Letters; Mathematics; Chemistry; Social

Sciences; Law; Education; Philosophy;
Engineering; Medicine; Theology.
Ce: Tele-Education.

Southern University of Chile
[Universidad Austral de Chile]
Independencia 641, Valdivia
Tel: 3961
Telex: 71035 unaus cl
Cable: independencia 641
Rector: Manfred Max Neef
Founded: 1955
F: Medicine; Veterinary Medicine; Agriculture;
Forestry; Philosophy and Humanities; Economics
and Business Administration; Science; Judicial
and Social Sciences; Fishery and Oceanography;
Engineering.

University of Chile
[Universidad de Chile]
Alameda Bernardo O'Higgins 1050, Santiago
Tel: +56(2) 698-9539
Fax: +56(2) 698-1891
Rector: Jaime Lavados Montes (1990-94)
Pro-Rector: Atilano Lamana Pola
Founded: 1738, 1839, 1842
F: Architecture and Town Planning; Arts;
Science; Agriculture and Forestry; Economics
and Administration; Physics and Mathematics;
Chemistry and Pharmacy; Veterinary Medicine;
Law; Philosophy and Humanities; Medicine;
Dentistry; Social Sciences.
I: Political Science; International Studies;
Nutrition and Food Technology.
D: Extension.

Catholic University of Concepción
[Universidad Católica de la Sant. Concepción]
Arturo Prat 88, Concepción
Rector: Pbro. Eliseo Escudero Herrero

University of Concepción
[Universidad de Concepción]
Victor Lamas No 1290, Casilla 20-C, Concepción
Tel: +56(41) 225-364
Fax: +56(41) 227-455
Telex: 260005 teuco cl
Cable: halcon rectoria
Rector: Augusto Parra Muñoz (1990-94)
Secretario General: Carlos Álvárez Núñez
Founded: 1919
F: Science; Agricultural, Veterinary and Forestry
Sciences; Biology and Natural Sciences;
Economic and Administrative Sciences; Juridical
and Social Sciences; Education, Humanities and
Fine Arts; Pharmacy; Engineering; Medicine;
Odontology.
Ce: Applied Economic Geology (Multinational);
Environmental Sciences (Multinational).

University 'Arturo Prat' Iquique
[Universidad 'Arturo Prat' Iquique]
Avenida 11 de Septiembre 2120, Iquique
Tel: 22472
Telex: 323126 unapiq ck
Rector: Enrique Diaz Vasquez
Founded: 1984
D: Economics and Management; Education and
Humanities; Marine Sciences; Engineering;
Science.
Ce: Desert Studies.

La Serena University
[Universidad de La Serena]
Avenida Raúl Bitrn s/n, La Serena
Tel: +56(51) 226-080
Fax: +56(51) 211-473
Telex: 220044 unise Cl
Rector: Jaime Pozo Cisternas (1990-)
Secretario General: Luis Núñez Olivares
Founded: 19⁸¹
F: Engineering; Sciences; Humanities; S; Limarí
Agriculture (Ovalle).
L: Applied Research.

University of Magallanes
[Universidad de Magallanes]
Angamos y Zenteno S/N, Punta Arenas
Tel: +56(61) 224-523
Fax: +56(61) 212-973
Cable: 380004 umag
Rector: Victor Fajardo Morales
Founded: 1964, 1981
F: Engineering; Humanities and Social
Sciences; Science.
I: Patagonia Studies.

University of Los Lagos, Osorno
[Universidad de Los Lagos]
Fuschslocher S/No, Osorno
Rector: Daniel López S.

Metropolitan University of Educational Sciences Santiago
[Universidad Metropolitana de Ciencias de la
Educación]
Avenida José Pedro Alessandri 774, Santiago
Tel: +56(2) 225-7731
Rector: Jesus González López
Founded: 1986
F: Arts and Physical Education; Philosophy and
Education; Science; History, Geography, and
Letters.
I: Entomology.

Metropolitain University of Technology, Santiago
[Universidad Tecnologica Metropolitana]
Dieciocho 161, Santiago
Rector: Luis Pinto Faverio

University of Santiago de Chile
[Universidad de Santiago de Chile]
Avenida Sur 3469, Santiago Poniente, Casilla
4637, Correo 2, Santiago
Tel: +56(2) 761-011
Rector: Eduardo Morales Santos
Founded: 1947, 1981
F: Engineering; Humanities; Science; Economics
and Administration.
S: Technology.
Ce: Computer.

Catholic University of Maule, Talca
[Universidad Catolica del Maule]
Avenida San Miguel S/N, Talca
Rector: Roberto Montecinos Espiñoza

University of Talca
[Universidad de Talca]
2 Norte 685, Talca
Tel: +56(71) 226-055
Fax: +56(71) 228-054
Rector: Alvaro Rojas Marín (1991-95)
Secretario General: Carlos Hojas Alonso
Founded: 1981
F: General Studies; Law; Natural Resources;
Management Sciences.
I: Educational Research; Humanities.

University of Tarapacá
[Universidad de Tarapacá]
General Velasquez 1775, Arica
Tel: 42600
Telex: 221036
Cable: Untar Cl
Rector: Luis Tapia Iturrieta
Founded: 1982
F: Administration and Economics; Science;
Education; Humanities and Letters; Engineering.
I: Agriculture; Anthropology and Archaeology.

Frontier University Temuco
[Universidad de la Frontera Temuco]
Avenida Francisco Salazar 01145, Temuco
Tel: +56(45) 252-835
Fax: +56(45) 252-547
E-Mail: @uchcecvm.cec.uchile.cl
Telex: 267038 ufro-cl
Rector: Heinrich von Boer
Secretario General: Fernando Matamala
Founded: 1981
F: Medicine; Engineering; Education and
Humanities; Agriculture.
I: Informatics; Agroindustry.

Catholic University of Temuco
[Universidad Católica de Temuco]
Avenida Alemania 0211, Temuco
Rector: Monsñorjorge Hourton Poisson

Catholic University of Valparaíso
[Universidad Católica de Valparaíso]
Avenida Brasil 2950, Casilla 4059, Valparaíso
Tel: +56(32) 251-024
Fax: +56(32) 212-746
E-Mail: BITNET
Telex: 230389 ucval cl
Rector: Bernardo Donoso Riveros (1990-93)
Secretario General: Reinhard Zorn Gardeweg
Founded: 1928
F: Architecture and Town Planning; Basic
Science and Mathematics; Law and Social
Sciences; Philosophy and Education;
Engineering; Natural Resources; Economics and
Administration; Agriculture.
I: Religious Sciences.

Technical University 'Federico Santa María' Valparaíso
[Universidad Técnica 'Federico Santa María']
Avenida Placeres 401, Casilla 110-V, Valparaíso
Tel: +56(32) 660-176
Telex: 230338 utfsm-cl
Cable: Casilla 110-V
Rector: Adolfo Arata Andriani
Founded: 1932
F: Engineering; Science; Economics and
Administration.

University of Educational Sciences 'Playa Ancha' Valparaíso
[Universidad de Playa Ancha de Ciencias de la
Educación]
Avenida Playa Ancha 850, Valparaíso
Tel: +56(32) 281-1758
Fax: +56(32) 285-041
Rector: Norman Cortes Larrieu
Secretario General: Patricio Sanhueza Vivanco
Founded: 1985
F: Humanities; Physical Education; Natural and
Exact Sciences; Education Sciences; Arts.

University of Valparaíso
[Universidad de Valparaíso]
Errázuriz 2190, Casilla 123-V, Valparaíso
Tel: +56(32) 213-071
Fax: +56(32) 252-125
Rector: Agustín Squella Narducci
Founded: 1912, 1981
F: Medicine; Law and Social Sciences;
Architecture; Dentistry.
I: Mathematics and Physics; Humanities;
Economic and Management Sciences;
Oceanology Research.
S: Architecture; Civil Engineering; Design; Law;
Social Service; Medicine; Nursing and Midwifery;
Chemistry and Pharmacy; Psychology; Dentistry;
Commercial Engineering; Auditing.

PRIVATE INSTITUTIONS

University of Aconcagua
[Universidad de Aconcagua]
Santo Domingo 31, San Felipe
Tel: +56 511-414
Rector: Rodrigo Oliver Varas
Founded: 1989

University 'Jose Santos Ossa', Antofagasta
[Universidad 'José Santos Ossa', Antofagasta]
Antonino Toro 851, Antofagasta
Rector: Jaime Valenzuela Acuña
Founded: 1992

Contemporary University Arica
[Universidad Contemporana]
21 de Mayo 354, Arica
Tel: +56 252-268
Rector: Normas Reyes Caballero
Founded: 1989
Commerce; Civil Industrial Engineering.

Adventist University of Chile
[Universidad Adventista de Chile]
Km. 12 Chillan a Tanilvoro-casilla 7-D, Chillan
Tel: +56(42) 222-901
Founded: 1989
Agriculture; Commerce; Civil and Agroindustrial Engineering; Accountancy.

Maritime University of Chile
[Universidad Maritima de Chile]
Alvarez 2138 Chorrillos, Viña del Mar
Tel: +56(32) 670-264
Rector: Juan Carlos Toledo de la Maza
Founded: 1990
Commerce; Civil Industrial Engineering; Architecture.

San Sebastián University Concepción
[Universidad San Sebastián]
Diagonal Pedro Aguirre Cerde 1225, Concepción
Tel: +56(41) 230-116
Rector: Carmen Vidal Montecino
Founded: 1989
Commerce; Psychology.

University for Development Concepción
[Universidad del Desarrollo]
Trinitarias 180, Concepción
Tel: +56(41) 242-549
Rector: Luis Ernesto Silva Bafalluy
Founded: 1990
Commerce; Architecture; Law; Civil Engineering.

University 'Francisco de Aguirre', La Serena
[Universidad 'Francisco de Aguirre', La Serena]
Manuel Rodriguez 436, La Serena
Tel: +56 224-858
Rector: Rene Larraguibel Smith
Founded: 1990

University 'Bolivariana' Las Condes-Salvador
[Universidad Bolivariana]
Avenida Las Condes 9430, Las Condes-Salvador
Tel: +62 494-1785
Rector: Francisco Vio Grossi
Founded: 1988
Commerce; Law; Architecture; Anthropology; Psychology; Journalism.

University of Las Condes
[Universidad Las Condes]
Avenida Las Condes 12438, Santiago
Tel: +56(2) 242-5500
Rector: Olga Rondanelli Hidalgo
Founded: 1987
S: Economics; Business Administration; Law.

Regional University 'El Libertador', Quillota
[Universidad Regional El Libertador, Quillota]
O'Higgins 322, Quillota
Tel: +56 310-055
Rector: Alfredo Calvo Apablaza
Psychology.

University 'Leonard Da Vinci' Rancagua
[Universidad 'Leonard Da Vinci']
Avenida República de Chile 592, Rancagua
Tel: +56(72) 224-491
Fax: +56(72) 222-440
Rector: Carlos Olivares Faundez
Founded: 1989
Computer Engineering.

Central University San Bernardo
[Universidad Central]
Avenida José Joaquín Prieto 10001, San Bernardo
Tel: +56 558-5621
Rector: Hugo Gálvez Gajardo
Founded: 1983
F: Architecture and Fine Arts; Law; Social Sciences; Economic and Administrative Sciences; Physical and Mathematical Sciences.
S: Political Science and Administration; Early Childhood Education.
Ce: Social Housing Architecture.

Autonomous Indoamerican University Santiago
[Universidad Autónoma Indoamericana]
Manuel Rodriguez 0351, Santiago
Tel: +56 851-0163
Rector: Moipa Brncic Isaza
Founded: 1989
Commerce.

Iberomerican University of Science and Technology Santiago
[Universidad Iberoamericana de Cienicas y Tecnología]
Moneda 1488/1490, Santiago
Tel: +56 671-0826
Rector: Jaime Lavin Mosquera
Commerce; Agriculture; Food Technology; Civil Engineering; Veterinary Science; Forestry.

International University 'Sek' Santiago
[Universidad Internacional 'Sek']
Villa La Reina, Casilla Postal N, Santiago
Tel: +56(2) 226-4567
Fax: +56(2) 211-4471
Rector: Francisco Guiral Segovia (1989-93)
Secretario General: Francisco Guiral Segovia
Founded: 1988
Economics; Psychology and Educational
Sciences; Law; Cultural Heritage Studies.

Mayor University Santiago
[Universidad Mayor]
Américo Vespucio 357, Providencia, Santiago
Tel: +56(2) 228-9751
Fax: +56(2) 228-6468
Rector: Rubén Covarrubias Giordano (1992-96)
Founded: 1988
S: Architecture; Forestry; Engineering and
Computer Sciences; Agriculture; Veterinary
Science; Industrial Graphics and Textiles.
Ce: Lifelong Education.

National University Andres Bello Santiago
[Universidad Nacional Andres Bello]
Avenida República 252, Santiago
Tel: +56(2) 696-6787
Rector: Monica Madariaga Gutierrez
Founded: 1988
Architecture; Accountancy; Computer Sciences;
Psychology; Journalism; Aquiculture; Law; Civil
Engineering; Construction.

Panamerican University of Science and Arts Santiago
[Universidad Panamericána de Ciencias y Artes]
Traslaviña 436, Yiña del Mar
Tel: +56(32) 685-201
Rector: Jaime Lavin Mosquera
Founded: 1989
Achitecture.

Royal University Santiago
[Universidad Real]
Avenida Las Condes 6830, Santiago
Tel: +56(2) 211-2631
Founded: 1988
Commerce; Psychology; Civil Engineering;
Accountancy; Education; Law; Architecture;
Journalism; Public Relations; Environmental
Design; Business Administration; Technical
Studies.

San Andrés University Santiago
[Universidad San Andrés]
Elena Blanco 1145, Providencia, Santiago
Tel: +56(2) 274-2432
Rector: Jose Elias Aboid
Founded: 1989
Commerce.

Santo Tomás University Santiago
[Universidad Santo Tomás]
Biarritz 1970, Providencia, Santiago
Tel: +56(2) 225-6327
Rector: Fernando Monckeberg
Founded: 1988
F: Sylviculture; Economics and Administration;
Humanities; Education.

University Academy of Christian Humanism Santiago
[Universidad Academia de Humanismo Cristiano]
Alonso Ovalle 1475, Santiago
Tel: +56(2) 695-4831
Fax: +56(2) 695-4824
Rector: Orlando Mella Valenzuela
Secretario General: Alejandro Saavedra
D: Commerce; Political Science; Sociology;
Anthropology; Social Work; Psychology; Social
Communication; Culture and Religion.

University 'Alonso de Ovalle', Santiago
[Universidad 'Alonso de Ovalle', Santiago]
Dieciocho 232, Santiago
Tel: +56(2) 698-6532
Rector: Alberto Naudon Del Rio
Founded: 1988

University of the Americas Santiago
[Universidad de Las Américas]
Manuel Montt 948, Providencia, Santiago
Tel: +56(2) 223-1135
Fax: +56(2) 225-8520
E-Mail: BITNET
Rector: Mario Albornoz Galdamez
Founded: 1988
Engineering; Economics and Administration;
Agriculture.

University the Andes Santiago
[Universidad de Los Andes]
General Bustamante 86, Santiago
Tel: +56(2) 499-388
Rector: Raul Bertelsen Repetto
Founded: 1989
Medicine; Law.

University of Arts, Science and Communications Santiago
[Universidad de Artes, Ciencias y Communicaciones]
Avenida Salvador 1222, Santiago
Tel: +56(2) 251-5900
Fax: +56(2) 776-414
Rector: Andres Guiloff Dimtstein
Founded: 1989
Commerce; Psychology; Architecture.

University of Arts and Social Sciences Arcis of Santiago
[Universidad de Artes y Ciencias Sociales Arcis]
Huerfanos 1710, Santiago
Tel: +56 699-1261
Rector: Luis Torres Acuña
Founded: 1989

Commerce, Economics, and Business
Administration; Graphic Design; Fine Arts; Dance;
Theatre; Journalism and Social Communication;
Social Service; Sociology.

University of 'Bernardo O'Higgins', Santiago
[Universidad 'Bernardo O'Higgins', Santiago]
Venida Viel 1497, Santiago
Tel: +56(2) 555-3039
Rector: Mario Correa Bacuñan
Founded: 1990

Catholic University of 'Blas Cañas, Santiago
[Universidad Catolica 'Blas Cañas', Santiago]
Jofre 462, Santiago
Tel: +56(2) 639-3032
Rector: Carlos Ortiz Hentiquez
Founded: 1990

University of Computer Sciences Santiago
[Universidad de Ciencias de la Informática]
Bernard Morín 495, Providencia, Santiago
Tel: +56(2) 223-8108
Fax: +56(2) 204-9096
Founded: 1989
S: Computer Sciences and Civil Engineering;
Psychology; Commercial Engineering; Executive
Engineering; Civil Engineering.
D: Informatics.

University Diego Portales Santiago
[Universidad Diego Portales]
Avenida Ejército 260, Santiago
Tel: +56(2) 672-1533
Rector: Manuel Montt Balmaceda
Founded: 1982
F: Business Administration; Law; Human
Sciences.

University 'Finis Terrae' Santiago
[Universidad 'Finis Terrae']
Pedro de Valdivia 1530, Santiago
Tel: +56(2) 274-8084
Fax: +56(2) 209-4135
Rector: Pablo Baraona Urzua
Secretario General: Roberto Guerrero
Founded: 1981
F: Law; Commercial Engineering; Social
Sciences; Architecture and Design.

University 'Gabriela Mistral' Santiago
[Universidad 'Gabriela Mistral']
Avenida Ricardo Lyon 1177, Santiago
Tel: +56(2) 204-7512
Rector: Alicia Romo Roman
Founded: 1981
S: Law; Business and Economics; Psychology;
Education; Social Communication; Civil
Engineering.

University 'Mariano Egaña' Santiago
[Universidad Mariano Egaña]
Providencia 2640, Santiago
Tel: +56(2) 233-2356
Rector: Germán Ceron Lopez
Founded: 1988
Commerce; Accountancy.

University 'Mariscal Sucre' Santiago
[Universidad Mariscal Sucre]
Hernando de Aguirre 2353, Santiago
Tel: +56(2) 696-1276
Rector: Luis Ferreto Mellafe
Founded: 1989
Commerce; Psychology; Civil Industrial
Engineering; Distance Education; Distance
Pedagogy; Distance Public Administration.

University of the Pacific Santiago
[Universidad del Pacífico]
Avenida Las Condes 11121, Santiago
Tel: +56(2) 215-2626
Rector: Julio Ortuzar Prado
Founded: 1990
Commerce.

University of the Republic Santiago
[Universidad La República]
Agustinas 1831, Santiago
Tel: +56(2) 697-0562
Fax: +56(2) 671-8457
Rector: Jorge Carvajal Muñoz
Secretary-General: Manuel Figueroa Santos
Founded: 1988
D: Commerce; Psychology; Architecture; Law;
Civil Industrial Engineering; Sociology.

University of the Southern Cone Salvador
[Universidad del Cono Sur]
Avenida República 190, Salvador
Tel: +56(2) 715-620
Founded: 1989
Commerce.

University of Teaching Santiago
[Universidad Educares]
Luis Rodríguez Velaso 4746, Santiago
Tel: +56(2) 208-0641
Rector: Gabriel de Pujada Hermosilla
Founded: 1989
Commerce; Psychology; Education; Ecology;
Physical Education; Psychopedagogy; Design and
Graphic Art; Agroindustrial Studies; Industrial
Management.

Technical University 'Vicente Pérez Rosales', Santiago
[Universidad Tecnologica 'Vicente Pérez
Rosales', Santiago]
Brown Norte 290, Santiago
Tel: +56(2) 274-5432
Rector: Karin Riedemann Hall
Founded: 1991

Autonomous University of the South Temuco
[Universidad Autónoma del Sur]
Porvenir 580, Temuco
Tel: +56 240-651
Founded: 1989
Commerce; Law.

University of Temuco
[Universidad de Temuco]
Avenida Alemania 0280, Temuco
Tel: +56 213-402
Rector: Aner Borgeaud Padilla
Founded: 1989
*Commerce; Architecture; Law; Forestry;
Psychology; Journalism.*

University 'Adolfo Ibañez', Valparaíso
[Universidad 'Adolfo Ibañez']
Balmeceda 1625 Recreo, Valparaíso
Tel: +56(32) 366-2676
Rector: Gonzalo Ibañez Santa Maria
Founded: 1988
Commerce; Civil Engineering; Law.

University of the Sea Viña del Mar
[Universidad del Mar]
Amunátegui 1838, Viña del Mar
Tel: +56(32) 625-544
Rector: Raul Baeza Aspee
Founded: 1989
*Commerce; Civil Industrial Engineering;
Computer Sciences.*

University of Viña del Mar
[Universidad Viña del Mar]
Diego Portales 90, Agua Santa, Viña del Mar
Tel: +56(32) 662-041
Rector: Barham Madain Ayub
Founded: 1988
*Commerce; Civil Engineering and Computer
Sciences; Architecture; Journalism.*

OTHER INSTITUTIONS

Instituto Profesional Adventista
Fundo Las Mariposas, Camino Tanilvoro Km 12,
Coihueco, Chillan
Tel: +56 222-901
Founded: 1982

Instituto Profesional Agrario Adolfo Matthei
Avenida Alcalde Soriano s/n, Casilla 58-A,
Osorno
Tel: +56 232-640
Founded: 1981
Agriculture.

Instituto Profesional Academia de Idiomas y Estudios Profesionales (A.I.E.P.)
Avenida Holanda 116 Providencia, Santiago
Tel: +56(2) 233-2368
Founded: 1989
Languages and Professional Studies.

Instituto Profesional Aleman de Valparaíso
Pilkcomayo s/n, Cerro Concepción, Valparaíso
Tel: +56(32) 217-548
Founded: 1988

Instituto Profesional Aleman Wilhelm Von Humboldt
Avenida 6150, Las Condes, Santiago
Tel: +56(2) 220-3167
Founded: 1988

Instituto Profesional ALPES
Republica 430, Santiago
Tel: +56(2) 689-0016
Founded: 1990

Instituto Profesional Andalien
Balmaceda 1048, Temuco
Tel: +56 215-813
Founded: 1990

Instituto Profesional la Araucana
Monijitas 506, Santiago
Tel: +56(2) 697-2104
Founded: 1988

Instituto Profesional de la Araucania
Avenida Alemania 0587, Temuco
Tel: +56 212-192
Founded: 1987

Instituto Profesional ARCIS
Huerfanos 1710, Santiago
Tel: +56(2) 699-1261
Founded: 1990

Instituto Profesional ARCOS
Campos de Deporte 121, Nuñoa, Santiago
Tel: +56(2) 204-4985
Founded: 1989

Instituto Profesional de las Artes Valero
Almirante Simpson 28, Santiago
Tel: +56(2) 634-5734
Founded: 1990
Arts.

Instituto Profesional de Atacama
O'Higgins 340, Copiapó
Tel: +56 214-017
Founded: 1988

Instituto Profesional de Aysen
Avenida Baquedano 237, Coyhaique
Founded: 1990

Instituto Profesional del Bio Bio
Victor Lamas 1299, Concepción
Tel: +56(41) 243-574
Founded: 1990

Instituto Profesional Blas Cañas
Carmen 264, Santiago
Tel: +56(2) 393-032
Founded: 1981

Instituto Profesional Campus
Avenida Manuel Montt 948, Providencia, Santiago
Tel: +56(2) 274-2647
Founded: 1983

Instituto Profesional 'Carlos Casanueva'
Ramón Carnicer 65, Santiago
Founded: 1993

Instituto Profesional Carlos Thielemann Martín
San Juan de Dios Pení 469, La Serena
Tel: +56 225-888
Founded: 1990

Instituto Profesional CENAFORM
General del Canto 367, Providencia, Santiago
Tel: +56(2) 251-3712
Founded: 1989

Instituto Profesional Centros de Estudios Turisticos
Marchant Perira 1077, Providencia, Santiago
Tourism.

Instituto Profesional Chileño Británico de Cultura
Santa Lucía 124, Santiago
Tel: 56(2) 638-2156
Founded: 1982
Culture.

Instituto Profesional de Ciencias de la Computación Acuario Data
Jofré 462, Santiago
Tel: +56(2) 689-2420
Founded: 1990
Data Processing.

Instituto Profesional CIISA
Avenida Pedro de Valdivia 2103, Providencia, Santiago
Tel: 56(2) 204-7677

Instituto Profesional de Computación
Almirante Barroso 37, Santiago
Tel: +56(2) 696-4816
Founded: 1989
Computation.

Instituto Profesional de las Comunicaciones Procom
Ernesto P. Lagarrigue 180, Santiago
Tel: +56(2) 776-399
Communication.

Instituto Profesional CONANDES
Arturo Prat 330, Arica
Tel: +56 251-441
Founded: 1989

Instituto Profesional de Concepción
Lincoyān 444, Concepción
Tel: +56(41) 230-116
Founded: 1990

Instituto Profesional CROVNLIET
Almirante Pastene 167, Providencia, Santiago
Tel: +56(2) 41827
Founded: 1990

Instituto Profesional de Desarrollo Regional Los Leones
Avenida Libertador Bdo. O'Higgins 393, Santiago
Tel: +56(2) 633-8190
Founded: 1990
Regional Development.

Instituto Profesional Diego Portales
Maipú 301, Concepción
Tel: +56(41) 229-454
Founded: 1988

Instituto Profesional 'Dr. Virginio Gómez G.'
Prat 451, Santiago
Tel: +56(2) 322-544
Founded: 1989

Instituto Profesional D.U.O.C.
Dário Urzúa 2100, Providencia, Santiago
Tel: +56(2) 225-8734
Founded: 1983

Instituto Profesional EACE
Avenida Salvador 1633 Ñuñoa, Salvador
Tel: +56(2) 274-7636
Founded: 1990

Instituto Profesional ECACEC
Avenida República 188-190, Santiago
Tel: +56(2) 695-2938
Founded: 1990

Instituto Profesional de Economia y Administración de Santiago
Vergara 702, Santiago
Tel: +56(2) 696-2887
Founded: 1989
Economics; Administration.

Instituto Profesional Educares
Luis Rodríguez Velasco 4746, Las Condes, Santiago
Tel: +56(2) 208-0641
Founded: 1981

Instituto Profesional Escuela Latinoamericana de Idiomas (ELADI)
Avenida José Miguel Infante 927, Providencia, Santiago
Tel: +56(2) 251-8111
Founded: 1988

Instituto Profesional ENAC
Echaurren 26, Santiago
Tel: +56(2) 698-8714
Founded: 1989

Instituto Profesional Epson
Avenida Apoquindo 5229 y Nueva Los Leones 0281
Tel: +56 212-3289
Founded: 1993

Instituto Profesional ESANE del Norte
Esmeralda 2040, Antofagasta
Founded: 1990

Instituto Profesional Escuela Superior de Comercio Exterior (ESCE)
Libertador Bdo. O'Higgins 1282, Valparaíso
Tel: +56(2) 214-942
Founded: 1989
External Commerce.

Instituto Profesional Escuela de Comunicación Monica Herrera
Avenida Ricardo Lyon 227, Providencia, Santiago
Tel: +56(2) 231-5335
Founded: 1982
Communication.

Instituto Profesional Escuela de Contadores Auditores de Santiago
Avenida Providencia 2640, Santiago
Tel: +56(2) 233-2356
Founded: 1982
Accountancy and Auditing.

Instituto Profesional Escuela Moderna de Música
Pio X 2446 Providencia, Santiago
Tel: +56(2) 232-2774
Founded: 1988
Music.

Instituto Profesional Escuela Nacional de Relaciones Públicas
Lota 2340, Providencia, Santiago
Tel: +56(2) 232-1900
Founded: 1989
Public Relations.

Instituto Profesional Escuela Superior de Negocios
Reusch 440, Temuco
Tel: +56 244-313
Marketing.

Instituto Profesional ESUCOMEX
Almirante Pastene 266, Providencia, Santiago
Tel: +56(2) 251-0011
Founded: 1989

Instituto Profesional de Estudios Superiores Blas Cañas
Jofré 462, Santiago
Tel: +56(2) 639-3032
Founded: 1981

Instituto Profesional GAMMA
Dieciocho 18, Santiago
Tel: +56(2) 672-3333
Founded: 1990

Instituto Profesional Guillermo Subercaseaux
Agustinas 1476, Santiago
Tel: +56(2) 698-1971

Instituto Profesional Helen Keller
Blanco 1081, Valparaíso
Tel: +56(32) 254-016
Founded: 1989

Instituto Profesional Hogar Catequistico
Avenida Miguel Claro 337, Providencia, Santiago
Tel: +56(2) 235-9879
Founded: 1989

Instituto Superior de Artes y Ciencias de la Comunicación (IACC)
Avenida Salvador 1222, Providencia, Santiago
Tel: +56(2) 274-4897
Founded: 1987
Arts; Communication.

Instituto Profesional INACAP
Avenida Chesterton 7028, Las Condes, Santiago
Tel: +56(2) 229-9000
Founded: 1981

Instituto Profesional INCACEA
Avenida Cristóbal Colón 6607, Las Condes, Santiago
Tel: +56(2) 229-3157
Founded: 1989

Instituto Profesional IPEVE
Avenida República 240-237, Santiago
Tel: +56(2) 698-5508

Instituto Profesional ITES
Uno Norte 363, Viña del Mar
Tel: +56(32) 977-635
Founded: 1983

Instituto Profesional Iquique English College
J.J. Pérez 419, Iquique
Tel: +56 412-409
Founded: 1981

Instituto Profesional ITESA
Avenida Repúblic 78, Santiago
Tel: +56(2) 699-4092
Founded: 1990

Instituto Profesional John F. Kennedy
Vergara 167, Santiago
Tel: +56(2) 698-4125
Founded: 1990

Instituto Profesional José Santos Ossa
Antonino Toro 851, Antofagasta
Tel: +56 247-795
Founded: 1989

Instituto Profesional Juan Bohon
Los Carreras 851, La Serena
Tel: +56 211-793
Founded: 1990

Instituto Profesional Latinoamericano de Comercio Exterior
Dieciocho 182, Providencia, Santiago
Tel: +56(2) 699-4760
External Commerce.

Instituto Profesional Libertador de Los Andes
Avenida Libertador, Bernardo O'Higgins 197, Los Andes
Tel: +56 424-954
Founded: 1981

Instituto Profesional de Los Angeles
Avenida Ricardo Vicuña 776, Los Angeles
Founded: 1989

Instituto Profesional Luis Galdames
María Luisa Santander 466, Providencia, Santiago
Tel: +56(2) 223-4581
Founded: 1984

Instituto Profesional de Administracion y Negocios de Manpower
Avenida Ricardo Lyon 891, Providencia, Santiago
Tel: +56(2) 384-774
Founded: 1981
Manpower Administration.

Instituto Profesional de Massachusetts
Tres Sur 1048, Talca
Tel: +56 225-713
Founded: 1990

Instituto Profesional del Maule
Cuatro Oriente 1279, Talca
Founded: 1988

Instituto Profesional del Pacífico
Avenida Las Condes 11121, Santiago
Tel: +56(2) 215-2626
Founded: 1982

Instituto Profesional Providencia
Dr. Hernán Alessandri 644, Providencia, Santiago
Tel: +56(2) 223-8635
Founded: 1982

Instituto Profesional SOEDUC
Combate Las Coimas 299, San Felipe
Tel: +56 511-640
Founded: 1990

Instituto Profesional del Sur
Anthauer 933, Osorno
Tel: +56 233-827
Founded: 1988

Instituto Profesional Teatro La Casa
Romero 2421, Santiago
Tel: +56(2) 681-5959
Founded: 1982

Instituto Profesional de Temuco
Avenida Alemania 0281, Temuco
Tel: +56 235-972
Founded: 1988

Instituto Profesional de Valparaíso
Errázuriz 1090, Valparaíso
Tel: +56(32) 252-338
Founded: 1988

Instituto Profesional de Viña del Mar
Diego Portales 90 Agua Santa, Viña del Mar
Tel: +56(32) 662-041
Founded: 1985

Instituto Profesional VIPRO
Brown Norte 290 Ñuñoa, Santiago
Tel: +56(2) 274-5432
Founded: 1987

Instituto Profesional Virginio Gómez
Prat 451, Los Angeles
Founded: 1989

Instituto Profesional Wilhelm von Humboldt
Avenida Kennedy 6150, Las Condes, Santiago
Tel: +56(2) 220-3167
Founded: 1988

Instituto Profesional ZIPTER
Padre Mariano 94, Providencia, Santiago
Tel: +56(2) 251-8435
Founded: 1989

Instituto Profesional San Bartolomé de La Serena
Avenida Estadio 1739, La Serena
Tel: +56 221-179
Founded: 1988

NATIONAL ACADEMIC BODIES

Ministry of Education
[Ministerio de Educación]
Avenida el Libertador Bernardo O'Higgins, Santiago
Tel: +56(2) 671-0292
Fax: +56(2) 671-6164
Ministro: Jorge Arrate Mac Niven

Consejo de Rectores Universidades Chilenas
Alameda 1371, 48 piso, Casilla 14798, Santiago
Tel: +56(2) 696-4286
Founded: 1954

Council of Private Professional Institutes
[Consejo de Institutos Profesionales Privados]
Avenida Ricardo Lyon 891, Santiago
Tel: +56(2) 384-774

Chilean National Commission for Unesco
[Comisión Nacional Chilena de Cooperación con la Unesco]
Oficina de Relaciones Internacionales, Ministerio de Educación Pública, Avenida Libertador Bernardo O'Higgins 1371, Santiago
Tel: +56(2) 698-3351
Fax: +56(2) 698-7831
Telex: 240-567 meduc cl
Cable: unescom santiago +
Tel: +56(2) 671-0518
Fax: +56(2) 696-8874
Telex: 240.567 nedyc ck
Presidente: Jorge Arrate MacNiven, Minister of Education Secretaria Ejecutiva: María Josefina Lira Bianchi

CHINA

UNIVERSITIES AND TECHNICAL UNIVERSITIES

Anhui Normal University
Wuhu (Anhui Province)
Tel: +86 2065
Cable: 1234
President: Yijin Du
Founded: 1949, 1970, 1972
D: Chinese Language and Literature; Political Science; History; Music and Fine Arts; Chemistry; Education; Biology; Geography; Mathematics; Physics; Physical Education; Correspondence Courses.
Research I.: Chinese Language; Education Science; Higher Education; Organic Chemistry.
Ut: Evening Studies.

Anhui University
Hefei (Anhui Province)
Tel: +86(551) 62655
D: Language Literature; History; Philosophy; Economy; Law; Library; Foreign Languages; Mathematics; Physics; Chemistry; Biology; Radio-Electronics; Computer.

Anhui University of Labour
District of Xuancheng (Anhui Province)

Beijing Agricultural Engineering University
Qinghua Donglu, Beijing 100083
Tel: +86(1) 201-6303
Fax: +86(1) 201-6320
Telex: 222573 rimet cn
Cable: 9125
President: Zhixin Wing
Secretary-General: Xiaosan Jiang
Founded: 1952
D: Agricultural Mechanization; Farm Power and Machinery; Water Conservancy and Building Engineering; Electronics and Electric Power Engineering; Food Engineering.
I: Rural Development; Agricultural Mechanization; New Fodder Resources Development; Livestock Engineering.

Beijing Agricultural University
Yuanmingyuan West Road 2, Haidian District, Beijing 100094
Tel: +86(1) 258-2330
Fax: +86(1) 258-2332
Telex: 222487 bau cn
Cable: 5832 beijing
President: Yuanchun Shi
Founded: 1905, 1949, 1954
D: Agronomy; Horticulture; Plant Protection; Soil and Plant Nutrition; Animal Husbandry; Agrometeorology; Food Science; Land Resource Science; Agricultural Applied Chemistry.
C: Veterinary Medicine; Agricultural Economics and Management; Biological Sciences.
Ce: Agricultural Remote Sensing (National Application and Training).

Research I: Agricultural Economics; Agricultural Engineering Installational.
I: Preplanting and Dost Harvest Technology; Plant Ecological Engineering; Applied Chemistry; Agricultual Resources, Environment and Remote Sensing; Agricultural Education; Animal Science for Agriculture and Biology.
Lab: National Agrobiotechnology.

Beijing Medical University
38 Xue Yuan Lu, Beijing 100083
Tel: +86(1) 201-7601
Fax: +86(1) 201-5681
Telex: 222782 bmu cn
President: Debing Wang
Founded: 1912
F: Nursing.
S: Basic Medicine; Pharmaceutical Studies; Public Health; Stomatology; Clinical Medicine No.1; Clinical Medicine No.2; Clinical Medicine No.3.
I: Mental Health; Clinical Pharmacology; Clinical Medicine; Basic Medicine; Pharmaceutical Science; Child and Adolescent Research; Environmental Medicine; Sports Medicine; Urology; Drug Dependence Research; Cancer Research (Beijing); Hematology; Hepatology.

Beijing Normal University
[Beijing Shifan Daxue]
19 Xin Jie Kou Wai Street, Beijing 100875
Tel: +86(1) 201-2288
Fax: +86(1) 201-1674
President: Fukang Fang
Founded: 1902
D: Mathematics; Physics; Chemistry; Chinese Language; History.
I: Low Energy Nuclear Physics; Modern Education Technology; History; Foreign Education.

Beijing Polytechnical University
Ping Le Yuan 100, Chao Yang District, Beijing 100022
Tel: +86(1) 771-1177
Fax: +86(1) 771-4088
Cable: 2971 beijing
President: Hu Wang
Standing Vice-President: Shaopu Cai
Founded: 1960
D: Mechanical Engineering; Industrial Automation; Electronic Engineering; Civil Engineering; Chemistry and Environmental Engineering; Applied Physics; Computer Sciences (DCS); Applied Mathematics; Metallic Materials Science and Engineering; Thermal Science and Engineering; Social Sciences; Architecture; Graduate; Basic Machine-Building Fundamentals; Basic Science.
Ce: Computer; Audio-Visual Assistant Education.
C: Economical Management.

Beijing University
Hai Dian, Beijing 100871 (Beijing Municipality)
Tel: +86(1) 256-1166
Fax: +86(1) 256-3883
Telex: 22239 pkuni cn
President: Shuqing Wu
Founded: 1898
D: *Mathematics; Probability and Statistics;
Mechanics; Physics; Geophysics; Technological
Physics; Radio Electronics; Computer Science;
Chemistry; Biology; Geology; Geography;
Psychology; Chinese Language and Literature;
History; Archaeology; Philosophy; International
Politics; Economics; International Economics;
Economics Management; Law; Library and
Information Sciences; Sociology; Oriental
Languages and Literature; Western Languages
and Literature; Russian Language and Literature;
English Language and Literature; Politics and
Administrative Management.*

Beijing University of Aeronautics and Astronautics (BUAA)
37 Xue Yuan Road, Beijing 100083
Tel: +86(1) 201-7251
Fax: +86202-8356
Telex: 222700 buaa cn
Cable: 0085
President: Shituan Shen (1988-)
Secretary-General: Baojun Liu
Founded: 1952
D: *Materials Science and Engineering;
Electronics Engineering; Automatic Control;
Propulsion; Aircraft Design and Applied
Mechanics; Computer Sciences; Manufacturing
Engineering; Applied Mathematics and Physics;
Mechanical and Electrical Engineering; Social
Sciences; Foreign Languages; Systems
Engineering.*
C: *Continuing Education; Management;
Astronautics.*
I: *Higher Education; Thermal Power
Engineering; Fluid Mechanics; Computer
Software Engineering; Manufacturing Engineering
I; Robotics; Plant Engineering; Reliability
Engineering; Solid Mechanics; Unmanned Aircraft
Design.*

Beijing University of Foreign Studies
2 North Xisanhuan Avenue, Haidan District,
Beijing 100081 (Beijing Municipality)
Tel: +86(1) 89-0351
Fax: +86(1) 831-1956
Telex: 222378
President: Fuxiang Wang
Founded: 1941, 1954
D: *English I.; English II.; Russian; French;
German; Spanish; Afro-Asian Languages; Eastern
European Languages; Arabic; Japanese;
Chinese; Interpreter Training (UN).*

Beijing University of Posts and Telecommunications
42 Xue Yuan Road, Haidian District, Beijing
100088
Tel: +86(1) 201-1974
Fax: +86(1) 202-8643
Telex: 222341 buptf cn
President: Xiang-hua Zhu (1989-93)
Director: Xiu-feng Li
Founded: 1955
D: *Telecommunications Engineering; Radio
Engineering; Management Engineering;
Computer Engineering; Mechanical Engineering;
Information Engineering; Applied Science and
Technology; Social Science; Foreign Languages;
Basic Courses Teaching.*
S: *Graduate Studies.*
F: *Correspondence Courses.*
I: *Scientific Research; Chemical Protection;
Optical Communication and Opto-electronic
Information Processing; Modern Communication
Technology.*
Ce: *Computer Aided Design (CAD); Computer;
Training.*

Beijing University of Science and Technology
30 Xueyuan Lu, Beijing 100083 (Beijing
Municipality)
Tel: +86(1) 201-9944
Fax: +86(1) 201-7283
Telex: 22036 biaat cn ext, ust beijing
Cable: 7441
President: Jingbo Li
Vice-President: Tianjung Yang
Founded: 1952
D: *Geology; Mining and Mineral Engineering;
Metallurgy; Metal Forming; Materials Science
and Engineering; Surface Sciences and
Corrosion Engineering; Thermal Energy
Engineering; Mechanical Engineering;
Automation; Computer Sciences; Mathematics
and Mechanics; Physics; Chemistry; Physical
Chemistry; Management; Social Sciences;
Foreign Languages.*
I: *Materials Physics; Metallurgy; Mechanical
Engineering; Material Science; Physical
Chemistry of Metallurgical Process; History of
Metallurgy and Materials; Geology; Mining
Research; Automatica Control; Thermal
Engineering; Applied Physics; Management
Science; Computer and System Science; Metal
Forming.*
Research I.: *Material's Failure; Higher
Education; Rolling Technological Innovation
(Designing).*
Ce: *Corrosion and Protection.*

China Capital Medical University Beijing
10 Sitoutiao, Beijing (Beijing Municipality)
Tel: +86(1) 33-9484
Medicine.

China Textile University Shanghai
1882 Yanan West Road, Shanghai 200051
(Shanghai Municipality)
Tel: +86(21) 259-9800
President: Yongchung Jiang
Registrar: Duoxiang Zhang
Founded: 1951
*D: Textile Engineering I; Textile Engineering II;
Textile Chemistry; Man-made Fibres; Mechanical
Engineering; Electrical Engineering and
Computer Science; Basic Science; Clothing
Technology; Industrial Management; Social
Science.*

China University of Mining and Technology Xuzhou
Xuzhou 221008 (Jiangsu Province)
Tel: +86(516) 88653
Fax: +86(516) 30393
Telex: 34076 xpttb cn
Cable: 2233
President: Shiji Peng (1982-)
Administration Officer: Tingen Zhang
Founded: 1909
*D: Mining Engineering; Mine Construction; Coal
Geology; Automation Engineering; Mechanical
Engineering; Mining Machinery; Coal Preparation
and Utilization; Mining Surveying and
Geophysical Prospecting; Social Sciences;
Applied Mathematics and Mechanics; Technical
Foreign Languages; Physical Education.
C: Economics and Trade; Continuing Education.*

Central University for Nationalities
27 Baishiqiao Road, Haidian District, Beijing
(Beijing Municipality)
Tel: +86(1) 890771

Chinese University of Political Science and Law Beijing
41 Xueyuan South Road, Haidian District, Beijing
(Beijing Municipality)
Tel: +86(1) 201-5517
Political Science; Law.

Chongqing University
Shapingba, Chongqing 630044 (Sichuan Province)
Tel: +86 66-4893
Telex: 62216 cquy cn
Cable: Chongqing 6234
President: Leguan Gu (1987-)
Founded: 1929
*D: Mechanical Engineering I; Mechanical
Engineering II; Thermal Power Engineering;
Electrical Engineering; Mining; Metallurgy; Radio
Engineering; Computer Sciences; Applied
Mathematics; Applied Physics; Applied
Chemistry; Foreign Languages; Physical
Education; Social Science; Engineering;
Automation.
C: Management Engineering; Evening Studies.
I: Bioengineering; Optical-Electronic Precision
Mechanics.*

East China Normal University Shanghai
3663 Zhongshan Road (North), Shanghai 200062
(Shanghai Municipality)
Tel: +86(21) 54-8461
Telex: 333 28 ecnu cn
Cable: 0187
Founded: 1951
*D: Education; Political Education; Philosophy;
Economics; Chinese Language and Literature;
History; Foreign Languages; Library and
Information Sciences; Mathematics; Mathematic
Statistics; Physics; Electronic Science and
Technology; Chemistry; Biology; Computer
Science; Psychology; Geography; Computer
Technology in Education; Environmental
Sciences; Physical Education; Fine Arts; Lifelong
Education.
I: Graduate; Educational Management.*

East China University of Chemical Technology Shanghai
130 Meilong Road, Shanghai 200237 (Shanghai
Municipality)
Tel: +86(21) 439-4280
Fax: +86(21) 439-0142
Telex: 33428 ecict cn
Cable: 9006
President: Chen Min-Heng
Vice-President: Lin Zhu-Yuan
Founded: 1952
*D: Chemical Engineering; Chemical Engineering
for Energy Resource; Biochemical Engineering;
Fine Chemical Engineering; Polymer Science and
Engineering; Inorganic Materials Science;
Environmental Engineering; Mechanical
Engineering; Automation and Electronic
Engineering; Mathematics; Physics; Chemistry;
Foreign Languages for Science and Technology;
Social Sciences; Computer Sciences; Process
Equipment; Management; Industrial Design;
Petroleum Processing.
S: Fundamental Education.
Research I.: Biochemical Engineering; Chemical
Reaction Engineering; Chemical Engineering;
Materials Science and Engineering; Process
Equipment; Fine Chemical Engineering;
Specialized Chemical.*

Fudan University Shanghai
220 Handan Road, Shanghai (Shanghai
Municipality)
Tel: +86(21) 548-4906
Fax: +86(21) 549-1875
Telex: 33317
President: Z.Y. Hua
*S: Technological Science; Management;
Economics; Life Science; Journalism; Cultural
Relics and Museum Science.
D: Chinese Language and Literature; Foreign
Languages and Literature; Journalism; Sociology;
History; Economics; World Economics;
International Politics; Philosophy; Law;
Mathematics; Statistics and Operational*

Research; Physics; Nuclear Science; Chemistry; Biochemistry; Microbiology and Microbiological Engineering; Physiology and Biophysics; Environmental and Resources Biology; Biotechnology; Electrical Engineering; Computer Science; Materials Science; Applied Mechanics; Light Source and Illumination Engineering; Management Science; Economic Management.

Fujian Normal University
23 Linghou Road, Lunshan District, Fuzhou (Fujian Province)
Tel: +86(591) 41-616
D: Education; Political Education; Languages and Literature; History; Geography; Biology; Mathematics; Physics; Chemistry; Philosophy; Music; Fine Arts; Foreign Languages.

Fuzhou University
Industrial Road, Fuzhou (Fujian Province)
Tel: +86(591) 71-0845
Fax: +86(591) 71-3866
Cable: 8383
President: Qian Kuang-wu (1992-)
Founded: 1958
D: Mathematics; Computer Science; Physics; Chemistry; Civil and Architectural Engineering; Geology and Mining Engineering; Mechanical Engineering; Light Industry; Electrical Engineering; Chemical Engineering; Foreign Languages; Industrial Management; Arts and Crafts; Finance and Trade; Accounting; Planning and Statistics.
C: Finance and Economics.
Research I: Automation; Electrical Engineering; Structural Engineering; Mathematics; Chemical; Material; Modern Physics Technology; Micro-Wave Communication Technology; Civil Prospecting and Designing; Gas-Sensitive Sensor; Software; Higher Education; Environment Protection; Canadian Affairs.
Research Ce.: Solid Material.

Gansu Agricultural University
Yingmentan, Anning District, Lanzhou 730070 (Gansu Province)
Tel: +86 68-011
President: Hengjue Hu
Founded: 1958
D: Animal Husbandry; Veterinary Science; Grassland Science; Agronomy; Plant Protection; Soil Science and Agrochemistry; Forest Science; Horticulture; Agricultural Engineering; Agricultural Economics.

Gansu Normal University
Lanzhou (Gansu Province)
Education.

Gansu University of Technology
57 Langongping, Lanzhou 730050 (Gansu Province)
Tel: +86 35-951
Telex: 72135 uotng cn
Cable: 3695
Founded: 1958

D: Mechanical Engineering I; Mechanical Engineering II; Automatic Control; Architecture and Structural Engineering; Management Engineering; Basic Science (Instructional and Research); Evening Studies; Cadres (Training).
I: Machine Manufacturing Engineering; Welding Techniques; Fracture Technology; Fluid Power Machinery.

Guangxi Normal University
Guilin (Guangxi Autonomous Region of Zhuang Nationality)
Tel: +86(771) 2915
D: Languages and Literature; Foreign Languages; History; Physics; Mathematics; Chemistry; Biology; Education.

Guangxi University
Nanning (Guangxi Autonomous Region of Zhuang Nationality)
Tel: +86(771) 28-823
D: Philosophy; Economics; Law; Foreign Languages; Chemical Industry; Mathematics; Physics; Chemistry; Light Industry; Languages and Literature; Engineering.

Guizhou University
Huaxi, Guiyang (Guizhou Province)
Tel: +86(851) 2218
D: Mathematics; Physics; Chemistry; Languages and Literature; History; Law; Foreign Languages; Philosophy.

Hainan University Haikou
Haikou (Guandong Province)

Hangzhou University
34 Tien Mu Shan Road, Hangzhou (Zhejiang Province)
Tel: +86(571) 81-224
Telex: 9600
President: Shanhong Shen
Founded: 1958
D: Political Science; Chinese Language and Literature; Philosophy; Economics; Law; Tourism; Finance; Journalism; Foreign Languages; History; Education; Psychology; Mathematics; Physics; Chemistry; Biology; Geography; Computer Sciences; Physical Culture; Regional Planning and Urban Sciences; Electronic Engineering; Foreign Languages of Non-Majors; Physical Culture of Non-Majors.

Harbin Medical University
1 Baojian Road, Nangang District, Harbin (Heilong Jiang Province)
Tel: +86(451) 62-941
Medicine.

Harbin Normal University
24 Hexing Road, Nangang District, Harbin (Heilong Jiang Province)
Tel: +86(451) 62-912
Education.

Harbin Polytechnical University
166 West Dazhi Street, Harbin (Heilong Jiang Province)
Tel: +86(451) 33-051

Harbin University of Science and Technology
22 Xue Fu Road, Nangang District, Harbin 150080 (Heilong Jiang Province)
Tel: +86(451) 61-081
Fax: +86(451) 61-849
Cable: 2500
Founded: 1958, 1978
D: *Mechanical Engineering I; Mechanical Engineering II; Electronic Engineering; Computer; Technological Physics; Management Engineering; Basic Studies.*
C: *Adult Education.*
Research I.: *Computer Auxiliary Design (Scientific); Optimization Design and Laser; Function Analysis.*
I: *Mechanical Engineering.*

Hebei Agricultural University
Nanguan, Baoding (Hebei Province)
Tel: +86 2956
Agriculture.

Hebei Teachers' University
Yuhua Zhonglu, Shijiazhuang 050016 (Hebei Province)
Tel: +86(631) 64-9941
Cable: 2345
President: Li Mengxing
Registrar: Gu Jiachang
Founded: 1906
D: *Education; Mathematics; Chemistry; Geography; Physical Culture; Chinese Language and Literature.*
Research Ce.: *Hebei Audio-visual Technology.*
Research I.: *Population; Education Science; Substitute Fuel.*

Hebei University
He Zuolu Road, Baoding 071002 (Hebei Province)
Tel: +86(312) 22-929
Telex: 26294 bdpbl cn
Cable: 0181 baoding
Founded: 1921, 1960
D: *Physics; Mathematics; Electronics; Chemistry; Biology; Chinese Language; History; Philosophy; Education; Foreign Languages; Economics; Law; Library Science and Informatics.*
I: *History; Bioengineering.*
Research I: *Japan.*
Ce: *Physics and Chemistry (Analytical); Computer.*

Hebei University of New Medicine
5 Changan West Road, Shijiazhuang 050017 (Hebei Province)
Tel: +86(631) 48-744
Fax: +86(631) 161-4092
President: Baolin Wei
Founded: 1915, 1932
Medicine Sciences; Stomatology; Pharmacy; Public Health.

Hefei Polytechnical University
Tunxi Road, Hefei (Anhui Province)
Tel: +86(551) 74-711
Telex: 90040
President: Shenggu Gu
Registrar: Shijie Yu
Founded: 1921

Hehai University Nanjing
Xikang Road 1, Nanjing 210024 (Jiangsu Province)
Tel: +86(25) 32-106
Telex: 34101 ectuw cn
Cable: 5478 nanjing
Founded: 1952
D: *Hydraulic Engineering; Navigation and Ocean Engineering; Irrigation and Drainage Engineering; Hydrology and Water Resouces; Engineering Surveying; Architectural Engineering; Management Engineering; Mechanics; Hydraulic Engineering Automation; Basic Studies; Correspondence Courses; Foreign Languages; Social Science.*
Research I: *Coast and Ocean Engineering; Environmental Engineering; Water Resources and Hydroelectric Power.*

Heilongjiang August 1st University of Land Reclamation
District of Mishan (Heilongjiang Province)
Telex: 1331
President: Zhang Wanshuang
Founded: 1958
D: *Agriculture; Mechanical Engineering; Farm Economics; Veterinary Medicine.*
F: *English Language Training; Farm Management Training.*

Heilongjiang University
24 Xue Fu Road, Nankang District, Harbin (Heilongjiang Province)
Tel: +86(451) 64940-9
Founded: 1942, 1958
D: *Chinese; History; Philosophy; Economics; Law; Russian Studies; English; Japanese; Library and Information Sciences; Mathematics; Computer Sciences; Physics; Chemistry.*
I: *Lexicography; Applied Mathematics; Soviet Studies; Foreign Literature; Sensor and Sensing Techniques; Linguistics; Russian; Economics.*
S: *Evening Studies.*

*Henan University
Kaifeng (Henan Province)
President: Jin Dexing
Founded: 1912, 1984
C: *Adult Education; Shaolin Wushu; Chinese Language; Sciences; Economics Trade; Physical Education.*

Huanan Normal University Guangzhou
Guangzhon (Guandong Province)
Education.

Huazhong Agricultural University Wuhan
Shizhishan, Wuhan 430070 (Hubei Province)
Tel: +86 71-5681
President: Sun Ji-Zhong
Founded: 1925, 1985
D: *Agriculture; Plant Protection; Soil Science and Agricultural Chemistry; Animal Husbandry and Veterinary Medicine; Horticulture and Sericulture; Agricultural Engineering; Food Science and Technology; Fisheries; Agricultural Economics; Basic Studies; Social Science; Lifelong Education.*
Ce: *Agricultural Economics Management (Training); Language; Swine Breeding; Cotton; Biotech.*

Hunan Medical University
22 Beizhang Road, Changsha 410078 (Hunan Province)
Tel: +86(731) 24-411
Fax: +86(731) 44-329
Telex: (731) 24-411
Cable: 6829
President: Jiadian Luo (1987-94)
Founded: 1914, 1953, 1988
F: *Medicine; Laboratory Studies; Anaesthesiology; Stomatology; Medical Library and Information Sciences; Preventive Medicine; Mental Health.*
I: *Cardiology; Mental Health; Oncology; Medical Genetics; Combined Western and Chinese Traditional Medicine; Medical Education Research; Preventive Medicine.*
Training Ce: *English; Clinical Pharmacology; Medical Genetics; Medical Equipment and Instrument Maintenance.*

Hunan University
Yuelushan, Changsha (Hunan Province)
Tel: +86(731) 83-171

Inner Mongolia Normal University Hohhot
Hohhot (Inner Mongolia Autonomous Region)
Education.

Jiangxi Agricultural University
Meiling, Nanchang (Jiangxi Province)
Tel: +86(791) 53-923
President: Ouyang Liang
Founded: 1980
Agriculture.

Jiangxi Normal University
77, Beijing West Road, Nanchang (Jiangxi Province)
Tel: +86(791) 67-801
D: *Chinese; Political Education; Foreign Languages; History; Education; Music; Painting; Mathematics; Computer Sciences; Physics; Chemistry; Geography; Physical Education; Education Communication.*

Jiangxi University
Disi Jiaotong Road, Nanchang (Jiangxi Province)
Tel: +86(791) 67-800
President: Dai Zhi-zhong (1983-)
Founded: 1958
D: *Chinese Language and Literature; Journalism; Law; History; Economics; Mathematics; Physics; Chemistry; Biology; Foreign Languages and Literatures; Philosophy; Evening Studies.*
I: *Computer Sciences.*
Ce: *Audio-visual.*

Jiaying University
Meizigang (Hill), Meizhou 514015 (Guangdong)
Tel: +86 23-2539
Cable: 2393
Founded: 1982, 1985
D: *Economics; Finance; Foreign Languages; Electronics; Mathematics; Physics; Chemistry; Biology; Geography; Chinese; Politics and History.*
I: *Research in Higher Learning; Customs and Culture of Hakka Research.*

Jilin Agricultural University
Jingyue Xiang, Nanguan District, Changchun 130118 (Jilin Province)
Tel: +86(431) 42-112
Founded: 1948, 1959
D: *Soil Science and Agricultural Chemistry; Agronomy; Animal Science; Agricultural Engineering; Agricultural Economics; Horticulture and Local Special Products; Science; Professional Teachers.*
I: *Comprehensive Technology of Agricultural Modernization; Cysticercosis.*

Jilin Polytechnical University
Changchun (Jilin Province)
Tel: +86(431) 27044
Telex: 83016 booth cn

Jilin University
79 Jiefang Road, Changchun 130023 (Jilin Province)
Tel: +86(431) 82-2331
Fax: +86(431) 82-3907
Telex: 83040 jlu cn
Cable: 1513
President: Wu Zhuoqun (1986-)
Founded: 1946, 1950, 1958
D: *Mathematics; Physics; Chemistry; Computer Sciences; Molecular Biology; Chinese Language and Literature; History; Economics; Law;*

Philosophy; Political Science; Foreign Languages and Literature; Marxism-Leninism Teaching and Research; Foreign Languages as a Second Language; International Economics; Management Science; Economic Management; Economic Law; Electronic Sciences; International Law; Archaeology; Environmental Sciences; Materials Science.
I: Mathematics; Atomic and Molecular Physics; Theoretical Chemistry; Materials Science; Demography; Classical Works; Systems Science; Japanese Affairs.
S: Graduate.
Ce: Computer; Modern Instrumental Analysis and Testing.

Jinan University Guangzhou
Shipai, Guangzhou 510632 (Guangdong Province)
Tel: +86(20) 77-4511
Fax: +86(20) 51-6941
Telex: 44645 jun cn
Cable: 0870 guangzhou
President: Liang Lingguang
Founded: 1906, 1927
C: Economics; Medicine; Liberal Arts; Science and Technology; Adult and Lifelong Education.
D: Foreign Languages and Literature; Chinese Language and Literature; Journalism; History; Chemistry; Applied Physics; Biology; Mathematics; Computer Sciences; Electronic Engineering; Economics; Finance; Business Administration; Commerce; Accountancy; Statistics and Planning; Chinese as Foreign Language.
I: Southeast Asia Studies; Overseas Chinese Studies; Economic Studies of Hong Kong's Special Economic Zones; Chinese Culture and History; Bioengineering Technology.
Research Ce: Hydrophyte; Reproduction Immunology.

Jishou University
District of Jishou (Hunan Province)

Lanzhou University
78 Tianshui Road, Lanzhou 730000 (Gansu Province)
Tel: +86 28-111
Fax: +86 41-7576
Telex: 72144
President: Zhide Hu

Liaoning University
Chongshan West Road, Huanggu District, Shenyang (Liaoning Province)
Tel: +86(24) 62-541
Cable: 6275
Founded: 1958
D: Chinese; History; Philosophy; Law; Foreign Languages; Computer Technology; Mathematics; Physics; Chemistry; Biology; Economics; Industrial Administration; Planning and Statistics; Finance and Insurance; Finance and Accounting.
I: Japanese.

Research I: Demographic Studies; Foreign Language (Training).

Nanjing Forestry University
Longpan Road, Nanjing (Jiangsu Province)
Tel: +86(25) 65-3231
Fax: +86(25) 50-2936
Telex: 342234 jpec cn
Cable: 2651
President: Wang Ming-Xiu (1984-)
Founded: 1952, 1984
D: Forestry; Wood Industry; Forestry Engineering; Chemical Engineering; Forestry Machinery; Forestry Economics and Management; Correspondence Courses; Evening Studies.
Research I: Bamboo.

Nanjing University
11 Hankou Road, Nanjing (Jiangsu Province)
Tel: +86(25) 63-7551
Fax: +86(25) 30-2728
Telex: 34151 prcnu cn
Cable: 0909
President: Qu Qinyue (1984-)
Founded: 1902
D: Chinese Language and Literature; Foreign Languages and Literature; History; Philosophy; Law; Political Science; Economics; Management Science; Library Science; Mathematics; Computer Sciences; Astronomy; Physics; Information Physics; Chemistry; Biology; Biochemistry; Geology; Geography; Atmospheric Science; Environmental Sciences; Foreign Language Instruction; Lifelong Education.
Ce: Chinese and American Studies; Computer; Materials Analysis; Audio-visual.

*Nankai University
94 Weijin Road, Tianjin 300071 (Tianjin Municipality)
Tel: +86(22) 35-8825
Fax: +86(22) 34-4853
Telex: 23133 nanki cn
Cable: 0589
President: Mu Guoguang (1986-94)
Registrar: Zhang Zili
Founded: 1919
D: Chinese Language and Literature; History; Philosophy; Economics; International Economics; Economic Management; Foreign Languages and Literature; Mathematics; Physics; Chemistry; Biology; Electronics; Computer Sciences; Environmental Science; Library Science; Political Science; Law; Finance; Tourism; Sociology; Accounting; Oriental Art.
Research I: Economics; International Economics; Demography; History; Ancient Chinese Bibliographical Collation; Law; Elemento-Organic Chemistry; Modern Optics; Polymer Chemistry; Molecular Biology; Applied Chemistry; Transportation Economics; Taiwan Economics.

I: *Mathematics (Nankai); New Energy Chemistry Materials; Latin American History.*

Ningxia University
21 Wencui Road, Yinchuan (Ningxia Autonomous Region of Hui Nationality)
Tel: +86(951) 77-800

Norman Bethune University of Medical Sciences Changchun
6 Xinmin Street, Changchun 130021 (Jilin Province)
Tel: +86 645-911
Fax: +86 644-739
Telex: 83016 booth cn
President: Yuanyao Chen (1991-)
Founded: 1939, 1978
S: *Basic Medical Sciences; Preventive Medicine; Dentistry; Health.*
F: *Library and Information Science.*
D: *Social Sciences; Adult Education; Animal Medicine.*
Research I: *Basic Medical Sciences; Environmental Medicine; Radiation Medicine; Endemic Diseases; Cerebrovascular Diseases; Surgery; Respiratory Diseases; Hepatic Diseases; Gerontology; Pharmaceutical Sciences; Higher Medical Education Management.*
Ce: *Neurology (National Training); Audiovisual; Computer; Molecular Biology; Radioisotope; Electronmicroscopy; Japanese Language Training for Sasakawa Medical Scholars.*
C: *First Clinical; Second Clinical; Third Clinical.*

Northeast Agricultural University Harbin
Gongbin Road, Xiangfang District, District of Acheng, Harbin 150030 (Heilongjiang Province)
Tel: +86(451) 55-981
Cable: 1333
Founded: 1948
D: *Bioengineering; Agricultural Engineering; Laboratory Centre; Horticulture; Agricultural Economics; Food Science; Plant Protection; Agricultural Education; Social Sciences; Basic Disciplines; Physical Training; Animal Husbandry; Veterinary Medicine; Agronomy.*

Northeast Normal University Changchun
Changchun (Jilin Province)
Tel: +86(431) 68-4088
Fax: +86(431) 68-4003
President: Qichang Huang (1986-)
Vice-President: Jingsi Zhou
Founded: 1946, 1950
D: *Education; Chinese Language and Literature; History; Mathematics; Biology; Physics; Chemistry; Physical Culture; Geography.*
I: *Japanese Studies; History of Ancient Civilization.*
Ce: *Lifelong Education; Tests and Analyses.*

*Northeast University of Technology Shenyang
Shenyang (Liaoning Province)
Tel: +86(24) 48-2157
Telex: 80033 Neit Cn
Cable: 2168
President: Lu Zhongwu (1984-)
Founded: 1923, 1950
D: *Mining Engineering; Mineral Engineering; Metallurgy; Non-Ferrous Metallurgy; Metallic Materials; Metal Processing; Thermal Engineering; Mechanical Engineering I; Mechanical Engineering II; Automation; Computer Sciences and Engineering; Physics; Chemistry; Mechanics; Foreign Languages; Physical Education; Social Science; Correspondence Courses.*

Northern Jiaotong University Beijing
Shangyuancun, Xizhimenwai, Beijing (Beijing Municipality)
Tel: +86(1) 89-0561
President: Shujing Zhang
Founded:
D: *Telecommunications; Civil Engineering; Mechanical Engineeering; Computer Sciences and Technology; Industrial Management; Railway Transportation; Electronic Engineering; Management Engineering; Physics; Mathematics; Economics; Correspondence Courses; Evening Studies.*
Sec: *Foreign Languages.*

Northwest University Xi'an
Daxue Dong Road, Xi'an 710069 (Shaanxi Province)
Tel: +86(29) 71-5036
Telex: 70005 nwuvs cn
Founded: 1912

Northwestern Agricultural University Yangling
Yangling (Shaanxi Province)
Tel: +86(910) 6007
Cable: 6007 Yanling
Founded: 1934, 1985
D: *Agriculture; Plant Protection; Soil Science and Agrochemistry; Horticulture; Agricultural Economics; Agricultural Machinery; Hydraulics; Animal Husbandry; Veterinary Medicine; Food Technology; Basic Studies.*
Research Ce: *Agriculture in Arid and Semi-Arid Areas.*
Ce: *Rural Economics and Management; Computer; Cadres (Training).*

*Northwestern Polytechnical University Xi'an

127 West Youyi Road, Xi'an 710072 (Shaanxi Province)
Tel: +86(29) 53-351
Fax: +86(29) 75-1959
Telex: 70185 nwtuy cn
Cable: Xi'an 5300
President: Hengzhi Fu (1984-)
Secretary-General: Guojin Tao
Founded: 1957
C: Astronautics; Management Science; Marine Engineering.
S: Graduate.
D: Aero-Engines; Aircraft Engineering; Aircraft Manufacture Engineering; Applied Mathematics; Material Science and Engineering; Applied Physics; Architecture Engineering; Automatic Control; Computer Sciences and Engineering; Engineering Mechanics; Electronic Engineering; Aircraft and Propulsion; Foreign Languages; Marine Control Engineering; Marine Electronic Engineering; Mechanical Engineering; Space Flight and Control; Lifelong Education; Correspondence Courses; Social Sciences.
I: Aircraft Structure; Pilotless Aircraft Technology; Undersea Technology; Materials and Heat Technology; Computer Sciences and Information Engineering; Natural Dialectics; Vibration Engineering; Xi'an Dies Development; Applied Mathematics; Acoustic English; Aerodynamics; Electronic Science and Technology; Fire Control; Electrical Machine and Control Technoloyg (REPM); Shanxi Province Non-Conventional Machine Technology; Industry Intelligent Control; Application Specific Integrated Circuit(ASIC); High Technology Application.
Ce: Foreign Training; Computer.

Overseas Chinese University Quanzhou

Quanzhou (Fujian Province)
Tel: +86(595) 4921

People's University of China Beijing

39 Haidian Road, Haidian District, Beijing (Beijing Municipality)
Tel: +86(1) 256-3399
Fax: +86(1) 256-6374
Telex: 222653 pucbj cn
Cable: 0086 beijing
President: Yuan Baohua (1985-)
Founded: 1937, 1950
S: Graduate.
C: Economics; Economic Planning and Statistics; Industrial And Commercial Management; Labour and Personnel Administration; Law; Journalism; Archives; Correspondence Courses.
I: History of Development of Marxism-Leninism; Population History; Chinese Language and Writing; History of Qing (Manchurian) Dynasty; Administration Studies; Sociology; Soft Science; Education in Marxist Theory.

Ce: Information; Chinese (for foreign students); Audio-visual.

Qinghai Normal University

38 Wusi Street, Xining (Qinghai Province)
Tel: +86(971) 55-451
Telex: 5400
Founded: 1956, 1956, 1958
Education.

Qinghai University

40 Ningzhang Road, Xining 810016 (Qinghai Province)
Tel: +86(971) 40-948
Cable: 2239
Founded: 1958
D: Mechanical Engineering; Chemical Engineering; Plant Protection; Agronomy; Mining; Hydroelectrical Engineering; Civil Engineering; Chinese Language; Elementary Courses; Administrative Engineering.
Ce: Soft Science Research; Scientific and Technical Information; Computer.

Qinghua University Beijing

1 Qinghuayuan, Haidian District, Beijing 100084 (Beijing Municipality)
Tel: +86(1) 256-7733
Fax: +86(1) 256-2768
Telex: 22617 qhtsc cn
Founded: 1911
S: Sciences; Economics and Management; Architecture; Lifelong Education; Graduate.
D: Architecture; Urban Planning and Design; Automation; Automobile Engineering; Chemical Engineering; Civil Engineering; Computer Sciences and Technology; Electrical Engineering; Electronic Engineering; Engineering Mechanics; Engineering Physics; Environmental Engineering; Materials Science and Engineering; Mechanical Engineering; Precision Instrumentation and Mechanical Techniques; Thermal Engineering; Applied Mathematics; Chemistry; Modern Applied Physics; Economics; International Trade and Finance; Management Engineering; Management Information Systems; Chinese Language and Literature; Foreign Language; Social Sciences.

Shandong Normal University

38 Wenhua East Road, Jinan (Shandong Province)
Tel: +86(531) 43-711
Telex: 39103 bthjh cn c/o na. 59
Education.

Shandong Polytechnical University

Wenhua Road, Jinan (Shandong Province)
Tel: +86(531) 25-081
Telex: 1260
Founded: 1951, 1984
D: Mechanical Engineering; Metallurgy; Thermal Power Engineering; Electrical Engineering; Electric Power Engineering; Electronics;

Computer Sciences and Engineering; Hydraulic
Engineering; Industrial Management; Basic
Studies; Evening Studies; Correspondence
Courses.

Shandong University
5 Hungjialou Town, Jinan (Shandong Province)
Tel: +86(531) 64-3861
Fax: +86(531) 64-2167
Telex: 390007
Founded: 1901, 1958
D: *Chinese Language and Literature; History;
Foreign Languages and Literature; Economics;
Philosophy; Social Sciences; Sociology;
Mathematics; Physics; Chemistry; Optics; Law;
Computer Sciences; Biology; Microbiology;
Management; Electronics; Library Science;
Aerospace Technical English.*

Shanghai Fisheries University
334 Jun Gong Road, Shanghai 200090
Tel: +86(21) 543-1090 (Ex.)
Fax: +86(21) 543-4358
President: Meilong Li (1985-)
Secretary-General: Tiansheng Wang
Founded: 1912, 1952, 1985
D: *Aquaculture; Food Science and Technology;
Fisheries Engineering; Fishery Economics and
Management; Basic Studies; Social Science;
Cadres (Training).*
Ce: *Agriculture Ministry (Pelagic Fisheries
Training).*
Research I: *Pelagic Fisheries; Ichthyology; Food
Science and Technology; Fisheries Higher
Education.*

Shanghai International Studies University
550 Da Lian Road(W), Shanghai
Tel: +86(21) 542-0900
Fax: +86(21) 542-0225
Telex: 33505 sisu cn
Cable: 0369
President: Dai Wei-Dong
Founded: 1949
D: *Languages and Literature; International
Trade; Foreign Affairs Management; Chinese as
a Foreign Language; Educational Communication
and Technology; International Journalism;
International Economic Law; Linguistics and
Applied Linguistics.*
Research Ce: *Foreign Languages and
Literatures; German-Speaking Areas.*
Research I: *Soviet Studies; Middle East Culture.*

Shanghai Jiaotong University
1954 Huashan Road, Shanghai (Shanghai
Municipality)
Tel: +86(21) 431-0310
Telex: 33262 jiash cn
Founded: 1896

Shanghai Polytechnical University
149 Yanchang Road, Shanghai (Shanghai
Municipality)
Tel: +86(21) 65-0744

Shanghai Second Medical University
280 Chong Qing Nan Road, Shanghai 200025
Tel: +86(21) 26-0760
President: Yifei Wang
Founded: 1952
F: *Medicine (3); Pediatrics.*
D: *Biomedical Engineering; Medical Sciences;
Social Sciences; Nursing; Medical Nutrition;
Health Management.*
S: *Basic Medical Sciences; Stomatology.*
Ut: *Night.*

Shanghai University
1220 Xinzha Road, Shanghai (Shanghai
Municipality)
Founded: 1920
C: *Liberal Arts; Engineering; Business
Management; Fine Arts; International Business;
Political Science.*
Research I: *Sociology; Archaeology.*

Shanghai University of Engineering Science
435 Xin Chun Road, Shanghai (Shanghai
Municipality)
Tel: +86(21) 661-1420
Telex: 142
President: Jiang Shang Xin
D: *Managerial Engineering; Textile Engineering;
Mechanical Engineering; Electrical Engineering;
Clothing Technology.*

Shanghai University of Science and Technology
South Gate, Jiading Town, Shanghai (Shanghai
Municipality)
Tel: +86(21) 95-2932
Science and Technology.

Shantou University
Tuopu Town, Shantou 515063 (Guandong
Province)
Tel: +86(754) 22-1128
Fax: +86(754) 22-1120
Telex: 45448 stuni cn
Cable: 2828
Founded: 1981
D: *Chinese Language and Literature; Foreign
Languages and Literature; Mathematics; Physics;
Chemistry; Biology; Architectural Engineering;
Computer and Information Engineering; Art
Design; Electro-Mechanic Engineering;
Economics; History; Law.*
C: *Medical.*
Training Ce: *Chinese Language for Foreign
Students.*
Research Ce: *Taiwan, Hong Kong and Overseas
Chinese Literature.*
Research I: *Tumor Pathology; Applied
Computer Science; Laws Concerning China's
SEZ.*

Shaanxi Teachers University
Xi'an 710062 (Shaanxi Province)
Tel: +86(29) 52-946
Fax: +86(29) 52-946
Founded: 1944, 1960

D: Education; Chinese Language and Literature; Political Education; History; Geography; Biology; Mathematics; Physics; Computer Sciences; Chemistry; Physical Education; Arts and Music; Foreign Languages; Audio-visual Education; Correspondence Courses.
S: Adult Education; Evening.

Shanxi Agricultural University
Taigu (Shanxi Province)
Tel: +86 241
Agriculture.

Shanxi University
36 Wucheng Road, Taiyuan (Shanxi Province)
Tel: +86(351) 73-441
Cable: 0982
Founded: 1920
D: Chinese; History; Chemistry; Foreign Languages; Physics.
C: Teachers.
I: Photo-Electron Research; Molecular Science Research; Loess Plateau.
Research I: History.

Shanxi University of Coal and Chemical Technology
Taiyuan (Shanxi Province)
Tel: +86(351) 66-602
Coal and Chemical Technology.

Shenzhen University
Nantou, Shenzhen 518060 (Guandong Province)
Tel: +86(775) 66-0277
Fax: +86(755) 66-0462
Cable: 3356
President: Youhai Wei
Director: Shuping Liang
Founded: 1983
D: Economics; Management; Law; Chinese Culture and Public Communications; Foreign Languages; Public Administration; Precision Machinery and Instruments; Electronic Engineering; Architecture; Civil Engineering; Soft Science; Applied Chemistry; Applied Physics; International Finance and Trade; Physical Education.
Ce: Computer; Audio-visual.
C: Adult Education.
Research I: Advanced Technology; Special Zone Economic Studies; Audio-visual Technology; New Energy Design.
L: Life Science.

Sichuan Institute of Foreign Languages
Lieshimu, Shapingba, Chongqing (Sichuan Province)
Tel: +86 66-1737
Telex: 62218 sifl cn
Cable: 1818
President: Lan Ren-Zhe (1990-94)
Founded: 1950
D: English; Teacher Education; Russian; French; German; Japanese; Chinese as a Foreign

Language; Foreign Trade; Students Preparing to Study Abroad; Chinese for International Students; Adult Education.
I: Higher Education Research; Foreign Language Lexicography Research; Foreign Children's Literature.
Research I: Sinology Abroad.
Ce: Canadian Studies; Audio-visual.

Sichuan Normal University
Chengdu, Sichuan 610066
Tel: +86(28) 44-2612
Telex: 600099 scnu cn
Cable: 4636
President: Wang Jun Neng (1992-96)
Founded: 1952, 1986
D: Chinese Language and Literature; Political Education; Foreign Languages; Mathematics; Physics; Chemistry; Geography; Education; Biology; Chinese; Lifelong Education; International Education; History; Art; Physical Education.
Ce: Electronic Computer.
I: Ancient Chinese Literature; Chinese Language; Solid State Physics; Educational Science.

Sichuan University
29 Wangjiang Road, Chengdu 610064 (Sichuan Province)
Tel: +86(28) 555-9432
Fax: +86(28)558-2187
Telex: 60159 scun cn
Cable: 2345 chengdu city, china
President: Chen Junkai (1989-94)
Founded: 1905
D: Humanities; Social Sciences; Engineering; Science.

South China Agriculture University Guangzhou
Wushan, Guangzhou
Tel: +86(20) 551-1299
Fax: +86(20) 551-1393
Cable: 6340 Guangzhou
President: Lu Yong-gen (1989-93)
Founded: 1952, 1964
D: Agronomy; Soil and Agricultural Chemistry; Plant Protection; Horticulture; Sericulture; Agricultural Economics; Animal Husbandry; Veterinary Medicine; Agricultural Engineering; Agricultural Biology; Basic Courses; Social Science.
Sec: Physical Education.
C: Adult Education; Forestry.

Southwest China Jiaotong University Sichuan Province
District of Emei (Sichuan Province)
Tel: +86 2361

142

Southwest China Teachers' University Chongqing

2 Tiansheng Road, Chongqing 630715 (Sichuan Province)
Tel: +86(82) 153-3901
Fax: +86(82) 153-805
Cable: 0350
President: Zhong Zhang-Cheng
Secretary-General: Wang Chang-Kai
Founded: 1950
D: *Chinese Language and Literature; Foreign Languages and Literature; Education; Political Education; History; Library and Information Sciences; Mathematics; Physics; Chemistry; Biology; Geography; Computer Sciences; Audio-visual Education; Music; Physical Culture; Arts.*

Southwest University of Forestry Kuming

District of Anning, Kunming (Yunnan Province)
Tel: +86(871) 515-7217
Telex: 2825
President: Wang Chun-lin
Founded: 1939, 1983
D: *Forestry; Forestry Protection; Forestry Industry.*

Suzhou University

1 Shizi Street, Suzhou 215006 (Jiangsu Province)
Tel: +86(512) 22-3614
Fax: +86(512) 77-1918
President: Lishang Jiang
Registrar: Zhulei Bao
Founded: 1901
S: *Law; Finance and Economics; Engineering.*
Research Ce: *Central.*
D: *Mathematics; Physics; Chemistry; Political Science; History; Chinese; Physical Education Training; Foreign Languages.*

*Taiyuan University of Technology

11 West Yingze Street, Taiyuan (Shanxi Province)
Tel: +86(351) 66-5608
Fax: +86(351) 64-1142
President: G.T. Yang
Founded: 1902, 1953, 1984
D: *Hydraulic Engineering; Mechanical Engineering I; Mechanical Engineering II; Electrical Engineering; Thermal Energy Engineering; Information Systems Engineering; Computer Sciences and Engineering; Chemical Engineering; Applied Chemistry; Mathematics and Mechanics; Civil and Environmental Engineering; Basic Theory; Management Engineering; Evening Studies.*

Talimu University of Agriculture and Land Reclamation

District of Akesu (Oygur Xingjian Autonomous Region)
Agriculture.

Tianjin Normal University

Weijin Road, Hexi District, Tianjin (Tianjin Municipality)
Tel: +86(22) 33-4713
Education.

Tianjin University

Qilitai, Nankai District, Tianjin 300072 (Tianjin Municipality)
Tel: +86(22) 31-8715
Telex: 23288 tuico cn
President: Yongshi Wu
Secretary-General: Zhaoji Yu
Founded: 1885, 1952
S: *Graduate; Management; Petrochemical Engineering; Adult Education.*
D: *Chemical Engineering; Applied Chemistry; Precision Instruments Engineering; Electronic Engineering; Electrical Engineering and Automation; Thermoenergy Engineering; Mechanical Engineering; Architecture; Civil Engineering; Hydraulic Engineering; Computer Engineering and Science; Maritime Engineering and Naval Architecture; Management Engineering; Technical Economics; Foreign Languages; Mathematics; Physics; Mechanics; Chemistry; Humanities and Social Sciences; Materials Science and Engineering.*
Ce: *Computer; Analysis; Precision Instruments; Geothermal Research and Training; Petroleum Development; Development for Chemical Separation Techniques.*
Research Ce: *Industrial Economics Development and Strategy; Computer-Aided Design.*

Tianjin University of Commerce

East Entrance of Jinba Road, Northern Suburbs of Tianjin, Tianjin
Tel: +86(22) 57-3169
Fax: +86(22) 57-3169
Telex: 23174 tiptb cn (53)
Cable: 3614
President: Bingwei Li
Founded: 1984
D: *Commercial Enterprise Management; Management Engineering; Refrigeration Engineering; Food Engineering; Packing Engineering; Politics and Laws; Basic Studies; Training Cadres; Hotel and Catering Management.*
I: *Commercial Comprehensive Designs; Freezing Technology.*

Tongji Medical University Wuhan

Hang Kong Lu, Wuhan (Hubei Province)
Tel: +86 35-6811
Founded: 1907, 1985
F: *Basic Medical Sciences; Pharmacy; Forensic Medicine.*
S: *Public Health.*
I: *Family Planning; Organ Transplantation; Cardiovascular Disease; Basic Medicine; Chinese and Western Medicine; Environmental Medicine; Social Medicine.*
Ce: *Experimental Medicine Research; Medical Training.*
Sec: *Lifelong Education.*

Tongji University Shanghai

1239 Siping Road, Shanghai (Shanghai Municipality)
Tel: +86(21) 545-5080
Fax: +86(21) 545-8965
Telex: 33488 tjidc cn
Cable: 3658
President: Gao Tingyao (1989-93)
Founded: 1907
S: Mechanical Engineering; Structural Engineering; Architecture and Urban Planning; Environmental Engineering; Management Engineering; Graduate; Correspondence and Continuing Education.
D: Applied Mathematics; Engineering Mechanics; Physics; Applied Chemistry; Road and Traffic Engineering; Surveying; Underground Building and Engineering; Marine Geology; Materials Science and Engineering; Electrical Engineering; Computer Sciences and Engineering; Social Science; Foreign Languages; German.
Ce: Computer; Measurement and Testing.
I: Environmental Protection Technology; Acoustics; Radiation and Immunity Analytical Technology (Shanghai).
Research I: Japan; German; Disaster Prevention and Relief (Shanghai).

*University of Electronic Science and Technology of China, Chengdu

4 North Jian She Road, Chengdu (Sichuan Province)
Tel: +86(28) 333-3312
Fax: +86(28) 333-4131
Telex: 60202
Cable: 6061
President: Sheng-Gang Liu (1986-)
Founded: 1956
D: Radio and Telecommunications Technology; Electromagnetic Field Engineering; Management Engineering; Humanities; Applied Mathematics; Applied Physics; Electronic Technology; Physical Education and Art; Automation; Materials Science and Engineering.
I: Electronic Engineering; dult Education.
Research I: Microelectronics Technology; Information Systems; Electronic Systems.

University of International Business and Economics Beijing

Huixin Dongjie, Hepingjie Beikou, Beijing 100029 (Beijing Municipality)
Tel: +86(1) 422-5522
Fax: +86(1) 421-2022
Telex: 22009 cchdp cn
Cable: 2161
Founded: 1954, 1984
F: International Business Communications; Foreign Languages; International Business; Customs Administration; International Business Management; International Economic Co-operation; International Economic Law; Political

Science; German; Economic Information Management.
Ce: Audio-visual; Business English Training; Lifelong Education; Teacher Training.
D: Correspondence Courses.
I: International Business Research; Pacific Asian Business.

University of Medicine of China Shenyang

Shenyang (Liaoning Province)
Tel: +86(24) 32-578
Cable: 3257
Founded: 1931, 1948
Medicine.

University of Petroleum Dongying

149 Taian Street, Dongying 257062 (Shandong Province)
Tel: +86(5461) 22-1011
Fax: +86(5461) 22-2923
Telex: 39314 faosl cn
Cable: 7108
D: Petroleum Engineering; Petroleum Exploration; Chemical Engineering; Mechanical Engineering; Automation; Management Engineering; Mathematics and Physics.
I: Zell Drilling; Heavy Oil; Petroleum Exploration; Applied Tribology.
Ce: Oil Exploration and Development Techniques (UN-Assisted Training); Computer.

University of Science and Technology of China Hefei

24 Jin Zhai Road, Hefei (Anhui Province)
Tel: +86(551) 63-300
Cable: 4430
Founded: 1958
D: Mathematics; Physics; Modern Chemistry; Modern Physics; Modern Mechanics; Radio and Electronics; Earth and Space Sciences; Biology; Precision Technology; Science Management (in preparation).

West China University of Medical Sciences Chengdu

Chengdu 61004 (Sichuan Province)
Tel: +86(28) 58-1130
Fax: +86(28) 58-3252
Telex: 60251 ucums cn
Cable: 7777 Chengdu
President: Yang Guangha (1988-)
Founded: 1910, 1959
S: Medicine; Stomatology; Public Health; Pharmacy; Basic Medical Studies.
D: Professional Retraining; Forensic Medecine; Foreign Languages; Sociology.
I: Stomatology; Oncology.

Wuhan Technical University of Surveying and Mapping

39 Luoyu Road, Wuhan 430070 (Hubei Province)
Tel: +86(27) 71-5571
Fax: +86(27) 71-4185
Telex: 40210 wtusm cn
Cable: 6852

D: Engineering Surveys; Photogrammetry and Remote Sensing; Geodesy; Cartography; Printing Enginering; Optical Instrumentation; Electronic Engineering; Computer Sciences and Engineering; Architectural Engineering; Social Sciences; Basic Studies.
National L: Remote Sensing Information Engineering in Surveying and Mapping.
Ce: Urban and Rural Surveys, Planning and Management (Education); Computer.
Research I: Surveying and Mapping.

Wuhan University
Wuhan 430072 (Hubei Province)
Tel: +86(27) 81-2712
Fax: +86(27) 71-2661

Wuhan University of Hydraulic and Electric Engineering
Wuhan 430072 (Hubei Province)
Tel: +86(27) 81-2212
Fax: +86(27) 81-4496
Telex: c/o 40170 wctel cn
Cable: 5750 wuhan
D: Hydraulic Engineering; River Engineering; Water Power Engineering; Civil Engineering; Mechanical Engineering; Electrical Engineering; Computer and Electronic Engineering; Hydraulic Power Engineering; Thermal Power Engineering; Management Engineering; Basic Science; Foreign Languages; Social Science.
Research I: Water Conservancy and Hydraulic and Electric Power; Electrical Engineering; Hydraulic Construction; Irrigation and Drainage; Electro-mechanical Pumping Station; River Engineering; Hydraulic Power Engineering; Thermal Power Science; Computer and Electronic Application; Social Science; Higher Learning Education.

Wuhan University of Iron and Steel Technology
Wuhan (Hubei Province)
Tel: +86(27) 66-3212
Cable: 7006
President: Ren Delin
Founded: 1958, 1984
D: Mining and Ore Technology; Metallurgy; Machinery; Industrial Automation; Chemical Engineering; Industrial Management; Materials Science.
Research Ce: Industrial Raw Materials; Materials Science; Development of Metallurgical and Mining Machinery.
Ce: Computerized Materials Analysis.

Xiamen University
Shi Ming Road South, Xiamen (Fujian Province)
Tel: +86(592) 22-5102
Fax: +86(592) 22-7402
Telex: 93003 bthxm cn
Cable: 0633 xiamen
President (Acting): Lin Zugeng (1989-)
Founded: 1921

D: Chinese Language and Literature; History; Anthropology; Foreign Languages and Literature; Journalism and Communication Sciences; Economics; Planning and Statistics; Accountancy; Business Management; Finance and Banking; Foreign Trade; Philosophy; Politics; Law; Mathematics; Physics; Chemistry; Biology; Oceanography; Electronic Engineering; Computer Sciences; Instruments Technology; Music; Fine Arts; Architecture.
I: Southeast Asia Studies; Taiwan Problems; Higher Education; Chinese Language and Literature; Anthropology; Environmental Science.
Research Ce: Cancer.
C: Overseas Correspondence.

Xi'an Jiaotong University
26 Xianning Road, Xi'an 710049 (Shaanxi Province)
Tel: +86(29) 33-2911
Fax: +86(29) 33-5471
Telex: 70123 xjtu cn
Cable: 2827
President: Shi Weixiang
Founded: 1896
D: Management; Mechanical Engineering; Energy and Power Engineering; Electrical Engineering; Electronic Engineering; Information and Control Engineering; Computer Science; Materials Engineering; Architecture and Construction; Chemical Engineering; Mathematics; Physics; Foreign Languages; Social Sciences; Economic Management; Engineering Mechanics; Machinery Science.
Ce: Foreign Students.

Xinjiang Normal University
Urumqi (Oygur Xinjiang Autonomous Region)
Education.

Xinjiang University
Urumqi (Oygur Xinjiang Autonomous Region)
Tel: +86(991) 22-929

Xiangtan University
Xiangtan (Hunan Province)
Tel: +86 24-812

Xizang (Tibet) University
Lhasa (Xizang Autonomous Region)
Founded: 1984

Yan'an University
Yan'an (Shaanxi Province)

Yanbian University
Yanji (Jilin Province)
Tel: +86(433) 3167

Yunnan Agricultural University
District of Xundian (Yunnan Province)
Tel: +86(871) 23-901
Agriculture.

Yunnan University

52 North Cuihu Road, Kunming (Yunnan Province)
Tel: +86 51-267
Founded: 1910, 1960

Zhejiang Agricultural University

172 Kai Xuan Road, Hangzhou 310029 (Zhejiang Province)
Tel: +86(571) 42-605
Telex: 351016 zau cn
Cable: 2418
D: *Agronomy; Plant Protection; Soil Science and Agrochemistry; Horticulture; Sericulture; Tea Science; Animal Husbandry and Veterinary Medicine; Agricultural Engineering; Economics and Management; Environmental Sciences; Food Science and Technology; Social Science; Nuclear-Agricultural Sciences; Basic Studies.*
C: *China Agricultural Administration.*
Sec: *Correspondence Courses.*
Research I: *Biotechnology; Pesticide Environmental Toxicology; Edible Fungus.*
I: *Agro-Ecology; Food Science.*
Ce: *Silk Research; Plant Quarantine Training.*

Zhejiang Normal University

Beishan Road, Jinhua City (Zhejiang Province)
Tel: +86 23-801
Telex: 3800
Founded: 1956, 1985
D: *Chinese Language and Literature; Foreign Languages; Political Education; History; Mathematics; Physics; Chemistry; Biology; Geography; Physical Education; Arts; Education; Correspondence Courses.*
Research I: *Mathematics; Children's Literature; Pedagogical Science.*

Zhejiang University

20 Yugu Road, Hangzhou 310027 (Zhejiang Province)
Tel: +86(571) 57-2244
Fax: +86(571) 57-1797
E-Mail: dma zunet/china.ira.uka.de
Telex: 35040 zufao cn
Cable: 0420
President: Yongxiang Lu (1988-96)
Founded: 1897, 1928
D: *Applied Mathematics; Physics; Chemistry; Mechanics; Earth Science; Electrical Engineering; Chemical Engineering; Civil Engineering; Mechanical Engineering; Information and Electronic Engineering; Photoelectronics and Scientific Instrumentation; Materials Science and Engineering; Energy Engineering; Polymer Science and Engineering; Computer Sciences and Engineering; Management Engineering; Philosophy and Sociology; Chinese Language and Literature; Biological Science and Technology; Foreign Languages; Economics; Architecture.*
Ce: *Computer and Information; Audio-visual and News.*

Zhejiang University of Medicine

157 Yian Road, Hangzhou 310006 (Zhejiang Province)
Tel: +86(571) 72-2700
Telex: 35036 zmu cn
Cable: Hangzhou, PRC
Founded: 1912, 1960
D: *Medicine; Pharmacy; Stomatology; Premedical Courses; Biomedical Engineering; Nutrition; Nursing; Lifelong Education.*
S: *Public Health.*
I: *Tumour Research; Infectious Diseases; Cardiology; Demography; Cardio- cerebro-vascular Problems; Geriatrics; Materia Medica.*

Zhengzhou University

129 Daxue Road, Zhengzhou (Henan Province)
Tel: +86(371) 46-455

Zhongnan University of Technology Changsha

Yuelushan, Changsha 410085 (Hunan Province)
Tel: +86(731) 83-111
Fax: +86(731) 82-817
Telex: 98190 csuot cn
Cable: 4349 changsha
Founded: 1951, 1955
C: *Mining and Metallurgy; Mechanical and Electrical Engineering; Science and Liberal Arts; Correspondence Courses; Graduate Studies.*
Research I: *Higher Education; Powder Metallurgy; Diwa Theory Metallurgy.*
Ce: *Robotics Research; Applied Quantum Chemistry.*

Zhongshan (Sun Yat-Sen) University Guangzhou

Guangzhou (Guangdong Province)
Tel: +86(20) 44-6300
Telex: 44604 zsufo cn
Cable: 8775
President: Zeng Haimin
Founded: 1924, 1926
D: *Management; Anthropology; Mathematics; Computer Sciences; Mechanics; Physics; Radioelectronics; Chemistry; Biology; Geography; Geology; Meteorology; Chinese Language and Literature; History; Law; Philosophy; Economics; Foreign Languages and Literature; Sociology; Library Science; Lifelong Education.*
I: *Materials Science; Computer Software; Polymer Science; Microelectronics; Southeast Asian History; Hong Kong and Macau Studies; Demography; Ancient Chinese Books and Records; Marxist Philosophy History.*
Research I: *Entomology; Environmental Science.*

OTHER INSTITUTIONS

Aba Teachers College

District of Wenchuan (Sichuan Province)
Teacher Training.

Anhui Agricultural Institute
Hefei (Anhui Province)
Agriculture.

Anhui College of Traditional Chinese Medicine
Wuhu (Anhui Province)
Chinese Medicine.

Anhui Electrical and Mechanical Institute
Wuhu (Anhui Province)
Electronics and Mechanics.

Anhui Institute of Finance
Bengbu (Anhui Province)
Finance.

Anhui Institute of Technology
Liu-An Road, Hefei (Anhui Province)
Tel: +86(551) 7553
Fax: +86(551) 255-553
Technology.

Anhui Medical College
Hefei (Anhui Province)
Medicine.

Anqing Teachers College
Anqing (Anhui Province)
Teacher Training.

Anshan Institute of Iron and Steel Technology
Zhonghua Road, Tiedong District, Anshan
(Liaoning Province)
Tel: +86(412) 25931
Iron and Steel technology.

Anshan Teachers School
Anshan (Liaoning Province)
Teacher Training.

Anshun Teachers School
Anshun (Guizhou Province)
Teacher Training.

Anyang Teachers School
Anyang (Henan Province)
Teacher Training.

Baicheng Teachers School
Baicheng (Jilin Province)
Teacher Training.

Baiqan Agricultural School
Hui County (Henan Province)
Agriculture.

Baoding Teachers School
Baoding (Hebei Province)
Teacher Training.

Baoji Teachers College
Baoji (Shaanxi Province)
Teacher Training.

Baoshan Teachers School
District of Baoshan (Yunnan Province)
Teacher Training.

Baotou Institute of Iron and Steel Technology
Baotou (Inner Mongolia)
Iron and Steel Technology.

Baotou Medical College
Baotou (Inner Mongolia)
Medicine.

Beijing Broadcasting Institute
Dinfuzhuang, Beijing (Beijing Municipality)
Tel: (1) 571461
Broadcasting.

Beijing College of Finance and Trade
68 Tsao Ling Front Street, Hsuan Wu District,
Beijing (Beijing Municipality)
Tel: +86(1) 1631
Trade; Finance.

Beijing College of Traditional Chinese Medicine
11 Beihuandong Road, Chaoyang District, Beijing
(Beijing Municipality)
Tel: +86(1) 462731
Chinese Medicine.

Beijing Dancing Academy
Beijing (Beijing Municipality)
Dance.

Beijing Film Academy (BFA)
Zhu-xin-zhuang, Beijing (Beijing Municipality)
Cinema.

Beijing Institute of Chemical Fibres
Heping Street, Chaoyang District, Beijing (Beijing
Municipality)
Tel: +86(1) 466931
Chemical Fibres.

Beijing Institute of Chemical Technology
15 Beisanhuan East Road, Chaoyang District,
Beijing
Tel: +86(1) 464089
Chemical Technology.

Beijing Institute of Civil Engineering and Architecture
Beijing (Beijing Municipality)
Civil Engineering; Architecture.

Beijing Institute of Commerce
11 Fu Cheng Road, Beijing (Beijing Municipality)
Tel: +86(1) 890341
Commerce.

Beijing Institute of Economics
Hongmiao Chaoyangmen, Beijing (Beijing
Municipality)
Tel: +86(1) 593831
Economics.

Beijing Institute of Foreign Trade
68 Tsao Ling Front Street, Husan Wu (District
Beijing)
Foreign Trade.

Beijing Institute of Forestry
Beijing (Beijing Municipality)
Tel: +86(1) 277179
Telex: 9131
Forestry.

Beijing Institute of Light Industry
Beijing (Beijing Municipality)
Tel: +86(1) 892497
Cable: 8765
Light Industry.

Beijing Institute of Physical Culture
Yuanmingyuan East Road, Beijing (Beijing
Municipality)
Tel: +86(1) 282231
Physical Culture.

**Beijing Institute of Procurements and
Handling of Commodities**
Beijing (Beijing Municipality)
Commodities.

Beijing Institute of Technology
7 Baishiqiao, Haidian District, Beijing (Beijing
Municipality)
Tel: +86(1) 890321
Telex: 22011 bit cn
Technology.

Beijing Language Institute
Xueyuan Road, Haidian District, Beijing (Beijing
Municipality)
Tel: +86(1) 2017531
Languages.

Beijing Medical College No. 2
Beijing (Beijing Municipality)
Medicine.

**Beijing Metallurgical Institute of Mechanical
and Electrical Engineering**
Beijing (Beijing Municipality)
Mechanical Engineering; Electrical Engineering.

Beijing Printing Institute
Beijing (Beijing Municipality)
Tel: +86(1) 9233981
Telex: 3469
Printing.

Beijing School of Meteorology
Beijing (Beijing Municipality)
Meteorology.

Beijing Second Foreign Languages Institute
Dingfuzhuang, Chaoyang District, Beijing (Beijing
Municipality)
Tel: +86(1) 571331
Foreign Languages.

Beijing Teachers College
Huayuancun, Haidian District, Beijing (Beijing
Municipality)
Tel: +86(1) 890841
Fax: +86(841) 9536
Teacher Training.

**Beijing Teachers College of Physical
Education**
No 21 Bei San Huan West Road, Hai Dian
District, Beijing (Beijing Municipality)
Tel: +86(1) 5522
Teacher Training; Physical Education.

Beijing Technical School of Electronics
Beijing (Beijing Municipality)
Electronics.

**Beijing Technical School of Petrochemical
Technology**
Beijing (Beijing Municipality)
Petrochemical technology.

Bengbu Medical College
108 Zhi Huai Road, Bengbu 233000 (Anhui
Province)
Tel: +86(552) 4412
Medicine.

Bijie Teachers School
Bijie (Guizhou Province)
Teacher Training.

Binzhou Medical College
Binzhou (Shandong Province)
Medicine.

Binzhou Teachers School
Binzhou (Shandong Province)
Teacher Training.

Central Academy of Arts and Crafts
34 Donghuan North Road, Beijing (Beijing
Municipality)
Tel: +86(1) 596391
Arts and Crafts.

Central Academy of Drama
139 Dong Mianhua Lane, Jiaodaoku, Beijing
(Beijing Municipality)
Tel: +86(1) 445269
Drama.

Central Academy of Fine Arts
5 Xiaoweihutong, Dongcheng District, Beijing
(Beijing Municipality)
Tel: +86(1) 596391
Fine Arts.

Central Conservatory of Music
43 Baojia Road, Xicheng District, Beijing (Beijing
Municipality)
Tel: +86(1) 667120
Music.

Central Institute of Finance
19 Xueyuan South Road, Xizhimenwai, Beijing
(Beijing Municipality)
Tel: +86(1) 891562
Finance.

Central Shanxi Teachers School
Yuci (Shanxi Province)
Teacher Training.

Changchun College of Geology
27 Fu Jin Road, Changchun (Jilin Province)
Tel: +86(431) 24781
Telex: Telex: 1967
Geology.

Changchun College of Traditional Chinese Medicine
Changchun (Jilin Province)
Chinese Medicine (Traditional).

Changchun Institute of Optics and Precision Mechanics
7 Weixing Road, Changchun (Jilin Province)
Tel: +86(431) 55931
Optics; Precision Mechanics.

Changchun Institute of Post and Telecommunications
Changchun (Jilin Province)
Post and telecommunications.

Changchun Teachers College
Changchun (Jilin Province)
Teacher Training.

Changde Teachers School
Changde (Hunan Province)
Teacher Training.

Changsha Railway Institute
148 Shaoshan Road, Changsha (Hunan Province)
Tel: +86(731) 35211
Railway Engineering.

Changsha Transportation College
Changsha (Hunan Province)
Transportation.

Changwei Medical College
Weifang (Shandong Province)
Medicine.

Changwei Teachers School
(Shandong Provinceeifang)
Teacher Training.

Chaohu Teachers School
Chaohu (Anhui Province)
Teacher Training.

Chaoyang Teachers School
Chaoyang (Liaoning Province)
Teacher Training.

Chengde Medical College
Chengde (Hebei Province)
Medicine.

Chengde Teachers School
Chengde (Hebei Province)
Teacher Training.

Chengdu College of Geology
Shilidian, Northeastern Suburb, Chengdu 610059 (Sichuan Province)
Tel: +86(28) 34712
Geology.

Chengdu College of Traditional Chinese Medicine
13 Xinlo Road, Chengdu (Sichuan Province)
Tel: +86(28) 21611
Chinese Medicine.

Chengdu Institute of Meteorology
Chengdu (Sichuan Province)
Meteorology.

Chengdu Institute of Physical Culture
2 Tiyuan Road, Southern Suburb, Chengdu (Sichuan Province)
Tel: +86(28) 54811
Physical Culture.

Chengdu Institute of Telecommunication Engeneering
4 Jianshe Road, Chengdu (Sichuan Province)
Tel: +86(28) 33312
Telex: 60202
Telecommunication Engineering.

Chenzhou Teachers School
Chenzhou (Hunan Province)
Teacher Training.

China Civil Aviation Institute
Tianjin (Tianjin Province)
Tel: +86(22) 247602
Civil Aviation.

China Institute of Mining Technology
Chongqing (Sichuan Province)
Mining Technology.

China Mining Institute
Xuzhou (Jiangsu Province)
Tel: +86(516) 88653
Mining.

China National Academy of Fine Arts
218 Nanshan Road, Hangzhou (Zhejiang Province)
Tel: +86(571) 707-9585
Fax: +86(571)707-0039
Fine Arts.

Chinese Aviation Pilot School
Guanghan (Sichuan Province)
Aviation.

Chinese Institute of Police
Shenyang (Liaoning Province)
Police Studies.

Chongqing Civil Engineering Institute
Shapingba District, Chongqing (Sichuan Province)
Tel: +86(811) 661989
Telex: 5120
Civil Engineering.

Chongqing Institute of Post and Telecommunications
Chongqing (Sichuan Province)
Post and Telecommunications.

Chongqing Institute of River and Highway Transport
Chongqing (Sichuan Province)
River and Highway Transport.

Chongqing Medical College
Chongqing (Sichuan Province)
Medicine.

Chongqing Teachers College
Chongqing (Sichuan Province)
Teacher Training.

Chuzhou Teachers School
Chuzhou (Anhui Province)
Teacher Training.

Dali Medical College
Dali (Yunnan Province)
Medicine.

Dali Teachers College
Dali Xia-guang, Dali Bai National Autonomous Region (Yunnan Province)
Teacher Training.

Dalian Institute of Aquatic Products
(Liaoning Provincealian)
Aquatic Products.

Dalian Institute of Foreign Languages
Dalian (Liaoning Province)
Languages.

Dalian Institute of Light Industry
Dalian (Liaoning Province)
Light Industry.

Dalian Institute of Technology
Luanjincum, Ganjingxi District, Dalian (Liaoning Province)
Tel: +86 91511
Telex: 86231 dit cn
Technology.

Dalian Maritime Institute
Lingshuiqiao, Dalian (Liaoning Province)
Tel: +86 91611
Maritime Studies.

Dalian Medical College
220 Xinghai Street, Dalian (Liaoning Province)
Tel: +86 491242
Medicine.

Dalian Railway Institute
Xishancun, Shahekon District, Dalian (Liaoning Province)
Tel: +86 44323
Railways.

Dandong Teachers School
Dandong (Liaoning Province)
Teacher Training.

Daqing Petroleum Institute
Anda County (Heilongjiang Province)
Tel: +86 31133
Petroleum Engineering.

Daqing Teachers School
Daqing (Heilongjiang Province)
Teacher Training.

Datong Medical School
Datong (Shanxi Province)
Medicine.

Daxian Teachers School
District of Daxian (Sichuan Province)
Teacher Training.

Dezhou Teachers School
Dezhou (Shandong Province)
Teacher Training.

East China Institute of Chemical Technology
130 Meilong Road, Shanghai (Shanghai Municipality)
Tel: +86(21) 380811
Telex: 33428 ecict cn
Chemical Technology.

East China Institute of Geology
Nanchang (Jiangxi Province)
Geology.

East China Institute of Metallurgy
Hu Dong Road, Maanshan 243002 (Anhui Province)
Tel: +86(555) 73235
Cable: 2699
Metallurgy.

East China Institute of Political Science and Law
1575 Wanghangdu Road, Shanghai (Shanghai Municipality)
Tel: +86(21) 520611
Political Science and Law.

East China Institute of Technology
200 Xiaolingwei, Nanjing (Jiangsu Province)
Tel: +86(25) 43145
Technology.

East China Petroleum Institute
Dongying (Shandong Province)
Tel: +86 24901
Petroleum Engineering.

Enshi Medical School
Enshi (Hubei Province)
Medicine.

Enshi Teachers School
Enshi (Hubei Province)
Teacher Training.

Foreign Affairs College
24 Zhan Lan Road, Beijing (Beijing Municipality)
Tel: +86(1) 890151
Foreign Affairs.

Foshan School of Veterinary Medicine
Foshan (Guangdong Province)
Veterinary Medicine.

Foshan Teachers School
Foshan (Guangdong Province)
Teacher Training.

Fujian Agricultural College
Fuzhou (Fujian Province)
Tel: +86(591) 50721
Agriculture.

Fujian College of Forestry
Xiqing, Nanping (Fujian Province)
Tel: +86 4982
Forestry.

Fujian College of Traditional Chinese Medicine
Fuzhou (Fujian Province)
Chinese Medicine.

Fujian Institute of Physical Culture
Xiamen (Fujian Province)
Physical Culture.

Fujian Medical College
Central 817 Road, Fuzhou (Fujian Province)
Tel: +86(591) 57861
Medicine.

Fujian School of Civil Engineering
Fuzhou (Fujian Province)
Civil Engineering.

Fuling Teachers School
Fuling (Sichuan Province)
Teacher Training.

Fuqing Teachers School
Fuqing (Fujian Province)
Teacher Training.

Fushun Institute of Petroleum
Fushun (Liaoning Province)
Petroleum Engineering.

Fuxin Mining Institute
Zhongua Road, Fuxin (Liaoning Province)
Tel: +86(418) 4321
Mining.

Fuyang Teachers College
Fuyang (Anhui Province)
Teacher Training.

Fuzhou Teachers School
Fuzhou (Fujian Province)
Teacher Training.

Fuzhou Teachers School
Fuzhou (Jiangxi Province)
Teacher Training.

Gannan Medical School
Ganzhou (Jiangxi Province)
Medicine.

Gannan Teachers School
Ganzhou (Jiangxi Province)
Teacher Training.

Gezhouba Institute of Hydroelectrical Engineering
Yichang (Hubei Province)
Tel: +86 22011
Hydroelectrical Engineering.

Guandong Institute for Minor Nationalities
Guangzhou (Guangdong Province)
Languages and Culture.

Guangdong Institute of Finance and Economics
Guangzhou (Guangdong Province)
Finance and Economics.

Guangdong Institute of Mechanical Engineering
Guangzhou (Guangdong Province)
Tel: +86 77461
Cable: 7003 guangzhou
Mechanical Engineering.

Guangdong Institute of Technology
729 East Dong Road, Guangzhou (Guangdong Province)
Tel: +86 776597
Technology.

Guangdong Medical and Pharmaceutical College
Baoggang Haizhou District, Guangzhou (Guangdong Province)
Tel: +86 429040
Medicine and Pharmaceuticals.

Guangxi Academy of Arts
Nanning (Guangxi Autonomous Region of Zhuang Nationality)
Arts.

Guangxi Agricultural College
Nanning (Guangxi Autonomous Region of Zhuang Nationality)
Tel: +86(771) 21223
Cable: 5100
Agriculture.

Guangxi College of Traditional Chinese Medicine
Nanning (Guangxi Autonomous Region of Zhuang Nationality)
Chinese Medicine.

Guangxi Institute of Nationalities
Nanning (Guangxi Autonomous Region of Zhuang Nationality)
Nationalities.

Guangxi Institute of Technology
Nanning (Guangxi Autonomous Region of Zhuang Nationality)
Technology.

Guangxi Medical College
Taoyuan Road, Nanning (Guangxi Autonomous
Region of Zhuang Nationality)
Tel: +86(771) 21477
Medicine.

**Guangxi Youjiang Teachers School for
Minor Nationalities**
Baise (Guangxi Autonomous Region of Zhuang
Nationality)
Teacher Training.

Guangzhou Academy of Fine Arts
257 Changgang East Road, Haizhou District,
Guangzhou (Guangdong Province)
Tel: +86(20) 449883
Fine Arts.

**Guangzhou College of Traditional Chinese
Medicine**
10 Jichang Road, San Yuan Li, Guangzhou
(Guangdong Province)
Tel: +86(20) 661233
Chinese Medicine.

Guangzhou Conservatory of Music
Guangzhou (Guangdong Province)
Music.

**Guangzhou Institute of Foreign Languages
(GIFL)**
Huangpodong, Guangzhou (Guangdong Province)
Tel: +86(20) 662303
Languages.

Guangzhou Institute of Foreign Trade
Guangzhou (Guangdong Province)
Tel: +86 601907
Fax: +86 601-660
Foreign Trade.

Guangzhou Institute of Physical Education
Maoer Hill Shaheding, Guangzhou (Guangdong
Province)
Physical Education.

Guangzhou Medical College
Guangzhou (Guangdong Province)
Medicine.

Guangzhou Teachers College
Guangzhou (Guangdong Province)
Teacher Training.

Guilin Institute of Electronics
Guilin (Guangxi Autonomous Region of Zhuang
Nationality)
Electronics.

Guilin Institute of Geology
Guilin (Guangxi Autonomous Region of Zhuang
Nationality)
Tel: +86 2796
Cable: 2695
Geology.

Guilin Medical School
Guilin (Guangxi Autonomous Region of Zhuang
Nationality)
Medicine.

**Guiyang College of Traditional Chinese
Medicine**
8 Shidong Road, Guiyang (Guizhou Province)
Tel: +86(851) 22633
Chinese Medicine.

Guiyang Medical College
Beying Road, Guiyang (Guizhou Province)
Tel: +86(851) 23948
Medicine.

Guiyang Teachers College
Guiyang (Guizhou Province)
Teacher Training.

Guizhou Agricultural College
Huaxi, Guiyang (Guizhou Province)
Tel: +86(851) 2319
Agriculture.

Guizhou Institute of Finance and Economics
Guiyang (Guizhou Province)
Finance and Economics.

Guizhou Institute for Minor Nationalities
Guiyang (Guishou Province)
Languages and Culture.

Guizhou Institute ofTechnology
Caijiaguan, Guiyang (Guizhou Province)
Tel: +86(851) 42756
Cable: 1114
Technology.

Guyuan Teachers School
District of Guyuan (Ningxia)
Teacher Training.

Handan Teachers School
Handan (Hebei Province)
Teacher Training.

Hangzhou Electronic Engineering Institute
Hangzhou (Zhejiang Province)
Electronical Engineering.

Hangzhou Institute of Commerce
Jiao Gong Road, Hangzhou (Zhejiang Province)
Tel: +86(571) 81024
Telex: 5096
Commerce.

Hanshan Teachers School
District of Chaoan (Guangdong Province)
Teacher Training.

Hanzhong Teachers College
Hanzhong (Shaanxi Province)
Teacher Training.

Harbin Institute of Civil Engineering and Architecture
144 Xidazhi Street, Nangang District, Harbin (Heilongjiang Province)
Tel: +86(451) 33512
Civil Engineering; Architecture.

Harbin Institute of Electrical Technology
Da-qing Road, Harbin (Heilongjiang Province)
Tel: +86(451) 55941
Electrical Engineering.

Harbin Institute of Shipbuilding Engineering
Wenmiao Jie, 11/F, Nangangqu, Harbin (Heilongjiang Province)
Tel: +86(451) 32571
Shipbuilding Engineering.

Harbin Monetary School
Harbin (Heilongjiang Province)
Finance.

Harbin Teachers School
Harbin (Heilongjiang Province)
Teacher Training.

Hebei College of Chinese Traditional Medicine
Shijiazhuang (Hebei Province)
Chinese Medicine.

Hebei Institute of Chemical Technology
Shijiazhuang (Hebei Province)
Chemical Technology.

Hebei Institute of Civil Engineering and Architecture
Zhangjiakou (Hebei Province)
Civil Engineering; Architecture.

Hebei Institute of Coal Mining and Civil Engineering
Xingtai (Hebei Province)
Coal Mining; Civil Engineering.

Hebei Institute of Finance and Trade
Shijiazhang (Hebei Province)
Finance; Trade.

Hebei Institute of Geology
Zhangjiakou (Hebei Province)
Geology.

Hebei Institute of Mechanical and Electrical Engineering
Shijiazhuang (Hebei Province)
Mechanical and Electrical Engineering.

Hebei Institute of Mining and Metallurgy
Tangshan (Hebei Province)
Mining; Metallurgy.

Hebei Institute of Technology
Yihao Road Dingzigu, Tianjin (Hebei Province)
Tel: +86(22) 67355
Technology.

Hebei School of Forestry
Yixian (Hebei Province)
Forestry.

Hebei School of Water Conservancy
Cangzhou (Hebei Province)
Water Conservation.

Hebei Teachers College
Hongqing Road, Qiaoxi District, Shijiazhuang (Hebei Province)
Tel: +86(311) 34262
Teacher Training.

Hechi Teachers School
Yishan (Guangxi Autonomous Region of Zhuang Nationality)
Teacher Training.

Hefei Institute of Geology
Hefei (Anhui Province)
Geology.

Heilongjiang College of Traditional Chinese Medicine
Harbin (Heilongjiang Province)
Chinese Medicine.

Heilongjiang Hydraulic Institute
Harbin (Heilongjiang Province)
Tel: +86 61903
Hydraulics.

Heilongjiang Institute of Commerce
Harbin (Heilongjiang Province)
Commerce.

Heilongjiang Institute of Mining
Jixi1 (Heilongjiang Province)
Mining.

Heilongjiang Nong-ken Normal College
Acheng (Heilongjiang Province)
Tel: +86 2546
Education.

Heilongjiang School of Finance
Harbin (Heilongjiang Province)
Finance.

Henan Agricultural Institute
Zhengzhou (Henan Province)
Agriculture.

Henan College of Traditional Chinese Medicine
Jinshui Road, Zhengzhou (Henan Province)
Tel: +86(371) 26695
Chinese Medicine.

Henan Institute of Finance and Economics
Zhengzhou (Henan Province)
Finance; Economics.

Henan Medical College
Zhengzhou (Henan Province)
Medicine.

Hengshui Teachers School
Hengshui (Hebei Province)
Teacher Training.

Hengyang Medical College
(Hunan Province)
Medicine.

Hengyang Teachers School
Hengyang (Hunan Province)
Tel: +86 25971
Teacher Training.

Hetian Teachers School
District of Hetian (Xingiang Province)
Teacher Training.

Heze Medical School
District of Heze (Shandong Province)
Medicine.

Heze Teachers School
(Shandong Province)
Teacher Training.

Huaibei Teachers College for Coal
Huaibei (Anhui Province)
Teacher Training (Coal).

Huainan Mining Institute
Huainan (Anhui Province)
Tel: +86 4797
Mining.

Huainan Teachers School
Huainan (Anhui Province)
Teacher Training.

Huaiyang Teachers School
Huaiyang (Jiangsu Province)
Teacher Training.

Huanggang Teachers School
District of Huanggang (Hubei Province)
Teacher Training.

Huangshi Teachers College
Huangshi (Hubei Province)
Teacher Training.

Huashan Medical School for Metallurgy
Huaying (Shaanxi Province)
Metallurgy.

Huazhong Institute of Technology
Wuhan (Hubei Province)
Tel: +86(27) 870152
Technology.

Huazhong Teachers College
Wuhan (Hubei Province)
Teacher Training.

Hubei Academy of Fine Arts
38 Huazhoncuan, Wuhan (Hubei Province)
Tel: +86(27) 877201
Fine Arts.

Hubei Agricultural Machinery Institute
Wuhan (Hubei Province)
Agricultural Machinery.

Hubei College of Education
23 Wuluo Road, Wuchang (Hubei Province)
Education.

Hubei College of Traditional Chinese Medicine
110 Yunjia Bridge, Wuhan (Hubei Province)
Tel: +86(27) 75694
Chinese Medicine.

Hubei Institute of Finance and Economics
Wuhan (Hubei Province)
Finance; Economics.

Hubei Institute of Light Industry
Ma-fang-shan Wuchang, Wuhan (Hubei Province)
Light Industry.

Hubei Medical College
39 Donghu Road, Wuhan (Hubei Province)
Tel: +86(27) 811495
Medicine.

Huiyang Teachers School
Huiyang (Guangdong Province)
Teacher Training.

Huizhou Teachers School
Tunxi (Anhui Province)
Tel: +86 3130
Teacher Training.

Hulan Teachers School
Hulan (Heilongjiang Province)
Teacher Training.

Hunan Agricultural Institute
East Lake Eastern Suburb, Changsha (Hunan Province)
Tel: +86(731) 24871
Agriculture.

Hunan College of Traditional Chinese Medecine
84 Shaoshan, Ghangsha (Hunan Province)
Tel: +86(731) 32275
Traditional Chinese Medicine.

Hunan Institute of Finance and Economics
Changsha (Hunan Province)
Finance; Economics.

Hunan Medical College
Bei Zhan Road, Changsha (Hunan Province)
Tel: +86(731) 24411
Medicine.

Hunan School of Commerce
Changsha (Hunan Province)
Commerce.

Hunan Teachers College
Changsha (Hunan Province)
Teacher Training.

Ili Teachers College
Ining (Xingiang Province)
Teacher Training.

Inner Mongolia Engineering College
Hohhot (Inner Mongolia)
Tel: +86(471) 44933
Telex: 85004 itcc cn
Engineering.

Inner Mongolia Forestry College
Hohhot (Inner Mongolia)
Tel: +86(471) 44665
Forestry.

Inner Mongolia Institute of Agricultural and Animal Husbandry
Hohhot (Inner Mongolia)
Tel: +86(471) 44746
Agriculture; Animal Husbandry.

Inner Mongolia Institute of Finance and Economics
Hohhot (Inner Mongolia)
Finance; Economics.

Inner Mongolia Medical College
Hohhot (Inner Mongolia)
Medicine.

Institute of Chinese Music
Beijing (Beijing Municipality)
Chinese Music.

Institute of Chinese Opera
Beijing (Beijing Municipality)
Chinese Opera.

Institute of International Politics
Beijing (Beijing Municipality)
International Politics.

Institute of International Relations
Poshangchun, Haidian District, Beijing (Beijing Municipality)
Tel: +86(1) 285631
International Relations.

Jiamusi Institute of Technology
Jiamusi (Heilongjiang Province)
Technology.

Jiamusi Medical College
Jiamusi (Heilongjiang Province)
Medicine.

Jiamusi Teachers School
Jiamusi (Heilongjiang Province)
Tel: +86 21857
Teacher Training.

Jian Teachers School
Jian (Jiangxi Province)
Teacher Training.

Jiangsu Agricultural Institute
Western Suburb, Yangzhou (Jiangsu Province)
Tel: +86 42521
Agriculture.

Jiangsu Commercial School
Yangzhou (Jiangsu Province)

Jiangsu Institute of Chemical Technology
Changzhou (Jiangsu Province)
Chemical Technology.

Jiangsu Institute of Technology
Zhenjiang (Jiangsu Province)
Tel: +86(511) 24071
Technology.

Jiangsu School of Public Security
Nanjing (Jiangsu Province)
Public Security.

Jiangxi College of Traditional Chinese Medicine
Nanchang (Jiangxi Province)
Traditional Chinese Medicine.

Jiangxi Institute of Finance and Economics
Nanchang (Jiangxi Province)
Finance; Economics.

Jiangxi Institute of Technology
Nanchang (Jiangxi Province)
Technology.

Jiangxi Medical College
Bayidadao, Nanchang (Jiangxi Province)
Tel: +86(791) 64936
Medicine.

Jianjing Teachers School
District of Yongchuan (Sichuan Province)
Teacher Training.

Jiaozuo Mining Institute
Jiaozuo (Henan Province)
Mining.

Jiaxing Teachers School
District of Wuxing (Zhejiang Province)
Teacher Training.

Jiaying Teachers School
(Guangdong Province)
Tel: +86 23624
Teacher Training.

Jilin Academy of Arts
Changchun (Jilin Province)
Arts.

Jilin Institute of Chemical Technology
Jilin (Jilin Province)
Chemical Technology.

Jilin Institute of Civil Engineering and Architecture
Changchun (Jilin Province)
Civil Engineering; Architecture.

Jilin Institute of Finance and Economics
Changchun (Jilin Province)
Finance; Economics.

Jilin Institute of Forestry
Jilin (Jilin Province)
Forestry.

Jilin Institute of Technology
Changchun (Jilin Province)
Technology.

Jilin Mechanical and Electrical School
Changchun (Jilin Province)
Mechanics and Electrics.

Jilin Physical Culture Institute
Changchun (Jilin Province)
Physical Culture.

Jilin Teachers College
Jilin (Jilin Province)
Teacher Training.

Jimei Navigation Institute
Xiamen (Fujian Province)
Tel: +86(592) 28151
Navigation.

Jimei Teachers School
Xiamen (Fujian Province)
Teacher Training.

Jingdezhen Porcelain Institute
Jingdezhen (Jiangxi Province)
Porcelain Techniques.

Jingzhou Teachers School
Jingzhou (Hubei Province)
Teacher Training.

Jining Medical School
Jining (Shandong Province)
Medicine.

Jining Teachers School
Jining (Shandong Province)
Teacher Training.

Jinzhou Institute of Technology
Jinzhou (Liaoning Province)
Technology.

Jinzhou Medical College
190 Lean Street, Jinzhou (Liaoning Province)
Tel: +86(416) 5943
Medicine.

Jinzhou Teachers College
Jinzhou (Liaoning Province)
Teacher Training.

Jiujiang Teachers School
Jiujiang (Jiangxi Province)
Tel: +86 3591
Teacher Training.

Kaifeng Medical School
Kaifeng (Henan Province)
Medicine.

Keshan Teachers School
Keshan (Heilongjiang Province)
Teacher Training.

Keshi Teachers College
Keshi (Xingiang Province)
Teacher Training.

Kunming Institute of Technology
Lianhuanchi, Northern Suburb, Kunming (Yunnan Province)
Tel: +86(871) 29021
Technology.

Kunming Medical College
Renmin Road, Kunming (Yunnan Province)
Tel: +86(871) 81966
Medicine.

Kunming Teachers College
Kunming (Yunnan Province)
Teacher Training.

Kunming Teachers School
Kunming (Yunnan Province)
Teacher Training.

Laiyang Agricultural College
Laiyang (Shandong Province)
Tel: +86 777
Agriculture.

Lanfang Teachers School
District of Anci (Hebei Province)
Teacher Training.

Lanzhou College of Traditional Chinese Medicine
Lanzhou (Gansu Province)
Traditional Chinese Medicine.

Lanzhou Institute of Commerce
Lanzhou (Gansu Province)
Commerce.

Lanzhou Medical College
7 Donggang West Road, Lanzhou (Gansu Province)
Tel: +86(931) 24311
Medicine.

Lanzhou Railway Institute
3 West Anning Road, Lanzhou (Gansu Province)
Tel: +86(931) 66221
Railways.

Lanzhou Teachers School
Lanzhou (Gansu Province)
Teacher Training.

Leizhou Teachers School
Zhanjiang (Guangdong Province)
Tel: +86 38255
Teacher Training.

Leshan Teachers School
Leshan (Sichuan Province)
Teacher Training.

Liangshan College of Education
Xichang (Sichuan Province)
Education.

Lianyungang Chemical Mining School
Lianyungang (Jiangsu Province)
Chemical Mining.

Liaocheng Teachers Institute
Liaocheng (Shandong Province)
Teacher Training.

Liaoning College of Traditional Chinese Medicine
Beling Street, Shenyang (Liaoning Province)
Tel: +86(24) 62567
Traditional Chinese Medicine.

Liaoning Institute of Construction Engineering
Shenyang (Liaoning Province)
Construction Engineering.

Liaoning Institute of Finance and Economics
Dalian (Liaoning Province)
Finance and Economics.

Liaoning School of Commerce
Jinzhou (Liaoning Province)
Commerce.

Liaoning Teachers College
Huanghe Street, Duanggu District, Liaoning (Liaoning Province)
Tel: +86(24) 65302
Teacher Training.

Linyi Teachers School
Fei County (Shandong Province)
Teacher Training.

Lishui Teachers School
District of Lishui (Zhejiang Province)
Teacher Training.

Liuan Teachers School
District of Liuan (Anhui Province)
Teacher Training.

Lu Xun Academy of Fine Arts
1 Sanhao Street, Heping District, Shenyang (Liaoning Province)
Tel: +86(24) 482635
Fine Arts.

Luoyang Institute of Technology
Luoyang (Henan Province)
Technology.

Luoyang Medical School
Luoyang (Henan Province)
Medicine.

Luoyang Teachers School
Luoyang (Henan Province)
Teacher Training.

Luzhou Medical College
Luzhou (Sichuan Province)
Medicine.

Maanshan Mining Institute
Maanshan (Anhui Province)
Mining.

Maanshan School of Commerce
Maanshanu (Anhui Province)
Commerce.

Medical College of Inner Mongolia Nationality
Hohhot (Inner Mongolia)
Medicine.

Mengzi Teachers School
District of Mengzi (Yunnan Province)
Teacher Training.

Mianyang Agricultural School
Mianyang (Sichuan Province)
Agriculture.

Mianyang Teachers School
Mianyang (Sichuan Province)
Teacher Training.

Mudanjiang Medical School
Mudanjiang (Heilongjiang Province)
Medicine.

Mudanjiang Teachers College
Mudanjiang (Heilongjiang Province)
Teacher Training.

Nanchang Institute of Aircraft Industry
Nanchang (Jiangxi Province)
Aircraft Industry.

Nanchong Medical School
Nanchong (Sichuan Province)
Medicine.

Nanchong Teachers College
10 Renminxi Road, Nanchong (Sichuan Province)
Tel: +86 2244
Teacher Training.

Nanjing Academy of Arts
15 Huju Road, Nanjing (Jiangsu Province)
Tel: +86(25) 31250
Telex: 34136 glynj cn
Arts.

Nanjing Aeronautical Institute
29 Yu dao Street, Nanjing (Jiangsu Province)
Tel: +86(25) 46752
Telex: 34155 nanj cn
Cable: 3057
Aeronautics.

Nanjing Chemical Engineering and Energetics
Nanjing (Jiangsu Province)
Chemical Engineering and Energetics.

Nanjing College of Traditional Chinese Medicine
282 Nanzhong Road, Nanjing (Jiangsu Province)
Tel: +86(25) 41337
Traditional Chinese Medicine.

Nanjing Institute of Chemical Technology
5 Xinmofan Road, Nanjing (Jiangsu Province)
Chemical Engineering.

Nanjing Institute of Civil Engineering and Architecture
Nanjing (Jiangsu Province)
Civil Engineering; Architecture.

Nanjing Institute of Food Economics
14 Hongmiao Lane, Fujian Road, Nanjing
(Jiangsu Province)
Tel: +86(25) 86033
Food Economics.

Nanjing Institute of Meteorology
Panchenggi Pukou District, Nanjing (Jiangsu Province)
Tel: +86(25) 51343
Meteorology.

Nanjing Institute of Pharmacy
24 Tongia Xiang, Nanjing (Jiangsu Province)
Tel: +86(25) 34371
Pharmacy.

Nanjing Institute of Physical Culture
Nanjing (Jiangsu Province)
Physical Culture.

Nanjing Institute of Posts and Telecommunications
38 Guandong Road Sanpailou, Nanjing (Jiangsu Province)
Tel: +86(25) 33862
Post and Telecommunications.

Nanjing Institute of Technology
Sipailou, Nanjing (Jiangsu Province)
Tel: +86(25) 34691
Telex: 34137
Technology.

Nanjing Medical College
Hanzhong Road, Nanjing (Jiangsu Province)
Tel: +86(25) 42696
Medicine.

Nanjing Railway Medical College
87 Dingjiaqiao Road, Nanjing (Jiangsu Province)
Tel: +86(25) 31508
Medicine.

Nanjing School of River Navigation
Nanjing (Jiangsu Province)
River Navigation.

Nanjing Teachers College of Education
Nanjing (Jiangsu Province)
Teacher Training.

Nanning Teachers College
Nanning (Guangxi Autonomous Region of Zhuang Nationality)
Teacher Training.

Nanning Teachers School
Nanning (Guangxi Autonomous Region of Zhuang Nationality)
Teacher Training.

Nanping Teachers School
Nanping (Fujian Province)
Teacher Training.

Nantong Medical College
19 Qixiu Road, Nantong (Jiangsu Province)
Tel: +86(513) 7191
Medicine.

Nantong Teachers School
Nantong (Jiangsu Province)
Teacher Training.

Nantong Textile School
Nantong (Jiangsu Province)
Textiles.

Neijiang Teachers School
Neijiang (Sichuan Province)
Teacher Training.

Ningbo Teachers School
Ningbo (Zhejiang Province)
Teacher Training.

Ningde Teachers School
District of Ningde (Fujian Province)
Teacher Training.

Ningxia Agricultural College
Yongning County, Ningxia (Ningxia)
Agriculture.

Ningxia Institute of Technology
Yinchuan (Ningxia)
Technology.

Ningxia Medical College
Southern Suburb, Yinchuan (Ningxia)
Tel: +86(951) 2831
Medicine.

North China Institute of Electrical Power
12 Qingnian Road, Baoding (Hebei Province)
Tel: +86 4951
Electrical Power.

North China Institute of Industrial Agricultural Engineering
Xingtai (Hebei Province)
Industrial Agricultural Engineering.

North China Institute of Water Conservancy and Hydro-Power
62 Zhonghua Street, Handan (Hebei Province)
Tel: +86 24860
Water Conservation and Hydro-Power.

Northeast College of Forestry
Harbin (Heilongjiang Province)
Tel: +86(451) 63163
Forestry.

Northeast Institute of Electric Power
Changchun Road, Jilin (Jilin Province)
Tel: +86(431) 44186
Electric Power.

Northeast Institute of Heavy Machinery
Heping Street, Fulaerji District, Qiqihar
(Heilongjiang Province)
Tel: +86 83984
Heavy Machinery.

Northwest Institute of Civil Engineering
Xi'an (Shaanxi Province)
Civil Engineering.

Northwest Institute of Forestry
Wugong (Shaanxi Province)
Forestry.

Northwest Institute of Light Industry
West Renmin Road, Xi'anyang (Shaanxi Province)
Tel: +86(910) 4389
Light Industry.

Northwest Institute for Minor Nationalities
4 Xibeixincun, Lanzhou (Gansu Province)
Tel: +86(931) 24011
Cable: 111
Languages and Culture.

Northwest Institute of Political Science and Law
Changannan Road, Xi'an (Shaanxi Province)
Tel: +86(29) 52056
Law; Political Science.

Northwest Institute of Telecommunication Engineering
2 Taibai Road, Xi'an (Shaanxi Province)
Tel: +86(29) 55801
Telecommunication Engineering.

Northwest Teachers College
51 Anning East Road, Lanzhou (Gansu Province)
Tel: +86(931) 66151
Teacher Training.

Qingdao Medical College
10 Huangtai Road, Qingdao (Shandong Province)
Tel: +86(532) 24523
Medicine.

Qinghai Animal Husbandry and Veterinary College
Xining (Ningxia)
Animal Husbandry and Veterinary Medicine.

Qinghai College for Minor Nationalities
25 Bayi Road, Xining (Ningxia)
Tel: +86(971) 75340
Languages and Culture.

Qinghai Educational College
91 Ba Yi Road, Xining (Ningxia)
Tel: +86(971) 55137
Education.

Qinghai Institute of Engineering and Agriculture
Xining (Ningxia)
Engineering; Agriculture.

Qinghai Medical College
84 Kun Lun Road, Xining (Ningxia)
Medicine.

Qingyang Teachers School
District of Qingyang (Gansu Province)
Teacher Training.

Qiqihar Institute of Light Industry
Qiqihar (Heilongjiang Province)
Light Industry.

Qiqihar School of Medicine
Qiqihar (Heilongjiang Province)
Medicine.

Qiqihar Teachers College
Qiqihar (Heilongjiang Province)
Teacher Training.

Quanzhou Teachers School
Quanzhou (Fujian Province)
Teacher Training.

Qufu Teachers Institute
Qufu (Shandong Province)
Teacher Training.

Qujing Teachers School
District of Qujing (Yunnan Province)
Teacher Training.

Shaanxi College of Traditional Chinese Medicine
Weiyang Road, Xi'an (Shaanxi Province)
Tel: +86(910) 2766
Traditional Chinese Medicine.

Shaanxi Institute of Finance and Economics
Cuihua Road, Xi'an (Shaanxi Province)
Tel: +86(29) 52221
Finance and Economics.

Shaanxi Institute of Mechanical Engineering
Jin Hua Road, Xi'an (Shaanxi Province)
Tel: +86(29) 31236
Mechanical Engineering.

Shaanxi Institute of Technology
(Shaanxi Province)
Technology.

Shaanxi Pedagogical Institute
Xing Shan Si Dong Jie 11, Xiao Zhai, Xi'an
(Shaanxi Province)
Pedagogy.

Shandon College of Oceanography
5 Yushan Road, Qingdao (Shandong Province)
Tel: +86(532) 84361
Oceanography.

Shandong Academy of Arts
Jinan (Shandong Province)
Arts.

Shandong Academy of Medicine
Jing Shi Road 35, Jinan (Shandong Province)
Medicine.

Shandong Agricultural Institute
District of Taian (Shandong Province)
Agriculture.

Shandong Institute of Agricultural Mechanization
Zibo (Shandong Province)
Agricultural Mechanization.

Shandong Institute of Building Materials
Zibo (Shandong Province)
Building Materials.

Shandong Institute of Chemical Technology
Quingdao (Shandong Province)
Chemical Technology.

Shandong Institute of Civil Engineering
Jinan (Shandong Province)
Civil Engineering.

Shandong Institute of Economics
Jinan (Shandong Province)
Tel: +86(531) 44161
Economics.

Shandong Institute of Light Industry
Jinan (Shandong Province)
Light Industry.

Shandong Institute of Metallurgy
Quingdao (Shandong Province)
Metallurgy.

Shandong Institute of Physical Culture
Jinan (Shandong Province)
Physical Culture.

Shandong Institute of Textile Technology
Quingdao (Shandong Province)
Textile Technology.

Shandong Institute of Traditional Chinese Medicine
23 Jingshi Road, Jinan (Shandong Province)
Tel: +86(531) 4694
Traditional Chinese Medicine.

Shandong Mining Institute
District of Taian (Shandong Province)
Tel: +86(538) 3310
Mining.

Shanghai Agricultural College
Shanghai (Shanghai Municipality)
Tel: +86 389081
Agriculture.

Shanghai College of Traditional Chinese Medicine
530 Lingling Road, Shanghai (Shanghai Municipality)
Tel: +86(21) 388400
Traditional Chinese Medicine.

Shanghai Conservatory of Music
20 Fenyang Road, Shanghai (Shanghai Municipality)
Tel: +86(21) 370137
Music.

Shanghai Customs School
Shanghai (Shanghai Municipality)
Customs.

Shanghai Drama Institute
630 Huashan Road, Shanghai (Shanghai Municipality)
Tel: +86(21) 521909
Drama.

Shanghai First Medical College
Shanghai (Shanghai Municipality)
Medicine.

Shanghai Institute of Finance and Economics
Shanghai (Shanghai Municipality)
Finance and Economics.

Shanghai Institute of Foreign Trade
119 Ti Yu Hui Lu, Shanghai (Shanghai Municipality)
Tel: +86(21) 598181
Telex: 33531 sioft cn
Cable: 3074
Foreign Trade.

Shanghai Institute of Foreign Trade
Shanghai (Shanghai Municipality)
Tel: +86(21) 598181
Telex: 33531 sioft can
Foreign Trade.

Shanghai Institute of Mechanical Engineering
516 Jun Gong Road, Shanghai 200093 (Shanghai Municipality)
Tel: +86(21) 433040
Mechanical Engineering.

Shanghai Institute of Physical Culture
650 Qingyuanhuan Road, Shanghai (Shanghai
Municipality)
Tel: +86(21) 480545
Physical Culture.

Shanghai Maritime College
1550 Pudong Street, Shanghai (Shanghai
Municipality)
Tel: +86(21) 84094
Maritime Studies.

Shanghai Railway Institute
Zhennan Road, Shanghai (Shanghai Municipality)
Tel: +86(21) 506344
Railway Engineering.

Shanghai Railways Medical College
Shanghai (Shanghai Municipality)
Medicine.

Shanghai School of Building Materials
Shanghai (Shanghai Municipality)
Building Materials.

**Shanghai School of Medical Apparatus and
Instruments**
Shanghai (Shanghai Municipality)
Medical Equipment.

**Shanghai School of Petrochemical
Technology**
Shanghai (Shanghai Municipality)
Petrochemical Technology.

**Shanghai School of Science and
Technology**
Shanghai (Shanghai Municipality)
Science; Technology.

Shanghai School of Textile Industry
Shanghai (Shanghai Municipality)
Textile Industry.

Shanghai School of Tourism
Shanghai (Shanghai Municipality)
Tourism.

Shanghai Technical College of Metallurgy
121 Caobao Road, Shanghai 201103 (Shanghai
Municipality)
Metallurgy.

Shangqiu Teachers School
Shangqiu (Henan Province)
Teacher Training.

Shangrao Teachers College
No. 21 Maojialing, Shangrao City (Jiangxi
Province)
Tel: +86 2440
Teacher Training.

Shanxi Institute of Finance and Economics
Taiyuan (Shanxi Province)
Finance and Economics.

Shanxi Medical College
10 Xinjian South Road, Taiyuan (Shanxi Province)
Tel: +86(351) 21511
Medicine.

Shanxi Teachers College
Linfen (Shanxi Province)
Teacher Training.

Shaoguan Teachers College
Da Tang Road, Shaoguan (Guangdong Province)
Tel: +86 5707
Teacher Training.

Shaoxing Teachers School
Shaoxing (Zhejiang Province)
Teacher Training.

Shaoyang Teachers School
Shaoyang (Hunan Province)
Teacher Training.

**Shenyang Aeronautical Engineering
Institute**
Huang-He Street, Shenyang (Liaoning Province)
Aeronautical Engineering.

Shenyang Agricultural Institute
Maguanqiao Dongling, Shenyang (Liaoning
Province)
Tel: +86(24) 4479
Agriculture.

Shenyang Conservatory of Music
Shenyang (Liaoning Province)
Music.

Shenyang Institute of Chemical Technology
Shenyang (Liaoning Province)
Chemical Technology.

Shenyang Institute of Pharmacy
Wenhua Road, Shenhe District (Henyang)
Tel: +86(24) 482706
Pharmacy.

Shenyang Institute of Physical Culture
Shenyang (Liaoning Province)
Physical Culture.

Shenyang Institute of Technology
Wenhua Road, Heping District, Shenyang
(Liaoning Province)
Tel: +86(24) 483081
Telex: 80033 neit cn
Technology.

**Shenyang Mechanical and Electrical
Institute**
Shenyang (Liaoning Province)
Mechanics and Electrics.

**Shenyang Metallurgical and Machinery
School**
Shenyang (Liaoning Province)
Metallurgy; Machines.

Shenyang School of Gold Technology
Shenyang (Liaoning Province)
Tel: +86 4141
Gold Technology.

Shenyang School of Pharmacy
Shenyang. (Liaoning Province)
Pharmacy.

Shenyang Teachers College
Shenyang (Liaoning Province)
Teacher Training.

Shihezi Agricultural College
Shihezi (Xingiang Province)
Tel: +86 2392
Agriculture.

Shihezi Medical College
Shihezi (Xingiang Province)
Medicine.

Shijiazhuang Institute of Technology for Railway Employees
Shijiazhuang (Hebei Province)
Technology for Railway Employees.

Shijiazhuang Teachers School
Shijiazhuang (Hebei Province)
Teacher Training.

Sichuan Agricultural Institute
Yaan (Sichuan Province)
Agriculture.

Sichuan Conservatory of Music
Chengdu (Sichuan Province)
Music.

Sichuan Institute of Animal Husbandry and Veterinary Medecine
Rongchang (Sichuan Province)
Animal Husbandry; Veterinary Medicine.

Sichuan Institute of Building Materials
District of Mianyang (Sichuan Province)
Building Materials.

Sichuan Institute of Chemical Technology
Zigong (Sichuan Province)
Chemical Technology.

Sichuan Institute of Finance and Economics
Guanghuachan, Chengdu (Sichuan Province)
Tel: +86(28) 23116
Finance and Economics.

Sichuan Institute of Fine Arts
Huangjueping, Jiulongpo District, Chongqing (Sichuan Province)
Tel: +86(811) 23423
Fine Arts.

Sichuan Institute of Technology
Chendu, Pi County (Sichuan Province)
Technology.

Simao Teachers School
District of Simao (Yunnan Province)
Teacher Training.

Siping Teachers College
Siping (Jilin Province)
Teacher Training.

South Central Institute of Political Science and Law
Wuhan (Hubei Province)
Tel: +86 701-620
Fax: +86 703-056
Political Science; Law.

South China College of Tropical Agriculture
District of Danxian, Hainan (Guangdong Province)
Tropical Agriculture.

South China (Huanan) Institute of Technology
Wushan, Guangzhou 7003 (Guangdong Province)
Tel: +86(20) 774433
Technology.

South Guizhou Teachers School for Nationalities
Duyun (Guizhou Province)
Teacher Training.

Southeast Guizhou Teachers School for Nationalities
District of Kaili (Guizhou Province)
Teacher Training.

Southeast Shanxi Medical School
Changzhi (Shanxi Province)
Medicine.

Southeast Shanxi Teachers School
Changzhi (Shanxi Province)
Teacher Training.

Southern Institute of Metallurgy
Ganzhou (Jiangxi Province)
Metallurgy.

Southwest Agricultural College
Chongqing (Sichuan Province)
Tel: +86(811) 3964
Agriculture.

Southwest Institute for Minor Nationalities
Chengdu (Sichuan Province)
Languages and Culture.

Southwest Institute of Petroleum
6 Shiyou East Road, Nanchong (Sichuan Province)
Tel: +86 2278
PetroleumEngineering.

Southwest Institute of Political Science and Law
Shapingba, Chongqing (Sichuan Province)
Tel: +86(811) 661223
Political Science; Law.

Suihua Teachers School
Suihua (Heilongjiang Province)
Teacher Training.

Suzhou Institute of Silk Technology
Xiangmen Road, Suzhou (Jiangsu Province)
Tel: +86(512) 25614
Silk Technology.

Suzhou Medical College
48 Renmin Road, Suzhou (Jiangsu Province)
Tel: +86(512) 25696
Telex: 36302 sitlx cn
Medicine.

Suzhou Railway Teachers College
Suzhou (Jiangsu Province)
Teacher Training.

Suzhou Sericulture School
District of Wuxian (Jiangsu Province)
Sericulture.

Suzhou Teachers School
Suzhou (Jiangsu Province)
Teacher Training.

Taian Teachers School
Taian (Shandong Province)
Teacher Training.

Taishan Medical College
Taian (Shandong Province)
Medicine.

Taiyuan Institute of Heavy Machinery
Rongliu Road, Taiyuan (Shanxi Province)
Tel: +86(351) 66521
Heavy Machinery.

Taiyuan Machinery Institute
Shanglancun, Beixao District, Taiyuan (Shanxi
Province)
Tel: +86(351) 59411
Machinery.

Taiyuan Teachers College
Taiyuan (Shanxi Province)
Tel: +86(351) 2370
Teacher Training.

Taizhou Teachers School
Lihai County (Zhejiang Province)
Teacher Training.

Tangshan Coal Medical College
Tangshan (Hebei Province)
Medicine.

Tangshan Teachers School
Tangshan (Hebei Province)
Teacher Training.

**Teachers College for Inner Mongolia
Nationality**
Tongliao (Inner Mongolia)
Teacher Training.

**Teachers School for Hainan Li and Miao
Autonomous Zhou**
Tongshen (Guangdong Province)
Teacher Training.

**Teachers School of Zhaowudameng
Mongolian Nationality**
Chifeng (Inner Mongolia)
Teacher Training.

Tianjin Agricultural Institute
Tianjin (Tianjin Province)
Agriculture.

**Tianjin College of Traditional Chinese
Medecine**
Xihucun, Nankai District, Tiajin (Tianjin Province)
Tel: +86(22) 23737
Traditional Chinese Medicine.

Tianjin Institute of Finance and Economics
25 Zhujiangdao, Hexi District, Tianjin (Tianjin
Province)
Tel: +86(22) 82657
Finance and Economics.

Tianjin Institute of Fine Arts
Tianjin (Tianjin Province)
Fine Arts.

Tianjin Institute of Foreign Languages
137 Machangdao, Hexi District, Tianjin (Tianjin
Province)
Tel: +86(22) 397101
Foreign Languages.

Tianjin Institute of Foreign Trade
Tianjin (Tianjin Province)
Foreign Trade.

Tianjin Institute of Light Industry
1486 Dagu Nanlu, Tianjin (Tianjin Province)
Tel: +86(22) 82965
Light Industry.

Tianjin Institute of Physical Culture
Tianjin (Tianjin Province)
Physical Culture.

Tianjin Institute of Science and Technology
Tianjin (Tianjin Province)
Science; Technology.

Tianjin Institute of Textile Technology
89 Cheng Linzhung Road, Hedong District, Tianjin
(Tianjin Province)
Tel: +86(22) 43251
Textiles Industry.

Tianjin Medical College
62 Qi Xiang Tai Road, Tianjin (Tianjin Province)
Medicine.

Tianjin Medical School
22 Qixiangtai Road, Heping District, Tianjin
(Tianjin Province)
Tel: +86(22) 332691
Medicine.

CHINA

Tianjin Music Conservatory
5 Shiyijing Road, Hedong District, Tianjin (Tianjin Province)
Tel: +86(22) 42882
Music.

Tianjin Teachers College
Tianjin (Tianjin Province)
Teacher Training.

Tianjin Technical Teachers Institute
Tianjin (Tianjin Province)
Technical Teacher Training.

Tianshui Teachers School
Tianshui (Gansu Province)
Teacher Training.

Tibet College of Agriculture and Animal Husbandry
District of Linzhi (Tibet)
Agriculture; Animal Husbandry.

Tibet Institute for Minor Nationalities
Xianyang (Tibet)
Languages and Culture.

Tibet Teachers College
Lhasa (Tibet)
Teacher Training.

Tieling Teachers College
Tieling (Liaoning Province)
Teacher Training.

Tonghua Teachers College
Tonghua (Jilin Province)
Teacher Training.

Tongling School of Finance and Economics
Tonglingu (Anhui Province)
Finance and Economics.

Tongren Teachers School
District of Tongren (Guizhou Province)
Teacher Training.

Wannan Agricultural Institute
Xuancheng (Anhui Province)
Agriculture.

Wannan Medical College
Wuhu (Anhui Province)
Tel: +86(553) 5947
Medicine.

Weinan Teachers School
District of Weinan (Shaanxi Province)
Teacher Training.

Wenzhou Medical College
Yixueyuan Road, Wenzhou (Zhejiang Province)
Tel: +86 4941
Medicine.

Wenzhou Teachers School
Wenzhou (Zhejiang Province)
Teacher Training.

West Henan School of Medicine
District of Yanshi (Henan Province)
Medicine.

Wuhan College of Geology
Yuijashan, Wuhan (Hubei Province)
Tel: +86(27) 70481
Geology.

Wuhan Institute for Building Materials
Wuhan (Hubei Province)
Building Materials.

Wuhan Institute for Cereal Preservation and Processing
Wuhan (Hubei Province)
Cereal Preservation and Process.

Wuhan Institute of Chemical Technology
Wuhan (Hubei Province)
Tel: +86 870-369
Chemical Technology.

Wuhan Institute of Physical Culture
(Hubei Provinceuhan)
Physical Culture.

Wuhan Institute of Technology
Wuhan (Hubei Province)
Technology.

Wuhan Institute of Textile Technology
Wuhan (Hubei Province)
Textile Technology.

Wuhan Institute of Urban Construction
Wuhan (Hubei Province)
Urban Construction.

Wuhan Institute of Water Conservancy and Electric Power
Luojia Hill, Wuhan (Hubei Province)
Tel: +86(27) 812212
Water Conservation; Electric Power.

Wuhan Metallurgical Medical School
Wuhan (Hubei Province)
Medicine.

Wuhan School of Building Construction for Metallurgical Industry
Wuhan (Hubei Province)
Metallurgical Industry.

Wuhan School of River Transport
Wuhan (Hubei Province)
Tel: +86(27) 661491
River Transport.

Wuhan Teachers College
Wuhan (Hubei Province)
Teacher Training.

Wuhu Teachers School
Wuhu (Anhui Province)
Teacher Training.

Wuxi Institute of Light Engineering
Wuxi (Jiangsu Province)
Tel: +86(510) 21243
Light Engineering.

Xiamen Institute of Aquatic Products
(Fujian Province)
Aquatic Products.

Xi'an Academy of Fine Arts
Xingguosi, Xi'an (Shaanxi Province)
Tel: +86(29) 52517
Fine Arts.

Xi'an Institute of Foreign Languages
Xi'an (Shaanxi Province)
Foreign Languages.

Xi'an Institute of Geology
4 Yan'ta Road, Xi'an (Shaanxi Province)
Tel: +86(29) 52991
Geology.

Xi'an Institute of Highways
Cuihua Road, Xi'an (Shaanxi Province)
Tel: +86(29) 52927
Highway Engineering.

Xi'an Institute of Metallurgy and Construction Engineering
13 Yan'ta Road, Xi'an (Shaanxi Province)
Tel: +86(29) 51293
Construction Engineering.

Xi'an Institute of Petroleum
Xi'an (Shaanxi Province)
PetroleumEngineering.

Xi'an Institute of Physical Culture
Xi'an (Shaanxi Province)
Physical Culture.

Xi'an Institute of Technology
Xi'an (Shaanxi Province)
Technology.

Xi'an Institute of Textile Technology
Jin Hua Road, Xi'an (Shaanxi Province)
Tel: +86(29) 31963
Textile Technology.

Xi'an Medical College
Xi'an (Shaanxi Province)
Medicine.

Xi'an Mining Institute
14 Yan'ta Road, Xi'an (Shaanxi Province)
Tel: +86(29) 52931
Mining.

Xi'an Music Conservatory
Xi'an (Shaanxi Province)
Music.

Xiangtan Mining Institute
Xiangtan (Hunan Province)
Mining.

Xiangtan Teachers School
Xiangtan (Hunan Province)
Teacher Training.

Xianning Teachers School
Xianning (Hubei Province)
Teacher Training.

Xianyang Teachers School
Xianyang (Shaanxi Province)
Teacher Training.

Xiaogan Teachers School
Xiaogan (Hubei Province)
Tel: +86 3906
Teacher Training.

Xichang Agricultural College
Mapinda, Xichang (Sichuan Province)
Tel: +86 3334
Agriculture.

Xin County Teachers School
Xin County (Shanxi Province)
Teacher Training.

Xingjiang August 1st Agricultural College
Zhimancheng, Urumqi (Xingiang Province)
Tel: +86(991) 42141
Agriculture.

Xingjiang Institute of Finance and Economics
Urumqi (Xingiang Province)
Finance and Economics.

Xingjiang Institute of Petroleum
Urumqi (Xingiang Province)
Petroleum.

Xingjiang Institute of Technology
Youhao Road, Urumqi (Xingiang Province)
Tel: +86(991) 41911
Technology.

Xingjiang Medical College
Urumqi (Xingiang Province)
Medicine.

Xingyi Teachers School
District of Xingyi (Guizhou Province)
Teacher Training.

Xinxiang Medical College
Ji County (Henan Province)
Medicine.

Xinxiang Teachers College
Xinxiang (Henan Province)
Teacher Training.

Xinyang Teachers College
Xinxiang (Henan Province)
Teacher Training.

Xuchang Teachers School
Xuchang (Henan Province)
Tel: +86 4853
Teacher Training.

Xuzhou Medical College
Xuzhou (Jiangsu Province)
Tel: +86 24932
Medicine.

Xuzhou Teachers College
57 Heping Road, Xuzhou (Jiangsu Province)
Tel: +86(516) 88750
Teacher Training.

Xuzhou Teachers School
Xuzhou (Anhui Province)
Teacher Training.

Yanan Medical College
Yanan (Shaanxi Province)
Medicine.

Yanbei Teachers School
Shuo County (Shanxi Province)
Teacher Training.

Yanbian Agricultural Institute
District of Yanji (Jilin Province)
Agriculture.

Yanbian Medical College
Yanji (Jilin Province)
Medicine.

Yanbian Teachers School
Yanji (Jilin Province)
Teacher Training.

Yancheng Teachers College
District of Yancheng (Jiangsu Province)
Teacher Training.

Yancheng Technical School
District of Yancheng (Jiangsu Province)
Technical Training.

Yangzhou Industrial School
Yangzhou (Jiangsu Province)
Industrial Studies.

Yangzhou Medical School
Yangzhou (Jiangsu Province)
Medicine.

Yangzhou Teachers College
The Shore of the Slender West Lake, Yangzhou
(Jiangsu Province)
Tel: +86 43011
Teacher Training.

Yantai Teachers College
Yantai (Shandong Province)
Tel: +86 23567
Teacher Training.

Yichang Medical School
Yichang (Hubei Province)
Medicine.

Yichang Teachers School
Yichang (Hubei Province)
Teacher Training.

Yichun Teachers School
Yichun (Jiangxi Province)
Teacher Training.

Yinchuan Teachers School
Helan (Ningxia)
Teacher Training.

Yingkou Teachers College
Yingkou (Liaoning Province)
Teacher Training.

Yishui Medical School
District of Yishui (Shandong Province)
Medicine.

Yiyang Teachers School
Yiyang (Hunan Province)
Teacher Training.

Youijiang Medical College for Nationalities
Baise (Guangxi Autonomous Region of Zhuang
Nationality)
Medicine.

Yueyang Teachers School
Yueyang (Hunan Province)
Teacher Training.

Yulin Teachers School
Yulin (Guangxi Autonomous Region of Zhuang
Nationality)
Teacher Training.

Yunnan Academy of Arts
Kunming (Yunnan Province)
Arts.

**Yunnan College of Traditional Chinese
Medicine**
Kunming (Yunnan Province)
Traditional Chinese Medicine.

Yunnan Institute of Finance and Trade
Kunming (Yunnan Province)
Finance; Trade.

Yunnan Institute for Minor Nationalities
Lianhuachi, Kunming (Yunnan Province)
Tel: +86(871) 23298
Languages and Culture.

Yunnan Institute of Technology
Huancheng Donglu, Kunming (Yunnan Province)
Tel: +86(871) 29031
Technology.

Yunnan School of Political Science and Law
Kunming (Yunnan Province)
Political Science; Law.

Yunyang Teachers School
Jun County (Hubei Province)
Teacher Training.

Yuxi Agricultural School
Xinan County (Henan Province)
Agriculture.

Zhangjiakou Medical College
Zhangjiakou (Hebei Province)
Medicine.

Zhangjiakou School of Agriculture
District of Xuanhua (Hebei Province)
Agriculture.

Zhangjiakou Teachers School
Zhangjiakou (Hebei Province)
Teacher Training.

Zhangye Teachers School
District of Zhangye (Gansu Province)
Teacher Training.

Zhangzhou Teachers School
Zhangzhou (Fujian Province)
Teacher Training.

Zhanjiang Agricultural School
Zhanjiang (Guangdong Province)
Agriculture.

Zhanjiang Fisheries College
40 Jiefang Road, Zhanjiang (Guangdong Province)
Tel: +86 21233
Fisheries.

Zhanjiang Medical College
Zhanjiang (Guangdong Province)
Medicine.

Zhaoqing Education College
Xing Hu, Zhaoqing City (Guangdong Province)
Tel: +86 23071
Education.

Zhaotong Teachers School
District of Zhaotong (Yunnan Province)
Teacher Training.

Zhejiang College of Traditional Chinese Medicine
Qhingchun Road, Hangzhou (Zhejiang Province)
Tel: +86(571) 71568
Traditional Chinese Medicine.

Zhejiang Fisheries Institute
District of Putuo (Zhejiang Province)
Tel: +86 3851
Fisheries.

Zhejiang Institute of Forestry
District of Lin'an (Zhejiang Province)
Forestry.

Zhejiang Institute of Silk Textiles
88 Wenyi Road, Hangzhou (Zhejiang Province)
Tel: +86(571) 85814
Silk Textiles Techniques.

Zhejiang Institute of Technology
Mishi Lane, Hangzhou (Zhejiang Province)
Tel: +86(571) 88514
Technology.

Zhejiang School of Metallurgical Economics
District of Jiande (Zhejiang Province)
Metallurgical Economics.

Zhelimu Animal Husbandry Institute
Tongliao (Inner Mongolia)
Animal Husbandry.

Zhelimu Medical College
Tongliao (Inner Mongolia)
Medicine.

Zhengzhou Institute for Cereal Preservation and Processing
Songshan Road, Zhengzhou (Henan Province)
Tel: +86(371) 47915
Cereal Preservation and Processing.

Zhengzhou Institute of Light Industry
Zhengzhou (Henan Province)
Tel: +86 32076
Light Industry.

Zhengzhou Institute of Technology
52 Wenhua Road, Zhengzhou (Henan Province)
Tel: +86(371) 32114
Technology.

Zhengzhou School of Aeronautics Engineering Management
Zhengzhou (Henan Province)
Aeronautics Engineering Management.

Zhengzhou School of Animal Husbandry and Veterinary Medicine
Xinan County (Henan Province)
Animal Husbandry; Veterinary Medicine.

Zhengzhou School of Mechanical and Electrical Engineering for Textile Technology
Zhengzhou (Henan Province)
Textile Technology.

Zhengzhou Teachers School
Zhengzhou (Henan Province)
Teacher Training.

Zhenjiang Medical School
Zhenjiang (Jiangsu Province)
Medicine.

Zhenjiang Shipbuilding Institute
P.O. Box 414, Zhenjiang (Jiangsu Province)
Tel: +86 22292
Shipbuilding.

Zhenjiang Teachers School
Zhenjiang (Jiangsu Province)
Teacher Training.

Zhongnan China Institute of Forestry
Zhuzhou (Hunan Province)
Tel: +86 31631
Forestry.

Zhongnan Institute for Minor Nationalities
Wuhan (Hubei Province)
Languages and Culture.

Zhongshan (Sun-Yat-Sen) Medical College
74 Zhongshanerlu, Guangzhou (Guangdong Province)
Tel: +86(20) 778223
Medicine.

Zhoukou Teachers School
Zhoukou (Henan Province)
Teacher Training.

Zunyi Medical College
Waihuan Road, Zunyi (Guizhou Province)
Tel: +86 3191
Medicine.

Zunyi Teachers School
Zunyi (Guizhou Province)
Teacher Training.

NATIONAL ACADEMIC BODIES

Ministry of Education
35 Damucanghutong, Xidan, (Beijing)
Tel: +86(1) 662730

National Commission of the People's Republic of China for Unesco
Ministry of Education, 35 Damucanghutong, Xidan, (Beijing)
Tel: +86(1) 662730
Telex: 22014 sede cn
Cable: Cunescocom beijing

COLOMBIA
UNIVERSITIES AND OTHER UNIVERSITY INSTITUTIONS

PUBLIC INSTITUTIONS

University of Antioquía
[Universidad de Antioquía]
Calle 67 No 5-108 Ciudad Universitaria, Apartado aéreo 1226, Medellín
Tel: +57(4) 210-5000
Fax: +57(4) 211-0672
Rector: Rafael Aubad López
Founded: 1801, 1822
F: Arts; Economics; Natural and Exact Sciences; Human Sciences; Social Sciences; Law; Education; Nursing; Engineering; Medicine; Veterinary Medicine and Animal Husbandry; Dentistry; Pharmacy; Public Health.
I: Political Science; Regional Studies; Physical Education.
S: Bacteriology and Clinical Chemistry; Food and Nutrition; Library Science.

Ce: Medical Research; Natural and Exact Sciences Research; Economic Research; Research for Environmental Sciences; Research for Energy Sources; Public Health Research.
D: Distance Education.

University of the Atlantic Barranquilla
[Universidad del Atlántico]
Carrera 43 Nos. 50-53, Apartado aéreo 1890, Barranquilla (Atlántico)
Tel: +57(958) 313-513
Rector: Ubaldo Enríque Meso Ricardo
Founded: 1941, 1946
P: Education; Economics; Architecture; Chemical Engineering; Chemistry and Pharmacy; Dietetics and Nutrition; Law.
I: Mathematics.
S: Painting; Music.

College of Public Administration 'ESAP' Bogotá
[Escuela Superior de Administración Pública 'ESAP' Bogotá]
Diagonal 40 No. 46A-37, Santa Fé de Bogotá
Tel: (1) 269-9147
Founded: 1958
Political and Administrative Sciences.

District University 'Francisco José de Caldas' Bogotá
[Universidad Distrital 'Francisco José de Caldas' Bogotá]
Carrera 15 No. 57-43, Apartado aéreo 8668, Santafé de Bogotá
Tel: +57(1) 255-8252
Fax: +57(1) 310-5235
Rector: Lombardo Rodríguez López
Founded: 1950, 1963
P: Education.

National University of Education Bogotá
[Universidad Pedagógica Nacional]
Calle 23 No. 11-73, Apartado aéreo 75144, Santafé de Bogotá
Tel: +57(1) 235-2044
Fax: +57(1) 211-1293
Rector: Adolfo Rodríguez Bernal
Founded: 1936, 1955, 1962
F: Science and Technology; Arts and Humanities; Education.
Ce: Education Research; Adult Education.

School of Public Administration, Santafé de Bogotá
[Escuela Superior de Administración Pública-ESAP]
Diagonal 40 No.46a-37, Apartado aéreo 29745, Santafé de Bogotá
Tel: +57(1) 222-4700
Fax: +57(1) 222-4356
Rector: Samuel Ospina Marin
Founded: 1958
Public Administration.

MEDDELLÍN BRANCH
[SECCIONAL MEDELLÍN]
Calle 56 (Bolívia) No 45-34, Apartado aéreo 5042,
Medellín (Antioquia)
Tel: +57(94) 254-3780
Fax: +57(94) 254-4051
Vicerector: Leider Mario Tobon Tobon

School of Police Studies Santa Fé de Bogotá
[Escuela de Policia 'General Santander']
Avenida 27 no. 44-01, Autopista sur-Muzu U,
Apartado aéreo 4670, Santafé de Bogotá
Tel: +57(91) 238-1674
Fax: +57(91) 710-8692
Rector: Ismael Trujillo Polanco
Police Studies.

University of Caldas
[Universidad de Caldas]
Calle 65 No. 26-10, Apartado aéreo 275,
Manizales (Caldas)
Tel: +57(968) 851-712
Fax: +57(968) 862-520
Rector: Jorge Raad Aljure
Founded: 1937, 1943
S: Medicine; Veterinary Medicine and Animal Husbandry; Agriculture; Law; Home Economics; Nursing; Fine Arts; Philosophy and Letters; Social Work; Geology.
De: Education.

Institute of Fine Arts Cali
[Instituto Departamental de Bellas Artes]
Avenida 2 Norte No. 7-38, Cali (Valle)
Tel: +57(923) 673-364
Fax: +57(923) 685-583
Rector: Ramón Daniel Espinosa Rodríguez
Fine Arts.

University of Cartagena
[Universidad de Cartagena]
Centro Carrera 6 No.36-100, Apartado aéreo
1382, Cartagena (Bolívar)
Tel: +57(53) 600-676
Fax: +57(53) 600-380
Rector: Manuel Agustín Sierra Navarro
Founded: 1774, 1827
F: Medicine; Dentistry; Chemistry and Pharmacy; Nursing; Law; Social Work; Economics; Civil Engineering.
P: Accountancy; Business Administration.

University of Cauca
[Universidad del Cauca]
Calle 5, No. 4-70, Apartado aéreo 1384, Popayán
(Cauca)
Tel: +57 243-020
Fax: +57 244-851
Rector: Carlos Alberto Collazos Muñoz
Founded: 1827, 1850, 1857, 1883, 1964
F: Law and Political and Social Sciences; Health Sciences; Civil Engineering; Electronics and Telecommunications; Accountancy; Humanities; Education.

People's University of César
[Universidad Popular del César]
Carrera 9 No. 14-32, Apartado aéreo 590,
Valledupar (César)
Tel: +57(955) 720-030
Fax: +57(955) 731-878
Rector: José Antonio Murgas Aponte
Founded: 1972, 1976
F: Education; Business Administration and Accountancy; Health Sciences.

Technological University of Chocó 'Diego Luís Córdoba'
[Universidad Tecnológica del Chocó 'Diego Luís Córdoba']
Carrera 2 No. 25-22, Apartado aéreo 292, Quibdó
(Chocó)
Tel: +57 711-589
Fax: +57 711-763
Rector: Diomedes Londoño Maturna
Founded: 1972, 1975
P: Education; Social Work; Public Works Technology; Business Administration; Fishery Technology; Agricultural Technology.

National University of Colombia
[Universidad Nacional de Colombia]
Ciudad Universitaria, Apartado 14490, Santafé de
Bogotá
Tel: +57(1) 244-2830
Fax: +57(1) 221-9891
Rector: Guillermo Paramo Rocha
Founded: 1825, 1935
F: Arts; Science; Human Sciences; Economics; Law and Political and Social Sciences; Engineering; Nursing; Medicine; Dentistry; Agriculture; Veterinary Medicine and Animal Husbandry; Agriculture (Medellín); Architecture (Medellín); Science (Medellín); Human Sciences (Medellín); Mining (Medellín); Engineering (Manizales); Agricultural Sciences (Palmira).

MANIZALES BRANCH
[SECCIONAL MANIZALES]
Carrera 27 No. 64- 60, Apartado aéreo 127,
Manizales (Caldas)
Tel: +57(968) 862-733
Fax: +57(968) 863-220
Vicerector: Carlos Enríque Ruíz
Founded: 1950

MEDELLÍN BRANCH
[SECCIONAL MEDELLIN]
Carrera 65 Calle 64, Autopista Norte, Apartado
aéreo 568 Medellín (Antioquia)
Tel: +57(94) 230-0540
Fax: +57(94) 230-2029
Vicerector: María Clara Echavarría
Founded: 1887

PALMIRA BRANCH
[SECCIONAL PALMIRA]
Carrera 32, Chapinero-Palmira, Apartado aéreo
237, Palmira (Valle)
Tel: +57(931) 727-616
Fax: +57(931)732-477
Vicerector: Franco Alirio Vallejo C.
Founded: 1934

University of Education and Technology of Colombia
[Universidad Pedagógica y Tecnológica de
Colombia]
Carretera Central del Norte, Apartado aéreo
1094, Tunja (Boyacá)
Tel: +57 422-174 ext. 18
Fax: +57 425-268
Rector: Carlos Hernando Forero Robayo
Founded: 1842, 1933, 1953, 1968
F: Engineering; Economics; Agricultural
Engineering; Education; Science; Health
Sciences.

CHIQUINQUIRA BRANCH
[SECCIONAL CHIQUINQUIRA]
Calle 14A No. 2-37, Apartado aéreo 16,
Chiquinquirá (Boyacá)
Tel: +57(98726) 2598
Vicerector: María Rosalba Sánchez Matamoros

DUITAMA BRANCH
[SECCIONAL DUITAMA]
Carrera 18 Calle 23, Apartado aéreo 1070,
Duitama, Boyacá
Tel: +57(987) 602-181
Vicerector: Otto Caro Niño

SOGAMOSO BRANCH
[SECCIONAL SOGAMOSO]
Calle 4 Sur No. 15-134, Apartado aéreo 332,
Sogamoso (Boyacá)
Tel: +57(987) 703-670
Vicerector: Justo Ignacio Báez Torres

University of Córdoba
[Universidad de Córdoba]
Kilómetro 3 vía Cereté, Apartado aéreo 354,
Montería (Córdoba)
Tel: +57 863-278
Fax: +57 860-054
Rector: Jorge Guerra Trujillo
Founded: 1966
F: Veterinary Medicine and Animal Husbandry;
Agriculture; Sciences; Health Sciences;
Education; Fishery.

Technological University of East Llanos
[Universidad de Los Llanos Orientales]
Apartado aéreo 2621, Km. 11, Via Puerto López,
Villavicencio (Meta)
Tel: +57 23449
Fax: +57 34892
Rector: Miguel Eduardo Villarreal Torres
Founded: 1974

P: Education; Nursing; Veterinary Medicine and
Animal Husbandry.
I: Environmental Research.

University of Amazonas Florencia
[Universidad de La Amazonia Florencia]
Avenida Circunvalación, Barrio-Porvenir,
Apartado aéreo 192, Florencia (Caquetá)
Tel: +57 2905
Fax: +57 8231
Rector: Ernesto Fajardo Castro
F: Education; Accountancy; Animal Husbandry.

University of La Guajira
[Universidad de La Guajira]
Calle 26 Carrera 6, Salida a Valledupar,
Apartado aéreo 172, Riohacha (La Guajira)
Tel: +57 273-856
Fax: +57 273-856
Rector: Francisco Justo Pérez Van-Leenden
Founded: 1976
F: Business Administration; Industrial
Engineering; Languages.

Technological University of Magdalena
[Universidad Tecnológica del Magdalena]
Avenida del Ferrocarril, Apartado aéreo 731,
Santa Marta (Magdalena)
Tel: +57 208-692
Fax: +57 208-692
Rector: Oswaldo Pérez Molina
Founded: 1958
F: Agricultural Engineering; Agricultural
Economics; Fishing Technology; Education;
Administration.

Columbian Politechnic 'Jaime Isaza Cadavid' Medellín
[Politécnico Colombiano 'Jaime Isaza Cadavid']
Carrera 48 No 7-151 El Poblado, Apartado aéreo
4932, Medellín (Antioquia)
Tel: +57(94) 266-5700
Fax: +57(94) 266-3635
Rector: Libardo Alvarez Lopera
Founded: 1964

RIONEGRO BRANCH
[SECCIONAL RIONEGRO]
Calle 51 no. 51-13 Rionegro, Rionegro (Antioquia)
Tel: +57 2712-823
Vicerector: Carlos Mario Mejía Sánchez

University of Nariño
[Universidad de Nariño]
Torobajo-Carrera 22 No. 18-109, Apartado aéreo
1175, Pasto (Nariño)
Tel: +57(277) 235-654
Fax: +57(277) 235-175
Rector: Guillermo Narvaez Ramírez (E)
Founded: 1689, 1904
F: Science and Education; Plastic Arts; Law;
Civil Engineering; Agriculture; Animal Husbandry;
Economics; Sciences and Technologies of the
Pacific.
P: Hydroculture; Music.

South Colombian University Neiva
[Universidad Surcolombiana]
Avenida Pastrana Borrero Carrera 1, Apartado
aéreo 385, Neiva (Huila)
Tel: +57 745-444
Fax: +57 745-443
Rector: Jorge Antonio Polania Puentes
Founded: 1968, 1976
*F: Accountancy and Administration; Education;
Health Sciences; Engineering.*
D: Distance Education; Extension.

University of Pamplona
[Universidad de Pamplona]
Calle 6 No. 2-102 El Carmen, Apartado aéreo
1046, Pamplona (Norte de Santander)
Tel: +57 682-960
Fax: +57 680-581
Rector: Ciro Alfonso Caicedo
Founded: 1960
P: Education; Food Technology.

Technological University of Pereira
[Universidad Tecnológica de Pereira]
La Julita, Apartado aéreo 97, Pereira (Risaralda)
Tel: +57 352-781
Fax: +57 354-446
Rector: Javier Arroyave Ochoa
Founded: 1958
*P: Education; Electrical Engineering;
Mechanical Engineering; Industrial Engineering;
Medicine.*
I: Polytechnical.

University of Quindío
[Universidad del Quindío]
Carrera 15, Calle 12 Norte, Apartado aéreo 460,
Armenia (Quindío)
Tel: +57 452-181
Rector: Henry Valencia Naranjo
Founded: 1960
*P: Education; Public Accountancy; Civil
Engineering; Mechanical Engineering; Electrical
Engineering; Medicine; Industrial Engineering;
Topography.*

Industrial University of Santander
[Universidad Industrial de Santander 'UIS']
Ciudad Universitaria-Carrera 27, Calle 9,
Apartado aéreo 678, Bucaramanga (Santander)
Tel: +57(973) 343-655
Fax: +57(973) 350-541
Rector: José Gómez Duarte
Founded: 1948
*F: Science; Human Sciences and Education;
Engineering; Engineering; Health Sciences;
Distance Education.*
D: Extension and Lifelong Education.

University 'Francisco de Paula' Santander
[Universidad 'Francisco de Paula' Santander]
Avenida Gran Colombia 12 E-96, Apartado aéreo
1055, Cúcuta (Norte de Santander)
Tel: +57 753-172
Fax: +57 753-893
Rector: Carlos Ivan Paez Blanco (E)
Founded: 1962
*F: Technology; Engineering; Business
Administration; Education.*
D: Distance Education.

OCAÑA BRANCH
[SECCIONAL OCAÑA]
Carrera 9 no. 10-52, bApartado aéreo 30, Ocaña
(Norte de Santander)
Tel: +57 623-344
Fax: +57 624-501
Vicerector: Gustavo Casadiego Angarita

University Institute of La Paz
[Instituto Universitario de La Paz]
Avenida Santander, Calle 9 No. 10-22,
Barrancabermeja (Santander)
Tel: +57(976) 221-908
Fax: (976) 222-711
Rector: Juan de Dios Castilla Amel

University Unit of South Bogotá (Distance Education)
[Unidad Universitaria del Sur de Bogotá
(Formación a Distancia)]
Carrera 53 No.14-39, Apartado aéreo 42891,
Santafé de Bogotá
Tel: +57(1) 255-3216
Fax: +57(1) 255-3479
Rector: Gabriel Jaime Cardona Orosco
Founded: 1981
*F: Administration; Engineering; Agriculture;
Social Sciences and Humanities.*

University of Sucre
[Universidad de Sucre]
Calle 19 No. 22-58, Apartado aereo 406, Sincelejo
(Sucre)
Tel: +57(95) 821-240
Rector: Gustavo Vergara Arrazola
Secretario General: Alfredo Salinas
Founded: 1978
*F: Science and Humanities; Agricultural
Engineering; Agricultural Production; Health
Sciences.*

Conservatory of Tolima
[Conservatorio del Tolima]
Caalle 9 no. 1-18, Apartado aéreo 615, Ibague
(Tolima)
Tel: +57 631-118
Fax: +57 635-378
Rector: Amina Melendro de Pulecio

COLOMBIA

University of Tolima
[Universidad del Tolima]
Barrio Santa Elena, Apartado aéreo 546, Ibagué
(Tolima)
Tel: +57(982) 644-219
Fax: +57(982) 644-869
Rector: Edgar Machado
Founded: 1945
*F: Business Administration; Agricultural
Engineering; Forestry; Veterinary Medicine and
Animal Husbandry; Education; Technology.*
I: Science.
D: Distance Education; Extension.

University of Valle del Cauca
[Universidad del Valle del Cauca]
Ciudad Universitaria, Meléndez, Apartado aéreo
25360, Cali (Valle del Cauca)
Tel: +57(23) 391-486
Fax: +57(23) 398-484
Rector: Jaime Enríque Galarza Sanclemente
Founded: 1945
*F: Engineering; Health Sciences; Architecture;
Social Sciences and Economics; Humanities;
Education; Science; Business Administration.*

Central University of Valle del Cauca
[Universidad Central del Valle del Cauca]
Carrera 26 No. 30-58, Apartado aéreo 297, Tuluá
(Valle)
Tel: +57(926) 244-375
Fax: +57(926) 244-337
Rector: Nestor Grajales Lopez
*P: Business Administration; Physical Education;
Social Sciences; Law; Accountancy.*

PRIVATE INSTITUTIONS

Autonomous University of Caribe Barranquilla
[Universidad Autónoma del Caribe]
Calle 90 No. 46-112, Barranquilla (Atlántico)
Tel: +57(958) 452-605
Fax: +57(958) 452-478
Rector: Mario Ceballos Araujo
Founded: 1967
*P: Business Administration; Architecture;
Communication; Accountancy; Sociology; Hotel
Administration.*

Education Corporation for Development 'Simón Bolivar' Barranquilla
[Corporación Educativa Mayor del Desarrollo
'Simón Bolívar']
Carrera 59 No. 59-76, Apartado aéreo 50595,
Barranquilla (Atlántico)
Tel: +57(58) 358-963
Fax: +57(58) 411-265
Rector: José Eusebio Consuegra Bolívar
Founded: 1972
*Education; Social Work Sociology; Economics;
Social Studies; Law.*

Metropolitan University Barranquilla
[Universidad Metropolitana]
Carrera 42F No. 75B-169, Apartado aéreo 50576,
Barranquilla (Atlántico)
Tel: +57(958) 356-344
Fax: +57(958) 583-378
Rector: Eduardo Acosta Bendek
Founded: 1973

University Corporation Costa Barranquilla (UNICOSTA)
[Corporación Universitaria de la Costa
(UNICOSTA)]
Calle 58 No. 55-66, Barranquilla (Atlántico)
Tel: +57(958) 511-974
Fax: +57(958) 417-678
Rector: Ramiro Alfonso Moreno Noriega
Founded: 1969
*Education; Economics Business Administration;
Architecture; Civil Engineering; Law.*

University of the North Barranquilla
[Universidad del Norte]
Kilometro 5 Carretera a Puerto Colombia,
Apartado aéreo 1569, Barranquilla
Tel: +57(958) 568-910
Fax: +57(958) 568-852
Rector: Jesús Ferro Bayona (1980-)
Founded: 1966
*S: Engineering; Business Administration; Law;
Humanities and Social Sciences; Health
Sciences.*
*Ce: Lifelong Education; Graduate Studies;
Cayena Culture; Research; Regional Studies.*
L: Immunology.

*Central University Foundation Bogotá
[Fundación Universidad Central]
Carrera 5 No. 21-38, Santafé de Bogotá
Tel: +57(1) 2848-249
Fax: +57(1) 2811-608
Rector: Jorge Enríque Molina Mariano
Founded: 1966
*P: Public Accountancy; Economics; Business
Administration; Publicity.*

College of Nuestra Señora del Rosario Bogotá
[Colegio Mayor de Nuestra Señora del Rosario]
Calle 14 No. 6-25, Santafé de Bogotá
Tel: +57(1) 282-0088
Fax: +57(1) 281-8583
Rector: Mario Suárez Melo
Founded: 1653
*P: Business Administration; Economics; Law;
Medicine; Physiology; Phonoaudiology; Therapy;
Philosophy and Letters.*

University Corporation of 'Antonio Nariño' Bogotá

[Corporación Universitaria 'Antonio Nariño']
Calle 20 Sur No. 13-61, Apartado aéreo 44564,
Santafé de Bogotá
Tel: +57(1) 272-4630
Fax: +57(1) 209-3888
Rector: Ricardo Aníbal Lozada Márquez
Founded: 1976
*Data Systems; Mechanical Automation;
Automotive Mechanics; Dance and Theatre;
Social Sciences; Chemistry and Biology;
Mathematics and Physics; Business
Administration; Public Accountancy; Engineering.*

University of the Andes Bogotá

[Universidad de Los Andes]
Apartado aéreo 4976, Carrera 1A, No. 18-A-70,
Santafé de Bogotá
Tel: +57(1) 282-4066
Fax: +57(1) 284-1890
Rector: Arturo Infante Villarreal
Founded: 1948
*Engineering; Economics; Law; Sciences;
Humanities and Social Sciences; Architecture;
Management.*
Ce: *Studies on Economic Development.*
D: *Regional Development.*
P: *Lifelong Education.*

University Foundation of America Bogotá

[Fundación Universidad de América Bogotá]
Avenida Circunvalar No. 20-53, Apartado Aéreo
11374, Santafé de Bogotá
Tel: +57(1) 281-5715
Fax: +57(1) 243-6672
Rector: Gustavo Hitzig B.
Founded: 1952
P: *Architecture; Economics; Industrial
Engineering; Mechanical Engineering; Chemical
Engineering; Petroleum Engineering.*

University Foundation 'Jorge Tadeo Lozano' Bogotá

[Fundación Universidad de Bogotá 'Jorge Tadeo
Lozano']
Calle 23 No. 4-47, Santafé de Bogotá
Tel: +57(1) 283-4610
Fax: +57(1) 282-6197
Founded: 1954
P: *Business Administration; Agriculture; Foreign
Commercial Studies; Public Accountancy;
Communication Sciences; Economics;
Geography; Marine Biology; Publicity;
Architectural Design and Decoration; Industrial
Design; Graphic Design; Diplomatic and
International Studies; Food Technology;
Agricultural Administration; Marketing
Technology; Systems Technology and Data
Processing; Architecture (Cartagena); Foreign
Commercial Studies (Cartagena); Tourism
(Cartagena).*

CARTAGENA BRANCH
[SECCIONAL CARTAGENA]
Carrera 4, No. 38-40 Plaza de la Merced,
Apartado aéreo 1310, Cartagena (Bolivar)
Tel: +57(53) 653-169
Fax: +57(53) 644-714
Vicerector: Augusto de Pombo Pareja

University Institution 'Sergio Arboledo' Bogotá

[Institución Universitaria 'Sergio Arboledo']
Calle 74 No. 14-14, Santafé de Bogotá
Tel: +57(1) 212-3981
Fax: +57(1) 212-066
Rector: Rodrigo Noguera Laborde

University 'La Gran Colombia' Bogotá

[Universidad 'La Gran Colombia']
Apartado aéreo 7909, Carrera 6 No. 13-40,
Santafé de Bogotá
Tel: +57(1) 343-8047
Fax: +57(1) 282-8386
Rector: José Galat Noumer
Founded: 1951
P: *Education; Architecture; Public Accountancy;
Law and Political Science; Economics; Civil
Engineering; Law (Armenia); Economics
(Armenia).*

ARMENIA BRANCH
[SECCIONAL ARMENIA]
Avenida Bolivar Carrera 14 No.7-47, Apartado
aéreo 262, Armenia (Quindo)
Tel: +57 454-791
Fax: +57 454-781
Vicerector: Alcides Londoño Fernandez

University of La Sabana Bogotá

[Universidad de La Sabana]
Calle 70 No. 12-19, Apartado aéreo 53753,
Santafé de Bogotá
Tel: +57(1) 249-6830
Fax: +57(1) 676-0808
Founded: 1971, 1979
F: *Education; Health Sciences; Law;
Administration and Economics; Engineering;
Social Communication.*

University of La Salle Bogotá

[Universidad de La Salle]
Apartado aéreo 28638, Carrera 2 No. 10-70,
Santafé de Bogotá
Tel: +57(1) 283-0900
Fax: +57(1) 286-8391
Rector: José Vicente Henry Valbuena, F.S.C.
(1993-)
Founded: 1964
P: *Education; Business Administration;
Agricultural and Cattle Administration; Library
Science; Economics; Civil Engineering;
Architecture; Philosophy and Letters; Languages;
Statistics; Optometry; Social Work; Animal
Husbandry; Electrical Engineering; Food
Engineering; Ambiental and Sanitary
Engineering; Chemistry and Biology;*

COLOMBIA

Mathematics and Physics; Design and Electronic
Automatization Engineering.
D: Advanced Studies.

University of San Buenaventura Bogotá
[Universidad de San Buenaventura]
Transversal 26 No. 172-08, Apartado aéreo 75010,
Santafé de Bogotá
Tel: +57(1) 677-5707
Fax: +57(1) 677-3003
Rector: Ruben Darío Vanegas Montoya
Founded: 1964
P: Education; Philosophy; Theology; Education
(Cali); Law (Cali); Accountancy (Cali); Economics
(Cali); Electronic Engineering (Cali); Architecture
(Cali); Religious Sciences (Cali); Special
Education (Cali); Psychology (Medellín);
Sociology (Medellín); Education (Medellín).

CALI BRANCH
[SECCIONAL CALI]
La Umbria-Carretera a Pance, Cali (Valle)
Tel: +57(923) 306-902
Fax: +57(932) 552-006
Vicerector: Luís Javier Uribe Munöz

CARTAGENA BRANCH
[SECCIONAL CARTAGENA]
Calle Real de Ternera-Cartagena, Apartado
aéreo 7833, Cartagena (Bolivar)
Tel: +57(53) 611-517
Fax: +57(53) 630-943
Vicerector: Alberto Montealegre González

MEDELLÍN BRANCH
[SECCIONAL MEDELLÍN]
Carrera 56C No. 51-90, Apartado aéreo 7370,
Medellín (Antioquia)
Tel: +57(94) 511-3600
Fax: +57(94) 231-6191
Vicerector: Germán Alonso Bautista Romero

*University Santo Tomás Bogotá
[Universidad Santo Tomás]
Apartado aéreo 75032, Carrera 9a No. 51-23,
Santafé de Bogotá 2
Tel: +57(1) 211-0085
Fax: (1) 211-6368
Rector: Alvaro Galvis Ramírez, O.P.
Founded: 1580, 1966
F: Civil Engineering; Electronics; Accountancy;
Economics and Administration; Sociology;
Psychology; Law and Political Science;
Philosophy and Letters; Architecture
(Bucaramanga); Dentistry (Bucaramanga);
Economics (Bucaramanga).

BUCARAMANGA BRANCH
[SECCIONAL BUCARAMANGA]
Carrera 18 No. 9-27, Bucaramanga, Santander
Tel: +57(973) 332-342
Fax: (973) 331-383
Vicerector: José Antonio Balaguera Cepeda

Xavier Pontifical University Bogotá
[Pontificia Universidad Javeriana]
Carrera 7 No. 40-62, Apartado aéreo 56710,
Santafé de Bogotá
Tel: +57(1) 287-5791
Fax: +57(1) 285-3348
Rector: Gerardo Arango Puerta
Founded: 1623, 1704, 1930, 1937
F: Theology; Architecture and Design;
Economics and Administration; Science; Law;
Social Sciences; Canon Law; Nursing; Social
Communication; Philosophy; Psychology;
Engineering; Medicine; Dentistry; Interdisciplinary
Studies; Economics and Administration (Cali);
Humanities and Social Sciences (Cali);
Engineering (Cali).
D: Religious Sciences (Cali); Modern
Languages.
P: Distance Education; Adult Education.
I: Aesthetic Research; Energetics; Human
Genetics Research; Environmental Development
Studies; Legal Studies and Research;
Geophysics.

CALI BRANCH
[SECCIONAL CALI]
Calle 18 No.118-250 Via a Pance, Apartado aéreo
26239, Cali (Valle)
Tel: +57(23) 396-727
Fax: +57(23) 396-785
Vicerector: Javier González Rodríguez

Autonomous University of Bucaramanga
[Universidad Autónoma de Bucaramanga]
Calle 48 No. 39-234, Apartado aéreo 1642,
Bucaramanga (Santander)
Tel: +57(97) 436-111
Fax: +57(97) 433-958
Rector: Gabriel Burgos Mantilla
Founded: 1952
F: Law; Social Communication; Business
Administration; Accountancy; Education.
Ce: Research.

University Santiago of Cali
[Universidad Santiago de Cali]
Apartado aéreo 4102, Calle 5, Carrera 62, Cali
(Valle del Cauca)
Tel: +57(23) 515-342
Rector: Diego Gustavo Maya Silva
Founded: 1958
P: Education; Law; Business Administration;
Accountancy.

Autonomous University Foundation of Colombia
[Fundación Universitaria Autónoma de Colombia]
Carrera 5 No. 11-43, Santafé de Bogotá
Tel: +57(1) 281-8624
Fax: +57(1) 342-9464
Rector: Alfredo Vázquez Carrizosa
Founded: 1971
F: Economics; Industrial Engineering; Systems
Engineering; Law.

Catholic University of Colombia
[Universidad Católica de Colombia]
Carrera 15 No. 47-31, Apartado aéreo 29832,
Santafé de Bogotá
Tel: +57(1) 285-3912
Fax: +57(1) 288-5828
Rector: José Edgar Gómez Betancourt
Founded: 1970
P: *Data Technology; Psychology; Law;
Economics; Civil Engineering; Industrial
Engineering; Architecture.*

Co-operative University of Colombia
[Universidad Cooperativa de Colombia]
Avenida Caracas No. 37-63, Apartado aéreo
13673, Santafé de Bogotá
Tel: +57(1) 245-4778
Fax: +57(1) 287-4010
Founded: 1958
*Educational Administration; Economics; Business
Administration; Sociology; Educational
Administration (Barrancabermeja); Administration
(Barrancabermeja); Economics
(Barrancabermeja); Educational Administration
(Bucaramanga); Economics (Bucaramanga);
Business Administration (Bucaramanga);
Educational Administration (Medellín);
Administration and Planning (Medellín);
Economics (Medellín); Commercial Engineering.*

BARRANCABERMEJA BRANCH
[SECCIONAL BARRANCABERMEJA]
Carrera 24 No. 6-33, Barrio El Recreo, Apartado
aéreo 514, Barrancabermeja (Santander)
Tel: +57(976) 224-120
Fax: +57(976) 221-997
Vicerector: Fernando Mosquera Zuñiga

BUCARAMANGA SECTION
[SECCIONAL BUCARAMANGA]
Calle 30 No. 33-51, Apartado aéreo 2019,
Bucaramanga (Santander)
Tel: +57(976) 341-917
Fax: +57(976) 354-229
Vicerector: Alfonso Prietro García

MEDELLÍN BRANCH
[SECCIONAL MEDELLÍN]
Calle 50 No. 41-70, Apartado Aéreo 50630,
Medellín, Antioquia
Tel: +57(4) 239-9685
Fax: +57(4) 249-7024
Vicerector: Genaro Galeano Franco

SANTA MARTA BRANCH
[SECCIONAL SANTA MARTA]
Calle 32 No. 2-14, Apartado aéreo 715, Santa
Marta (Magdalena)
Tel: +57 232-850
Fax: +57 212-550
Vicerector: Eduardo Angulo Mestre

*External University of Colombia
[Universidad Externado de Colombia]
Calle 12 No. 1-17 Este, Apartado aéreo 034141,
Santafé de Bogotá
Tel: +57(291) 282-6066
Fax: +57(291) 284-3769
E-Mail: Bitnet: unesterna@andescol
Rector: Fernando Hinestrosa
Founded: 1886, 1958
F: *Law and Social and Political Sciences;
Economics; Finance and International Relations;
Social Work; Education; Social Communication.*

Free University of Colombia
[Universidad Libre de Colombia]
Calle 8 No. 5-80, Santafé de Bogotá
Tel: +57(1) 286-9466
Fax: +57(1) 282-0469
Rector: Jorge Enríque Córdoba P.
Founded: 1923
P: *Law; Education; Accountancy; Metallurgical
Engineering; Industrial Engineering; Law
(Barranquilla); Medicine (Barranquilla); Dentistry
(Barranquilla); Law (Cali); Business
Administration (Cali); Accountancy (Cali);
Medicine (Cali); Education (Cúcuta); Law
(Cúcuta); Accountancy (Cúcuta); Economics
(Pereira); Law (Pereira); Education (Socorro).*

*INCCA University of Colombia
[Universidad INCCA de Colombia]
Apartado aéreo 14817, Carrera 13 No. 24-15,
Bogotá
Tel: +57(1) 286-5200
Fax: +57(1) 282-4932
Rector: Jose Enrique Conti Bautista
Secretario General: José Gregorio Avellaneda
Pulido
Founded: 1955, 1970
F: *Natural and Basic Sciences; Human and
Social Sciences; Technology; Economic Sciences;
Judicial and State Sciences; Graduate Studies.*

Pilot University Corporation of Colombia
[Corporación Universidad Piloto de Colombia]
Carrera 9 No. 45A-44, Apartado aéreo 53658,
Santafé de Bogotá
Tel: +57(1) 285-6450
Rector: José Alberto Alvarado Jimenez
Founded: 1962
F: *Architecture; Systems Engineering;
Economics; Accountancy; Systems Engineering
(Girardot); Administration (Girardot).*

BARRANQUILLA BRANCH
[SECCIONAL BARRANQUILLA]
lle 46 No. 48-170, Apartado aéreo 1752,
Barranquilla (Atlántico)
Tel: +57(958) 568-953
Fax: +57(958) 415-110
Vicerector: Manuel Medina Pareja
Founded: 1956

[SECCIONAL CALI]
Diagonal 37A No. 3-29, Apartado aéreo 1040, Cali
(Valle)
Tel: +57(23) 587-161
Fax: +57(23) 570-318
Vicerector: Libardo Orejuela Diaz

CUCUTA BRANCH
[SECCIONAL CUCUTA]
Avenida Canal Bogotá, Margen Izquierdo Inters,
Apartado aéreo 180, Cúcuta (Norte de Santander)
Tel: +57(970) 746-351
Fax: +57(970) 781-033
Vicerector: Raul López

PEREIRA BRANCH
[SECCIONAL PEREIRA]
Carrera 7 No. 40-03, Apartado aéreo 1330,
Pereira (Risaralda)
Tel: +57(961) 366-016
Fax: +57(961) 366-024
Vicerector: Darío García Montoya

SOCORRO BRANCH
[SECCIONAL SOCORRO]
Calle 15 No. 16-58, Socorro (Santander)
Tel: +57(977) 272-639
Fax: +57(977) 272-181
Vicerector: Ana Elisa Niño de Gast

GIRARDOT BRANCH
[SECCIONAL GIRARDOT]
Carrera 19 No. 17-33, Apartado aéreo 543,
Girardot (Cundinamarca)
Tel: +57 28-505
Fax: +57 28-873
Vicerector: Hugo Aranguren Riaño

The Autonomous University Corporation of Manizales
[Corporación Autónoma Universitaria de
Manizales]
Antigua Estación del Ferrocarril, Apartado aéreo
441, Manizales (Caldas)
Tel: +57(968) 810-450
Fax: +57(968) 810-290
Rector: José Ignacio Restrepo Abondano
*Industrial Design; Physiotherapy; Odontology;
Economics; Systems Engineering; Mechanical
Engineering.*

Catholic University of Manizales
[Universidad Católica de Manizales]
Carrera 23 Nos. 60-63, Apartado Aéreo 357,
Manizales (Caldas)
Tel: +57(968) 860-019
Fax: +57(968) 860-575
Rectora: Mabel Jaramillo Restrepo (1984-)
Founded: 1954, 1983
*F: Education; Health Sciences; Bacteriology;
Language Therapy; Nutrition and Dietetics;
Advertising; Tourism Administration; Education
Administration and Planning; Educational,
Orientation and Counselling; Education and*

*Religious Sciences; Preuniversitary Studies in
Health.*
S: Medical Microbiology; Educational Planning.
D: Humanities; Language Sec.
*Ce: Research; Human Communication Studies
(C.E.C.H.).*

University Foundation of Manizales
[Fundación Universitaria de Manizales
FUNDEMA]
Carrera 9 No. 19-03, Apartado aéreo 868,
Manizales (Caldas)
Tel: +57(968) 841-450
Fax: +57(968) 841-443
Rector: Hugo Salazar García

Latin American Autonomous University 'Unaula' Medellín
[Universidad Autónoma Latinoamericana
'Unaula']
Carrera 55 No. 4951, Medellín (Antioquia)
Tel: (4) 231-1199
Founded: 1966
*P: Education; Law; Accountancy; Industrial
Engineering; Economics; Sociology.*

Pontifical Bolivariana University Medellín
[Universidad Pontificia Bolivariana]
Apartado aéreo 1178, Calle 52 No. 40-88,
Medellín (Antioquia)
Tel: +57(4) 249-7199
Fax: +57(4) 239-6683
Rector: Mgr. Darío Munero Vélez (1988-)
Founded: 1936
*F: Social Sciences; Architecture and Design;
Law and Political Science; Engineering;
Medicine; Education and Humanities; Religious
Sciences.*
D: Lifelong Education.
Ce: Evening Studies; Development Research.

BUCARAMANGA BRANCH
[SECCIONAL BUCARAMANGA]
Calle 33 No. 21-18 Seminario Floridablan,
Bucaramanga (Santander)
Tel: +57 425-598
Fax: +57 388-390
Vicerector: Jesús Quiroz Crispin

University of Medellín
[Universidad de Medellín]
Apartado aéreo 1983, Carrera 87 No. 30-65, Los
Alpes (Belén), Medellín (Antioquia)
Tel: +57(4) 238-3906
Fax: +57(4) 341-4913
Rector: Enríque Alberto Olano Asuad
Secretario General: César Augusto Fernández
Posada
Founded: 1950
*P: Education; Law; Industrial Economics;
Administration; Statistics; Civil Engineering;
Accountancy.*
*S: Public Government; Political Science; Latin
American Literacy; Penal Law and Criminology.*

Marian University Pasto
[Universidad Mariana]
Calle 18 No. 34-104, Apartado aéreo 811, Pasto
(Nariño)
Tel: +57(927) 233-616
Fax: +57(927) 230-874
Rector: Nisla Elizabeth Young Espinosa
Founded: 1967
*Business and Accounting; Philosophy and
Theology; Spanish and English Language;
Nursing; Public Accounting; Systems Engineering;
Education.*

University School of Administration, Finance and Technology 'EAFIT' Medellín
[Universidad Escuela de Administración y
Finanzas y Tecnologías 'EAFIT']
Apartado aéreo 3300, Avenida Las Vegas,
Carrera 49 No. 7-50, Medellín (Antioquia)
Tel: +57(4) 266-4324
Fax: +57(4) 266-4284
Rector: Guillermo Sanín Arango
Founded: 1960
S: Administration; Engineering.
Ce: Lifelong Education.

Catholic University of the East Rionegro
[Fundación Universitaria Católica de Oriente
Ríonegro]
Calle 41 No. 45-201, Apartado aéreo 008,
Ríonegro (Antioquia)
Tel: +57(94) 531-3912
Fax: +57(94) 531-3972
Rector: Darío Gómez Zuluaga

OTHER INSTITUTIONS

PUBLIC INSTITUTIONS

Centro de Estudios Superiores 'María Goretti'
Avenida de Las Américas, Pasto, Nariño
Tel: +57(277) 215-357
Fax: +57(277) 212-314
Rector: Ancelmo Cardona
*Architecture; Ceramics; Education; Business
Administration; Topography; Systems
Technology.*

Fundación Centro de Investigación Docencia y Consultoria Administrativa 'CIDCA'
Carrera 18 No. 38-19, Santafé de Bogotá
Tel: +57(1) 320-0011
Fax: +57(1) 245-5963
Rector: Harold Celio del Valle
*International Business; Accountancy; Systems
Engineering; Electronics; Electromechanics.*

Fundación Escuela Colombiana de Mercadotecnia
Calle 50 No. 40-39, Apartado aéreo 4983,
Medellín (Antioquia)
Tel: +57(4) 216-1672
Fax: +57(4) 239-4854
Rector: Julio César Agudelo Tangarife
Founded: 1970
Business.

Instituto Técnico Central
Calle 13 No. 16-74, Santafé de Bogotá
Tel: +57(1) 282-4013
Fax: +57(1) 342-0017
Rector: Carlos Gabriel Gómez Restrepo
Electromechanics.

Instituto Tecnológico de Electrónica y Comunicaciones 'ITEC'
Transversal 49 No. 105-84, Apartado aéreo 14515,
Santafé de Bogotá
Tel: +57(1) 253-6040
Fax: +57(1) 253-6266
Rector: Orlando Hidalgo Santos
*Telecommunications; Electronics and
Communication.*

Instituto Tecnológico Pascual Bravo
Calle 73, No. 73A-226 Sector de Pilarica,
Apartado aéreo 6821, Medellín (Antioquia)
Tel: +57(4) 234-5082
Fax: +57(4) 264-7577
Rector: Martha Lucía Arango Gaviria
Founded: 1938
Electronics; Mechanics; Industrial Systems.

Tecnológico de Antioquia
Calle 53 No. 40-65, Apartado aéreo 11421,
Medellín (Antioquia)
Tel: +57(4) 239-3756
Fax: +57(4) 239-8979
Rector: Humberto Saldarriaga Carmona
*Agriculture; Education; Gerontology; Business
Administration; Systems Technology.*

Unidades Tecnológicas de Santander
Carrera 30 No. 9-40, Apartado aéreo 899,
Bucaramanga (Santander)
Tel: +57(76) 358-366
Fax: +57(76) 346-3666
Rector: Alvaro Ramírez Cordero
Founded: 1963
Electronics; Electromechanics; Topography.

PRIVATE INSTITUTIONS

Centro Educacional de Computos y Sistemas 'CEDESISTEMAS'
Carrera 49 No. 54-63, Apartado aéreo 223,
Medellín, Antioquia
Tel: +57(4) 241-8132
Fax: +57(4) 513-1407
Rector: Alvaro Gil Gil
Founded: 1976
Business Administration; Computer Science.

Colegio de Estudios Superiores de Administración (CESA)
Diagonal 35 No. 5-41, Apartado aéreo 6528,
Santafé de Bogotá
Tel: +57(1) 285-3408
Fax: +57(1) 288-5974
Rector: Marco Fidel Rocha Rodríguez
Administration Studies.

Colegio Odontológico Colombiano
Carrera 9 No. 13-40, Apartado aéreo 34196,
Santafé de Bogotá
Tel: +57(1) 341-5141
Rector: Miguel Antonio Yepes Parra
Dentistry.

Corporación Educativa (ESUMER)
Calle 76 No. 80-126 Robledo, Apartado aéreo,
51822, Medellín, Antioquia
Tel: +57(4) 264-6011
Fax: +57(4) 264-9855
Rector: Fernan Angel Zuluaga Hoyos
Founded: 1964
International Business; Financial Administration.

Corporación Educativa del Caribe
Carretera Troncal Occidente Via Corozal,
Apartado aéreo 248, Sincelejo, Sucre
Tel: +57(52) 821-402
Fax: +57(52) 823-882
Rector: Noel Morales Calao
Child Education; Accountancy.

Corporación Escuela de Administración de Empresas 'EAE'
Avenida Alférez Real 5, Km. 14, Apartado aéreo
2144, Cali (Valle)
Tel: +57(23) 552-462
Fax: +57(23) 551-525
Rector: José Francisco Engel Wenski
Founded: 1969
Marketing; Management.

Corporación Internacional para el Desarrollo Educativo (CIDE)
Calle 41 No. 27A-52, Santafé de Bogotá
Tel: +57(1) 268-0462
Fax: +57(1) 268-0566
Rector: Rafael Enríque Ulloa Barrios
Art and Publicity; Photography; Education; Computer Science; Industrial Design; Nutrition; Systems Engineering.

Corporación Universitaria Adventista
Carrera 84 No. 33AA-01, Apartado aéreo 877,
Medellín Antioquia
Tel: +57(4) 250-7948
Fax: +57(4) 250-6428
Rector: Gamaliel Flores Gómez
Theology; Music; Management.

Corporación Universitaria Autónoma de Occidente
Calle 9B No. 29A-67, Barrio Champagnat,
Apartado aéreo 3119, Cali, Valle
Tel: +57(23) 565-415
Fax: +57(23) 581-233
Rector: Luís Hernan Pérez Paez
Founded: 1969
Journalism; Economics; Engineering.

Corporación Universitaria de Ibague
Barrio Ambalá-Carrera 22, Calle 67, 2Apartado
aéreo 487, Ibague, Tolima
Tel: +57(82) 640-616
Fax: +57(82) 640-619
Rector: Leonidas López Herran
Commerce; Accountancy; Engineering.

Corporación Universitaria Lasallista de Medellín
Calle 54A No. 30-01, Piso 5, Apartado aéreo
50130, Medellín, Antioquia
Tel: +57(4) 249-1533
Fax: +57(4) 239-7595
Rector: Guillermo Latorre Restrepo
Food Technology Education; Preschool Education.

Corporación Tecnológica de Bogotá
Carrera 21 No. 54-67, Apartado aéreo 5189,
Santafé de Bogotá
Tel: +57(1) 248-1223
Fax: +57(1) 217-5754
Rector: Alberto Francisco Gómez Téllez
Data Systemization; Electrochemistry; Plastics; Industrial Chemistry; Pharmaceutics.

Corporación Tecnológica de Bolívar
Calle del Bouquet, Carrera 21 No. 25-92,
Apartado aéreo 1372, Cartagena, Bolívar
Tel: +57(53) 604-968
Fax: +57(53) 604-317
Rector: Luís Enríque Borja Barón
Founded: 1945
Systems Technology; Economics; Business.

Corporacion Tecnológica (Centrosistemas)
Carrera 29 No. 50-54, Apartado aéreo 3910,
Bucaramanga (Santander)
Tel: +57(796) 474-660
Fax: +57(796) 430-273
Rector: Jairo Castro Castro
Financial Administration; Public Works; Electronics; Systems Technology; Computer Graphics.

Corporación Tecnológica de Ciencias Empresariales
Calle 46 No. 3-65, Santafé de Bogotá
Tel: +57(1) 287-9737
Fax: +57(1) 245-3789
Rector: Julio Alberto Moyano Ferrer
Publicity; International Business; Marketing; Business Administration.

Corporación Tecnológica de Santander
Carrera 29 No. 47-32, Apartado aéreo 40223,
Bucaramanga (Santander)
Tel: +57(76) 479-392
Fax: +57(76) 436-002
Rector: Fernando Vargas Mendoza
*Textile Design; Occupational Health; Marketing
and Publicity; Hotel Administration; Tourism;
Financial and Systems Administration; Computer
Science; Food Administration.*

Corporación Universitaria de Ciencias Agropecuarias
Calle 222, No. 54-25, Apartado aéreo 34204,
Santafé de Bagotá
Tel: +57(1) 676-1258
Fax: +57(1) 676-1132
Rector: Germán Anzola Montero
*Animal Husbandry; Food Engineering; Veterinary
Studies.*

Corporación Universitaria de Colombia (IDEAS)
Calle 69 No. 7-77, Santafé de Bogotá
Tel: +57(1) 255-8321
Fax: +57(1) 217-9073
Rector: Jairo Tapias Ospina
Computer Science.

Corporación Universitaria del Meta
Carrera 32 No. 34A-31, Barrio San Fernando,
Apartado aéreo 3244, Villavicencio, Meta
Tel: +57(866) 31149
Fax: +57(866) 31150
Rector: Rafael María Mojica García
*Management; Public Accountancy; Systems
Accountancy.*

Corporación Universitaria 'Rafael Nuñez'
Calle de la Soledad 5-06, Apartado aéreo 1637,
Cartagena, Bolívar
Tel: +57(53) 647-578
Fax: +57(53) 600-134
Rector: Miguel Henriquez Emiliani
Special Education; Public Accountancy.

Corporación Universitaria Santa Rosa de Cabal
Calle 14 No. 27-80, Apartado aéreo 1371, Santa
Rosa de Caball, Risaralda
Tel: +57(63) 643-000
Fax: +57(63) 642-058
Rector: José López

Corporación Universitaria del SINU
Carrera 3 No. 29-26, Apartado aéreo 1199,
Montería, Córdoba
Tel: +57(401) 822-467
Fax: +57(401) 822-988
Rector: Elias Bechara Zainum
Social Work; Business Administration; Law.

Escuela de Administración de Negocios
Calle 72 No. 9-71, Apartado aéreo 100888,
Santafé de Bogotá
Tel: +57(1) 211-2716
Fax: +57(1) 249-4255
Rector: Hildebrando Perico Afanador
Founded: 1968
Business Administration; Systems Engineering.

Escuela Colombiana de Ingeniería 'Julio Garavito'
Autopista del Norte Km 13, Apartado aéreo
14520, Santafé de Bogotá
Tel: +57(1) 676-0236
Fax: +57(1) 676-0479
Rector: Eduardo Silva Sánchez
Founded: 1972
*Civil Engineering; Systems Engineering;
Electrical Engineering.*

Escuela Colombiana de Medicina
Transversal 9A bis No. 133-25, Apartado aéreo
100998, Santafé de Bogotá
Tel: +57(1) 274-3096
Fax: +57(1) 625-2030
Rector: Miguel Antonio Rangel Franco
Medicine; Dentistry.

Escuela de Ingeniería de Antioquia
Calle 25 Sur No. 42-73, Envigado Zúñiga,
Apartado aéreo 7516, Medellín, Antioquia
Tel: +57(4) 331-7843
Fax: +57(4) 331-7851
Rector: Alberto Quevedo Díaz
*Civil Engineering; Geological Engineering;
Administration.*

Fundación Centro Universitario de Bienestar Rural
Vereda Periconegro-Puerto Tejada, Apartado
aéreo 6555, Puerto Tejada, Cauca
Tel: +57(28) 282-412
Fax: +57(28) 536-491
Rector: Edmundo Gutiérrez Ramírez
Rural Education.

Fundación Escuela de Ciencias de la Salud de la Sociedad de Cirugía de Bogotá
Calle 10 No. 18-75, Hospital San José, Santafé de
Bogotá
Tel: +57(1) 201-9158
Rector: Alberto Villaneda Soto
Founded: 1976
Health Sciences.

Fundación Escuela de Medicina 'Juan N. Corpas'
Avenida Corpas Km. 3 Suba, Apartado aéreo
2787, Santafé de Bogotá
Tel: +57(1) 681-3637
Fax: +57(1) 683-4481
Rector: Jorge Piñeros Corpas
Founded: 1972
Medicine.

Fundación Instituto Universitario de Ciencia y Tecnología 'Konrad Lorenz'
Calle 70A No. 10-52, Apartado aéreo 250724,
Santafé de Bogotá
Tel: +57(1) 212-5121
Fax: +57(1) 212-8365
Director: Juan Alberto Aragon Bateman
Psychology; Management.

Fundación Universitaria Agraria de Colombia
Calle 170 No. 50-90, Apartado aéreo 34152,
Santafé de Bogotá
Tel: +57(1) 672-1630
Fax: +57(1) 672-3773
Rector: Fidel Huertas Bernal
Animal Husbandry; Civil Engineering; Food Technology.

Fundación Universitaria del Area Andina
Calle 71 No. 13-21, Apartado aéreo 50814,
Santafé de Bogotá
Tel: +57(1) 248-9054
Fax: +57(1) 211-5477
Rector: Pablo Oliveros Marmolejo

Fundación Universitaria de García Rovira, Norte y Gutiérrez
Ciudad Universitaria-Málaga, Málaga, Santander
Tel: +57(76) 607-353
Rector: Luis Adriano Diaz Torres
Animal Husbandry; Forestry; Business Administration.

Fundación Universitaria 'Los Libertadores'
Carrera 10 No. 65-98, Apartado aéreo 75087,
Santafé de Bogotá
Tel: +57(1) 235-0688
Fax: +57(1) 232-1979
Rector: Hernan Linares Angel
Journalism; Hotel Administration; International Business.

Fundación Universitaria 'Luis Amigo'
Transversal 51A No. 67B-134, Apartado aéreo
11001, Medellín, Antioquia
Tel: +57(4) 230-1804
Fax: +57(4) 230-2181
Rector: Marino Martínez Pérez
Re-educational Pedagogy; Family Studies; Business.

Fundación Universitaria 'María Caño'
Carrera 42 No. 50-69, Apartado aéreo 5096,
Medellín, Antioquia
Tel: +57(4) 245-9696
Rector: Jairo Hernández Navas
Physiotherapy; Occupational Therapy.

Fundación Universitaria Monserrate
Calle 72 No. 11-41, Santafé de Bogotá
Tel: +57(1) 217-4912
Fax: +57(1) 249-4959
Rector: Berta Revollo Bravo
Founded: 1948
Education (preschool level); Social Work.

Fundación Universitaria de Popayan
Calle 5 No. 7-78, Apartado aéreo 742, Popayan,
Cauca
Tel: +57(282) 221-920
Fax: +57(282) 221-920
Rector: José Bernardo Ayerbe Mosquera
Stockraising; Mining; Ecology.

Fundación Universitaria San Martín
Calle 61A No. 14-28, Santafé de Bogotá
Tel: +57(1) 255-5919
Fax: +57(1) 235-8356
Rector: Jaime Villamizar Lamus
Publicity; Dentistry.

Instituto de Ciencias de la Salud
Calle 10A No.22-04, El Poblado, Apartado aéreo
54591, Medellín, Antioquia
Tel: +57(4) 268-0364
Fax: +57(4) 266-6046
Rector: Hernan Velez Atehortua
Health Science; Medicine; Dentistry.

Instituto Tecnológico de Administración y Economía (ITAE)
Calle 35 No. 9-81, Apartado aéreo 2147,
Bucaramanga (Santander)
Tel: +57(796) 422-080
Rector: Eduardo Sierra Barreneche
Founded: 1972
Fashion Design and Textile Applications; Art and Architectural Decoration; Industrial Management.

Instituto Universitario de Historia de Colombia
Carrera 9 No. 9-52, Apartado aéreo 9649 Santafé
de Bogotá
Tel: +57(1) 282-5316
Fax: +57(1) 282-5316
Rector: Antonio Cacua Prada
Founded: 1966
History of Columbia.

Politécnico Grancolombiano
Calle 57 Carrera 3 Este, Apartado aéreo 90853,
Santafé de Bogotá
Tel: +57(1) 212-6064
Fax: +57(1) 217-6146
Rector: César Tulio Delgado Hurtado
Advertisement; Business Administration; Accountancy; Systems Engineering.

Universidad Católica Popular del Risaralda
Avenida sur-Parque, Metropolitano Cafe,
Apartado aéreo 2435, Pereira, Risaralda
Rector: Francisco Nel Jiménez Gómez
*Industrial Economics; Business Administration;
Accountancy.*

NATIONAL ACADEMIC BODIES

Ministry of Education
[Ministerio de Educación Nacional]
Avenida El Dorado, Santa Fé de Bogotá
Tel: +57(1) 222-4903
Fax: +57(1) 222-0324
Telex: 42456 sgmen co
Ministro: Maruja Pachón de Villamizar

**Colombian Institute for the Development of
Higher Education (ICFES)**
[Instituto Colombiano para el Fomento de la
Educación Superior (ICFES)]
Calle 17 No. 3-40, Apartado aéreo 6319, Santa Fé
Bogotá
Tel: 281-9311
Fax: 286-8045
Director General: Balo Barbano
Secretaria General: Patricia Linares Prieto

Colombian Universities Association
[Asociación Colombiana de Universidades
(ASCUN)]
Apartado aéreo 012300, Calle 93, No. 16-43,
Santaafé de Bogotá
Tel: +57(1) 218-5145
Fax: +57(91) 218-5098
Presidente: Otoniel Fernńdez Villegas
Secretario general: Alfonso Borrero, S.J.
Founded: 1958

Colombian National Commission for Unesco
[Comisión Nacional Colombiana de Cooperación
on la Unesco]
Ministerio de Educación Nacional, Avenida El
Dorado, Oficina 510, Santa Fé de Bogotá
Tel: +57(1) 222-4691
Fax: +57(1) 222-0324
Telex: 42456 sgmen
Presidente: Maruja Pachón de Villamizar,
Minister of Education
Secretaria Ejecutiva: María del Rosario Ortíz
Santos

CONGO

UNIVERSITIES

*University Marien Ngouabi Brazzaville
[Université Marien Ngouabi]
B.P. 69, Brazzaville
Tel: +242 812-436
Telex: 5331 kg
Recteur: Christophe Bouramoué
Secrétaire général: Marie Alphonse Aya
Founded: 1959, 1971, 1977

F: *Letters and Human Sciences; Sciences
(Dolisie); Law; Economics (Pointe-Noire).*
I: *Management; Rural Development (Ouesso);
Physical Education and Sport (Makabana); Health
Sciences; Teacher Training (Loubomo).*
S: *Technical Education; Administration and
Training for the Magistrature; Teacher Training.*

NATIONAL ACADEMIC BODIES

Ministry of National Education
[Ministère de l'Éducation nationale]
B.P. 493, Brazzaville
Tel: +242 812-460
Fax: +242 833-987
Ministre: Naasson Loutete Dangui

Congo National Commission for Unesco
[Commission nationale congolaise pour l'Unesco]
Tour Nabemba (14é étage), B.P. 493, Brazzaville
Tel: +242 831-986
Cable: unesco brazzaville
Président: Naasson Loutete Dangui, Minister of
Education
Secrétaire général: Jean-Marie Adoua

COSTA RICA

UNIVERSITIES

PUBLIC INSTITUTIONS

Technological University of Costa Rica
[Universidad Tecnológica de Costa Rica]
Apartado 159, Cartago
Tel: +506 515-333
Telex: 515-348
Founded: 1971
D: *Business Administration; Agricultural
Administration; Electronics; Agricultural
Engineering; Industrial Engineering; Forestry
Engineering; Industrial Production; Industrial
Design; Computer Sciences; Civil Engineering;
Wood Technology; Agriculture; Metallurgy;
Drawing; Production Supervising; Security and
Occupational Hygiene.*
Ce: *Computer; Contruction Experimental;
Information Technology; Wood (Experimental).*

SAN CARLOS REGIONAL BRANCH
[SEDE REGIONAL DE SAN CARLOS]
Santa Clara de San Carlos, Alajuela

University of Costa Rica
[Universidad de Costa Rica]
C 21 a 4 y 6, San José
Tel: +506(234) 243-660
Fax: +506(234) 255-822
Telex: 330027
Rector: Luis Garita Bonilla

COSTA RICA

P: Agriculture; Education; Economics; Fine Arts;
Basic Sciences; Social Sciences; Engineering;
Letters.
Ce: Public Administration Research and
Qualification(CICAP); Geophysics Research
(CIGEFI); Cereals and Seeds Research (CIGRAS);
Research on Abnormal Blood Diseases and
Related Disorders (CIAHATA).

National University Heredia
[Universidad Nacional]
Apartado 86, Heredia
Tel: +506 376-363
Fax: +506 380-086
Telex: 7550 unavi cr
Founded: 1973
F: Philosophy and Letters; Social Sciences;
Earth and Marine Sciences; Exact and Natural
Sciences; Health Sciences.
Ce: Research and Teaching in Education;
General Studies.

BRUNCA REGIONAL BRANCH
[SECCION REGIONAL BRUNCA]
San Isidro del General Pérez, Zeledón, San José

CHOROTEGA REGIONAL BRANCH
[SECCION REGIONAL CHOROTEGA]
Liberia, Guanacaste

State University of Distance Education San José
[Universidad Estatal a Distancia]
Ap. 2 de Plaza González Víquez, San José
Tel: +506(234) 241-689
Fax: +506(234) 534-990
Telex: 3003 uned cr
Founded: 1977
S: Education; Management; Health Studies;
Natural and Applied Sciences; Social and Human
Sciences.

PRIVATE INSTITUTIONS

Adventist University of Central America Alajuela
[Universidad Adventista de Centro América]
Carretera a Iriquís, La Ceiba, Alajuela
Tel: +506 415-622
Fax: +506 411-282
Telex: 7034
Cable: ucadve
Founded: 1986
S: Business Administration; Theology;
Education.
Ce: Research.

182

Interamerican University of Costa Rica
[Universidad Interamericana de Costa Rica]
P.O. Box 6495-1000, San José, San Pedro de
Montes de Oca
Tel: +506(234) 346-262
Fax: +506(234) 538-744
President: William J. Salom
Registrar: Cecilia Gómez
Founded: 1990
P: Business Administration for Managers.

Latin American University of Costa Rica
[Universidad Latina de Costa Rica]
C 21 a 4 y 6, San José
Tel: +506(234) 553-833
Fax: +506(234) 339-420
Telex: 33-0027
Rector: Maria Lorena Madaibal (1992-)
Secretario General: Jorge Barahona
Founded: 1979
P: International Relations; Education
Administration; Education; Business
Administration; Publicity; Economics; Journalism.
I: Research; Education Research.

PASO CANÕAS REGIONAL BRANCH
[SEDE REGIONAL DE PASO CANÕAS]
Corredores, Puntarenas

*Autonomous University of Central America San José
[Universidad Autónoma de Centro América]
Apartado 7637, 1000 San José
Tel: +506(234) 334-0701
Fax: +506(234) 240-0391
Telex: 2907
Rector: Guillermo Malavassi Vargas
Founded: 1976
Administrative Engineering; Computer Sciences;
Architecture; Fine Arts; Law; Economics; Social
Sciences; Political Science.

STUDIUM GENERALE COSTARRICENSE
Apartado 7651-1000, San José
Tel: +506(234) 223-6766
Fax: +506(234) 222-6528
Dean: Mario Granados
Accountancy; Architecture; Business
Administration; Civil Engineering; Computer
Science; Economics; Electrical Engineering;
History; Journalism; Law; Music; Philology;
Philosophy; Public Administration.

COLLEGIUM ACADEMICUM
Apartado 1703-1002, San José
Tel: +506(234) 221-8919
Dean: Gastón Certad
Business Administration; Computer Science;
International Relations; Law.

MONTERREY COLLEGE
[COLEGIO MONTERREY]
Apartado 5103-1000, San José
Tel: +506(234) 222-9863
Fax: +506(234) 222-3062
Dean: Rufino Gil
*Accountancy; Banking and Finance; Business
Administration; Human Resources; Psychology;
Public Administration.*

COLLEGE OF PLASTIC ARTS
[COLEGIO DE ARTES PLASTICA]
Apartado 6177-1000, San José
Tel: +506(234) 221-0053
Fax: +506(234) 221-0053
Dean: Wilberth Villegas
*Design for Advertising; Educational Sciences,
Nursing; Fine Arts; Industrial Design; Music.*

AUTONOMOUS SCHOOL OF MEDICINE
[ESCUELA AUTÓNOMA DE CIENCIAS MEDICAS]
Apartado 638-1007, San José
Tel: +506(234) 231-2194
Fax: +506(234) 221-4538
Dean: Alvaro Fernández-Salas
*Administration of Health Centres; Health
Sciences; History of Medicine; Human
Morphology; Medicine; Occupational Medicine.*

FREE SCHOOL OF LAW
[ESCUELA LIBRE DE DERECH]
Apartado 715-2010, San José
Tel: +506(234) 221-3660
Fax: +506(234) 221-8763
Dean: Ricardo Guerrero
Law.

'LEONARDO DA VINCI COLLEGE
[COLEGIO 'LEONARDO DA VINCI']
Apartado 44-1009, San José
Tel: +506(234) 233-7035
Dean: Teresita Bonilla
*Business Administration; Civil Engineering;
Industrial Administration; Industrial Engineering;
Public Relations.*

SANTO TOMAS DE AQUINO COLLEGE
[COLEGIO SANTO TOMAS DE AQUINO]
Apartado 250-2100, San José
Tel: +506(234) 223-2767
Fax: +506(234) 257-0104
Dean: Luis Carlos Donato
*Banking and Finance; Business Administration;
Computer Science; Industrial Engineering; Law.*

COLLEGIUM FIDELITAS
[COLEGIO FIDELITAS]
Apartado 8063-1000, San José
Tel: +506(234) 253-0262
Fax: +506(234) 253-9576
Dean: Lipcia Munguía
*Accountancy; Banking and Finance; Business
Administration; Educational Science; Electrical
Engineering; Industrial Engineering.*

ANDRES BELLO COLLEGE
[COLEGIO ANDRES BELLO]
Apartado 455-2010, San José
Tel: +506(234) 223-9282
Fax: +506(234) 233-0598
Dean: Herberth Sasso
*Educational Science; International Relations;
Nursing; Psychology; Public Relations; Tourism.*

COLLEGIUM SANCTUS IUDAS TADAEUS
Apartado 7676-1000, San José
Tel: +506(234) 233-4255
Fax: +506(234) 233-3973
Dean: Helia Betancourt
Educational Science; Journalism.

COLLEGIUM SANTA PAULA
Apartado 3595-1000, San José
Tel: +506(234) 221-6810
Fax: +506(234) 221-5331
Dean: María Eugenia Vargas
Occupational Therapy; Physical Therapy.

Central Costa Rican University San José
[Universidad Central Costarricense]
C 21 a 4 y 6, San José
Tel: +506(234) 330-027
Founded: 1990
*P: Computer Science; Education; Business
Administration.*

**International University of the Americas San
José**
[Universidad Internacional de las Américas]
Calle 23, a 7 y 9, San José
Tel: +506(234) 335-304
Fax: +506(234) 223-216
Rector: Miguel Angel Guitiérrez Alvarez
Manager: Alvaro Pazos Baldioceda
Founded: 1986
*P: Business Administration; International
Commerce; Publicity; Medicine; International
Relations; Systems Engineering; Industrial
Engineering; Electro-Mechanical Engineering;
English; Tourism; Accountancy; Law; Education
(pre-school level).*

PÉREZ ZELEDÓN REGIONAL CENTRE
[CENTRO REGIONAL PÉREZ ZELEDÓN]
San Isidro del General, San José

**Latin American University of Sciences and
Technology San José**
[Universidad Latinoamericana de Ciencias y
Tecnología]
Apartado 10235, 1000 San José
Tel: +506(234) 239-155
Fax: +506(234) 224-542
Founded: 1986
*Business Administration; Accountancy; Tourism;
Computer Sciences; Research and Development.*

Panamerican University San José
[Universidad Panamericana]
Calle 23 y ctl. y 1, San José
Telex: 21-2176
Founded: 1988
P: English; Education; Computer Sciences; Business Administration; Administration; Architecture; Publicity Design; Tourism; Public Accountancy; Human Resources Administration; Public Relations; Civil Engineering; Industrial Engineering.

OTHER INSTITUTIONS

Centro Agronómico Tropical de Investigación y Enseñanza
Turrialba
Tel: +506 56-6431
Fax: +506 56-1533
Founded: 1942
Tropical Agriculture.

Escuela de Agricultura de la Región Húmeda (EARTH)
Curridabat
Tel: +506 53-5454
Fax: +506 53-4597
Founded: 1989
Tropical Agriculture.

Instituto Centroamericano de Administración Pública
Apartado 10025, 1000 San José
Tel: +506(234) 22-3133
Founded: 1954
Public Administration.

Université pour la Paix/Universidad para la Paz
Ciudad Colón, Apartado 199-1250, Escazú
Tel: +506 49-1511
Fax: +506 49-1929
Telex: 2331 macaze cr
Founded: 1980
Peace Studies.

NATIONAL ACADEMIC BODIES

Ministry of Public Education
[Ministerio de Educación Pública]
Apartado 10087-1000, San José
Tel: +506(234) 220-229
Fax: +506(234) 552-868
Ministro: Eduardo Doryan Garrón

National Council of Rectors
[Consejo Nacional de Rectores (CONARE)]
San Pedro de Montes de Oca, Apartado 374-2050, San José
Tel: +506(234) 24-3066
Fax: +506(234) 34-0374
President: Arturo Jofré Vartanián
Director: José Andrés Masís Bermúdez
Founded: 1974

Costa Rica Commission for Cooperation with Unesco
[Comisión Costarricense de Cooperación con la Unesco]
Ministerio de Educación Pública, San Pedro de Montes de Oca, San José
Tel: +506(234) 240-4320
Fax: +506(234) 244-320
Telex: 2107
Cable: comisión unesco sanjosé
Presidente: Eduardo Doryan Garrón, Minister of Education
Secretario Permanente: Nelly Maía Ramón Jara de Venegas

CÔTE D'IVOIRE

UNIVERSITIES

*National University of Côte d'Ivoire
[Université nationale de Côte d'Ivoire]
B.P.V. 34, Abidjan
Tel: +225 44-35-31
Fax: +225 44-35-31
Telex: 26138 rectu ci
Recteur: Semi-Bi Zan (1993-)
Secrétaire général: Julienne Badia
International Relations: Gérard Lezou Dago
Founded: 1959, 1964

UNIVERSITY CENTRE OF COCODY
[CENTRE UNIVERSITAIRE DE COCODY]
Cocody
Vice-Recteur: Asseypo Hazuhouot
Founded: 1994
F: Science and Techniques; Medicine; Law; Economics and Management; Letters, Arts and Human Sciences; Pharmany; Dentistry-Stomatology.
I: Tropical Ecology; Applied Linguistics; New Energy Research; Negro-African Literature and Aesthetics; Ethno-Sociological Studies; Tropical Geography; African History, Art and Archaeology; Criminology.
Ce: French Studies; Lifelong Education; Communication Research; Teaching and Applied Psychological Research; Social Studies; Juridical Studies.

UNIVERSITY CENTRE OF ABOBO-ADJAMÉ
[CENTRE UNIVERSITAIRE D'ABOBO-ADJAMÉ]
Abobo-Adjamé
Vice-Recteur: Daouda Aïdara
Founded: 1994
S: Nature and the Environment.
Ce: Medical and Veterinary Entomology (Bouaké).

UNIVERSITY CENTRE OF BOUAKÉ
[CENTRE UNIVERSITAIRE DE BOUAKÉ]
Bouaké
Vice-Recteur: François Kouakou N'Guessan
Founded: 1994
S: Letters; Law and Economics.

OTHER INSTITUTIONS

Ecole nationale supérieure agronomique
Yamoussoukra
Directeur: Mathias Zengbe
Founded: 1965, 1994
Agriculture.

Ecole nationale supérieure de Statistique et d'Economie appliquée
B.P. 3, Abidjan 08
Tel: +225 44-08-40
Fax: +225 44-39-88
Directeur: François Yattien-Amiguet
Founded: 1961
Statistics and Applied Economics.

Ecole nationale supérieure des Travaux publics
B.P. 148, Abidjan
Tel: +225 64-01-00
Telex: 22606 ensipa ci
Directeur: Sylvain Kacou
Founded: 1963
Public Works.

Ecole normale supérieure
B.P. 10, Abidjan 08
Tel: +225 44-43-23
Fax: +225 44-38-23
Directeur: Touré Vakaba
Founded: 1964
D: Arts and Letters; Languages; Science and Technology; History and Geography; Educational Science.

Institut national supérieur de l'Enseignement technique (INSET)
B.P.V. 79, Abidjan
Tel: +225 44-42-88
Telex: 2288
Directeur: Boubouo Nahounou
Founded: 1975
S: Engineering; Industrial Technology; Commerce; Technology.

Institut pédagogique national de l'Enseignement technique et professionel (IPNETP)
B.P. 2098, Abidjan
Tel: +225 44-67-69
Fax: +225 44-58-37
Directeur: Souleymané Bah
Secrétaire général: André Tebily
International Relations: Mamadou Diomandé
Founded: 1975
Technical and Vocational Education.

NATIONAL ACADEMIC BODIES

Ministry of National Education
[Ministère de l'Education nationale]
B.P.V. 120, Abidjan 01
Tel: +225 22-44-17
Fax: +225 22-69-08
Telex: 23377 mineduca abidjan
Ministre: Pierre Kipré

Côte d'Ivoire National Commission for Unesco
[Commission nationale ivoirienne pour l'Unesco]
Ministère de l'Education nationale, chargé de l'Enseignement secondaire et supérieur, 15, avenue Noguès, Abidjan 01
Tel: +225 32-48-25
Fax: +225 21-22-25
Telex: 22151 unesco ci
Secrétaire général: Abdou Touré

CROATIA

UNIVERSITIES

University of Osijek
[Sveučilište u Osijeku]
Ul. Bracé Radića 15, 54 000 Osijek
Tel: +385(54) 31-822
Fax: (54) 24-750
Founded: 1975
F: Economics; Law; Education; Agriculture; Biotechnology; Civil Engineering; Mechanical Engineering Sciences; Electrical Engineering; Agriculture; History.
Ce: Social Research of Slavonija and Baranja Slavonski Brod.

University of Rijeka
[Sveučilište Vladimir Bakarić u Rijeci]
Trg Riječke Rezolucije 7/I,P.P. 179, 51000 Rijeka
Tel: +385(51) 36-036
Fax: +385(51) 39-539
Rector: Elso Kuljanićić
Secretary-General: Glavni Tajnik
Founded: 1973
F: Medicine and Stomatology; Technical, Mechanical, Shipbuilding and Electrical Engineering; Civil Engineering; Maritime Studies;

Economics; Hotel Management; Economics and
Tourism; Law; Education; Agriculture and
Tourism.
Ce: Sea Research.

University of Split
[Sveučilište u Splitu]
Livanjska 5, 58 000 Split
Tel: +385(58) 49-966
Founded: 1974
F: Law; Electrical, Mechanical and Marine
Engineering; Economics; Philosophy; Chemical
Engineering; Civil Engineering; Tourism and
Foreign Trade; Oceanography and Fisheries;
Adriatic Agricultural Research.

*University of Zagreb
[Sveučilište u Zagrebu]
Trg Maršala Tita 14, 41000 Zagreb
Tel: +385(41) 464-244
Fax: +385(41) 464-388
E-Mail: rektorat@irb.ac.mail.yu
Rector: Marijan Šunjió
Secretary: Marijan Perkovió
Founded: 1669
F: Agriculture; Architecture; Economics;
Electrical Engineering; Chemical Engineering and
Technology; Organization and Computer
Sciences; Political Sciences; Traffic Engineering;
Mechanical Engineering and Naval Architecture;
Study of the Handicapped; Physical Education
and Sports; Pharmacy and Biochemistry;
Philosophy; Surveying; Civil Engineering; Printing
Technology; Catholic Theology; Medicine;
Metallurgy; Law; Food and Biotechnology;
Natural Sciences and Mathematics; Mining,
Geology, and Petroleum Engineering; Dentistry;
Forestry; Textile Technology; Veterinary
Medicine; Drama; Fine Arts; Music; Agriculture;
Technical Sciences; Economics; Immunology;
Physics, Chemistry, Biology, Genetics, Medical
Research, Marine Biology; Philosophy; Social
Research; Applied Social Research; Physics;
Migrations and Minorities; Medical Research and
Occupational Medicine; History of Art;
Development and International Relations.
Ce: Computer.

NATIONAL ACADEMIC BODIES

Ministry of Education, Culture and Sport
Trg. Bruze 6, 41 000 Zagreb
Tel: +385(41) 410-449
Fax: +385(41) 410-421
Minister: Vesna Giradi-Jurkić

Croatian National Commission for Unesco
Trg. Bruze 6, 41 000 Zagreb
Tel: +385(41) 469-024
Fax: +385(41) 410-421
Chairman: Ivan Supicié
Secretary-General: Dino Milinović

CUBA

UNIVERSITIES

University of Camagüey
[Universidad de Camagüey]
Carretera de Circunvalación, Camagüey
Tel: +53 61019
Telex: 031201
Founded: 1967, 1974
F: Agriculture and Animal Husbandry;
Technology.
I: Economics; Education.

University of Havana
[Universidad de La Habana]
Calle San Lázaro, Esquina L, Vedado, Ciudad de
La Habana
Tel: +53(7) 73231
Telex: 511277 esc matematicas uh
Rector: Fernando Rojas Avalos
Founded: 1728
F: Biology; Geography; Cybernetics; Physics;
Chemistry; Science and Nuclear Technology;
Philosophy and History; Arts and Letters;
Journalism; Foreign Languages; Psychology;
Law; Economic Planning; Accountancy and
Finance; Political Economics; Pharmacy and
Food Technology; Preparatory; Encounter
Courses for Workers and Correspondence
Courses.
Ce: Computer Sciences; Demographic Studies.

Central University of Las Villas
[Universidad Central de Las Villas]
Carretera a Camajuaní Kilómetro 10, Santa
Clara, Las Villas
Tel: +53 81178
Fax: +53 81682
Telex: 41130 univ las villas
Rector: Luis Gómez Gutiérrez
Founded: 1952
F: Industrial Engineering; Mechanical
Engineering; Electrical Engineering; Chemical
and Sugar Technology; Civil Engineering and
Architecture; Chemistry and Physics; Letters;
Economics; Law; Psychology; Cybernetics and
Mathematics; Languages (Preparatory);
Agriculture; Veterinary Medicine; Encounter
Courses for Workers and Correspondence
Courses.
I: Computer Sciences.
D: Marxism-Leninism; Physical Education, Sport
and Recreation.

*University of Oriente
[Universidad de Oriente]
Avenida Patricio Lumumba s/n, Apartado postal
436, Santiago de Cuba, Oriente
Tel: +53 33011
Fax: +53 32689
Telex: 061-145
Rector: Manuel Blanco Milá
Secretario General: Oscar Sánchez del Campo
Delgado
Founded: 1947
*F: Technology; Social Sciences and Humanities;
Agriculture; Natural Sciences and Mathematics;
Law.*
I: Economics; Education.
Ce: Scientific Research.

OTHER INSTITUTIONS

**Centro Nacional de Investigaciones
Científicas**
Avenida 25, Calle 158, Reparto Cubanacán, La
Habana
Tel: +53(7) 219-587
Scientific Research.

Centro Universitario de Holguín
Miró No. 125 e/, Frexes y Aguilera, Holguín
Founded: 1976

Centro Universitario de Matanzas
Calle Medio No. 100 e/, Zaragoza y Manzaneda,
Matanzas
Tel: +53(52) 2612
Founded: 1976

Centro Universitario de Pinar del Río
Martí No. 270 esq. a 27 de Noviembre, Pinar del
Río
Founded: 1976

**Instituto Superior Agrícola de Ciego de
Avila**
Ciego de Avila
Tel: +53(33) 25702
Telex: 32146
Founded: 1978
Agriculture.

Instituto Superior de Arte
Calle 120 No. 1110 e/, 9na y 13 Cubanacán, La
Habana
Founded: 1976
Arts.

**Instituto Superior de Ciencias
Agropecuarias de La Habana**
Quinta de los Molinos, Avenida Salvador Allende
y Luaces, La Habana
Founded: 1976
Agriculture and Stockraising.

**Instituto Superior de Ciencias Médicas de
Camagüey**
Hospital Provincial y Politécnico de la Salud,
Camagüey 1
Tel: +53 8536
Founded: 1981
Medicine.

**Instituto Superior de Ciencias Médicas de
La Habana**
146 No. 2504 e/31 y 25 Cubanacán, La Habana
Founded: 1976
Medicine.

**Instituto Superior de Ciencias Médicas de
Santiago de Cuba**
Avenida de las Américas e/1, Santiago de Cuba
Tel: +53(226) 6679
Founded: 1976
Medicine.

**Instituto Superior de Ciencias Médicas de
Villa Clara**
Arias No. 9 Hospital Provincial e/, Doble Via y
Circunvalación, Sta. Clara, Villa Clara
Tel: +53(42) 27820
Founded: 1976
Medicine.

**Instituto Superior de Cultura Física Manuel
Fajardo**
Sta. Catalina e/, Primelles y Boyeros, La Habana
Tel: +53(7) 406-171
Founded: 1976
Physical Education.

Instituto Superior de Servicio Exterior
22 e/1ra y 3ra Miramar, La Habana
Tel: +53(7) 25097
Founded: 1976
External Services.

**Instituto Superior Minero Metalúrgico de
Moa**
Moa, Holguín
Founded: 1976
Metallurgy.

Instituto Superior Pedagógico
Carretera de Circunvalación, Camagüey
Founded: 1976
Teacher Training.

**Instituto Superior Pedagógico de
Guantánamo**
Guantánamo
Teacher Training.

Instituto Superior Pedagógico de Holguín
Calle Quinta e/, Maceo y Hospital, Holguín
Founded: 1976
Teacher Training.

Instituto Superior Pedagógico de la Educación Técnica y Profesional
Avenida Vantroi y Rancho Boyeros, La Habana
Founded: 1976
Teacher Training (Technical and Professional).

Instituto Superior Pedagógico de La Habana
La Habana
Teacher Training.

Instituto Superior Pedagógico de Las Villas
Universidad Central, Carretera de Camaguani
Km. 10, Santa Clara, Villa Clara
Founded: 1976
Teacher Training.

Instituto Superior Pedagógico de Lenguas Modernas
Ciudad Libertad Marianao, La Habana
Founded: 1976
Teacher Training (Modern Languages).

Instituto Superior Pedagógico de Manzanillo
Veguitas Manzanillo, Granma
Founded: 1976
Teacher Training.

Instituto Superior Pedagógico de Matanzas
Calle Rio e/ Matanzas y Medio, Matanzas
Founded: 1976
Teacher Training.

Instituto Superior Pedagógico de Pinar del Río
Colon Rpto. Llamalari, (Antigua Sec. Básica Frank Pais), Pinar del Río
Founded: 1976
Teacher Training.

Instituto Superior Pedagógico de Santiago de Cuba
Avenida Patricio Lumumba s/n, Santiago de Cuba
Founded: 1976
Teacher Training.

Instituto Superior Politécnico José A. Echeverría
CUJAE Marianao, La Habana
Tel: +53 200641
Telex: 511153 ccft cujac
Founded: 1976

Instituto Superior Técnico de Cienfuegos
Cienfuegos
Tel: +53(432) 21521
Telex: 042141
Technical Studies.

NATIONAL ACADEMIC BODIES

Ministry of Education
[Ministerio de Educación]
Ospiso e/. Mercaderes y San Iganacio, Habana Vieja, La Habana
Tel: +53(7) 624-011
Fax: +53(7) 622-547
Ministro: Luis I. Gómez Gutiérrez

Directorate of International Organizations
[Dirección de Organismos Internacionales]
Ministerio de Relaciones Exteriores, Calle 5a, entre G & H Vedado, La Habana
Tel: +53(7) 305-031
Telex: 511122

Cuban National Commission for Unesco
[Comisión Nacional Cubana de la Unesco]
Avenida Kohly 151, Nuevo Vedado, La Habana
Tel: +53(7) 36161
Fax: +53(7) 313-123
Cable: concun habana
Presidente: Oscar García Fernández
Secretaria Permanente: María Josefa Vilaboy Morales

CYPRUS

UNIVERSITIES

University of Cyprus
[Panepistimio Kyprou]
odos Kallipoleos 75, P.O. Box 537, Nicosia
Tel: +357(2) 366186
Fax: +357(2) 366198
E-Mail: admin@jupiter cca.ucy.cy
Chairperson, Interim Governing Board: Nelly Tsouyopoulos
Director, Administration and Finance: Nikos Vakis
Founded: 1992
S: Humanities and Social Sciences; Economics and Management; Pure and Applied Sciences.

OTHER INSTITUTIONS

Forestry College, Prodromos
Prodromos, Limassol
Tel: +357(5) 462064
Fax: +357(5) 462646
Director: Christos Alexandrou (1989-)
Founded: 1951
Forestry.

Higher Hotel Institute, Cyprus
P.O. Box 4812, Nicosia
Tel: +357(2) 305001
Fax: +357(2) 314672
Telex: 2850 xenia cy
Director: Andreas Papadopoulos (1993-)
Senior Officer: Andreas Varnavas
Founded: 1969
Hotel Management.

Higher Technical Institute, Cyprus
P.O. Box 2423, Nicosia
Tel: +357(2) 494454
Fax: +357(2) 494953
Director: Demetrios Lazarides (1991-)
Administration Officer: Agni Daniel
Founded: 1968
D: Civil Engineering; Electrical Engineering; Marine Engineering; Mechanical Engineering; Computer Studies.

Mediterranean Institute of Management (MIM)
P.O. Box 536, Nicosia
Tel: +357(2) 377992
Fax: +357(2) 376872
Cable: producentre
Director: Herodotos Michaelides (1987-)
Secretary: Nitsa Zannetou
Founded: 1976
Business Management.

School of Nursing
General Hospital, Nicosia
Tel: +357(2) 451111
Founded: 1955
Nursing.

NATIONAL ACADEMIC BODIES

Ministry of Education and Culture
[Ypourgion Paideias kai Politismou]
Odos Gr. Afxentiou, Nicosia
Tel: +357(2) 303331
Fax: +357(2) 445021
Telex: 5760 mineduc cy

Cyprus National Commission for Unesco
Ministry of Foreign Affairs, Nicosia
Tel: +357(2) 302427
Fax: +357(2) 451881
Telex: 3001 2
Cable: minforeign nicosia
Chairman: Tasos Panayides

CZECH REPUBLIC

UNIVERSITIES AND TECHNICAL UNIVERSITIES

*Charles University
[Univerzita Karlova]
Ovocný trh 5, 116 36 Praha 1
Tel: +42(2) 2449-1111
Fax: +42(2) 2422-9487
E-Mail: karel maly@ruk.cun.cz
Telex: 122818 up pho
Rektor: Karel Malý (1994-)
Kvestor: Jan Winkler
International Relations: Jaroslav Vacek
Founded: 1348, 1882, 1918, 1945
F: Mathematics and Physics; Natural Sciences; Law; Philosophy and Letters; Medicine I; Medicine II; Medicine III; General Medicine (Plzeň); General Medicine (Hradec Králové); Pharmacy (Hradec Králové); Education; Physical Education and Sport; Catholic Theology; Goose Theology; Gospel Theology; Social Sciences.

*Czech Technical University
[České vysoké učení technické]
Zíkova 4, 166 35 Praha 6
Tel: +42(2) 332-1111
Fax: +42(2) 332-7493
E-Mail: hanzl@vc.cvut.cz
Rektor: Stanislav Hanzl (1991-94)
Kvestor: Zdeněk Vospěl
International Relations: Jan Hlavička
Founded: 1707, 1803, 1864
F: Civil Engineering; Mechanical Engineering; Electrical Engineering; Nuclear Science and Physical Engineering; Architecture; Transport.

J.E. Purkyně University
[Univerzita Jana Evangelisty Purkyně]
České mládeže 8, 400 11 Ústí nad Labem
Tel: +42(47) 45241
Fax: +42(47) 43010
Rektor: Jan Kopka (1994-)
Kvestor: Vladislav Trefil
International Relations: Vice-Rektor, Josef říha
Founded: 1964, 1977
F: Pedagogy; Environmental Studies; Social Studies and Economics.

*Masaryk University
[Masarykova univerzita]
Žerotinovo Nám. 9, 601-77 Brno
Tel: +42(5) 4221-5183
Fax: +42(5) 4212-8266
E-Mail: schmidt@rect.muni.cz
Cable: mu brno
Rektor: Eduard Schmidt (1994-)
Kvestor: František Gale
International Relations: Vice-Rektor, Jiři Šramet
Founded: 1919, 1945, 1989
F: Natural Science; Medicine; Law; Education; Economics and Administration; Philosophy.

Palacký University
[Univerzita Palackého]
Křížkovského 8, 771 47 Olomouc
Tel: +42(68) 5508
Fax: +42(68) 264-16
E-Mail: jarab@risc.upol.cz
Rektor: Josef Jařab (1994-)
Kvestor: Jiři Jirka
International Relations: Vice-Rektor, Jaroslav Macháček
Founded: 1573, 1946
F: Medicine; Natural Sciences; Philosophy; Education; Theology; Body Culture; Law.
Ce: Computer; Optics L.

Silesian University
[Slezská univerzita]
Bezručovo nám 13, 746 01 Opava
Tel: +42(653) 218-030
Fax: +42(653) 218-019
Rektor: Martin Černohorský (1994-)
Kvestor: Jaroslav Kania
International Relations: Vice-Rektor, Zdeněk Stuchlík
Founded: 1991

F: Philosophy and Natural Sciences; Business Sciences.

Technical University
[Vysoké učení technické]
Kounicova 67a, 601 90 Brno
Tel: +42(5) 4132-1217
Fax: +42(5) 4121-1309
E-Mail: vavrin ro.vutrb.cz
Rektor: Petr Vavřín (1994-)
Kvestor: Alexander Černý
International Relations: Vice-Rektor, Helena Zemánková
Founded: 1849, 1945
F: Civil Engineering; Mechanical Engineering; Electrical Engineering; Technology (Zlín); Chemistry; Business Sciences; Plastic Arts.
D: Architecture.

Technical University
[Vysoká škola strojní a textilní]
Hálkova 6, 461 17 Liberec
Tel: +42(48) 254-41
Fax: +42(48) 233-17
E-Mail: zdenek.kovar vslib.cz
Rektor: Zdeněk Kovář
Kvestor: Petr Strádal
International Relations: Vice-Dean, Radko Kovář
Founded: 1953
F: Textile Engineering; Mechanical Engineering; Education; Business Administration.

*Technical University Ostrava
Třída 17 Listopadu, 708 33 Ostrava-Poruba
Tel: +42(69) 6991-111
Fax: +42(69) 691-8507
E-Mail: tomas.cermak@vsb.cz
Telex: 52568 vsbos
Rector: Tomáš Čermák (1994-)
Kvestor: Stanislav Dziob
International Relations: Vice-Rektor, Václav Roubíček
Founded: 1716, 1763, 1770, 1894
F: Mining Engineering and Geology; Metallurgy; Electrotechnicsand Informatics; Economics; Engineering.

University of Agriculture
[Vysoká škola zemědělská]
Zemědělská 1, 613 00 Brno
Tel: +42(5) 4521-1838
Fax: +42(5) 4521-1128
E-Mail: rektor pok0.vs2br.cz
Rektor: Pavel Jelínek (1991-93)
Kvestor: V.L. Bulla
Founded: 1919
F: Agriculture; Agricultural Economics; Forestry; Horticulture (Lednice, Moldavia).

University of Agriculture
[Vysoká škola zemědělská]
Kamýcká 129, 165 21 Praha-Suchdol 6
Tel: +42(2) 338-1111
Fax: +42(2) 338-2063
E-Mail: hron pefl.vsz.cz
Rektor: Jan Hron (1994-)
Kvestor: Miloš Frýbort
International Relations: Vice-Rektor, Pavel Kovář
Founded: 1906
F: Agriculture; Operations and Economics; Forestry; Technics.

University of Economics
[Vysoká škola ekonomická]
Nám. Winstona Churchilla 4, 130 67 Praha 3
Tel: +42(2) 2409-5111
Fax: +42(2) 2422-0657
E-Mail: seger@vse.cz
Rektor: Jan Seger (1994-)
Kvestor: Jiří Kříž
International Relations: Vice-Rektor, Jaroslava Durčáková
Founded: 1949, 1953
F: Finance and Accounting; International Relations; Company Commerce; Information and Statistics; National Economy.

University of Ostrava
[Ostravská univerzita]
Dvořákova 7, 701 03 Ostrava
Tel: +42(69) 622-6066
Fax: +42(69) 622-2803
E-Mail: hubacek@oudec.osu.cz
Rektor: Jaroslav Hubacek (1994-)
Kvestor: Ladislav Kudela
International Relations: Vice-Rektor, Miroslav Havrlant
Founded: 1953, 1959, 1991
F: Natural Sciences; Philosophy; Pedagogy; Health and Social Care.

University of Pardubice
[Univerzita Pardubice]
Nám Čs. Legií 565, 532 10 Pardubice
Tel: +42(40) 513-221
Fax: +42(40) 514-530
E-Mail: rektor@hlb.upce.cz
Cable: všcht pardubice
Rektor: Ladislav Kudláček (1994-)
Kvestor: Viří Maršálek
International Relations: Vice-Rektor, Jaroslav Churáček
Founded: 1950
F: Chemical Technology; Economics and Administration; Transport.

University of South Bohemia
[Jihočeská univerzita]
Ul. Branišovska 31, 370 05 České Budějovice
Tel: +42(38) 402-20
Fax: +42(38) 402-20
E-Mail: divisek@jcu.cz
Rektor: Jirí Divíšek (1991-94)
Kvestor: Václav Přibáň

International Relations: Vice-Rektor, František Sehnal
Founded: 1991
F: Agriculture; Biological Science; Education; Health and Social Care; Theology.

University of Veterinary Sciences and Pharmaceutics
[Vysoká škola veterinární a farmaceutická]
Palackého 1-3, 612 42 Brno
Tel: +42(5) 4132-1107
Fax: +42(5) 4121-1151
E-Mail: zima@csbrmu 11.bitnet
Rektor: Stanislav Zima (1994-)
Kvestor: Oldřich Sova
International Relations: Vice-Rektor, Josef Illek
Founded: 1918
F: Veterinary Medicine; Veterinary Hygiene and Ecology; Pharmaceutics.

University of West Bohemia
[Západočeská univerzita]
Americká 42, 306 14 Plzeň
Tel: +42(19) 355-51
Fax: +42(19) 220-019
Telex: 154 292
Rektor: Jiří Holenda (1994-)
Kvestor: Josef Průša
International Relations: Vice-Rektor, Jiří Pinkner
Founded: 1991
F: Mechanical Engineering; Electrical Engineering; Applied Sciences; Economics; Education; Law.

OTHER INSTITUTIONS

Akademie múzickych umení
Tržiště 18, Praha 1
Tel: +42(2) 530-949
Fax: +42(2) 530-501
Rektor: Jaroslav Vostrý (1994-)
Kvestor: Tamara Čuříková
International Relations: Vice-Rektor, Peter Toperczer
Founded: 1945, 1951
Music; Theater Art; Film and Television Art.

Akademie výtvarných umění
U Akademie 4, Praha 7
Tel: +42(2) 373-641
Fax: +42(2) 375-781
Rektor: Milan Knižák (1994-)
Kvestor: Vladimír Kalugin
International Relations: Vice-Rektor, Jiří Kotalík
Founded: 1896
Fine Arts.

Janáčkova akademie múzických umění
Komenského nám. 6, Brno
Tel: +42(5) 4232-1307
Fax: +42(5) 4221-3286
Rektor: Alena Štěpánková-Veselá (1994-)
Kvestor: Eduard Gondek
International Relations: Vice-Rektor, Arnošt Parsch
Founded: 1947
Music; Theatre.

Vysoká skola chemicko-technologická
Technická 5, Praha 6
Tel: +42(2) 332-1111
Fax: +42(2) 2431-1082
E-Mail: rse@vscht.cz
Telex: 122744 vsch c
Rektor: Ivan Stibor (1994-)
Kvestor: Jiří Pelc
International Relations: Vice-Kvestor, Josef Koubek
Founded: 1953
Chemical Technology.

Vysoká škola umělecko-průmyslová
Nám J. Palacha 80, Praha 1
Tel: +42(2) 2481-1172
Fax: +42(2) 232-6884
Rektor: Josef Hlaváček (1984-)
Kvestor: Jirí Halík
International Relations: Vice-Rektor, Jiří Šetlík,
Applied Arts
Founded: 1946

Vysoká skola veterinárnía Farmaceutická
Palackého 1, Brno
Tel: +42(5) 4132-1107
Fax: +42(5) 4121-1151
E-Mail: zima@csbrmv 11.bitnet
Telex: 63039
Rektor: Stanislav Zima (1994-)
Kvestor: Oldõicm Sova
International Relations: Vice-Rektor, Josef Illek
Founded: 1918
Veterinary Medicine; Veterinary Hygiene and Ecology; Pharmaceutics.

Vysoká skola zemědelská
Kamycká ul. 129 Suchdol, Praha 6
Tel: +42(2) 338-1111
Fax: +42(2) 338-2063
E-Mail: hron@pefl.vsz.cz
Telex: 122323 vszp c
Rektor: Jan Hron (1994-)
Kvestor: Miloš Frýbort
International Relations: Vice-Rektor, Pavel Kolář
Founded: 1906
Agriculture.

NATIONAL ACADEMIC BODIES

Czech Ministry of Education, Youth and Physical Education
[Ministerstvo školství, mládeže a těcovýchovy]
Karmelitská 7, 11812 Praha 1
Tel: +42(2) 531-651
Fax: +42(2) 531-322
Minister: Ivan Pilip (1994-)
Secretary: Vladimír Ševela
International Relations: Deputy Minister, Emanuel Ondráček

Czech Rectors' Conference
[Česká Konference Rektorů (ČKR)]
Masaryk University, Žerotínovo nám9, 601 77
Tel: +42(5) 4214-8270
Fax: +42(5) 4212-8272
E-Mail: crc.secretary@muni.cz
President: Stanislav Hanzl, Rector, Czech Technical University
Secretary-General: Marie Fojtíková

Czech Commission for Unesco
[Zeská Komise pro Spolvpráci s Unesco]
Toskánsky palác, Hradčanské nám. 5, 11800 Praha 1
Tel: +42(2) 3115581
Telex: 123323
Cable: unescoczechoslovak prague
Secretary-General: Jaroslava Moserová

DENMARK

UNIVERSITIES AND TECHNICAL UNIVERSITIES

Academy of Music
[Nordjysk Musikkonservatorium]
Ryesgade 52, 9000 Aalborg
Tel: +45 812-7744
Music.

*Aalborg University
[Aalborg Universitetscenter]
Postbox 159, 9100 Aalborg
Tel: +45 9815-8522
Fax: +45 9815-1522
Telex: 69790 aub dk
Rector: Sven Caspersen (1976-)
Universitetsdirektør: Peter Lykke
Founded: 1971
F: Social Sciences; Technology and Science; Humanities.

The Aarhus School of Business
[Handelshøjskolen i Aarhus]
Fuglesangs Allé 4, 8210 Aarhus V
Tel: +45 86-15-55-88
Fax: +45 86-15-46-79
Rector: Morten Balling (1993-97)
Administrator: Jan Halle
Founded: 1939
F: Business Administration; Modern Languages.

Royal Academy of Music, Aarhus
[Det jyske Musikkonservatorium]
Fuglesangs Allé 26, 8210 Aarhus V
Tel: +45 89-48-33-88
Rector: Erik Bach (1992-)
Administrator: Sander Angelsø
Founded: 1927
Music.

*University of Aarhus
[Aarhus Universitet]
Ndr. Ringgade 1, 8000 Aarhus C
Tel: +45 8942-1166
Fax: +45 8619-7029
Rector: Henning Lehmann (1983-98)
Universitets direktør: Stig Møller
Founded: 1928, 1934
F: Arts; Health Science; Social Sciences; Theology.

Copenhaghen Business School
[Handelshøjskolen i København]
Struenseegade 7-9, 2200 København N
Tel: +45 38-15-38-15
Fax: +45 38-15-20-15
Rector: Finn Junge-Jensen (1987-)
Administrationschief: Jakob Voltelen
Founded: 1917
F: Economics and Business Administration; Modern Languages.

*University of Copenhagen
[Københavns Universitet]
Nørregade 10, Postboks 2177, 1017 København K
Tel: +45 45-35-32-26-26
Fax: +45 45-35-32-26-28
E-Mail: kjm@adm.ku.dk
Telex: 22221 unicop dk
Cable: unicop
Rector: Kjeld Møllgaard (1994-97)
Universitetsdirektør: Peter Plenge
Founded: 1479
F: Theology; Law; Health Sciences; Humanities; Science.

The Royal Danish Academy of Fine Arts, School of Architecture
[Det kongelige danske Kunstakademi, Arkitektskolen]
Kongens Nytorv 1, 1050 København K
Tel: +45 33-12-68-60
Fax: +45 33-12-75-98
Rector: Ebbe Melgaard (1990-)
Administrator: Dorte Andersen
Founded: 1754
S: Restoration and Building Archaeology; Building Science; Building Design; Town and Landscape Planning; Design; Visual Communication.

The Royal Danish Academy of Fine Arts, Schools of Visual Art
[Det kongelige danske Kunstakademi, Billedkunstkolen]
Kongens Nytorv 1, 1050 København K
Tel: +45 33-12-75-98
Rector: Else Marie Bukdahl (1985-)
Administrator: Dorte Andersen
Visual Art.

The Royal Danish Academy of Music
[Det kongelige danske Musikkonservatorium]
Niels Brocks Gade 1, 1574 København V
Tel: +45 33-12-42-74
Fax: +45 33-14-09-11
Rector: Steen Pade (1993-)
Administrator: Bjarne Østergård
Founded: 1867
Music.

Engineering Academy of Denmark
[Danmarks Ingeniørakademi]
Bygning 101, 2800 Lyngby
Tel: +45 45-87-75-00
Fax: +45 42- 88-17-99
Telex: 37529 dth diad
Rector: Hans Peter Jensen
Administrationschef: Henrik Moltke
Founded: 1957
D: *Chemical Engineering; Mechanical and Production Engineering; Civil Engineering; Electrical Engineering; Food Science and Technology.*

*Technical University of Denmark
[Danmarks Tekniske Universtit]
Anker Engelundsvej, 2800, Lyngby
Tel: +45 42-88-22-22
Fax: +45 42-88-17-99
Telex: 37529 dthdia dk
Rector: Hans Peter Jensen (1986-95)
Administrationschef: Henrik Moltkeer
Founded: 1829
D: *Chemical Engineering; Electrical Engineering; Civil and Construction Engineering; Mechanical Engineering.*

Funen Academy of Music
[Det fynske Musikkonservatorium]
Islandsgade 2, 5000 Odense
Tel: +45 66-11-06-63
Music.

*Odense University
[Odense Universitet]
Campusvej 55, 5230 Odense M
Tel: +45 66-158-600
Fax: +45 66-158-428
Telex: Oubibl-59918
Rector: Henrik Tvarnø (1993-97)
Universitetsdirektør: Helge Muhle Larsen
Founded: 1966
F: *Natural Sciences; Health Sciences; Humanities.*
S: *Business and Economics.*

*Roskilde University
[Roskilde Universitetscenter]
Marbjergvej 35, Postbox 260, 4000 Roskilde
Tel: +45 46-75-77-11
Fax: +45 46-75-74-01
Rector: Henrik Toft Jensen (1989-98)
Universitetsdirektør: Erik Ebbe
Founded: 1970
F: *Humanities; Natural Sciences; Social Sciences.*

Southern Denmark Business School
[Handelshøjskole Syd]
Grundtvigs Allé 150, 6400 Sønderborg
Tel: +45 74-43-42-25
Fax: 74-43-01-93
Rector: Jens Hohw (1993-)
Administrator: N.H. Assing
Founded: 1984
Business Economics; Business Language.

West Jutland Academy of Music
[Vestjysk Musikkonservatorium]
Islandsgade 50, 6700 Esbjerg
Music.

OTHER INSTITUTIONS

Arkitektskolen i Aarhus
8000 Aarhus C
Tel: +45 13-08-22
Fax: +45 86-13-06-45
Rector: Gøsta Knudsen (1991-96)
Administrator: Ole Graah
Founded: 1965
F: *Building Design; Urban Design; Landscape and Garden Design; Restoration of Houses and Parts of Towns; Industrial Design; Furniture and Interior Design.*

Danmarks Biblioteksskole
Birketinget 6, 2300 København S
Tel: +45 31-58-60-66
Fax: +45 32-84-02-01
Rector: Ole Harbo
Administrator: Edvard Jeppesen
Founded: 1956
Library Sciences.

Danmarks Farmaceutiske Højskole
Universitetsparken 2, 2100 København
Tel: +45 31-37-08-50
Fax: +45 35-37-57-44
Rector: Birthe Jensen (1988-97)
Administrator: Bjørn Andersen
Founded: 1892
Pharmacy.

Danmarks Højskole for Legemsøvelser
Nørre Allé 51, 2200 København N
Tel: +45 31-39-25-55
Fax: +45 35-36-24-14
Rector: Ivar Berg-Sørensen
Founded: 1911
Physical Education.

Danmarks Jordemoderskole, Afdelingen Aalborg
Vesterbro, 21 D, 9000 Aalborg
Tel: +45 98-11-05-88
Fax: +45 98-11-02-00
Rector: Lisbeth Drevs
Midwifery.

Danmarks Jordemoderskole, Afdelingen i København
Rigshospitaletafsnit 72-1-1, Tagensovej, 18, 2100 København N
Tel: +45 35-45-72-16
Fax: +45 35-36-18-10
Telex: 15784 rhblod dk
Rector: Bente Zebitz
Midwifery.

Danmarks Journalisthojskole
Olof Palmes Alle 11, 8200 Aarhus N
Tel: +45 86-16-11-22
Fax: +45 86-16-89-10
Rector: Kim Minke (1994-)
Administrator: Mogens Schmidt
Journalism.

Danmarks Laererhøjskole Emdrupborg
Emdrupvej 101, 2400 Kobenhavn NV
Tel: +45 31-69-66-33
Fax: +45 39-66-00-81
Rector: Tom Ploug Olsen
Konstitueret Administrationschef: Bente Lomholt
Founded: 1856
Education.

Den kongelige Verterinaer- og Landbohøjskole
Bülowsvej 13, 1870 Frederiksberg C
Tel: +45 35-28-28-28
Fax: +45 35-28-20-79
Rector: Bent Schmidt-Nielsen (1987-)
Administrationschef: Ernst Gravesen
Founded: 1858
F: Veterinary Science; Agriculture.

Den Sociale Højskole i Aarhus
Stenvej 4, 8270 Højbjerg
Tel: +45 86-27-66-22
Fax: +45 86-27-74-76
Rector: Christen Christensen
Social Work.

Den Sociale Højskole i Esbjerg
Storegade 182, 6705 Esbjerg
Tel: +45 75-13-35-00
Fax: +45 75-12-09-04
Rector: Grethe Erichsen
Social Work.

Den Sociale Højskole i København
Randersgade 10, 2100 København
Tel: +45 1-42-46-01
Fax: +45 31-42-07-61
Rector: Carl Einar Jørgensen
Social Work.

Den Sociale Højskole i Odense
Campusvej 55, 5230 Odense M
Tel: +45 66-15-86-00
Fax: +45 65-93-09-34
Rector: Lise Ferch
Social Work.

Ingeniørhøjskolen, Aarhus Teknikum
Dalgas Avenue, 2, 9 8000 Aarhus C
Tel: +45 86-13-62-11
Fax: +45 86-13-64-88
Rector: H. Svanhede Pedersen
Administrator: Aage Jjørnager
Engineering.

Ingeniørhøjskolen, Esbjerg Teknikum
Niels Bohrsvej, 8, 6700 Esbjerg
Tel: +45 79-12-76-66
Fax: +45 75-45-36-43
Rector: Kurt Kallestrup
Administrator: P. Bundgaard
Engineering.

Ingeniørhøjskolen, Haslev Teknikum
Braabyvej 45, 4690 Haslev
Tel: +45 56-31-14-00
Fax: +45 56-31-10-33
Rector: Finn Torp
Administrator: E. Keincke
Engineering.

Ingeniørhøjskolen, Helsingør Teknikum
Rasmus Knudsensvej, 50, 3000 Helsingør
Tel: +45 49-21-66-22
Fax: +45 49-21-33-24
Rector: Gert Christoffersen
Engineering.

Ingeniørhøjskolen, Horsens Teknikum
Chr. M. Ostergaardsvej 4, 8700 Horsens
Tel: +45 75-62-88-11
Fax: +45 75-62-64-56
Rector: Poul Holm Nielsen
Administrator: Povl Thomsen
Engineering.

Ingeniørhøjskolen, Københavns Teknikum
Lautripvang 15, 2750 Ballerup
Tel: +45 44-97-80-88
Fax: +45 44-97-81-72
Rector: Verner Davgaard
Administrator: Niels Wohlert
Engineering.

Ingeniørhøjskolen, Odense Teknikum
Niels Bohr Allé 1, 5230 Odense M
Tel: +45 66-13-08-27
Fax: +45 66-13-48-27
Rector: Bent Poulsen
Administrator: Flemming Johansen
Engineering.

Ingeniørhøjskolen, Sønderborg Teknikum
Voldgade 5, 6400 Sønderborg
Tel: +45 74-42-55-50
Fax: +45 74-43-17-35
Rector: K. Clemen Jørgensen
Administrator: Mathias Madsen
Engineering.

Ingeniørhøjskolen, Vestjysk Teknikum
Valdemarsvej, 339, 7400 Herning
Tel: +45 97-21-03-88
Fax: +45 97-12-98-97
Rector: Poul Holm Nielsen
Administrator: Mathias Madsen
Engineering.

Midtjysk Handelscenter
Gl. Landevej 2, 7400 Herning
Tel: +45 97-22-25-44
Fax: +45 97-21-33-87
Business Studies.

Rytmisk Musikkonservatorium
Dr. Prieones Vej, 3, 1854 Frederiksberg C
Music.

Socialpadagogisk Højskole
Kastelsvej 60, 2100 København
Tel: +45 31-42-34-34
Fax: +45 31-42-14-85
Rector: Elsa Schmidt
Social Education.

NATIONAL ACADEMIC BODIES

Ministry of Education
[Undervisningsministeriet]
Frederiksholms Kanal 26, 1220 København K.
Tel: +45 33-92-50-00
Fax: +45 33-92-55-47
Minister: Ole Vig Jensen

Ministry of Education, Department of Higher Education
[Undervisningsministeriet Universitetsafdelingen]
Frederiksholms Kanal 28, 1220 København K
Tel: +45 33-92-55-00

Ministry of Education, Department of International Relations
[Undervisningministeriet, Der Internationale afdeling]
Frederiksholms Kanal 25, 1220 København K.
Tel: +45 33-92-50-00
Fax: +45 33-95-55-67
Telex: 16243

Ministry of Research
[Forskningsministeriet]
H. C. Andersens Boulevard 40, 1553 København V
Tel: +45 33-11-43-00

Danish Ministry of Cultural Affairs
[Kulturministeriet]
Nybrogade 2, 1203 København K
Tel: +45 33-92-33-70

The Danish Rectors' Conference
[Rektorkollegiet]
Frederiksholms Kanal 26, 1220 København K
Tel: +45 33-92-53-00
Fax: +45 33-92-50-75
Telex: 16243 rks dk
Rector: Hans Peter Jensen
Secretary-General: Ellen Hansen
Founded: 1967

The Danish Federation of Professional Associations
[Akademikernes Centralorganisation (AC)]
Norre Voldgade 29, 1358 København K
Tel: +45 33-12-85-40
Fax: +45 33-93-85-40
Chairman: Alex Nielsen
Director: Jorgen Friis Christensen
Founded: 1972

Danish National Commission for Unesco
[Den Danske Unesco National Kommission]
Frederiksholms Kanal 21, 1220 København K
Tel: +45 33-92-5000
Fax: +45 33-92-55-67
Telex: 112-112
Cable: daunesco copenhagen
Chairman: Erik W. Thulstrop
Secretary-General: Ernst Goldschmidt

DOMINICAN REPUBLIC

UNIVERSITIES

Technological University Azua
[Universidad Tecnológica del Sur]
c/Duarte 46, Azua
Founded: 1984
Education; Technical Studies; Agricultural Engineering; Accountancy; Administration; Nursing.

Dominican Adventist University Bonao
[Universidad Adventista Dominicana]
Apartado postal 770, Sonador, Bonao
Tel: +1809(525) 3533
Founded: 1982
D: Sciences; Psychology; Business Administration; Theology; Education; Agronomy; Secretarial Studies.
Ce: Research.

195

Cibao Technological University
[Universidad Tecnológica del Cibao]
Aut. Duarte, Km. 1 1/2, Avenida Universitaria,
Apartado postal 401, La Vega
Tel: + 1809 573-3863
Fax: + 1809 573-6194
Rector: Ramón Benito Angeles Fernández
Secretario General: Juan Homaldo Veras
Founded: 1983
S: Humanities and Education; Law; Agronomy;
Computer Science; Bioanalysis; Secretarial
Studies; Engineering and Architecture;
Technology; Dentistry; Medicine; Sciences;
Administration and Accountancy.

University Nordestana San Franciso de Macorís
[Universidad Nordestana]
P.O. Box 239, San Francisco de Macorís
Tel: + 1809 588-3239
Founded: 1978
F: Medicine; Agriculture; Law; Economics and
Social Sciences; Engineering.
D: Extension.

Central University of the East San Pedro de Macorís
[Universidad Central del Este]
Avenida Circunvalación, San Pedro de Macorís
Tel: + 1809 529-3562
F: Medicine; Law and Political Science;
Economics and Social Sciences; Engineering and
Architecture; Humanities.

*Catholic University 'Madre y Maestra' Santiago
[Universidad Católica 'Madre y Maestra']
Autopista Duarte Km 1/2, Santiago
Tel: + 1809 583-0441
Fax: + 1809 581-7750
Telex: 346-1032
Rector: Mgr. Agripino Núñez Collado
Founded: 1962
S: Engineering; Health Sciences; Science and
Humanities; Social and Administration Sciences;
Hotel Administration.
D: Lifelong Education.

Technological University of Santiago
[Universidad Tecnológica de Santiago]
Apartado postal 21423, Santiago
Tel: + 1809 582-7156
Fax: + 1809 582-7644
Founded: 1974
F: Economics and Social Sciences; Engineering
and Architecture; Secretarial Studies; Languages;
Psychology.

Autonomous University of Santo Domingo
[Universidad Autónoma de Santo Domingo]
Avenida Alma Mater, Ciudad Universitaria, Santo
Domingo
Tel: + 1809 533-1104
Fax: + 1809 533-1106
Cable: uniausd
Rector: Julio Ravelo Astacio
Founded: 1538
F: Humanities; Science; Economics and Social
Sciences; Law; Engineering and Architecture;
Medicine; Agriculture and Veterinary Science.
C: Basic Studies (for first year students).

Catholic University of Santo Domingo
[Universidad Católica de Santo Domingo]
c/Santo Domingo 3, La Julia, Santo Domingo
Founded: 1984
D: Humanities; Social Communication;
Theology; Education.

Dominican University College of Professional Studies Santo Domingo
[Universidad Colegio Dominicano de Estudio
Profesionales]
Prol. Independencia, Km. 9 1/2, Carretera
Sánchez, Santo Domingo
Founded: 1985
F: Economics and Social Sciences; Humanities;
Science and Technology; Juridical Studies;
Agriculture; Health Sciences.

Dominican University O&M Santo Domingo
[Universidad Dominicana O&M]
Apartado postal 509, Avenida Independencia,
Santo Domingo
Founded: 1978

National University 'Pedro Henrúquez Ureña' Santo Domingo
[Universidad Nacional 'Pedro Henríquez Ureña']
Avenida John F. Kennedy, Km. 5 1/2, Santo
Domingo
Tel: + 1809 565-6651
Rector: Jaime A. Viñas Román
F: Science; Humanities, Education and
Sciences; Health Sciences; Engineering;
Architecture and Arts; Agriculture and Veterinary
Science.
I: Biomedical Sciences.

University 'APEC' Santo Domingo
[Universidad 'APEC']
Avenida Bolívar 173, Santo Domingo
Tel: + 1809 687-0021
Fax: + 1809 685-5581
Chancellor: Nicolás Pichardo
Academic Vice-Chancellor: Baltasar González
Camilo
Founded: 1965, 1983
F: Administration; Humanities and Science.
S: Languages; Technology; Computer Science;
Arts; Law; Business; Accountancy; Banking and
Economics; Tourism; Marketing.

University of Dentistry Santo Domingo
[Universidad Odontológica Dominicana]
Prol. 27 de Febrero, Las Caobas, Santo Domingo
Founded: 1985
Dentistry.

University Eugenio María de Hostos Santo Domingo
[Universidad Eugenio María de Hostos]
Avenida Abraham Lincoln 753, Santo Domingo
Tel: + 1809 532-2495
Founded: 1981
*F: Health Sciences; Science and Technology;
Economics and Administration; Humanities and
Social Sciences.*

University Iberomericana Santo Domingo
[Universidad Iberomericana]
Apartado postal 1600, Avenida Francia 129, Santo
Domingo
Founded: 1982
*F: Architecture and Art; General Studies;
Economics; Health Sciences; Agriculture.*

University Interamericana Santo Domingo
[Universidad Interamericana]
Dr. Baez 4, Santo Domingo
Founded: 1982
*Communication Studies; Psychology; Public
Relations; Statistics; Sociology; Education;
Computer Sciences; Tourism; Agricultural
Administration; Administration; Secretarial
Studies; Business Administration; Law.*

University Ulises Francisco Espaillat Santo Domingo
[Universidad Ulises Francisco Espaillat]
c/Rafael A. Sánchez 52, Apartado postal 22432,
Ciudad Santo Domingo
Founded: 1986
Political and Social Sciences.

OTHER INSTITUTIONS

Instituto Nacional de Ciencias Exactas
c/Conde, Edificio Baquero, Apartado postal 1796,
Santo Domingo
Founded: 1974
Exact Sciences.

Instituto Superior de Agricultura
La Herradura, Apartado postal 166, Santiago
Tel: + 1809 582-6621
Founded: 1986
Agriculture.

Instituto Técnico Superior
c/Juan Sánchez Ramírez 23, Gazcue, Apartado
postal 711-2, Santo Domingo
Founded: 1987
Technical Studies.

Instituto Tecnológico de Santo Domingo
Avenida de Los Próceres Galá, Apartado postal
249, Santo Domingo
Tel: + 1809 567-9271
Telex: 4181 intec law
Founded: 1973
Technology.

Instituto Tecnológico del Cibao Oriental
Cotuí
Founded: 1983
Technology.

NATIONAL ACADEMIC BODIES

State Secretariat for Education, Fine Arts and Culture
[Secretaría de Estado de Educación, Bellas Artes
y Cultos]
Avenida Máximo Gómez, Santo Domingo
Tel: + 1809 688-4600
Fax: + 1809 682-0788
Secretary of State: Jacqueline Malagón

National Council for Higher Education
[Consejo Nacional de Educacion Superior
CONES)]
Calle Vicente Celestino Duarte 19, Santo
Domingo
Tel: + 1809 687-1684
Secreario Ejecutivo: José Andres Aibar

Dominican Association of University Rectors
[Asociación Dominicana de Rectores de
Universidades (ADRU)]
Calle Luperón esq. Hostos, Ciudad Colonial,
Santo Domingo
Tel: + 1809 689-0003
Fax: + 1809 921-3559
Chairman: Jesús María de Jesús Moya
Secretary: Gertrudys de Mieses
Founded: 1981

Dominican National Commission for Unesco
[Comisión Nacional Dominicana de la Unesco]
Secretaría de Estado de Educación, Bellas Artes
y Cultos, Avenida Máximo Gómez, Santo
Domingo
Tel: + 1809 689-9410
Fax: + 1809 682-0788
Cable: comic unesco secuducacion santo
domingo
Presidenta ex-officio: Jacqueline Malagón,
Secretary of State for Education
Secretaria General: Luisa Lamouth de Robles

ECUADOR

UNIVERSITIES AND TECHNICAL UNIVERSITIES

PUBLIC INSTITUTIONS

Technical University of Ambato
[Universidad Técnica de Ambato]
Ciuddela Ingahurco, Apartado de Correos 334,
Ambato
Tel: +593(2) 822191
Founded: 1959
F: *Administration and Management;
Accountancy and Auditing; Education and
Development; Engineering.*

University of Azuay
[Universidad del Azuay]
Ciudad Universitaria, Azuay
Tel: +593 828878
Fax: +593 817995
Rector: Juan Cordero
Founded: 1990
F: *Philosophy; Administration; Design; Science
and Technology; Law and Social Sciences.*

Technical University of Babahoyo
[Universidad Técnica de Babahoyo]
Via Flores, Apartado 66, Babahoyo
Founded: 1971
F: *Education; Agriculture.*

State University of Bolivar
[Universidad Estatal de Bolivar]
Apartado postal 92, Guaranda
Tel: +593 980121
Fax: +593 980123
Rector: Gabriel Galarza L.
Founded: 1989
F: *Administration; Agriculture; Medicine;
Education.*

Institute of Technology of Chimborazo
[Escuela Superior Politécnica de Chimborazo]
Kilómetro 1 Panamericana Sur, P.O. Box 4703,
Ríobamba
Tel: +593(2) 961969
Rector: Rodrigo Jaramillo Garcés (1987-)
Founded: 1969, 1973
F: *Agriculture; Animal Husbandry; Dietetics and
Nutrition; Mechanical Engineering; Science;
Business Administration; Chemistry; Physical
Education; Physics and Mathematics.*

University of Cuenca
[Universidad de Cuenca]
Avenida 12 de Abril, Apartado de Correos 168,
Cuenca
Tel: +593(7) 824365
Founded: 1868
F: *Law; Medicine; Engineering; Philosophy,
Letters, and Education; Chemistry; Dentistry;
Architecture; Economics; Fine Arts.*
D: *Languages.*
I: *Physical Education.*

Agricultural University of Ecuador
[Universidad Agraria del Ecuador]
Quito
Agriculture.

Technical University of Esmeraldas
[Universidad Técnica de Esmeraldas]
Avenida Nuevo Horizonte, Esmeraldas
Founded: 1970
F: *Agriculture; Education; Administration.*
I: *Cultural Studies; Scientific Research.*

Institute of Technology of the Littoral, Guayaquil
[Escuela Superior Politécnica del Litoral
Guayaquil]
Calle Rocafuerte y Loja, Guayaquil
Tel: +593(4) 303733
Cable: Espol
Founded: 1958
D: *Electrical Engineering; Mechanical
Engineering; Naval Engineering; Geological,
Mining, and Petroleum Engineeering.*
I: *Physics; Mathematics; Chemistry; General
Studies.*
S: *Nursing; Communications Technology.*

University of Guayaquil
[Universidad de Guayaquil]
Calle Chile 900, Apartado 471, Guayaquil
Tel: +593(4) 325432
Telex: 4179 uguaye-ed
Founded: 1867, 1897
F: *Law and Social Sciences; Medicine;
Mathematics and Physics; Philosophy, Letters
and Education; Agricultural Engineering;
Chemistry; Dentistry; Natural Sciences;
Economics; Architecture; Chemical Engineering;
Social Communication; Industrial Engineering;
Psychology; Veterinary Medicine and Animal
Husbandry; Administration; Physical Education;
Diplomatic Studies.*

Technical University of the North, Ibarra
[Universidad Técnica del Norte]
Avenida Pérez Guerrero y Olmedo, Casilla 199,
Ibarra
Tel: +593 952833
Rector: Antonio Posso
Founded: 1986
F: *Education; Administration; Applied Sciences;
Textile Engineering; Health Sciences.*

National University of Loja
[Universidad Nacional de Loja]
Ciudadela Universitaria 'La Argilia', Loja
Tel: +593(4) 960252
Telex: 4135-unloja-ed
Founded: 1859
F: *Jurisprudence; Veterinary Science;
Agriculture; Medicine; Administration;
Philosophy, Letters and Education; Science and
Technology; Arts.*
I: *Languages.*
U: *Popular.*

Technical University of Machala
[Universidad Técnica de Machala]
Calle Tarque entre Sucre y 9 de Octubre,
Machala
Founded: 1969
F: Agriculture and Veterinary Medicine;
Chemistry; Sociology; Administration and
Accountancy; Civil Engineering.

Technical University of Manabí
[Universidad Técnica de Manabí]
Ciudadela Universitaria, Portoviejo, Manabí
Tel: +(593)652677
Founded: 1952
F: Mathematics, Physics, and Chemistry;
Agricultural Engineering; Agriculture; Veterinary
Medicine; Social Sciences and Education;
Administration and Economics; Nursing.

State Technical University of Quevedo
[Universidad Técnica Estatal de Quevedo]
Vía a Quito s/n, Casilla 74, Quevedo, Los Rios
Tel: +593(7)51430
Founded: 1984
S: Forestry Engineering; Animal Livestock
Engineering; Agro-Business Administration; Soils
and Water Management Technology; Agricultural
Mechanization Technology.
I: Agricultural Research.

Central University of Ecuador Quito
[Universidad Central del Ecuador]
Avenida América y Alfredo Pérez Guerrero,
Apartado 166, Quito
Tel: +593(2) 524714
Founded: 1586, 1622, 1786, 1897
F: Law; Medicine; Engineering; Philosophy,
Letters and Education; Economics;
Administration; Agriculture; Veterinary Medicine
and Animal Husbandry; Chemistry and
Pharmacy; Dentistry; Architecture and Town
Planning; Fine Arts; Psychology.

National University of Technology Quito
[Escuela Politécnica Nacional Quito]
Calle Isabel la Católica y Vientimilla, Apartado
Correos 2759, Quito
Tel: +593(2) 507126
Fax: +593(2) 567848
Telex: 22650 Espona
Rector: Alfonso Espinosa Ramón (1990-95)
Founded: 1870, 1935
F: Chemical Engineering; Electrical
Engineering; Mechanical Engineering; Civil
Engineering; Geology; Computer Engineering;
Sciences.
I: Basic Sciences; Technology; Nuclear
Sciences; Technological Research; Social
Sciences; Geophysics.

Armed Forces Politechnic Quito
[Escula Politecnica del Ejercito]
Gral. Pazminõ y Avenida Colombia, Quito
Tel: +593(2) 543533
Fax: +593(2) 504988
Rector: Jorge Vergara Ordoñeaz
Founded: 1977
Engineering; Education.

PRIVATE INSTITUTIONS

Catholic University of Cuenca
[Universidad Católica de Cuenca]
Calle Bolívar y Benigno Malo, Apartado de
Correos 19A, Cuenca
Tel: +593(7) 842606
Fax: +593(7) 831040
Telex: 04-8567 ucacue ed
Cable: ucacue
Rector: César Cordero Moscoso (1975-96)
Dean of Foreign Students in Europe: Franz
Kanehl, UCACUE, Humboldtstrasse 11, 4000
Düsseldorf, Germany
Founded: 1970
F: Law and Political and Social Sciences;
Education and Psychology; Medicine and Health
Sciences; Economics and Business; Commercial
Engineering and Accounting; Business
Engineering and Administration; Chemical
Engineering and Industry; Agriculture, Mines, and
Animal Husbandry; Engineering and Systems;
Physical Education and Sports; Journalism and
Communications; Social Work and Service;
Secretarial Studies; Teacher Training and
Languages (elementary level); Education;
Nursing and Medical Technology.

University of the Holy Ghost Guayaquil
[Universidad Espiritu Santo de Guayaquil]
Guayaquil

Catholic University of Guayaquil
[Universidad Católica de Santiago de Guayaquil]
Km. 21/2 Avenida Carlos Julio Arosemena,
Apartado 4671, Guayaquil
Tel: +593(4) 202130
Founded: 1962
F: Architecture; Engineering; Economics;
Medicine; Law; Philosophy; Technology.

Civil University 'Vicente Rocafuerte' Guayaquil
[Universidad Laica 'Vicente Rocafuerte']
Avenida de las Américas, Apartado 1133,
Guayaquil
Tel: +593(4) 287200
Founded: 1963
F: Architecture; Education; Economics;
Administration; Civil Engineering; Law and Social
Sciences; Journalism; Agricultural Engineering.
Ce: Research.

International University Sek Guayaquil
[Universidad International Sek Guayaquil]
Guayaquil

Technical University of Loja
[Universidad Técnica Particular de loja]
Barrio San Cayetano, Apartado de Correos 608,
Loja
Tel: +593(4) 961836
Fax: +593(4) 963159
Telex: (04) 4533 unitel ed
Rector: Néstor Silverio Jiménez
Secretary-General: Carlos Ramírez Romero
Founded: 1971
F: Civil Engineering; Agroindustrial Engineering;
Economics; Architecture; Computer Sciences;
Mining; Languages; Arts and Sciences;
Secretarial Studies Sciences; Accountancy and
Auditing.
Ce: Research.
I: Educational Research; Economics Research.

Civil University 'Eloy Alfaro' of Manabí
[Universidad Laica 'Eloy Alfaro' de manabí]
Vía San Mateo, Casilla 2732, Manta, Manabí
Tel: +593(4) 610288
Fax: +593(4) 614095
Founded: 1985
F: Education; Medicine; Administration;
Engineering; Dentistry; Law, Social and Political
Sciences; Economics; Architecture; Marine
Sciences; Social Work; Communication Studies
Sciences; Accountancy and Auditing.

Equinox University of Technology Quito
[Universidad Técnológica Equinoccial]
Rumipamba y Borgeois 210, Casilla 2764, Quito
Tel: +593(2) 442288
Rector: Alvaro Trueba Barahona
Director General Administrativo y Financiero:
José Benítez Celi
Founded: 1986
F: Applied Administrative Sciences; Economics;
Arts; Social Sciences; Agriculture; Engineering.
Ce: Research.
D: Languages.

Pontifical Catholic University of Ecuador Quito
[Pontificia Universidad Católica del Ecuador
Quito]
12 de Octubre 1076 y Roca, Apartado 17 01 2184,
Quito
Tel: +593(2) 529240
Fax: +593(2) 567117
E-Mail: puce.edu.ec
Rector: Julio Terán Dutari, S.J. (1985-95)
Secretario General: Manuel Freire Sánchez
Founded: 1946
F: Law; Economics; Engineering; Education;
Human Sciences; Nursing; Theology and
Philosophy; Administration; Exact and Natural
Sciences; Linguistics and Literature.

S: Social Work; Psychology; Medical
Technology.
I: Economic Research.
Ce: Latin American Studies (CECA); Museology
and History; Transport Research.

NATIONAL ACADEMIC BODIES

PUBLIC INSTITUTIONS

Ministery of Public Education, Sports and Culture
[Ministerio de Educación Pública, Desportos y
Cultura]
Mejia 322, Quito
Tel: +593(2) 540701
Fax: +593(2) 503537
Ministro: Rosalía Arteaga Serrano

National Council for Universities and Technical Universities
[Consejo Nacional de Universidades y Escuelas
Politécnicas]
9 de Octubre 624 y Carrión, Quito
Tel: +593(2) 569897
Fax: +593(2) 21442
Telex: 563685
Presidente: Teodoro Coello Váquez
Secretario General: Gonzalo Muñoz
Founded: 1966

Ecuador National Commission for Unesco
[Comisión Nacional Ecuatoriana de la Unesco]
Calle Buenos Aires 136, Quito
Tel: +593(2) 540701
Fax: +593(2) 503537
President: Rosalía Arteaga Serrano, Minister of
Education
Secretario Permanente: Fernando Chamorro

EGYPT

UNIVERSITIES

Ain Shams University
Kasr el Zaafran, Abbassia, Cairo
Tel: +20(2) 820-230
Fax: +20(2) 284-7822
E-Mail: postmaster@shams.eun.eg.
Telex: 94070-u-shms-un
President: Abd El Wehab Mohamed Abd El Hafez
(1992-)
Secretary-General: Helmy Moafy
International Relations: Vice-President, Post-
Graduate Studies and Research, Aly Ramzy Abd
El Megid Ramzy
Founded: 1950
F: Arts; Law; Commerce; Science; Medicine;
Engineering; Agriculture; Education; Languages.

C: For Women (Education).
Higher I: Nursing.
I: Environmental Studies and Research;
Postgraduate Childhood Studies; Business
Statistics Research.
C: Science Education; Middle East Research;
Computer; Research for the Development of
English Language Teaching; Papyrological
Studies; Business Research; Information System;
Public Service; Research and Training on Vectors
of Diseases.

Al-Azhar University Cairo
Cairo
Tel: +20(2) 623-281
Fax: +20(2) 611-404
Telex: 21945 skircw
Rector: Abd-El-Fattah Hussieny El-Sheikh (1987-)
Secretary-General: Saed Sayed Farag
International Relations: General Rector, Cultural
and Scientific Relations, Mahmoud Abd El Sattar
Abd El Haleik
Founded: 1970, 1961
F: Arabic Language; Theology; Law; Islamic
Religion; Islamic Daowa (Fundamentals); Islamic
Studies; Language and Translation; Commerce;
Science; Medicine; Dentistry; Pharmacy;
Engineering; Agriculture; Education; Islamic
Culture (for girls); Arabic Language (Assiut);
Theology (Assiut); Law (Assiut); Arab Language
(Mansoura); Islamic Religion (Mansoura); Arabic
Language (Zagazig); Islamic Religion (Zagazig);
Arabic Language (Menofeiya); Islamic Religion
(Menofeiya); Law (Tanta); Islamic Religion
(Tanta); Arabic Language (El-Behera); Law (El
Behera).

*Alexandria University
22 Al-Guish Avenue, Chatby, Alexandria
Tel: +20(3) 596-2924
Fax: +20(3) 596-0720
E-Mail: postmaster@alex.eun.eg.
Telex: 54467 univy un
President: Essam Salem (1992-)
Secretary-General: Ahmed Talaat El Beshbeshy
International Relations: Vice-President,
Postgraduate Studies and Research, Ibrahim Aly
Abd El Latif
Founded: 1942, 1953
F: Arts; Arts (Damanhour); Law; Commerce;
Commerce (Damanhour); Science; Medicine;
Dentistry; Education; Education (Damanhour);
Veterinary Medicine (Edfina); Pharmacy;
Engineering; Tourism and Hotel Management;
Agriculture; Agriculture (Sabha Basha);
Agriculture (Damanhour); Fine Arts; Physical
Education (Men); Physical Education (Women).
Higher I: Nursing; Public Health.
I: Medical Research; Postgraduate Studies and
Research.
Ce: Public Services; Postgraduate Science
Research.

The American University in Cairo
113 Kasr El-Aini Street, P.O. Box 2511, Cairo
11511
Tel: +20(2) 354-2964
Fax: +20(2) 355-7565
E-Mail: internet auc-acs.evn.eg
Telex: 92224 aucai un
Cable: victorious
President: Donald McDonald (1990-)
Senior Vice-President and Provost: Andrew Kerek
International Relations: John Swanson
Founded: 1919
S: Humanities and Social Sciences; Business,
Economics and Communication; Sciences and
Engineering.
Ce: Adult and Continuing Education; Desert
Development; Social Research.

*Arab Academy for Science and Technology (AAST)
Gamal Abdel Nasser Avenue, Miami, P.O. Box
10219, Alexandria
Tel: +20(3) 560-2366
Fax: +20(3) 560-2144
Telex: 54160 acad un
Cable: arabcademy
President: Gamal El-Din Ahmed Mokhtar (1972-)
Director (Admissions and Registration): Abd El
Khalek A. Saleh
Founded: 1972
C: Maritime Studies and Technology;
Engineering and Technology; Management and
Technology.
Ce: Research and Consultancy.

Assiut University
Assiut
Tel: +20(88) 323-000
Fax: +20(88) 322-564
E-Mail: assiut@frcu.eun.eg.
Telex: 92863 asun un
Cable: assiut university-egypt
Rector: M.R. El Tahlawi (1991-)
Secretary-General: Sayed Mohamed Sayed
International Relations: Vice-President,
Postgraduate Studies and Research, Farouk
Mahmoud Khalil
Founded: 1949, 1976
F: Science; Science (Sohag); Science (Qena);
Science (Aswan); Engineering; Medicine;
Agriculture; Pharmacy; Veterinary Medicine;
Education; Law; Commerce; Education (Sohag);
Physical Education; Education (Aswan); Education
(Qena); Arts (Sohag); Arts (Qena); Commerce
(Sohag); Social Services (Aswan).
Higher I: Nursing.

Cairo University
Orman, Giza, Cairo
Tel: +20(2) 572-7066
Fax: +20(2) 628-884
E-Mail: postmaster@cairo.eun.eg.
Telex: 94372 uncai un
President: Mofid Mahmoud Shehab (1993-)
Secretary-General: Mokhar Aly El-Shehawy

International Relations: Vice-President, Postgraduate Studies and Research, Farouk Ismail Mohamed
Founded: 1908, 1925
F: Arts; Arts (Beni Suef); Law; Law (Beni Suef); Economics and Political Science; Commerce; Commerce; Science; Medicine; Dentistry; Pharmacy; Engineering; Engineering (El-Fayoum); Agriculture; Agriculture (El-Fayoum); Veterinary Medicine; Veterinary Medicine (Beni Suef); Mass Communication; Arabic and Islamic Studies (Dar El-Olum); Arabic and Islamic Studies (Fayoum); Archaeology; Education (El-Fayoum); Education (Beni Suef); Social Service (El-Fayoum); Physiotherapy; Urban Planning.
Higher I: Nursing.
I: Tumour Studies; Educational Studies and Research; Statistical Studies and Research; African Studies and Research.

Helwan University Cairo
96 Ahmed Oraby Street, El-Mohandeseen, Embababa P.O., Cairo
Tel: +20(2) 344-4038
Fax: +20(2) 345-5461
E-Mail: helwan@f.r.cu.eun.eg.
Telex: 3455461
President: Mohamed Mahmoud El-Gohary
Secretary-General: Laila Khaled El-Afendy
International Relations: Vice-President, Postgraduate and Research, Hamdiya Maimoud Zahran
Founded: 1975
F: Engineering and Technology; Engineering and Technology (Mataria); Art Education; Fine Arts; Fine Arts (Alexandria); Applied Arts (Giza); Musical Education; Agriculture; Commerce and Business Administration; Education; Science; Tourism and Hotel Management; Home Economics; Physical Education; Physical Education.

Mansoura University
P.O. Box 35516, 35516 Mansoura
Tel: +20(50) 355-405
Fax: +20(50) 353-584
E-Mail: postmaster@mans.eun.eg.
Telex: 23738 mans un
President: M.H.M. Emarah (1990-)
Secretary-General: Gamal Mahmoud Dawood
International Relations: Vice-President, Postgraduate Studies and Research, Abd El Raouf Mohamed Mahdy
Founded: 1972
F: Education; Science; Commerce; Commerce (Demietta); Engineering; Agriculture; Law; Arts; Pharmacy; Medicine; Dentistry; Science (Demietta); Education (Demietta).

*Menoufia University
Gamal Abdel Nasser Street, Shebin El-Kom
Tel: +20(48) 342-16
Fax: +20(2) 777-620
E-Mail: postmaster@shebin.feun.eg.
Telex: 23832 muske un
President: Sakr Ahmed Sakr (1993-)
Secretary-General: Mahmoud Basyouni Sultan
International Relations: Vice-President, Postgraduate Studies and Research, Abd El Hady Abd el Nasser
Founded: 1976
F: Agriculture; Engineering and Technology; Electronics (Menouf); Education; Science; Commerce; Medicine; Arts; Law; Home Economics.
Higher I: Nursing.
I: Liver Studies and Research.

Minia Uinia University
Minia
Tel: +20(286) 324-460
Fax: +20(286) 326-243
E-Mail: postmater@minia.eun.eg.
Telex: 24000 mnuv
President: Gamal Abou El Makarem Rizk (1991-)
Secretary-General: Ahmed Fathi Mohamed Fayed
International Relations: Vice-President, Postgraduate Studies Research, Maher Mostafa Kamel Ahmed
Founded: 1976
F: Agriculture; Arts and Human Sciences; Education; Engineering and Technology; Sciences; Physical Education (for Men); Medicine; Fine Arts; Arabic Studies.

Senghor University Alexandria
[Senghor Université/Université internationale de Langue française au Service du Développement africain]
1 Midan Ahmed Orabi, El Mancheya, Alexandria
Tel: +20(3) 819-971
Fax: +20(3) 819-974
Telex: 55 917 senghr
Recteur: Souleymane Seck (1993-)
Vice-Recteur: Nahwat Abdalla
Founded: 1990
D: General Administration; Environmental Management; Nutrition and Health Studies; Heritage Management.

Suez Canal University
Ek-Shik Zaid, Ismailia
Tel: +20(264) 224-009
Fax: +20(264) 325-208
E-Mail: suez@frcu.eun.eg.
Cable: 63297 scu.fm.um.
President: Ahmed Dewdar Basyouny (1993-)
Secretary-General: Mohamed Abdel Rahman El-Kady
International Relations: Abd El Fatah Mohamed Abd El Wehab
Founded: 1976

F: *Natural Sciences; Agriculture; Veterinary Medicine; Medicine; Commerce; Commerce (Port Said); Education; Education (El-Arish); Education (Port Said); Education (Suez); Petroleum Engineering and Mining (Suez); Environmental Agricultural Sciences (El-Arish); Engineering and Technology (Port Said); Physical Education (Port Said); Tourism and Hotel Management.*
Higher I: *Nursing (Port Said).*
Ce: *Public Service; Fish Research; Ecological Research Studies of Sinai; Medical Research.*

Tanta University
El-Geish, Tanta
Tel: +20(240) 327-928
Fax: +20(240) 322-785
Telex: 23605 un tha
President: Shawky El-Saud Khater (1993-)
Secretary-General: Abdel Rahman Hassan
Founded: 1975
F: *Education (Kfar El Shiekh); Education; Arts; Science; Engineering; Medicine; Pharmacy; Dentistry; Commerce; Law; Nursing; Agriculture; Veterinary Medicine; Physical Education (Men).*
Higher I: *Nursing.*

Zagazig University
Zagazig
Tel: +20(255) 322-417
Fax: +20(255) 245-452
E-Mail: postmaster@zagazig.eun.eg.
Telex: 92860 zu un
President: Ramzy El-Shaire (1991-)
Secretary-General: Samia Sayed Ahamed Shalaby
International Relations: Vice-President, Postgraduate Studies and Research, Mohamed Samir Tobar
Founded: 1974
F: *Commerce; Education; Agriculture (Moshtohor); Agriculture; Veterinary Medicine; Arts; Law; Law (Benha); Science; Medicine; Pharmacy; Engineering; Physical Education (for Men); Physical Education (for Women); Commerce (Benha); Education (Benha); Arts (Benha); Medicine (Benha); Science (Benha); Veterinary Medicine (Moshtohor); Engineering (Shoubra).*
Higher I: *Nursing.*
I: *Production Efficiency; Ancient Near Eastern Studies.*
Ce: *Computer.*

OTHER INSTITUTIONS

College of Industrial Education
Shark-El-Nil P.O. Box 65513, Beni-Suef
Tel: +20(82) 223-067
Director: Mohamed Fouad Elfafeh Ibrahim (1992-94)
International Relations: Ibrahim Eltayeb, Registrar
Founded: 1992
Industrial Studies.

College of Industrial Education
Al-Sawah, Cairo
Tel: +20(2) 454-7544
Director: Abdel Rahman Moussa (1990-94)
International Relations: Safy El-Ghandour
Founded: 1989
Production Technology; Automations and Tractors; Refrigeration and Air-Conditioning; Electrical Engineering; Electronics.

Faculty of Kindergarten Education
Mohamed Amin Shohaieb Street 12A, Alexandria
Tel: +20(3) 546-8757
Fax: +20(3) 546-8757
Director: Seham Mohamed Badr (1989-94)
International Relations: Nadia Hafez
Education (Kindergarten Level).

Faculty of Kindergarten Education
Dokki, Cairo
Tel: +20(2)
Education (kindergarten level).

Faculty of Special Education
AMein Shohayeb Street, Alexandria
Tel: +20(3) 545-4313
Director: Abdul-Fallah Ahmed Haggag (1988-94)
International Relations: Shawkey Abdul-Sallam
Home Economics; Art and Music.

Faculty of Special Education
Ramleh, Alexandria
Education.

Faculty of Special Education
Abbassia, Cairo
Education.

Faculty of Special Education
Dokki, Cairo
Education.

Faculty of Special Education
El-Fayoum
Tel: +20(84) 324-965
Director: Abd El-Fatah Mahmoud El-Shershaby (1990-94)
Founded: 1990
D: *Home Economics; Arts; Infant-food.*

Faculty of Special Education
Kena
Tel: +20(96) 327-571
International Relations: M.T. Isamail
Founded: 1989
D: *Arts; Music; Home Economics; Education Technology; Kindergarten Education.*

Faculty of Special Education
Mansoura
Tel: +20(50) 357-171
Director: Hussein A.Sonbol
Founded: 1990
D: *Home Economics; Arts; Music; Educational Technology; Educational Information.*

Faculty of Special Education
Ashmuon, Menoufia
Education.

Faculty of Special Education
Taha Hussein Street, Minia
Tel: +20(86)
Director: Mohammed Ali-Nasr (1990-94)
Founded: 1990
D: Home Economics; Arts; Music; Technology; Mass Media.

Faculty of Special Education
Port-Said
Education.

Faculty of Special Education
Tanta
Tel: +20(40) 314-225
Fax: +20(40) 314-225
Director: Abdel Hameed M.Noweir (1992-94)
International Relations: Mamdooh K.El Nefawy
Founded: 1988
D: Arts; Music; Educational Technology; Home Economics; Educational Media.

Faculty of Special Education
El Sayadeen, Zagazig, El Sharkia
Tel: +20(55) 345-515
Director: Hamed Maher Ezz (1991-94)
Founded: 1991
D: Arts; Music; Educational Technology; Home Economics; Educational Mass Media; Basic Education.

Higher Institute of Agricultural Cooperative Studies
Shaba El-Kema, Cairo
Tel: +20(2) 224-850
Agriculture.

Higher Institute of Co-operative and Agricultural Guidance
Assiut
Tel: +20(88) 322-2815
Administrative Studies.

Higher Institute of Hydraulic Stations
Aswan
Hydraulic Engineering.

Higher Institute of Social Service
Ed Rossafa Street.13 Moharam Bek, Alexandria
Tel: +20(3) 492-4151
Director: Samea Mohamed Fahmi
Social Service.

Higher Institute of Social Service
Aswan
Tel: +20(97) 314-995
Social Service.

Higher Institute of Social Service
Kafr Al Sheikh
Tel: +20(47) 323-184
Social Service.

Higher Institute of Social Service
Nafar El-Kolaby, Cairo
Tel: +20(2) 779-100
Director: S.A.Abdel El-Latif
Social Service.

Higher Institute of Social Service
Damanhour
Director: Mohamed Tathy Akasha
Social Service.

Higher Institute of Social Service
Kafr El-Seikh
Social Service.

Higher Institute of Social Service
Port-Said
Tel: +20(66) 324-365
Director: Farak Mohamed Shalabi
Social Service.

Higher Institute of Technology
Stadium Street, Banha
Tel: +20(13) 230-297
Fax: +20(13) 230-297
Director: Ahmed Soliman Huzayyin (1993-94)
Founded: 1988
D: Electrical Engineering; Mechanical Engineering; Civil Engineering; Basic Studies.

Higher Institute of Technology
El-Asher Min Ramadan City
Tel: +20(15) 363-597
Technology.

NATIONAL ACADEMIC BODIES

Supreme Council of Universities
Cairo University Building, Giza, Cairo
Tel: +20(2) 728-877
Fax: +20(2) 728-722
E-Mail: postmaster@egfrcuvx.bitnet
Telex: 92312 frcu un
President: Hussein Kamel Baha'a Eldine
Secretary-General: Salah Eldin Morsi
Founded: 1950

Egyptian National Commission for Unesco
7 Kuwait Street, Dokki, Guizeh, P.O. Box 12311, Cairo
Tel: +20(2) 360-9641
Fax: +20(2) 716-947
Cable: unescedu
Chairman: Hussein Kamel Baha'a Eldine, Minister of Education
Secretary-General: Fawzi Abdel Zaher

EL SALVADOR

UNIVERSITIES

PUBLIC INSTITUTIONS

University of El Salvador
[Universidad de El Salvador]
Ciudad Universitaria, Final 25 Avenida Norte, San Salvador
Tel: +503(25) 7922
Telex: 20794
Rector: Fabio Castillo
Founded: 1841, 1847
F: Medicine; Law and Social Sciences; Agriculture; Science and Humanities; Engineering; Chemistry and Pharmacy; Dentistry; Economics.

University of the East San Miguel
[Universidad de Oriente]
4a Calle Pte. 709, San Miguel
Tel: +503(61) 1180
Rector: Roberto Gustave Torres
Founded: 1982
F: Engineering, Architecture and Agriculture; Science and Humanities; Law and Economics; Health Sciences.

Western University of El Salvador, Santa Ana
[Universidad Occidental de El Salvador]
6a Avenida Sur 52, Apartado postal 270, Santa Ana
Tel: +503(40) 0222
Rector: Roberto Molina Castro
F: Engineering; Economics; Science and Humanities.

PRIVATE INSTITUTIONS

American University of El Salvador
[Universidad Americana San Salvador]
Centro Profesional Presidente, Edif. 'A' la. Planta, Apartamento No 4, Colonia San Benito, San Salvador
Tel: +503(79) 0680
Cable: amschool
Rector: Ricardo Gavidia Castro (1982)
Secretario General: Rolando Palacios
Founded: 1978, 1982
F: Sciences and Humanities.
C: Economics.

Metropolitan University of El Salvador
[Universidad Metropolitana de El Salvador]
1a Avenida Norte y 5a Calle Poniente 405, San Salvador
Tel: +503(21) 0189
F: Economics; Science and Humanities; Engineering.

Pedagogical University of El Salvador
[Universidad Pedagógica de El Salvador]
7a Avenida Nte. 421, San Salvador
Tel: +503(22) 16142
Rector: Luis Alfonso Aparicio
Secretario General: José Antonio Arias Martell
Founded: 1982
Education.

Polytechnic University of El Salvador
[Universidad Politécnica de El Salvador]
17 Calle Poniente 243, Apartado postal 1441, San Salvador
Tel: +503(21) 1866
Rector: Rigoberto Vitelio Melaro
Founded: 1979
F: Engineering and Architecture; Economics.

Interamerican University 'Simon Bolívar' San Miguel
[Universidad Interamericana 'Simón Bolívar']
12 C.O. y 2a Avenida Nte 105, an Miguel
Tel: +503(61) 0975
Rector: Orlando Guillermo Rivas Paniagua

University of La Paz
[Universidad de La Paz]
4a Avenida Sur 606a, San Miguel
Tel: +503(61) 0813
Rector: Javier Urrutia

University 'Capitain General Gerardo Barrios' San Miguel
[Universidad 'Capitain General Gerardo Barrios']
4a Calle Poniente 209, San Miguel
Tel: +503(61) 2947
Rector: Raúl Rivas Quintanilla
Founded: 1982
F: Engineering and Architecture; Economics; Science and Humanities; Law and Social Sciences; Agriculture.

Central American University 'José Simón Cañas' San Salvador
[Universidad Centroamericana 'José Simeón Cañas']
Apartado postal (01) 168, San Salvador
Tel: +503(73) 4400
Fax: +503(73) 1010
Telex: 30018 Proca
Cable: Ucasal, Autopista Sur
Rector: Miguel Francisco Estrada Lemus, S.J.
Secretario General: Mario Cerna Torres
Founded: 1965
F: Economics; Engineering; Humanities and Natural Sciences.

Christian University of the Assemblies of God San Salvador
[Universidad Cristiana de las Asambleas de Dios]
27 Calle Oriente 134, San Salvador
Tel: +(503) 25-5046
Rector: Adrian Fernando Archila Morales
Founded: 1983
Science and Humanities.

Evangelical University of El Salvador San Salvador

[Universidad Evangélica de El Salvador]
63 Avenida Sur y Pje. 1 No. 138, San Salvador
Tel: +503(98) 3105
Rector: Carlos Humberto Vigil Navarrete
Founded: 1981
F: Medicine; Dentistry; Science and Humanities; Engineering; Agriculture.

Lutheran Salvadorean University San Salvador

[Universidad Luterana Salvadoreña]
Km. 3 1/2 Carretera a Los Planes de Renderos, Autopista a Comalpa, Esquina Nor-Oriente, San Salvador
Tel: +503(70) 1470
Rector: Medardo Enresto Gómez Palacios

Open University of San Salvador

[Universidad Modular Abierta]
3a Calle Pte. 1126, San Salvador
Tel: +503(74) 4029
Rector: Judith Virginia Mendoza de Diaz
Founded: 1982
F: Economics; Science and Humanities.

New University San Salvador

[Universidad Nueva San Salvador]
Calle Arce y 23 Av. Sur No. 1243, San Salvador
Tel: +503(21) 2288
Rector: Rafael Hernán Contreras Rodríguez
Founded: 1981
F: Economics; Science and Humanities; Law and Social Science; Pure and Applied Sciences; Health Sciences; Dentistry; Political Science.

Panamerican University of San Salvador

[Universidad Panamericana]
5a Avenida Norte 17, Mijacanos, San Salvador
Tel: +503(81) 0276
Rector: Oscar Armando Moran Folgar
Founded: 1989

Salvadorean University 'Alberto Masferrer' San Salvador (USAM)

[Universidad Salvadoreña 'Alberto Masferrer' (USAM)]
19 Avenida Norte, entre 3a Calle Poniente y Alameda 'Juan Pablo II', San Salvador
Tel: +503(21) 1136
Fax: +503(22) 8006
Rector: Amilcar Avendaño y Ortíz
Secretaria General: Daysi Carolina M. de Gómez
Founded: 1979
F: Medicine and Surgery; Chemistry and Pharmaco-Biology; Dentistry; Veterinary Medicine; Law and Social Sciences.
I: Science and Technological Research.

Salvadorean University 'Isaac Newton' San Salvador

[Universidad Salvadoreña 'Isaac Newton']
1a Avenida Nte. 838, San Salvador
Tel: +503(22) 2131
Rector (Acting): Juan Francisco López
Founded: 1982
F: Science and Humanities; Economics; Engineering and Architecture.

Salvadorean University San Salvador

[Universidad Salvadoreña]
Calle San Antonio Abad y Avenida Alvaredo 164, Colonia Buenos Aires, San Salvador
Tel: +503(25) 8861
Rector: Ricardo Francisco Alfaro Sandoval
Founded: 1982
F: Engineering; Economics.

University 'Albert Einstein' San Salvador

[Universidad 'Albert Einstein']
Urb. Lomas de San Francisco, Calle Circunvalación, Block L, Lote No. 6, San Salvador
Tel: +503(73) 3780
Rector: Jorge Luis Hernández Flores
Founded: 1973
Engineering and Architecture.

University of the Americas San Salvador

[Universidad las Américas de El Salvador]
3a Calle Ote. 111, Apartado postal 2318, San Salvador
Tel: +503(21) 7647
Rector: René Guillermo Mata
Founded: 1982
F: Economics; Law and Social Sciences.

University of Business Administration San Salvador

[Universidad de Administración de Negocios]
Avenida Roosevelt y 4a Avenida Sur 4517, San Salvador
Tel: +503(23) 4962
Rector: Victor Benjamin Fuentes
Business Administration.

University 'Don Bosco' San Salvador

[Universidad 'Don Bosco']
Ciudadela 'Don Bosco', Cantón Venecia, Calle Plan del Pino, San Salvador
Tel: +503(25) 8878
Rector: Federico Miguel Huguet Rivera
Founded: 1983
F: Science and Humanities; Engineering.

University 'Dr. Andres Bello' San Salvador

[Universidad 'Dr. Andres Bello']
49 Avenida Sur 737, an Salvador
Tel: +503(24) 0021
Rector: Marco Tulio Magaña Escalanteua

University 'Dr. José Matías Delgado' San Salvador

[Universidad 'Dr. José Matías Delgado']
Km. 8 1/2 Carretera a Santa Tacla, Apartado
postal 1849, Nueva San Salvador
Tel: +503(78) 1424
Rector: David Escobar Galindo
Founded: 1977
F: Law.
S: .Liberal and Fine Arts; Applied Arts;
Economics; Accountancy; Business
Administration and Marketing; Public
Administration; Banking Administration.

University 'Dr. Manuel Luis Escamilla' San Salvador

[Universidad 'Dr. Manuel Luis Escamilla']
47 Avenida Norte y 1a, Calle Poniente 2514, San
Salvador
Tel: +503(23) 0727
Rector: Adela Cabezas de Rosales

University 'Francisco Gavidia' San Salvador

[Universidad 'Francisco Gavidia']
Alameda Roosevelt 2937, San Salvador
Tel: +503(24) 5962
Rector: Mario Antonio Ruiz Ramírez
Founded: 1981
F: Economics; Social Sciences.

University of Integrated Education San Salvador

[Universidad de Educación Integral (Sistema
Modular)]
Edificio Campo Marte 6 2a Planta, Avenida Norte
11C.P. y 3a, San Salvador
Tel: +503(26) 5504
Rector: Manuel Antonio Rivas Santana

University 'Leonardo Da Vinci' San Salvador

[Universidad 'Leonardo Da Vinci']
Avenida Roosevelt 2139, San Salvador
Tel: +503(23) 6034
Rector: Carlos Benjamín Valiente Ortíz
Founded: 1981
Economics.

University of Science and Development San Salvador

[Universidad de Ciencia y Desarrollo]
Col. Escalón, Avenida Manuel Enrique Araujo,
San Salvador
Tel: +503(79) 3788
Rector: José Roberto Campos Anaya

University of Technology San Salvador

[Universidad Tecnológica]
Calle Arce 1020, San Salvador
Tel: +503(71) 5058
Rector: José Mauricio Loucel
Founded: 1980
D: Economics; Engineering and Architecture;
Humanities and Natural Sciences.

University 'Tomás Alba Edison' San Salvador

[Universidad 'Tomás Alba Edison']
23 Calle Poniente, Avenida Las Víctorias 1, San
Salvador
Tel: +503(25) 4207
Rector: José Juan Interiano (1985-)
Secretario General: Leopoldo Samayoa
Founded: 1978, 1985
F: Economics; Engineering.
D: Ecology; Technology; Administration of New
Products; Democratic Economics.

Autonomous University of Santa Ana

[Universidad Autónoma de Santa Ana]
9a Calle Poniente 22, Avenida Sur, Santa Ana
Tel: +503(41) 0811
Rector: Guillermo Martínez Mendoza
Founded: 1982
F: Economics; Health Studies; Law; Science and
Humanities.

Catholic University of the West Santa Ana

[Universidad Católica de Occidente]
1a Calle Pte. 32, Santa Ana
Tel: +503(41) 3217
Fax: +503(41) 2655
Rector: Mons. Marco René Revelo Contreras
Secretario General: Margarito Calderón
Founded: 1982
F: Science and Humanities; Industrial
Engineering; Economics; Agricultural
Engineering; Juridical and Social Sciences.
I: Human Promotion; Rural Development.

Santaneca Science and Technology University Santa Ana

[Universidad Santaneca de Ciencia y Tecnología]
9a. Calle Poniente No 1, Santa Ana
Tel: +503(41) 2399
Rector: Ovidio Antonio Agreda Cardona
Secretario General: Juan Francisco Linares
Linares
Founded: 1982
F: Science and Humanities; Economics;
Engineering and Architecture.

Technical University of Latin America San Salvador

[Universidad Técnica Latinoamericana]
4a Avenida Norte 3-6, Nueva San Salvador
Tel: +503(28) 4775
Rector: Rosendo Mauricio Sermeño Palacios
Founded: 1981
F: Engineering; Economics; Animal Husbandry;
Social Sciences and Humanities.

University of Sonsonate

[Universidad de Sonsonate]
2a Avenida Nte. 6-6, Sonsonate
Tel: +503(51) 0866
Rector: Jesús Adalberto Diaz
Founded: 1982
F: Engineering and Natural Sciences;
Economics and Social Sciences.

OTHER INSTITUTIONS

Instituto Tecnológico Centroamericano
Km. 11, Carretera a Nueva San Salvador, San
Salvador
Tel: +503(28) 1166
Founded: 1989

Instituto Tecnológico de Chalatenango
Final C. Morazán, Barrioo El Calvario,
Chalatenango
Tel: +503(35) 2526

Instituto Tecnológico Metropolitano
Urbanización José Simón Cañas, Calle Principal
Colonia Zacamil, San Salvador

Instituto Tecnológico de San Vicente
Final Calle C. Miranda, San Vicente
Tel: +503(33) 0250

Instituto Tecnológico de Santa Ana
Avenida Santa Ana California, y 31 Calle Pte.,
Santa Ana
Tel: +503(41) 4348

Instituto Tecnológico de Sonsonate
Colonia 14 de diciembre, 25 Calle Pte. y Avenida
Morazán, Sonsonate
Tel: +503(51) 0634

Instituto Tecnológico de Usulután
Final 7a Calle Ote., y Avenida El Molino,
Usulután
Tel: +503(62) 0406

Instituto Tecnológico de Zacatecoluca
Avenida Juna Manuel Rodríguez, y Calle al
Volcán, Zacatecoluca
Tel: +503(34) 0462

NATIONAL ACADEMIC BODIES

Ministry of Education
[Ministerio de Educación]
6a Calle Oriente 435, San Salvador
Tel: +503(28) 0608
Fax: +503(28) 3200
Minister: Cecilia Gallardo de Cano

**El Salvador National Commission for
Unesco**
[Comisión Nacional Salvadoreña de Cooperación
con la Unesco]
Ministerio de Educación, Nueva San Salvador,
Apartado postal 1175, San Salvador
Tel: +503(28) 0377
Fax: +503(28) 3200
Presidente: Cecilia Gallardo de Cano, Ministro de
Educación
Secretario Ejecutivo: José Ramiro Velasco
Barrera

ERITREA

UNIVERSITIES

*Asmara University
P.O. Box 1220, Asmara
Tel: +291(1) 113-600
Telex: 42091
Cable: Asmuniv
President: Tewolde-Berhan G. Egziabher
Founded: 1958, 1968
*F: Natural Sciences; Social Sciences; Language
Studies; Law; Arid Zone Agriculture (In process
of development).
I: African Studies; Appropriate Technology.
D: Extension.*

NATIONAL ACADEMIC BODIES

Ministry of Education
P.O. Box 5610, Asmara
Tel: +291(1) 113-044
Fax: +291(1) 113-866

ESTONIA

UNIVERSITIES

Estonian Academy of Music
[Eesti Muusikaakadeemia]
Vabaduse pst. 130, Tallinn 0009
Tel: +372(2) 514-510
Fax: +372(2) 446-745
Rector: Peep Lassmann (1992-)
Vice-Rector: Marje Lohuaru
Founded: 1919
Music.

Estonian Agricultural University
[Eesti Póllumajandusülikool]
Rija 12, Tartu 2400
Tel: +362(7) 431-800
Fax: +372(7) 431-573
Telex: 173839 ader
Rector: Mait Klaassen (1993-)
Vice-Rector: Henn Elmet
International Relations: Toomas Tael
Founded: 1951
*F: Agronomy; Forestry and Land Engineering;
Economics and Social Sciences; Agricultural
Engineering; Veterinary Medicine.
I: Animal Husbandry.*

Tallinn Art University
[Tallinna Kunstiülikool]
Tartu mnt. 1, 0001 Tallin
Tel: +372(2) 421-481
Fax: +372(2) 432-659
Rector: Jaak Kangilaski (1989-)
Founded: 1989
D: *Painting; Stage Design; Printmaking; Sculpture; Ceramics; Glasswork; Textiles; Fashion Design; Leatherwork; Architecture; Industrial Design; Interior Design; History of Art; Social Studies; Universal Painting; Drawing; Construction; Languages.*

Tallinn Pedagogical University
[Tallinna Pedagookikaülikool]
Narva mnt. 25, 0100 Tallinn
Tel: +372(2) 425-868
Fax: +372(2) 312-588
E-Mail: tbach@tpedi.ioc.ee
Rector: Talis Bachmann (1992-)
Assistant to the Rector: Ena Martin
International Relations: Reet Kääni
Founded: 1919
F: *Languages; Mathematics and Natural Sciences; Educational Sciences; Social Sciences; Fine Arts; Physical Education.*
Ce: *Health Education; Psychodiagnostics; School Counselling; Advertising; Public Administration; Social Work; Sports; In-Service Training; Language; Computer; Cognitive Neuroscience (Research).*

Tallinn Technical University
[Tallinna-Tehnikaülikool]
Ehitajate tee 5, 0026 Tallinn
Tel: +372(2) 532-441
Fax: +372(2) 532-446
E-Mail: aarna@ce.ttu.ee
Telex: 173 101 stjut su
Rector: Olav Aarna (1991-)
Head of Administration: Jüri Tanner
International Relations: Madli Ganihhina
Founded: 1918, 1938
F: *Computer and Systems Engineering; Civil Engineering; Power Engineering; Humanities; Mechanical Engineering; Chemistry; Economics and Business Administration; Mathematics and Physics.*
Ce: *Continuing Education.*

*University of Tartu
[Tartu Ülikool]
18 Ülikooli St., 2400 Tartu
Tel: +372(7) 441-315
Fax: +372(7) 435-440
Telex: 173 243 taun
Rector: Peeter Tulviste (1993-98)
Scientific Secretary: Veera Ant
International Relations: Riina Laidvee
Founded: 1802, 1919

F: *Theology; Law; Medicine; Philosophy; Biology and Geography; Economics; Mathematics; Physical Education; Physics and Chemistry; Social Sciences.*

OTHER INSTITUTIONS

Eesti Merehariduskeskus
Estonia pst. 10, Tallinn 0100
Tel: +372(2) 411-168
Rector: Valdur Aret (1992-)
Prorector: Eugen Olle
Founded: 1992
Marine Education.

Eesti Riigikaitse Akadeemia
Kase St. 61, 0020 allinn
Tel: +372(2) 238-574
Fax: +372(2) 238-137
Rector: Eduard Raska (1993-97)
Chancellor: Feliks Angelstok
International Relations: Urmas Rei
Founded: 1992
Public Service Studies.

Narva Kõrgkool
Anveldi 14, 2000 Narva
Tel: +372(35) 22005
Fax: +372(35) 31995
Rector: Nina Sepp (1991-)
Executive: Nikolai Bashkirov
International Relations: Vyacheslav Konovalov
Founded: 1991
Teacher Training.

Tallinna Kõrgem Tehnikakool
Pärnu mnt. 62, 0010 Tallinn
Tel: +372(2) 453-689
Fax: +372(2) 450-956
Rector: Arvi Altmäe (1992-)
Prorector: Enno Lend
International Relations: Eve Otsa
Founded: 1992
Architecture; Building; Mechanical Engineering; Transportation and Logistics; General Studies.

Tartu Lennukolledž
Kreutzwaldi 58A, 2480 Tartu
Tel: +372(7) 422-277
Fax: +372(7) 422-277
Rector: Villu Mikita (1993-)
Administrative Director: Kaido Kaska
International Relations: Mart Enneveer
Founded: 1993
Aviation Studies.

Tartu Operajate Seminar
Salme la, 400 artu
Tel: +372(7) 434-042
Fax: +372(7) 434-042
Rector: August Solo (1973-)
Founded: 1828
Teacher Training.

Viljandi Kultuurikolledz
Laidoneri plates 8, 2900 Viljandi
Tel: +372(43) 53598
Fax: +372(43) 53598
Rector: Enn Siimer (1991-)
Administration Director: Juta Külm
Founded: 1991
Theatre Art; Dance; Folkmusic; Library Studies.

Virumaa Körgkool
Järvelüla tee 35, 2020 Kohtla-Jörve
Tel: +372(33) 47801
Fax: +372(33) 49781
E-Mail: vk@vk.edu.ee
Rector: Heino Türkson (1991-)
Executive Director: Viivi Ilves
International Relations: Head, Department of Humanities, Ene Jöemägi
Founded: 1992
Humanities; Real Sciences.

NATIONAL ACADEMIC BODIES

Estonian Ministry of Culture and Education
[Eesti Vabariigi Kulturt ja Haridusminsteerium]
11 Tönismagi St., 0100 Tallinn
Minister: Paul Eeerik Rumno

Council of Rectors of Estonian Universities
Ehitajate tee 5, 0108 Tallinn
President: Olav Aarna

Estonian National Commission for Unesco
23, Suur-Karja, 0001 Tallinn
Tel: +372(2) 441-431
Fax: +372(6) 313-757
Chairman: Yaak Kangilaski
Secretary-General: Doris Kareva

ETHIOPIA

UNIVERSITIES

*Addis Ababa University
P.O. Box 1176, Addis Ababa
Tel: +251(1) 11-59-14
Fax: (1)+251 55-38-11
Telex: 21205
Cable: aa Univ
President (Acting): Duri Mohammed
Founded: 1961, 1975
F: Law; Education; Medicine; Business and Economics; Science; Technology; Veterinary Medicine.
C: Social Sciences; Agriculture (Abassa); Teachers'; Medicine (Gondar).
S: Pharmacy; Graduate Studies; Library Science; Information Science for Africa.
I: Ethiopian Studies; Development Research; Languages; Educational Research.
D: Lifelong Education.

BAHIR DAR TEACHERS' COLLEGE
P.O. Box 79, Bahir Dar, W. Gojjam
Founded: 1971
Teacher Education.

COLLEGE OF AGRICULTURE
P.O. Box 5, Awassa Sidamo
Founded: 1976
Agriculture (Awassa Sidamo).

COLLEGE OF SOCIAL SCIENCES
Sidist Kilo Campus, P.O. Box 1176, Addis Ababa
Founded: 1951
Social Sciences.

FACULTY OF EDUCATION
Sidist Kilo Campus, P.O. Box 1176, Addis Ababa
Founded: 1962
Education.

UNIVERSITY OF LAW
Sidist Kilo Campus, P.O. Box 1176, Addis Ababa
Founded: 1963
Law.

FACULTY OF MEDICINE
Black Lion Hospital Compound, P.O. Box 1176, Addis Ababa
Founded: 1965
Medicine.

FACULTY OF SCIENCE
Arat Kilo Campus, P.O. Box 1176, Addis Ababa
Founded: 1951
Science.

FACULTY OF TECHNOLOGY
Northern Campus, Amist Kilo Campus, P.O. Box 385, Addis Ababa
Founded: 1953
Technology.

FACULTY OF TECHNOLOGY
Southern Campus, .O. Box 518, Addis Ababa
Founded: 1954
Technology.

FACULTY OF VETERINARY MEDICINE
Debre Zeit, P.O. Box 342, E. Shoa
Founded: 1963
Veterinary Medicine.

GONDAR COLLEGE OF MEDICAL SCIENCES
P.O. Box 196, Gondar
Founded: 1954
Medical Sciences (Gondar).

INSTITUTE OF LANGUAGE STUDIES
Sidist Kilo Campus, P.O. Box 1176, Addis Ababa
Founded: 1951
Language Studies.

Alemaya University of Agriculture
P.O. Box 138, Dire Dawa, Harar
Tel: +251(5) 11-13-99
President: Ephraim Mamo
Academic Vice-President: Mitiku Haile
Founded: 1954, 1985
F: Agriculture; Forestry.

D: *Natural and Social Sciences.*
P: *Continuing Education.*
Ce: *Agricultural Research (Alemaya);*
Agricultural Research (Debrezeit).

OTHER INSTITUTIONS

Arba Minch Water Technology Institute
P.O. Box 21, Arba Minch, N. Omo
Tel: 70
Founded: 1986
Water Technology.

College of Urban Planning
P.O. Box 1023, Addis Ababa
Tel: +253(1) 550-206
Telex: 21551
Cable: nupi et
Founded: 1970
Urban Planing.

Jimma Institute of Health Sciences
P.O. Box 378, Jimma, Illubabor
Tel: (7) 111340
Founded: 1983
Health Sciences.

Kotebe College of Teacher Education
P.O. Box 31248, Addis Ababa
Tel: (1) 611555
Founded: 1969
Teacher Education.

NATIONAL ACADEMIC BODIES

Ministry of Education
Higher Education, Main Department, P.O. Box
30747, Addis Ababa
Tel: +251(1) 552-519
Fax: +251(1) 550-8777
Minister: Mrs. Gennet Zeweide

Ethiopian National Agency for Unesco
P.O. Box 2996, Addis Ababa
Tel: +251(1) 552-519
Chairperson: Mrs. Gennet Zeweide, Minster of
Education
Secretary-General: Aberra Makonnen

FIJI

UNIVERSITIES

*University of the South Pacific
P.O. Box 1168, Suva
Tel: +679 313-900
Fax: +679 301-305
Telex: 2276 usp f
Founded: 1970
S: *Pure and Applied Sciences; Humanities;*
Social and Economic Development; Agriculture.

ALAFUA CAMPUS
P.O. Box 890, Alafua, Western Samoa

UNIVERSITY CENTRE
Raratong, Cook Island
Founded: 1970

UNIVERSITY CENTRE
Tarawa, Kiribati
Founded: 1970

UNIVERSITY CENTRE
Nauru
Founded: 1970

UNIVERSITY CENTRE
Honiara, Solomon Islands
Founded: 1970

UNIVERSITY CENTRE
Funafuti, Tuvalu
Founded: 1970

UNIVERSITY CENTRE
Port Villa, Vanuatu
Founded: 1970

UNIVERSITY CENTRE
Apia, Western Samoa
Founded: 1970

OTHER INSTITUTIONS

Corpus Christi Training College
Suva
Founded: 1958

Lautoka Teachers' College
Lautoka
Founded: 1977
Teacher Training.

The Fiji Institute of Technology
Suva
Tel: +679 381-044
Founded: 1963
Technology.

The Fiji School of Agriculture
Koronivia
Founded: 1954
Agriculture.

The Fiji School of Medicine
Tamavua Suva
Founded: 1883
Medicine.

The Fiji School of Nursing
Tamavua, Suva
Nursing.

NATIONAL ACADEMIC BODIES

Ministry of Education, Women, Culture, Science and Technology
Malela House, Suva
Tel: +679 312-387
Fax: +679 303-511
Minister: Mrs. Taufa Vakatale

Fiji National Commission for Unesco
Ministry of Education, Women, Culture, Science
and Technology, Malela House, Suva
Tel: +679 314-477
Fax: +679 303-511
Telex: 2167
Minister: Mrs. Taufa Vakatale, Minister of
Education
Secretary: Isireli Senibulu

FINLAND

UNIVERSITIES AND UNIVERSITY INSTITUTIONS

*Åbo Akademi University
[Abo Akademi]
Domkyrkotorget 3, FIN-20500 Abo
Tel: +358(21) 65-43-11
Fax: +358(21) 51-75-53
E-Mail: INTERNET: abo.fi, earn/bitnet: finabo
Telex: 62301 aabib h fi
Rektor: Bengt Stenlund (1988-98)
Förvaltningsdirektör (Administrative Director):
Roger Broo
International Relations: Heidi Granqvist
Founded: 1918
*F: Arts; Mathematics and Natural Sciences;
Economics and Political Science; Chemical
Engineering; Theology; Education (Vasa); Social
and Caring Sciences (Vasa).*
*I: Archipelago; Social Research; Parasitology;
Religious and Cultural History; Industrial
Pollution Control; Human Rights; Women's
Studies; Comparative Nordic Politology and
Administration; Folklore; Advanced Management
Systems Research.*
*Ce: Language; Computer; Extension Studies;
Biotechnology.*
L: Accelerator.
S: Teacher Training (Vasa).

Academy of Fine Arts
[Kuvataideakatemia]
Yrjönkatu 18, FIN-00120 Helsinki
Tel: +368(0) 64-35-01
Fax: +368(0) 60-45-42
Rehtori: Outi Heiskanen (1994-97)
Director of Administration: Hallintojohtaja
International Relations: Riitta Salmi
Founded: 1848, 1985
*D: Painting; Printmaking; Sculpture; Time and
Space Based Arts (Media-Arts); General Studies.*

*College of Veterinary Medicine, Helsinki
[Eläinlääketieteellinen korkeakoulu]
Hämeentie 57, FIN-00580 Helsinki
Tel: +358(0) 39-31-141
Fax: +358(0) 39-31-799
E-Mail: alitaloh@vetmed.fi
Telex: 123203 elkk fl
Rehtori: Ilkka Alitalo (1985-95)
Hallintojohtaja (Administration Head): Ritva
Niiniluoto
International Relations: Riitta Kaitajärvi
Founded: 1945
*D: Basic Veterinary Medicine; Clinical Sciences;
Food and Environmental Hygiene.*

**Helsinki School of Economics and Business
Administration**
[Helsingin kauppakorkeakoulu]
Runeberginkatu 14-16, FIN-00100 Helsinki
Tel: +358(0) 43-131
Fax: +358(0) 43-13-217
E-Mail: +INTERNET: elehtine@hkkk.fi
Telex: 122220 econ sf
Rehtori: Veikko Jääskeläinen (1992-97)
Hallintojohtaja (Head of Administration): Matti
Sarakontu
International Relations: Leena Masalin
Founded: 1904
*D: Business Administration and Management
Systems; Accounting and Finance; Marketing and
Production Economics; Economics; Law and
Social Sciences; Mathematics and Statistics;
Languages.*
*Ce: International; Management Development;
Small Business.*
P: Development Co-operation (PRODEC).
*I: Basic Research in Administration and
Economics.*

*Helsinki University of Technology
[Teknillinen korkeakoulu]
Otakaari 1, FIN-02150 Espoo
Tel: +358(0) 4511
Fax: +358(0) 46-50-77
E-Mail: username@hut.fi
Telex: 125161 htkk fi
Cable: 12591
Rehtori: Paavo Vronen (1994-97)
Hallintojohtaja (Administrative Director): Esa
Luomala
Founded: 1849, 1879, 1908
*F: Information Technology; Civil Engineering
and Surveying; Mechanical Engineering;
Electrical Engineering; Process Engineering and
Materials Science; Architecture.*
*Ce: Computer; Arctic Offshore Research;
Metsähovi Radio Research; Urban and Regional
Studies; Continuing Education; Language.*
L: Low Temperature Physics.

Sibelius Academy
[Sibelius-Akatemia]
Döbelninkatu 2, FIN-00260 Helsinki
Tel: +358(0) 40-54-41
Fax: +358(0) 40-50-46-00
E-Mail: postmaster@siba.fi
Rehtori: Lassi Rajamaa (1993-96)
Hallintojohtaja (Director of Administration): Seppo Suihko
International Relations: Kristiina Saalonen
Founded: 1882, 1924, 1939
D: Theory of Music and Composition; Solo Performance; Music Education; Church Music; Jazz Music; Folk Music; Orchestral and Choral Conducting.
Ce: Opera Studies; Continuing Education.

*Swedish School of Economics and Business Administration
[Svenska handelshögskolan]
Arkadiagatan 22, 0100 Helsinki
Tel: +358(0) 40-30-31
Fax: +358(0) 40-30-33-33
E-Mail: INTERNET: firstname@shh.fi
Rektor: Marianne Stenius (1993-96)
Förvaltningsdirektör (Administrative Director): Kristian Dufholm
International Relations: Maini Mannerkoski
Founded: 1909
D: Accounting; Business Law; Economics; Entrepreneurship and Management; Finance; Marketing and Economic Geography; Modern Languages; Organization and Management; Political Science; Statistics and Computer Sciences.
I: Research.

Theatre Academy
[Teatterikorkeakoulu]
P.O. Box 148, FIN-00511 Helsinki
Tel: +358(0) 77-39-31
Fax: +358(0) 77-39-32-00
Rehtori: Kari Rentola (1994-97)
Hallintojohtaja (Administrative Director): Riitta Väisänen
Founded: 1979
D: Acting; Directing and Dramaturgy; Dance; Swedish; Sound and Lighting Design (Tampere).

*University of Art and Design Helsinki (UIAH)
[Taideteollinen korkeakoulu]
Hämeentie 135c, FIN-00560 Helsinki
Tel: +358(0) 75-631
Fax: +358(0) 75-63-223
E-Mail: INTERNET: uiah.fi
Rehtori: Yrjö Sotamaa (1986-94)
Hallintojohtaja (Administrative Director): Ilkka Huovio
International Relations: International Affairs Coordinator, Marjaana Kurkinen
Founded: 1871, 1973

F: Art Education; Visual Communication; Industrial and Environmental Design; General Studies.
D: Graphic Design; Stage Design; Film and Television; Photography; Interior Architecture and Furniture Design; Industrial Design; Textile Design; Ceramic and Glass Design; Clothing and Fashion Design; Craft Design.
I: Finnish Design Management; Research in Industrial Arts.
Ce: Advanced Studies.

*University of Helsinki
[Helsingin yliopisto]
P.O. Box 33 (Hallituskatu 8), FIN-00014 Helsingin
Tel: +358(90) 19-11-911
Fax: +358(90) 19-13-008
E-Mail: username@helsinki.fi
Telex: 124690 unih fi
Rehtori: Risto Ihamuotila (1992-95)
Hallintojohtaja (Director of Administration): Sinikka Mertano
International Relations: Vararehtori (Vice-Rector), Paul Fogelberg
Founded: 1640
F: Theology; Law; Medicine; Arts; Science; Education; Social Sciences; Agriculture and Forestry.
I: International Economic Law; Women's Study (Christina); Historical Research (Renvall); Development Studies; Biotechnology; Electron Microscopy; Seismology; High Energy Physics; Higher Energy Physics Research; Verification of Chemical Disarmament; Mathematical Research (Rolf Nevanlinna).
S: Social Science (Swedish).
Ut: Comparative Linguistics Research.
Ce: Continuing Education (Helsinki); Computer; Language.

*University of Joensuu
[Joensuun yliopisto]
P.O. Box 111, FIN-80101 Joensuu
Tel: +358(73) 151-2050
Fax: +358(73) 151-050
E-Mail: BITNET/EARN:intnl@finujo
INTERNET:intnl@joyl.joensuu.fi
Telex: 46223 joy fi
Rehtori: Paavo Pelkonen (1994-98)
Hallintojohtaja (Director of Administration): Matti Halonen
Founded: 1969, 1984
F: Education; Humanities; Science; Social Sciences; Forestry.
S: Translation Studies (Savonlinna, English, German, Russian).
D: Teacher Education.
I: Karelian Research.
Ce: Language; Computer; Extension Studies; Research and Development for Information Technology in Education.
Stations: Mekrijärvi Research.

FINLAND

*University of Jyväskylä
[Jyväskylän yliopisto]
P.O. Box 35, FIN-40351 Jyväskylä
Tel: +358(41) 60-12-11
Fax: +358(41) 60-10-11
E-Mail: sallinen@halko.jyu.fi
Telex: (library): 28219
Rehtori: Aino Sallinen (1992-97)
Hallintojohtaja (Administrative Director): Juho Hukkinen
International Relations: Marita Selosmaa
Founded: 1863, 1934, 1966
F: Education; Social Sciences; Humanities; Mathematics and Natural Sciences; Sport and Health Sciences.
I: Educational Research; Environmental Research.
Ce: Language; Economic Research; Language for Finnish Universities; Computer; Continuing Education.

*University of Kuopio
[Kuopion yliopisto]
P.O. Box 1627, FIN-70211 Kuopio
Tel: +358(71) 16-22-11
Fax: +358(71) 16-21-31
E-Mail: tuomo.teittinen@uku.fi
Telex: 42218 kuf sf
Rehtori: Ossi V. Lindqvist (1994-98)
Hallintojohtaja (Administrative Director): Tuomo Teittinen
Founded: 1966, 1984
F: Natural Sciences and Environmental Sciences; Medicine; Dentistry; Pharmacy; Social Sciences.
I: Public Health Research; Virtanen.
Ce: Language; Computer; Training and Development; Animal (National Laboratory).

*University of Lapland
[Lapin yliopisto]
P.O. Box 122, FIN-96101, Rovaniemi
Tel: +358(60) 32-42-08
Fax: +358(60) 32-42-07
E-Mail: osnelma@.levi.urova.fi
Telex: 37130 lapyo fi
Rehtori: Esko Riepula (1979-97)
Hallintojohtaja (Administrative Director): Juhani Lillberg
International Relations: Outi Snellman
Founded: 1979
F: Law; Education; Social Sciences; Art and Design.
I: Nordic Law.
Ce: Language; Arctic; Continuing Education.

*Lappeenranta University of Technology
[Lappeenrannan teknillinen korkeakoulu]
Skinnarilaankatum, P.O. Box 20, FIN-53851 Lappeenranta
Tel: +358(53) 62-111
Fax: +358(53) 62-12-350
E-Mail: juhani.jaakkola@lut.fi
Telex: 58290 ltkk sf
Rehtori: Juhani Jaakkola (1977-)

Hallintojohtaja (Administrative Director): Arto Oikkonen
International Relations: Helena Salo
Founded: 1969
D: Information Technology; Mechanical Engineering; Energy Technology; Industrial Engineering and Management; Chemical Technology; Business Administration.
Ce: Computer; Language; Continuing Education.

*University of Oulu
[Oulun yliopisto]
Kirkkokatu 11A, P.O. Box 191, FIN-90101 Oulu 10
Tel: +358(81) 55-34-011
Fax: +358(81) 37-11-58
E-Mail: marja.karjalainen@oulu.fi
Telex: 32375-oylin fi
Rehtori: Lauri Lajunen (1993-97)
Hallintojohtaja (Administrative Director): Pekka Heikkinen
International Relations: Marja Karjalainen
Founded: 1958
F: Humanities; Science; Medicine; Technology; Education.
I: Research of Northern Finland; Space Research.
Ce: Computer Services; Continuing Education; Language; Biocenter; Ecocenter.
Ut: Science Studies; Collagen Research.

*Tampere University of Technology
[Tampereen teknillinen korkeakoulu]
P.O. Box 527, FIN-33101 Tampere
Tel: +358(31) 31-62-111
Fax: +358(31) 31-62-170
E-Mail: INTERNET: tlepisto@adm.tut.fi
Telex: 22-313 ttktr-fi
Rehtori: Timo Lepistö (1985-98)
Hallintojohtaja (Director of Administration): Seppo Loimio
International Relations: Eila Hirvonen
Founded: 1965
F: Electrical Engineering; Mechanical Engineering; Civil Engineering; Architecture; Materials Engineering; Information Technology.
I: Information Technology Research.
Ce: Computer; Language; Lifelong Education (EDUTECH).

*University of Tampere
[Tampereen yliopisto]
Kalevantie 4, P.O. Box 607, FIN-33101 Tampere
Tel: +358(31) 21-56-111·
Fax: +358(31) 21-34-473
E-Mail: hvioka@uta.fi
Telex: 22263 tayk fi
Rehtori: J.K. Visakorpi (1993-96)
Hallintojohtaja (Administrative Director): Timo Lahti
International Relations: Kirsi-Marja Marnela
Founded: 1925, 1930, 1966
F: Social Sciences; Humanities; Economics and Administration; Medicine; Education.

I: Social Sciences Research; Speech Studies; Extension Studies.
Sect: Vocational Studies.
Ce: Computer; Language Teaching.

*Turku School of Economics and Business Administration
[Turun kauppakorkeakoulu]
Rehtorinpellonkatu 3, FIN-20500 Turku
Tel: +358(21) 63-83-11
Fax: +358(21) 63-83-299
E-Mail: mercurius@abo.fi
Telex: 62310 tkkk fi
Rehtori (Rector): Reino Kanerva (1978-97)
Hallintojohtaja (Administrative Director): Arno Leino
International Relations: Maija Vähämäki
Founded: 1950, 1977
D: Accounting and Finance; Administration; Marketing; Economics; Languages.
I: European Studies; East-West Trade.
Ce: Business Research and Development; Continuing Education; Finland Future; Computer.

*University of Turku
[Turun yliopisto]
FIN-20500 Turku
Tel: +358(21) 633-51
Fax: +358(21) 63-36-363
E-Mail: skoivisto@sara.cc.utu.fi
Telex: 62123 tyk sf
Rehtori: Keijo Paunio (1993-96)
Hallintojohtaja (Head of Administration): Esko Välimäki
International Relations: Vararehtori (Vice-Rector), Keijo Virtanen
Founded: 1920
F: Humanities and Arts; Social Sciences; Mathematics and Natural Sciences; Medicine; Education; Law.
I: Achipelago Research; Subarctic Research (Kevo).
Ut: Cardiorespiratory Research; Sociology of Education Research.
Ce: Maritime Studies; Language; Extension Studies; Biotechnology; Environmental Research (Satakunta).
Observatory: (Tuokla).

*University of Vaasa
[Vaasan yliopisto]
WWolffintie 36, P.O. Box 297, FIN-65101 Vaasa
Tel: +358(61) 32-48-111
Fax: +358(61) 32-48-208
E-Mail: ari.salminen@uwasa.fi
Telex: 74262 vyk fi
Rehtori: Ari Salminen (1994-98)
Hallintojohtaja (Head of Administration): Lars Nyqvist
International Relations: Päivi Laukkanen
Founded: 1966, 1980

F: Business Administration; Accounting and Industrial Management; Social Sciences; Humanities.
Ce: Continuing Education; Economic Research (Western Finland); Computer.

NATIONAL ACADEMIC BODIES

Opetusministerio
P.O. Box 293, Meritullinkatu 10, FIN-00171 Helsinki
Tel: +358(0) 13-41-71
Fax: +358(0) 65-67-65
Telex: 122079 mined fi

Council for Higher Education
[Korkeakouluneuvosto]
Pohjoisranta 4 A 9, P.O. Box 293, FIN-00171 Helsinki
Tel: +358(0) 13-41-71
Fax: +358(0) 65-67-58
Puheenjohtaja (Chairman): Reijo Vihko (1993-96)
Pääsihteeri (Secretary-General): Matti Hosia

Suomen korkeakoulujen rehtorien neuvosto
University of Helsinki, Fabinaninkatu 33, P.O. Box 3, FIN-00100 Helsinki
Tel: +358(0) 191-2335
E-Mail: markkanen@hylk.helsinki.fi
Puheenjohtaja (Chairman): Ossi V. Lindgavist (1993-94)
Pääsihteeri (Secretary-General): Tapio Markkane

Centre for International Mobility (CIMO)
[Kansainvälisen henkilövaihdon keskus CIMO]
Hakaniemenkatu, P.O. Box 343, FIN-00531 Helsinki
Tel: +358(0) 77-47-70-33
Fax: +358(0) 77-47-70-64
E-Mail: cimoinfo@oph.fi
Johtaja (Director): Lauri Lantto (1991-)
Apulaisjohtaja (Deputy Director): Anneli Milén
International Relations: Merja Lankinen
Founded: 1991

Finnish National Commission for Unesco
[Suomen Unescotoimikunta]
Ministry of Education, Meritullinhatu 10, P.O. Box 293, FIN-00171 Helsinki
Tel: +358(0) 13-41-71
Fax: +358(0) 13-41-75-86
Telex: 122079 mined fi
Cable: finnunesco helsinki
Puheenjohtaja (Chairperson): Maria-Lüsa Nevala (1993-95)
Pääsihteeri (Secretary-General): Inkeri Aarnio-Lwoff

FRANCE

UNIVERSITIES AND POLYTECHNIC INSTITUTES

PUBLIC INSTITUTIONS

University of Provence (Aix-Marseilles I)
[Université de Provence (Aix-Marseille I)]
3, Place Victor Hugo, 13331 Marseille Cedex 3
Tel: +33 91-10-60-00
Fax: +33 91-10-60-06
Président: Vincent-Paul Kaftandjian (1992-)
Secrétaire général: William Barkate
International Relations: Michel Giraud
Founded: 1413, 1896, 1970
Ut: History; Anglo-American Language, Literature and Civilization; Oriental and Slavonic Languages and Civilizations; Romance and Latin American Languages, Literature and Civilizations; Germanic Languages, Literature and Civilizations; Letters; Fine Arts, Letters, and Expression; Psychology; Sociology and Ethnology; Philosophy and Human Sciences; Mathematics and Computer Science; Physics; Chemistry; Natural Sciences; Mediterranean Studies; Geography.
I: Mechanics of Turbulence; Petroleum Chemistry and Industrial Organic Synthesis; Labour Studies.
Ce: Lifelong Education; Distance Education.

University of Aix-Marseilles II
[Université d'Aix-Marseille II]
Le Pharo, Jardin E. Duclaux, 58 boulevard Charles Livon, 13284 Marseille Cedex 07
Tel: +33 91-39-65-00
Fax: +33 91-31-31-36
Président: Claude Mercier
Secrétaire général: Paul Patriarche
International Relations: Patrick Regli
Founded: 1413, 1896, 1973
F: Economics (Aix); Medicine; Pharmacy; Dentistry.
Ut: Science (Luminy); Physical Education and Sport.
S: Engineering; Journalism and Communication.
I: Technology (IUT, Aix); Banking, Finance and Insurance (IUP); Fluid Mechanics; Labour (Aix); Mechanics of Turbulence; Geography (Aix); Human Biometrics and Careers Advising.
Ce: Tropical Health and Medicine; Communication; Lifelong Education.

University of Law, Economics and Science (Aix-Marseilles III)
[Université de Droit, d'Économie et des Sciences (Aix-Marseille III)]
3, avenue Robert Schuman, 13628 Aix-en-Provence Cedex 01
Tel: +33 42-59-99-20
Fax: +33 42-64-03-96
Telex: 420727 udesam

Président: Christian Louit
Secrétaire général: Jacques Moreau
International Relations: Maurice Flory
Founded: 1413, 1896, 1973
F: Applied Economics; Science and Technology; Law and Political Science.
Ut: Juridical Research; Science; Scientific and Technical Research; Education.
S: Physics; Synthesis and Chemical Engineering.
I: Business Administration; Business Law; Political Science; Accountancy; Analytical Chemistry and Quality Control; Regional Development; French (for foreign students); Technology (IUT, Marseille); Natural Colloid Research.
Ce: Tourism; Lifelong Education.

University of Picardie Jules-Verne, Amiens
[Université de Picardie-Jules Verne]
Chemin du Thil, 80025 Amiens Cedex 01
Tel: +33 22-82-72-72
Fax: +33 22-82-75-00
Président: Paul Personne (1994-)
Secrétaire général: Gilles Gay
International Relations: Bernard Risbourg
Founded: 1964, 1970
F: Law, Political and Social Science; Economy and Management; Letters; Philosophy and Human Sciences; History and Geography; Medicine; Pharmacy; Mathematics and Computer Sciences; Applied and Basic Sciences; Science and Technology; Foreign Languages and Cultures, and Communication Research.
I: General Administration; Psychoanalysis and Health Social Practices; Technology (IUT); Business Administration; Art.
Ce: Administrative and Political Research; Industrial Systems Research.

University of Angers
[Université d'Angers]
30, rue des Arènes, B.P. 3532, 49035 Angers Cedex
Tel: 41-23-23-23
Fax: 41-23-23-00
Telex: 41-86-96-23 unangers
Président: Pierre Jallet
Secrétaire général: Jean-Claude Connin
International Relations: Dominique Dubois
Founded: 1971, 1972
Ut: Medicine and Pharmacy; Environmental Sciences; Law, Economics, and Social Sciences; Letters and Human Sciences; Structures and Materials Science.
I: Technology (IUT); Industrial Systems Engineering (IUP); Transport, Hotel Management and Tourism (IUP).
Ce: Lifelong Education.

University of Artois
[Université d'Artois]
9, rue du Temple BP665, 2030 Arras Cedex
Tel: +33 (21) 60-30-70
Fax: +33 (21) 60-37-37
Administrateur provisoire: Alain Lottin
Secrétaire général: Marie-Paule Dejonghe
International Relations: Jacques Lesenne
*Ut: Letters; Languages; Economic and Social
Administration (IUT); Mathematics, Physics,
Chemistry and Biology (Lens); Economics;
History and Geography.
I: Technology (IUT, Lens); Technology (IUT,
Béthune).*

University of Avignon
[Université d'Avignon et des Pays de Vaucluse]
35, rue Joseph Vernet, BP 218, 8400 Avignon
Cedex
Tel: +33 90-82-68-10
Fax: +33 90-85-19-03
Telex: 432-526
Président: Bernard Blavoux (1992-)
Secrétaire général: Michel Patin
International Relations: Joel Mahe
Founded: 1972, 1984
*Ut: Letters and Human Sciences; Exact and
Natural Sciences; Applied Sciences and
Languages; Law, Political and Economic
Sciences.
I: Technology (IUT).
Ce: Lifelong Education.*

University of Franche-Comté, Besançon
[Université de Franche-Comté]
3,rue Goudimel, 25030 Besançon Cedex
Tel: +33 81-66-66-66
Fax: +33 81-66-60-09
Président: Michel Woronoff
Secrétaire général: Michel Roignot
International Relations: Patrick A. Lehmann
Founded: 1422, 1691, 1896, 1971
*Ut: Letters and Human and Social Sciences;
Science and Technology; Law, Economics and
Political Science; of Medicine and Pharmacy;
Observatory; Physical Education.
Ce: Applied Linguistics; Distance Education.
I: Lifelong Education; Technology (IUT);
Mechanical Engineering (IUP); Administration
(IUPAG); Technology (IUT, Belfort).*

University of Bordeaux I, Talence
[Université Bordeaux I]
351, cours de la Libération, 33405 Talence Cedex
Tel: +33 56-84-60-00
Fax: +33 56-80-08-37
Président: Marc Penouil
Secrétaire général: Manuel-Robert Edouard
International Relations: Dominique
Lacone-Labarthe
Founded: 1441, 1896, 1970
*Ut: Earth Sciences; Mathematics and Data
Processing; Physics; Chemistry; Biology;
Juridical Sciences (Pessac); Basic Economics
(Pessac); Advanced Economics (Pessac);
Regional Development (Pessac); Regional
Geological Studies.
S: Electronics and Radioelectrical Engineering;
Chemical and Physical Engineering.
I: Political Studies; Food Technology;
Professional Studies (IUP); Management Studies;
Mathematics Research; Marine Biology.
Ce: Lifelong Education; Technology (IUT
Gradignan).
Observatory.*

University of Bordeaux II
[Université Bordeaux II]
146, rue Léo Saignat, 33076 Bordeaux Cedex
Tel: +33 57-57-10-10
Fax: +33 56-99-03-80
Telex: unib II 572237 f
Président: Jacques Beylot
Secrétaire général: Jean-Paul Selsis
International Relations: Michel Le Bras
Founded: 1441, 1896, 1970
*Ut: Medical Sciences I; Medical Sciences II;
Medical Sciences III; Pharmaceutical Sciences;
Odontology; Tropical Medicine and Biology;
Biochemistry and Cellular Biology; Social and
Psychological Sciences.
I: Applied Human Sciences; Industrial
Pharmacy; Oenology; Physical Education and
Sport; Practical Modern Languages; Data
Processing Applied to Medical Sciences;
Electronic Microscopy; Audio-visual
Communication; Lifelong Education; Public
Health.
Ce: Medical Pedagogy; Applied Computer
Science; Medical Practitioners; Legal Medicine;
Industrial Medicine and Ergonomics.
S: Medical and Biological Sciences (Doctorate).*

University of Bordeaux III
[Université Michel de Montaigne Bordeaux III]
Domaine Universitaire, Esplanade Michel de
Montaigne, 33405 Talence Cedex
Tel: +33 56-84-50-50
Fax: +33 56-84-50-90
(1994-)
Secrétaire général: A. Marie Dudezert
International Relations: Michel Jouve
Founded: 1441, 1896, 1970
*Ut: Letters and Arts; Philosophy; History;
Geography and Regional Studies; Regional
Development and Natural Resources; German
and Scandinavian Studies; Studies of English-
speaking Countries; Iberian and Latin American
Studies; Foreign Languages and Civilizations.
I: Technology (IUT, Gradignan); Professional
Studies (IUP); Information Sciences,
Communication and Art.
Ce: Ancient History and Archaeology; Earth
Population Studies; Iberian Studies; Urban Space
Studies; Distance Education; Lifelong Education.*

University of Western Brittany, Brest
[Université de Bretagne Occidentale]
Rue des Archives, B.P. 808, 29285 Brest Cedex
Tel: +33 98-01-60-00
Fax: +33 98-31-60-01
Président: Jean-Claude Bodère (1992-)
Secrétaire général: René Firmin
International Relations: Philippe Cahuzac
Founded: 1461, 1896, 1970
Ut: Letters and Social Sciences; Science and Technology; Medicine; Law and Economics; Dentistry.
I: Marine Studies; Professional Studies (IUP); Environmental Studies; Technology (IUT); Technology (IUT, Quimper); Technology (IUT, Lorient); Ce; Breton and Celtic Studies.

University of Caen
[Université de Caen]
Esplanade de la Paix, 14032 Caen Cedex
Tel: +33 31-45-55-00
Fax: +33 31-45-56-00
Telex: 170270
Président: Claude Larsonneur (1993-)
Secrétaire général: Jean-Pierre Gohel
International Relations: Max Robba
Founded: 1437, 1970
Ut: Law and Political Science; Economics and Management; Medicine; Pharmaceutical Sciences; Human Sciences; Life and Behavioural Sciences; Soil Sciences and Regional Development; Modern Languages; History; Sciences; Physical Education and Sport; Food Technology and Nutrition.
I: Technology; Technology (Cherbourg); Business Administration; Professional Studies (IUP); Materials Science; Biochemistry and Applied Biology; Preparatory Administrative Studies (IPAG).
Ce: French (for foreign students); Computer; Lifelong Education; Distance Education.

University of Cergy-Pontoise
[Université de Cergy-Pontoise]
33, boulevard du Port, 95011 Cergy Cedex
Tel: +33 (1)3425-6000
Fax: +33 (1)3425-2904
Administrateur Provisoir: Bernard Rasult
Secrétaire général: Marlène Celermajor
International Relations: Jean-Marie Imhoff
Founded: 1993
Ut: Human Sciences; Science and Technology.
I: Technology (IUT); Professional Studies (IUP).

University of the Savoie, Chambéry
[Université de Savoie]
27, rue Marcoz, B.P. 1104, 73011 Chambéry Cedex
Tel: +33 79-75-85-85
Fax: +33 79-75-84-44
Président: Pierre Baras (1994-)
Secrétaire général: Bernard Cavarec
Ut: Science and Technology; Letters, Human and Social Sciences; Languages and Communication.

S: Environmental Engineering and Construction; Engineering (Annecy).
I: Technology (IUT, Annecy); Professional Studies (IUP).
Ce: Lifelong Education.

University of Clermont-Ferrand I
[Université d'Auvergne (Clermont-Ferrand I)]
49, boulevard Gergovia, B.P. 32, 63001 Clermont-Ferrand Cedex
Tel: +33 73-34-77-77
Fax: +33 73-35-55-18
Président: Michel Doly
Secrétaire général: Jean Ortoli
International Relations: Jean-Paul Azam
Founded: 1854, 1896, 1970
F: Juridical and Political Sciences; Economics and Management; Medicine; Pharmacy; Dentistry.
I: Hydrology and Bioclimatology; Technology (IUT); Preparatory Administrative Studies (IPAG); Lifelong Education.

University Blaise-Pascal (Clermont-Ferrand II)
[Université Blaise-Pascal (Clermont-Ferrand II)]
34, avenue Carnot, B.P. 185, 63006 Clermont-Ferrand Cedex 1
Tel: +33 73-40-63-63
Fax: +33 73-40-64-31
Président: Jean-Marc Monteil (1992-97)
Secrétaire général: Alain Roume
International Relations: Jacques-Philippe Saint-Gerand
Founded: 1854, 1896, 1970, 1987
Ut: Exact and Natural Sciences; Scientific and Technical Research; Letters and Human Sciences; Applied Foreign Languages and Communication; Psychology, Social Sciences, and Education; Technology.
S: Chemical Engineering.
I: Physical Education and Sport; Physics; Psychology and Applied Social Sciences; Mathematics Research; I. of Technology (IUT, Montluçon); Foreign Commerce (IUP); Industrial Systems Engineeing (IUP).
Ce: Distance Education; Computer.

University of Corsica
[Université Pascal Paoli-Corse]
7, avenue Jean Nicoli, B.P. 52, 20250 Corte, Corsica
Tel: +33 95-45-00-00
Fax: +33 95-46-03-21
Président: Antoine F. Bernardini
Secrétaire général: Robert Alberti
International Relations: Jacques Orsoni
Founded: 1976
Ut: Letters, Languages and Human Sciences; Sciences and Techniques.
D: Economics and Management; Law.
I: Technology (IUT).

University of Burgundy, Dijon
[Université de Bourgogne]
Campus de Montmuzard, B.P. 138, 21004 Dijon Cedex
Tel: +33 80-39-50-00
Fax: +33 80-39-50-69
Telex: unbourg 352245
Président: Jocelyne Pérard (1993-)
Secrétaire général: Dominique Martiny
International Relations: François Pitavy
F: Law and Political Sciences; Economics and Business Administration; Letters and Philosophy; Foreign Languages and Communication; Human Sciences; Science, and Technology; Pharmaceutical and Biological Sciences; Medicine; Earth Sciences.
Ut: Human Sciences and the Environment; Physical Education and Sport.
I: Technology (IUT); Technology (IUT, Le Creusot); Preparatory Administrative Studies (IPAG); Automobile and Transport Studies (ISAT, Nevers); Oenology; Educational, Teaching and Cultural Studies (IUP).
Ce: Lifelong Education.

University of the Littoral, Dunkirk
[Université du Littoral]
9, quai de la Citadelle, B.P. 1022, 59375 Dunkerque Cedex 1
Tel: +33(28) 23-73-73
Fax: +33(28) 23-73-13
Président: Alain Dubrulle
Secrétaire général: Riwonana Joffrès
International Relations: Dominique Engrand
Founded: 1993
Ce: Applied Foreign Languages (Boulogne-sur-Mer); English (Boulogne-sur-Mer); German (Boulogne-sur-Mer); Law (Boulogne-sur-Mer); Economics (Boulogne-sur-Mer); Industrial Technology (Calais); Life Sciences (Calais); Mathematics (Calais); Physics (Calais); Materials Sciences (Dunkirk); Chemistry (Dunkirk); Modern Languages (Dunkirk); Economic and Social Administration (Dunkirk); Applied Mathematics and Social Sciences (Dunkirk).
I: Technology (IUT); Industrial Systems Engineering (IUP, Calais, Dunkirk).

University of Evry-Val d'Essonne
[Université d'Evry-Val d'Essonne]
Boulevard des Coquibus, 91025 Evry Cedex
Tel: +33 1-69-47-70-00
Fax: +33 1-69-47-70-07
Administrateur provisoire: Michel Fayard
Secrétaire général: Colette Liot
International Relations: Albert Lumbroso
Founded: 1993
Ut: Science and Technology; Human Sciences, Law, Economics and Social Sciences.
I: Technology (IUT); Professional Studies (IUP).
Ce: Lifelong Education.

National Polytechnic Institute of Grenoble
[Institut National Polytechnique de Grenoble]
46, avenue Félix-Viallet, 38031 Grenoble Cedex
Tel: +33 76-57-45-00
Fax: +33 76-57-45-01
Telex: inpg 320 205 f
Président: Maurice Renaud
Secrétaire général: Pierre Balme
International Relations: Marité Janot-Giorgetti
Founded: 1901, 1971
S: Electronics and Radio-Engineering; Electronical and Metallurgical Engineering; Electrical Engineering; Physical Engineering; Hydraulic Engineering; Applied Mathematics and Data Processing; Paper Technology; Industrial Engineering.
Ce: Lifelong Education.

University 'Joseph Fourier' (Grenoble I)
[Université Joseph Fourier (Grenoble I)]
621, Avenue Centrale, Domaine universitaire, B.P. 53, Saint Martin d'Hères, 38041 Grenoble Cedex
Tel: +33 76-51-46-00
Fax: +33 76-51-48-48
Telex: 980134 F
Cable: Exacsciences 38 Grenoble
Président: Daniel Bloch (1994-)
Sécretaire général: Jean-Jacques Pellegrin
International Relations: Alain Nemoz
Founded: 1339, 1896, 1970
Ut: Physical Education and Sport; Biology; Chemistry; Geography; Geology; Computer Sciences and Applied Mathematics; Mathematics; Mechanical Engineering; Medicine (La Tronche); Pharmacy (La Tronche); Physics; Science and Techniques; Mechanics.
I: Technology (IUT); Mathematics and Computing (IUP).
Observatory.

University Pierre Mendès-France (Grenoble II)
[Université Pierre Mendès-France (Grenoble II)]
Domaine universitaire St. Martin d'Hères, B.P. 47, 38040 Grenoble Cedex
Tel: +33 76-82-54-00
Fax: +33 76-82-56-54
Telex: unisog 980-910 F
Président: André Siganos (1994-)
Secrétaire général: Nicole Malassigné
International Relations: Jacqueline Domenach
Founded: 1339, 1896, 1970
Ut: Economics; Economic Development and Social Change; Law; Human Sciences (History, Arts, Philosophy, Social Geography); Human and Social Sciences, and Applied Mathematics.
I: Political Studies; Business Administration; Technology (IUT); Technology (IUT, Valence).
Ce: Lifelong Education.

University Stendhal (Grenoble III)
[Université Stendhal (Grenoble III)]
Domaine St. Martin d'Hères, B.P. 25, 38040
Grenoble Cedex
Tel: +33 76-82-43-00
Fax: +33 76-82-43-84
Telex: unisog 980910 F
Président: André Sigamos
Secrétaire général: Jean-Louis Reffet
Founded: 1339, 1896, 1970
*Ut: Classic and Modern Letters; Communication;
Languages; Foreign Languages, Literature and
Civilizations; English and Anglo-American
Language, Literature and Civilization.*
I: Information and Communication (IUP).
*Ce: French Studies (for foreign students);
Lifelong Education.*

University of Le Havre
[Université du Havre]
25 rue Philippe Lebon, B.P. 1123, 76063 Le Havre
Cedex
Tel: +33 35-19-55-00
Fax: 35-21-49-59
Président: Michel Leduc
Secrétaire général: Jacques Riou
International Relations: Michel Hiscock
Founded: 1984
F: International Trade; Science and Techniques.
*I: Technology (IUT); Commerce and Marketing
(IUP).*
Ce: Lifelong Education.

University of Science and Technology (Lille I) Villeneuve d'Ascq
[Université des Sciences et Technologies de Lille
(Lille I)]
Domaine Universitaire scientifique, 59655
Villeneuve d'Ascq Cedex
Tel: +33 20-43-43-43
Fax: +33 20-43-49-95
Telex: Euror 136339F
Président: Pierre Louis (1992-)
Secrétaire général: Yves Chaimbault
International Relations: Vincent Cordonnier
Founded: 1560, 1896, 1970
*Ut: Economic and Social Sciences;
Mathematics; Data Processing, Electronics and
Automation; Physics; Chemistry; Biology; Earth
Sciences; Geography; Marine and Regional
Biology (Wimereux); Agriculture.*
S: Chemical Engineering; Engineering.
*I: Research on the Teaching of Mathematics;
Fluid Mechanics; Business Administration;
Mathematics and Computer Sciences (IUP);
Commerce and Marketing (IUP); Management
(IUP); Technology (IUT, Lille).*
Ce: Lifelong Education.

University of Law and Health Sciences (Lille II)
[Université du Droit et de la Santé (Lille II)]
42, rue Paul Duez, 59800 Lille
Tel: +33 20-52-56-29
Fax: +33 20-88-24-32
Président: Jean Léonardelli (1994-)
Secrétaire général: Guy Bailleul
International Relations: Alain Vernes
*Ut: Medicine; Pharmacy; Physical Education and
Sport (Ronchin).*
*F: Dentistry; Juridical, Political and Social
Sciences (Villeneuve d'Ascq).*
*I: Speech Therapy; Pharmaceutical Chemistry;
Forensic and Social Medicine; Technology (IUT,
Roubaix); Lifelong Education.*

Charles de Gaulle University of Human Sciences, Literature and Arts (Lille III) Villeneuve d'Ascq
[Université Charles de Gaulle Sciences
humaines, Lettres et Arts (Lille III)]
B.P. 149 'Pont de Bois', 59653 Villeneuve d'Ascq
Cedex
Tel: +33 20-33-60-00
Fax: +33 20-91-91-71
Président: Bernard Alluin (1994-)
Secrétaire général: Pascal Joly
International Relations: Dominique Roselle
Founded: 1560, 1896, 1970
*Ut: History, History of Art, and Archaeology;
Language, Literature and Civilizations of English-
speaking Countries; German Studies; Roman,
Slavonic and Oriental Studies; Ancient
Languages; French Linguistics and Literary
Studies; Mathematics, Economics, and Social
Sciences; Philosophy; Psychology; Readaptation
Technology.*
D: Applied Foreign Languages; Education.
*I: Technology (IUT, Tourcoing); Information and
Communication (IUP, Roubaix).*
Ce: Lifelong Education.

University of Limoges
[Université de Limoges]
Hôtel Burgy, 13 rue de Genève, 87065 Limoges
Cedex
Tel: +33 55-45-76-01
Fax: +33 55-45-76-34
Président: Jean-Claude Vareille
Secrétaire général: Yvan Tchéfranoff
International Relations: Maurice Dumont
Founded: 1626, 1909, 1970
F: Medicine; Pharmacy; Law and Economics.
Ut: Letters and Human Sciences; Sciences.
S: Engineering (ENSIL).
*I: Research on the Teaching of Mathematics;
Preparatory Administrative Studies (IPAG);
Communication (IRCON) (Regional); Technology
(IUT); Management (IUP).*
*Ce: Environmental Research (CRIDEAU); Law
and Economics of Sport; Lifelong Education.*

*University Claude Bernard (Lyons I) Villeurbanne
[Université Claude Bernard (Lyon I)]
43, boulevard du 11 novembre 1918, 69622 Villeurbanne Cedex
Tel: +33 72-44-80-00
Fax: +33 72-43-10-20
Telex: 330 208
Président: Gérard Fontaine
Secrétaire général: Jacques Flacher
International Relations: Edgar Elbaz
Founded: 1809, 1896, 1970
Ut: Medicine (Grange-Blanche); Medicine (Alexis-Carrel); Medicine (Lyon Nord); Medicine (Lyon Sud); Pharmacy; Dentistry; Physical Education and Sport.
I: Readaptation Techniques; Material Sciences; Engineering and Technological Development; Chemistry, and Molecular and Cellular Biology; Systems Analysis; Earth, Ocean, Atmospheric, Space and Environmental Sciences; Scientific and Technical Engineering (ISTIL) (Lyon); Observatory; Environmental Engineering (IUP); Technology (IUT); Technology (IUT, Villeurbanne).
Ce: Lifelong Education.

*University of Lyons II
[Université Lumière (Lyon II)]
86, rue Pasteur, 69365 Lyon Cedex 07
Tel: +33 78-69-70-00
Fax: +33 78-69-56-01
Telex: 330637
Président: Eric Froment
Secrétaire général: Jean Bayle
International Relations: Jean Claude Lasserre
Founded: 1809, 1896, 1970
F: Economics and Management; Juridical Studies (Bron); Psychology and Social Sciences; Languages; History and Geography, Arts and Environmental Sciences (Bron).
I: Psychological, Sociological, and Pedagogical Sciences; Labour Studies; Teacher Training; Political Studies; Technology (IUT, Bron).
Ce: French (for foreign students); Lifelong Education.

University Jean Moulin (Lyons III)
[Université Jean Moulin (Lyon III)]
1, rue de l'Université, B.P. 0638, 69239 Lyon Cedex 02
Tel: +33 72-72-20-20
Fax: +33 72-72-20-50
Telex: 380-311 F
Président: Henri Roland (1994-)
Secrétaire général: Jean-Claude Migraine-George
International Relations: Olivier Moreteen
Founded: 1809, 1896, 1973
F: Law; Philosophy; Letters and Civilizations; Languages.
I: Business Administration; Labour Studies; History of Christianity; Technology (IUT); International Affairs (IUP); Health Services

Management (IUP); Rhone Studies; Population Studies; Indo-European Studies.
Ce: Lifelong Education.

University of Maine-Le Mans
[Université du Maine-Le Mans]
Avenue Olivier Messiaen, B.P. 535, 72017 Le Mans Cedex
Tel: +33 43-83-30-00
Fax: +33 43-83-30-77
Président: Alain Pleurdeau
Secrétaire général: Denise Landry
International Relations: Jean-Louis Fourquet
Founded: 1969, 1976
F: Science; Letters and Humanities; Law and Economics.
Ce: Lifelong Education.
I: Electrical Engineering and Industrial Computing (IUP); Management and Social Engineering (IUP); Technology (IUT).

University of Metz
[Université de Metz]
Ile du Saulcy, B.P. 794, 57012 Metz Cedex 1
Tel: +33 87-31-50-50
Fax: +33 87-31-50-55
Telex: unimetz 930462 F
Président: Gérard Nauroy (1993-)
Secrétaire général: J. Diebolt
International Relations: Jean-Louis Bretonnet
Founded: 1970
Ut: Mathematics, Informatics, and Mechanics; Basic and Applied Sciences; Letters and Human Sciences; Law.
I: Technology (IUT); Mechanical Engineering (IUP); Industrial Systems Engineering (IUP); Information and Communication (IUP); Franco-German of Economics and Technology of Sarreguemines; Business Administration.
Ce: Lifelong Education.

University of Montpellier I
[Université de Montpellier I]
5, boulevard Henri IV, B.P. 1017, 34006 Montpellier Cedex
Tel: +33 67-41-74-00
Fax: +33 67-41-02-46
Président: Yves Loubatières (1994-)
Secrétaire général: Jacques Cronert
International Relations: Jean Castel
Founded: 1220, 1896, 1970
Ut: Law and Social Sciences; Economics; Business Administration; Juridical, Economic and Social Research; Industrial Pharmacy; Pharmacy; Dentistry; Medicine; Food Technology.
I: Industrial Pharmacy (European); Business (ISEM); Health Services (IUP); Commerce and Marketing (IUP); Engineering and Management (IUP).
Ce: Administrative Studies; Lifelong Education.

Languedoc University of Science and Technology (Montpellier II)

[Université des Sciences et Techniques du Languedoc (Montpellier II)]
Place Eugène Bataillon, 34095 Montpellier Cedex 05
Tel: +33 67-14-30-30
Fax: +33 67-14-30-31
Telex: stmont 490944 F
Président: Yves Escoufier (1994-)
Secrétaire général: Bernard Biau
International Relations: Pierre Vitse
Ut: Fundamental and Applied Sciences.
S: Chemical Engineering.
I: Engineering Sciences (ISIM); Business Administration; Electrical Engineering and Industrial Computing (IUP); Mathematic Engineering and Computing (IUP); Technology (IUT); Technology (IUT, Nimes).
Ce: Lifelong Education.

University Paul Valéry (Montpellier III)

[Université Paul Valéry (Montpellier III)]
Route de Mende, B.P. 5043, 34032 Montpellier Cedex 1
Tel: +33 67-14-20-00
Fax: +33 67-14-20-52
Président: Jules Maurin
Secrétaire général: Stanislas Kubiak
International Relations: Pierre Vitoux
Founded: 1220, 1896, 1970
Ut: Letters, Philosophy, Arts and Linguistics; Anglo-American, German, Slav and Oriental Studies; Human and Environmental Sciences; Economics, Mathematics and Social Sciences; Sociology and Ethnology; Romance and Mediteranean Languages.
D: Lifelong Education.

Haute-Alsace University (Mulhouse)

[Université de Haute-Alsace (Mulhouse)]
2, rue des Frères Lumière, 68093 Mulhouse Cedex
Tel: +33 89-59-63-00
Fax: +33 89-59-63-19
Telex: 880400F; F21198 (telex par télématique)
Président: Gilles Prado
Secrétaire général: Alain Collange
International Relations: Jean-Pierre Gérard
Founded: 1970, 1975, 1977
Ut: Science and Techniques; Polytechnic Research.
F: Letters and Human Sciences; Economics and Social Sciences.
S: Chemical Engineering; Textile Engineering; Applied Sciences for Engineering.
I: Commerce and Marketing (IUP); Technology (IUT); Technology (IUT, Colmar).
Ce: Lifelong Education.

National Polytechnical Institute of Lorraine Vandoeuvre-les-Nancy

[Institut National Polytechnique de Lorraine]
2, Avenue de la Forêt-de-Haye, B.P. 3, 54501 Vandoeuvre-les-Nancy
Tel: +33 83-59-59-59
Fax: +33 83-59-59-55
Président: Michel Lucius
Secrétaire général: Noël Gand
International Relations: Jean-Paul Tisot
Founded: 1872, 1970, 1976
Ut: Industrial Systems Engineering.
S: Materials Engineering (European); Industrial Techniques; Electrical and Mechanical Engineering; Agriculture and Food Industries; Mining; Chemical Industries; Applied Geology and Prospecting.
D: Lifelong Education.

University of Nancy I

[Université de Nancy I]
24-30, rue Lionnois, B.P. 3069, 54013 Nancy Cedex
Tel: +33 83-32-81-81
Fax: +33 83-32-95-90
Telex: Nancyun 960646 F
Président: Jean-Pierre Finance (1994-)
Secrétaire général: Georges Paull
International Relations: Georges Rocci
Founded: 1572, 1896, 1970
Ut: Medicine; Pharmaceutical Sciences; Dentistry; Sciences of Matter; Biological Sciences; Sport and Physical Education; Mathematics, Computing and Automation; Science and Technologies of Engineering; Science and Technology of the Wood Industry; Computing and Applications (ESIAL).
I: Technology (IUT, Longwy); Electrical Engineering and Industrial Informatics (IUP).

University of Nancy II

[Université Nancy II]
25, rue Baron Louis, B.P. 454, 54001 Nancy Cedex
Tel: +33 83-34-46-00
Fax: +33 83-30-05-65
Président: René Hodot (1991-96)
Secrétaire général: Pascal Aimé
International Relations: Henriah Holec
Founded: 1572, 1896, 1970
Ut: Literature; Foreign Languages and Literature; History and Geography; Knowledge of Mankind; Language Sciences; Mathematics and Computer Sciences; Law, Economics, and Management.
I: Administrative and Political Studies; Commerce; Labour Studies; Technology (IUT); Audio-visual and Cinema Studies (European); Preparatory Administrative Studies (IPAG); Banking, Finance and Insurance (IUP); Information and Communication (IUP).
Ce: European; Distance Education.

*University of Nantes
[Université de Nantes]
1, quai de Tourville, B.P. 1026, 44035 Nantes
Cedex 01
Tel: +33 40-99-83-83
Fax: +33 40-99-83-00
Telex: 700579
President: Jacques-Henri Jayez (1992-)
Secrétaire général: Christian Palu-Laboureu
Founded: 1962, 1970
*Ut: Medicine; Pharmacy; Dentistry; Law and
Political Science; Economics; History and
Sociology; Foreign Languages; Letters and
Human Sciences; Science.*
*I: Geography and Regional Development;
Business Administration; Preparatory
Administrative Studies (IPAG); Electronic
Techniques; Thermodynamics and Materials
(ISITEM); Banking, Finance and Insurance (IUP);
Chemical Engineering (IUP); Technology (IUT);
Technology (IUT, Saint-Nazaire).*
Ce: Lifelong Education.

University of Nice-Sophia Antipolis
[Université de Nice-Sophia Antipolis]
Parc Valrose, 28, avenue Valrose, 06108 Nice
Cedex 02
Tel: +33 93-52-98-98
Fax: +33 93-51-91-91
Président: Jean-Pierre Laheurte
Secrétaire général: Alain Deliau
International Relations: Pascal Arnaud
Founded: 1965, 1970
*Ut: Dentistry; Law of International Business and
Development; Physical Education and Sport;
Culture and Space; Sciences.*
*F: Medicine; Law and Economics; Letters and
Human Sciences.*
*S: Computer Sciences; Engineering (Nice-
Sophia-Antipolis).*
*I: Management (IUP); Mediterranean Studies;
Economics (IUP); Technology (IUT); Business
Administration.*
*Ce: Geodynamic and Astronomical Studies;
Preventive Medicine; Mature Students; Lifelong
Education.*

University of Orléans
[Université d'Orléans]
Château de la Source, B.P. 6749, 45067 Orléans
Cedex 02
Tel: +33 38-41-71-71
Fax: +33 38-41-70-69
Président: Didier Billard (1992-)
Secrétaire général: Christophe Courtin
International Relations: Julie Sabiani
Founded: 1962, 1970
*Ut: Law, Economics and Management; Basic
and Applied Sciences; Sciences and Advanced
Technologies; Sport and Physical Education.*
F: Letters and Human Sciences.

*I: Technology (IUT); Technology (IUT, Bourges);
Technology (IUT, Châteauroux); Chemical
Engineering (IUP); Management (IUP).*
Ce: Lifelong Education.

University of Paris I (Panthéon-Sorbonne)
[Université de Paris I (Panthéon-Sorbonne)]
12, Place du Panthéon, 75231 Paris Cedex 05
Tel: +33 1-46-34-97-00
Fax: +33 1-46-34-20-56
Président: Yves Jegouzo (1994-)
Secrétaire général: Tristan Chalon
Founded: XIIthc., 1970
*Ut: Management and Economics of Enterprises;
Economics; Economic and Social Administration,
and Labour and Social Studies; Business Law;
Law, Administration and Public Sector; Political
Science; International and European Studies; Art
History and Archaeology; Plastic Arts and
Science of Art; Geography; History; Mathematics,
Computer Sciences and Statistics; Philosophy.*
*I: Business Administration; Economic and Social
Development Studies; Social Sciences of Labour;
Demography; Mathematics and Applied
Economics; Tourism.*
*D: Languages; Law; Social Sciences; Physical
and Sports Activities.*
Ce: Audio-visual; Lifelong Education.

*University Panthéon-Assas (Paris II)
[Université Panthéon-Assas (Paris II)]
12, place du Panthéon, 75231 Paris Cedex 05
Tel: +33 1-44-41-57-00
Fax: +33 1-44-41-55-13
Président: Philippe Ardant (1993-)
Secrétaire général: Renaud Rhim
Founded: XIIthc., 1970
*Ut: Private General Law; Economics; Penal
Studies and Criminology and Social Adjustment;
History and Sociology of Institutions and
Economy; Business Law; Public Administration;
Political Science; European, International and
Comparative Legal and Economic Studies.*
*I: French Press; Criminology; International
Studies; Comparative Law; Business Law; Roman
Law; Juridical Studies.*
*D: Labour Studies; Social Psychology and
Juridical Sociology; Modern Languages and
Civilizations; Computer Sciences.*
Ce: Lifelong Education.

University of the New Sorbonne (Paris III)
[Université de la Sorbonne Nouvelle (Paris III)]
17, rue de la Sorbonne, 75230 Paris Cedex 05
Tel: +33 1-40-46-28-80
Fax: +33 1-43-25-74-71
Président: Suzy Halimi
Secrétaire général: Eliane Lagarde-Klepping
Founded: XIIthc., 1970
*Ut: Language and Literature and Civilizations of
English-speaking countries; Linguistics and
Phonetics; Italian and Romanian; Iberian and
Latin American Studies; General and
Comparative Literature; French (for teaching*

abroad); German; Oriental and Arab Studies;
French and Latin Literature and Linguistics.
S: Interpreters and Translators.
I: Latin American Languages and Civilizations;
Theatre; Cinema and Audio-visual Studies.
D: Physical Education.
Ce: Lifelong Education.

University of Paris-Sorbonne (Paris IV)
[Université Paris-Sorbonne (Paris IV)]
1, rue Victor Cousin, 75230 Paris Cedex 05
Tel: (1) 40-46-22-11
Fax: (1) 40-46-25-88
Président: Jean-Pierre Poussou (1993-)
Secrétaire générale: Annie Richard-Lebrun
International Relations: Jean-Pierre Poussou
Founded: XIIthc., 1970
Ut: History of Art and Archaeology; French
Literature; French Language; Latin; Greek;
History; Geography; Philosophy; Germanic
Studies; Slavonic Studies; English and North
American Studies; Italian and Romanian Studies;
Iberian and Latin American Studies; Music and
Musicology.
I: Western Modern Civilizations; Information and
Communication Sciences; Applied Human
Sciences.
D: Mathematics and Data Processing (Applied
to Human Sciences); Arabic and Islamic Studies;
Experimental Studies.
Ce: Applied Foreign Languages; Sciences of
Language; French and Comparative Literatures;
Foreign Literatures and Cultures; Philosophy and
Social Sciences; Classical World and its Legacy;
Medieval Studies; History and Modern
Civilizations; Geography and Urban Studies;
Contemporary Societies; History of Art and
Archaeology; Sciences of Religions and Religious
Anthropology; Lifelong Education.

University René Descartes (Paris V)
[Université René Descartes (Paris V)]
12, rue de l'Ecole de Médecine, 75270 Paris
Cedex 06
Tel: +33 1-40-46-16-16
Fax: +33 1-40-46-16-15
E-Mail: minitel 3615 code paris5
Telex: 250821F Paris V
Président: Pierre Villard (1994-)
Secrétaire général: C. Potier
Founded: XIIthc., 1970
Ut: Social Sciences; Psychology; Educational
Sciences; Mathematics and Computer Sciences;
General and Applied Linguistics; Forensic
Medicine and Medical Law; Biomedical Studies;
Physical Education and Sports.
F: Medicine (Hôpital Cochin-Port Royal);
Medicine (Hôpital Necker-Enfants Malades);
Medicine (Hôpital Paris-Ouest); Dentistry;
Pharmaceutical and Biological Sciences; Law.

I: Psychology; Technology (IUT).
Ce: Lifelong Education.

*University Pierre and Marie Curie (Paris VI)
[Université Pierre et Marie Curie (Paris VI)]
4, place Jussieu, 75252 Paris Cedex 05
Tel: +33 1-44-27-44-27
Fax: +33 1-44-27-38-29
Telex: 200-145
Président: Jean Claude Legrand (1991-)
Secrétaire général: Pierre Endrivet
International Relations: Minko Balkansi
Founded: XIIthc., 1970
Ut: Pure Theoretical and Applied Mathematics;
Calculation and Mathematics; Data Processing;
Mechanics, Energetics and Robotics; Electronics,
Electrical Engineering, Automation, and Applied
Physics; Theoretical and Applied Physics;
Chemistry; Life Sciences; Earth Sciences and
Environment Studies; Marine Observatories
(Roscoff, Banuyls, and Villefranche-sur-Mer).
F: Medicine (Hôpital Saint-Antoine); Medicine
(Hôpital Broussais); Medicine (Hôpital Pitié-
Salpêtrière); Dentistry.
S: Chemistry.
I: Science and Technology.
D: Modern Languages; Physical Education and
Sport.
Ce: Lifelong Education.

*University Denis-Diderot (Paris VII)
[Université Denis-Diderot (Paris VII)]
2, place Jussieu, 75251 Paris Cedex 05
Tel: +33 1-44-27-44-27
Fax: +33 1-44-27-69-64
Telex: 270075 pariset
Président: Jean-Pierre Dedonder
Secrétaire général: Pierre Maussion
International Relations: Pierre Chartier
Founded: XIIthc., 1970
Ut: Mathematics; Physics; Chemistry; Biology
Sciences of Nature and Life; Biochemistry;
Sciences of Texts and Documents; Social
Sciences; Clinical Human Sciences;
Anthropology, Ethnology, and Science of
Religions; Area Studies; East Asian Studies;
Medicine (Xavier Bichat); Medicine (Lariboisière-
Saint-Louis); Dentistry; English Studies; Earth
Sciences.
I: Technology (IUT); Mathematic Didactics
Research; Mathematics and Industrial Computing
(IUP).
D: Physical Education and Sport; Applied
Languages; Didactics of Scientific Disciplines;
Linguistics; Management and Protection of the
Environment; Cinema, Communication and
Information.
D: Lifelong Education; Continuing Education.
Ce: Computer Assisted Teaching (National).

224

University of Vincennes at Saint-Denis (Paris VIII)
[Université de Vincennes à Saint-Denis (Paris VIII)]
2, rue de la Liberté, 93526 Saint-Denis Cedex 02
Tel: +33 1-49-40-67-89
Fax: +33 1-48-21-04-46
Président: Jean-Claude Mela (1994-)
Secrétaire général: Bernard Civeyrac
Founded: XIIthc., 1970
*Ut: Arts, Philosophy, and Aesthetics;
Administration Studies; Territorial, Economic and
Social Studies; Literature, History, and Sociology;
Foreign Languages and Culture; Computer
Sciences, Linguistics, and Technology;
Psychology; Communication and Education.
I: Urban Studies.*

University Paris-Dauphine (Paris IX)
[Université Paris-Dauphine (Paris IX)]
Place du Maréchal de Lattre-de-Tassigny, 75775
Paris Cedex 16
Tel: +33 1-44-05-44-0511 +33 1-44-05-41-41
Telex: 699322 upd
Président: Ivar Ekeland
Secrétaire général: Josette Mouly
International Relations: Guy Terny
Founded: XIIthc., 1970
*Ut: Business Administration and Applied
Economics (1st cycle); Business Administration
(2nd cycle); Applied Economics (2nd cycle);
Organization Sciences (3rd cycle); Mathematics
of Decision-Making; Computer Sciences.
Ce: Lifelong Education.*

University of Paris X (Nanterre)
[Université de Paris X (Nanterre)]
200, avenue de la République, 92001 Nanterre
Cedex
Tel: +33 1-40-97-72-00
Fax: +33 1-40-97-75-71
Telex: 63-08-98 upxnant
Président: Michel Imberty (1994-)
Secrétaire général: Monique Fayeton
International Relations: Danièle Frison
Founded: XIIthc., 1970
*Ut: Physical and Sports Techniques; Anglo-
American Studies; Germanic, Slavonic, Iberian
and Italian Studies and Applied Foreign
Languages; Economics, Management, Applied
Mathematics and Social Sciences; Letters,
Linguistics and Philosophy; Juridical and Political
Sciences; Psychology and Educational Sciences;
Economics, Management, Applied Mathematics
and Social Sciences and Administration.
I: Technology (IUT, Ville-d'Avray).
Ce: Lifelong Education.*

University Paris-Sud (Paris XI) Orsay
[Université Paris-Sud (Paris XI)]
Centre scientifique, 15, rue Georges Clémenceau,
91405 Orsay Cedex
Tel: +33 1-69-41-67-50
Fax: +33 1-69-41-61-35
Telex: 692166 F
Président: Alain Gaudemer
Secrétaire général: Pierre Lafond
International Relations: Jean-François Vinson
Founded: XIIthc., 1970
*Ut: Basic Scientific and Medical Studies (1st
cycle); Pharmacy and Biology (Châtenay-
Malabry); Linear Accelerator; Medicine (Kremlin-
Bicêtre); Juridicial and Economic Sciences
(Sceaux); Human Hygiene and Ecology
(Châtenay-Malabry); Therapeutic Chemistry
(Châtenay-Malabry).
S: Sciences; Electrical Engineering.
I: Preparatory Administrative Studies (IPAG);
Electrical Engineering and Industrial Computing
(Cachan); Commerce and Marketing (Sceaux);
Technology (IUT, Orsay); Technology (IUT,
Cachan); Technology (IUT, Sceaux).
Ce: Lifelong Education.*

University of Paris Val-de-Marne (Paris XII)
[Université Paris Val-de-Marne (Paris XII)]
61, avenue du Général de Gaulle, 94010 Créteil
Cedex
Tel: +33 1-45-17-10-00
Fax: +33 1-42-07-70-12
Telex: 211752 upvm
Président: Bernard Dizambourg (1991-96)
Secrétaire général: Pierre Ulrich
International Relations: Pierre-Louis Fagnez
Founded: XIIthc., 1970
*Ut: Medicine; Law and Political Science (La
Varenne-St.-Hilaire); Letters and Human
Sciences; Economics and Management (La
Varenne-St. Hilaire); Sciences and Technology;
Business Administration and Exchanges;
Communication and Social Integration.
I: Town Planning; Technology (IUT); Preparatory
Administrative Studies (IPAG); Transport, Hotel
Management and Tourism (IUP); Commerce and
Marketing (IUP).
D: Lifelong Education.*

University of Paris-Nord (Paris XIII)
[Université Paris-Nord (Paris XIII)]
Avenue Jean-Baptiste Clément, 93430
Villetaneuse
Tel: +33 1-49-40-30-00
Fax: +33 1-49-40-33-33
Telex: 610670 usinor
Président: Jean-François Mela
Secrétaire général: Jean-Paul Barbier
International Relations: Pierre Jaisson

Founded: XIIthc., 1970
Ut: *Law and Social and Political Sciences; Economics and Management; Communication Sciences; Letters and Human Sciences.*
I: *Information and Communication (IUP); Banking, Finance, and Insurance (IUP); Management (IUP); Technology (IUT); Technology (IUT, Saint-Denis).*
Ce: *Science and Polytechnical (Saint-Denis); Medical and Biological Sciences (Bobigny); Lifelong Education.*

University of Pau
[Université de Pau et des Pays de l'Adour]
B.P. 576, 64012 Pau University Cedex
Tel: +33 59-92-30-00
Fax: +33 59-80-83-80
Président: Claude Laugenie
Secrétaire général: Jean Ravon
International Relations: Jean-Pierre Montfort
Founded: 1970
F: *Letters, Languages, and Human Sciences; Exact and Natural Sciences; Law, Economics and Management; Sciences and Techniques.*
S: *Engineering.*
I: *Business Administration; Materials Engineering (IUP); Management (IUP); Technology (IUT, Bayonne); Technology (IUT, Pays de l'Adour).*
D: *Mature Students.*
Ce: *Lifelong Education (FORCO).*

University of Perpignan
[Université de Perpignan]
52, avenue de Villeneuve, 66860 Perpignan Cedex
Tel: +33 68-66-20-00
Fax: +33 68-66-20-19
Telex: 505005
Président: Jean Sagnes
Secrétaire général: Serge Reyna
Founded: 1970
F: *Human, Legal, Economic and Social Sciences; Exact and Natural Sciences.*
I: *Business Administration; Transport, Hotel Management and Tourism (IUP); Industrial Systems (IUP); Technology (IUT).*
Ce: *Lifelong Education.*

University of Poitiers
[Université de Poitiers]
15, rue de Blossac, 86034 Poitiers Cedex
Tel: +33 49-45-30-30
Fax: +33 49-45-30-50
Telex: 793 450f
Président: Alain Tranoy (1994-)
Secrétaire général: Hélène Brochet-Toutini
Founded: 1431, 1970
Ut: *Juridical and Social Sciences; Economics; Basic and Applied Sciences; Languages and Literatures; Human Sciences; Physical Education and Sport; Medicine and Pharmacy.*
S: *Mechanical and Aeronautical Engineering; Engineering.*

I: *Business Administration; Industrial Systems Engineering (IUP); Commerce and Marketing (IUP); Technology (IUT); Technology (IUT, Angoulême).*
D: *Audio-Visual Studies.*
Ce: *Medieval Studies; Aerodynamic and Thermic Studies; Lifelong Education.*

*University of Rheims Champagne-Ardennes
[Université de Reims Champagne-Ardennes]
23, rue Boulard, 51096 Reims Cedex
Tel: +33 26-05-30-00
Fax: +33 26-05-30-98
Président: Claude Séverin (1992-97)
Secrétaire général: Jean-Pierre Leclère
Founded: 1967, 1970
Ut: *Law and Political Science; Letters and Human Sciences; Medicine; Dentistry; Pharmacy; Economics and Management; Exact and Natural Sciences.*
S: *Packaging.*
I: *Teacher Training; Technical Training (Charleville-Mézières); Technology (IUT); Technology (IUT, Troyes).*
Ce: *Lifelong Education; Distance Education.*

University of Rennes I
[Université de Rennes I]
2, rue du Thabor, 35065 Rennes Cedex
Tel: +33 99-25-36-36
Fax: +33 99-25-36-00
Président: Jacques Lenfant (1994-)
Secrétaire générale: Annie Julien
International Relations: Marie-Liesse Hoube
Founded: 1461
Ut: *Juridical Sciences; Economics and Applied Economics; Medical Sciences; Pharmaceutical and Biological Sciences; Dentistry; Structure and Properties of Matter; Behavioural and Environmental Sciences; Mathematics; Philosophy.*
S: *Applied Sciences and Technology (Lannion).*
I: *Computer Science and Communication; Management; Preparative Administrative Studies (IPAG); Political Studies; Computing Sciences and Random Systems (Research); Mathematics (Research); Research and Technologies Applied to Health; Mathematics and Computing; Technology (IUT); Technology (IUT, Lannion).*

University of Haute-Bretagne (Rennes II)
[Université de Haute-Bretagne (Rennes II)]
6, avenue Gaston-Berger, 35043 Rennes Cedex
Tel: +33 99-33-52-52
Fax: +33 99-33-51-75
Président: André Lespagnol
Secrétaire général: Hervé Latimier
International Relations: Patrick Thoreau
Founded: 1461, 1970
Ut: *Physical Education and Sports; Arts, Letters and Communication; Social Sciences; Human Sciences; Foreign and Regional Languages and Cultures.*

I: Labour Social Sciences; Information and Communication (IUP); Mathematics and Computing (IUP); Technology (IUT, Vannes).
Ce: Lifelong Education.

University of La Rochelle
[Université de La Rochelle]
23, rue Albert Einstein, 17071 La Rochelle Cedex 9
Tel: +33 46-459-114
Fax: +33 46-449-376
Administrateur provisoire: Yves Pimont
Secrétaire général: Gérard Mazières
Founded: 1993
Ut: Law; Sciences and Techniques; Human Sciences.
I: Commerce and Marketing (IUP); Mathematics and Industrial Computing (IUP); Technology (IUT).

University of Rouen-Haute-Normandie
[Université de Rouen-Haute Normandie]
1 Rue Thomas Becket, B.P. 138, 76821 Mont-Saint-Aignan Cedex
Tel: +33 35-14-60-00
Fax: +33 35-14-63-48
Telex: 770127 univrou
Président: Jean-Marie Carpentier (1993-)
Secrétaire général: Emile Poirier
International Relations: Bernard Maitrot
Founded: 1966, 1970
Ut: Law, Economics and Management; Letters and Human Sciences; Medicine and Pharmacy; Psychology, Sociology and Education; Science and Technology; Physical Education and Sport.
I: Business Administration; Preparatory Administrative Studies (IPAG); Mathematics and Industrial Computing (IUP); Technology (IUT).
Ce: Lifelong Education.

Jean Monnet University Saint-Etienne
[Université Jean Monnet-Saint-Etienne]
34, rue Francis Baulier, 42023 Saint-Etienne Cedex 02
Tel: +33 77-42-17-00
Fax: +33 77-42-17-99
Telex: 300816 unistet
Président: Bernard Etlicher
Secrétaire général: Pierre Bessenay
International Relations: Yves Bouveret
Founded: 1970
F: Law and Management; Arts, Communication, and Education; Letters, Languages and Human Sciences; Science and Technology; Medicine.
I: Labour Studies; French Language (for foreign students); Advanced Studies (ISTASE); Industrial Systems (IUP); Management (IUP); Technology (IUT); Technology (IUT, Roanne).
Ce: Lifelong Education.

Louis Pasteur University (Strasbourg I)
[Université Louis Pasteur (Strasbourg I)]
4, rue Blaise Pascal, 67070 Strasbourg Cedex
Tel: +33 88-41-60-00
Fax: +33 88-60-75-50
Telex: 870260 ulp
Président: Adrien Schmitt
Secrétaire général: Jacques Soulas
International Relations: Monique Flasaquer
Founded: 1537
Ut: Pharmaceutical Sciences; Mathematics and Computer Sciences.
F: Medical Sciences; Odontological Sciences; Chemistry; Physics; Life and Earth Sciences; Behavioural and Environmental Sciences; Economics and Management; Geography.
S: Advanced Studies in Physics; Polymer Engineering (Graduate); Biotechnology; Chemical Industries (European).
I: Engineering Science (IUP, for Senior citizens); Technology (IUT).
Ce: Primatology.
D: Further Education.
Astronomical Observatory.

University of Human Sciences (Strasbourg II)
[Université des Sciences humaines (Strasbourg II)]
22, rue Descartes, 67084 Strasbourg Cedex
Tel: +33 88-41-73-00
Fax: +33 88-41-73-54
Président: Albert Hamm (1993-)
Secrétaire général: René Deshayes
Founded: 1437, 1970
Ut: Classical Languages;; Foreign Languages, Literature and Civilizations; Philosophy, Linguistics, and Communication; Social Sciences; Historical Sciences; Arts; Applied Languages and Human Sciences; Physical Education and Sport.
I: Protestant Theology; Catholic Theology; Translation and Interpretation; French Studies.
Ce: Distant Education.
D: Lifelong Education.

Robert Schuman University (Strasbourg III)
[Université Robert Schuman (Strasbourg III)]
1, Place d'Athènes, 67084 Strasbourg Cedex
Tel: 88-41-42-00
Fax: 88-61-30-37
Président: Gilbert Knaub (1990-)
Secrétaire général: Alain Mège
International Relations: Vlad Constantinesco
Founded: 1437, 1970
Ut: Law, Political Science and Management; Law, Political and Social Sciences (Research).
I: Labour Studies; Political Studies; Economics and Business Administration; European Studies; Comparative Law; Commerce; Technology (IUT).
Ce: Journalism; International Study of Industrial Ownership; Foreign Languages; Lifelong Education; Financial and Administrative Research; Environmental Law; Financial Policies

Studies; German Studies.; History of Institutions Research; Computer; International and European Studies; Political Studies.; History of International Relationship Research; Strategy and Defence Studies; Labour Sciences Research.

University of Toulon and the Var
[Université de Toulon et du Var]
Avenue de l'Université, B.P. 132, 83957 La Garde Cedex
Tel: +33 94-14-20-00
Fax: +33 94-14-21-57
Président: François Resch
Secrétaire général: Bernard Rieupouilh
International Relations: Jean-Jacques Corre
Founded: 1970
Ut: Law; Economics and Management; Sciences and Techniques; Letters and Human Sciences.
I: Engineering; Technology (IUT).
Ce: French Studies (for foreign students during summer); Lifelong Education.

National Polytechnic Institute of Toulouse
[Institut National Polytechnique de Toulouse]
Place des Hauts-Murats, B.P. 354, 31006 Toulouse Cedex
Tel: +33 62-24-54-00
Fax: +33 61-53-67-21
Président: Henri Angelino
Secrétaire général: Jean-Louis Bonzinae
International Relations: Henri Angelino
Founded: 1906, 1970
S: Agriculture; Electrical Engineering, Electronics, Computer Sciences and Hydraulics; Chemistry; Chemical Engineering.
D: Industrial Systems; Physical Education and Sports.
Ce: Lifelong Education.

University of Social Sciences (Toulouse I)
[Université des Sciences sociales (Toulouse I)]
Place Anatole France, 31042 Toulouse Cedex
Tel: +33 61-63-35-00
Fax: +33 61-63-37-98
Président: Bernard Saint-Girons (1993-)
Secrétaire général: Danièle Roulland
International Relations: Jean-Pierre Theron
Founded: 1229, 1970
Ut: Law (1st, 2nd and 3rd cycle); Economics (1st, 2nd and 3rd cycle); Economic and Social Administration (1st, 2nd and 3rd cycle); Computer Sciences (2nd and 3rd cycle).
I: Political Studies (1st and 2nd cycle); Comparative Law of Latin Countries; Criminology and Penal Sciences; International Studies and Development; Economics (IUP); Management (IUP); Town Planning and Construction Laws; Rural Legislation and Economics; Technology (IUT, Rodez (1st cycle)).
Ce: Documentation and European Research (CEDRE); Foreign Languages and Civilizations Research; Study and Research of Legal Texts of Southern France; Fiscal Research Studies; Contemporary History of Institutions; Police

Research Studies; Interdisciplinary Social Research; Military Research; Economic and Statistic Research (CRES); Legal and Economic Studies of Employment; Economic Development Programming; Economic and Finance Research; Studies of the Development of International Specialization; Business Administration Research; Productive Organizations Studies; Social Science Informatics Research.

University of Toulouse-le-Mirail (Toulouse II)
[Université de Toulouse-le-Mirail (Toulouse II)]
5, allées Antonio Machado, 31058 Toulouse Cedex
Tel: +33 61-50-42-50
Fax: +33 61-50-42-09
Président: Georges Mailhos
Secrétaire général: Jean Rebout
International Relations: Romain Gaignard
Founded: 1229, 1970
Ut: Philosophy; Psychology; Social Sciences (Ramond-Ledrut); Classical Languages and Letters; Letters, Languages and Music; History, History of Art and Archaeology; Geography and Development; Mathematics, Data Processing, Statistics, Economics and Management; Hispanic and Hispano-American Studies; Audio-visual Studies; Anglophone Studies; Foreign Languages, Literature and Civilizations.
I: Audio-visual Studies (IUP); Pluridisciplinary Latin-American Studies (IPEALT); Technology (IUT).
Ce: Lifelong Education.

University Paul Sabatier (Toulouse III)
[Université Paul Sabatier (Toulouse III)]
118, route de Narbonne, 31062 Toulouse Cedex
Tel: +33 61-55-66-11
Fax: +33 61-55-64-70
Telex: 521880 f
Président: Jean-Claude Martin
Secrétaire général: Albertine Verdaguer
Founded: 1229, 1970
Ut: Medical Sciences (Purpan); Medical Sciences (Rangueil); Pharmaceutical Sciences; Dentistry; Physical Education and Sport; Mathematics, Computer Sciences and Management; Physics, Chemistry, and Automation; Life and Earth Sciences; Modern Languages.
I: Electrical Engineering and Industrial Computing (IUP); Industrial Systems Technology (IUP); Industrial Mathematics (IUP); Mathematic Engineering and Computing (IUP); Civil Engineering and Infrastructures (IUP); Bio-Engineering (IUP); Technology (IUT); Technology (IUT, Tarbes).
Ce: Lifelong Education.
Observatory.

University of Tours
[Université François Rabelais de Tours]
3, rue des Tanneurs, 37041 Tours Cedex
Tel: +33 47-36-66-00
Fax: +33 47-36-64-10
Telex: 751 194f
Président: Henri Mouray
Secrétaire général: Pierre Richard
International Relations: Claude Doubinsky
Founded: 1962
Ut: *Medicine; Pharmaceutical Sciences; Sciences and Techniques; Law, Economics and Social Sciences; English and Applied Foreign Languages; Planning and Development; Renaissance Studies.*
F: *Classical and Modern Languages, Literature and Civilizations; Arts and Human Sciences.*
S: *Industrial Computer Sciences; Engineering (Blois).*
I: *French; Technology (IUT); Technology (IUT, Blois).*
Ce: *Lifelong Education.*

University of Valenciennes and Hainaut-Cambrésis
[Université de Valenciennes et du Hainaut-Cambrésis]
Le Mont-Houy, B.P. 311, 59304 Valenciennes Cedex
Tel: +33 27-14-12-34
Fax: +33 27-14-11-00
Telex: 810270 uni vhc
Président: Claude Tournier
Secrétaire général: Henri-Dominique Mennecier
International Relations: Edmond Nogacki
Founded: 1970
I: *Science and Technology; Juridical and Economic Sciences and Management; Letters, Languages and Arts.*
S: *Mechanics and Energetics; Data Processing and Production; Industrial Studies; Preparatory Administrative Studies (IPAG); Training and Educational Research; Electrical Engineering and Industrial Computing (IUP); Technology (IUT).*

University of Versailles Saint-Quentin-en-Yvelines
[Université de Versailles Saint-Quentin-en-Yvelines]
23, rue du Refuge, 78035 Versailles Cedex
Tel: +33 1-39-25-41-04
Fax: +33 1-39-25-41-07
Administrateur provisoire: Michel Garnier
Secrétaire général: Danièle Saillant
International Relations: Armelle Chopard
Founded: 1993

PRIVATE INSTITUTIONS

*Catholic University of the West, Angers
[Université Catholique de l'Ouest]
3, place André Leroy, B.P. 808, 49008 Angers Cedex 01
Tel: +33 41-81-66-00
Fax: +33 41-81-66-09
Recteur: Claude Cesbron (1991-)
Secrétaire général: Patrick Lerays
Founded: 1875
F: *Theology.*
I: *Education; Modern Languages; Applied Mathematics; Psychology and Applied Social Sciences; Education and Communication; Letters and History; Pastoral Studies; Pure and Applied Scientific Research; Applied Ecology; Physical Education.*
S: *Commerce; Electronic Engineering; Chemistry.*
Ce: *French Studies.*

*Catholic University of Lille
[Fédération Universitaire et Polytechnique de Lille]
60, boulevard Vauban, BP 109, 59016 Lille Cedex
Tel: (20) 13-40-00
Fax: (20) 13-40-90
Président: Gaston Vandecandelaere (1991-94)
Directeur des Services généraux: Charles Hénin
Founded: 1873, 1974
F: *Theology; Law and Economics; Medicine; Letters and Human Sciences; Sciences.*
S: *Electronics and Micro-computing (ISEN); Translators and Interpreters; Higher Industrial Studies; Higher Commercial Studies; Social Service; Midwifery; Delegates of the Free F. of Medicine; Secretarial Sciences; Physiotherapy and Chiropody; Nursing and Child Welfare; Teacher Training; Bilingual and Trilingual Secretarial Studies; Social Work; Textile Engineering and Technology (ESTIT).*
I: *Accountancy; French Studies; Agricultural Studies (ISA); Religious Education; Sacred Music; Catechism Teachers; Advanced Science and Technology; Civil and Mechanical Engineering (ICAM); Microelectronics-Solid State Physics; Business Studies Applied to Engineering; Acoustics; Chemical Physics; Geology; Strategy and Techniques for Communication; Scientific Economics and Management (ISEG).*
Ce: *Economic and Administrative Research; Religious Studies; Teacher Training (Lille, Arras, Cambrai); Lifelong Education.*

Catholic University of Lyons
[Université Catholique de Lyon]
25-29 rue du Plat, 69288 Lyon Cedex 02
Tel: +33 72-32-50-12
Fax: +33 72-32-50-19
Recteur: Mgr Christian Ponson (1991-)
Secrétaire général: Claude Blond
Founded: 1875

F: Theology; Philosophy; Law, Economics, and Social Sciences; Letters and Human Sciences; Chemistry, Physics, and Electronics; Science.
S: Biochemistry and Biology; Translation; Laboratory Technology.
I: Education; Pastoral Studies; Economic and Social Development; Christian History; Family Studies; Agriculture; Romance Linguistics; Sacred Music; French Language and Culture.
Ce: Bioethical.

*Catholic Institute of Paris
[Institut Catholique de Paris]
21, rue d'Assas, 75270 Paris Cedex 06
Tel: + 1-44-39-52-00
Fax: +33 1-45-44-27-14
Recteur: Patrick Valdrini
Secrétaire général: Félix d'Herouville
Founded: 1875
Ut: Theology and Religious Sciences.
F: Philosophy; Canon Law; Letters.
S: Library Science; Psycho-Pedagogical Training; Psychology; Organic and Mineralogical Chemistry; Economics and Social Sciences; Ancient Oriental Languages.
I: Pastoral Studies; Liturgy; Liturgical Music; Science and Theology of Religions; Social Studies; Education; Religious Studies; French Language and Culture; Interpreters and Translators; Electronics; Geology; Agriculture (Beauvais).
Ce: Law, Economics, and Political Science; Secretarial Studies; Library Science; Mature Students and Senior Citizens; Lifelong Education.

*Catholic Institute of Toulouse
[Institut Catholique de Toulouse]
31, rue de la Fonderie, 31068 Toulouse Cedex
Tel: +33 61-52-62-35
Fax: +33 61-25-82-75
Recteur: André Dupleix (1994-)
Founded: 1877
F: Theology; Canon Law; Letters and Human Sciences.
S: Science; General Education; Education; Secretarial Studies; Agriculture (Purpan).
I: Religions and Pastoral Studies; Sacred Music; Education.
C: Occitanie Studies (by correspondence).
Ce: Hygiene and Social Studies; African Studies; Teacher Training; International (Social Sciences); Religious Training; Audio-Visual; Lifelong Education.

SPECIALIZED PUBLIC INSTITUTIONS

[Les Grands Etablissements]

Central School of Paris
[Ecole Centrale des Arts et Manufactures (Ecole centrale de Paris)]
Grande Voie des Vignes, 92295 Châtenay-Malabry Cedex

Tel: +33 41-13-13-65
Fax: +33 46-60-3-6-10
E-Mail: Earn-Bitnet
Telex: 634991F ECP Paris
Directeur: Daniel Gourisse
Secrétaire général: Maurice Simon
Founded: 1829, 1991
D: Economics, and Social and Human Sciences; Applied Mathematics and Data Processing; Chemistry; Materials Science; Energetics; Mechanical Engineering; Electrical Engineering; Civil Engineering.
Ce: Lifelong Education.

'Collège de France' Paris
['Collège de France']
11, place Marcelin Berthelot, 75231 Paris Cedex
Tel: +33 1-44-27-12-11
Fax: +33 1-44-27-11-09
Founded: 1530
Mathematics, Physics, and Natural Sciences; Philosophy and Social Sciences; History, Philology, and Archaeology.

Institute of Political Studies Paris
[Institut d'Etudes politiques de Paris]
27, rue Saint-Guillaume, 75341 Paris Cedex 07
Tel: +33 1-45-49-50-50
Directeur: Alain Lancelot
Founded: 1872, 1945, 1969
Political, Social and Economic Sciences; Lifelong Education.

National Conservatoire of 'Arts et Métiers' Paris
[Conservatoire National des Arts et Métiers (CNAM)]
292, rue Saint-Martin, 75141 Paris Cedex 03
Tel: +33 1-40-27-20-00
Fax: +33 1-42-71-93-29
Administrateur général: Guy Fleury
Founded: 1794, 1819
D: Mathematics and Data Processing; Physics and Meteorology; Chemistry and Biology; Industrial Materials; Mechanics; Energetics; Electronics and Automation; Nuclear Sciences; Civil Engineering; Regional Development Sciences; Economics and Management; Labour Studies.
Ce: Lifelong Education.

National Institute of Eastern Languages and Civilizations Paris
[Institut national des Langues et Civilisations orientales (INALCO)]
2, rue de Lille, 75343 Paris Cedex 07
Tel: +33 1-49-26-42-00
Fax: +33 1-49-26-42-99

Président: André Bourgey
Secrétaire général: Silvio Sangalli
Founded: 1971
*Modern Languages and Civilizations of: Africa,
China, Korea-Japan, Central and Eastern Europe,
Near East and North Africa, South-East Asia,
High Asia, Oceania, South Asia, Russia-Eurasia,
the Americas; International Exchange
Preparation; International Higher Studies;
Intercultural Communication; Multilingual
Engineering; Automatic Languages Processing.*

National Museum of Natural History Paris

[Muséum national d'Histoire naturelle]
Jardin des Plantes, 57, rue Cuvier, 75231 Paris
Cedex 05
Tel: +33 1-40-79-30-00
Directeur: Henry Delubmey
Secrétaire général: Daniel Cuvier
Founded: 1635
*Tropical Agriculture; Entomology; Ethnology;
Geology; Palaeontology; Zoology.*

National School of 'Arts et Métiers' Paris

[Ecole nationale supérieure d'Arts et Métiers]
151, boulevard de l'Hôpital, 75640 Paris Cedex 13
Tel: +33 1-44-24-63-20
Telex: 220064F etrav ext 379 f
Directeur général: Guy Gautherin
Founded: 1912, 1963
*Science and Applied Science; Economics and
Law; Humanities; Lifelong Education.*

National School of Archival Studies Paris

[Ecole nationale des Chartes]
19, rue de la Sorbonne, 75005 Paris
Tel: +33 1-46-33-41-82
Fax: +33 1-43-29-89-75
Directeur: Yves-Marie Bercé
Secrétaire général: Marie-Clotilde Hubert
Founded: 1821
*Palaeography; History of Books and Bibliography;
History of French Institutions; History of Private
Law; Archives and Diplomatic Studies; Sources of
Literature; Roman Philology; Archaeology.*

Observatory of Paris

[Observatoire de Paris]
61, avenue de l'Observatoire, 75014 Paris
Tel: +33 1-40-51-22-21
Telex: 270776 obs
Cable: obs paris
Président: Michel Combes
Secrétaire général: Catherine Merrien
International Relations: Annie Baglin
Founded: 1821
Astronomy; Geodesy.

'Palais de la Découverte' Paris

['Palais de la Découverte']
Avenue Franklin D. Roosevelt, 75008 Paris
Tel: +33 1-40-74-80-00
Fax: +33 1-40-74-81-81
E-Mail: Minitel 3615 decouverte
Directeur: Michel Demazure
Secrétaire général: Michèle Guillaumin
Founded: 1937
*D: Mathematics; Astronomy; Physics; Earth
Sciences; Chemistry; Biology; Medicine.*

Physics of the Globe Institute Paris

[Institut de Physique du Globe]
Tour 24, place Jussieu, 75005 Paris
Tel: +33 1-44-27-44-27
Fax: +33 1-44-27-36-12
Telex: 202810
Directeur: Jean Louis Le Mouel
Founded: 1921
Physics of the Globe.

Practical School of Higher Studies Paris

[Ecole pratique des hautes Etudes (EPHE)]
45-47, rue des Ecoles, Galerie Claude Bernard,
75005 Paris
Tel: +33 1-40-46-33-97
Fax: +33 1-40-46-33-98
Président: Monique Adolphe
Founded: 1868
*Sec: Natural Sciences (IIIrd Section); History
and Philology (IVth Section); Religious Sciences
(Vth Section).*

School of Higher Studies in Social Sciences Paris

[Ecole des hautes Etudes en Sciences sociales
(EHESS)]
54, boulevard Raspail, 75006 Paris
Tel: +33 1-49-54-25-25
Fax: +33 1-45-44-93-11
Président: Marc Augé (1990-95)
Secrétaire général: Charles Carriere
Founded: 1975
*D: History; Sociology, Social Anthropology, and
Psychology; Economics; Cultural Affairs.*

National School of Information and Library Sciences Villeurbanne

[Ecole nationale supérieure des Sciences de
l'Information et des Bibliothèques]
17-21, boulevard du 11 Novembre 1918, 69623
Villeurbanne Cedex
Tel: +33 72-44-43-43
Fax: +33 72-44-27-88
Directeur: Jacques Kériguy
Secrétaire général: Pierre Blanc
Library Science.

GRANDES ECOLES

PUBLIC INSTITUTIONS

Centre d'Etudes supérieures des Techniques industrielles (CESTI/ISMCM)
3, rue Ferdinand Hainaut, 93407 Saint-Ouen
Tel: +33 49-45-29-00
Fax: +33 49-45-29-91
Directeur: Henri Veysseyre
International Relations: Tuong Vinh
Founded: 1956
Industrial Techniques.

Centre national d'Etudes agronomiques des Régions chaudes (CNEARC/ESAT)
101, avenue Agropolis, 34033 Montpellier 01
Tel: +33 67-61-70-00
Fax: +33 67-41-02-32
Directeur: Alain Ruellan
Agriculture (Tropical).

Institut des Sciences de l'Ingénieur de Clermont-Ferrand (CUST)
24, avenue des Landais, 63174 Aubière
Tel: +33 73-40-75-00
Fax: +33 73-40-75-10
Directeur: Michel Troquet
International Relations: André Lavaure
Engineering Sciences.

Direction de l'Enseignement supérieur des Télécommunications (DEST)
46, rue Barrault, 75634 Paris 13
Tel: +33 1-45-81-77-77
Fax: +33 1-45-88-66-68
Directeur: Michel Camus
International Relations: Brigitte Krulic
Telecommunications.

Ecole de l'Air (EA)
Base Aérienne, 13661 Salon de Provence Air
Tel: +33 90-53-90-90
Fax: +33 90-53-00-10
Commandant: Gilbert Dumaz
International Relations: Marc Guillaume
Aviation Studies.

Ecole d'Architecture de Nancy (EAN)
Parc de Rémincourt, 54602 Villers-les-Nancy
Tel: +33 83-90-83-90
Fax: +33 83-27-39-74
Directeur: Denis Grandjean
Architecture.

Ecole centrale de Lille (EC)
Cité scientifique de Lille, B.P. 48, 59651 Villeneuve-d'Ascq
Tel: +33 20-33-53-53
Fax: +33 20-33-54-99
Directeur: Jean-Claude Gentina
International Relations: Pierre Borne
Engineering and Technology.

Ecole centrale de Lyon (ECL)
36, avenue Guy Collonghue, 69130 Ecully
Tel: +33 72-18-60-00
Fax: +33 78-43-39-62
Directeur: Etienna Pascaud
International Relations: Léo Vincent
Founded: 1857
Engineering and Technology.

Ecole centrale de Nantes (ECN)
1, rue Noé, 44072 Nantes 03
Tel: +33 40-37-16-00
Fax: +33 40-74-74-06
Directeur: Pierre Vaussy
International Relations: Michel Lucas
Engineering and Technology.

Ecole centrale de Paris (ECP)
Grandes Voie des Vignes, 92295 Chatenay Malabray
Tel: +33 1-41-13-10-00
Fax: +33 1-49-60-36-10
Directeur: Daniel Gourisse
International Relations: Daniel Peigne
Engineering and Technology.

Ecole européenne des hautes Etudes des Industries chimiques de Strasbourg (EHICS)
1, rue Blaise Pascal, B.P. 0407, 67008 Strasbourg
Tel: +33 88-41-68-00
Fax: +33 88-61-78-52
Directeur: Jean-Claude Bernier
International Relations: Jean-Louis Leibengut
Chemical Industries.

Ecole nationale supérieure des Techniques industrielles et des Mines d'Alès (EMA)
6, avenue de Clavières, 30319 Alès
Tel: +33 66-78-50-00
Fax: +33 66-78-50-34
Directeur: Henri Pugnère
Founded: 1843
Industrial Techniques; Mining.

Ecole nationale supérieure des Techniques industrielles et des Mines de Douai (EMD)
941, rue Charles Bourseul, B.P. 838, 59508 Douai
Tel: +33 27-93-22-22
Fax: +33 27-93-23-31
Directeur: Maurice Cotte
International Relations: Bernard Blondeel
Industrial Techniques; Mining.

Ecole nationale supérieure des Mines de Nancy (EMN)
Parc de Saurupt, 54042 Nancy
Tel: +33 83-58-42-32
Fax: +33 83-57-97-94
Directeur: Claude Cremet
International Relations: Abdahlan Sfeier
Mining.

Ecole nationale d'Administration (ENA)
13, rue de l'Université, 75007 Paris
Tel: +33 1-49-26-45-45
Fax: +33 1-42-60-26-95
Directeur: Raymond-François Le Bris (1995-)
International Relations: Bernard Boube
Founded: 1945
Administration; Territorial Administration; European Studies.

Ecole nationale de l'Aviation civile (ENAC)
7, avenue Edouard Belin, B.P. 4005, 31055 Toulouse
Tel: +33 62-17-40-00
Fax: +33 62-17-40-23
Directeur: Alain Soucheleau
International Relations: Jean-Marc Alliot
Founded: 1948
Civil Aviation.

Ecole nationale du Génie de l'Eau et de l'Environnement de Strasbourg (ENGEES)
1, quai Koch, B.P. 1039, 67070 Strasbourg
Tel: +33 88-25-34-50
Fax: +33 88-37-04-97
Directeur: Daniel Loudière
International Relations: Jean-Marc Hoffmann
Water and Environmental Engineering.

Ecole nationale du Génie rural, des Eaux et Forêts (ENGREF)
19, avenue du Maine, 75732 Paris Cedex 15
Tel: +33 1-49-88-00
Fax: +33 1-45-49-88-27
Directeur: Denis Ballay
International Relations: Robert Moreau
Founded: 1874
Rural Engineering; Forestry.

Ecole nationale d'Ingénieurs de Belfort (ENI)
Espace Bartholdi-Belfort Technopôle, 90016 Belfort
Tel: +33 84-58-23-00
Fax: +33 84-54-00-62
Directeur: Claude Chicoix
International Relations: Claude Chicoix
Founded: 1962
Engineering.

Ecole nationale d'Ingénieurs de Brest (ENI)
Technopôle Brest-Iroise, 29608 Brest
Tel: +33 98-05-66-00
Fax: +33 98-05-66-10
Directeur: François Ropars
International Relations: Gérard Lemarie
Founded: 1961
Engineering.

Ecole nationale d'Ingénieurs de Metz (ENI)
Ile du Saulcy, 57045 Metz 1
Tel: +33 87-34-69-00
Fax: +33 87-34-69-35
Directeur: Pierre Padilla
International Relations: Armand Bemer
Founded: 1962
Engineering.

Ecole nationale d'Ingénieurs de Saint-Etienne (ENI)
58, rue Jean Parot, 42023 Saint-Etienne 2
Tel: +33 77-43-84-84
Fax: +33 77-43-84-99
Directeur: Thomas Mathia
International Relations: Robert Meillier
Founded: 1961
Engineering.

Ecole nationale d'Ingénieurs de Tarbes (ENI)
47 Chemin d'Azereix, B.P. 1629, 65016 Tarbes
Tel: +33 62-44-27-00
Fax: +33 62-44-27-27
Directeur: Bernard Mugniery
International Relations: Yves-Pol Hemonin
Founded: 1963
Engineering.

Ecole nationale d'Ingénieurs des Travaux agricoles de Bordeaux (ENITA)
1, cours du Général de Gaulle, 33175 Gradignan
Tel: +33 56-04-03-03
Fax: +33 56-80-90-56
Directeur: Jean Magne
International Relations: Jean Magne
Founded: 1962
Agriculture.

Ecole nationale d'Ingénieurs des Travaux agricoles de Clermont-Ferrand (ENITA)
Marmilhat, RN 89, 63370 Lempdes
Tel: +33 73-98-13-13
Fax: +33 73-98-13-00
Directeur: Robert Hénaff
International Relations: André Nil
Agriculture.

Ecole nationale d'Ingénieurs des Travaux agricoles (ENITHP)
2, rue Le Nôtre, 49045 Angers Cedex 01
Tel: +33 41-22-54-54
Fax: +33 41-73-45-57
Directeur: André Nil
International Relations: Yves Guiheneuf
Agriculture (Horticulture).

Ecole nationale d'Ingénieurs des Travaux des Techniques des Industries agricoles et alimentaires (ENITIAA)
Chemin de la Géraudière, 44072 Nantes 03
Tel: +33 40-40-03-00
Fax: +33 40-59-63-36
Directeur: Bernard Guerin
International Relations: Annie Lambert
Agriculture; Food Technology.

Ecole nationale de la Météorologie (ENM)
Avenue Gustave Coriolis, 31057 Toulouse Cédex
Tel: +33 61-07-90-90
Fax: +33 61-07-96-30
Directeur: Daniel Rousseau
International Relations: Daniel Rousseau
Meteorology.

Ecole nationale des Ponts et Chaussées (ENPC)
28, rue des Saints-Pères, 75343 Paris 07
Tel: +33 1-44-58-27-00
Fax: +33 1-44-58-34-09
Directeur: Jacques Lagardère
International Relations: Philippe Sardin
Founded: 1747
Civil Engineering.

Ecole normale supérieure (ENS)
45, rue d'Ulm, 75230 Paris Cedex 05
Tel: +33 1-44-32-30-00
Fax: +33 1-43-29-73-69
Directeur: Etienne Guyon
Founded: 1794
Education and Research.

Ecole normale supérieure (ENS)
61, avenue du Président-Wilson, 94235 Cachan
Tel: +33 1-47-40-20-00
Fax: +33 1-47-40-20-74
Directeur: Bernard Decombs
International Relations: Claude Bortolussi
Founded: 1912
Education and Research.

Ecole normale supérieure de Fontenay-Saint Cloud (ENS)
31, avenue Lombart, B.P. 81, 92260 Fontenay Aux Roses
Tel: +33 1-41-13-24-00
Fax: +33 1-41-13-24-09
Directeur: Michel Coquery
International Relations: Michel Coquery
Founded: 1887
Education and Research.

Ecole normale supérieure de Lyon (ENS)
46, allée d'Italie, 69364 Lyon 07
Tel: +33 72-72-80-00
Fax: +33 72-72-80-80
Directeur (Acting): Jean Giraud
International Relations: Pierre Servoz-Gavin
Education and Research.

Ecole nationale supérieure agronomique (ENSA)
9, place Viala, 34060 Montpellier 01
Tel: +33 67-61-22-00
Fax: +33 67-61-25-80
Directeur: Paul Raymond
International Relations: Guy Banel
Founded: 1872
Agriculture.

Ecole nationale supérieure agronomique (ENSA)
65, rue de Saint-Brieuc, 35042 Rennes
Tel: +33 99-28-50-00
Fax: +33 99-28-75-10
Directeur: Pierre Thivend
International Relations: Philippe Ruffio
Founded: 1826
Agriculture.

Ecole nationale supérieure agronomique (ENSA)
145, avenue de Muret, 31076 Toulouse
Tel: +33 61-42-83-98
Fax: +33 61-42-30-29
Directeur: Dominique Coquart
International Relations: Jacques Moreau
Agriculture.

Ecole nationale de la Statistique économique (ENSAE)
3, avenue Pierre Larousse, 92245 Malakoff
Tel: +33 1-41-17-51-55
Fax: +33 1-41-17-64-80
Directeur: Alain Trognin
International Relations: Pascal Lahaye
Economic Statistics.

Ecole nationale supérieure de l'Aéronautique et de l'Espace (ENSAE-SUPAERO)
10, avenue Edouard-Belin, B.P. 4032, 31055 Toulouse
Tel: +33 62-17-80-80
Fax: +33 62-17-83-30
Directeur: Jean-Claude Ripoll
International Relations: Alexandre Huynh
Founded: 1909
Aeronautical and Space Engineering.

Ecole nationale supérieure d'Agronomie et des Industries alimentaires (ENSAIA)
2, avenue de la Forêt de la Haye, 54505 Vandoeuvre-les-Nancy
Tel: +33 83-59-59-59
Fax: +33 83-59-58-04
Directeur: Joël Hardy
International Relations: Joël Hardy
Agriculture and Food Technology.

Ecole nationale supérieure des Arts et Industries de Strasbourg (ENSAIS)
24, boulevard de la Victoire, 67084 Strasbourg
Tel: +33 88-14-47-00
Fax: +33 88-24-14-90
Directeur: André Colson
International Relations: André Colson
Arts and Industrial Engineering.

Ecole nationale supérieure des Arts et Industries textiles (ENSAIT)
2, place des Martyrs de la Resistance, 59070 Roubaix 1
Tel: +33 20-25-64-64
Fax: +33 20-24-84-06
Directeur: Christian Vasseur
International Relations: Christiane Billaz
Arts and Industrial Textiles.

Ecole nationale supérieure de Biologie appliquée à la Nutrition et à l'Alimentation
Campus Universitaire, 1, Esplanade Erasme, 21000 Dijon
Tel: +33 80-39-66-01
Fax: +33 80-39-66-11
Directeur: Denis Lorient
International Relations: Andrée Voilley
Applied Biology; Nutrition and Food Technology.

Ecole nationale supérieure de Chimie de Clermont-Ferrand (ENSC)
Ensemble scientifique des Cézeaux, 24, avenue des Landais, B.P. 187, 63174 Aubière
Tel: +33 73-40-71-45
Fax: +33 73-40-70-95
Directeur: Jacques Gelas
International Relations: Marie-Thérèse Fournier
Founded: 1908
Chemistry.

Ecole nationale supérieure de Chimie de Lille (ENSC)
Domaine Universitaire scientifique, B.P. 108, 59652 Villeneuve-d'Ascq Cedex
Tel: +33 20-43-49-92
Fax: +33 20-47-05-99
Directeur: Alain Lablache-Combler
International Relations: Alain Lablache-Combler
Founded: 1894
Chemistry.

Ecole nationale supérieure de Chimie de Montpellier (ENSC)
8, rue de l'Ecole normale, 34075 Montpellier 1
Tel: +33 67-14-43-00
Fax: +33 67-14-43-53
Directeur: Patrick Geneste
International Relations: Lucien Doljac
Founded: 1908
Chemistry.

Ecole nationale supérieure de Chimie de Mulhouse (ENSC)
3, rue Alfred Werner, 68093 Mulhouse
Tel: +33 89-42-70-20
Fax: +33 89-59-98-59
Directeur: Jean-Pierre Fouassier
International Relations: Jacques Streith
Founded: 1908
Chemistry.

Ecole nationale supérieure de Chimie de Paris (ENSC)
11, rue Pierre-et-Marie-Curie, 75231 Paris 05
Tel: +33 1-44-27-66-87
Fax: +33 1-43-25-79-75
Directeur: Bernard Tremillon
International Relations: Edmond Francke
Chemistry.

Ecole nationale supérieure de Chimie de Rennes (ENSC)
Avenue du Général Leclerc, 35700 Rennes
Tel: +33 99-87-13-00
Fax: +33 99-87-13-99
Directeur: Henri Patin
International Relations: Pierre Briend
Founded: 1919
Chemistry.

Ecole nationale supérieure de Chimie de Toulouse (ENSC)
118, route de Narbonne, 31077 Toulouse
Tel: +33 61-17-56-56
Fax: +33 61-17-56-00
Directeur: Roland Morancho
International Relations: Jean-Pierre Gorrichon
Chemistry.

Ecole nationale supérieure de Chimie et de Physique de Bordeaux (ENSCP)
351, cours de la Libération, 33405 Talence
Tel: +33 56-84-65-65
Fax: +33 58-84-66-33
Directeur: Henry Gasparoux
International Relations: Alain Levasseur
Founded: 1891
Chemistry and Physics.

Ecole nationale supérieure de l'Electronique et de ses Applications (ENSEA)
6, Avenue du Ponceau, 95014 Cergy Pontoise
Tel: +33 1-30-73-66-66
Fax: +33 1-30-76-66-67
Directeur: Roger Ceschi
International Relations: Daniel Pasquet
Founded: 1952
Electronics.

Ecole nationale supérieure d'Electrochimie et d'Electrométallurgie de Grenoble (ENSEEG)
Domaine Universitaire, B.P. 75, 38403 Saint-Martin-d'Hères
Tel: +33 76-82-65-00
Fax: +33 76-82-66-30
Directeur: Pierre Hicter
International Relations: Jean-Claude Poignet
Electro-chemistry and Electro-metallurgy.

Ecole nationale supérieure d'Electrotechnique, d'Electronique, et d'Informatique et d'Hydraulique de Toulouse (ENSEEIHT)
2, rue Charles Camichel, 31071 Toulouse
Tel: +33 61-58-82-00
Fax: +33 61-62-09-76
Directeur: Desiré Amoros
International Relations: Serge Lefeuvre
Electrical Engineering and Automation;
Electronics and Microelectronics; Hydraulics.

Ecole nationale supérieure d'Electricité et de Mécanique (ENSEM)
2, avenue de la Forêt de Haye, 54516 Vandoeuvre les Nancy
Tel: +33 83-59-59-59
Fax: +33 83-44-07-63
Directeur: Jean-Claude Braun
International Relations: Jean-François Aubry
Electrical and Mechanical Engineering.

Ecole nationale supérieure d'Electronique et de Radioélectricité de Bordeaux (ENSERB)
351, cours de la Libération, 33405 Talence
Tel: +33 56-80-84-50
Fax: 56-37-20-23
Directeur: Bernard Leroux
International Relations: Jacques Pistre
Founded: 1920
Electronics; Radio-electrical Techniques.

Ecole nationale supérieure d'Electronique et de Radioélectricité de Grenoble (ENSERG)
23, avenuue des Martyrs, B.P. 257, 38031 Grenoble
Tel: +33 76-85-60-00
Fax: +33 76-8560-60
Directeur: Michel Baribaud
International Relations: Etienne Pic
Electronics; Radio-electrical Techniques.

Ecole nationale supérieure de Géologie et de Prospection minière (ENSG)
94, avenue de Lattre-de-Tassigny, B.P. 452, 54001 Nancy
Tel: +33 83-32-85-86
Fax: +33 83-30-21-37
Directeur: Bernard Durand
International Relations: Jean-Louis Vigneresse
Geology; Mining.

Ecole nationale des Sciences géographiques (ENSG.Géo)
22, avenue Pasteur, 94160 Saint-Mandé
Tel: 43-74-12-15
International Relations: Henri Journoud
Founded: 1941
Geography; Surveying; Cartography.

Ecole nationale supérieure d'Horticulture (ENSH)
4, rue Hardy, 78009 Versailles
Tel: +33 1-39-50-60-87
Fax: +33 1-39-51-57-85
Directeur: Iain Riquois
International Relations: Noëlle Dorion
Founded: 1873
Horticulture.

Ecole nationale supérieure d'Hydraulique et de Mécanique de Grenoble (ENSHMG)
Domaine Universitaire, B.P. 53, 38402 Saint-Martin-d'Hères
Tel: +33 76-82-50-00
Fax: +33 76-82-50-01
Directeur: Yves Fautrelle
International Relations: Odile Lantz
Hydrology; Mechanical Engineering.

Ecole nationale supérieure des Industries agricoles et alimentaires (ENSIA)
1, Avenue des Olympiades, 91305 Massy
Tel: +33 1-69-93-50-50
Fax: +33 1-69-20-02-30
Directeur: Bernard Guerin
International Relations: Elisabeth Dumoulin
Founded: 1893
Agricultural Industries; Food Technology.

Ecole nationale supérieure des Industries chimiques de Nancy (ENSIC)
1, rue de Grandville, 5400142 Nancy
Tel: +33 83-17-50-00
Fax: +33 93-35-08-11
Directeur: Alain Storck
International Relations: Tatiana Görner
Industrial Chemistry.

Ecole nationale supérieure d'Ingénieurs de Constructions aéronautiques (ENSICA)
49 avenue Léon-Blum, 31056 Toulouse
Tel: +33 61-58-75-00
Fax: +33 61-58-75-24
Directeur: Jean-Louis Fréson
International Relations: Didier Delorme
Founded: 1948
Aeronautic Construction Technology.

Ecole nationale supérieure d'Ingénieurs électriciens de Grenoble (ENSIEG)
Domaine Universitaire, B.P. 46, 38402 Saint-Martin-d'Hères
Tel: +33 76-82-62600
Fax: +33 76-82-63-01
Directeur: Christian Masselot
International Relations: Max Ginier-Gillet
Electrical Engineering.

Ecole nationale supérieure des Ingénieurs des Etudes et Techniques d'Armement (ENSIETA)
2, rue François Verny, 29806 Brest 9
Tel: +33 98-34-88-00
Fax: +33 98-34-88-46
Directeur: Claude le Roy
International Relations: Nicolas Ogloblinsky
Armaments Techniques.

Ecole nationale supérieure d'Ingénieurs de Génie chimique (ENSIGC)
Chemin de la Loge, 31078 Toulouse
Tel: +33 62-25-23-00
Fax: +33 62-25-23-18
International Relations: Christophe Gourdon
Chemical Engineering.

Ecole nationale supérieure d'Informatique et de Mathématiques appliquées de Grenoble (ENSIMAG)

213, avenue de la Bibliothèque, B.P. 53, 38041 Grenoble 9
Tel: +33 76-82-72-33
Fax: +33 76-82-72-99
Directeur: Guy Mazere
International Relations: Catherine Bellon
Computer Sciences; Applied Mathematics.

Ecole nationale supérieure de Mécanique énergétique de Valenciennes (ENSIMEV)

Le Mont Houy, B.P. 311, 59304 Valenciennes
Tel: +33 27-14-12-02
Fax: +33 27-14-12-00
Directeur: Yves Ravalard
International Relations: René Cavel
Energetics.

Ecole nationale supérieure des Industries textiles de Mulhouse (ENSITM)

11, rue Alfred Werner, 68093 Mulhouse
Tel: +33 89-59-63-20
Fax: +33 89-59-63-39
Directeur: Auguste Kirschner
International Relations: Jean-Yves Drean
Founded: 1861
Textile Engineering.

Ecole nationale supérieure des Mines de Paris (ENSM)

60, boulevard Saint-Michel, 75272 Paris 06
Tel: +33 1-40-51-90-90
Fax: +33 1-43-54-18-98
Directeur: Jacques Lévy
International Relations: Jacques Lévy
Founded: 1783
Mining.

Ecole nationale supérieure des Mines de Saint-Etienne (ENSM)

158, cours Fauriel, 42023 Saint-Etienne 02
Tel: +33 77-42-01-23 F+33 77-42-00-00
Directeur: Philippe Hirtzman
International Relations: Francis Lancelot
Founded: 1816
Mining.

Ecole nationale supérieure de Mécanique et d'Aérotechnique (ENSMA)

Site Futurscope, B.P. 109, 86960 Chasseneuil du Poitou
Tel: +33 49-49-80-80
Fax: +33 49-49-80-00
Directeur: Claude Gasc
International Relations: Jean-Pierre Romain
Founded: 1948
Mechanical Engineering; Aerotechniques.

Ecole nationale supérieure de Mécanique et des Microtechniques (ENSMM)

La Bouloie, Route de Gray, 25030 Besançon
Tel: 81 66 66 16
Directeur: Jean-Louis Vaterkowski
International Relations: Pierre Baptiste
Founded: 1927
Mechanical Engineering; Micro-techniques.

Ecole nationale supérieure de Physique de Grenoble (ENSP)

rue de la Houille Blanche, 38402 Saint-Martin-d'Héres
Tel: +33 76-82-62-00
Fax: +33 76-82-64-70
Directeur: Jean-Pierre Longequeue
International Relations: Michel Schlenker
Applied Physics.

Ecole nationale supérieure de Physique de Marseille (ENSP)

Domaine Universitaire de St. Jérôme, avenue Normandie Niemen, 13397 Marseille 20
Tel: +33 91-28-80-89
Fax: +33 91-28-88-13f
Directeur: Serge Huard
International Relations: Thierry Kakouridis
Founded: 1959
Applied Physics.

Ecole nationale supérieure de Physique de Strasbourg (ENSP)

Parc d'Innovation, Boulevard Sébastian Brant, 67400 Ilkirch
Tel: +33 88-6550-00
Fax: +33 88-65-52-49
Directeur: François Becker
Applied Physics.

Ecole nationale supérieure du Pétrole et des Moteurs (ENSPM)

228-232, avenue Napoleón Bonaparte, B.P. 311, 92506 Rueil-Malmaison
Tel: +33 1-47-49-02-14
Fax: +33 1-47-52-70-36
Directeur: Jean Masseron
International Relations: Jean-Christophe Fleche
Founded: 1925
Petroleum Production; Motors.

Ecole nationale supérieure des Télécommunications (ENST)

46, rue Barrault, 75634 Paris 13
Tel: +33 1-45-81-77-77
Fax: +33 1-45-89-79-06
Directeur: Alain Sirot
International Relations: Jennifer Molet
Founded: 1878
Telecommunications.

Ecole nationale supérieure des Télécommunications de Bretagne (ENST)
Technopôle de Brest Iroise, B.P. 832, 29285 Brest
Tel: +33 98-00-11-11
Fax: +33 98-45-51-33
Directeur: Francis Jutand
International Relations: Vanina Savelli
Telecommunications.

Ecole nationale supérieure de Techniques avancées (ENSTA)
32, boulevard Victor, 75015 Paris
Tel: +33 1-45-52-44-08
Fax: +33 1-45-82-55-87
Directeur: Pierre Sintes
Founded: 1969
Advanced Technologies.

Ecole nationale des Travaux publics de l'Etat (ENTPE)
Rue Maurice Audin, B.P. 2, 69518 Vaulx-en-Velin
Tel: +33 72-04-70-70
Fax: +33 72-04-62-54
Directeur: Daniel Sené
International Relations: Michel Daugreilh
Founded: 1891
Public Works and Civil Engineering.

Ecole nationale vétérinaire d'Alfort (ENV)
7, avenue du Général de Gaulle, 94704
Maisons-Alfort
Tel: +33 1-43-96-71-00
Fax: +33 1-43-96-71-25
Directeur: André Parodi
International Relations: Brigitte Joseph-Enriquez
Founded: 1765
Veterinary Medicine.

Ecole nationale vétérinaire de Lyon (ENV)
1, avenue Bourgelat, B.P. 83, 69280 Marcy l'Etoile
Tel: +33 78-87-00-84
Fax: +33 78-87-82-62
Directeur: Michel Lapras
International Relations: Claude Jean-Blain
Veterinary Medicine.

Ecole nationale vétérinaire de Nantes (ENV)
Route de Gachet, 4408726 Nantes 03
Tel: +33 40-68-77-77
Fax: +33 40-68-77-78
Directeur: Kacqies Sevestre
International Relations: Xavier Mahler
Veterinary Medicine.

Ecole nationale vétérinaire de Toulouse (ENV)
23, chemin des Capelles, 31076 Toulouse
Tel: +33 61-19-38-00
Fax: +33 61-19-38-18
Directeur: George Van Haverbeke
International Relations: Jean Sautet
Founded: 1829
Veterinary Medicine.

Ecole polytechnique
Route de Saclay, 91128 Palaiseau
Tel: +33 1-69-33-47-36
Fax: +33 1-69-33-30-21
Directeur: Henry Marescaux
International Relations: Roland Seneor
Founded: 1794
Mathematics; Economics; Mechanical Engineering; Physics; Chemistry; Humanities and Social Sciences.

Institut national agronomique Paris-Grignon (INA-PG)
16, rue Claude-Bernard, 75231 Paris 05
Tel: +33 1-44-08-16-61
Fax: +33 1-44-08-17-00
Directeur: Paul Vialle
Agriculture.

Institut national des Sciences appliquées de Lyon (INSA)
20, avenue Albert-Einstein, 69621 Villeurbanne
Tel: +33 72-43-83-83
Fax: +33 72-73-85-00
Directeur: Joël Rochat
International Relations: Henri Botta
Founded: 1957
Applied Sciences.

Institut national des Sciences appliquées de Rennes (INSA)
20, avenue des Buttes-de-Coësmes, 3504331
Rennes
Tel: +33 99-28-64-00
Fax: +33 99-63-67-05
Directeur: René Dabard
International Relations: Yves Morice
Founded: 1966
Applied Sciences.

Institut national des Sciences appliquées de Rouen (INSA)
Place Emile Blondel, B.P.08, 76131
Mont-Saint-Aignan
Tel: +33 35-52-83-00
Fax: +33 35-52-83-20
Directeur: Gilbert Touzot
International Relations: José Souza de Cursi
Applied Sciences.

Institut national des Sciences appliquées de Toulouse (INSA)
Complexe scientifique de Rangueil, 31077
Toulouse
Tel: +33 61-55-95-13
Fax: +33 61-55-95-00
Directeur: Marc Courvoisier
International Relations: Françoise Voillet
Founded: 1963
Applied Sciences.

Institut national supérieur de Formation agro-alimentaire (INSFA)
65, rue de Saint Brieuc, 35042 Rennes
Tel: +33 99-28-54-92
Fax: +33 99-28-75-10
Directeur: Pierre Thivend
Food Technology.

Institut national des Télécommunications (INT)
9, rue Charles Fourier, 91011 Evry
Tel: +33 1-60-76-40-40
Fax: +33 1-60-77-65-29
Directeur: Daniel Cané
International Relations: Louis Rambaud
Telecommunications.

Institut de Recherche et d'Enseignement supérieur aux Techniques de l'Electronique (IRESTE)
La Chantrerie, B.P. 3003, 44087 Nantes 03
Tel: +33 40-68-30-00
Fax: +33 40-68-30-66
Directeur: Yves Thomas
International Relations: Jacqueline Boniffay
Electronics Techniques.

Institut supérieur d'Agriculture (ISA)
41, rue du Port, 59046 Lille
Tel: +33 20-30-83-14
Fax: +33 20-40-05-83
Directeur: Pascal Codron
International Relations: Dean Hipple
Agriculture.

Institut des Sciences de l'Ingénieur de Montpellier (ISIM)
place Eugène Bataillon, 34095 Montpellier 05
Tel: +33 67-14-31-60
Fax: +33 67-14-45-14
Directeur: Serge Peytavin
International Relations: François Schue
Engineering.

Institut des Sciences de la Matière et du Rayonnement (ISMRA)
6, boulevard du Maréchal Juin, 14050 Caen
Tel: +33 31-45-27-50
Fax: +33 31-45-27-60
Directeur général: Jean-Charles Vienot
International Relations: Michel Louvel
Materials Sciences.

Université de Technologie de Compiègne (UTC)
Rue Roger Couttolenc, B.P. 233, 60206 Compiègne
Tel: +33 44-23-44-23
Fax: 44-23-43-00
Président: Michel Lavalou
International Relations: Jean-Louis Boiteux
Mechanical Technology; Biological Technology; Chemical Technology; Computer Engineering; Human Sciences and Technology.

Ecole supérieure de Commerce (CERAM)
rue Dostoïevski, B.P. 085, 06902, Sophia Antipolis
Tel: +33 93-95-45-45
Fax: +33 93-65-45-24
Directeur: Maxime Crener
International Relations: Bernard Ricciardi
Commerce.

Centre d'Etudes supérieures industrielles (CESI)
6, boulevard de l'Europe, 91033 Evry
Tel: +33 1-60-78-12-67
Fax: +33 1-60-78-52-04
Directeur: Janusz Meilcrek
Industrial Studies.

Centre d'Etudes supérieures industrielles (CESI)
297, rue de Vaugirard, 75015 Paris
Tel: +33 1-44-19-23-45
Fax: +33 1-42-50-25-06
Directeur: Jacques Bahry
Industrial Studies.

Centre de Formation et de Perfectionnement des Journalistes (CEPJ)
33, rue du Louvre, 75002 Paris
Tel: +33 1-44-82-20-00
Fax: +33 1-82-20-02
Directeur: Yves Agnès
Founded: 1946
Journalism.

Ecole européenne des Affaires (EAP)
6, avenue de la Port de Champeret, 75838 Paris
Tel: +33 1-44-09-30-00
Fax: +33 1-44-09-3359
Directeur: Michel Raimbault
International Relations: Michel Raimbault
Business Management (European).

Ecole catholique d'Arts et Métiers de (ECAM)
40 montée Saint-Barthélemy, 69321 Lyon Cedex 05
Tel: +33 78-37-81-81
Fax: +33 72-40-22-39
Directeur: Jean Guy
International Relations: Pierre-Marie Gueritey
Founded: 1900
Engineering.

Ecole de hautes Etudes commerciales du Nord (EDHEC)
58 Rue du Port, 59046 Lille
Tel: +33 20-15-45-00
Fax: +33 20-15-45-01
Directeur: Olivier Oger
International Relations: Pascal Onraed
Commerce.

Ecole pour les Etudes et la Recherche en Informatique et Electronique (EERIE)
Parc scientifique Georges Besse, 30000 Nimes
Tel: +33 66-38-70-00
Fax: +33 66-84-05-06
Directeur: Jean-Claude Ippolito
Computer Sciences and Electronics.

Ecole française d'Ingénieurs des Industries papetieres et graphiques (EFPG)
Domaine Universitaire, B.P. 65, 38402 Saint-Martin-d'Hères
Tel: +33 76-82-69-00
Fax: +33 76-82-69-33
Directeur: Christian Voillot
International Relations: Jacques Silvy
Paper Technology.

Ecole française d'Electronique et d'Informatique (EFREI)
110, rue Amyot, 75005 Paris
Tel: +33 1-47-07-05-95
Fax: +33 1-43-37-42-96
Directeur: Henri Meunier
International Relations: Christine Loevenbruch
Founded: 1936
Electronics; Computer Sciences.

Ecole d'Ingénieurs de Tours (EIT)
rue Marcel Dassault, B.P. 0407, 37004 Tours
Tel: +33 47-27-20-20
Fax: +33 47-27-93-25
Directeur: Gérard Gaillot
International Relations: Fabienne Mignon
Engineering.

Ecole polytechnique féminine (EPF)
3 bis, rue Lakanal, 92330 Sceaux
Tel: +33 1-41-13-01-51
Fax: +33 1-46-60-39-94
Directeur: Alain Jeneveau
International Relations: Erna Ortodoro
Founded: 1925
Technology.

Ecole supérieure d'Agriculture d'Angers (ESA)
55, rue Rabelais, 49007 Angers 01
Tel: +33 41-23-55-55
Fax: +33 41-23-55-00
Directeur: Aymard Honoré
International Relations: Jean Bourgeois
Agriculture.

Ecole supérieure d'Agriculture de Purpan (ESAP)
75, voie du Toec, 31076 Toulouse
Tel: +33 61-49-23-11
Fax: +33 61-31-91-48
Directeur: Pierre Tapie
International Relations: Evelyne Francal
Agriculture.

Ecole supérieure de Commerce d'Amiens Picardie (ESC)
18, place Saint-Michel, 80038 Amiens 1
Tel: +33 22-82-23-00
Fax: +33 22-82-23-01
Directeur: Roger Mezin
International Relations: Elena Spaletti
Founded: 1942
Management.

Ecole supérieure de Commerce de Bordeaux (ESC)
680, Cours de la Libération, 33405 Talence
Tel: +33 58-84-55-55
Fax: +33 56-84-55-00
Directeur: Georges Viala
International Relations: Jean Lefèbvre
Management.

Ecole supérieure de Commerce de Brest (ESC)
2, avenue de Provence, 29272 Brest
Tel: +33 98-34-44-44
Fax: +33 98-34-44369
Directeur: Jacques Baguenard
International Relations: Gilles Gueguen
Management.

Ecole supérieure de Commerce de Clermont-Ferrand (ESC)
4, boulevard Trudaine, 63037 Clermont-Ferrand
Tel: +33 73-98-24-24
Fax: +33 73-98-24-49
Directeur: Henri Verdier
International Relations: Michael Bryant
Founded: 1919
Management.

Ecole supérieure de Commerce de Dijon (ESC)
29, rue Sambin, 21000 Dijon
Tel: +33 80-75-59-00
Fax: +33 80-72-59-99
Directeur: Christian Bérard
International Relations: Henri Heugel
Management.

Ecole supérieure de Commerce de Grenoble (ESC)
12, rue Pierre Semard, 38003 Grenoble 01
Tel: +33 76-70-60-60
Fax: +33 76-70-60-99
Directeur: Jean-Paul Léonardi
International Relations: Thierry Grange
Management.

Ecole supérieure de Commerce Le Harve/Caen (ESC)
30, rue Richelieu, 376087 Le Havre
Tel: +33 32-92-59-99
Fax: +33 35-42-11-16
Directeur: Michel Poté
International Relations: Armel Esnol
Management.

Ecole supérieure de Commerce de Lille (ESC)
avenue Gaston Berger, 59045 Lille
Tel: +33 20-49-31-31
Fax: +33 20-49-04-56
Directeur: Jean-Pierre Debourse
International Relations: Philippe Evrard
Management.

Ecole supérieure de Commerce de Lyon (ESC)
23, Avenue Guy de Collongue, B.P. 174, 69132 Ecully
Tel: +33 78-33-78-00
Fax: +33 78-33-61-69
Directeur: Bruno Dufour
International Relations: Ian Tovey
Management.

Ecole supérieure de Commerce de Marseille (ESC)
Domaine de Luminy, B.P. 911, 13009 Marseille 9
Tel: +33 91-41-24-90
Fax: +33 91-26-81-62
Directeur: Charles-Henri Besseyre des Horts
International Relations: Michèle Pentagrossa
Management.

Ecole supérieure de Commerce de Montpellier (ESC)
2300, avenue des Moulins, 34034 Montpellier
Tel: +33 67-10-25-00
Fax: +33 67-45-13-56
Directeur: Didier Jourdan
International Relations: Salvador Begueria
Management.

Ecole supérieure de Commerce de Nantes Atlantique (ESC)
8, route de la Jonelière, 44003 Nantes 01
Tel: +33 40-37-34-34
Fax: +33 40-37-34-07
Directeur: Aïssa Dermouche
International Relations: Martine Froissart
Management.

Ecole supérieure de Commerce de Pau (ESC)
3, rue Saint John Perse, 64000 Pau
Tel: +33 59-92-64-64
Fax: +33 59-92-64-55
Directeur: Laurent Hua
International Relations: Alan Gibson
Management.

Ecole supérieure de Commerce de Poitiers (ESC)
11, rue de l'Ancienne Comédie, 86000 Poitiers
Tel: +33 49-60-58-00
Fax: +33 49-60-58-30
Directeur: Albert Hirbarrondo
International Relations: Viviane Bourdin
Management.

Ecole supérieure de Commerce de Reims (ESC)
B.P. 302, 51061 Reims Cedex
Tel: +33 26-08-06-04
Fax: +33 26-04-69-63
Directeur: Pierre Lamborelle
International Relations: Paul Crowther
Founded: 1929
Management.

Ecole supérieure de Commerce de Rouen (ESC)
Boulevard André-Siegfried, B.P. 34, 76130 Mont-Saint-Aignan
Tel: +33 32-82-74-00
Fax: +33 35-76-06-62
Directeur: Jean-Claude de Schletere
International Relations: Françoise Castem
Founded: 1871
Management.

Ecole supérieure de Commerce de Toulouse (ESC)
20, Boulevard Lascrosses, 31068 Toulouse
Tel: +33 61-29-49-49
Fax: +33 61-29-49-94
Directeur: Jacques Ain
International Relations: William McNulty
Founded: 1903
Management.

Ecole supérieure de Commerce de Tours (ESC)
1, rue Léo-Delibes, B.P. 0535, 37005 Tours
Tel: +33 47-71-71
Fax: +33 47-71-72-10
Directeur: Guy Leboucher
International Relations: Eugénie Draper
Management.

Ecole supérieure de Chimie industrielle de Lyon (ESCIL)
43, boulevard du 11 Novembre 1918, 69616 Villeurbane
Tel: +33 44-84-96
Fax: +33 78-93-13-96
Directeur: Jean-Claude Charpentier
International Relations: Jean Huet
Industrial Chemistry.

Ecole supérieure de Chimie organique et minérale (ESCOM)
13, boulevard de l'Hautil, 95092 Cergy Pontoise
Tel: +33 1-30-75-60-20
Fax: +33 30-75-60-21
Directeur: Dominique Raynaud
International Relations: Laura Green
Organic and Mineral Chemistry.

Ecole supérieure de Commerce de Paris (ESCP)
79, avenue de la République, 75543 Paris Cedex 11
Tel: +33 1-49-23-20-00
Fax: +33 1-43-55-99-63
Directeur: Mme Véronique de Chantérac
International Relations: Olivier Delaroche
Management.

Ecole supérieure d'Electronique de l'Ouest (ESEO)
4, rue Merlet-de-la-Boulaye, 49024 Angers 01
Tel: +33 41-86-67-67
Fax: +33 41-87-99-27
Directeur: Victor Hamon
International Relations: Victor Hamon
Founded: 1956
Electronics.

Ecole supérieure d'Informatique, Electronique et Automatique (ESIEA)
9, rue Vésale, 75005 Paris
Tel: +33 1-43-37-78-43
Fax: +33 1-43-36-27-02
Directeur: Jean-Louis Marulaz
International Relations: Peter Wilson
Computer Sciences; Electronics; Automation.

Ecole supérieure d'Ingénieurs en Electrotechnique et Electronique (ESIEE)
2, Cité Descartes, B.P. 99, 93160 Noisy
Tel: +33 1-45-92-65-00
Fax: +33 45-92-66-99
Directeur: Jacques Perrin
International Relations: Jean-Louis Meslier
Founded: 1904
Electrotechniques and Electronics.

Ecole supérieure d'Ingénieurs en Génie électrique (ESIGELEC)
1, rue Maréchal Juin, 76131 Mont-Saint-Aignan
Tel: +33 35-52-80-20
Fax: +33 35-52-80-80
Directeur: Dominique Valentin
International Relations: Daniel Lierville
Founded: 1901
Electrical Engineering.

Ecole supérieure d'Ingénieurs de Marseille (ESIM)
IMT Technopôle de Château-Gombert, 13454 Marseille
Tel: +33 91-05-44-44
Fax: +33 91-05-43-43
Directeur: Philippe Zanin
International Relations: Philippe Durourcq
Engineering.

Ecole supérieure d'Ingénieurs et de Techniciens pour l'Agriculture(ESITPA)
rue Grande, B.P. 607, 27106 Val-de-Reuil
Tel: +33 59-14-59
Fax: +33 32-59-87-32
Directeur: Georges Bastine
International Relations: Georges Molmy
Founded: 1919
Agricultural Engineering.

Ecole spéciale de Mécanique et d'Electricité (ESME)
4, rue Blaise-Desgoffe, 75006 Paris
Tel: +33 1-45-48-03-70
Fax: +33 1-45-44-80-66
Directeur: Jean Doceul
International Relations: Denys Pine des Granges
Founded: 1905
Mechanical and Electrical Engineering.

Ecole supérieure d'Optique (ESO)
B.P. 147, 91403 Orsay
Tel: +33 1-69-41-68-01
Fax: +33 1-69-41-31-92
Directeur: Christian Imbert
International Relations: Alain Aspect
Founded: 1920
Optics.

Ecole supérieure de Physique et de Chimie industrielles (ESPCI)
10, rue Vauquelin, 75231 Paris 05
Tel: +33 1-40-79-44-00
Fax: +33 1-40-79-44-25
Directeur: Pierre-Gilles de Gennes
International Relations: Lucien Monnerie
Founded: 1882
Physics and Industrial Chemistry.

Ecole supérieure du Soudage et de ses Applications (ESSA)
90, rue des Vanesses, B.P. 50362, 95942 Roissy CDG
Tel: +33 1-49-90-36-00
Fax: +33 1-49-90-36-59
Directeur: Mihran Dadlan
Welding.

Ecole supérieure des Sciences commerciales d'Angers (ESSCA)
1, rue Lakanal, B.P. 2007, 49016 Angers 01
Tel: +33 41-73-47-47
Fax: +33 41-73-47-48
Directeur: Christian Brulard
International Relations: Alain Ouvrieu
Management.

Ecole supérieure des Sciences économiques et commerciales (ESSEC)
Avenue Bernard Hirsch, B.P. 105, 95021 Cergy-Pontoise
Tel: +33 1-34-43-30-00
Fax: +33 1-34-43-30-01
Directeur: Maurice Thévenet
International Relations: Fréderic Jenny
Management.

Ecole supérieure des Techniques aerospatiales (ESTA)
Bâtiment 502 bis, Complexe scientifique d'Orsay, 91405 Orsay
Tel: +33 1-69-28-68-57
Fax: +33 1-69-28-06-20
Directeur: Alain Durollet
International Relations: Guy Robin
Founded: 1930
Aerospatial Techniques.

Ecole supérieure des Sciences et Technologies de l'Ingénieur de Nancy (ESSTIN)
Parc Robert Bentz, 2, rue Jean Lamour, 54500 Vandoeuvre les Nancy
Tel: +33 83-50-33-33
Fax: +33 83-54-21-73
Directeur: Robert Mainard
International Relations: Françoise Clerc
Engineering Sciences.

Ecole supérieure des techniques industrielles et des textiles (ESTIT)
1, allée Lakaonal, B.P. 209, 59654 Villeneuve-d'Ascq
Tel: +33 20-91-35-21
Fax: +33 20-91-03-18
Directeur: Bernard Avrin
International Relations: David Grant Douglas
Industrial and Textile Techniques.

Ecole spéciale des Travaux publics, du Bâtiment et de l'Industrie (ESTP)
57, boulevard Saint-Germain, 75240 Paris 05
Tel: +33 1-44-41-11-18
Fax: +33 1-44-41-11-12
Directeur: Serge Eyrolles
International Relations: Jacques Fargier
Public Works.

Ecole universitaire d'Ingénieurs de Lille (EUDIL)
Cité scientifique, 59655 Villeneuve d'Ascq
Tel: +33 1-44-41-11-18
Fax: +33 1-44-41-11-12
Directeur: Pierre Legrand
International Relations: Lievin Devos
Engineering.

Ecole des hautes Etudes commerciales (HEC)
1, rue de la Libération, B.P. 31, 78350 Jouy-en-Josas
Tel: +33 1-39-67-70-00
Fax: +33 1-39-67-70-75
Management.

Ecole des hautes Etudes industrielles (HEI)
13, rue de Toul, 59046 Lille
Tel: +33 20-30-83-14
Fax: +33 20-42-81-46
Directeur: Michel Vittu
International Relations: Fredericka Beets
Industrial Studies.

Institut catholique d'Arts et Métiers (ICAM Lille)
6, rue Auber, 59046 Lille
Tel: +33 20-93-58-55
Fax: +33 20-93-14-89
Directeur: Guy Carpier
International Relations: Frédéric Geoffroy
Founded: 1898
Engineering; Economics and Computer Sciences.

Institut catholique d'Arts et Métiers (ICAM Nantes)
35, avenue du Champ de Manoeuvres, 44470 Carquefou
Tel: +33 40-52-40-52
Fax: +33 40-52-40-99
International Relations: Rémi de Maindreville
Engineering.

Institut commercial de Nancy (ICN)
4, rue Michel Ney, 54037 Nancy
Tel: +33 83-39-64-50
Fax: +33 83-39-68-80
Directeur: Jacques Thevenot
International Relations: David Long
Founded: 1905
Management.

Institut de Chimie et Physique industrielles (ICPI)
31, place Bellecour, 69288 Lyon 02
Tel: +33 72-32-51-51
Fax: +33 72-32-51-29
Directeur: Michelle Gelin
International Relations: Claude Bourgeois
Industrial Chemistry and Physics.

Institut supérieur agricole de Beauvais (ISAB)
rue Pierre Waguet, B.P. 313, 60026 Beauvais
Tel: +33 44-0625-25
Fax: +33 44-06-25-26
Directeur: André Blanchard
International Relations: Krysia de Kergorlay
Agriculture.

Institut supérieur d'Agriculture Rhône-Alpes (ISARA)
31, place Bellecour, 69288 Lyon 02
Tel: +33 72-32-51-00
Fax: +33 20-54-56-66
Directeur: Jacques Riauté
International Relations: Marguerite Paraire
Agriculture.

Institut supérieur d'Electronique du Nord (ISEN)
41, boulevard Vauban, 59046 Lille
Tel: +33 20-30-62-20
Fax: +33 20-54-56-66
Directeur: Jean-Noël Decarpigny
International Relations: Evelyn Litton
Electronics.

Institut supérieur d'Electronique de Paris (ISEP)
28, rue Notre Dame des Champs, 75270 Paris Cedex 06
Tel: +33 1-49-54-52-44
Fax: +33 1-49-54-52-01
Directeur: Jacques Caumartin
International Relations: Yves Serizier
Founded: 1955
Electronics.

Institut textile et chimique de Lyon (ITECH Lyon)
181-203, avenue Jean Jaurès, 69342 Lyon 07
Tel: +33 78-72-28-31
Fax: +33 78-61-03-33
Directeur: Jean-Pierre Gallet
International Relations: Nathalie Pinton
Textiles and Chemical Engineering.

Ecole supérieure d'Electricité (SUPELEC)
Plateau du Moulon, 911920 Gif-sur-Yvette
Tel: +33 1-69-85-12-12
Fax: +33 1-69-85-12-34
Directeur: Bernard Pincibono
International Relations: Antoine Sorba
Founded: 1894
Electrical Engineering.

OTHER INSTITUTIONS

PUBLIC INSTITUTIONS

Antenne pédagogique d'Architecture
B.P. 47, 95000 Cergy Cedex
Architecture.

Centre de Documentation et de Recherches européennes, comparatives et internationales
9, rue J.-Macé, 35000 Rennes
Tel: +33 99-38-03-01
Documentation; European Studies; International Studies.

Centre de Formation de Conseillers d'Orientation
3 bis, rue Bart, 59000 Lille
Tel: +33 20-17-09-29
Vocational Guidance and Counselling.

Centre départemental d'Education ouvrière du Nord de la France
sac postal 19, 59650 Villeneuve-d'Ascq
Founded: 1954
Workers' Adult Education.

Centre européen universitaire de Nancy
15, place Carnot, 54042 Nancy Cedex
Tel: +1 83-36-52-84
Founded: 1950
Law and Political Science; Economics; Contemporary European Studies.

Centre national d'Etudes supérieures de la sécurité sociale
27 rue des Docteurs Charcot, 42031 St. Etienne Cedex
Tel: +33 77-57-72-74
Social Security Studies.

Centre régional d'Education physique
Rue des Marettes, 35802 Dinard
Tel: +33 99-46-16-23
Physical Education.

Centre régional d'Education physique et sportive
Château de Mirande, rue Pierre de Coubertin, 21000 Dijon Cedex
Tel: +33 80-65-46-12
Physical Education and Sports.

Centre régional d'Education physique et sportive
1, avenue Foch, 54311 Essey-les-Nancy
Tel: +33 83-27-58-51
Founded: 1929
Physical Education and Sports.

Centre régional d'Education physique et sportive
Château de Boivre, Vouneuil-sous-Biard, 86000 Poitiers
Tel: +33 49-53-31-24
Physical Education and Sports.

Centre régional d'Education physique et sportive
Rue des Marettes, 35802 Rennes Cedex
Tel: +33 99-46-16-25
Physical Education and Sports.

Centre régional d'Education physique et sportive
4, allée du Sommerhof, 67035 Strasbourg Cedex 3
Tel: +33 88-30-38-64
Physical Education and Sports.

Conservatoire national supérieur d'Art dramatique
2 bis, rue du Conservatoire, 75009 Paris
Tel: +33 1-42-46-12-91
Drama.

Conservatoire national supérieur de Musique
14, rue de Madrid, 75008 Paris
Tel: +33 1-42-93-15-20
Founded: 1795
Music.

Ecole d'Architecture de Bordeaux
Domaine de Raba, Cours de la Libération, 33405 Talence Cedex
Tel: +33 56-80-65-44
Fax: +33 56-37-03-23
Architecture.

Ecole d'Architecture de Clermont-Ferrand
71, boulevard Côte-Blatin, 63000
Clermont-Ferrand
Tel: +33 73-93-18-55
Founded: 1968
Architecture.

Ecole d'Architecture de Grenoble
10, Galerie des Baladins, 38000 Grenoble
Tel: +33 76-23-31-72
Founded: 1927
Architecture.

Ecole d'Architecture de Lyon
3 rue Maurice Audin, 69120 Vaulxieu Velin
Tel: +33 1-72-04-69-55
Architecture.

Ecole d'Architecture de Marseille-Luminy
Domaine de Luminy, 70 Route Leon Lachamps,
13288 Marseille-Luminy Cedex 2
Tel: +33 91-26-80-80
Founded: 1752
Architecture.

Ecole d'Architecture de Nantes
La Mulotière', Rue Massenet, 44300 Nantes
Tel: +33 40-76-07-33
Founded: 1946
Architecture.

Ecole d'Architecture de Normandie
27 rue Lucien Fromage, 76160 Darnetal
Tel: +33 35-08-07-71
Architecture.

Ecole d'Architecture de Paris-Belleville
7880, rue Rebeval, 75019
Tel: +33 1-42-41-33-60
Founded: 1648
Architecture.

Ecole d'Architecture de Paris-la-Défense
158 rue Salvador Allende, 92023 Nanterre Cedex
Tel: +33 1-47-76-01-05
Architecture.

Ecole d'Architecture de Paris-la-Seine
14, rue Bonaparte, 75272 Paris Cedex 06
Tel: +33 1-42-72-81-11
Architecture.

Ecole d'Architecture de Paris-la-Villette
144, rue de Flandre, 75019 Paris
Tel: +33 1-42-08-79-70
Architecture.

Ecole d'Architecture de Paris-Villemin
11, quai Malaquais, 75272 Paris Cedex 06
Tel: +33 1-42-60-34-57
Architecture.

Ecole d'Architecture de Paris-Tolbiac
5, rue du Javelot, 75645 Paris Cedex 13
Tel: +33 1-45-82-27-27
Architecture.

Ecole d'Architecture de Rennes
34, rue Hoche, 35000 Rennes
Tel: +33 99-62-21-77
Architecture.

Ecole d'Architecture de Saint-Etienne
1, rue Buisson, 42000 Saint-Etienne
Tel: +33 77-32-69-31
Architecture.

Ecole d'Architecture de Strasbourg
8 Bd. Wilson, B.P. 37, 67000 Strasbourg
Tel: +33 88-32-25-35
Architecture.

Ecole d'Architecture du Languedoc-Roussillon
1, rue 91 Plan des Quatre-Seigneurs, 34090
Montpellier
Tel: +33 67-63-34-30
Architecture.

Ecole d'Architecture de Versailles
2, avenue de Paris, 78000 Versailles
Tel: +33 39-51-52-51
Architecture.

Ecole du Louvre
34, quai du Louvre, 75041 Paris Cedex 01
Tel: 42 60 25 50
Founded: 1882
Archaeology, History of Arts, Museology.

Ecole municipale des Arts décoratifs
1, rue de l'Académie, 67000 Strasbourg
Tel: +33 88-35-38-58
Decorative Arts.

Ecole nationale d'Assurances
292, rue Saint-Martin, 75003
Tel: +33 42-71-24-14
Founded: 1946
Insurance.

Ecole nationale des Beaux-Arts
3, rue Michelet, 21000 Dijon
Tel: +33 80-30-21-27
Founded: 1766
Fine Arts.

Ecole nationale des Beaux-Arts
10, rue Neyret, 69001 Lyon
Tel: +33 78-28-13-67
Fine Arts.

Ecole nationale des Beaux-Arts
1, avenue Boffrand, 54000 Nancy
Tel: +33 83-40-16-25
Founded: 1702
Fine Arts.

Ecole nationale des Beaux-Arts et des Arts appliqués à l'Industrie de Bourges
7, rue Edouard Branly, 18000 Bourges
Tel: +33 48-70-11-45
Founded: 1824
Fine Arts.

Ecole nationale du Cadastre
76, chemin du Calquet, 31081 Toulouse Cedex
Tel: +33 61-49-30-87
Cadastral Surveying.

Ecole nationale de la Concurrence et de la Consommation
6, rue Saint-Maur, 75011 Paris
Tel: +33 43-79-41-10
Commerce.

Ecole nationale de Formation agronomique
Route de Narbonne, B.P. 87, 31326 Castenet
Tolosan Cedex
Tel: +33 61-73-04-25
Agricultural Education.

Ecole nationale des Douanes
86 Boulevard Orléans, 76037 Rouen
Tel: +33 46-24-94-97
Fax: +33 35-62-08-55-434
Founded: 1947
Customs and Excise.

Ecole nationale du Génie rural, des Eaux et des Forêts
14 rue Girardet, 54042 Nancy Cedex
Tel: +33 83-35-10-20
Rural Engineering; Forest.

Ecole nationale des Haras
Le Pin au Haras, 61310 Exmes
Tel: +33 33-67-92-79
Founded: 1892
Horse Breeding.

Ecole nationale des Impôts
1, rue Ledru, 63033 Clermont-Ferrand Cedex
Tel: +33 73-93-88-44
Founded: 1951
Taxation.

Ecole nationale d'Ingénieurs des Travaux agricoles de Dijon
21 boulevard Olivier de Serres, 21802 Quetigny
Cedex
Tel: +33 80-46-30-01
Agricultural Engineering.

Ecole nationale d'Ingénieurs de Travaux agricoles de Marmilhat
63370 Lempdes-Clermont-Ferrand, 63370
Lempdes-Clermont-Ferrand
Tel: +33 73-92-52-36
Agricultural Engineering.

Ecole nationale d'Ingénieurs des Techniques des Industries agricoles et alimentaires
Chemin de la Geraudière, 44072 Nantes Cedex
03 44072
Tel: +33 40-40-03-00
Agricultural and Food Technology.

Ecole nationale d'Ingénieurs des Travaux ruraux et des Techniques sanitaires
1, quai Koch, B.P. 1039F, 67070 Strasbourg Cedex
Tel: +33 88-25-34-50
Founded: 1960
Civil Engineering (Rural); Public Health Engineering.

Ecole nationale Louis Lumière
8, rue Rollin, 75005 Paris
Tel: +33 43-54-10-17
Founded: 1926
Photography; Cinematography; Sound and Videonics.

Ecole nationale de la Magistrature
8, rue Chanoinesse, 75004 Paris
Tel: +33 43-26-22-11
Magisterial Studies.

Ecole nationale de la Magistrature
9, rue du Maréchal-Joffre, 33080 Bordeaux Cedex
Tel: +33 56-52-05-50
Fax: +33 56-81-82-63
Magisterial Studies.

Ecole nationale de la Marine marchande
95, traverse Prat, 13008 Marseille
Tel: +33 91-73-02-98
Marine Engineering.

Ecole nationale de la Marine marchande
38, rue Joseph-Blanchart, 44100 Nantes
Tel: +33 40-73-64-80
Marine Engineering.

Ecole nationale de la Marine marchande
Rue Pierre-Loti, 22500 Paimpol
Tel: +33 96-20-80-27
Marine Engineering.

Ecole nationale de la Marine marchande
Rue de la Victoire, 35400 Saint-Malo
Tel: +33 99-40-83-46
Marine Engineering.

Ecole nationale de la Santé publique
Avenue du Professeur Léon Bernard, 35043
Rennes Cedex
Tel: +33 99-59-29-36
Founded: 1945
Public Health.

Ecole nationale des Services du Trésor
Bois de la Grange Noisiel, 77420 Champs-sur-
Marne Cedex
Tel: +33 60-05-92-04
Public Finance.

Ecole nationale de la Statistique et de l'Administration économique
3, avenue Pierre Larousse, 92241 Malakoff Cedex
Tel: +33 45-40-10-11
Founded: 1942
Economic Administration.

Ecole nationale supérieure agronomique
145, avenue de Muret, 31076 Toulouse Cedex
Tel: +33 61-42-83-98
Agriculture (including Animal Husbandry).

Ecole nationale supérieure des Arts appliqués et des Métiers d'Art
63, rue Olivier-de-Serres, 75015 Paris
Tel: +33 45-30-20-66
Applied Arts.

Ecole nationale supérieure des Arts décoratifs
31, rue d'Ulm, 75005 Paris
Tel: +33 43-29-86-79
Founded: 1766
Decorative Arts.

Ecole nationale supérieure des Arts et Industries
24, boulevard de la Victoire, 67084 Strasbourg Cedex
Tel: +33 88-35-55-05
Founded: 1875
Engineering and Technology.

Ecole nationale supérieure des Arts et Industries textiles de Roubaix
2, place des Martyrs de la Résistance, 59070 Roubaix Cedex 01
Tel: +33 20-25-64-64
Founded: 1885
Textile Engineering.

Ecole nationale supérieure des Beaux-Arts
17, quai Malaquais, 75272 Paris Cedex 06
Tel: +33 42-60-34-57
Fine Arts.

Ecole nationale supérieure de Céramique industrielle
47 avenue Albert Thomas, 87065 Limoges Cedex
Tel: +33 55-45-22-22
Founded: 1893
Industrial Ceramics.

Ecole nationale supérieure de Police
8, avenue Gambetta, 69450 St. Cyr-au-Mont d'Or
Tel: +33 78-64-02-88
Founded: 1941
Police Studies.

Ecole nationale supérieure des Sciences agronomiques appliquées
26, boulevard Docteur Petitjean, B.P. 588, 21016 Dijon Cedex
Tel: +33 80-66-54-12
Founded: 1920
Agricultural Science.

Ecole nationale supérieure des Sciences de l'Information et des Bibliothèques
17-21, boulevard du 11 novembre 1918, 69621 Villeurbanne
Tel: +33 78-89-64-45
Information and Library Science.

Ecole nationale des Techniques industrielles et de Mines de Nantes
3 rue Marcel Sembat, 44049 Nantes Cedex 04
Tel: +33 40-73-74-70
Founded: 1991
Industrial Technology; Mining Technology.

Ecole régionale des Beaux-Arts
30, rue Hoche, 35000 Rennes
Tel: +33 99-28-55-78
Founded: 1881
Fine Arts.

Ecole supérieure d'Agronomie tropicale dépendant du Centre national d'Etudes agronomiques des Régions chaudes
Avenue du Val-de-Montjenaud, 34033 Montpellier Cedex
Tel: +33 67-54-55-33
Tropical Agriculture.

Ecole supérieure de Formation agricole
44, rue Rabelais, 49044 Angers Cedex
Tel: +33 41-88-58-12
Agricultural Education.

Ecole supérieure d'Interprètes et de Traducteurs de l'Université de Paris Sorbonne Nouvelle
Place du Maréchal-de-Lattre de-Tassigny, 75116 Paris
Tel: +33 45-05-14-10
Founded: 1957
Interpretation and Translation.

Ecole technique supérieure des Travaux maritimes
Rue Maurice-Audin, 69120 Vaulx-en-Velin
Tel: +33 78-80-82-69
Maritime Construction.

Institut d'Elevage et de Médecine vétérinaire des Pays tropicaux
10, rue Pierre-Curie, 94704 Maisons-Alfort
Tel: +33 43-68-88-73
Founded: 1920
Tropical Stockbreeding and Veterinary Medicine.

Institut d'Etudes sociales
21, rue d'Assas, 75006 Paris
Tel: +33 1-42-22-41-80
Founded: 1924
Social Studies.

Institut d'Etudes supérieures d'Industries et d'Economie laitières
16, rue Claude-Bernard, 75231 Paris Cedex 05
Tel: +33 1-47-07-16-45
Dairy Industry and Economics.

Institut d'Etudes supérieures des Techniques de l'organisation
Conservatoire national des Arts et Métiers, 292, rue Saint-Martin, 75141 Paris Cedex 03
Tel: +33 1-42-71-24-14
Founded: 1956
Organization Techniques.

Institut européen d'Etudes commerciales supérieures
3, avenue d'Alsace, 67000 Strasbourg
Tel: +33 1-88-36-56-77
Founded: 1919
Commerce.

Institut des hautes Etudes européennes
5, rue Schiller, 67000 Strasbourg Cedex
Tel: +33 88-35-02-69
Founded: 1953
European Studies.

Institut d'Informatique d'Entreprise (Conservatoire national des Arts et Métiers)
18, allée Jean-Rostand, 91002 Evry Cedex
Tel: +33 1-60-77-97-40
Computer Sciences; Economics and Management.

Institut national d'Administration publique
2, avenue de l'Observatoire, 75006 Paris
Tel: +33 1-43-20-12-60
Founded: 1966
Public Administration.

Institut national d'Etude du Travail et d'Orientation professionnelle
41, rue Gay-Lussac, 75005 Paris
Tel: +33 43-29-12-23
Founded: 1928
Professional Orientation.

Institut national de Promotion supérieure agricole
Rue des Champs Prévois, 21100 Dijon
Tel: +33 80-66-72-27
Agriculture.

Institut national des Sciences et Techniques nucléaires
B.P. 6, 91191 Gif-sur-Yvette Cedex
Tel: +33 69-08-24-19
Founded: 1956
Nuclear Sciences and Techniques.

Institut national du Sport et de l'Education physique
11, avenue du Tremblay, 75012 Paris
Tel: +33 1-48-08-41-20
Founded: 1933
Physical Education and Sports.

Institut national des Techniques économiques et comptables
292, rue Saint-Martin, 75141 Paris Cedex 3
Tel: +33 1-42-71-24-14
Finance and Accountancy.

Institut national des Techniques de la Documentation
292, rue Saint-Martin, 75141 Paris Cedex
Tel: +33 1-48-87-64-40
Founded: 1950
Documentation Technique.

Institut de Préparation aux Fonctions sociales et éducatives spécialisées
8, rue Joliot Curie, 51100 Reims
Tel: +33 26-06-22-88
Specialized Education.

Institut des Professeurs de Français à l'Etranger
46, rue Saint-Jacques, 75005 Paris
Tel: +33 1-43-29-12-13
Founded: 1920
French Language and Culture.

Institut régional d'Administration
quai des Martyrs de la Libération, B.P. 208, 20291 Bastia, Corse Cedex
Tel: +33 95-32-22-00
Administration.

Institut régional d'Administration
49, rue Jean-Jaurès, B.P. 213, 59018 Lille
Tel: +33 20-52-02-02
Fax: +33 20-85-07-13
Administration.

Institut régional d'Administration
15, avenue de Lyon, 57000 Metz
Tel: +33 87-75-44-11
Administration.

Institut régional d'Administration
6, route de la Jonelière, 44300 Nantes
Tel: +33 40-74-34-77
Administration.

Institut régional d'Administration
1, avenue Dutrievoz, B.P. 2016, 69616 Villeurbanne Cedex
Tel: +33 78-89-89-41
Founded: 1970
Administration.

Institut régional d'Education physique
Campus II Boulevard Maréchal-Juin, 14032 Caen Cedex
Physical Education.

Institut régional d'Education physique
200, avenue de la République, 92001 Nanterre Cedex
Physical Education.

Institut régional d'Education physique
1, rue Lacretelle, 75015 Paris
Tel: +33 1-48-28-55-62
Founded: 1928
Physical Education.

Institut régional d'Education physique et sportive
3, place de la Victoire, 33076 Bordeaux Cedex
Tel: +33 56-91-34-24
Founded: 1928
Physical Education and Sports.

Institut régional d'Education physique et sportive
Rue Paul Doumer, 63000 Clermont-Ferrand
Tel: +33 73-93-93-17
Founded: 1929
Physical Education and Sports.

Institut régional d'Education physique et sportive
9, chemin Latéral, 59790 Ronchin
Tel: +33 20-52-52-35
Founded: 1928
Physical Education and Sports.

Institut régional d'Education physique et sportive
118, rte de Narbonne, 31077 Toulouse Cedex
Tel: +33 61-52-98-44
Founded: 1929
Physical Education and Sports.

Institut régional de Gestion
35, place Pey-Berland, 33076 Bordeaux Cedex
Tel: +33 56-52-99-88
Founded: 1956
Management.

Institut scientifique et technique de l'Alimentation
292, rue Saint-Martin, 75003 Paris
Tel: +33 1-48-87-37-38
Food Science and Technology.

Institut supérieur des Matériaux et de la Construction Mécanique (Ecole de spécialisation)
3, rue Fernand Hainaut, 93407 Saint-Ouen Cedex
Tel: +33 46-06-40-85
Founded: 1948
Material and Mechanical Manufacturing.

Institut technique de Banque
292, rue Saint-Martin, 75141 Paris Cedex 03
Tel: +33 1-48-87-64-40
Founded: 1950
Banking.

Institut technique de Prévision économique et sociale
292, rue Saint-Martin, 75141 Paris Cedex 03
Tel: +33 1-42-71-24-14
Economic and Social Planning.

Institut Universitaire de Formation continue
La Bouloie, Route de Gray, 25030 Besançon Cedex
Tel: +33 1-81-50-32-66
Founded: 1973
Continuing Education.

PRIVATE INSTITUTIONS

Centre d'Enseignement du Management
3, rue Cassette, 75006 Paris
Tel: +33 1-45-44-38-80
Management.

Centre d'Enseignement du Management Collège des Sciences sociales et économiques
3, rue Cassette, 75006 Paris
Tel: +31 1-45-44-38-80
Manegement; Social Sciences; Economics.

Centre d'Etudes préparatoires aux Organisations internationales
16, rue Miollis, 75015 Paris
Tel: +33 1-45-66-97-58
International Studies.

Centre Parisien de Management
108, boulevard Malesherbes, 75017 Paris
Tel: +33 1-47-66-51-34
Founded: 1973
Management.

Ecole d'Anthropologie
1, place d'Iéna, 75116 Paris
Tel: +33 1-47-93-09-84
Founded: 1876
Anthropology.

Ecole du Chef d'Entreprise et des Cadres supérieurs
24, rue Hamelin, 75116 Paris
Tel: +33 45-53-31-59
Founded: 1944
Business Administration.

Ecole dentaire de Paris (Société de l'Ecole et du Dispensaire dentaire de Paris)
45, rue de la Tour-d'Auvergne, 75009 Paris
Tel: +33 1-48-78-74-86
Founded: 1880
Dentistry.

Ecole de Formation d'Educateurs spécialisés de l'Enfance et de l'Adolescence inadaptées
21000 Dijon
Preschool Education; Teacher Training for Handicapped Children.

Ecole de Formation Psycho-Pédagogique
22, rue Cassette, 75005 Paris
Tel: +33 1-45-48-80-46
Founded: 1946
Applied Psychology; Education; Medical Studies.

Ecole française libre des Attachés de Presse
61, rue Pierre-Charron, 75008 Paris
Tel: +33 43-59-07-79
Press and Public Relations.

Ecole Franco-Allemande de Commerce et d'Industrie
12, Cours St. Eloi, 75012 Paris
Tel: +33 43-44-06-53
Commerce.

Ecole internationale de Langue et de Civilisation françaises-Alliance française
101, boulevard Raspail, 75270 Paris Cedex 06
Tel: +33 45-44-38-28
Founded: 1914
French Language and Civilization.

Ecole Libre des hautes Etudes sociales (Ecole des hautes Etudes internationales, Ecole supérieure de Journalisme)
4, place St-Germain-des-Prés, 75006 Paris
Tel: +33 42-22-68-06
Founded: 1889
Social Sciences; International Studies; Journalism.

Ecole libre de Marketing et de Publicité
61, rue Pierre Charron, 75008 Paris
Tel: +33 43-59-07-79
Marketing; Advertising.

Ecole de Notariat
17, rue Chevreuil, 49000 Angers
Tel: +33 41-88-72-12
Founded: 1892
Notarial Studies.

Ecole de Notariat
22, allée de Tourny, 33000 Bordeaux
Tel: +33 56-52-76-91
Notarial Studies.

Ecole de Notariat
Rue de la Rotonde, 63000 Clermont-Ferrand
Tel: +33 73-93-85-31
Founded: 1913
Notarial Studies.

Ecole de Notariat
3, rue du Lycée, 21000 Dijon
Tel: +33 80-67-15-71
Founded: 1908
Notarial Studies.

Ecole de Notariat
7 rue de Pamelda, 59044 Lille Cedex
Tel: +1 20-54-54-52
Notarial Studies.

Ecole de Notariat
15, quai Claude-Bernard, 69007 Lyon
Tel: +33 78-72-80-33
Founded: 1902
Notarial Studies.

Ecole de Notariat
Avenue des Apothicaires, 34010 Montpellier
Tel: +33 67-54-16-38
Notarial Studies.

Ecole de Notariat
119, rue de Coulmiers, 44000 Nantes
Tel: +33 40-74-08-76
Founded: 1905
Notarial Studies.

Ecole de Notariat
65 Bd. Raynaud, 06100 Nice
Tel: +33 93-52-62-69
Notarial Studies.

Ecole de Notariat
28, quai de la Fontaine, 30000 Nîmes
Tel: +1 66-67-03-82
Notarial Studies.

Ecole de Notariat
15 bis, rue Poullain-Duparc, 35000 Rennes
Tel: +1 99-79-08-34
Founded: 1892
Notarial Studies.

Ecole de Notariat
39, rue du Champ-aux-Oiseaux, 76042 Rouen Cedex
Tel: +33 35-70-50-41
Founded: 1893
Notarial Studies.

Ecole de Notariat
2, rue des Juifs, 67000 Strasbourg
Tel: +33 88-32-10-55
Notarial Studies.

Ecole de Notariat
32, rue de Richelieu, 37000 Tours
Tel: +33 47-05-60-20
Notarial Studies.

Ecole nouvelle d'Organisation économique et sociale
62, rue de Miromesnil, 75008 Paris
Tel: +33 45-22-53-86
Founded: 1937
Business Administration; Accountancy; Transport Services.

Ecole d'Optique-Lunetterie
14, rue Nicolas Leblanc, 59000 Lille
Tel: +33 20-57-38-52
Optics and Spectacle Techniques.

Ecole pratique de Service social
139, boulevard du Montparnasse, 75006 Paris
Tel: +33 43-22-44-97
Founded: 1913
Social Service.

Ecole de Psychologues practiciens
21, rue d'Assas, 75270 Paris Cedex 06
Tel: +33 1-45-48-17-75
Applied Psychology.

Ecole supérieure d'Application des Corps gras
Rue Monge, Parc industriel de Pessac, 33600 Pessac
Tel: +33 56-36-00-44
Founded: 1952
Technology of Fats.

Ecole supérieure du Bois
6-8, avenue de Saint Mandé, 75012 Paris
Tel: +33 1-46-28-09-33
Founded: 1934
Wood Technology; Forestry.

Ecole supérieure de Commerce de Rennes
4 avenue des Français libres, 35000 Rennes
Tel: +33 99-31-00-31
Commerce.

Ecole supérieure de Commerce de Saint-Etienne
21 rue d'Arcole, 42000 Saint-Etienne
Tel: +33 47-32-87-85
Commerce.

Ecole supérieure de Commerce et d'Administration des Entreprises
9, rue Emile-Zola, 76000 Le Havre
Tel: +33 35-21-12-18
Founded: 1871
Commerce; Business Administration.

Ecole supérieure de Commerce et d'Administration des Entreprises
Domaine Universitaire de Luminy, Case 911, 13288 Marseille Cedex
Tel: +33 91-41-01-60
Founded: 1872
Commerce; Business Administration.

Ecole supérieure de Commerce et d'Administration des Entreprises
2300, avenue des Moulins, 34030 Montpellier Cedex
Tel: +33 67-40-42-43
Founded: 1897
Commerce; Business Administration.

Ecole supérieure de Commerce et d'Administration des Entreprises
3 rue Saint-John Perse, 64000 Pau
Tel: +33 59-92-64-64
Commerce; Business Administration.

Ecole supérieure de Commerce et d'Administration des Entreprises
Domaine de Raba, Cours de la Libération, 33405 Talence Cedex
Tel: +33 56-80-70-50
Founded: 1874
Business Administration.

Ecole supérieure de Commerce et d'Administration des Entreprises de Bourgogne et de Franche Comté
29, rue Sambin, 21000 Dijon
Tel: +33 80-72-12-40
Founded: 1899
Commerce; Business Administration.

Ecole supérieure de Commerce et d'Administration des Entreprises de Bretagne
2, avenue de Provence, B.P. 214, 29272 Brest Cedex
Tel: +33 98-34-44-44
Founded: 1962
Commerce; Business Administration.

Ecole supérieure du Cuir, des Peintures, des Encres et des Adhésifs
181, avenue Jean-Jaurès, 69342 Lyon Cedex 7
Tel: +33 78-72-28-31
Leather Technology; Paints; Varnish; Adhesives.

Ecole supérieure d'Electricité Antenne de Rennes
Avenue de la Boulais, 35510 Cesson Sevigne
Tel: +33 99-00-21-00
Electrical Engineering.

Ecole supérieure des Industries textiles de Lyon
43, cours Général-Giraud, 69283 Lyon Cedex 01
Tel: +33 78-27-07-00
Founded: 1884
Textile Industry.

Ecole supérieure des Industries textiles d'Epinal
86, rue d'Alsace, 88000 Epinal
Tel: +33 29-35-50-52
Founded: 1905
Spinning; Weaving.

Ecole supérieure de Journalisme
50, Rue Gauthier de Chatillon, 59000 Lille
Tel: +33 20-54-48-21
Journalism.

Ecole supérieure de Journalisme
4, place St-Germain-des-Prés, 75006 Paris
Tel: +33 1-42-22-68-06
Journalism.

Ecole supérieure de Métrologie
941 rue Charles Bourseul, 59508 Douai Cedex
Tel: +33 27-87-16-14
Metrology.

Ecole supérieure des Professions immobilières
2, impasse du Mont Tonnerre, 75015 Paris
Tel: +33 47-83-48-75
Founded: 1954
Estate Agent Studies.

Ecole supérieure technique de Biologie appliquée
56, rue Planchat, 75020 Paris
Tel: +33 43-71-47-40
Applied Biology.

Ecole supérieure de Traducteurs, Interprètes, et Cadres du Commerce extérieur
60, boulevard Vauban, 59046 Lille Cedex
Tel: +33 20-30-88-27
Founded: 1961
Interpretation and Translation; Foreign Trade.

Ecole technique des Surintendantes d'Usines et de Services sociaux
8 villa du Parc Montsouris, 75014 Paris
Tel: +33 45-65-00-70
Founded: 1917
Industrial Social Service.

Ecole technique supérieure privée de Chimie de l'Ouest
60, rue Michelet, 49000 Angers
Tel: +33 41-88-98-33
Founded: 1950
Chemistry.

Groupe Ecole de Commerce de Nantes
8, route de la Jonelière, 44003 Nantes Cedex
Tel: +33 40-37-34-34
Fax: +33 40-37-34-04
Founded: 1900
Commerce.

Institut des Actuaires français
243, rue St. Honoré, 75001 Paris
Tel: +33 1-48-78-46-72
Actuarial Sciences.

Institut d'Economie scientifique et de Gestion
1 rue François Baës, 59800 Lille
Tel: +33 20-54-58-92
Economics and Management.

Institut européen d'Administration des Affaires
Boulevard de Constance, 77305 Fontainebleau Cedex
Tel: +33 60-72-40-00
Founded: 1958
Business Administration.

Institut européen des hautes Etudes internationales
B.P. 176, 06023 Nice Cedex
Tel: +33 1-92-94-21-20
International Studies.

Institut français de Gestion
31320 Castenet Tolosan
Tel: +33 61-53-59-27
Management.

Institut de Gestion international agroalimentaire
56 Campus Avenue du Parc, 95033 Cergy-Pontoise Cedex
Tel: +33 30-73-28-88
Agriculture and Food Technology.

Institut international supérieur de Formation des Cadres de Santé
162, avenue Lacassagne, 69424 Lyon Cedex 03
Tel: +33 78-54-54-12
Founded: 1965
Health Education.

Institut libre des hautes Etudes économiques et commerciales
35, cours Xavier Arnozan, 33000 Bordeaux
Tel: +33 56-44-95-97
Economics and Commerce.

Institut libre d'Etudes des Relations internationales
12, rue des Saints-Pères, 75006 Paris
Tel: +33 42-96-51-48
Founded: 1948
International Relations.

Institut libre d'Etudes supérieures de la Côte-d'Azur
37, rue d'Antibes, 06400 Cannes
Tel: +33 93-43-43-82
International Studies.

Institut océanographique
195, rue Saint-Jacques, 75005 Paris
Tel: +33 1-43-25-63-10
Founded: 1906
Oceanography.

Institut polytechnique des Sciences appliquées
12, rue Béranger, 75003 Paris
Tel: +33 1-42-72-95-03
Applied Sciences.

Institut de Psychanalyse
187, rue Saint-Jacques, 75005 Paris
Tel: +33 1-46-33-32-90
Psychoanalysis.

Institut supérieur de Gestion
45, rue Spontini, 75016 Paris
Tel: +33 1-47-81-21-14
Management.

Institut supérieur international du Parfum, de la Cosmétique et de l'Aromatique alimentaire
18, rue Mansart, 78010 Versailles
Tel: +33 39-54-82-85
Perfume and Cosmetic Techniques; Food Flavouring.

Institut supérieur d'Interprétariat et de Traduction
21, rue d'Assas, 75270 Paris Cedex 06
Tel: +33 42-22-33-16
Founded: 1957
Interpretation and Translation.

Institut supérieur des Sciences techniques et d'Economie commerciale
24, rue Hamelin, 75016 Paris
Tel: +33 1-47-27-88-70
Science and Technology; Economics.

NATIONAL ACADEMIC BODIES

Ministry of Higher Education and Research
[Ministère de l'Enseignement supérieur et de la Recherche]
1, rue Descartes, 75231 Paris 05
Tel: +33 1-46-34-35-35
Ministre: François Fillon

National Centre for University and School Social Services
[Centre national des Oeuvres universitaires et scolaires (CNOUS)]
69, quai d'Orsay, 75007 Paris
Tel: +33 1-44-48-53-00
Fax: +33 1-45-55-48-49
Directeur: Paul Pierre Valli
Founded: 1955

Conference of University Presidents
[Conférence des Présidents d'Universités (CPU)]
12, rue de l'Ecole de Médecine, 75270 Paris 06
Tel: +33 1-43-54-50-49
Fax: +33 1-43-26-16-51
Président: François Fillon, Ministre de l'Enseignement supérieur et de la Recherche
Vice-Présidents: Bernard Dizambourg, Bernard Alluin, Adrien Schmitt, Suzy Halimi
Founded: 1971

Rectors' Conference
[Conférence des Recteurs]
Houssiniere, B.P. 9752, 44076 Nantes 03
Tel: +33 40-37--37-37
Président: Jean-Claude Maistre, Recteur, Académie de Nantes
Founded: 1967

National Office for Information on Study and the Professions
[Office national d'Information sur les Enseignements et les Professions (ONISEP)]
B.P. 86, 77423 Marne-la-Vallée Cedex 02
Tel: +33 64-80-35-00
Fax: +33 64-80-35-01
Directeur: Henry Pradeaux
Founded: 1970

Union of Catholic Establishments of Higher Education
[L'Union des Etablissements d'Enseignement supérieur catholique (UDESCA)]
21 rue d'Assas, 75270 Paris Cedex 06
Tel: +33 1-45-48-61-43
Fax: +33 1-45-44-27-14
Chairman: Paul Guiberteau
Founded: 1875

Commission of the French Republic for Unesco
[Commission de la République française pour l'Education, la Science et la Culture (Unesco)]
42, avenue Raymond Poincaré, 75116 Paris
Tel: +33 1-40-66-66-28
Fax: +33 1-47-04-94-65
Telex: 645187
Président: Jean Sirinelli
Secrétaire général: Georges Poussin

FRENCH POLYNESIA

UNIVERSITIES AND UNIVERSITY CENTRES

French University of the Pacific Papeete
[Université française du Pacifique]
B.P. 4635, Papeete, Tahiti
Tel: +689 421-680
Fax: +689 410-131
Président: Francis Dubus (1993-)
Secrétaire général: Philippe Ribière
International Relations: Gérard Nardou, Director for International Cooperation
Founded: 1987
D: Law; Science; Languages.

University Centre of French Polynesia
[Centre universitaire de Polynésie française]
B.P. 6570, FAA Aéroport, Tahiti
Tel: +689 421-680
Fax: +689 410-131
D: Law; Science; Letters.

GABON

UNIVERSITIES

*University Omar Bongo Libreville
[Université Omar Bongo]
Boulevard Léon M'ba, B.P. 13.131, Libreville
Tel: +241 73-20-33
Fax: +241 73-20-72
Telex: ung 5336 gø
Recteur: Daniel Ona-Ondo (1993-)
Secrétaire général: Emmanuel Ango-Meye
Founded: 1970
F: Law; Letters and Human Sciences.
S: Education; Forestry and Hydraulics; Technical Teacher Training; Management Studies.
Ce: Health Sciences.

HIGHER SCHOOL OF TEACHER TRAINING
[ECOLE NORMALE SUPÉRIEURE]
B.P. 17009, Libreville
Tel: +241 76-31-59
Fax: +241 73-20-73
Telex: uob 5336 go
Directeur: Augustin Moussirou Mouyama (1994-)
Secrétaire général: Samuel Nze
Founded: 1972

GABON

NATIONAL INSTITUTE OF MANAGEMENT
[INSTITUT NATIONAL DES SCIENCES DE GESTION]
B.P. 190, Libreville
Tel: +241 73-28-45
Fax: +241 73-20-73
Directeur: Fabien Okoue-Metogo (1991-)
Secrétaire général: Lucien Nzong
Founded: 1973
Accountancy; Commercial Techniques; Finance; Marketing.

NATIONAL SCHOOL OF FORESTRY
[ECOLE NATIONALE D'ETUDES FORESTIÈRES DU CAP
ESTÉRIAS]
B.P. 3960, Libreville
Tel: +241 76-83-45
Fax: +241 74-84-42
Directeur: Martin Mabala (1987-)
Directeur des Etudes: Vincent de Paul
Mourambou
Founded: 1957, 1975
Forestry and Water Techniques.

NATIONAL SCHOOL OF MAGISTRATURE
[ECOLE NATIONALE DE MAGISTRATURE]
B.P. 46, Libreville
Tel: +241 72-00-06
Directeur: Antoine Oliveira (1983-)
Secrétaire général: M. Mouelet
Founded: 1971

NATIONAL SCHOOL OF SECRETARIAL STUDIES
[ECOLE NATIONALE DE SECRÉTARIAT]
B.P. 17014, Libreville
Tel: +241 76-18-22
Directeur: Mme Orango-Berre (1994-)
Secrétaire général: Léopold-Paulin Gnangogneny
Office Computerization; Languages; Law.

TECHNICAL TEACHER TRAINING SCHOOL
[ECOLE NORMALE SUPÉRIEURE DE L'ENSEIGNEMENT
TECHNIQUE]
B.P. 3989, Libreville
Tel: +241 73-29-88
Fax: +241 73-20-73
Telex: uob 5336 go
Directeur: Paul Nang Ndong
Secrétaire général: Jeanne Fouefoue
Mechanical Manufacturing; Electronic Mechanical Construction; Civil Engineering; Automobile Engineering; Wood Technology; Metallic Structures.

University of Sciences and Techniques of Masuku
[Université des Sciences et Techniques de Masuku]
B.P. 901.913, Franceville
Tel: +241 67-74-49
Fax: +241 67-75-20
Telex: 6723 go

Recteur: Jacques Lebibi (1992-)
Secrétaire général: Anselme Ponga
Founded: 1986
Science; Engineering.

NATIONAL ACADEMIC BODIES

Ministry of National Education
[Ministère de l'Education nationale]
Libreville
Tel: +241 76-12-52
Fax: +241 76-14-48
Telex: 5501 go
Ministre: Paulette Missambo (1991-)
Secrétaire général: Sidoine Mbouna
International Relations: Directeur, Jeanne-Thérèse Mboumba-Rekoula
Founded: 1960

Gabon National Commission for Unesco
[Commission nationale gabonaise pour l'Unesco]
Ministère de l'Education nationale, B.P. 264, Libreville
Tel: +241 76-42-65
Fax: +241 76-42-65
Telex: 5501 go
Président: Paulette Moussavou Missambo, Minister of Education (1991-)
Secrétaire général: Marie-Madeleine Avome-Nze
Founded: 1961

THE GAMBIA

OTHER INSTITUTIONS

Gambia College
Brikama
Tel: +220 714
Founded: 1978

NATIONAL ACADEMIC BODIES

Ministry of Education
Bedford Place Building, Banjul
Tel: +220(22) 227-236
Fax: +220(22) 228-140
Minister: Alhaji A.E.W.F. Badjie

The Gambia National Commission for Unesco
15 Marina Place, P.O. Box 1133, Banjul
Tel: +220(22) 225-214
Fax: +220(22) 225-297
Telex: 2204 presof gb9
Cable: unesco natcom mined banjul
Chairman: G.W.L. Thomas
Secretary-General: Alieu Badara Saja Taal

GEORGIA

UNIVERSITIES

Abhaz University
[Abhazskij Gosudarstvennyj Universitet]
Ul. Cereteli 9, 384900 Suhumi
Tel: +7 24374
Founded: 1932, 1979
*D: Commerce; Law; Philology; Foreign
Languages; History and Law; Mathematics;
Physics; Biology; Geography; Pedagogy;
Economics; Research.*

Georgian Technical University
[Gruzinskij Tehniceskij Universitet]
Ul. Kostava 77, 380075 Tbilisi
Tel: +7(8832) 360-762
Fax: +7(8832) 365-590
Chancellor: G.G. Tchogovadze
Founded: 1922, 1990
Technology.

*Tbilisi University
[Tbilisskij Gosudarstvennyj Universitet]
Prosp. Čavčavadz 1, 380028 Tbilisi
Tel: +7(8832) 314-792
Rector: Vazha M. Okudjava
Founded: 1918
*F: History; Philology; Journalism; Philosophy
and Psychology; West European Languages and
Literature; Law; Economics; Cybernetics and
Applied Mathematics; Physics; Mathematics and
Mechanics; Chemistry; Biology; Geology and
Geography; Oriental Studies; Industrial and Trade
Economics; Business Economics.
I: Applied Mathematics Research.
D: Evening Studies; Correspondence Courses.*

OTHER INSTITUTIONS

Gorijskij Ekonomiceskij Institut
Prosp. Cavcavadze 57, 383500 Gori
Economics.

**Gruzinskij Gosudarstvennyj Teatral'nyj
Institut**
Prosp. Rustaveli 17, 380004
Drama.

Kutaisskij Politehniceskij Institut
Prosp. Molodezi 62, 384014 Kutaisi
Tel: +7 5-48-74
Technology.

**Tbilisskaja Gosudarstvennaja Akademija
Hudozestv**
Ul. Griboedova 22, 380008 Tbilisi
Fine and Applied Arts; Architecture.

**Tbilisskaja Gosudarstvennaja
Konservatorija**
Ul. Griboedova 8, 380004 Tbilisi 4
Music.

**Tbilisskij Gosudarstvennyj Medicinskij
Institut**
Prosp. V. Psavela 33, 380077 Tbilisi 77
Medicine.

NATIONAL ACADEMIC BODIES

Ministry of Education
Ul. Chitadze 6, 390018 Tbilisi
Tel: +7(8832) 989-428
Fax: +7(8832) 997-249
Minister: T. Kvachantiradze

Georgian National Commission for Unesco
Ministry of Foreign Affairs, Ul. Chitadze 4, 380018
Tbilisi
Tel: +7(8832) 989-428
Fax: +7(8832) 997-249
Telex: 212184 slava su
President: Alexander Chikvaidze, Minister of
Foreign Affairs
Secretary-General: Petr Metreveli

GERMANY

UNIVERSITIES AND UNIVERSITY INSTITUTIONS

***Rhenish-Westphalian Technical University
of Aachen**
[Rheinisch-Westfälische Technische Hochschule]
Templergraben 55, 52052 Aachen
Tel: +49(241) 80-01
Fax: +49(241) 80-4413
Telex: 08/32704 thac d
Rektor: Klaus Habetha (1987-95)
Kanzler: Jürgen Kessler
Founded: 1870, 1948
*F: Mathematics and Natural Sciences;
Architecture; Civil Engineering; Mechanical
Engineering; Mining and Metallurgy; Philosophy;
Economics; Electrical Engineering; Medicine.
I: Plastic Technology; Wool Research;
Rationalization Research; Biomedical
Technology; Pre-University Course for Foreign
Students.
A: Technical (Wuppertal-Elberfeld).
Ce: Interdisciplinary for Environmental
Protection; Hydrotechnology Research; Laser
Technology Research; Production Technology
Research; Ceramic Processing and Application
Techniques Research; Experimental Station for
Inland Shipbuilding (Duisburg); House of
Technology (Essen).*

*University of Augsburg

[Universität Augsburg]
Universitätsstrasse 2, 86159 Augsburg
Tel: +49(821) 598-1
Fax: +49(821) 598-5505
Rektor: Reinhard Blum (1991-95)
Kanzler: Dieter Köhler
Founded: 1970
F: *Economics and Social Sciences; Law;
Catholic Theology; Mathematical and Natural
Sciences; Philosophy I; Philosophy II.*
D: *Professional Further Training; Sports.*

*University of Bamberg

[Otto-Friedrich-Universität Bamberg]
Kapuzinerstrasse 16, 96047 Bamberg
Tel: +49(951) 863-0
Fax: +49(951) 863-1005
Rector: Alfred Hierold (1992-96)
Kanzler: Alfred Hemmerlein
Founded: 1972, 1979
F: *Catholic Theology; Education, Philosophy,
and Psychology; Languages and Literatures;
History and Geography; Economics, Business
Administration, and Social Sciences.*
S: *Social Work; Computers.*
I: *Physical Education.*
Ce: *Lifelong Education; Sociological Research;
History of the German Language (Research);
Islamic Art (Research).*

*University of Bayreuth

[Universität Bayreuth]
Universitätsstrasse 30, 95447 Bayreuth
Tel: +49(921) 55-1
Fax: +49(921) 55-2208
Präsident: Helmut Büttner (1991-97)
Kanzler: Wolf-Peter Hentschel
Founded: 1972
F: *Mathematics and Physics; Biology,
Chemistry, and Earth Sciences; Law and
Economics; Languages and Literature; Cultural
Sciences.*
I: *Music and Drama Research; Experimental
Geochemistry and Geophysics Research;
Macromolecular Research; African Studies;
Materials Science; Earth Eco-Systems Research
(BITÖK).*
Ce: *Economic Research; Computer; African
Culture; Language.*

*Free University of Berlin

[Freie Universität Berlin]
Altensteinstrasse 40, 14195 Berlin
Tel: +49(30) 838-1
Fax: +49(30) 831-6571
Telex: 0184019 fubln-d
Präsident: Johann Wilhelm Gerlach (1991-95)
Kanzler: Kurt Hammer
Founded: 1970
D: *Basic Medicine; Clinical Medicine (Steglitz);
Clinical Medicine (Charlottenburg); Dentistry;
Veterinary Medicine; Law; Economics and
Business Administration; Philosophy and Social*
*Sciences I; Philosophy and Social Sciences II;
Communication Sciences; Education; History;
Classical Studies and Archaeology; Political
Science; German Philology; Modern Languages
and Literature; Mathematics; Physics; Chemistry;
Pharmacy; Biology; Earth Sciences; Physical
Education.*
I: *Social Science Research; Eastern Europe;
Latin American Studies; North American Studies;
Data Processing; Didactics and Curricula
Research; Media Processing; Women's Studies.*
L: *Language; Veterinary.*

*Humboldt University Berlin

[Humboldt-Universität zu Berlin]
Unter den Linden 6, 10099 Berlin
Tel: +49(30) 2093-0
Fax: +49(30) 2093-2770
E-Mail: press@pr.hu-berlin.de
Telex: 112833 unbn d
President: Marlis Dürkop
Founded: 1809, 1948, 1989
F: *Medicine ('Charité'); Law; Economics;
Theology; Social Sciences; Education; Physical
Education; Rehabilitation; Philosophy and History;
Cultural Studies; German; Philologies; Asian and
African Studies; Linguistics; Mathematics;
Physics; Electronics; Computer Science; Biology;
Chemistry; Psychology; Pharmacy; Geography;
Nutrition and Food Technology; Agriculture and
Horticulture; Veterinary Medecine.*

Technical University of Berlin

[Technische Universität Berlin]
Strasse des 17. Juni 135, 10623 Berlin
Tel: +49(30) 314-0
Fax: +49(30) 314-26760
Telex: 184 262 tubln d
Präsident: Manfred Fricke (1985-)
Kanzler: Alfred Klein
Founded: 1799, 1879, 1946
D: *Communications and Historical Sciences;
Social and Planning Sciences; Mathematics;
Physics; Synthetic and Analytical Chemistry;
Physical and Applied Chemistry; Building
Construction and Surveying; Architecture;
Mechanics and Thermodynamics; Processing
Technology; Construction and Manufacturing;
Transport; Food Technology and Biotechnology;
Agriculture; International Rural Development;
Mining and Earth Sciences; Materials
Technology; Economics; Electrical Engineering;
Computer Sciences; Environmental Studies;
Educational Sciences.*
I: *Turbulence Research.*

*University of Bielefeld

[Universität Bielefeld]
Universitätsstrasse 25, 33615 Bielefeld
Tel: +49(521) 106-00
Fax: +49(521) 106-5844
Telex: 932362 unibi
Rektor: Helmut Skowronek (1992-96)
Kanzler: Karl Hermann Huvendick
Founded: 1969

F: History and Philosophy; Linguistics and Literature; Mathematics; Education; Physics; Law; Sociology; Biology; Chemistry; Economics; Psychology and Physical Education; Theology, Geography, Music and Art; Technology.
I: Didactics of Mathematics; Population and Social Policy Research; Mathematical Economics.
C: Teacher Training; Science Studies; Interdisciplinary Research; Science Transfer; Women's Studies.

*University of the Ruhr, Bochum
[Ruhr-Universität Bochum]
Universitätsstrasse 150, 44780 Bochum
Tel: +49(234) 700-1
Fax: +49(234) 709-4201
Telex: 0825860
Rektor: Manfred Bormann (1994-98)
Kanzler: Bernhard Wiebel
Founded: 1961
F: Protestant Theology; Catholic Theology; Philosophy, Education, and Journalism; History; Languages and Literature; Law; Economics; Social Sciences; Mechanical Engineering; Civil Engineering; Electrical Engineering; Mathematics; Physics and Astronomy; Geosciences; Chemistry; Biology; Psychology; Medicine; Physical Education.

*Rhenish Friedrich-Wilhelm University of Bonn
[Rheinische Friedrich-Wilhelms-Universität Bonn]
Regina-Pacis-Weg 3, 53111 Bonn
Tel: +49(228) 73-1
Fax: +49(228) 73-5579
Telex: 886657 unibo d
Rektor: Max G. Huber (1992-96)
Kanzler: Reinhard Lutz
Founded: 1777, 1786, 1818
F: Protestant Theology; Catholic Theology; Law and Economics; Medicine; Philosophy; Mathematics and Natural Sciences; Agriculture; Educational Sciences.
I: Old Catholic Theology; Late Classical Antiquity Research; Discrete Mathematics; Oriental Languages Seminar.

University of Bremen
[Universität Bremen]
Bibliotheksstrasse, 28359 Bremen
Tel: +49(421) 218-1
Fax: 1+49(421) 218-4259
Telex: 245-811
Rektor: Jürgen Timm (1982-97)
Kanzler: Gerd-R diger K ck
Founded: 1971
D: Physics and Electrical Engineering; Chemistry and Biology; Mathematics and Computer Sciences; Mechanical and Process Engineering; Geology; Law; Economics; Geography, History and Social Sciences; Religion, Psychology, and Political and Social Sciences; Languages, Art, and Music; Sport, and Labour and Cultural Sciences; Educational Sciences.

*Carolo-Wilhelmina Technical University of Brunswick
[Technische Universität Carolo-Wilhelmina zu Braunschweig]
Pockelsstrasse 14 (Forum), 38106 Braunschweig
Tel: +49(531) 391-0
Fax: +49(531) 391-4577
Telex: 952526
Präsident: Bernd Rebe (1983-)
Founded: 1745, 1877, 1968
F: Mechanical and Electrical Engineering; Natural Sciences.
D: DPhilosophy and Social Sciences; Mathematics, Computer Sciences and Economics; Chemistry, Pharmacy, and Biological Sciences; Physics and Earth Sciences; Architecture; Mechanical Engineering; Construction Engineering; Educational Sciences; Electrical Engineering.
I: Wood Research; Physical Education; Agricultural Technology and Sugar Manufacturing.
Ce: Computer; Lifelong Education.

*Technical University of Chemnitz
[Technische Universität Chemnitz-Zwickau]
Strasse der Nationen 62, 09111 Chemnitz
Tel: +49(371) 531-0
Fax: +49(371) 531-1342
Telex: 32483 tud
Rektor: Günther Hecht (1991-)
Kanzler: Peter Rehling
Founded: 1836, 1953, 1963, 1986
D: Mathematics; Chemistry; Physics; Mechanical Engineering I; Mechanical Engineering II; Mechanical Engineering III; Materials Science; Electrical Engineering; Computer Sciences; Teacher Training; Economics and Law.

Technical University of Clausthal
[Technische Universität Clausthal]
Adolph-Roemer-Strasse 2A, 38678 Clausthal-Zellerfeld
Tel: +49(5323) 72-0
Fax: +49(5323) 72-3500
Telex: 953828 tuclz d
Rektor: Claus Marx (1993-94)
Kanzler: Peter Kickartz
Founded: 1775, 1864, 1968
F: Natural Sciences and Humanities; Mining, Metallurgy, and Mechanical Engineering; Mathematics and Computer Sciences; Physics; Chemistry; Geology; Mining and Mineralogy; Material Sciences and Metallurgy; Mechanical and Process Engineering.

College of Physical Education of Cologne
[Deutsche Sporthochschule Köln]
Carl-Diem-Weg 6, 50933 Köln
Tel: +49(221) 4982-1
Fax: +49(221) 499-5505
Telex: 8882291 UNIK-D

Rektor: Joachim Mester (1991-95)
Kanzler: Eike Reschke
Founded: 1947, 1970
Physical Education.

University of Cologne
[Universität zu Köln]
Albertus-Magnus-Platz, 50923 Köln
Tel: +49(221) 470-0
Fax: +49(221) 470-5151
Telex: 08882291 (unikd)
Rektor: Ulrich Matz (1993-97)
Kanzler: Johannes Neyses
Founded: 1388, 1919
F: Economics and Social Sciences; Law; Medicine; Philosophy; Mathematics and Natural Sciences; Education; Education for the Handicapped.

*University of Constance
[Universität Konstanz]
Universitätsstrasse 10, 78464 Konstanz
Tel: +49(7531) 88-1
Fax: +49(7531) 88-3688
Telex: 0733359 univ. d.
Rektor: Bernd Rüthers (1991-95)
Kanzler: Jürgen Hess
Founded: 1966
F: Mathematics; Physics; Chemistry; Biology; Social Sciences; Economics and Statistics; Law; Philosophy and History; Administrative Science.

Technical University Cottbus
[Technische Universität Cottbus]
Karl-Marx-Strasse 17, 03044 Cottbus
Tel: +49(355) 69-0
Fax: +49(355) 69-2156
Telex: 379139
Rektor: Günter Spur (1991-)
Kanzler: Peter Langer
Founded: 1969
Building Technology.

*Technical University of Darmstadt
[Technische Hochschule Darmstadt]
Karolinenplatz 5, 64289 Darmstadt
Tel: +49(6151) 16-0
Fax: +49(6151) 16-5489
Telex: 419579
Präsident: Helmut Böhme (1987-95)
Kanzler: Hanns H. Seidler
Founded: 1836, 1895
D: Law and Economics; Social Sciences and History; Education Science, Psychology and Sport Science; Material Science; Mathematics; Physics; Mechanics; Chemistry; Biology; Geo-Sciences and Geography; Surveying; Constructional Engineering; Architecture; Mechanical Engineering; Electrical Energy Engineering; Electrical Communications Technology; Control and Data Processing; Computer Sciences.

University of Dortmund
[Universität Dortmund]
August-Schmidt-Strasse 4, 44227 Dortmund
Tel: +49(231) 755-1
Fax: +49(231) 755-5145
Telex: 822 465
Rektor: Albert Klein (1994-98)
Kanzler: Klaus Anderbrügge
Founded: 1965
D: Mathematics; Physics; Chemistry; Chemical Engineering; Computer Sciences; Mechanical and Industrial Engineering; Electrical Engineering; Urban and Regional Planning; Economics and Social Sciences; Statistics; Construction Engineering; Education and Biology; Special Education and Rehabilitation of the Handicapped; Human Sciences; Language and Literature; Music, Arts, Sport, and Geography.
I: Occupational Health; Spectrochemistry; Environmental Studies; Robotics Research; Transport Technology.
Ce: Didactics; Computer; Lifelong Education.

*Technical University of Dresden
[Technische Universität Dresden]
Mommsenstrasse 13, 01069 Dresden
Tel: +49(351) 463-0
Fax: +49(351) 471-7985
Telex: 328102
Rektor: Günther Landgraf (1990-94)
Kanzler: Alfred Post
Founded: 1828, 1851, 1890
F: Mathematics and Sciences; Electrical Engineering and Electronics; Mechanical Engineering; Informatics; Civil Engineering, Hydraulics, and Forestry; Economics; Humanities and Social Science; Law; Educational Science; Medicine (in process of development); Transport Sciences (in process of development).
Ce: Applied Languages; Computer; Technology.

*University of Duisburg
[Universität Gesamthochschule-Duisburg]
Lotharstrasse 65, 47048 Duisburg
Tel: +49(203) 379-0
Fax: +49(203) 379-3333
Telex: 855793 unidud
Rektor: Gernot Born (1986-95)
Kanzler: Rudolf Baumanns
Founded: 1972
D: Philosophy, Theology, and Social Sciences; Education, Psychology, and Physical Education; German and Romance Languages and Literature; Fine and Applied Arts; Economics; Biology, Chemistry, and Geography; Mechanical, Industrial and Marine Engineering; Mining Engineering, Foundry and Glass Technology, Ceramics; Electrical Engineering; Physics and Technology; Mathematics.

*Heinrich-Heine-University of Düsseldorf
[Heinrich-Heine-Universität Düsseldorf]
Universitätsstrasse 1, 40225 Düsseldorf
Tel: +49(211) 311-1
Fax: +49(211) 311-5193
E-Mail: BITNET: kaiserd0rud81
Telex: 8587 348 uni d
Rektor: Gert Kaiser (1983-95)
Kanzler: Ulf Pallme König
Founded: 1907, 1965, 1989
F: *Medicine; Mathematics and Natural Sciences;
Philosophy; Economics.*
I: *Diabetic Research; Dietetics and Nutrition;
Environmental Hygiene.*
Ce: *Neurological Therapy.*

*Catholic University of Eichstätt
[Katholische Universität Eichstätt]
Ostenstrasse 26, 85072 Eichstätt
Tel: +49(8421) 20-1
Fax: +49(8421) 20-474
Telex: 55941 Lraeid
Präsident: Nikolaus Lobkowicz (1990-96)
Kanzler: Manfred Hartl
Founded: 1972, 1980
F: *Catholic Theology; Education and Philosophy;
Modern Languages and Literature; History and
Social Sciences; Mathematics and Geography;
Business Administration; Religious Education;
Social Service.*
I: *Latin American Studies.*
P: *Special Collaboration with University of
Würzburg (Transmission of Knowledge in Late
Middle Ages).*
Ce: *Ethnology of Old European Languages
Research.*

College of Education of Erfurt/Mühlhausen
[Pädagogische Hochschule Erfurt/Mühlhausen]
Nordhäuser Strasse 63, 99089 Erfurt
Tel: +49(361) 737-0
Fax: +49(61) 737-1999
Rektor: Ulrich Pommer (1993-97)
Kanzler: Martin Rudolph Kellner
Founded: 1953, 1969
D: *Biology; Chemistry; Mathematics; Physics;
Technical Education, Handicraft and Music;
Education; German; Foreign Languages; Art;
Social Sciences.*

Universität Erfurt
Geschäftsstelle, Kramerbrücke 9-11, 99084 Erfurt
Tel: +49(361) 643-9086
Gründungsbeauftragter: Klaus Dieter Wolff (1993-)

***Friedrich Alexander University of
Erlangen-Nuremberg**
[Friedrich-Alexander-Universität
Erlangen-Nürnberg]
Schlossplatz 4, 91054 Erlangen
Tel: +49(9131) 85-0
Fax: +49(9131) 85-2131
Telex: 06-29 830 unier d

Rektor: Gothard Jasper (1990-98)
Kanzler: Thomas A.H. Schöck
Founded: 1743, 1961
F: *Protestant Theology; Law; Medicine;
Philosophy I; Philosophy II; Natural Sciences I;
Natural Sciences II; Natural Sciences III;
Economics and Social Sciences; Technology;
Education.*
I: *Biomedical Engineering; Franconian Studies
and General Regional Studies; Philosophy and
History(Interdisciplinary) of Science.*
Ce: *Regional Computer; Social Science
Research; Astrophysics (Bamberg); Sports.*

*University of Essen
[Universität-Gesamthochschule-Essen]
Universitätsstrasse 2, 45141 Essen
Tel: +49(201) 183-1
Fax: +49(201) 183-3536
Telex: 8579091 uni d
Rektor: Elmar Lehmann (1992-96)
Kanzler: Elmar Lengers
Founded: 1972
D: *Philosophy, Religious Studies, and Social
Sciences; Education, Psychology, and Physical
Education; Languages and Literature; Fine and
Applied Arts; Economics; Mathematics; Physics;
Chemistry; Architecture and Bio-Geosciences;
Construction Engineering; Surveying; Mechanical
Engineering; Energetics, Processing Engineering,
and Electronics; Medicine.*

Educational College Flensburg-University
[Bildungswissenschaftliche Hochschule
Flensburg-Universität]
Mürwikerstrasse 77, 24943 Flensburg
Tel: +49(461) 31300
Fax: +49(461) 38543
Rector: Hans Schulte (1992-95)
Kanzler: Dieter Hass
Founded: 1946
Education.

Europa University Viadrina Frankfurt (Oder)
[Europa-Universität Viadrina Frankfurt (Oder)]
Grosse Scharrnstr. 59, 15230 Frankfurt (Oder)
Tel: +49(335) 5534-0
Fax: +49(335) 5534-305
Rektor: Hans Weiler (1993-97)
Kanzler: Josef Schmücker

**Johann Wolfgang Goethe University of
Frankfurt**
[Johann Wolfgang Goethe-Universität Frankfurtam
Main]
Senckenberganlage 31, 60325 Frankfurt am Main
Tel: +49(69) 798-1
Fax: +49(69) 798-8383
Telex: 413932 unif d
Präsident: Werner Meissner (1994-2000)
Kanzler: Wolfgang Busch
Founded: 1914, 1932

D: Law; Medicine; Philosophy; Economics; Educational Sciences; Psychology; Protestant Theology; Catholic Theology; Social Sciences; History; Classical Philology and Fine Arts; Philology; Eastern and Non-European Languages and Culture; Mathematics; Physics; Chemistry; Biochemistry and Pharmacy; Biology; Earth Sciences; Geography; Labour Studies and Physical Education; Computer Sciences.

Freiberg Mining Academy
[Bergakademie Freiberg]
Akademiestrasse 6, 09599 Freiberg
Tel: +49(3731) 51-0
Fax: (3731) 22195
Telex: (41) 322391 baf d
Rektor: Dietrich Stoyan (1991-97)
Kanzler: Wilhelm Wahlers
Founded: 1765, 1905, 1946
Sec: Economics.
D: Mathematics; Physics; Chemistry; Earth Sciences; Geotechnics and Mining Engineering; Processing Technology and Silicate Industry; Metallurgy and Materials Manufacturing Engineering; Material Sciences; Mechanical and Power Engineering; Technical Computer Science; History of Science and Technology.
I: Foreign Languages.

*Albert Ludwig University of Freiburg im Breisgau
[Albert-Ludwigs-Universität Freiburg im Breisgau]
Heinrich-von-Stephan-Strasse 25, 79100 Freiburg/Breisgau
Tel: +49(761) 203-0
Fax: +49(761) 203-4369
Telex: 772740-60 ufd
Rektor: Manfred Löwisch (1991-95)
Kanzler: Friedrich-Wilhelm Siburg
Founded: 1457
F: Theology; Law; Economics; Medicine; Philosophy; I; II; III; IV; Mathematics; Physics; Chemistry and Pharmacy; Biology; Earth Sciences; Forestry.

College of Education of Freiburg
[Pädagogische Hochschule Freiburg]
Kunzenweg 21, 79117 Freiburg
Tel: +49(761) 682-1
Fax: +49(761) 682-402
Rektor: Rudolf Denk (1994-84)
Leitender Verwaltungsbeamter: Peter Mollus
Founded: 1962, 1971
Education.

Justus Liebig University of Giessen
[Justus Liebig-Universität Giessen]
Ludwigstrasse 23, 35390 Giessen
Tel: +49(641) 702-1
Fax: +49(641) 702-2099
Telex: 176419013
Präsident: Heinz Bauer (1987-95)
Founded: 1607, 1946

D: Law; Economics; Social Sciences; Education; Physical Education and Fine Arts; Psychology; Theology; History; German Language and Literature; English and Anglo-American Literature; Mediterranean and East European Languages and Literature; Mathematics; Physics; Chemistry; Biology; Veterinary Medicine; Nutrition and Home Economics; Earth Sciences and Geography; Medicine; Agriculture.
Ce: Data Processing; Radiation; Continental Agricultural and Economic Research; Basic Philosophy of Science; Teacher Training; Regional Development Research.
I: Tropical Studies.

*Georg August University of Göttingen
[Georg-August-Universität Göttingen]
Gosslerstrasse 5-7, 37073 Göttingen
Tel: +49(551) 39-0
Fax: +49(551) 39-9612
Telex: 96703
Präsident: Hans Ludwig Schreiber (1992-96)
Kanzler: Klaus Volle
Founded: 1737
F: Theology; Law; Medicine; History and Philosophy; Mathematics; Physics; Chemistry; Earth Sciences; Biology; Forestry; Agriculture; Economics; Social Sciences; Education.

*Ernst Moritz Arndt University of Greifswald
[Ernst-Moritz-Arndt-Universität Greifswald]
Domstrasse 11, 17487 Greifswald
Tel: +49(3834) 63-0
Fax: +49(3834) 63-311
Telex: 398167
Rektor: Hans Jürgen Zobel (1990-94)
Kanzler: Carl Heinz Jacob
Founded: 1456, 1815, 1946
F: Jurisprudence; Medicine; Theology; Philosophy; Mathematics and Natural Sciences.
D: Biology; Chemistry; Pharmacy; Geological Sciences; Geography.
I: German Philology; Music Sciences and Music Pedagogics; Arts; Educational Psychology (in process of development); Slavonic Studies; English and American Studies; Romance Studies; History; Scandinavian Studies; Foreign Languages; Philosophy (in process of development); Physical Education.
Ce: Computer.

*Distance Teaching University of Hagen
[FernUniversität-Gesamthochschule-Hagen]
Feithstrasse 152, 58084 Hagen
Tel: +49(2331) 987-01
Fax: +49(2331) 987-330
Telex: 233-1716
Rektor: Günter Fandel (1993-97)
Kanzler: Ralf Bartz
Founded: 1974
F: Economics; Law; Mathematics; Computer Sciences; Electronics; Social Sciences and Education.

I: Distance Study Research.
Ce: Distance Study Development; Computer.

*Martin Luther University of Halle-Wittenberg

[Martin-Luther-Universität Halle-Wittenberg]
Universitätsplatz, 06099 Halle/S.
Tel: +49(345) 832-0
Fax: +49(345) 29515
Rektor: Gunnar Berg (1993-94)
Kanzler: Wolfgang Matschke
Founded: 1817, 1933
Sec: History; Philosophy; Law; German
Language and Literature and Fine Arts; Modern
Languages and Literature; Foreign Languages;
Mathematics; Biological Sciences; Physics;
Classical and Oriental Studies; Teacher Training;
Dentistry; Pharmacy; Agriculture; Economics;
Education; Chemistry; Physical Education;
Theology; Teacher Training; Dentistry;
Geography.
D: Medicine.
I: Social Sciences; Preparation of Students
Studying Abroad; Biotechnicum.
Ce: European Enlightenment International
Research; Computer.

College for Economic and Political Sciences Hamburg

[Hochschule für Wirtschaft und Politik Hamburg]
Von-Melle-Park 9, 20146 Hamburg
Tel: +49(40) 4123-1
Fax: +49(40) 4123-4150
Präsident: Lothar Zechlin (1992-97)
Verwaltungsleiter: Horst-Volkert Thiel
Sociology; Economics.

Technical University of Hamburg-Harburg

[Technische Universität Hamburg-Harburg]
Denickestrasse 22, 21073 Hamburg
Tel: +49(40) 7718-0
Fax: +49(40) 7718-2040
Präsident: Hauke Trinks (1993-99)
Leitender Verwaltungsbeamter: Justus Woydt
Founded: 1978
S: Mechanical Engineering; Electrical and
Electronical Engineering; Processing Technology
and Technical Engineering; Civil Engineering.
D: Town, Environment and Technology
Research; Systems Engineering Research; Civil
Engineering Research; Information and
Communication Technologies Research;
Materials, Design, and Manufacturing Research;
Processing Technology and Energy Systems
Research.

University of the Federal Armed Forces of Hamburg

[Universität der Bundeswehr Hamburg]
Holstenhofweg 85, 22043 Hamburg
Tel: +49(40) 6541-1
Fax: +49(40) 6541-2774
Telex: 0214952
Präsident: Gerhard Strunk (1992-98)
Kanzler: Eckard Redlich
Founded: 1972
D: Electrical Enginering; Mechanical
Engineering; Economic and Administrative
Sciences; Educational Science.
Ce: Didactics; Language; Computer.

*University of Hamburg

[Universität Hamburg]
Edmund-Siemens-Allee 1, 20146 Hamburg
Tel: +49(40) 4123-1
Fax: +49(40) 4123-2449
Präsident: Jürgen Lüthje (1991-97)
Leitender Verwaltungsbeamter: Hartmut
Halfmeier
Founded: 1919
D: Theology; Law I; Law II; Economics;
Medicine; Philosophy and Social Sciences;
Education; Languages; History; Fine Arts;
Oriental Studies; Mathematics; Physics;
Chemistry; Biology; Earth Sciences; Psychology;
Computer Sciences; Physical Education.
I: Shipbuilding; Radio and Television; Peace
Research and Security; Integration Research;
International Tax; Drama.
Ce: Computer; University Didactics
(Interdisciplinary).

Hanover Medical School

[Medizinische Hochschule Hannover]
Konstanty-Gutschow-Strasse 8, 30625 Hannover
Tel: +49(511) 532-1
Fax: +49(511) 532-5576
Rektor: Reinhard Pabst (1993-95)
Kanzler: Wolfgang Franke-Stehmann
Founded: 1963
*Medicine; Dentistry; Biochemistry; Pharmacy;
Public Health Medical Technology and
Informatics; Training for Technicians and Nurses.*

Hanover School of Veterinary Medicine

[Tierärztliche Hochschule Hannover]
Bischofsholer Damm 15, 30173 Hannover
Tel: +49(511) 856-6
Fax: +49(511) 856-7685
Rektor: Detlef Simon (1993-95)
Kanzler: Hans Linnemann
Founded: 1778, 1887
Veterinary Medicine.

*University of Hanover
[Universität Hannover]
Welfengarten 1, 30167 Hannover
Tel: +49(511) 762-0
Fax: +49(511) 762-3456
Telex: 923868
Präsident: Hinrich Seidel (1979-97)
Kanzler: Jan Gehlsen
Founded: 1831, 1847, 1968, 1978
D: Mathematics; Physics; Chemistry; Geo
Sciences; Biology; Architecture; Civil Engineering
and Geodesy; Mechanical Engineering; Electrical
Engineering; Horticulture; Landscape
Architecture and Environmental Planning;
Literature and Languages; History, Philosophy,
and Social Sciences; Education Sciences II; Law;
Economics; Educational Sciences I.

*Rupert Charles University of Heidelberg
[Ruprecht-Karls-Universität Heidelberg]
Grabengasse 1, 69117 Heidelberg
Tel: +49(6221) 54-1
Fax: +49(6221) 54-2618
Telex: 46 15 15 unihd d
Rektor: Peter Ulmer (1991-95)
Kanzler: Siegfried Kraft
Founded: 1386
F: Theology; Law; Basic Medical Sciences;
Theoretical Medicine; Clinical Medicine I; Clinical
Medicine II; Clinical Medicine (Mannheim);
Philosophy and History; Oriental Studies and
Antiquities; Modern Languages; Economics;
Social and Behavioural Sciences; Mathematics;
Chemistry; Physics and Astronomy; Biology;
Earth Sciences; Pharmacy.
I: South Asia.
Ce: Molecular Biology; Scientific Calculation.

University College of Education of Heidelberg
[Pädagogische Hochschule Heidelberg]
Keplerstrasse 87, 69120 Heidelberg
Tel: +49(6221) 477-0
Fax: +49(6221) 477-432
Rektor: Ludwig Schwinger (1994-98)
Founded: 1962, 1971
Ut: I; II; III; IV; V; VI.
I: Computer Sciences; Applied Linguistics in the
Rehabilitation of the Handicapped; Further
Education.

University of Hildesheim
[Universität Hildesheim]
Marienburger Platz 22, 31141 Hildesheim
Tel: +49(5121) 883-0
Fax: +49(5121) 86156
Rektor: Rudolf Weber (1990-94)
Kanzlerin: Marina Frost
Founded: 1978
D: Educational Sciences; Social Work and
Cultural Education; Languages; Mathematics,
Computer Sciences, and Natural Sciences.
Ce: Computer; Lifelong Education and Distance
Study.

*University of Hohenheim
[Universität Hohenheim]
Schloss, 70599 Stuttgart (Hohenheim)
Tel: +49(711) 459-0
Fax: +49(711) 459-3289
Telex: 722959
Präsident: Wolfgang Haubold (1990-94)
Kanzler: Konrad Stahlecker
Founded: 1818, 1904, 1919, 1967
F: General and Applied Natural Sciences;
Biology; Agriculture I; Agriculture II; Economics
and Social Sciences.
I: Agricultural Chemistry; Seed Cultivation;
Agricultural Mechanics and Construction;
Apiculture.

*Technical University of Ilmenau
[Technische Universität Ilmenau]
Max-Planck-Ring 14, 98693 Ilmenau
Tel: +49(3677)69-0
Fax: +49(3677)69-1701
E-Mail: postmaster@tu-ilmenau.de
Rektor: Eberhart Köhler (1990-95)
Kanzler: Bernhard Haupt
Founded: 1953, 1963
F: Mathematics and Natural Sciences;
Informatics and Automation Cybernetics;
Electrical Engineering and Information
Techniques; Mechanical Engineering; Economic
Sciences.
D: Foreign Languages.

*Friedrich Schiller University of Jena
[Friedrich-Schiller-Universität Jena]
Fürstengraben 1, 07743 Jena
Tel: +49(3641) 6300
Fax: +49(3641) 63-2345
E-Mail: gerd. wechsung @ kerwaltung. uni jena.
dbp. de
Telex: 331506 unid
Rektor: Georg Machnik (1993-97)
Kanzler: Klaus Kübel
Founded: 1548, 1558
F: Physics, Astronomy and Technical Science;
Mathematics; Chemistry; Biology; Philosophy;
Psychology, Education and Sports; Economics;
Theology; Law.
D: Medicine.
Ce: Computer.

University of Kaiserslautern
[Universität Kaiserslautern]
Erwin-Schrödinger-Strasse, 67663 Kaiserslautern
Tel: +49(631) 205-0
Fax: +49(631) 205-3200
Telex: 45627 unikl d
Präsident: Klaus Landfried (1987-99)
Kanzler: Hermann Fahse
Founded: 1970
F: Mathematics; Chemistry and Food
Technology; Biology; Mechanical Engineering;
Electrical Engineering; Architecture, Planning,
Environmental Studies, and Education;
Economics and Social Sciences; Computer
Sciences; Physics.

College of Education of Karlsruhe
[Pädagogische Hochschule Karlsruhe]
Bismarckstrasse 10, 76133 Karlsruhe
Tel: +49(721) 23991
Fax: +49(721) 28150
Rektor: Otto Bardong (1992-95)
Leitender Verwaltungsbeamter: Günter Taube
Founded: 1768, 1962
Education.

*University of Karlsruhe
[Universität Fridericiana zu Karlsruhe
(Technische Hochschule)]
Kaiserstrasse 12, 76128 Karlsruhe
Tel: +49(721) 608-0
Fax: +49(721) 608-4290
E-Mail: (X.400) S=postmaster; W=verwaltung;
P=uni-Karlsruhe; a=dbp; c=de
Telex: 17721166
Rektor: Heinz Kunle (1983-95)
Kanzler: Gerhard Selmayr
Founded: 1825, 1865, 1885, 1967
F: Mathematics; Physics; Chemistry; Biological
and Earth Sciences; Social Sciences and
Humanities; Architecture; Civil Engineering and
Surveying; Mechanical Engineering; Chemical
Engineering; Electrical Engineering; Computer
Sciences; Economics.
I: Regional Planning; Applied Computer
Sciences; Applied Cultural Science (Interfaculty);
Automation and Robotics-IAR (German-French);
Environmental Research (German-French).
Ce: Computer.
International Seminar for Science and Teaching
in Chemical Engineering, Technical and Physical
Chemistry.

University of Kassel
[Universität-Gesamthochschule Kassel]
Mönchebergstrasse 19, 34125 Kassel
Tel: +49(561) 804-0
Fax: +49(561) 804-2330
Telex: 99572 Ghkks d
Präsident: Hans Brickmann (1989-95)
Kanzler: Hans Gädeke
Founded: 1970
D: Humanities and Education; Ergonomics and
Vocational Education; Psychology, Physical
Education, and Music; Social and Political
Sciences; Applied Social Sciences and Law;
Economics and Business Administration;
Romance and English Languages; German; Art;
Graphic Art and Industrial Design; Architecture;
Town Planning and Landscape Architecture; Civil
Engineering; Mechanical Engineering; Electrical
Engineering; Mathematics; Physics; Chemistry
and Biology; Agriculture; International
Agricultural Studies; Social Studies; Visual
Communication.

*Christian Albrecht University of Kiel
[Christian-Albrechts-Universität zu Kiel]
Olshausenstrasse 40, 24118 Kiel
Tel: +49(431) 880-00
Fax: +49(431) 880-2072
E-Mail: postmaster @ rz.uni-kiel.dbp.de
Telex: 292656
Rektorin: Karin Peschel (1992-96)
Kanzler: Horst Neumann
Founded: 1665, 1773, 1867, 1945
F: Theology; Law; Economics and Social
Sciences; Medicine; Philosophy; Mathematics and
Natural Sciences; Agriculture.
I: World Economics; Science Education; Marine
Sciences.
Ce: Maritime Earth Sciences Research
(GEOMAR).

Koblenz School of Corporate Management
[Wissenschaftliche Hochschule zur
Unternehmensführung Koblenz]
Haus d'Ester, Heerstrasse 52, 5414 Vallendar
Tel: (261) 225-76
Fax: (261) 659-09111
E-Mail: geonet whu.koblenz
Cable: whuk
Founded: 1984
Ce: Triad for Comparative Management;
Financial Management.
Area: Marketing Management; Management
Information Systems; Accountancy and Control;
Economics.

University of Koblenz-Landau of Mainz
[Universität Koblenz-Landau Mainz]
Hegelstrasse 59, 55122 Mainz
Tel: +49(6131) 37460-0
Fax: +49(6131) 37460-40
Präsident: Hermann Saterdag (1988-94)
Kanzler: Reiner Wanner
Founded: 1949, 1964, 1969
F: Educational Science; Philology; Natural
Science; Computer Sciences (Koblenz);
Psychology (Landau).
I: Media Didactics (Koblenz); Educational
Research (Landau); Computer Sciences
(Koblenz).
Ce: Sex Sciences and Education Research
(Landau).

*University of Leipzig
[Universität Leipzig]
Augustusplatz 9-11, 04109 Leipzig
Tel: +49(341) 719-0
Fax: +49(341) 209325
Telex: 311432 uni d
Rektor: Cornelius Weiss (1991-)
Kanzler: Peter Gutjahr-Löser
International Relations: Director, International &
European Affairs, Svend Poller
Founded: 1409, 1953, 1991
I: Philosophy; Political Science; Literature;
Cultural Sciences; German for Foreign Students;

Sociology; Physical Education; Interpreter Training.
F: Law; Theology; Medicine; Veterinary Medicine; Economics; Sport Sciences.
Sec: History; Sciences; Psychology; Communication and Media Sciences; German Philology; Theoretical and Applied Linguistics; Foreign Languages; Oriental and African Studies; Mathematics and Computer Sciences; Physics; Chemistry; Biosciences; History of Art and Archaeology.
D: Lifelong Education.

Lübeck Medical University
[Medizinische Universität zu Lübeck]
Ratzeburger Allee 160, 23538 Lübeck
Tel: +49(451) 500-0
Fax: +49(451) 500-3016
Telex: 026 492 ul
Rektor: Wolfgang Henkel (1990-96)
Kanzler: Wolf-Dieter von Detmering
Founded: 1964, 1973
F: Technical and Scientific; Medical.

College of Education of Ludwigsburg
[Pädagogische Hochschule Ludwigsburg]
Reuteallee 46, 71634 Ludwigsburg
Tel: +49(7141) 140-0
Fax: +49(7141) 140-434
Rector: Siegfried Krauter (1994-98)
Leitender Verwaltungsbeamter: Frieder Miller
Founded: 1962, 1971
F: Education; Languages; Mathematics and Natural Sciences; Social Sciences and Theology; Cultural and Technical Studies.
D: Special Education (Reutlingen); Further Education.
Ce: Didactic Research.

Lüneburg University
[Universität Lüneburg]
Wilschenbrucher Weg 84, 21335 Lüneburg
Tel: +49(4131) 714-0
Fax: +49(4131) 714-428
Präsident: Hartwig Donner (1989-97)
Kanzler: Hans-Georg Schultz-Gerstein
Founded: 1946, 1978
D: Educational Sciences; Economics and Social Sciences; Applied Cultural Studies.
Ce: Lifelong Education.

Academy of Medicine of Magdeburg
[Medizinische Akademie Magdeburg]
Leipziger Strasse 44, 31920 Magdeburg
Tel: (91) 670
Founded: 1954
Medicine; Nursing.

*Otto-von-Guerick University of Magdeburg
[Otto-von-Guerick-Universität Magdeburg]
Universitätsplatz 2, 39106 Magdeburg
Tel: +49(391) 5592-0
Fax: +49(391) 5592-153
E-Mail: tuvg; e-mail: akaa et dmdtu.11 bitnet
Telex: 351214tumd
Rektor: Jürgen Dassow (1993-96)
Founded: 1953, 1961, 1987
F: Production Engineering; Mechanical Engineering; Thermal Engineering; Electrical Engineering; Computer Science; Mathematics; Natural Sciences; Educational Sciences; Economics (in process of development); Foreign Languages; Sports.

Johannes Gutenberg University of Mainz
[Johannes Gutenberg-Universität Mainz]
Saarstrasse 21, 55122 Mainz
Tel: +49(6131) 39-0
Fax: +49(6131) 39-2919
Telex: 4187 476 uni d
Präsident: Josef Reiter (1991-97)
Kanzler: Dieter Vogel-Arnoldi
Founded: 1477, 1946
F: Theology; Theology; Law and Economics; Medicine; Philosophy and Education; Social Sciences; Philology I; Philology II; Philology III; History; Mathematics; Physics; Chemistry and Pharmacy; Biology; Earth Sciences; Applied Linguistics (Germersheim); Fine Arts; Music; Sport.
Sec: Lifelong Education.
Ce: Medical-Scientific Research; Material-Scientific Research; Environmental Research.

*University of Mannheim
[Universität Mannheim]
Schloss, 68131 Mannheim
Tel: +49(621) 292-0
Fax: +49(621) 292-2587
Telex: 26276211776
Rektor: Otto H. Jacobs (1988-94)
Kanzler: Dietmar Ertmann
Founded: 1907, 1946, 1967
F: Law; Industrial Management Studies; Economics and Statistics; Social Sciences; Philosophy, Psychology, and Educational Sciences; Languages and Literature; History and Geography; Mathematics and Data Processing.
Ce: Computer.

*University of Marburg
[Philipps-Universität Marburg]
Biegenstrasse 10, 35032 Marburg/Lahn
Tel: +49(6421) 28-1
Fax: +49(6421) 28-500
E-Mail: AuslAmt@Mailgate.Verwaltung.Uni-Maarburg.de
Telex: 482372 UMR D
Präsident: Dietrich Simon (1988-94)
Kanzler: Bernd Höhmann
Founded: 1527

D: *Law; Economics; Social Sciences and Philosophy; Psychology; Theology; History; Classical Studies; General and Germanic Linguistics and Philology; Modern German Literature and Arts; Modern Languages and Literature; Non-European Languages and Literature; Mathematics; Physics; Physical Chemistry; Chemistry; Pharmacy and Chemistry of Foods; Biology; Earth Sciences; Geography; Medicine; Education.*

*Technical University of Munich
[Technische Universität München]
Arcisstrasse 21, 80333 München
Tel: +49(89) 2105-1
Fax: +49(89) 2105-2000
Telex: 522854 tumue d
Präsident: Otto Meitinger (1987-95)
Kanzler: Heinrich Lampersberger
Founded: 1827, 1868, 1877, 1970
D: *Mathematics and Computer Sciences; Physics; Chemistry, Biology, and Earth Sciences; Economics and Social Sciences; Construction Engineering and Surveying; Architecture; Mechanical Engineering; Electrical Engineering; Agriculture and Horticulture (Weinhenstephan); Brewing, Food Technology and Dairy Science (Weinhenstephan); Medicine.*
I: *Environmental Planning and Research.*
Ce: *Physical Education.*

University of the Federal Armed Forces Munich
[Universität der Bundeswehr München]
Werner-Heisenberg-Weg 39, 85579 Neubiberg
Tel: +49(89) 6004-1
Fax: +49(89) 6004-3560
Telex: 5215800
Präsident: Hans Georg Lössl (1994-2000)
Kanzler: Hans Lerch
Founded: 1973
F: *Construction and Surveying; Electrical Engineering; Computer Sciences; Aviation and Aerospace Engineering; Education; Social Sciences; Economics and Organizational Sciences; Mechanical Engineering (Polytechnical); Business Administration (Polytechnical); Electrical Engineering (Polytechnical).*

*Ludwig-Maximilians-University of Munich
[Ludwig-Maximilians-Universität München]
Geschwister Scholl-Platz 1, 80539 München
Tel: +49(89) 2180-0
Fax: +49(89) 2180-2322
E-Mail: steinmann@rektorat.verwaltung.uni-muenchen.dbp.de
Telex: 529860 univm
Rektor: Wulf Steinmann (1982-94)
Kanzler: Hendrik Rust
Founded: 1472, 1800, 1826
D: *Theology; Theology; Law; Industrial Economics; Political Economics; Forestry; Medicine; Veterinary Medicine; History and Fine*

Arts; Philosophy, Theory of Science, and Statistics; Psychology and Pedagogics; Anthropology; Languages and Literature I; Languages and Literature II; Social and Behavioural Sciences; Mathematics; Physics; Chemistry and Pharmacy; Biology; Earth Sciences.
L: *Nuclear Physics (in conjunction with the Technical University, Munich).*
Ce: *Linguistic Research; Japanese Studies; Molecular Biology.*

University of Münster
[Westfälische Wilhelms-Universität Münster]
Schlossplatz 2, 48149 Münster
Tel: +49(251) 83-1
Fax: +49(251) 83-4831
Telex: 892529 UNIM sd
Rektor: Maria Wasna (1990-94)
Kanzler: Klaus Triebold
Founded: 1780, 1818, 1902, 1907
F: *Theology; Theology; Law; Economics and Social Sciences; Medicine; Philosophy; Mathematics and Natural Sciences.*
D: *Social Sciences; Philosophy; Psychology; Education, Sociology, and Communications; History; Germanic Studies; English Studies; Romance and Slav Studies; Classical and Non-European Studies; Earth Sciences; Mathematics; Physics; Chemistry; Biology; Physical Education; German Language and Literature, Arts.*
Ce: *Mature Students.*

Carl von Ossietzky University of Oldenburg
[Carl von Ossietzky Universität Oldenburg]
Ammerländer Heerstrasse 114-116, 26129 Oldenburg
Tel: +49(441) 798-0
Fax: +49(441) 798-3000
Telex: 25655
Präsident: Michael Daxner (1986-98)
Kanzler: Wolf-Dietrich von Fircks
Founded: 1970
F: *Education; Communication and Fine Arts; Social Sciences; Economics and Law; Philosophy, Psychology, and Physical Education; Biology; Chemistry; Physics; Mathematics; Computer Sciences; Languages and Literature.*
I: *Marine Chemistry and Biology.*

University of Osnabrück
[Universität Osnabrück]
Schloss/Neuer Graben, 49074 Osnabrück
Tel: +49(541) 969-0
Fax: +49(541) 969-4570
E-Mail: BITNET dos uni 1 internet uni-osnabrueck. de
Präsident: Rainer Künzel (1990-96)
Kanzler: Christoph Ehrenberg
Founded: 1970
D: *Social Sciences; Cultural Geosciences; Education and Cultural Sciences; Physics; Biology/Chemistry; Mathematics/Informatics; Language and Literature; Psychology;*

Economics; Law; Catholic Theology (Osnabrück and Vechta); Education Theory, Psychology and Sports (Vechta); Languages, Art and Music (Vechta); Sciences and Mathematics (Vechta); Social and Cultural Sciences; Working Group of Health Sciences.
Ce: Computer.
I: European Law; Financial Law and Tax Law; Private International Law and Comparative Law; Procedural Law and General Comparison of Procedures; Local Government Law; Empirical Economic Research; Church and Society; Migration and Intercultural Research Studies (IMIS); Cultural History of 'Frühe Neuzeit'.

University of Paderborn
[Universität-Gesamthochschule-Paderborn]
Warburger Strasse 100, 33098 Paderborn
Tel: +49(5251) 60-0
Fax: +49(5251) 60-2519
E-Mail: eunet/usenet
Telex: 936776 unipb d
Rektor: Hans Albert Richard (1991-95)
Kanzler: Ulrich Hintze
Founded: 1972
D: Philosophy, and Religious and Social Sciences; Education, Psychology, and Physical Education; Languages and Literature; Fine Arts and Music; Economics and Business Studies; Physics; Chemistry and Chemical Engineering; Landscape Architecture; Environmental Protection Technology; Agriculture (Soest); Mechanical Engineering I; Mechanical Engineering II (Meschede); Mechanical Engineering III (Soest); Electrical Engineering and Electronics; Telecommunication Technology (Meschede); Electrical Power Engineering (Soest); Mathematics and Computer Sciences.
L: Computer-Aided Design.

*University of Passau
[Universität Passau]
Dr.-Hans-Kapfinger-Strasse 22, 94032 Passau
Tel: +49(851) 509-0
Fax: +49(851) 509-130
Rektor: Karl-Heinz Pollok (1976-97)
Kanzler: Karl August Friedrichs
Founded: 1973
F: Catholic Theology; Law; Economics; Mathematics and Data Processing; Philosophy.
I: East Bavaria Home Research; New Psychology History; Agricultural Law; International and Foreign Law.

University of Potsdam
[Universitt Potsdam]
Am Neuen Palais 10, 14469 Potsdam
Tel: +49(331) 977-0
Fax: +49(331) 972163
Rektor: Rolf Mitzner (1991-95)
Kanzler: Jens Prüss

*University of Regensburg
[Universität Regensburg]
Universitätsstrasse 31, 93053 Regensburg
Tel: +49(941) 943-1
Fax: +49(941) 943-2305
Telex: 65658 unire d
Rektor: Helmut Altner (1989-97)
Kanzler: Hans-Hagen Zorger
Founded: 1962
F: Theology; Law; Economics; Medicine; Philosophy, Physical Education and the Fine Arts; Education and Psychology; History, Social Sciences, and Geography; Languages and Literature; Mathematics; Physics; Pre-Clinical Medicine and Biology; Chemistry and Pharmacy.

*University of Rostock
[Universität Rostock]
Universitätsplatz 1, 18051 Rostock
Tel: +49(381) 498-0
Fax: +49(381) 498-1006
Telex: 398460
Rektor: Gerhard Maess (1990-)
Kanzler: Joachim Wittern
Founded: 1419, 1946
I: Biology; Chemistry; History; Latin American Studies; Pedagogics and Psychology; Physics; Linguistics and Literature; Physical Education; Electronic Engineering; Mathematics; Informatics; Archaeology; Romance Linguistics and Literature (in process of developement); Applied Linguistics; Philosophy (in process of development).
F: Business and Management and Social Sciences; Medicine; Theology; Law; Agricultural Technology; Mechanical Engineering and Shipbuilding.

University of the Saar
[Universität des Saarlandes]
Im Stadtwald, 66123 Saarbrücken
Tel: +49(681) 302-0
Fax: +49(681) 302-3900
Telex: 518/6817533
Präsident: Günther Hönn (1992-96)
Kanzler: Hartwig Cremers
Founded: 1947, 1948
F: Law and Economics; Medicine (Homburg); Philosophy; Mathematics and Natural Sciences.
I: Physical Education.

University of Education of Schwäbisch Gmünd
[Pädagogische Hochschule Schwäbisch Gmünd]
Oberbettringer Strasse 200, 73525 Schwäbisch Gmünd
Tel: +49(7171) 606-1
Fax: +49(7171) 606-212
Rektor: Karl Setzen (1994-98)
Leitender Verwaltungsbeamter: Hartmut Kies
Founded: 1825, 1947, 1962
F: Educational Sciences; Languages; Mathematics and Natural Sciences; Social Sciences and Theology; Arts and Crafts.

D: Lifelong Education; Media Education; Multicultural Education.

*University of Siegen
[Universität-Gesamthochschule-Siegen]
Am Herrengarten 3, 57072 Siegen
Tel: +49(271) 740-1
Fax: +49(271) 740-4899
E-Mail: eickbush@aaa.unisiegen.d400.de
Telex: 271-383
Rektor: Klaus Sturm (1989-97)
Kanzler: Johann Peter Schäfer
Founded: 1972, 1980
D: Philosophy, History, Geography, and Religious and Social Sciences; Education, Psychology, and Physical Education; Languages and Literature; Fine Arts and Music; Economics and Business Administration; Mathematics; Physics; Chemistry and Biology; Architecture and Town Planning; Civil Engineering; Mechanical Engineering; Electrical Engineering.
I: Humanities and Social Sciences (Research); Empirical Literature and Media Research; Research Project on Aesthetics, Pragmatism and History of German Television; Language in Industry, Business and Other Vocational Areas; European Regional Research.
Ce: Monetary Macroeconomics(Research); Sensor Systems (Research); Humanities (Graduate); Computer; Chemistry (Graduate).
L: Surface Technology.

School of Administrative Sciences of Speyer
[Hochschule für Verwaltungswissenschaften Speyer]
Freiherr-vom-Stein-Strasse 2, 67324 Speyer
Tel: +49(6232) 654-0
Fax: +49(6232) 654-208
Rektor: Hans-Herbert v. Arnim (1993-95)
Leitender Verwaltungsbeamter: Hans Döring
Founded: 1947, 1950
Administrative Sciences.
I: Public Administration Research.

*University of Stuttgart
[Universität Stuttgart]
Keplerstrasse 7, 70174 Stuttgart
Tel: +49(711) 121-0
Fax: +49(711) 121-2150
Telex: 72-17-03 unis d
Rektorin: Heide Ziegler (1992-96)
Kanzler: Joachim Schwarze
Founded: 1829, 1840, 1890, 1967
F: Civil Engineering and Surveying; Architecture and Town Planning; Chemistry; Electrical Engineering; Energetics; Production Technology; Earth and Biological Sciences; History and Social and Economic Sciences; Aeronautics and Space Technology; Mathematics and Computer Sciences; Philosophy; Physics; Chemical Engineering.

Ce: Computer Science; Language; Infrastructure Planning; Computer.
I: Biomedical Technology; Computer Applications; Textile Research; Sport; Computer Applications II.

University of Trier
[Universität Trier]
Universitätsring 15, 54296 Trier
Tel: +49(651) 201-1
Fax: +49(651) 201-4299
E-Mail: btx20285
Telex: 472680 unitr
Präsident: Jörg Hasler (1987-95)
Kanzler: Ignaz Bender
Founded: 1970, 1975
D: Education, Philosophy, and Psychology; Languages and Literature; History, Political Science, Classical Archaeology, Egyptology, Art History, and Papyrology; Management Economics, Sociology, Political Economy, Mathematics, and Ethnology; Law; Geography/Geosciences.
I: Cusanus Studies; Labour Legislation and Labour Relations in the European Community.

*Eberhard Karl University of Tübingen
[Eberhard-Karls-Universität Tübingen]
Wilhelmstrasse 7, 72074 Tübingen
Tel: +49(7071) 29-1
Fax: +49(7071) 29-5990
Telex: 7262867 utzv d
Präsident: Adolf Theis (1972-96)
Kanzler: Georg Sandberger
Founded: 1477
F: Protestant Theology; Catholic Theology; Law; Economics and Business Administration; Medicine; Philosophy; Social and Behavioural Sciences; Modern Languages; History; Antiquities and Cultural Sciences; Mathematics; Physics; Chemistry and Pharmacy; Biology; Earth Sciences and Geography; Informatics.
I: German Distance Studies; Special Pedagogics (Reutlingen).
Ce: Data Processing.

University of Ulm
[Universität Ulm]
Albert-Einstein-Allee, 89081 Ulm-Donau
Tel: +49(731) 502-01
Fax: +49(731) 502-2038
Telex: 7212 567 uniuld
Founded: 1967
F: Clinical Medicine; Theoretical Medicine; Natural Sciences and Mathematics; Mathematics and Economics; Engineering; Computer Sciences.

University of Architecture and Building of Weimar
[Hochschule für Architektur und Bauwesen Weimar-Universität-]
Geschwister-Scholl-Strasse 8, 99423 Weimar
Tel: +49(3643) 58-0
Fax: +49(3643) 61710
E-Mail: capous
Telex: 618950 habw
Rector: Gerd Zimmermann (1992-95)
Kanzler: Heiko Schultz
Founded: 1860, 1926, 1954
F: Architecture, Town and Regional Planning; Civil Engineering; Computer Science and Mathematics; Art and Cultural Science.
I: Material Research and Testing.

College of Education of Weingarten
[Pädagogische Hochschule Weingarten]
Kirchplatz 2, 88250 Weingarten
Tel: +49(751) 501-0
Rektor: Rudolf Meissner (1994-98)
Leitender Verwaltungsbeamter: Hubert Kaiserauer
Founded: 1949, 1962
Education.

Private University of Witten/Herdecke
[Private Universität Witten/Herdecke]
Alfred-Herrhausen-Str.50, 58448 Witten
Tel: +49(2302) 926-0
Fax: +49(2302) 926-929
Präsident: Konrad Schily (1987-)
Kaufman Geschäftsführer: Bernhard Stöhr
Founded: 1983
F: Medicine; Business Administration; Dentistry; Oriental Studies.

*University of Wuppertal
[Bergische Universität-Gesamthochschule-Wuppertal]
Gaussstrasse 20, 42097 Wuppertal
Tel: +49(202) 439-1
Fax: +49(202) 439-2899
Telex: 8592262 bughw
Rector: Erich Hödl (1991-95)
Kanzler: Klaus Peters
Founded: 1972
D: Social Sciences; Philosophy and Theology, and History; Education; Languages and Literature; Economics; Mathematics; Architecture; Art, Design, Music, and Printing Technology; Natural Sciences I; Natural Sciences II; Construction Engineering; Mechanical Engineering; Electrical Engineering; Security Technology.
Ce: Computer.

*Bayerische Julius-Maximilians University of Würzburg
[Bayerische Julius-Maximilians-Universität Würzburg]
Sanderring 2, 97070 Würzburg
Tel: +49(931) 31-1
Fax: +49(931) 15123
Telex: 9318152
Präsident: Theodor Berchem (1994-2000)
Kanzler: Bruno Forster
Founded: 1402, 1582
F: Theology; Law; Medicine; Arts I; Arts II; Arts III; Biology; Chemistry and Pharmacy; Earth Sciences; Mathematics and Information Science; Physics and Astronomy; Economics.
S: Medical Assistants; Physiotherapy; Physical Rehabilitation; Midwifery; Nursing; Dietetics; Child Care.

OTHER INSTITUTIONS

Fachhochschule Aachen
Kalverbenden 6, 52066 Aachen
Tel: +49(241) 6009-0
Fax: +49(241) 6009-1090
Rektor: Hermann-Josef Buchkremer (1991-1995)
Kanzler: Peter Michael Reusch

Fachhochschule Aalen
Beethovenstrasse 1, 73430 Aalen
Tel: +49(7361) 576-0
Fax: +49(7361) 576-250
Rektor: Helmut Rosswag (1989-97)
Kanzler: Heinz Kistner

Fachhochschule Augsburg
Baumgartnerstrasse 16, 86161 Augsburg
Tel: +49(821) 5586-0
Fax: +49(821) 5586-222
Präsident: Hans Benedikt (1988-94)
Kanzler: Ernst Mayr

Philosophisch-Theologische Hochschule der Selesianer Don Boscos Benediktbeuern-Theologische Fakultät
Don-Bosco-Strasse 1, 83671 Benediktbeuren
Tel: +49(8857) 88-216
Fax: +49(8857) 88-376
Rektor: Otto Wahl (1988-94)
Theology (Catholic); Philosophy.

Alice-Salomon Fachhochschule für Sozialarbeit und Sozialpädagogik Berlin
Karl-Schrader-Strasse 6, 10781 Berlin
Tel: +49(30) 21458-1
Fax: +49(30) 216-6411
Rektorin: Christine Labonté-Roset (1994-98)
Kanzler: Klaus Johannssen
Social Work; Education.

**Deutsche Bundepost Telekom
Fachhochschule Berlin**
Ringbahnstrasse 130, 12103 Berlin
Tel: +47(30) 7574-4500
Fax: +49(30) 752-2070
Telex: 183660 fhbln d
Rector: Egon Hilt (1992-)
Verwaltungsdirektorin: Dagmar Drutschmann
Telecommunications.

Europäische Wirtschaftshochshule Berlin
Europacenter, 10789 Berlin
Tel: +49(30) 254-8020
Fax: +49(30) 254-80231
Rector: Jürgen Weitkamp
Registrar: Gert Elstermann
Founded: 1973
*D: Economics; International Business; Finance
and Accounting; Organization and Human
Resources; Computer Science; Marketing.*

**Evangelische Fachhochschule Berlin,
Fachhochschule für Sozialarbeit und
Sozialpädagogik**
Reinerzstrasse 40/41, 14193 Berlin
Tel: +49(30) 829-9080
Fax: +49(30) 82990-836
Rektor: Dieter Peter Weber (1992-97)
Kanzlerin: Heidemarie Kirschnick
Social Work; Social Pedagogy.

**Fachhochschule für Technik und Wirtschaft
Berlin**
Treskowallee 8, 10313 Berlin
Tel: +49(30) 5019-0
Fax: +49(30) 509-0134
Gründugsrektor: Günter Siegel
Kanzler: Holger Langkutsch
Technology; Economics.

Fachhochschule für Wirtschaft Berlin
Badensche Strasse 50-51, 10825 Berlin
Tel: +49(30) 867-1
Fax: +49(30) 867-8270
Rector: Jürgen Kunze (1992-96)
Kanzler: Norbert Nerlich
Economics.

Katholische Fachhochschule Berlin (KFB)
Köpenicker Allee 39-57, 10318 Berlin
Tel: +49(30) 501010-0
Fax: +49(30) 509-9342
Rektor: Klaus Kliesch (1993-97)
Verwaltungsleiter: Siegfried Lehmann

Hochschule der Künste Berlin
Ernst-Reuter-Platz 10, 10587 Berlin
Tel: +49(30) 3185-0
Fax: +49(30) 3185-2635
Präsident: Olaf Schwencke (1992-96)
Kanzler: Jürgen Schleicher
Founded: 1969
Arts.

Hochschule für Musik 'Hanns Eisler' Berlin
Charlottenstrasse 55, 10117 Berlin
Tel: +49(30) 2090-2411
Fax: +49(30) 2090-2408
Rektorin: Annerose Schmidt (1990-96)
Kanzler: Günter Schwarz
Founded: 1950
Music.

**Hochschule für Schauspielkunst 'Ernst
Berlin'**
Schnellerstrasse 104, 12439 Berlin
Tel: +49(30) 636-2261
Fax: +49(30) 636-1994
Rektor: Klaus Völker (1993-97)
Founded: 1905, 1981
*Sec: Acting; Directing; Puppetry; Philosophy and
Cultural History.*

Kunsthochschule Berlin-Weissensee
Bühringstrasse 20, 13086 Berlin
Tel: +49(30) 471-4061
Fax: +49(30) 471-5082
Rektor: Alfred Hückler (1992-96)
Kanzlerin: Silvia Durin
Founded: 1947
Arts.

Fachhochschule Biberach
Karlstrasse 11, 88400 Biberach
Tel: +49(7351) 582-0
Fax: +49(7351) 582-119
Rektor: Bernhard Schilling (1991-95)
Kanzler: RR Walter Büchele

Fachhochschule Bielefeld
Kurt-Schumacher-Strasse 6, 33615 Bielefeld
Tel: +49(521) 106-01
Fax: +49(521) 106-2600
Telex: 932362 unibi
Rektor: Heinrich Ostholt (1993-97)
Kanzler: Gerd Böhlig

Kirchliche Hochschule Bethel
Remterweg 45, 33617 Bielefeld
Tel: +49(521) 144-3948+49(521) 144-4700
Rektor: Hermann Braun (1994-95)
Kirchen-Verwaltungsdirektor: Hans-Ulrich Hein
Theology (Protestant).

**Evangelische Fachhochschule Rheinland-
Westfalen-Lippe Bochum**
Immanuel-Kant-Strasse 18-20, 44803 Bochum 1
Tel: +49(234) 36901-0
Fax: +49(234) 36901-100
Rektor: Gottfried Schmidt (1988-96)
Kanzler: Klaus Meinert

Fachhochschule Bergbau Bochum
Herner Strasse 45, 4630 Bochum
Tel: +49(234) 968-02
Fax: +49(234) 968-3606
Telex: 825-701

Fachhochschule Bochum
Universitätsstrasse 150, 44801 Bochum
Tel: +49(234) 700-1
Fax: +49(234) 709-4219
Rektor: Heinz Becker (1989-97)
Kanzler: Rainer Ambrosy

Fachhochschule Brandenburg
Magdeburger Strasse 53, 14770 Brandenburg
Tel: +49(3381) 303-612
Fax: +49(3381) 303-611

Fachhochschule Braunschweig-Wolfenbüttel
Salzdahlumer Strasse 46-48, 38302 Wolfenbüttel
Tel: +49(5331) 301-0
Fax: +49(5331) 301-153
Kanzler: Wilfried Kroll

Hochschule für Bildende Künste Braunschweig
Johannes-Selenka-Platz 1, 38118 Braunschweig
Tel: +49(531) 391-9122
Fax: +49(531) 391-9292
Präsident: Dieter Welzel (1989-)
Kanzler: Götz von Götz
Founded: 1963

Hochschule Bremen
Neustadtwall 30, 28199 Bremen
Tel: +49(421) 5905-0
Fax: +49(421) 5905-292
Telex: 244750
Rektor: Ronald Mönch (1991-96)
Kanzler: Jürgen-Peter Henckel

Hochschule für Künste Bremen
Am Wandrahm 23, 28195 Bremen
Tel: +49(421) 30890-0
Fax: +49(421) 30890-45
Rektor: Jürgen Waller (1989-1994)
Kanzler: Klaus Güse
Arts.

Hochschule Bremerhaven
An der Karlstadt 8, 27568 Bremerhaven
Tel: +49(471) 4823-0
Fax: +49(471) 4823-115
Rektor: Heinz-Jürgen Scheibe (1991-96)
Kanzlerin: Renate Bitter

Fachhochschule Coburg
Friedrich-Streib Strasse 2, 96450 Coburg
Tel: +49(9561) 317-0
Fax: +49(9561) 317-109
Präsident: Gerhard Lindner (1994-98)
Kanzler: Klaus Schubert

Evangelische Fachhochschule Darmstadt
Zweifalltorweg 12, 64293 Darmstadt
Tel: +49(6151) 8798-0
Fax: +49(6151) 879858
Rektor: Thomas Dell-George (1990-94)
Kanzler: Gustav Fetzer

Fachhochschule Darmstadt
Haardtring 100, 64295 Darmstadt
Tel: +49(6151) 16-02
Fax: +49(6151) 16-8949
Rektor: Manfred Kremer (1983-96)
Kanzlerin: Ellen Göbel

Hochschule für Musik Detmold
Neustadt 22, 32756 Detmold
Tel: +49(5231) 7407-0
Fax: +49(5231) 7407-72
Rektor: Martin Christoph Redel (1993-97)
Kanzler: Friedrich Kramer
Music.

Deutsche Bundepost Telekom Fachhochschule Dieburg
Max-Planck-Strasse 2, 64807 Dieburg
Tel: +49(6071) 28-0
Fax: +49(6071) 28-2752
Telex: 4191840 fhdi
Rektor: Eberhard Mathée (1982-)
Verwaltungsdirektor: Ralf Siegbert Blum
Telecommunications.

Fachhochschule Dortmund
Sonnenstrasse 96, 44139 Dortmund
Tel: +49(231) 9112-0
Fax: +49(231) 9112-313
Rektor: Hans-Jürgen Kottman (1989-97)
Kanzler: Hans-Joachim von Buchka

Evangelische Fachhochschule für Sozialarbeit Dresden
Vosstrasse 2, 01219 Dresden
Tel: +49(351) 471-5991
Fax: +49(351) 471-5993
Gründungsrektor: Ulfrid Kleinert (1991-95)
Kanzler: Stefan Mertenskötter
Social Work.

Hochschule für Bildende Künste Dresden
Günzstrasse 34, 01307 Dresden
Tel: +49(3751) 44020
Fax: +49(3751) 459-0025
Rektor: Horst Hirsig (1993-96)
Kanzler: Hans-Jürgen Schönemann
Founded: 1764
Fine Arts.

Hochschule für Kirchenmusik der Ev.-Luth. Landeskirche SachsensDresden
Käthe Kollwitz Ufer 97, 01309 Dresden
Tel: +49(351) 30440
Fax: +49(351) 30440
Rektor: Christfried Brödel
Church Music.

Hochschule für Musik 'Carl Maria von Weber' Dresden
Wettiner Platz 13, 01067 Dresden
Tel: +49(351) 495-2103
Fax: +49(351) 459-2103
Rektor: Wilfried Krätzschmar (1991-)
Kanzler: Peter Neuner
Founded: 1856
Music.

Hochschule für Technik und Wirtschaft Dresden (FH)
Friedrich-List-Platz 1, 01069 Dresden
Tel: +57(351) 462-3102
Fax: +57(351) 462-2285
Rektor: Wolfgang Braun (1992-96)
Kanzler: Hannes Neumann
Technical Sciences; Economics.

Fachhochschule Düsseldorf
Universitätsstrasse, 40225 Düsseldorf
Tel: +49(211) 311-1
Fax: +49(211) 311-5303
Rektor: Paul Kuff (1991-95)
Kanzler: Harald Lutter

Kunstakademie Düsseldorf
Eiskellerstrasse 1, 40213 Düsseldorf
Tel: +49(211) 1396-0
Fax: +49(211) 1396-225
Rektor: Markus Lüpertz (1987-96)
Kanzler: Peter Michael Lynen
Founded: 1773
Arts.

Robert-Schumann-Hochschule Düsseldorf
Fischerstrasse 110, 40476 Düsseldorf
Tel: +49(211) 491-2011
Fax: +49(211) 491-1618
Rektor: Helmut Kirchmeyer (1987-95)
Kanzler: Werner Kowal

Fachhochschule Eberswalde
Alfred-Möller-Strasse, 16225 Eberswalde
Tel: +49(3334) 65-0
Fax: +49(3334) 65-425
Telex: 161445
Gründungsrektor: Gunther Wolff (1992-)
Verwaltungsleiter: Dieter Rudolph

Fachhochschule Ostfriesland Emden
Constantiaplatz 4, 26723 Emden
Tel: +49(4921) 807-0
Fax: +49(4921) 807-201
Rektor: Harro Ohlenburg (1989-95)
Kanzler: Peter Reissaus

Fachhochschule Erfurt
Schlüterstr. 1, 99089 Erfurt
Tel: +49(361) 6700-401
Fax: +49(361) 6700-413
Rektorin: Gisela Rauschhofer (1993-97)
Kanzler: Rudolf Tilly

Philosophisch-Theologisches Studium Erfurt
Domstr. 10, 99084 Erfurt
Tel: +49(361) 590-770
Fax: +49(361) 590-7720
Rektor: Franz George Friemel (1993-94)
Philosophy; Theology.

Fachhochschule für Sozialwesen Esslingen
Flandernstrasse 101, 73732 Esslingen
Tel: +49(711) 397-21
Fax: +49(711) 397-3875
Rektor: Falk Roscher (1993-97)
Leitender Verwaltungsbeamter: Gerhard Wörner
Social Science.

Fachhochschule für Technik Esslingen
Kanalstrasse 33, 73728 Esslingen
Tel: +49(711) 397-3000
Fax: +49(711) 397-3100
Rektor: Dieter Birkle (1985-97)
Kanzler: Klaus Bandl
Technical Science.

Folkwang-Hochschule Essen
Klemensborn 39, 45239 Essen
Tel: +49(201) 4903-0
Fax: +49(201) 4903-288
Rektor: Wolfgang Hufschmidt (1988-96)

Hochschule für Kirchenmusik der Evangelischen Landeskirche in Baden-Württemberg Esslingen
Mülberger Str. 37, 73728 Esslingen
Tel: +49(711) 316-7508
Fax: +49(711) 316-7684
Rektor: Gero Soergel (1990-)
Church Music.

Fachhochschule Flensburg
Kanzleistrasse 91-93, 24943 Flensburg
Tel: +49(461) 805-1
Fax: +49(461) 805-300
Rektor: Ernst-Gottfried Schmidt (1994-97)
Kanzler: Klaus Arnold

Fachhochschule Frankfurt am Main
Nibelungenplatz 1, 60318 Frankfurt am Main
Tel: +49(69) 1533-0
Fax: +49(69) 1533-2400
Rektor: Johann Schneider (1991-94)
Kanzler: Reiner Frey

Hochschule für Bankwirtschaft (HfB) Frankfurt am Main
Sternstrasse 8, 60318 Frankfurt am Main
Tel: +49(69) 154008-0
Fax: +49(69) 154008-115
Rektor: Helmut Reinboth
Banking.

Hochschule für Musik und Darstellende Kunst Frankfurt am Main
Eschersheimer Landstrasse 29-39, 60322 Frankfurt am Main
Tel: +49(69) 154007-0
Fax: +49(69) 154007-108
Rektor: Hans-Dieter Resch (1991-95)
Kanzlerin: Angelika Amend
Founded: 1938
Music; Fine Arts.

Staatliche Hochschule für Bildende Künste (Städelschule) Frankfurt am Main
Dürerstrasse 10, 60596 Frankfurt
Tel: +49(69) 605008-0
Fax: +49(69) 60500-866
Rektor: Kasper König (1988-1994)
Kanzler: Jürgen Grumann
Founded: 1942
Fine Arts.

Philosophisch-Theologische Hochschule Sankt GeorgenFrankfurt am Main
Offenbacher Landstrasse 224, 60599 Frankfurt am Main
Tel: +49(69) 6061-0
Fax: +49(69) 6061-330
Rektor: Johannes Beutler (1992-94)
Philosophy; Theology (Catholic).

Fachhochschule für Sozialwesen, Religions-Pädagogik und Gemeindediakonie Freiburg
Bugginger Strasse 38, 79114 Freiburg
Tel: +49(761) 47812-0
Fax: +49(761) 47812-30
Rektor: Joachim Walter (1992-96)
Kanzler: Dieter Maertins
Social Work; Religious Education (Protestant); Pastoral Care.

Katholische Fachhochschule Freiburg-staatlich anerkannt-Hochschule für Sozialwesen, Religionspädagogik und Pflege Freiburg
Wölflinstrasse 4, 79104 Freiburg
Tel: +49(761) 200-0
Fax: +49(761) 200-444
Rektor: Herbert Pielmaier (1989-97)
Leitender Verwaltungsbeamter: Hans-Dieter Link

Staatliche Hochschule für Musik Freiburg
Schwarzwaldstrasse 141, 79095 Freiburg
Tel: +49(761) 31915-0
Fax: +49(761) 31915-42
Rektor: Johann-Georg Schaarschmidt (1980-96)
Leitender Verwaltungsbeamter: Manfred Klimanski
Founded: 1946
Music.

Fachhochschule Weihenstephan Freising
Weihenstephaner Berg, 85354 Freising 12
Tel: +49(8161) 71-3339
Fax: +49(8161) 71-4207
Präsident: Josef Herz (1989-97)
Kanzler: Wolfgang Simon

Theologische Hochschule Friedensau
An der Ihle 5 A, 39291 Friedensau
Tel: +49(3921) 78130
Rektor: B.Ed. Pfeiffer (1993-95)
Kanzler: Roland Nickel
Theology.

Fachhochschule Fulda
Marquardstrasse 35, 36039 Fulda
Tel: +49(661) 9640-0
Fax: +49(661) 9640-199
Rektor: Joseph Dehler (1982-94)
Kanzler: Erwin Jacobs

Theologische Fakultät Fulda
Domplatz 2, 36037 Fulda
Tel: +49(661) 87220
Fax: +49(661) 87224
Rektor: Balthasar Gareis (1992-95)
Theology (Catholic).

Fachhochschule Furtwangen
Gerwigstrasse 11, 78120 Furtwangen
Tel: +49(7723) 920-0
Fax: +49(7723) 920-610
Telex: 772315
Rektor: Walter Zahradnik (1987-95)

Fachhochschule Gelsenkirchen
Neidenburger Str.10, 45897 Gelsenkirchen
Tel: +49(209) 9596-0
Fax: +49(209) 595-379
Gründungsrektor: Peter Schulte (1993-97)
Kanzler: Günter Scholz

Fachhochschule Giessen-Friedberg
Wiesenstrasse 14, 35390 Giessen
Tel: +49(641) 309-1
Fax: +49(641) 309-301
Rektor: Jürgen Hagedorn (1993-97)
Kanzlerin: Eva Maria Bleutge

Burg Giebichenstein-Hochschule für Kunst und Design Halle
Neuwerk 7, 06108 Halle
Tel: +49(345) 850-0
Fax: +49(345) 850-109
Rektor: Johannes Langenhagen (1992-94)
Kanzler: Wolfgang Stockert
Founded: 1915
Arts; Design.

Evangelische Hochschule für Kirchenmusik Halle
Emil-Abderhalden-Str. 10, 06108 Halle
Tel: +49(345) 21327
Fax: +49(345) 23495
Rektor: Helmut Gleim
Verwaltungsleiter: Joachim Voigt
Church Music.

Evangelische Fachhochschule für Sozialpädagogik der Diakonenanstalt des Rauhen Hauses Hamburg
Horner Weg 170, 22111 Hamburg
Tel: +49(40) 65591-180
Rektor: Wolfgang Braun (1986-96)
Social Education.

Fachhochschule Hamburg
Winterhuder Weg 29, 22085 Hamburg
Tel: +49(40) 29188-1
Fax: +49(40) 29188-3217
Präsident: Rolf Dalheimer (1975-99)
Leitender Verwaltungsbeamter: Heinrich Göring

Hochschule für Bildende Künste Hamburg
Lerchenfeldt 2, 22081 Hamburg
Tel: +49(40) 2984-3255
Fax: +49(40) 2984-3241
Präsidentin: Adrienne Goehler (1989-95)
Leitender Verwaltungsbeamter: Peter Hielscher
Founded: 1954
Fine Arts.

Hochschule für Musik und Theater Hamburg
Harvestehuder Weg 12, 20148 Hamburg
Tel: +49(40) 44195-0
Fax: +49(40) 4419-5666
Präsident: Hermann Rauhe (1978-96)
Leitender Verwaltungsbeamter: Bernhard Lange
Music and Drama.

Evangelische Fachhochschule Hannover
Blumhardtstrasse 2, 30625 Hannover
Tel: +49(511) 5301-0
Fax: +49(511) 5301-195
Rektor: Manfred Bergs (1984-96)
Kanzler: Dietmar Kohlstedt

Fachhochschule Hannover
Ricklinger Stadtweg 118, 30459 Hannover
Tel: +49(511) 4503-0
Fax: +49(511) 4503-120
Rektor: Rolf Hüper (1992-94)
Kanzler: Christoph Wiedemann

Hochschule für Musik und Theater Hannover
Emmichplatz 1, 30175 Hannover
Tel: +49(511) 3100-1
Fax: +49(511) 3100-200
Präsident: Peter Becker (1993-97)
Kanzler: Roland Scholl
Founded: 1957
Music and Dance.

Fachhochschule Harz
Friedrichstrasse 57-59, 38855 Wernigerode
Tel: +49(3943) 359-0
Fax: +49(3943) 359-109
Rektor: Karsten Kirsch (1994-97)
Kanzler: Klaus Bernert

Fachhochschule Westküste Heide
Rungholtstr.9, 25746 Heide
Tel: +49(481) 8555-0
Fax: +49(481) 8555-20
Rektor: Hans-Jürgen Block (1994-2000)
Economics; Technical Sciences.

Fachhochschule Heidelberg-Staatlich anerkannte Fachhochschule der Stiftung Rehabilitation
Bonhoefferstrasse 1, 69123 Heidelberg
Tel: +49(6221) 882-567
Fax: +49(6221) 88-2787
Telex: 461675 bfwd
Rektor: Horst Methner (1978-97)
Kanzler: Michael Nagy
Architecture; Business Administration; Social Studies.

Hochschule für Jüdische Studien Heidelberg
Friedrichstrasse 9, 69117 Heidelberg
Tel: +49(6221) 22576
Fax: +49(6621) 167-696
Rektor: Julius Carlebach (1989-)
Founded: 1979
Jewish Studies.

Hochschule für Kirchenmusik der Evangelischen Landeskirche in BadenHeidelberg
Hildastr. 8, 69115 Heidelberg
Tel: +49(6221) 27062
Rektor: Wolfgang Herbst (1976-98)
Church Music.

Fachhochschule Heilbronn
Max-Planck-Strasse 39, 74081 Heilbronn
Tel: +49(7131) 504-0
Fax: +49(7131) 504-0
Rektor: Otto Grandi (1989-97)
Leitender Verwaltungsbeamter: Eberhardt Harst

Philosophisch-Theologische Hochschule der Redemptoristen Hennef
Waldstrasse 9, 53773 Hennef
Tel: +49(2242) 82556
Rektor: Josef Schmitz (1978-)
Philosophy; Theology (Catholic).

Hochschule für Kirchenmusik der Evangelischen Kirche von Westfalen Herford
Parkstr. 6, 32049 Herford
Fax: +49(5221) 81017
Rektor: Uwe Karsten Gross (1994-)
Church Music.

Fachhochschule Hildesheim-Holzminden
Hohnsen 3, 31134 Hildesheim
Tel: +49(5121) 881-0
Fax: +49(5121) 881-125
Rektor: Johannes Kolb (1989-95)
Kanzler: Gerd Sutor

Märkische Fachhochschule Iserlohn
Frauenstuhlweg 31, 58644 Iserlohn
Tel: +49(2371) 566-0
Fax: +49(2371) 566-274
Telex: 823137
Rektor: Michael Teusner (1993-97)
Kanzler: Hellmut Cramer

Fachhochschule Isny, Naturwissenschaftlich-Technische Akademie Prof. Dr. Grübler
Seidenstrasse 12-35, 88316 Isny/Allgäu
Tel: +49(7562) 9707-0
Fax: +49(7562) 9707-71
Rektor: Willy Dilger
Natural Sciences.

Fachhochschule Jena-Hochschule für Technik und Wirtschaft
Tatzendpromenade 1 b, 07745 Jena
Tel: +49(3641) 23085
Fax: +49(3641) 22864
Rektor: Werner Bornkessel (1991-97)
Kanzler: Rainer Gutsch
Technical Science; Economics.

Fachhochschule Karlsruhe
Moltkestrasse 4, 76133 Karlsruhe
Tel: +49(721) 169-0
Fax: +49(721) 169-200
Rektor: Werner Fischer (1990-94)
Leitender Verwaltungsbeamter: Udo Bitter

Staatliche Akademie der Bildenden Künste Karlsruhe
Reinhold-Frank-Strasse 67, 76133 Karlsruhe
Tel: +49(721) 845018-0
Fax: +49(721) 848150
Rektor: Andreas Franzke (1988-96)
Leitender Verwaltungsbeamter: Rüdiger Weis
Founded: 1854
Fine Arts.

Staatliche Hochschule für Gestaltung Karlsruhe
Durmersheimer Str. 55, 76185 Karlsruhe
Tel: +49(721) 9541-0
Fax: +49(721) 9541-206
Gründungsrektor: Heinrich Klotz (1991-)
Leitender Verwaltungsbeamter: Manfred Erlewein
Design.

Staatliche Hochschule für Musik Karlsruhe
Wolfartsweierer Str.7a, 76131 Karlsruhe
Tel: +49(721) 6629-50
Fax: +49(721) 6629-66
Rektorin: Fany Solter (1984-1996)
Leitender Verwaltungsbeamter: Wolfram Scherer
Founded: 1929
Music.

Fachhochschule Kempten-Hochschule für Technik und Wirtschaft
Immenstädter Strasse 69, 87435 Kempten
Tel: +49(831) 2523-0
Fax: +49(831) 2523-104
Rektor: Klaus Seidel (1994-98)
Kanzler: Volker Büchner
Technical Science; Economics.

Fachhochschule Kiel
Grenzstrasse 3, 24149 Kiel
Tel: +49(431) 2199-0
Fax: +49(431) 2199-86
Rektor: Peter Jochimsen (1993-97)
Kanzler: Dietmar Wabbel

Fachhochschule für Bibliotheks- und Dokumentationswesen in Köln
Claudiusstrasse 1, 50678 Köln
Tel: +49(221) 8275-3376
Fax: +49(221) 331-8538
Rektor: Helmut Jüngling (1991-95)
Kanzlerin: Brigitte Husmann
Library Science; Documentation.

Fachhochschule Köln
Claudiusstrasse 1, 50678 Köln
Tel: +49(221) 8275-1
Fax: +49(221) 8275-3131
Telex: 873330 fhsk d
Rektor: Joachim Metzner (1989-1997)
Kanzler: Karlfriedrich Lange von Stocmeier

Hochschule für Musik Köln
Dagobertstrasse 38, 50668 Köln 1
Tel: +49(221) 912818-0
Fax: +49(221) 131204
Rektor: Franz Müller-Heuser (1990-97)
Kanzlerin: Isabel Pfeiffer-Poensgen
Music.

Katholische Fachhochschule Nordrhein-Westfalen Köln
Wörthstrasse 10, 50668 Köln 1
Tel: +49(221) 7757-0
Fax: +49(221) 723-062
Rektor: Winfried Hofmann (1991-95)
Erhard Fries

Kunsthochschule für Medien Köln
Peter-Welter-Platz 2, 50676 Köln
Tel: +49(221) 201-890
Fax: +49(221) 201189-17
Rektor: Klaus Katz (1991-94)
Kanzler: Horst Rossa
Arts; Media Studies.

Rheinische Fachhochschule Köln
Hohenstaufenring 16-18, 50674 Köln 1
Tel: +49(221) 20302-0
Fax: +49(221) 2030-245
Rektor: Manfred Wolf (1991-94)

Fachhochschule Konstanz
Brauneggerstrasse 55, 78462 Konstanz
Tel: +49(7531) 206-0
Fax: +49(7531) 206-117
Rektor: Olaf Harder (1980-1996)
Leitender Verwaltungsbeamter: Axel Schuler

Institüt für Kommunikations-Design an der Fachhochschule Konstanz
Seestrasse 33, 78464 Konstanz
Tel: +49(7531) 50103
Fax: +49(7531) 57139
Direktor: Peter Andermatt (1989-)
Communications and Design.

Fachhochschule Anhalt (Bernburg-Dessau-Köthen)
Bernburger Strasse 52-57, 06366 Köthen
Tel: +49(3496) 67-0
Fax: +49(3496) 2152
Telex: 047720
Rektor: Klaus Hertwig (1991-96)
Kanzler: Wolf-Günter Rasche

Süddeutsche Hochschule für Berufstätige-Staatlich anerkannte Fachhochschule der AKAD Lahr
Otto-Hahn-Str.5, 77933 Lahr/Schwarzwald
Tel: +49(7821) 26065
Fax: +49(7821) 23413
Rektor: Kurt W. Schönherr (1991-)
Continuing Education.

Fachhochschule Landshut-Hochschule für Wirtschaft-Sozialwesen-Technik
Am Lurzenhof 1, 84036 Landshut
Tel: +49(871) 506-0
Fax: +49(871) 506-506
Präsident: Hans-Joachim Fischer (1989-94)
Kanzler: Hansgeorg Falterer
Economics; Social Work; Technical Science.

Fachhochschule Lausitz
Grossenhainer Str.57, 01968 Senftenberg
Tel: +49(3573) 85-0
Fax: +49(3573) 85-209
Gründungsrektor: Roland Sessner (1991-94)
Kanzler: Guido Kalka

Fachhochschule Leipzig der Deutschen Bundespost Telekom
Gustav-Freytag-Str.43-45, 04277 Leipzig
Tel: +49(341) 3933-0
Fax: +49(341) 313032
Gründungsrektor: Uwe Rabenhorst
Telecommunications.

Hochschule für Grafik und Buchkunst Leipzig
Wächerstrasse 11, 04107 Leipzig
Tel: +49(341) 2135-0
Fax: +49(341) 312401
Rektor: Arno Rink (1987-1993)
Kanzlerin: Martina Petermann
Founded: 1764
Graphic and Book Design.

Hochschule für Musik und Theater 'Felix-Mendelssohn-Bartholdy' Leipzig
Grassisstrasse 8, 04107 Leipzig
Tel: +49(341) 216-530
Fax: +49(341) 21653-47
Rektor: Siegfried Thiele (1990-94)
Kanzler: Uwe Schmitz
Founded: 1843
Music and Drama.

Hochschule für Technik, Wirtschaft und Kultur Leipzig (FH)
Karl Liebknecht-Strasse 132, 04227 Leipzig
Tel: +49(341) 3928-0
Fax: +49(341) 3928-456
Telex: 51 552 tehael
Founded: 1992
Technical Science; Economics; Culture.

Ostdeutsche Hochschule für BerufstätigeLeipzig
Konradstr.52, 04315 Leipzig
Tel: +49(341) 689-1202
Fax: +49(341) 689-1203
Gründungsrektor: Kurt W. Schönherr (1992-)
Continuing Education.

Fachhochschule Lippe
Liebigstrasse 87, 32657 Lemgo
Tel: +49(5261) 702-0
Fax: +49(5261) 702-222
(1989-97)
Kanzler: Helmuth Hoffstetter

Fachhochschule Lübeck
Stephensonstrasse 3, 22562 Lübeck
Tel: +49(451) 500-0
Fax: +49(451) 500-5100
Telex: 026492 ul
Rektor: Christian Jentsch (1993-96)
Kanzler: Horst Drewello

Musikhochschule Lübeck
Grosse Petersgrube 17-29, 23552 Lübeck 1
Tel: +49(451) 1505-0
Fax: +49(451) 1505-300
Rektor: Friedhelm Döhl (1991-94)
Founded: 1933
Music.

Evangelische Fachhochschule für Sozialwesen Ludwigshafen
Maxstrasse 29, 67059 Ludwigshafen
Tel: +49(621) 59113-0
Rektor: Dieter Wittmann (1987-95)
Verwaltungsleiter: Wilfried Kramer
Social Sciences.

Fachhochschule Nordostniedersachsen Lüneburg
Munstermannskamp 1, 21335 Lüneburg
Tel: +49(4131) 706-0
Fax: +49(4131) 706-111
Rektor: Hermann J.Weihe (1991-97)
Kanzler: Roland Schmidt

Fachhochschule Magdeburg
Am Krökentor 2, 39104 Magdeburg
Tel: +49(391) 551-091
Rektor: Hans-Jürgen Kaschade (1991-98)

Fachhochschule Rheinland-Pfalz Mainz
Seppel-Glückert-Passage 10, 55116 Mainz
Tel: +49(6131) 2392-0
Fax: +49(6131) 2392-12
Präsident: Wulf-R. Fischer (1994-2000)
Kanzler: Dieter Eckert

Katholische Fachhochschule für Sozialarbeit, Sozialpädagogik und Praktische Theologie Mainz
Saarstrasse 2, 55122 Mainz 1
Tel: +49(6131) 3866-0
Fax: +49(6131) 3866-50
Rektorin: Hanneliese Steichele (1992-95)
Kanzler: Alfred Staub
Social Work; Social Education; Theology.

Fachhochschule für Sozialwesen Mannheim
Pettenkoferstrasse 24-26, 68169 Mannheim 1
Tel: +49(621) 3926-0
Fax: +49(621) 3926-222
Rektor: Joachim Auer (1988-96)
Leitender Verwaltungsbeamter: Giselher Rupp
Social Work.

Fachhochschule für Technik Mannheim
Speyerer Strasse 4, 68163 Mannheim 1
Tel: +49(621) 292-6400
Fax: +49(621) 292-6425
Rektor: Dietmar von Hoyningen-Huene (1989-97)
Kanzler: Eckard Grunewald
Technical Science.

Staatliche Hochschule für Musik Heidelberg-Mannheim
N7, 18, 68161 Mannheim
Tel: +49(621) 292-0
Fax: +49(621) 292-2072
Rektor: Gerald Kegelmann (1989-97)
Leitender Verwaltungsbeamter: Engelbert Stich
Founded: 1971
Music.

Städtische Fachhochschule für Gestaltung Mannheim
E3, 16, 68159 Mannheim
Tel: +49(621) 293-2774+49(621) 101-452
Rektor: Klaus Bessau (1991-95)
Leitender Verwaltungsbeamter: Christa Niefnecker
Design.

Fachhochschule Merseburg
Geusaer Strasse, 06217 Merseburg
Tel: +49(3461) 46-0
Fax: +49(3461) 46-2906
Rektorin: Johanna Wanka (1994-97)
Kanzler: Bernd Janson

Hochschule für Technik und Wirtschaft Mittweida (FH)
Technikumplatz 17, 09648 Mittweida
Tel: +49(3727) 58-0
Fax: +49(3727) 58-1379
Telex: 77520 ihsmit
Rektor: Reinhard Schmidt (1992-96)
Verwaltungsdirektor: Lothar Otto
Founded: 1969
Technical Science; Economics.

Evangelische Fachhochschule für Religionspädagogik und Gemeindediakonie Moritzburg
Bahnhofstr.9, 01468 Moritzburg
Tel: +49(35207) 427
Fax: +49(35207) 656
Rektor: Peter Meis (1992-96)
Kanzler: Thomas Schmitt
Religious Education; Pastoral Care.

Akademie der Bildenden Künste München
Akademiestrasse 2, 80799 München 40
Tel: +49(89) 3852-0
Fax: +49(89) 395-684
Rektor: Otto Steidle (1993-95)
Kanzlerin: Cornelia v. Crailsheim
Founded: 1770
Fine Arts.

Fachhochschule München
Lothstrasse 34, 80335 München
Tel: +49(89) 1265-0
Fax: +49(89) 1265-1490
E-Mail: 898147 = fhm
Präsident: Walther Kessler (1976-94)
Kanzler: Uwe Brockhausen

Hochschule für Fernsehen und Film München
Frankenthaler Strasse 23, 81539 München
Tel: +49(89) 680004-0
Fax: +49(89) 680004-89
Präsident: Helmut Oeller (1988-96)
Kanzlerin: Sabine Walz-Jaeger
Founded: 1967
D: Communications Sciences; Film Techniques; Cinema and Television Programmes; Documentary Films and Television Advertising.

Hochschule für Musik in München
Arcisstrasse 12, 80333 München 2
Tel: +49(89) 5591-01
Fax: +49(89) 280-381
Präsident: Cornelius Eberhardt (-1995)
Kanzler: Martin Henkel-Ernst
Founded: 1924
Music.

Hochschule für Philosophie (Philosophische Fakultät S.J.)
Kaulbachstrasse 33, 80539 München 22
Tel: +49(89) 2386-2300
Fax: +49(89) 2386-2302
Rektor: Peter Ehlen (1988-97)
Kanzler: Karl Frings
Philosophy.

Katholische Stiftungsfachhochschule München
Preysingstrasse 83, 81667 München 80
Tel: +49(89) 48092-1
Fax: +49(89) 480-1907
Rektor: Karljörg Schäflein (1990-98)
Verwaltungsleiter: Obermaier-van Deun

Fachhochschule Münster
Hüfferstrasse 27, 48149 Münster
Tel: +49(251) 83-1
Fax: +49(251) 83-9739
Telex: 892529 Uni MSD
Rektor: Peter Pleyer (1990-94)
Kanzler: Hans Michatsch

Kunstakademie Münster-Hochschule für Bildende Künste Münster
Scheibenstrasse 109, 48153 Münster
Tel: +49(251) 97217-0
Fax: +49(251) 791674
Rektor: Gunter Keusen (1993-97)
Kanzler: Hans Lesener
Fine Arts.

Philosophisch-Theologische Hochschule der Franziskaner und KapuzinerMünster
Hörsterplatz 4, 48147 Münster
Rektor: Edilbert Schülli (1993-96)
Sekretär: Ildefons Vanderheyden
Philosophy; Theology (Catholic).

Fachhochschule Neubrandenburg
Brodaer Strasse 2, 17033 Neubrandenburg
Tel: +49(395) 4513-0
Fax: +49(395) 4513-212
Rektor: Hans-Joachim Memmler (1991-)
Kanzler: Heinrich Rudolf Zimmer

Augustana-Hochschule in Neuendettelsau
Waldstrasse 11, 91564 Neuendettelsau
Tel: +49(9874) 509-0
Fax: +49(9874) 509-95
Rektor: Helmut Utzschneider (1993-95)

Fachhochschule Niederrhein
Reinarzstrasse 49, 47805 Krefeld 1
Tel: +49(2151) 822-0
Fax: +49(2151) 822-555
Rektor: H. Ostendorf (1994-98)

Akademie der Bildenden Künste in Nürnberg
Bingstrasse 60, 90480 Nürnberg 30
Tel: +49(911) 9404-0
Fax: +49(911) 9404-150
Präsident: Rainer Beck (1987-96)
Leitender Verwaltungsbeamter: Herbert Fürstenhöfer
Founded: 1662
Fine Arts.

Evangelische Stiftungsfachhochschule Nürnberg
Burgschmietstrasse 10, 90419 Nürnberg 90
Tel: +49(911) 372790
Fax: +49(911) 3727911
Präsident: Roland Proksch (1991-95)
Kanzler: Uwe Reissmann

Georg-Simon-Ohm-Fachhochschule Nürnberg
Kesslerplatz 12, 90489 Nürnberg 21
Tel: +49(911) 5880-0
Fax: +49(911) 5880-269
Rektor: Klaus-Frieder Zander (1994-98)
Kanzler: Henning Hofmeister

Fachhochschule für Kunsttherapie der Freien Kunstschule Nürtingen
Sigmaringer Strasse 15, 72622 Nürtingen
Rektor: Fritz Marburg (1993-)
Art Therapy.

Fachhochschule Nürtingen
Neckarsteige 6-10, 72622 Nürtingen
Tel: +49(7022) 701-309
Fax: +49(7022) 701-303
Rektor: Eduard Mändle (1977-97)
Leitender Verwaltungsbeamter: Roland Bosch

Lutherische Theologische Hochschule Oberursel
Altkönigstrasse 150, 61440 Oberursel, Taunus
Tel: +49(6171) 24340
Rektor: Volker Stolle (1993-95)
Theology.

European Business School of Oestrich-Winkel
Schloss Reichartshausen, 65375 Oestrich-Winkel
Tel: +49(6723) 69-0
Fax: +49(6723) 3064
Präsident: Klaus Evard (1971-)
Geschäftsführung: Klaus Evard
Founded: 1971
D: Economics; Marketing; International Finance and Trade; Practical Computer Sciences; Information Management; Theoretical Computer Sciences; Business Administration; International Management; Management Accounting; Auditing and Tax; Organizational Behaviour; Operational Environmental Economics; Finance; Applied Informatics.
I: Marketing; Ecology and Environmental Management; Finance Management; Law and Business Administration (International); Multilingual Business Communications; System Development Research and Consulting; International Economics and Management Research.

Hochschule für Gestaltung Offenbach
Schlossstrasse 31, 63065 Offenbach
Tel: +49(69) 80059-0
Fax: +49(69) 880791
Rektor: Wolfgang Sprang (1994-98)
Kanzlerin: Sponheimer-Bram
Design.

Fachhochschule Offenburg
Badstrasse 24, 77652 Offenburg
Tel: +49(781) 205-0
Fax: +49(781) 205-214
Rektor: Arno Voegele (1993-97)

Fachhochschule Oldenburg
Ofener Strasse 16-19, 26121 Oldenburg
Tel: +49(441) 7708-0
Fax: +49(441) 7708-100
Rektor: Klaus Zwilling (1992-95)
Kanzler: Helmut Heine

Fachhochschule Osnabrück
Albrechtsstrasse 30, 49076 Osnabrück
Tel: +49(541) 969-0
Fax: +49(541) 969-2066
Rektor: Erhard Mielenhausen (1989-95)
Kanzler: Werner Volkert

Freie Kunst-Studienstätte Ottersberg
Am Wiesterbruch 66-68, 28870 Ottersberg
Rektor: Hermanus Westendorp (1991-95)
Art.

Fachhochschule der Wirtschaft Paderborn
ürstenalle 3-5, 33103 Paderborn
Tel: +49(5251) 3102-69
Fax: +49(5251) 3102-14
Leiter: Franz Wagner (1993-)
Economics.

Theologische Fakultät Paderborn
Kamp 6, 33098 Paderborn
Tel: +49(5251) 1216
Rektor: Michael Kunzler (1992-94)
Quästor: Friedrich Siebecke
Theology.

Fachhochschule Pforzheim-Hochschule für Gestaltung, Technik ünd Wirtschaft
Tiefenbronner Strasse 65, 75175 Pforzheim
Tel: +49(7231) 603-0
Fax: +49(7231) 603-205
Telex: 17723159
Gründungsrektor: Rupert Huth (1992-95)
Leitender Verwaltungsbeamter: Wolfgang Hohl
Design; Technical Sciences; Economics.

Nordakademie Pinneberg-Staatlich anerkannte Fachhochschule mit dualen Studiengängen
An der Mühlenau 14, 25421 Pinneberg
Tel: +49(4101) 512-991
Fax: +49(4101) 512-992
Rektor: George Plate (1992-95)
Kanzler: Jörg Meier

Fachhochschule Potsdam
Friedrich-Ebert-Strasse 4, 14467 Potsdam
Tel: +49(331) 2884-0
Fax: +49(331) 2884-222
Rektor: Helmut Knüppel (1994-98)
Kanzler: Volker Bley

Hochschule für Film und Fernsehen 'Konrad Wolf' Potsdam-Babelsberg
Karl-Marx-Strasse 33/34, 14482 Potsdam
Tel: +49(331) 78981-83
Fax: +49(331) 75073
Rektor: Wolf-Dieter Panse (1990-)
Kanzler: Udo Funke
Cinema and Television.

Fachhochschule Regensburg
Prüfeningerstrasse 58, 93049 Regensburg
Tel: +49(941) 4607-0
Fax: +49(941) 4607-102
Präsident: Erich Kohnhäuser (1990-98)
Kanzler: Maximilian Roth

Hochschule für Berufstätige Rendsburg
Kieler Strasse 53, 24768 Rendsburg
Tel: +49(4331) 5227
Fax: +49(4331) 28612
Präsident: Kurt W.Schönherr (1980-)
Kanzler: Ernst Kunz
Continuing Education.

Evangelische Fachhochschule für Sozialwesen Reutlingen
Ringelbachstrasse 221, 72762 Reutlingen
Tel: +49(7121) 2414-0
Fax: +49(7121) 2414-29
Rektor: Gottfried Hermann (1992-96)
Kanzler: Manfred Möller
Social Studies.

Fachhochschule für Technik und Wirtschaft Reutlingen
Alteburgstrasse 150, 72762 Reutlingen
Tel: +49(7121) 271-0
Fax: +49(7121) 271-224
Rektor: Georg Obieglo (1981-1997)
Leitender Verwaltungsbeamter: Winfried Hermanutz
Technical Science; Economics.

Fachhochschule Rosenheim
Marienberger Strasse 26, 83024 Rosenheim
Tel: +49(8031) 805-0
Fax: +49(8031) 805-105
Präsident: Hans Zang (1986-94)
Kanzler: Helmut Hanika

Hochschule für Musik und Theater Rostock
Am Bussebart 11, 18055 Rostock
Tel: +49(381) 25409
Gründungsrektor: Wilfried Jochims (-1998)
Kanzler: Bernhard Marusiak
Music and Drama.

Hochschule der Bildenden Künste Saar
Keplerstrasse 3-5, 66117 Saarbrücken
Tel: +49(681) 5867-601
Fax: +49(681) 5847-287
Rektor: Horst Gerhard Haberl (1993-97)
Verwaltungsleiter: Heinrich Scherber
Fine Arts.

Hochschule für Technik und Wirtschaft des Saarlandes (HTW)
Goebenstrasse 40, 66117 Saarbrücken 1
Tel: +49(681) 5867-0
Fax: +49(681) 5867-122
Rektor: Helmut Groh (1992-96)
Kanzler: Guido Arbeck
Technical Science; Economics.

Fachhochschule für Bergbau Saarbrücken
Trierer Strasse 4, 66111 Saarbrücken
Tel: +49(681) 405-3486
Fax: +49(681) 405-3534
Rektor: Jürgen Leonhardt (1992-96)
Verwaltungsleiter: Klaus-Peter Schäfer
Mining.

Katholische Fachhochschule für Sozialwesen (Sozialarbeit u. Sozialpädagogik) Saarbrücken
Rastpfuhl 12a, 66113 Saarbrücken
Tel: +49(681) 97132-0
Fax: +49(681) 97132-40
Rektor: Reiner Feth (1993-97)
Verwaltungsleiterin: Rosie Becker
Social Work; Social Education.

Musikhochschule des Saarlandes

Bismarckstrasse 1, 66111 Saarbrücken
Tel: +49(681) 62408-9
Fax: +49(681) 638250
Rektor: Klaus Velten (1991-95)
Leitender Verwaltungsbeamter: Alfons Simon
Founded: 1957
Music.

Philosophisch-Theologische Hochschule SVD St. Augustin

Arnold-Janssen-Strasse 30, 53754 St. Augustin
Tel: +49(2241) 237-222
Rektor: Karl-Josef Rivinius (1992-)
Studiensekretär: Hermann Kochanek
Philosophy; Theology.

Fachhochschule Schmalkalden

Blechhammer 4 u.9, 98564 Schmalkalden
Tel: +49(3683) 688-0
Fax: +49(3683) 2558
Rektor: Jens Goebel (1993-97)
Kanzler: Thomas Losse

Fachhochschule für Gestaltung Schwäbisch Gmünd

Rektor-Klaus-Strasse 100, 73525 Schwäbisch Gmünd
Tel: +49(7171) 602-603
Fax: +49(7171) 69259
Rektor: Harald Stetzer (1991-95)
Leitender Verwaltungsbeamter: Franz Reif
Design.

Fachhochschule Albstadt-Sigmaringen

Anton-Günter-Strasse 51, 72488 Sigmaringen
Tel: +49(7571) 7208-0
Fax: +49(7571) 7208-29
Rektor: Lutz Ringewelski (1992-96)
Leitender Verwaltungsbeamter: Werner Rombach

Fachhochschule Stralsund

Grosse Parower Strasse 145, 18435 Stralsund
Tel: +49(3831) 3679
Fax: +49(3831) 367680
Gründungsrektor: Günter Jorke (1991-)
Kanzler: Manfred Hülsmann

Fachhochschule für Bibliothekswesen Stuttgart

Feuerbacher Heide 38-42, 70192 Stuttgart 1
Tel: +49(711) 22742-0
Fax: +49(711) 2274-233
Rektor: Peter Vodosek (1990-98)
Leitender Verwaltungsbeamter: Peter Marquardt
Library Science.

Fachhochschule für Druck Stuttgart

Nobelstrasse 10, 70569 Stuttgart 80, Vaihingen
Tel: +49(711) 685-2807
Fax: +49(711) 685-6650
Rektor: Bernd Kaiser (1990-98)
Leitender Verwaltungsbeamter: Gerold Müller
Printing Technology.

Fachhochschule für Technik Stuttgart

Willi-Bleicher-Strasse 29, 70174 Stuttgart
Tel: +49(711) 121-0
Fax: +49(711) 121-2666
Rektor: Martin Stohrer (1993-97)
Leitender Verwaltungsbeamter: Gerhard Blöchle
Technical Science.

Merz-Akademie Stuttgart

Teckstrasse 58, 70190 Stuttgart 1
Tel: +49(771) 26866-0
Fax: +49(771) 26866-21
E-Mail: makad@stuttgart.de
Direktor: Markus Merz (1983-
Verwaltungsleiterin: Sabine Natterer
Design.

Staatliche Akademie der Bildenden Künste Stuttgart

Am Weissenhof 1, 70191 Stuttgart 1
Tel: +49(711) 2575-0
Fax: +49(711) 2575-102
Rektor: Wolfgang Henning (1991-94)
Leitender Verwaltungsbeamter: Günter Oelberger
Founded: 1761
Fine Arts.

Staatliche Hochschule für Musik und Darstellende Kunst Stuttgart

Urbanplatz 2, 70182 Stuttgart
Tel: +49(711) 212-1
Fax: +49(711) 640-2393
Rektor: Rolf Hempel (1990-94)
Leitender Verwaltungsbeamter: Werner Proksch
Founded: 1922
Performing Arts; Music.

Theologische Fakultät Trier

Universitätsring 19, 54296 Trier
Tel: +49(651) 201-3520
Fax: +49(651) 201-3951
Rektor: Jost Eckert (1991-95)
Dekan: Ekkart Sauser
Theology.

Staatliche Hochschule für Musik Trossingen

Schultheiss-Koch-Platz 3, 78647 Trossingen 1
Tel: +49(7425) 9491-0
Fax: +49(7425) 9491-48
Rektor: Jürgen Weimer (1980-96)
Leitender Verwaltungsbeamter: Erwin Amann
Music.

Fachhochschule Ulm

Prittwitzstrasse 10, 89075 Ulm/Donau
Tel: +49(731) 502-08
Fax: +49(731) 502-8270
Rektor: Günther Hentschel (1989-97)
Leitender Verwaltungsbeamter: Herbert Jarosch

Wissenschaftliche Hochschule für Unternehmensführung (WHU) Otto-Beisheim-Hochschule Vallendar
Burgplatz 2, 56179 Vallendar
Tel: +49(261) 6509-0
Fax: +49(261) 6509-111
Rektor: Adolf-Friedrich Jacob (1992-94)
Economics.

Theologische Hochschule Vallendar der Pallotiner
Pallottistrassse 3, 56179 Vallendar
Tel: +49(261) 6402-1
Fax: +49(261) 6402-290
Rektor: Franz Courth (1992-94)
Theology.

Katholische Fachhochschule NorddeutschlandVechta
Abt. Vechta, Driverstrasse 23, 49377 Vechta
Tel: +49(4441) 9226-0
Fax: +49(4441) 5140
Rektor: Adolf Anderl (1991-95)
Kurator: Hanns Huning

Fachhochschule Wedel (PTL Wedel Prof. Dr. H. Harms)
Feldstrasse 143, 22880 Wedel, Holstein
Tel: +49(4103) 8048-0
Fax: +49(4103) 8048-39
Rektor: Dirk Harms
Geschäftsführer: Dirk Harms

Gustav-Siewerth-Akademie, Staatlich anerkannte wissenschaftliche HochschuleWeilheim
Oberbierbronnen 1, 79809 Weilheim-Bierbronnen
Tel: +49(7755) 699
Fax: +49(7755) 364
Rektor: Remigius Bäumer (1993-98)
Kanzler: August Weh
Science.

Hochschule für Musik 'Franz Liszt' Weimar
Platz der Demokratie 2/3, 99423 Weimar
Tel: +49(3643) 555-0
Fax: +49(3643) 61865
Rektor: Wolfram Huschke (1993-97)
Kanzlerin: Sieglinde Welker
Founded: 1872
Music.

Fachhochschule Ravensburg Weingarten
Doggenriedstrasse, 88250 Weingarten
Tel: +49(751) 501-0
Fax: +49(751) 49240
Rektor: Gregor Zibold (1990-98)
Leitender Verwaltungsbeamter: Peter Holländer

Fachhochschule Wiesbaden
Kurt-Schumacher-Ring 18, 65197 Wiesbaden
Tel: +49(611) 9495-01
Fax: +49(611) 444696
Rektor: Clemens Klockner (1985-97)
Kanzler: Peter Mertens

Fresenius Akademie-Fachhochschule Fresenius Wiesbaden
Dambachtal 20, 65193 Wiesbaden
Tel: +49(611) 5807-0
Fax: +49(611) 5807-41
Rektor: Wilhelm Fresenius

Technische Fachochschule Wildau
Friedrich-Engels-Strasse 63, 15742 Wildau
Tel: +49(3375) 500-365-368
Fax: +49(3375) 500-324
Gründungsrektor: Wilfried Arlt (1992-95)
Verwaltungsleiterin: Renate Wilde
Technical Science.

Fachhochschule Wilhelmshaven
Friedrich-Paffrath-Strasse 101, 26389 Wilhelmshaven
Tel: +49(4421) 804-1
Fax: +49(4421) 804-304
Rektor: Dietrich Kirsch (1992-95)
Kanzler: Hans-Joachim Baier

Kirchliche Hochschule Wuppertal
Missionsstrasse 9b, 42285 Wuppertal, Barmen
Tel: +49(202) 2820-0
Fax: +49(202) 2820-101
Rektor: Siegfried Kreuzer (1994-95)
Siegward Kunath
Theology (Protestant).

Fachhochschule Würzburg-Schweinfurt-Aschaffenburg
Abt. Würzburg:Münzstrasse 12, 97070 Würzburg
Tel: +49(931) 304-0
Fax: +49(931) 304-159
Präsident: Wolfgang Fechner (1989-95)
Kanzler: Jürgen Herzog

Hochschule für Musik Würzburg
Hofstallstrasse 6/8, 97070 Würzburg
Tel: +49(931) 50641
Fax: +49(931) 14408
Präsident: Franz Hennevogl (1987-1995)
Kanzler: Erich Lurz
Music.

Hochschule für Technik, Wirtschaft und Sozialwesen Zittau-Görlitz
Theodor-Körner-Allee 16, 02763 Zittau
Tel: +49(3583) 61-0
Fax: +49(3583) 510-626
Telex: 328223
Rektor: Peter Dierich (1992-97)
Kanzler: Peter Reinhold
Technical Science; Economics; Social Studies.

Hochschule für Technik und Wirtschaft Zwickau
Dr.-Friedrichs-Ring 2A, 08056 Zwickau
Tel: +49(375) 53536-0
Fax: +49(375) 536-1011
Telex: 321224
Cable: 77038 ihzrz
Rektor: Horst-Dieter Tietz (1992-
Kanzler: Joachim Körner
Founded: 1969
Technical Science; Economics.

NATIONAL ACADEMIC BODIES

Federal Ministry for Education and Science
[Bundesministerium für Bildung und Wissenschaft (Abteilung 4, Hochschulenwissenschaft Politik)]
Heinemannstrasse 2, 53175 Bonn
Tel: +49(228) 571-0
Fax: +49(228) 57-2096

Standing Conference of the Ministers of Education and Cultural Affairs in the Federal Republic of Germany
[Staändige Konferenz der Kultusminister der Länder in der Bundesrepublik Deutschland]
Nassestrasse 8, 53113 Bonn
Tel: +49(228) 501-0
Fax: (228)+49 501-301
Telex: 886 587 kmkd
Secretary-General: Joachim Schulz-Hardt

Conference of Rectors and Presidents of Universities
[Hochschulrektorenkonferenz (HRK)]
Ahrstrasse 39, 53175 Bonn
Tel: +49(228) 887-0
Fax: (228) 887-110
Telex: (228) 887-110
President: Hans-Uwe Erichsen
Secretary-General: Josef Lange
International Relations: Ruediger Juette
Founded: 1949, 1990

Federal Government-Länder Commission for Educational Planning and Research Promotion
[Bund-Länder-Kommission für Bildungsplanung und Forschungsförderung]
Friedrich-Ebert-Allee 39, 53113 Bonn
Tel: +49(228) 54020
Fax: +49(228) 5402-150

Alexander-von-Humboldt Foundation Fondation Alexander-von-Humboldt
[Alexander-von-Humboldt-Stiftung]
Jean-Paul-Strasse 12, 53173 Bonn
Tel: +49(228) 833-0
Fax: +49(228) 833-199
President: Reimar Lüst
Secretary-General: Heinrich Pfeiffer
Founded: 1860, 1953

Donors' Association for the Promotion of Science and Humanities
[Stifterverband für die Deutsche Wissenschaft]
Barkhovenallee 1, 45239 Essen-Bredeney
Tel: +49(201) 72210
Fax: +49(201) 714-6968
Telex: 857544
President: Klaus Liesen
Secretary-General: Horst Niemeyer
Founded: 1920

German Academic Exchange Service/Office allemand d'échanges universitaires
[Deutscher Akademischer Austauschdienst]
Kennedyallee 50, 53175 Bonn
Tel: +49(228) 88201
Fax: +49(228) 882-444
President: Theodor Berchem
Secretary-General: Christian Bode
Founded: 1925, 1950

German Association of University Professors
[Deutscher Hochschulverband (DHV)]
Rheinallee 18, 53173 Bonn
Tel: +49(228) 364-002
Fax: +49(228) 353-403
President: Hartmut Schiedermair
Secretary: Michael Hartmar
Founded: 1952

German Foundation of International Development/Fondation allemande pour le Développement international
[Deutsche Stiftung für Internationale Entwicklung (DSE)]
Hans-Böckler-Strasse 5, 53225 Bonn
Director-General: Hans-Rimbert Hemmer
Deputy Director-General: Peter Sötje
Founded: 1959

German National Association for Student Affairs
[Deutsches Studentenwerk (DSW)]
Weberstrasse 55, 53113 Bonn
Tel: +49(228) 26906-23
Fax: +49(228) 26906-39
President: Albert von Mutius
Secretary-General: Horst Bachmann
Founded: 1921

German National Scholarship Foundation
[Studienstiftung des Deutschen Volkes e.V.]
Mirbachstrasse 7, 53175 Bonn
Tel: +49(228) 820-960
President: Manfred Eigen
Secretary-General: Hartmut Rahn
Founded: 1925

German Research Community
[Deutsche Forschungsgemeinschaft (DFG)]
Kennedyallee 40, 5300 Bonn 2
Tel: +49(228) 8851
Fax: +49(228) 885-2221
President: Hubert Markl
Secretary-General: Burkhart Müller
Founded: 1920, 1949

Higher Education Information System Ltd.
[Hochschule-Informations-System GmbH]
Goseriede 9, 30159 Hannover

Max Planck Society for the Advancement of Science
[Max-Planck-Gesellschaft zur Förderung der Wissenschaften e.V.]
Residenzstrasse 1A, Postfach 647, 80333 München
Tel: +49(89) 21080
Fax: +49(89) 2108
Telex: 522203
President: Hans F. Zacher
General Secretary: Wolfgang Hasenclever
Founded: 1948

Science Council
[Wissenschaftsrat]
Brohler Strasse 11, 50968 Köln
Tel: +49(221) 3776-0
Fax: +49(221) 388-440
President: Dieter Simon
Secretary-General: Winfried Benz
Founded: 1957

German Commission for Unesco
[Deutsche Unesco-Kommission]
15 Colmantstrasse, 5300 Bonn 1
Tel: +49(228) 692-091
Fax: +49(228) 636-912
Telex: 886326 duk d.co bonn
President: Peter P. Canisius
Secretary-General: Traugott Schöfthaler

GHANA

UNIVERSITIES

*University of Cape Coast
University Post Office, Cape Coast
Tel: +233(42) 2440-9
Fax: +233(42) 2449
Telex: 2552 ucc gh
Vice-Chancellor: S.K. Adjepong (1991-)
Registrar: K. Kunadu
International Relations: C.E. Ameyaw
Founded: 1962, 1971
S: Agriculture.
F: Arts; Education; Science; Social Sciences.
Ce: Development Studies.
I: Education.

University for Development Studies
P.O. Box 1350, Tamale
Tel: +233(71) 2078
Vice-Chancellor (Acting): R.B. Bening
Registrar: Paul Effah
Founded: 1992
F: Agriculture; Integrated Development Studies; Applied Sciences (in preparation).
S: Medicine and Health Science (in preparation).

*University of Ghana
P.O. Box 25, Legon
Tel: +233(21)667-706
Fax: +233(21) 667-701
Telex: 2556 ugl gh
Cable: university, legon
Vice-Chancellor: George Benneh (1992-)
Registrar: G.F. Daniel
Founded: 1948, 1957, 1961
F: Agriculture; Arts; Law; Medicine; Science; Social Studies.
S: Administration; Communication Studies; Performing Arts; Public Health.
I: Adult Education; African Studies; Population Studies.
Ce: Tropical Clinical Pharmacology and Therapeutics; International for Music and Dance.
United Nations U. I. for Natural Resources in Africa (UNU/INRA).

INSTITUTE OF ADULT EDUCATION
Legon, P.O. Box, Accra
Founded: 1948
Adult Education.

INSTITUTE OF AFRICAN STUDIES
Legon, P.O. Box 75, Accra
Founded: 1961
African Studies.

INSTITUTE OF STATISTICAL, SOCIAL AND ECONOMIC RESEARCH
Legon, P.O. Box 74, Accra
Founded: 1962
Statistical, Social and Economic Research.

NOGUCHI MEMORIAL INSTITUTE FOR MEDICAL RESEARCH
Legon, Accra
Tel: +233(21) 667-701
Fax: +233(21) 667-701
Founded: 1979
Medical Research.

REGIONAL INSTITUTE FOR POPULATION STUDIES
Legon, P.O. Box 96, Accra
Founded: 1972
Population Studies.

SCHOOL OF ADMINISTRATION
Legon, P.O. Box 78, Accra
Founded: 1962
Administration.

SCHOOL OF COMMUNICATION STUDIES
Legon, P.O. Box 53, Accra
Founded: 1972
Communication Studies.

SCHOOL OF PERFORMING ARTS
Legon, Accra
Tel: +233(21) 667-701
Fax: +233(21) 667-701
Performing Arts.

UNIVERSITY OF GHANA MEDICAL SCHOOL
P.O. Box 4236, Accra
Founded: 1964
Medicine.

*University of Science and Technology
University Post Office, Kumasi
Tel: +233(51) 3137
Fax: +233(51) 3137
Telex: 2555 ust gh
Cable: kumasitech, kumasi ghana
Vice-Chancellor: Eugene H. Amonoo-Neizer
(1992-97)
Registrar and Secretary: S.O. Gyimah-Kessie
Founded: 1951, 1961
*F: Agriculture; Environmental and Development
Studies; Law; Pharmacy; Science; Social
Sciences.*
C: Art.
*S: Medical Sciences; Engineering; Mines
(Tarkwa).*
*I: Mining and and Mineral Engineering;
Renewable Natural Resources; Technical
Education (ITE).*
*Ce: Technology Consultancy (TCC); Land
Administration Research (LARC); Cultural
Studies; Dairy/Beef Cattle Research.*
Bureau: Integrated Rural Development (BIRD).

INSTITUTE OF MINING AND MINERAL ENGINEERING
Tarkwa, Kumasi
Founded: 1976
Mining.

INSTITUTE OF RENEWABLE NATURAL RESOURCES
Kumasi
Tel: +233(51) 5351
Founded: 1982
Renewable Natural Resources.

OTHER INSTITUTIONS

**Ghana Institute of Management and Public
Administration**
Achimota, P.O. Box 50, Accra
Tel: +233(21) 667-682
Fax: +233(21) 667-681
Telex: 2551 gimpa gh
Director-General: T.B. Wereko (1986-94)
Secretary: E.A. Cooper
Founded: 1961
*Div: Human Resource Development;
Management Research; Consultancey;
Postgraduate; Strategic Studies/Policy Analysis;
Administration.*

University College of Education of Winneba
P.O. Box 25, Winneba
Tel: +233 041361
Principal: Nathaniel Kofi Pecku
Registrar: Justice Nii Aryeetey
Founded: 1992
*Div (Education): Science; Languages; General
Culture and Social Studies; Applied Arts and
Technology; Specialized and Professional Studies
in Education.*

NATIONAL ACADEMIC BODIES

Ministry of Education and Culture
P.O.B. M45, Accra
Tel: +233(21) 665-421

Ghana National Commission for Unesco
Ministry of Education and Culture, P.O.B. 2739,
Accra
Tel: +233(21) 665-421
Fax: +233(21) 662-718
Telex: 2700
Chairman: Harry Sawyerr
Secretary: John Kusi-Achampong

GREECE

UNIVERSITIES AND TECHNICAL UNIVERSITIES

Aegean University
[Panepistimion Aegaeou]
odos Karantoni 8, Mytilini
Tel: +30(251) 25979
Fax: +30(251) 23783
Founded: 1984
F: Social Sciences (Mytilini).
*D: Business Administration (Chios);
Mathematics (Samos); Primary and Preschool
Education (Rhodes).*

Agricultural University of Athens
[Georgikon Panepistimion Athinon]
odos odos 75, Athinai 11855
Tel: +30(1) 346-1944
Fax: +30(1) 346-0885
Telex: 225018 agsa gr
Rector: Michael Loukas
Secretary-General: Constantinos Tsakoumakis
International Relations: Maria Yerogiannaki
Founded: 1920
*F: Crop Science; Animal Sciences; Agricultural
Biology and Biotechnology; Agricultural
Economics; Food Science and Technology; Land
Reclamation and Agricultural Engineering;
Science.*

**Athens University of Economics and
Business**
[Ikonomikon Panepistimion Athinon]
odos Patission 76, Athinai 10434
Tel: +30(1) 8211-124
Fax: +30(1) 8228-419
E-Mail: INTERNET: postmast
cr@aueb.ariadne-t.gr
Telex: 2253 63 asoe gr
Rector: Georgios K. Christou (1992-95)
Secretary-General: Sotiris Benos
International Relations: Eleni Maniati
Founded: 1920
*D: Economics; Business Administration;
Statistics; International and European Economic*

Studies; Management Science and Marketing; Informatics.
Ce: Research.

*National Technical University of Athens
Iroon polytechniou 9, Athinai 10682
Tel: +30(1) 772-8104
Fax: +30(1) 772-8127
Telex: ntua 221682
Rector: Nikolaos Markatos
International Relations: Bozana Gyzi
Founded: 1836, 1887, 1929
D: Civil Engineering; Mechanical Engineeering; Electrical Engineering; Architecture; Chemical Engineering; Rural Surveying and Engineering; Mining and Metallurgical Engineering; Naval Architecture and Marine Engineering; General Science.
Ce: Computer.

Panteios University of Economic and Political Sciences Athens
[Panteion Panepestimion Ikonomikon kai Politicon Epistimon]
odos Leoforos Syngrou 136, Athinai 17671
Tel: +30(1) 922-0100
Fax: +30(1) 922-3100
Telex: 224296 pspe
Founded: 1930, 1937
D: Political Science and International Studies; Public Administration; Sociology; Communication and Mass Media Studies; Urban and Regional Development; Social Anthropology, Geography and Politics; Law (General); Psychology.
I: Regional Development; International Relations.
Ce: Political Research; International Affairs; Social Morphology and Social Politics; Criminology; Research of Greek Modern Society; Study of Ancient Greek and Hellenistic Law; Research of State Politics.

School of Fine Arts
[Anotati Scholi Kalon Technon]
odos 28 Octovriou 42, Athinai 10682
Tel: +30(1) 361-7643
Fax: +30(1) 360-1093
Founded: 1910
Fine Arts.

*University of Athens
[Ethnikon kai Kapodistriakon Panepistimion Athinon]
odos Panepistimiou 30, 10679 Athinai
Tel: +30(1) 363-1813
Fax: +30(1) 364-7337
Telex: 223815/univ. gr.
Rector: Petros A. Gemtos
International Relations: Sophia Manoussaka
Founded: 1837
F: Theology; Law, Economics, and Political Science; Health Sciences; Humanities; Applied Sciences.
D: Theology; Pastoral Theology; Law; Economics; Political Sciences and Public Administration; Medicine; Dentistry; Pharmacy; Nursing; Literature; History and Archaeology; Philosophy, Education, and Psychology; English Language and Literature; French Language and Literature; German Language and Literature; Physics; Chemistry; Mathematics; Biology; Geology; Physical Education and Sport; Teacher Training; Teacher Training; Informatics.

Institute of Home Economics Athens
[Idryma Ikiakis Ikonomias]
odos Skoufa-Iraklitou 8, Athinai 10673
Tel: +30(1) 362-2835
Fax: +30(1) 321-749-814
Founded: 1990
Home Economics.

Technical University of Crete
[Polytechnion Kritis]
Venizelou 34, Chania 73132
Tel: +30(821) 42176
Fax: +30(821) 53571
President: John Tegopoulos
Registrar: Emmanuel Vandoulaki
Founded: 1977
D: Mechanical Engineering (in process of development); Chemical and Environmental Engineering; Electronic and Computer Engineering; Mineral Resources Engineering; Production and Management Engineering; Basic Sciences.
Ce: Computer.

University of Crete
[Panepistimion Kritis]
odos Dimitrakaki 17, Rethymnon
Tel: +30(831) 25313
Fax: +30(831) 27956
Telex: 601 262728 mpuc gr
Rector: Georgios Grammatikakis (1990-96)
Secretary-General: Stamatios Kokkinakis
International Relations: Spyros Pnevmaticos
Founded: 1973
S: Philosophy (Rethymnon); Science (Iraklion); Health Sciences (Iraklion).
D: Education.

Ionian University, Corfu
[Ionian Panepistimion]
Megaro Capopodistria, Corfu 49100
Tel: +30(661) 45614-5
Fax: +30(661) 22549
Rector: Elly Yotopoulou
Secretary-General: Popi Kanellou
Founded: 1984
Foreign Languages Translation, and Interpretation; Music; History; Library Science (from 1993).

University of Ioannina
[Panepistimion Ioanninon]
odos Domboli 30, Ioannina 45110
Tel: +30(651) 25915
Fax: +30(651) 74112
E-Mail: BITNET: pubrel@grioanun
Telex: 6322160 pnps
Rector: Ioannis D. Vergados (1991-94)
Secretary-General: Loukas Papaloukas
International Relations: Victoria Tsoumari
Founded: 1964, 1970
S: Philosophy; Science; Medicine.
D: Teacher Training (elementary level); Teacher Training (pre-school level).
Ce: Aquatic Biology Research; Computer.

*University of Macedonia
[Panepistimion Makedonias]
156, Egnatias, Thessaloniki 546 21
Tel: +30(31) 844-825
Fax: +30(31) 844-536
Telex: 410-497 umac gr
Cable: umac gr
Rector: Yannis Tsekouras
Secretary-General: Michalis Eleftheriadis
Founded: 1948
Sec: Economics; Business Administration; International and European Economic Studies; Accounting and Finance; Applied Informatics.

*University of Patras
[Panepistimion Patron]
Spilios Papathanassopoulos, Patrai 261 10
Tel: +31(61) 991-822
Fax: +30(61) 991-996
Telex: 312447 unpa gr
Prytanis (Rector): Stamatios Alahiotis (1994-97)
Secretary-General (Acting): Spilios Papathabnassopoulos
Founded: 1964
S: Natural Sciences; Engineering; Health Sciences; Humanities and Social Sciences; Economics.
I: Computer Technology; Chemical Engineering and High Temperature Process.

*University of Piraeus
[Panepistimion Pireos]
Karaoli and Dimitriou 80, Piraeus 18534
Tel: +30(1) 417-3159
Fax: +30(1) 417-9064
Telex: 241321
Rector: Theodore Gamaletsos
Secretary-General: A. Gotsis
International Relations: N. Alefandris
Founded: 1938
D: Economics; Business Administration; Statistics and Actuarial Science; Banking and Financial Management; Maritime Studies; Industrial and Operations Management; Informatics.
Ce: Research.

*Aristotle University of Thessaloniki
[Aristoteleion Panepistimion Thessalonikis]
University Campus, Thessaloniki 54006
Tel: +30(31) 909-431
Fax: +30(31) 996-6725
Telex: 0412181 auth gr
Rector: Antonios Mantis
Secretary-General: Dimitrios Batzios
International Relations: John Vassilion
Founded: 1925
F: Theology; Philosophy; Sciences; Law and Economics; Geotechnical Sciences; Health Sciences; Technology; Fine Arts.
S: Physical Education and Athletics.
I: Modern Greek Studies (Manolis Triantafyllidis Foundation).
Ce: Byzantine Research.

University of Thessaly
[Panepistimion Thesalias]
Argonafton kai Mavrocordatou, 38221 Volos
Tel: +30(421) 24785
Fax: +30(421) 24689
Founded: 1984
F: Humanities; Production Sciences.
D: Medicine; Physical Education and Athletics.

Dimocritus University of Thrace
[Dimocrition Panepistimion Thrakis]
Dimocritou 17, Comotini 69100
Tel: +30(531) 261-112
Fax: +30(531) 29398
Telex: 462205 duth gr
Rector: Evangelos Galoussis (1991-94)
Secretary-General: Susana Markidou
Founded: 1974
F: Law; Engineering (Xanthi); Medicine (Alexandroupolis).
D: Civil Engineering; Electrical Engineering; Physical Education and Sport; Educational Sciences (primary level); Educational Sciences (pre-school level); History and Ethnology.

NATIONAL ACADEMIC BODIES

Ministry of National Education, Division of Higher Education
[Ipourgion Pedias, Diefthinsis Anotatis Ekpedefseos]
odos Mitropoleos 15, Athinai 10185
Tel: +30(1) 323-7480
Fax: +30(1) 324-8264
Telex: 216059

Interuniversity Centre for the Recognition of Degrees and Diplomas Obtained Abroad (D.I.K.A.T.S.A.)
Leoforos Syngrou 112, Athinai 11741
Tel: +30(1) 922-2533

GREECE

Greek National Commission for Unesco
Ministry of Education, odos Academias 3, Athinai
10671
Tel: +30(1) 361-0581
Fax: +30(1) 362-0726
Telex: 218213-216593 ypex gr
Cable: grecunesco athens
President: Constantine Tsamadoj

GUADELOUPE

UNIVERSITIES

University of the French Antilles and Guyane
[Université des Antilles et de la Guyane]
Boulevard Légitimus, B.P. 771, 97173 Pointe-à-Pitre Cedex
Tel: +590 82-38-22
Fax: +590 91-06-57
Telex: Univag 919739 GLV
Président: Jean-Claude William (1994-99)
Secrétaire général: Raphaël Bourdy
International Relations: Eric Nabajoth, Vice-Président
Founded: 1970, 1982
Ut: Letters and Human Sciences (Martinique); Exact and Natural Sciences; Law and Economics; Medicine; Law and Economics (Martinique); Science and Techniques in Physical and Sporting Activities.
I: Higher Education (Guyane); Technology (Guyane).

GUATEMALA

University 'Francisco Marroquín' Guatemala
[Universidad Francisco Marroquín]
6 Calle Final, Zona 10, Guatemala
Tel: +502(2) 346886
Fax: +502(2) 346896
Cable: ufama guatemala
Rector: Fernando Monterroso
Secretario General: Juan F. Bendfeldt
Founded: 1971
S: Economics and Business Administration; Law; Architecture; Medicine; Dentistry; Systems Engineering and Computer Sciences; Theology; Economics and Business Administration (Graduate); Social Sciences (Graduate).
I: Public Accountancy and Auditing; Art.
D: Education, History and Communication; Psychology; Philosophy; Extension; Teacher Training (secondary level); Political Studies; Religious Science; History of Art.

University 'Mariano Gálvez' Guatemala
[Universidad 'Mariano Gálvez']
3a Avenida 9-00, Zona 2, Apartado 1811, Guatemala
Tel: +502(2) 534339
Founded: 1966
F: Economics; Law and Social Sciences.

University Rafael Landívar Guatemala
[Universidad Rafael Landívar]
Vista Hermosa 111, Zona 16, Guatemala
Tel: +502(2) 692151
Fax: +502(2) 692756
Founded: 1961
F: Economics; Humanities; Law and Social Sciences; Industrial Engineering; Architecture; Agriculture.
S: Teacher Training (secondary level).
I: Political and Social Sciences; Psychology.
Ce: Social Development.

University of San Carlos Guatemala
[Universidad de San Carlos de Guatemala]
Ciudad Universitaria, Zona 12, Guatemala
Tel: +502(2)2 760790
Rector: Alfonso Fuentes Soria
Secretario General: Hector Adolfo Cifuentes Mendoza
Founded: 1676, 1945
F: Agriculture; Economics; Architecture; Law and Social Sciences; Medicine; Chemistry and Pharmacy; Humanities; Engineering; Medicine and Animal Husbandry; Dentistry.

University of the Valley Guatemala
[Universidad del Valle de Guatemala]
Apartado postal 82, Guatemala
Tel: +502(2) 692827
Fax: +502(2) 380212
Founded: 1961
F: Science and Humanities; Social Sciences; Education.
I: Educational Research.

NATIONAL ACADEMIC BODIES

Ministry of Education
[Ministerio de Educación]
Palacio Nacional, Guatemala
Tel: +502(2) 224202
Fax: +502(2) 2537386
Ministro: Celestino Alfredo Tay Coyoy

Guatemalan Commission for Cooperation with Unesco
[Comisión Guatemalteca de Cooperación con la Unesco]
3a Avenida 10-29, Zona 1, Apartado postal 2630, Guatemala
Tel: +502(2) 29825
Cable: guateunesco guatemala ca
Secretaria: Estela G. de Luna

GUINEA

UNIVERSITIES

University of Conakry
[Université de Conakry]
B.P. 1147, Conakry
Tel: +224 46-16-39
Recteur: Mohamed Lamine Kaba
Secrétaire général: Aliou V. Diallo
Founded: 1962, 1984, 1989
F: Law and Economics; Letters and Human Sciences; Medicine and Pharmacy; Science.
I: Polytechnic.
Ce: Computer; English Studies (CELA); French Studies (CELF); Applied Technology (CTA); Teledetection Studies and Research (CERT).

University of Kankan
[Université de Kankan]
B.P. 203, Kankan
Tel: +224 20-93
Recteur: Sekou Konaté (1985-)
Founded: 1963, 1967, 1984
F: Social Sciences; Natural Sciences.

OTHER INSTITUTIONS

Institut supérieur agronomique et vétérinaire Valéry Giscard d'Estaing
B.P. 131, Faranah
Tel: +224 81-02-15
Founded: 1976
Agriculture and Veterinary Medicine.

Institut supérieur des Mines et Géologie de Boké
Boké
Mining and Geology.

Institut supérieur des Sciences de l'Education de Manéah
B.P. 795, Conakry
Educational Sciences.

NATIONAL ACADEMIC BODIES

Ministry of Higher Education and Scientific Research
[Ministère de l'Eseignement supérieur et de la Recherche scientifique]
Conakry
Tel: +224 44-38-04
Ministre: Charles Pascal Tolno

Guinea National Commission for Unesco
[Commission nationale guinéenne pour l'Unesco]
Ministère de l'Education supériere et de la Recherche scientifique, B.P. 964, Conakry
Tel: +224 44-49-57
Fax: +224 44-20-12
Telex: 22331 mdec ge
Président: Aliou Banire Diallo
Secrétaire général: Ibrahima Magassouba

GUYANA

UNIVERSITIES

University of Guyana
P.O. Box 101110, Georgetown
Tel: +592(2) 54841
Cable: uniguy
Vice-Chancellor and Principal: D.R. Craig
Registrar: G.N. Cave
Founded: 1963
F: Education; Health Sciences; Natural Sciences; Social Sciences; Technology.
S: Agriculture.

NATIONAL ACADEMIC BODIES

Ministry of Education and Cultural Development
26 Brickdam, Georgetown
Tel: +592(2) 63094
Fax: +592(2) 585111
Minister: Dale Bisnauth

Guyana National Commission for Unesco
'Dargan House', 90 Robb and Oronoque Streets, P.O. Box 1014, Georgetown
Tel: +592(2) 54-306
Fax: +592(2) 58-511
Cable: mined geogetown
Chairman: Dale Bisnauth, Minister of Education and Cultural Development

HAITI

UNIVERSITIES

State University of Haïti
[Université d'État d'Haïti]
25-35, rue Bonne Foi, Boite postale 2279, Port-au-Prince
Tel: +509 2-3210
Founded: 1944
F: Law and Economics; Sciences; Humanities; Dentistry; Medicine and Pharmacy; Agriculture and Veterinary Science; Ethnology.
S: Teacher Training.
I: Business Administration and International Studies; African Research and Studies.
Ce: Applied Linguistics.

NATIONAL SCHOOL OF ARTS
[ECOLE NATIONALE DES ARTS (ENARTS)]
226, rue Monseigneur Guilloux, Port-au-Prince
Arts.

SCHOOL OF LAW OF CAYES
[ECOLE DE DROIT DES CAYES]
rue Sténio Vincent, Cayes, Haiti
Law.

SCHOOL OF LAW OF FORT-LIBERTÉ
[ECOLE DE DROIT DE FORT-LIBERTÉ]
Fort-Liberté
Law.

SCHOOL OF LAW OF GONAIVES
[ECOLE DE DROIT DES GONAIVES]
Gonaives
Tel: +509 74-0397
Law.

SCHOOL OF LAW OF SAINT-MARC
[ECOLE DE DROIT DE SAINT-MARC]
Saint-Marc
Law.

INSTITUTE OF ELECTRONIC TECHNOLOGY
[INSTITUT DE TECHNOLOGIE ÉLECTRONIQUE D'HAÏTI]
159, rue Enterrement, Port-au-Prince
Tel: +509 22-9232
Electronics.

SCHOOL OF NURSING OF CAP-HAÏTIEN
[ECOLE DES INFIRMIÈRES DU CAP-HAÏTIEN]
Cap-Haïtien
Nursing.

NATIONAL SCHOOL OF NURSING OF PORT-AU-PRINCE
[ECOLE NATIONALE DES INFIRMIÈRES DE PORT-AU-PRINCE]
rue Monseigneur Guilloux, Port-au-Prince
Tel: +509 22-5236
Nursing.

G.O.C. INSTITUT POLYTECHNIQUE
1, Impasse Alouette Nazon, Port-au-Prince

CENTRE FOR TECHNICAL STUDIES, PLANNING AND APPLIED
ECONOMICS (CTPEA)
[CENTRE DE TECHNIQUES, DE LA PLANIFICATION ET
D'ECONOMIE APPLIQUÉE (CTPEA)]
B.P. 1796, Port-au-Prince
Tel: +509 22-3554
*Technical Studies, Planning and Applied
Economics.*

*University of Quisqueya
[Université de Quisqueya]
Angle rue Charéron et Boulevard Harry Truman,
Boite postale 796, Port-au-Prince
Tel: +509 23-7430
Founded: 1988
*F: Agriculture and Environmental Science;
Economics and Administration; Engineering;
Education; Law.*

OTHER INSTITUTIONS

America English School
120, rue des Miracles, Port-au-Prince
Tel: +509 22-5103

**Centre d'Enseignement commercial et
technique**
26, rue Dr. Audain, Port-au-Prince
Tel: +509 22-7776
Commercial Training and Techniques.

**Centre d'Etudes commerciales et
techniques**
25, Bois Verna, Port-au-Prince
Tel: +509 45-0440
Commercial and Technical Studies.

**Centre d'Etudes universitaires et de
Formation continue**
87, Haut de Turgeau, Port-au-Prince
Tel: +509 45-3383

Centre Universitaire international d'Haïti
6, rue Marcadieu Bourdon, Port-au-Prince
Tel: +509 22-9973

Collège Universitaire Caraïbe
Delmas 29, No. 7, Port-au-Prince
Tel: +509 45-2166

Ecole de Commerce Gérard A. Joseph
Delmas, Port-au-Prince
Tel: +509 46-1427
Commerce.

Ecole de Commerce Julien Graan
4, avenue Christophe, Port-au-Prince
Tel: +509 45-2245
Commerce.

Ecole de Commerce Maurice Laroche
26, chemin des Dalles, Port-au-Prince
Tel: +509 22-3798
Commerce.

Ecole de Secrétariat bilingue Christ-Roi
Entrée Christ-Roi Bourdon, Port-au-Prince
Tel: +509 22-1290
Bilingual Secrétarial Studies.

Ecole de Secrétariat de Direction
68, rue Capois, Port-au-Prince
Tel: +509 22-1465
Secretarial Studies.

Ecole moyenne de Technique géologues
Route Nationale, Port-au-Prince
Tel: +509 22-5301
Geology.

**Ecole technique de Commerce et de
Langues vivantes**
146, avenue Christophe, Port-au-Prince
Tel: +509 22-3998
Commerce and Modern Languages.

English Spanish Accounting School
11, rue des Miracles, Port-au-Prince
Tel: +509 22-5103
Accountancy.

First School
Place Dantès Destouches, Port-au-Prince
Tel: +509 22-4755

Institut Adventista Franco-Haïtien
Diquini 63, Port-au-Prince
Tel: +509 34-1195

Institut des hautes Etudes commerciales et économiques
275, avenue John Brown, Port-au-Prince
Tel: +509 22-1550
Commerce and Economics.

Institut Lope de Vega
24, lière Impasse Lavaud, Port-au-Prince
Tel: +509 45-5585

Institut supérieur des Sciences économiques et politiques
180, avenue John Brown, Port-au-Prince
Economic and Politicial Sciences.

Institut supérieur technique d'Haïti
22, avenue du Chili, Port-au-Prince
Tel: +509 22-6159
Technology.

Institut universitaire d'Etudes spécialises
208, Lalue, Port-au Prince

International Correspondance School (ICS)
96, rue Capois, Port-au-Prince
Tel: +509 22-3222

Jamaica School of Business
58, avenue John Brown, Port-au-Prince
Tel: +509 22-7534
Business Studies.

Nouvelle Ecole de Commerce
160, rue Dr. Aubry, Port-au-Prince
Tel: +509 22-0749
Commerce.

Professional School
22, ruelle Dufort, Port-au-Prince
Tel: +509 45-3383

NATIONAL ACADEMIC BODIES

Haitian National Commission for Unesco
[Commission nationale haïtienne de Coopération avec l'Unesco]
Ministère de l'Education nationale, 5, avenue Marie-Jeanne, Port-au-Prince
Tel: +509 20-747
Telex: 20108
Secrétaire permanent: Jean Noël

HOLY SEE

UNIVERSITIES

*Pontifical Gregorian University Rome
[Pontificia Università Gregoriana]
Piazza della Pilotta 4, 00187 Roma
Tel: +39(6) 67011
Fax: +39(6) 67015413
Cable: Pugi Roma
Rector: Giuseppe Pittau, S.J.
Administrative Director: Sandro Barlone
International Relations: Arij Roest Crollius
Founded: 1553

F: *Theology; Canon Law; Philosophy; Ecclesiastical History; Missiology; Social Sciences.*
I: *Spiritual Theology; Psychology; Religious Sciences.*
S: *Latin Language and Literature.*
Ce: *Social Communication (Interdisciplinary).*

Pontifical Lateran University Rome
[Pontificia Universitàs Lateranensis]
Piazza S. Giovanni in Laterano 4, 00184 Roma
Tel: +39(6) 698-86401
Fax: +39(6) 698-86133
Rettore: Umberto Betti, OFM
Segretario Generale: Daniele Micheletti
Founded: 1773, 1913, 1959
F: *Theology; Canon Law; Civil Law; Philosophy.*
I: *Pastoral Studies; Family Studies; Moral Theology; Religious Life; Religious Sciences; Patristic Studies.*

Pontifical University of St. Thomas Aquinas in Rome
[Pontificia Studiorum Universitas A S. Thoma Aquinate in Urbe]
Largo Angelicum 1, 00184 Roma
Tel: +39(6) 670-21
Fax: +39(6) 679-0407
Rettore: Edward Kaczyński, O.P.
Segretario Generale: Bruno Esposito, O.P.
Founded: 1580, 1906, 1963
F: *Theology; Canon Law; Philosophy; Social Sciences.*
I: *Spiritual Studies; Religious Sciences; Theology.*

Pontifical Urban University Rome
[Pontificia Universitas Urbaniana]
Via Urbano VIII 16, 00165 Roma
Tel: (6) 686-8640
Fax: (6) 6830-8363
Cable: urban university-vatican
Rettore: Daniel Acharuparambil, O.C.D.
Segretatio Generale: Mario Colombo, P.I.M.E.
F: *Philosophy; Theology; Canon Law; Missiology.*
I: *Missionary Catechesis; Study of Atheism.*
Ce: *Chinese Studies.*

Salesian Pontifical University Rome
[Università Pontificia Salesiana]
Piazza Ateneo Salesiano 1, 00139 Roma
Tel: (6) 872-90141
Fax: (6) 8729-0222
Cable: università salesiana 00139 roma
Rettore: Raffaele Farina (1992-95)
Segretario Generale: Mario Morra
Founded: 1904, 1940, 1973
F: *Theology; Canon Law; Philosophy; Education.*
I: *Classical Studies; Religious Sciences; Social Communication Sciences; Social Education; Catechetic; History of Canon Law.*

OTHER INSTITUTIONS

Pontificia Facultas Scientiarum Educationis Auxilium
Via Cremolino 141, 00166 Roma
Tel: +39(6) 6155-0790
Fax: +39(6) 6156-4640
Preside: Enrica Rosanna
Segretaria: Carla Sartoria
Founded: 1966

Pontificia Facultas Theologica Marianum
Viale Trenta Aprile 6, 00153 Roma
Tel: +39(6) 581-4441
Fax: +39 (6) 588-0292
Preside: Ignacio Mará Calabuig Adán
Founded: 1866, 1955
Theology.

Pontificia Facultas Theologica S. Bonaventurae
Via del Serafico 1, 00142 Roma
Tel: +39(6) 519-2007
Fax: +39 (6) 519-2067
Preside: Orlando Todisco
Segretario: Julian Zalbanini
Founded: 1587, 1955
Theology.

Pontificia Facultas Theologica S. Teresianum
Piazza San Pancrazio 5A, 00152 Roma
Tel: +39(6) 581-2362
Fax: +39(6) 580-9050
Preside: Jesus Castellano Cervera
Segretario: Dario Cumer
Founded: 1935
Theology.

Pontificium Athenaeum Anselmianum
Piazza dei Cavalieri di Malta 5, 00153 Roma
Tel: +39(6) 57911
Fax: +33(6) 574-6863
Rettore: Pius Tragan
Segretario Generale: Mario Morra
Founded: 1687, 1867
Theology; Philosophy.
I: Liturgical.

Pontificium Athenaeum Antonianum
Via Merulana 124, 00185 Roma
Tel: +39(6) 703-739
Fax: +39(6) 779-749
Rettore: José Antonio Merino Abad
Segretario Generale: Giuseppe Denedetto Xnereb
Founded: 1933
Theology; Canon Law; Philosophy.

Pontificium Athenaeum Regina Apostolorum
Via Aurelia Antica 4601, 00165 Roma
Tel: +39(6) 663-2906
Fax: +39(6) 663-2805
Rettore: Alvaro Corcuera Martínez del Rio
Segretario: Daniel Reynolds
Founded: 1993

Pontificium Athenaeum Sanctae Crucis
Piazza S. Apollinare 49, 00186 Roma
Tel: +39(6) 654-3752
Fax: +39(6) 689-7021
Rettore: Lluis Clavell Ortiz-Repiso
Segretario Generale: Giuseppe Gerola
Founded: 1985

Pontificium Institutum Altioris Latinitatis
Piazza dell'Ateneo Salesiano 1, 00139 Roma
Tel: +39(6) 872-901
Preside-Decano: Enrico Dal Covolo
Segretario: Sergio Gelici
Founded: 1964

Pontificium Institutum Archaeologiae Christianae
Via Napoleone III 1, 00185 Roma
Tel: +39(6) 446-5574
Fax: +39(6) 446-9197
Rettore: Patrick Saint-Roch
Founded: 1925
Archaeology.

Pontificium Institutum Biblicum
Via della Pilotta 25, 00187 Roma
Tel: +39(6) 679-6453
Fax: +39(6) 6701-6151
Rettore: Klemens Stock
Founded: 1909
Biblical Studies.

Pontificium Institutum Musicae Sacrae
Via di Torre Rossa 21, 00165 Roma
Tel: +39(6) 663-8792
Founded: 1911, 1931
Sacred Music.

Pontificium Institutum Studiorum Arabicorum et Islamisticae
Viale di Trastevere 89, 00153 Roma
Tel: +39(6) 589-2676
Fax: +39(6) 588-2595
Preside: André Ferré
Founded: 1960
Arabic and Islamic Studies.

Pontificium Institutum Studiorum Orientalium
Piazza di Santa Maria Maggiore 7, 00185 Roma
Tel: +39(6) 446-5589
Fax: +39(6) 446-5576
Rettore: Clarence Gallagher
Segretario: Jakov Kulič
Founded: 1917
Oriental Studies.

NATIONAL ACADEMIC BODIES

Congregation for Catholic Education
[Congregatio de Institutione Catholica]
Piazza Pio XII, 00193 Roma
Tel: +39(6) 6988-4167
Fax: +39(6) 6988-4172
Prefect: Pio Laghi
Secretary: José Saraiva Martins
Founded: 1588

HONDURAS

UNIVERSITIES

National Autonomous University of Honduras
[Universidad Nacional Autónoma de Honduras]
Ciudad Universitaria, Tegucigalpa D.C.
Tel: +504 32-22-08
Founded: 1845
F: Law and Social Sciences; Medicine; Engineering; Economics; Dentistry; Chemistry and Pharmacy.
I: Economic Research.
D: Extension.
Ce: General Studies; General Studies (San Pedro Sula); General Studies (La Ceiba); Industrial Studies.

REGIONAL UNIVERSITY CENTRE, ATLÁNTICA
[CENTRO UNIVERSITARIO REGIONAL LITORAL ATLÁNTICO]
La Ceiba, Atlántica

REGIONAL UNIVERSITY CENTRE OF THE NORTH
[CENTRO UNIVERSITARIO REGIONAL DEL NORTE]
San Pedro Sula, Cortes

University of San Pedro Sula
[Universidad de San Pedro Sula]
18 Avenida, 6 calle, N.O., San Pedro Sula, Cortés

José Cecilio del Valle University Tegucigalpa
[Universidad José Cecilio del Valle]
Apartado postal 917, Tegucigalpa, D.C.
Tel: +504 22-89-61
Fax: +504 37-05-75
Rector: Irma Acosta De Fortin
Founded: 1978
Engineering; Administration and Accountancy; Computer Science.

National Pedagogical University 'Francisco Morazán' Tegucigalpa
[Universidad Pedagógica Nacional 'Francisco Morazán']
Boulevard Miraflores, Apartado Postal 3394, Tegucigalpa, D.C.
Tel: +504 32-74-17
Rector: Roque Ramos Motiño
Founded: 1990
S: Human Sciences.
I: Science and Technology.
D: Natural Sciences; Business Education; Technical Industry Education; Mathematics; Home

Economics Education; Education; Social Sciences; Languages and Literature; Physical Education; Plastic Arts.
Ce: University.

OTHER INSTITUTIONS

Escuela Agrícola Panamericana
El Zamorano, Francisco Morazán
Tel: +504 332-717
Telex: 3111 1567
Founded: 1942
Agriculture.

NATIONAL ACADEMIC BODIES

Ministry of Public Education
[Ministerio de Educación Pública]
la Calle, entre 2a, 3a y 4a Avenidas, Tegucigalpa, D.C.
Tel: +504 227-090
Fax: +504 224-931
Ministro: Xenobia Rodas de León Gómez

Honduras National Commission for Unesco
[Comisión Nacional Hondureña Cooperación con la Unesco]
Ministerio de Educación Pública, la Calle, entre 2a, 3a y 4a Avenidas, Teguagalpa, D.C.
Tel: +504 227-497
Fax: +504 222-216
Cable: mineducacion tegucigalpa
Coordinadora General: Blanca Regina Osorio

HONG KONG

UNIVERSITIES

*The Chinese University of Hong Kong
Shatin, New Territories, Hong Kong
Tel: +852 2609-8899
Fax: +852 2603-5115
E-Mail: clara@uab.msmail.cuhk.hk
Telex: 50301 cuhk hx
Cable: sinoversity
Vice-Chancellor: Charles. K. Kao (1987-)
Registrar (Acting): Ho Wan Siu-wan
International Relations: Director, Office of Academic Links, Mark Sheldon
Founded: 1963
F: Arts; Business Administration; Medicine; Science; Social Sciences; Education; Engineering.
S: Graduate; Continuing Studies.
I: Asia-Pacific Business; Asia-Pacific Studies; Biotechnology; Chinese Studies; Science and Technology; Humanities Research.

*City University of Hong Kong
83 Tat Chee Avenue, Kowloon, Hong Kong
Tel: +852 2788-7654
Fax: +852 2788-1167
Telex: 45531 cpoly hx
Vice-Chancellor: Patrick Cheng Yiu-Chung (1989-)
Director of Administration: Keith Houghton
Founded: 1984
F: Business; Science and Technology; Law.
C: Higher Vocational Studies.
P: Humanities and Social Sciences.

Hong Kong Polytechnic
Hung Hom, Kowloon, Hong Kong
Tel: +852 2766-5111
Fax: +852 2766-3374
E-Mail: Bitnet hkpoly@hkpcc.hkp.hk
Telex: 38967 polyx hx
Director: Poon Chung-kwong (1991-98)
Associate Director (Administration): Miranda
Leung Po-chu
International Relations: Alexander Tzang
Hing-chung
Founded: 1972
F: Applied Science and Textiles; Business and
Information Systems; Communication;
Construction and Land User; Engineering; Health
and Social Studies.

Hong Kong University of Science and Technology
Tai Po Tsai, Clear Water Bay, Kowloon, Hong
Kong
Tel: +852 358-6000
Fax: +852 736-3303
Vice-Chancellor: Chia-Wei Woo
Founded: 1988
S: Business and Management; Engineering;
Humanities and Social Sciences; Science.
Ce: Language.

Lingnan College
15 Stubbs Road, Hong Kong
Tel: +852 2572-2226
Fax: +852 2838-1601
E-Mail: yaokath
Cable: redgrey
President: John T.S. Chen (1981-)
Registrar: Lok-wood Mui
International Relations: College Secretary,
Katherine Y.B. Yao
Founded: 1967
F: Arts; Business; Social Sciences.
Research Ce: Asian Pacific Studies;
International Business Studies; Modern Literature
in Chinese.

*The University of Hong Kong
Pokfulam Road, Hong Kong
Tel: +852 859-2111
Fax: +852 858-2549
Telex: 71919 cereb hx
Cable: university hong kong
Vice-Chancellor: Wang Gungwu (1986-)
Registrar: M.G. Spooner
Founded: 1911
F: Architecture; Arts; Dentistry; Education;
Engineering; Law; Medicine; Science; Social
Sciences.
Ce: Asian Studies; Urban Planning and
Environmental Management; Kadoorie
Agricultural Research; Language; Social
Sciences Research.
I: Marine Science; Molecular Biology.
S: Professional and Continuing Education.

OTHER INSTITUTIONS

Haking Wong Technical Institute
702 Lai Chi Kok Road, Cheung Sha Wan
Kowloon, Hong Kong
Tel: +852 361-5161
Fax: +852 725-2342
Principal: James Kung
Executive Officer: Ivy Leung
Founded: 1977
D: Commercial Studies; Construction; Electrical
Engineering; Hotel-Keeping and Tourism Studies;
Marine Engineering and Fabrication; Mechanical
Engineering.

Hong Kong Baptist College
224 Waterloo Road, Kowloon, Hong Kong
Tel: +852 339-7400
Fax: +852 339-7373
President: Daniel G.W. Tse
Academic Registrar: Clement K. Young
Founded: 1956

Hong Kong Technical College (Chai Wan)
30 Shing Tai Road, Hong Kong
Tel: +852 595-8333
Fax: +852 505-4200
Principal: Frederick K.W. Mak
Senior Executive Officer: Regina Koo
Founded: 1993
D: Applied Science; Business Administration;
Computing and Mathematics; Electronic
Engineering; Hotel Catering and Tourism
Management; Manufacturing Engineering.

Hong Kong Technical College (Tsing Yi)
20 Tsing Yi Road, Tsing Yi Island, New
Territories, Hong Kong
Tel: +852 2436-8333
Fax: +852 2434-5652
Senior Executive Officer: Celia Ip
Founded: 1993
D: Business Administration; Computing and
Mathematics; Construction; Design; Electrical and
Communications Engineering; Manufacturing
Engineering; Mechanical Engineering.

Kwai Chung Technical Institute
20 Hing Shing Road, Kwai Chung New
Territories, Hong Kong
Tel: +852 2424-6221
Fax: +852 2410-1278
Principal: W.C. Tam
Executive Officer: Josalin Tse
Founded: 1975
*D: Commercial Studies; Electrical Engineering;
Manufacturing Engineering; Mechanical
Engineering; Textiles Industries.*

Kwun Tong Technical Institute
25 Hiu Ming Street, Kwun Tong Kowloon, Hong
Kong
Tel: +852 2727-4331
Fax: +852 2346-6012
Principal: G.A.V. Ribeiro
Executive Officer: Philip Keung
Founded: 1975
*D: Clothing Technology; Commercial Studies;
Electronic Engineering; Mechanical Engineering;
Printing.*

Lee Wai Lee Technical Institute
30 Renfrew Road, Kowloon, Hong Kong
Tel: +852 2338-361
Fax: +852 2336-3459
Principal: M.C. Lau
Executive Officer: Anita Lee
Founded: 1979
*D: Commercial Studies; Design; Electronic
Engineering; General Studies; Manufacturing
Engineering; Mechanical Engineering; Motor
Vehicle Engineering.*

Morrison Hill Technical Institute
6 Oi Kwan Road, Wan Chai, Hong Kong
Tel: +852 2574-5321
Fax: +852 2572-9847
Principal: Y.W. Yang
Executive Officer: Alice Chan
Founded: 1970
*D: Computing Studies; Commercial Studies;
Construction; Electronic Engineering; Mechanical
Engineering; General Studies.*

Sha Tin Technical Institute
21 Yuen Wo Road, Sha Tin New Territories, Hong
Kong
Tel: +852 2606-6227
Fax: +852 2694-7029
Principal: Kenneth Ng
Executive Officer: Grace Lau
Founded: 1986
*D: Applied Science; Computing Studies;
Commercial Studies; Design; Electronic
Engineering; General Studies; Manufacturing
Engineering.*

Tuen Mun Technical Institute
Tsing Wun Road, Tuen Mun New Territories,
Hong Kong
Tel: +852 2463-0066
Fax: +852 2454-5654
Principal: Y.M. Mo
Executive Officer: Evan Ho
Founded: 1986
*D: Commercial Studies; Construction; Electronic
Engineering; Manufacturing Engineering;
Computing Studies.*

NATIONAL ACADEMIC BODIES

Education Department
Wu Chung House, 213 Queen's Road East,
Wanchai, Hong Kong
Tel: +852 2891-0088
Fax: +852 2893-0853

HUNGARY

UNIVERSITIES

PUBLIC INSTITUTIONS

Academy of Drama and Film Budapest
[Szinház-és Filmművészeti Főiskola]
Vas u. 2/c, 1088 Budapest
Tel: +36(1) 138-4727
Fax: +36(1) 138-4749
Rector: Péter Huszti
Founded: 1865
Drama; Cinematography.

*Budapest University of Economic Sciences
[Budapesti Közgazdaságtudományi Egyetem]
Fövám tér 8, 1093 Budapest
Tel: +36(1) 117-6268
Fax: +36(1) 117-8883
Telex: 22-4186
Rector: Rudolf Andorka
Secretary-General: Pál Varjas
Founded: 1920, 1948, 1990
*F: Management and Business Administration;
Economics; Social Sciences; Postgraduate
Studies.*
Div: Basic Economic Studies.

*Eötvös Loránd University Budapest
[Eötvös Loránd Tudományegyetem]
Egyetem tér 1/3, 1364 Budapest
Tel: +36(1) 266-3119
Fax: +36(1) 266-4025
Telex: 22-5467 elte h
Rector: Miklós Szabó
Secretary-General: Gyula Kisfaludy
Founded: 1561, 1950
F: Arts; Law and Political Science; Science.
I: Sociology; Teachers Training (primary level:).

Franz Liszt Academy of Music Budapest
[Liszt Ferenc Zeneműbvészeti Főiskola]
Liszt Ferenc tér 8, 1061 Budapest
Tel: +36(1) 122-5434
Fax: +36(1) 121-4097
Rector: István Lantos
Founded: 1875, 1971
Artistic Studies.

Haynal Imre University of Health Sciences Budapest
[Haynal Imre Egészégtudományi Egytem]
Szabolcs u. 35, 1135 Budapest
Tel: +36(1) 126-1248 F+36(1) 129-9031
Rector: Gábor Brooser
Health Sciences.

Hungarian Academy of Craft and Design Budapest
[Magyar Iparművészeti Főiskola]
Zugligeti u. 11/25, 1121 Budapest
Tel: +36(1) 176-1722
Fax: +36(1) 176-7488
Rector: Imre Schrammel
Founded: 1880, 1949
Craft and Design; Teacher Training.

Hungarian Academy of Fine Arts Budapest
[Magyar Képzőművészeti Főiskola]
Andrássy út. 69/71, 1062 Budapest
Tel: +36(1) 142-8556
Fax: +36(1) 142-1563
Rector: Lajos Sváby
Founded: 1871, 1949
Fine Arts; Art Theory (2).

Hungarian University of Physical Education Budapest
[Magyar Testnevelési Egyetem]
Alkotás ú. 44, 1123 Budapest
Tel: +36(1) 142-8556
Fax: +36(1) 142-1563
Rector: Lajos Sváby
Founded: 1925, 1975, 1989
Physical Education and Sport.

*Semmelweis University of Medicine Budapest
[Semmelweis Orvostudományi Egyetem]
Üllobi út 26, 1085 Budapest VII
Tel: +31(1) 118-0236
Fax: +36(1) 113-5090
E-Mail: walton@nkcs sote.hu
Telex: 226720
Rector: Miklós Réthelyi (1993-99)
Founded: 1769, 1951
F: Medicine; Dentistry; Pharmacy.

*Technical University of Budapest
[Budapesti Műszaki Egyetem]
Műegyetem rakpart 3, 1111 Budapest XI
Tel: +36(1) 181-2179
Fax: +36(1) 185-2218
Telex: 225931 muegy
Rector: Péter Bíróer
Secretary-General: József Vajda
Founded: 1782, 1872

F: Civil Engineering; Mechanical Engineering; Architecture; Chemical Engineering; Electrical Engineering; Engineering Transportation; Natural and Social Sciences.
Ce: Engineering (International).

University of Horticulture and Food Industry Budapest
[Kertészeti és Élelmiszeripari Egyetem]
Villányi út 35-43, 1118 Budapest
Tel: +36(1) 185-0666
Fax: +36(1) 166-6220
E-Mail: h 960héa. huella. bitnet
Rector: Tibor Deák
Secretary-General: Tibor Kovacs
Founded: 1853, 1943, 1968, 1986
F: Horticulture; Food Processing Industry.
C: Food Industry (Szeged); Horticulture (Kecskemét).
I: Viticulture and Oenology Research (Kecskemét); Viticulture and Oenology (Pécs Trans-Danubian Research); Oenology and Viticulture (Eger Research).

University of Veterinary Science Budapest
[Állatorvostudományi Egyetem]
István u.2, P.O. Box 2, 1400 Budapest
Tel: +36(1) 122-2660
Fax: +36(1) 142-6518
Telex: 224439
Rector: László Frenyó (1991-94)
Secretary-General: Tibor Jankovits
Founded: 1787, 1952, 1962
Veterinary Science; Research (Ulló).

Kossuth Lajos University Debrecen
[Kossuth Lajos Tudományegyetem]
Egytem tér 1-3, 4010 Debrecen
Tel: (52) 521-6666
Fax: (52) 521-0007
E-Mail: h1937@ella.uucp
Telex: (61) 72-200
Rector: Zoltán Abádi-Nagy
Registrar: László Vargas
Founded: 1538, 1912, 1949
F: Arts; Sciences.

University of Agricultural Sciences Debrecen
[Agrártudományi Egyetem]
Böszörményi út 138, 4015 Debrecen
Tel: +36(52) 415-873
Fax: +36(52) 413-385
Telex: 72-2111 h
Rector: Jakob Loch (1992-95)
Secretary-General: György Nádas
Founded: 1868, 1970
F: Agricultural Sciences; Agricultural Water and Environmental Management (Szarvas).
C: Animal Husbandry (Hódmezövásárhely); Research I. (Karcag).

University of Medicine Debrecen
[Debreceni Orvostudományi Egyetem]
Nagyerdei körut 98, 4012 Debrecen
Tel: +36(52) 417-571
Fax: +36(52) 419-807
Rector: Lajos Gergely
Founded: 1912
Medicine and Dentistry; Nursing, Medical Informatics, Social Work.

*Gödöllö University of Agriculture
[Gödöllö Agrártudományi Egyetem]
Páter Károly út 1, 2103 Gödöllö
Tel: +36(28) 310-971
Fax: +36(28) 310-804
E-Mail: h 3423 rek huella.bitnet; kocsis rkt.gau.hu
Telex: 224892 gate h
Cable: gate gödöllö hungary
Rector: Károly Kocsis
Secretary-General: László Guth
Founded: 1945
F: Agricultural Sciences; Agricultural Engineering; Economic and Social Sciences.
C: Agriculture (Gyöngyös, Mezötúr, Nyíregháza).
I: Environmental Management and Landscape Planning; Agricultural Teacher Training; Foreign Languages; Scientific Education; Manager Training and Business (Budapest); Agricultural Research (Kompolt).

Pannon University of Agriculture Keszthely
[Pannon Agrártudományi Egyetem]
Deák Ferenc út 16, 8360 Keszthely
Tel: +36(83) 312-257
Fax: +36(83) 3198-105
Rector: László Várnagy
Founded: 1797, 1970
F: Agriculture (Georgikon); Agricultural Sciences (Mosonmagyaróvár); Animal Science (Kaposvár).

*University of Miskolc
[Miskolci Egyetem]
3515 Miskolc-Egyetemváros
Tel: +36(46) 365-111
Fax: +36(46) 312-862
E-Mail: rekto@gp;d.uni-miskolc.hu
Telex: 62223 nmemis h
Rector (Acting): Ottó Farkas
Founded: 1735, 1990
F: Mining Engineering; Metallurgical Engineering; Mechanical Engineering; Law and Political Sciences; Metallurgical Technology (Dunaujváros); Economics.
I: Humanities.

Janus Pannonius University Pécs
[Janus Pannonius Tudományegyetem Pécs]
Szántó Kovács János u. 1/b, 7633 Pécs
Tel: +36(72) 310-581
Fax: +36(72) 310-527
Rector: Károly Barakonyi
Founded: 1921, 1982
F: Law and Political Science; Economics and Business; Humanities; Sciences.

Pécs University of Medicine
[Pécsi Orvostudományi Egyetem]
Szigeti-út 12, 7624 Pécs
Tel: +36(72) 314-086
Fax: +36(72) 326-244
Telex: 12311 pote h
Rektor: Gábor Kelényi
Chief-Secretary: Ernö Antal
Founded: 1923, 1951
Medicine; Dentistry.

University of Forestry and Wood Sciences Sopron
[Erdészeti és Faipari Egyetem]
Bajcsy-Zsilinszky út 4, 9400 Sopron
Tel: +36(99) 311-100
Fax: +36(99) 311-103
E-Mail: h9898efe@ella. hu
Telex: 249126
Rector: András Winkler
Founded: 1808, 1962
F: Forestry; Wood Technology Engineering; Surveying and Country Planning (Székesfehérvár).
C: Paper Industry and Wood Technology.

Albert Szent-Györgyi Medical University Szeged
[Szent-Györgyi Albert Orvostudományi Egyetem]
Dugonics tér 13, 6722 Szeged
Tel: +36(62) 312-729
Fax: +36(62) 312-729
E-Mail: patak@recof.szote.u-szeged.hu
Telex: 82-441
Rektor: Loránd L. Fráter
Founded: 1872, 1921, 1951
F: Medicine; Pharmacy.
C: Health Sciences.
I: Social Sciences; Foreign Languages.
Ce: Medical Education; Computing.

Attila József University Szeged
[József Attila Tudományegyetem]
Dugonics tér 13, 6701 Szeged
Tel: +36(62) 324-022
Fax: +36(62) 310-412
E-Mail: hlo52rek@ella.hu
Telex: 82 4ol jate h
Rektor: János Csirik
Secretary-General: István Monok
Founded: 1921, 1940, 1945, 1962
F: Law; Arts; Science.
L: Cybernetics.
Ce: Language.

University of Veszprém
[Veszprémi Egyetem]
Egyetem út 10, 8201 Veszprém
Tel: +36(88) 422-617
Fax: (88) 426-016
Telex: 32397
Cable: egyetem veszprém
Rector: János Liszi (1992-95)
Secretary-General: Lakatos Lászlóné
Founded: 1949, 1951
F: Engineering; Teacher Training.

OTHER INSTITUTIONS

PUBLIC INSTITUTIONS

Apáczai Csere János Tanítóképzô Fôiskola Győr
Liszt Ferenc út 42, 9022 Győr
Tel: +36(96) 329-934
Director-General: Sándor Cseh
Teacher Training (primary level).

Bánki Donát Gépipari műszaki Fôiskola Budapest
Népszínház utca 8, 1081 Budapest
Tel: +36(1) 134-3925
Fax: +36(1) 133-6761
Director-General: Imre Czinege
Engineering; Teacher Training (Technical).

Bárczi Gusztáv Gyógypedagógiai Tanárképző Fôiskola Budapest
Bethlen tér 2, 1071 Budapest
Tel: +36(1) 142-1379
Fax: +36(1) 122-6447
E-Mail: h-50981ll@ellahu
Director-General: Sándor Illyés
Special Education.

Berzsenyi Dániel Tanárképzô Fôiskola Szombatheli
Károlyi Gáspár tér 4, 9701 Szombathely
Tel: +36(94) 329-911
Fax: +36(94) 312-248
E-Mail: h 2892pus@ella.hu
Director-General: János Pusztay
Teacher Training.

Bessenyei György Tanárképző Fôiskola Nyíreghyháza
Sóstói út 31/b, 4401 Nyíregyháza
Tel: +36(42) 341-202
Fax: +36(42) 341-202
E-Mail: h6534 foi ella.hu
Director-General: Gábor Székely
Teacher Training.

Budapesti Tanítóképző Fôiskola
Kiss János altábornagy út 40, 1126 Budapest
Tel: +36(1) 156-3482
Fax: +36(1) 202-38
Director-General: Géza Nagyszentpéteri
Teacher Training (primary level).

Comenius Tanítóképző Fôiskola Sárospatak
Eötvös út 7, 3950 Sárospatak
Tel: +36(74) 324-211
Fax: +36(74) 324-329
Director-General: Sándor Komáromy
Primary Teacher Training.

Eötvös József Tanítóképzô Fôiskola Baja
Szegedi út 2, 6500 Baja
Tel: +36(79) 321-655
Fax: +36(79) 321-819
E-Mail: ella 8675
Director-General: Klára Fátrai
Teacher Training (primary level).

Eszterházi Károly Tanárképzô Fôiskola Eger
Szabadság tér 2, 3301 Eger
Tel: +36(36) 410-975
Fax: +36(36) 410-119
E-Mail: dr.sandor orban h2331 orb.@ella.hu
Director-General: Sándor Orbán
Teacher Training.

Gépipari és Automatizálási műszaki FôiskolaKecskemét
Izsáki út 10, 6001 Kecskemét
Tel: +36(76) 481-291
Fax: +36(76) 481-304
Director-General: László Madarász
Mechanical Engineering and Automation.

Hajdúböszörményi Óvóképző Fôiskola
Désány I. u. 7-9, 4220 Hajdúböszörmény
Tel: +36(55) 371-433
Fax: +36(55) 371-559
Pre-School Teacher Training.

Illyés Gyula Pedagógiai Fôiskola Szedszárd
Rákóczi út 1, 7100 Szekszárd
Tel: +36(74) 312-133
Fax: +36(74) 311-679
Director-General: János Gergely
Pedagogy.

Juhász Gyula Tanárképzô Fôiskola Szeged
Aprilis 4-e út 6, 6725 Szeged
Tel: +36(62) 310-495
Fax: +36(74) 311-679
Director-General: István Szalay
Teacher Training.

Kandó Kálmán Villamosipari Mûszaki Fôiskola Budapest
Tavaszmező utca 15-17, 1084 Budapest
Tel: +36(1) 210-1442
Fax: +36(1) 134-2132
Director-General: Péter Keresztes
Engineering; Business Management; Electrical Engineering Teaching.

Kecskeméti Tanítóképző Fôiskola Kecskmét
Kaszap utca 6-14, 6000 Kecskemét
Tel: +36(76) 321-444
Fax: +36(76) 483-282
Director-General: Márta Dovala
Primary Teacher Training.

Kereskedelmi és Gazdasági Föiskola Szolnok
Ady E. u. 9, 5000 Szolnok
Tel: +36(56) 379-677
Fax: +36(56) 426-719
Director-General: István Molnár
Commerce and Economics.

Kereskedelmi és Vendéglátóipari Föiskola Budapest
Alkotmány u. 9-11, 1054 Budapest
Tel: +36(1) 1327150
Fax: +36(1) 132-6164
Telex: 20-2522
Director-General: Lásló Csismadia
Commerce, Catering and Tourism.

Könnyüipari Müszaki Föiskola Budapest
Doberdó út 6, 1034 Budapest
Tel: +36(1) 250-0333
Fax: +36(1) 188-6763
Director-General: József Erdélyi
Light Industry.

Külkereskedelmi Föiskola Budapest
Ecseri út 3, 1097 Budapest
Tel: +36(1) 157-2683
Fax: +36(1) 157-5243
Director-General: Károly Iványi
Foreign Trade.

Magyar Táncmüvészeti Föiskola Budapest
Andrássy út 25, 1061 Budapest VI
Tel: +36(1) 267-8646
Fax: +36(1) 268-0828
Director-General: Jeni Gál
Founded: 1950, 1983
Dance.

Pénzügyi és Számviteli Föiskola Budapest
Buzogány u. 10-12, 1149 Budapest
Tel: +36(1) 163-1855
Fax: +36(1) 183-4799
E-Mail: h8662 laz@ella.hu
Director-General: József Roóz
Finance and Accountancy.

Pollack Mihály müszaki Föiskola Pécs
Boszorkány u. 2, 7624 Pécs
Tel: +36(72) 314-682
Director-General: István Kistelegdi
Technology.

Széchényi István Föiskola Györ
Hédervári u. 3, 9026 Györ
Tel: +36(96) 429-722
Fax: +36(96) 329-263
Director-General: Tamás Szekeres
Engineering; Busines Management.
echnical Teaching.

Tanítóképzö Föiskola Jászberény
Rákóczi út 53, 5102 Jászberény
Tel: +36(57) 312-155
Fax: +36(57) 311-551
Director-General: József Nagy
Primary Teacher Training; Cultural Management Training; Library Science.

Ybl Miklós Müszaki Föiskola Budapest
Thökököly út 74, 1146 Budapest
Tel: +36(1) 142-6315
Fax: +36(1) 122-9602
Director-General: Lajos Pozsgai
Engineering; Business Management; Teacher Training (Technical).

PRIVATE INSTITUTIONS

Gábor Dénes müszaki Informatkai Föiskola Budapest
Hévizi út 6/E, Budapest
Tel: +36(1) 188-8350f+36(1) 250-1222
Director-General: Magda Kovács
Technical Informatics.

Modern Üzleti Tudományok Föiskola Tatabánya
Stúdium tér, Tatabánya
Tel: +36(34) 310-142
Fax: +36(34) 310-142
Director-General: József Kandikó
Modern Business Studies.

Mozgássérültek Petö András Nevelöképzö és Nevelöintézte Budapest
Kútvölgyi út 6, 1125 Budapest
Tel: +36(1) 201-4533
Fax: +36(1) 155-6649
Director-General: Mrs. Gy. Kozma
Motor Disabilities; Physiotherapy.

NATIONAL ACADEMIC BODIES

Ministry of Education and Culture
Szalay út 10-14, 1055 Budapest
Tel: +36(1) 269-3171
Fax: +36(1) 132-1932
Minister: Ferenc Mádl

Coordination Office for Higher Education
The House of Professors, Atjósi Dürer sor 19-21, 1146 Budapest
Tel: +36(1) 153-4261
Fax: +36(1) 142-8157
General Director: Tibor Gyula Nagy

Hungarian Accreditation Committee
The House of Professors, Atjósi Dürer sor 19-21, 1146 Budapest
Tel: +36(1) 251-3479
Fax: +36(1) 142-8157
E-Mail: rozsnyai@fki.huninet.hu
International Relations: Christina Rozsnyai
Founded: 1993

Hungarian Rectors' Conference
Atósi Dürer sor 19-21, 1146 Budapest
President: József Hŕnori

Hungarian National Commission for Unesco
Ministry of Culture and Education, Szalay út 10-
14, 1363 Budapest
Tel: +36(1) 1313-526
Fax: +36(1) 1313-536
Telex: 225-935
Cable: hungarounesco budapest
Chairman: Béla Köpeczi
Secretary-General: Karoly Ginter

ICELAND

UNIVERSITIES

University of Akureyri
[Háskólinn á Akureyri]
Thingvallastraeti, 600 Akureyri
Tel: +354(6) 30900
Fax: +354(6) 30999
E-Mail: ha@ismennt.is
Rector: Thorsteinn Gunnarsson (1994-99)
Executive Director: Olafur Búi Gunnlaugsson
Founded: 1987
*F: Economics; Nursing; Education; Fisheries
Studies.*

Agricultural College, Hvanneyri
[Baendaskólinn á Hvanneyri]
Hvanneyri,311 Borgarnes
Tel: +354(93) 700-00
Fax: +354(93) 700-48
Rector: Magnús B. Jonsson
Founded: 1947
Agriculture.

Technical College of Iceland
[Taekniskóli Íslands]
Höfdabakka 9, 112 Reykjavík
Tel: +354(1) 814-933
Fax: +354(1) 673-260
Rector: Gudbrandur Steinthorsson
Founded: 1964
*D: Electrical Engineering; Mechanical
Engineering; Construction; Management; Medical
Technology.*

*University of Iceland
[Háskóli Íslands]
1101 Reykjavik
Tel: +354(1) 694-300
Fax: +354(1) 213-31
E-Mail: thordkri@rhi.hi.is
Telex: 2307
Rektor: Sveinbjörn Björnsson (1991-97)
Director, Academic Affairs: Thórdur Kristinsson
International Relations: Thóra Magnúsdóttir
Founded: 1911
*F: Theology; Medicine; Law; Economics;
Philosophy; Engineering; Science; Dentistry;
Social Sciences; Nursing; Physiotherapy.*

University College of Education, Iceland
[Kennaraháskóli Íslands]
Stakkahlíd, 105 Reykjavík
Tel: +354(1) 633-800
Fax: +354(1) 633-833
E-Mail: thorir@ismbnnt.is
Rector: Thorir Olafsson (1991-95)
Dean of Academic Affairs: Erla Kristjansdottir
Founded: 1908, 1971
Education and Teacher Training.

NATIONAL ACADEMIC BODIES

Ministry of Culture and Education
[Menntamáláraduneytid]
Sölvhólsgötu 4, 150 Reykjavík
Tel: +354(1) 609-500
Fax: +354(1) 623-068
E-Mail: rø2krist@ismennt.is
Minister: Olafur G. Einarsson (1991-95)
Secretary-General: Gudridur Sigurdardottir
Founded: 1947

Icelandic National Commission for Unesco
Ministry of Culture and Education, Sölvhólsgötu
4, 150 Reykjavík
Tel: +354(1) 609-500
Fax: +354(1) 623-068
E-Mail: rø2.gudny@ismennt.is
Telex: 2111 iskult is
Chairman: Stefán Stefánsson
Secretary-General: Gudny Helgadóttir
Founded: 1964

INDIA

UNIVERSITIES AND TECHNICAL UNIVERSITIES

Agra University
Paliwal Park, Agra, Uttar Pradesh 282004
Tel: +91(562) 64164
Cable: agra university, agra, uttar pradesh
Vice-Chancellor: S.S. Gupta
Registrar: C.P. Srivastava
Founded: 1927
*F: Arts; Commerce; Education; Fine Arts; Home
Science; Homeopathic Medicine; Law; Medicine;
Science.
I: Basic Sciences; Home Science; Social
Sciences; Hindi Studies and Linguistics.*

**University of Agricultural Sciences,
Bangalore**
Hebbal, Bangalore, Karnataka 560065
Tel: +91(80) 330984
Telex: 8458393 uask in
Cable: univagris, bangalore
Vice-Chancellor: K.V. Devaraj
Registrar: H.R. Reddy
Founded: 1964
*F: Agriculture; Animal and Veterinary Sciences;
Basic Sciences and Humanities.*

University of Agricultural Sciences, Dharwad
Krishinagar, Dharwad, Karnataka 580005
Tel: +91(836) 42521
Telex: 865244 agcdin
Cable: univagris, dharwad
Vice-Chancellor: P. Vittal Rai
Registrar: S.S. Pathanashetti
Founded: 1986
F: Agriculture; Animal Sciences.

Alagappa University
Alagappapuram, Alagappa Nagar, Karaikudi,
Tamil Nadu 623004
Tel: +91(4565) 2039
Vice-Chancellor: K. Nagappan
Registrar: K. Jayaraman
Founded: 1985
*F: Arts; Commerce; Corporate Secretaryship;
Education; Physical Education; Science.*

*Aligarh Muslim University, Aligarh
Aligarh, Uttar Pradesh 202002
Tel: +91(571) 400220
Telex: 564-230 amu in
Cable: muslim university, aligarh, u.p.
Vice-Chancellor: M.N. Faruqui
Registrar: A.K. Kazi
Founded: 1920
*F: Arts; Commerce; Engineering and
Technology; Law; Life Sciences; Medicine; Unani
Medicine; Science; Social Sciences; Theology.
C: Women's; J.N. Medical; Engineering and
Technology (Z.H.).
I: Petroleum Studies.
Ce: Advanced Study; West Asian Studies.
University Polytechnic.
Women's Polytechnic.*

University of Allahabad
Allahabad, Uttar Pradesh 211002
Tel: +91(532) 608157
Cable: university, allahabad
Vice-Chancellor: U.N. Gupta
Registrar: R.P. Singh
Founded: 1887, 1922
*F: Arts; Commerce; Engineering; Law;
Medicine; Science.*

*All India Institute of Medical Sciences
Ansari Nagar, New Delhi 110029
Tel: +91(11) 862663
Telex: 3173042-aims in
Cable: medinst new delhi
Director: S.K. Kacker
Registrar: R.K. Puri
Founded: 1956
Medical Sciences; Nursing.

Amravati University
Amravati University Campus, P.B., Amravati,
Mahrashtra 444602
Tel: +91(721) 62373
Fax: +91(891) 55547
Telex: 0721-227-amv in
Cable: amuni, amravati
Vice-Chancellor: G.V. Patil
Registrar: K.G. Khamare
Founded: 1983
*F: Arts; Ayurvedic Medicine; Commerce;
Education; Engineering; Home Sciences; Law;
Medicine; Science; Social Sciences.*

Andhra University
Waltair, Visakhapatnam, Andhra Pradesh 530003
Tel: +91(891) 54871
Cable: university,visakhapatnam
Vice-Chancellor: M. Gopalakrishna
Registrar: P.V.S. Rama Rao
Founded: 1926
*C: Arts and Commerce; Engineering; Law;
Science and Technology.*

Andhra Pradesh Agricultural University
Rajendranagar, Hyderabad, Andhra Pradesh
500030
Tel: +91(842) 245161
Telex: 0425-6939 apau in
Cable: agriversity,hyderabad
Vice-Chancellor: M.V. Rao
Registrar: Bhaskara Prasad
Founded: 1964
*F: Agriculture; Home Science; Postgraduate
Studies; Veterinary Science.
C: Agricultural (Aswaraopet); Agricultural
(Bapatla); Agricultural (Naira); Agriculture
(Rajendranagar); Home Science (Bapatla); Home
Science (Hyderabad); Veterinary Science
(Rajendranagar); Veterinary Science (Tirupati);
C.V. Agriculture (Tirupati).*

Anna University
Sardar Patel Road, Guindy, Madras, Tamil Nadu
600 025
Tel: +91(44) 235-1445
Telex: 041-21077 annu in
Cable: annatech, madras
Vice-Chancellor: M. Anandakrishnan
Registrar: G. Ramaryan
Founded: 1978, 1982
*F: Applied Engineering; Architecture and
Regional Planning; Engineering; Science and
Humanities; Technology.
S: Computer Science and Engineering;
Electrical and Electronics Engineering;
Electronics and Communication Engineering;
Instrumentation and Electronics Engineering.
Ce: Biotechnology; Environmental Studies;
Ramanujan Computing; Water Resources; Crystal
Growth; Ocean Data; New and Renewable
Sources of Energy.*

Annamalai University

Annamalainagar P.O., Tamil Nadu 608002
Tel: +91(4144) 22249
Telex: 4602-201 auin
Cable: university, annamalainagar
Vice-Chancellor: M.G. Muthukumarasamy
Registrar: P.R. Karpagaganapathy
Founded: 1928
F: Agriculture; Arts; Dentistry; Education; Engineering and Technology; Fine Arts; Indian Languages; Medicine; Science.

Arunachal University

Doimukh P.O., Itanagar, Arunachal Pradesh 791111
Tel: +91(3781) 1253
Cable: arunversity, itanagar
Vice-Chancellor: A.C. bhagbati
Registrar: Joram Begi
Founded: 1984
F: Commerce; Education; Environmental Sciences; Languages; Life Sciences; Physical Sciences; Social Sciences.

Assam University

Regional Engineering College Campus, Siechar, Assam 788010
Tel: +91 22611
Vice-Chancellor: J.B. Bhattacharjee

Assam Agricultural University

Jorhat, Assam 785013
Tel: +91(376) 20965
Fax: +91(37) 320919
Telex: 206 aau in
Cable: agrivarsity, jorhat
Vice-Chancellor: U.C. Upadhyay (1992-)
Registrar: M.C. Sharma
Founded: 1969
F: Agriculture; Home Science; Veterinary Sciences.

Avadh University

Avadh University Campus, Faizabad, Uttar Pradesh 224001
Tel: +91(5272) 2135
Cable: university, faizabad, u.p.
Vice-Chancellor: K.P. Nautiyal
Registrar: A.N. Seth
Founded: 1975
F: Arts; Commerce; Education; Engineering and Technology; Law; Science.
D: Mathematics and Statistics; Solid State Physics and Electronics; Economics and Rural Development; History, Culture and Archaeology.

Avinashilingam Institute for Home Science and Higher Education for Women

Coimbatore, Tamil Nadu 641043
Tel: +91(422) 41786
Telex: 855-459-adu-in
Cable: saradalaya, coimbatore
Vice-Chancellor: Rajammal P. Devadas
Registrar: Saroja Prabhakaran
Founded: 1957, 1988

F: Education; Home Science; Humanities; Science.

Awadhesh Pratap Singh University

[Awadhesh Pratap Singh Vishwavidyalaya]
Rewa, Madhya Pradesh 486003
Tel: +91(7662) 22277
Fax: +91(7662) 22175
Cable: university, rewa
Vice-Chancellor: J.S. Rathore
Registrar: M.P. Agnihotri
Founded: 1968
F: Arts; Commerce; Education; Engineering; Home Science and Social Sciences; Life Sciences; Medicine; Science.

B.N. Mandal University

Madhepura, Bihar 852113
Vice-Chancellor: Ram Badan Yadav
Registrar: Abdus Sami

*Banaras Hindu University

Varanasi, Uttar Pradesh 221005
Tel: +91(542) 331852
Fax: +91(542) 312059
Telex: 0545-304 bhu in
Cable: hindu university, varanasi
Vice-Chancellor: D.N. Mishra
Registrar: R.C.P. Sinha
Founded: 1915
F: Agriculture; Arts; Ayurveda; Commerce; Education; Engineering and Technology; Law; Management Studies; Medicine; Performing Arts; Sanskrit Vidya Dharm Vigyan; Science; Social Sciences; Visual Arts.

Banasthali University

[Banasthali Vidyapith]
P.O. Banasthali Vidyapith, Rajasthan 304022
Tel: +91(1438) 8341
Fax: +91(1438) 8365
Cable: banasthali vidyapith, rajasthan
President: Sushila Vyas
Secretary: Diwakar Shastri
Founded: 1935, 1943, 1983
F: Education; Fine Arts; Home Science; Humanities; Science; Social Sciences.

Bangalore University

Jnana Bharathi, Bangalore, Karnataka State 560056
Tel: +91(80) 3303023
Fax: +91(80) 355295
Cable: unibangalore, bangalore
Vice-Chancellor: N.R. Shetty
Registrar: A.M. Pathan
Founded: 1964
F: Arts; Commerce; Communication; Education; Engineering; Law; Medicine; Mental Health and Neurosciences; Oncology; Science; Technology.

Barkatullah University
[Barkatullah Vishwavidyalaya]
Hoshangabad Road, Bhopal, Madhya Pradesh
462006
Tel: +91(755) 547103
Cable: university bhopal
Vice-Chancellor: K.C. Nair
Registrar: D.S. Dakwall
Founded: 1970, 1988
F: Arts; Commerce; Education; Engineering;
Home Science; Law; Life Sciences; Medicine;
Science; Social Sciences; Technical Education.

Bengal Engineering College
P.O. Botanic Garden, Howrah, West Bengal
711103
Tel: +91(33) 6604561
Director: B. Sen

Maharaja Sayajirao University of Baroda
Vadodara, Gujarat 390002
Tel: +91(272) 329338
Fax: +91(265) 329283
Telex: 0175 678 mus in
Cable: universiti, vadodara
Vice-Chancellor: Suresh Dalal (1993-)
Registrar: D.P. Chayya
Founded: 1949
F: Arts; Science; Commerce; Education and
Psychology; Medicine; Technology and
Engineering; Fine Arts; Home Science; Social
Work; Law; Management Studies; Performing
Arts.

Berhampur University
Bhanja Bihar,District Ganjam, Orissa 760007
Tel: +91(6872) 2122
Telex: 0673-262-buni-in
Cable: berhampur university, berhampur,
dist.ganjam
Vice-Chancellor: R.C. Das
Registrar: R.N. Mishra
Founded: 1966
D: Botany; Business Administration; Chemistry;
Commerce; Computer Science; Economics;
English; History; Home Science; Industrial
Relations and Personnel Mannagement;
Journalism and Mass Communication; Law;
Linguistics; Marine Science; Mathematics; Oriya;
Physics; Political Science; Zoology.

Tilak Manjhi Bhagalpur University
Bhagalpur, Bihar 812007
Tel: +91(641) 22153
Cable: university, bhagalpur, bihar
Vice-Chancellor: Sunil Saran
Registrar: V.S. Yadav
Founded: 1960
F: Arts; Social Sciences; Commerce; Education;
Engineering; Law; Medicine; Science.

Bharathiar University
Coimbatore, Tamil Nadu 641046
Tel: +91(422) 42222
Telex: 855-488 unib in
Cable: unibharathiar, coimbatore
Vice-Chancellor: K.M. Marimuthu
Registrar: S.P. Viswanathan
Founded: 1982
F: Arts; Sciences; Social Sciences.
S: Management and Entrepreneurial
Development.
D: Economics; Linguistics; Tamil; Psychology;
Sociology; Population Studies; Commerce;
Educational Technology; Mathematics; Physics;
Chemistry; Botany; Zoology; Statistics; Computer
Science; Environmental Science; Biotechnology;
Physical Education; Distance Education.

Bharathidasan University
Palkalaiperur, Tiruchirapalli, Tamil Nadu 620024
Tel: +91(431) 896271
Telex: 0455-253 bard-in
Cable: bard, tiruchirapalli
Vice-Chancellor: V.R. Muthukkaruppan (1994-)
Registrar: C. Thangamuthu
Founded: 1982
F: Arts; Science; Education; Indian and Other
Languages; Energy.
I: Irrigation Management Training;
Management.
Ce: for Adult Continuing and Extension
Education.

Bhavnagar University
Gaurishanker Lake Road, Bhavnagar, Gujarat
364002
Tel: +91(278) 20006
Cable: university,bhavnagan
Vice-Chancellor: J.K. Bhatt
Registrar: D.A. Vaishnav
Founded: 1978
F: Arts; Commerce; Education; Engineering;
Law; Rural Studies; Science.

Bhoj Open University
Old Confidential Building, Barkatullah University,
Bhopal, Madhya Pradesh 462026
Tel: +91(755) 587236
Vice-Chancellor: K.C. Nair
Registrar: S.K. Dey

Bidhan Chandra Agricultural University
[Bidhan Chandra Krishi Viswavidyalaya]
Mohanpur, Nadia, West Bengal 741252
Tel: haringhata H54
Cable: krishibidhan, haringnghata
Vice-Chancellor: D.K. Dasgupta
Registrar: A.K. Banerjee
Founded: 1974
Agriculture; Veterinary and Animal Sciences.

Baba Sahab Bhim Rao Ambedkar Bihar University
Muzaffarpur, Bihar 842001
Tel: +91(621) 243071
Cable: bihvarsity, mazaffarpur
Vice-Chancellor: A.K. Biswarto
Registrar: M. Jha
Founded: 1952
F: Arts; Commerce; Education; Engineering; Law; Medicine; Science; Social Science.

Birla Institute of Technology
Mesra, Ranchi, Bihar 835215
Tel: (651) 301565
Fax: +91(651) 306303
Cable: technology, ranchi
Director: S. Venkateswaran
Registrar: G. Sahay
Founded: 1955, 1972, 1986
D: Mechanical Engineering; Electrical and Electronics Engineering; Civil Engineering; Electronics and Communication Engineering; Production Engineering; Computer Engineering; Pharmaceutical Science; Space Engineering and Rocketry; Business Administration.
Ce: Microprocessor Research; Rocketry Research; Plasma Research.
Science and Technology Entrepreneurs' Park (BIT).

*Birla Institute of Technology and Science
District Jhunjhunu, Pilani, Rajasthan 333031
Tel: +91(1596) 42090
Fax: +91(1596) 42123
E-Mail: bits@sirnetd.ernet.in
Cable: bits, pilani
Director: S. Venkateswaran
Registrar: J.L. Arora
Founded: 1964
F: Humanities; Social Sciences; Science and Technology.

Birsa Agricultural University
Kanke, Ranchi, Bihar 834006
Tel: +91(651) 73500
Cable: agriversity ranchi
Vice-Chancellor: R. Kerketta
Registrar: C.S.P. Singh
Founded: 1981
F: Agriculture; Forestry; Veterinary Science and Animal Husbandry.

University of Bombay
University Road, Fort, Bombay, Maharashtra State 400032
Tel: +91(22) 273623
Fax: +91(22) 2652832
Cable: bombay university, bombay 32
Vice-Chancellor: S.D. Karnik
Registrar: Jairam D. Chavan
Founded: 1857, 1904, 1928, 1953
F: Arts; Ayurvedic Medicine; Commerce; Dentistry; Fine Arts; Law; Medicine; Science; Technology.

Bundelkhand University
Jhansi, Uttar Pradesh 284129
Tel: +91 8321
Telex: 341198
Cable: university, jhansi
Vice-Chancellor: Kalyan Singh
Registrar: O.P. Srivastava
Founded: 1975
F: Arts; Science; Commmerce; Education; Agriculture; Law; Medicine.

University of Burdwan
Rajbati, Burdwan, West Bengal 713104
Tel: +91(341) 3238
Telex: 2001-203-buwb-in
Cable: burdsity, burdwan
Vice-Chancellor: M. Bhattacharyya
Registrar: M.K. Chatterjee
Founded: 1960
F: Arts; Engineering and Technology; Science.

University of Calcutta
College Street, Calcutta, West Bengal 700073
Tel: +91(33) 380071
Telex: 021-2752-univ-in
Cable: university calcutta
Vice-Chancellor: R.N. Basu
Registrar: T.K. Mukherjee
Founded: 1857
F: Agriculture and Veterinary Science; Arts; Commerce; Education, Journalism and Library Science; Engineering and Technology; Fine Arts, Music and Home Science; Law; Medicine; Science.

University of Calicut
P.O. Calicut University, Calicut, Kerala 673635
Tel: +91(495) 440044
Telex: 0804-243 unic-in
Cable: unical, calicut
Vice-Chancellor: A.N.P. Ummerkutty
Registrar: T.K. Ummer
Founded: 1968
F: Ayurveda; Commerce; Education; Engineering; Fine Arts; Homeopathy; Humanities; Journalism; Languages; Law; Medicine; Science; Dentistry.

Central Agricultural University
Iroisenba, Imphal, Manibur
Vice-Chancellor: M.P. Singh
Registrar: O.P. Bhatnagar
Agriculture.

Central Institute of English and Foreign Languages
Hyderabad, Andhra Pradesh 500007
Tel: +91(842) 868131
Fax: +91(40) 868225
Telex: 425-7089 cef in
Cable: english hyderabad
Director: S.K. Verma
Registrar: G. Venkateshwer Rao
Founded: 1958, 1972, 1973
English; Foreign Languages.

Central Institute of Higher Tibetan Studies
Sarnath, Varanasi, Uttar Pradesh 221007
Tel: +91(542) 385148
Telex: 545-332 ihts in
Director: S. Rinpoche
Registrar: K.P. Singh
Founded: 1967, 1988
F: Adhunik Vidya; Hetu Avam Adhyatma Vidya; Shabda Vidya.

Central Institute of Fisheries Education
P.B. 7392, Jaiprakash Road, Seven Bungalows, Versova, Bombay, Maharashtra 400061
Tel: +91(22) 6261-4446
Telex: 011-7821
Cable: fishinst, bombay
Director: S.D. Tripathi
Registrar: S.L. Dua
Founded: 1961
Fisheries.

Chandra Shekhar Azad University of Agriculture and Technology
Nawabanj, Kanpur, Uttar Pradesh 208002
Tel: +91(512) 294661
Fax: +91(512) 210408
Cable: agrivarsity, kanpur
Vice-Chancellor: P.S. Yadav
Registrar: D.C. Kulshrestha
Founded: 1975
Agriculture; Veterinary Science and Animal Husbandry.
D: Home Science.

Chaudhary Charan Singh Haryana Agricultural University
Hisar, Haryana 125004
Tel: +91(1662) 273720
Fax: +91(1662) 73552
Telex: 345-216-hau-in
Cable: agrivarsity, hisar
Vice-Chancellor: Sarvadanand Arya
Registrar: S.N. Roy
Founded: 1970
C: Agriculture; Animal Sciences; Basic Sciences and Humanities; Home Science; Sports; Veterinary Sciences.

Chaudhary Charan Singh Meerut University
Meerut, Uttar Pradesh 250005
Tel: +91(12) 75454
Cable: universityn leeryt
Vice-Chancellor: Ravindra Kuman
Registrar: Har Prakash
Founded: 1965
F: Agriculture; Arts; Commerce; Education; Law; Medicine; Science.

Chitrakut Gramoday University
[Chitrakut Gramoday Vishwavidyalay]
Chitrakut, Satna, Madhya Pradesh 210204
Tel: +91(7672) 411
Vice-Chancellor: R.N. Kapoor
Registrar: S.P. Tewari
Founded: 1991

Cochin University of Science and Technology
Cochin University P.O., Cochin, Kerala 682022
Tel: +91(484) 855619
Fax: +91(484) 856595
Telex: 885-5019 cu in
Cable: unicochin, kochi 22
Vice-Chancellor: S. Balaraman
Registrar: S.M.M. Mohamed
Founded: 1971, 1986
F: Engineering; Environmental Studies; Humanities; Law; Marine Sciences; Science; Social Sciences; Technology.

Dayalbagh Educational Institute
P.O. Dayalbagh, Agra, Uttar Pradesh 282005
Tel: +91(562) 50959
Cable: dayalinst, agra
Director: P.S. Satsangi
Registrar: R.M.M. Singh
Founded: 1981
F: Arts; Commerce; Education; Engineering; Science.

Deccan College Postgraduate and Research Institute
Pune, Maharashtra 411006
Tel: +91(212) 660113
Fax: +91(212) 660104
Cable: deccolinst, pume
Director: V.N. Misra
Registar: S.T. Bhane
Founded: 1921, 1852, 1939, 1990
D: Linguistics; Archaeology.

*University of Delhi
Delhi 110007
Tel: +91(11) 2521521
Fax: +91(11) 6886427
Telex: 3178099 duin
Cable: university, delhi, india
Vice-Chancellor: Upendra Baxi
Registrar: S.K. Wasan
Founded: 1922
F: Applied Sciences and Humanities; Arts; Ayurvedic and Unani Medicine; Education; Interdisciplinary and Applied Sciences; Law; Management Studies; Mathematics; Medical Science; Music and Fine Arts; Science; Social Sciences; Technology.

Devi Ahilya University
[Devi Ahilya Vishwavidyalaya]
University House, Indore, Madhya Pradesh 452001
Tel: +91(731) 433352
Fax: +91(731) 433615
Telex: 0735-261-davv-in
Cable: university, indore
Vice-Chancellor: S.S. Chandel
Registrar: C.P. Modi
Founded: 1964, 1983

F: *Arts; Ayurvedic Studies; Commerce;*
Dentistry; Education; Engineering; Engineering
Sciences; Life Sciences/Home Science;
Management Studies; Medicine; Pharmacy;
Science; Social Sciences and Law.

Dibrugarh University
Dibrugarh, Assam 786004
Tel: +91(373) 70239
Cable: university, dibrugarh
Vice-Chancellor: M.M. Sharma
Registrar: B.C. Saikia
Founded: 1965
F: *Arts; Commerce; Medicine; Science and*
Technology.

Doctor Babasahib Ambedkar Marathwada University
Aurangabad, Maharashtra 431004
Tel: +91(2432) 31069
Cable: marathsity, aurangabad (deccan)
Vice-Chancellor: G.B. Shindi
Registrar: B.R. Arbad
Founded: 1958
F: *Arts; Ayurveda; Commerce; Education;*
Engineering; Law; Medicine; Science; Social
Sciences; Fine Arts; Homeopathy; Management
Science; Physical Education.

Dr. B.R. Ambedkar Open University, Hyderabad
6-3-645 Somajiguda, Hyderabad, Andhra Pradesh
500482
Tel: +91(40) 210197
Cable: opvarsity, hyderabad
Vice-Chancellor: S. Bashiruddin
Registrar: M. Satyanarayana Rao
Founded: 1982
F: *Arts; Commerce; Science; Social Sciences.*

Doctor Babasahib Amdedkar Technological University
Leonere District, Raigarh, Maharashtra 402103
Tel: +91(7762) 381
Cable: technology kolaba
Vice-Chancellor: V.R. Deshparde
Registrar: D.P. Mishra
Engineering; Technology.

Doctor Bhimrao Ambedkar University
1/16 Viram Khand, Gomti Nagar, Lucknow, Uttar
Pradesh 226016
Tel: +91(522) 392591

Doctor Harisingh Gour University Sagar
[Doctor Harisingh Gour Vishwavidyalaya Sagar]
Gour Nagar, Sagar, Madhya Pradesh 470003
Tel: +91(7582) 0143
Cable: university, sagar
Vice-Chancellor: R.N. Tripathi
Registrar (Administration): Krishnajee Tiwari
Founded: 1946, 1983
F: *Arts; Ayurved; Commerce; Education;*
Engineering; Law; Life Sciences; Science; Social
Sciences; Technology; Management Studies.

Doctor Yashwant Singh Parmar University of Horticulture and Forestry
Oachghat, Solan, Himachal Pradesh Nauni
173230
Tel: +91(1792) 219
Fax: +91(1792) 2888
Cable: vanudyan, solan
Vice-Chancellor: B.R. Sharma (1991-)
Registrar: J.K. Nadda
Founded: 1985
F: *Horticulture.*
C: *Forestry.*
D: *Extension Education; Research.*
Ce: *Computer Science and Instrumentation.*
Station: *Seed Production; Regional Horticultural*
Research (Jachh, Sharbo, Bajaura, Dhaulakuar,
Kandaghat, Tabo, Nagrota Bhagwan, Seobagh,
Manala); Temperate Horticulture Research
(Kotkhai).

Forest Research Institute
Dehra Dan, Uttar Pradesh 248006
Tel: +91 25277
Cable: vanudyan
Vice-Chancellor: N.K. Joshi
Registrar: Rajive Kumar
Forestry (Research).

Gandhigram Rural Institute
Gandhigram, Indigul Anna District, Tamil Nadu
624302
Tel: +91(4557) 323
Fax: +91(4537) 2323
Cable: gramvarsity, gandhigram
Vice-Chancellor: D.K. Oza
Registrar: R. Balasubramanian
Founded: 1956, 1976
F: *Agriculture and Animal Husbandry; English*
and Foreign Languages; Rural Development;
Rural Health and Sanitation; Rural Oriented
Sciences; Rural Social Sciences; Tamil, Indian
Languages and Rural Arts.

Gauhati University
Guwahati, Assam 781014
Tel: +91(361) 7042
Fax: +91(361) 70133
Cable: university, guwahati
Vice-Chancellor: N.K. Chaudhury
Registrar: M.C. Bhuyan
Founded: 1948
F: *Arts; Commerce; Engineering; Law;*
Medicine; Science.

*Goa University
Taleigao Plateau, Sub-P.O. Goa University, Goa
403203
Tel: +91(832) 224184
Cable: unigoa, goa
Vice-Chancellor: P.R. Dubhashi (1990-95)
Registrar: Shri G. V. Kamat
Founded: 1985
F: *Applied Sciences; Arts, Humanities and*
Social Sciences; Commerce and Management

Studies; Education; Engineering and Technology;
Fine and Performing Arts; Law; Medicine; Pure
Sciences.
I: Management Studies (Goa); Management
Training and Research (Vidya Vikas Mandal);
Oceanography (National).
Ce: Historical Research (Xavier).

Gokhale Institute of Politics and Economics
Pune, Maharashtra 411004
Tel: +91(212) 344287
Cable: gokhalinst
Director: D.C. Wadhwa
Politics; Economics.

University of Gorakhpur
Gorakhpur, Uttar Pradesh 273009
Tel: +91(551) 333060
Cable: university, gorakhpur
Vice-Chancellor: V.S. Pathak
Registrar: R.N. Singh
Founded: 1956
F: Agriculture; Arts; Science; Commerce; Law;
Engineering.

Govind Ballabh Pant University of Agriculture and Technology
District Nainital, Pantnagar, Uttar Pradesh 263145
Tel: +91(5942) 33663
Cable: pantvarsity, pantnagar
Vice-Chancellor: S.C. Mudgal
Registrar: B.P. Singh
Founded: 1960, 1972
F: New Education.
C: Agriculture; Basic Sciences and Humanities;
Fisheries; Forestry and Hill Agriculture; Home
Science; Postgraduate Studies; Technology;
Veterinary Sciences.

Gujarat University
Navrangpura, Gujarat 380009
Tel: +91(79) 441654
Fax: +91(79) 441654
Cable: unigujarat, ahmedabad
Vice-Chancellor: M.N. Desai
Registrar: M.S. Shah
Founded: 1950
F: Arts; Commerce; Education; Law; Medicine;
Science; Engineering and Technology.

Gujarat Agricultural University
Dantiwada Campus, Sardar Krushinagar, District
Banasnantha, Gujarat 385506
Tel: +91(2742) 3425-266
Telex: 1204 206 gaud in
Cable: Krushi, sardar krushinagar
Vice-Chancellor: Govindbhai Shekhda
Registrar (Administration): M.S. Patel
Founded: 1972
F: Agricultural Engineering and Technology;
Agriculture; Dairy Science; Forestry and
Horticulture; Home Economics; Postgraduate
Studies; Veterinary Science and Animal
Husbandry.

Gujarat Ayurved University
Jamnagar, Gujarat 361008
Tel: +91(288) 76854
Cable: ayu, jarnnagar
Vice-Chancellor: B.T. Trivedi
Registrar: P.M. Mamtora
Founded: 1966
Ayurvedic Medicine.

*Gujarat University
[Gujarat Vidyapith]
Mahatma Gandhi Campus, Ashram Road,
Ahmedabad, Gujarat 380014
Tel: +91(79) 429392
Fax: +91(79) 429547
Telex: 121-6254 guvi in
Cable: gujarat vidyapith, ahmedabad
Vice-Chancellor: Ramlal Parikh
Registrar: V.R. Tripathi
Founded: 1920
F: Education; School Education; Social
Sciences.
C: Social Services (for Girls); Social Services
(for Boys).
I: Tribal Research.
Ce: Studies in Modern Indian Languages and
Literature; Studies in Rural Management; Krishi
Vigyan Kendra (Farm-Science Training); Peace
Research; Appropriate Technology.

Gulbarga University
Jnana Ganga, Gulbarga, Karnataka 585106
Tel: +91(8472) 21446
Fax: +91(8472) 21632
Telex: 0895-208 gulu
Cable: unigul gulbarga
Vice-Chancellor: N. Rudraiah
Registrar: K.S. Ramanjanappa
Founded: 1980
F: Arts; Commerce; Education; Engineering;
Law; Medicine; Science and Technology; Social
Sciences.

Guru Ghasidas University
Bilaspur, Madhya Pradesh 495009
Tel: +91(7752) 7752
Cable: vidhwavidyalaya, bilaspur, madhya
pradesh
Vice-Chancellor: R.L. Singh
Registrar: P.B. Trivedi
Founded: 1983
F: Arts; Commerce; Education; Engineering;
Home Science; Law; Life Science; Physical
Education; Science; Social Science.

Gurukula Kangri University
[Gurukula Kangri Vishwavidyalaya]
Hardwar, Uttar Pradesh 249404
Tel: +91(1334) 427366
Cable: gurukula, hardqar
Vice-Chancellor: Dharampal
Registrar: Jaidev Vedalankar
Founded: 1900
F: Humanities; Science.

Guru Nanak Dev University

Amritsar, Punjab 143005
Tel: +91(183) 258802
Fax: +91(183) 258820
Telex: 0384-274-gndu-in
Cable: university, amritsar
Vice-Chancellor: G.S. Randhawa
Registrar: Darshan Singh
Founded: 1969
F: Agriculture, Forestry and Food Technology;
Applied Sciences; Arts and Social Sciences;
Ayurvedic Medicine; Dental Sciences; Economics
and Business; Education; Engineering and
Technology; Fine Arts and Aesthetics; Humanities
and Religious Studies; Languages; Laws; Medical
Sciences; Physical Education; Physical Planning;
Sciences.

University of Health Sciences Andhra Pradesh

Vijayawada, Andhra Pradesh 520005
Tel: +91(866) 477206
Telex: 475269 uhs in
Cable: health university, vijaywada
Vice-Chancellor: C.S. Bhastravan
Registrar-in-Charge: M. John Apprao
Founded: 1986
F: Ayurveda; Dentistry; Homeopathy; Modern
Medicine; Naturopathy; Nursing; Pharmacy;
Unani.

Hemwati Nandan Bahuguna Garhwal University

Srinagar, District Garhwal, Uttar Pradesh 246174
Tel: +91(194) 2167
Telex: unigarh, sriragar 246 174
Vice-Chancellor: B.S. Rajput
Registrar: R.S. Gupta
Founded: 1973, 1989
F: Arts; Science; Commerce; Education; Law.

Himachal Pradesh Agricultural University

[Himachal Pradesh Krishi Vishva Vidyalaya]
Palampur, Himachal Pradesh 176062
Tel: +91(1894) 2121
Cable: himkrishi palampur
Vice-Chancellor: R.P.S. Tyagi
Registrar: Chamel Singh
Founded: 1978
Agriculture; Veterinary and Animal Sciences.

Himachal Pradesh University

Summer Hills, Shimla, Himachal Pradesh 171005
Tel: +91(177) 3513
Cable: himversity, shimla
Vice-Chancellor: P.S. Negi
Registrar: A.R. Chauhan
Founded: 1970
F: Ayurveda; Commerce and Management
Studies; Education; Engineering and Technology;
Languages; Law; Medicine Science; Performing
and Visual Arts; Science; Social Sciences.
Ce: Agro-Economic Research.

*University of Hyderabad

Central University P.O., Hyderabad, Andhra
Pradesh 500134
Tel: +91(40) 253951
Fax: +91(40) 253145
Telex: 425-2050 uhyd in
Cable: central varsity hyderabad
Vice-Chancellor: Govardhan Mehta (1994-)
Registrar: P. Muralikrishna
Founded: 1974
S: Chemistry; Humanities; Life Sciences;
Mathematics and Computer/Information Sciences;
Performing Arts, Fine Arts and Communication;
Physics; Social Sciences.
D: Applied Linguistics and Translation Studies;
Regional Studies; Comparative Literature.

Indian Agricultural Research Institute New Delhi

Pusa, New Delhi 110012
Tel: +91(11) 5754595
Fax: +91(11) 5740722
Telex: 3177161 iari in
Cable: krishipusa, new delhi
Director: Ram Badan Singh (1995-)
Registrar (Academic): A.K. Chaturvedi
Founded: 1905
Agricultural Research (postgraduate).

Indian Institute of Science

Bangalore, Karnataka 560012
Tel: +91(80) 344411
Fax: +91(80) 341683
E-Mail: ernet-in
Telex: 0845-8349 bg iisc in
Cable: 'science' bangalore
Director: C.N.R. Rao
Registrar: P.S. Venkateswaran
Founded: 1909
F: Engineering; Science; Biochemistry.
Ce: Reproductive Biology and Molecular
Endocrinology; Genetic Engineering; Ecological
Sciences; Excellence in Chemistry (Supported by
CSIR); Material Research; Electronics Design and
Technology; Supercomputer Education and
Research; Aerospace Engineering; Atmospheric
Sciences; Theoretical Studies; Foreign
Languages; Application of Science and
Technology to Rural Areas (ASTRA); Continuing
Education; Scientific and Industrial Consultancy.

Indian Institute of Technology Bombay

Powai, Bombay, Maharashtra 400076
Tel: +91(22) 5786530
Fax: +91(22) 5783480
Telex: 011-71385 iitb in
Cable: technology, bombay
Director: Suhas P. Sukhatme (1995-)
Registrar: D.K. Ghosh
Founded: 1958, 1961
F: Planning; Research and Development.
Ce: Energy Studies; Studies in Resources
Engineering.

INDIA

Indian Institute of Technology, Delhi
Hauz Khas, New Delhi 110016
Tel: +91(11) 666979
Fax: +91(11) 6862037
Telex: 31-73087 iit in
Cable: technology, new delhi
Director: N.C. Nigam
Registrar: Amarjit Singh
Founded: 1961, 1963
Chemistry; Civil Engineering; Electrical Engineering; Mechanical Engineering; Textile Technology; Computer Sciences; Natural Sciences; Humanities; Social Sciences.

Indian Institute of Technology, Kanpur
Kanpur, Uttar Pradesh 208016
Tel: +91(512) 214151
Telex: 0325-269 iitk-in
Cable: technology, kanpur
Director: R.C. Mehratra
Registrar: V. Narasimhan
Founded: 1960, 1962
D: Chemistry; Computer Science and Engineering; Aerospace Engineering; Mathematics; Nuclear Engineering and Technology; Physics.

Indian Institute of Technology Kharagpur
P.O. Kharagpur Technology, Kharagpur, West Bengal 721302
Tel: +91(3222) 2221
Fax: +91(3222) 2303
Telex: 06401 201 itkg in
Cable: technology, kharagpur
Director: K.L. Chopra
Registrar: S. Chander
Founded: 1950, 1956
*D: Architecture and Regional Planning; Chemistry; Computer Science and Engineering; Electronics and Electrical Communication Engineering; Aerospace Engineering; Agricultural Engineering; Chemical Engineering; Civil Engineering; Electrical Engineering; Industrial Engineering and Management; Mechanical Engineering; Metallurgical Engineering; Mining Engineering; Geology and Geophysics; Humanities and Social Sciences; Mathematics; Naval Architecture; Physics and Meteorology.
Ce: Cryogenic Engineering; Materials Science; Rubber Technology; Rural Development; Computer.*

Indian Institute of Technology, Madras
Madras, Tamil Nadu 600036
Tel: +91(44) 235-1365
Fax: (91) 235-0509
Telex: 41-8926-iitm-in
Cable: technology, madras
Director: N.V.C. Swamy
Registrar: V. Shanmugam
Founded: 1959
Technology.

Indian School of Mines
Dhanbad, Bihar 826004
Tel: +91(326) 832040
Fax: +91(326) 832040
Telex: 0629-214 ism
Cable: scolomin, dhanbad 826004
Director: Gurdyal Prasad (1991-)
Registrar: M. Ramakrishna
Founded: 1926, 1967
*D: Mining Engineering; Petroleum Engineering; Engineering and Mining Machinery; Applied Geology; Applied Geophysics; Fuel and Mineral Engineering.
Ce: Continuing Education; Longwall Mine Mechanization; Mine Environment.*

Indian Statistical Institute
203 Barrackpore Trunk Road, Calcutta, West Bengal 700035
Tel: +91(33) 526694
Fax: +91(33) 566680
Telex: 21-2210 stat in
Cable: statistica calcutta 700035
Director: B.L.S. Prakasa Rao
Chief Administrative Officer: P.K. Bandyopadhyay
Founded: 1932, 1959
Statistical Studies.

*Indian Veterinary Research Institute
Izatnagar, Uttar Pradesh 243122
Tel: +91(771) 74069
Telex: 577-205 ivri in
Cable: vetex izatnagar
Director: D.S. Kashyap
Registrar: S.R. Kashyap
Founded: 1889, 1983
Veterinary Science.

Indira Gandhi Agricultural University
[Indira Gandhi Krishi Vishwa Vidyalaya]
Raipur, Madhya Pradesh 492012
Tel: +91(771) 424481
Fax: +91(771) 429532
Cable: ikrishi, raipur-492012
Vice-Chancellor: Kirti Singh
Registrar: R.K. Mishra
Founded: 1987
Agriculture; Dairy Technology; Veterinary Science and Animal Husbandry.

Indira Gandhi Institute of Medical Sciences
Sheikhpuna, Puna, Bihar 800014
Director: S.S. Ambasta

Indira Gandhi National Open University
IGNOU Campus, Maidan Garhi, New Delhi 110068
Tel: +91(11) 6865922
Fax: +91(11) 6868492
Telex: 31-73023 ignou in
Cable: ignou, new delhi
Vice-Chancellor: V.C. Kulandai Swamy
Registrar (Administration): K. Narayanan
Founded: 1985
S: Continuing Education; Education; Engineering and Technology; Humanities; Management Studies; Sciences; Social Sciences.

University of Music and Fine Arts
[Indira Kala Sangit Vishwavidyalaya]
Khariagarh Distr. Rajnandgam, Madhya Pradesh
491861
Tel: +91 232
Cable: university, khairagarh
Vice-Chancellor: Ku. Sharayu Kalekar
Registrar: M.K. Gangajaliwale
Founded: 1956
*F: Dance; Fine Arts and Arts; Folk Music and
Art; Music; Painting.*

International Institute for Population Sciences
Govandi Station Road, Deonar, Bombay,
Maharashtra 400088
Tel: +91(22) 5563254
Fax: +91(22) 5563207
Cable: demography, bombay
Director: K.B. Pathak
Administrative Officer: R. Bashyam
Founded: 1956, 1985
*Development Studies; Fertility Studies;
Mathematical Demography and Statistics;
Migration and Urban Studies; Population Policies
and Development; Public Health and Mortality
Studies.*

Jadavpur University
P.O. Jadavpur University, Calcutta, West Bengal
700032
Tel: (91)(33) 735508
Fax: +91(33) 4736236
Telex: 21-4160 vc juin
Cable: unijad, caleutta-700032
Vice-Chancellor: S.C. Son
Registrar: B. Banerjea
Founded: 1955
F: Arts; Engineering and Technology; Science.

Jai Narain Vyas University
Jodhpur, Rajasthan 342001
Tel: +91(291) 32947
Telex: 552-285-avrc-in
Cable: university, jodhpur
Vice-Chancellor: V. Srinivasan
Registrar: Doongar Daria
Founded: 1962
*F: Arts, Social Sciences and Education;
Commerce and Management Studies;
Engineering; Law; Science.*

Jai Prakash University
[Jai Prakash Vishwavidyalaya]
Chapra, Bihar 841301
Tel: +91(326) 656072
Vice-Chacellor: S.N. Sinha
Registrar: J.P. Sharma

Jain Vishva Bharati Institute
P.B. 8, P.O. Ladnun, Rajasthan 341306
Tel: +91 2116
Cable: amritayan, ladnun 341306
Vice-Chancellor: Ramjee Singh
Registrar: Nalinik Shastree
Founded: 1991

Jamia Hamdard University
[Jamia Hamdard]
Hamdard Nagar, New Delhi 110062
Tel: +91(11) 6433685
Fax: +91(11) 6468824
Telex: 31-62942
Cable: jamham, new delhi
Vice-Chancellor: M. Rasheeduzzafar
Registrar: M. Hamidullah Bhat
Founded: 1989
*F: Islamic Studies and Humanities Mohd Amin;
Pharmacy; Science; Unani Medicine.*

Jamia Millia Islamia University
[Jamia Millia Islamia]
Jamia Nagar, New Delhi 110025
Tel: +91(11) 6836867
Cable: jamia, new delhi
Vice-Chancellor: Bashiruddin Ahmed
Registrar: Khwaja M. Shahid
Founded: 1920, 1963
*F: Education; Engineering and Technology;
Humanities and Languages; Law; Natural
Sciences; Social Sciences.*

University of Jammu
Bahu Wali Rakh, New Campus, Jammu, Jammu
and Kashmir 180004
Tel: +91(191) 43682
Cable: university, Jammu
Vice-Chancellor: Y.R. Malhotra
Joint Registrar: O.P. Sharma
Founded: 1948, 1969
*F: Arts; Commerce; Education; Law; Medicine;
Music and Fine Arts; Oriental Learning; Science;
Social Sciences.*

Jawaharlal Nehru Agricultural University
[Jawaharlal Nehru Krishi Vishwavidyalaya]
P.O. Box 80, Krishnigar, Jabalpur, Madhya
Pradesh 482004
Tel: +91(761) 343606
Telex: 765-313 jkvj in
Cable: Krishiviswa, jabalpu
Vice-Chancellor: K.S. Johar
Registrar: S.N. Sharma
Founded: 1964
*Agricultural Engineering; Agriculture; Veterinary
Science and Animal Husbandry.*

*Jawaharlal Nehru University
New Mehrauli Road, New Delhi 110067
Tel: +91(11) 667676
Telex: 31-73167 jnu in
Cable: jayenu, new delhi
Vice-Chancellor: Yoginder K. Alagh
Registrar: K.P. Sankaran Unny
Founded: 1969
*S: Computer and Systems Sciences;
Environmental Sciences; International Studies;
Languages; Physical Sciences; Life Sciences;
Social Sciences.*

Jawaharlal Nehru Technological University
Masab Tank, Mahaveer Marg, Hyderabad,
Andhra Pradesh 500028
Tel: +91(40) 228388
Fax: +91(40) 227648
Telex: 425-6846-jntu-in
Cable: technology, hyderabad
Vice-Chancellor: I. Gopal Reddy
Registrar: G.A. Ghosh
Founded: 1972
F: Architecture; Chemistry; Engineering;
Humanities and Languages; Management
Sciences; Mathematics; Physics.
S: Lifelong and Distance Education.

Jiwaji University
Vidya Vihar, Gwalior, Madhya Pradesh 474011
Tel: +91(751) 341348
Fax: +91(751) 341450
Cable: university, gwalior
Vice-Chancellor: K.K. Singh
Registrar: S.K. Bagde
Founded: 1964
F: Arts; Ayurveda; Commerce; Education;
Engineering; Home Science; Law; Life Sciences;
Medicine; Physical Education; Science; Social
Science.

Kakatiya University
Vidyaranyapuri, Warangal, Andhra Pradesh
506009
Tel: +91(8712) 79344
Telex: 825-230-kucn-in
Cable: kakatiya
Vice-Chancellor: K. Jayashankar
Registrar: A. Shankaraiah
Founded: 1976
F: Arts; Commerce; Education; Engineering and
Technology; Law; Medicine; Pharmaceutical
Sciences; Science; Social Sciences; Unani
Medicine.

University of Kalyani
P.O. Kalyani, District Nadia, West Bengal 741235
Tel: +91(3162) 690
Cable: kalyani
Vice-Chancellor: A.K. Roy
Registrar: P. Sircar
Founded: 1960
F: Arts and Commerce; Education; Science.

**Kameshwar Singh Darbhanga Sanskrit
University**
Kameshwara Nagar, Darbhanga, Bihar 846004
Tel: +91 2178
Cable: savita, darbhanga
Vice-Chancellor: Upadhyay
Registrar: Ramchandra Jha
Founded: 1961
F: Astrology and Jyotish; Ayurvedic Medicine;
Darshan; Fine Arts; Puranas; Sahitya; Vyakarana
and Linguistics; Sociology; Vedas.

Kannada University
District Bellary, Hampi, Karnataka 583211
Tel: +91(8394) 5334
Fax: +91(8394) 5355
Vice-Chancellor: Chardrashekhra Kambav
Registrar: K.V. Narayana

Kanpur University
Kalyanpur, Kanpur, Uttar Pradesh 208024
Tel: +91(512) 250450
Cable: university, kanpur
Vice-Chancellor: V.N. Upadhyaya
Registrar: R.S. Bansal
Founded: 1966
F: Agriculture; Arts; Ayurvedic and Unani
Medicine; Business and Industrial Management;
Commerce; Education; Engineering and
Technology; Law; Medicine; Science; Social
Sciences.

Karnatak University
Ravate Nagar, Dharwad, Karnataka 580003
Tel: +91(83) 42016
Fax: +91(836) 42464
Telex: 865320 kud in
Cable: unikarnatak, dharwwod
Vice-Chancellor: S. Rame Gowda
Registrar: B.P. Kamiram
Founded: 1949
F: Arts; Commerce; Education; Engineering;
Indian System of Medicine; Law; Management;
Medicine; Science and Technology; Social
Sciences.

Kashi Vidyapith
Varanasi, Uttar Pradesh 221002
Tel: +91(542) 54160
Fax: +91(542) 52269
Cable: kashividyapith, varanasi
Vice-Chancellor: R.K. Tripathi
Registrar: R.C. Sharma
Founded: 1921
F: Arts and Humanities; Commerce; Education;
Law; Social Sciences; Social Work.

Kerala Agricultural University
P.O. Vellanikkara, Trichur, Kerala 680654
Tel: +91(487) 23432
Telex: 887-268 kau-in
Cable: agrivarsity, trichur
Vice-Chancellor: A.M. Michael
Registrar: E.K. Majhi
Founded: 1971
F: Agricultural Engineering; Agriculture;
Fisheries; Veterinary and Animal Sciences.

University of Kerala
University P.O., Thiruvanathapuram, Kerala
695034
Tel: +91 75631
Cable: university, thiruvanathapuram
Vice-Chancellor: J.V. Vilanilam
Registrar: P.V. Nair
Founded: 1937, 1957, 1974

F: *Applied Science; Arts; Ayurveda; Commerce; Dentistry; Education; Engineering and Technology; Fine Arts; Homeopathy; Law; Management Studies; Medicine; Oriental Studies; Physical Education; Science; Social Sciences.*

Konkan Agricultural University
[Konkan Krishi Vidyapeeth]
Dapoli, District Ratnagiri, Maharashtra 415712
Tel: +91(2358) 2064
Fax: +91(2358) 2074
Telex: 01-1903209-kku-in
Cable: konkanagri dapoli
Vice-Chancellor: Arvind Sawant
Registrar: A.D. Dixit
Founded: 1972
F: *Agriculture; Fisheries; Veterinary Science.*

Kota Open University
Pushpa Niwas, Station Road, Kota, Rajasthan 324002
Tel: +91(744) 21254
Telex: 305-257 kou-in
Vice-Chancellor: T.N. Bhardwaja
Registrar: S.K. Agarwal
Founded: 1987
F: *Commerce and Management; Education; Science and Technology; Social Science and Humanities.*

Kumaun University
Nainital, Uttar Pradesh 263001
Tel: +91(5942) 2068
Cable: kumaun university, nainital
Vice-Chancellor: M.C. Joshi
Registrar: R.C. Pant
Founded: 1973
F: *Arts; Commerce; Education; Law; Science.*

Kurukshetra University
Kurukshetra, Haryana 132119
Tel: +91(1744) 30039
Fax: +91(1744) 30277
Cable: dharmakshetra, kurukshetra, haryana
Vice-Chancellor: B.S. Dahiya
Registrar: Jyoti Arora
Founded: 1956
F: *Arts and Languages; Ayurioveda; Commerce and Management; Education; Engineering and Technology; Indian Studies; Law; Science; Social Sciences.*

Kuvempu University
B.R. Project, Shimoga District, Karnataka 577115
Tel: +91(8182) 35222
Fax: +91(8182) 35255
Cable: janana sahyadri, br project
Vice-Chancellor: K.N.V. Rao
Registrar: I.H. Pujarraj
Founded: 1987
F: *Arts; Commerce; Education; Engineering; Law; Medicine; Science and Technology.*

Lalit Narayan Mithila University
Darbhanga, Bihar 846004
Tel: +91(6272) 22428
Cable: unimithila, darbhanga
Vice-Chancellor: B. Jayashankar
Registrar: S.Z. Rahman
Founded: 1972
F: *Commerce; Education; Humanities; Law; Medicine; Science; Social Science.*

University of Lucknow
Badshahbagh, Lucknow, Uttar Pradesh 226007
Tel: +91(522) 381583
Cable: university luchnow
Vice-Chancellor: M.S. Sodha
Registrar: R.K. Singh
Founded: 1921
F: *Architecture; Arts; Ayruveda; Commerce; Dentistry; Education; Engineering and Technology; Fine Arts; Law; Medicine; Science.*

University of Madras
University Centenary Building, Chepauk, Triplicane P.O., Madras, Tamil Nadu 600005
Tel: +91(44) 568778
Telex: 416376 unom in
Cable: university, madras
Vice-Chancellor: S. Sathikh (1990-93)
Registrar: P. Govindarajulu
Founded: 1857
F: *Arts; Commerce; Engineering; Fine Arts; Indian and Other Languages; Law; Medicine; Science; Teaching; Management Sciences.*

Madurai Kamaraj University
Palkalai Nagar, Madurai, Tamil Nadu 625021
Tel: +91(452) 85471
Cable: university, madurai
Vice-Chancellor: M.D.K. Kuthalingam
Registrar: N.S. Venkala Suppu
Founded: 1966, 1978
S: *Biological Sciences; Mathematical Sciences; Physics.*
I: *Artemia Research and Training.*

Magadh University
Bodh-Gaya, Bihar 824234
Tel: +91(631) 20835
Cable: magvarsity, bodh-gaya, bihar state
Vice-Chancellor: A.B. Prasad
Registrar: A.K. Srivastava
Founded: 1962
F: *Commerce; Humanities; Law; Management; Medicine; Science; Social Sciences.*

Maharshi Dayanand Sarswati University, Ajmer
Ajmer, Rajasthan 305001
Tel: +91(145) 52337
Vice-Chancellor: Kanta Ahuja
Registrar: S.D. Khan
Founded: 1987
F: *Arts; Commerce; Education; Fine Arts, Music and Dramatics; Law; Management; Sanskrit Studies; Social Sciences.*

Maharshi Dayanand University
Rohtak, Haryana 124001
Tel: +91(1262) 72327
Cable: varsity, rohtak
Vice-Chancellor: V.C. Sharma
Registrar: T.C. Gupta
Founded: 1976
*F: Ayurvedic and Unani Systems of Medicine;
Commerce and Business Management;
Education; Engineering; Humanities; Law; Life
Sciences; Medical Sciences; Physical Sciences;
Social Sciences.*

Mahatma Gandhi University
Priyadarshini Hills, Athirampuzha P.O., Kottayam,
Kerala 686562
Tel: +91(481) 7605
Telex: 288-mguk-in
Vice-Chancellor: A. Sukumaran Nair
Registrar: M.C. Chacko
Founded: 1983, 1988
*F: Education; Fine Arts; Science; Social
Sciences; Arts; Ayurveda; Commerce;
Engineering; Homeopathy; Law; Medicine;
Oriental Studies.*

Mahatma Phule Agricultural University
[Mahatma Phule Krishi Vidyapeeth]
Rahuri, District Ahmednagar, Maharashtra 413722
Tel: +91(241) 43208
Cable: krishivid rahuri
Vice-Chancellor: S.K. Dorge
Registrar: S.N. Karle
Founded: 1967
*F: Agricultural Engineering; Agriculture;
Veterinary Science.*

Makhalnal Chaturvedi National University Institute of Journalism
E-8/76 Arera Colony, P.B. No. RSN/60, Bhopal,
Madhya Pradesh 462016
Tel: +91(755) 65307
Director-General: Radeshyam Sharma
Executive Director: Arvind Chaturvedi
Founded: 1990
*D: Journalism; Public Relations; Mass
Communication; Newspaper Management;
Computer Programming and Applications.*

Mangalore University
Mangalagangothri, Karnataka 574199
Tel: +91(824) 742276
Fax: +91(824) 742367
Telex: 258 pgc in
Cable: university, mangalore
Vice-Chancellor: M.I. Savadatti
Registrar: K.M. Kaveriappa
Founded: 1980
*F: Arts; Commerce; Education; Engineering and
Technology; Law; Medicine; Science.*

Manipal Academy of Higher Education
Madhav Nagar, Manipal, Karnataka 576119
Tel: +91(8252) 71000
Fax: +91(8252) 70500
Telex: 833-209-mphe-in
Director: Ramdas M. Pai
Registrar: P.L.N.G. Rao

Manipur University
Canchipur, Imphal, Manipur 795003
Tel: +91 20529
Telex: 286-205
Cable: manvarsity, imphal
Vice-Chancellor: I.S. Khaiden
Registrar: Th. Joychandra Singh
Founded: 1980
F: Humanities; Science; Social Science.

Manonmaniam Sundaranar University
Kokkirakulam, Tirunelveli, Tamil Nadu 627009
Tel: +91(462) 71964
Fax: +91(462) 25785
Telex: 433 259 msu-in
Cable: university, tirunelveli
Vice-Chancellor: V. Vasanthi Devi
Registrar: S. Silvanathan
Founded: 1990
*F: Arts; Education; Science and Engineering.
S: Computer and Mathematical Sciences; Fine
Arts; Housing Aesthetics and Sports; Humanities
and Social Scienses; International Studies; Life
and Environmental Sciences; Management,
Commerce and Economical Sciences; Physical
Studies; Space and Satellite Studies; Tamil and
Other Indian Languages.*

Marathwada Agricultural University
[Marathwada Krishi Vidyapith]
P.O. Krishinagar, Parbhani, Maharashtra 431402
Tel: +91(2452) 2110
Cable: university, parbhani
Vice-Chancellor: V.K. Patil
Registrar: S.T. Kachwe
Founded: 1972
*F: Agricultural Engineering; Agricultural
Technology; Agriculture; Home Science;
Horticulture; Veterinary Science.*

Mohan Lal Sukhadia University
Pratapnagar, Udaipur, Rajasthan 313001
Tel: +91(294) 29166
Cable: university, udaipur
Vice-Chancellor: R.K. Rai
Registrar: K.C. Gupta
Founded: 1962, 1982
*F: Commerce and Management Studies; Law;
Postgraduate Studies; Science; Social Sciences
and Humanities.*

Mother Teresa Women's University
13 Race Course Road, Guindy, Madras, Tamil Nadu 600032
Tel: +91(44) 234880
Cable: women's university, madras
Vice-Chancellor: S. Lakshmi
Registrar: Sathyavathi Manual
Founded: 1984
F: Adult and Continuing Education; Computer Science; Economics; Education; English; Family Life Management; History Studies; Music; Psychology; Sociology; Tamil.

*University of Mysore
Crawford Hall, P.B. No. 406, Mysore, Karnataka 570005
Tel: +91(821) 23555
Fax: +91(821) 21263
Telex: 0846-226 (uom in)
Cable: unireg, mysore
Vice-Chancellor: M. Madaiah
Registrar: S.K. Pattanayak
Founded: 1916
F: Arts; Science and Technology; Commerce; Education; Engineering; Law; Medicine.

Nagaland University
Nagaland
Vice-Chancellor: I. Yangar Ao
Founded: 1994

Nagarjuna University
Nagarjunanagar, Guntur, Andhra Pradesh 522510
Tel: +91(863) 83269
Fax: +91(863) 83378
Telex: 0471218-naga in
Cable: university, nagarjunanagar
Vice-Chancellor: Y.C. Simhadri
Registrar: P. Muralidhandu
Founded: 1976
F: Ayurveda; Commerce; Education; Engineering; Fine Arts; Humanities; Law; Medicine; Natural Science; Oriental Learning; Physical Science; Social Science.

Nagpur University
Rabindranath Tagore Marg, Nagpur, Maharashtra 440001
Tel: +91(712) 525417
Fax: +91(712) 532841
Cable: nagpur university, nagpur
Vice-Chancellor: M.T. Gabhe
Registrar (Acting): S. Desar
Founded: 1923
F: Arts; Ayurvedic Medicine; Commerce; Education; Engineering and Technology; Home Science; Law; Medicine; Science; Social Science.

Narendra Deva University of Agriculture and Technology
Narendranagar, Kumarganj, Faizabad, Uttar Pradesh 224229
Tel: +91(5272) 4832
Cable: agrivarsity, faizabad
Vice-Chancellor: S.S. Khanna
Registrar: S.M. Shamim
Founded: 1975
Agriculture.

National Dairy Research Institute
Karnal, Haryana 132001
Tel: +91(184) 22800
Fax: +91(184) 20042
Telex: 396-204 ndri in
Cable: dairysearch, karnal
Director: S.C. Sarma
Registrar: R.S. Sobangi
Founded: 1955
Dairy Research.

National Law School of India University
Nagarbhavi, Bangalore, Karnataka 560072
Tel: +91(280) 351624
Fax: +91(280) 351674
Cable: lawvarsity
Director: N.R. Madhava Menon (1988-93)
Registrar: R. Krishnappa
Founded: 1987
Law.

National Museum Institute of the History of Art, Conservation and Museology
Janpath, New Delhi 110011
Tel: +91(11) 3018159
Fax: +91(11) 3019821
Telex: 31-66553 nmnd in
Cable: museotute
Director-General: R.C. Sharma
Registrar: R.K. Gupta
Founded: 1989
History of Art, Conservation and Museology.

National Sanskrit University
[Rashtriya Sanskrit Vidyapith]
Tirupati, Andhra Pradesh 517507
Tel: +91(8574) 23937
Cable: vichya peetham, tirapali
Vice-Chancellor: R. Mahadevan
Registrar: C.S. Pandey
Founded: 1864
Sanskrit Studies.

Nizam's Institute of Medical Sciences
Panajagutta, Hyderabad, Andhra Pradesh 500482
Tel: +91(842) 229316
Telex: 425 6478 nims in
Cable: nims, thydaabad
Director-in-Charge: I. Dinakar
Executive Registrar: Koteswara Rao
Founded: 1989
Medical Sciences.

University of North Bengal
P.O. North Bengal University, Rajarammohunpur,
District Darjeeling, West Bengal 734430
Tel: +91(3556) 255
Cable: north bengal
Vice-Chancellor: K.N. Chatterjee
Registrar: T.K. Chatterjee
Founded: 1962
F: Arts, Commerce and Law; Science.

North-Eastern Hill University
Lower Lachaumiere, Shillong, Meghalaya 793001
Tel: +91(364) 760075
Fax: +91(364) 760074
Telex: sh-0137
Cable: nehu, shillong
Vice-Chancellor (Acting): Barrister Pakem
Registrar (Acting): A. Patton
Founded: 1973
F: Languages.
*S: Agricultural Sciences and Rural
Development; Education; Environmental
Sciences; Life Sciences; Physical Sciences;
Social Sciences.*

North Gujarat University
Post Box No. 21, Rajmahel Road, Patan, Gujarat
384265
Tel: +91(2766) 3427
Cable: university, patan
Vice-Chancellor: D.A. Gandi
Registrar: D.S. Barad
Founded: 1986
*F: Arts; Commerce; Education; Law; Science;
Technology.*

North Maharashtra University
P.B. 80, Jalgaion, Maharashtra 425001
Tel: +91(257) 27289
Cable: uttamvidya, jalgaon
Vice-Chancellor: N.K. Thakare
Registrar: S.P. Joglekar
Founded: 1990
*F: Arts; Commerce; Education; Law; Medicine;
Ayurveda; Mental, Moral and Social Sciences;
Engineering; Science.*

Orissa University of Agriculture and Technology
Bhubaneswar, District Puri, Orissa 751003
Tel: +91(674) 402868
Cable: agritech, bhubaneswar
Vice-Chancellor: I.C. Mohapatra
Registrar: P.C. Behera
Founded: 1962
*C: Agricultural Engineering and Technology;
Agriculture; Basic Science; Engineering and
Technology; Fishery; Home Science; Veterinary
Science and Animal Husbandry.*

Osmania University
Hyderabad, Andhra Pradesh 500007
Tel: +91(40) 868951
Fax: +91(40) 869020
Telex: 425-7090 osmu in
Cable: university, hyderabad, deccan 500007
Vice-Chancellor: M. Malla Reddy
Registrar: Hanumanlu Polasa
Founded: 1918
*F: Arts; Commerce; Education; Engineering;
Law; Science; Social Science; Technology.*

Pandit Ravishankar Shukla University
Raipur, Madhya Pradesh 492010
Tel: +91(771) 533957
Fax: +91(771) 534283
Cable: university, raipur
Vice-Chancellor: R.K. Thakur
Registrar: H.L. Gupta
Founded: 1963
*F: Arts; Ayurveda; Commerce; Education;
Engineering; Home Science; Law; Life Sciences;
Medicine; Science; Social Sciences.*

*Panjab University Chandigarh
Chandigarh, Union Territory 160014
Tel: +91(172) 541945
Telex: 395 464 rsic in
Cable: university, chandigarh
Vice-Chancellor: T.N. Kapoor (1991-94)
Registrar: B.L. Gupta
Founded: 1947
*F: Arts; Business Management and Commerce;
Dairying, Animal Husbandry and Agriculture;
Design and Fine Arts; Education; Engineering
and Technology; Languages; Law; Medical
Sciences; Pharmaceutical Sciences; Sciences.*

Patna University
Patna, Bihar 800005
Tel: +91(612) 50531
Cable: patversity, patna, bihar state
Vice-Chancellor: M. Mohiuddin
Registrar: B.K. Verma
Founded: 1917
*F: Commerce; Education; Engineering; Fine
Arts; Humanities; Law; Medicine; Science; Social
Sciences.*
I: Public Administration.

Pondicherry University
Kalapet, Pondicherry 605001
Tel: +91(413) 852175
Fax: +91(413) 857265
Vice-Chancellor: A. Gnanam
Registrar: S.G. Bhat
Founded: 1985
*S: Ecology (Salim Ali); Management; Performing
Arts.*
I: International Studies.
*D: Biology; Chemistry; Commerce; Economics;
English; French; Futurology; History;
Mathematics; Philosophy; Physical Education and
Sports; Physics; Sanskrit; Tamil.*

*University of Poona
Ganeshkhind, Pune, Maharashtra 411007
Tel: +91(212) 333868
Fax: +91(212) 333899
Cable: unipuna, pune
Vice-Chancellor: Shridhar C. Gupte
Registrar: S.P. Bhosale
Founded: 1948
F: Arts; Ayurveda; Commerce; Education;
Engineering; Law; Medicine; Mental, Moral and
Social Sciences; Science.

Postgraduate Institute of Medical Education and Research, Chandigarh
Sector 12, Chandigarh, Union Territory 160012
Tel: +91(172) 541376
Telex: 395-315-pbi in
Cable: postgradmed, chanchigarh
Director: B.N.S. Walia
Registrar: M.L. Ranga
Founded: 1962, 1967
Medical Education and Research (postgraduate).

*Punjab Agricultural University
Ludhiana, Punjab 141004
Tel: +91(161) 401794
Fax: +91(161) 401794
Telex: 0386-473 coae-in
Cable: agrivarsity, ludhiana
Vice-Chancellor: A.S. Khehra
Registrar: J.B. Goyal
Founded: 1962
C: Agricultural Engineering; Agriculture; Basic
Sciences and Humanities; Home Science (Kaoni);
Home Science (Ludhiana); Veterinary Science;
Postgraduate Studies.
S: Energy Studies for Agriculture; Extension
Education.

Punjabi University
Patiala, Patiala 147002
Tel: +91(175) 822378
Fax: +91(175) 822418
Telex: 394-219 pup
Cable: university, patiala
Vice-Chancellor: J.S. Puar (1989-)
Registrar: Tirath Singh
Founded: 1962
F: Arts and Social Sciences; Ayurveda and
Unani Medicine; Business, Administration and
Commerce; Dental Science; Education;
Humanities and Religious Studies; Languages;
Law; Life Sciences; Medicine (Faridkot); Physical
Sciences; Vocational Courses; Engineering.
I: Advanced Studies in Rural Development
(Guru Kashi,Prem Kumar); Advanced Studies in
Urdu (Nawab Sher Khan, Malerkotla).
D: Correspondence Courses.
Ce: Guru Kanshi Regional (Bhatinda); Audio-
Visual Research; Social Change (Research);
Economic Change.

Punjabrao Agriculture University
[Punjabrao Krishi Vidyapeeth]
P.O. Krishinagar, Akola, District Akola,
Maharashtra 444104
Tel: +91(724) 25365
Telex: 725-215 pkvin
Cable: university, akola
Vice-Chancellor: B.G. Bathkal
Registrar: S.D. Lokhande
Founded: 1969
F: Agricultural Engineering; Agriculture;
Veterinary Science.

Purvanchal University
Jaunpur, Uttar Pradesh 222002
Tel: +91(5452) 2009
Vice-Chancellor: U.P. Singh
Registrar: G.S. Mishra
Founded: 1987
F: Arts; Commerce; Agriculture; Business
Administration; Education; Law; Science.

Rabindra Bharati University
56-A Barrackpore Trunk Road, Calcutta, West
Bengal 700050
Tel: +91(33) 522018
Vice-Chancellor: Pabitra Sarkar
Registrar: R.C. Mitra
Founded: 1962
F: Arts; Fine Arts; Visual Arts.
Ce: Study and Research on Tagore.

Rajasthan Agricultural University
Bikaner, Rajasthan 334001
Tel: +91(151) 25977
Fax: +91(151) 26476
Telex: 03505-208 rkvb in
Cable: agriversity, bikaner
Vice-Chancellor: R.K. Patel (1994-)
Registrar: Suneed Dhariwal
Founded: 1987
Ce: Agriculture; Agriculture (Udaipur);
Agriculture (Jobner-Jaipur); Veterinary and
Animal Sciences; Technology and Agricultural
Engineering; Home Science (Bikaner); Home
Science (Udaipur); Dairy Science.
D: Extension Education.
Stations/Laboratories: Agricultural Experiment
Station.

Rajasthan University Udaipur
[Rajasthan Vidyapeeth Udaipur]
Saletia Ground, Udaipur, Rajasthan 313001
Tel: +91(294) 27987
Cable: vidyapeeth, udaipur
Vice-Chancellor: D.P. Sharma
Founded: 1937, 1987
F: Arts and Commerce; Education; Social Work.

University of Rajasthan
Gandhinagar, Jaipur, Rajasthan 302004
Tel: +91(141) 511863
Cable: university, jaipur
Vice-Chancellor: T.K.N. Unnithan
Registrar: J.K. Sachdeva
Founded: 1947

F: Arts; Ayurveda; Commerce; Education; Engineering and Technology; Fine Arts, Music and Dramatics; Law; Management Studies; Medicine and Pharmaceutics; Science; Social Sciences.

Rajendra Agricultural University
P.O. Pusa, Samastipur, Bihar 848125
Tel: +91(6274) 226
Cable: agriversity, pusa
Vice-Chancellor: K.S. Chauhan (1993-)
Registrar: M.S. Haque
Founded: 1970
F: Agricultural Engineering; Agriculture; Basic Science; Home Science; Veterinary and Animal Husbandry.

Ranchi University
Ranchi, Bihar 834008
Tel: +91(651) 302600
Cable: unidurga, ranchi
Vice-Chancellor: K.K. Nag
Registrar: A. Prasad
Founded: 1960
F: Humanities; Science; Commerce; Education; Engineering; Law; Medicine; Social Sciences.

Rani Durgavati University
[Rani Durgavati Vishwavidyalaya]
Saraswati Vihar, Jabalpur, Madhya Pradesh 482001
Tel: +91 320785
Cable: unidurga jabalpur
Vice-Chancellor: G.S. Misra
Registrar: D.S. Darkwale
Founded: 1957, 1983
F: Arts; Ayurveda; Commerce; Engineering; Home Science; Law; Life Science; Mathematical Sciences; Medicine; Science; Social Sciences; Management.

Rohilkhand University
Bareilly, Uttar Pradesh 243001
Tel: +91(581) 73658
Cable: ruversity, bareilly
Vice-Chancellor: Bhoomittra Dev
Officiating Registrar: K.V. Singh
Founded: 1975
F: Agriculture; Arts; Commerce; Education; Law; Life Science; Science.

University of Roorkee
Roorkee, Uttar Pradesh 247667
Tel: +91(1332) 72742
Fax: +91(1332) 73560
Telex: 597-201 uor in
Cable: university, roorkee
Vice-Chancellor: H.C. Visvesvaraya
Registrar: P.C. Mohan
Founded: 1847, 1948

I: Paper Technology.
D: Architecture and Planning; Bio-Sciences and Biotechnology; Chemistry; Earth Sciences; Chemical Engineering; Civil Engineering; Earthquake Engineering; Electronics and Computer Engineering; Mechanical and Industrial Engineering; Metallurgical Engineering; Humanities and Social Sciences; Hydrology; Mathematics; Physics.
Ce: Computer.

Sambalpur University
Jyoti Vihar, P.O. Burla, Sambalpur, Orissa 768019
Tel: +91(663) 7158
Cable: university, sambalpur
Vice-Chancellor: A.K. Samantraj
Registrar: Issac Behera
Founded: 1967
C: V.S.S. Medical; Regional Engineering; Sambalpur Homeopathic Medical; Lajpat Rai Law; Engineering.
S: Life Science.
I: Visual and Performing Arts (Sundargarh); Advance Teacher Studies (Dr. P.M.).
D: Anthropology and Sociology; Chemistry; Computer Science and Application; Earth Science; Economics; English; Environmental Sciences; History; Home Science; Law; Library and Information Science; Mathematics; Oriya; Physics; Political Science and Public Administration; Statistics; Sociology; Business Administration.

Sampurnanand Sanskrit University
[Sampurnanand Sanskrit Vishvavidyalaya]
Varanasi, Uttar Pradesh 221002
Tel: +91(542) 44089
Cable: shrutam, varanasi
Vice-Chancellor: V. Venkatachalam
Registrar: G.S. Misra
Founded: 1958
D: Bauddha Darshana; Comparative Philosophy; Dharmashastra; Education; Home Science; Jain Darshana; Jyotish; Library Science; Mimansa; Modern Languages and Linguistics; Nyaya; Pali; Politics and Economics (Ancient and Modern); Prakrit and Jainagam; Puranetihasa; Sahitya; Veda; Vedanta; Vyakarana; Yoga Tantra.

Sanjay Gandhi Postgraduate Institute of Medical Sciences
P.B. No. 375, Lucknow, Uttar Pradesh 226001
Tel: +91(522) 51993
Telex: 535-411 sg-pgi in
Cable: ayurvigyan, lucknow
Director: S.S. Agarwal
Executive Registrar: S.E. Sinha
Founded: 1983
Medical Sciences (postgraduate); Nursing; Medical Technology.

Sardar Patel University

P.B. No. 10, Vallabh Vidyanagar, Gujarat 388120
Tel: +91(2692) 30808
Telex: 172 251 vuia in
Cable: university, vallabh vidyanagar, gujarat
Vice-Chancellor: D.D. Jadeja
Registrar: Chandrakant Patel
Founded: 1955, 1966
*F: Arts; Business Studies; Education;
Engineering and Technology; Home Science;
Law; Homeopathy; Medicine and Pharmacy;
Science.*

Saurashtra University

Kalavad Road, Rajkot, Gujarat State 360005
Tel: +91(281) 40450
Cable: university, rajkot
Vice-Chancellor: Jayeshbhai Desai
Registrar: J.M. Udani
Founded: 1967
*F: Arts; Commerce; Education; Home Science;
Law; Medicine; Rural Studies; Science;
Technology.*

School of Planning and Architecture

4 Block B, Indraprastha Estate, New Delhi 110002
Tel: +91(11) 331-7892
Fax: +91(11) 331-9435
Cable: schoolplan, new delhi
Director: Sreemay Bash
Registrar: D.R. Bains
Founded: 1955, 1959, 1979
Architecture and Town Planning.

Sher-E-Kashmir University of Agricultural Sciences and Technology

Post Box No. 262, Srinagar, Jammu and Kashmir
190001
Tel: +91(194) 73459
Cable: agrisity srinagar
Vice-Chancellor: M.A. Dar
Registrar: H.M. Tahir
Founded: 1982
*F: Agriculture; Veterinary Sciences and Animal
Health (Nowshehra).*
*D: Animal Production (Shuhama); Sericulture
(Mirgund).*

Shivaji University

Vidyanagar, Kolhapur, Maharashtra 416004
Tel: +91(231) 25122
Fax: +91(231) 24033
Telex: 195-226-suk in
Cable: unishivaji, kolhapur
Vice-Chancellor: A.T. Varute
Registrar: B.P. Sabale
Founded: 1962
*F: Arts; Ayurvedic Medicine and Surgery and
Homeopathic Medicine and Surgery; Commerce;
Education; Engineering and Technology; Law;
Medicine; Science; Social Science.*

Shreemati Nathibai Damodar Thackersey Women's University

1 Nathibai Thackersey Road, Bombay,
Maharashtra 400020
Tel: +91(22) 291879
Fax: +91(22) 2864091
Cable: uniwomen, bombay
Vice-Chancellor: Suma Chitnis
Registrar: A.G. Bhalwankar
Founded: 1916
*F: Arts; Commerce; Education; Fine Arts; Home
Science; Library Science; Nursing; Social
Sciences.*

Shri Jagannath Sanskrit University

[Shri Jagannath Sanskrit Vishvavidyalaya]
Shri Vihar, Puri, Orissa 752002
Tel: +91(6752) 2669
Cable: shrivihar, puri-752001
Vice-Chancellor: Tribikram Pati
Registrar: B. Beura
Founded: 1981
*F: Dharmashastra; Nyaya; Sahitya;
Sarvadarshan; Vedanta; Vyakaran.*

Shri Lal Bahadur Shastri National Sanskrit University

[Shri Lal Bahadur Shastri Rashtriya Sanskrit
Vidyapeeth]
Shahee Jeet Singh Marg, Katwaria Sarai, New
Delhi 110016
Tel: +91(11) 6868274
Cable: Vidyapeetham, new dalhi
Vice-Chancellor: Mandan Mishra
Registrar: Ch. Sambaiah
Sanskrit Studies.

sidhu Kanhu University

Dumka, Santal Pargana, Bihar 814101
Tel: +91(6434) 6434
Vice-Chancellor: Amar Kumar Singh
Registrar: M. Sowaid

South Gujarat University

Udhna-Magdalla Road, Post Box No. 49, Surat,
Gujarat 395007
Tel: +91(261) 667141
Cable: soguni surat
Vice-Chancellor: B.A. Parikhi
Registrar: N.K. Desai
Founded: 1967
*F: Arts; Commerce; Education; Engineering;
Law; Medicine; Rural Studies; Science.*

South Indian Society for the Propagation of Hindi

[Dakshina Bharat Hindi Prachar Sabha]
P.B. No. 1419, Thyagarayanagar, Madras, Tamil
Nadu 600017
Tel: +91(44) 441824
Cable: dakshin madras
Pro-Vice-Chancellor (Honorary): B.D. Jatti
Registrar: A. Ramaswamy
Founded: 1918

F: Education; Hindi Language and Literature (Madras, Ernakulum Complexes); Comparative Literature, Journalism, Lexicology, Modern Hindi Literature, Translation and Drafting (Dharwad-Karnataka and Hyderabad Complexes).

Sree Chitra Tirunal Institute for Medical Sciences and Technology
P.O. Trivandrum Medical College, Trivandrum, Kerala 695011
Tel: +91(471) 443085
Fax: +91(471) 446433
Telex: 435-290 scmc in
Cable: chitramet, thiruvananthapuram
Director: M.S. Valiathan
Registrar: G.N.A. Nayar
Founded: 1973, 1981
Biomedical Engineering and Technology; Medical Sciences.

Sree Sankaracharya University of Sanskrit
Kaladi, Kerala 683574
Vice-Chancelor: R. Ramachndran Nair
Sanskrit Studies.

Sri Chandrasekharendra Nyaya Shastra Mahavidyalaya
Kancheepusam, Tamil Nadu 631503

Sri Krishnadevaraya University Anantapur
Sri Venkateswarapuram (P.O.), Anantapur, Andhra Pradesh 515003
Tel: +91(8554) 23444
Fax: +91(8554) 22150
Cable: s.k. university, anantapur
Vice-Chancellor: M.J. Kesavamurthy
Registrar: D. Venkata Raju
Founded: 1981
F: Arts; Commerce; Law; Sciences; Management.
Ce: Planning and Development Studies; Rayalaseema Development Studies.

Sri Padmavati Women's University
[Sri Padmavati Mahila Visvadyalayam]
Tirupati, District Chittoor, Andhra Pradesh 517502
Tel: +91(8574) 21876
Cable: Mahilalaya, tirupati
Vice-Chancellor: Philomena Royappa Reddy
Registrar: Y.P. Reddy
Founded: 1983
D: Applied Mathematics; Communication and Journalism; Computer Science; Education; English Language and Literature; Law; Microbiology; Music; Nutrition and Child Development; Physical Education; Sericulture; Social Work; Telugu Studies; Women Development Studies Ce.

Sri Sathya Sai Institute of Higher Learning
Prasanthinilayam, Anantapur District, Andhra Pradesh 515134
Tel: +91(8574) 2039
Cable: sainstitut
Vice-Chancellor: S. Sampath
Registrar: K. Hanumanthappa
Founded: 1981
F: Arts; Business Management; Science.

Sri Venkateswara University
Tirupati, District Chittoor, Andhra Pradesh 517502
Tel: +91(8574) 21727
Cable: university, tirupati
Vice-Chancellor: P. Jayarama Reddy
Registrar: K. Jayadeva Reddy
Founded: 1954
F: Arts; Commerce; Education; Engineering; Law; Oriental Learning; Science; Biology and Earth Sciences; Humanities and Extension Studies; Mathematical and Physical Sciences; Social and Behavioural Sciences; Fine Arts.

Tamil University
Administrative Buildings, Tanjavur, Tamil Nadu 613005
Tel: +91(4362) 20040
Cable: valartamil, thanjavur
Vice-Chancellor: Avvai Natarajan
Registrar: S. Sivakamasundari
Founded: 1981
F: Arts; Developing Tamil; Language; Manuscriptology; Science.
S: Philosophy; Indian Languages.
D: Adult Education.
Ce: Tribal Research; Underwater Archaeology; Computer.

Tamil Nadu Agricultural University
Coimbatore, Tamil Nadu 641003
Tel: +91(422) 41788
Fax: +91(422) 41672
Telex: 855360 tnau in
Cable: farmvar, coimbatore, tamil nadu
Vice-Chancellor: S. Sankaran
Registrar: C. Ramaswami
Founded: 1971
F: Agriculture; Agricultural Engineering; Veterinary and Animal Sciences; Fishery; Horticulture.

Tamil Nadu Dr. M.G.R. Medical University
Periyar Building, 52 E.V.K. Sampath Salai, Vepery, Madras, Tamil Nadu 600007
Tel: +91(44) 588796
Fax: +91(44) 563277
Telex: 041-6273/muly in
Cable: mediclave, madras
Vice-Chancellor: B.P. Rajan
Registrar: Khaja Kaled Rahman
Founded: 1987
F: Medicine; Pharmacy; Dentistry; Nursing; Science.

Tamil Nadu Veterinary and Animal Sciences University
Madras Veterinary College Campus, Vepery,
Madras, Tamil Nadu 600007
Tel: +91(44) 581586
Telex: 041-5049-mvc in
Cable: univet, madras
Vice-Chancellor: V. Gnanaprakasam
Registrar: D. Padamananaban
Veterinary and Animal Sciences.

Tata Institute of Social Sciences
[Tata Samajik Vighyan Sanstha]
Deonar, Post Box No. 8313, Bombay,
Maharashtra 400088
Tel: +91(22) 5560108
Fax: +91(22) 5562912
Cable: fernstalk, chembur, bombay 400071
Vice-Chancellor: Armaity S. Desai (1992-)
Registrar: S.K. Bandyopadhyay
Founded: 1936, 1956
D: Criminology and Correctional Administration; Family and Child Welfare; Medical and Psychiatric Social Work; Personnel Management and Industrial Relations; Research Methodology; Urban and Rural Community Development; Social Welfare Administration; Health Services Studies; Extra Mural Studies.

Tezpur University
District Sonitpurt, Tezpur, Assam 784001
Vice-Chancellor: K.M. Pathak

Telugu University
Lalithakala Kshetram, Saroobagh, Public
Gardens, Hyderabad, Andhra Pradesh 500001
Tel: +91(842) 234676
Cable: telvers, hyderabad
Vice-Chancellor: P. Jagannatham
Registrar: N. Sivarama Murthy
Founded: 1985
S: History, Culture and Archaeology; Language Development; Literature.
Ce: Comparative Studies; Telugu.

Thapar Institute of Engineering and Technology
Patiala, Punjab 147001
Tel: +91(175) 812007
Telex: 392-207 trdc in
Cable: thaparinst, patiala
Director: M.P. Kapoor (1993-)
Registrar: Amarjit Juneja
Founded: 1955, 1985
S: Basic and Applied Sciences and Humanities; Humanities, Culture and Liberal Arts; Bio-Technology.
D: Civil Engineering and Construction Technology; Computer Science and Engineering; Electrical and Electronics Engineering; Mechanical and Industrial Engineering; Chemical Engineering.

Tilak Maharashtra Vidyapeeth
[Tilak Maharashtra Vidyapeeth]
Vidyapeeth Bhavan, Gultekadi, Pune,
Maharashtra 411037
Tel: A.R. Kulkarni
Cable: timavee, pune
Vice-Chancellor: H.P. Deshmukh
Registrar: V.K. Nulkar
Founded: 1921
F: Arts; Ayurveda; Education; Social Sciences.

Tripura University
College Road, Agartala, Tripura 799004
Tel: +91(381) 5434
Fax: +91(381) 5434
Cable: trivarsity, agartala
Vice-Chancellor (Acting): Y.D. Pande (1993-)
Registrar: B.K. Bajpaie
Founded: 1987
F: Arts; Sciences.

Utkal University
P.O. Vani Vihar, Bhubaneswar, District Puri,
Orissa 751004
Tel: +91(674) 52850
Cable: utkalvihar bhubaneswar
Vice-Chancellor: S. Acharya
Registrar: P.K. Patra
Founded: 1943
F: Arts; Commerce; Education; Engineering; Law; Medicine; Science.

Veer Kunwar Singh University
Ara, Bihar 802301
Vice-Chancellor: Surendra Nath Sirgn Registrar:
A.M.M. Kamal

Vidyasagar University
Midnapore, West Bengal 721101
Tel: +91 2329
Cable: university, midnapore
Vice-Chancellor: S.N. Ghosh
Registrar (Acting): A.K. Chakrabarti
Founded: 1981
F: Arts and Commerce; Science.

Vikram University
Ujjain, Madhya Pradesh 456010
Tel: +91(734) 52070
Cable: university, ujjain
Vice-Chancellor: Jokhan Singh
Registrar: S.C. Condal
Founded: 1957
F: Arts; Ayurveda; Commerce; Education; Engineering; Law; Life Sciences; Management Studies; Science; Social Sciences.
Ce: Adult/Continuing Education and Extension P.

Vinoba Bhave University
P.B. No.31, Hazanbagh, Brhar 825301
Tel: +91(9546) 2387
Vice-Chancellor: Vinodini Terway
Registrar: K.N. Gope

Visva-Bharati
P.O. Santiniketan, District Birbhum, West Bengal 731236
Tel: +91(3463) 52751
Fax: +91(3463) 52672
Telex: 203201 rabi in
Cable: visvabani, santiniketan
Vice-Chancellor: S. Bhattacharya
Registrar: Hironmay Chakravarthy
Founded: 1921, 1951
I: Sino-Indian Studies and Research; Hindi Studies and Research; Fine Arts and Crafts; Rural Reconstruction; Agriculture; Postgraduate Studies; Music and Dance; Science; Humanities and Social Sciences; Education.

Yashawantrao Chavan Maharashtra Open University
College Road, Nasik, Maharashtra 422005
Tel: +91(253) 70060
Fax: +91(253) 77244
Vice-Chancellor: R.G. Takawale
Registrar: B.D. Chaure
Founded: 1989
F: Arts.
D: Agriculture; Audio-visual; Commerce and Management; Computer Science; Education; Humanities; Instructional Technology; Planning and Co-ordination; Research and Development; Science and Technology; Student Evaluation; Student Services.
Ce: Computer.

NATIONAL ACADEMIC BODIES

Ministry of Human Resources Development
Department of Education, 534 Shastri Bhavan, New Delhi 110001
Tel: +91(11) 333936
Telex: 3161336 eouc in
Minister: Arjun Singh

Association of Indian Universities
16 Kotla Road, New Delhi 110002
Tel: +91(11) 3312429
Fax: +91(11) 3315105
Telex: 31-66180
President: R.G. Takawale, Vice-Chancellor, Yashwantrao Chavan Maharashtra Open University, Nashik (1994-)
Secretary-General: K.B. Takwale
Founded: 1925

University Grants Commission
Bahadur Shah Zafar Marg, New Delhi 110002
Tel: +91(11) 3311241
Fax: +91(11) 331
Telex: 3165913 ugc in
Chairman: G. Ram Reddy (1993-)
Secretary: I.J. Khanna
Founded: 1953

Indian National Commission for Co-operation with Unesco
Ministry of Human Resources Development, Department of Education, Room 203, (C) Wing 534, Shastri Bhavan, New Delhi 110001
Tel: (Secretariat)+91 384589
Telex: 3161336
Cable: educind new delhi
President: Arjun Singh
Secretary-General: S.V. Giri

INDONESIA

UNIVERSITIES

STATE INSTITUTIONS

Airlangga University
[Universitas Airlangga]
Jalan Airlangga 4-6, Surabaya 60286, East Java
Tel: +62(31) 41348
Fax: +62(31) 42557
Telex: 36138
Cable: unair
Rektor: Bambang Rahino Setokoesoemo (1989-)
Founded: 1954
S: Medicine; Dentistry; Law; Economics; Pharmacy; Social and Political Sciences; Mathematics and Natural Sciences; Veterinary Medicine.
C: Health Sciences.
Research Ce: Nutrition; Traditional Medicine; Enviromental Health; Regional Development; Law Development.

Andalas University
[Universitas Andalas]
Limau Manis, Padang 25163, West Sumatra
Tel: +62(751) 28981
Cable: unand
Rektor: Fachri Ahmad
Founded: 1956
F: Medicine; Law; Letters; Economics; Agriculture; Animal Husbandry; Science.

Bengkulu University
[Universitas Bengkulu]
Jalan Raya Kandang Limun, Bengkulu 38371
Tel: +62(736) 21170
Fax: +62(736) 41793
Rektor: Nitza Arbi
Founded: 1992
F: Law; Economics; Social and Political Sciences; Agriculture; Education.

Brawijaja University
[Universitas Brawijaja]
Jl. Mayor Jendral Haryono 169, Malang 65114,
East Java
Tel: +62(341) 51611
Fax: +62(341) 65420
Telex: 31873 ia
Rektor: Z.A. Achmady
Chief of General Administration: Sam Siahaya
Founded: 1957, 1963
F: Law; Economics; Administration; Agriculture;
Animal Husbandry; Engineering; Medicine;
Fishery; Polytechnics; Postgraduate Studies.
P: MIPA.

Cenderawasih University
[Universitas Cenderawasih]
Jalan Sentini, Abepura, Jayapura, Irian Barat
Tel: +62(976) 81301
Fax: +62(976) 81674
Telex: 76138 uncen ia
Cable: ucen japura
Rektor: August Kafiar
Founded: 1962
F: Law; Agriculture; Teacher Training;
Education; Social and Political Sciences.
I: Anthropology; Educational Research; Public
Administration Development.

Diponegoro University
[Universitas Diponegoro]
Jalan Imam Barjo, SH 1-3, P.O. Box 270,
Semarang 50241
Tel: +62(24) 318-381
Telex: 22315 undip sm
Rektor: Muladi S.H.
Founded: 1956, 1961
F: Law; Economics; Engineering; Medicine;
Social and Political Sciences; Letters and
Education; Animal Husbandry and Fishery.
L: Coastal Area Development (Jepara).
D: Biology.
Ce: Educational Systems and Development;
Computer and Data Processing.

Gadjah Mada University
[Universitas Gadjah Mada]
Bulaksumur, Yogyakarta 55281
Tel: +62(274) 88688
Fax: +62(274) 88974
Telex: 25135
Cable: ungam
Rektor: Mochamad Adnan (1990-94)
Pembantu Rektor II: Bambang Riyanto
Founded: 1949
F: Biology; Economics; Pharmacy; Philosophy;
Geography; Law; Social and Political Sciences;
Medicine; Dentistry; Veterinary Medicine;
Forestry; Mathematics and Natural Sciences;
Agriculture; Animal Husbandry; Psychology;
Letters; Engineering; Agricultural Technology;
Postgraduate Studies.
Ce: Population Studies; Rural and Regional
Development; Culture; National Planning and
Development; Japanese Studies; Environmental
Studies; Traditional Medicine.

General Soedirman University
[Universitas Jenderal Soedirman]
Kampus Unsoed, Grendeng P.O. Box 15,
Purwokerto 53122, Central Java
Tel: +62 21892
Rektor: Sobardi
Founded: 1963
F: Law; Agriculture; Biology; Animal Husbandry;
Economics.

Haluoleo University
[Universitas Haluoleo]
Jalan Mayjen S. Parmen, Kendari 93121,
Sulawesi Tenggara
Tel: +62(401) 21834
Rektor: Soleh Solahuddin
Founded: 1964, 1981
F: Education; Economics; Social and Political
Sciences; Agriculture.
I: Social Research; Community Service.
Ce: Ecological Studies; Population Studies;
Computer Science and Information Systems;
Rural Areas Development Studies.
Open U.

Hasanuddin University
[Universitas Hasanuddin]
Jalan Perintis Kemerdekaan, Kampus
Tamalanera, Ujung Pandang 90245
Tel: +62(411) 510-200
Cable: unhas
Rektor: Basri Hasanuddin
Founded: 1949, 1965
F: Economics; Law; Medicine; Engineering;
Public Health; Dentistry; Letters; Social and
Political Sciences; Agriculture; Animal
Husbandry; Mathematics and Natural Sciences.

*University of Indonesia Jakarta
[Universitas Indonesia]
Jalan Salemba Raya 4, Jakarta Pusat 10430
Tel: +62(21) 727-0020
Telex: 45680 ui jkt-ia
Cable: univ
Rektor: M.K. Tadjuddin
Pembantu Rektor II (Administrative): M. Legowo
Founded: 1950
F: Medicine; Dentistry; Mathematics and
Sciences; Engineering; Law; Economics; Letters;
Psychology; Political and Social Sciences; Public
Health; Postgraduate Studies; Polytechnic.
I: Research; Social Services.
Ce: Institutional Development Research; Health
Research; Social and Cultural Studies; Research
of Human Resources and Environment; Research
of Sciences and Technology; Education and
Social Services; Regional Development; Services
on Social Communication; Justice and the Role
of Law.

Jambi University
[Universitas Jambi]
Jln.Prof.Dr.Sri. Soedewi Masjchun Sofwan, SH
Jambi. 36122
Tel: +62(741) 23198
Rektor: S.B. Samad
Founded: 1963
*F: Law; Economics; Agriculture; Animal
Husbandry; Education; Teacher Training.*
Ce: Computer; Research.

Jember University
[Universitas Jember]
Jalan Kalimantan III/24, Kampus Bumi Tegal,
Jember, East Java
Tel: +62(331) 21270
Rektor: Simanhadi Widyaprakosa
Registrar: Made Pedungan Sardha
Founded: 1957, 1964
*F: Law; Social and Political Sciences;
Agriculture; Teachers Training and Educational
Sciences; Letters; Economics.*
Ce: Computer; Research.
Agricultural Polytechnic.

Lambung Mangkurat University
[Universitas Lambung Mangkurat]
Jalan Brigjen H. Hasan Basri, P.O. Box 219,
Banjarmasin 70023
Tel: +62(511) 54177
Fax: +62(511) 4195
Cable: unlam banjarmasin
Rektor: H. Supardi (1960-)
Founded: 1958, 1960
*F: Law; Economics; Social and Political
Sciences; Agriculture; Teacher Training and
Education; Forestry; Fishery; Civil Engineering;
Medicine.*
Ce: Environmental Study; Research.
Polytechnic.

Lampung University
[Universitas Lampung]
Jalan Prof. Dr. Sumantai Brojonegorol, Bander
Lampung
Tel: +62(721) 72767
Cable: unila
Rektor: Alhusiduki Hamim
Founded: 1961, 1965
*F: Economics; Law; Education; Teacher
Training; Agriculture.*

Mahendradatta University
[Universitas Mahendradatta]
Jalan Ken Arok 5, Denpasar
Tel: +62(361) 34827
Rektor: Jimmy J. Soputan (1987-)
Central Administrative Director: Shri Wedastera
Suyasa
Founded: 1963, 1984
*F: Social and Political Sciences; Law; Technical
and Industrial Management.*
*Ce: Social and Political Science Research; Law
Research; Technical Research.*

Mataram University
[Universitas Mataram]
Jalan Pendidikan 37, Kotak Pos 20, Mataram,
Ampenan 88125
Tel: +62 23007
Founded: 1962
*F: Economics; Law; Agriculture; Animal
Husbandry.*

Mulawarman University
[Universitas Mulawarman]
Jalan Kampus Gunung Kelua 5, Samarinda, P.O.
Box 68, Samarinda, Kalimantan Timur
Tel: +62(541) 41118
Cable: unmul samarinda
Rektor: Yunus Rasyid (1989-98)
Founded: 1962
*F: Social and Political Sciences; Economics;
Agriculture; Forestry; Teacher Training;
Education.*
I: Forestry Research.
*Ce: Computer; Language; Environmental
Studies.*

North Sumatra University
[Universitas Sumateria Utara]
Jalan Dr. T. Mansyur 9, Kampus USU, Medan
20155
Tel: (61) 23210
Telex: 51753
Rektor: Jusuf Hanafiah
Founded: 1957
*F: Agriculture; Medicine; Law; Engineering;
Economics; Mathematics and Natural Sciences;
Letters; Dentistry.*

Nusa Cendana University
[Universitas Nusa Cendana]
Jalan Adi Sucipto, Penfui, Kupang Timor
Tel: +62 21680
Cable: undana
Rektor: Moses Rupilu Toelihere
Founded: 1962
*F: Administration; Education and Teacher
Training; Education; Law; Agriculture; Animal
Husbandry.*
*Ce: Research; Environmental Life Study;
Population Study; Assessment and Development
of Dry Land Farming; Assessment and
Development of the Province; Social Service.*

Open University Pondok Cabe
[Universitas Terbuika]
Jalan Cabe Raya, Pondok Cabe Kotak Pos,
Cipatat, West Java 15411
Tel: +62(21) 749-0941
Fax: +62(21) 749-0417
Telex: 47498, ater ia
Rektor: B.S. Brotosiswoyo
Founded: 1984
*Education and Teacher Training; Economics;
Social and Political Sciences; Mathematics and
Natural Sciences.*

Padjadjaran University
[Universitas Padjadjaran]
Jalan Dipati Ukur 35, Bandung 40132
Tel: +62(22) 832-7178
Cable: unpad
Rektor: H. Maman P. Rukmana
Founded: 1952, 1957
*F: Law; Social and Political Sciences;
Economics; Letters; Psychology; Medicine;
Dentistry; Agriculture; Animal Husbandry; Natural
Sciences; Communication Studies.
I: Parasitology; Natural Sciences; Ecology;
Religious Studies; Social Research; Cultural
Studies.
D: Extramural Studies.*

Palangka Raya University
[Universitas Palangka Raya]
Kampus CINPAR, Jalan Yos Sudarso, Tanjung
Nyaho, Palangka Raya
Tel: +62(514) 21722
Cable: unpar palangka raya
Rektor: Amris Makmur
Founded: 1963
*F: Teacher Training; Economics; Education;
Agriculture.*

Pattimura University
[Universitas Pattimura]
Jalan Ir. M. Putuhenan, Kotak Pos 95, Kampus
Unpatti Poka-Ambon, Ambon
Tel: +62 69520
Fax: +62 69560
Cable: kotak pos 95
Rektor: Jan Laurens Nanere (1973-)
Pembantu Rektor I (Administrative): P.J.
Siwabessy
Founded: 1956, 1963
*F: Law; Social and Political Sciences;
Agriculture and Forestry; Animal Husbandry and
Fishery; Economics; Teacher Training;
Technology.
Ce: Research; Public Service.*

Riau University
[Universitas Riau]
Jalan Pattimura 9, Pekanbaru, Riau 28131
Tel: +62(761) 21341
Rektor: Mohammad Diah
Founded: 1962
*F: Mathematics and Natural Sciences;
Economics; Social and Political Sciences;
Fishery; Education.*

Sam Ratulangi University
[Universitas Sam Ratulangi]
Kampus Unsrat, Bahu, Manado
Tel: +62(431) 63586
Rektor: R.S. Tangkudung
Founded: 1965
*F: Medicine; Agriculture; Animal Husbandry;
Law; Economics; Social and Political Sciences;
Engineering; Letters; Fishery; Education; Teacher
Training.*

Sebelas Maret University
[Universitas Sebelas Maret]
Jalan Ir. Soetami 36A, Kentingan, Surakarta
57125
Tel: +62 36633
Rektor: Koneto Wibisono Siswomihardjo
Founded: 1976
*F: Education; Teacher Training and Education;
Letters; Social and Political Sciences; Law;
Economics; Medicine; Agriculture; Engineering.
Ce: Educational Systems Development.*

Sriwijaya University
[Universitas Sriwijaya]
Jalan Srijaya Negara, Palembang 30319
Tel: +62(711) 358-688
Cable: rektor unseri
Rektor: Amran Halim
Founded: 1953, 1960
*F: Economics; Law; Engineering; Medicine;
Agriculture; Teacher Training; Education.*

Syiah Kuala University
[Universitas Syiah Kuala]
Komplek Darussalam, Banda Aceh 23111
Tel: +62(21) 22721
Fax: +62(21) 22721
Telex: usk bna 54153
Cable: unsyiah
Rektor: Ali Basyah Amin (1991-)
Pembantu Rektor I (Academic): Ridhwan Ibrahim
Founded: 1959, 1961
*F: Economics; Law; Veterinary Medicine and
Animal Husbandry; Engineering; Agriculture;
Teacher Training and Education; Medicine.
Ce: Language; Public Service; Research.
Open University.
Polytechnic.*

Tadulako University
[Universitas Tadulako]
Kampus Bumi Bahari, Taduleko, Palu 94111
Tel: +62 22355
Rektor: Musji Amal Pagiling
Founded: 1981
*F: Law; Social and Political Sciences;
Agriculture; Education; Teacher Training.*

Tanjungpura University
[Universitas Tanjungpura]
Jalan A Yani, Pontianak 78122, Kalimantan Barat
Tel: +62 39636
Rektor: Mahmud Akil
Founded: 1965
*F: Law; Economics; Agriculture; Engineering;
Social and Political Sciences; Teacher Training;
Education.*

Udayana State University
[Universitas Udayana]
Kampus Bukit, Jimbaran, Denpasar, Bali 80361
Tel: +62(361) 71854
Founded: 1962
*F: Letters; Medicine; Animal Husbandry; Law
and Social Sciences; Engineering; Agriculture;
Economics; Education; Teacher Training.*

PRIVATE INSTITUTIONS

Adventist University of Indonesia Bandung
[Universitas Advent Indonesia]
Jalan Cisarua-Lembang, d/a Kanton Pos
Cipagaanti, Bandung
Tel: +62(22) 4583
Rektor: R.A. Hutagaol
Founded: 1948, 1962, 1982
*D: Theology; Education; Business
Administration; Biology.*
C: Nursing.

Amir Hamzah University
[Universitas Amir Hamzah]
Jalan Sampali (Medan Estate), Medan
Rektor: Mahadi
Founded: 1981
Law; Economics.

Atma Jaya Catholic University of Indonesia
[Universitas Katolik Indonesia Atma Jaya]
Jalan Jendral Sudirman 51, Jakarta Selatan
12930
Tel: +62(21) 570-3306
Cable: unikatolik
Rektor: Mariana Setiadarma (1987-)
Founded: 1960
*F: Economics; Public Administration; Education
and Teacher Training; Mechanical and Electrical
Engineering; Law; Medicine; Psychology.*
Ce: Atma Jaya Research; Ethical Research.
I: Languages.

Atmajaya Usung-Pandang University
[Universitas Atmajaya Usung-Pandang]
Jalan Tanjung Alang 23-Ujung, Pandang 90134
Tel: +62(411) 81038
Rector: S.J. Jobs (1990-93)
Pembantu Rektor: A. Soehardjono
Founded: 1981
F: Economics; Electro Technics; Law.
Ce: Agrarian Law Research.

Atmajaya University Yogyakarta
[Universitas Atmajaya]
Jalan Babarsari 44, Yogyakarta
Rektor: Silvester A. Khodi
Founded: 1965
Law; Economics; Engineering.

17 August 1945 University Banyuwangi
[Universitas 17 Agustus 1945 Banyuwangi]
Jalan Adi Sucipto 26, Banyuwangi, East Java
Tel: +62(333) 41980
Rektor: I.G. Kurtjana
Founded: 1980
*F: Economics; Social and Political Sciences;
Law; Agriculture; Teacher Training and
Education.*

17 August 1945 University Cirebon
[Universitas 17 Agustus 1945 Cirebon]
Jalan Siliwangi 41, Cirebon
Tel: +62 4312
Rektor: Endi Syamsalgbacri
Founded: 1964
Public and Business Administration; Law.

17 August 1945 University Jakarta
[Universitas 17 Agustus 1945]
Jalan Sunter Permai, Podosnoro, Jakarta Cetara
Tel: +62(21) 687-301
Rektor: L. Aroean
Founded: 1952
*F: Social and Political Sciences; Law; Public
and Business Administration; Engineering;
Pharmacy; Economics.*

17 August 1945 University Samarinda
[Universitas 17 Agustus 1945 Samarinda]
Jalan Ir. H. Juanda, Air Puteh, Samarinda
Tel: +62 43390
Rektor: H.M. Ardan
Founded: 1965
*Law; Social and Political Sciences; Economics;
Engineering.*

17 August 1945 University Semarang
[Universitas 17 Agustus 1945 Semarang]
Jalan Seteran Dalam 9, Semarang 50134
Tel: +62(24) 318-202
Rektor: Sujanto
Founded: 1963
*F: Law; Social and Political Sciences;
Economics; Engineering.*
I: Research and Development.

17 August 1945 University Surabaya
[Universitas 17 Agustus 1945 Surabaya]
Jalan Semolowaru 45, Surabaya
Tel: +62(31) 578-755
Rektor: Soeparman Hadipranoto
Founded: 1964
*Public and Business Administration; Economics;
Law; Industrial Technology.*

Bojonegoro University
[Universitas Bojonegoro]
Jalan Lettu Suyitno 2, Bojonegoro
Tel: +62 81984
Rektor: Soebijakto
Founded: 1981
Law; Social and Political Sciences; Agriculture.

Bung Hatta University
[Universitas Bung Hatta]
Jalan Sumatera, Ulak Karang, Padang, Sumatra
Barat 251331
Tel: +62(751) 516-78
Fax: +62(751) 554-75
Rektor: Sjofjan Asnawi (1990-94)
Registrar: Mas Eriza
Founded: 1981
*F: Economics; Law; Teacher Training and
Education; Letters; Engineering; Fisheries.*

Ce: Co-operative Studies; Cultural Studies and Development; Language Training and Development; Fisheries Studies and Development.

Christian University of Indonesia Jakarta
[Universitas Kristen Indonesia]
Jalan Mayjen Sutoyo, Cawang, Jakarta 13630
Tel: +62) 809-0311
Fax: +62) 809-3948
Rektor: Maurits Simatupang
Founded: 1953
F: Engineering; Letters; Medicine; Law; Economics; Education and Teacher Training.

Christian University of Indonesia Tomohon
[Universitas Kristen Indonesia Tomohon]
Jalan Kakaskasen III, Tomohon 95362 (North Sulawesi)
Tel: +62 511-45
Rektor: E.A. Worang
Pembantu Rektor (Administrator): Willy Najoan
Founded: 1965
F: Theology; Education and Teacher Training; Psychology; Mathematical and Natural Sciences; Law; Veterinary Medicine; Public Health; Technical Engineering; Agricultural Technology; Christian Education.
Ce: Research and Development; Environmental Studies.

Darma Agung University
[Universitas Darma Agung]
Jalan Bantam 21, Medan
Tel: +62 28931
Rektor: Lukito Sukahar
Founded: 1957
Law; Social and Political Science; Economics; Education and Teacher Training; Engineering; Agriculture; Industrial and Textile Engineering; Letters.

Darul'Ulum University of Jombang
[Universitas Darul'Ulum]
Jalan Merdeka 29A, Jombang, East Java
Tel: +62(321) 815-17
Fax: +62(321) 816-31
Rektor: H. Lukman Hakim Musta'in (1991-93)
Secretary: Qomaruzzaman
Founded: 1965
F: Law; Social and Political Sciences; Education Engineering; Economics; Agriculture; Pedagogy; Psychology.
I: Research and Development; Islamic Studies.
Ce: Training for Foreign Languages; Computer.

Dr. R. Mustopo University
[Universitas Prof. Dr. R. Mustopo]
Jalan Hanglekir 1/8 Blok, H. Kebayoran Baru, Jakarta
Tel: +62(21) 7702-69
Rektor: Wibowo
Founded: 1958, 1962
F: Dentistry; Social and Political Science; Economics; Communication Studies.

Dr. Soetomo University Surabaya
[Universitas Dr. Soetomo Surabaya]
Jalan Semolowaru, Surabaya
Tel: +62(31) 60118
Rektor: Ida Bagus Alit
Administration; Fisheries; Education.

Gresik University
[Universitas Gresik]
Jalan Arief Rakhmar Hakim 2B, Gresik
Tel: +62 81918
Rektor: Mudjiono
Founded: 1981
Engineering; Education; Law Economics.

Ibn Khaldun Bogor University
[Universitas Ibn Khaldun Bogor]
Jalan R.E. Martadinata 2-4, Bogor
Tel: +62(251) 211-12
Rektor: Hafidhuddin
Founded: 1961
F: Economics; Law; Islamic Law; Engineering; Islamic Theology; Education; Islamic Education.

Ibn Khaldun University Jakarta
[Universitas Ibnu Khaldun]
Jalan Pemuda 1 Kav. 97, Rawamangun, Jakarta Timur
Tel: +62 488-0599
Rektor: H. Amura
Founded: 1956, 1960
F: Journalism and Mass Communication; Social and Political Sciences; Law; Agriculture; Economics; Islamic Studies; Shari'a.

Indonesia Muda University
[Universitas Indonesia Muda]
Jalan Letjen Suprapto 22, Jakarta
Founded: 1965
Engineering; Law.

Islamic University of Bandung
[Universitas Islam Bandung]
Jalan Tamansari 1, Bandung 40116
Tel: +62(22) 50368 +
Tel: +62(22) 446-136
Rektor: Achmad Tirtosudero
Founded: 1959
F: Law; Psychology; Engineering; Economics; Mathematics and Natural Sciences; Communication; Islamic Law (Shari'a); Islamic Theology; Islamic Education.
I: Research and Extension.

Islamic University of Indonesia Yogyakarta
[Universitas Islam Indonesia]
Jalan Cik Ditiro 1, Yogyakarta
Tel: +62(274) 3091
Rektor: H.L. Soejoeti
Founded: 1945, 1951
F: Economics; Law; Civil Engineering; Textile Technology.

Islamic University of Jakarta
[Universitas Islam Jakarta]
Jalan Balai Rakyat, Utan Kayu, Jakarta
Tel: +62 452-86
Rektor: Nazaruddin
Founded: 1951
F: Law; Economics.

Islamic University of Malang
[Universitas Islam Malang]
Jalan Mayjen Haryono 193, Malang
Rektor: Tholchah Hasan
Founded: 1981
*Law; Agriculture; Economics; Engineering;
Education and Teacher Training.*

Islamic University of North Sumatra
[Universitas Islam Sumatera Utara]
Jalan Sisingamangaraja, Teladan, Medan 20217
Tel: +62(61) 243-82
Rektor: Yasuf Rangkuti
Founded: 1952
*F: Law; Letters; Economics; Education and
Teacher Training; Social and Political Science;
Agriculture; Medicine; Engineering; Islamic Law;
Islamic Teaching; Islamic Communication.*

Islamic University of Nusantara
[Universitas Islam Nusantara]
Jalan Sukarno Hatta, Bandung
Tel: +62(22) 411-43
Rektor: Tb. Abin Syamsuddin Makmun
Founded: 1959
Economics; Law; Education.

Islamic University of Riau
[Universitas Islam Riau]
Jalan Prof. Moh. Younes SH 29, Pekanbaru, Riau
Tel: +62 21016
Rektor: H. Zaini Kunin
Pembantu Rektor (Academic): Tengku Dahril
Founded: 1962
*F: Law; Theology; Engineering; Agriculture;
Economics; Social and Political Sciences;
Education.*
I: Legal Aid Studies; Research.
*Ce: Rural Development Studies; Management
Development.*

Islamic University 'Sheikh Yusuf'
[Universitas Islam 'Syekh Yusuf' Tangerang]
Babakan, Tangerang, Jawa Barat
Tel: +62 22340
Rektor: Salura
Founded: 1966, 1975
*F: Social and Political Sciences; Law; Theology;
Engineering; Education.*

Islamic University of Sultan Agung
[Universitas Islam Sultan Agung]
Jalan Raya Kaligawe, Semarang
Tel: +62(24) 2844
Cable: unissula
Founded: 1962
F: Law; Economics; Engineering; Medicine.

Jakarta University
[Universitas Jakarta]
Jalan Pulo Mas Barat, Villa Tarah Mas, Jakarta
Rektor: H.M. Singh Maraf
Founded: 1965
*Engineering; Law; Public and Business
Administration.*

Janabadra University
[Universitas Janabadra]
Jalan Tetara Rakyat Mataram 57, Yogyakarta
Tel: +62(274) 61039
Rektor: Sedjito Sosrodihardjo
Founded: 1958
Law.

Jayabaya University
[Universitas Jayabaya]
Jalan A. Yani, By-Pass, Jakarta
Tel: +62(21) 414-771
Rektor: Achjani Atmakusuma (1962-)
Founded: 1958
*F: Economics; Law; Political and Social
Sciences; Engineering.*

Kediri University
[Universitas Kediri]
Jalan Mastrip 32, Kediri
Tel: +62 61002
Rektor: H. Borgoes Sasmito
Founded: 1980
*Law; Social and Political Science; Agriculture;
Economics; Engineering.*

Khairun University
[Universitas Khairun]
Jalan Bandara Abdallah, Ternate, Maluku Utara
97728
Tel: +62 21550
Rektor: Jusuf Abdulrahman
Secretary-General: Abdul Hamid Hasan
Founded: 1964
*F: Law; Economics and Development Studies;
Education.*

Krida Coacana Christian University
[Universitas Kristen Krida Coacana]
Jalan Tanjung Duren Raya 4, Jakarta 11470
Tel: +62(21) 599-601
Rektor: Rudi C. Tarcimingkeng
Founded: 1967
F: Medicine; Engineering; Economics.
I: Social Welfare.

Krisnadwipayana University
[Universitas Krisnadwipayana]
Jatiwaringin, Pondok Gede, P.O. 7774/jatm,
Jakarta
Tel: +62 846-2230
Rektor: R. Moehono
Founded: 1952
*Engineering; Public and Business Administration;
Law; Economics.*

Madura University
[Universitas Madura]
Jalan djokotole 43, Pamekasan
Rektor: H. Hadiatoellah
Founded: 1978
Law; Economics; Social and Political Science; Education.

Mahasaraswati University
[Universitas Mahasaraswati]
Jalan Kembodja, Denpasar
Tel: +62(361) 27019
Rektor: I. Gusti Made Tamba (1963-)
Founded: 1962
F: Agriculture; Law; Economics; Education and Teacher Training; Civil Engineering; Dentistry.
Ce: Research.
L: Language.

Merdeka University Madiun
[Universitas Merdeka Madiun]
Jalan Pahlawan 25, P.O. Box 12, Madiun
Tel: +62 4427
Rektor: Soerjano
Founded: 1979
Law; Economics; Social and Political Sciences; Engineering.

Merdeka University Malang
[Universitas Merdeka Malang]
J1. Terusan Raya Dieng 62-64, Malang 65146
Tel: +62(341) 28395
Fax: +62(341) 64994
Rektor: Wahjoetomo
Pembantu Rektor (Academic): Suwarso
Founded: 1964
F: Law; Economics; Engineering; Political and Social Sciences.
D: Tourism.

Methodist University of Indonesia Medan
[Universitas Methodist Indonesia]
Jalan Hang Tuah 8, Medan
Tel: +62(61) 536-735
Rektor: L. Hutahuruk
Founded: 1965
Letters; Medicine; Agriculture.

Mount Klabat University
[Universitas Klabat]
Airmadidi-Manado, P.O. Box 3, Sulawesi Utara
Tel: +62(431) 91042
Cable: adventist manado
Founded: 1965
Agriculture; Business Administration; Secretarial Studies; Theology; Education.

Maranatha Christian University
[Universitas Kristen Maranatha]
Jalan Cihampelas 169, Bandung
Tel: +62(22) 81212
Rektor: Yusuk Gundi S.
Founded: 1965
Medicine; Engineering; Psychology; Letters.

Muhammadiyah University of Jakarta
[Universitas Muhammadiyah Jakarta]
Jln. KH. Ahmad Dahlan Cirendeu Ciputat, Jakarta Selatan 15419
Tel: +62 741-894
Rektor: Roeslan Saleh (1955-)
Founded: 1955
F: Engineering; Law; Social and Political Sciences; Economics; Agriculture; Islamic Education; Islamic Law; Theology.
I: Research and Development; Social Service; Islamic and Muhammadiyah Organization.
Ce: Energy and the Environment (Research); Technology and Development (Research); Applied Biotechnology (Study); Economic Research and Development.

Muhammadiyah University of Jember
[Universitas Muhammadiyah Jember]
Jalan Karimata, 43, Kotak Pos 104, Jember 68121, East Java
Tel: +62 21640
Rektor: Mohammed Ionak (1981-)
Founded: 1981
F: Agriculture; Law; Education and Teacher Training; Economics; Social and Political Sciences; Technology.
I: Research and Social Development.

Muhammadiyah University of Magelang
[Universitas Muhammadiyah Magelang]
Jalan Tidar 21, Magelang
Tel: +62 2082
Rektor: Masanan Andara
Founded: 1964
Economics; Law; Education.

Muhammadiyah University of Malang
[Universitas Muhammadiyah Malang]
Jalan Bandung 1, Malang 65113
Tel: +62(341) 51253
Fax: +62(341) 82060
Rektor: H.A. Malik Fadjar (1992-96)
Founded: 1965
F: Education and Teacher Training; Social and Political Sciences; Law; Economics; Engineering; Agriculture; Psychology; Husbandry; Islamic Education; Islam.
Ce: Social Sciences and Indonesian Islamic Studies.

Muhammadiyah University of Mataram
[Universitas Muhammadiyah Mataram]
Jalan K.H.A. Dahlan 1, Mataram
Tel: +62 23723
Rektor: H. Agusfian Wahab
Founded: 1980
F: Social and Political Sciences; Education; Civil Engineering; Agriculture.

Muhammadiyah University of North Sumatra
[Universitas Muhammadiyah Sumatera Utara]
Jalan Gedung Arca 53, Medan
Tel: +62(61) 20217
Rektor: H. Dalmi Iskandar
Founded: 1957
Education; Sociology; Economics; Agriculture.

Muhammadiyah University of Surakarta
[Universitas Muhammadiyah Surakarta]
Jalan A. Yanis, Pabelau P.O. Box 1, Surakarta
Rektor: H.A. Malit Fajar
Founded: 1958
Education and Teacher Training.

Muhammadiyah University of Ujung Pandang
[Universitas Muhammadiyah Ujung Pandang]
Jalan Ranggong 21, Ujung Pandang
Tel: +62(411) 21879
Rektor: Djamalludin Amien
Founded: 1963
Education and Teacher Training; Social Work; Social and Political Sciences; Economics.

Muhammad Sroedji University
[Universitas Muhammad Sroedji]
Jalan Sriwijayo 32, Jember
Rektor: Moch. Nurullah
Founded: 1981
Social and Political Sciences; Education; Economics; Engineering; Law.

Muria Kudus University
[Universitas Muria Kudus]
Kampus Gondang Ilanis, Bal P.O. Box 53, Bawah, Kudus
Tel: +62 22229
Rektor: Abd. Latief Nawawi
Founded: 1980
Economics; Law; Education and Teacher Training.

Muslim University of Indonesia Ujung Pandang
[Universitas Muslim Indonesia]
Jalan Kakatua 27, Ujung Pandang
Rektor: H. Abdurahman A. Basalamah
Founded: 1954
Economics; Law; Engineering.

Narotama University
[Universitas Narotama]
Jalan A.R. Hakim 51, Surabaya
Tel: +62(31) 596-404
Rektor: R. Djoko Soemadijo
Founded: 1981
Economics; Law; Engineering.

National University Jakarta
[Universitas Nasional]
Jalan Sawo Manila, Pejaten, Pasar Minggu, Jakarta 12510
Tel: +62(21) 782-700
Rektor: S.T. Alisjahbana
Administratur: El Amry B. Putera
Founded: 1949, 1953
F: Political Science; Biology; Law; Economics; Language and Literature; Mathematics and Physics; Engineering; Agriculture.
Ce: Islamic Studies; Japanese Studies.

Ngurah Rai University
[Universitas Ngurah Rai]
Jalan Patih Jelantik 9, Denpasar, Bali
Tel: +62(361) 34017
Rektor: I. Ketut Wirata Sindhu
Founded: 1979
Law; Economics; Social and Political Sciences; Engineering.

Nommensen (HKBP) University
[Universitas HKBP Nommensen]
Jalan Dr. Soetomo 4A, Medan 20234, Sumatera Utara
Tel: +62(61) 511-426
Telex: 51577 nom mon
Rektor: Danlay Purnama Tampubolon
Founded: 1954
F: Economics; Public and Business Administration; Education and Teacher Training; Engineering; Animal Husbandry; Law; Arts; Agriculture.
D: Research; Batak Studies.

Pakuan University
[Universitas Pakuan]
Jalan Pakuan, P.O. Box 353, Bogor
Tel: +62 312-206
Founded: 1961, 1980
F: Law; Economics; Education and Teacher Training; Letters; Technology; Mathematics and Natural Sciences.
I: Research and Development; Academic Services to the Community.
L: Computer; Language.

Pancasila University Jakarta
[Universitas Pancasila]
Srengseng Sawah, Pasar Minggu, Jakarta 12640, Selatan
Tel: +62(21) 727-0086
Rektor: Awaloeddin Jamin
Founded: 1966
F: Law; Economics; Pharmacy; Engineering.

Pancasakti University Tegal
[Universitas Pancasakti Tegal]
Jalan Pancasakti 2, Tegal
Tel: +62 21082
Rektor: Seosilo Hardjo
Founded: 1979
F: Social and Political Sciences; Fishery; Teacher Training.

Parahyangan Catholic University
[Universitas Katolik Parahyangan]
Jalan Ciumbuleuit 94, Bandung 40141, Jawa
Barat
Tel: +62(22) 83691
Fax: +62(22) 81110
Cable: unpar, bandung
Rektor: Pande Radja Silalahi (1990-94)
Academic and Student Registrar: Cecilia Lauw
Founded: 1955, 1958, 1962
*F: Economics; Law; Social and Political
Sciences; Engineering; Philosophy and Religion.*

Pasundan University
[Universitas Pasundan]
Jalan Tamansari 8, Bandung
Tel: +62(22) 51309
Rektor: Tsetje Sukarna Hasan
Founded: 1960
*Law; Economics; Engineering; Education and
Teacher Training.*

Paul Christian University of Indonesia
[Universitas Kristen Indonesia Paulus]
Jalan Cenderawasih 65, Ujung Pandang
Tel: +62(411) 83259
Rektor: M. Towoliu Harmanses
Founded: 1965
Engineering; Law; Economics; Letters.

Pekalongan University
[Universitas Pekalongan]
Jalan Teutara Pelagar 49, Pekalongan
Tel: +62 21096
Rektor: M. Ichsan Lain
Founded: 1981
Economics; Law; Fishery.

Pembangunan Panca Budi University
[Universitas Pembangunan Panca Budi]
Subroto, Km 415, Medan 20122
Tel: +62(61) 519-571
Rektor: Abd Khalik Fajduani
Founded: 1961
*F: Law; Philosophy; Economics; Agriculture;
Architecture; Technology.*

Pepabri University of Ujung Pandang
[Universitas Pepabri Ujung Pandang]
Jalan Syarif Alqadri 32A, Ujung Pandang
Tel: +62(411) 83773
Rektor: H. Mustari Talli
*Social and Political Sciences; Engineering;
Administration.*

Petra Christian University
[Universitas Kristen Petra]
Siwalankerto 121-131, Tromolpos 5304, Surabaya
60002
Tel: +62(31) 813-040
Rektor: Wasis
Founded: 1961
Letters; Engineering; Economics.

Proclamation '45 University
[Universitas Proklamasi '45]
Jalan Dagen 129, Yogyakarta
Tel: +62 2021
Rektor: Hidayat Mukmina
Founded: 1964
Law; Economics; Social and Political Sciences.

Sarjanawiyata Tamansiswa University
[Universitas Sarjanawiyata Tamansiswa]
Jalan Kusumanegara 121, Yogyakarta 55165
Tel: +62(274) 62265
Rektor: Imam Barnadib (1989-93)
Founded: 1955
*F: Teacher Training and Education; Agriculture;
Economics.*

Satya Wacana Christian University
[Universitas Kristen Satya Wacana]
Jalan Diponegoro 52-60, Salatiga 50711, Java
Tel: +62(298) 81362
Fax: +62(298) 81420
Telex: 22364 ukswsa
Vice-Chancellor: Willi Toisuta (1983-93)
Registrar: Hot Pasaribu
Founded: 1956, 1962, 1977
*F: Law; Economics; Theology; Agriculture;
Biology; Electronics; Teacher Training and
Education.*
*D: Natural Sciences and Mathematics; General
Studies.*
*Ce: Language; Computer; Advancement of
Teaching; Research in Science and Technology.*

Siliwangi University
[Universitas Siliwangi]
Jalan Siliwangi, P.O. Box 65, Tasikmalaya 46115,
West Java
Tel: +62 21634
Rektor: H. Mashudi
Founded: 1979
*F: Teacher Training and Education; Economics;
Agriculture; Engineering.*

Simalungun University
[Universitas Simalungun]
Jalan Sisingamangaraja Barat, Pematang Siantar
Tel: +62 24719
Rektor: Muller Damanik
Founded: 1966
*F: Economics; Agriculture; Law; Engineering;
Education and Teacher Training.*

Slamet Riyadi University Surakarta
[Universitas Slamet Riyadi Surakarta]
Jalan Sumpah Permuda 18, Joglo Kadipiro,
Surakarta, Central Java
Tel: +62 7839
Rektor: Sarwono
Founded: 1980
*F: Law; Economics; Agriculture; Social and
Political Sciences; Teacher Training and
Education.*
Ce: Research and Community Service.

Soegijapranata Catholic University
[Universitas Katholik Soegijapranata]
Pandanaraw 100, Semarang 50241, Central Java
Tel: +62(24) 316-142
Fax: +62(24) 313-795
Rektor: M. Sastrapratedja (1989-93)
Pembantu Rektor: A. Widanti Soebiyanto
Founded: 1982
*F: Economics; Civil Engineering; Law;
Psychology.
I: English Language Training; Socio-Economic
Research; Applied Research for Eco-Settlement.
Ce: Health Psychology (Research).*

Soerjo University
[Universitas Soerjo]
Jalan Jurusan, Ngawi Cepu, Ngawi
Founded: 1981
Law; Social and Political Science; Agriculture.

Sunan Giri University
[Universitas Sunan Giri]
Jalan Citarum 1, Surabaya
Tel: +62(31) 578-225
Founded: 1976
*Engineering; Economics; Social and Political
Science; Law.*

Surabaya University
[Universitas Surabaya]
Jalan Ngagel Jaya Selatan 169, Surabaya
Tel: +62(31) 60866
Rektor: Soebijono Tjitrowinoto
Founded: 1966
*Pharmacy; Law; Economics; Psychology;
Engineering.*

Swadaya Gunung Jati University
[Universitas Swadaya Gunung Jati]
Jalan Dervi Sartika 1, Cirebon
Rektor: Saleh Sachyana
Founded: 1960
*Law; Economics; Education and Teacher
Training.*

Tarumanagara University
[Universitas Tarumanagara]
Jalan Letjen S Parman 1, Jakarta 11440
Tel: +62(21) 591-747
Rektor: A. Kahono
Founded: 1962
Medicine; Engineering; Law; Economics.

Tidar University of Magelang
[Universitas Tidar Magelang]
Jalan Kapten Suparman, Magelang
Tel: +62 2438
Rektor: A. Gambiro
Pembantu Rektor I: Jojok Tarunawijaya
Founded: 1979
*F: Economics; Education and Teacher Training;
Agriculture; Social and Political Sciences;
Engineering.
I: Research; Public Service.*

Tri Dharma University
[Universitas Tri Dharma]
Jalan Kapten Tendean 26, Balikpapan
Rektor: M. Simanjantak
Founded: 1978
*Law; Engineering; Education and Teacher
Training.*

Trisakti University
[Universitas Trisakti]
Jalan Kiyai Tapa, Grogol, Jakarta 11440
Tel: +62(21) 566-3231/3
Fax: +62(21) 567-3001
Rektor: Mulyatno Sindhudarmoko (1990-94)
Vice-Rector for Personnel, Administration, and
Finance Affairs: Itjang D. Gunawan
Founded: 1965
*F: Law; Economics; Medicine; Dentistry; Civil
Engineering and Planning; Industrial Technology;
Mineral Technology; Landscape Architecture and
Environmental Technology.
C: Transportation Management.
A: Tourism; Accountancy; Insurance; Graphic
Technology.
I: Research.
Ce: Computer.*

Tunas Pembangunan University
[Universitas Tunas Pembangunan]
Jalan Walanda Maramis 31, Cengklik, Surakarta
Rektor: Soenarso
Founded: 1980
Engineering; Economics; Agriculture; Education.

Veterans University of the Republic of Indonesia
[Universitas Veteran Republik Indonesia]
Jalan G. Bawakaraeng 72, Ujung Pandang
Tel: +62(411) 324-181
Rektor: H.I.M. Salman
Founded: 1961
*Education and Teacher Training; Social and
Political Sciences; Engineering.*

Widya Karya Catholic University
[Universitas Katholik Widya Karya]
Jalan Bondowoso 2, P.O. Box 121, Malang
Tel: +62 28171
Rektor: Riyadi Sarojo J.
Founded: 1982
Economics; Agriculture; Engineering.

Widya Mandala Catholic University
[Universitas Katholik Widya Mandala]
Jalan Dinoyo 42-44, Surabaya 60265
Tel: +62(31) 684-478
Rektor: Soetrisoro
Founded: 1960
*F: Education and Teacher Training; Pharmacy;
Economics; Engineering; Agricultural Technology.
Ce: Applied Research.*

Wijayakusuma University Purwokerto
[Universitas Wijayakusuma Purwokerto]
Kampus Unwiku Karangsalam, P.O. Box 85,
Purwokerto, Jawa Tengah
Tel: +62(281) 21889
Founded: 1980
F: Law; Social and Political Sciences;
Economics; Engineering; Animal Husbandry.
I: Research.

Wijayakusuma University of Surabaya
[Universitas Wijayakusuma Surabaya]
Jalan Dukuh Kupang XXV, Surabaya 60225
Tel: +62(31) 675-77
Rektor: Trimojono
Founded: 1980
F: Engineering; Agriculture; Law; Economics;
Social and Political Sciences; Education and
Teacher Training; Medicine; Veterinary Medicine.
I: Research and Public Services.

Wisnu Wardhana University
[Universitas Wisnu Wardhana]
Jalan Dr Cipto 17, Malang
Tel: +62 26018
Rektor: Sako Wiyono
Founded: 1981
Law; Economics; Agriculture; Education and
Teacher Training.

OTHER INSTITUTIONS

STATE INSTITUTIONS

Institut Keguruan dan Ilmu Pendidikan, Bandung
Jalan Dr. Setiabudi 229, Bandung
Tel: +62(22) 83162
Rektor: Abdal Kodir
Founded: 1954
Teacher Training and Education; Mathematics;
Social Sciences; Technology; Health Education.

Institut Keguruan dan Ilmu Pendidikan, Jakarta
Kampus Rawamangun Muka, Jakarta 13220
Tel: +62(21) 81811
Rektor: Anah S. Suparno
Founded: 1963
Education.

Institut Keguruan dan Ilmu Pendidikan, Malang
Jalan Surabaya 6, Malang
Tel: +62 51312
Rektor: Hadi Soeparto
Founded: 1954
Education.

Institut Keguruan dan Ilmu Pendidikan, Manado
Kampus IKIP Negeri, Mandando, Tondano
Tel: +62 51193
Rektor: Max Wulleer
Founded: 1965
Education.

Institut Keguruan dan Ilmu Pendidikan, Medan
Jalan William Iskander, Medan, Estate
Tel: +62 327-704
Rektor: Sukarna
Founded: 1965
Education; Letters; Mathematics; Social Sciences;
Engineering; Health Education.

Institut Keguruan dan Ilmu Pendidikan, Padang
Kampus IKIP, Air Tawar, Padang
Tel: +62(751) 53902
Rektor: Mohammed Ansyan
Founded: 1954
Education; Letters; Mathematics; Social Sciences;
Engineering; Health Education.

Institut Keguruan dan Ilmu Pendidikan, Semarang
Jalan Kelud Utara, Semarang 50232
Tel: +62(24) 311-502
Rektor: Retmono
Founded: 1965
Education; Letters; Social Sciences; Mathematics;
Health Education.

Institut Keguruan dan Ilmu Pendidikan, Surabaya
Kampus IKOP, Jalan Ketintang, Surabaya 60231
Tel: +62 839-009
Rektor: Soerono Martorahardjo
Founded: 1965
Education.

Institut Keguruan dan Ilmu Pendidikan, Ujung Pandang
Kampus IKIP, Gunung Sari Baru, Ujung Pandang
Tel: +62(411) 83930
Telex: 71173 ikip up
Rektor: H. Sjahruddin Kaseng
Founded: 1965
Education.

Institut Keguruan dan Ilmu Pendidikan, Yogyakarta
Kampus IKIP, Karang Malang, Yogyakarta
Tel: +62(274) 86168
Rektor: Djohar
Founded: 1965
Education.

Institut Pertanian Bogor
Jalan Raya Padjajaran, Bogor 16144
Tel: +62 323-081
Rektor: H. Sitanala Arsyad
Founded: 1963

Institut Teknologi Bandung
Jalan Taman Sari 64, Bandung
Tel: +62(22) 250-3149
Telex: 28324 itb bd
Rektor: Wiranto Arisonundar
Founded: 1959

Institut Teknologi Sepulah Nopember, Surabaja
Jalan Keputih, Sukolilo, Surabaja
Tel: +62(31) 594-7264
Telex: 31224 intexs sb
Rektor: Oedjoe Djoemaman
Founded: 1960
Mathematics; Technology.

PRIVATE INSTITUTIONS

Institut Keguruan dan Ilmu Pendidikan
Jalan Curgkrungan, Karanganom, Cetara
Tel: +62 22363
Rektor: H. Sutoyo
Founded: 1965
Education.

Institut Keguruan dan Ilmu Pendidikan Muhammadiyah, Jakarta
Jalan Limau II, Blok B-I, Kebayoran Baru, Jakarta
Tel: +62(21) 773-177
Rektor: H. Agustiar
Founded: 1957
Education.

Institut Keguruan dan Ilmu Pendidikan, Mataram
Jalan Pemuda, Mataram
Tel: +62 22082
Rektor: Indun
Founded: 1967
Education; Mathematics; Letters.

Institut Keguruan dan Ilmu Pendidikan Aswasliyah, Medan
Jalan Sisingamangaraja, Medan
Rektor: H. Salim Siregar
Founded: 1963
Education.

Institut Keguruan dan Ilmu Pendidikan Gunung Sitoli, Nias
Jalan Yos Sudarso 118/E, Nias
Tel: +62 21616
Founded: 1965
Education.

Institut Keguruan dan Ilmu Pendidikan Muhammadiyah, Purwokerto
Jalan Dukuh Waluh, Kembaran, Purwokerto
Tel: +62 41751
Rektor: Djarwoto Aminoto
Founded: 1965
Education.

Institut Keguruan dan Ilmu Pendidikan Muhammadiyah, Purworejo
Jalan KHA Dahlan 3, Purworejo
Tel: +62 21494
Rektor: H. Arba'in Mahkmud
Founded: 1964
Education.

Institut Keguruan dan Ilmu Pendidikan Veteran Jawa Tengah, Semarang
Jalan Pawiatan Lukur IV, Semarang
Tel: +62(24) 316-105
Rektor: Kaboel Soemardjo
Founded: 1962
Education; Social Sciences; Technology.

Institut Keguruan dan Ilmu Pendidikan Veteran, Sukohardjo
Kampus Jambor, Sukohardjo
Rektor: Soenarjo
Founded: 1968
Social Education; Letters; Mathematics.

Institut Keguruan dan Ilmu Pendidikan PGRI, Surabaya
Jalan Ngagel Dadi IIIB, Surabaya
Tel: +62(31) 581-097
Rektor: H.A. Hudan Dardiri
Founded: 1971
Education; Letters; Mathematics; Social and Political Sciences; Technology.

Institut Keguruan dan Ilmu Pendidikan Saraswati
Jalan Pahlawan No.2, Tabanan
Tel: +62 91267
Rektor: Gusti Ngurah Raka Haryna
Founded: 1965
Social Sciences; Mathematics; Letters.

Institut Keguruan dan Ilmu Pendidikan PGRI, Wates
Jalan Kembang No.5, Margosari Kulonprogo, Wates Yogykarta
Tel: +62(274) 183
Rektor: R. Skoeadji
Founded: 1969
Education; Social Sciences.

Institut Keguruan dan Ilmu Pendidikan Muhammadiyah, Yogyakarta
Jalan Kapas 6, Samaki, Yogyakarta
Tel: +62(274) 63515
Rektor: H. Noeng Muhadjir
Founded: 1960
Education.

Institut Keguruan dan Ilmu Pendidikan PGRI, Yogyakarta
Jalan PGRI I, Senosewu KM 3, Kotak Pos 123, Yogyakarta
Tel: +62(274) 88808
Rektor: Sela Hadisingrat
Founded: 1962
Education; Social Sciences.

Institut Keguruan dan Ilmu Pendidikan Veteran, Yogyakarta

Jalan Glendeagon, Babarsari, Yogyakarta
Tel: +62(274) 5630
Rektor: H. Soerawar
Founded: 1967
Social Sciences; Education; Mathematics; Technology.

Institut Kesenian Jakarta

Jalan Cikini Raya 37, Jakarta
Tel: +62(21) 324-807
Rektor: Toeti Heraty Narhadi
Founded: 1970
Art; Art and Sciences; Film and Television.

Institut Manajemen Koperasi Indonesia

Jalan Raya Bandung, KM 205 Jatinangor, Sumedang
Rektor: Yuyan Wirasasmeta
Founded: 1981
Finance and Management; Productivity Management; Manpower Management.

Institut Teknologi Nasional, Malang

Jalan Bendungan Sigura-gura 2, Malang
Tel: +62 51951
Rektor: R. Iswandi Kertasentana
Founded: 1962
Technology.

Institut Teknologi Pembangunan, Surabaya

Jalan Balongsari Praja V/1, Tandes, Surabaya
Tel: +62(31) 713-802
Rektor: Moedjiarto
Founded: 1980
Technology.

NATIONAL ACADEMIC BODIES

Directorate-General of Higher Education

[Direktorat Jenderal Pendidikan Tinggi]
Jalan Pintu, Senayan, Jakarta 10002
Tel: +62(21) 573-1988
Director-General: Bambang Soehendro (1993-)
Secretary: B.B. Mewengkang

Indonesian National Commission for Unesco

Ministry of Education and Culture, Jalan Jenderal Soedirman-Senayan, Gedung C, Lt. 7, Jakarta 10270
Tel: +62(21) 573-3127
Fax: +62(21) 573-3127
Telex: 65615 deppk
Cable: indonatcom jakarta
Chairman: Wardiman Djajonegoro, Minister of Education
Secretary: Mohammad Afieq

IRAN

UNIVERSITIES

Ahvaz University of Medical Sciences

Golestan Road, Ahvaz
Tel: +98(61) 833-936
Fax: +98(61) 35200
Chancellor: M. Mombini
Founded: 1986
Medicine.

Allmeh Tabatabai University Tehran

Karimkhan Zand Avenue, North Aban, Tehran
Tel: +98(21) 894-187
Fax: +98(21) 892-536
Chancellor: M. Haliji
Founded: 1984
Basic Sciences; Human Sciences.

Al'zahra University Tehran

Vanak Avenue, Tehran
Tel: +98(21) 682-721
Fax: +98(21) 685-187
Chancellor: A. Koohian
Founded: 1964, 1975
Basic Sciences; Human Sciences.

Amir Kabir University of Technology Tehran

Hafez Avenue, Tehran
Tel: +98(21) 646-8055
Fax: +98(21) 641-3969
Telex: 214269
Chancellor: M. Salimi
Engineering.

Arak Teacher's Training University

Beheshti Street, Arak
Tel: +98(861) 22048
Fax: +98(861) 26007
Chancellor: M. Taheri
Founded: 1986
Basic Sciences; Human Sciences.

Arak University of Medical Sciences

Shahid Shiroodi Street, Arak
Tel: +98(2531) 800-9563
Fax: +98(2531) 36211
Chancellor: M. Dalvandi
Medicine.

Ardebil University of Medical Sciences

Ardebil
Tel: +98(451) 32053
Fax: +98(451) 39692
Chancellor: M.Pirmoazzen
Medicine.

Art University

499 Valiasr Avenue, Park Daneshjo, Tehran
Tel: +98(21)48089
Chancellor: M. Askari
Founded: 1980
Arts.

AZAD Private (Open) University
Enghelab Avenue, Corner of Felestin Street,
Tehran
Tel: +98(21) 646-6310
Fax: +98(21) 646-2314
President: A. Jassbi
Founded: 1982
*Science; Human Sciences; Technical Sciences
and Engineering; Medical Sciences.*

Babol University of Medical Sciences
Ganj Afrooz, P.O. Box 569, Babol
Tel: +98(11) 313-0069
Fax: +98(11) 82181
Chancellor: M.Khaleghnezhad
Founded: 1986
Medicine.

Bandar Abbas University of Medical Sciences
Bandar Abbas
Tel: +98(761) 30612
Fax: +98(761) 31991
Chancellor: M.Moedi
Medicine.

Birjand University
Birjand
Tel: +98(561) 22565
Fax: +98(561) 27045
Chancellor: M. Karimpoor
Basic Sciences; Human Sciences.

Birjand University of Medical Sciences
Moalem Street, Birjand
Tel: +98(561) 27571
Fax: +98(561) 26898
Chancellor: M. Mohaghegh
Medicine.

Bou Ali Sina University
Abbas Abad, Hamadan
Tel: +98(81) 20952
Fax: +98(81) 25046
Chancellor: M. Keypoor
*Basic Sciences; Human Sciences; Technical
Sciences and Engineering.*

Bushehr Faculty of Medical Sciences
P.O. Box 3631, Bushehr
Tel: +98(771) 23226
Fax: +98(771) 26154
Chancellor: M. Mohaghegh
Medicine.

Bushehr University
Dovas, School of Engineering, Bushehr
Chancellor: M. Khajeh
Agriculture.

*Esfahan University
Darvazeh Shiraz, Esfahan
Tel: +98(31) 271-071
Fax: +98(31) 277-396
Telex: 312295 ireu
Chancellor: Hassan Razmjoo
Vice-Chancellor (Finance and Administration):
Reza Enshaie
Founded: 1936, 1958
*F: Admnistrative Sciences and Economics;
Educational Sciences; Engineering; Foreign
Languages; Letters and Humanities; Pure
Sciences.*
D: Physical Education.

Esfahan University of Medical Sciences
Darvazeh Shiraz, Esfahan
Tel: +98(31) 685-141
Fax: +98(31) 685-145
Telex: 212308 emsu ir
Chancellor: Hamid-Reza Jamshidi
Founded: 1986
Medicine.

Esfahan University of Technology
Esfahan
Tel: +98(31) 03291-3040
Fax: +98(31) 827-079
Telex: 312764
Chancellor: M. Saghaiyan Nezhad
Founded: 1977
Agriculture; Technical Sciences and Engineering.

Fasa Faculty of Sciences
Fasa
Tel: +98(731) 7091
Fax: +98(731) 7092
Chancellor: M. Mohebbi
Sciences.

Ferdowsi University of Mashhad
Mashhad
Tel: +98(51) 807-504
Fax: +98(51) 031-2360
Chancellor: M. Kazempoor
Vice-Chancellor for Administration: Hassan-Ali
Azarnoush
Founded: 1937, 1949, 1956
*Basic Sciences; Human Sciences; Technical
Sciences and Enginering.*

Ghazvin University of Medical Sciences
Shahid Bahonar Boulevard, Ghazvin
Tel: +98(281) 36006
Fax: +98(281) 307-430
Chancellor: M. Riyazi
Medicine.

Gilan University Rasht
Saadi Avenue, Rasht
Tel: +98(231) 31999
Fax: +98(231) 37022
Telex: 232100
Chancellor: M. Varsey
Founded: 1977
*Basic Sciences; Human Sciences; Technical
Sciences and Engineering.*

Gilan University of Medical Sciences
Namjo Street, Rasht
Tel: +98(231) 31282
Fax: +98(231) 32460
Chancellor: M. Ghanbari
Founded: 1986
Medicine.

Gurgan University of Agriculture
Shahed Beheshti Street, Gurgan
Tel: +98(271) 24827
Chancellor: M. Enayati
Agriculture.

Hamadan University of Medical Sciences
Abbas Abad Boulevard, Hamadan
Tel: +98(81) 220-773
Fax: +98(81) 220-683
Chancellor: M. Abolhassani
Founded: 1986
Medicine.

Hormozgan University
Ayatollah Ghafari Street, Bandar Abbass
Tel: +98(761) 37322
Chancellor: M. Zomorrodian
*Marine Sciences; Technical Sciences and
Engineering.*

Ilam Faculty of Medical Sciences
Ashori Street, Ilam
Tel: +98(841) 32296
Fax: +98(841) 21841
Chancellor: M. Keykhavandi
Medicine.

Ilam University
Ilam
Chancellor: M. Piri
*Basic Sciences; Technical Sciences and
Engineering.*

Iman Khomeini International University
East of Felestini Street, Ghazvin
Tel: +98(281) 32247
Fax: +98(281) 0281-331
Chancellor: M. Taghikhani
*Basic Sciences; Human Sciences; Technical
Sciences and Engineering.*

Imam Sadegh University
Chamran Exp'way, Saadat Abad, Tehran
Tel: +98(21) 604-001
Chancellor: M. Mahdavi Kani
Founded: 1983
Human Sciences.

Iran University of Medical Sciences
Corner of Gandhi and 20th Avenue, P.O. Box
1587-6171, Tehran 15179
Tel: +98(21) 688-191
Fax: +98(21) 801-7399
Chancellor: S.J. Sadjadi (1989-)
Vice-Chancellor: A.H. Hajitarkhani
Founded: 1974
F: Medicine.

*S: Nursing and Midwifery; Paramedical
Sciences; Public Health; Medical Management
and Documentation Services; Rehabilitation
Sciences.
I: Psychiatric; Endocrinology and Metabolism.
Ce: Research and Training for Laboratory
Sciences.*

Iran University of Science and Technology Tehran
Narmak-East Farjam Street, Tehran 16844
Tel: +98(21) 771-1205
Fax: +98(21) 771-143
Chancellor: M. Mollabashi
Founded: 1938, 1977
*C: Civil Engineering; Mechanical Engineering;
Chemical Engineering; Electrical Engineering and
Electronics; Industrial Engineering; Architecture
and Urban Planning; Science; Physics;
Metallurgy; Language Arts.*

Jahrom Faculty of Medical Sciences
Jahrom
Tel: +98(791) 31520
Fax: +98(791) 31523
Chancellor: M. Shahi
Medicine.

Kashan Teacher's Training University
Amir Kabir Street, Km. of 5 Fin Road, Kashan
Chancellor: M. Shamekhi
Basic Sciences; Human Sciences.

Kashan University of Medical Sciences
P.O. Box 87155-111, Kashan
Tel: +98(2521) 21112
Fax: +98(2521) 311-3188
Chancellor: M. Seyyedi
Medicine.

Kerman University of Medical Sciences
Jomhori Boulevard, Kerman
Tel: +98(341) 44930
Fax: +98(341) 40389
Chancellor: M. Ziaeddini
Founded: 1986
Medicine.

Kermanshah University of Medical Sciences
Sorkheh Lizeh, Kermanshah
Tel: +98(431) 58945
Fax: +98(431) 708-094
Chancellor: M. Razi
Medicine.

Khaje-Nasiral'din Tousi University of Technology
Valiasr Avenue, Mirdamad Street, Tehran
Tel: +98(21) 888-3001
Fax: +98(21) 801-7469
Chancellor: M. Ardabili
Technical Sciences and Engineering.

Kordestan University
Pasdaran Avenue, Sanandaj
Chancellor: M. Yosrebi
Basic Sciences; Human Sciences.

Kordestan University of Medical Sciences
Pasdaran Street, Sanandaj
Tel: +98(471) 30205
Fax: +98(471) 33600
Chancellor: M. Derafshi
Medicine.

Lorestan Faculty of Medical Sciences
Motahary Street, Khoramabad
Tel: +98(661) 22030
Fax: +98(661) 311-4078
Chancellor: M. Karimian
Medicine.

Lorestan University
Falakol'Aflak Street, Khoramabad
Tel: +98(661) 25777
Fax: +98(661) 22782
Chancellor: M. Tavakkol
Basic Sciences.

Mashhad University of Medical Sciences
University Street, Mashhad
Tel: +98(51) 8013-006
Fax: +98(51) 813-007
Chancellor: M. Bahrami
Founded: 1986
Medicine.

*Mazandaran University
P.O. Box 416, Babolsar
Tel: +98(2491) 33180
Fax: +98(2491) 33702
Telex: 215424
Chancellor: M. Sheikhol-Eslami
International Relations: Ellen Vuosalo Tavokoli
Founded: 1980
C: Sciences; Economics; Engineering; Agricultural Science.

Mazandaran University of Medical Sciences
Sari-Moalem Square, Babolsar
Tel: +98(151) 28240
Fax: +98(151) 546-835
Chancellor: M. Babamahmoodi
Medicine.

Payam-e-Nour University
Lashkarak Road, Tehran
Tel: +98(21) 280-925
Fax: +98(21) 288-511
Chancellor: M. Zohoor
Human Sciences (by correspondence).

Petroleum University
Kot Abdollah Km. of 10, Ahvaz
Tel: +98(61) 2061
Chancellor: A. Enayat
Founded: 1939
Technical Sciences and Engineering.

Rafsanjan University of Medical Sciences
Iman Street, Rafsanjan
Tel: +98(3431) 6962
Fax: +98(3431) 6310
Chancellor: M. Sadeghi
Medicine.

Razi University
Beheshti Boulevard, Kermanshah
Tel: +98(831) 28050
Fax: +98(831) 26183
Chancellor: M. Khodai
Founded: 1972
Basic Sciences; Human Sciences; Technical Sciences and Engineering.

Sabzevar Teacher's Training University
Km. of 5 Old Tehran Road, Sabzevar
Tel: 99721
Chancellor: M. Mohammadian
Basic Sciences; Human Sciences.

Semnan University
Hevdah Shahrivar Boulevard, Semnan
Tel: +98(2231) 34802
Fax: +98(2231) 21005
Chancellor: M. Taherian
Founded: 1975
Basic Sciences; Human Sciences.

Shahed University
Valisr and Taleghani Intersection, Rahimzadeh Lane, Tehran
Tel: +98(21) 320-2255
Chancellor: A.A. Noor Bala
Founded: 1975
Basic Sciences; Human Sciences; Technical Sciences and Engineering.

Shahid Bahonar University
P.O. Box 133, Jomhori Boulevard, Kerman
Tel: +98(341) 44682
Fax: +98(341) 42716
Chancellor: M. Akbari
Founded: 1975
Human Sciences; Technical Sciences and Letters.

Shahid Beheshti University
Evin 19834, Tehran
Tel: +98(21) 295-156
Fax: +98(21) 290-430
Chancellor: Hadi Nadimi
Founded: 1959
Basic Sciences; Human Sciences; Technical Sciences and Engineering.

Shahid Beheshti University of Medical Sciences
Evin, Tehran
Tel: +98(21) 299-691
Fax: 98(21) 296-052
Chancellor: M. Tabatabay
Medicine.

Shahid Chamran University
Goestan Street, Ahvaz
Tel: +98(61) 32041
Fax: +98(61) 48048
Telex: 612075 cuai ir
Chancellor: M. Zargham
Founded: 1955
Basic Sciences; Human Sciences; Technical Sciences and Engineering.

Shahr-e-Kord University
Km. of 2 Saman Road, Shahr-e-Kord
Tel: +98(2231) 34802
Chancellor: M. Edris
Founded: 1978

Shahr-e-Kord University of Medical Sciences
Varzesh Street, Shahr-e-Kord
Tel: +98(381) 30061
Chancellor: M. Safay
Medicine.

Sharif University of Technology
Azadï Avenue, P.O. Box 3406, Tehran
Tel: +98(21) 600-5210
Fax: +98(21) 601-2983
Chancellor: Mohammad Etemadi
Founded: 1965, 1979
Basic Sciences; Technical Sciences and Engineering.

Shahrood Faculty of Medical Sciences
Shohada Street, Shahrood
Tel: +98(2731) 31850
Fax: +98(2731) 34090
Chancellor: M. Ajami
Medicine.

Shahrood University
Hafte Tir Sp., Shahrood
Chancellor: M. Farhadi
Basic Sciences.

*Shiraz University
Zand Avenue, 71345 Shiraz
Tel: +98(71) 59220
Fax: +98(71) 32227
Telex: 332169 shu ir
Chancellor: Gholam Hossein Zamani
Founded: 1962
C: Agriculture; Education; Electronic Industry; Engineering; Law; Letters and Human Sciences; Veterinary Medicine.

Shiraz University of Medical Sciences
Zand Street, Shiraz
Tel: +98(71) 332-366
Fax: +98(71) 59317
Chancellor: Malak Hosseyni
Founded: 1986
Medicine.

*Sistan and Baluchistan University
P.O. Box 161-98135, Khash Road, Zahedan
Tel: +98(541) 27091
Fax: +98(541) 26888
Cable: dasibal
Chancellor: Habibollah Dahmardeh
Founded: 1975
C: Engineering; Agriculture; Marine Engineering; Sciences.

Tabriz Sahand University of Technology
Azadi Street, Golgasht Road, Tabriz
Chancellor: M. Keynezhad
Technical Sciences and Engineering.

Tabriz Teacher's Training University
Taleghany Avenue, Ma'raj Street, Tabriz
Tel: +98(41) 64465
Fax: +98(41) 64465
Chancellor: M. Irandoost
Basic Sciences; Human Sciences.

*Tabriz University
29 Bahman Boulevard, Tabriz 51664
Tel: +98(41) 341-300
Fax: +98(41) 344-013
Telex: 412045 tbun
Chancellor: M.A.AHosseinpour Faizi
Founded: 1946, 1975, 1979
F: Agriculture; Education and Psychology; Engineering; Persian Literature and Foreign Languages; Science; Human and Social Sciences.
I: Chemistry; Urban Research; Persian History and Culture.
Ce: Astronomical Research and Observatory.

Tabriz University of Medical Sciences
29th Bahman Avenue, Poorsina, Tabriz
Tel: (41) 369-190
Fax: (41) 342-761
Telex: 412045 tbun-ir
Chancellor: Hussein Sadeghi Shoja
Registrar: M.H. Zarrintan
Founded: 1986
F: Medicine; Pharmacy; Dentistry; Public Health and Nutrition; Nursing and Midwifery; Laboratory Science; Rehabilitation.

Tarbiat Modares University
Chamran Exp'way and Jalal Al'Ahmad Intersection, Tehran
Tel: +98(21) 800-9720
Fax: +98(21) 800-6544
Chancellor: Seyed Esfahani
Basic Sciences; Human Sciences; Technical Sciences and Engineering (all graduate level).

Tehran Teacher's Training University
Shahid Mofateh, Tehran
Tel: +98(21) 882-5010
Fax: +98(21) 836-654
Chancellor: M. Medghalchi
Founded: 1930, 1976
Basic Sciences; Human Sciences.

*Tehran University
Avenue Enghelab, Tehran
Tel: +98(21) 646-9824
Fax: +98(21) 640-9348
Telex: 213944 ir ibb
Chancellor: M. Afrooz
Founded: 1934, 1941
F: Letters and Humanities; Fine Arts; Science;
Engineering; Agriculture; Natural Sciences; Law
and Political Sciences; Education; Islamic
Theology and Culture; Social Sciences;
Economics; Management and Administration;
Veterinary Medicine; Foreign Languages.
I: Geophysics; Comparative Law; Biochemistry
and Biophysics.
Ce: Environmental Studies; International
Studies.

Tehran University of Medical Sciences
Enghelab Street/Quds Street, Tehran
Tel: +98(21) 640-5666
Fax: +98(21) 641-6537
Chancellor: M. Bastan Hagh

Urmia University
Shahid Beheshti Street, Urmia
Tel: +98(441) 45910
Fax: +98(441) 43442
Telex: 442081 urmu ir
Chancellor: S.M. Razavi-Rohani (1991-)
Founded: 1967, 1976
F: Agriculture; Science; Veterinary Medicine;
Persian Literature and Humanities.
I: Technology and Engineering.

Urmia University of Medical Sciences
Jahad Street, Urmia
Tel: +98(441) 32296
Fax: +98(441) 21841
Chancellor: M. Lamey
Founded: 1986
Medicine.

Valiasr Rafsanjan University
Motahary Street, 22 Bahman Square, Tehran
Chancellor: M. Gholampoor
Agriculture.

Yazd University
Daneshjo Boulevard, Yazd
Tel: +98(351) 48223
Fax: +98(351) 48223
Chancellor: Jalil Shahi
Technical Sciences and Engineering.

Yazd University of Medical Sciences
Bafgh Road, Safaeeyeh, Yazd
Tel: +98(351) 45446
Fax: +98(351) 45445
Chancellor: M. Kazemi
Medicine.

Yazoj University of Medical Sciences
Motahari Street, Yazoj
Tel: +98(741) 7229
Fax: +98(741) 5689
Chancellor: M. Salehi
Medicine.

Zahedan University of Medical Sciences
Shariati Street, Zahedan
Tel: +98(541) 28110
Fax: +98(541) 30884
Chancellor: M. Shahriari
Medicine.

Zanjan University
Km. of 6 Zanjan and Tabriz Road, Zanjan
Chancellor: M. Karimi
Basic Sciences.

Zanjan University of Medical Sciences
Parvin Aetesami Street, Zanjan
Tel: +98(2821) 29455
Fax: +98(2821) 29632
Chancellor: M. Poor Hosseyni
Medicine.

OTHER INSTITUTIONS

Ardebil University
University Street, Ardebil
Tel: +98(451) 21871
Chancellor: M. Mostaghim
Agriculture.

Damghan Faculty of Science
Cheshmeh Ali Road, Damghan
Tel: 4666
Director: M. Naderi
Science.

Faculty of Industrial Safety and Occupational Health
Saveh Road, Yaftabad, Tehran
Tel: +98(21) 669-5785
Director: M. Noormohammadi
Industrial Safety and Occupational Health.

NATIONAL ACADEMIC BODIES

Ministry of Culture and Higher Education
Avenue Nejatollahi, Tehran
Tel: +98(21) 890-197
Fax: +98(21) 882-7293
Minister: S. M. Hashemi Golpayegani

Institute for Research and Planning in Higher Education
1 Golfam Street, Africa Avenue, Tehran
Tel: +98(21) 808-9876
Fax: +98(21) 222-0338

National Council for Scientific and Industrial Research
31 Alvand Street, Tehran
Tel: +98(21) 680-436
Fax: +98(21) 686-0588
Chairman: M. Habibi

Iranian National Commission for Unesco
1188 Enghelab Avenue, Rostam Building, P.O. Box 11365-4498, Tehran 13158
Tel: +98(21) 640-8355
Fax: +98(21) 646-8387
Telex: 212889
Chairman: S.M. Reza Hashemi Golpayegani, Minister of Culture and Higher Education
Secretary-General: Akbar Haji Ebrahim Zargar

IRAQ

UNIVERSITIES

University of Al-Anbar
Al-Anbar
Tel: +964 886-4814
Fax: +964 887-8849
President: Abdul Rahman Abdul Karim Al-Ani (1990-)
Executive Director: Mustafa Shahb Ahmed
Founded: 1987
C: Education; Education (for girls); Science; Medicine.

University of Al-Qadisiya
P.O. Box 381, Diwania, Al-Qadisiya
Tel: +964(366) 28066
Telex: 216500 unqad
President: F.H. Hussen
Executive Director: J.A. Hashim
International Relations: E.A.M. Ai-Heety
Founded: 1988
C: Education; Administration and Economics; Art; Veterinary Medicine; Medicine.

Al-Mustansiriyah University Baghdad
[Al-Jami'at Al-Mustansiriyah]
P.O. Box 14022, Waziriyah, Baghdad
Tel: +964(3) 416-8500
Fax: +964(1) 416-0021
Telex: 2122566
Cable: musbad irak
President: Riadh Hamid Al-Dabbagh (1982-)
Registrar: Yousif Rabie Yousif
International Relations: Hisham A. Shihatha
Founded: 1963, 1964, 1965, 1974
C: Arts; Science; Medicine; Education; Engineering; Economics and Administration; Teacher Training.
I: National and Socialist Studies.

Ce: Modern Languages; Middle East Studies; Development of Teaching Methods; Teaching Arabic to Foreigners; Computer.

University of Babylon
[Jami'at Babil]
P.O. Box 4, Hilla
Tel: +964 885-1398
Fax: +964 885-1398
President: Yehya T. Al-Rawi (1991-)
Vice-President: Ali M. K. Al-Rikabi
International Relations: Director of Scientific Affairs, Saad J. Taj-Aldeen
Founded: 1991
C: Fine Arts Education; Law; Science; Engineering; Physical Education; Education; Medicine.

University of Baghdad
[Jami'at Baghdad]
Jadyriya, Baghdad
Tel: +964(1) 776-7819
Fax: +964(1) 776-3592
Telex: 2197 jamit
Cable: jamit
President: Abdul Ilah Al Khashab (1992-)
Assistant President (Administrative Affairs): M.B.Enad
International Relations: Assistant President (Student Affairs), Sadik F. Diab
Founded: 1958, 1969
C: Law and Political Science; Arts; Education; Agriculture; Science; Medicine; Pharmacy; Dentistry; Veterinary Medicine; Alsharea'; Nursing; Administration and Economics; Physical Education; Engineering; Fine Arts.
Ce: Psychiatry; Palestinian Studies Research; Psychology and Educational Research; Natural History Research; Arab-Scientific Research; Administration and Economics Research; Medical Research; Dental Research; Computer.

University of Technology Baghdad
[Al-Jami'at Al-Technologia]
P.O. Box 35010, Baghdad
Tel: +964(1) 719-6021
Telex: 214-9
Cable: Unitech
President: Dakhil H. Jerew (1993-)
Vice-President: Jasim M. Al-Samarai
International Relations: Wamidh Dhyaa Eldeen
Founded: 1960, 1975
D: Mechanical Engineering; Electrical Engineering; Building and Construction Engineering; Applied Sciences; Technical Education; Production Engineering and Metallurgy; Control and Systems Engineering; Chemical Engineering; Architecture; Computer Science; Higher Education.
Ce: Lifelong Education; Consulting Engineering.

University of Basrah
[Jami'at Al-Basrah]
Garmat Ali, Basrah
Tel: +964(40) 417-851
Telex: 207025 ik
President: Akram Mohammed Subhi Mohammed
(1993-)
Vice-President: Majeed Hashim
International Relations: Riyad Salin Haddad
Founded: 1964, 1967
C: Science; Engineering; Medicine; Agriculture;
Economics and Administration; Arts; Education;
Physical Education; Law.
Ce: Arab Gulf Studies; Computer; Marine
Sciences.

Jami'at Al-Kufa
[University of Kufa]
P.O. Box 21, Kufa
Tel: +964(333) 346-109
Fax: +964(333) 346-049
Telex: 216304 kf uni ik
President: Dhafir Dawood Sul Iqman (1991-)
Vice-President: Aqueel Abid Yassin
International Relations: Director (Scientific
Department and Cultural Affairs), Sabah Nema
Al-Thamir
Founded: 1988
C: Education (for girls); Art; Science;
Engineering; Administration and Economics;
Medicine.
Ce: Kufa Studies; Cultural and Social Activities.
Ut: Continuing Education.

University of Mosul
[Jami'at Al-Mosul]
Al-Majmoaa, Mosul
Tel: +964 812-611
Fax: +964 815-060
Telex: 8015 engcolmo
Cable: Mosul Uni
President: Kubais S.A. Fahady (1993-)
Assistant President: Sadullah. N. Al-Niemi
International Relations: Director (Scientific
Affairs), Talib H. Ali
Founded: 1967
C: Medicine; Engineering; Science; Agriculture
and Forestry; Arts; Administration and
Economics; Education; Veterinary Medicine;
Physical Education; Dentistry; Law;
Pharmacology; Teacher Training; Nursing.
Ce: Computer; Dams and Water Resources
Research; Turkish Studies; Mosul Document
Centre.

*University of Salahaddin
[Jami'at Salahaddin]
Erbil
Tel: (66) 266-28
Telex: 218510
Cable: zanco
President: Khusrow Ghani Shali
Founded: 1968
F: Science; Engineering; Agriculture; Arts;
Administration; Education; Medicine.

University of Tikrit
P.O. Box 42, Tikrit
Tel: +964(21) 824-531
Fax: +964(21) 825-730
Telex: 216700
Cable: 5434164
President: A.K. Shaaban (1987-)
Vice-President: Amin S. Badawy
International Relations: A. Hassaballah
Founded: 1988
C: Engineering; Education (for girls); Medicine;
Education; Agriculture.

OTHER INSTITUTIONS

Institute of Administration
Al-Risafa, Baghdad
Tel: +964(1) 416-5004
Dean: Saad Zanad Darwish (1987-)
Founded: 1969
D: Secretarial Studies; Banking; Insurance
Management; Store Management; Accounting;
Computer Systems; Statistics.

Institute of Applied Arts
Zafaraniy, Baghdad
Tel: +964(1) 773-4040
Dean: Nashwan Abdulwahhab Abdulrazak
Founded: 1969
D: Design; Clothing; Interior Design; Textiles;
Glass and Architectural Decorating.

Institute of Technical Instructors
P.O. Box 24029, Zaaferania, Baghdad
Tel: +964(1) 773-0194
Dean: M.W. Al-Alousl
Founded: 1987
D: Mechanical Engineering; Electronics;
Automotive Engineering; Electrical Engineering.

Institute Technology-Babylon
P.O. Box 87, Abu-Garak, Babylon
Tel: +964 886-4841
Dean: Akram Jafar Hassani Al-Hilly (1993-)
International Relations: Dean, Akram Jafar
Hassani Al-Hilly
Founded: 1976
D: Accounting; Store Management; Mechanics;
Civil Engineering; Surveying; Machine and
Equipment; Electronics; Community Health;
Nursing.

Institute of Technology-Baghdad
P.O. Box 29008, Baghdad
Tel: +964(1) 773-1491
Fax: +964(1) 773-1041
Telex: 212769 instech ik
Dean: Raddi Muhsin Al-Zubaidi (1993-)
Founded: 1972
D: Civil Engineering; Irrigation and Operating of
Water Projects; Surveying; Electrical Engineering;
Electronics; Mechanical Engineering; Machinery
and Equipment; Chemical Industry.

Technical Institute-AlAmaua
P.O. Box 34, Al-Amara
Dean: Kasim Abdul Jabar Al-Satair (1985-)
International Relations: Kasim Abdul Jabar
Al-Satair
Founded: 1979
D: Electrical Engineering; Civil Eengineering;
Surveying; Mechanical Engineering; Electronics;
Machinery and Equipment; Chemical Industry;
Accounting; Store Management; Nursing.

Technical Institute-Al-Anbar
P.O. Box 7, Al-Anbar
Tel: +964 543-3664
Telex: 213244 imtik
Dean: Obaid Mahmood Mihssen Al-Zubay (1981-)
Founded: 1977
D: Civil Engineering; Electrical Engineering;
Mechanical Engineering; Mechinery and
Equipment; Chemical Industries; Computer
Syetems; Community Health; Accounting; Stores
Administration; Secretarial Studies.

Technical Institute-Al-Dour
Al-Dour
Tel: +964(218) 62461
Dean: Kasim Faisal Hassan (1988-94)
Founded: 1988
D: Electronics; Mechanical Engineering;
Accounting; Pharmacy.

Technical Institute-Al-Huwayja
Al-Huwayja
Tel: +964 42638
Dean: Mahfoud Hamdoon Alsawaf (1992-)
Founded: 1980
D: Irrigation and Water; Mechanical
Engineering; Machinery and Equipment;
Secretarial Studies; Store Management.

Technical Institute-Al-Mansor
Al-Mansor, Baghdad
Tel: +964 543-3695
Dean: Mohammed Abdul Kader Yousif
Founded: 1988
D: Electrical Engineering; Library Management;
Medical Management; Clinical Pathology;
Pharmacy; Optometry.

Technical Institute-Al-Najaf
P.O. Box 263, Abu-Suckair Road, Al-Najaf
Tel: +964(30) 361-184
Founded: 1978
D: Civil Engineering; Electrical Engineering;
Communications; Mechanical Engineering;
Machinery and Equipment; Accounting; Computer
Systems.

Technical Institute-Al-Nasiriyah
Baghdad Street, Al-Nasiriyah
Tel: +964(42) 231-315
Dean: Saleh Abdul-Reda Rashid
Founded: 1980
D: Electrical Engineering; Mechanical
Engineering; Accounting; Secretarial Studies;
Judicial Management; Community Health.

Technical Institute-Al-Qadissiya
Al-Qadissiya
Tel: +964 885-3953
Dean: Abas Hussin Jawad (1991-)
Founded: 1988
D: Mechanical Engineering; Accounting; Store
Management; Community Health.

Technical Institute-Al-Shatra
Al-Shatra, Thikar
Tel: +964 717-2052
Dean: Talib K. Hussain (1986-94)
Founded: 1979
D: Surveying; Electrical Engineering;
Mechanical Engineering; Mechinery and
Equipment; Store Management; Animal
Production; Plant Productioin; Agricultural
Machines.

Technical Institute-Al-Simawa
P.O. Box 15, Al-Samawa
Tel: +964 888-5220
Dean: A.A.B. Mahamad (1983-)
Founded: 1989
D: Surveying; Electrical Enginerring; Mechanical
Engineering; Accounting; Nursing.

Technical Institute-Basrah
Bab-Alzubair, P.O. Box 272, Basrah
Tel: +964 217-985
Telex: 207116
Dean: Kamal A. Al-Chalaby (1988-)
Founded: 1973
D: Secretarial Studies; Accounting; Store
Management; Computing Systems; Mechanical
Engineering; Machinery and Equipment;
Electronics; Electrical Engineering; Civil
Engineering; Surveying; Chemical Industries;
Clinical Pathology; Pharmacy; Anaesthetics;
Community Health; Nursing.

Technical Institute-Kafa
Al-Najaf, Kufa
Tel: +964 885-3581
Dean: Ryad Mohammed Al-Aanyi (1994-)
Founded: 1980
D: Electrical Engineering; Mechanical
Engineering; Machinery and Equipment;
Secretarial Studies; Store Management; Clinical
Pathology; Community Health; Pharmacy; Plant
Production.

Technical Institute-Kerbala
Hindya Road, P.O. Box 30, Kerbala
Dean: Hussain Mohamad Ahmed (1980-)
D: Electrical Engineering; Mechanical
Engineering; Accounting; Community Health.

Technical Institute-Kirkuk
P.O. Box 104, Kirkuk
Tel: +964(50) 219-142
Telex: 5602
Cable: teknitute
Dean: Sami Abdul-Hamid Al-Kineen (1993-)
Founded: 1988

D: Civil Engineering; Surveying; Electronics; Electrical Engineering; Mechanical Engineering; Machinery and Equipment; Chemical Industry; Nursing; Community Health; Store Management; Accounting; Computer Systems.

Technical Institute-Kut
P.O. Box, Wasit, Kut
Tel: +964 885-2751
Dean: Abdul-Jabbar Khalalef Al-Jumaily (1980-94)
Founded: 1980
D: Irrigation and Water Projects Operating; Surveying; Mechanical Engineering; Mechinery and Equipment; Accounting; Store Management; Clinical Pathology; Community Health.

Technical Institute-Musaib
Babylon-Baghdad General Street,
Musaib-Babylon
Tel: +964 886 2147
Dean: Ali K. Ibrahim (1990-)
Founded: 1979
D: Plant Production; Animal Production; Soil; Agricultural Machines; Machinery and Equipment; Mechanical Engineering; Irrigation and Water Project Operating; Accounting; Electrical Engineering.

Technical Institute-Mosul
Majtmoah-Mosul
Tel: +964 812-081
Fax: +964 886-3556
Telex: 298-060
Dean: Mazin R. Khalil (1993-)
Founded: 1976
D: Civil Engineering; Irrigation and Drainage; Surveying; Electrical Engineering; Electronics; Mechanical Engineering; Machinery and Equipment; Chemical Industry; Industry Accounting; Secretary Studies; Store Management; Library Management; Computer Systems; Clinical Pathology; Community Health; Radiation; Anaesthetics; Plant Production; Animal Production; Agricultural Machines and Equipment.

Technical Institute-Naynawa
P.O. Box, Namrood, Naynawa-Mosul
Tel: +964(6) 092-1909
Dean: Samer Abdulrazak Yasin Al-Abdaly (1978-94)
Founded: 1980
D: Accounting; Electronics.

Technical Institute-Suwara
P.O. Box 5, Wassit, Suwaira
Tel: +964 885-2365
Dean: Muayad Abdul Rahman Al-Mubarck (1987-)
Founded: 1987
D: Mechanical Engineering; Accounting.

Technical Institute of Administration
Zaaferania, Baghdad
Tel: +964 773-8745
Fax: +964 213-370
Dean: Mohammad Abdul-Aal Amin (1989-)
Founded: 1976
D: Secretarial Studies; Store Management; Accounting; Computers; Judicial Management; Tourism.

NATIONAL ACADEMIC BODIES

Ministry of Higher Education and Scientific Research
Baghdad
Telex: 212385 balemali ik

Iraqi National Commission for Unesco
Ministry of Education, Baghdad
Tel: +964(1) 886-0000
Fax: +964(21) 885-1989
Telex: 212259 educate ik
Cable: incu baghdad
Chairman: Hikmat Abdullah Al-Bazaz, Minister of Education
Secretary-General: Khalid Ibrahim Hamash

IRELAND

UNIVERSITIES AND UNIVERSITY COLLEGES

*Dublin City University
Glasnevin, Dublin 9
Tel: +353(1) 704-5000
Fax: +353(1) 360-830
E-Mail: internet: cdcu.ie
Telex: 30690 dcu ei
President: Daniel O'Hare (1977-)
Secretary: Martin Conry
Founded: 1975, 1989
F: Computing and Mathematical Sciences; Humanities; Engineering and Design; Education; Science and Paramedical Studies.
S: Applied Languages; Communication; Biological Sciences; Chemical Sciences; Physical Sciences; Electronic Engineering; Computer Applications; Mathematical Sciences; Mechanical and Manufacturing Engineering.
Ce: Distance Learning (National); Technologies in Education (National); National Information Technology in Education; Language Technology (National); Communication Technology and Culture Research (COMTEC).

The University of Dublin, Trinity College
Dublin 2
Tel: +353(1) 677-2941
Fax: +353(1) 677-2694
Telex: Dublin 93782 tcd ei
Cable: Trinity, Dublin
Provost: Thomas Noel Mitchell (1991-2001)
Secretary: Michael Gleeson
Founded: 1592

F: Arts; Arts; Business, Economic and Social Studies; Engineering and Systems Sciences; Health Science; Science.
S: Graduate.
C: Irish of Ecumenics; Church of Ireland Theological.
Ce: Pharmaceutical Biotechnology (National); Optronics Ireland.
Ut: Metals Processing Research; Polymer Materials Research; Vision Sensor Research.
L: Hitachi Dublin.

*University of Limerick

Plassey Technological Park, Limerick
Tel: +353(61) 333-644
Fax: +353(61) 330-316
E-Mail: heanet, janet, bitnet, internet
Telex: 70609 ulei
President: Edward M. Walsh (1970-)
Registrar: P. Leo Colgan
Founded: 1972, 1989
C: Business; Engineering and Science; Humanities.
F: Education.
Ce: Applied Mathematics Research; CIME Research; Environmental Research; Lightwave Technology Research; Materials Research; Quality Management (National); Power Electronics and Circuit Design; Software Re-engineering; Telecommunications Research; European Public Policy Research; Plassey Management and Technical.
Ut: Advanced Manufacturing Technology.

*National University of Ireland/ Ollscoil na hEireann

49 Merrion Square, Dublin 2
Tel: +353(1) 676-7246
Fax: +353(1) 661-9665
Cable: natuniv, dublin
Chancellor: Michael Mortell (1976-)
Registrar: John Nolan
Founded: 1908
F: Arts; Philosophy and Sociology; Celtic Studies; Law; Science; Medicine; Engineering and Architecture; Commerce; Agriculture; Food Science and Technology; Veterinary Medicine.

UNIVERSITY COLLEGE, CORK
Cork
Tel: +353(21) 276-871
Fax: +353(21) 273-072
Telex: 26050
Cable: u.c.c. ireland
President: Michael P. Mortell (1989-99)
Registrar: M. Aidan Moran
Founded: 1849, 1880, 1908
F: Arts; Celtic Studies; Commerce; Science; Law; Dairy Science; Engineering; Medicine.
Ce: National Microelectronics Research; National Food Biotechnology; Plant Biotechnology; Executive Systems Research (ESRC); European Social Research; Hydraulics and Maritime Research.

UNIVERSITY COLLEGE DUBLIN
Belfield, Dublin 4
Tel: +353(1) 269-4409
Telex: 32693 ei
President: Art Cosgrove (1986-96)
Registrar: John J. Kelly
Founded: 1851, 1979, 1908
F: Arts; Law; Commerce; Science; Medicine; Engineering and Architecture; Agriculture; Veterinary Medicine.
S: Architecture.
Ce: Accounting and Taxation Research; Advanced Manufacturing Technology Centre (AMT); Bioengineering Research (BRC); Development Studies; Drama Studies; Economic Research; Energy Conversion Research; Engineering Ceramics Research; Engineering Metals Processing Research; Engerprise and Small Business; Equality Studies; European Economics and Public Affairs (CEEPA); Family Studies; Film Studies; Health Economics; Information Technology; International Marketing Studies; International Marketing Studies; Language Centre; Local Heritage Studies; Marketing Studies; Optoelectronics Research; Plant Science; Quality and Services Management; Relativity Theory; Retail Studies; Safety, Health and Welfare at Work; Science Policy Research; Services Industries Research; Social and Organizational Psychology; Social Science Research; Tribology Design; Water Resources Research; omen's Education, Research and Resource.

UNIVERSITY COLLEGE, GALWAY
Galway
Tel: +353(91) 244-11
Fax: +353(91) 257-00
Telex: 50023
President: Colm Ó Heocha (1975-)
Registrar: M.F. McCarthy
Founded: 1845, 1908
F: Arts; Celtic Studies; Commerce; Engineering; Law; Medicine; Science.
Ce: Alltech European Biosciences Research; Manufacturing Research; National Nutrition Surveillance; Social Sciences Research.
I: Martin Ryan Marine Science.
L: Optoelectonics; Board of Adult and Continuing Education.

SAINT PATRICK'S COLLEGE
Maynooth, County Kildare
Tel: +353(1) 628-5222
Fax: +353(1) 628-9063
Master: Séamus Smyth (1994-)
Registrar: Peter Carr
Founded: 1795, 1895, 1908
F: Theology; Philosophy; Arts; Science; Celtic Studies.

OTHER INSTITUTIONS

Church of Ireland College of Education
96 Upper Rathmines Road, Dublin 6
Tel: +353(1) 497-0033
Fax: +353(1) 497-0878
Founded: 1811
Education.

CRAWFORD COLLEGE OF ART AND DESIGN
Sharman Crawford Street, Cork
Tel: +353(21) 966-777
Fax: +353(21) 962-267
Founded: 1978
Art and Design.

Dublin Institute of Technology
30 Upper Pembroke Street, Dublin 2
Tel: +353(1) 661-1688
Fax: +353(1) 661-1696
Founded: 1978
Technology.

DUBLIN COLLEGE OF CATERING
Cathal Brugha Street, Dublin 1
Tel: +353(1) 874-7886
Fax: +353(1) 874-3634
Catering.

COLLEGE OF COMMERCE
Rathmines, Dublin 6
Tel: +353(1) 497-0666
Fax: +353(1) 496-6088
Commerce.

COLLEGE OF MARKETING AND DESIGN
40 Mountjoy Square, Dublin 1
Tel: +353(1) 836-3000
Fax: +353(1) 874-0505
Marketing and Design.

COLLEGE OF MUSIC
Adelaide Road, Dublin 2
Tel: +353(1) 478-4788
Fax: +353(1) 478-4738
Music.

COLLEGE OF TECHNOLOGY
Bolton Street, Dublin 1
Tel: +353(1) 872-7177
Fax: +353(1) 872-7879
Technology.

COLLEGE OF TECHNOLOGY
Kevin Street, Dublin 8
Tel: +353(1) 475-7541
Fax: +353(1) 478-0282
Technology.

Dun Laoghaire School of Art and Design
Carriglea Park, Kill Avenue, Dun Laoghaire, Co. Dublin
Tel: +353(1) 280-1138
Fax: +353(1) 280-33454
Art and Design.

Froebel College of Education
Sion Hill, Blackrock, Co. Dublin
Tel: +353(1) 288-8520
Founded: 1943
Education.

LIMERICK COLLEGE OF ART, COMMERCE AND TECHNOLOGY
Moylish Park, Limerick
Tel: +353(61) 513-44
Art, Commerce and Technology.

Mary Immaculate College
South Circular Road, Limerick
Tel: +353(61) 314-923
Fax: +353(61) 313-632
Founded: 1898
Teacher Training (primary level).

Mater Dei Institute of Education
Clonliffe Road, Dublin 3
Tel: +353(1) 837-6027
Education.

National College of Industrial Relations
Sandford Road, Dublin 6
Tel: +353(1) 497-2917
Fax: +353(1) 497-2200
Industrial Relations.

St. Angela's College of Education for Home Economics
Lough Gill, Sligo
Tel: +353(71) 420-51
Fax: +353(71) 445-85
Education for Home Economics.

St. Catherine's College of Education for Home Economics
Sion Hill, Blackrock, Co. Dublin
Tel: +353(1) 288-4989
Fax: +353(1) 283-4858
Education for Home Economics.

St. Mary's Training College
Marino, Dublin 9
Tel: +353(1) 833-5111
Fax: +353(1) 833-5290
Teacher Training (primary level).

St. Patrick's College
Drumcondra, Dublin 9
Tel: +353(1) 837-6191
Fax: +353(1) 837-6197
Founded: 1875
Teacher Training; Education Research; Special Education.

Shannon College of Hotel Management
Shannon Airport, Co. Clare
Tel: +353(61) 471-444
Fax: +353(61) 475-160
Hotel Management.

The National College of Art and Design
100 Thomas Street, Dublin 8
Tel: +353(1) 671-1377
Fax: +353(1) 671-1748
Art and Design.

The Royal College of Physicians of Ireland
6 Kildare Street, Dublin 2
Tel: +353(1) 661-6677
Founded: 1667
Medicine.

The Royal College of Surgeons
123 St. Stephen's Green, Dublin 2
Tel: +353(1) 478-0200
Fax: +353(1) 478-0934
Founded: 1784
Surgery.

THOMOND COLLEGE OF EDUCATION
Castletroy, Limerick
Tel: +353(61) 334-488
Founded: 1976
Education.

NATIONAL ACADEMIC BODIES

Department of Education
[Ann Roinn Oideachais]
Marlborough Street, Dublin 1
Tel: +353(1) 873-4700
Fax: +353(1) 872-9553
Minister: Niamh Bhreathnach

Conference of the Heads of Irish Universities (C.H.I.U.)
49 Merrion Square, Dublin 2
Tel: +353(1) 767-246
Fax: +353(1) 619-665
Chairman: Thomas Mitchell
Executive Officer: John Nolan

Irish National Commission for Unesco
International Section, Department of Education,
Marlbourough Street, Dublin 1
Tel: +353(1) 873-4700 Exe 2433
Fax: +353(1) 8729-553
Telex: 31136 educ
Cable: neo dublin
Chairman: Dónal Thornhill
Secretary: Seán Harkin

ISRAEL

UNIVERSITIES AND TECHNICAL UNIVERSITIES

Bar-Ilan University
Ramat-Gan 52900
Tel: +972(3) 531-8500
Fax: +972(3) 535-4184
Telex: 361311
Cable: unibarilan
President: Shlomo Eckstein (1992-95)
Rector: Moshe Kaveh
Director-General: Shabtai Lubel
Founded: 1955
F: Jewish Studies; Humanities; Social Sciences; Natural Sciences; Law.

Ben-Gurion University of the Negev
[Universitat Ben Gurion Ba-Negev]
P.O. Box 653, Beer-Sheva 84105
Tel: +972(7) 461-111
Fax: +972(7) 237-682
E-Mail: acsecğumail.bgu.ac.il(Tslila Zagagi)
Telex: 5253 unasi il
President: Avishay Braverman (1990-)
Rector: Nachum Finger
Director-General: Eli Keidar
International Relations: President, Avishay Braverman
Founded: 1964, 1969, 1973
F: Humanities and Social Sciences; Natural Sciences; Engineering Sciences; Health Sciences.
I: Desert Research (Jacob Blaustein, Sde Boker Campus); Applied Research; Research and Archives (David Ben-Gurion).
S: Continuing Education.

University of Haifa
[Universitat Haifa]
Mount Carmel, Haifa 31905
Tel: +972(4) 240-111
Fax: +972(4) 342-104
E-Mail: mrecto4@Haifa.uvm
President (Acting): Yehuda Hayuth (1993-
Rector: Morcechai Shechter
International Relations: Yael Metser
Founded: 1963, 1972
F: Humanities; Social Sciences and Mathematics; Law; Education.
S: Social Work; Graduate Studies; Education (Kibbutz Movement Oranim).
Ce: Educational Administration and Evaluation; Rehabilitation Research and Human Development; Family Research and Study; Gerontology Research and Study; Study of Israel and its Settlements (jointly with the Ben-Zvi Foundation); Leon Recanati for Maritime Studies; Natural Resources and Environment Research; Study of Psychological Stress (R.D. Wolfe); Jewish-Arab; Policy and Security Studies; Jewish Education in the Diaspora; External Studies; Youth Policy; Education Research and

Advancement of Higher Education among Arabs in Israel.
I: Golan Research; Research into Christian Activities in Palestine in the 19th Century (Gottlieb Schumacher); Middle Eastern Studies (Gustav Heinemann); Haifa and Galilee Research; Research and Studies of Zionism (Herzl); Alternatives in Education; Public Policy; Research and Development in Arab Education; Study and Research of the Kibbutz and the Co-operative Idea; Study of French History and Culture; Evolution; Holocaust Studies (Strochlitz); Shipping and Aviation Research; Archaeology (Zinman); Study of the History of the Bund, the History of the Jewish Labor in Eastern Europe, and Yiddish Culture.
P: Peace Studies and Conflict Resolution in the Middle East (Bertha von Suttner).
L: Psychological.

*The Hebrew University of Jerusalem

[Ha'Universita Ha'Ivrit Bi'Yerushalayim].
Mount Scopus, Jerusalem 91905
Tel: +972(2) 882-111
Fax: +972(2) 322-545
Telex: 26458 scopm il
Cable: scopus
President: Hanoch Gutfreund (1993-97)
Rector: Yehoshua Ben-Arieh
Director-General: Moshe Vigdor
International Relations: Yehudit Birk
Founded: 1918, 1925, 1948, 1981
F: Humanities; Social Sciences; Law; Mathematics and Natural Sciences; Agriculture; Medicine; Dentistry.
S: Pharmacy; Education; Veterinary Medicine; Applied Science and Technology; Social Work; Library and Archive Studies; Overseas Students; Business Administration; Nutritional Science; Occupational Therapy; Nursing; Public Health and Community Medicine.

Open University of Israel

[Ha'Universita Ha'Petuha]
16 Klausner Street, Tel-Aviv 61-392
Tel: +972(3) 646-0460
Fax: +972(3) 642-3639
E-Mail: LEA.ALént.openu.ac.il
President: Menahem E. Yaari (1992-97)
Director-General: Ehud Or
International Relations: Director, Public Affairs Department, Elissa Allerhand
Founded: 1974
Natural Sciences; Life Sciences; Mathematics; Computer Science; Humanities; Social Sciences; Education; Economics; Management; Jewish Studies; Music and Art.

*Technion-Israel Institute of Technology

[Technion-Machon Technologi Le'Israel]
Technion City, Haifa 32000
Tel: +972(4) 292-593
Fax: +972(4) 325-537
Telex: telcon 46406
Cable: technion haifa
President: Zehev Tadmor (1990-)
Vice-President for Administration and Finance: Michael Rubinowitch
International Relations: Paul Singer
Founded: 1912
F: Civil Engineering; Architecture and Town Planning; Mechanical Engineering; Electrical Engineering; Chemistry; Chemical Engineering; Physics; Mathematics; Agricultural Engineering; Aerospace Engineering; Industrial Engineering and Management; Medicine; Computer Science; Materials Engineering; Food Technology and Biotechnology; Nuclear Engineering; Education; D; Biology; Biomedical Engineering; I; Transportation Research; Advanced Studies in Science and Technology; Medical Sciences Research; Solid State; Space Research; Water Research; Computer; Pre-University Studies; Continuing Education and External Studies.

Tel Aviv University

[Universitat Tel Aviv]
P.O. Box 39040, Ramat-Aviv 69978
Tel: +972(3) 640-8111
Fax: +972(3) 640-8601
President: Yoram Dinstein
Rector: Dan Amir (1993-)
General Director: David Lanir
International Relations: Director, Interacademic Affairs, Abel Schechter
Founded: 1953, 1956
F: The Arts; Social Sciences; Exact Sciences; Humanities; Management; Law; Life Sciences; Engineering; Medicine.
S: Social Work; Education; Continuing Medical Education; Dentistry; Health Professions.

*Weizmann Institute of Science

[Makhon Weizmann Lemada]
P.O. Box 26, Rehovot 76100
Tel: +972(8) 343-111
Fax: +972(8) 466-966
Telex: 381300
Cable: weizinst
President: Haim Harari (1988-98)
Vice-President (Finance and Administration): David Schlachet
Founded: 1934, 1949
F: Mathematics; Physics; Chemistry; Biophysics and Biochemistry; Biology.
D: Science Teaching.
Ce: Computer.
S: Graduate.

OTHER INSTITUTIONS

Beit-Berl Teachers' Training College
Beit-Berl Post 44905
Tel: +972(9) 906-333
Fax: +972(9) 454-104
President: Aaron Seidenberg (1990-)
Registrar: Shunamit Lifshitz
International Relations: Gad Arensberg
Founded: 1971
Teacher Training.

Bezalel Academy of Arts and Design
Mt. Scopus, P.O.B. 24046, Jerusalem 91240
Tel: +972(2) 893-333
Fax: +972(2) 823-094
Telex: 26452 bezal il
Head: Ran Sapoznik (1991-)
Deputy Director, Finance: Dan Canaan
International Relations: Director of Public Affairs,
Hannah Aschheim
Founded: 1906
Arts; Design.

College of Management-Academic Studies in Tel-Aviv
9 Shoshana Persitz Street, Tel-Aviv 61480
Tel: +972(3) 690-2020
Fax: +972(3) 699-0460
Chairman: Seev Neumann (1992-)
Director: Eliezer Fuchs
Founded: 1977
Management-Academic Studies.

The David Yellin Teachers College
P.O. Box 3578, Jerusalem 91035
Tel: +972(2) 533-111
Fax: +972(2) 521-548
Director: Itay Zimran (1988-)
Administrative Director: Margalit Matityahu
International Relations: Academic Director, Aaron
Shai
Founded: 1913
Teacher Training.

Gordon Teachers' College
73 Tchernikhovski str., Haifa 35705
Tel: +972(4) 335-547
Fax: +972(4) 337-044
Dean: Joseph Goldstein (1989-)
Administrator: Z.Zimerman
International Relations: Ella Mazor
Founded: 1952
Teacher Training.

Jerusalem College of Technology
P.O. Box 16031, Jerusalem 91160
Tel: +972(2) 422-075
E-Mail: ysefbřachot.jct.ac.il
President: Joseph S. Bodenheimer (1993-)
Director: Yosef Apter
International Relations: Joel Gering
Founded: 1969
*Electronics; Applied Physics/Electro-Optics;
Computer Science; Applied Mathematics;
Managerial Accounting.*

The Jerusalem Rubin Academy of Music and Dance
Givat Ram, Jerusalem 91904
Tel: +972(2) 759-911
Fax: +972(2) 527-713
Head: Avner Biron (1994-)
Director-General: Micha Tal
International Relations: Sharon Tabor-Pintz
Founded: 1947
Music; Dance.

THE CONSERVATORY/THE HIGH SCHOOL
7 Smolenskin Street, Jerusalem 92101
Tel: +972(2) 619-443
Fax: +972(2) 630-537

Levinsky College of Education
15 Shoshana Persitz, P.O. Box 48130, Tel-Aviv
61480
Tel: +972(3) 690-2404
Fax: +972(3) 699-3546
Head: Abraham Rocheli (1981-)
Administrator-General: Moshe Shalev
International Relations: Hana Gordon
Founded: 1913
*Education (Early Childhood, Special Education,
High School, Elementary School); Mathematics;
Biology; Music; English Studies; Arabic Studies;
Humanistic Studies.*

Mihlalah, Jerusalem College
Bayit Vegan, P.O. Box 16078, Jerusalem 91160
Tel: +972(2) 750-911
Fax: +972(2) 750-917
Rektor: Yehudah Copperman (1964-)
Deputy Director-General: Yaakov Bar Or
International Relations: Louis Applbaum
Founded: 1964
C: Teacher Training.
*S: Jewish Studies (Chananh Wolfson); Education
(Joseph and Faye Tannenbaum); Overseas
Students (Linda Pinsky).*
Ce: Holocaust Education (Serena Abeles Raab).
*I: Treatment of Children with Learning
Disabilities.*
P: Russian Immigrants (Preparatory).

Oranim, School of Education of the Kibbutz Movement
Tivon 36006
Tel: +972(4) 838-811
Fax: +972(4) 838-738
Dean: Yuval Dror (1990-)
Vice-Dean: Michael Ofer
Founded: 1951
*Liberal Arts (Haifa University); Teacher Training;
In-service Teacher Training; Research on Kibbutz
Education; Special Education (Zweig); Midrash-
Informal Jewish Studies.*

ORT Braude College
P.O.Box 78, Karmiel 20101
Tel: +972(4) 882-020
Fax: +972(4) 882-016
Director: Phinhas Shwinger (1989-)
Administrative Director: Shimon Haker
Founded: 1988
*Electrical Engineering; Mechanical Engineering;
Industrial Engineering; Biotechnology
Engineering.*

'ORT' College for Teachers in Technology
Givat Ram Campus, Jerusalem 95435
Tel: +972(2) 520-610
Fax: +972(2) 520-610
HeadRector: S.Zitronblatt: J.Shappir
Teacher Training (Technology).

Ruppin Institute of Agriculture-Academic Program
Emek Hefer 60960
Tel: +972(9) 683-067
Fax: +972(9) 683-090
E-Mail: rupin@ccsg.tau.ac.il
Director: Eliezer Levin (1995-)
Academic Director: Yoram Amiel
International Relations: Victor Friedman
Founded: 1949
Agriculture.

Shenkar College of Textile Technology and Fashion
24 Anna Frank Street, Ramat-Gan 52526
Tel: +972(3) 752-1133
Fax: +972(3) 752-1141
Telex: 341118 btv il
President: Amotz Weinberg (1994-)
Director-General: Yigal Freiman
International Relations: Adi Ganani
Founded: 1970
Textile Technology; Fashion.

State Teachers' College-Seminar Hakibuttzim
Derech Namir 149, Tel-Aviv 62507
Tel: +972(3) 690-2323
Fax: +972(3) 699-0269
Head: Ahuva Laor (1987-94)
Administrative Director: Efraim Zohari
International Relations: Ruth Yakir
Founded: 1939
*Education (early childhood, elementary, special,
junior high school levels); Physical Education,
Movement and Dance; Research and
Development in Education; Theatre Arts;
Computers in Education; Study of Democracy and
Co-Existence; Teaching of the Holocaust;
Academic Literacy.*

Talpiot Teachers' College
10 Hazerem Street, Tel-Aviv
Tel: +972(3) 512-8555
Fax: +972(3) 512-8570
Principal: M. Babchick (1987-94)
Executive Director: Chaim Amit
International Relations: Nava Horovitz
Founded: 1937
Teacher Training.

The Zinman College of Physical Education at the Wingate Institute
Wingate Post Office, Netanya 42902
Tel: +972(9) 639-222
Fax: +972(9) 650-960
Rector: Zvi Artzi (1994-)
International Relations: Mike Garmise
Founded: 1944
Physical Education.

NATIONAL ACADEMIC BODIES

Ministry of Education and Culture
34 Shivtey Yisrael Street, Jerusalem 91911
Tel: +972(2) 292-245
Fax: +972(2) 292-752
Minister: Amnon Rubinstein (1993-)
Director-General: Simshon Shoshani

Council for Higher Education
[Hamoetza Lehaskala Gehova]
P.O.B. 4037, Jerusalem 91040
Tel: +972(2) 663-131
Fax: +972(2) 660-625
Chairman: Amnon Rubinstein (1993-)
Director-General: Gury Zilkha
International Relations: Secretary, Techia Karcz
Founded: 1958

Committee for the Evaluation of Foreign Academic Degrees
Ministry of Education and Culture, Jerusalem 91911
Tel: +972(2) 293-700
Fax: +972(2) 293-706
Head: Yair Levin
Director: Nira Gur-Arieh
Founded: 1973

Israel National Commission for Unesco
Ministry of Education and Culture, Jerusalem 91911
Tel: +972(2) 293-746
Fax: +972(2) 293-745
Cable: isrunesco jerusalem
President: Amnon Rubinstein
Founded: 1952

ITALY

UNIVERSITIES AND TECHNICAL UNIVERSITIES

University of Ancona
[Università degli Studi di Ancona]
Piazza Roma 23, 60100 Ancona
Tel: +39(71) 282-12
Fax: +39(71) 220-2324
Rector: Guido Bossi (1991-96)
Administrative Director: Sandro Ferri
International Relations: Marta Sabbatini
Founded: 1969, 1970
F: *Agriculture; Mathematics, Physics and Natural Sciences; Engineering; Medicine and Surgery; Economics and Commerce.*

University of Aquila
[Università dell'Aquila]
Piazza Vicenzo Rivera 1, 67100 L'Aquila
Tel: +39(862) 431111
Fax: +39(862) 412948
Rector: Giovanni Schippa (1981-1995)
Administrative Director: Laura Paoni
International Relations: Pier Ugo Foscolo
Founded: 1952
F: *Economics and Commerce; Letters and Philosophy; Mathematics, Physics, and Natural Sciences; Engineering; Medicine and Surgery.*

Polytechnic Institute of Bari
[Politecnico di Bari]
Via Celso Ulpiani/13, 70125 Bari
Tel: +39(80) 243-501
Architecture; Engineering.

*University of Bari
[Università degli Studi di Bari]
Piazza Umberto I, 70100 Bari
Tel: +39(80) 311-111
Fax: +39(80) 314-641
Telex: 810598 Univba I
Rector: Aldo Cossu
Administrative Director: Innocenzo Santoro
International Relations: Michele Aresta
Founded: 1924
F: *Law; Economics and Commerce; Medicine and Surgery; Pharmacy; Agriculture; Letters and Philosophy; Mathematics, Physics, and Natural Sciences; Veterinary Medicine; Teacher Training; Foreign Languages and Literature.*

University of Bergamo
[Universita degli studi di Bergamo]
Via Salvecchio, 19, 24100 Bergamo
Tel: +39(35) 277111
Fax: +39(35) 277205
Rector: Pietro Enrico Ferri (1984-96)
Administrative Director: Domenico Danisi
International Relations: Pietro Enrico Ferri
F: *Economy and Commerce; Engineering; Foreign Languages and Literature.*

*University of Bologna
[Università degli Studi di Bologna]
Via Zamboni 33, 40126 Bologna
Tel: +39(51) 259-111
Fax: +39(51) 259-034
Rector: Fabio Roversi-Monaco (1985-94)
Administrative Director: Ines Fabbro
International Relations: Carmela Maldarizzi
Founded: 11th, 1802
F: *Law; Political Science; Economics and Commerce; Statistics, Demography, and Actuarial Sciences; Letters and Philosophy; Teacher Training; Medicine and Surgery; Mathematics, Physics, and Natural Sciences; Industrial Chemistry; Pharmacy; Engineering; Agriculture; Veterinary Medicine.*
I: *Music and Drama.*
S: *Modern Languages; Interpretation and Translation.*

University of Brescia
[Università degli Studi di Brescia]
Piazza Mercato 15, 25121 Brescia
Tel: +39(30) 29881
Fax: +39(30) 298-8329
Telex: 304116 univbs I
Rector: Augusto Preti (1983-1995)
Administrative Director: Franco Quarantelli
International Relations: Gian Primo Cella
Founded: 1982
F: *Medicine and Surgery; Engineering; Economics and Commerce.*

University of Cagliari
[Università degli Studi di Cagliari]
Via Università 40, 09100 Cagliari, Sardinia
Tel: +39(70) 6751
Fax: +39(70) 669-425
Telex: 043 790269 unic i
Rector: Pasquale Mistretta (1991-94)
Administrative Director: Fabrizio Ficorella
International Relations: Fabrizio Ficorella
Founded: 1607
F: *Law; Political Science; Economics and Commerce; Arts and Philosophy; Teacher Training; Medicine and Surgery; Mathematics, Physics, and Natural Sciences; Pharmacy; Engineering.*
D: *Neuroscience; Experimental Biology; New Chemical Sciences.*

University of Calabria
[Università degli Studi della Calabria]
Via Brodolini, 87036 Roges di Rende (Cosenza)
Tel: +39(984) 4911
Fax: +39(984) 463-505
Rector: Giuseppe Frega
Administrative Director: Sergio Livoli
Founded: 1972
F: *Letters and Philosophy; Mathematics, Physics, and Natural Sciences; Engineering; Pharmacy; Economics.*

*University of Camerino
[Università degli Studi di Camerino]
Via del Bastione, 62032 Camerino, C.A.P.
Tel: +39(737) 40111
Fax: +39(737) 40298
Telex: 560024 unicam
Rector: Mario Giannella (1983-1995)
Administrative Director: Sergio Sabietti
International Relations: Ignazio Buti
Founded: 1336, 1816, 1861, 1958
*F: Law; Mathematics, Physics, and Natural
Sciences; Pharmacy; Architecture; Veterinary
Medicine.*

University of Cassino
[Università degli Studi di Cassino]
Via Marconi, 10, 03043 Cassino (Frosinone)
Tel: +39(776) 2991
Fax: +39(776) 310-562
Rector: Federico Rossi (1990-1997)
Administrative Director: Luigi Peluso Cassese
International Relations: Paolo de Paolis
Founded: 1979
*F: Teacher Training; Economics and Commerce;
Engineering; Letters and Philosophy.*

Free University Institute 'Carlo Cattaneo' Castellanza
[Libero Istituto Universitario 'Carlo Cattaneo']
Corso Matteotti, 22, 21053 Castellanza (Varese)
Tel: +39(331) 480-747
Economics and Commerce.

*University of Catania
[Università degli Studi di Catania]
Piazza dell'Università, 2, 95129 Catania
Tel: +39(95) 310-355
Fax: +39(95) 325-194
Rector: Gaspare Rodolico (1974-1995)
Administrative Director: Sebastiano Spadaro
International Relations: Salvatore Rodono
Founded: 1434
*F: Law; Political Science; Economics and
Commerce; Letters and Philosophy; Medicine and
Surgery; Mathematics, Physics and Natural
Sciences; Pharmacy; Agriculture; Engineering;
Teacher Training.*

University of Chieti
[Università degli Studi 'Gabriele d'Annunzio'di
Chieti]
Via dei Vestini, 66013 Chieti
Tel: +39(871) 3551
Fax: +39(871) 355-343
Rector: Uberto Crescenti (1985-1994)
Administrative Director: Marco Napoleone
International Relations: Gabriella di Peppe
Founded: 1961,
*F: Mathematics, Physics, and Natural Sciences;
Pharmacy; Economics and Commerce (Pescara);
Foreign Languages and Literature (Pescara);
Letters and Philosophy; Architecture (Pescara);
Medicine and Surgery.*

University of Ferrara
[Università degli Studi di Ferrara]
Via Savonarola 9, 44100 Ferrara
Tel: +39(532) 203-181
Fax: +39(532) 48927
International Relations: Anna Maria Poltronieri
Founded: 1391, 1598, 1860, 1942
*F: Architecture; Engineering; Letters and
Philosophy; Law; Medicine and Surgery;
Mathematics, Physics, and Natural Sciences;
Pharmacy.*

University of Florence
[Università degli Studi di Firenze]
Piazza San Marco 4, 50121 Firenze
Tel: +39(55) 27571
Fax: +39(55) 599-887
Telex: 572400 Unifi
Rector: Paolo Blasi (1991-1994)
Administrative Director: Carlo Vidoni Guidoni
International Relations: Luigi Amaducci
Founded: 1321, 1859, 1872, 1924
*F: Law; Political and Social Sciences;
Economics and Commerce; Letters and
Philosophy; Teacher Training; Medicine and
Surgery; Pharmacy; Architecture; Agriculture;
Mathematics, Physics, and Natural Sciences;
Engineering.*

*University of Genoa
[Università degli Studi di Genova]
Via Balbi 5, 16126 Genova
Tel: +39(10) 20991
Fax: +39(10) 2099227
Telex: 271114
Rector: Sandro Pontremoli (1990-1996)
Administrative Director: Domenico Pellitteri
International Relations: Giuseppe Aceti
Founded: 1471, 1773
*F: Law; Political Science; Economics and
Commerce; Letters and Philosophy; Foreign
Languages and Literature; Teacher Training;
Medicine and Surgery; Mathematics, and
Physical and Natural Sciences; Pharmacy;
Engineering; Architecture.*

University of Lecce
[Università degli Studi di Lecce]
Viale Gallipoli, 39, 73100 Lecce
Tel: +39(832) 4061
Fax: +39(832) 246-993
Telex: 860830 Unstle I
Rector: Angelo Rizzo (1993-)
Administrative Director: Stanislao Natali
International Relations: Raffaele De Giorgi
Founded: 1966
*F: Letters and Philosophy; Teacher Training;
Mathematics, Physics, and Natural Sciences;
Engineering; Banking and Commerce.*

*University of Macerata
[Università degli Studi di Macerata]
Piaggia dell'Università 2, 62100 Macerata
Tel: +39(733) 2581
Fax: +39(733) 232639
Rector: Alberto Febbrajo (1991-94)
Administrative Director: Tito Morelli
International Relations: Adam Roberto
Founded: 1290, 1540
F: Law; Letters and Philosophy; Political Science.

University of Messina
[Università degli Studi di Messina]
Piazza Universit@, 98100 Messina
Tel: +39(90) 716-111
Fax: +39(90) 717-762
Rector: Guglielmo Stagno d'Alcontres (1983-1995)
Administrative Director: Vincenzo Ferluga
International Relations: Girolamo Cotroneo
Founded: 1548
F: Law; Political Science; Economics and Commerce; Engineering; Statistical, Demographic and Actuarial Sciences; Letters and Philosophy; Teacher Training; Medicine and Surgery; Veterinary Medicine; Pharmacy; Mathematics, Physics, and Natural Sciences.

*Catholic University of the Sacred Heart Milan
[Università Cattolica del Sacro Cuore]
Largo Agostino Gemelli 1, 20123 Milano
Tel: +39(2) 72341
Fax: +39(2) 723-42210
Telex: 321033 ucatmi
Cable: universcatmi
Rector: Adriano Bausola (1983-95)
Administrative Director: Domenico Lofrese
International Relations: Guido Castelli
Founded: 1920
F: Law; Political Science; Economics and Commerce; Letters and Philosophy; Teacher Training (Milan and Brescia); Agriculture (Piacenza); Medicine and Surgery (Rome); Mathematics, Physical and Natural Sciences (Brescia); Bank Financial and Insurance Sciences; Foreign Languages and Literature.

*Polytechnic Institute of Milan
[Politecnico di Milano]
Piazza Leonardo da Vinci 32, 20133 Milano
Tel: +39(2) 23991
Fax: +39(2) 239-92206
Telex: polimi 1333467
Rector: Emilio Massa (1990-96)
Administrative Director: Giorgio Coppini
International Relations: Giancarlo Spinelli
Founded: 1863
F: Engineering; Architecture.

University of Commerce 'Luigi Bocconi' Milan
[Università Commerciale 'Luigi Bocconi']
Via R. Sarfatti 25, 20136 Milano
Tel: +39(2) 58361
Fax: +39(2) 583-62000
Telex: uniboci 316003
Rector: Mario Monti (1989-94)
Administrative Director: Enrico Resti
International Relations: Carlo Secchi
Founded: 1902
F: Economics.

University Institute of Modern Languages Milan
[Istituto Universitario di Lingue Moderne]
Via Filippo de Liscate, 12, 20145 Milano
Tel: +39(2) 582-181
Modern Languages and Literature.

University of Milan
[Università degli Studi di Milano]
Via Festa del Perdono 7, 20122 Milano
Tel: +39(2) 58351
Fax: +39(2) 58304482
Telex: 320484
Rector: Paolo Mantegazza (1984-96)
Administrative Director: Piero Cassani
International Relations: Fausto Pocar
Founded: 1924
F: Economics and Commerce; Law; Political Science; Letters and Philosophy; Medicine and Surgery; Pharmacy; Mathematics, Physics, and Natural Sciences; Agriculture; Veterinary Medicine; Science (Como, Varese).

University of Modena
[Università degli Studi di Modena]
Via Università 4, 41100 Modena
Tel: +39(59) 329-111
Fax: +39(59) 218-661
Rector: Carlo Cipolli (1993-96)
Administrative Director: Antonio Salvini
International Relations: Maria Rosaria Tosco
Founded: 1175
F: Law; Medicine and Surgery; Mathematics, Physics, and Natural Sciences; Pharmacy; Economics; Engineering.

University of Molise
[Università degli Studi del Molise]
Via Mazzini, 8, 86100 Campobasso
Tel: +39(874) 4041
Founded: 1982
F: Economics and Social Sciences; Law; Agriculture.

University Institute of Oriental Studies Naples
[Istituto Universitario Orientale]
Piazza S. Giovanni Maggiore 30, 80133 Napoli
Tel: +39(81) 551-7815
Fax: =39(81) 760-5242
Telex: 721089 iuo i
Rector: Adriano Rossi (1992-95)
Nicola De Dominicis
International Relations: Marina Guidetti
Founded: 1732
F: Letters and Philosophy; Foreign Languages and Literature; Political Sciences; Islamic Studies.

University Institute of Teacher Training 'Suor Orsola Benincasa' Naples
[Istituto Universitario pareggiato di Magistero 'Suor Orsola Benincasa']
Corso Vittorio Emmanuele, 292, 80121 Napoli
Tel: +39(81) 419-327
Founded: 1901
Teacher Training.

University Institute of Naval Studies Naples
[Istituto Universitario Navale]
Via Ammiraglio Acton 38, 80133 Napoli
Tel: +39(81) 552-0327
Fax: +39(81) 552-1485
Telex: 710417 navale i
Rector: Gennaro Ferrara (1986-95)
Administrative Director: Ferdinando Fiengo
International Relations: Giancarlo Spezie
Founded: 1920
Economics; Marine Sciences.

Second University of Naples
[SSeconda Università degli Studi di Napoli]
Via Santa Maria di Costantinopoli, 104, 80138 Napoli
Tel: +39(81) 296-803
F: Architecture (Aversa); Medicine and Surgery (Caserta); Mathematics, Physics, and Natural Sciences (Caserta); Economics and Commerce (Capula); Law (Santa Maria Capua Vetere); Environmental Sciences (Caserta); Engineering (Aversa).

University 'Federico II' of Naples
[Università degli Studi 'Federico II' di Napoli]
Corso Umberto 1, 80138 Napoli
Tel: +39(81) 547-7111
Fax: +39(81) 547-7234
Rector: Fulvio Tessitore (1993-96)
Administrative Director: Tommaso Pelosi
International Relations: Ovidio Mario Bucci
Founded: 1224
F: Agriculture; Architecture; Economics and Commerce; Pharmacy; Law; Letters and Philosophy; Engineering; Medicine and Surgery; Veterinary Medicine; Mathematics, Physics and Natural Sciences; Political Science.

University of Padua
[Università degli Studi di Padova]
Via VIII Febbraio 2, 35122 Padova
Tel: +39(49) 828-3111
Fax: +39(49) 828-3099
Telex: unpadu 430176
Rector: Gilberto Muraro (1993-96)
Administrative Director: Dino Artmann
International Relations: Benedetto Scimemi
Founded: 1222
F: Law; Political Science; Statistical, Demographic, and Actuarial Sciences; Letters and Philosophy; Teacher Training; Medicine and Surgery; Mathematics, Physics and Natural Sciences; Pharmacy; Engineering; Agriculture; Psychology; Veterinary Medicine.
I: Nuclear Physics (I.N.F.N.).

University of Palermo
[Università degli Studi di Palermo]
Piazza Marina 61, 90100 Palermo
Tel: +39(91) 270-111
Fax: +39(91) 611-0448
Rector: Antonino Gullotti (1993-96)
Carmelo Fallica
International Relations: Giovanni Giudice
Founded: 1779, 1806
F: Law; Letters and Philosophy; Economics and Commerce; Medicine and Surgery; Mathematics, Physics, and Natural Sciences; Engineering; Architecture; Agriculture; Pharmacy; Teacher Training; Political Sciences.

*University of Parma
[Università degli Studi di Parma]
Via Cavestro, 7, 43100 Parma
Tel: +39(521) 2041
Fax: (521) 207-521
Telex: 530327
Rector: Nicola Occhiocupo (1989-95)
Administrative Director: Maurizio Castelli
International Relations: Enzo Molina
Founded: 1964
F: Law; Letters and Philosophy; Agriculture; Economics; Pharmacy; Medicine and Surgery; Veterinary Medicine; Mathematics, Physics, and Natural Sciences; Engineering.

*University of Pavia
[Università degli Studi di Pavia]
Strada Nuova 65, 27100 Pavia
Tel: +39(382) 3871
Fax: +39(382) 21389
E-Mail: BITNET:maint+Uipvccn +attention of
Telex: 312841 unipav i
Rector: Roberto Schmid (1988-94)
Administrative Director: Gesuino Piga
International Relations: Antonio Savini
Founded: 1825, 1361
F: Law; Political Sciences; Economics; Letters and Philosophy; Medicine and Surgery; Mathematics, Physics, and Natural Sciences; Pharmacy; Engineering.
S: Musical Paleography and Philology.

University of Italian Studies for Foreigners Perugia

[Università Italiana per Stranieri di Perugia]
Piazza Fortebraccio 4, 006100 Perugia
Tel: +39(75) 57461
Fax: +39(75) 62014
Telex: 662079 unstra i
Rector: Giorgio Spitella
Administrative Director: Carmelo Saetta
Italian Language and Culture (for Foreigners).

University of Perugia

[Università degli Studi di Perugia]
Piazza della Università, 06100 Perugia
Tel: +39(75) 5851
Fax: +39(75) 585-2078
Telex: 662078
Rector: Giancarlo Dozza (1976-94)
Administrative Director: Carmelo Saetta
International Relations: Giancarlo Dozza
Founded: 1200, 1308
F: Law; Political Science; Letters and Philosophy; Teacher Training; Medicine and Surgery; Mathematics, Physics and Natural Sciences; Pharmacy; Agriculture; Veterinary Medicine; Economics and Commerce; Engineering.

Higher School of University and Advanced Studies Pisa

[Scuola Superiore di Studi Universitari e di Perfezionamento]
Via Carducci 40, 56100 Pisa
Tel: +39(50) 559241
Social Sciences; Experimental and Applied Sciences.

School of Education Pisa

[Scuola Normale Superiore]
Piazza dei Cavalieri 6, Pisa
Tel: +39(50) 597-111
Fax: +39(50) 563-513
Telex: 590548 snspi i
Director: Emilio Picasso (1991-95)
Administrative Director: Daniele Sevieri
International Relations: Alfredo Stussi
Founded: 1813
Letters and Philosophy; Mathematics, Physics and Natural Sciences.

University of Pisa

[Università degli Studi di Pisa]
Lungarno Pacinotti 43, 56100 Pisa
Tel: +39(50) 920000
Fax: +39(50) 42446
Telex: Univpi 590035
Rector: Luciano Modica (1993-96)
Administrative Director: Giorgio Coluccini
International Relations: Guido Paduano
Founded: 1343
F: Law; Economics; Letters and Philosophy; Political Science; Foreign Languages and Literature; Medicine and Surgery; Mathematics, Physics and Natural Sciences; Pharmacy; Engineering; Agriculture; Veterinary Medicine.

Basilicata University, Potenza

[Università degli Studi della Basilicata]
Via Nazario, Sauro, 85, 85100 Potenza
Tel: +39(971) 474111
Fax: +39(971) 54847
Telex: 812492 unstba i
Rector: C. D. Fonseca
Administrative Director: I. Santoro
Founded: 1982
F: Mathematics, Physics, and Natural Sciences; Engineering; Agriculture; Letters and Philosophy.

University of Reggio Calabria

[Università degli Studi di Reggio Calabria]
Via Zecca, 4, 89125 Reggio Calabria
Tel: +39 (965) 332-202
Rector: Antonio Quistelli
Administrative Director: Salvatore Leonardi
Founded: 1982
F: Architecture; Agriculture; Engineering; Law (Catanzaro); Medicine and Surgery (Catanzaro). S: Pharmacy.

Free University Institute of Bio-Medicine Rome

[Libero Instituto Universitario 'Campus Bio-medico']
Via Lancelloti, 18, 00186 Roma
Tel: +39(6) 683-00887
Founded: 1939
F: Medicine and Surgery.

Free International University of Social Studies Rome

[Libera Università Internazionale degli Studi Sociali]
Viale Pola 12, 00198 Roma
Tel: +39(6) 674-861
Fax: +39(6) 674-86300
Rector: Mario Arcelli (1992-95)
Administrative Director: Giovanni Nocco
International Relations: Maria Sticchi Damiani
F: Political Science; Economics and Commerce; Law.

Free University 'Maria SS. Assunta'

[Libera Università 'Maria SS Assunta']
Via della Transpontina 21, 00100 Roma
Tel: +39(6) 686-5945
Founded: 1939
F: Letters and Philosophy; Teacher Training.

University of Rome 'La Sapienza'

[Università degli Studi di Roma 'La Sapienza']
Piazzale Aldo Moro 5, 00185 Roma
Tel: 39(6) 499-12860
Fax: +39(6) 445-2824
Telex: 620564 unisap
Rector: Giorgio Tecce (1988-94)
Administrative Director: Ernesto Nicolai
International Relations: Dino Guerritore
Founded: 1303, 1935
F: Law; Political Science; Economics and Commerce; Statistics, Demography, and Actuarial Science; Letters and Philosophy; Psychology;

Mathematics, Physics, and Natural Sciences;
Sociology; Engineering; Architecture; Medicine
and Surgery; Pharmacy.
S: Aerospatial Engineering; Archivists and
Librarians.

University of Rome Tor Vergata
[Università degli Studi di Roma Tor Vergata]
Via Orazio Raimondo, 8, 00173 Roma
Tel: +39(6) 72591
Rector: Aldo Brancati (1993-96)
Administrative Director: Nunzio Quintorio
Law; Letters and Philosophy; Economy; Medicine
and Surgery; Mathematics, Physics, and Natural
Sciences; Engineering.

Third University of Rome
[Terza Università degli Studi di Roma]
Via C. Segré Rector: Biancamaria Tedeschini
Lalli (1993-)
F: Architecture; Economy; Engineering; Letters
and Philosophy; Mathematics, Physics and
Natural Sciences.

University of Salerno
[Università degli Studi di Salerno]
Via Valle dell'Imo, 84084 Fisciano, Salerno
Tel: +39(89) 961111
(1987-995)
Administrative Director: Mario Rosario Cavaliere
International Relations: Angelo Trimarco
F: Law; Pharmacy; Economics and Commerce;
Engineering; Letters and Philosophy; Economic
and Social Sciences; Teacher Training; Political
Sciences; Mathematics, Physics, and Natural
Sciences.

*University of Sassari
[Università degli Studi di Sassari]
Piazza Università, 21, 07100 Sassari, Sardinia
Tel: +39(79) 228-211
Fax: (79) 228-816
Telex: 790299 sacer i
Rector: Giovanni Palmieri (1991-94)
Administrative Director: Orazio Nicotra
International Relations: Paola Olla Brundu
Founded: 1562, 1617, 1766
F: Law; Medicine and Surgery; Pharmacy;
Veterinary Medicine; Agriculture; Mathematics,
Physics, and Natural Sciences; Letters and
Philosophy; Political Sciences; Economics and
Commerce.
Ce: Spectroscopy; Electronic Microscopy.

University of Italian Studies for Foreigners Siena
[Università per stranieri di Siena]
Via dei Termini, 6, 53100 Siena
Tel: +39(577) 49260
Founded: 1939
Italian Language and Culture (for foreigners).

University of Siena
[Università degli Studi di Siena]
Via Banchi di Sotto 55, 53100 Siena
Tel: +39(577) 298-000
Fax: +39(577) 298-202
Telex: 572459
Rector: Luigi Berlinguer (1985-94)
Administrative Director: Jolanda Dei Semplici
International Relations: Annalisa poggialini
Founded: 1240, 1859
F: Law; Engineering; Medicine and Surgery;
Pharmacy; Economics and Banking; Mathematics,
Physics, and Natural Sciences; Teacher Training;
Letters and Philosophy.

University of Teramo
[Università degli Studi di Teramo]
Viale Cruciole, 120, 64100 Teramo
Tel: +39(861) 2661
Founded: 1939
F: Veterinary Medicine; Law; Political Sciences.

University of Trento
[Università degli Studi di Trento]
Via Belenzani 12, 38100 Trento
Tel: +39(461) 881-111
Fax: +39(461) 881-299
Telex: univin 400674
Rector: Fulvio Zuelli (1990-96)
Administrative Director: Vitaliano Agostini
International Relations: Elisabetta Tonini
Founded: 1962, 1972, 1982
F: Sociology; Mathematics, Physics, and Natural
Sciences; Economics and Commerce; Law;
Letters and Philosophy; Engineering.

International Higher School of Advanced Studies Trieste
[Scuola Internazionale Superiore di Studi
Avanzati di Trieste]
Via Beirut, 2-4, 34013 Trieste
Tel: +39(40) 37871
Founded: 1939
Advanced Studies.

*University of Trieste
[Università degli Studi di Trieste]
Piazzale Europa 1, 34100 Trieste
Tel: +39(40) 676-3811
Fax: +39(40) 676-3093
Telex: 460865 univts
Rector: Giacomo Borruso (1990-96)
Administrative Director: Gioacchino Pafumi
International Relations: Mauro Graziani
Founded: 1877, 1924
F: Law; Political Sciences; Economics; Letters
and Philosophy; Teacher Training; Medicine and
Surgery; Mathematics, Physics, and Natural
Sciences; Pharmacy; Engineering.
S: Translation and Interpretation.

Polytechnic Institute of Turin
[Politecnico di Torino]
Corso Duca degli Abruzzi 24, 10129 Torino
Tel: +39(11) 564-6111
Fax: +39(11) 564-6329
Telex: 220646 polito i
Rector: Rodolfo Zich (1987-97)
Administrative Director: Maria A. Zecchini Piglia
International Relations: Gian Federico Micheletti
Founded: 1859, 1906
F: Architecture; Engineering.
S: Aerospace Engineering.

University of Turin
[Università degli Studi di Torino]
Via Giuseppe Verdi 8, 10124 Torino
Tel: +39(11) 88021
Fax: +39(11) 818-2218
Rector: Mario Dianzani (1984-96)
Administrative Director: Franca Vercelli Fisicaro
International Relations: Oreste Calliano
Founded: 1404, 1713
F: Agriculture; Economics and Commerce;
Pharmacy; Law; Letters and Philosophy; Teacher
Training; Medicine and Surgery; Veterinary
Medicine; Mathematics, Physics, and Natural
Sciences; Political Science.

*University of Udine
[Università degli Studi di Udine]
Via Antonini 8, 33100 Udine
Tel: +39(432) 297-284
Fax: +39(432) 556-259
E-Mail: crin@uduniv.cineca.it
Telex: 450412 univud i
Rector: Marzio Strassoldo di Graffembergo
(1992-95)
Administrative Director: Giacomo Minuti
International Relations: Mauro Bertagnino
Founded: 1978
F: Agriculture; Engineering; Mathematics,
Physics, and Natural Sciences; Letters and
Philosophy; Foreign Languages and Literature;
Medicine and Surgery; Economics and Banking.
Ce: Computer; Audiovisual Language;
International and Plurilinguistics.

University of Urbino
[Università degli Studi di Urbino]
Via Saffi 2, 61029 Urbino
Tel: +39(722) 3015 + 39(722) 2690
International Relations: Cesare Cangiotti
Founded: 1506, 1826, 1923
F: Law; Economics; Letters and Philosophy;
Political Sciences; Teacher Training; Sociology;
Pharmacy; Environmental Science; Mathematics,
Physics, and Natural Sciences.

University Institute of Architecture Venice
[Istituto Universitario di Architectura]
S. Croce Campazzo dei Tolentini 191, 30125
Venezia
Tel: +39(41) 529-7711
Fax: +39(41) 529-7780
Rector: M. Folin
Administrative Director: Francesco Quatraro
Founded: 1926
Architecture.

*University of Venice
[Università degli Studi di Venezia]
Ca' Foscari, Dorsoduro 3246, 30123 Venezia
Tel: +39(41) 529-8111
Fax: +39(41) 529-8321
Telex: 410638
Rector: Paolo Costa (1992-95)
Administrative Director: Antonino Domina
International Relations: Rosella Mamoli Zorzi
Founded: 1868, 1968
F: Economics; Foreign Languages and
Literature; Letters and Philosophy; Mathematics,
Physics and Natural Sciences.

University of Verona
[Università degli Studi di Verona]
Via S. dell'Artigliere 8, 37129 Verona
Tel: +39(45) 809-8111
Fax: +39(45) 809-8255
Telex: 481106
Rector: Mario Marigo (1992-95)
Administrative Director: Renzo Piccoli
International Relations: Maria Teresa Bindella
F: Medicine and Surgery; Letters and
Philosophy; Economics and Commerce;
Mathematics, Physics and Natural Sciences;
Literature and Philosophy; Foreign Languages
and Literature; Natural Sciences and
Biotechnology.
S: Social Workers.
Ce: East-West Studies and European
Integration; Studies and Research on Social and
Economic Development Planning.

Viterbo State University
[Università degli Studi della Tuscia]
Via San Giovanni Decollato 1, 01100 Viterbo
Tel: +39(761) 2571
Fax: +39(761) 325-785
Telex: 614076 tusvit i
Rector: Gian T. Scarascia Mugnozza (1982-96)
Administrative Director: Franco Fracassa
International Relations: Lorenzo Venzi
Founded: 1979
F: Agriculture; Modern Foreign Languages and
Literature; Mathematics, Physics and Natural
Sciences; Conservation of Cultural Property.

NATIONAL ACADEMIC BODIES

Ministry of Universities and Scientific and Technological Research
[Ministero della Università e della Ricersa Scientifica e Tecnologica]
Piazzale Kennedy, 20, 00144 Roma
Tel: +39(6) 59911
Fax: +39(6) 584-9211
Minister: Francesco D'Onofrio

Standing Conference of Italian University Rectors
[Conferenza Permanente dei Rettori delle Università Italiane]
Via Salaria, 113, 001 Roma
Tel: +39(6) 853-52761

National Council for Science and Technology
[Consiglio Nazionale della Sciencia e della Tecnologia]
Piazzala Kennedy, 20, 00144 Roma
Tel: +39(6) 59911
Telex: 614079 piuniv i

National University Council
[Consiglio Universitario Nationale]
Piazza Kennedy, 20, 00144 Roma
Tel: +39(6) 59911

Italian National Commission for Unesco
[Commission Nationale Italiana per l'Unesco]
Piazza Firenze 27, 00186 Roma
Tel: +39(6) 687-3713
Fax: (6) 687-3684
Telex: 626641 italun i
Chairman: Tullia Carettoni Romagnoli
Secretary General: Luigi Capogrossi

JAMAICA

UNIVERSITIES

*The University of the West Indies
Mona, Kingston
Tel: P.B.X. +1809 92-71660
Telex: 2123 univers ja
Cable: univers ja
Vice-Chancellor: The Hon. Sir Alister McIntyre (1988-)
Registrar: Byron Robertson
Founded: 1948, 1962
F: Medicine; Arts and General Studies; Natural Sciences; Social Sciences; Education; Law; Agriculture; Engineering.

I: Social and Economic Research; International Relations; Mass Communication (Caribbean).
S: Social Sciences (Graduate); Continuing Studies.

OTHER INSTITUTIONS

Caribbean Graduate School of Theology
14 West Avenue Constant Spring, Kingston 8
Tel: +1809(925) 7358
Founded: 1986
Theology.

College of Agriculture
Port Antonio, P.O. Box 170, Postland
Tel: +1809(993) 3246
Founded: 1982
Agriculture.

College of Arts, Sciences and Technology
237 Old Hope Road, Kingston 6
Tel: +1809(92) 71680
Founded: 1958
Arts, Sciences and Technology.

West Indies College
Mandeville, Manchester
Tel: +1809(962) 2204

NATIONAL ACADEMIC BODIES

Ministry of Education and Culture
2 National Heroes Circle, P.O. Box 202, Kingston
Tel: +1809(922) 1400
Minister: Burchell Whiteman

The University Council of Jamaica (UCJ)
25 Dominica Drive, 7th Floor, 'The Towers', Kingston 5, Jamaica West-Indies
Tel: +1809(929) 7312
Fax: +1809(929) 7312
Chairman: Keith Panton
Executive Director: Ethley D. London
Founded: 1987

Jamaica National Commission for Unesco
25 Dominica Drive, Kingston
Tel: +1809(926) 5480
Fax: +1809(92) 98468
Cable: jamunesco kingston
Chairman: Burchell Whiteman, Minister of Education
Secretary-General: Sylvia Thomas

JAPAN

UNIVERSITIES AND COLLEGES WITH GRADUATE SCHOOLS

NATIONAL INSTITUTIONS

Aichi University of Education
[Aichi Kyoiku Daigaku]
Hirosawa, Igaya-cho, Kariya-shi, Aichi-ken 448
Tel: +81(566) 36-3111
President: Shigeru Shojyaku
Secretary-General: Osamu Nakanishi
Founded: 1873, 1966
Education.

Akita University
[Akita Daigaku]
1-1 Tegata Gakuen-machi, Akita-shi, Akita 010
Tel: +81(188) 33-5261
President: Naoyoshi Niino
Secretary-General: Naoaki Hayashi
Founded: 1949
C: Allied Medical Science and Technology.
S: Medicine; Medicine (Graduate); Education (Graduate).
D: Advanced Studies in Special Education for the Mentally Handicapped.
Ce: Education; Mining; Education Technology.
I: Natural Resources Research.
L: Central Medical Research.

Asahikawa Medical College
[Asahikawa Ika Daigaku]
Nishikagura 4-5, Asahikawa, Hokkaido 078
Tel: +81(166) 65-2111
Telex: 922492
President: Tetsuya Sjhimizu
Secretary-General: Yutaka Kashino
Founded: 1973
Medicine; Animal Medical Research.

*Chiba University
[Chiba Daigaku]
1-33 Yayoi-cho, Inage-ku, Chiba 263
Tel: +81(43) 251-1111
Fax: +81(43) 290-2041
President: Ryo Yoshida (1994-98)
Secretary-General: Hiroshi Kusaka
International Relations: Miyuki Fukuda
Founded: 1949
F: Letters; Law and Economics; Education; Pharmaceutical Sciences; Engineering; Horticulture; Science.
F: Medicine; Nursing.
C: Arts and Sciences; Chemical Analysis.
Ce: Pathogenic Fungi and Microbial Toxicoses (Research); Remote Sensing and Image Research; Information Processing; Health Sciences; Radioisotope Research; International Student.

Chofu-shi University of Electro-Communications
[Denki-tsushin Daigaku]
1-5-1 Chofugaoka, Chofu-shi, Tokyo 182
Tel: +81(424) 83-2161
Telex: 2822446 uec j
President: Minoru Sumita
Director of Administration: Yuzo Taruki
Founded: 1918, 1949
F: Electro-Communications.
S: Electro-Communications (Graduate); Information Systems (Graduate).
I: Laser Science.
Ce: Information Proceeding.
Observatory: Space Radio Wave Observatory (Sanadachu).

Ehime University
[Ehime Daigaku]
10-13 Dogo-Himata, Matsuyama-shi, Ehime 790
Tel: +81(899) 24-7111
Fax: +81(899) 24-7149
President: Ryo fukunishi
Secretary-General: Toshinao Moriya
Founded: 1949
F: Law and Literature; Education; Science; Engineering; General Education.
S: Medicine; Agricultural Sciences (Graduate).
C: Agriculture.
Ce: Advanced Instrumentation for Chemical Analysis; Data Processing; Health Administration.

Fukui Medical School
[Fukui Ika Daigaku]
23 Shimoaizuki, Matsuoka-cho, Fukui 910-11
Tel: +81(776) 61-3111
Fax: +81(776) 61-3535
President: Kanji Torizuka (1989-92)
Secretary-General: Susumu Saito
Founded: 1978
Medicine; Laboratory Animals Research; Medical Research; Medical Information Science; Radio-Isotope Research.

Fukui University
[Fukui Daigaku]
9-1 Bunkyo, 3-chome, Fukui-shi, Fukui 910
Tel: +81(776) 23-0500
Fax: +81(776) 27-8518
President: Tadashi Shimada (1987-93)
Director-General: Hisashi Ujiie
Founded: 1949
F: Education; Engineering.
Ce: Co-operative Research.
I: Low Temperature Physics (Experimentsing Experimental Applied Physics).

Fukuoka University of Education
[Fukuoka Kyoiku Daigaku]
729 Akama, Munakata-shi, Fukuoka 811-41
Tel: +81(940) 35-1200
President: Takahide Tashiro
Secretary-General: Shigeru Yoshida
Founded: 1943, 1949
Education.

Fukushima University
[Fukushima Daigaku]
2 Sugumichi, Asakawa, Fukushima-shi,
Fukushima 960-12
Tel: +81(245) 48-5151
President: Jun Hoshino
Secretary-General: Akio Okuda
Founded: 1949
Economics; Education.

Gifu University
[Gifu Daigaku]
1-1 Yanagido, Gifu-shi, Gifu-ken 501-11
Tel: +81(582) 30-1111
Fax: +81(582) 30-1260
President: Akira Katoh (1949-)
Secretary-General: Hiroshi Takeda
Founded: 1949
F: Education; Engineering; Agriculture; General Education.
S: Medicine; Nursing.
I: Equilibrium Research; Anaerobic Bacteriology; Development of Mountain Regions.
Ce: Co-operative Research.

The Graduate University for Advanced Studies
[Sogo Kenkyu Daigakuin Daigaku]
4259 Nagatsuda-cho, Midori-ru, Yokohama-shi,
Kanagawa 227
Tel: +81(45) 922-1661
President: Saburo Nagakura
Secretary-General: Yuji Ukita
Culture Study; Statistics and Physical Sciences; Life Science.

Gunma University
[Gunma Daigaku]
4-2 Aramaki-Machi, Maebasi-shi, Gunma 371
Tel: +81(272) 32-1611
President: Eiichi Ishikawa
Secretary-General: Katsuyuki Utagawa
Founded: 1949
F: Education; Engineering; General Studies.
C: Technology; Medical Care and Technology.
S: Medicine.
I: Endocrinology.

Hamamatsu University School of Medicine
[Hamamatsu Ika Daigaku]
3600 Handa-cho, Hamamatsu-shi, Shizuoka
431-31
Tel: +81(53) 435-2111
President: Yoshiro Kawashima
Secretary-General: Hiroshi Harada
Founded: 1974
Medicine; Photon Medical Research.

Hirosaki University
[Hirosaki Daigaku]
1 Bunkyo-cho, Hirosaki-shi, Aomori-ken 036
Tel: +81(172) 36-2111
President: Wataru Teshirogi
Secretary-General: Sho Suzuki
Founded: 1949

F: Humanities; Education; Science; Agriculture.
S: Medicine; Allied Medical Sciences.
C: Liberal Arts.

*Hiroshima University
[Hiroshima Daigaku]
1-1-89, Higashisenda-machi, Naka-ku, Hiroshima-shi, Hiroshima 730
Tel: +81(82) 241-1221
Fax: +81(82) 242-1561
Cable: hiruniv hiroshima
President: Yasuo Harada
Secretary-General: Yoshiyuki Kato
International Relations: Yasuhiro Ogawa
Founded: 1949
F: Integrated Arts and Sciences; Letters; Education; Economics; Law; Science; Engineering; Applied Biological Science; School Education (Elementary, Junior High School levels; Education of the Visually Handicapped, Hearing Impaired, and Mentally Retarded).
S: Medicine; Dentistry; Nursing; Dental Hygienists; Dental Technicians.
I: Nuclear Medicine and Biology Research; International Education; Cultural Studies of the Seto Inland Sea; Early Childhood Education (Research); Regional Economic Research; Replacement Medicine (Research); Peace Science; Waste Waters Treatment.
Ce: Higher Education Research; Information Processing; Integrated Systems (Researchd Process Technology, Computer System Architecture); Cryogenic; Gene Science; Health Service; Instrument for Chemical Analysis; Regional Geography (Research); Educational Study and Practice (Research); Radioisotope.
L: Crystal Physics; Amphibian Biology; Plant Chromosome and Gene Stock; Fisheries.

*Hitotsubashi University
[Hitotsubashi Daigaku]
2-1 Naka, Kunitachi-shi, Tokyo 186
Tel: +81(425) 72-1101
Fax: +81(425) 75-0868
Telex: 2842107 hitots j
President: Kinya Abe
Secretary-General: Kazumi Ida
International Relations: Shigeru Kure
Founded: 1875, 1920, 1949
F: Commerce; Economics; Law; Social Studies.
I: Economic Research.

*Hokkaido University
[Hokkaido Daigaku]
Nishi 5, Kita 8-jo, Kita-ku, Sapporo-shi, Hokkaido
060
Tel: +81(11) 716-2111
Fax: +81(11) 746-9488
President: Tsutomu Hiroshige (1991-95)
Secretary-General: Takashi Okabayashi
International Relations: Katsutoshi Nakamura
Founded: 1872, 1918, 1947
F: Letters; Education; Law; Economics; Science; Pharmaceutical Sciences; Engineering; Agriculture; Veterinary Medicine; Fisheries.

C: Medical Technology.
S: Medicine; Dentistry; Environmental Science (Graduate).
D: General Education.
I: Language and Culture Studies; Low Temperature Science; Electronic Science (Research); Immunological Science; Radioisotope Science (Central); Study of North Eurasian Cultures; Planning of Industrial Education; Algological Research; Balneotherapeutic Research; Cancer; Animal Experiments; Metals Research; North Pacific Fisheries (Research).
Ce: Catalysis Research; Slavic Research; Computing; Information Processing Education; Instrumental Analysis; Experimental Plants and Animals; Molecular Genetics (Research); Interface Quantum Electronics (Research); Health Administration; Earthquake Prediction (Research); Physical Education.
Ut: Chromosome Research; Child Development (Research and Clinical).
L: Ocean Bottom Seismology; Usujiri Fisheries; Sea-Ice Research; Electronics Instruments; Animal Experiments.

Hokkaido University of Education
[Hokkaido Kyoiku Daigaku]
1-3 Ainosato 5-3, Kita-ku, Sapporo-shi, Hokkaido 002
Tel: +81(11) 778-8811
Fax: +81(11) 778-8840
President: Kazuyuki Tanimoto
Director: Atsuro Ohara
Founded: 1943, 1949
Education; Research and Guidance for Teaching Practice.

Hyogo University of Education
[Hyogo Kyoiku Daigaku]
942-1 Shimokume, Yashiro-cho, Kato-gun, Hyogo-ken
Tel: +81(795) 44-1101
President: Shusaku Sato
Education.

Ibaraki University
[Ibaraki Daigaku]
2-1-1 Bunkyo, Mito-shi, Ibaraki 310
Tel: +81(292) 26-1621
Fax: +81(292) 25-0792
President: Kanehisa Hashimoto
Secretary-General: Kunio Ogata
Founded: 1949
F: Humanities; Education; Science; Engineering; Agriculture.
C: General Education.
Ce: Health; Co-operative Research and Development; Instrumental Analysis; Computer; Education and Research of Lifelong Learning.

Iwate University
[Iwate Daigaku]
3-18-8 Ueda, Morioka-shi, Iwate 020
Tel: +81(196) 23-5171
President: Shoji Funakoshi
Secretary-General: Naoaki Hayashi
Founded: 1949
F: Humanities and Social Science; Agriculture; Engineering; Education.

Japan Advanced Institute of Sciences and Technology, Hokuriku
[Hokuriku Sentan Kagaku Gijutsu Daigakuin Daigaku]
15 Asahidai, Tatsukuchi-cho,11Nomi-gun, Ishikawa 923-12
Tel: +81(761) 51-1111
President: Tominaga Keii
Secretary-General: Mitsugu Tamagaki
Informatics; Material Sciences.

Joetsu University of Education
[Joetsu Kyoiku Daigaku]
1 Yamayashiki-machi, Joetsu-shi, Niigata 943
Tel: +81(255) 22-2411
Fax: +81(255) 22-3403
President: Akira Kato
Secretary-General: Shinichi Do
Founded: 1978
D: School Education; Early Childhood and Special Education; Languages; Social Studies; Science; Fine Arts and Music; Physical Education, Home Economics, and Industrial Arts.
Ce: Educational Research and Development; Skills Training; Demonstration and Research for the Handicapped; Research and Training in Educational Information; Health.

Kagawa Medical School
[Kagawa Ika Daigaku]
1750-1 Ikenobe, Miki-cho, Kita-gun, Kagawa 761-07
Tel: +81(878) 98-5111
Fax: +81(878) 98-7109
President: Shozo Irino (1991-94)
Secretary-General: Akira Ohkubo
Founded: 1978
Medicine.

Kagawa University
[Kagawa Daigaku]
1-1, Saiwai-cho, Takamatsu-shi, Kagawa 760
Tel: +81(878) 61-4141
President: Tomotoshi Okaichi
Secretary-General: Yukio Shinoda
Founded: 1923, 1949
F: Education; Economics; Agriculture; Humanities and Social Science.

*Kagoshima University

[Kagoshima Daigaku]
1-21-24 Kourimoto, Kagoshima-shi, Kagoshima 890
Tel: +81(992) 54-7141
Fax: +81(992) 59-4986
President: Shozo Hayasaka (1987-)
Secretary-General: Jinichiro Kawasaki
International Relations: takeyoshi Kaneko
Founded: 1949
F: Law and Letters; Education; Science; Medicine; Dentistry; Engineering; Agriculture; Fisheries.
I: Cancer Research; Laboratory Animal Sciences.
S: Allied Medical Sciences.
Ce: Liberal Arts; The South Pacific; Information Processing; Educational Research and Training.
L: Fishery Research.

*Kanazawa University

[Kanazawa Daigaku]
1-1 Marunouchi, Kanazawa-shi, Ishikawa 920
Tel: +81(762) 62-4281
Fax: +81(762) 64-1003
President: Akira Okada (1993-)
Secretary-General: Susumu Katsuyama
Founded: 1949
F: Letters; Education; Law; Economics; Science; Medicine; Pharmacy; Pharmaceutical Science; Engineering.
C: Liberal Arts.
S: Natural Science and Technology (Graduate); Allied Medical Professions.
I: Cancer Research; Extension; Gene Research.
Ce: Radioisotope; Information Processing.

National Institute of Fitness and Sports Kagoshima Kanoya

[Kanoya Taiiku Daigaku]
1 Shiromizu-cho, Kanoya-shi, Kagoshima 891-23
Tel: +81(994) 46-4111
Fax: +81(994) 46-2516
President: taketoshi Imamura
Secretary-General: Whei Isowaki
Founded: 1981
C: Fitness and Sports Sciences.
Ce: Marine Sports; Foreign Language.

Kitami Institute of Technology

[Kitami Kogyo Daigaku]
165 Koen-cho, Kitami-shi, Hokkaido 090
Tel: +81(157) 24-1010
Fax: +81(157) 61-9530
President: Makoto Hirabayashi (1990-94)
Secretary-General: Shuji Kaneda
Founded: 1960, 1966
D: Applied Mechanical Engineering; Mechanical Engineering; Electrical Engineering; Electronic Engineering; Industrial Chemistry; Environmental Engineering; Civil Engineering; Developmental Engineering; General Education.

*Kobe University

[Kobe Daigaku]
1-1 Rokkodai-cho, Nada-ku, Kobe-shi, Hyogo 657
Tel: +81(78) 881-1212
Fax: +81(78) 861-6718
President: Masahiro Suzuki
Secretary-General: Osamu Kikukawa
International Relations: Isao Oya
Founded: 1949
F: Letters; Education; Law; Economics; Business Administration; Science; Medicine; Engineering; Agriculture.
C: Liberal Arts.
S: Allied Medical Sciences; Humanities and Social Sciences (Graduate).
I: Economics and Business Administration Research.
Ce: Information Processing; Co-operative Research and Development; Molecular Biology.

Kobe University of Mercantile Marine

[Kobe Shosen Daigaku]
5-1-1, Fukaeminami-machi, Higashinada-ku, Kobe-shi, Hyogo 658
Tel: +81(78) 453-2332
Fax: +81(78) 412-9721
President: Tokujiro Inoue
Secretary-General: Nobuo Fukazawa
Founded: 1917, 1920, 1952
D: Maritime Science; Transportation and Information Systems Engineering; Ocean Electro-Mechanical Engineering; Power System Engineering.
I: Marine Cargo Transportation Research.

Kochi Medical School

[Kochi Ika Daigaku]
Kohasu, Oko-cho, Nankoku-shi, Kochi 783
Tel: (888) 66-5811
President: Isamu Kitamura (1992-96)
Secretary-General: Kazuyoshi Tada
Founded: 1976
F: Medicine.
I: Laboratory Animals.
L: Medical Research.
Ce: Medical Information Science.

Kochi University

[Kochi Daigaku]
2-5-1 Akebono-cho, Kochi-shi, Kochi 780
Tel: +81(888) 44-0111
Fax: +81(888) 40-3481
President: Mitusaki Nakauchi
Director-General: Hidetaka Sano
Founded: 1949
F: Science; Humanities; Education; Agriculture.
I: USA Marine Biological.
L: Hydrothermical Chemistry (Research).

*Kumamoto University
[Kumamoto Daigaku]
2-39-1 Kurokami, Kumamoto-shi, Kumamoto 860
Tel: +81(96) 344-2111
Fax: +81(96) 345-9562
President: Yoshimasa Morino (1990-94)
Secretary-General: Naoki Shimada
Founded: 1949
F: Letters; Education; Law; Science; Pharmaceutical Sciences; Engineering; General Education.
C: Medical Technology and Nursing.
S: Medicine; Science and Technology (Graduate).
Ce: Co-operative Research; Health; Educational Practice and Guidance; Molecular Embryology and Genetics; Animal Research; Engineering Research Equipment.
L: High Energy Rate.

Kyoto Institute of Technology
[Kyoto Kogei Sen-i Daigaku]
Hashigami-cho, Matsugasaki, Sakyo-ku, Kyoto-shi, Kyoto 606
Tel: +81(75) 791-3211
Fax: +81(75) 712-8961
President: Tomomasa Tstsumi
Secretary-General: Kunitake Ueoka
Founded: 1949
F: Engineering and Design; Textile Science.
C: Technical.
Ce: Information Processing; Waste-Water Treatment.

*Kyoto University
[Kyoto Daigaku]
Yoshida-Honmachi, Sakyo-ku, Kyoto-shi, Kyoto 606-01
Tel: +81(75) 753-7531
Fax: +81(75) 753-2092
President: Hiroo Imura (1991-95)
Secretary-General: Makoto Tamura
Founded: 1897, 1919, 1947, 1949
F: Letters; Education; Law; Economics; Science; Medicine; Pharmaceutical Sciences; Engineering; Agriculture.
C: Liberal Arts and Sciences; Medical Technology.
S: Human and Environmental Studies (Graduate).
I: Chemical Research; Research in the Humanities; Chest Disease Research; Atomic Energy; Wood Research; Food Science (Research); Disaster Prevention Research; Theoretical Physics (Yukawa); Virus Research; Economic Research; Mathematical Sciences (Research); Research Reactor; Primate Research.
Ce: Southeast Asian Studies; Data Processing; Radiation Biology; Radio Atmospheric Science; Ecological Research; Radioisotope Research; Environment Preservation; Information Processing (Educational); African Area Studies;

Molecular Biology and Genetics; Biomedical Engineering (Research); Student Exchange; Student Health; Sports Science (Research); Archaeological Operations.
L: Plasma Physics.

Kyoto University of Education
[Kyoto Kyoiku Daigaku]
7 Fukakusa-Fujinomori-cho, Fushimi-ku, Kyoto-shi, Kyoto 612
Tel: 75-641-9281
President: Naoki Kamo
Secretary-General: Kazuo Nakata
Founded: 1876
Education.

Kyushu Institute of Design
[Kyushu Geijutsukoka Daigaku]
9-1 Shiobaru,4-chome, Minami-ku, Fukuoka-shi, Fukuoka 815
Tel: +81(92) 553-4407
Fax: +81(92) 553-4593
President: Yoshinori Ando (1992-94)
Secretary-General: Takao Higuchi
Founded: 1968
Design.

*Kyushu University
[Kyushu Daigaku]
6-10-1 Hakozaki, Higashi-ku, Fukuoka 812
Tel: +81(92) 641-1101
Fax: +81(92) 641-4509
President: Koji Wada (1991-95)
Director-General, Administration Office: Susumu Shimomiya
International Relations: Yukio Kiuchi
Founded: 1903, 1911, 1947
F: Literature; Education; Law; Economics; Science; Medicine; Dentistry; Pharmaceutical Sciences; Engineering; Agriculture.
C: General Education.
S: Engineering Sciences (Graduate); Health Sciences.
I: Medical Bioregulation; Applied Mechanics (Research); Advanced Materials Study; Health Science; Languages and Cultures; Biotron; Tropical Agriculture.
Ce: Information Processing (Education); Coal Mining Materials (Research); Radioisotope; Advanced Instrumental Analysis; Computer; Foreign Students (Education).
L: Genetic Information (Research); High Voltage Electron Microscopy (Research); Waste Water Treatment.

Mie University
[Mie Daigaku]
1515 Kamihama-cho, Tsu-shi, Mie 514
Tel: +81(592) 32-1211
Fax: +81(592) 32-1136
President: Yasuo Takemura
Director of Administration Bureau: Katsuyuki Kurosaki
Founded: 1949

F: *Humanities and Social Sciences; Education (primary, junior high, handicapped, kindergarten levels); Engineering; Bioresources.*
S: *Medicine.*

Miyagi University of Education
[Miyagi Kyoiku Daigaku]
Aramaki Aoba, Aoba-Ku, Sendai 980
Tel: +81(22) 214-3303
Fax: +81(22) 214-3309
President: Terutake Ito (1990-93)
Secretary-General: Hisao Ohtsuka
Founded: 1965
F: *Education.*
I: *Science Education Research.*
Ce: *Teacher; Information Processing.*

Miyazaki Medical College
[Miyazaki Ika Daigaku]
5200 Kihara, Kiyotake-cho, Miyazaki-gun, Miyazaki 889-16
Tel: +81(985) 85-1510
President: Kazuo Kinoshita
Secretary-General: Teiji Kjusakabe
Founded: 1947
Medicine.

Miyazaki University
[Miyazaki Daigaku]
7710 Oaza Kumano, Miyazaki-shi, Miyazaki 880
Tel: +81(985) 58-2811
President: Hajime Ikeda
Secretary-General: Michitoshi Urabe
Founded: 1949
F: *Agriculture; Education; Engineering.*

Muroran Institute of Technology (MIT)
[Muroran Kogyo Daigaku]
27-1 Mizumoto-cho, Muroran-shi, Hokkaido 050
Tel: +81(143) 44-4181
Fax: +81(143) 47-3126
President: Takashi Arakawa (1991-)
Head of Administration Bureau: Tadasu Yurugi
International Relations: Kiyohito Izumi
Founded: 1949
D: *Civil Engineering and Architecture; Mechanical Systems Engineering; Computer Science and Systems Engineering; Electrical and Electronics Engineering; Materials Science and Engineering; Applied Chemistry; Civil and Environmental Engineering; Production and Information Systems Engineering; Chemical and Materials Engineering.*
Ce: *Information Processing (Educational); Cooperative Research and Development.*

Nagaoka Technological University
[Nagaoka Gijutsukagoku Daigaku]
1603-1, Kamitomioka-machi, Nagaoka-shi, Niigata 949-54
Tel: +81(258) 46-6000
President: Yasuzo Uchida
Secretary-General: Marinasa Isono
Founded: 1976
F: *Engineering.*

Ce: *Language; Analysis; Technological Development; Computer; Radioisotope; Sound and Vibration Technology.*

Nagasaki University
[Nagasaki Daigaku]
1-14 Bunkyo-machi, Nagasaki-shi, Nagasaki 852
Tel: +81(958) 47-1111
Founded: 1949
F: *Education; Economics; Pharmacy; Engineering; Fisheries; Liberal Arts.*
S: *Medicine; Dentistry.*
I: *Tropical Diseases Research; South East Asia Research; Atomic Disease.*

Nagoya Institute of Technology
[Nagoya Kogyo Daigaku]
Gokiso-cho, Showa-ku, Nagoya-shi, Aichi 466
Tel: +81(52) 732-2111
President: Hirotomo Yoshida
Secretary-General: Masao Kawasaki
Founded: 1905, 1949
Engineering.

*Nagoya University
[Nagoya Daigaku]
Furo-cho, Chikusa-ku, Nagoya-shi, Aichi 464-01
Tel: +81(52) 781-5111
Fax: +81(52) 782-8863
Telex: iaunag j 4427565
President: Nobuo Kato (1992-96)
Director-General: Masahito Nishio
Founded: 1871, 1931, 1939, 1949
S: *Letters; Education; Law; Economics; Science; Medicine; Engineering; Agricultural Sciences; International Development (Graduate); Human Informatics (Graduate).*
C: *General Education; Medical Technology.*
F: *Language and Culture (for foreign students).*
I: *Environmental Medicine (Research); Water Research (Research).*
Ce: *Radioisotope Research; Chemical Instrument; Information Processing (Education); Advanced Energy Conversion (Research); Gene Research; Computation; Health, Physical Fitness and Sports (Research); Co-operative Research in Advanced Science and Technology; Plasma Science; Dating and Materials Research.*
L: *Solar-Terrestrial Environment.*

Nara College of Education
[Nara Kyoiku Daigaku]
Takabatake-cho, Nara-shi, Nara 630
Tel: +81(742) 27-9111
Telex: 23-8057
President: Shigeru Goto (1989-95)
Secretary-General: Katsuyuki Udagaw
International Relations: Takashi Watanabe
Founded: 1949
Education.

Nara Institute of Science and Technology
[Nara Sentan Kagaku Gijutsu Daigakuin Daigaku]
4259 Nagatsuda-cho, Midori-ru, Yokohama-shi,
Kanagawa 227
Tel: +81(7437) 2-5111
President: Akira Sakurai
Secretary-General: Yutaka Kimura
Founded: 1993
Informatic Science; Bio-Science.

*Nara Women's University
[Nara Joshi Daigaku]
Kitauoyahigashi-machi, Nara-shi, Nara 630
Tel: +81(742) 20-3330
President: Hajime Tamura
Secretary-General: Teruhiko Sumiyoshi
Founded: 1908, 1949
F: Letters; Science; Home Economics.

Naruto University of Teacher Education
[Naruto Kyoiku Daigaku]
Takashima, Naruto-shi, Tokushima 772
Tel: +81(886) 87-1311
Fax: +81(886) 87-1396
President: Junya Noji
Secretary-General: Hideo Kono
Founded: 1981
*F: School Education; Language and Social
Sciences; Science; Arts; Health and Living
Sciences.*
*Ce: School Education; Health Service; Training
for Practical Skills.*

National Defence Medical College
[Boei Ika daigakko]
3-2 Namiki, Tokorozawa-shi, Saitama 359
Tel: +81(429) 95-1211
President: Toshiro Ogata
Secretary-General: Kiichi Ogino
Founded: 1973
Medicine.

*Niigata University
[Niigata Daigaku]
8050, Ikarashi 2-nocho, Niigata-shi, Niigata 950-21
Tel: +81(25) 262-6098
Fax: +81(25) 262-6539
President: Terukazu Muto (1992-96)
Secretary-General: Keiju Nakamura
Founded: 1910, 1949
*F: Humanities; Education; Law; Economics;
Science; Engineering; Agriculture.*
C: Commerce; Biomedical Technology.
S: Medicine; Dentistry.
*I: Brain Research; Hazards in Snowy Areas
(Research); Nephrology; Laboratory Animals.*
*Ce: Materials of Brain Diseases; Information
Processing.*
D: General Education.

Obihiro University of Agriculture and Veterinary Medicine
[Obihiro Chikusan Daigaku]
Inada-cho, Obihiro-shi, Hokkaido 080
Tel: +81(155) 48-5111
President: Sadao Sakamura
Secretary-General: Isao Kanesaka
Founded: 1941, 1949
*Animal Husbandry; Agriculture; Veterinary
Medicine.*

*Ochanomizu Women's University
[Ochanomizu Joshi Daigaku]
2-1-1 Otsuka, Bunkyo-ku, Tokyo 112
Tel: +81(3) 3943-3151
President: Jiro Ota
Secretary-General: Nobuyuki Tsuzukihashi
Founded: 1874, 1989
*F: Letters and Education; Science; Home
Economics.*
I: Food Chemistry Research.

Oita Medical College
[Oita Ika Daigaku]
1-1506 Idaigaoka, Hazama-cho, Oita-gun, Oita
879-56
Tel: +81(975) 49-4411
President: Ryosaburo Takaki
Secretary-General: Hiroji Yamaguchi
Medicine; Sciences.

*Oita University
[Oita Daigaku]
700 Dannoharu, Oita-shi, Oita 870-11
Tel: +81(975) 69-3311
Fax: +81(975) 67-5926
President: Arata Nomura (1994-98)
Secretary-General: Shinichi Watanabe
Founded: 1949
*D: Education; Economics; Engineering;
Education (Graduate).*
*S: Economics (Graduate); Engineering
(Graduate).*
Ce: Computer.

*Okayama University
[Okayama Daigaku]
1-1, Naka 1-chome, Tsushima, Okayama-shi,
Okayama 700
Tel: +81(86) 252-1111
Fax: +81(86) 254-6104
President: Katsuaki Takahashi
Secretary-General: Kimihiro Ito
International Relations: Senji Hirokaki
Founded: 1949
*F: Letters; Education; Law; Economics; Science;
Pharmaceutical Sciences; Engineering;
Agriculture.*
*C: General Education; Medical; Dentistry; Health
Sciences.*
*I: Bioresources (Research); Study of the Earth's
Interior.*
*Ce: Educational Technology; Development of
Teaching Capacity; Computer; Isotope;*

Administration for Environmental Science and
Technology; Gene Research; International
Students.
L: Surface Science (Research).

*Osaka University
[Osaka Daigaku]
1-1 Yamadaoka, Suita-shi, Osaka 565
Tel: +81(6) 877-5111
Fax: +81(6) 878-1366
Telex: 5286207 osaku J
Cable: handai
President: Junjiro Kanamori
Secretary-General: Masahiko Kasuya
International Relations: Yuki Nakajyo
Founded: 1931, 1947
F: Letters; Human Sciences; Law; Economics;
Science; Medicine; Dentistry; Pharmaceutical
Sciences; Engineering; Engineering Science;
Language and Culture; Health and Sports
Sciences.
C: General Education; Biomedical Technology.
I: Microbial Diseases (Research); Scientific and
Industrial Research; Social and Economic
Research; Protein Research; Welding Research;
Laser Engineering; Molecular and Cellular
Biology.
Ce: Low Temperature; Ultra High Voltage
Electron Microscopy (Research); Information
Processing; Radioisotope Research; Extreme
Materials (Research); Computer; Nuclear Physics
(Research); Genome Information Research;
Superconducting Materials and Electronics
(Research); Photoenergetics of Organic Materials
(Research).

Osaka University of Education
[Osaka Kyoiku Daigaku]
4-88 Minami-Kawahori-cho, Tennoji-ku, Osaka-
shi, Osaka 543
Tel: +81(729) 76-3211
President: Shigeya Kinoshita
Secretary-General: Shikonari Higashiyama
Founded: 1949
Education (day and evening courses).

Osaka University of Foreign Studies
[Osaka Gaikokugo Daigaku]
1-1, Higashi 8-chome, Aomadani, Minoo-shi,
Osaka 562
Tel: +81(727) 28-3111
President: Osamu Ikeda
Secretary-General: Norio Ueno
Founded: 1921, 1949
Foreign Studies (day and evening courses);
Japanese Studies for Foreign Students.

Otaru University of Commerce
[Otaru Shoka Daigaku]
3-5-21 Midori, Otaru-shi, Hokkaido 047
Tel: +81(134) 23-1101
Fax: +81(134) 22-0467
President: Iomasa Yamada (1992-96)
Director, Administration Bureau: Akira Kawasaki
Founded: 1910, 1949
Commerce; Language.

Ryukyus University
[Ryukyu Daigaku]
1 Senbaru, Nishihara-cho, Nakagami-gun,
Okinawa 903
Tel: +81(988) 87-0101
President: Keishin Sunakawa
Secretary-General: Hiroshi Yamamori
International Relations: Hiroshi Yamamori
Founded: 1950, 1966, 1972
F: Law and Literature; Letters; Education;
Sciences; Engineering; Agriculture; Medicine.
Ce: Tropical Agriculture Research.
L: Marine.
D: General Education.

Saga Medical College
[Saga Ika Daigaku]
1-1, Nabeshima 5-chome, Saga-shi, aga 849
Tel: +81(952) 31-6511
President: Keiichi Matsuura
Secretary-Genral: Masahide Uchida
Founded: 1976
Medicine.

Saga University
[Saga Daigaku]
1 Honjo-machi, Saga-shi, Saga 840
Tel: +81(952) 24-5191
Founded: 1949
Education; Economics; Science and Engineering;
Agriculture.

Saitama University
[Saitama Daigaku]
255 Shimo-Okubo, Urawa-shi, Saitama 338
Tel: +81(488) 52-2111
President: Kiyoshi Horikawa
Secretary-General: Hiroyuki Ito
International Relations: Motohiro Iizuka
Founded: 1949
Liberal Arts; Education; Economics; Science and
Engineering.

Shiga University
[Shiga Daigaku]
1-1-1 Banba, Hikone-shi, Shiga 522
Tel: +81(749) 22-5600
Fax: +81(749) 27-1005
President: Hisao
Secretary-General: Hiroshi Ogi
Founded: 1922, 1949
F: Education; Economics.
I: Lake Science (Research); School Education;
Economics and Business Research.

Shiga University of Medical Science
[Shiga Ika Daigaku]
Seta-Tsukinowacho, Otsu-shi, Shiga 520-21
Tel: +81(775) 48-2111
Founded: 1974
Medicine; Molecular Neurobiology Research.

Shimane Medical University
[Shimane Ika Daigaku]
89-1 Enya-cho, Izumo-shi, Shimane 693
Tel: +81(853) 23-2111
Fax: +81(853) 22-9304
President: Akina Hirakawa (1990-94)
Secretary-General: Masahiko Ishii
Founded: 1975
Medicine; Experimental Animals.

Shimane University
[Shimane Daigaku]
1060 Nishikawatsu-cho, Matsue-shi, Shimane 690
Tel: +81(852) 32-6100
Fax: +81(852) 32-6019
President: Miyuki Yamada (1991-95)
Secretary-General: Isamu Kanetsuka
Founded: 1949
F: Law and Literature; Education; Science;
Agriculture.
I: Marine Biology; Molecular Genetics
(Research); Research and Training for
Educational Practice; Coastal Lagoon
Environments (Research).

*Shinshu University
[Shinshu Daigaku]
3-1-1 Asahi, Matsumoto-shi, Nagano 390
Tel: +81(263) 35-4600
Founded: 1949
F: Arts; Education; Economics; Science;
Medicine; Engineering; Agriculture; Textile
Technology; Liberal Arts.
S: Allied Medical Sciences.
I: Nature Education Research; Adaptation
Medicine; High Polymer Research.
Ce: Engineering Education.
L: Natural Science Research.

Shizuoka University
[Shizuoka Daigaku]
836 Otani, Shizuoka-shi,Shizuoka 422
Tel: +81(54) 237-1111
President: Mamoru Nagai
Secretary-General: Takashi Moriya
Arts; Education; Science; Engineering;
Agriculture; Liberal Arts.

*Tohoku University
[Tohoku Daigaku]
2-1-1 Katahira, Aoba-ku, Sendai-shi, Miyagi 980
Tel: +81(22) 227-6200
Fax: +81(22) 221-6032
President: Jun-Ichi Nishizawa
Secretary-General: Shiro Hirota
International Relations: Kiyoshi Kakemizu
Founded: 1907, 1949

F: Arts and Letters; Education; Law; Economics;
Science; Medicine; Dentistry; Pharmacy;
Engineering; Agriculture.
C: General Education; Medical Sciences.
I: Material Research; Genetic Ecology;
Advanced Materials Processing; Tuberculosis
and Cancer Research; Scientific Measurement
Research; Fluid Science; Electrical
Communication Research; Chemical Reaction
Science.
Ce: Cryogenics; Applied Information Research;
Cyclotron Radioisotope; Computer.

Tokushima University
[Tokushima Daigaku]
2-24 Shinkura-cho, Tokushima-shi, Tokushima 770
Tel: +81(886) 22-5131
President: Katsuyuki Takeda
Secretary-General: Mechio Matsumoto
Founded: 1949
F: Education; Pharmacy; Engineering.
C: General Education.
S: Medicine; Dentistry; Nursing; Midwifery; X-
Ray Technicians; Laboratory Technicians.
I: Enzyme Research; Marine Biology.

Tokyo Gakugei University
[Tokyo Gakugei Daigaku]
4-1-1 Nukui-Kita-machi, Koganei-shi, Tokyo 184
Tel: +81(423) 25-2111
President: Otohiko Hasumi
Secretary-General: Tadao Hirakawa
Founded: 1949
Teacher Training.

*Tokyo Institute of Technology
[Tokyo Kogyo Daigaku]
2-12-1 Ohokayama, Meguro-ku, Tokyo 152
Tel: +81(3) 3726-1111
Fax: +81(3) 3726-4714
Telex: 2466360 titech j
Cable: Titechookayama
President: Yasuharu Suematsu
Director-General: Kenji Abe
International Relations: Kazuki Shigemori
Founded: 1881, 1929
F: Science; Engineering; Bioscience and
Biotechnology.
S: Interdisciplinary Graduate of Science and
Engineering (Nagatsuta).
L: Resources Utilization; Precision and
Intelligence; Engineering Materials (Research);
Nuclear Reactors (Research).

Tokyo Medical and Dental University
[Tokyo Ikashika Daigaku]
1-5-45, Yushima, Bunkyo-ku, Tokyo 113
Tel: +81(3) 3813-6111
Fax: +81(3) 3813-6111
President: Hajime Yamashita
Secretary-General: Saiichiro Ito
Founded: 1928, 1944, 1946, 1955

Medicine; Dentistry; Medical and Dental
Engineering; Medical Research; Stomatognathic
Science; Microbiology Research; General
Education.

Tokyo National University of Fine Art and Music
[Tokyo Geijutsu Daigaku]
12-8 Ueno Park, Taito-ku, Tokyo 110
Tel: (3) 3828-6111
Telex: 3828-6108
President: Ikuo Hirayama (1989-93)
Secretary-General: Shigeru Aoki
Founded: 1949
Fine Arts; Music.

*The University of Tokyo
[Tokyo Daigaku]
7-3-1 Hongo, Bunkyo-ku, Tokyo 113
Tel: +81(3) 3812-2111
Fax: +81(3) 5689-7344
Telex: j25510 unitokyo
Cable: Tokuniv
Socho (President): Hiroyuki Yoshikawa
Jimukyokucho (Director-General): Jiro Sato
Founded: 1877, 1923, 1949
F: Law; Medicine; Engineering; Letters; Science;
Agriculture; Economics; Education; Pharmacy.
C: Arts and Science.
I: Medical Science; Earthquake Research;
Oriental Culture; Social Science; Socio-
Information and Communication Studies;
Industrial Science; Historiographical; Applied
Microbiology; Nuclear Studies; Ocean Research;
Cosmic Ray; Solid State Physics.
Ce: Computer; Cryogenic; Radioisotope;
Nuclear Research; Educational Computer;
Environmental Science; Advanced Science and
Technology (Research).
L: Molecular Genetics Research.

Tokyo University of Agriculture and Technology
[Tokyo Noko Daigaku]
3-8-1 Harumi-cho, Fuchu-shi, Tokyo 183
Tel: +81(423) 64-3311
President: Shinji Sakagami
Secretary-General: Kazuyuki Takahashi
Founded: 1949
Agriculture; Engineering; General Education.

Tokyo University of Fisheries
[Tokyo Suisan Daigaku]
4-5-7 Konan, Minato-ku, Tokyo 108
Tel: +81(3) 3471-1251
President: Shoichi Tanaka
Secretary-General: Hiroshi Yamashita
Founded: 1888, 1897, 1949
Fishery; Pisciculture; Marine Environmental
Science and Technology; Food Technology;
Aquaculture; General Education; Fishery
Resources Research.

Tokyo University of Foreign Studies
[Tokyo Gaikokugo Daigaku]
4-51-21 Nishigahara, Kita-ku, Tokyo 114
Tel: +81(3) 3917-6111
President: Takuya Hara
Secretary-General: Masatsugu Katsuyama
Founded: 1897, 1899, 1949
Foreign Languages and Literature; Study of
Languages and Cultures of Asia and Africa.

Tokyo University of Mercantile Marine
[Tokyo Shosen Daigaku]
2-1-6 Etchujima, Koto-ku, Tokyo 135
Tel: +81(3) 5245-7300
President: Hisashi Kugumiya
Secretary-General: Toshiaki Sawagawa
Founded: 1875, 1949
Mercantile Marine Engineering and Navigation;
Navigation Research.

Tottori University
[Tottori Daigaku]
4-101 Koyama-cho Minami, Tottori-shi, Tottori 680
Tel: +81(857) 28-0321
President: Shinji Hayashi
Secretary-General: Satoyuki Saito
Founded: 1949
F: Education; Engineering; Medicine;
Agriculture; General Education.
C: Medical Care Technology.
I: Neurological Sciences; Steroid Research.
Ce: Laboratory Animal Research; Kansouchi
Kenkyu.

Toyama Medical and Pharmaceutical University
[Toyama Ikayakka Daigaku]
2630 Sugitani, Toyama-shi, Toyama 930-01
Tel: +81(764) 34-2281
Fax: +81(764) 34-1463
President: Takao Yamazaki (1988-94)
Administrator: katumi Osida
Founded: 1893, 1975
Medicine; Pharmacy; Wakan-Yaku (Traditional
Sino-Japanese Medicines) (Research).

Toyama University
[Toyama Daigaku]
3910 Gofuku, Toyama-shi, Toyama 930
Tel: +81(764) 41-1271
President: Chitaru Oguro
Secretary-General: Osamu Imada
Founded: 1949
F: Humanities; Education; Economics; Science;
Pharmacy; Engineering.
C: General Education.
Ce: Computer.
L: Radioisotope.

Toyohashi University of Technology
[Toyohashi Gijutsukagaku Daigaku]
1-1 Hibarigaoka, Tempaku-cho, Toyohashi-shi,
Aichi 441
Tel: +81(532) 47-0111
Fax: +81(532) 47-2957
Telex: 4322-201 jpntut
President: Shin-ichi Sasaki (1990-94)
Director-General: Tomio Yamashita
Founded: 1976
D: *Energy Engineering; Production Systems
Engineering; Electrical and Electronic
Engineering; Information and Computer Science;
Materials Science; Regional Planning;
Knowledge-based Information Engineering;
Humanities and Social Engineering.*
Ce: *Language; Physical Fitness, Sport and
Health (Research); Technology Development;
Chemometrics; Manufacturing Technology;
Computer.*
L: *Radioisotope.*

*Tsukuba University
[Tsukuba Daigaku]
1-1-1 Tennodai, Tsukuba-shi, Ibaraki 305
Tel: +81(298) 53-2111
Fax: +81(298) 53-6019
Telex: 3652580 untuku j
Cable: Untuku Tsuchiura Japan
President: Reona Esaki (1992-)
Secretary-General: Naomi Onodera
Founded: 1949
C: *Humanities; Social Sciences; Natural
Sciences; Comparative Culture; Japanese
Language and Culture; Human Sciences;
Biological Sciences; Agriculture and Forestry;
Socio-Economic Planning; International Relations;
Information Sciences; Engineering Systems;
Engineering Sciences; Medical Technology and
Nursing.*
S: *Medicine; Health and Physical Education; Art
and Design; Teachers of Acupuncture and
Physical Therapy.*
I: *Philosophy; History and Anthropology;
Literature and Linguistics; Modern Languages
and Cultures; Education; Psychology; Special
Education; Social Sciences; Socio-Economic
Planning; Biological Sciences; Agriculture and
Forestry; Agricultural and Forest Engineering;
Applied Biochemistry; Mathematics; Physics;
Chemistry; Geoscience; Applied Physics;
Materials Science; Engineering Mechanics;
Information Sciences and Electronics; Health and
Sport Sciences; Art and Design; Basic Medical
Sciences; Clinical Medicine; Community
Medicine.*
Ce: *Foreign Language; Sport and Physical
Education; Educational Media; Tandem
Accelerator; Cryogenics; Science Information
Processing; Radioisotope; Chemical Analysis;
Machining; Computational Physics.*

University of Library and Information Sciences Tsukuba-gun
[Toshokan Joho Daigaku]
1-2 Kasuga, Tsukuba-shi, Ibaraki 305
Tel: +81(298) 52-0511
President: Kazuo Onodera
Secretary-General: Mitsuhiko Katsumura
Library and Information Sciences.

Utsunomiya University
[Utsonomiya Daigaku]
350 Mine-machi, Utsunomiya-shi, Tochigi 320
Tel: +81(286) 36-1515
President: Kiyoji Tsufura
Founded: 1949
F: *Education; Engineering; Agriculture.*
C: *Education.*
I: *Wood Control.*

Wakayama University
[Wakayama Daigaku]
930 Sakaedani, Wakayama-shi, Wakayama 640
Tel: +81(734) 54-0361
Fax: +81(734) 54-0387
President: Asao Ono
Secretary-General: Koichi Mori
Founded: 1871, 1922, 1949
F: *Education; Economics.*
I: *Economic Studies.*
Ce: *Computer.*

Yamagata University
[Yamagata Daigaku]
1-4-12 Kojirakawa-machi, Yamagata-shi,
Yamagata 990
Tel: +81(236) 31-1421
Fax: +81(236) 31-1891
Founded: 1949
F: *Letters and Social Sciences; Education;
Science; Engineering; Agriculture; General
Education.*
S: *Medicine.*

Yamanashi University
[Yamanashi Daigaku]
4-4-37 Takeda, Kofu-shi, Yamanashi 400
Tel: +81(552) 52-1111
President: So Ito
Secretary-General: Kinya Sakurai
Founded: 1949
F: *Liberal Arts and Education; Engineering.*
I: *Fermentation Research; Inorganic Synthesis
Research.*

Yamaguchi University
[Yamaguchi Daigaku]
1677-1 Yoshida, Yamaguchi-shi, Yamaguchi 753
Tel: +81(839) 22-6111
Fax: +81(839) 22-0445
President: Naotoshi Murakami
Secretary-General: Hajime Kayanuma
International Relations: Sumiko Tokunaga
Founded: 1949
F: *Humanities; Education; Economics; Science;
Engineering; Agriculture; Liberal Arts.*

S: *Medicine.*
I: *East Asian Economic Research.*

Yamanashi Medical University
[Yamanashi Ika Daigaku]
1110 Shimokato, Tamaho-cho, Nakakoma-gun,
Yamanashi 409-38
Tel: +81(552) 73-1111
Fax: +81(552) 73-7108
President: Hiroshi Suzuki
Secretary-General: Kiyozo Adachi
Founded: 1978
*Medicine; Research Laboraoty; Animal
Experiments.*

Yokohama National University
[Yokohama Kokuritsu Daigaku]
156 Tokiwadai, Hodogaya-ku, Yokohama-shi,
Kanagawa 240
Tel: +81(45) 335-1451
Fax: +81(45) 341-2582
President: Tokio Ota
Secretary-General: Michiaki Murakami
Founded: 1949
F: *Education; Economics; Business
Administration; Engineering.*
I: *Environmental Science and Technology.*
S: *International and Business Law (Graduate).*

PUBLIC INSTITUTIONS

Aichi Prefectural University of Fine Arts
[Aichi Kenritsu Geijutsu Daigaku]
1-1 Sagamine, Yazako, Nagakute-cho, Aichi-gun,
Aichi 480-11
Tel: +81(561) 62-1180
President: Kamon Tatehata
Secretary-General: Akihiko Okubo
Founded: 1966
Music; Fine Arts.

Fukuoka Women's University
[Fukuoka Jyoshi Daigaku]
1-1-1 Kasumigaoka, Higashi-ku, Fukuoka-shi,
Fukuoka 813
Tel: +81(92) 661-2411
President: Shizu Tokumoto
Secretary-General: Joji Honmatsu
Founded: 1923
Letters; Domestic Sciences.

Fukushima Medical College
[Fukushima Kenritsu Ika Daigaku]
1 Hikoriga-oka, Fukushima-shi, Fukushima 960-12
Tel: +81(245) 48-1211
Fax: +81(245) 48-3836
President: Haruki Wakasa
Secretary-General: Ieharu Sato
Founded: 1944, 1947, 1952
Medicine; Rehabilitation.

Gifu Pharmaceutical University
[Gifu Yakka Daigaku]
6-1 Mitahora-higashi 5-chome, Gifu-shi, Gifu 502
Tel: +81(582) 37-3931
Fax: +81(582) 37-5979
President: Mizuo Mizuo
Secretary-General: Hideo Murase
Founded: 1932, 1946
*Public Health Pharmacy; Manufacturing
Pharmacy.*

Himeji Institute of Technology
[Himeji Kogyo Daigaku]
2167 Shosha, Himeji-shi, Hyogo 671-22
Tel: +81(792) 66-1661
President: Chiyoe Yamanaka
Secretary-General: Noriaki Noro
Founded: 1944, 1949
F: *Engineering; Science; General Education.*
I: *Environment Research.*

Kanazawa College of Art
[Kanazawa Bijutsu Kogei Daigaku]
5-11-1 Kodatsuno, Kanazawa-shi, Ishikawa 920
Tel: +81(762) 62-3531
Fax: +81(762) 62-6594
President: Fujio Kitade
Secretary-General: Akihide Nagaashima
Founded: 1946, 1950, 1955
Art.

Kitakyushu University
[Kitakyushu Daigaku]
4-2-1 Kitagata, Kokuraminami-ku, Kitakyushu-shi,
Fukuoka 802
Tel: +81(93) 962-4436
President: Tetsuro Nakatani
Secretary-General: Keiji Mizukami
Founded: 1946, 1950, 1952
F: *Foreign Studies; Economics; Letters; Law.*
I: *Industrial and Social Research.*

Kobe City University of Foreign Studies
[Kobe-shi Gaikokugo Daigaku]
9-1 Gakuen-higashi-machi, Nishi-ku, Kobe-shi,
Hyogo 651-21
Tel: +81(78) 794-8121
President: Yoshio Yukida
Secretary-General: Mamoru Kamogawa
Founded: 1946, 1949
Foreign Studies; Foreign Studies (Research).

Kobe University of Commerce
[Kobe Shoka Daigaku]
8-2-1, Gakuen Nishimachi, Nishiku, Kobe-shi,
Hyogo 651-21
Tel: +81(78) 794-6161
President: Tetsuya Nose
Founded: 1929, 1944, 1948
D: *Economics; Business Administration;
Management Science; Arts and Natural Science;
Extramural Studies.*
I: *Economic Research.*

Kumamoto Women's College
[Kumamoto Joyoshi Daigaku]
2432-1 Mizuarai, Kengun-cho, Kumamoto-shi,
Kumamoto 862
Tel: +81(96) 383-2929
President: Hiroshi Matsugaki
Secretary-General: Akitoshilto
Founded: 1949
Letters; Living Sciences.

Kyoto City University of Arts
[Kyoto Shiritsu Geijutsu Daigaku]
13-6 Kutsukake-cho, Ooe, Nishigyo-ku, Kyoto-shi,
Kyoto 610-11
Tel: +81(75) 332-0701
President: Shunpei Ueyama
Secretary-General: Osamu Masumoto
Founded: 1909, 1950, 1969
Fine Arts; Music.

Kyoto Prefectural University
[Kyoto Furitsu Daigaku]
1-5 Shimogamo-Hangi-cho, Sakyo-ku, Kyoto-shi,
Kyoto 606
Tel: +81(75) 781-3131
Founded: 1949
*Letters and Domestic Science; Science of Living;
Agriculture.*

Kyoto Prefectural University of Medicine
[Kyoto Furitsu Ika Daigaku]
465 Kajii-cho, Kawaramachi-dori Hirokoji-agaru,
Kamigyo-ku, Kyoto-shi, Kyoto 602
Tel: +81(75) 251-5111-8
President: Setsuya Fujita
Secretary-General: Akio Dohata
Founded: 1872, 1880, 1922
*Medicine; Neurological Diseases and Geriatrics
(Research).*

Kyushu Dental College
[Kyushu Shika Daigaku]
2-6-1 Manazuru, Kokurakita-ku, Kitakyushu-shi,
Fukuoka 803
Tel: +81(93) 582-1131
Fax: +81(93) 582-6000
President: Akitatsu Shimamura (1989-94)
Secretary-General: Toshiki Tanaka
Founded: 1921, 1949
F: Dentistry.
S: Dentistry (Graduate); Dental Hygiene.
Ce: Animal Research.

Nagasaki Prefectural College
[Nagasaki Kenritsu Daigaku]
123 Kawashimo-cho, Sasebo-shi, Nagasaki 858
Tel: +81(956) 47-2191
President: Takeshi Suzuki
Secretary-General: Kazuhiro Mori
Founded: 1957
Economics.

Nagoya City University
[Nagoya Shiritsu Daigaku]
1 Kawasumi, Mizuho-cho, Mizuho-ku, Nagoya-shi,
Aichi 467
Tel: +81(52) 851-5511
President: Yoetsu Hachisuka
Secretary-General: Masami Nagata
Founded: 1950
F: Pharmacy; Economics; Medicine.
C: General Education.
S: Nursing.
Ce: Computer.

Nara Medical University
[Nara Kenritsu Ika Daigaku]
Shijocho 840, Kashihara-shi, Nara 634
Tel: +81(7442) 2-3051
President: Hyoe Ishikawa
Secretary-General: Masanori Tsuji
Founded: 1945
Medicine.

Okinawa Prefectural College of Fine Arts
[Okinawa Kenritsu Geijutsu Daigaku]
1-4 Tonokura-cho, Shuri Naha-shi, Okanawa 903
Tel: +81(98) 831-5000
President: Masao Yamamoto
Secretary-General: Tetsuo Yoshimoto
Founded: 1928
Fine Arts.

*Osaka City University
[Osaka Shiritsu Daigaku]
3-3-138 Sugimoto, Sumiyoshi-ku, Osaka-shi,
Osaka 558
Tel: +81(6) 605-2011
President: Kenjiro Yamamoto
Secretary-General: Ryuhei Sugiyama
Founded: 1949
F: Commerce (day and evening courses);
Economics (day and evening courses); Law (day
and evening courses); Letters (day and evening
courses); Science; Engineering; Science of
Living.
S: Medicine.
Ce: General Education.
I: Economic Research; Atomic Energy
Research.

Osaka Prefectural University
[Osaka Furitsu Daigaku]
1-1 Gakuen-machi, Sakai-shi, Osaka 593
Tel: +81(722) 52-1161
President: Takao Heisa
Secretary-General: Shigenari Mizutori
Founded: 1949
F: Engineering; Agriculture; Economics.
S: Integrated Arts and Sciences; Social Welfare.
Ce: Computer.
L: Engineering.

Osaka Women's University
[Osaka Joshi Daigaku]
2-1 Daisen-cho, Sakai-shi, Osaka 590
Tel: +81(722) 22-4811
President: Masaaki Ueda
Secretary-General: Shigeru Mori
Founded: 1924
Arts and Sciences.

Sapporo Medical College
[Sapporo Ika Daigaku]
Nishi 17-chome, Minami 1-jo, Chuo-ku, Sapporo-
shi, Hokkaido 060
Tel: +81(11) 611-2111
President: Akira Yachi (1992-96)
Secretary-General: Kenichi Kamiyama
Founded: 1945, 1950, 1958
Medicine; Cancer Research; Marine Medicine.

Shizuoka Prefectural University
[Shizuoka Kenritzu Daigaku]
52-1 Yada, Shizuoka-shi, Shizuoka 422
Tel: +81(54) 264-5102
Fax: +81(54) 264-5099
President: Koji Uchizono (1987-)
Secretary-General: Koetzu Yamamichi
Founded: 1986
*F: Pharmaceutical Sciences; Food and
Nutritional Sciences; International Relations;
Administration and Informatics.*

Tokyo Metropolitan Institute of Technology
[Tokyo Toritsu Kagaku Gijutsu Daigaku]
6-6 Asahigaoka, Hino-shi, Tokyo 191
Tel: +81(425) 83-5111
President: Kanji Negishi
Secretary-General: Nobuyuki Araki
Founded: 1986
Engineering.

*Tokyo Metropolitan University
[Tokyo Toritsu Daigaku]
1-1 Minami-Ohsawa, Hachiojo-Shi, Tokyo 192-03
Tel: +81(3) 717-0111
Fax: +81(3) 718-4661
President: Masami Yamazumi (1989-93)
Secretary-General: Koichi Sakamoto
Founded: 1949
*F: Social Sciences and Humanities; Law;
Economics; Science; Technology.
Ce: Urban Studies.*

Wakayama Medical College
[Wakayama Kenritsu Ika Daigaku]
9-Kyuban-cho, Wakayama-shi, Wakayama 640
Tel: +81(734) 31-2151
Cable: Wakayama Idai
President: Norihiko Komai
Secretary-General: Ishio Nakayama
Founded: 1945, 1948
Medicine.

Yokohama City University
[Yokohama Shiritsu Daigaku]
22-2 Seto, Kanazawa-ku, Yokohama-shi,
Yokohama 236
Tel: (45) 787-2311
President: Noboru Takasugi (1990-94)
Secretary-General: Tsutomu Kono
Founded: 1928, 1949
*F: Economics and Business Administration;
Liberal Arts and Science.
S: Medicine.
I: Economics Research; Biological Research
(Kihara).
D: General Education.*

PRIVATE INSTITUTIONS

Aichi University
[Aichi Daigaku]
1-1 Machihata-machi, Toyohashi-shi, Aichi 441
Tel: +81(532) 47-4111
Fax: +81(532) 47-4132
Founded: 1946, 1949
*F: Law; Business Administration; Economics;
Literature.
I: General Education; International Affairs;
Managerial Research; Community Research;
Chuba District Industry Research.
C: Junior (Women).
S: Graduate.
Ce: Data Processing.
D: Japanese (for foreign students).*

*Aichi Gakuin University
[Aichi Gakuin Daigaku]
12 Araike, Iwasaki, Nisshin-cho, Aichi-gun, Aichi
470-01
Tel: (5617) 3-1111
Fax: +81(5617) 3-4449
Telex: 1180
President: Tadataka Koide
Secretary-General: Shinji Sugihara
Founded: 1950, 1953
*F: Letters; Commerce; Business Administration;
Law; Dentistry.
I: Zen Studies; Law and Religion; Business
Administration; Foreign Languages; Cultural
Studies.
D: Liberal Arts.
Ce: Foreign Language Audio-visual Education;
Education for Information Processing; Data
Processing.*

Aichi Institute of Technology
[Aichi Kogyo Daigaku]
1247 Yachigusa, Yachigusa-cho, Toyoda-shi,
Aichi 470-03
Tel: +81(565) 48-8121
Founded: 1912, 1954, 1959
Engineering (day and evening courses).

Aichi Medical University
[Aichi Ika Daigaku]
21 Yazako Karimata, Nagakute-cho, Aichi-gun,
Aich 480-11
Tel: +81(561) 62-3311
Fax: +81(561) 62-4866
President: Itsuro Sjobue
Founded: 1971
*Medicine; Nursing; Medical Science of Aging;
Molecular Science of Medicine.*

Aichi Shukutoku Daigaku
[Aichi Shukutoku University]
9 Katahira, Nagakute-cho, Aichi-gun, Aichi 480-11
Tel: +81(561) 62-4111
Rector: Motofumi Kobayashi
Secretary-General (Acting): Goro Yanagi
Founded: 1975
Letters.

*Aoyama Gakuin University
[Aoyama Gakuin Daigaku]
4-4-25 Shibuya, Shibuya-ku, Tokyo 150
Tel: (3) 3409-8111
Fax: (3) 3409-7923
President: Shoichi Naito (1991-95)
Secretary-General: Kunizo Kasai
International Relations: Sakae Shimizu
Founded: 1904, 1949
*C: Literature (day and evening courses);
Economics (day and evening courses); Law;
Science and Engineering.
S: Business Administration (day and evening
courses); International Politics, Economics and
Business.
I: Research.
Ce: Information Science Research.*

Asahi University
[Asahi Daigaku]
1851 Hozumi, Hozumi-cho, Motosu-gun, Gifu
501-02
Tel: +81(5832) 6-6131
President: Keizaburo Miyata
Secretary-General: Hiroshi Tanaka
Founded: 1971, 1985
Business Administration; Dentistry; Law.

Asahikawa Daigaku
[Asahikawa University]
23-1-9 Nagayama 3-jo, Asahikawa-shi, Hokkaido
079
Tel: +81(166) 48-3121
President: Tsuyoshi Miki
Secretary-General: Koyo Oishi
Founded: 1968
Economics.

Ashikaga Kogyo Daigaku
[Ashikaga Institute of Technology]
268-1 Omae-cho, Ashikaga-shi, Tochigi 326
Tel: +81(284) 62-0605
President: Yoshinobu Wada
Secretary-General: Goro Okahira
Founded: 1967
Engineering.

Ashiya University
[Ashiya Daigaku]
13-22 Rokurokuso-cho, Ashiya-shi, Hyogo 659
Tel: +81(797) 23-0661
Fax: +81(797) 23-1901
President: Shigekazu Fukuyama (1964-)
Founded: 1964
Education.

Asia University
[Ajia Daigaku]
5-24-10 Sakai, Musashino-shi, Tokyo 180
Tel: +81(422) 54-3111
Fax: +81(422) 55-8232
International Relations: Tsutomu Aoshima
Founded: 1941, 1955
*Business Administration; Economics; Law; Asian
Studies; International Relations.*

Azabu University
[Azabu Daigaku]
1-17-71 Fuchinobe, Sagamihara-shi, Kanagawa
229
Tel: +81(427) 54-7111
President: Tsunenori Nakamura
Secretary-General: Mitsugu Takahashi
International Relations: Yoshito Wakao
Founded: 1890, 1950
Environmental Health; Veterinary Science.

Baika Women's College
[Baika Joshi Daigaku]
2-19-5 Shukunosho, Ibaraki-shi, Osaka 567
Tel: +81(726) 43-6221
Fax: +81(726) 41-5244
President: Mitsunobu Ootsuka (1989-91)
Secretary-General: Kazumi Nakamoto
International Relations: Kimio Teranoto
Founded: 1878, 1964
Literature.

Baiko Women's College
[Baiko Jogakuin Daigaku]
365 Myoji-cho, Yoshimi, Shimonoseki-shi,
Yamaguchi 759-65
Tel: +81(832) 86-2221
President: Yasumasa Sato
Founded: 1964
Literature.

Bukkyo University
[Bukkyo Daigaku]
96 Kitahananobo-cho, Murasakino, Kita-ku,
Kyoto-shi, Kyoto 603
Tel: +81(75) 491-2141
President: Kjoji Takahashi
Secretary-General: Tatsuo Miyaguchi
Founded: 1887, 1949, 1967
Letters; Sociology; Education.

Bunka Women's College
[Bunka Joshi Daigaku]
3-22-1 Yoyogi, Shibuya-ku, Tokyo 151
Tel: +81(3) 3299-2310
President: Jun Oonuma
Secretary-Genenarl: Masahiro Ishikawa
Founded: 1964
Domestic Economy; Letters.

Bunkyo Daigaku
[Bunkyo Daigaku]
3337 Minami-Ogishima, Koshigaya-shi, Saitama 343
Tel: +81(489) 74-8811
President: Jun Nagaoka
Secretary-General: Hiroaki Yoshii
Education; Human Sciences; Letters; Informatics; International Relations.

Chiba College of Economics
[Chiba Keizai Daigaku]
3-59-5, Todoroki-machi, Inage-ku, hiba-shi, Chiba 263
Tel: +81(43) 253-9111
President: Tsutomu Sakuma
Secretary-General: Yoshiyuki Mochizuki
Economics.

Chiba Institute of Technology
[Chiba Kogyo Daigaku]
2-17-1 Tsudanuma, Narashino-shi, Chiba 275
Tel: +81(474) 75-2111
President: Hisafuji Watanabe
Executive Director: Akira Takahashi
Founded: 1942, 1950
Technology.

*Chiba University of Commerce
[Chiba Shoka Daigaku]
1-3-1 Konodai, Ichikawa-shi, Chiba 272
Tel: +81(473) 72-4111
Fax: +81(473) 71-6881
President: Yasumasa Hayakawa
Secretary-General: Yoshihiko Tojo
Founded: 1922, 1928, 1944, 1950
Commerce and Economics; Economic Research.

*Chubu University
[Chubu Daigaku]
1200 Matsumoto-cho, Kasugai-shi, Aichi 487
Tel: +81(568) 51-1111
Fax: +81(568) 51-1141
President: Kazuo Yamada (1975-)
Secretary-General: Ryozo Ohnishi
Founded: 1938, 1962, 1964, 1984
C: Engineering; Business Administration and Information Sciences; International Studies.
I: Science and Technology (Research); Industry and Economics (Research); International Studies (Research).
Ce: Production Engineering (Innovation).

Chukyo University
[Chukyo Daigaku]
101-2 Yagoto Honmachi, Showa-ku, Nagoya-shi, Aichi 466
Tel: (52) 832-2151
President: Kiyohiro Umemura
Secretary-General: Hiroshi Terakawa
International Relations: Atsushi Seki
Founded: 1927, 1954, 1956
Commerce; Physical Education; Letters; Law; Education; Economics.

Chukyo Women's U.
[Chukyo Joshi Daigaku]
55 Yokone-cho, Ofu-shi, Aich 474
Tel: +81(562) 46-1291
President: Taro Tanioka
Secretary-General: Kunio Ishihara
Founded: 1963
Physical Education; Domestic Sciences.

*Chuo University
[Chuo Daigaku]
742-1 Higashinakano, Hachioji-shi, Tokyo 192-03
Tel: +81(426) 74-2111
Fax: +81(426) 74-2214
President: Tomonosuke Takagi
Secretary-General: Hideyuki Ishii
International Relations: Oko takahashi
Founded: 1885, 1905, 1949
F: Law (day and evening courses); Economics (day and evening courses); Commerce (day and evening courses); Science and Engineering (day and evening courses); Literature (day and evening courses).
D: Law (by correspondence).
I: Comparative Law in Japan; Accountancy; Economic Research; Business Research; Social Science; Cultural Science; Health and Physical Education.
Ce: Computer.

Daido Institute of Technology
[Daido Kogyo Daigaku]
2-21 Daido-cho, Minami-ku, Nagoya, Aichi 457
Tel: +81(52) 612-6111
President: Yasuhisa Tozawa
Secretary-General: Shiro Shinko
Founded: 1964
Engineering.

Daito Bunka University
[Daito Bunka Daigaku]
1-9-1 Takashimadaira, Itabashi-ku, Tokyo 175
Tel: +81(3) 3935-1110
Fax: +81(3) 3932-6902
President: Shigeyuki Hozumi
Registrar: Hiroko Onaka
Founded: 1923, 1949
F: Literature; Economics and Business Administration; Foreign Languages; Law; International Relations.
I: Oriental Studies; Calligraphy.
P: Japanese Language (for foreign students).

*Dokkyo University (Dokkyo Group)

[Dokkyo Daigaku]
1-1 Gakuen-cho, Soka-shi, Saitama 340
Tel: +81(489) 42-1111
Fax: +81(489) 42-4312
E-Mail: bitnet: ogatell@jpndkyo
President: Heihachiro Yoshino
Secretary-General: Yusei Kodama
Founded: 1864
F: Foreign Languages; Economics; Law; Liberal Arts.
I: Foreign Language Teaching.
Ce: Data-Processing and Computer Science.

Dokkyo University School of Medicine

[Dokkyo Ika Daigaku]
880 Kitakobayashi, Mibu-machi, Shimotsga-gun, Tochigi 321-02
Tel: +81(282) 86-1111
President: Masaharu Yoshimura
Secretary-General: Yoshiaki Aizawa
Founded: 1972
Medicine.

*Doshisha University

[Doshisha Daigaku]
Imadegawa-dori, Karasuma-Higashiiru, Kamigyo-ku, Kyoto-shi, Kyoto 602
Tel: +81(75) 251-3223
Fax: +81(75) 251-3057
President: Tajiro Iwayama
President: Akira Nishimura
Founded: 1875, 1912, 1949
F: Theology; Letters (day and evening courses); Law (day and evening courses); Economics (day and evening courses); Commerce (day and evening courses); Engineering.
Ce: American Studies.
I: Humanities and Social Science Research; Science and Engineering Research.

Doshisha Women's College of Liberal Arts

[Doshisha Joshi Daigaku]
Tanabecho, Tsuzuki-gun, Kyoto 610-03
Tel: +81(7746) 5-8411
President: Sanehide Kodama
Secretary-General: Takao Masuda
Founded: 1876, 1949
Liberal Arts; Home Economics.

Elizabeth University of Music

[Erizabeto Ongaku Daigaku]
4-15 Nobori-cho, Naka-ku, Hiroshima-shi, Hiroshima 730
Tel: +81(82) 221-0918
Fax: +81(82) 221-0947
President: Jiro Kosaki
Founded: 1948, 1952, 1963
Music (co-educational).

Ferris Women's College

[Ferris Jogakuin Daigaku]
37 Yamate-cho, Naka-ku, Yokohama-shi, Kanagawa 231
Tel: +81(45) 681-5150
President: Toru Yuge
Secretary-General: Kazuko Hisamori
Founded: 1947
Letters; Music.

Fujita Health University

[Fujita Hoken'eisei Daigaku]
1-98 Dengakugakubo, Kutsukake-cho, Toyoake-shi, Aichi 470-11
Tel: +81(562) 93-2600
Fax: +81(562) 93-4593
President: Hiroshi Watanabe
Founded: 1972
Medicine; Hygiene; Comprehensive Medical Science.

Fukui Institute of Technology

[Fukui Kogyo Daigaku]
3-6-1 Gakuen, Fukui-shi, Fukui 910
Tel: +81(776) 22-8111
President: Kenzo Kanai
Secretary-General: Tsuneo Nishida
Founded: 1965
Engineering.

Fukuoka Dental College

[Fukuoka Shika Daigaku]
2-15-1,Tamura, Sawara-ku, Fukuoka-shi, Fukuoka 814
Tel: +81(92) 661-3030
President: Tetsuo Ishiki
Secretary-General: Isamu Ide
Dentistry.

Fukuoka Institute of Technology

[Fukuoka Kogyo Daigaku]
3-30-1 Wajirohigashi, Higashi-ku, Fukushima-shi, Fukuoka 811-02
Tel: +81(92) 606-3131
President: Kaku Nakajima
Secretary-General: Tsutau Hashizume
Founded: 1963
Engineering.

Fukuoka University

[Fukuoka Daigaku]
8-19-1 Nanakuma, Jonan-ku, Fukuoka-shi, Fukuoka 814-01
Tel: +81(92) 871-6631
International Relations: Isao Takagi
Founded: 1934, 1949, 1956
F: Law; Humanities; Economics; Commerce; Science; Engineering; Medicine; Pharmacy; Physical Education.
S: Nursing.
I: Research.
Ce: Radioisotope; Computer.

Fukuyama University
[Fukuyama Daigaku]
Sanzo, 1-banchi, Gakuen-cho, Fukuyama-shi,
Hiroshima 729-02
Tel: +81(849) 36-2111
Fax: +81(849) 36-2213
President: Shigeru Miyachi
Secretary-General: Tsugio Itsuta
Founded: 1975
F: Economics; Pharmacy and Pharmaceutical
Science; Engineering.
C: Liberal Arts.
I: Industrial Science; Marine Bioresources
(Research).
Ce: Human Science (Research).

*Gakushuin University
[Gakushuin Daigaku]
1-5-1 Mejiro, Toshima-ku, Tokyo 171
Tel: +81(3) 3986-0221
Fax: +81(3) 5992-1005
Cable: gakushudai
President: Tozo Hayakawa
Secretary-General: Noboru Mekai
Founded: 1877, 1949
F: Law; Economics; Letters; Science.
I: Oriental Cultures (Research).
Ce: Computer.

Higashi Nippon Gakuen University
[Higashi Nippon Gakuen Daigaku]
1757 Kanazawa, Tobetsu-cho, Ishikari-gun,
Hokkaido 061-02
Tel: +81(1332) 3-1211
President: Kinai Tomita
Founded: 1974
Pharmacy; Dentistry.

Himeji Dokkyo University (Dokkyo Group)
[Himeji Dokkyo Daigaku]
7-2-1 Kami-Ohno, Himeji-shi, Hyogo 670
President: Tomokazu Nishikawa
Secretary-General: Fukuo Takeda
Founded: 1987
Law; Economics and Information Sciences;
Foreign Languages; Liberal Arts.

Hiroshima Bunkyo Women's College
[Hiroshima Bunkyo Joshi Daigaku]
1-2-1 Kabe-higashi, Asakita-ku, Hiroshima-shi,
Hiroshima 731-02
Tel: +81(82) 814-3191
Fax: +81(82) 815-2097
Founded: 1957, 1962
Letters; Regional Cultures Research.

Hiroshima Institute of Technology
[Hiroshima Kogyo Daigaku]
2-1-1, Miyake, Saeki-ku, Hiroshima-shi, Hiroshima
731-51
Tel: +81(829) 21-3121
President: Noboru Tsuru
Secretary-General: Nobuyuki Akiyama
Founded: 1961
Engineering; Environmental Design.

Hiroshima Shudo University
[Hiroshima Shudo Daigaku]
1717 Otsuka, Numata-cho, Asa-Minami-ku,
Hiroshima-shi, Hiroshima 731-31
Tel: +81(82) 848-2121
President: Shinji Fujita
Founded: 1952, 1973
Commercial Sciences; Humanities and Sciences;
Law.

Hiroshima University of Economics
[Hiroshima Keizai Daigaku]
5-37-1 Gion, Asa Minami-ku, Hiroshima-shi,
Hiroshima 731-01
Tel: +81(82) 871-1000
Founded: 1907, 1967, 1984
Economics; Regional Economics (Research);
ComputerSciences.

Hokkaido College of Dairy Farming
Hokkaido
[Rakuno Gakuen Daigaku]
582-1 Bunkyodai-Midorimachi, Ebetsu-shi,
Hokkaido 069
Tel: +81(11) 386-1111
President: Kazuyoshi Hirao
Secretary-General: Toshiharu Kikuchi
Founded: 1933, 1959
Dairy Farming.

Hokkaido Institute of Pharmaceutical
Sciences
[Hokkaido Yakka Daigaku]
7-1 Katsuraoka-cho, Otaru-shi, Hokkaido 047-02
Tel: +81(134) 62-5111
President: Keichi Ito
Secretary-General: Hideki Kodaira
Founded: 1974
Pharmaceutical Sciences.

*Hokkaigakuen University
[Hokkaigakuen Daigaku]
4-1-40 Asahi-machi, Toyohira-ku, Sapporo-shi,
Hokkaido 062
Tel: +81(11) 841-1161
President: Takayuki Sakaue (1992-96)
Director-General: Kazuo Saito
Founded: 1887, 1950, 1952
F: Economics; Law; Engineering.
I: Development Research.
D: General Education.

Hokkaido Institute of Technology
[Hokkaido Kogyo Daigaku]
419-2 Maeda, Teine, Nishi-ku, Sapporo-shi,
Hokkaido 061-24
Tel: +81(11) 681-2161
President: Mikio Arie
Secretary-General: Engineering
Founded: 1953
Engineering.

Hokkaido Tokai University
[Hokkaido Tokai Daigaku]
224 Chuwa, Kamui-cho, Asahikawa-shi, Hokkaido 070
Tel: +81(166) 61-5111
President: Yoshio Mihara
Secretary-General: Isao Shimizu
Founded: 1977
International Culture; Engineering.

Hokuriku University
[Hokuriku Daigaku]
1-1 Taiyogaoka, Kanazawa-shi, Ishikawa 920-11
Tel: +81(762) 29-1161
Fax: +81(762) 29-1393
President: Eishin Kyuno
Secretary-General: Koichi Nakagawa
Founded: 1975
S: Pharmacy; Foreign Languages; Law; Liberal Arts.

Hokusei Gakuen University
[Hokusei Gakuen Daigaku]
3-1 Oyachi Nishi 2-chome, Atsubetus-ku, Sapporo-shi, Hokkaido 004
Tel: +81(11) 891-2731
Fax: +81(11) 892-6097
President: Nobuo Tsuchihashi
Secretary-General: Tadayuki Ohtsu
Founded: 1887, 1962
Literature; Economics.

*Hosei University
[Hosei Daigaku]
17-1, Fujimi 2 chome, Chiyoda-ku, Tokyo 102
Tel: +81(3) 3264-9315
Fax: +81(3) 3238-9873
Telex: J29683
President: Bakuji Ari (1988-)
Secretary-General: Isamu Okakura
International Relations: Tei Kawaguchi
Founded: 1880, 1889, 1903, 1949
F: Law; Letters; Economics; Engineering; Business Administration; Social Sciences.
S: Correspondence Education.
I: Social Research (Ohara); Okinawan Studies; Modern Law and Politics (Boissonade); Japan Statistic Research; Comparative Economic Studies; Nogami Memorial Noh Theater Research.
Ce: Computer; Athletic Research; Ion Beam Technology (Research); Business and Industrial Research.

Hoshi University
[Hoshi Yakka Daigaku]
2-4-41 Ebara, Shinagawa-ku, Tokyo 142
Tel: +81 3786-1011
President: Yutaka Kasuya
Secretary-General: Hajime Yoshinuma
Founded: 1941, 1963
Pharmaceutical Sciences.

Hyogo College of Medicine
[Hyogo Ika Daigaku]
1-1 Mukogawa-cho, Nishinomiya-shi, Hyogo 663
Tel: +81(798) 45-6111
Founded: 1971
Medicine.

*International Christian University
[Kokusai Kirisutokyo Daigaku]
3-10-2 Osawa, Mitaka-shi, Tokyo 181
Tel: +81(422) 33-3131
Fax: +81(422) 33-9887
Cable: inchristun Mitaka Japan
President: Kunio Oguchi
Secretary-General: Akira Shibanuma
International Relations: Thomas T. Wynant
Founded: 1949
C: Liberal Arts.
D: Humanities; Social Sciences; Natural Sciences; Languages; Education; International Studies.
I: Educational Research and Service; Social Science Research; Study of Christianity and Western and Eastern Culture; Asian Cultural Studies; Peace Research.

International University of Japan
[Kokusai Daigaku]
777 Anachi-shinden, Munami uonuma-gun, Niigata 949-72
Tel: +81(257) 77-1111
Fax: +81(257) 79-4441
Telex: 3238347 iuj j
President: Shuntaro Shishido
Secretary-General: Hiroshi Murakami
Founded: 1982
International Relations (Graduate); International Management (Graduate); Middle East Studies; Global Communication.

Ishinomaki Senshu University
[Ishinomaki Senshu Daigaku]
Shin-mito 1-banchi, Minamisakai, Ishinomaki-shi, Miyagi 986
Tel: +81(225) 22-7711
President: Yasumi Ogura
Secretary-General: Hironari Ono
Science and Engineering; Business Administration.

Iwaki Meisei University
[Iwaki Meisei Daigaku]
5-5-1, Iino, Chuodai, Iwaki-shi, Fukushima 970
Tel: +81(226) 29-5111
President: Tatsusaburo Suzuki
Secretary-General: Hisayoshi Yasui
Science and Engineering; Humanities; Liberal Arts.

Iwate Medical University
[Iwate Ika Daigaku]
19-1 Uchimaru, Morioka-shi, Iwate 020
Tel: +91(196) 51-5111
Founded: 1928, 1952

F: Medicine; Dentistry.
Ce: Cyclotron Research.

*Japan Women's University
[Nihon Joshi Daigaku]
2-8-1 Merjirodai, Bunkyo-ku, Tokyo 112
Tel: +81(3) 3943-3131
Fax: +81(3) 3942-6518
President: Misako Miyamoto
Secretary-General: Nobuo Makino
Founded: 1901, 1948
*F: Home Economics; Humanities; Integrated
Arts and Social Sciences; Science.*
*I: Child Studies; Rural Life Research; Education
for Women; Computer Research.*
D: Correspondence Courses.

The Japanese Red Cross College of Nursing
[Nihon Sekijuji Kango Daigaku]
4-1-3 Hiroo, Shibuya-ku, Tokyo 150
Tel: +81(33) 409-0875
President: Masao Takahashi
Founded: 1966
Nursing.

Jichi Medical School
[Jichi Ika Daigaku]
3311-1 Yakushiji, Minamikawachi-machi,
Kawachi-gun, Tochigi 329-04
Tel: +81(285) 44-2111
President: Kiku Nakao
Secretary-General: Kiyoshi Nakachi
Founded: 1972
Medicine; Hematology; Nursing.

*The Jikei University School of Medicine
[Tokyo Jikei-kai Ika Daigaku]
3-25-8 Nishi-shinbashi, Minato-ku, Tokyo 105
Tel: +81(3) 3433-1111
Fax: +81(3) 3435-1922
President: Tetsuo Okamura
Administrative Director: Yoshiki Tanaka
Founded: 1881, 1921, 1952
S: Medicine; Nursing.
I: Medical Science.
*Ce: Continuing Medical Education; Laboratory
Animal; Radioisotope Research; Education and
Research.*
L: Space Medicine.

Jissen Women's University
[Jissen Joshi Daigaku]
4-1-1 Osakaue, Hino-shi, Tokyo 191
Tel: +81(425) 85-0311
Fax: +81(425) 85-0771
President: Masami Yoshikawa (1988-)
Secretary-General: Kiyoshi Uchida
Founded: 1899, 1925, 1949
F: Literature; Home Economics.
*D: Japanese Literature; English Literature;
Aesthetics and Art History; Food Science;
Clothing Science.*
I: Japanese Arts and Literature Materials.

Josai University
[Josai Daigaku]
1-1 Keyakidai, Sakodo-shi, Saitama 350-02
Tel: +81(492) 86-2233
President: Taijiro Matsuura
Secretary-General: Shizuo Nakamura
Founded: 1965
Economics; Science; Pharmacy.

Juntendo University
[Juntendo Daigaku]
2-1-1 Hongo, Bunkyo-ku, Tokyo 113
Tel: +91(3) 3813-3111
Fax: +81(3) 3814-9100
President: shozo Ishii
Secretary-General: Hisato Iida
Founded: 1839, 1944, 1950
Health and Physical Education; Medicine.

Kagawa Nutrition College
[Joshi Eiyo Daigaku]
3-9-21 Chiyoda, Sakado-shi, Saitama 350-02
Tel: +81(492) 82-3601
President: Yoshiko Kagawa
Director, Educational Affairs: Tadao Miyasaka
Founded: 1961
Nutrition; Nutrition and Research.

Kanagawa Dental College
[Kanagawa Shika Daigaku]
82 Inaoka-cho, Yokusuka-shi, Kanagawa 238
Tel: +81(468) 25-1500
President: Akira Yamanaka
Secretary-General: Morihisa Saito
Founded: 1964
Dentistry.

Kanagawa Institute of Technology
[Kanagawa Kogyo Daigaku]
1030 Shimoogino, Atsugi-shi, Kanagawa 243-02
Tel: +81(462) 41-1211
President: Hidehiko Takeyama
Founded: 1975
Engineering.

*Kanazawa Institute of Technology
[Kanazawa Kogyo Daigaku]
7-1 Ogigaoka, Nonoichi-machi, Ishikawa 921
Tel: +81(762) 48-1100
Fax: +81(762) 48-6189
E-Mail: kitamura@kitmast.cisp.kanazawa-it.ac.jp
Telex: 5122456kit Ic j
Cable: kit
Chancellor: Tsuyoshi Sato (1992-)
Managing Director: Yoshio Izumiya
Founded: 1965
*D: Mechanical Engineering; Mechanical
Systems Engineering; Electrical Engineering;
Electronics; Information and Computer
Engineering; Managerial Engineering; Civil
Engineering; Architecture; Liberal Arts.*
*I: Information Sciences Research; Structural
Engineering Research; Environmental Science
Research; Materials System Research; Urban
Planning Research; Basic Foreign Languages*

Education Research; Electron Device Systems Research; Applied Computer Sciences Research. *Ce: Basic Engineering; Information Processing Services.*

Kanazawa Medical University
[Kanazawa Ika Daigaku]
1-1 Daigaku, Uchinade-machi, Kahoku-gun, Ishikawa 920-02
Tel: +81(762) 86-2211
Fax: +81(762) 86-0224
President: Yasuaki Yamasaki
Founded: 1972
Medicine.

Kanagawa University
[Kanagawa Daigaku]
3-27-1 Rokkakubashi, Kanagawa-ku, Yokohama-shi, Kanagawa 221
Tel: +81(45) 481-5661
Fax: +81(45) 491-7915
President: Morihisa Fujimoto
Secretary-General: Hiroshi Kubo
International Relations: Kunitomo Sakurai
Founded: 1929, 1949
F: Economics (day and evening courses); Foreign Languages; Law (day and evening courses); Engineering (day and evening courses); Business Administration; Science.

Kanda College of Foreign Languages
[Kanda Gaigo Daigaku]
1-4-1 Wakaba, Mihama-ku, Chiba-shi, Chiba 261
Tel: +81(43) 273-1233
President: Kazuko Inoue
Secretary-General: Toru Sato
Foreign Languages.

Kansai Medical University
[Kansai Ika Daigaku]
1 Fumizono-cho, Moriguchi-shi, Osaka 570
Tel: +81(6) 992-1001
President: Yutaka Tashiro
Secretary-General: Takara Nishi
Founded: 1928, 1947, 1954
Medicine; Liver Research.

Kansai University
[Kansai Daigaku]
3-3-35 Yamate-cho, Suita-shi, Osaka 564
Tel: +81(6) 388-1121
Fax: +81(6) 330-3027
President: Akio Onishi
Secretary-General: Kiyoshi Kitada
International Relations: Teiichi Kawata
Founded: 1886, 1905, 1948
F: Law; Letters; Economics; Commerce; Sociology; Engineering.
I: Economic and Political Studies; Oriental and Occidental Studies; Industrial Technology; Legal Studies; Human Rights Studies.
Ce: Archaeological Studies.

Kansai University of Foreign Studies
[Kansai Gaikokugo Daigaku]
16-1 Kitakatahoko-cho, Hirakata-shi, Osaka 573
Tel: +81(720) 56-1721
President: Sadato Tanimoto
Secretary-General: Saburo Fujino
International Relations: Hajime Yamamoto
Founded: 1876
Foreign Languages.

Kanto Gakuen University
[Kanto Gakuen Daigaku]
200 Fujaku, Ota-shi, Gunma 370
Tel: +81(276) 31-2711
President: Junichi Matsudaira
Secretary-General: Toru Kishi
Founded: 1876
Economics; Law.

*Kanto Gakuin University
[Kanto Gakuin Daigaku]
4834 Mutsuhura-cho, Kanazawa-ku, Yokohama-shi, Kanagawa 236
Tel: +81(45) 786-7002
Fax: +81(45) 786-7038
President: Tsuneo Ikawa (1987-)
Acting Secretary-General: Iwao Miwa
International Relations: Kinshiro Nakaura
Founded: 1949
F: Economics; Engineering; Humanities; Letters; Law.
I: Economics Research; Architectural and Environmental Engineering; Technological Research.
Ce: Computer.

Kawasaki Medical College
[Kawasaki Ika Daigaku]
577 Matsushima, Kurashiki-shi, Okayama 701-01
Tel: +81(86) 462-1111
President: Yoshio Mochizuki
Secretary-General: Risuke Yakushiji
Founded: 1970
Medicine.

*Keio University
[Keio Gijuku Daigaku]
2-15-45 Mita, Minato-ku, Tokyo 108
Tel: +81(3) 3453-4511
Fax: +81(3) 3769-2047
Telex: 34532 keioic j
President: Yasuhiko Torii (1993-)
Secretary-General: Takao Fukudome
Founded: 1858, 1890
F: Letters; Economics; Law; Business Administration and Commerce; Science and Technology.
I: Cultural and Linguistic Studies; Communications Research; Physical Education; Oriental Culture; Audio-Visual Language.
S: Medicine; Foreign Languages; Correspondence Courses; Business.
C: Nursing.

Ce: Computer; Area Studies; Teacher Training; Economic and Social Observatory.

Kinjo Gakuin Daigaku
2-1723 Omori, Moriyama-ku, Nagoya-shi, Aichi 463
Tel: +81(52) 798-0180
President: Kazuie Sanuki
Secretary-General: Kei Mizukawa
International Relations: Hiroshi Imanaka
Founded: 1927
Letters; Domestic Sciences.

Kinki University
[Kinki Daigaku]
3-4-1 Kowakae, Higashi-Osaka-shi, Osaka 577
Tel: +81(6) 721-2332
President: Masataka Seko
Secretary-General: Shozo Misonoo
International Relations: Jitsuichi Naka
Founded: 1949
F: Jurisprudence; Economics and Business Administration; Science and Technology; Pharmacy; Agriculture; Medicine; Letters.
I: Oriental Medicine.

Kitakyushu University of Occupational and Environmental Health
[Sangyo Ika Daigaku]
1-1 Iseigaoka, Yahata-nishi-ku, Kitakyushu-shi, Fukuoka 807
Tel: +81(93) 603-1611
Fax: +81(93) 602-5482
Cable: uoeh kitakyushu
President: Akira Koizumi (1978-92)
Secretary-General: Yoshio Kuramoto
Founded: 1978
S: Medicine; Nursing and Medical Technology; Occupational and Community Health Nursing; Medical Science (Graduate).
I: Industrial Ecological Sciences.
Ce: Occupational Health Training.

Kitasato University
[Kitasato Daigaku]
5-9-1 Shirokane, Minato-ku, Tokyo 108
Tel: +81(3) 3444-6161
President: Bonro Kobayashi
Secretary-General: Kazuo Tahara
Founded: 1962, 1964
Hygienic Sciences; Pharmaceutical Sciences; Veterinary Medicine and Animal Husbandry; Medicine (Sagamihara-shi); Fisheries Sciences; Nursing.

Kobe Gakuin University
[Kobe Gakuin Daigaku]
518 Arise, Ikawadani-cho, Nishi-ku, Kobe-shi, Hyogo 651-21
Tel: +81(78) 974-1551
Fax: +81(78) 974-5689
President: Takao Hama
Secretary-General: Masayuki Takemura
International Relations: Masatoyo Aoki

Founded: 1966
Nutrition; Law; Economics; Pharmacy; Humanities and Sciences.

Kobe Jogakuin University
[Kobe Jogakuin Daigaku]
4-1 Okadayama, Nishinomiya-shi, Hyogo 662
Tel: +81(798) 52-0955
Fax: +81(798) 51-8535
President: Sachiko Kodama (1989-94)
Secretary-General: Akira Yoshida
Founded: 1875, 1891, 1948
S: Letters; Music; Home Economics; Human Sciences.
I: Research.

Kobe Women's College of Pharmacy
[Kobe Joshi Yakka Daigaku]
4-19-1 Motoyamakita-machi, Higashinada-ku, Kobe-shi, Hyogo 658
Tel: +81(78) 453-0031
Fax: +81(78) 453-0205
President: Naotaka Nagakura
Secretary-General: Katsumi Matsui
Founded: 1920, 1949
Pharmacy.

Kobe Women's University
[Kobe Joshi Daigaku]
2-1 Aoyama, Higashi-suma, Suma-ku, Kobe-shi, Kobe 654
Tel: +81(78) 731-4416
Fax: +81(78) 732-5161
President: Kaname Yukiyoshi (1966-)
Secretary-General: Osamu Ando
Founded: 1950, 1966
Literature; Home Economics.

Kogakkan University
[Kogakkan Daigaku]
1704 Kodakujimoto-cho, Ise-shi, Mie 516
Tel: +81(596) 22-0201
President: Shogo Tani
Secretary-General: Isao Okada
Founded: 1882, 1903, 1940, 1962
Letters.

Kogakuin University
[Kogakuin Daigaku]
1-24-2 Nishi Shinjku, Shinjuku-ku, Tokyo 160
Tel: +81(3) 3324-1211
President: Kaoru Hongo
Founded: 1888, 1949
Engineering.

*Kokugakuin University
[Kokugakuin Daigaku]
4-10-28 Higashi, Shibuya-ku, Tokyo 150
Tel: +81(3) 5466-0111
President: Akira Haruta
Secretary-General: Yoshio Shibasaki
Founded: 1882, 1919, 1948
F: Letters; Law; Economics.
I: Japanese Culture and Classics.

Kokushikan University
[Kokushikan Daigaku]
4-28-1 Setagaya, Setagaya-ku, Tokyo 154
Tel: +81(3) 5481-3111
President: Toshio Hato
Secretary-General: Yoshiro Sekiguchi
International Relations: Akira Tsuruho
Founded: 1953, 1958
F: Political Science and Economics (day and evening courses); Law; Literature; Engineering; Physical Education.
I: Political Science and Education Research; Accountancy Research; Comparative Law Research; Iraq Ancient Culture Research.
Ce: Computer.

Komazawa University
[Komazawa Daigaku]
1-23-1 Komazawa, Setagaya-ku, Tokyo 154
Tel: +81(3) 3418-9010
President: Keiichi Abe
Secretary-General: Taizo Watanabe
International Relations: Takeshi Sakamoto
Founded: 1759, 1882, 1952
F: Buddhism; Arts and Sciences; Economics; Law; Business Management; Foreign Languages; Physical Education.
I: Religious Social Research; Buddhist Economics.

Konan Women's University
[Konan Joshi Daigaku]
6-2-23 Morikita-machi, Higashinada-ku, Kobe-shi, Hyogo 658
Tel: +81(78) 431-0391
Fax: +81(78) 412-7177
President: Hiroshi Miyagi (1972-)
Secretary-General: Yoshio Nagasaka
Founded: 1955, 1964
Letters.

*Konan University
[Konan Daigaku]
8-9-1 Okamoto, Higashinada-ku, Kobe-shi, Hyogo 658
Tel: +81(78) 431-4341
Fax: +81(78) 413-2676
President: Kazunori Yuasa (1990-)
Secretary-General: Takeshi Nouzou
International Relations: Keiko Imai
Founded: 1919, 1951
F: Liberal Arts; Science; Economics; Law; Business Administration.
I: Interdisciplinary Studies.
Ce: Information Processing.

Koriyama Women's College
[Koriyama Joshi Daigaku]
3-25-2 Kasei, Koriyama-shi, Fukushima 963
Tel: +81(249) 32-4848
President: Tomisa Sekiguchi
Secretary-General: Osamu Sekiguchi
Founded: 1950
Domestic Sciences.

Koshien University
[Koshien Daigaku]
10-1 Momijigaoka, Takarazuka-shi, Hyogo 665
Tel: +18(797) 87-5111
President: Tojiro Kawamura
Secretary-General: Tsuneo Yokoyama
Founded: 1967
Nutrition; Administration.

Koyasan University
[Koyasan Daigaku]
Koyasan, Ito-gun, Wakayama 648-02
Tel: +81(736) 56-2921
Fax: +81(736) 56-2746
Cable: Kii-Koya
President: Hidenori Wada
Chief Secretary: Kosei Kusunoki
Founded: 1886, 1926
F: Letters.
I: Culture of Esoteric Buddhism.

Kumamoto Institute of Technology
[Kumamato Kogyo Daigaku]
4-22-1 Ikeda, Kumamoto-shi, Kumamoto 860
Tel: +81(96) 326-3111
President: Yoshitaka Nakayama
Secretary-General: Isao Matsuo
International Relations: Hitoshi Maemura
Founded: 1965, 1967
Engineering.

Kumamoto University of Commerce
[Kumamoto Shoka Daigaku]
2-5-1 Oe, Kumamoto-shi, Kumamoto 862
Tel: +81(96) 364-5161
President: Shigemichi Iwano
Secretary-General: Seiji Yamashita
International Relations: Ryusuke Furuta
Founded: 1950
Commerce; Economics; Liberal Arts.

Kunitachi College of Music
[Kunitachi Ongaku Daigaku]
5-5-1 Kashiwa-cho, Tachikawa-shi, Tokyo 190
Tel: +81(425) 36-0321
Fax: +81(425) 35-2313
President: Bin Ebisawa (1991-)
Head: Yoshiharu Ishizawa
Founded: 1926, 1950
Music; Music (Research); Organological Research; Computer Music and Music Technology.

Kurume University
[Kurume Daigaku]
67 Asahi-machi, Kurume-shi, Fukuoka 830
Tel: +81(942) 35-3311
President: Kyozo Koketsu
Secretary-General: Moriya Uchida
Founded: 1928, 1950
F: Letters; Law.
S: Commerce; Medicine.
I: Industrial Economics; Cardiovascular Diseases; Clinical Pathology; Brain Diseases.

*Kwansei Gakuin University
[Kwansei Gakuin Daigaku]
1-1-155 Uegahara, Nishinomiya-shi, Hyogo 662
Tel: +81(798) 53-6111
Fax: +81(798) 51-0915
Cable: crescent nishinomiya
President: Kazuo Tsuge (1989-95)
University Secretary: Hisao Inoue
International Relations: Michikazu Saeki
Founded: 1889, 1912, 1932
S: Theology; Humanities; Sociology; Law;
Economics; Business Administration; Science.
I: Industrial Research; Integrated Educational
Research and Development.
Ce: Information Processing Research.

Kwassui Women's College
[Kwassui Joshi Dayaku]
1-50 Higashi-Yamate-machi, Nagasaki-shi,
Nagasaki 850
Tel: +81(958) 22-4107
President: Yuzuru Hirohata
Secretary-General: Toshinao Eto
International Relations: Akira Wataya
Founded: 1952
Letters.

Kyorin University
[Kyorin Daigaku]
6-20-2 Shinkawa, Mitaka-shi, Tokyo 181
Tel: +81(422) 47-5511
President: Kazuo Takeuchi
Secretary-General: Mitsuyuki Yokoi
Founded: 1966, 1970
Social Sciences; Foreign Languages.
S: Allied Health; Medicine.

Kyoritsu Pharmaceutical University
[Kyoritsu Yakka Daigaku]
1-5-30 Shibakoen, Minato-ku, Tokyo 105
Tel: +81(3) 3434-6241
President: Masashi Tomota
Secretary-General: Tadao Koyama
Founded: 1930, 1949
Pharmacy.

Kyoritsu Women's University
[Kyoritsu Joshi Daigaku]
2-2-1 Hitotsubashi, Chiyoda-ku, Tokyo 101
Tel: +81(3) 3237-2433
Founded: 1886, 1925, 1949
Home Economics; Arts and Letters; International
Culture.

Kyoto Pharmaceutical University
[Kyoto Yakka Daigaku]
5 Misasaginakauchi-cho, Yamashina-ku, Kyoto-
shi, Kyoto 607
Tel: +81(75) 581-3161
Fax: +81(75) 594-5454
President: Katsuya Ohata
Secretary-General: Masaaki Hishigi
Founded: 1884, 1919, 1949
Pharmacy; Molecular and Cellular Biology for
Pharmaceutical Sciences (in preparation).

Kyoto Sangyo University
[Kyoto Sangyo Daigaku]
Motoyama, Kamigamo, Kita-ku, Kyoto-shi, Kyoto
603
Tel: +81(75) 701-2151
President: Sukekata Kashiwa
Secretary-General: Tsuyoshi Tsubota
Founded: 1965
F: Economics; Business Administration; Law;
Foreign Languages; Science; Engineering.
D: Liberal Arts.
I: Computer; World Affairs; Linguistics
(International).

Kyoto Seika University
[Kyoto Seika Daigaku]
137 Kino, Iwakura, Sakyo-ku, Kyoto-shi Kyoto 606
Tel: +81(75) 702-5200
President: Atsuhiro Shibatani
Founded: 1968
Fine Arts; Humanities.

*Kyoto University of Foreign Studies
[Kyoto Gaikokugo Daigaku]
6 Saiin Kasame-cho, Ukyo-ku, Kyoto-shi, Kyoto
615
Tel: +81(75) 322-6012
Fax: +81(75) 311-8989
Telex: 5422102 gadai j
Chancellor: Yoshikazu Morita (1976-)
Secretary-General: Motohiro Izutsu
Founded: 1947, 1959
Foreign Studies.

Kyoto Women's University
[Kyoto Joshi Daigaku]
35 Kitahiyoshi-cho, Imakumano, Higashiyama-ku,
Kyoto-shi, Kyoto 605
Tel: +81(75) 531-1111
President: Naosada Kano
Secretary-General: Genki Shibahara
Founded: 1920, 1949
Literature; Home Sciences.

Kyushu Sangyo University
[Kyushu Sangyo Daigaku]
2-3-1 Matsukadai, Higashi-ku, Fukuoka-shi,
Fukuoka 813
Tel: +81(92) 673-5050
President: Tsutomu Yanagase
Secretary-General: Masashi Hiramatsu
Founded: 1959, 1963
F: Art; Engineering; Commerce; Management;
Economics; Liberal Arts.

Kyushu Tokai University
[Kyushu Tokai Daigaku]
9-1-1 Toroku, Oe-cho, Kumamoto-shi, Kumamoto
862
Tel: +81(96) 382-1141
Fax: +81(96) 381-7956
Founded: 1964, 1973
S: Engineering; Agriculture.
I: Industrial Science and Technical Research.
Ce: Computer; Space Information.

Matsuyama University
[Matsuyama Daigaku]
4-2 Bunkyo-cho, Matsuyama-shi, Ehime 790
Tel: +81(899) 25-7111
President: Mitsuru Miyasaki (1992-94)
Secretary-General: Toshio Yamasaki
Founded: 1923, 1949
F: Economics; Business Administration;
Humanities; Law.
I: General Regional Research.

Meiji College of Oriental Medicine
[Meiji Shinkyu Daigaku]
Hiyoshi-cho, Funai-gun, Kyoto 629-03
Tel: +81(771) 72-1181
President: Takeshi Yonezawa
Secretary-General: Tyosei Odawara
Founded: 1983
Accupuncture and Moxibustion.

Meiji College of Pharmacy
[Meiji Yakka Daigaku]
1-35-23 Nozawa, Setagaya-ku, Tokyo 154
Tel: +81(3) 3424-1001
President: Takeshi Ooishi
Secretary-General: Yu Oshima
Founded: 1902, 1949
Pharmacy.

*Meiji Gakuin University
[Meiji Gakuin Daigaku]
1-2-37 Shirokanedai, Minato-ku, Tokyo 108
Tel: +81(3) 5421-5111
Fax: +81(3) 5421-5458
E-Mail: compuserve
Telex: J44762 prime
Cable: meiji gakuin 0115269
President: Kan'ichi Fukuda
Secretary-General: KatsumiHajiwara
Founded: 1877, 1949
F: Literature; Economics; Sociology and Social
Work; Law; International Studies; General
Education.
I: Linguistics and Cultural Studies; Foreign
Language Education; Christian Research;
Industry and Economy (Research); Law
Research; General Education; Sociology and
Social Welfare; International Peace Research
(Meigaku).

*Meiji University
[Meiji Daigaku]
1-1 Kanda Surugadai, Chiyoda-ku, Tokyo 101
Tel: +81(3) 3296-4545
Fax: +81(3) 3296-4360
Telex: 2227034 meiji u
President: Kaoru Okano
Secretary-General: Masacazu Tsutsuii
International Relations: Shohichi Usui
Founded: 1881, 1903, 1925, 1949
S: Law; Commerce; Political Science and
Economics; Arts and Letters; Science and
Technology; Agriculture; Business
Administration.

I: Social Sciences; Cultural Sciences; Science
and Technology.
Ce: Computer.

Meijo University
[Meijo Daigaku]
1-501 Shiogamaguchi, Tenpaku-ku, Nagoya-shi,
Aichi 468
Tel: +81(52) 832-1151
President: susumu Maruse
Secretary-General: Hideaki Kiyomi
Founded: 1924, 1949
F: Law; Commerce; Science and Technology;
Agriculture; Pharmacy.

*Meikai University
[Meikai Daigaku]
1-1 Keyakidai, Sakado-shi, Saitama 350-02
Tel: +81(492) 85-5511
President: Yuriko Ohtsuka (1994-)
Secretary-General: Takuzo Adachi
Founded: 1970
Dentistry; Foreign Languages; Economics.

Meisei University
[Meisei Daigaku]
2-1-1 Hodokubo, Hino-shi, Tokyo 191
Tel: +81(425) 91-5111
President: Mitsuo Kodama
Secretary-General: Senichi Yamada
Founded: 1964
Science and Technology; Humanities; Information
Processing; Japanese Culture.

Mukogawa Women's University
[Mukogawa Joshi Daigaku]
6-46 Ikebiraki-cho, Nishinomiya-shi, Hyogo 663
Tel: +81(798) 47-1212
Fax: +81(798) 47-1800
President/Chancellor: Akira Kusaka (1967-)
Secretary-General: Ryo Okawara
International Relations: Tetsuaki Shimizu
Founded: 1939, 1949
C: Letters; Home Economics; Music.
S: Pharmaceutical Sciences.
I: Linguistic Cultures; Infant Education
Research; Education; Aesthetics in Everyday Life.

Musashi Institute of Technology
[Musashi Kogyo Daigaku]
1-28-1 Tamazutsumi, Setagaya-ku, Tokyo 158
Tel: +81(3) 3703-3111
President: Shoichi Kohama
Secretary-General: Shigeo Hakamura
Founded: 1929, 1949
F: Mechanical Engineering; Electrical and
Electronic Engineering; Electronics and
Communication Engineering; Architecture; Civil
Engineering; Industrial Engineering.
I: Atomic Energy Research.
Ce: Information Processing.

Musashi University

[Musashi Daigaku]
1-26-1 Toyotama-kami, Nerima-ku, Tokyo 176
Tel: +81(3) 3991-1191
President: Tsuyoshi Sakurai
Secretary-General: Minoru Watanabe
Founded: 1922, 1949, 1969
Economics; Humanities.

Musashino Academy of Music

[Musashino Ongaku Daigaku]
1-13-1 Hazawa, Nerima-ku, Tokyo 176
Tel: +81(3) 3992-1121
Fax: +81(3) 3991-7599
Cable: Musamusik
President: Naoyoshi Fukui
Founded: 1929, 1949
Music; Education and Culture Research.

Musashino Art University

[Musashino Bijutsu Daigaku]
1-736 Ogawa-cho, Kodaira-shi, Tokyo 187
Tel: +81(423) 41-5011
Fax: +81(423) 42-6452
President: Hiroshi Mizuo
Secretary-General: Mikio Honjyo
International Relations: Yoshio Sagawa
Founded: 1929, 1962
*D: Japanese Painting; Painting; Sculpture;
Visual Communication Design; Industrial, Interior
and Craft Design; Scenography, Display, and
Fashion Design; Architecture; Science of Design;
Imaging Arts and Sciences.*

Nagasaki Institute of Applied Science

[Nagasaki Sogo Kagaku Daigaku]
536 Aba-machi, Nagasaki-shi, Nagasaki 851-01
Tel: +81(958) 39-3111
President: Osamu Ishino
Secretary-General: Yasushi Egashira
Founded: 1942, 1965
Engineering.

Nagoya University of Commerce and Business Administration

[Nagoya Shoka Daigaku]
Sagamine, Nisshin-cho, Aichi-gun, Aichi 470-1
Tel: +81(5617) 3-2111
Fax: +81(5617) 3-1202
E-Mail: BITNET:@jpnnucba
Telex: 4496002 nucba
President: Hiroshi Kurimoto (1981-)
Secretary-General: Shigeru
Founded: 1950, 1953
*D: Commerce; Business Administration;
International Economics; Management
Information Systems.
Ce: Language Education.*

Nakamura Gakuen College

[Nakamura Gakuen Daigaku]
5-7-1 Beppu, Jonan-ku, Fukuoka-shi, Fukuoka 814
Tel: +81(92) 851-2531
President: Torao Yamamoto
Secretary-General: Saburo Zaitsu
Founded: 1965
Domestic Sciences.

*Nanzan University

[Nanzan Daigaku]
18 Yamazato-cho, Sowa-ku, Nagoya-shi, Aichi 466
Tel: +81(52) 832-3111
Fax: +81(52) 833-6985
Cable: Nanzandaigaku Nagoya
President: Hans Jürgen Marx, S.V.D. (1993-)
Secretary-General: Yuro Yamamoto
Founded: 1932, 1949
*F: Economics; Arts and Letters; Foreign Studies;
Law; Business Administration.
I: Anthropology; Religions and Cultures;
Japanese Social Ethics.
Ce: Japanese Studies; American Studies; Latin
American Studies; Australian Studies; European
Studies.*

Nara University

[Nara Daigaku]
1500 Sanryo-cho, Nara-shi, Nara 631
Tel: +81(742) 44-1251
President: Ichiro Suizu
Secretary-General: Miyoshi Imanishi
Founded: 1969
Letters; Sociology; Liberal Arts.

*Nihon University

[Nihon Daigaku]
8-24 Kudan-Minami 4-chome, Chiyoda-ku, Tokyo 102
Tel: +81(3) 5275-8000
Telex: 29496 nichidai j
Cable: Nihondaigaku
President: Shigenori Kinoshita
Founded: 1889, 1903, 1949
*C: Law; Humanities and Science; Economics;
Commerce; Arts; International Relations; Science
and Technology; Industrial Technology;
Engineering; Medicine; Agriculture and
Veterinary Medicine; Pharmacy.
S: Dentistry; Dentistry (Matsudo).
D: Correspondance Courses.*

Nihon Social Welfare University

[Nihon Fukushi Daigaku]
Okuda, Mihama-cho, Chita-gun, Aichi 470-32
Tel: +81(569) 78-2211
President: Masaru Osawa
Secretary-General: Teruo Watanabe
International Relations: Minoru Kawada
Founded: 1953, 1957
Social Welfare; Economics.

Niigata College of Pharmacy
[Niigata Yakka Daigaku]
5-13-2 Kamishin'ei-cho, Niigata-shi, Niigata 950-21
Tel: +81(25) 269-3171
President: Jiro Yajima
Secretary-General: Sukematsu Mori
Founded: 1977
Pharmacy.

Nippon College of Physical Education
[Nippon Taiiku Daigaku]
7-1-1 Fukazawa, Setagaya-ku, Tokyo 158
Tel: +81(3) 5706-0995
Fax: +81(3) 5706-0912
President: Eijyu Watai
Secretary-General (Acting): Takeo Terada
Founded: 1891, 1949
Physical Education; Health Education; Martial Arts; Social Recreation.

Nippon Dental University
[Nippon Shika Daigaku]
1-9-20 Fujimi, Chiyoda-ku, Tokyo 102
Tel: +81(3) 3261-8311
President: Izumi Nakahara
Secretary-General: Tadashi Taga
Founded: 1907
Dentistry; Dentistry (Niigata).

Nippon Institute of Technology
[Nippon Kogyo Daigaku]
4-1 Gakuendai, Miyashiro-machi, Minamisaitama-gun, Saitama 345
Tel: +81(480) 34-4111
Fax: +81(480) 34-2941
President: Kiyoyasu Ohkawa (1991-95)
Secretary-General: Haruo Hirose
Founded: 1967
D: Mechanical Engineering; Electrical Engineering; Architectural Engineering; Systems Engineering; Liberal Arts.
Ce: Machining and Processing; Materials Testing; Information Technology; Electrical Laboratory; Building Engineering.
L: Ultra High Voltage.

*Nippon Medical School
[Nippon Ika Daigaku]
1-1-5 Sendagi, Bunkyo-ku, Tokyo 113
Tel: +81(3) 3822-2131
President: Tasuku Shoji
Secretary-General (Acting): Goro Asano
International Relations: Kosho Sato
Founded: 1904, 1912, 1925
Medicine; Gerontology; Tumour and Infectious Diseases Studies.

Nippon Veterinary and Zootechnical College
[Nippon Juichikusan Daigaku]
1-7-1 Kyonan-cho, Musashino-shi, Tokyo 180
Tel: +81(422) 31-4151
Fax: +81(422) 33-2094
President: Masaharu Takahashi
Secretary-General: Akehiro Okitani
Founded: 1871, 1949
Veterinary Medicine and Animal Husbandry.

Nippon Women's College of Physical Education
[Nihon Joshi Taiiku Daigaku]
8-19-1 Kitakarasuyana, Setagayaku, Tokyo 157
Tel: +81(33) 300-2251
President: Masahiko Udo
Secretary-General: Takayuki Shimojyu
Founded: 1965
Physical Education.

Nisho Gakusha University
[Nisho Gakusha Daigaku]
6-16 Sanban-cho, Chiyoda-ku, Tokyo 102
Tel: +81(3) 3261-7406
President: Hiroyoshi Amagai
Secretary-General (Acting): Nobuo Kuriyama
Founded: 1928, 1949
Literature; International Politics and Economics.

Obirin University
[Obirin Daigaku]
3758 Tokiwa-cho, Machida-shi, Tokyo 194-02
Tel: +81(427) 97-2661
President: Kazuo Ono
Secretary-General: Kintei Ogawa
Founded: 1950
Letters; Economics; International Studies.

Okayama University of Science
[Okayama Rika Daigaku]
1-1 Ridai-cho, Okayama-shi, Okayama 700
Tel: +81(86) 252-3161
President: Tsutomu Kake
Secretary-General: Satoshi Shimizu
Founded: 1964
C: Sciences; Engineering.
I: Earth Science (Research).
Ce: Information Processing; Micro-Analysis; Ultra Low Temperature.

Osaka College of Music
[Osaka Ongaku Daigaku]
1-1-8 Shonai-Saiwa-machi, Toyonaka-shi, Osaka 561
Tel: +81(6) 334-2131
Fax: +81(6) 333-0286
President: Yuzuru Nagai (1988-)
Secretary-General: Toyosuke Kurita
Founded: 1915, 1948, 1958
Music.

Osaka College of Physical Education
[Osaka Taiiku Daigaku]
1558-1, Noda, Kumatori-chi, Sennan-gun, Oosaka 590-04
Tel: +81(726) 324-3141
President: Tetsu Beppu
Secretary-General: Takayoshi Muto
Founded: 1965
Physical Education.

Osaka Dental University

[Osaka Shika Daigaku]
5-31, Otemae, 1-Chome Chuo-Ku, Osaka-shi,
Osaka 540
Tel: +81(6) 943-6521
Fax: +81(6) 943-8051
President: Hironori Sagawa
Secretary-General: Fukashi Furuki
Founded: 1911, 1952
Dentistry.

Osaka Electro-Communications University

[Osaka Denkitsushin Daigaku]
18-8 Hatsu-cho, Neyagawa-shi, Osaka 572
Tel: +81(720) 24-1131
President: Kuniya Fukuda
Secretary-General: Toru Ogawa
Founded: 1961
Engineering.

Osaka Gakuin University

[Osaka Gakuin Daigaku]
2-36-1 Kishibe-Minami, Suita-shi, Osaka 564
Tel: +81(6) 381-8434
Fax: +81(6) 382-4363
President: Yoshiyasu Shirai
Registrar: Yasuhiro Takei
Founded: 1962, 1963
*F: Commerce; Economics; Law; Foreign
Languages.*
C: Accounting.
D: Correspondence Courses.

Osaka Industrial University

[Osaka Sangyo Daigaku]
3-1-1 Nakagaito, Daito-shi, Osaka 574
Tel: +81(720) 75-3001
President: Michiyoshi Kuwahara
Secretary-General: Hideaki Hakayama
Founded: 1965
*Liberal Arts; Business Administration;
Economics; Engineering.*

Osaka Institute of Technology

[Osaka Kogyo Daigaku]
5-16-1 Omiya, Asahi-ku, Osaka-shi, Osaka 535
Tel: +81(6) 952-3131
Fax: +81(6) 953-9496
President: Tomio Ito (1987-)
Secretary-General: Hajime Murakami
Founded: 1922, 1949
Engineering (daytime and evening courses).

Osaka Kokusai University

[Osaka Kokusai Daigaku]
3-50-1 Sugi, Hirakata-shi, Osaka 573-01
Tel: +81(720) 58-1616
President: Shogo Okuda
Secretary-General: Masahiro Yoshida
International Relations: Kazuo Sato
*Business Administration Informatics; Politics and
Economics.*

Osaka Medical College

[Osaka Ika Daigaku]
2-7 Daigaku-machi, Takatsuki-shi, Osaka 569
Tel: +81(726) 83-1221
Fax: +81(726) 81-3723
President: Hideo Matsumoto
Secretary-General: Tadao Tsujikura
Founded: 1927, 1952
Medicine.

Osaka University of Arts

[Osaka Geijutsu Daigaku]
469 Higashiyama, Kanan-cho, Minami-Kawachi-
gun, Osaka 585
Tel: +81(721) 93-3781
President: Kinsaku Nakane
Secretary-General: Isamu Fujii
International Relations: Motoyoshi Arai
Founded: 1964
Arts.

Osaka University of Economics

[Osaka Keizai Daigaku]
2-2-8 Osumi, Higashi-yodogawa-ku, Osaka-shi,
Osaka 533
Tel: +81(6) 328-2431
President: Takeshi Kamijima
Secretary-General: Iori Nakada
Founded: 1932, 1936, 1949
*F: Economics (day and evening divisions);
Business Administration (day and evening
divisions).*
*I: Japanese Economic History Research; Small
Business Undertaking Research; Industrial and
Economics Research; Business Administration.*

Osaka University of Pharmaceutical Sciences

[Osaka Yakka Daigaku]
2-10-65 Kawai, Matsubara-shi, Osaka 580
Tel: +81(723) 32-1015
President: Harutoshi Kubota
Secretary-General: Koji Kono
Founded: 1925, 1950
Pharmaceutical Sciences.

Otani Women's College

[Otani Joshi Daigaku]
Shigakudai, Nishikiori, Tondabayashi-shi, Osaka
584
Tel: +81(721) 24-0381
President: Megumi Sato
Secretary-General: Minoru Higashi
Founded: 1966
Letters.

Otani University

[Otani Daigaku]
Kamifusa-cho, Koyama, Kita-ku, Kyoto-shi, Kyoto
603
Tel: +81(75) 432-3131
President: Toshiaki Terakawa
Secretary-General: Meigyo Kuchiki
Founded: 1882, 1922, 1949
Letters.

Otemon Gakuin University
[Otemon Gakuin Daigaku]
2-1-15 Nishiai, Ibaraki-shi, Osaka 567
Tel: +81(726) 43-5421
Fax: +81(726) 43-5427
President: Yukio Goto
Secretary-General: Tsutomu Nakagawa
Founded: 1888
F: Economics; Letters.
Ce: Australian Studies; Education Research.

Otsuma Women's University
[Otsuma Joshi Daigaku]
12 Sanban-cho, Chiyoda-ku, Tokyo 102
Tel: +81(3) 5275-6074
Fax: +81(3) 3261-8119
President: Hideyasu Nakagawa
Secretary-General: Norihiko Okamura
Founded: 1908, 1942, 1949
F: Domestic Science; Literature.
S: Social Information Studies.
*P: General Education (Sayamadai Campus);
General Education (Tama Campus).*
I: Human Living Sciences.

O'u University
[O'u Daigaku]
31-1 Mosumi-do, Tomita-machi, Koriyama-shi,
Fukushima 963
Tel: +81(429)32-8931
PresidentSecretary-General: Mitsufusa Yoshimi:
Shinichi Soeda
Dentistry; Letters.

Rissho University
[Rissho Daigaku]
4-2-16 Osaki, Shinagawa-ku, Tokyo 141
Tel: +81(3) 3492-6616
President: Hoyo Watanabe
Secretary-General: Toshiteru Maeda
Founded: 1904, 1924, 1949
*F: Buddhism; Literature; Economics; Business
Administration; Law.*
*I: Nichiren Faith and Teachings (Research);
Comprehensive Study of the Lotus Sutra;
Industrial Management (Research); Legal
Research; Human Sciences (Research).*
Ce: North Sumatra Area Studies (Research).

Ritsumeikan University
[Ritsumeikan Daigaku]
561-1 Kitamachi, Toji-in, Kita-ku, Kyoto-shi, Kyoto
603-77
Tel: +81(75) 465-1111
President: Masateru Oonami
Secretary-General: Rikito Kohata
International Relations: Andre Brune
Founded: 1900, 1913
*F: Humanities; Law; Economics; Business
Administration; Industrial Sociology; Letters;
Science and Engineering; International Relations.*
*I: Cultural Sciences Research; Science and
Engineering Research.*

Ryukoku University
[Ryukoku Daigaku]
67 Tsukamoto-cho, Fukakusa, Fushimi-ku, Kyoto-
shi, Kyoto 612
Tel: +81(75) 642-1111
President: Takamaro Shigaraki
Secrerary-General: Kiyonori Hasu
International Relations: Nakatami Miyakawa
Founded: 1679, 1900, 1949
*F: Literature; Economics; Business
Administration; Law; Science and Technology;
Social Study.*
*I: Buddhist Cultural Studies; Social Sciences
Research.*

Ryutsu-Keizai University
[Ryutsu-Keizai Daigaku]
120 Hirahata, Ryguasaki-shi, Ibaraki 301
Tel: +81(297) 64-0001
Fax: +81(297) 64-0011
President: Koji Saeki
Registrar: Yoshiharu Ogawa
Founded: 1965
F: Economics; Sociology.
I: Distribution Studies.
*Ce: Languages and Cultural Exchange;
Information Processing; Physical Education.*

Seiwa College
[Seiwa Daigaku]
7-54 Okadayama, Nishinomiya-shi, Hyogo 662
Tel: +81(798) 52-0724
President: Tsugikazu Nishigaki
Secretary-General: Yuichi Tanishima
Education.

Sakushin Gakuin College
[Sakushin Gakuin Daigaku]
908 Takeshita-cho, Utsunomiya-shi, Tochigi
321-32
Tel: +81(286) 67-7111
President: Hideo Yamamoto
Secretary-General: Seiwa Akeno
Business Administration.

St. Andrew's University
[Momoyama Gakuin Daigaku]
237-1 Nishino, Sakai-shi, Osaka 588
Tel: +81(722) 36-1181
President: Harunari Yamasaki
Secretary-General: Hidenobu Morinishi
International Relations: Hiroshi Emura
Founded: 1959
*Letters; Sociology; Economics; Business
Administration.*

St. Luke's College of Nursing
[Seiroka Kango Daigaku]
10-1 Akashi-cho, Chuo-ku, Tokyo 104
Tel: +81(3) 3543-6391
President: Shigeaki Hinohara
Secretary-General: Shoichi Ishii
Founded: 1920, 1964
Nursing.

St. Marianna University School of Medicine
[Sei Marianna Ika Daigaku]
2-16-1, Sugao, Miyamae-ku, Kawasaki-shi,
Kanagawa 216
Tel: +81(44) 977-8111
Fax: +81(44) 977-5542
President: Kazuo Hasegawa
Secretary-General: Makoto Watanabe
Founded: 1971
*Medicine; Intractable Disease Treatment
Research.*

*St. Paul's University
[Rikkyo Daigaku]
34-1 Nishi Ikebukuro 3-chome, Toshima-ku, Tokyo
171
Tel: +81(3) 3985-2231
Fax: +81(3) 985-8784
Cable: rikkyodaigaku
President: Yotaro Hamada
Secretary-General: Shigeki Tomizawa
International Relations: Daikichi Harada
Founded: 1874, 1883, 1920, 1949
F: General Education.
*C: Arts; Economics; Social Relations; Science;
Law and Politics.*
*I: American Studies; Christian Education;
Atomic Energy; Latin American Studies; Industrial
Relations; Social Welfare; Tourism.*
D: Asian Studies.
*Ce: Psychological and Educational Clinical;
Computer.*

Saitama Medical School
[Saitama Ika Daigaku]
38 Morohongo, Morayama-machi, Iruma-gun,
Saitama 350-04
Tel: +81(492) 95-1111
President: Masanobu Ishida
Secretary-General: Kiyohiro Maruki
Founded: 1972
Medicine.

Sanno College
[Sangyo Noritsu Daigaku]
1573 Kami-kasuya, Isehara-shi, Kanagawa 259-11
Tel: +81(463) 92-2211
President: Takehiko Matsuda
Secretary-General: Kenichi Takizawa
Founded: 1979
Administrative Informatics.

*Seijo University
[Seijo Daigaku]
6-1-20 Seijo, Setagaya-ku, Tokyo 157
Tel: +81(3) 3482-1181
Fax: +81(3) 3484-2698
President: Toshio Yamada
Secretary-General: Reiko Shimano
Founded: 1917, 1926, 1950
F: Economics; Arts and Literature; Law.
I: Economic Studies; Folklore Studies.

Seikei University
[Seikei Daigaku]
3-3-1 Kichijoji, Kita-machi, Musashino-shi, Tokyo
180
Tel: +81(422) 37-3531
Fax: +81(422) 56-0116
President: Yuya Ueno
Secretary-General: Tatsuji Fuse
International Relations: Setsu Kato
Founded: 1912, 1949
F: Economics; Engineering; Humanities; Law.
*Ce: Asian and Pacific Studies; Information
Processing.*

Seinan Gakuin University
[Seinan Gakuin Daigaku]
6-2-92, Nishijin, Sawara-ku, Fukuoka-shi, Fukuoka
814
Tel: +81(92) 841-1311
Fax: +81(92) 823-3227
President: Teruo Tanaka
Secretary-General: Joemon Watanabe
International Relations: Ryuta Murakami
Founded: 1916, 1949
*Theology; Literature; Commerce; Economics;
Law.*

Seisen Women's College
[Seisen Joshi Daigaku]
3-16-21 Higashi Gotanda, Shinagawa-ku, Tokyo
141
Tel: +81(3) 3447-5551
President: Saeko Tayama
Secretary-General: Kunio Ishikawa
Founded: 1950
Letters.

*Senshu University
[Senshu Daigaku]
3-8-1 Kandajimbo-cho, Chiyoda-ku, Tokyo 101
Tel: +81(3) 3265-6211
Fax: +81(3) 3265-6821
President: Seiji Mochizuki (1992-94)
Secretary-General: Hiroshi Suzuki
Founded: 1880, 1913, 1922, 1949
*S: Economics; Law; Business Administration;
Commerce; Letters.*
*I: Social Sciences; Law and Political Science;
Business Administration; Commerce;
Accountancy; Humanities; Physical Education;
Legal Studies; Information Sciences.*

Setsunan University
[Setsunan Daigaku]
17-8 Ikedanaka-machi, Neyagawa-shi, Osaka 572
Tel: +81(720) 26-5101
President: Susumu Fujita
Secretary-General: Hajime Murakami
Founded: 1975
*Engineering; International Culture; Administrative
Informatics; Law.*

Shibaura College of Technology
[Shibaura Kogyo Daigaku]
3-9-14 Shibaura, Minato-ku, Tokyo 108
Tel: +81(3) 3452-3201
Fax: +81(3) 5476-2949
President: Osamu Oomoto
Secretary-General: Kenkichi Imai
International Relations: Kakuichiro Adachi
Founded: 1927, 1949
Engineering; System Engineering; Education and Research.

Shikoku Christian College
[Shikoku Gakuin Daigaku]
3-2-1 Bunkyo-cho, Zentsuji-shi, Kagawa 765
Tel: +81(877) 62-2111
President: Yasuo Nakazono
Secretary-General: Kosaku Sugimoto
Founded: 1950, 1959, 1962
Literature; Sociology.

Shirayuri Women's College
[Shirayuri Joshi Daigaku]
1-25 Medorigaoka, Chofu-shi, Tolyo 182
Tel: +81(3) 3326-5050
President: Teruko Kataoka
Secretary-General: Yasuko Fukui
Founded: 1946
Letters.

Showa College of Pharmaceutical Sciences
[Showa Yakka Daigaku]
3-3165, Higashi-Tamagawagakuen, Machida-shi,
Tokyo 194
Tel: +81(427) 21-1511
President: Seisho Tobinaga
Secretary-General: Tatsuo Tanaka
Founded: 1930, 1949
Pharmaceutical Sciences.

Showa Women's University
[Showa Joshi Daigaku]
1-7 Taishido, Setagaya-ku, Tokyo 154
Tel: +81(3) 3411-5111
Fax: +81(3) 3487-6850
E-Mail: jpnswu 10
President: Kusuo Hitomi
Secretary-General: Kazunobu Shibata
Founded: 1920, 1949
Literature; Domestic Science; English and American Literature; Living Arts; Modern Culture; Women's Culture; Child Education Research.

Showa University
[Showa Daigaku]
1-5-8 Hatanodai, Shinagawa-ku, Tokyo 142
Tel: +81(3) 3784-1151
President: Junichi Ishii
Secretary-General: Kei Kura
Founded: 1928, 1952, 1964
Medicine; Pharmaceutical Sciences; Dentistry.

Shukutoku University
[Shukutoku Daigaku]
200 Daiganji-cho, Chiba-shi, Chiba 280
Tel: +81(472) 65-7331
President: Takatoshi Hasegawa
Secretary-General: Hiroo Yokoyama
Founded: 1965
Sociology.

*Soka University
[Soka Daigaku]
1-236 Tangi-cho, Hachioji-shi, Tokyo 192
Tel: +81(426) 91-2211
Fax: +81(426) 91-2039
Rector: Kazuo Takamatsu
Secretary-General: Eiichi Fukada
International Relations: Masaki Kita
Founded: 1971
F: Economics; Law; Letters; Business Administration; Education; Engineering.
I: Peace Studies; Applied Economics; Asian Studies; Japanese Studies; Life Science; Systems Science; Comparative Study of Cultures.
Div: General Culture.
Ce: Language and Culture Research.
D: Correspondence Courses.

*Sophia University Tokyo
[Jochi Daigaku]
7-1 Kioicho, Chiyoda-ku, Tokyo 102
Tel: +81(3) 3238-3111
Fax: +81(3) 3238-3137
Telex: htlotani j24140
Cable: sophiauniv tokyo
President: Keiji Otani (1993-)
Secretary-General: Shigeru Fujisaki
International Relations: Yoko Ayusawa
Founded: 1913, 1928
F: Theology; Humanities; Law; Economics; Foreign Studies; Comparative Cultures; Science and Technology.
I: Life Science; Study of Social Justice; Christian Culture; International Relations; Comparative Culture; Asian Cultures; Culture of German-speaking Areas; Oriental Religions; Medieval Thought; Ibero-American; International Communication Linguistic; American and Canadian Studies.

Sugiyama Jogakuen University
[Sugiyama Jogakuen Daigaku]
17-3 Hoshigaoka-motomachi, Chikusa-ku, Nagoya-shi, Aichi 464
Tel: +81(52) 781-1186
President: Akiyoshi ehara
Secretary-General: Kunio Takahashi
Founded: 1949, 1972
Home Economics; Letters; Human Relations.

Surugadai University
[Surugadai Daigaku]
697 Ichinoki, Oaza Asu, Hanno-shi, Saitama 357
Tel: +81(429) 72-1111
President: Toshio Iino
Secretary-General: Seigo Miura
Law; Economics.

Taisho University
[Taisho Daigaku]
3-20-1 Nishisugamo, Toshima-ku, Tokyo 170
Tel: +81(3) 3918-7311
President: Ryosho Hayashi
Secretary-General: Noritake Okamoto
Founded: 1926, 1949
Humanities.

Takarazuka School of Formative Arts
[Takarazuka Zokeigeijutsu Daigaku]
7-27 tsutsujigaoka, Hanayashiki, Takarazuka-shi,
Hyogo 665
Tel: +81(727) 56-1231
President: Jun Igarashi
Secretary-General: Teruo Takada
Formative Arts.

Takushoku University
[Takushoku Daigaku]
3-4-14 Kobinata, Bunkyo-ku, Tokyo 112
Tel: +81(3) 3947-2261
President: Toshimi Oosakai
Secretary-General: Yukio Sano
Founded: 1900
*Commerce; Political Science and Economics;
Foreign Languages; Technology.*

Tama Art University
[Tama Bijutsu Daigaku]
3-15-34 Kaminoge, Setagaya-ku, Tokyo 158
Tel: +81(3) 3702-1141
President: Kenshi Goto
Secretary-General: Hisao Yada
Founded: 1935, 1947, 1953
Arts and Design.

Tama College of Administrative Informatics
[Tama Daigaku]
4-1-1 Hijirigaoka, Tama-shi, Tokyo 206
Tel: +81(423) 37-7111
President: Kasuo Noda
Secretary-General: Keiichi Jyoto
Administrative Informatics.

*Tamagawa University
[Tamagawa Daigaku]
6-1-1 Tamagawa Gakuen, Machida-shi, Tokyo 194
Tel: +81(427) 28-3111
Fax: +81(427) 28-1181
President: Tetsuro Obara (1973-)
Secretary-General: Yoshiaki Ikeda
Founded: 1929, 1947
F: Agriculture; Engineering; Arts and Education.

I: Educational Research.
D: Correspondence Courses.

Teikyo University
[Teikyo Daigaku]
2-11-1 Kaga, Itabashi-ku, Tokyo 173
Tel: +81(3) 3964-1211
Telex: +81(3) 3962-5067
President: Shoichi Okinaga
Founded: 1966
*S: Liberal Arts; Economics; Law (All Hachioji
Campus); Medicine; Pharmacy and Biological
Pharmacy (Sagamiko Campus); Science and
Engineering (Utsunomiya Campus).*

Teikyo University of Technology
[Teikyo Gijyutsu Kagaku Daigaku]
2289-23 Uruido Aza Otani, Ichihara, Chiba 290-01
Tel: +81(436) 74-5511
President: Yoshinosuke Yasojima
Secretary-General: Toshiharu Hayashi
Founded: 1987
Informatics; Health and Welfare (Special).

Tezukayama University
[Tezukayama Daigaku]
7-1-1 Tezukayama, Nara-shi, Nara 631
Tel: +81(742) 45-4701
President: Michio Morinaga
Secretary-General: Makoto Saito
Founded: 1964
Liberal Arts; Economics.

Toho University
[Toho Daigaku]
5-21-16 Omori Nishi, Ota-ku, Tokyo 143
Tel: +81(3) 3762-4151
President: Shusuke Hirano
Secretary-General: Akira Yamaki
Founded: 1925
*Pharmaceutical Sciences; Physical Sciences;
Medicine.*

Tohoku College of Pharmacy
[Tohoku Yakka Daigaku]
4-4-1 Komatsushima, Aoba-ku, Sendai-shi, Miyagi
983
Tel: +81(22) 234-4181
Founded: 1939, 1949
Pharmaceutical Sciences; Cancer Research.

Tohoku Fukushi (Welfare) University
[Tohoku Fukushi Daigaku]
1-8-1 Kunimi, Aoba-ku, Sendai-shi, Miyagi 981
Tel: +81(22) 233-3111
President: Kazuo Sasaki
Secretary-General: Sakae Otake
Founded: 1958, 1962
*Social Welfare; Buddhist Social Welfare
(Research); Buddhist Social Education
(Research); Public Administration (Research).*

*Tohoku Gakuin University
[Tohoku Gakuin Daigaku]
1-3-1 Tsuchitoi, Sendai-shi, Miyagi 980
Tel: +81(22) 264-6411
Fax: +81(22) 264-3030
President: Tetsuo Seino (1982-)
International Relations: Tsutau Sakurai
Founded: 1886, 1891
*F: Letters; Economics; Law; Engineering;
Liberal Arts.*

Tohoku Institutions of Technology
[Tohoku Kogyo Daigaku]
35-1 Yagiyama-Kasumi-chi, Taihaku-ku, Sendai-
shi, Miyagi 982
Tel: +81(22) 229-1151
President: Shunichi Iwasaki
Secretary-General: Naoshi Chiba
Founded: 1964
Engineering.

Toin Gakuen Yokohama University
[Toin Gakuen Yokohama Daigaku]
1614 Tetsumachi, Midori-ku, Yokoyama-shi,
Kanagaka 225
Tel: +81(45) 972-5881
President: Noboru Ukawa
Secretary-General: Shigeo Kato
Law; Engineering.

*Tokai University
[Tokai Daigaku]
1117 Kitakaname, Hiratsuka, Kanagawa 259-12
Tel: +81(463) 58-1211
Fax: +81(463) 35-2458
Telex: 47796 tokaic j
Cable: tokai daigaku
President: Norio Tatsuro (1991-)
Director-General, Academic Affairs: Hideaki
Kanie
International Relations: Shigeru Shimizu
Founded: 1942, 1946
*S: Letters; Political Science and Economics;
Law; Humanities and Culture; Physical Education;
Science; Engineering; Engineering II; High
Technology for Human Welfare; Marine Science
and Technology; Medicine.*
*Ce: Foreign Language; Foreign Student
Education; Licensed Professional Training;
Research and Information; Space Information;
Okinawa Regional Research; Asia Minor and
Balkan Research.*
*Research I: Strategic Peace and International
Affairs; Industrial Science; Civilization; Social
Sciences; Oceanic Development; Arts; Medical;
Education; Sports Medical Science.*
Japanese Language Course.

Tokiwa Daigaku
1-430-1 Miwa, Mito-shi, Ibaraki 310
Tel: +81(292) 32-2611
President: Hidemichi Morosawa
Secretary-General: Hideto Kimoto
Founded: 1983
Human Sciences.

Tokushima Bunri University
[Tokushima Bunri Daigaku]
180 Nishihama, Yoamashiro-cho, Tokushima-shi,
Tokushima 770
Tel: +81(886) 22-9611
Fax: +81(886) 26-2998
President: Takashi Soeda
Secretary-General: Takashi Kamada
International Relations: Shoji Kume
Founded: 1895, 1966
*F: Domestic Science; Music; Pharmaceutical
Sciences; Literature; Engineering.*

Tokyo College of Informatics
[Tokyo Jyoho daigaku]
1200-2 Yato-machi, Wakaba-wu, Chiba-shi, Chiba
265
Tel: +81(43) 236-1101
President: Yujiro Hayashi
Secretary-General: Katsuyuki Makishima
Business Administration and Informatics.

Tokyo College of Pharmacy
[Tokyo Yakka Daigaku]
1432-1 Horinouchi, Hachioji-shi, Tokyo 192-03
Tel: +81(426) 76-5111
President: Tomio Yamakawa
Secretary-General: Atsuko Sanbe
Founded: 1880, 1949
Pharmacy.

Tokyo Denki University
[Tokyo Denki Daigaku]
2-2 Kanda-Nishikicho, Chiyoda-ku, Tokyo 101
Tel: +81(3) 5280-3311
President: Sogo Okamura
Secretary-General: Susumu Kanaya
Founded: 1907, 1939, 1949
*Engineering (day and evening courses); Science
and Engineering.*

Tokyo Dental College
[Tokyo Shika Daigaku]
1-2-2, Masago, Chiba-shi, Chiba 260
Tel: +81(43) 279-2222
Fax: +81(472) 79-2052
President: Hiroshi Sekine
Secretary-General: Kasuyoshi Namikai
Founded: 1890, 1907
Dentistry.

Tokyo Kasei Daigaku
1-18-1 Kaga, Itabashi-ku, Tokyo 173
Tel: +81(3) 3961-5226
President: Tsukasa Shimizu
Secretary-General: Kenichi Yamamoto
Founded: 1922
Domestic Sciences; Letters.

Tokyo Engineering University
[Tokyo Koka Daigaku]
1401-1 Katakura-cho, Hachioji-shi, Tokyo 192
Tel: +81(426) 37-2111
President: Noboru Takagi
Secretary-General: Wataru Kawachi
Founded: 1986
Engineering.

Tokyo Institute of Polytechnics
[Tokyo Kogei Daigaku]
1583 Iiyama, Atsugi-shi, Kanagawa 243-02
Tel: +81(462) 41-0454
Fax: +81(462) 42-3000
President: Sakae Tanaka
Secretary-General: Katsuhiko Kurioka
Founded: 1923
Engineering.

Tokyo International University
[Tokyo Kokusai Daigaku]
1-13-1 Matoba-Kita, Kawagoe-shi, Saitama 350
Tel: +81(492) 32-1111
Fax: +81(492) 34-3824
E-Mail: jpntiu 01 bitnet
President: Yasuo Kaneko
Secretary-General: Toshimasa Yamada
Founded: 1965
S: Business and Commerce; International
Studies and Human Relations; Economics.
Graduate S: Business and Commerce;
International Relations; Sociology.

Tokyo Theological College
[Tokyo Shingaku Daigaku]
3-10-30 Osawa, Mitaka-shi, Tokyo 181
Tel: +81(422) 32-4185
President: Kikuo Matsunaga (1983-87)
Secretary-General: Noboru Takemae
Founded: 1943
Theology.

Tokyo Keizai University
[Tokyo Keizai Daigaku]
1-7 Minamicho, Kokubunji-shi, Tokyo 185
Tel: +81(423) 21-1941
President: Buntaro Tomizuka
Secretary-General: Shigeru Kobayashi
Founded: 1900, 1949
Economics; Business Administration (day and
evening courses).

Tokyo Medical College
[Tokyo Ika Daigaku]
6-1-1 Shinjuku, Shinjuku-ku, Tokyo 160
Tel: +81(3) 3351-6141
President: Hisao Ito
Secretary-General: Masahiko Kjomura
Founded: 1916, 1946
Medicine.

Tokyo Music College
[Tokyo Ongaku Daigaku]
3-4-5 Minami-ikebukuro, Toshima-ku, Tokyo 171
Tel: +81(3) 3982-3186
President: Taiichi Uemura
Secretary-General: Kazuo Miyawaki
Founded: 1954
Music.

*Tokyo Woman's Christian University
[Tokyo Joshi Daigaku]
2-6-1 Zempukuji, Suginami-ku, Tokyo 167
Tel: +81(3) 3395-1211
Fax: +81(3) 3399-3123
Cable: twcutjd tokyo
President: Makoto Yamamoto (1992-96)
Secretary-General: Kazuhiro Hobo
Founded: 1918, 1948
C: Arts and Sciences; Culture and
Communication; Women's Studies.
I: Comparative Studies of Culture.

Tokyo Women's Medical College
[Tokyo Joshi Ika Daigaku]
8-1 Kawada-cho, Shinjuku-ku, Tokyo 162
Tel: +81(3) 3353-8111
Fax: +81(3) 3353-6793
Telex: twmlib j 232-2317
President: Morimasa Yoshioka (1983-95)
Secretary-General: Eisei Tazaki
Founded: 1900, 1951
F: Medicine.
S: Nursing.
I: Heart of Japan; Clinical Endocrinology.
Ce: Diabetes; Maternal and Pernatal.

Tokyo University of Agriculture
[Tokyo Nogyo Daigaku]
1-1-1 Sakuragaoka, Setagaya-ku, Tokyo 156
Tel: +81(3) 3420-2131
President: Toshiro Matsuda
Secretary-General: Takuo Ideo
Founded: 1891, 1925
Agriculture; Biological Industry.

*Science University of Tokyo
[Tokyo Rika Daigaku]
1-3 Kagurazaka, Shinjuku-ku, Tokyo 162
Tel: +81(3) 3260-4271
Fax: +81(3) 3260-4370
Telex: sciencuniv
President: Tetsuji Nishikawa
Secretary-General: Toshitaka Sygiyama
Founded: 1881, 1949
F: Science; Pharmacy; Engineering; Science
and Technology; Industrial Science and
Technology; Business Administration.
I: Science Technology (Research).

Toyo Eiwa Women's College
[Toyo Eiwa Jyogakuin Daigaku]
32-1 Mihomachi, Midori-ku, Yokoyama-shi,
Kanagaka 226
Tel: +81(45) 922-5511
President: Kokichi Asakura
Secretary-General: Hiroshi Yokoyama
Humanities.

Toyo University
[Toyo Daigaku]
5-28-20 Hakusan, Bunkyo-ku, Tokyo 112
Tel: +81(3) 3945-7220
Fax: +81(3) 3942-2489
President: Akira Suganuma
Secretary-General: Shogo Maatsuoka
Founded: 1887, 1906
*F: Literature; Economics; Business
Administration; Law; Sociology; Engineering.*
*I: Asian Studies; Business Administration
(Research); Economic Research; Social
Relations; Asia-Africa Cultural Research;
Comparative Law (Research); Industrial
Technology (Research); Child and Juvenile
Problems.*
Ce: Informatics Research and Education.

Toyota Technological Institute
[Toyota Kogyo Daigaku]
2-12 Hisakata, Tempaku-ku, Nagoya-shi, Aichi 468
Tel: +81(52) 802-1111
Fax: +81(52) 802-6069
President: Kiyosi Kobayashi
Secretary-General: Minoru Miki
Founded: 1981
*Engineering; Computer Sciences; CAD;
SemiconductorSciences.*

*Tsuda College
[Tsudajuku Daigaku]
2-1-1 Tsuda-machi, Kodaira-shi, Tokyo 187
Tel: +81(423) 42-5111
Fax: +81(423) 41-2444
President: Yuriko Ohtsuka
Secretary-General: Shiro Hojnma
Founded: 1900, 1948
*D: English Language and Literature;
Mathematics; International and Cultural Studies.*
*I: Research in Language and Culture;
International Studies; Mathematics and Computer
Science.*
Ce: Computer; Health Service; Audio-visual.

Tsurumi College
[Tsurumi Daigaku]
2-1-3 Tsurumi, Tsurumi-ku, Yokohama-shi,
Kanagawa 230
Tel: +81(45) 581-1001
President: Naomichi Takasaki
Secretary-General: Eiji Suzaki
Founded: 1924, 1953, 1963
Literature; Dentistry.

University of East Asia
[Toa Daigaku]
15-2 Kasuno, Shimonoseki-shi, Yamaguchi 751
Tel: +81(832) 56-1111
President: Takefumi Namai
Secretary-General: Keizo Tokushige
F: Economics; Engineering.
S: Designing.

*University of the Sacred Heart Tokyo
[Seishin Joshi Daigaku Tokyo]
4-3-1 Hiroo, Shibuya-ku, Tokyo 150
Tel: +81(3) 3407-5811
Fax: +81(3) 5485-3884
Cable: Seishingakuin, Tokyo
President: Tetsuko Nakagawa, R.S.C.J. (1993-)
Secretary-General: Masami Kodera
Founded: 1907, 1948, 1950
*Foreign Languages and Literature; Japanese
Language and Literature; History and Social
Sciences; Education; Philosophy; General
Cultural Subjects.*

*Waseda University
[Waseda Daigaku]
1-6-1 Nishi-waseda, Shinjuku-ku, Tokyo 169-50
Tel: +81(3) 3203-4141
Fax: +81(3) 3208-1032
Telex: 2323280 waseda j
Cable: wasedauniv
President: Chumaru Koyama
Secretary-General: Takehiko Kawase
Founded: 1882, 1902, 1949
*S: Political Science and Economics; Law;
Literature I; Literature II (evening division);
Education; Commerce; Science and Engineering;
Social Sciences (evening division); Human
Sciences.*
*I: Social Sciences; Systems Science;
Comparative Law; Language Teaching; Research
in Business Administration; Research in
Contemporary Political and Economic Affairs.*
*Ce: Advanced Research for Human Sciences;
Japanese Language; Informatics.*
D: International.
*L: Science and Engineering Research; Kagami
Memorial for Materials Science and Technology.*

Yachiyo International College
[Yachiyo Kokusai Daigaku]
210 Matsubara, Makino, Yachiyo-shi, Chiba 261
Tel: +81(474) 88-2111
President: Kiyoshi Takase
Secretary-General: Teruzo Komiya
Politics and Economics.

UNIVERSITIES AND COLLEGES WITHOUT GRADUATE SCHOOLS

PUBLIC INSTITUTIONS

Aichi Kenritsu Daigaku
3-28 Takada-cho, Mizuho-ku, Nagoya-shi, Aichi
467
Tel: +81(52) 851-2191
Rector: Kimio Shiozawa
Secretary-General: Sumihiro Yamada
Founded: 1950
Letters; Foreign Languages.

Aizu Daigaku
Tsuruga, Aizuwakamatsu-shi, Fukushima 965
Tel: +81(242) 37-2500
President: Toshiyasu Kunii
Secretary-General: Kasuo Yamazaki
Founded: 1993
Computer Science and Technology.

Aomori Koritsu Daigaku
153-4 Yamazaki, Aomori-shi, Aomori 030-01
Tel: +81(177) 64-1555
President: Katsuyasu Kato
Secretary-General: Toro Yamazaki
Founded: 1993
Business Administration and Economics.

Gunma Kenritsu Joshi Daigaku
1395-1 Kaminote, Tamamura-machi, Sawa-gun,
Gunma 370-11
Tel: +81(270) 65-8511
President: Toshio Hiraoka
Secretary-General: Hiroji Hayashi
Founded: 1980
Letters.

Hiroshima Joshi Daigaku
1-1-71 Ujina-higashi, Minami-ku, Hiroshima-shi,
Hiroshima 734
Tel: +81(82) 251-5178
President: Michio Kawakami
Secretary-General: Mitsuhiko Yaegaki
Founded: 1928
Letters; Domestic Sciences.

Kochi Joshi Daigaku
5-15 Eikokuji-cho, Kochi-shi, Kochi 780
Tel: +81(888) 73-2156
Rector: Junko Ikekawa
Secretary-General: Masaaki Nakamura
Founded: 1949
Domestic Sciences; Letters.

Shimonoseki Shiritsu Daigaku
2-1-1 Daigaku-cho, Shimonoseki-shi, Yamaguchi
751
Tel: +81(832) 52-0288
President: Hiroyuki Ooya
Secretary-General: Masami Sawabuchi
Founded: 1956
Economics; International Commerce.

Miyazaki Kentitsu Daigaku
1-1-2 Funazuka, Miyazaki-shi, Miyazaki 880
Tel: +81(985) 20-2000
President: Yoshihiro Hirashima
Secretary-General: Masaharu Hidaka
Founded: 1993
Humanities.

Okayama Kenritsu Daigaku
111 Kuboki, Sojya-shi, Okayama 719-11
Tel: +81(8669) 4-2111
President: Kiyoo Kosaka
Secretary-General: Atsumi Ono
Founded: 1993
*Health and Welfare; Information Technology;
Designing.*

Takasaki Keizai Daigaku
1300 Kaminamie-machi, Takasaki-shi, Gumma
370
Tel: +81(273) 43-5417
President: Manabu Ishii
Secretary-General: Ryo Matsuhashi
Founded: 1952
Economics.

Tsuru Bunka Daigaku
3-8-1 Tahara, Tsuru-shi, Yamanashi 402
Tel: +81(554) 43-4341
President: Tsunekichi Shirao
Secretary-General: Kazuo Sonoda
Founded: 1953
Letters.

Yamaguchi Joshi Daigaku
3-2-1 Sakurabatake, Yamaguchi-shi, Yamaguchi
753
Tel: +81(839) 28-0211
President: Osamu Takayama
Secretary-General: Masayuki Mori
Founded: 1941
Letters; Domestic Sciences.

PRIVATE INSTITUTIONS

Akita Keizai Hoka Daigaku
46-1 Morisawa, Tezakura, Shimokita, Akita-shi,
Akita 010
Tel: +81(188) 36-3313
President: Toshio Oofuchi
Secretary-General: Shinichi Murai
Founded: 1953
Economics; Law.

Aomori Daigaku
2-3-1, Kohata, Aomori-shi, Aomori 030
Tel: +81(177) 38-2114
Rector: Yoshio Sakagami
Secretary-General: Takafumi Kimura
Founded: 1962
Business Administration; Sociology; Engineering.

Atomi Gakuen Joshi Daigaku
1-9-6 Nakaro, Niiza-shi, Saitama 352
Tel: +81(484) 78-3333
President: Hedemichi Wada
Secretary-General: Yosunori Hikita
Founded: 1969
Letters.

Beppu Daigaku
82 Kita-ishigaki, Beppu-shi, Oita 874-01
Tel: +81(977) 67-0101
President: Shunichi Nishimura
Secretary-General: Hiroaki Asada
Founded: 1946
Letters.

Chuo Gakuin Daigaku
451 Kujike, Abiko-shi, Chiba 270-11
Tel: +81(471) 83-6502
President: Saburo Ishimoto
Secretary-General: Susumu Inomata
Founded: 1966
Commerce; Law.

Dai-ichi Keizai Daigaku
3-11-25 Gojo, Dazaifu-shi, Fukuoka 818-01
Tel: +81(92) 922-5131
President: Yasuhisa Tsuzuki
Secretary-General: Hiroshi Asakawa
Founded: 1968
Economics.

Dai-ichi Kogyo Daigaku
1-10-2 Chuo, Kokubu-shi, Kagoshima 899-43
Tel: +81(995) 45-0640.
President: Yashihisa Tsuzuki
Secretary-General: Jun Asai
Technology.

Dai-ichi Yakka Daigaku
22-1 Tamagawa-cho, Minami-ku, Fukuoka-shi,
Fukuoka 815
Tel: +81(92) 541-0161
President: Yasuhisa Tsuzuku
Founded: 1960
Pharmacy.

Doho Daigaku
7-1 Inabaji-cho, Nakamura-ku, Nagoya-shi, Aichi
453
Tel: +81(52) 411-1111
President: Yutei Ikeda
Founded: 1921
Letters; Social Welfare.

Dohto Daigaku
7-1 Ochiishi-cho, Mombetsu-shi, Hokkaido 094
Tel: +81(1582) 4-8101
President: Masamichi Hayashi
Secretary-General: Yasuyoshi Kondo
Founded: 1978
Social Welfare; Fine Arts; Theacher Training.

Eichi Daigaku
2-18-1 Wakoji, Amagasaki-shi, Hyogo 661
Tel: +81(6) 491-5000
President: Hirotsugu Inoue
Secretary-General: Masatoshi Oda
Founded: 1963
Letters.

Fuji Daigaku
450-3 Shimoneko, Hanamaki-shi, Iwate 025
Tel: +81(198) 23-6221
President: Tamisuke Shigekura
Secretary-General: Kaichi Sugibayashi
Founded: 1965
Economics.

Fuji Joshi Daigaku
Nishi 2-chome, Kita 16-jo, Kita-ku, Sapporo-shi,
Hokkaido 001
Tel: +81(11) 736-0311
President: Yoshiko Nagata
Secretary-General: Hiroshi Kudo
Founded: 1950
Letters; Human Life.

Gifu Joshi Daigaku
80 Taromaru, Gifu-shi, Gifu 501-25
Tel: +81(582) 29-2211
President: Mikio Hori
Secretary-General: Fusao Shibata
Founded: 1968
Domestic Sciences; Letters.

Gifu Keizai Daigaku
5-56 Kitagata-cho, Ogaki-shi, Gifu 503
Tel: +81(584) 74-5151
President: Terumichi Osako
Secretary-General: Keisho Mukai
Founded: 1967
Economics.

Hachinohe Daigaku
13-98 Mihono, Hachinohe-shi, Aomori 031
Tel: +81(178) 25-2711
President: Mitsutake Sato
Secretary-General: Masaaki Sakamoto
Founded: 1981
Commerce.

Hachinohe Kogyo Daigaku
88-1 Obiraki, Myo, Hachinohe-shi, Aomori 031
Tel: +81(178) 25-3111
President: Koichi Murakami
Secretary-General: Toru Yanagiya
Founded: 1972
Engineering.

Hakodate Daigaku
51-1 Takaoka-cho, Hakodate-shi, Hokkaido 042
Tel: +81(138) 57-1181
President: Hiroshi Kawamura
Secretary-General: Keizo Tobiyama
Founded: 1965
Commerce.

Hakuoh Daigaku
1177 Daigyoji, Oyama-shi, Tochige 323
Tel: +81(285) 22-1111
President: Toshio Harada
Secretary-General: Yoshishichiro Kakinuma
Business Administration; Law.

Hanazona Daigaku
8-1 Tsubonouchi-cho, Nishinokyo, Nakagyo-ku,
Kyoto-shi, Kyoto 604
Tel: +81(75) 811-5181
President: Muneoki Morinaga
Secretary-General: Soko Murakuchi
Founded: 1949
Letters; Welfare.

Hannan Daigaku
5-4-33 Amamihigashi, Matsubara-shi, Osaka 580
Tel: +81(723) 32-1224
President: Tetsuro Kawaqhima
Secretary-General: Takashi Tamaoki
Founded: 1950
Commerce; Economics.

Hirosaki Gakuin Daigaku
13-1 Minori-cho, Hirosaki-shi, Aomori 036
Tel: +81(172) 34-5211
President: Hidenori Toyoshima
Secretary-General: Takashi Kasai
Letters.

Hiroshima Jogakuin Daigaku
4-13-1 Ushita-Higashi, Hiroshima-shi, Hiroshima
732
Tel: +81(82) 228-0386
President: Akira Endo
Secretary-General: Shigenobu Hatakeyama
Founded: 1932
Letters; Living Sciences.

Hiroshima-Denki Daigaku
6-20-1 Nakano, Aki-ku, Hiroshima-shi, Hiroshima
739-03
Tel: +81(82) 893-0381
President: Kaizo Kuwahara
Secretary-General: Akira Nakakura
Founded: 1967
Engineering.

Hokkaigakuen Kitami Daigaku
235 Hokko, Kitami-shi, Hokkaido 090
Tel: +81(157) 22-2721
President: Masao Morimoto
Secretary-General: Mitsuyuki Kuhira
Founded: 1977
Commerce.

Hyogo Kenritsu Kango Daigaku
13-7, Kita-oji-machi, Akashi-shi, Hyogo 673
Tel: +81(78) 925-0860
President: Yuko Minami
Secretary-General: Nagisa Kashiwagi
Founded: 1993
Nursing.

Ibaraki Kirisutokyo Daigaku
6-11-1 Omika-cho, Hitachi-shi, Ibaraki 319-12
Tel: +81(294) 52-3215
President: Shoji Uemura
Secretary-General: Mitsuo Takeda
Founded: 1967
Letters.

Jobu Daigaku
634-1 Toyazuka-machi, Isezaki-shi, Gunma 372
Tel: +81(270) 32-1010
President: Sada Machida
Secretary-General: Toranosuke Uehara
Founded: 1986
Commerce; Administrative Informatics.

Joshi Bijutsu Daigaku
1900 Asamizo-dai, Sagamihara-shi, Kanagawa
228
Tel: +81(427) 78-6111
President: Michiya Matsushima
Secretary-General: Katsuhiko Muto
Founded: 1929
Arts.

Kagoshima Joshi Daigaku
1904 Uchi, Hayato-cho, Aira-gun, Kagoshima
899-51
Tel: +81(995) 43-1111
President: Sueo Nakamura
Secretary-Genral: Yuichi Takenouchi
Founded: 1978
Letters.

Kagoshima Keizai Daigaku
8850 Shimofukomoto-cho, Kagoshima-shi,
Kagoshima 891-01
Tel: +81(992) 61-3211
President: Noriyoshi Nokuo
Secretary-General: Kiyonori Yamaguchi
Founded: 1950
Economics; Sociology.

Kamakura Joshi Daigaku
1420 Iwase, Kamakura-shi, Kanagawa 247
Tel: +81(467) 44-2111
President: Noriko Matsumoto
Founded: 1943
Domestic Sciences.

Kanazawa Keizai Daigaku
101 Ushi, Gosho-machi, Kanazawa-shi, Ishikawa
920
Tel: +81(762) 52-2236
President: Shigeto Konishi
Secretary-General: Minoru Bota
Founded: 1967
Economics.

Keiai Keizai Daigaku
1-5-21 Anagawa, Chiba-shi, Chiba 263
Tel: +81(43) 251-6363
President: Junko Hara
Secretary-General: Masao Mitsuhashi
Founded: 1950
Economics.

Kobe Kaisei Joshi Gakuin Daigaku
2-7-1 Aotani-cho, Nada-ku, Kobe-shi, Hyogo 657
Tel: +81(78) 801-2277
President: Atsuko Hirai
Founded: 1950
Letters.

Kobe Kokusai Daigaku
5-1-1-Manabigaoka, Tarumi-ki, rumi-ku, Kobe-shi,
Hyogo 655
Tel: +81(78) 709-3851
President: Isao Sasaki
Secretary-General: Yoshio Yakubo
Founded: 1968
Economics.

Koka Joshi Daigaku
38 Kadono-cho, Nishi-Kyogoku, Ukyo-ku, Kyoto-shi, Kyoto 615
President: Ryoji Abe
Secretary-General: Eiichi Makimoto
Founded: 1944
Arts; Music.

Kokusai Budo Daigaku
841 Aza Monomizuka, Shinga, Katsuura-shi, Chiba 299-52
Tel: +81(470) 73-4111
President: Yu Inagaki
Secretary-General: Ryoichiro Toyota
Founded: 1984
Physical Training.

Kurume Kogyo Daigaku
2228 Kamitsu-machi, Kurume-shi, Fukuoka 830
Tel: +81(942) 22-2345
President: Masaru Takada
Secretary-General: Torata Murakami
Founded: 1971
Engineering.

Kyoto Gakuen Daigaku
1-1, Nanjo Otani, Sokabe-cho, Kameoka-shi, Kyoto 621
Tel: +81(771) 22-2001
President: Kaichi Kiuchi
Secretary-General: Shoichi Fujibayashi
Founded: 1969
Economics; Law.

Kyoto Tachibana Joshi Daigaku
34 Oyake Yamada-cho, Yamashina-ku, Kyoto-shi, Kyoto 607
Tel: +81(75) 571-1111
President: Manzo Chiji
Secretary-General: Jiro Ashida
Founded: 1967
Letters.

Kyushi Joshi Daigaku
1-1 Jiyagaoka, Yahatanishi-ku, Kitakyushu-shi, Fukuoka 807
Tel: +81(93) 691-3331
President: Yoshimi Fujikawa
Secretary-General: Motoshige Kusaba
Domestic Sciences; Letters.

Kyushu Kokusai
5-9-1 Edamitsu, Yahatahigashi-ku, Kitakyushu-shi, Fukuoka 805
Tel: 81(93) 671-8910
President: Masaharu Yamada
Secretary-General: Shinji Tashiro
Founded: 1947
Law and Economics.

Kyushu Kyoritsu Daigaku
1-8 Jiyugaoka, Yahatanishi-ku, Kitakyushu-shi, Fukuoka 807
Tel: +81(93) 691-3331
President: Yuichi Matake
Founded: 1965
Economics; Engineering.

Matsumoto Shika Daigaku
1780 Hirooka, Gobara, Shiojiri-shi, Nagano 399-07
Tel: +81(63) 52-3100
President: Shigeo Kobayashi
Secretary-General: Koshi Nomoto
Founded: 1972
Dentistry.

Matsusaka Daigaku
1846 Kubo-cho, Matsusaka-shi, Mie 515
Tel: +81(598) 29-1122
President: Mitsuhiro Umemura
Secretary-General: Jiro Uno
Founded: 1982
Political Sciences and Economics.

Mimasaka Joshi Daigaku
32 Kamigawara, Tsuyama-shi, Okayama 708
Tel: +81(868) 22-7718
President: Taku Sugiyama
Secretary-General: Yu Sakate
Founded: 1951
Domestic Sciences.

Minami Kyushu Daigaku
Hibariga-oka, Takanabe-cho, Koyu-gun, Miyazaki 884
Tel: +81(983) 23-0793
President: Masatoshi Inosaki
Founded: 1965
Horticulture.

Miyagi Gakuin Joshi Daigaku
9-1-1 Sakuragaoka, Aoba-ku, Sendai-shi, Miyagi 981
Tel: +81(22) 279-1311
President: Tosaku Nosaka
Secretary-General (Acting): Hidetoshi Hasegawa
Founded: 1946
Art and Science.

Morioka Daigaku
808 Sunagome, Takizawa-mura, Iwate-gun, Iwate 020-01
Tel: +81(196) 88-5555
President: Tomio Takahashi
Secretary-General: Jinsho Sugiyama
Letters (Education).

Musashino Joshi Daigaku
1-1-20 Shin-machi, Hoya-shi 202, Tokyo
Tel: +81(424) 68-3111
President: Shoji Okochi
Founded: 1950
Letters.

Nagano Daigaku
Shimonogo, Ueda-shi, Nagano 386-12
Tel: +81(268) 38-2350
President: Fumio Marui
Secretary-General: Toei Hori
Founded: 1966
Industial Sociology.

Nagoya Gakuin Daigaku
1350 Kamishinano-cho, Seto-shi, Aichi 480-12
Tel: +81(561) 42-0350
President: Takao Nishimura
Secretary-General: Ryuichi Nakaya
Founded: 1964
Economics; Commerce.

Nagoya Geijutsu Daigaku
280 Furui, Kumanosho, Nishikasugai-gun, Aichi
481
Tel: +81(568) 24-0315
President: Shunzo Oshima
Secretary-General: Masaharu Matsui
Founded: 1970
Music; Fine Arts.

Nagoya Joshi Daigaku
4-30 Shioji-cho, Mizuho-ku, Nagoya-shi, Aichi 467
Tel: +81(52) 852-1111
President: Ichiro Koshihara
Secretary-General: Takuo Kondo
Founded: 1964
Domestic Sciences; Letters.

Nagoya Keizei Daigaku
61-1 Uchikubo, Inuyama-shi, Aichi 484
Tel: +81(568) 67-0511
President: Hiroaki Sueoka
secretary-General: Tetsuhito Ishikawa
Founded: 1979
Economics; Law.

Nagoya Ongaku Daigaku
7-1 Inabaji-cho, Nakamura-ku, Nagoya-shi, Aichi
468
Tel: +81(52) 411-1111
President: Sekiryou Sumida
Secretary-General: Tetsuei Shikano
Founded: 1976
Music.

Nara Sangyo Daigaku
3-12-1 Tatsunokita, Sango-cho, Ikomo-gun, Nara
636
Tel: +81(745) 73-7800
President: Toshiro Ise
Secretary-General: Masaru Murata
Founded: 1984
Economics; Law.

Nihon Shakai-Jigyo Daigaku
3-1-30 Takeoka, Kiyose-shi, Tokyo 204
Tel: +81(424) 92-6111
President: Fumio Miura
Secretary-General: Mizumaru Hozumi
Founded: 1950
Social Welfare.

Nippon Bunka Daigaku
977 Katakura-cho, Hachioji-shi, Tokyo 192
Tel: +81(426) 36-5211
President: Chikamasa Ninagawa
Founded: 1978
Law.

Nippon Bunri Daigaku
1727-162, Ichigi, Oita-shi, Oita 870-03
Tel: +81(975) 92-1600
President: Yukio Suga
Secretary-General: Yoshimi Sato
Founded: 1967
Engineering; Commerce and Economics.

Nishi Tokyo Kagaku Daigaku
2525 Yatsusawa, Uenohara-cho, Kitatsuru-gun,
Yamanashi 409-01
Tel: +81(554) 63-4411
Fax: +81(554) 63-4430
President: Shinroku Saito
Secretary-General: Masao Tamaki
Founded: 1987, 1990
*Science and Engineering; Electronics and
Information Science; Bioscience; Materials;
Management Engineering; Liberal Arts and
Sciences.*

Nishikyushu Daigaku
4490-9 Hirayama, Osaki, Kanzaki-machi, Kanzaki,
Saga 842
Tel: +81(952) 52-4191
President: Eiji Ichimaru
Secretary-General: Kasuchika Tsutsumi
Founded: 1968
Domestic Sciences.

Nishinippon Kogyo Daigaku
1633 Aratsu, Kanda-cho, Miyako-gun, Fukuoka
800-03
Tel: +81(9302) 3-1491
Fax: +81(9302) 4-7900
President: Junichi Okabe
Secretary-General: Masanari Imamiya
Founded: 1967
Engineering.

Notorudamu Joshi Daigaku
1 Minami-Nonogami-cho, Shimogamo, Sakyo-ku,
Kyoto-shi, Kyoto 606
Tel: +81(75) 781-1173
Fax: +81(75) 702-4060
President: Osamu Mizukoshi
Founded: 1961
Letters; English Language and Literature.

Notre Dame Seishin Joshi Daigaku
2-16-9 Ifuku-cho, Okayama-shi, Okayama 700
Tel: +81(86) 252-1155
President: Mie Saiga
Founded: 1944
Letters; Domestic Sciences.

Okayama Shoka Daigaku
2-10-1 Tsushima-Kyo-machi, Okayama-shi,
Okayama 700
Tel: +81(86) 252-0642
President: Hiroshi Ijiri
Secretary-General: Kantaro Mitsueda
Founded: 1965
Commerce; Law and Economics.

Okinawa Daigaku
747 Kokuba, Naha-shi, Okinawa 902
Tel: +81(98) 832-3216
President: Seiichi Sakukawa
Secretary-General: Seiko Uehara
Founded: 1961
Law and Economics.

Okinawa Kokusai Daigaku
276-2 Ginowan, Ginowanshi, Okinawa 901-22'
Tel: +91(98) 892-1111
President: Reiji Hirashiki
Secretary-General: Shigenobu Kanashiro
Founded: 1961
Law; Commerce and Economics; Letters; Liberal Arts.

Osaka Keizai Hoka Daigaku
6-10 Gakuoniji, Yao-shi, Osaka 581
Tel: +81(729) 41-8211
President: Hiroshi Kubota
Secretary-General: Hiroshi Ishiyama
International Relations: Tamotsu Nakajima
Founded: 1971
Economics; Law; Liberal Arts.

Osaka Kokusai Joshi Daigaku
6-21-57 Fujita-cho, Moriguchi-shi, Osaka 570
Tel: +81(6) 902-0791
President: Shogo Okuda
Secretary-General: Tamotsu Takeda
International Relations: Hajime Hayashi
Founded: 1965
Human Sciences; Domestic Sciences.

Osaka Shoin Joshi Daigaku
4-2-26 Hishiyanishi, Higashi Osaka-shi, Osaka 577
Tel: +81(6) 723-8181
President: Takehiko Touzu
Founded: 1925
Arts and Sciences.

*Osaka Shogyo Daigaku
4-1-10 Mikuriya Sakae-machi, Higashiosaka-shi, Osaka 577
Tel: +81(6) 781-0381
Fax: +81(6) 781-8438
E-Mail: BITNET: nodeno.jpnoucoi
President: Taro Tanioka
Secretary-General: Kozo Inui
Founded: 1928, 1949, 1952
F: Commerce and Economics.
I: Industry and Management; Commercial History.
Ce: Information Processing.

Otemae Joshi Daigaku
6-42 Ochayasho-cho, Nishinomiya-shi, Hyogo 662
Tel: +81(798) 34-6331
Fax: +81(798) 23-4761
President: Takeo Hibino
Head Officer, Administration: Yu Fukui
Founded: 1966
F: Literature.
I: History Research; Anglo-Norman Research.

Reitaku Daigaku
2-1-1 Hikarigaoka, Kashiwa-shi, Chiba 277
Tel: +81(471) 73-3601
President: Mototaka Hiroike
Secretary-General: Yusuhiro Imuta
International Relations: Masayuki Tajima
Founded: 1942
Foreign Languages; International Economics.

Sagami Joshi Daigaku
2-1-1 Bukyo, Sagamihara-shi, Kanagawa 228
Tel: +81(427) 42-1411
President: Keikichi Takamatsu
Secretary-General: Koji Katano
Founded: 1909
Arts and Sciences.

Saitama Kogyo Daigaku
1690 Fusaiji, Okabe-machi, Osato-gun, Saitama 369-02
Tel: +81(485) 85-2521
President: Shuichi Suzuki
Secretary-General: Stsuo Mizuno
Engineering.

Sakuyo Ongaku Daigaku
1334-1 Yaide, Tsuyama-shi, Okayama 708
Tel: +81(868) 24-1811
President: Hideki Matsuda
Secretary-General: Takashi Isshiki
Founded: 1966
Music.

Sapporo Daigaku
7-3-1 Nishioka 3-jo, Toyohira-ku, Sapporo-shi, Hokkaido 062
Tel: +81(11) 852-1181
President: Shozo Uchiyama
Secretary-General: Isao Ishida
International Relations: Mitsuo Honda
Founded: 1967
Economics; Foreign Languages; Business Administration; Law; Liberal Arts.

Sapporo Gakuin Daigaku
11 Bunkyodai, Ebetsu-shi, Hokkaido 069
Tel: +81(11) 386-8111
President: Toshiaki Misawa
Secretary-General: Kiyoaki Abe
Founded: 1946
Commerce; Economics; Cultural Sciences; Law; Social Informatics.

Sendai Daigaku
2-18, Minami 2-chome, 2-18 Funaoka, Shibata-machi, Shibata-gun, Miyagi 989-16
Tel: +81(224) 55-1121
President: Tomi Mori
Secretary-General: Shigeru Haga
Founded: 1967
Physical Engineering.

Senzoku Gakuen Daigaku
2-3-1 Hisamoto, Takatsu-ku, Kawasaki-shi,
Kanagawa-ken 213
Tel: +81(44) 877-3211
Fax: +81(44) 856-2972
President: Toshikazu Maeda (1986-)
Secretary-General: Izo Murata
Founded: 1967
*Music; Opera; Choral Music; Conducting; Piano;
Advanced Sound Technology and Engineering.*

Shikoku Joshi Daigaku
123-1 Ebisuno, Furukawa, Ojin-cho, Tokushima-
shi, Tokushima 771-11
Tel: +81(886) 65-1300
President: Haruo Saito
Secretary-General: Kazuo Ohara
International Relations: Toshihiko Okamoto
Founded: 1961
Letters; Domestic Sciences.

Shinwa Joshi Daigaku
7-13-1 Suzurandai-kitamachi, Kita-ku, Kobe-shi,
Hyogo 651-11
Tel: +81(78) 591-1651
President: Kaoru Yamasaki
Secretary-General: Masami Ohiga
Founded: 1966
Letters.

Shitennoji Kokusai Bukkyo Daigaku
3-2-1 Gukuenmae, Habikino-shi, Osaka 583592
Tel: +81(7) 56-3181
President: Sonkyo Takifuji
Secretary-General: Ichiro Matoba
Letters.

Shoin Joshigakuin Daigaku
1-2-1 Shinoharaobaroyama-cho, Nadaku, Kobe-
shi, Hyogo 657
Tel: +81(78) 882-6122
President: Shigetoshi Tomoeda
Secretary-General: Junji Tanahashi
Founded: 1966
Letters.

Shokei Daigaku
155-7 Nirenoki, Shimizu-machi, Kumamoto-shi,
Kumamoto 860
Tel: +81(96) 338-8840
President: Tetsuto Sako
Secretary-General: Takushi Morita
Founded: 1975
Letters.

Shonan Koka Daigaku
1-1-25 Tsujido, Nishikaigan, Fujisawa-shi,
Kanagawa 251
Tel: +81(466) 34-4111
President: Eitaro Itoyama
Secretary-General: Shigenobu Nagano
Founded: 1963
Engineering.

Shuchiin Daigaku
545 Toji-cho Hachijo-sagaru, Mibu-dori, Minami-
ku, Kyoto-shi, Kyoto 601
Tel: +81(75) 681-6513
President: Enmei Imai
Founded: 1905
Buddhism.

Shujitso Joshi Daigaku
1-6-1 Nishigawara, Okayama-shi, Okayama 703
Tel: +81(86) 272-3185
President: Hitoshi Kimura
Secretary-General: Shogo Kaneda
Founded: 1979
Letters.

Soai Daigaku
4-4-1 Nanko-Naka, Suminoe-ku, Osaka-shi, Osaka
559
Tel: +81(6) 612-5900
President: Tomoumi Nakanishi
Secretary-General: Akira Horikawa
Music; Cultural Sciences.

Sonoda Gakuen Joshi Daigaku
7-29-1 Minami-Tsukaguchi-cho, Amagasaki-shi,
Hyogo 661
Tel: +81(6) 429-1201
President: Eiichi Hayashi
Secretary-General: Minoru Kawada
Founded: 1963
Letters.

Sugino Joshi Daigaku
4-6-19 Kamiosaki, Shinagawa-ku, Tokyo 141
Tel: +81(3) 3491-8151
President: Eiichi Iwasawa
Secretary-General: Hideko Sugino
Founded: 1950
Domestic Sciences.

Takachiho Shoka Daigaku
2-19-1 Omiya, Suginami-ku, Tokyo 168
Tel: +81(3) 3313-0141
President: Mamoru Fukui
Secretary-General: Yukio Takada
Founded: 1914
Commerce.

Tenri Daigaku
1050 Somanouchi-cho, Tenri-shi, Nara 632
Tel: +81(7436) 3-1511
President: Akinori Ookubo
Secretary-General: Yoshinobu Inokuchi
Founded: 1925
*Humanities; Letters; International Culture;
Physical Training; Liberal Arts.*

Tezukayama Gakuin Daigaku
1823 Imakuma, Sayama-cho, Minamikawachi-gun,
Osaka 589
Tel: +81(723) 65-0865
President: Hiromitsu Yamada
Secretary-General: Keiichi Ito
Founded: 1966
Letters.

Toho Gakuen Daigaku
1-41-1 Wakaba-shi, Chofu-shi, Tokyo 182
Tel: +81(3) 307-4101
President: Akira Miyoshi
Secretary-General: Mitsugu Yoshida
Founded: 1955
Music.

Toho Ongaku Daigaku
84 Imaizumi, Kawagoe-shi, Saitama 356
Tel: +81(492) 35-2157
President: Harumitsu Mimuroto
Secretary-General: Masaharu Sugaya
Founded: 1965
Music.

Tohoku Joshi Daigaku
1-2-1 Toyohara, Hirosaki-shi, Aomori 036
Tel: +81(172) 33-2289
President: Ichiro Toratani
Secretary-General: Jiro Ishioka
Founded: 1969
Domestic Science.

Tohoku Seikatsu Bunka Daigaku
1-18 Nijinooka, Izumi-ku, Sendai-shi, Miyagi 980
Tel: +81(22) 272-7511
President: Naosuke Sato
Secretary-General: Masamichi Sugawara
Founded: 1958
Domestic Science.

Tokai Joshi Daigaku
Kirino-cho Naka, Kakamigahara-shi, Gifu 504
Tel: +81(583) 89-2200
President: Noriro Ichijima
Secretary-General: Yoshio Sugie
Letters.

Tokoha Gakuen Daigaku
1000 Sena, Shizuoka-shi, Shizuoka 420
Tel: +81(54) 263-1125
President: Haruo Yoshikawa
Secretary-General: Akira Matahira
Education; Foreign Languages.

Tokuyama Daigaku
843-4-2 Kune-Kurigasako, Tokuyama-shi,
Yamaguchi 745
Tel: +81(834) 28-0411
President: Keiji Miyoshi
Secretary-General: Yoshio Uchiyama
Founded: 1971
Economics.

Tokyo Joshi Taiiku Daigaku
620 Tanikawakami, Aoyagi, Kunitachi-shi, Tokyo
186
Tel: +81(425) 72-4131
President: Yuichi Suzuki
Secretary-General: Shohei Nagao
Founded: 1962
Physical Training.

Tokyo Zokei Daigaku
1556, Utsunuki-cho, Hachioji-shi, Tokyo 193
Tel: +81(426) 37-8111
Rector: Takeshi Umimoto
Secretary-General: Kazuyuki Oda
Founded: 1966
Formative Arts.

Towa Daigaku
1-1-1 Chikushigaoka, Minami-ku, Fukuoka-shi,
Fukuoka 815
Tel: +81(92) 541-1511
Founded: 1967
Engineering.

Ueno Gakuen Daigaku
4-24-12 Higashiueno, Taito-ku, Tokyo 110
Tel: +81(33) 842-1021
President: Hiroshi Ishibashi
Secretary-General: Kimio Oi
International Relations: Akiko Yamawaki
Founded: 1952
Music.

Wako Daigaku
2160 Kanai-cho, Machida-shi, Tokyo 195
Tel: +81(44) 988-1431
President: Yasuhiko Sugiyama
Secretary-General: Masayuki Ochiai
Founded: 1966
Humanities; Economics.

Wayo Joshi Daigaku
2-3-1 Konodai, Ichikawa-shi, Chiba 272
Tel: +81(473) 71-1111
President: Kaoru Nakajima
Secretary-General: Keiichiro Kikuno
Founded: 1928
Letters and Domestic Sciences.

Yamanashi Gakuin Daigaku
2-4-5 Sakaori, Kofu-shi, Yamanashi 400
Tel: 81(552) 24-1450
President: Tadahiko Furuya
Secretary-General: Hirotoshi Mikami
Founded: 1951
Law; Commerce.

Yasuda Joshi Daigaku
6-13-1 Yasuhigashi, Asaminami-ku, Hiroshima-
shi, Hiroshima 731-01
Tel: +81(82) 878-8111
President: Makoto Kuwano
Secretary-General: Yoshihiko Yasuda
Founded: 1966
Letters.

Yokohama Shoka Daigaku
4-11-1 Higashi-Terao, Tsurumiku, Yokohama-shi,
Kangawa 230
Tel: +81(45) 571-3901
President: Kazuo Osawa
Secretary-General: Katsutoshi Sugimitsu
Founded: 1966
Commerce.

NATIONAL ACADEMIC BODIES

Ministry of Education, Science and Culture
3-2-2 Kasumigaseki 3-chome, Chiyoda-ku, Tokyo
Tel: +81(3) 3581-4211
Fax: +81(3) 581-9149

Central Council for Education
[Chuo Kyoiku Shingikai]
The Ministry of Education Science and Culture, 3-2-2 Kasumigaseki, Chiyoda-ku, Tokyo
Tel: +81(3) -581-4211

National University Association of Japan
[Kokuritsu Daigaku Kyokai]
Hongo 7-3-1, Bunkyo-ku, Tokyo 113
Tel: +81(3) 813-0467

Association of the Public (Local Government) Universities
[Koritsu Daigaku Kyokai]
c/o Kokuritsu Kyoiku Kaikannai, 3-2-3 Kasumigaseki Chiyoda-ku, Tokyo 100
Tel: +81(580) 20-46

Association of Private Universities of Japan
[Nihon Shiritsu Daigaku Kyokai]
4-2-25 Kudan-kita, Chiyoda-ku, /o, Shigaku-Kaikan d102
Tel: +81(3) 3261-7048
Fax: +81(3) 261-0769
President: Shige Yoshi Kitsutaka
Secretary-General: T. Maruyama
Founded: 1948

Japanese University Accreditation Association
[Daigaku Kijun Kyokai]
20-3 Honshio-cho, Shinjuku-ku, Tokyo 160
Tel: +81(3) 35105-17

National Institute for Educational Research
[Kokuritsu Kyoiku Kenkyu Sho]
6-5-22 Shimomeguro Meguro-ku, Tokyo 153
Tel: +81(3) 714-0111
Cable: ninstfedure tokyo
Director-General: Isao Suzuki
Founded: 1949

Japanese National Commission for Unesco
Ministry of Education Science and Culture, 3-2-2 Kasumigaseki 3-chome, Chiyoda-ku, Tokyo
Tel: +81(3) 581-4211 (ext. 2551)
Fax: +81(3) 581-9149
Cable: unescocom tokyo
Chairman: Yasunori Nishijima
Secretary-General: Yutaka Okamura

JORDAN

UNIVERSITIES

PUBLIC INSTITUTIONS

Al al-Bayt University
[Jami'at Al al-Bayt]
P.O. Box 772, Jubayha
Tel: +962(6) 84-01-90
Fax: +962(6) 84-67-21
President: Mohammed Adnan Al-Bakhit (1992-)
Founded: 1992
F: Arts and Sciences; Islamic Jurisprudence and Law; Economics and Public Administration.
I: Astronomy and Space Sciences; Islamic Art and Architecture; Bayt al-Hikmah (House of Wisdom).
Ce: Language; Computer.

Amman University College for Applied Engineering
[Kulliyat Amman Al-Jamiiya Lilhandassa Attatbikiya]
P.O. Box 15008, Marka, Amman
Tel: +962(6) 89-23-42
Fax: +962(6) 89-42-92
Dean: Mohammad A.K. Alia (1989-)
Deputy Dean: Ibrahim Abbas
International Relations: Ahmad Obeid
Founded: 1975, 1989
D: Electrical Engineering; Mechanical Engineering; Chemical Engineering; Civil Engineering; General Sciences.

*Jordan University of Science and Technology
[Jami'at Al-Ulum wa Al-Tiknolojia Al-Urdunia]
P.O. Box 3030, Irbid
Tel: +962(2) 29-51-11
Fax: +962(2) 29-51-23
Telex: 55545 just jo
President: Kamel Ajlouni (1986-95)
Vice-President: Sa'ad Hijazi
International Relations: Sa'ad Hijazi
Founded: 1986
F: Engineering; Medicine; Dentistry; Pharmacy; Nursing; Science; Agriculture; Veterinary Medicine.

*Mu'tah University
[Jami'at Mu'tah]
P.O. Box 7, Mu'tah
Tel: +962(6)61-78-60
Fax: +962(6)65-40-61
Telex: 63003 mu'tah jo
President: Abdulrahman Attiyat (1993-)
Vice-President (Academic): Shaher El-Hasan Al-Rashdan
International Relations: Director-General, Presidential Affairs, Fa'eq Hamdan
Founded: 1981

F: Sciences; Engineering; Arts; Law; Educational Sciences; Economics and Administrative Sciences; Agriculture; Nursing.

*The University of Jordan
[Al-Jami'ah Al-Urdunia]
Amman
Tel: +962(6) 84-35-55
Fax: +962(6) 84-10-50
Telex: 21629 unvj jo
President: Fawzi Gharaibeh (1991-)
Vice-President (Administrative): Sulaiman Arabiyat
International Relations: Mohammed Maqusi
Founded: 1962
F: Arts; Economics and Administration Sciences; Science; Shari'a (Islamic Law); Medicine; Agriculture; Educational Sciences; Engineering and Technology; Law; Physical Education; Nursing; Pharmacy; Dentistry; Postgraduate Studies.
Ce: Language; Computer; Islamic Culture; Water and Environment Research and Study; Human Ressources Development for Health Persqonnel; Strategic Studies; Phonetics Research; Documents and Manuscripts.

*Yarmouk University
[Jami'at Al-Yarmuk]
Irbid
Tel: +962(2) 27-11-00
Fax: +962(2) 27-47-25
Telex: 51533 yarmuk jo
Cable: yarmouk irbid jordan
President: Marwan R. Kamal (1994-98)
Vice-President: Ahmad Salem
International Relations: Muhammed Halawa
Founded: 1976
F: Science; Arts; Education and Fine Arts; Economics and Administration Sciences; Sharia and Islamic Studies; Physical Education.
C: Applied Engineering (Hijjawi).
I: Archaeology and Anthropology.
Ce: Jordanian Studies; Language; Educational Research and Development; Computer and Information; Theoretical Research and Development.

Zarqa University
[Jami'at Al-Zarqa]
University Liaison Office Ministry of Higher Education, P.O. Box 138, Amman
Tel: +962(6) 84-27-00
Fax: +962(6) 84-38-64
President: Mohammed Ahmad Hamdan (1992-)
Arts and Sciences; Administrative Sciences; Education.

PRIVATE INSTITUTIONS

Al-Isra University
[Jami'at Al-Isra]
P.O. Box 83, El-Amad, Ma'adaba
Tel: +962(8) 41710
Fax: +962(8) 41505
President: Abdul Bari Durra (1992-94)
Director (Administrative): Dawod Samoh
International Relations: Naif Khurma
Founded: 1991
F: Arts; Sciences; Law; Engineering; Pharmacy.

Al-Zayatoonah University, Al-Urdunia
[Jami'at Al-Zayatoonah, Al-Urdunia]
P.O. Box 130, 33117 Al-Urdunia
Tel: +962(8) 41573
Fax: +962(8) 41570
President: Azmi Kassim Al-Madi
Director (Administrative): Mahmoud Abu-Kishik
International Relations: Omar Awamleh
Founded: 1993
C: Arts and Humanities; Pharmacy and Nursing; Science.

Amman University
[Jami'at Amman]
Al-Siru Region/Suwaileh, Al Salt Main Road, P.O. Box 337, Jubeiha, Amman
Tel: +962(6) 83-51-66
Fax: +962(6) 83-33-15
President: Eid A. Al-Dahiyat (1990-94)
Director (Administrative): Mohammed Shaheen
International Relations: Maher L.D. Salim
Founded: 1990
F: Arts and Science; Economics and Administrative Sciences; Engineering; Law; Pharmacy and Medical Sciences.

Applied Science University
[Jami'at Al-Ulum Al-Tatbiqiya]
Shafa Badran, 11931 Amman
Tel: +962(6) 83-71-81
Fax: +962(6) 83-28-99
President: Bassam Abu-Gazaleh (1991-)
Vice-President: Seif Al-Wadi Romahi
International Relations: Sidqi Hattab, Director of Cultural and Public Relations
Founded: 1991
F: Arts; Law; Basic Sciences; Para-Medical Sciences; Pharmacy; Engineering; Economics.

Jerash University
[Jami'at Jerash]
P.O. Box 311, Amman
Tel: +962(4) 45-05-21
Fax: +962(4) 45-05-20
President: Mohammed Ahmad Suwwan (1993-)
Registrar: Ibraheem Ogla
International Relations: Issa Ibu-Zahra
Founded: 1993
F: Arts; Economics and Administration; Science; Agriculture; Islamic Studies (Al-Shariah); Law.

Jordan University for Women
[Jami'at Al-Banat Al-Urdunia]
P.O. Box 961343, Amman
Tel: +962(6) 71-55-46
Fax: +962(6) 71-55-70
Cable: jami'at al-banat
President: Mahmud Al-Samra (1993-95)
Registrar: Ali Yaghi
Founded: 1991
*F: Science; Architecture and Interior Design;
Arts; Pharmacy and Medical Technology;
Business Administration and Finance.*

Jordan Academy of Music/Higher Institute of Music
[Al-Akadimiya Al-Urdunia Lilmusiqa]
P.O. Box 962127, 11196 Amman
Tel: +962(6) 60-62-34/60-41-72
Fax: +962(6) 60-62-34
Dean (Acting): Nabil Darras (1993-)
Assistant Dean: Issa Haddad
Founded: 1990
Music.

Philadelphia University
[Jami'at Filadelfia]
P.O. Box 1101, Sweileh
Tel: +962 83-21-71
Fax: +962 83-21-72
President: Fuad Sheikh Salem (1993-)
Assistant President (Administration): Isam Najib
International Relations: Muffeed Abd Rabbo
Founded: 1989
*F: Engineering; Pharmacy; Science; Law;
Administrative Sciences and Economics; Arts.*

Princess Sumaya University College for Technology
[Kuliyat Al-Amira Sumaya Al-Jamiiya Liltiknolojia]
P.O. Box 925819, 11110 Amman
Tel: +962(6) 84-47-01
Fax: +962(6) 84-48-06
Telex: 21276
Cable: erramah
Dean: Mohammad Q. Al Quaryoty (1992-)
Dean Assistant: Mohammad Harb Hammad
Founded: 1991
Computer Science; Electronic Engineering.

NATIONAL ACADEMIC BODIES

Ministry of Education
P.O. Box 1646, Amman
Tel: +962(6) 68-50-81
Fax: +962(6) 66-60-19
Telex: 21396 educate jo
Minister: Abdur-Rauf Rawabdeh

Jordan National Commission for Unesco
Ministry of Education, P.O. Box 1646, Amman
Tel: +962(6) 69-47-31
Fax: +962(6) 66-60-19
Telex: 21396 educate jo
Cable: unesco jordan ministry education amman
Chairman: Abdur-Rauf Rawabdeh, Minister of Education

KAZAKHSTAN

UNIVERSITIES

Karaganda University
[Karagandinskij Gosudarstvennyj Universitet]
Universitetskaja ul. 28, 470074 Karaganda
Tel: +7 74-49-50
Founded: 1972
*F: History; Philology; Physics; Mathematics;
Biology; Chemistry; Economics; Law.*
D: Evening Courses; Correspondence Courses.

*Kazakh State University AlFarabi
[Kazahskij Al Farabi Gosudarstvennyj Universitet]
Al Farabi Avenue 71, 480121 Almaty
Tel: +7(327) 47-25-17
Fax: +7(327) 2-472609
Rector: Kopzhasar N. Naribaev
Founded: 1934
*F: Biology; Geography; Mechanics and
Mathematics; Physics; Chemistry; Eastern
Studies; History, Archaeology and Ethnography;
Journalism; Philosophy and Politilogy; Law;
Philology; Economics and Sociology; Preparatory
(for foreign students).*
*I: Experimental and Theoretical Physics
Research; New Chemical Technologies and
Materials Research; Biology and Biotechnology
Problems; Ecological Problems.*
*Ce: Research and Education of Al-Farabi, and
Spiritual.*

Kazakh National Technical University
[Kazahskij Nacional'nij Tehniceskij Universitet]
Ul. Stapaeva 22, 480013 Almaty
Tel: +7(327) 67-69-01
Rector: E.M. Shuihuldihov
Technology.

Kazakh State Technical University
[Kazakskij Gosudarstvennij Tehniceskij Universitet]
Ul. Sverdlova64, 637003 Pavlodar
Tel: +7 45-11-10
Rector: A.D. Frezorger
Technology.

OTHER INSTITUTIONS

Akmolinskij Inzenerno-Stroitel'nyj Institut
Ul. Tsiolkovskogo 2, 473021 Akmola
Tel: +7 4-29-53
Rector: A.G. Cekaev
Engineering.

Akmolinskij Medicinskij Institut
Prosp. Mira 51a, 473013 Akmola
Rector: V.G. Korpacev
Medicine.

Akmolinskij Sel'skohozjajstvennyj Institut
Prosp. Pobedy 116, 473012 Akmola
Tel: +7 5-89-16
Rector: B.O. Alimzhanov
Agriculture.

Alma-Atinskij Arhitekturno-Stroitel'nyj Institut
Ul. Obrucava 28, 480123 Almaty
Tel: +7(327) 49-46-11
Rector: N.A. Atrushkevic
Architecture and Construction.

Alma-Atinskaja Gosudarstvennaja Konservatorija im Kurmanynzi
Ul. Kirova 136, 480091 Almaty
Tel: +7(327) 63-78-63
Rector: D.K. Kastinov
Music.

Alma-Atinskij Energeticeskij Institut
Ul. Baitursinova 126, 480013 Almaty
Tel: +7(327) 67-57-40
Rector: G. Promlimov
Engergetics.

Alma-Atinskij Gosudarstvennyj Medicinskij Institut
Ul. Tole bi 88, 480012 Almaty
Tel: +7(327) 67-78-85
Rector: E.B. Belozerov
Medicine.

Alma-Atinskij Gosudarstvennyj Teatral'no-Hudozestvennyj Institut
Ul. Sovetskaja 28, 480100 Almaty
Tel: +7(327) 63-42-32
Theatre and Art.

Alma-Atinskij Institut Inzenerov Zeleznodoroznogo Transporta
Ul. Sevcenko 97, 480012 Almaty
Tel: +7(327) 68-55-07
Rector: I.S. Karabasov
Railway Engineering.

Alma-Atinskij Zooveterinarnyj Institut
Prosp. Abaja 28, 480047 Almaty 28
Tel: +7(327) 62-68-94
Rector: K.S. Sabdenov
Animal Husbandry and Veterinary Science.

Dzambulskij Gidromeliorativno Stroitel'nyj Institut
Ul. Kommunisticeskaja 91, 484039 Dzhambul
Tel: +7 4-36-81
Rector: D.T. Suleimenov
Food and Light Industries.

Karagandinskij Gosudarstvennyj Medicinskij Institut
Ul. Gogolja 40, 470061 Karaganda
Rector: M.T. Alijkparov
Medicine.

Karagandinskij Kooperativnyj Institut
Ul. Akademiceskaja 9, 470017 Karaganda
Tel: +7 56-63-76
Cooperative Studies.

Karagandinskij Politehniceskij Institut
Bul. Mira 56, 470041 Karaganda
Tel: +7 52-88-95
Rector: G.G. Piven'

Kazahskaja Gosudaarstvennaja Akademij Unravlenij
Ul. Dzandosova 55, 480035 Almaty
Tel: +7(327) 20-28-45
Rector: N.K. Mamirov
National Economy.

Kazahskij Himiko-Tehnologiceskij Institut
Prosp. Tavke-Nana 5, 486018 Cimkent
Tel: +7 3-40-49
Rector: T. Sh. Kajmerov
Chemical Technology.

Kazahskij Sel'skohozjajstvennyj Institut
Prosp. Abaja 8, 480021 Almaty
Tel: +7(327) 61-38-28
Rector: E. Zh. Zhumabekov
Agriculture.

Kostanajskij Sel'skohozjajstvennyj Institut
Ul. Sverdlova 119, 458011 Kustanaj
Tel: +7 5-26-24
Rector: S.B. Ismuzatov
Agriculture.

Rudnenskij Industrial'nyj Institut
Ul. 50-let. Oktjabrja 38, 459120 Rudnyi
Tel: +7 3-54-03
Rector: J.S. Ahmetov
Industrial Engineering.

Semipalatinskij Gosudarstvennyj Medicinskij Institut
Ul. Sovetskaja 103, 490050 Semipalatinsk
Tel: +7 2-22-51
Rector: T.K. Raisov
Medicine.

Semipalantinskij Tehnologičesicij Institut Mjasnoj j Moločnoj Promyšlennosti
Ul. Glinki 49, 490150 Semipalatinsk
Tel: +7 5-07-80
Mechnical Engineering; Technology; Engineering Economics.

Semipalatinskij Zoo-Veterinarnyj Institut
Ul. Urickogo 17, 490050 Semipalatinsk
Tel: +7 3-21-14
Rector: Z.K. Tokaev
Animal Husbandry and Veterinary Science.

Ust'-Kamenogorskij Stroitel'no-doroznyj Institut
Ul. Lugovaya 19, 492000 Ust' Kamenogorsk
Tel: +7 44-24-81
Rector: Yu. V. Batalov
Construction and Road Building.

Zapadno-Kazahstanskij Sel'skohozjajstvennyj Institut
Gorodok SHI, 417025 Ural'sk
Tel: +7 5-51-80
Rector: S. Sh. Dzubaev
Agriculture.

NATIONAL ACADEMIC BODIES

Ministry of Education
Almaty 100
Tel: +7(327) 61-16-43

Kazakhstan National Commission for Unesco
Ministry of Foreign Affairs, 167 Geltoksan Street, 480064 Almaty 64
Tel: +7(3272) 62-52-22
Fax: +7(3272) 63-76-33
Chairman: M. Zhukaav, Deputy Prime Minister
Executive Secretary: Kaïzat Issagliev

KENYA

UNIVERSITIES

PUBLIC INSTITUTIONS

Egerton University
P.O. Box 536, Njoro
Tel: +254(37 61620
Fax: +254(37) 61527
Telex: 33075-njoro
Cable: university njoro
Vice-Chancellor: J.C. Kiptoon (1992-)
Deputy Vice-Chancellor (Administration and Finance): R. Munavu
Founded: 1939, 1986, 1987
F: Agriculture; Arts and Social Sciences; Education and Human Resources; Science.
D: Research and Extension.

Jomo Kenyatta University of Agriculture and Technology
P.O. Box 62000, Nairobi
Tel: +254(151) 22646-9
Fax: +254(151) 21764
Vice-Chancellor: R.W. Michieka (1992-)
Deputy Principal (Administration): J.K. Yego
Founded: 1981, 1988, 1993
F: Agriculture; Engineering; Science.

Kenyatta University
P.O. Box 43844, Nairobi
Tel: +254(2) 81-07-59
Fax: +254(2) 81-07-59
Cable: kenuco
Vice-Chancellor: G.S. Eshiwani (1992-)
Deputy Vice-Chancellor (Academic Programmes): J.N. Mutio
Founded: 1972, 1985
F: Arts; Commerce; Education; Science; Environmental Studies; Bureau; Educational Research.

Maseno University College
Private Bag, Maseno
Tel: +254(35) 51008
Fax: +254(35) 51221
Principal: William R. Ochieng (1991-96)
Deputy Principal(Administration): D. Serem
Founded: 1990
F: Education; Arts; Science.
I: Research and Postgraduate Studies.
Ce: Interdisciplinary Studies.

Moi University
P.O. Box 3900, Eldoret
Tel: +254(321) 43001
Fax: +254(321) 43260
Telex: 35047
Cable: moi varsity, eldoret
Vice-Chancellor: S.O. Keya (1988-)
Chief Administrative Officer: J.K. Sang
Founded: 1984
F: Agriculture; Education; Forest Resources and Wildlife Management; Health Sciences; Information Sciences; Science; Social, Cultural and Development Studies; Technology.
S: Environmental Studies.
Ce: Human Resources Management.

*University of Nairobi
P.O. Box 30197, Nairobi
Tel: +254(2) 33-42-44
Fax: +254(2) 33-68-85
Telex: 22095 varsity ke
Cable: varsity, nairobi
Vice-Chancellor: F.J. Gichaga (1991-96)
Deputy Vice-Chancellor (Administration): S.O. Wandiga
Founded: 1956, 1964, 1970
F: Agriculture; Architecture, Design and Development; Arts; Commerce; Law; Medicine; Science; Veterinary Medicine; External Degrees Studies; Engineering; Education; Social Sciences.
I: African Studies; Diplomacy and International Studies; Computer Science; Development Studies; Population Studies and Research.
S: Journalism.

PRIVATE INSTITUTIONS

Catholic University of Eastern Africa
P.O. Box 24205, Nairobi
Tel: +254(2) 89-16-01
Fax: +254(2) 89-12-61
Rector: Msgr. Mbiku (1992-)

University of Eastern Africa, Baraton
P.O. Box 2500, Eldoret
Tel: +254(3231) 2625
Fax: +254(3231) 2263
Vice-Chancellor: Mishael Muze (1991-)
Deputy Vice-Chancellor: George Agoki
Founded: 1980, 1991
*F: Agriculture; Business Administration;
Education and Psychology (secondary level);
History and Social Sciences; Languages and
Communication; Theology; Religious and Biblic
Languages; Science and Mathematics;
Technology; Nursing.*

NATIONAL ACADEMIC BODIES

Ministry of Education
P.O. Box 30040, Nairobi
Tel: +254(2) 33-44-11
Fax: +254(2)21-42-87
Minister: Joseph J. Kamotho (1992-)
Permanent Secretary: S.S. Lesirima

Commission for Higher Education
P.O. Box 54999, Nairobi
Tel: +254(2) 22-87-53
Fax: +254(2) 22-22-18
Cable: comhigh
Secretary: J.M. Mungai (1985-)
Founded: 1985

Kenya National Commission for Unesco
Ministry of Education, Commerce House, P.O.
Box 72107, Nairobi
Tel: +254(2) 33-89-80
Fax: +254(2) 21-30-25
Cable: education nairobi
Chairman: Joseph J. Kammotho, Minister of
Education
Secretary-General: C.J. Chacha-Ogwe

KOREA DPR

UNIVERSITIES

Cha Gwang Su University
North Pyongan Province
Founded: 1961

Chagang University
Kanggye City, Chagang Province
Founded: 1970
F: Agriculture; Sericulture; Farm Machinery.

Chang Chol Gu University Pyongyang
Pyongchon District, Pyongyang
Founded: 1970
F: Cookery; Services; Tailoring; Management.
I: Commerce.

Changjasan University
Chagang Province
Founded: 1967

**Chosan University of Physical Education
Pyongyang**
Tongdaewon District, Pyongyang
Founded: 1958
Physical Education.

Changsusan University
Haeju City, South Hwanghae Province
Founded: 1959
Medicine.

Chinmyong University
North Hamgyong Province
Founded: 1948

Chong Jun Taek University of Economics
Wonsan City, Kangwon Province
Founded: 1960
*F: Planning; Supply and Administration;
Finance; Commercial Management.*

Chonrigil University
Chagang Province
Founded: 1953

Chongsong University
Hamhung City, South Hamgyong Province
Founded: 1946
Medicine.

Hambuk University
Ranam District, Chongjin City, North Hamgyong
Province
Founded: 1970
F: Agriculture; Farm Machinery; Pomiculture.

Hyesan University of Education No. 1
Ryanggang Province
Founded: 1967
Education.

Huichon University of Technology
Huichon City, Chagang Province
Founded: 1959
*F: Radio Engineering; Wire Communication
Engineering; Electro-Apparatus Engineering;
Mechanical Engineering.*

Myongsin University
South Pyongan Province
Founded: 1967

Inpung University
Kanggye City, Chagang Province
Founded: 1969
Medicine.

Kang Gon University
Sariwon City, North Hwanghae Province
Founded: 1971
Medicine.

Karimchon University
Hyesan City, Ryangang Province
Founded: 1971
Medicine.

Kim Hyong Gwon University of Education
South Hamgyong Province
Founded: 1961
Education.

Kim Il Sung University Pyongyang
Taesong District, Pyongyang
President: Pak Gwan O
Founded: 1946, 1953
F: *Economics; History; Philosophy; Law; Korean Language and Literature; Foreign Languages and Literature; Mathematics and Mechanics; Physics; Chemistry; Biology; Geography; Geology; Automation.*
I: *Juche Ideas; Social Sciences.*

Kim Hyong Jik University of Education
Pyongyang
Founded: 1946
Education.

Kim Chaek University of Technology Pyongyang
Central District, Pyongyang
President: Kim Gyong Wan
Founded: 1948
F: *Geological Prospecting; Mining Engineering; Metallurgy; Material Engineering; Machine Building; Mechanical Engineering; Shipbuilding; Electrical Engineering; Electronic Engineering; Communication; Automatic Engineering; Physical Engineering; Industrial Management.*

Kim Chol Ju University of Education
Pyongyang
Founded: 1946
Education.

Kim Je University Haeju City
Haeju City, South Hwanghae Province
Founded: 1960
F: *Agriculture; Pomiculture; Farm Machinery; Agronomics.*
I: *Agricultural Science Research.*

Kim Jong Suk University of Education
Ryanggang Province
Founded: 1967
Education.

Kim Jong Tae University
South Hwanghae Province
Founded: 1961

Koryo University of Pharmacy Hamhung City
Hamhung City, South Hamgyong Province
Founded: 1968
Pharmacy.

Kumya University
Sapo District, Hamhung City, South Hamgyong Province
Founded: 1958
F: *Agriculture; Pomiculture; Farm Machinery.*

Kumgang University
Kangwon Province
Founded: 1949

Kwangje University
Pyonghawa-Dong, Sinuiju City, Pyongan Province
Founded: 1969
Medicine.

Kwanso University
North Pyongan Province
Founded: 1947

Kye Ung Sang University
Sariwon City, North Hwanghae Province
F: *Agriculture; Biology; Agrochemistry; Pomiculture; Forest and River Protection; Farm Machinery; Agronomics.*

Kyongsong University
Pohang District, Chongjin City, North Hamgyong Province
Founded: 1948
Medicine.

Li Gye Sun University
North Hwanghae Province
Founded: 1953

Manpung University
Sinuiju City, North Pyongyang Province
Founded: 1969
F: *Agriculture; Pomiculture; Farm Machinery.*

Nampo University
Waudo District, Nampo City
Founded: 1967
F: *Agriculture; Horticulture; Farm Machinery.*

O Jung Hup University
North Hamgyong Province
Founded: 1961

Ponghwa University
Pyongsong City, South Pyongan Province
Founded: 1972
F: *Medicine.*

Pyongyang University of Agriculture
Ryongsong District, Pyongyang
Founded: 1981
F: Agriculture; Veterinary and Animal Husbandry.

Pyongyang University of Cinematics
Tongdaewon District, Pyongyang
Founded: 1953
F: Social Sciences; Creation; Direction; Cinematography; Actors; Technology; Cinematic Art.

Pyongyang University of Construction and Building Materials
Taedonggang District, Pyongyang
Founded: 1953
F: Architecture; Architectural Engineering; Construction Engineering; Building Materials; City Management; Construction and Building Materials.

Pyongyang University of Fine Arts
Tongdaewon District, Pyongyang
Founded: 1947
F: Korean Painting; Paintings; Graphic Art; Sculpture; Industrial Art; Crafts.
I: Fine Arts Research.

Pyongyang University of Foreign Studies
Taesong District, Pyongyang
Founded: 1949
F: Russian, Chinese, Arabic, Japanese; English; French and Spanish; Education.
I: Training; Education Theory; Simultaneous Interpretation.

Pyongyang University of Light Industry
Songyo District, Pyongyang
Founded: 1959
F: Textile Engineering; Machine Engineering; Chemical Engineering of Daily Necessities; Food Engineering; Management.
I: Light Industry; Food Research.

Pyongyang University of Mechanical Engineering
Taedonggang District, Pyongyang
F: Machinery; Mechanical Engineering; Construction Machinery; Automation; Design.
I: Mechanical Engineering.

Pyongyang University of Medicine
Central District, Pyongyang
Founded: 1948
F: Clinical Medicine; Korean Traditional Medicine; Basic Medicine; Hygiene; Pharmacy; Stomatology.

Pyongyang Music and Dance University
Taedonggang District, Pyongyang
Founded: 1948
F: National Instruments; Western Instruments; Vocal Technique; Dance; Composition; Preparatory.
I: Music and Dance.

Pyongyang University of Railways
Hyongjesan District, Pyongyang
Founded: 1959
Railway Engineering.

Ryanggang University
Hyesan City, Ryangang Province
Founded: 1955
F: Agriculture; Management; Forestry Engineering; Wood Processing.
I: Agricultural and Forestry Scientific Research.

Ryomyong University
North Hamgyong Province
Founded: 1946

Saenal University
South Hamgyong Province
Founded: 1961

Samgwang University
Nampo, South Pyongan Province
Founded: 1963

Sariwon University
North Hwanghae Province
Founded: 1963

Sinuiju University of Light Industry
Sinuiju City, North Pyongyang Province
Founded: 1982
Machine Engineering; Chemical Engineering; Textile Engineering; Food Technology.

Sohae University
Waudo District, Nampo City
Founded: 1977
Fisheries.

Songdowon University
Wonsan City, Kangwon Province
Medicine.

Songdo University
Kaesong
Founded: 1961

Tonghae University
Wonsan City, Kangwon Province
Founded: 1959
Fisheries.

University of Chemical Industry Hamhung City
Hoesang District, Hamhung City, South Hamgyong Province
Founded: 1947
F: Inorganic Chemical Engineering; Organic Chemical Engineering; High Polymers Chemical Engineering; Silicate Engineering; Machine Engineering.

University of Coal Mining Pyongsong City
Pyongsong City, South Pyongan Province
Founded: 1968
F: Coal Mining; Geological Engineering; Mechanical Engineering; Automation.

University of Geology Sariwon City
Sariwon City, North Hwanghae Province
Founded: 1970
Geology.

University of Hydraulics and Dynamics Hamhung City
Tonghungsan District, Hamhung City, South Hamgyong Province
Founded: 1959
F: Hydraulic Engineering; Electrical Engineering; Irrigation; Mechanical Engineering.

University of Mining and Metallurgical Engineering Chongjin City
Pohang District, Chongjin City, North Hamgyong Province
Founded: 1959
F: Geotechnology; Mining; Coal Engineering; Automation; Metallurgy; Mineral Analysis.

University of National Economy Pyongyang
Pyongyang
Founded: 1946
F: Industrial Management; Agricultural Management; Finance and Banking; Planning; Trade; Statistics.

University of Printing Technology Pyongyang
Pyongyang
Founded: 1984
Printing Engineering.

University of Science Pyongsong City
Pyongsong City, South Pyongan Province
Founded: 1967
F: Mathematics; Physics; Automation; Chemistry; Biology.

University of Sea Transport Rajin City
Rajin City, North Hamgyong Province
Founded: 1968
Navigation; Marine Engineering.

University of Veterinary and Animal Husbandry Pyongsong City
Pyongsong City, South Pyongan Province
Founded: 1955
Veterinary Medicine; Animal Husbandry.

Wonsan University of Agriculture
Wonsan City, Kwangwon Province
Founded: 1948
F: Agriculture; Agricultural Machines; Agronomics; Pomiculture; Sericulture; Agro-Chemistry; Agro-Biology; Irrigation Engineering.

OTHER INSTITUTIONS

Anju College of Coal Mining
South Pyongan Province
Founded: 1985
Coal Mining.

Anju College of Technology
South Pyongan Province
Founded: 1976
Technology.

Bukjung College of Technology
North Pyongan Province
Founded: 1960
Technology.

Chaeryong College of Tideland Reclamation
South Hwanghae Province
Founded: 1985
Reclamation.

Cho Ok Hwa College
South Hamgyong Province
Founded: 1968

Choe Hui Suk College
South Hamgyong Province
Founded: 1972

Chongjin College of Electronics and Automation
North Hamgyong Province
Founded: 1984
Electronics and Automation.

Chongjin College of Light Industry
North Hamgyong Province
Founded: 1984
Light Industry.

Chongjin College of Metallugical Engineering
North Hamgyong Province
Founded: 1984
Metallugical Engineering.

Chongjin College of Railway Management
North Hamgyong Province
Founded: 1985
Railway Management.

Chongjin College of Technology
North Hamgyong Province
Founded: 1960
Technology.

Chongju College of Railway Construction
North Pyongan Province
Founded: 1985
Railway Construction.

Chongsu College of Chemical Industry
North Pyongan Province
Founded: 1985
Chemical Industry.

Chonnae College of Technology
Kangwon Province
Founded: 1982
Technology.

Dongrim College of Technology
North Pyongan Province
Founded: 1976
Technology.

Dongson College
North Pyongan Province
Founded: 1968

February 26th College of Technology
Chagang Province
Founded: 1985
Technology.

Haeju College of Electronics and Automation
South Hwanghae Province
Founded: 1984
Electronics and Automation.

Haeju College of Light Industry
South Hwanghae Province
Founded: 1985
Light Industry.

Haeju College of Technology
South Hwanghae Province
Founded: 1961
Technology.

Haeju Teachers' Training College
South Hwanghae Province
Founded: 1968
Teacher Training.

Hamhung College of Chemical Industry
South Hamgyong Province
Founded: 1984
Chemical Industry.

Hamhung College of Computing Machines
South Hamgyong Province
Founded: 1985
Computing Machines.

Hamhung College of Electronics and Automation
South Hamgyong Province
Founded: 1984
Electronics and Automation.

Huichon College of Mechanical Engineering
Chagang Province
Founded: 1984
Mechanical Engineering.

Hungnam College of Technology
South Hamgyong Province
Founded: 1960
Technology.

Hwasong College of Technology
Pyongyang
Founded: 1983
Technology.

Hyesan College of Technology
Ryanggang Province
Founded: 1971
Technology.

Hyongbong College of Technology
South Pyongan Province
Founded: 1979
Technology.

Kaesong College of Light Industry
Kaesong
Founded: 1984
Light Industry.

Kangson College of Metallugical Engineering
Nampo, South Pyongan
Founded: 1984
Metallugical Engineering.

Kangson College of Technology
Nampo, South Pyongan Province
Founded: 1960
Technology.

Kapsan College of Technology
Ryanggang Province
Founded: 1984
Technology.

Kilju College of Forestry
North Hamgyong Province
Founded: 1984
Forestry.

Kim Jong Suk Teachers' Training College
North Hamggyong Province
Founded: 1972
Teacher Training.

Kimchaek College of Metallugical Engineering
South Hamgyong Province
Founded: 1984
Metallugical Engineering.

Kiyang College of Technology
Nampo, South Province
Founded: 1960
Technology.

Kogonwon College of Technology
North Hamgyong Province
Founded: 1981
Technology.

Komdok College of Technology
South Hamgyong Province
Founded: 1961
Technology.

Kusong College of Mechanical Engineering
North Pyongan Province
Founded: 1984
Mechanical Engineering.

Kusong College of Technology
North Pyongan Province
Founded: 1968
Technology.

Kyongsong College of Technology
North Hamgyong Province
Founded: 1961
Technology.

Li Su Bok College of Chemical Industry
South Pyongan Province
Founded: 1984
Chemical Industry.

Li Su Dok College
Kangwon Province
Founded: 1968

Ma Dong Hui College
North Hamgyong Province
Founded: 1968

May Fourth College of Technology
South Pyongan Province
Founded: 1984
Technology.

Munpyong College of Technology
Kangwon Province
Founded: 1960
Technology.

Musan College of Technology
North Hamgyong Province
Founded: 1960
Technology.

Namhung College of Technology
South Pyongan Province
Founded: 1983
Technology.

Nampo College of Medicine
Nampo, South Pyongan Province
Founded: 1985
Medicine.

Nampo College of Shipbuilding
Nampo, South Pyongan Province
Founded: 1985
Shipbuilding.

Nampo College of Technology
Nampo, South Pyongan Province
Founded: 1960
Technology.

Paeksan College
Chagang
Founded: 1968

Pohang College of Technology
North Hamgyong Province
Founded: 1964
Technology.

Pukchang College of Technology
South Pyongan Province
Founded: 1976
Technology.

Pukchong College of Horticulture
South Hamgyong Province
Founded: 1984
Horticulture.

Pyongchon College of Technology
Pyongyang
Founded: 1970
Technology.

Pyongsong College
South Pyongan Province
Founded: 1972

Pyongyang College of City Planning
Pyongyang
Founded: 1985
City Planning.

Pyongyang College of Computing Machines
Pyongyang
Founded: 1985
Computing Machines.

Pyongyang College of Construction
Pyongyang
Founded: 1984
Construction.

Pyongyang College of Printing
Pyongyang
Founded: 1984
Printing.

Pyongyang College of Surgery
Pyongyang
Founded: 1985
Surgery.

Pyongyang College of Technology
Pyongyang
Founded: 1960
Technology.

Pyongyang Electrical College
Pyongyang
Founded: 1984
Electrical Engineering.

Rahung College of Technology
South Hamgyong Province
Founded: 1976
Technology.

Rakwon College of Technology
North Pyongan Province
Founded: 1960
Technology.

Rakyon College of Technology
South Hwanghae Province
Founded: 1984
Technology.

Ranam College of Technology
North Hwanghae Province
Founded: 1984
Technology.

Ryongdung College of Technology
North Pyongan Province
Founded: 1979
Technology.

Ryongsong College of Food Industry
Pyongyang
Founded: 1982
Food Industry.

Ryongsong College of Mechanical Engineering
South Hamgyong Province
Founded: 1961
Mechanical Engineering.

Ryongyang College of Technology
South Hamgyong Province
Founded: 1976
Technology.

Samhung College
Pyongyang
Founded: 1968

Samjiyon College
Ryanggang Province
Founded: 1968

Samsong College
North Pyongan Province
Founded: 1968

Sapo College of Technology
South Hamgyong Province
Founded: 1961
Technology.

Sariwon College of Agricultural Chemicals
North Hwanghae Province
Founded: 1984
Agricultural Chemicals.

Sinchang College of Technology
South Pyongan Province
Founded: 1961
Technology.

Sinchon College of Agriculture
South Hwanghae Province
Founded: 1984
Agriculture.

Sinpo College of Fisheries
South Hamgyong Province
Founded: 1984
Fisheries.

Sinuiju College of Economics
North Pyongan Province
Founded: 1985
Economics.

Sinuiju College of Technology
North Pyongan Province
Founded: 1960
Technology.

Songjin College of Fireproof Material Technology
North Hamgyong Province
Founded: 1983
Fireproof Material Technology.

Songjin College of Technology
North Hamgyong Province
Founded: 1960
Technology.

Songlim College of Technology
North Pyongan Province
Founded: 1961
Technology.

Songpyong College of Technology
North Hamgyong Province
Founded: 1979
Technology.

Sosong College of Technology
Pyongyang
Founded: 1976
Technology.

Sukchon College of Agriculture
South Pyongan Province
Founded: 1984
Agriculture.

Sunchon College of Silicate Engineering
South Pyongan Province
Founded: 1976
Silicate Engineering.

Sunchon College of Technology
South Pyongan Province
Founded: 1961
Technology.

Sungho College of Technology
Pyongyang
Founded: 1961
Technology.

Sunhwa College
Nampo
Founded: 1968

Supung Electrical College
North Pyongan Province
Founded: 1984
Electrical Engineering.

Taean College of Technology
Nampo, South Pyongan Province
Founded: 1960
Technology.

Tanchon College of Geological Prospecting
South Hamgyong Province
Founded: 1984
Geological Prospecting.

Tanchon College of Technology
South Hamgyong Province
Founded: 1971
Technology.

Tokchon Automobile College
South Pyongan Province
Founded: 1984
Transport.

Tokchon College of Hydraulic Power Construction
South Pyongan Province
Founded: 1985
Hydraulic Power Construction.

Tokchon College of Technology
South Pyongan Province
Founded: 1960
Technology.

Tokhyon College of Technology
North Pyongan Province
Founded: 1978
Technology.

Tonghung College
South Hamgyong Province
Founded: 19˜2

Uiju College of Technology
North Pyongan Province
Founded: 1984
Technology.

Undok College of Coal Mining
North Hamgyong Province
Founded: 1985
Coal Mining.

Undok College of Technology
North Hamgyong Province
Founded: 1960
Technology.

Unhung College of Technology
Ryanggang Province
Founded: 1985
Technology.

Unsan College of Technology
North Pyongan Province
Founded: 1961
Technology.

Yangsil College
North Pyongan Province
Founded: 1972

NATIONAL ACADEMIC BODIES

State Committee for Education
Sung-Li Street, Central District, Pyongan
Tel: +850(2) 36804
Fax: +850(2) 814-410
Telex: (899)37 02 sn kp
President: Ryong Tchoé Ki

National Commission of the Democratic People's Republic of Korea for Unesco
Ministry of Foreign Affairs, Pyongyang
Tel: +850(2) 5350
Telex: 5350 unesco foreign ministry pyongyang
Chairman: Sou Heun Tchoé
Secretary-General: Tai Gyun Ri

KOREA REPUBLIC

UNIVERSITIES AND COLLEGES

NATIONAL INSTITUTIONS

Andong National University
388 Songchon-dong, Andong City, Kyongbuk
760-749
Tel: +82(571) 551-661
Fax: +82(571) 505-599
President: Kyu-Chang Nam (1991-95)
Senior Administrative OfficerDirector of General
Affairs: Ho-Jong Kim: Il-Hoo Yoon
Founded: 1948, 1965, 1979
C: Humanities; Social Sciences; Natural Sciences; Arts and Physical Education; Andong Culture.
I: Language Research; Andong Regional Social Development; Toegye; Social Science Research; Folklore; Basic Sciences.

Anseong National University
67 Seog Jeong-ri Anseong-eub, Anseong-gun,
Kyeonggi-do 456-749
Tel: +82(334) 73-2700
Fax: +82(334) 73-2704
President: Ki-Young Han (1939-)
Founded: 1939
F: Agriculture; Science and Engineering; Humanities and Social Sciences.

Busan National University
30 Changion-dong, Kumjong-gu, Busan 609-735
Tel: +82(51) 56-0171
Founded: 1946, 1953

C: *Engineering; Humanities; Social Sciences; Natural Sciences; Law and Political Science; Education; Business Administration; Pharmacy; Medicine; Dentistry; Home Economics; Arts.*
Graduate S: *Business Administration; Public Administration; Industrial Management; Education.*
I: *Coastal Region Development Research; Solid State Physics; Language Research; Unification Research; New Community Movement (Research); Science Education; Mechanical Technology.*
Ce: *Computer.*

Changwon National University
641-773 Sarim-dong, Changwon, Kyung-nam
Tel: +82(551) 83-2151
Fax: +82(551) 83-2970
Founded: 1971, 1982
F: *Liberal Arts; Economics and Management; Law and Administration; Natural Science; Arts and Music; Engineering and Technology.*
I: *Unification Research; Labour Problems Research; Industrial Management; Industrial Technology.*
Ce: *Computer.*

Cheju National University
1, Ara 1-Dong, Cheju 690-756
Tel: +82(64) 54-2114
Fax: +82(64) 55-6130
President: Jang-Gwon Koh
Founded: 1952
C: *Humanities; Law and Political Science; Economics and Commerce; Education; Agriculture; Ocean Sciences; Natural Sciences; Engineering.*
Graduate S: *General; Education; Business Administration; Public Administration.*

Chinju National University
150 Ch'ilan-dong, Chinju 660-758
Tel: +82(591) 52-2378
Fax: +82(591) 52-9554
President: Si Kyung Kim (1993-97)
Provost: Hyun Chul an
International Relations: Vice-President, Chul Wook Kim
Founded: 1910
D: *Agriculture; Animal Science; Forestry; Horticulture; Dairy Science and Technology; Food Processing; International Livestock Industry; Civil Engineering; Landscape Architecture; Landscape Architecture; Mechanics Engineering; Computer Science; Electronic Engineering; Environmental Engineering; Mechanical Design Engineering; Living Culture; Industrial Economics; Forest Products Technology; Fiber Crafts; Accounting.*
Ce: *Computer.*

Chonbuk National University
666-14 Dokjin-Dong 1-Ga, Chonju, Chonbuk 560-756
Tel: +82(652) 76-2001
Fax: +82(652) 76-0429
Telex: 760429
President: Myung-Soo Chang (1994-98)
Secretary-General: Sang-Hwan Chung
International Relations: Byung-Jun Rho
Founded: 1947
C: *Engineering; Agriculture; Law; Education; Social Science; Humanities; Art; Commerce; Natural Science; Dentistry; Veterinary Medicine; Clothing and Textiles.*
S: *Medical.*
Graduate S: *Business Administration; Education; Public Administration; Industrial Technology; Environment Studies.*
Ce: *Computer.*

Chonju National University of Education
128 Tongseohak-dong, Wansan-Ku, honju 560-757
Tel: +82(652) 81-7114
Fax: +82(652) 81-0102
President: Nam-Sik Chae (1991-95)
Registrar: Chin-Mo Kang
Founded: 1955
Education.

Chonnam National University
300 Yongbong-dong, Puk-gu, Kwangiu 500-757
President: Han Sun Choi (1992-96)
Secretary-General: Byung Suk Lee
International Relations: Dean, Planning and Research, Jong Youll Park
Founded: 1952
C: *Humanities; Natural Sciences; Business Administration; Law; Medicine; Dentistry; Agriculture; Engineering; Education.*
S: *Graduate.*

Chung-Ju National University
123 Komdan-ri, Lryu-myon, Jungwon-gun, Chungbuk 383-870
Tel: +82(441) 841-5000
Fax: +82(441) 853-1236
President: Seo Yeong-Kee (1993-97)
Registrar: Cho Mu-Jea
International Relations: Lee Ji-Heon
Founded: 1962
Engineering; Humanities and Social Science; Education; Industrial Science and Technology.

Chungbuk National University
48 Kaeshin-dong, Chongju, Chungbuk 360-763
Tel: +82(431) 63-2114
Fax: +82(431) 63-0612
President: Nang-Ho Lee (1994-98)
Secretary-General: Gi-Woo Lee
Founded: 1951, 1978
C: *Humanities; Social Sciences; Natural Sciences; Engineering; Agriculture; Education; Pharmacy; Medicine.*
S: *Graduate.*

Chungnam National University

Kung-dong, Yusong-ku, Taejon 305-764
Tel: +82(42) 821-5114
Fax: +82(42) 823-1469
Telex: cnucie k 45571
President: Duck-Kyun Oh
Founded: 1952
*C: Humanities; Social Science; Natural
Sciences; Economics and Management;
Engineering; Agriculture; Law; Pharmacy;
Medicine; Home Economics; Fine Arts and Music.*
Graduate S: *Business Administration;
Education; Public Administration; Public Health;
Industry.*
*I: Language Research; Basic Science Research;
Community Development Research; Unification
Research; American Studies; Educational
Research and Development; Environment
Science and Technology; Physical Education and
Sports Science; Research Biological Engineering;
Paekje Research; Humanities Research;
Research of Natural Sciences; Management and
Economics; Industrial Technology Research;
Agricultural Science and Technology; Law and
Public Administration; Medicine Development;
Community Medicine; Home Economics; Arts.*
Ce: Industrial Education Research.

Gunsan National University

Miryong-dong, Gunsan CT, Chonbuk 573-360
Tel: +82 60-1113
Fax: +82 62-5334
E-Mail: root@knusun 1. kunsan. ac. kr
President: Han Yeon-Jong (1991-95)
Director of General Affairs: Yoon Han-Chul
International Relations: Park Jong-Dae
Founded: 1965
*C: Humanities; Music and Arts; Social Sciences;
National Sciences; Engineering; Ocean Sciences
and Technology.*
S: Industry (Graduate).
*I: Ideology; Regional Development; Basic
Science; Contempotary Arts; Industrial
Development; Languages Research; Engineering;
Fisheries Science.*
Ce: Coastal Research.

Gyeongsang National University

92 Kajoa-dong, Chinju CT, Kyongnam 660-701
Tel: +82 751-5114
Fax: +82 759-8061
Founded: 1948, 1953, 1968, 1980
*C: Agriculture; Education; Law and Business
Management; Graduate S; Education.*
*I: Agricultural Resources Research; Applied
Science; Science; Computer Sciences; Education
Research and Development; Provincial Culture;
Humanities Research; Livestock Research; New
Community Movement (Research); Science
Research; Social Science Research.*
Ce: Computer.

Jeju National University

Ara-Dong, Cheju CT, Cheju-do 690-121
Tel: +82 23-6141
Founded: 1952
*D: Korean Language and Literature; English
Language and Literature; Law; Agriculture;
Veterinary Science; Fishery; Animal Husbandry;
Home Economics; Horticulture; Food Production;
Business Administration; Mathematics; Marine
Biology.*

Kangnung National University

San 1 Chipyen-dong, Kangnung, Kangwon-do
210-702
Tel: +82 42-7001
Fax: +82 43-7110
Present: Lee Cham Soo (1991-95)
International Relations: Nam Koong Yong
Founded: 1969, 1979
*D: Business Administration; Accountancy;
English Language and Literature; Korean
Language and Literature; Physics, Chemistry,
and Biology; Regional Development; Music and
Fine Arts.*
I: Saemul Research; Unification Research.

Kangwon National University

192-1, Hyoja-2 dong, Chunchon 2001-701
Tel: +82(351) 50-6111
Fax: +82(361) 51-9556
Founded: 1947, 1978
*C: Agriculture; Humanities and Social Sciences;
Education; Law; Business Administration; Natural
Sciences; Engineering; Forestry.*
Graduate S: *Education; Business and Public
Administration.*
Ce: Computer.

Kongju National University

182 Shinkwan-dong, Kong ju CT, hungnam,
314-701
Tel: +82(416) 50-8114
Fax: +82(416) 53-3157
Founded: 1948, 1954
*C: Education; Humanities and Social Sciences;
Natural Sciences; Engineering; Industrial
Sciences.*
Graduate S: *Education; Industrial Development.*

Korea Air and Correspondence University Seoul

169 Dongsung-dong, Chongro-ku, Seoul 110-791
Tel: +82(2) 740-4114
Fax: +82(2) 744-5882
President: In-Suk Chang (1991-94)
Dean of Academic AffairsSecretary-General:
Chong-Hun Lee: Sung-Il Lee
Founded: 1972, 1981
*D: General Education; Korean Language and
Literature; English Language and Literature;
Chinese Language and Literature; French
Language and Literature; Law; Public
Administration; Economics; Business*

Administration; Agriculture; Home Economics; Computer Sciences and Statistics; Education; Trade; Applied Statistics; Environmental Hygiene; Early Childhood Education.
I: Distance Learning; Educational Media Development.
Ce: Computer; Student Guidance.

Korea Maritime University Busan
1 Dongsam-dong, Yeongdo-ku, Busan 606-791
Tel: +82(410) 4114
Fax: +82(414) 2475
Telex: Komauni K53665
President: Joen Hyo-Jung (1992-96)
Director: Jang Han-Soo
Founded: 1945
Navigation; Marine Engineering; Mechanical Engineering; Maritime Law; Shipping Management; Naval Architecture; Electronics and Communication; Foreign Trade; Oceanography.

Korea National University of Education
Darak-ri, Kangnae-myeon, Cheongwon-gun, Chungbuk 363-791
President: Shin Kuk-Bom
Founded: 1984
Education.

Korea National University of Physical Education
88-15 Oryoon-dong Songpa-gu, Seoul 138-763
Tel: +82(2) 410-6700
Fax: +82(2) 418-1877
President: Sukyoung Song (1994-96)
Secretary-General: Euidong Kim
International Relations: Jongsoo Son
Founded: 1977
D: Physical Education.
S: Graduate.
Research: Physical Education and Sports Science; Physical Education.
Ce: Computer; Saemul Undong Research.

Kumoh National University of Technology
188 Shinpyung-dong, Kumi CT, Kyung Buk 730-701
Tel: +82(546) 467-4114
Fax: +82(546) 467-4050
President: Yong-Hyun Choi (1993-97)
Director of General Affairs: Young-Kyl Jang
Founded: 1979
D: Mechanical Engineering; Mechanical and Production Engineering; Mechanical and Precision Engineering; Engineering Science and Mechanics; Electronic Engineering; Electronics Communication; Electronic and Control Engineering; Architectural Engineering; Civil Engineering; Industrial Engineering; Polymer Science and Engineering; Materials Science and Engineering; Applied Mathematics.
I: Research of Manufacturing Productivity; Community Research.
S: Industry (Graduate).

Ce: Continuing Education; Computer Engineering.

Kyungpook National University
[Kyungpook Taehak-gyo]
1370 Sankyok-dong, Puk-gu, Taegu 702-701
Tel: +82(53) 955-5001-35
Fax: +82(53) 954-6806
Telex: publicd k 54400 (12)
President: Chan-Suk Park (1994-98)
Secretary-General: Tae-Jin Kim
Founded: 1952
C: Humanities; Social Sciences; Economics and Commerce; Engineering; Agriculture; Natural Sciences; Law; Education; Music and Visual Arts.
S: Medicine; Dentistry.
Graduate S: Education; Public Administration; Health; Business Administration; Industrial Engineering.
I: Language; Philosophy and Korean Studies (Toegye); Electronic Technology; Basic Science; Saemaul Research; Genetic Engineering; Peace Research; Research of Industrial Technology; Humanities; Agricultural Science and Technology; Law Research; Social Science Research; Economic and Managerial Research; Research of Physical Education and Sports Science; Environmental Science; Pacific Rim Studies; Electronic Technology; Science Education Research; Language.
Ce: Audio-Visual Education; Computer.

Miryang National University
1025-1, Naei-dong, Miryang, Kyongnam 627-130
Tel: +82(527) 354-3181
Fax: +82(527) 355-3181
President: Jung Do Sub
Chief of General Affairs: Kim Sei Han
Founded: 1923
Agriculture; Natural Science and Engineering; Humanities and Social Science; Industrial Scinece and Technology.

Mokpo National Maritime University
571-2 Jukgyo-dong, Mokpo, Chunnam 530-729
Tel: +82(631) 44-2141
Fax: +82(631) 40-7046
President: Jung-Chul Oh (1993-97)
Director of General Affairs: Jae-Hoon Kim
Founded: 1950
I: Student Guidance; Maritime Industry and Technology.

Mokpo National University
61, Toim-ri, Chonggye-myon, Muan-gun, Chonnam 534-729
Tel: +82(631) 72-8153
Fax: +82(636) 52-4793
President: Lee Tae-Geun (1994-98)
Founded: 1946, 1990
C: Humanities; Social Science; Natural Science; Engineering.
I: Welfare Improvement; Unification Research; Littoral Biota; Basic Sciences.

National Fisheries University of Pusan

599-1 Daeyeon 3-dong, Nam-gu, Pusan 608-737
Tel: +82(51) 622-3951
Fax: +82(51) 625-9947
Founded: 1946, 1964
F: *Fishing Technology; Food Science and
Technology; Fisheries Biology; Oceanography;
Social Sciences.*
I: *Marine Sciences; Fisheries Management;
Aquatic Organisms Pathology.*

Pusan National University

30 Changjeon-dong, Keumjong-ku, Pusan 607-035
Tel: +82(51) 510-0311-9
Fax: +82(51) 512-9049
President: Hyuk-Pyo Chang
Director of General Afffairs: Sung-Duck Kim
International Relations: Dean, Planning and
International Relations, Dong-Hyeon Jung
Founded: 1946
C: *Engineering; Humanities; Social Sciences;
Natural Sciences; Law; Education; Business;
Pharmacy; Medicine; Dentistry; Home Economics;
Arts.*
Graduate S: *Management; Public
Administration; Education; Industry.*

Pusan National University of Education

263 Keoje-1-dong, Dongrae-Ke, Pusan
Tel: +82(51) 500-7114
Fax: +82(51) 505-4908
President: Kap-Soo Ha
Dean of Academic Affairs: Jong-Kun Kim
Founded: 1955
Education.

Pusan National University of Technology

100, Yongdan-Dong, Nam-Gu, Pusan 608-739
Tel: +82(51) 626-0701
Fax: +82(51) 621-2821
President: Han Sang Sook (1992-96)
International Relations: Lee Jong Taik
Founded: 1924
*Engineering; Humanities and Social Science;
General Studies.*

Samchok National University

Samchok Saneob Taehakkyo
Tel: +82(397) 72-8611-19
Fax: +82(397) 72-8620
President: Young Dal Kim (1994-98)
Secretary-General: Jwa Young Lee
Founded: 1939
*Engineering; Humanities and Social Sciences;
Design and Arts.*

Sangju National Polytechnic University

386 Gajang-Dong, Sangju, Gyeongbuk 742-170
Tel: +82(582) 30-5120
Fax: +82(582) 32-6005
President: Lee Nang Woo
Founded: 1921

D: *Agronomy; Sericulture; Animal Science;
Horticulture; Forest Resources; Civil Engineering;
Food Engineering; Industrial Machinery
Egnineering; Silk Textile Engineering; Computer
Science; Nutrition and Food Science; Clothing
and Design; Electronic Engineering; Chemical
Engineering; Architectural Engineering;
Automotive Engineering; Industrial Economics;
Industrial Administration; Child Welfare.*
Ce: *Computer.*

Seoul National Polytechnic University

172 Kongneung-Dong, Nowon-Gu, Seoul 139-743
Tel: +82(2) 970-6114
Fax: 82(2) 970-6088
President: Dae-Byong Yoon (1991-94)
Secretary-General: Sung-Min Park
Founded: 1955
*Engineering; Plastic; Cultural and Social
Sciences.*

*Seoul National University

San 56-1, Shinnim-dong, Kwanak-gu, Seoul
151-742
Tel: +82(2) 808-5114
Fax: +82(2) 885-5272
Telex: Snurok k29664
President: Chong-un Kim (1991-95)
Dean of Academic Affairs: Myung Chey
International Relations: Dean of Planning and
Coordination, Dong-Kun Kim
Founded: 1946, 1975
C: *Humanities; Social Sciences; Natural
Sciences; Home Economics; Business
Administration; Engineering; Agriculture; Fine
Arts; Law; Education; Veterinary Medicine;
Pharmacy; Music; Medicine; Dentistry.*
Graduate S: *Public Administration;
Environmental Studies; Public Health.*
I: *Natural Products Research; Language
Research; Communication Research;
Environmental Science; Molecular Biology and
Genetics; Social Sciences; Economic Research
Law Research; Korean Culture; American
Studies; Saemaul Udong Studies; Basic Sciences.*

Sun Cheon National University

315 Maegok-dong, Sun Chon, Chonnam 540-742
Tel: +82(661) 50-3114
Fax: +82(661) 50-3117
President: Jin-Ho Kim
Secretary-General: Young-Soo Ji
International Relations: Seong-Soon Kim
Founded: 1935, 1982
S: *Agricultural; Educational; Humanities and
Social Science; Engineering; Natural Science.*
I: *Regional Development Research; Industrial
Technology Research; Natural Science Research.*
Ce: *Computer.*

Taejon National University of Technology
305-3 Samsung 2-Dong, Tong-Gu, Taejon 300172
Tel: +82(42) 630-0114
Fax: +82(42) 625-1485
President: Kang Yong-Sik (1988-)
Director: Hong Jong-Bong
International Relations: Lee Sang-Ho
Founded: 1927
*Engineering; Humanities and Social Science;
Liberal Arts.*

Yosu National Fisheries College
Kuk-dong, Yosu CT, Chonnam 550-180
Tel: +82 40-6114
Fax: +82 41-5520
President: Jeong-han Kim
Director of Academic Afffairs: Sang-soo Kim
International Relations: Director of Planning and
Research, Haeng-gihl Kim
Founded: 1917, 1987
*F: Fisheries and Ocean; Engineering; Science;
Humanities and Sociology.*
I: Fisheries Science; Industrial Technology.

PUBLIC INSTITUTIONS

Kaya University
San 120 Jinsanri, Koryeongeup Koryeongun,
Kyeong Buk 717-800
Tel: +82(543) 954-1437
Fax: +82(543) 954-6094
President: Lee Sang Hee (1993-95)
Founded: 1993
*Ceramic Engineering; Electronic Ceramic
Engineering; Industrial Design.*

Seoul City University
90, Chonnong-dong, Tongdaemun-gu, Seoul
130-743
Tel: +82 210-2114
Fax: +82 244-5301
President: Hong Shin
Dean of Acadenic Affairs: Chang-Seok Kim
Founded: 1918

University of Inchon
177 Towha-dong, Nam-gu, Ichon 402-749
Tel: +82 760-8114
Fax: +82 760-8056
President: Hwang Kyu-Bok (1994-98)
Dean of General Affairs: Moon Kun-Su
International Relations: Director of Planning and
Development, Shin Hyun-Jae
Founded: 1979
*F: Humanities; Natural Sciences; Social
Sciences; Engineering; Economics and Business
Administration; Art and Education.*
Graduate S: Education.

PRIVATE INSTITUTIONS

Ajou University
Wonchon-dong, Suwon CT, Kyongji-Do 442-749
Tel: +82(331) 219-2114
Fax: +82(331) 213-5158
International Relations: Ja-Yoon Koo
Founded: 1972
*C: Engineering; Business Administration;
Humanities; Social Sciences; Natural Sciences;
Medicine.*
Graduate S: Industry; Business Administration.

Busan Catholic College
8-12 Pugok Dong, Kumjong-Gu, Busan
Tel: +82(51) 515-0432
Fax: +82(51) 515-0435
Rector: Myoung Ok-Ahn (1994-97)
Academic Dean: Chan Gui-Suk
Founded: 1990
D: Theology; Nursing.

Busan University of Foreign Studies
Uam-dong, Nam-gu, Busan 608-060
Tel: +82(51) 643-5111-7
Fax: +82(51) 645-4525
President: Dong-Son Kim
Dean of Academic Affairs: Chang-Hee Lee
Founded: 1981
*F: Foreign Studies; Humanities and Social
Science; Economics and Trade; Natural Sciences
and Engineering.*
S: Evening; Graduate.
*I: Audio-Visual Education; Law; International
Studies; Foreign Language Training.*
*Ce: Linguistic Research; Cultural Studies; Social
Science Research; Computer; Trade and
Management Research.*

Busan Women's University
Gwaebop-dong, Buk-gu, Busan
Tel: +82(51) 305-1001
Fax: +82(51) 305-5206
President: Mu Nam Kim (1992-94)
Dean of Academic Affairs: Sang Seon Kwon
International Relations: Hong Seob Jeong
Founded: 1969
*C: Humanities and Social Sciences; Natural
sciences; Arts; Education.*

Catholic University Seoul
Haewha-dong, Chongno-gu, Seoul 110-530
Tel: +82(2) 740-9714
Fax: +82(2) 741-2801
President: Choi Chang-Mou
Founded: 1885, 1959
Theology; Medicine.

Chonbuk Sanup University of Technology

663, Soryong-Dong, Kunsan, Chonbuk 573-400
Tel: +82(654) 60-3114
Fax: +82(654) 60-3253
President: Tou-Shik Kang (1993-97)
Secretary-General: Hee Seong Kang
International Relations: Provost, Du-Seok Kim
Founded: 1977
*D: Mechanical Engineering; Electrical
Engineering; Electronic Engineering; Industrial
Chemistry; Architectural Engineering; Civil
Engineering; Food Engineering; Information and
Telecommunication Engineering; Computer
Engineering; Computer Science; Clothing and
Textile; Engineering Design; Recreation and
Leisure Sport; Business Administration; Tourism
Management; Accounting; International Trade;
Economics; Tourism and Interpretation; Public
Administration; Law; English; Nursey
Kindergarden.*

Chondang University

419 Sungnam-Ri, Muan-Kun, Chonnam
Tel: +82(636) 453-4960-8
Fax: +82(636) 453-4969
President: Bae Chong Moo
Executive Director: Kim CheHyung
Founded: 1994
*Div: Liberal Arts and Humanities; Business;
Engineering; General Studies.*

Chongju University

36 Naedok-dong, Chongju-shi
Tel: +82(431) 51-8114
Fax: +82(431) 51-8110
President: Jung Yong Tae (1994-98)
Founded: 1946
*C: Economics and Business Administration; Law
and Political Science; Liberal Arts and Science;
Natural Sciences and Engineering; Education;
Arts.*

Chonju Woosuk University

490 Hujong-ri, Samry-up, Wangju-gun, Chonbuk
565-800
Tel: +82(652) 290-1114
Fax: +82(652) 291-9312
President: Kim Jong-Chol
Executive Director: Jong-Pil Im
International Relations: Executive Director,
Kwang-Mun Park
Founded: 1979
*C: Humanities; Social Sciences; Natural
Sciences; Home Economics; Pharmacy; Oriental
Medicine; Education; Fine Arts; Life Science.*

Chosun University

375 Sosok-dong, Dong-gu, Kwangju 501-759
Tel: +82(62) 230-3334
Fax: +82(62) 232-3334
President: Chong Byung Hyou (1992-96)
Dean of Academic Affairs: Lee Sung Baik
International Relations: Director of Research and
International, Lee Woo Sun
Founded: 1946

*C: Law and Political Science; Liberal Arts and
Science; Education; Commerce and Economics;
Foreign Languages; Engineering; Medical;
Pharmacy; Dentistry; Physical Education.*

Chung-Ang University

221 Huksok-dong, Dongjak-ku, Seoul 156-756
Tel: +82(2) 810-2114
Fax: +82(2) 816-9938
Telex: cauniv k 24763
Cable: chunganguniv seoul
President: Min Ha Kim (1993-)
Dean of Planning: Hyuk Jae Yim
International Relations: Dean of International
Education, Dong Sung Kim
Founded: 1918, 1945, 1953
*C: Liberal Arts; Science; Engineering;
Education; Law; Political Science and Economics;
Business Administration; Industrial Studies;
Pharmacy; Medicine; Arts; Foreign Languages;
Social Sciences; Home Economics; Music;
Architecture and Construction.*
Graduate S.
Ce: Chung-Ang Research; Computer.
*I: Humanities; Education Research; Legal
Research; Economic Research; Social Sciences;
Management Research; Arts; Technology and
Science; Family Life; Medical Science;
Pharmaceutical Science; North-East Asian
Studies; Public Policy and Administration;
Japanese Studies; Music; Basic Sciences; Korean
Folklore; International Women's Study; Food and
Resource; Communication; Environmental
Sciences; Third World Studies; Genetic
Engineering; Australian Studies; Industrial
Management; Statistical Studies; Regional
Economy; Construction Technology.*

Daebul University

72 Sanho-Ri, Samho-Myeon, Yeong Arm-Grn,
Chonnam 526-890
Tel: +82(693) 71-0160
Fax: +82(693) 71-0165
President: Lee Kyung Soo (1994-96)
Chief, Office for Planning and Coordination: Yi
Sung Hoon
Founded: 1994
*D: Computer Science; Physics; Electrical
Engineering; Electronic Engineering; Industrial
Engineering; Chemical Engineering; Business
Administration; Computer Engineering; Industrial
Design; Architecture.*
*I: Industrial Technology; Environmental
Research; Regional Development; Study on
Korea and China Academic Exchange.*

Danho Educational Institution

San 117-6, Samgo-RiYoungin-Eup, Yongin-Coon,
Kyunggi-Dho
Tel: +82(335) 32-6471-80
Fax: +82(335) 32-6479
President: Kin Jung-Haeng (1992-95)
Executive Director: Kim Jong-Dai
International Relations: Song Ho-Dai
Founded: 1953

D: Judo; Combative Arts; Taekwondo; Physical Education; Leisure and Recreation; Special Physical Education; Dance; Industrial Design; Painting; Sports Management; Tourism Management; Management and Information Systems; Environment Health; Food Science and Nutrition; Computer Science and Statistics; Physical Therapy.
I: Martial Arts; Sports Science.

Dankook University Seoul
8 Hannam-dong, Yongsan-gu, Seoul 140-714
Tel: +82(2) 709-2114
Fax: +82(2) 792-5814
President: Hong Ro Yoon
Director of General Affairs: Jeong Sik Min
International Relations: Dean of Planning, Il Hyun Jeong
Founded: 1947
C: Liberal Arts and Science; Commerce and Economics; Law and Political Science; Engineering; Education; Evening Studies.
Graduate S: Business Administration; Education; Public Administration.
I: Oriental Studies; Anglo-American Studies; Research of New Community Movement; Industrial Research; Chinese Studies; Folk Arts; Technology Research; Statistics.

Dong Eui University
24 Kaya-dong, Busanjin-gu, Busan 614-010
Tel: +82(51) 804-1500
Fax: +82(51) 895-3727
President: Byung Don Lee (1992-)
Dean of General: Kwan Soo Lee
Founded: 1979
F: Liberal Arts; Law and Political Science; Business Administration and Economics; Science; Engineering; Fine Arts and Music.
I: Political Science; Industrial Management; Marine Biology.

Dong Yang University of Technology
574 Sanbub-Li, Punggi-Up, Youngju, Kyoungsangbuk-Do 751-800
Tel: +82(572) 30-1000
Fax: +82(572) 636-8523
President: Sunghea Choi (1994-98)
Founded: 1994
Electronic Engineering; Control and Instrumentation Engineering; Communication Engineering; Industrial Engineering.

Dong-A University Busan
Hadan 2-dong, Saha-gu, Busan 604-714
Tel: +82(51) 200-6114
Fax: +82(51) 201-5430
President: Soon-Gi Shin (1993-95)
Vice-President: Hae-woo Shin
International Relations: Head of Planning Office, Suh-ill Song
Founded: 1947, 1959
C: Humanities; Natural Sciences; Law; Social Sciences; Business Administration; Agriculture; Engineering; Physical Education; Arts; Medicine.

Graduate S: Business Administration; Education; Industry.
I: Sokdang Academic Research of Korean Culture; Language Research; Enviromental Problems Research; Business Management Research; Social Science Research; Research of Sports Science; German Studies; Law Studies; Basic Science Research; Korea Agricultural Technology Research; Korean Resources Development; Ocean Resources Research; Tourism and Leisure Research; Life Science Research; Research Industrial Medicine.
Ce: Population Research.

Dongduck Women's University
23-1 Hawolgok-dong, Sungbug-ku, Seoul 136-714
Tel: +82(2) 913-2001
Fax: +82(2) 913-0731
Predident: Kim Jong-Hyup (1992-96)
Vice-President: Cho Won-Young
International Relations: Dean of University Plans, Kim Duk-Sung
Founded: 1950
C: Humanities; Social Sciences; Natural Science; Pharmacy; Arts.
D: General Studies and Teaching.
I: Korean Studies; Business Administration; Natural Drugs Research.
Ce: Environmental Health Research; Industrial Design Research; Computer.

Dongguk University
26, 3-ga Pil-dong, Chung-gu, Seoul 100-715
Tel: +82(2) 260-3114
Fax: +82(2) 277-1274
E-Mail: userid@u4680.dongguk.ac.kr
President: Minn Byung Chun (1991-94)
Dean of Academic Affairs: Chung Byung Jo
International Relations: Lee Won Boo
Founded: 1906, 1930, 1940, 1946, 1953
C: Buddhism; Liberal Arts and Sciences; Law and Political Science; Economics and Commerce; Agriculture and Forestry; Engineering; Education.
Graduate S: Public Administration; Business Administration; Education.
I: Buddhist Research; National Security Research.
Ce: Dhyana; Buddhist Scriptures Translation; Computer.

Dongseo University
San 69-1, Jurye-Dong, Buk-Gu, Busan 616-010
Tel: +82(51) 313-2001
Fax: +82(51) 312-2389
E-Mail: jykim@won.donseo.ac.kr
President: Kim Jong Yule (1994-96)
Executive Director: Chang Hyeung Boo
International Relations: Director of Planning, Lee Jae Ik
Founded: 1991
C: Engineering; Natural Sciences; Arts.
I: Industry and Technology Development.
Ce: Computer; Continuing Education.

Dongshin University

Taehodong, Naju CT, Chonnam 520-714
Tel: +82(613) 30-3011
Fax: +82(613) 33-2909
President: Sang-Sup Lee (1991-95)
International Relations: Suk-Joo Lee
Founded: 1987
D: Architecture; Civil Engineering; Industrial Engineering; Environmental Engineering; Urban Planning; Inorganic Material Engineering; Information and Communication Engineering; Electrical and Electronics Engineering; Mathematics; Physics; Landscape Architecture; Computer Science and Staticstics; Clothing and Textiles; Food and Nutrition; Life-Physical Education; Prespartory Course for Oriental Medicine; Oriental Medicine; Korean Language and Literature; English Language and Literature; Japanese Language and Literature; Chinese Language and Literature; Economics; Management Information System.

Duksung Women's University

419, Sangmun-dong, Dobong-gu, Seoul 132-714
Tel: +82(2) 901-8000
Fax: +82(2) 901-8114
President: Young-Sook Joo (1994-97)
Dean of Academic Affairs
Founded: 1950
C: Humanities; Social Science; Natural Sciences; Pharmacy; Fine Arts.

Ewha Women's University

11-1, Tahyon-dong, Sudaemun-gu, Seoul 120-750
Tel: +82(2) 360-2114
Fax: +82(2) 360-2065
President: Hoo-Jung Yoon (1986-94)
Dean of the Office of Faculty and Academic Affairs: Seung-Hwan Lee
International Relations: Dean of International Institute, Soo-Young Auh
Founded: 1886, 1910, 1945
C: Liberal Arts; Natural Sciences; Music; Fine Arts; Physical Education; Education; Law and Political Science; Medicine; Nursing; Pharmacy; Home Economics.
Graduate S: Education; Industrial Design.

Hallym University

Okchon-dong, Chunchon CT, Kangwon 200-010
Tel: +82(361) 53-5411
Fax: +82(361) 51-9800
President: Bom Mo Chung
Vice-President: Heung Bong Cha
Founded: 1982
C: Humanities; Social Science; Natural Science; Medicine.

Han Nam University

Ojung-dong, Taeduk-Gu, Taejon CT, Chungnam 300-791
Tel: +82(42) 629-7114
Fax: +82(42) 629-5874
President: Pak Chong-Min
Vice-President: Yu Jung-Ok
Founded: 1956
C: Liberal Arts; Education; Natural Science; Engineering; Economics and Administration.
I: Natural Science; East-West Cultural Science; Regional Development; Language; Industrial Management; Chung-Cheon Cultural; Information Science; Japanese Studies; Social Science Research; Economics.
Ce: New Community Research; Study of Christianity and Culture.

Han Shin University

411 Yangsandong, Osan, Kyounggido 447-791
Tel: +82(2) 233-9438
Fax: +82(2) 72-3343
President: Chai Yong choo (1992-96)
Director of Academic Affairs: Jong Dae Lim
International Relations: Director of Planning and Management, Oong-Hyun Sung
Founded: 1940
F: Theology; Social Welfare; Humanities; Business and Economics; Natural Sciences.

Hankuk Aviation University

200-1, Hwajon Dong, Koyang-Shi, Kyonggi-Do 411-791
Tel: +82(2) 300-0114
Fax: +82(2) 307-5769
Predisent: Hyung-Jae Lee (1992-)
Dean of Academic Affairs: Hong-Chul Chung
International Relations: Dean of Planning and External Affairs, Soon-Kil Hong
Founded: 1952, 1968
D: General Studies; Flight Operation; Business Administration; Aeronautical Engineering; Telecommunication and Information Engineering; Avionics Engineering; Aviation Administration; Materials Engineering; Mechanical Engineering and Design; Computer Science; Telecommunication and Information Engineering; Flight Operation and Administration.
I: Electronic, Information and Telecommunication Development Research; Aviation Industry and Policy Studies.
Ce: Aviation Research; Computer.

Hankook University of Foreign Studies Seoul

270 Imun-dong, Tongdaemun-gu, Seoul 131-791
Tel: +82(2) 961-4114
Fax: +82(2) 960-7898
President: Ahn Byong Man (1994-98)
International Relations: Dean of Research and Cooperation, Choi Yong Soo
Founded: 1954

C: *Occidental Studies; Oriental Studies; Law and Political Science; Trade and Economics; Education; Liberal Arts and Natural Sciences.*
Graduate S: *Interpretation and Translation; International Trade; Education.*
Ce: *Language Research.*

Hanseo University
360 Taegok-li, Haemi-myen Seosan-kun, chungnam 352-820
Tel: +82(455) 60-1111
Fax: +82(455) 60-1119
President: Sokwoo Lee (1994-96)
Secretary-General: Kichul Ham
Founded: 1992
C: *Engineering; Humanities; Social Sciences; Natural Sciences; Law and Political Science; Education; Business Administration; Pharmacy; Medicine; Dentistry; Home Economics; Arts.*
Graduate S: *Business Administration; Public Administration; Industrial Management; Education.*
I: *Coastal Region Development Research; Solid State Physics; Language Research; Unification Research; Research of New Community Movement; Science Education; Mechanical Technology.*
Ce: *Computer.*

Hansung University Seoul
389 Samson-dong 2-ga, Songbuk-gu, Seoul 136-792
Tel: +82(2) 760-4211
Fax: +82(2) 760-4215
President: Won Hyung-Gap (1972-94)
Administrative Officer: Kim Kyung-Ja
Founded: 1972
C: *Humanities; Social Sciences; Arts; Natural Sciences.*
Graduate S: *Business Administration; Public Administration.*

Hanyang University Seoul
17 Haengdang-dong, Songdong-gu, Seoul 133-791
Tel: +82(2) 290-0114
Fax: +82(2) 292-1285
President: Hae-seong Lee
Dean of Academic Affairs: Mýeung-ho O
Founded: 1939, 1945, 1948, 1956
C: *Engineering; Medicine; Humanities; Social Sciences; Natural Sciences; Law; Commerce and Economics; Education; Home Economics; Music; Physical Education.*
Graduate S: *Industry; Business Administration; Public Administration; Education; Environmental Sciences; Banking.*
I: *Industrial Science (Research); Economic Research; Sino-Soviet Studies.*
Ce: *Local Autonomy.*

Honam University
148 Sangchon-dong, Seo-Ku, Kwangju 502-260
Tel: +82(62) 370-8114
Fax: +82(62) 370-8008
President: Lee Dai-Soon
Dean of Academic Affairs: Yu Choon-Sik
International Relations: Dean of Planning Affairs, Lee Sae-Jun
Founded: 1981
I: *East European Studies; Social Studies; Industrial Administration; Industrial Technology; Regional Development; Computer Sciences and Communications:; Athletics.*

Hong Ik University Seoul
72-1 Sangsu-dong, Mapo-gu, Seoul 121-791
Tel: +82(2) 320-1114
Fax: +82(2) 320-1122
E-Mail: hkkuh@gayakreonet.re.kr
President: Myeon Young Lee (1991-)
Vice-President for Academic Affairs: Sang Pil Shim
International Relations: Hakan Kuh
Founded: 1946, 1971
C: *Engineering; Business Administration and Economics; Fine Arts; Liberal Arts; Education.*
Graduate S: *Industrial Arts; Environmental Studies; Education.*
I: *Environmental Studies.*
Ce: *Computer.*

Hoseo University
Mt. 29-1 Sechul-Ri, Baebang-Myun, Asan-Kun, Choognam-Do 337-795
Tel: +82(418) 40-5114
Fax: +82(418) 548-1831
President: Suk Kyu Kang
Founded: 1979
C: *Human Sciences; Social Sciences; Natural Sciences; Engineering; Arts and Sports; Evening Courses.*
Graduate S: *Industry and Management.*

Hyosung Women's University Kyungbuk
Kumrak-dong, Hayang-eup, Kyungsan-gun, Kyungbuk 713-702
Tel: +82(541) 52-8001
Fax: +82(541) 52-8030
President: Do Sik Park
Chief Secretary: Gye-Bog Ahn
Founded: 1952
C: *Liberal Arts and Sciences; Law and Political Science; Education; Pharmacy; Art; Home Economics; Foreign Studies; Economics and Commerce; Music; Natural Sciences; Social Sciences.*
I: *Korean Women's Problem Research; Catholic Education Research.*

Hyupsung University
8-1 Sang-Ri Bongdan-Myun, Hwasungkun,
Kyunggido 455-890
Tel: +82(331) 292-7131-4
Fax: +82(331) 292-3131
President: Park Keun Soo (1993-96)
Founded: 1983
D: Theology; Humanities and Arts.

Incheon University
177 Towha-dong, Nam-gu, Incheon 402-749
Tel: +82 74-5301
Founded: 1979
*F: Humanities; Natural Sciences; Social
Sciences; Engineering; Business Administration.
I: Foreign Languages.
Ce: National Unification Research; Research of
New Community Movement; Industrial
Development Research.*

Inchon National University of Education
59-12 Sungeui-dong, Buk-gu, Inchon 403-050
Tel: +82(32) 540-1114
Fax: +82(32) 541-0580
President: Dong Hwa Chung (1993-97)
Dean of Academic Affairs: Jong Un Choi
Founded: 1962
*C: Engineering; Humanities; Social Sciences;
National Science; Law and Political Science;
Education; Business Administration; Pharmacy;
Medicine; Dentistry; Home Economics; Arts.
S: Graduate.
I: Solid State Physics; Language Research;
Unification Research; New Community
Movement; Science Education; Mechnical
Technology.
Ce: Computer.*

Inha University
253 Yonghyon-dong, Nam-gu, Inchon 402-751
Tel: +82(32) 860-7114
Fax: +82(32) 863-1333
Telex: 32771 inhauni k
President: Sung-Ok Cho
Vice-President: Byung-ha Choi
Founded: 1954, 1971
*C: Engineering; Natural Sciences; Business
Administration and Economics; Law and Public
Administration; Liberal Arts and Sciences;
Education.
Graduate S: Education; Business
Administration.*

Inje University
18-3, Obang-dong, Kimhae, Kyongsangnam-do
621-749
Tel: +82(525) 34-7111
Fax: +82(525) 34-0712
President: Nak Hwan Paik
Director of General Affairs: Young Euy Choi
Founded: 1979, 1989
*C: Medicine; Natural Sciences; Humanities and
Social Sciences; Public Health.*

*I: Medical; Medical Sciences; Industrial
Medicine; Basic Sciences.*

International University Seoul
Chongneung-dong, Songbuk-gu, Seoul 136-104
Tel: +82(2) 919-0411

JeonJu University
1200 Hyoja-dong, 3-Ga, Wansan-Gu, Chonju CT,
Chonbuk 560-759
Tel: +82(652) 220-2464
Fax: +82(652) 220-2464
E-Mail: jsc@jeondrs.jeonju.ac.kr
President: Chongik rhee (1993-94)
Director of Planning (Acting): Yoon-Seop Klm
International Relations: Jinsuk Chun
Founded: 1964
*C: Humanities; Law and Public Administration;
Economics and Business Administration;
Education; Natural Science and Engineering; Arts
and Sciences; Regional Science.*

Jeonju Woosuk University
Hujong-ri, Samrae-eup, Wanju-gun, Chonbuk
565-800
Tel: +82 73-8001
Founded: 1979
*S: Humanities; Social Sciences; Education;
Science; Pharmacy; Home Economics; Physical
Education and Art.*

Kang Nam University
San 62, Kukal-Ri, Kihueng-Eup, Yougin-Kun,
Kyunggi-Do 449-702
Tel: +82(331) 280-3500
Fax: +82(331) 281-3601
President: Joong Yun cho (1994-)
Founded: 1946
*C: Theology; Science and Engineering;
Business Administration; Humanities; Social
Sciences; Arts and Physical Education.*

Keimyung University
2139 Daemyung-dong, Daegu 705-701
Tel: +82(53) 626-1321
Fax: +82(53) 623-9935
E-Mail: ihsynn@kmucc;keimyung.ac.kr
President: Ilhi Synn (1988-)
Dean of General Affairs: daeil Hong
International Relations: Man Kee Choe
Founded: 1954, 1956, 1978
*C: Humanities; Teacher Training; Foreign
Studies; Business Administration; Social
Sciences; Law; Natural Sciences; Engineering;
Home Economics; Music; Fine Arts; Physical
Education; Evening.
S: Medicine.
I: International Education; Industrial
Management; Domestic Science; German
Studies; Japanese Studies; Chinese Studies;
Educational Studies; Industrial Technology;
Mathematical Sciences; Natural Sciences; Social
Sciences (Research); Medical Science; Arts and*

421

Culture; Theological Studies; Local Communication; Lifelong Education.
Ce: East-West; Behavioural Sciences.

King Sejong University Seoul
Kunja-dong, Songdong-gu, Seoul 133-150
Tel: +82(2) 467-5121
Founded: 1954

*Konkuk University
93-1, Mojin-dong, Seongdong-gu, Seoul 133-701
Tel: +82 450-3114
Fax: +82 452-3108
President: Yoon Hyoung-Sup (1994-98)
Vice-President: Hong Sung-Wha
International Relations: Hyung-Hoan Lee
Founded: 1946, 1959
C: Liberal Arts; Sciences; Engineering; Law and Political Science; Commerce and Economics; Animal Husbandry; Agriculture; Arts and Home Economics; Education; Humanities; Social Sciences; Natural Sciences; Medicine; Political Science; Art and Design.
I: Humanities; Industrial Science and Technology; Agriculture Development; Economics and Management; Genetic Engineering; Environmental Studies; Basic Sciences; Social Sciences; Public Administration Affairs; Animal Husbandry; Arts and Home Economics; Education; Cheongwon Humanities; Social Policy; Natural Sciences; Formative Arts; Medical Sciences; Chinese Affairs; Real Estate Policy.

Konyang University
San 30, Naedongri, Nonsan, Chungnam
Tel: +82(461) 33-2071
Fax: +82(461) 33-2070
President: Chang Kap Lee (1991-94)
Founded: 1991
C: Liberal Arts; Commerce; Science; Engineering; Class; Humanities; Business and Economics; Natural Science; Industrial Technology; Food Culture.
I: Research.
Ce: Computer.

Kookmin University Seoul
861-1 Chongnung-dong, Songbuk-gu, Seoul 136-702
Tel: +82(2) 910-4114
Fax: +82(2) 919-2100
President: Hyun Syng-Il (1992-96)
International Relations: Dean, External Affairs, Jun Jae-Bik
Founded: 1946, 1981
C: Liberal Arts; Law and Political Science; Economics and Business Administration; Engineering; Architecture and Design; Education; Forestry.

Korea Institute of Technology and Education
307, Gajean-Ri, Byungchon-Myon, Chonan-Gun Chungnam
Tel: +82(417) 60-1000
Fax: +82(417) 61-9504
President: Nack-Joo Lee (1992-96)
Director of Academic Affairs: Il-Hwan Park
Founded: 1991
D: Mechanical Engineering; Electrical Engineering; Electronic Engineering; Information and Communication Engineering; Industrial Design; Liberal Arts and Teacher Education.
Ce: Research of Industrial Technology and Manpower.

Korea University Seoul
1, 5-ka, Anam-dong, Sungbuk-gu, Seoul 136-701
Tel: +82(2) 920-1114
Fax: +82(2) 922-5820
Telex: korea ku 34138
President: Hong Il Sik (1994-98)
International Relations: Bong Young Chung
Founded: 1905, 1946
C: Law; Business Administration; Liberal Arts; Agriculture; Political Sciences and Economics; Science; Engineering; Medicine; Education.
Graduate S: Business Administration; Education; Food and Agriculture.

Korean Christian College Seoul
San 201, Ilwagik 6-dong, Kangseo-ku, Seoul 157-702
Tel: +82(2) 698-8876
Fax: +82(2) 698-8876
President: Lee Bong Hoon (1994-96)
Dean of Academic Affairs: Kim Jin Whae
Founded: 1958
D: Theology; Church Administration; Mission Language; Religious Philosophy; Church Music; Social Welfare; Children's Welfare.

Korean Sahmyook (Union) University Seoul
223 Kongneung 2-dong, Nohwon-gu, Seoul 139-742
Tel: +82(2) 972-3606 12
Fax: +82(2) 979-5318
Telex: kum sda k 25329
Cable: adventist, seoul, korea
President: Hong Ryang Kim
Academic Dean: Dae-Keuk Nam
Founded: 1906, 1961, 1985
D: Theology; English Language and Literature; Business Administration; Nursing; Pharmacy; Nutrition; Chemistry; Music; Biology; Horticulture; Industrial Education; Rehabilitation Therapy; Dairy Farming Resources.
Research I: Theological; Evangelist; Christian Education; Behavioural Science; Life Sciences; Language; Basic Science.

Korean Tourism University Kyongju City
Hyohyen-dong, Kyongju CT, Kyungbuk 780-210
Tel: +82 3-5558
Founded: 1988

Kosin College

149-1, Dongsam-dong, Yeongdo-ku, Pusan
606-701
Tel: +82(51) 414-6063
Fax: +82(51) 414-5349
President: Pyeng-seh Oh (1994-96)
Business Manager: Pyeng-hee Choi
International Relations: Director of Planning,
Yong-won Kang
Founded: 1970
D: Natural Sciences; Medicine; Theology;
Theology.

Kwan Dong University Kangreung

522 Naegok-dong, Kangreung CT, Kangwon
210-701
Tel: +82(391) 41-1011
Fax: +82(391) 41-1010
President: Young-Chul Paik
Founded: 1955, 1959
C: Education; Humanities; Social Sciences;
Engineering; Evening.

Kwangju Catholic College

Sangchon-dong, So-gu, Kwangju 502-260
Tel: +82(62) 372-0124-7
Fax: +82(62) 372-4377
President: Timothy Kim Min-Su (1993-97)
Academic Dean: Peter Song Hyun-Sub
Founded: 1962
C: Theology and Philosophy.

Kwangju University

592-1 Jinwol-Dong, Seo-Gu, Kwangju 502-703
Tel: +82(62) 670-2114
Fax: +82(62) 674-0078
President: Kim Ran-Soo (1990-94)
Executive Director, Office of Planning: Kim
Hyuk-Jong
International Relations: Ahn Young-Sup
Founded: 1983
C: Economics and Business; Social Sciences;
Liberal Arts and Science; Engineering; Arts.
Graduate S: Economics and Business; Mass
Communication.
I: Industrial Management; Korean Culture and
Art; University Development; Industrial
Technology; Social Sciences; International
Affairs.
Ce: Computer.

Kwangwoon University Seoul

447-1 Wolkye-dong, Nowon-gu, Seoul 139-701
Tel: +82(2) 910-5114
Fax: +82(2) 917-6147
President: Kang June-Gill (1994-98)
International Relations: Ra Keuk-Hwan
Founded: 1962, 1983
D: Engineering; Natural Sciences; Business
Administration and Economics; Law and Political
Science; Social Sciences.
Graduate S: Engineering and Management
Information.

Kyonggi University

Iui-ri, Suji-myon, Yongin-gun, Kyonggi 449-840
Tel: +82 6-2175
Founded: 1956, 1976
D: Physical Education; Korean Language and
Literature; English Language and Literature;
Tourism; Business Administration; Public
Administration; International Trade; Tourism
Development; Accountancy; Civil Engineering;
Architecture; Industrial Management.
I: Production Management; Tourism
Development; Social Studies; American Culture
and Language; Chinese Studies.

Kyongju University Kyongju City

Hyohyun-Dong, Kyongju, Kyungbuk 780-210
Tel: +82(561) 748-5551
Fax: +82(561) 748-5553
President: Joon Koo Lee (1994-)
Founded: 1988
D: Tourism Business Administration; Hotel
Administration; Tourism and Public
Administration; English and Tourism; Japanese
and Tourism; Cultural Assets; Advertising and
Public Relations; Tourism Landscape
architecture; Urban Engineering.

Kyung Hee University Seoul

1, Hoegi-dong, Dongdaemoon-ku, Seoul 130-701
Tel: +82(2) 961-0030
Fax: +82(2) 962-4343
President: Yong Il Kong (1994-96)
Registrars: Yong-Chul Shin; Chung-Mo Kang
Founded: 1949, 1951
C: Liberal Arts and Science; Law; Political
Sciences and Economics; Education; Home
Economics; Medicine; Oriental Medicine;
Dentistry; Pharmacy; Foreign Languages and
Literature; Social Sciences; Music; Physical
Education; Natural Sciences; Engineering;
Industry; Physical Education and Sports; Hotel
Administration (International).
S: Nursing; Education; Public Administration;
Business Administration; Technology and
Information Sciences; Journalism and Mass
Communication; Peace Studies.

Kyungnam University

449 Wolyong-dong, Habpo-gu, Masan 631-701
Tel: +82(551) 45-5000
Fax: +82(551) 46-6184
Telex: 533698
President: Jae Kyu Park (1986-)
Dean of Academic Affairs
International Relations: Maeng Yol Jang
Founded: 1946, 1982
C: Liberal Arts and Science; Education;
Commerce and Economics; Law and Political
Science; Engineering.
Graduate S: Education; Business
Administration.
I: Far Eastern Studies; Industrial Management;
Environmental Research.

423

Kyungpook Sanup University
33 Puho-Ri, Hayang-Up, Kyungsan-Gun,
Kyungsangpuk-Do 713-701
Tel: +82(541) 53-8001
Fax: +82(541) 53-8800
President: Lee Hyo Tae (1993-97)
Director of General Affairs: Cho Ho Hyun
International Relations: Weon S. Lee
Founded: 1963
C: Engineering; Humanities and Social
Sciences; Formative Arts.
Graduate S: Industry.
Research I: Industrial Technology; Regional
Industry and Business; Formative arts; Local
Autonomy.
Ce: Education; Computer.

Kyungsung University
Taeyon-dong, Nam-gu, Busan 608-736
Tel: +82(51) 623-5331
Fax: +82(51) 623-7803
President: Kim Dae-Sung (1993-95)
International Relations: Cho Dal-Gon
Founded: 1955
C: Liberal Arts; Law and Political Science;
Commerce and Economics; Sciences;
Engineering; Pharmacy; Arts.
Graduate S: International Trade; Industry;
Education.

Kyungwon University
San 65, Pokjon-dong, Sujong-gu, Songnam CT,
Kyonggi 461-701
Tel: +82(342) 752-3220
Fax: +82(342) 753-8828
President: Tai-Sik Sim (1994-97)
Director of Planning: Moo-Hong Joo
International Relations: Moo-Hong Joo
Founded: 1981

Mokwon University Taejon
24 Mok-dong, Chung-gku, Taejon CT, Chungnam
301-729
Tel: +82(42) 220-6114
Fax: +82(42) 256-2315
President: Pong-Bae Park (1990-)
Founded: 1954, 1980
C: Humanities; Social Sciences; Science and
Engineering; Music; Fine Arts; Liberal Arts and
Science.
Graduate S: Theology.
I: Industrial Management.
Ce: Computer.

Myong Ji University
50-3 Namgajwa-dong, Seodaemun-gu, Seoul,
120-728
Tel: +82(2) 300-1700
Fax: +82(2) 307-6196
President: Kun Koh (1994-98)
Vice-President: Jung-Sun Suh
International Relations: Dean of Planning and
Management Board, Pyun Chong-Kun
Founded: 1948, 1962, 1983

C: Humanities; Law and Political Science;
Business Administration and Economics; Science;
Engineering; Humanities and Social Science.
I: Public Administration Research; Industrial
Research; Humanities; Saemul.

*Pai Chai University
439-6 Toma-dong, Seo-ku, Taejon CT, Chungnam
302-162
Tel: +82(42) 520-5114
Fax: +82(42) 525-9334
President: Seung-Keun Rhee
Dean: Hea-Joon Chung
Founded: 1885, 1978, 1981
C: Liberal Arts; Social Sciences; Natural
Sciences; International Industry; Education;
General Education.
I: Early Childhood Education; Humanities;
Natural Sciences; Social Sciences; Advanced
Sciences and Technology; Educational Research;
Social Education; Audio-Visual Education;
International Education; Unification Research.

Pierson University
111 Youngyi-Dong, Pyongtaeg, Kyungki-Do
450-130
Tel: +82(333) 655-8701/5
Fax: +82(333) 54-1863
President: Dal-Jin Park (1988-)
Director of Planning and Control
Founded: 1912
D: Theology; Social Welfare; Korean Language
and Literature; Community Development;
Business Administration; Public Administration;
Economics; Music; Visual Art Design.

Pohang University of Science and Technology
San 31, Hyoja-dong, Pohang CT, Kyungbuk
790-784
Tel: +82(562) 279-2001
Fax: +82(562) 279-2020
E-Mail: chang@ vision.postech.ac.kr
Telex: K54312
President: Sooyoung Chang (1994-)
Dean of Academic Affairs: Jin Ho Kwak
International Relations: Eun Sook Choi
Founded: 1986
D: Mathematics; Physics; Chemistry; Life
Science; Materials Science and Metallurgical
Engineering; Mechanical Engineering; Industrial
Engineering; Electronic and Electrical
Engineering; Computer Science; Chemical
Engineering; General Education.
Graduate S: Information Technology.
Research Ce: Advanced Fluids Engineering;
Automation; Catalytic Technology; Biofunctonal
Molecules; Advanced Aerospace Materials;
Biotechnology; Super High-Speed Electronic;
Basic Science Research; Advanced Product and
Production Technology.
L: Accelerator; Information Research.

Pusan University of Foreign Studies
Uam-Dong, Nam-Gu, Pusan 608-060
Tel: +82(51) 643-5111-7
Fax: +82(51) 645-4525
President: Pong-Sik Park (1994-98)
Dean of Academic Affairs: Jeong-Son Kim
International Relations: Dean of Planning and
Development, Seong-Cheol Choi
Founded: 1981
*F: Foreign Studies; Humanities and Social
Science; Economics and Trade; Natural Sciences
and Engineering.*
*I: Audio-Visual Education; Law; International
Studies; Foreign Language Training.*
S: Evening; Graduate.
*Ce: Linguistic Research; Cultural Studies; Social
Science Research; Computer; Trade and
Management.*

Sacred Heart College for Women, Puchon City
[Songsim Yoja Daehak]
San 43-1, Yokkgok 2-Dong, Puchon City, Kyonggi
422-743
Tel: +82(32) 62-8251
Fax: +82(32) 665-9798
President: Jae Soon Kim, R.S.C.J. (1993-)
Dean of Studies: Yoong-il Kim
Founded: 1964
*D: Korean Language and Literature; English
Language and Literature; French Language and
Literature; Chinese Language and Literature;
Korean History; Social Service; Sociology;
Business Administration; Accountancy;
Psychology; Home Economics; Nutrition; Textile
Engineering and Clothing; Chemistry;
Mathematics; Biology; Music.*
*Graduate S: Korean Language and Literature;
English Language and Literature; French
Language and Literature; Social Service;
Chemistry.*
*I: Natural Sciences; Life Science; Religious
Educaton; Sacred Music; Research of Social
Sciences.*

Sang Ji College
Woosan-dong, Wonju CT, Kangwon 220-702
Tel: +82(374) 42-1121
Fax: +82(374) 42-2433
President: Chan-Kook Gim (1993-97)
Dean of Studies: Seung-Suck Oh
International Relations: Director of Planning and
Development, Myung-Hwan Kim
Founded: 1974
*D: Law; Public Administration; Economics;
Business Administration; Social Welfare.*

Sang Myung Women's University
Hongji-dong, Chongno-gu, Seoul 110-743
Tel: +82(2) 287-5114
Fax: +82(2) 396-6226
President: Jung-Bok Bang (1991-94)
Myung-Sook Han
International Relations: Hoo-Jee Lee
Founded: 1965

*D: Home Economics; Fine Arts; Physical
Education; Korean Literature; English Philology;
Music; Sociology.*

Sejong University, Seoul
98 Kunja-Dong, Sungdong-Gu, Seoul 133-747
Tel: +82(2) 460-0114
Fax: +82(2) 460-0405
President: Joong Hwa Lee (1991-95)
Director, University Planning: Kwang Sun Hong
International Relations: Hyun Ju Shin
Founded: 1947
*D: Korean Language; English; Japanese;
Education; History; Public Administration;
Economics; International Trade; Applied
Statistics; Business Administration; Finance and
Accounting; Tourism Administration; Hotel
Administration; Information Science;
Mathematics; Chemistry; Food Science; Home
Economics; Earth Science; Computer Science;
Physics; Fine Arts; Applied Arts; Gymnastics;
Dance; Music.*

Semyung University
San 21-1, Shinwol-Dong, Chechon-Si, Chungbuk
390-230
Tel: +82(443) 45-1125
Fax: +82(443) 44-2111
President: Kim Yub (1991-)
Founder and Chairman: Kwon Young Woo
Founded: 1987
*C: Humanities; Law; Business Administration;
Natural Sciences; Engineering; Oriental Medicine.*
*I: Human and Social Science Research;
Industrial Technology Research.*

Seoul Women's University
126 Kongreung-dong, Nowon-gu, Seoul 139-774
Tel: +82(2) 970-5114
Fax: +82(2) 978-7931
President: Koo-Young Chung (1984-95)
International Relations: Director for International
Cooperation, Misun Mun
Founded: 1960
*C: Humanities; Social Sciences; Natural
Sciences; Fine Arts and Physical Education.*
*I: Saemaul Studies; Rural Development;
Women's Studies.*

Seo Kyeong University
16-1, Chongneung-Dong, Songbuk-Gu, Seoul
136-704
Tel: +82(2) 940-7114
Fax: +82(2) 919-0345

Seonam University
720 Kwangchi-Dong, Namwon, Chonbuk 590-170
Tel: +82(671) 33-9300
Fax: +82(671) 33-9306
President: Hong-Ha Lee (1992-96)
Secretary-General: Eun-Seop Song
Founded: 1991

D: Korean Language and Literature; English Language and Litetarure; Public Administration; Law; Management Information Systems; Management; Computer Science; Computer Science and Statistics; Computer Science and Information Science; Mathematics; Physics; Chemistry; Biology; Electronic Engineering; Electrical Engineering; Chemical Engineeering; Civil Engineering; Architectural Engineering; Industrial Design.

Seoul Theological University
Bucheon 422-742
Tel: +82(32) 349-9381
Fax: +82(32) 349-9400
President: Keun Whan Kang (1992-96)
Founded: 1911
Theology; Christian Education; Social Work; Church Music.

Seowon University
231 Mochung-dong, Chungju CT, Chungbuk 360-742
Tel: +82(431) 62-8822
President: Shin-Hee Hong (1993-)
Registrar: Ki-Yang Pak
Founded: 1972
Humanities and Social Sciences; Education; Natural Sciences; Arts.

*Sogang University
Shinsu-dong, Mapo-gu, Seoul 121-742
Tel: +82(2) 705-8114
Fax: +82(2) 705-8204
Cable: jesuitmis
President: Park Hong, S.J. (1989-)
Vice-President: chung-Ho Suh
International Relations: Assistant to the President for International Affairs, Basil M. Price, S.J.
Founded: 1960, 1970
C: Social Science; Business Administration; Liberal Arts; Science and Engineering; Commerce.
Graduate S: Business Administration.
I: Humanities Research; Basic Science Research; Religious Studies; Communications and Culture; Economic and Business Research; East-Asian Studies; Labour and Management Studies; Technology Management; Accountancy; English; Industrial Technology Research; Philosophy.
D: General Education.

Songsim University
San 43-1, Yokgok 2-Dong, Wonmi-Gu, Kyonggi Do 422-743
Tel: +82(32) 342-9610
Fax: +82(32) 341-9798
President: Jae Soon Kim (1993-)
Dean of Academic Affairs: Seungil Back
International Relations: Seejae Lee
Founded: 1964
D: Korean Language and Literature; English Language and Literature; French Language and

Literature; Chinese Language and Literature; Korean History; Religious Studies; Social Work; Sociology; Business Administration; Accounting; Psychology; Home Management; Food and Nutrition; Clothing and Texitile; Chemistry; Mathematics; Biology; Computer Science; Music.
I: Natural Sciences; Life Sciences; Religious Education; Sacred Music; Social Sciences; Industrial Management.

Sookmyung Women's University
Chungpa-Dong 2Ka, Yongsan-gu, Seoul 140-742
Tel: +82(2) 710-9000
Fax: +82(2) 718-2337
Founded: 1938, 1955
C: Liberal Arts; Natural Sciences; Home Economics; Political Science and Economics; Music; Pharmacy; Fine Arts.
Research I: Political Affairs and Economics; Languages and Literature; Pharmaceutical Science; Reunification.
Ce: Asian Women (Research).

Soon Shin University
604-5, Dang Jung-Dong, Kunpo-Si, Kyung Gi-Do 435-742
Tel: +82(343) 52-8054-6
Fax: +82(343) 57-6517
President: Jeong Yull Park (1992-96)
Director for Planning and Coordination: In Kap Chung
International Relations: Provost, Kun Seung Lee
Founded: 1953
Theology.

Soonchungyang University
San 53-1, Eupnae-ri, Sinchang-myun, Asan-gun, Choongchungnam-Do
Tel: +82(418) 549-1114
Fax: +82(418) 42-4615
President: Tai-ho Cho (1993-97)
Director of Planning: Won-jik Lee
Founded: 1978, 1979
C: Humanities; Economics and Commerce; Sciences; Industrial Sciences; Medicine.
I: Cancer Research; Obstetrics and Gynaecology; Industrial Medicine; Population and Community Health Studies.

*Soong Sil University Seoul
1-1, Sangdo 5 Dong, Dongjak-ku, Seoul 156-743
Tel: +82(2) 820-0114
Fax: +82(2) 816-1513
President: Song-Chin Kim (1993-97)
Vice-President: Hoo-Bong Song
International Relations: Director of International Programs, Ja-Yoon Koo
Founded: 1897, 1905, 1971, 1987
C: Liberal Arts; Natural Sciences; Law; Social Sciences; Economics and Commerce; Engineering.
S: Industry (Graduate); Small Business Studies (Graduate); Information Science (Graduate); Labour and Industrial Relations (Graduate).

I: Humanities; Basic Sciences; Law; Social Sciences; Social Sciences (Christian); Industrial and Economics Research; Christian Culture; Small Business Development; Labour and Industrial Relations (Korean).
Ce: Computer.

Southern Seoul University
21 Maeju-Ri, Seonghwan-Eup, Cheonahn-Kun, Choongnam 333-800
Tel: +82(417) 580-2000
Fax: +82(417) 582-2117
President: Ho-Keun Kim (1994-)
Dean of Academic Affairs: Kwan-Hoo Yang
International Relations: Dean of Public Relations and Cooperation, BYung-Kweon Cheon
Founded: 1993
C: Engineering; Business; Art and Design; Liberal Arts.
I: Public Relations and Cooperation; Industrial Technology.
Ce: Computer; Audio-Visual.

St. Michael's (Anglican) University
1-1 Hang-Dong, Kuro-ku, Seoul 152-140
Tel: +82(2) 615-0005
Fax: +82(2) 683-8858
President: Jae Joung Lee (1993-97)
Executive Director for Accademic Affairs
International Relations: Hahn Kyung Kim
Founded: 1914
Arts and Science; Divinity.

Sun Moon University
381-7, Samryong-Dong, Chonan-Si, Choongnam 330-150
Tel: +82(417) 567-9671
Fax: +82(417) 61-2065
President: Yoon Se Won (1986-)
International Relations: Planning Director, Koh Jong Won
Founded: 1986
C: Theology; Humanities; Economics and Business; Natural Science; Engineering.
I: Korean Language; Unificaition Theology.
Ce: Theological Studies; Science and Advanced Technology.

Sung Kyul Christian University
147-2, Anyang 8-Dong, Mana-Gu, Anyang, Kyunggi-Do 430-742
Tel: +82(343) 43-3831
Fax: +82(343) 43-3831
President: Sung Kee-Ho (1989-98)
Dean Chaplain: Jeong Sang-Un
International Relations: Kim Kwang-Son
D: Theology; Christian Education; Pastoral Theology; Overseas Missons; Church Music; Community Development; Social Wealfare; Early Childhood Education; English Language and Literature; Business Administration; Public Administration; Computer Science; Computer Information; Computer Statistics.

Sung Kyun Kwan University
53, 3-ka Myungryun-dong, Chongro-gu, Seoul 110-745
Tel: +82(2) 760-0114
Fax: +82(2) 744-2453
President: Chang Eul-Byung (1991-94)
Academic Affairs Officer
International Relations: Song Jae-So
Founded: 1992, 1398, 1937
C: Liberal Arts; Science; Engineering; Law and Political Science; Economics and Commerce; Pharmacy; Confucian Studies; Agriculture; Home Economics; Education.
S: Economics; Library Science; Foreign Trade (Graduate); Industrial Development (Graduate).
I: Research of Oriental Culture; Science Research; Humanities; Social Sciences; Korean Industrial Studies.

Sungshin Women's University
249-1, 3ka, Tongson-dong, Songbug-gu, Seoul 136-742
Tel: +82(2) 920-7114
Fax: +82(2) 926-3120
President: Han Young-hwan (1991-95)
Dean of Academic Affairs: Ahn Myung-soo
International Relations: Kwon Yong-woo
Founded: 1963
D: Home Economics; Economics; Foreign Languages; Fine Arts; Korean Language and Literature; Music; Social Sciences.

Suweon University
Wawoo-ri,Pongdam-myon, Hwasong-gun, Kyonggi 445-890
Tel: +82(2) 33-1402
Founded: 1981

Suwon Catholic College
Wongrim-ri, Pongdam-myon, Hwasong-gun, Kyonggi-do 445-744
Tel: +82(331) 292-4521-4
Fax: +82(331) 292-4526
Rector: Sang-Ho Han (1994-)
Registrar: Kwang-am Hakwon
Founded: 1983

Taegu Catholic College
219, Namsan 3-Dong, Jung-Gu, Taegu 705-020
Tel: +82(53) 256-5358
Fax: +82(53) 252-9753
President: Kim Young Hwan (1993-)
Executive: Choi Whi In
Founded: 1981
Theology; Medicine.

Taegu Oriental Medical College
Chumchon-dong, Kyongsan-gun, Kyongbuk 713-800
Tel: +82 83-0551
Founded: 1980
Oriental Medicine.

Taegu University
15 Naeri-Ri, Jinryang-Myon, Kyongsan-Gun,
Kyongsangbuk-Do 713-714
Tel: +82(541) 50-5700
Fax: +82(541) 50-5820
President: Cho Ki Seob (1994-)
Founded: 1956

Taejeon University
96-3 Yongun-dong, Tong-gu, Taejon CT,
Chungnam 300-716
Tel: +82(42) 280-2114
Fax: +82(42) 283-8808
Founded: 1981
D: Korean Language and Literature; English;
National Ethics; Law; Public Administration;
Management Economics; International Trade;
Mathematics; Economics; Oriental Medicine;
Biology; Electronics; Architecture.

Taeshin University
708-113 Anyang 5-Dong, Manan-Gu, Anyang,
Kyung-Gi
Tel: +82(2) 855-2010
Fax: +82(343) 48-3870
President: Young Sil Kim (1991-94)
Executive Director: Hyung Suk Kim
International Relations: Associate Chief of
Academic Affairs, In Hwan Kim
C: Engineering; Humanities; Social Sciences;
Law and Political Science; Education; Business
Admininstration; Arts.

University of Ulsan
Mugo-dong, Ulsan CT, Kyongnam 680-749
Tel: +82(522) 77-3101
Fax: +82(522) 77-3101
E-Mail: sjlee@munsu.ulsan.ac.kr
President: Sangjoo Lee (1988-)
Dean of Academic Affairs: Muntae Park
International Relations: Director for Research and
International Exchange, Jinmoo Kim
Founded: 1969
D: Mechanical Engineering; Electrical
Engineering; Material Sciences; Civil
Engineering; Chemistry and Industrial Chemistry;
Architecture; General Studies.
C: Junior Technical.
Ce: Computer.

WonKwang University
344-2 Shinyong-dong, Iri CT, Chollabukdo 570-749
Tel: +82(653) 50-5111
Fax: +82(653) 50-5666
President: Kim Sam-Ryong (1986-94)
Vice-President: Ryu Byung-Duk
International Relations: Vice-President, Han
Ki-Doo
Founded: 1953
C: Liberal Arts and Science; Education; Law
and Political Science; Pharmacy; Commerce and
Economics; Education; Agriculture; Oriental
Medicine; Dentistry; Engineering; Home
Economics.

Yeungnam University
Taedong-dong, Kyongsan, Kyoungbook 712-749
Tel: +82(2) 393-3330
Fax: +82(2) 392-0618
President: Ryu Chang Ou
Founded: 1967
C: Liberal Arts; Science; Engineering; Law and
Political Science; Commerce and Economics;
Medicine; Pharmacy; Home Economics;
Education; Agriculture and Animal Husbandry;
Music; Fine Arts; Evening.
Graduate S: Business Administration;
Environmental Studies; Education.

*Yonsei University Seoul
134 Shinchon-dong, Sudaemun-gu, Seoul 120-749
Tel: +82(2) 361-2114
Fax: +82(2) 392-0618
Telex: yonsei K29127
President: Ja Song (1992-96)
Vice-President: Sok Duk Kim
International Relations: Director, Division of
Internation Education, Horace H. Underwood
Founded: 1885, 1957
C: Liberal Arts; Business Administration and
Economics; Science; Engineering; Theology;
Social Sciences; Law; Music; Home Economics;
Education and Physical Education; Medicine;
Dentistry; Nursing.
S: Graduate; Business Administration
(Graduate); Theology (Graduate); Education
(Graduate); Public Administration (Graduate);
Engineering (Graduate); Health Sciences and
Management (Graduate); International Studies
(Graduate).
I: Agricultural Development; Medical
Technology; Korean Studies; East and West
Studies; Urban Studies and Development;
Christianity and Korean Culture; Tropical
Medicine; Occupational Health Studies.
Ce: Korean-French.

OTHER INSTITUTIONS

NATIONAL INSTITUTIONS

Busan National Teachers College
Koje-dong, Tongnae-gu, Busan 607-070
Tel: +82(51) 84-5055
Founded: 1946
Teacher Training.

Jeon Ju National Teachers College
Dongsohak-dong, Chongju CT, Chonbuk 560-120
Tel: +82(6) 0051
Founded: 1936
Teacher Training.

PRIVATE INSTITUTIONS

Youngdong Institute of Technology
San 12-1 Chung Book Youngdong Koon,
Youngdong, Up Selkeli
Tel: +82(414) 40-1045
Fax: +82(414) 40-1039
President: Kim Jea Ku (1994-)
Registrar: Lee Wan Young
Founded: 1994
*Chemical Engineering; Heredity Engineering;
Computer Science; Electronics Engineering;
Communication Engineering; City Urban
Engineering; Architectural Engineering; Industry
Engineering.*

NATIONAL ACADEMIC BODIES

Ministry of Education
77 Sejong-ro, Chong-ro-gu, Seoul
Tel: +82(2) 720-3400
Fax: +82(2) 733-2322
Telex: 24758 munkyo k
Minister: Sook-he Kim

Korean Council for University Education (KCUE)
27-2 Youido-dong, Youngdongpo-ku, Seoul
150-742
Tel: +82(2) 783-3067
Fax: +82(2) 780-8311
Chairman: Chong Un Kim
Secretary-General: Byung-Rym Koo
International Relations: Executive Director,
Research Institute of Higher Education, Hyun
Chong Lee
Founded: 1982

The Korean Federation of Education Associations
142 Woomyon-dong, Seocho-ku, Seoul 137-140
Tel: +82(2) 576-5892/7
Fax: +82(2) 577-5965
Cable: korean education
President: Hyung-Won Yoon (1994-97)
Secretary-General: Yong-Am Park
International Relations: Director, International
Relations, Jae-Koo Woo
Founded: 1947

Korean National Commission for Unesco
Sungloon Building, 141 Samsung-Dong,
Kangnam-ku, Seoul 135-190
Tel: +82(2) 561-6754
Fax: +82(2) 568-7454
Telex: mocndm k23231-2
Cable: unesco seoul
Chairman: Sook-he Kim, Minister of Education
Secretary-General: In-suk Cha
International Relations: Chief, International
Cooperation Section, Hyun-soo Park
Founded: 1954

KUWAIT

UNIVERSITIES

*Kuwait University
[Jami'at al-Kuwait]
Khaldia, P.O. Box 5969, Kuwait Safat 13060
Tel: +965 481-1188
Telex: kt 22616
Rector: Faizhai M. Al-Kharafi (1993-)
Secretary-General: Hussain Al-Mahmoud
Founded: 1966
F: Medicine; Allied Health Sciences and Nursing.
C: Commerce, Economics and Political Science; Law; Arts; Science; Engineering and Petroleum Technology; Education; Shari'a (Islamic Law) and Islamic Studies.
Ce: Community Service and Continuing Education.

OTHER INSTITUTIONS

College of Basic Education
P.O. Box 34053, Adiuilia 73251
Tel: +965 251-4200
Education.

College of Business Studies
P.O. Box 43197, Hawalli 32046
Tel: +965 261-4962
Telex: KT 22615 A
Business Studies.

College of Health Sciences
P.O. Box 14281, Fayha 72853
Tel: +965 254-1044
Health Sciences.

College of Technological Studies
P.O. Box 42325, Shuwaikh 70654
Tel: +965 846-471
Telex: 22269 ptt trg
Technological Studies.

Public Authority for Applied Education and Training
P.O. Box 23167, Safat 13092
Tel: +965 241-3050
Telex: 22269
Founded: 1982
Education and Training.

NATIONAL ACADEMIC BODIES

Ministry of Education and Higher Education
P.O.Box 7, Safat
Tel: +965 481-7702
Fax: +965 483-7601
Minister: Ahmad Abdallah Al-Rube

Kuwait National Commission for Unesco
Post Box 3266, Safat 13033
Tel: +965 240-5331
Fax: +965 244-4403
Telex: 23656
Chairman: Ahmad Abdallah Al-Rube, Minister of Education
Secretary-General: Sulaiman Al-Onaizi

KYRGYZSTAN

UNIVERSITIES

*Kyrgyz University
[Kyrgyzskij Gosudarstvennyj Universitet]
Ul. Bishkek 537, 720024 Bishkek 24
Tel: +7 26-26-34
Founded: 1951
F: History; Law; Philology; Economics; Finance; Mathematics and Applied Mathematics; Physics; Geography; Biology; Foreign Languages; Chemistry.
D: Evening Studies; Correspondence Courses.

OTHER INSTITUTIONS

Biskekskij Politehniceskij Institut
Prosp. Mira 66, 720057 Bishkek
Tel: +7 42-14-62

Kirgizskij Gosudarstvennyj Medicinskij Institut
Ul. 50-let Oktjabrja 92, 720061 Bishkek
Medicine.

Kirgizskij Sel'skohozjajstvennyj Institut
Ul. Kommunisticeskaja 68, 720453 Bishkek
Tel: +7 4-54-11
Agriculture.

Kirgizskij Gosudarstvennyj Institut Iskusstv
Ul. Dzantoseva 115, 720460 Bishkek
Arts.

NATIONAL ACADEMIC BODIES

Ministry of Education
Bishkek

National Commission for the Kyrgyz Republic for Unesco
Ministry of Foreign Affairs, Ul Abdumonuov 205, Bishkek
Tel: +33(12) 22-69-22
Fax: +33(12) 22-57-35
Telex: 245185 ubter sy
Chairman: O. Ibraimov
Secretary-General: Adasch Toktosunova

LAO PEOPLE'S DEMOCRATIC REPUBLIC

UNIVERSITIES

Institute of Pedogogy Dongdok (IUP)
[Mahavithagnalay Sangkhou Dongdok]
Ministry of Education, Lanexang Road, B.P. 67, Vientiane
Tel: +856 413631
Director: Phankham Viphavanh (1989-94)
Founded: 1958
Pedagogy.

National Polytechnic Institute
[Mahavithagnalay Saphavisa 'Song Thanhva']
Ministry of Education, Lanexang Road, B.P. 67, Vientiane
Tel: +856(21) 312072
Fax: +856(21) 314382
Director: Tuyen Dongvan (1993-94)
Founded: 1984

University of Medical Sciences
[Mahavithagnalay Phaitsat]
Ministry of Public Health, P.O. Box 131, Vientiane
Tel: +856(21) 4034
Rector: Bounkouang Phichith (1991-94)
Director: Phienpheng Phone Sena
Founded: 1958
F: Medicine; Pharmacy.
S: Public Health; Dentistry.

OTHER INSTITUTIONS

Honghien Kalxang Sanhzoung Fayfa-Electronic
Ministry of Education, Lanexang Road B.P. 67, Vientiane
Tel: +856(21) 2423
Director: Somnuch Vorasanh
Founded: 1983
Electronics and Electrotechniques.

Honghien Kaset Naboung
Ministry of Agriculture and Forestry, B.P. 811, Vientiane
Director: Xayamang Vongsack (1992-94)
Founded: 1992
Agriculture.

Honghien Kosang Kehasathanh Sanhzung
Ministry of Communication, Transport, Post and Construction, Vientiane
Tel: +856(21) 414530
Director: Bounleam Sysoulat
Founded: 1983
Building and Architecture.

Honghien Khommanakhom Kholsong sanhzooung
Ministry of Communication, Transport, Post and Construction, Vientiane
Tel: +856(21) 312424
Director: Rathanamany Khounivong (1991-94)
Founded: 1974
Communication and Transport.

Honghien Kotmay
Ministry of Jutice, Vientiane
Tel: +856(21) 312010
Director: Soutta Chommanychanh (1989-94)
Founded: 1986
Law.

Honghien Pamay Sanhzung Dongdok
Ministry of Agruculture and Forestry, B.P. 811, Vientiane
Tel: +856(21) 414813
Director: Suchhongseng Saignaleut (1993-94)
Founded: 1986
Forestry.

Honghien Paysani Tholakhommanakhom Sanhzung
Ministry of Communication, Transport, Post and Construction, Vientiane
Tel: +856(21) 312427
Director: Insouane Bounnasy (1988-94)
Founded: 1988
Post and Telecommunications.

Honghien Sollaphathal Thad Thong
Ministry of Agriculture and Forestry, .P. 811 Vientiane
Tel: +856(21) 215019
Director: Phomkham Namkham (1985-94)
Founded: 1985
Irrigation.

NATIONAL ACADEMIC BODIES

Ministry of Education and Sports
Avenue Lane Xang, Vientiane
Tel: +856(21) 60-00
Fax: +856(21) 60-07
Minister: M. Phimmasone

Lao National Commission for Unesco
B.P. 67, Vientiane
Tel: +856(21) 216-004
Fax: +856(21) 212-108
Telex: 4320
Cable: laonatcom mineducation vientiane
Chairman: M. Phimmasone, Minister of Education
Secretary-General: Khamphao Phonekeo

LATVIA
UNIVERSITIES

Daugavpils Pedagogical University
[Daugavpils Pedagoğiska universitate]
Vienibas iela 13, 5407 Daugavpili
Tel: +371(2) 8-254-22180
Fax: +371(2) 8-254-22890
Rector: Bruno Jansons
Vice-Rector (Academic): Stanislavs Rabša
International Relations: Indrikis Krams
F: Biology and Chemistry; Physics and Mathematics; Humanities; Physical Culture; Music.

Academy of Arts
[Latvjas Makslas akademija]
Kalpaka bulv. 13, 1867 Riga
Tel: +371(2) 33-22-02
Fax: +371(2) 22-89-63
Rector: Indulis Zarinš
Vice-Rector (Academic): Atis Kampars
International Relations: Atis Kampars
Arts.

Institute of Medecine
[Latvijas Medicinas akademija]
Dzirciema iela 16, 1007 Riga
Tel: +371(2) 45-97-52
Fax: +371(8) 82-81-55
Telex: 161172 tema sv
Rector: Janis Vetra
Vice-Rector (Academic): Aija Žilevica
International Relations: Ilze Aizsilniece
Founded: 1949
F: Medicine; Stomatology; Pharmacy; Rehabilitation; Nursing.

Academy of Agriculture
[Latvijas Lauksaimniecibas universitate]
Liela iela 2, 3001 Jelgava
Tel: +371(30) 225-84
Fax: +371(30) 272-38
Telex: 161100 pkp su/for jelg 35 sinus
Rector: Voldemars Strikis
Vice-Rector (Academic): Peteris Bušmanis
International Relations: Inara Melgalve
Founded: 1937
F: Agricultural Engineering; Agriculture; Economics; Food Technology; Forestry; Rural Engineering; Veterinary Medicine.

Music Academy of Latvia
[Jazepa Vitola Latvijas Muzikas akademija]
Kr. Barona iela 1, 1050 Riga
Tel: +371(2) 22-86-84
Fax: +371(8) 82-02-71
Telex: 161186 forum su
Rector: Juris Karlsons
Vice-Rector: Arvids Luste
International Relations: Maija Sipola
Founded: 1920
Music.

Riga Technical University

[Rigas Tehniska universitate]
Kalku iela 1, 1055 Riga
Tel: +371(2) 22-58-85
Fax: +371(8) 82-00-94
Rector: Egons Lavendelis
Vice-Rector (Academic): Janis Gerhards
International Relations: Natalija Ivanova
Founded: 1861
F: *Instrumentation and Automation Engineering;*
Architecture; Computer Science and Computer
Engineering; Civil Engineering; Electrical and
Power Engineering; Engineering Economics;
Chemical Technology; Mechanical Engineering;
Radio Engineering and Telecommunications;
Textile and Clothing Technology.

Institute of Civil Aviation

[Rigas Aviacijas universitate]
Lomononosova iela 1, 1019 Riga
Tel: +371(2) 10-32-85
Fax: +371(2) 14-02-93
Telex: 161100 klp su rau
Rector: Vladimirs Hodakovskis
Vice-Rector (Academic): Jurijs Martinovs
International Relations: Vladimirs Silantjevs
Founded: 1919
F: *Mechanical Engineering; Radio Electronics*
and Computer Systems; Economics.

*University of Latvia

[Latvijas Universitáte]
Raina bulvari 19, 1586 Riga
Tel: +371(2) 22-86-11
Fax: +371(8) 82-01-13
Telex: 161172 tema su
Rector: Juris Zakis (1970-)
Vice-Rector (Academic): Juris Kruminš
International Relations: Aline Gržibovska
Founded: 1919
F: *Foreign Languages; Geography; History and*
Philosophy; Law; Management and Economic
Informatics; Philology; Physics and Mathematics;
Theology.

OTHER INSTITUTIONS

Latvijas Juras akademija

Kronvalda bulv. 6, 1010 Riga
Tel: +371(2) 32-11-61
Fax: +371(8) 83-01-38
Rector: Janis Berzinš (1991-)
Vice-Rector (Academic): Indulis Liepinš
International Relations: Irena Valevča
Founded: 1991
Maritime Studies.

Latvijas Kulturas akademija

Luzdas iela 24, 1003 Riga
Tel: +371(2) 14-01-75
Fax: +371(2) 22-88-83
Rector: Peteris Lakis (1991-)
Founded: 1991.
D: *History of Culture; International Studies; Film*
Directing.

Latvijas Policijas akademija

Ezermalasiela iela 8, 1028 Riga
Tel: +371(2) 55-14-37
Fax: +371(2) 55-10-70
Rector: Zenons Indrikovs (1991-)
Vice-Rector (Academic): Osvalds Joksts
International Relations: Osvalds Joksts
Founded: 1991
Police Studies.

Latvijas Republikas Nacionalas Aizsardzibas akademija

Ezermalas iela 8, 1028 Riga
Tel: +371(2) 52-28-10
Fax: +371(2) 52-28-10
Rector: Valdis Matiss (1991-)
Vice-Rector (Academic): Karlis Kreslinš
International Relations: Indulis Skrastin
Founded: 1991
Defence Studies.

Latvijas Sporta pedağoğijas akademija

Brivibas iela 333, 1037 Riga
Tel: +371(2) 52-05-95
Fax: +371(2) 22-50-39
Telex: tema su 161172
Rector: Uldis Gravitis
Vice-Rector (Academic): Viesturs Krauksts
International Relations: Uldis Švinks
Physical Education and Sports.

Liepajas Pedagoğiska augstskola

Lielaja iela 14, 3401 Liepaja
Tel: +371(2) 8-234-2401
Fax: +371(2) 8-234-24223
Rector: Karlis Dobelis
Vice-Rector (Academic): Roberts Veics
International Relations: Karlis Dobelis
Pedagogy.

Rezeknes Augstskola

Atbrivošanas aleja 90, 4600 Rezekne
Tel: +371(2) 8-246-23219
Fax: +371(2) 8-246-23709
Rector: Irena Silineviča (1993-)
Vice-Rector (Academic): Manfreds Šneps-Šneppe
International Relations: Manfreds Šneps-Sneppe
Founded: 1993

NATIONAL ACADEMIC BODIES

Ministry of Education, Culture and Science

[Izglitibas, Kulturas un Zinatnes Ministrija]
Valnu iela 2, 1098 Riga
Tel: +371(2) 22-24-15
Fax: +371(2) 21-39-92
Telex: 161172 tema su
Minister: Janis Vaivads

Latvia National Commission for Unesco

Pils Iaukums 4-415, 1804 Riga
Tel: +371(2) 22-27-62
Fax: +371(2) 22-74-05
President: Janis Vaivads, Minister of Education
Secretary-General: Rudite Grigorjeva

LEBANON

UNIVERSITIES

Balamand University
[Université de Balamand]
B.P. 100, Tripoli
Tel: +961(6) 610-133
Fax: +961(6) 866-650
President: Ghassan Tuéni
Founded: 1988
Theology; Fine Arts; Humanities.

*American University of Beirut
Beirut, or U.S. Office:, 850 Third Avenue (18th
Floor), New York, N.Y. 10022
Tel: +1(212) 319-2429
Fax: +1(212) 486-2867
Telex: (Beirut) 2081 le
President: Robert M. Haddad (1993-)
Registrar (Acting): Edward A. Mazloum
Founded: 1866, 1920
*F: Arts and Sciences; Medicine; Health
Sciences; Engineering and Architecture;
Agriculture and Food Sciences.*
D: Education.
S: Nursing.
Ce: Computer.

*Beirut Arab University
[Jâmi'at Bâyrut al-'Arabiya]
Tarik El-Jadidé, P.O. Box 11-5020, Beirut
Tel: +961(1)300-110
Telex: 22844 Abu
President: Mohamed Ali Abdelrahim
Founded: 1960
*F: Arts; Law; Commerce; Engineering;
Architecture; Science; Pharmacy.*

Lebanese American University
B.P. 4080, Beirut
Tel: +961(1) 811-968
Founded: 1950

*Lebanese University Beirut
[Al-Jâmi'ah al-Lubnaniyah]
Museum Square, Beirut
Tel: +961(1)386-817
Telex: 42151 Le Fansul
Recteur (Acting): Mohamed Majzoub (1993-)
Secrétaire général: Larifée Lakis
Founded: 1951, 1953
*F: Fine Arts; Science; Law, Political Science
and Administration; Letters and Human Sciences;
Education; Journalism and Communication;
Economics and Business Administration;
Engineering; Social Sciences; Agriculture; Public
Health; Medicine.*

*Notre Dame University, Louaizé
[Université Notre-Dame, Louaizé]
P.O. Box 72 Zouk Mikael, Zouk Mosbeh
Recteur: R.P. François Eid
Founded: 1978, 1987
*S: Business, Economics and Diplomacy;
Humanities; Natural and Applied Sciences.*

*St. Joseph University Beirut +Université
Saint Joseph +Jami'at al-Qiddis Yussuf
Rue Huvelin, B.P. 293, Beirut
Tel: +961(1) 324-900
Cable: medifac
Recteur: Jean Ducruet, S.J. (1975-)
Secretaire général: Henri Awit
Founded: 1881
I: Religious Sciences; Islamic-Christian Studies.
*F: Medicine; Pharmacy; Dentistry; Engineering;
Law and Political Science; Economics; Business
Administration and Management; Letters and
Human Sciences; Nursing and Midwifery.*
*I: Modern Languages and Translation; Teacher
Training (kindergarten, primary, handicapped);
Telecommunications.*
*Ce: Modern Arabic Studies; Banking; Insurance
Studies.*

University of the Holy Ghost
[Université Saint-Esprit]
Kaslik, Jounieh
Tel: +961(9) 912-019
Fax: +961(9) 914-941
Telex: 45777 usek le
Recteur: Elie Khalifée (1993-)
Secrétaire général: Ayoub Chahwan
Founded: 1949
*F: Theology; Philosophy and Human Sciences;
Business Administration and Commercial
Sciences; Arts; Fine and Applied Arts; Law;
Agricultural Sciences.*
I: Liturgy; Musicology; History; Education.
S: Music.
Sec: Foreign Languages.
*Ce: Research on Peace and Development
(Faculty of Philosophy and Human Sciences);
Documentation and Research.*

OTHER INSTITUTIONS

Al-Akadimiyah al-Lubnaniyah lil-Fûnûn
al-Jamîlah
Sin-El-Fil, POB 55251, Beirut
Tel: +961(1) 480-056
Founded: 1937
Fine Arts.

Kulliyat Al-Imam Al-Ouzai li-Dirasat
Al-Islamiyya
P.O. Box 14-5355, Beirut
Tel: +961(1) 317-708
Founded: 1979
Islamic Studies.

Kulliyat al-Sharq al-Awsat
B.P. 1170, Beirut
Founded: 1949
*Religious Studies; History; Business
Administration; Engineering; Natural Sciences.*

Kulliyat Idarat Al-Amal Al-Islamiya
P.O. Box 14-5355, Beirut
Tel: +961(1) 317-708
Founded: 1986
Business Administration.

Ma'had al-'Hikmat al-'Ali li-l-'Huqûq
1961 Rue de Hikmat, Beirut
Founded: 1961
Law.

Ma'had Haïkazian
Rue du Mexique, B.P. 1748, Beirut
Tel: +961(1) 349-230
Founded: 1955
Business Administration; Humanities, Languages and Literature; Science; Social and Behavioural Sciences.

NATIONAL ACADEMIC BODIES

Ministry of Culture and Higher Education
Immeuble Sofil, Beirut
Tel: +961(1) 300-970
Fax: +961(1) 423-432
Minister: Michel Edde

Lebanese National Commission for Unesco
Palais de l'Unesco, Beirut
Tel: +961(1) 300-962
Fax: +961(1) 310-243
President: Nagib Abou Haidar
Secretary-General: Hicham Nachabe

LESOTHO
UNIVERSITIES

*National University of Lesotho
P.O. 180, Roma via Maseru
Tel: +266 340-601
Fax: +266 340-000
Telex: 4303 lo
Cable: uniter roma
Vice-Chancellor: A.D. Baikie
Registrar: M.R. Likate
Founded: 1945, 1975
F: Agriculture; Education; Humanities; Law; Postgraduate Studies; Social Sciences.
I: Sciences.

NATIONAL ACADEMIC BODIES

Ministry of Education, Sports and Culture
P.O. 47, Maseru
Tel: +266 323-956
Fax: +266 310-206
Minister: P.B. Mosisli

Lesotho National Commission for Unesco
Ministry of Education, Sports and Culture, P.O. 47, Maseru
Tel: +226 315-932
Fax: +226 310-297
Telex: 4342 undevpro
Cable: unescom maseru
Chairman: P.B. Mosisli, Minister of Education
Secretary-General: Thjami Mashologu

LIBERIA
UNIVERSITIES

University of Liberia
P.O. Box 9020, Capital Hill, Monrovia
Tel: +231 222-448
President: Stephen Yekeson
Founded: 1851, 1951
S: Law.
I: African Studies and Research.
D: Lifelong Education.
Ce: Social Sciences and Humanities; Teacher Training; Agriculture and Forestry; Business and Public Administration; Science and Technology; Medicine.

OTHER INSTITUTIONS

Cuttington University College
P.O. Box 277, Monrovia
Tel: +231 224-243
Cable: pecusam
Founded: 1889

NATIONAL ACADEMIC BODIES

Ministry of Education
Broad Street, Monrovia
Fax: +231 515-515
Minister: Theophilius Sonpon

Liberian National Commission for Unesco
Ministry of Education, Room 403, Broad Street, Monrovia
Tel: +231 225-008
Fax: +231 226-144
Telex: 44449 minedu
Cable: natcom education ministry monrovia
Executive Secretary: Hawah Goll-Kotchi

LIBYA
UNIVERSITIES

Al-Arab Medical University
P.O.B. 18251, Benghazi
Tel: +218(61) 25007
Telex: 40204
Founded: 1984
F: Medicine; Dentistry.

University of Al-Fateh
P.O. Box 13482, Tripoli
Tel: +218(22) 36010/8
President: Ibraheim El-Muntaser
Founded: 1957
*F: Science; Agriculture; Engineering; Letters;
Petroleum Technology; Nuclear Engineering and
Electronics; Medicine; Pharmacy; Veterinary
Medicine; Education (Zawia).*

University of Garyounis
P.O. Box 1308, Benghazi
Tel: +218(61) 87462
Vice-Chancellor: Salem Shebani
Founded: 1955
*F: Letters and Education; Economics and
Commerce; Law; Science; Engineering;
Agriculture; Dentistry.
Ce: Research for Social Sciences and
Economics.*

Sebha University
P.O. Box 18758, Sebha
Tel: +218(071) 21575/76
Telex: 30622
President: Ali Mohammed Mohammed Saleh
Founded: 1983
*F: Education; Science.
Ce: Research for African Studies.*

OTHER INSTITUTIONS

Higher Institute of Electronics
P.O. Box 8645, Beni Walid/Souk Jin
Founded: 1976
Electronics.

Higher Institute of Mechanical and Electrical Engineering
P.O. Box 61160, Hon
Tel: +218 2154
Telex: 30254 ly
Founded: 1976
Mechanical and Electrical Engineering.

Higher Institute of Technology
P.O. Box 68, Brack
Tel: +218 45300
Founded: 1976
Technology.

NATIONAL ACADEMIC BODIES

Secretariat of the General People's Committee for Education and Scientific Research
Sirt
Tel: +218(21) 604-807
Fax: +218(21) 623-038
Secretary: Ma'atouk Mohammed Ma'atouk

National Commission for Education Science and Culture of the Libyan Arab Jamahiriya
P.O. Box 1091, Tripoli
Tel: +218(21) 41572
Fax: +218(21) 41760
Chairman: Ma'atouk Mohammed Ma'atouk,
Secretary of Education
Secretary-General: Mustafa Bushaala

LIECHTENSTEIN

OTHER INSTITUTIONS

Internationale Akademie für Philosophie
Obergass 75, 9494 Schaan
Tel: +41(75) 28675
Fax: +41(75) 28548
Founded: 1986
Philosophy.

Liechstenteinische Ingenieurschule
Marianumstrasse 45, 9490 Vaduz
Tel: +41(75) 29310
Fax: +41(75) 81487
Founded: 1961
Engineering.

NATIONAL ACADEMIC BODIES

Education Centre of the Principality of Liechtenstein
[Schulamt desFürstentums Liechtenstein]
Herrengasse, 9490 Vaduz
Tel: +41(75) 66751
Fax: +41(75) 66299

LITHUANIA

UNIVERSITIES

Kaunas Medical Academy
[Kauno Medicinos Akademija]
A. Mickevičiaus 9, 3000 Kaunas
Tel: +370(7) 226110
Fax: +370(7) 220733
Telex: 26 92 68 rasa
Rector: Vilius Grabauskas (1993-)
Vice-Rector for Academic Affairs: Rimvydas
Stropus
International Relations: Limas Kupčinskas
Founded: 1950
*F: Medicine; Pharmacy; Nursing; Stomatology.
I: Biomedical Research; Cardiology;
Endocrinology; Psychophysiology and
Rehabilitation (Palanga).*

Kaunas University of Technology
[Kauno Technologijos Universitetas]
K. Donelaicio 73, 3006 Kaunas
Tel: +370(7) 227044
Fax: +370(7) 202640
E-Mail: rastine@cr.ktu.lt
Rector: Kęstutis Kriščiunas (1992-)
Vice-Rector for Academic Affairs: Aleksandras Targamadze
International Relations: Head, Agency for Communications and Information, Robertas Kupstas
Founded: 1920, 1950
F: Automation Engineering; Power Engineering; Chemical Engineering; Management; Light Industry Engineering; Machine Building Engineering; Mechanical Engineering; Radio Electronics; Civil Engineering; Administration; Electrotechnics and Automatics; Computer Engineering; Fundamental sciences; Manufacturing.
I: Social and Humanitarian Studies.
Ce: Computer; Vibration Technology Research; Ultrasound Technology Research; Packing Technology Research; International Study; Physical Education and Health; Professional Improvement.

Kaunas Vytautas Magnus University
[Kauno Vytauto Dižiojo Universitetas]
Daukanto 28, 3000 Kaunas
Tel: +370(7) 222739
Fax: +370(7) 203858
E-Mail: rector@vmu-lira,lt.ee
Telex: 26 98 57 vytun
Rector: Bronius Vaškelis (1993-)
Vice-Rector for Academic Affairs: Vytautas Kaminskas
International Relations: Pranas Bruzga
Founded: 1922, 1950, 1989
F: Environmental Studies; Informatics; Business and Management; Humanities; Arts; Social Sciences; Theology and Philosophy.

Klaipeda University
[Klaipedos Universitetas]
Danes 17, 5800 Klaipeda
Tel: +370(61) 56315
Fax: +370(61) 56526
Rector: Stasys Vaitiekunas (1993-)
Vice-Rector for Studies: Vaiduties Laurenas
International Relations: Vanda Kavaliauskiene
Founded: 1950
F: Humanities; Natural Sciences; Pedagogics; Engineering.
Ce: Eastern Prussia and Western Lithuanian History; Systems Analysis Research.

Lithuanian Academy of Agriculture
[Lietuvos Žemes ukio Akadenija]
Noreikiškes, Kaunas Region 4324
Tel: +370(7) 296500
Fax: +370(7) 296531
Telex: 26 97 68 varpa
Rector: Rimantas Urbonas (1989-)
Secretary: Algirdas Motuzas
Founded: 1945
F: Agronomy; Economics; Water and Land Exploitation; Forestry; Farming Engineering.

Lithuanian Academy of Arts
[Lietuvos Dailes Akademija]
Maironio 6, 2600 Vilnius
Tel: +370(2) 613004
Fax: +370(2) 619966
Rector: Arvydas Saltenis (1994-)
Vice-Rector for Academic Affairs: Adomas Butrimas
International Relations: Kostas Bogdanas
Founded: 1793
F: Applied Arts; Fine Arts.
I: Arts of Vilnius Academy of Arts (Kaunas).
D: Communications and Arts (Klaipeda).

Lithuanian Academy of Veterinary Medicine
[Lietuvos Veterinarijos Akademija]
Tilžes 18, 3022 Kaunas
Tel: +370(7) 260383
Fax: +370(14) 261417
Rector: Vidmantas Bižokas (1993-)
Vice-Rector for Academic Affairs: Romas Gružauskas
International Relations: Henrikas Žilinskas
Founded: 1954
Veterinary Medicine; Cattle Breeding Technology.

Lithuanian Institute of Physical Education
[Lietuvos Kuno Kulturos Instituas]
Sporto 6, 3029 Kaunas
Tel: +370(7) 200577
Fax: +370(7) 204515
Rector: Albertas Skurvydas (1992-)
Vice-Rector for Academic Affairs: Arvydas Stasiulis
International Relations: Neringa Raslavičiute
Founded: 1945
Pedagogics; Coaching; Health; In-Service Training.

Lithuanian Police Academy
[Lietuvos Policijos Akademija]
Ateities 20, 2057 Vilnius
Tel: +370(2) 763918
Fax: +370(7) 354444
Telex: 30 32 34 'teise'
Rector: Alvydas Pumputis (1990-)
Vice-Rector for Academic Affairs: Egidijus Kurapka
International Relations: Arunas Stumbras
Founded: 1990

D: Criminology; Administrative Law; Psychology and Ethics; Philosophy; Operation Activities; Criminal Law; Civil Law; Constitutional Law; Applied Computer Science; Professional Tactics; Physical Training; Criminal Justice Process; Modern Languages.

Siauliai Pedagogical Institute
[Siaulių Pedagoginis Institutas]
P. Višinskio 25, 5400 Siauliai
Tel: +370(14) 33673
Fax: +370(14) 35459
Rector: Aloyza Gudavičius (1991-)
Vice-Rector for Studies: Vytautas Bikulčius
International Relations: Laima Stankevičiene.
Founded: 1954
Pedagogy; Special Education; Philology Education; Physics and Mathematics; Fine Arts; In-Service.

Vilnius Academy of Music
[Vilniaus Muzikos Akademija]
Gedimino pr. 42, 2001 Vilnius
Tel: +370(2) 612691
Fax: +370(2) 220093
Rector: Juozas Antanavičius (1994-)
Vice-Rector for Academic and Art Affairs:
Eugenijus Ignatonis
International Relations: Laima Bakiene.
Founded: 1949
Piano and Musicology; Instrumental and Vocal Music; Theatre and Cinema.

*Vilnius University
[Vilniaus Universiteras]
Universiteto 3, 2734 Vilnjus
Tel: +370(2) 623779
Fax: +370(2) 613473
Telex: 26 12 12 vu vu
Rector: Rolandas Pavilionis (1990-)
Vice-Rector for Academic Affairs: Saulius Vengris
International Relations: Algimantas Lipinaitis
Founded: 1579
F: Physics; Mathematics; Chemistry; Natural Sciences; Medicine; History; Philology; Law; Economics; Medicine; Communications; Improving Professional Qualifications; Humanities (Kaunas).
I: International Relations and Political Sciences; Journalism; Material Parameter and Applied Sciences.
Ce: Religion and Research; Women's Studies; Semiotics; Jewish Studies; Oriental Studies; Environmental Studies.

Vilnius Pedagogical University
[Vilniaus Pedagoginis Universitetas]
Studentų 39, 2034 Vilnius
Tel: +370(2) 738053
Fax: +370(2) 355692
Rector: A. Pakerys (1993-)
Vice-Rector for Academic Affairs: I. Musteikiene
International Relations: I. Navickiene.
Founded: 1935

F: Physics; Mathematics; Natural Sciences; History; Foreign Languages; Pedagogy and Psychology; Lithuanian Philology; Slav Philology.

Vilnius Technological University
[Vilniaus Technikos Universitetas]
Sauletekio al. 11, 2054 Vilnius
Tel: +370(2) 769600
Fax: +370(2) 765210
Rector: Edmundas Zavadskas (1990-)
Vice-Rector for Academic Affairs: A. Staškevičius
International Relations: Regimantas Ciupaila
Founded: 1969
F: Architecture; Electronics; Fundamental Research; Urban Engineering; Construction Engineering; Business Management; Mechanical Engineering; Transport.
I: Aviation.
Ce: Continuing Studies; International Studies.

NATIONAL ACADEMIC BODIES

Lithuanian Agency for Higher Education, Research and Development
Gedimino pr. 11, 2039 Vilnius
Tel: +370(2) 620964
Fax: +370(2) 614829
Director: Jonas Puodžius

Lithuanian Rectors' Conference
Universitero 3, 2734 Vilnius
Tel: +370(2) 623779
Fax: +370(2) 613473
Telex: 261 212 vu su
Chairman: Rolandas Pavilionis

Senate's Chairmen's Conference
K. Donelaičio 73, 3000 Kaunas
Tel: +370(2) 220411
Chairman: A. Ziliukas

Science Council of Lithuania
Gedimino pr. 3, 2600 Vilnius
Tel: +370(2) 614010
Fax: +370(2) 621939
Chairman: Leonas Kadžiulis

Lithuanian National Commission for Unesco
J. Basanavicias 5, 2683 Vilnius
Tel: +370(2) 622994
Fax: +370(2) 220520
President: Laimutis Telksnys
Secretary-General: Alfredas Jomantas

LUXEMBOURG

UNIVERSITIES

International University Institute of Luxembourg
[Institut universitaire international de Luxembourg]
162A, avenue de la Faïencerie, Luxembourg
Tel: +352(2) 466-644
Founded: 1958, 1974
Ce: Juridical Studies and Comparative Law; Political Economics; European Studies and Research.

University Centre of Luxembourg
[Centre universitaire de Luxembourg]
162A, avenue de la Faïencerie, Luxembourg 1511
Tel: +352(2) 466-644
Fax: +352(2) 466-644-508
Président: Pierre Seck (1987-)
Directeur administratif: Jean-Paul Mossong
Founded: 1848, 1968, 1974
D: Law and Economics; Letters and Human Sciences; Science; Education; Law; Mathematics.

OTHER INSTITUTIONS

Institut supérieur d'Etudes et de Recherches pedagogiques
Route de Dickirch, Walferdange
Tel: +352 33-34-201
Education.

Institut Supérieur de Technologie
rue R. Coudenhove-Kalergi, L-1359 Luxembourg
Tel: +352 43-66-61
Fax: +352 43-21-24
Founded: 1979
Mechanical, Electrical and Civil Engineering; Industrial Computing.

NATIONAL ACADEMIC BODIES

Ministry of National Education
[Ministère de l'Education nationale]
29, rue Aldringen, 2926 Luxembourg
Tel: +352(2) 478-5101
Fax: +353(2) 478-5110
Ministre: Marc Fischbach

Luxembourg National Commission for Cooperation with Unesco
[Commission nationale luxembourgeoise pour la Coopération avec l'Unesco]
Ministère de l'Education nationale, 29, rue Aldringen, 2920 Luxembourg
Tel: +353(2) 478-511
Fax: +352(2) 478-5113
Telex: 2111
Cable: commission unesco luxembourg
Président: Jean-Pierre Kraemer
Secrétaire général: Marc Turpel

MACAU

UNIVERSITIES

*University of Macau
[Universidade de Macau]
P.O. Box 3001, Macau
Tel: +853 397-4301
Fax: +853 320-694
Telex: 88397 uea om
Cable: uestasia
Rector: Tianqing Li
Administrator: Rufino Ramos
Founded: 1981, 1988, 1990
F: Arts; Business Administration; Social Sciences; Science and Technology.
S: Education.
P: Law.
D: Portuguese Studies; Foundation Studies.
Ce: Luso-Asiatic Studies; Macau Studies; Scientific Research; China Economic Research.

NATIONAL ACADEMIC BODIES

Education and Culture Services
[Serviços de Educação e Cultura]
Macau
Telex: 88346 edu om

MACEDONIA (REPUBLIC OF)

UNIVERSITIES

University of Bitola
[Univerzitet u Bitoli]
Bulevar 'I-vi Maj' bb, 97000 Bitola
Tel: +389(97) 23-788
Founded: 1979
F: Economics; Technology; Tourism; Law.
I: Tobacco Research; Hydrobiology; Ancient Slavic Culture; Agriculture; Education.

*'Sts. Kiril and Metodij' University-Skopje
[Univerzitet 'Sv. Kiril i Metódi' vo Skopju]
Bulevar 'Krste Misirkov' bb, 91 000 Skopje
Tel: +389(91) 116-323
Fax: +389(91) 116-370
Rector: Tomislav Čokrevski (1992-94)
Secretary-General: Duško Sokovski
International Relations: Frederika Popovska-Pavlovska (Vice-Rector), International Relations
Founded: 1949
F: Law; Economics; Philology; Philosophy; Architecture; Civil Engineering; Mechanical Engineering; Electrical Studies; Technology and Metallurgy; Mining and Geology (Štip); Natural Sciences and Mathematics; Civil Defence and Security; Medicine; Pharmacy; Dentistry; Physical Education; Agriculture; Veterinary Medicine; Forestry; Music; Art; Drama.

I: Economics; Social and Political Sciences; Seismology; Veterinary Medicine; Rice Studies; National History; Macedonian Language; Folklore.
A: Education; Education (Stip).
S: Agriculture (Strumica).

NATIONAL ACADEMIC BODIES

Former Yugoslav Republic of Macedonia National Commission for Unesco
Ministry of Culture, Ilindenska b.b., 91000 Skopje
Tel: +389(91) 220-823
Fax: +389(91) 225-810

MADAGASCAR

UNIVERSITIES

*University of Antananarivo
[Université d'Antananarivo]
B.P. 566, Ambohitsaina, Antananarivo
Tel: +261 241-14
Telex: 22304 recumt mg
Recteur: Emile Rakotomahanina Ralaisoa
Vice-Recteur: M. Andrianjatovo
International Relations: Christiane Andriamirado
Founded: 1955, 1960, 1976, 1988, 1992
S: Law, Economics, Administration, and Sociology; Sciences; Health Sciences; Polytechnic; Letters; Agriculture; Teacher Training.

NATIONAL CENTRE OF ENGLISH TEACHING
[CENTRE NATIONAL D'ENSEIGNEMENT DE LA LANGUE ANGLAISE]
B.P. 109 Antananarivo 101
Tel: +261 260-28
Directeur: Yolande Ramarosaona
Secrétaire général: Jean-Pierrot Raveloarison
Founded: 1985
English.

RADIO-ISOTOPES LABORATORY
[LABORATOIRE DE RADIO-ISOTOPES]
B.P. 3383, Antananarivo
Tel: +261 404-88
Directeur: Jean Andriantsoa
Founded: 1956
Radio-Isotopes Techniques.

MUSEUM OF ART AND ARCHAEOLOGY
[MUSÉE D'ART ET D'ARCHÉOLOGIE]
B.P. 564, Antananarivo
Tel: +261 210-47
Directeur: Jean-Aimé Rakotoarisoa
Executive Director: Guy Rakotovao
Founded: 1964
Art and Archaeology.

University of Antsiranana
[Université d'Antsiranana]
B.P. 0, Antsiranana
Tel: +261(8) 211-37
Fax: +261(8) 294-09
Recteur: M. Befeno
Directeur administratif: M. Jeannot
Founded: 1975, 1988, 1992
Polytechnic; Letters; Teaching Training.

University of Fianarantsoa
[Université de Fianarantsoa]
B.P. 1264, Fianarantsoa 301
Tel: +261(7) 508-02
Fax: +261(7) 510-19
Recteur: Pascal Ratalata
Directeur administratif: Jeannot Célestin Tatagera
Founded: 1977, 1988, 1992
S: Law; Sciences; Computer Science; Teacher Training (3rd level).

NATIONAL SCHOOL OF COMPUTER SCIENCES
[ECOLE NATIONALE D'INFORMATIQUE]
Fianarantsoa
Tel: +261(07) 508-01
Directeur: Cyprien Rakotoasimbahoaka
Founded: 1980
Computer Sciences.

University of Mahajanga
[Université de Mahajanga]
B.P. 652, Mahajanga
Tel: +261(6) 227-24
Fax: +261(6) 293-64
Recteur: M. Rajabo
Secrétaire général: François Hevidrazana
Founded: 1977, 1988, 1992
Dentistry; Sciences; Medicine.

University of Toamasina
[Université de Toamasina]
B.P. 591, Toamasina
Tel: +261(5) 324-54
Fax: +261(5) 336-15
Recteur: Eugène Régis Mangalaza
Directeur Administratif: André Bias Ramilamanana
Founded: 1977, 1988, 1992
S: Law, Economics, Business Administration, and Sociology; Letters.
Ce: Ethnological and Linguistic Studies and Research.

CENTRE FOR ETHNOLOGICAL AND LINGUISTIC STUDIES AND RESEARCH
[CENTRE D'ETUDES ET DE RECHERCHES ETHNOLOGIQUES ET LINGUISTIQUES]
Toamasina
Directeur: Gabriel Rabemahefa
Founded: 1985
Linguistics.

University of Toliary
[Université de Toliary]
B.P. 185, Toliary
Tel: +261(9) 410-33
Fax: +261(9) 418-02
Recteur: Jeanne Dina
Directeur administratif: Tsiebo Elysé
Andriantompoiniarivo
International Relations: Aurore Biviarisolo
Founded: 1977, 1988, 1992
Letters; Sciences; Teaching Training.

DOCUMENTATION AND RESEARCH CENTRE FOR ART AND
ORAL TRADITIONS OF MADAGASCAR
[CENTRE DE DOCUMENTATION ET DE RECHERCHE SUR L'ART
ET LES TRADITIONS ORALES À MADAGASCAR]
Toliary
Directeur: François Rabedimy
Founded: 1985
Art and Oral Traditions.

INSTITUTE OF MARINE SCIENCES
[INSTITUT HALIEUTIQUE ET DES SCIENCES MARINES (I.H.S.M.)]
Toliary
Marine Sciences.

TOLIARY MARINE STATION
[STATION MARINE DE TOLIARY]
B.P. 141, Toliary
Founded: 1970

INSTITUTE OF TROPICAL DENTISTRY (I.H.S.M.)
[INSTITUT D'ODONTO STOMATOLOGIE TROPICAL (I.O.S.T.)]
Mahajanga
Tropical Dentistry.

MALAWI

UNIVERSITIES

*University of Malawi
P.O. Box 278, Zomba
Tel: +265 522-622
Fax: +265 522-760
Telex: 45214 mi
Cable: university zomba
Vice-Chancellor: Brown B. Chimphamba (1991-95)
Registrar: Geofrey G. Chipungu
Founded: 1964
*F: Agriculture; Applied Studies; Commerce;
Education; Engineering; Humanities; Social
Sciences; Nursing; Medicine; Science.
I: Education.
Ce: Social Research; Educational Research and
Training; Management.*

BUNDA COLLEGE OF AGRICULTURE
P.O. Box 219, Lilongwe
Tel: +265 721-455
Agriculture.

CHANCELLOR COLLEGE
P.O. Box 280, Zomba
Tel: +265 522-222

KAMUZU COLLEGE OF NURSING
Private Bag 1, Lilongwe
Tel: +265 721-622
Nursing.

THE POLYTECHNIC
Private Bag 303, Chichiri, Blantyre 3
Tel: +265 632-144

NATIONAL ACADEMIC BODIES

State Secretariat for Higher Education
[Secrétariat d'Etat à l'Enseignement supérieur]
Antananarivo
Tel: +261(2) 271-85
Fax: +261(2) 238-97
Secrétaire d'Etat: Eléonore Nerine

Madagascar National Commission for Unesco
[Commission nationale malgache pour l'Unesco]
1, Naka Rabemanantsoa-Behoririka,
Antananarivo
Tel: +261(2) 217-61
Fax: +261(2) 284-96
Cable: comunesco
Président: Fulgence Fanony, Ministre de
l'Education
Secrétaire général: Hery-Zo Ralambomahay

NATIONAL ACADEMIC BODIES

Ministry of Education, Science and Culture
Private Bag 328, Lilongwe
Tel: +265 784-800
Fax: +265 782-873
Minister: The Hon. Sam Mpasu

Malawi National Commission for Unesco
Taurus House, P.O. Box 30278, Capital City,
Lilongwe 3
Tel: +265 784-000
Fax: +265 782-417
Telex: 4769 unesco mi
Cable: unesco lilongue 3 malawi
Executive Secretary: Francis S.D. Kakatera

MALAYSIA

UNIVERSITIES

*University of Agriculture, Malaysia
[Universiti Pertanian Malaysia]
43400 UPM Serdang, Selangor
Tel: +60(3) 948-6101
Fax: +60(3) 948-3244
Telex: uniper ma 37454
Cable: unipertama sungai besi
Vice-Chancellor: Syed Jalaludin bin Syed Salim
(1982-93)
Registrar: Shahdan bin Asri
Founded: 1971
F: Agriculture; Educational Studies;
Engineering; Fisheries and Marine Sciences;
Food Science and Biotechnology; Forestry;
Economics and Management; Science and
Environmental Studies; Veterinary Medicine and
Animal Science; Human Ecology.
S: Graduate Studies.
Ce: Extension and Continuing Education;
Applied Sciences Studies; Basic Sciences
Studies; Social Sciences and Management
Studies; Instructional Services; Computer.
I: Consultancy.

*International Islamic University
[Universiti Islam Antarabangsa]
P.O. Box 70, Jalan Sultan, 46700 Petaling Jaya,
Selangor
Tel: +60(3) 755-5322
Fax: +60(3) 757-9598
E-Mail: rector@its.iiu.my
Telex: islamu ma 37161
Rector: Abdul Hamid Ahmad Abu Sylayman
(1988-94)
Director: Jamaluddin bin Yacob
Founded: 1983
F: Economics and Management; Islamic
Revealed Knowledge and Human Sciences; Law;
Postgraduate Studies.
Ce: Research.

*University of Malaya
[Universiti Malaya]
Pantai Valley, 59100 Kuala Lumpur
Tel: +60(3) 756-0022
Fax: +60(3) 755-2975
Telex: ma 39845
Cable: univsel, kuala lumpur
Vice-Chancellor: Abdullah Sanusi bin Ahmad
(1994-97)
Registrar (Acting): Mustapa B. Haji Shamsuri
Founded: 1949, 1962
F: Arts and Social Sciences; Dentistry;
Economics and Administration; Engineering; Law;
Medicine; Science; Syariah; Usuluddin;
Education.

I: Advanced Studies.
Ce: Foundation Studies in Science; Language;
Cultural; Computer.
A: Malay Studies; Islamic.

ISLAM ACADEMY
[AKADEMIC ISLAM]
Kota Bharu Kelantan
Tel: +60(9) 926-491
Fax: +60(9) 926-580
Director: Hassan bin Yusuf (1994-)
Registrar: Idris Abdullah
Founded: 1981

National University of Malaysia
[Universiti Kebangsaan Malaysia]
43600 Bangi, Selangor
Tel: +60(3) 825-0001
Fax: +60(3) 825-6484
Telex: ma 31496
Cable: unikeb
Vice-Chancellor: Mohd. Sham bin Mohd. Sani
(1993-96)
Registrar: Baharuddin Haji Ishak
Founded: 1970
F: Business Management; Development
Sciences; Economics; Education; Engineering;
Islamic Studies; Law; Life Sciences; Mathematics
and Computer Sciences; Medicine; Physics and
Applied Sciences; Science and Natural
Resources; Social Sciences and Humanities.
I: Malay Language, Literature and Culture.
Ce: Quantitative Studies; Language.

Northern University of Malaysia
[Universiti Utara Malaysia]
Sintok, 06010 Jitra, Kedah
Tel: +60(4) 741-801
Fax: +60(4) 741-043
Telex: ma 42052
Cable: utamas
Vice-Chancellor: Shamsuddin bin Kassim
(1993-96))
Registrar (Acting): Latifah bte. Hassan
Founded: 1984
S: Accountancy; Economics and Public
Administration; Foundation Studies; Information
Technology; Languages and Scientific Thinking;
Management.
Ce: Business and Entrepreneurial Development.

University Malaysia Sarawak
Rumah Setia, Jalan Taman Budaya, 93000
Kuching, Sarawak
Tel: +60(82) 428-110
Fax: +60(82) 427-716
Mohd. Zawawi bin Haji Ismail (1992-95)
Manager, Human Resource Management: Mohd.
Bohhari M. Yasin
Faculties: Information Technology; Engineering.

University of Science Malaysia
[Universiti Sains Malaysia]
Minden 11800, Penang
Tel: +60(4) 657-7888
Fax: +60(4) 657-1526
Telex: ma 40254 usmlib
Cable: unisains, penang
Vice-Chancellor: Yang Berbahagia Dato Haji
Musa bin Mohamad
Registrar: Hajah Siti Mazenah Saad
Founded: 1969, 1972
*S: Biological Sciences; Chemical Sciences; Civil
Engineering; Educational Studies; Electrical and
Electronic Engineering; Housing, Building and
Planning; Humanities; Industrial Technology;
Management; Materials and Mineral Resources
Engineering; Mathematical and Computer
Sciences; Mechanical Engineering; Medical
Sciences; Mechanical Engineering (Sri Iskander);
Pharmaceutical Sciences; Social Sciences.*

*University of Technology Malaysia
[Universiti Teknologi Malaysia]
Campus Sekudai, Karung Berkunci, 791, 80990
Johor Bahru, Johor
Tel: +60(7) 576-160
Fax: +60(7) 566-722
E-Mail: nc@utmjb
Telex: ma 60-205
Cable: utekma johor bahuru
Vice-Chancellor: Ahmad Zaharuddin bin Idrus
(1994-97)
Registrar: Haji Ismail Ibrahim
Founded: 1925, 1946, 1972
*F: Built Environment; Chemical and Natural
Resources Engineering; Civil Engineering;
Computer Science and Information Systems;
Electrical Engineering; Mechanical Engineering;
Science; Surveying; Management and Human
Resources.*
*Ut: Instructions (Teaching Method Development,
Audio-Visual Aids in Teaching); Research and
Consultancy.*
*I: Noise and Vibration Studies; Coastal and
Offshore Engineering.*

KUALA LUMPUR CAMPUS
Jalan Semarak, Kuala Lumpur
Tel: +60(3) 292-9033
Fax: +60(3) 293-4344
Director: Ishak bin Abdul Rahman (1994-)
Registrar (Acting): Tuan Haji Johari bin Jendol
Founded: 1981

OTHER INSTITUTIONS

MARA Institute of Technology
Shah Alam, Selangor
Tel: +60 559-2950
Fax: +60 550-0226
Director: Haji Ahmad Zaidee bin Laidin (1994-97)
Registrar: Bahadon bin Jsmail
Founded: 1957

*S: Accountancy; Art and Design; Administration
and Law; Architecture, Planning and Surveying;
Applied Science; Business and Management;
Mathematical Sciences and Computing;
Engineering; Hotel Management and Tourism;
Library Science and Information; Library Science
and Information; Mass Communication;
Secretarial Sciences.*
Ce: Language.

JOHOR BRANCH
Beg Berkunci 527, 85009 Segamat, Johor
*S: Accountancy; Administration; Business
Management; Secretarial Sciences.*

KELANTAN BRANCH
Kem Kijang, Jalan Pantai Cinta Berahi, 15350
Kota Bahru, Kelantan
Tel: +60(9) 737-363
Fax: +60(9) 738-622
Principal: Abdullah Mohamad (1991-94)
*S: Accountancy; Business and Management;
Secretarial Sciences.*

MELAKA BRANCH
KM 26, Jalan Lendu, 78000 Alor Gajah, Melaka
Tel: +60(6) 565-231
Fax: +60(6) 563-963
Principal: Baharuddin Abdul Aziz (1991-)
*S: Accountancy; Administration and Law;
Business Management; Secretarial Sciences.*

PAHANG BRANCH
Lintasan Semarak, 26400 Bander Pusat Jengka,
Pahang Darul Makmur
Tel: +60(9) 466-3323
Fax: +60(9) 463-343
Principal: Nasudin Othman (1991-)
*S: Accountancy; Administration and Law;
Applied Science; Business Management;
Mathematical Sciences and Computing;
Secretarial Sciences.*

PERAK BRANCH
32040 Sri Manjung, Perak
Tel: +60(5) 688-3996
Fax: +60(5) 688-1311
Principal: Mohd. Salleh bin Haji Ismail (1994-95)
*S: Accountancy; Administration and Law;
Architecture and Town Planning; Business and
Management; Mathematical Science and
Computing; Secretarial Sciences.*

PERLIS BRANCH
P.O. Box 41, 02607 Arau, Perlis
Tel: +60(4) 986-1001
Fax: +60(4) 986-2233
Principal: Wan Abaid Wan Ismail (1993-95)
*S: Accountancy; Administration and Law;
Applied Science; Business and Management;
Secretarial Sciences.*

SABAH BRANCH
Beg Berkunci 71, 88997 Kota Kinabalu, Sabah
Tel: +60(88) 492-746
Fax: +60(88) 492-900
Principal: Baharudin Ismail (1993-95)
*S: Accountancy; Business and Management;
Administration and Law; Secretarial Sciences.*

SARAWAK BRANCH
Jalan Siol Kanan, Semariang, P.O. Box 1288,
93012 Kuching
Tel: +60(82) 441-219
Fax: +60(82) 443-522
Principal: Ibrahim Abu Shah (1994-95)
*S: Acountancy; Business and Management;
Secretarial Sciences.*

TERENGGANU BRANCH
Sura Hujung, 23000 Dungun, Terengganu
Tel: +60(9) 841-370
Fax: +60(9) 841-166
Principal: Muhammad bin Muda (1993-95)
*S: Accountancy; Admininstration and Law;
Business and Management; Mathematical
Sciences and Computing; Hotel Management and
Tourism; Secretarial Sciences.*

Tunku Abdul Rahman College
Jalan Genting Kelang, Wilayah Persekutuan,
Kuala Lumpur
Tel: +60(3) 423-3122
Principal: Lim Khaik Leong
Registrar: Chee Ah Kiow
Founded: 1969
*S: Business Studies; Technology; Art and
Science; Pre-University Studies.*
D: Extramural Studies.

NATIONAL ACADEMIC BODIES

Ministry of Education
Educational Planning and Research Division,
Level 2, 3 and 5, Block J, Pusat Bandar
Damansara, 50604 Kuala Lumpur
Tel: +60(3) 255-6900
Fax: +60(3) 255-4960
Cable: pendidikan
Minister: Amar Sulaiman bin Haji Daud

Malaysian National Commission for Unesco
Ministry of Education, Level 5, Block F (North),
Pusat Bandar Damansara, 50604 Kuala Lumpur
Tel: +60(3) 255-8655
Fax: +60(3) 254-4580
Telex: ma 33547
Cable: malnatcom kuala lumpur
Chairman: Amar Sulaiman bin Haji Daud,
Minister of Education
Secretary-General: Mohamed bin Omar

MALI
OTHER INSTITUTIONS

School of Higher Pratical Studies
[Ecole des hautes Etudes pratiques]
B.P. 242, Bamako
Tel: +223 22-21-47
Directeur: Siby Ginette Bellegarde (1994-)
Secrétaire général: Sadio Thiam
Founded: 1974
*D: Secretarial Studies; Management Informatics;
Commercial Techniques; Accountancy.*

Ecole nationale d'Administration
B.P. 276, Bamako
Tel: +223 22-27-19
Directeur: Mohamed Traoré (1994-)
Secrétaire général: Bernard Diallo
Founded: 1963
*D: Public Administration; Juridical Science;
Economics and Management.*

Ecole nationale d'Ingénieurs
B.P. 242, Bamako
Tel: +223 22-21-47
Fax: +223 22-50-38
Directeur: Bakary Sinenta (1994-)
Secrétaire général: Elise Goïta
Founded: 1963
*D: Industrial Engineering; Civil Engineering and
Topography; Basic Sciences; Administrative and
Commercial Techniques; Civil Engineering and
Mining.*

Ecole nationale de Médecine et de Pharmacie du Point G.
Point-G, Bamako
Tel: +223 22-52-77
Fax: +223 22-96-58
Directeur: Issa Traor 7e (1991-)
Secrétaire général: Bakary Mamadou Cissé
Founded: 1969
Medicine; Pharmacy.

Ecole nationale des Postes et Télécommunications
Bamako
Tel: +223 22-56-98
Fax: +223 22-71-95
Directeur: Mamadou Bamba (1983-)
Surveillant général: Jovite Dackono
Founded: 1969
Post and Telecommunications.

Ecole normale supérieure
B.P. 241, Bamako
Tel: +223 22-21-85
Directeur: Sekou B. Traoré (1994-)
Secrétaire géérale: Camara Lidia Stepanova
Founded: 1962
Teacher Training.

Institut polytechnique rural de Katibougou
B.P. 6, Koulikoro
Tel: +223 26-20-12
Directeur: Tahirou Traoré (1994-)
Secrétaire gńeéral: Mohamed Laminé Alpha
Founded: 1966
D: *Sciences; Agricultural Techniques; Stockraising; Economic and Social Sciences; Forestry and Rural Engineering.*

Higher Institute of Applied Training and Research
[Institut supérieur de Formation et Recherche appliquée]
B.P. 241, Bamako
Tel: +223 23-04-66
Fax: +223 23-04-66
Directeur: N'Golo Diarra (1994-)
Secrétaire général: Denis Dougnon
International Relations: Mme. Thiam
Founded: 1970
Applied Training and Research.

Ministry of National Education, Division of Higher Education
[Ministère de l'Education nationale, Direction nationale de l'Enseignement supérieur]
B.P. 71, Bamako
Tel: +223 22-87-20
Directeur: Salikou Sanogo
International Relations: Diarra Mountaga

Mali National Commission for Unesco
[Commission nationale malienne pour l'Unesco]
Ministère de l'Education nationale, B.P. 119, Bamako
Tel: +223 22-25-15
Fax: +223 22-82-97
Telex: 2412 miniplan
Président: Moustapha Dicko, Ministre de l'Education (1991-)
Founded: 1960

MALTA

*University of Malta
Msida
Tel: +356 333-903
Fax: +356 336-450
Telex: 407 hieduc mw
Cable: university malta
Rector: P. Serracino Inglott
Registrar: A. Gellel
International Relations: L.N. Agius
Founded: 1592, 1769, 1988
F: *Architecture and Civil Engineering; Arts; Dental Surgery; Economics, Management and Accountancy; Education; Law; Mechanical and Electrical Engineering; Medicine and Surgery; Science; Theology.*
Ce: *Communication Technology; Distance Learning; European Documentation and Research; International Business Studies.*
I: *Agriculture; Anglo-Italian Studies; Child Development; Energy Technology; Forensic Studies; Gerontology; Health Care; Linguistics; Masonry and Construction Research; Mediterranean; Social Welfare; Youth Studies.*
A: *Diplomatic Studies (Mediterranean).*

Ministry of Education
Beltissebh, Floriana
Tel: +356 239-842

Maltese National Commission for Unesco
Ministry of Education, Beltissebh, Floriana
Tel: +356 235-495
Fax: +356 221-634
Telex: 1515
Cable: external malta
Chairman: Roger Ellul Micallef
Secretary: J.G. Agius

MARTINIQUE

University of the Antilles and Guyane
[Université des Antilles et de la Guyane]
Route de Bellevue, 97260 Fort-de-France
Tel: +596 72-60-24
Président: Jacques Portecop
Founded: 1850, 1949, 1982
F: *Law and Economics (Schoelcher).*
Ut: *Letters and Human Sciences.*

Faculty of Letters and Human Sciences
[Faculté des Lettres et Sciences humaines]
B.P. 7207, 97275 Schoelcher Cedex
Letters and Human Sciences.

Martinique Academic Inspectorate, School Organisation Service
[Inspection académique de la Martinique, Service de l'Organisation scolaire]
B.P. 638 et 639, 97262 Fort-de-France Cedex
Tel: +596 72-60-60

MAURITANIA

UNIVERSITIES

University of Nouakchott
[Université de Nouakchott]
B.P. 798, Nouakchott
Tel: +222(2) 539-77
Fax: +222(2) 519-45
Telex: 710
Recteur: El Hacen Ould Lebatt
Secrétaire général: Mohamed Yehdih O. Tolba
Founded: 1986
F: Letters and Humanities; Law and Economics.

OTHER INSTITUTIONS

Centre supérieur d'Enseignement technique
B.P. 986, Nouakchott
Tel: +222(2) 530-17
Fax: +222(2) 544-29
Telex: 719 mtn nktt
Directeur: Mohamed Lemine
Founded: 1982
Technical Studies.

Ecole nationale d'Administration (ENA)
Nouakchott
Administration.

Ecole nationale de l'Enseignement maritime et des Pêches
Nouakchott
Maritime Studies; Fisheries.

Ecole normale supérieure
B.P. 990, Nouakchott
Tel: +222(2) 531-84
Fax: +222(2) 531-72
Directeur: Mohamed Ould Sidya
Founded: 1970, 1987
Teacher Training.

Institut Ben Abass
Nouakchott
Cultural Studies.

Institut supérieur des Etudes et Recherches islamiques (ISERI)
Nouakchott
Islamic Studies and Research.

Institut supérieur scientifique
B.P. 5026, Nouakchott
Tel: +222(2) 511-68
Fax: +222(2) 539-97
Telex: 598 mtn nktt
Directeur: Ahmedou O. Hamed
Founded: 1986

Physics; Chemistry; Mathematics and Computer Sciences; English; Languages; Geology; Biology.

NATIONAL ACADEMIC BODIES

Ministry of National Education
[Ministère de l'Education nationale]
B.P. 227, Nouakchott
Tel: +222(2) 523-62
Ministre: Moctar OUld Haye
Secrétaire général: Achour Ould Samba

Mauritania National Commission for Unesco
[Commission nationale pour l'Unesco]
B.P. 5115, Nouakchott
Tel: +222(2) 52802
Fax: +222(2) 52802
Président: Liman Ould Tegueddi, Minister of Culture and Islamic Guidance
Secrétaire général: Ahmed Beddy Oult Ahmedou Vall

MAURITIUS

UNIVERSITIES

*University of Mauritius
Réduit
Tel: +230 54-9642
Fax: +230 54-9642
Telex: 4621 unim iw
Cable: university mauritius
Vice-Chancellor: Jagadish Manrakhan
Registrar: M. Joynathsing
Founded: 1965
S: Agriculture; Engineering; Law, Management and Social Studies; Science.

SIR SEEWOOSAGUR RAMGOOLAM CENTRE FOR MEDICAL RESEARCH AND STUDIES
Redui
Founded: 1986
Medical Research and Studies.

OTHER INSTITUTIONS

Lycée Polytechnique Sir Guy Forget
Centre de Flacq
Tel: .33+692 53-28-70
Founded: 1982

Mauritius Institute of Education
Reduit
Tel: +230 541031
Founded: 1974
Education.

CURRICULUM DEVELOPMENT CENTRE
Beau Bassin
Founded: 1984
Curriculum Development.

MAURITIUS COLLEGE OF EDUCATION
Beau Bassin
Founded: 1942
Education.

Prof. Upadhyaya Industrial Trade Training Centre
Piton
Founded: 1982
Industrial Trade Training.

School of African, Oriental and Mauritian Studies
Moka
Tel: +230 48021
Founded: 1977
African, Oriental and Mauritian Studies.

Sir Kher Jagatsing Industrial Trade Training Centre
Beau Bassin
Industrial Trade Training.

NATIONAL ACADEMIC BODIES

Ministry of Education and Science
Rainbow House, Edith Cavell Street, Port Louis
Tel: +230 212-8574
Fax: +230 212-3783
Minister: Armoogum Parsuramen

Mauritius National Commission for Unesco
Ministry of Education and Science, Rainbow House, Edith Cavell Street (2nd floor), Port Louis
Tel: +230 208-3368
Fax: +230 212-3783
Cable: unesco education ministry port louis
Chairman: Armoogum Parsuramen, Minister of Education
Secretary-General: N.G. Naraido

MEXICO

UNIVERSITIES

PUBLIC INSTITUTIONS

*Autonomous University of Aguascalientes
[Universidad Autónoma de Aguascalientes]
Avenida Universidad s/n, Carretera al Club Campestre km. 2.5, 20100 Aguascalientes (Aguascalientes)
Tel: +52(49) 14-60-70
Fax: +52(49) 14-32-22
Presidente: Gonzalo González Hernández (1992-94)
Secretario General: Santiago Cortés Chávez
Founded: 1867, 1973
Ce: Basic Studies; Biomedical Sciences; Agriculture and Veterinary Medicine; Technology; Economics and Administration; Arts and Humanities.

*Autonomous University of Baja California
[Universidad Autónoma de Baja California]
Avenida Alvaro Obregón y Julián Carrillo s/n, 21100 Mexicali (Baja California)
Tel: +52(65) 52-23-79
Fax: +52(65) 52-95-40
Telex: 569888
Rector: Luis Llorens Baez (1991-95)
Secretario General: Luis Javier Garavito Elias
Founded: 1957
F: Architecture; Odontology; Law; Accountancy and Administration (Tijuana); Chemistry; Economics; Medicine (Tijuana); Odontology (Tijuana); Marine Sciences; Sciences.
S: Accountancy and Administration; Agricultural Training; Education Sciences; Engineering; Medicine; Nursing; Social and Political Sciences; Pedagogy; Translation; Law (Tijuana); Tourism; Humanities; Accountancy and Administration (Ensenada); Engineering (Ensenada); Engineering (Tecate).
I: Geography and History; Engineering; Social Research; Agriculture and Breeding Cattle Research; Veterinary Science Research; Educative Development and Research; History Research; Oceanology Research.

Autonomous University of Baja California South
[Universidad Autónoma de Baja California Sur]
Ciudad Universitaria, Km. 5 Carretera Al Sur, 23000 La Paz (Baja California Sur)
Tel: +52(112) 1-18-70
Fax: +52(112) 1-18-80
Rector: Jésus Druck González (1993-97)
Secretario General: Jorge Vale Sánchez
Founded: 1975
Ce: Social Sciences; Marine Sciences; Agricultural Sciences.
D: Extension.

Autonomous University of Campeche
[Universidad Autónoma de Campeche]
Ciudad Universitaria, 24030 Campeche (Campeche)
Tel: +52(981) 6-52-43
Fax: +52(981) 6-52-43
Rector: Juan José Casanova Isaac (1991-95)
Secretario General: Rafael Martínez Castro
F: Law; Engineering.
C: Chemistry and Biology; Commerce; Medicine; Political Science and Public Administration; Medicine; Accountancy; Technology; Dentistry.

Autonomous University of Carmen
[Universidad Autónoma del Carmen]
Avenida Concordia Esq. Avenida 56 s/n, 24180 Ciudad del Carmen (Campeche)
Tel: +52(938) 2-08-67
Fax: +52(938) 2-11-33
Rector: Eduardo del C. Reyes Sánchez
Secretario General: Melchor Ahumada Jiménez
Founded: 1967

F: Law; Education; Commerce and Administration; Fishery; Chemistry; Engineering.
S: Nursing; Languages; Commerce.

Autonomous University Chapingo
[Universidad Autónoma Chapingo]
Km. 38.5 Carretera México-Texcoco, 56230 Chapingo (Estado de México)
Tel: +52(595) 4-00-35
Fax: +52(595) 4-50-06
Rector: Carlos Orozco Alam (1991-95)
Director Académico: Agustín López Herrera
Founded: 1854, 1984
Agriculture.

*Autonomous University of Chiapas
[Universidad Autónoma de Chiapas]
Boulevard Belisario Domíguez Km 1081, Colina Universitaria, 29000 Tuxtla Gutiérrez (Chiapas)
Tel: +52(961) 5-10-21
Fax: +52(961) 5-06-64
Rector: Jorge Arias Zebadua (1991-94)
Secretario General: Pedro René Bodegas Valera
Founded: 1975
Administration; Physics and Mathematics; Biomedicine; Humanities; Law (San Cristóbal Las Casas); Sociology (San Cristóbal Las Casas); Business Administration (Tapachula); Agriculture (Tapachula); Acccountancy; Chemistry (Tapachula); Agriculture (Villa Flores); Agriculture (Huehuetan).

Autonomous University of Chihuahua
[Universidad Autónoma de Chihuahua]
Escorza y B. Carranza s/n, 31000 Chihuahua (Chihuahua)
Tel: +52(14) 15-79-44
Fax: +52(14) 15-93-85
Rector: Sergio Piña Marshall (1992-96)
Secretario General: Rubén Márquez Meléndez
Founded: 1954
F: Agriculture; Accountancy and Administration; Law; Physical Education; Nursing and Midwifery; Philosophy and Letters.
S: Public Administration and Political Science.

Autonomous University of Ciudad Juárez
[Universidad Autónoma de Ciudad Juárez]
Avenida López Mateos 20, Apartado postal 1594D, 32310 Ciudad Juárez (Chihuahua)
Tel: +52(16) 16-56-92
Fax: +52(16) 16-21-11
Rector: Wilfrido Campbell Saavedra (1992-96)
Secretaria General: Adriana Saucedo García
Founded: 1973
Biomedicine; Social Sciences and Administration; Engineering.

Autonomous University of Coahuila
[Universidad Autónoma de Coahuila]
Bulevar Venustiano Caranza y Licenciado Salvador González Lobo, 25280 Saltillo (Coahuila)
Tel: +52(84) 15-73-92
Fax: +52(84) 15-38-53
Rector: Alejandro Dávila Flores (1994-97)
Secretario General: José Ignacio Méndez Lastra
Founded: 1867, 1957
F: Education; Law.
S: Chemistry; Economics; Civil Engineering; Architecture; Psychology; Nursing and Midwifery; Social Work; Plastic Arts; Medicine.

NORTH UNIT
[UNIDAD NORTE]
Calle Morelia No. 1007, Guadalupe, Apartado postal No. 529, Monclova (Coahuila)
Tel: +52(863) 3-39-13
Coordinador: Alberto Ramírez Beeza
Engineering; Social and Administration; Chemistry.

TORREÓN UNIT
[UNIDAD TORREÓN]
Blvd. Revolución 590 Ote., Torreón (Coahuila)
Tel: +52(17) 12-23-79
Fax: +52(17) 16-74-88
Social and Administrative Sciences; Political and Social Sciences; Engineering; Biological and Health Sciences.

University of Colima
[Universidad de Colima]
Avenida Universidad 333, 28000 Colima (Colima)
Tel: +52(331) 2-85-10
Fax: +52(331) 4-30-06
Telex: 62248 ucolme
Rector: Fernando Moreno Peña (1989-97)
Secretario General: Lorenzo Hernández Arreguin
Founded: 1940, 1960
F: Education; Accountancy and Administration; Medicine; Mechanical and Electrical Engineering; Biological Sciences; Architecture; Law.
S: Political and Social Sciences; Social Work; Economics; Civil Engineering; Chemistry; Nursing; Veterinary Medicine and Animal Husbandry; Marine Sciences; Letters and Communication; Foreign Languages.

Juárez University of the State of Durango
[Universidad Juárez del Estado de Durango]
Constitución 404 Sur, 34000 Durango (Durango)
Tel: +52(181) 2-56-05
Fax: +52(181) 2-56-05
Rector: Juan Francisco Salazar Benitez (1992-96)
Secretario General: María Elena Valdés de Reyes
Founded: 1872, 1957

S: Law; Medicine; Accountancy and Administration; Mathematics; Forestry; Social Work; Sociology; Music; Dentistry; Nursing and Midwifery; Commerce; Veterinary Medicine and Animal Husbandry; Zoology (Gómez Palacio); Food Technology (Gómez Palacio); Agricultural Engineering (Gómez Palacio); Civil Engineering (Gómez Palacio); Medicine (Gómez Palacio).

University of Guadalajara
[Universidad de Guadalajara]
Avenida Juárez 975, 44100 Guadalajara (Jalisco)
Tel: +52(36) 25-22-42
Fax: +52(36) 26-06-68
Telex: 0681744 xhug mex
Rector: Raul Padilla López (1989-95)
Secretario General: Guillermo Arturo Gómez Reyes
Founded: 1791
F: Administration; Agronomy; Agriculture (Autlán); Accountancy; Architecture; Chemistry; Dentistry; Economics; Engineering; Geography; Law; Medicine; Philosophy and Letters; Psychology; Science; Social Work; Tourism; Veterinary Medicine and Animal Husbandry; Veterinary Medicine and Animal Husbandry (Ciudad Guzmán).
S: Nursing; Nursing (Ocotlán); Nursing (Ciudad Guzman); Plastic Arts; Polytechnic; Polytechnic (Ocatlán).
I: Human Settlement; Astronomy and Meteorology; Botany; Development of Capital Goods; Economic and Regional Studies; Social Studies; Geography and Statistics; Limnology; Wood, Cellulose and Paper Studies; Infectious and Experimental Pathology; Psychiatry and Psychosomatic Disorders; Public Health Research (regional).
D: National Political and Government Studies.

University of Guanajuato
[Universidad de Guanajuato]
Lascuraín de Retana 5, 36000 Guanajuato (Guanajuato)
Tel: +52(473) 2-23-94
Fax: +52(473) 2-71-48
Rector: Juan Carlos Romero Hicks (1991-97)
Secretario General: Arturo Lara López
Founded: 1732, 1870, 1945
S: Accountancy and Administration; Law; Mining, Geology, and Metallurgy; Medicine; Chemistry; Electronics, and Mechanical and Electrical Engineering; Architecture; Plastic Arts; Business Administration; Interior Design; Nursing and Midwifery (4); Philosophy and Letters; Civil Engineering; Topography; Music; Industrial Relations; Agriculture and Animal Husbandry; Psychology; Mathematics; Auxiliary Accountancy.
I: Physics; Education Research.
Ce: Agriculture and Food Technology Research; Language.

Autonomous University of Guerrero
[Universidad Autónoma de Guerrero]
Avenida Abasolo 33, 39020 Chilpancingo (Guerrero)
Tel: +52(747) 2-25-36
Fax: +52(747) 2-29-10
Rector: Gabino Olea Campos (1993-96)
Secretario General: Fausto Solís Leyva
Founded: 1869
S: Philosophy and Letters; Engineering; Education.
C: Law; Architecture and Town Planning; Economics; Biological and Chemical Sciences; Veterinary Medicine and Animal Husbandry (Ciudad Altamirana); Earth Sciences (Taxco el Viejo).

ACAPULCO UNIT
[UNIDAD ACAPULCO]
Prolongación Niños Héroes No. 133, Acapulco (Guerrero)
Tel: +52(748) 5-03-53
Coordinador: Felix González Figueroa
Social Sciences; Economic and Administrative Sciences; Health Sciences.

IGUALA UNIT
[UNIDAD IGUALA]
Periférico Pte. s/n, Col. Villa de Guadalupe, 40010 Iguala (Guerrero)
Tel: +52(733) 2-41-85
Coordinador: Bartolo Hernández Santa Anna
Agriculture.

Autonomous University of the State of Hidalgo
[Universidad Autónoma del Estado de Hidalgo]
Abasolo 600, 42000 Pachuca (Hidalgo)
Tel: +52(771) 5-53-40
Fax: +52(771) 5-53-40
Rector: Gerardo Sosa Castelán (1994-97)
Secretario General: Juan Manuel Camacho Beltrán
Founded: 1869, 1961
I: Law and Social Sciences; Accountancy and Administration; Industrial Engineering; Exact Sciences.
S: Medicine; Dentistry; Social Work; Nursing.

University of the West, Los Mochis
[Universidad de Occidente]
Avenida Benito Juárez 435, Poniente, Apartado postal 936, 81200 Los Mochis (Sinaloa)
Tel: +52(681) 5-10-61
Fax: +52(681) 5-39-00
Rector: Ernesto Cebreros Murillo (1993-96)
Secretario General: Cutberto Hernández Caro
Founded: 1980
D: Administration; Engineering; Psychology; Communication; Law; Biology; Accountancy and Economics; Mathematics.
I: Anthropological and Social Research; Aquacultural and Fishing Development Technology Research.

GUAMUCHIL UNIT
[UNIDAD GUAMUCHIL]
José María Vigil y Blvd. Lazaro, Cardenas,
Guamuchil (Sinaloa)
Tel: +52(673) 2-03-83
Coordinador General: Everardo Angulo Valle
Social and Administrative Sciences; Biology and Health Sciences; Engineering.

GUASAVE UNIT
[UNIDAD GUASAVE]
Corregidora y Zaragoza, 81000 Guasave
(Sinaloa)
Tel: +52(687) 2-27-00
Coordinador General: Jesús Teodoro Ramírez Jacobo
Social and Administrative Sciences; Engineering.

GULIACÁN UNIT
[UNIDAD GULIACÁN]
Blvd. Madero No. 334 Pte., 80000 Guliacán
(Sinaloa)
Tel: +52(67) 50-30-36
Coordinador General: J. Heriberto Sánchez Gaxiola
Social and Administrative Sciences; Engineering.

LOS MOCHIS UNIT
[UNIDAD LOS MOCHIS]
Blvd. Macario Gaxiola y Carretera, Internacional,
Apartado postal No. 936, 81200 Los Mochis
(Sinaloa)
Tel: +52(681) 5-60-60
Coordinador General: José Alfredo Hernández Mexia
Social and Administrative Sciences; Engineering; Biology.

MAZATLÁN UNIT
[UNIDAD MAZATLÁN]
Avenida del Mar No. 1200, 82110 Mazatlán
(Sinaloa)
Tel: +52(69) 83-64-04
Coordinador General: Roberto Tirado García
Social and Administrative Sciences; Natural Sciences.

*Metropolitan Autonomous University
[Universidad Autónoma Metropolitana]
Boulevard Manuel Avila Camacho 90, Col. El
Parque, 53390 Naucalpan de Juárez (Estado de México)
Tel: +52(5) 5-76-79-00
Fax: +52(5) 5-76-65-29
Telex: 1772152 aumrme
Rector: Julio Rubio Oca (1993-97)
Secretario General: M.C. Magda Fresman Orozco
Founded: 1973

AZCAPOTZALCO UNIT
[UNIDAD AZCAPOTZALCO]
Avenida San Pablo 180, Col. Reynosa
Tamaulipas, Delegación Azcapotzalco, 02200
México (D.F.)
Tel: +52(5) 3-82-43-10
Fax: +52(5) 3-82-40-52
Rector: Edmundo Jacobo Molina
Engineering; Social and Human Sciences; Arts and Design.

IZTAPALAPA UNIT
[UNIDAD IZTAPALAPA]
Avenida Michoacán y la Purisima, Col. Vicentina
Delegación Iztapalapa, 09340 México (D.F.)
Tel: +52(5) 6-12-22-65
Fax: +52(5) 6-12-08-85
Rector: José Luis Gazuuez Mateos
Biomedical and Health Sciences; Basic Sciences and Engineering; Human and Social Sciences.

UNIDAD XOCHIMILCO
Calz. del Huesco 1100, Col. Villa Quietud,
Delegación Coyoacán, 04969 México (D.F.)
Tel: +52(5) 5-94-66-56
Fax: +52(5) 7-24-51-75
Rector: Avedis Aznavurian Apajian
Biology and Health Sciences; Social and Human Sciences; Arts and Design.

Autonomous University of the State of Mexico
[Universidad Autónoma del Estado de México]
Instituto Literario 100 Oriente, 50000 Toluca
(Estado de México)
Tel: +52(72) 13-47-32
Fax: +52(72) 14-55-46
Rector: Marco Antonio Morales Gómez (1993-97)
Secretario Académico: Gilberto Cortez Bastida
Founded: 1828, 1943, 1956
F: Accountancy and Administration; Agricultural Sciences; Architecture and Fine Arts; Behavioural Sciences; Chemistry; Political Sciences; Tourism; Veterinary Medicine.
S: Urban and Regional Planning; Sciences; Anthropology.

*National Autonomous University of Mexico (UNAM)
[Universidad Nacional Autónoma de México (UNAM)]
Ciudad Universitaria, 04510 México (D.F.)
Tel: +52(5) 548-40-40
Fax: +52(5) 550-87-72
Telex: 1777429 unamme
Rector: José Sarukhán Kermez (1989-97)
Secretario General: Salvador Malo
Founded: 1551, 1910, 1929, 1944
F: Architecture; Science; Political and Social Sciences; Chemistry; Business Administration and Accountancy; Law; Economics; Nursing and Midwifery; Philosophy and Letters; Engineering; Medicine; Dentistry; Veterinary Medicine and Animal Husbandry; Psychology; Higher Studies (Cuautitlán).

S: Plastic Arts; Music; Social Work.
Ce: Atmospheric Sciences; Ecology; Instruments; Research on Nitrogen Fixing; Genetic Engineering and Biotechnology.
I: Astronomy; Biology; Marine Sciences and Limnology; Nuclear Sciences; Physics; Cellular Physiology; Geophysics; Geography; Geology; Engineering; Biomedical Research; Applied Mathematics and Systems; Research in Materials; Mathematics; Chemistry.
National Astronomical Observatories: (San Pedro Mártir; Tonantzintla, and Zacatecas).

NATIONAL SCHOOL OF PROFESSIONAL STUDIES ACATLÁN
[ESCUELA NACIONAL DE ESTUDIOS PROFESIONALES ACATLÁN]
Av. Alcanfores y San Juan, Totoltepec, 53150 Sta. Cruz Acatlán (Estado de México)
Tel: +52(5) 3-73-16-77
Fax: +52(5) 3-73-24-25
Director: Victor José Valencia Gómez
Economic and Administrative Sciences; Social Sciences and Humanities; Engineering.

NATIONAL SCHOOL OF PROFESSIONAL STUDIES ARAGÓN
[ESCUELA NACIONAL DE ESTUDIOS PROFESIONALES ARAGÓN]
Prof. Carlos Hank G. y Hacienda, Rancho-Seco de Aragón, 57170 Ciudad Nezahualcóyotl (Estado de México)
Tel: +52(5) 7-80-29-33
Fax: +52(5) 7-94-32-45
Director: Claudio Carl Merrifield Castro
Economic and Administrative Sciences; Social Sciences; Engineering.

NATIONAL SCHOOL OF PROFESSIONAL STUDIES IZTACALA
[ESCUELA NACIONAL DE ESTUDIOS PROFESIONALES IZTACALA]
Avenida Los Barrios s/n, Unidad Los Reyes Iztacala, 54090 Tlalnepantla (Estado de México)
Tel: +52(5) 5-65-72-75
Fax: +52(5) 3-90-58-43
Directora: Arlette López Trujillo
Natural and Exact Sciences; Health Sciences.

NATIONAL SCHOOL OF PROFESSIONAL STUDIES ZARAGOZA
[ESCUELA NACIONAL DE ESTUDIOS PROFESIONALES ZARAGOZA]
J.C. Bonilla No. 66, Col. Ejército Oriente, 09230 México (D.F.)
Tel: +52(5) 7-44-10-76
Fax: +52(5) 7-44-12-17
Director: Benny Weyss Steider
Chemistry; Health Sciences; Natural Sciences.

FACULTIES OF HIGHER STUDIES CUAUTITLÁN
[FACULTAD DE ESTUDIOS SUPERIORES CUAUTITLÁN]
Carretera Cuautitlán Teoloyucan Km. 2.5, Apartado postal 25, Cuautitlán Izcalli (Estado de México)
Tel: +52(5) 8-72-09-84
Fax: +52(5) 8-72-68-97
Director: Jaime Keller Torres
Social Sciences; Administration; Engineering; National Sciences.

National Pedagogical University of México

[Universidad Pedagógica Nacional]
Km. 1/2 Carretera al Ajusco, Héroes de Padierna, 14200 México (D.F)
Tel: +52(5) 6-45-64-69
Fax: +52(5) 6-45-53-40
Rector: Eduardo Maliachi y Velasco (1993-)
Secretario Administrativo: Salvador Heredia Reyes
Founded: 1979
Education.

AGUASCALIENTES UNIT
[UNIDAD AGUASCALIENTES]
Pedro Parga No. 231, Col. Centro, 20000 Aguascalientes (Aguascalientes)
Tel: +52(49) 13-07-31
Fax: +52(49) 13-61-24
Director: Antonio Ortíz Sandoval
Education.

COLIMA UNIT
[UNIDAD COLIMA]
Gabriel León Polanco Esq., Leonardo Yañez Centeno, Fracc. Alfredo Bonfil, 28950 Colima (Colima)
Tel: +52(331) 2-56-63
Fax: +52(331) 2-56-63
Director: Roberto A. Merlo Aguilera
Education.

MEXICALI UNIT
[UNIDAD MEXICALI]
Río Mocorito y José Antonio Torres, Landa s/n, Col. Independencia, 21290 Mexicali (Baja California)
Tel: +52(65) 66-20-80
Director: Sergio Gómez Montero
Education.

Michoacan University of Saint Nicholas of Hidalgo Morelia

[Universidad Michoacana de San Nicolás de Hidalgo]
Edificio 'A' Cd. Universitaria, Morelia (Michoacán de Ocampo)
Tel: +52(43) 16-70-20
Fax: +52(43) 16-33-35
Rector: Daniel Trujillo Mesina (1990-35)
Secretario General: Román Armando Luna Escalante
Founded: 1843, 1542, 1917, 1939
F: Medicine; Dentistry; Law and Sociology; Agrobiology (Uruapan).
S: Civil Engineering; Mechanical Engineering; Chemistry; Wood Technology; Architecture; Chemistry; Pharmacy and Biological Sciences; Nursing; Accountancy and Administration; Physics and Mathematics; Biological Sciences; Philosophy; History; Veterinary Medicine and Zoology.
C: Agriculture (Apatzingan).

Autonomous University of the State of Morelos

[Universidad Autónoma del Estado de Morelos]
Avenida Universidad 1001, 62210 Cuernavaca
(Morelos)
Tel: +52(73) 13-65-97
Fax: +52(73) 13-34-95
Telex: 173392 uamme
Rector: Alejandro Montalvo Pérez (1988-94)
Secretario General: Antonio Miranda Sotelo
Founded: 1939, 1872, 1953
F: Accountancy and Business Administration;
Chemistry and Industrial Engineering.
S: Agriculture; Law and Social Sciences;
Biology; Psychology; Medicine; Education and
Human Communication; Architecture.

Autonomous University of Nayarit

[Universidad Autónoma de Nayarit]
Ciudad de la Cultura 'Amado Nervo', 63190 Tepic
(Nayarit)
Tel: +52(321) 3-13-20
Fax: 52(321) 3-25-21
(1991-94)
Secretario General: Juan Rafael Esparza Meza
Founded: 1962, 1975
S: Agriculture (Xalisco); Industrial Chemical
Engineering; Economics; Tourism; Commerce
and Administration; Law; Medicine; Dentistry;
Veterinary Medicine and Animal Husbandry;
Fisheries; Nursing.

*Autonomous University of Nuevo León

[Universidad Autónoma de Nuevo León]
Ciudad Universitaria, 64000 Monterrey (Nuevo
León)
Tel: +52(83) 52-28-85
Fax: +52(83) 76-77-57
Telex: 382989 unalnme
Rector: Manuel Silos Martínez (1991-94)
Secretario General: Reyes Tamez Guerra
Founded: 1826, 1933, 1971
F: Agriculture; Architecture; Biology;
Mathematics and Physics; Chemistry;
Accountancy and Administration; Law and Social
Sciences; Economics; Nursing; Philosophy and
Letters; Political Science; Communication
Sciences; Civil Engineering; Mechanical and
Electrical Engineering; Medicine; Dentistry; Sport;
Psychology; Public Health Administration; Social
Work; Veterinary Medicine and Animal
Husbandry; Political Science; Communication
Sciences; Earth Sciences; Forestry; Visual Arts;
Music.
S: Scenic Arts.

'Benito Juárez' Autonomous University of Oaxaca

[Universidad Autónoma 'Benito Juárez' de
Oaxaca]
Ciudad Universitaria, Ex-Hacienda 'Cinco
Señores', 68120 Oaxaca (Oaxaca)
Tel: +52(951) 1-06-88
Fax: +52(951) 1-06-88
Telex: 18601 ubjome
Rector: Homero Pérez Cruz (1992-96)
Secretario General: Odavías Martínez Soriano
Founded: 1827, 1955
F: Accountancy and Public Administration;
Medicine and Surgery.
S: Law and Social Sciences; Medicine;
Chemistry; Architecture; Veterinary Medicine and
Zoology; Nursing; Dentistry.

Benements Autonomous University of Puebla

[Benements Universidad Autónoma de Puebla]
4 Sur No. 104, 72000 Puebla (Puebla)
Tel: +52(22) 46-99-71
Fax: +52(22) 32-32-69
Telex: 178350 iuapme
Rector: José Doger Corte (1990-96)
Secretario General: Victor Espíndola Cabrera
Founded: 1937, 1956
S: Public Administration; Architecture;
Accountancy; Physics and Mathematics;
Chemistry; Law and Social Sciences; Economics;
Nursing and Midwifery; Philosophy and Letters;
Civil Engineering; Chemical Engineering;
Medicine; Veterinary Medicine and Zoology
(Tecamachalco); Dentistry; Languages; Music.
I: Scientific Research.
D: Physical Education; Extension.

Autonomous University of Querétaro

[Universidad Autónoma de Querétaro]
Centro Universitario, Cerro de las Campanas,
76010 Querétaro (Querétaro)
Tel: +52(42) 16-76-59
Fax: +52(42) 16-49-17
Rector: José Alfredo Cepeda Garrido (1994-97)
Secretario Administrativo: Jorge Léon Camacho
Founded: 1625
F: Chemistry; Engineering; Accountancy and
Business Administration; Law; Psychology;
Veterinary Medicine and Animal Husbandry.
S: Medicine; Sociology; Nursing; Languages;
Journalism.
I: Fine Arts.

Autonomous Agricultural University 'Antonio Narro', Saltillo

[Universidad Autónoma Agraria 'Antonio Narro']
Buena Vista, 25315 Saltillo (Coahuila)
Tel: +52(84) 17-31-84
Fax: +52(84) 17-36-44
Telex: 038128
Rector: Eduardo Fuentes Rodriguez (1993-94)
Secretario General: José Luis Berlanga Flores
Founded: 1923

F: Agronomy; Engineering; Socioeconomic
Science; Animal Science.

LA LAGUNA UNIT
[UNIDAD LA LAGUNA]
Carretera a Santa Fé y Periférico, 27000 Torreón
(Coahuila)
Director: JosJaime Lozano García
Founded: 1980
Health Sciences; Agricultural Engineering.

Autonomous University of San Luis Potosí
[Universidad Autónoma de San Luis Potosí]
Alvaro Obregón 64, 78000 San Luis Potosí (San
Luis Potosí)
Tel: +52(48) 12-02-82
Fax: +52(48) 18-19-21
E-Mail: lastras a. sep rodríguez al. medellín p
Rector: Alfonso Lastras Ramírez
Secretario General: Jaime Valle Méndez
Founded: 1859, 1923
F: Commerce and Administration; Law;
Economics; Science; Engineering.
S: Agriculture; Chemistry; Stomatology; Nursing;
Medicine; Psychology; Habitat.
I: Geology; Educational Sciences; Physics;
Metallurgy; Agriculture and Stockraising; Arid
Zones Research; Humanistic Research; Economic
Research; Law Research.
D: Communication Sciences.
Ce: Language; Chemistry Research.

HUASTECA UNIT
[UNIDAD ZONA HUASTECA]
Carretera Valles Tampico Km. 3.5, Calle
Romualdo del Campo s/n, Col. Las Aguilas,
Apartado postal No. 163, 79000 Ciudad Valles
(San Luis Potosí)
Tel: +52(138) 2-36-44
Director: Eduardo Abut Ramos
Chemistry; Social and Administrative Sciences;
Engineering.

MEDIA UNIT
[UNIDAD ZONA MEDIA]
Carretera Rioverde-San Ciro Km. 4, Apartado
postal No. 84, 79610 Rioverde (San Luis Potosí)
Tel: +52(487) 2-14-99
Directora: Milka Elena Escalera Chävez
Administration; Enginneering.

Autonomous University of Sinaloa
[Universidad Autónoma de Sinaloa]
Angel Flores y Riva Palacio s/n, 80000 Culiacán
(Sinaloa)
Tel: +52(67) 13-93-91
Fax: +52(67) 12-50-95
Rector: Rubén Rocha Moya
Secretario General: Jorge Luis Guevara Reynaga
Founded: 1873, 1965
F: Law and Social Sciences.
C: Agriculture; Agriculture (Juan José Rios).
S: Biology; Accountancy and Administration;
Engineering (Los Mochis); Engineering

(Mazatlán); Economics; Marine Sciences; Fishery;
Social Sciences; Medicine and Surgery; Social
Work; Nursing; Meteorology; Plastic Arts; Physics
and Mathematics; Philosophy; Agricultural
Administration; Dentistry; Psychology; Veterinary
Medicine and Zoology.
I: Languages.
Ce: Musical.

University of Sonora
[Universidad de Sonora]
Campos de la Universidad, 83000 Hermosillo
(Sonora)
Tel: +52(62) 13-15-81
Fax: +52(62) 12-02-83
Rector: Jorge Luis Ibarra Mendivil
Secretario General: Manuel Sánchez Lucero
Founded: 1938
S: Law and Social Sciences; Psychology and
Communications Studies; Engineering;
Chemistry; Agronomy and Stockraising;
Engineering (Caboria); Chemistry (Caboria); Law
and Sciences (Caboria).
D: Social Sciences; Accountancy and
Administration; Economics; Humanities; Physics;
Mathematics; Geology; Chemistry and Biology.

NORTHERN REGIONAL UNIT
[UNIDAD REGIONAL NORTE]
Avenida Universidad e Irigoyen, Col. Ortiz,
Apartado postal No. 234, 83600 Caboria (Sonora)
Tel: +52(637) 2-22-82
Vice-Rector: Eduardo Canseco Vilchis
Social and Administrative Sciences; Technology
and Engineering; Chemistry; Agriculture; Natural
Sciences.

SOUTHERN REGIONAL UNIT
[UNIDAD REGIONAL SUR]
Lazaro Cárdenas No. 100, 85900 Navojoa
(Sonora)
Tel: +52(642) 2-47-04
Vice-Rector: Fabian Galindo Duarte
Social and Administrative Sciences; Natural and
Exact Sciences; Chemistry; Agriculture.

*Technical Institute of Sonora
[Instituto Tecnológico de Sonora]
5 de Febrero 818 Sur, 85000 Ciudad Obregón
(Sonora)
Tel: +52(641) 7-07-83
Fax: +52(641) 7-07-31
Rector: Oscar Russo Vogel
Founded: 1955, 1973
D: Agriculture; Administration and Accountancy;
Psychology; Industrial Engineering; Civil
Engineering and Hydrology; Chemistry and
Chemical Engineering; Humanities; Veterinary
Medicine and Animal Husbandry; Mathematics
and Physics; Nursing (2); Extension.

UNIDAD GUYAMAS
Carretera Al Aeropuerto Km. 3, Apartado postal
No. 870, 35400 Guyamas (Sonora)
Tel: +52(622) 2-71-32
Telex: 120482
Director: Ignacio Palomares Urrea
*Industrial Engineering; Electronical Engineering;
Electrical Engineering; Civil Engineering;
Chemical Engineering; Administration; Public
Accountancy; Chemistry.*

'Juárez' Autonomous University of Tabasco

[Universidad 'Juárez' Autónoma de Tabasco]
Zona de la Cultura, Carretera Frontera s/n, 86020
Villahermosa (Tabasco)
Tel: +52(931) 229-93
Fax: +52(931) 216-37
Rector: Fernando Rabelo Ruíz de la Peña
(1988-96)
Academic Services Secretary: Walter Ramírez
Izquierdo
Founded: 1879, 1958
*D: Economics and Administration; Social
Sciences and Humanities; Health Sciences;
Engineering and Technology; Basic Studies;
Agriculture and Stockraising; Basic Sciences;
Informatics.
Ce: Social Sciences and Humanities Research;
Health Research; Biology and Biotechnology
Research; Agriculture Research; Economics-
Administration Research; Engineering and
Technology Research; Basic Sciences Research.*

CENTRAL UNIT
[UNIDAD CENTRO]
Avenida Universitaria No. 246, 86040
Villahermosa (Tabasco)
Tel: +52(931) 2-29-93
Fax: +52(931) 2-16-37
Rector: Fernando Rabelo Ruiz de la Peña
*Economic and Administrative Sciences; Social
and Human Sciences; Health Sciences; Education
and Arts.*

CHONTALPA UNIT
[UNIDAD CHONTALPA]
Carretera Cunduacán-Jalpa Km. 1, Conduacán
(Tabasco)
Tel: +52(933) 6-03-00
Fax: +52(933) 6-03-42
Director General: Rodolfo Mayo Oropeza
*Engineering and Technology; Basic Sciences;
Economic and Administrative Sciences.*

SIERRA UNIT
[UNIDAD SIERRA]
Carretera Villahermosa-Teapa Km. 25, Corresp.
Avenida Universidad s/n, Apartado postal No.
298, 86000 Villahermosa (Tabasco)
Tel: +52(93) 12-72-11
Fax: +52(93) 12-16-37
Director General: Arturo E. Priego Ramírez
Agriculture and Stockraising; Biology.

Autonomous University of Tamaulipas

[Universidad Autónoma de Tamaulipas]
Calle Matamoros 8-altos, 87000 Ciudad Victoria
(Tamaulipas)
Tel: +52(131) 2-71-69
Fax: +52(131) 2-00-70
Telex: 31260 uatyme
Rector: Humberto Filizola Haces
Secretario General: Fernando Arizpe García
Founded: 1956
*F: Law; Agriculture; Commerce and
Administration; Social Work; Veterinary Medicine
and Zoology; Education; Agriculture (Ciudad
Mante); Commerce and Administration (Nuevo
Laredo); Law and Social Sciences (Tampico);
Engineering (Tampico); Architecture (Tampico);
Nursing and Midwifery (Tampico); Medicine
(Tampico); Commerce and Administration
(Tampico); Dentistry (Tampico); Medicine (H.
Matamoros); Nursing (Matamoros); Chemistry
(Reynosa); Agro-Industrial Sciences (Reynosa).
C: Music (Tampico).*

Autonomous University of Tlaxcala

[Universidad Autónoma de Tlaxcala]
Avenida Universidad 1, 90000 Tlaxcala (Tlaxcala)
Tel: +52(246) 2-11-67
Fax: +52(246) 2-11-67
Rector: Juan Méndez Vásquez (1991-95)
Secretario Académico: Magdiel Xicotencatl Presa
Founded: 1976
*D: Social Sciences and Administration;
Education; Human Sciences; Industrial
Engineering and Chemistry; Agriculture; Health
Sciences.*

University of Veracruz

[Universidad Veracruzana]
Zona Universitaria, Lomas del Estadio, 91090
Xalapa (Veracruz)
Tel: +52(281) 7-34-27
Fax: +52(281) 7-63-70
Telex: 015516 diuvme
Rector: Emilio Gidi Villarreal (1992-95)
Secretario Académico: Jorge Ramírez Juárez
Founded: 1944
*F: Business Administration; Agriculture;
Anthropology; Architecture; Bioanalysis; Biology;
Dentistry; Music; Theatre; Commerce;
Engineering; Physics; Dance; Law; Economics;
Statistics; Philosophy; History; Languages;
Chemistry; Spanish Literature; Mathematics;
Medicine; Nutrition; Pedagogics; Psychology;
Sociology; Dentistry (Ciudad Mendoza); Medicine
(Ciudad Mendoza); Mechanical and Electrical
Engineering (Ciudad Mendoza); Administration
(Coatzacoalcos); Engineering (Coatzacoalcos);
Chemistry (Coatzacoalcos); Agriculture
(Córdoba); Biology (Córdoba); Architecture
(Córdoba); Medicine (Minatitlán); Dentistry
(Minatitlán); Social Work (Minatitlán); Commerce*

(Nogales); Architecture (Poza Rica); Engineering (Poza Rica); Chemistry (Poza Rica); Medicine (Poza Rica); Dentistry (Poza Rica); Psychology (Poza Rica); Pedagogics (Poza Rica); Social Work (Poza Rica); Commerce (Veracruz); Administration (Veracruz); Pedagogics (Veracruz); Tourism (Veracruz); Engineering (Veracruz); Physics (Veracruz); Psychology (Veracruz); Dentistry (Veracruz); Naval Engineering (Veracruz); Chemistry (Veracruz); Veterinary Medicine and Zoology (Veracruz); Bioanalysis (Veracruz); Medicine (Veracruz); Nutrition (Veracruz); Journalism (Veracruz); Agriculture (Tuxpán); Biology (Tuxpán); Veterinary Medicine and Zoology (Tuxpán); Commerce (Tuxpán).

Autonomous University of Yucatán
[Universidad Autónoma de Yucatán]
Calle 60 y 57, 97000 Mérida (Yucatán)
Tel: +52(99) 24-80-00
Fax: +52(99) 28-25-57
Rector: Carlos M. Pasos Novelo (1991-94)
Secretario General: Carlos Nuñez Erosa
Founded: 1624, 1922
F: Anthropology; Architecture; Business Administration and Accountancy; Law; Economics; Engineering; Chemical and Industrial Engineering; Mathematics; Medicine; Veterinary Medicine; Dentistry; Psychology; Education.
S: Chemistry; Nursing.

Autonomous University of Zacatecas
[Universidad Autónoma de Zacatecas]
Galeana No. 1, 98000 Zacatecas (Zacatecas)
Tel: +52(492) 2-91-09
Fax: +52(492) 2-64-55
Rector: Virgilio Rivera Delgadillo (1992-96)
Secretario General: Hector Martínez Cantú
Founded: 1832, 1920, 1959, 1968
S: Agriculture; Chemistry; Accountancy and Administration; Law; Economics; Nursing; Engineering; Mining; Medicine; Dentistry; Veterinary Medicine and Animal Husbandry; Social Sciences.
Ce: Mathematics; Languages.

Veracruz Pedagogical University
[Universidad Pedagógica Veracruzana]
Calle Nicolás Bravo 6, 91000 Jalapa (Veracruz)
Tel: +52(281) 794-43
Director: Hector Herrera Bustamente
Education.

PRIVATE INSTITUTIONS

University Anáhuac
[Universidad Anáhuac]
Avenida Lomas de Anáhuac s/n Fracc. Lomas Anáhuac, 52760 Huixquilucan (Estado de Mexico)
Tel: +52(5) 589-2200
Fax: +52(5) 589-9796
Rector: Raymund Cosgrave (1990-96)
Secretario General: Gregorio López Zarraga
Founded: 1965

S: Medicine; Communications; Social Sciences; Actuarial Sciences; Psychology; Architecture; Computer Sciences; Law; Economics; Education; Business Administration; Tourism; Industrial Design; Engineering.

Anáhuac University of the South
[Universidad Anáhuac del Sur]
Avenida de las Torres 131, Col. Oliver de los Padres, 01780 México (D.F.)
Tel: +52(5) 6-83-11-00
Rector: J.F. Dermont McKluskey
Founded: 1964
S: Graphic Design; Actuarial Sciences; Business Administration and Accountancy; Engineering; Tourism; Computer Science; Industrial Relations.

University of Bajío A.C.
[Universidad del Bajío A.C.]
Falda del Cerro Gordo s/n, Fraccionamiento Lomas del Campestre, 37150 León (Guanajuato)
Tel: +52(47) 17-17-40
Fax: +52(47) 18-55-11
Telex: 1772861 Ulsame
Rector: Ronaldo Henderson Calderón
Founded: 1968, 1973
S: Administration; Communication Studies; Dentistry; Accountancy; Veterinary Medicine and Zoology; Tourism and Hotel Management; Engineering; Architecture; Law; Computer Engineering; Agriculture.
Ce: Art and Design; Extension.

Benavente Lasallista University Celaya
[Universidad Lasallista Benavente]
Avenida Universidad s/n, 38040 Celaya (Guanajuato)
Tel: +52(461) 2-52-27
Fax: +52(461) 2-59-71
Rector: Hector Aquilar Tamayo
Law.

University of Celaya
[Universidad de Celaya]
Carretera Panamericana Km. 269, 36000 Guanajuato (Guanajuato)
Tel: +52(461) 390-99
Fax: +52(461) 396-00
Rectora: Marcela Díez de Batta (1988-)
Rector and Administrative Officer: M.B. Marcela Diez de Batta
Founded: 1988
F: Business; Sciences; Humanities; Co-ordinator.
Ce: Experimental Propagation of Plants; Historical Research.

University Chapultepéc
[Universidad Chapultepéc]
Eugenia No 1010, Col. de Valle, 03100 México (D.F.)
Tel: +52(5) 23-68-49
Rector: Francisco Lejarza Gallegos
S: Commerce and Administration; Medicine; Architecture; Law; Systems Engineering.

Regional University 'Miguel Hidalgo' Ciudad Madero
[Universidad Regional 'Miguel Hidalgo']
16 de Septiembre 102 Ote, Col. Arbol Grande,
89490 Ciudad Madero (Tamaulipas)
Rector: Luciano Herrera Peña
S: Social Sciences; Administration; Nursing; Nutrition; Physical Education.

Mexican American University of the North, Ciudad Reynosa
[Universidad México Americana del Norte]
Guerrero y Plutarco Elías Calles 1317, Col. de Prado, 88560 Ciudad Reynosa (Tamaulipas)
Tel: +52(89) 22-20-02
Fax: +52(89) 22-85-68
Rectora: Edith Cantu de Luna
Director Ejecutivo: Francisco Abel Treviño
Founded: 1982
I: Economic and Administrative Sciences; Communication Sciences; Exact Sciences; Biological and Health Sciences; Law.

University Cuauhtémoc
[Universidad Cuauhtémoc]
Jalpan y Tlacomulco. Colonia La Paz, 72160 Puebla (Puebla)
Tel: +52(22) 48-20-44
Rector: Francisco Martínez Briones
Founded: 1977
S: Commerce and Administration; Law; Engineering; Dentistry; Psychology.

University Cuetlaxcoapan, S.C.
[Universidad Cuetlaxcoapan, S.C.]
Boulevard Valsequillo y 3B Sur. Residencial Boulevares, 72000 Puebla (Puebla)
Tel: +52(22) 43-22-44
Rector: Salvador Calva Morales
Veterinary Medicine; Animal Science.

Autonomous University of Fresnillo
[Universidad Autónoma de Fresnillo]
Prolongación Avenida Hidalgo s/n, 99000 Fresnillo (Zacatecas)
Tel: +52(493) 2-32-10
Fax: +52(493) 2-32-10
Rector: Ismael Bárcenas Ríos
F: Econonmics and Administrative Sciences; Computer Systems; Engineering.

Autonomous University of Guadalajara
[Universidad Autónoma de Guadalajara]
Avenida la Patria 1201, 3a, Sección Lomas del Valle, 44100 Guadalajara (Jalisco)
Tel: +52(3) 6-41-32-52
Fax: +52 (36) 6-42-54-27
Telex: 682785 uag pme
Rector: Luis Garibay Gutiérrez (1957-)
Secretario General: Carlos Pérez Vizcaíno
Founded: 1935
D: Medicine; Science and Technology; Humanities and Social Sciences; Business Administration; Education; Architecture.

S: Dentistry; Nursing; Civil Engineering; Mechanical and Electrical Engineering; Computer Sciences; Agricultural Engineering; Biology; Mathematics; Accountancy; Tourism; Economics; Industrial Design; Plastic Arts; Anthropology; Philosophy and Letters; Languages; Psychology; Communication Studies; Computer Sciences.
I: Humanities and Social Sciences; Biology; Exact and Earth Sciences.
Ce: Industrial Development Research (CIDI); Economic Research (CIEN); Lifelong Education.

*Technical and Higher Studies Institute of the West, Guadalajara
[Instituto Tecnológico y de Estudios Superiores de Occidente]
Fuego 1031 Jardines Del Bosque, 31175 Guadalajara (Jalisco)
Tel: +52(3) 6-69-35-30
Fax: +52(3) 6-69-35-85
E-Mail: myance@mexicano.gdl.iteso.mx
Rector: Pablo Humberto Posada Velázquez, S.J. (1992-)
Director General Académico: Pablo Lasso Gómez
Founded: 1957, 1968, 1975
S: Architecture; Human Social Sciences.
D: Physics and Mathematics; Social Sciences; Engineering; Economics and Administration; Postgraduate Studies; Extension.
Ce: Computer; Agriculture and Stockraising.

Kino University, A.C. Hermosillo
[Universidad Kino, A.C.]
Marruecos Final Oriente, Col. Casa Blanca, 83070 Hermosillo (Sonora)
Tel: +52(62) 13-50-66
Fax: +52(62) 13-50-66
Rector: Adolfo Hernández Muńoz
Founded: 1985
D: Social Sciences; Management Sciences; Research.

University of the New World La Herradura
[Universidad Nuevo Mundo]
Bosque Moctezuma 124, 53920 Fracc. La Herradura (Estado de México)
Tel: +52(5) 5-89-17-11
Rector: Guillermo Amat
Mass Communication; Business Administration; Accountancy; Law; Graphic Design; Industrial Design; Philosophy; Mechanical Engineering; Psychology.

La Laguna Autonomous University, A.C.
[Universidad Autónoma de la Laguna, A.C.]
Avenida Juárez Ote. 87, 27000 Torreón (Coahuila)
Tel: +52(17) 16-10-65
Fax: +52(17) 16-03-99
Rector: Pedro Héctor Rivas Figueroa
Secretario: Carlos Manuel Guereca López
Founded: 1988
C: Administration Sciences; Sciences and Humanities; Research.

Madero University
[Universidad Madero]
Prol. 45 Poniente No. 7117, Col. Nva. Zavaleta,
Puebla (Puebla)
Tel: +52(22) 84-59-59
Fax: +52(22) 84-60-40
Director: Donacio Alvarado Hernández (1986-)
Founded: 1982
S: *Social Sciences; Business; Ecology (in process of development).*
D: *Research; Cultural Research for the Community.*

University of Mazatlán, A.C.
[Universidad de Mazatlán, A.C.]
Guillermo Nelson 100 Desp. 104, 82000 Mazatlán
(Sinaloa)
Tel: +52(69) 82-54-91
Rector: Fernando A. Orrantía Arellano
Mechanical Engineering Administration; Business Administration; Law; Public Accountancy; Computer Systems Administration.

University of Sciences and Humanities of the Pacific, Mazatlán
[Universidad de Ciencias y Humanidades del Pacífico]
Belisario Domínguez y Compañia 1800, 82000
Mazatlán (Sinaloa)
Tel: +52(69) 82-75-42
Directora: María Magdalena Gonzáles de Lizárraga
Administration; Psychology; Public Relations.

University of the Mayab
[Universidad del Mayab]
Km. 15.5 Carretera Mérida-Progresso, 927000
Mérida (Yucatán)
Tel: +52(99) 24-51-88
Fax: +52(99) 22-00-06
Rector: Carlos Villalva Talavera
Administration; Law; Computer Science; Communication Sciences; Psychology.

University of the Americas Mexico
[Universidad de las Américas, A.C.]
Puebla 223, Col. Roma, 067000 Mexico (D.F.)
Tel: +52(5) 5-25-40-66
Fax: +52(5) 5-11-60-40
Rectora: Margarita Gómez-Palacio Muñoz (1988-)
Founded: 1940, 1985
D: *Business Administration; Psychology; International Studies; Education; General Education Studies.*
Ce: *Language.*
I: *Oaxacan Studies.*

*Autonomous Technical Institute of México
[Instituto Tecnológico Autónomo de México]
Rio Hondo 1, Tizapán, San Angel, 10200 México
(D.F.)
Tel: +52(5) 5-50-82-28
Fax: +52(5) 5-50-76-37
E-Mail: BITNET:majeenheer itamvms1
Rector: Arturo Fernández Pérez (1992-)
Registrar: José Luis Espíndola
Founded: 1946, 1963
D: *Accountancy and Administration; Social Sciences; Computer Sciences; Economics; General Studies; Applied Mathematics and Actuarial Sciences; Law.*
Ce: *Economic Research and Analysis; Public Policy; International Business; Extension; Competitiveness Studies.*

Hispanic Mexican University México
[Universidad Hispano Mexicana]
Emilio Castelar 63 Esq. con Eugenio Sué 44, Col.
Polanco, 11590 México (D.F.)
Tel: +52(5) 5-45-17-82
Rector: Ezequiel Tomás Biosca
Tourism; Administration; International Relations.

*Iberian-American University México
[Universidad Iberoamericana]
Prolongación Paseo de la Reforma 880, Col.
Lomas de Santa Fé, 01210 México D.F.
Tel: +52(5) 5-70-61-98
Fax: +52(5) 7-26-90-48
Rector: Carlos Vigil Avalos
Founded: 1943, 1952
D: *Business Administration; Economics; Accountancy; Architecture and Town Planning; Art; Industrial and Graphic Design; Nutrition and Food Technology; Civil Engineering; Mechanical and Electrical Engineering; Engineering and Chemical Engineering; Physics; Mathematics; Systems Technology; Political and Social Sciences; Communication; Law; Psychology; Human Development; Religious Sciences; Philosophy; History; Letters.*
Ce: *Didactics; Social Service; Extension.*

'GOLFO-CENTRO' UNIT
[PLANTEL GOLFO-CENTRO]
Calzada Ignacio Zaragoza 284, Col. Los Pinos,
72240 Puebla (Puebla)
Tel: +52(22) 30-44-48
Fax: +52(22) 30-44-60
Rector: Armando Rugarcía Torres
Social and Administrative Sciences; Engineering; Health Sciences.

LAGUNA UNIT
[PLANTEL LAGUNA]
Carretera Nueva a San Pedro Km. 4.5, 27000
Torreón (Coahuila)
Tel: +52(17) 17-99-38
Fax: +52(17) 18-90-45
Rector: Victor Raúl Durana Valerio
Social and Administrative Sciences; Engineering and Technology.

LEÓN UNIT
[PLANTEL LEÓN]
Libramiento Norte Km. 3, 37000 León
(Guanajuato)
Tel: +52(47) 11-38-77
Fax: +52(47) 11-54-77
Rector: Carlos Velasco Arzac
*Social and Administrative Sciences; Engineering
and Technology; Agriculture and Stockraising.*

NORTH-WEST UNIT
[PLANTEL NORDESTE]
Blvd. Aguacaliente y Privada Pinos, 22420
Tijuana (Baja California)
Tel: +52(66) 30-15-77
Fax: +52(66) 30-15-91
Rector: Agustín Rozada Rebollar
Engineering and Technology; Social Sciences.

Intercontinental University México
[Universidad Intercontinental]
Avenida Insurgentes Sur 4303, 14420 México
(D.F.)
Tel: +52(5) 73-85-44
Rector: Juan José Corona López
Founded: 1976
S: *Architecture; Communication Sciences;
Accountancy and Administration; Law;
Philosophy; Design; Dentistry; Education;
Psychology; Theology; Tourism.*

*La Salle University México
[Universidad La Salle]
Avenida Benjamin Franklin 47, 06140 México
(D.F.)
Tel: +52(5) 2-71-03-91
Fax: +52(5) 2-71-85-85
Cable: ulsalle mexico
Rector: Mtro. Lucio Tazzer De Schrijver
Vice-Rector: Ambrosio Luna Sallas
Founded: 1962
S: *Accountancy and Administration; Law;
Engineering; Architecture; Medicine; Chemistry;
Philosophy; Religious Sciences.*
D: *Education; Lifelong Education.*

Latin University, A.C. México
[Universidad Latina, A.C.]
Chihuahua 202, 006700 México (D.F.)
Tel: +52(5) 5-64-54-29
Fax: +52(5) 5-64-54-29
Rector: Carlos E. Cuenca Dardón
Administration; Accountancy.

Latin American University México
[Universidad Latinoamericana]
S.C., Gabriel Mancera 1402, Col. del Valle, 03100
México (D.F.)
Tel: +52(5) 6-04-53-52
Rector: Rubén Rodríguez y Rodríguez
Founded: 1976
S: *Dentistry; Communications and Public
Relations; Administration and Accountancy;
Informatics; Law.*

Mexican University of Technology México
[Universidad Mexicana de Tecnología]
Czda. de Tlalpan 450, Col. Viaducto, 08200
México (D.F.)
Tel: +52(5) 5-30-98-04
Fax: +52(5) 5-30-32-83
Telex: 1771-300 achame
Rectora: María del Carmen Pérez Herrera
Founded: 1959, 1982
D: *Law; Accountancy; Business Administration;
Computer Sciences.*

Panamerican University México
[Universidad Panamericana]
Augusto Rodin 498, Col. Mixcoac, 03910 México
(D.F.)
Tel: +52(5) 5-98-27-79
Fax: +52(5) 611-2265
Rector: Carlos Llano Cifuentes (1990-93)
Vice-Rector: Jesús Magaña Bravo
Founded: 1966, 1978
S: *Administration; Law; Economics; Philosophy;
Industrial and Electromechanical Engineering;
Education; Institution Administration.*
I: *Higher Business Studies; Business
Administration; Education; Juridical Research.*

GUADALAJARA UNIT
[UNIDAD GUADALAJARA]
Prol. Cah. Circunvalación Pte. No. 49, Ciudad
Granja, 45010 Zapopar (Jalisco)
Tel: +52(3) 6-27-12-09
Director General: Sergio Villanueva Varela
*Social and Administrative Sciences; Engineering
and Technology.*

University Simón Bolívar México
[Universidad Simón Bolívar]
Avenida Río Mixcoac 48, Col. Insurgentes
Mixcoac, 03920 México (Distrito Federal)
Tel: +52(5) 5-98-17-17
Directora General: Clotilde Montoya Juárez
*Biology; Graphic Design; Food Technology;
Computer Systems; Chemistry, Pharmacy and
Biology.*

Technical University of Mexico
[Universidad Tecnológica de México]
Avenida Marina Nacional 162, Col. Anáhuac,
11320 México (D.F.)
Tel: +52(5) 5-27-65-65
Fax: +52(5) 3-99-15-76
Rector: Manuel Campuzano Treviño (1994-)
Founded: 1966
F: *Dentistry; Administrative and Social
Sciences.*

University of Miguel Alemán
[Universidad Miguel Alemán]
Antonio Alzate y Press Palmito, Col. Hercilia,
88300 Ciudad Miguel Alemán (Tamaulipas)
Tel: +52(897) 2-15-77
Rector: Roberto Ramírez Ramírez
F: *Architecture; Accountancy and
Administration; Law and Social Sciences.*

University of Montemorelos
[Universidad de Montemorelos]
Apartado postal 16, Montemorelos (Nuevo León)
Tel: +52(826) 3-32-22
Fax: +52(826) 3-27-08
Rector: Ismael Castillo Osuna
Founded: 1942, 1973
S: *Education; Accountancy and Administration; Nursing; Medicine; Fine Arts; Chemistry and Biology; Theology.*

Mexican University of the North East, Monterrey
[Universidad Mexicana del Noreste]
Quinta Zona 409, Col. Caracol, 64810 Monterrey (Nuevo León)
Tel: +52(83) 40-12-05
Fax: +52(83) 40-12-05
Rector: Juan Antonio González Aréchiga
Founded: 1976
D: *Administration and Social Sciences; Engineering and Science; Systems Engineering; Library Science; Cultural Diffusion; Education Systems.*

*Regiomontana University A.C. Monterrey
[Universidad Regiomontana A.C.]
Villagrán Sur 328, 64000 Monterrey (Nuevo León)
Tel: +52(83) 42-52-94
Fax: +52(83) 44-34-70
Rector: Pablo A. Logoria Treviño
Secretario General: Hector Valdes Treviño
Founded: 1951, 1969
D: *Humanities and Social Sciences; Engineering and Exact Sciences; Architecture and Design; Communication and Cultural Studies; Business Administration; Graduate Studies; Training and Development.*

*University of Monterrey
[Universidad de Monterrey]
Avenida Morones Prieto 4500 Pte., San Pedro, 66238 Garza García (Nuevo León)
Tel: +52(8) 338-50-38
Fax: +52(8) 338-56-19
E-Mail: fazcunag@ummac01.mty.udem.mx
President: Francisco J. Azcúnaga Guerra
Registrar: José Miguel Facundo
Founded: 1969
D: *Art, Design, and Environmental Sciences; Economic and Administrative Sciences; Education and Humanities; Engineering, Exact and Natural Sciences; Health Sciences; Law and Social Sciences.*
S: *Nursing and Midwifery; Nursing.*
P: *Research and Development.*
Ce: *Training and Development; Health and Development.*

University of the North, Monterrey
[Universidad del Norte]
Venustiano Carranza 1350 Nte., 64000 Monterrey (Nuevo León)
Tel: +52(83) 48-97-30
Fax: +52(83) 48-96-24
Director General: Antonio J. González Villarreal
D: *Engineering; Administration.*

University of the North East, Monterrey
[Universidad del Noroeste]
Avenida Serdan 14 Ote., 83000 Monterrey (Nuevo León)
Tel: +52(62) 17-01-78
Fax: +52(62) 17-38-85
Rector: Horacio Soria Salazar
Founded: 1979
F: *Administration Sciences; Social Sciences; Engineering.*
Ut: *Education.*
Ce: *Child Development Studies.*

Motolinía del Pedregal University
[Universidad Motolinía del Pedregal]
Avenida de las Fuentes 525, Pedregal de San Angel, 01900 México (D.F.)
Tel: +52(5) 5-68-83-24
Directora: Rosa María Osorio
Design.

Motolinía University
[Universidad Motolinía, A.C.]
Cerrado de Ameyalco 227, Col. del Valle, 03100 México (D.F.)
Tel: +52(5) 5-23-48-13
Directora General: Luz María Portillo Arroyo
Founded: 1918
Law; Chemistry.

Franco-Mexican University Naucalpan
[Universidad Franco-Mexicana]
Colina del Kan 1, Fracc. Boulevares, 53140 Naucalpan (Estado de México)
Tel: +52(5) 3-93-37-30
Rector: Javier Muñoz Orozco
Business Administration and Tourism; Communication Studies; Accountancy; Law; Education; Psychology; Industrial Relations.

Regional University of the South East, Oaxaca
[Universidad Regional del Sureste]
Prolongación 20 de Noviembre s/n, Col. Alemán, 62120 Oaxaca (Oaxaca)
Tel: +52(951) 6-83-83
Rector: Leonel Rodríguez Aragón
Founded: 1977
S: *Administration and Accountancy; Architecture; Dentistry; Law and Social Sciences; Medicine; Psychology; Chemistry; Nursing; Technology; Computer Science.*

*University of the Americas-Puebla
[Universidad de las Américas]
Catarina Mártir, Apartado postal 100, 72820
Cholula (Puebla)
Tel: +52(22) 29-20-01
Fax: +52(22) 29-20-09
E-Mail: ecardenas@udlapvms.pue.udlap.mx
Rector: Enrique Cárdenas Sánchez
Founded: 1940, 1963, 1968, 1970
F: Administration; Basic Sciences; Engineering;
Humanities; Social Sciences.
I: Advanced Studies.

People's Autonomous University of the State of Puebla
[Universidad Popular Autónoma del Estado de Puebla]
Edificio Central, 21 Sur 1103, 72160 Puebla
(Puebla)
Tel: +52(22) 32-21-38
Fax: +52(22) 32-62-91
Telex: 178432
Rector: M.A. Mario Eglesias García Teruel
Humanities; Technology; Health Sciences;
Economics and Administration; Agriculture.

Autonomous University of the North East, Saltillo
[Universidad Autónoma del Noreste]
Monclova 1561, Col. República, 25280 Saltillo
(Coahuila)
Tel: +52(84) 16-46-77
Fax: +52(84) 16-31-53
Rector: Lauro Saucedo Reyna (1989-)
Secretario General: Gabriel Duran Maltos
Founded: 1974
Architecture; Accountancy; Industrial Engineering
Administration; Industrial and Systems
Engineering; Mechanical Engineering
Administration; Business Administration;
Educative Administration; Tourism; Human
Resources Administration; Political Science and
Public Administration; Law; Graphic Design;
Human Development; Psychology; Computer
Sciences.

CIUDAD ACUÑA UNIT
[UNIDAD CIUDAD ACUÑA]
Guerrero Villaldana s/n, Ciudad Acuña (Coahuila)

MONCLOVA UNIT
[UNIDAD MONCLOVA]
Blvd. Benito Juárez y, Avenida de los Reyes s/n,
Monclova (Coahuila)
Tel: +52(863) 5-25-66
Rector: José Luis Garzón Valdés
Social and Administrative Sciences; Engineering.

PIEDRAS NEGRAS UNIT
[UNIDAD PIEDRAS NEGRAS]
Avenida E. Carranza 1300, Col. Mundo Nuevo,
Piedras Negras (Coahuila)
Tel: +52(878) 3-29-44
Director: José Raúl García Treviño
Social and Administrative Sciences; National and
Exact Sciences; Engineering.

SABINAS UNIT
[UNIDAD SABINAS]
Cuauhtemoc No. 2552, Cd. fondadores, 26740
Sabinas (Coahuila)
Tel: +52(861) 3-07-42
Fax: +52(861) 3-07-32
Directora: Claudia Arizte Cepada
Social and Administrative Sciences; Engineering.

University of the Centre of México San Luis Potosí
[Universidad del Centro de México]
Capitan Caldera 75, 78250 San Luis Potosí (San
Luis Potosí)
Tel: +52(481) 3-12-94
Rector: José Jesús Sierra Ortega

SALTILLO UNIT
[UNIDAD SALTILLO]
Enrique Reyna y Américas, Unidad Saltillo
(Coahuila)
Directora: Lorena Fernandez Rodríguez
Social and Administrative Sciences; Engineering.

TORREÓN UNIT
[UNIDAD TORREÓN]
Avenida Morelos 946 pte., Torreón (Coahuila)
Tel: +52(17) 16-84-58
Director: Marco Antonio Leal Olivares
Social and Administrative Sciences; Engineering.

University of the Sierra, A.C.
[Universidad de la Sierra, A.C.]
Avenida de los Técnicos s/n, Fracc. El Paraíso,
73160 Huauchinango (Puebla)
Tel: +52(776) 2-24-88
Fax: +52(776) 2-25-99
Rector: Alberto Jiménez Morales
Business Administration; Public Accountancy;
Law.

University of the North East, Tampico
[Universidad del Noreste]
Prolongación de la Avenida Hidalgo S/N,
Apartado postal 184 o 469, Tampico (Tamaulipas)
89000
Tel: +52(12) 28-1156
Fax: +52(12) 28-1153
Rector: José Sierra Flores
Secretario General: Luciano Fernández Cavazos
Founded: 1970, 1977
S: Medicine; Dentistry; Psychology; Biology;
Chemistry; Nursing; Communication; Design.
Ce: Computer.

University of Tepeyac
[Universidad del Tepeyac]
Callao 842, Col. Lindavista, 07300 México (D.F.)
Tel: +52(5) 5-77-64-22
Rector: Rodrigo Valle-Orozco (1975-)
Academic Principal: Rocio Eguren Monter
Founded: 1941, 1975
S: Architecture; Business Administration;
Communication Sciences; Accountancy; Law;
Tourism; Engineering.

Ce: Language; Computer; Research.
D: Psychology; Public Relations.

University 'Don Vasco',A.C. Uruapan

[Universidad 'Don Vasco',A.C.]
Carretera Uruapan Patzcuaro Km. 100, 60110
Uruapan (Michiocán)
Tel: +52(452) 4-25-26
Fax: +52(452) 4-69-60
Rector: José Luis Sahagun de la Parra
Administration; Accountancy; Architecture; Social Work; Graphic Design; Education; Civil Engineering; Agricultural Stockraising Development Planning.

*University of Valle de Atemajac

[Universidad del Valle de Atemajac]
Avenida Tepeyac 4800, Fracc. Prados Tepeyac,
45050 Guadalajara (Jalisco)
Tel: +52(3) 6-20-02-23
Fax: +52(3) 6-20-02-23
Rector: Santiago Méndez Bravo
Founded: 1960, 1979
D: Humanities and Social Sciences;
Engineering; Economics and Administration;
Research.
Ce: Lifelong Education.

LA PIEDAD UNIT
[PLANTEL LA PIEDAD]
Avenida La Salle No. 1, Fracc. Vasco de Quiroga,
59300 La Piedad (Michoacán)
Tel: +52(352) 2-47-50
Fax: +52(532) 2-48-50
Director: Luis Armando González González
Social and Administrative Sciences.

University of Valle del Bravo

[Universidad del Valle del Bravo]
Herón Ramírez 155 Nte, Col. Rodríguez, 88630
Ciudad Reynosa (Tamaulipas)
Tel: +52(89) 24-94-10
Fax: +52(89) 24-97-14
Rector: Hector García Herrera
Secretario General: César Augusto González
Soberón
*Business Administration; Public Accountancy;
Law; Communications; Tourism; Spanish
Literature; Psychology; Biology; Medicine,
Surgery and Obstetrics; Dentistry; Agricultural
Engineering Administration; Civil Engineering;
Mechanical Engineering; Electrical Engineering
Administration; Petroleum Engineering; Industrial
Administration Engineering; Industrial Relations;
Agricultural and Zoological Engineering;
Architecture; Computer Science Systems.*

BELLAVISTA UNIT
[UNIDAD BELLAVISTA]
Veracruz y Madero s/n, Col. Bellavista, 88630
Ciudad Reynosa (Tamaulipas)
Tel: +52(89) 24-91-49
Director: Ariel Nava Rodríguez
Economic and Administrative Sciences.

CENTRAL UNIT
[UNIDAD CENTRO]
Pedro J. Méndez y Pino Suarez No. 235, Col.
Centro, 88500 Ciudad Reynosa (Tamaulipas)
Tel: +52(89) 22-40-92
Director: Fernando Flores Arteaga
Engineering and Technology.

CIUDAD VICTORIA UNIT
[UNIDAD CIUDAD VICTORIA]
Victoria
Tel: +52(131) 2-01-80
Fax: +52(131) 2-13-92
Vice-Rector: Salomón Beltrán Caballero
*Economic and Administrative Sciences; Health
Sciences.*

MANTE UNIT
[UNIDAD MANTE]
Mante
Tel: +52(123) 2-26-18
Fax: +52(123) 2-23-38
Vice-Rectora: Bertha Margarita Delgado García
*Social Sciences; Economic and Administrative
Sciences.*

MATAMOROS UNIT
[UNIDAD MATAMOROS]
Diagonal Cuauhtemoc y 7a. No. 13, 87350 H.
Matamoros (Tamaulipas)
Tel: +52(891) 6-51-80
Fax: +52(891) 6-49-94
Vice-Rector: Victor Manuel Garza Mendoza
*Economic and Administrative Sciences;
Engineering and Technology; Social Sciences.*

NUEVO LAREDO UNIT
[UNIDAD NUEVO LAREDO]
Nuevo Laredo
Tel: +52(871) 4-96-20
Fax: +52(871) 5-11-81
Vice-Rector: Jorge Luis López Vargas
Social Sciences; Medicine.

TAMPICO UNIT
[UNIDAD TAMPICO]
Tampico
Tel: +52(12) 13-98-64
Fax: +52(12) 13-98-44
Vice-Rectora: María de Lourdea García de
Castilla
*Economic and Administrative Sciences;
Engineering.*

University of Valle de México

[Universidad del Valle de México]
Tehuantepec 250, Colonia Roma Sur, 06760
México (D.F.)
Tel: +52(5) 2-64-05-08
Fax: +52(5) 5-74-04-22
Rector: Jesús M. Nájera M. (1990-)
Founded: 1960, 1968
*Architecture (Tlalpan, San Rafael); Economics
and Administration; Social Sciences; Exact
Sciences.*
Ce: Computer.

LOMAS VERDES UNIT
[PLANTEL LOMAS VERDES]
Avenida de las Aves, 53220 Naucalpán (Estado
de México)
Tel: +52(5) 3-43-37-45
Fax: +52(5) 3-43-26-20
Vice-Rector (Acting): Jesús M. Nájera M.
*Social and Administrative Sciences; Engineering;
Technology.*

ROMA UNIT
[PLANTEL ROMA]
Mérida No. 33, Col. Roma, 06700 México (D.F.)
Tel: +52(5) 5-33-69-15
Fax: +52(5) 2-08-03-32
Director General: Luis Guillermo del Pino
Fuentes
*Social and Administrative Sciences; Engineering
and Technology.*

SAN RAFAEL UNIT
[PLANTEL SAN RAFAEL]
Sadi Carnot 57, Col. San Rafael, 06470 México
(D.F.)
Tel: +52(5) 7-05-74-77
Fax: +52(5) 7-05-27-00
Vice-Rector: José Antonio Outon Mato
*Social and Administrative Sciences; Engineering
and Technology.*

TLALPAN UNIT
[PLANTEL TLALPAN]
San Juan de Dios 6, Col. Huipulco, 14380 México
(D.F.)
Tel: +52(5) 2-27-02-10
Vice-Rector: Luis Silva Guerrero
*Engineering and Technology; Social and
Administrative Sciences; Natural Sciences.*

SAN ANGEL UNIT
[PLANTEL SAN ANGEL]
San Jerónimo 82 San Angel, 01100 México (D.F.)
Tel: +52(5) 5-50-37-52
Fax: +52(5) 5-50-66-65
Directora General: María de la Luz Paniagua
Jimenéz
Computer Sciences; Administration.

University of Valle de Puebla, A.C.
[Universidad del Valle de Puebla, A.C.]
Avenida 12 Oriente 204, 72000 Puebla (Puebla)
Tel: +52(22) 37-51-16
Fax: +52(22) 43-04-94
Rector: Jaime Illescas López
*Administration; Public Accountancy; Industrial
Relations; Tourism; Computer Science
Administration.*

University of Valle de Toluca
[Universidad del Valle de Toluca]
Calle 21 de Marzo 101, Toluca (Estado de
México)
Tel: +52(72) 14-22-42
Rector: Jesús Barrera Legorreta
*Economics and Administration; Architecture and
Town Planning; Accountancy; Social Sciences.*

University 'Christopher Columbus' Veracruz
[Universidad 'Cristóbal Colón']
Carretera Boticaria Km. 1 1/2, 91930 Veracruz
(Veracruz)
Tel: +52(29) 37-70-77
Fax: +52(29) 37-68-55
Rector: Francisco Cubells Salas
*S: Architecture; Computer Science and
Administration; Law; Pedagogics; History of Art;
Agricultural Development; Psychology.*

University Villa Rica Veracruz
[Universidad Villa Rica]
Avenida Díaz Mirón 2242, 91700 Veracruz
(Veracruz)
Tel: +52(29) 21-20-01
Fax: +52(29) 21-54-40
Rector: Ignacio R. Rodríguez Moreno
*Accountancy and Administration; Law;
Economics; Psychology.*

MOCAMBO UNIT
[UNIDAD MOCAMBO]
Prolongación Avenida Costa Verde, Esq.
Progreso, Fracc. Jardines de Mocambo, 91990
Boca del Río (Veracruz)
Tel: +52(29) 21-20-01
Fax: +52(29) 21-54-40
Rector: Ignacio R. Rodríguez Moreno
*S: Accountancy and Administration; Law;
Economy; Psychology; Engineering; Architecture.*

Women's University of Veracruz-Llave
[Universidad Femenina de Veracruz-Llave]
Balboa 524, 91910 Veracruz (Veracruz)
Tel: +52(29) 37-14-60
Rectora: Gemma Odila Garzón Arcos
Social Work.

José Vasconcelos University Victoria de Durango
[Universidad José Vasconcelos]
Guadalupe 312 norte, 34000 Victoria de Durango
(Durango)
Tel: +52(181) 3-37-51
Rector: Enrique Medina Vidaña
*D: Psychology; Communications; Design;
Pedagogy; Lifelong Education.*

University Xicotepetl, A.C.
[Universidad Xicotepetl, A.C.]
Aldama 122, 73080 Col. Xicotepec de Juarez
(Puebla)
Tel: +52(776) 4-13-10
Fax: +52(776) 4-11-32
Director General: José Luis Aldana López
Founded: 1983
*D: Veterinary Medicine and Zoology;
Agricultural and Plant Engineering; Agricultural
Business Administration; Business
Administration; Public Accountancy.*

OTHER INSTITUTIONS

PUBLIC INSTITUTIONS

Benemérita y Centenaria Escuela Nacional de Maestros
Calz. México-Tacuba No. 75, Col. Un Hogar Para Nosotros, 11330 México (D.F.)
Tel: +52(5) 3-41-06-81
Director: Gilberto Juárez Millán
Education.

Benemérito Instituto Normal del Estado (Gral. Juan Crisostomo Bonilla)
Blvd. Hermanos Serdan s/n, Col. Valle del Rey, Puebla (Puebla)
Tel: +52(22) 48-33-76
Director General: Alejandro Pérez Morales
Teacher Training.

Centro de Desarrollo Professional para la Educación Agropecuaria
Claudio Bernard No. 159, Col. Doctores, 06720 México (D.F.)
Tel: +52(5) 5-78-31-83
Director: Victor Manuel Rosas López
Agricultural Education Development.

Centro de Enseñanza Técnica Industrial
Avenida del Chaco 3223, Fraccionamiento Providencia, 44620 Guadalajara (Jalisco)
Tel: +52(3) 3-41-64-29
Director: Armando J. Medina Palomera
Engineering.

Centro de Estudios Superiores de Comunicación Educativa de Tlaxcala
Domicílio Conocido, Col. Ignacio Zaragoza No. 3, 90160 Totolac (Tlaxcala)
Tel: +52(246) 2-74-00
Director: Leonardo Vargas Machado
Educational Communication.

Centro de Estudios Superiores de Educacion Rural 'Luís Hidalgo Monroy'
Domicílio Conocido en Acececa, Apartado postal No. 18, 92100 Tantoyuca (Veracruz)
Tel: +52(129) 5-01-84
Director: Froylán Jésus Pajín Molina
Rural Education.

Centro de Estudios Superiores del Estado de Sonora
Calle Ley Federal del Trabajo Final Col. Apolo, 83100 Hermosillo (Sonora)
Tel: +52(62) 15-71-01
Fax: +52(62) 15-70-47
Director General: Luis Alfredo Montaño Lagarda
Engineering; Ecology; Business Administration; International Commerce.

UNIDAD ACADEMICA DE SAN LUIS RIO COLORADO
Carretera a Sonoyta Km. 6.5, San Luís Río Colorado (Sonora)
Tel: +52(653) 4-13-59
Fax: +52(653) 4-42-49
Director: Héctor Manuel Cervantes Soto
Economic and Administrative Sciences; Agronomy; Industrial Engineering.

Centro de Estudios Superiores Navales
Revillagigedo No. 11, 1er Piso, Col. Centro, 06056 México (D.F.)
Tel: +52(5) 5-10-22-68
Director (Acting): Hugo Acosta Aguilar
Marine Studies.

Centro de Estudios Superiores Turísticos, A.C. (Coahuila)
Presidente Cárdenas 651, 25000 Saltillo (Coahuila)
Tel: +52(84) 12-63-73
Directora: Alicia E. Barajas Sosa
Tourism.

Centro de Estudios Tecnológicos del Mar en la Paz
Terrenos del Conchalito s/n, 23000 La Paz (Baja California Sur)
Tel: +52(112) 2-49-06
Director: Guillermo González López
Marine Technology.

Centro Interamericano de Estudios de Seguridad Social 'Jesús Reyes Heroles'
Calle San Ramon s/n, Esq. San Jeronimo, Unidad Independencia, Apartado postal No. 990-87, 10100 México (D.F.)
Tel: +52(5) 5-95-00-11
Director: Alvaro Carranza Uriolagoitta
Social Security Studies.

Centro Interdisciplinario de Investigación y Docencia en Educación
Avenida Universidad No. 282 Pte., Apartado postal No. 752, 76000 Querétaro (Querétaro)
Tel: +52(42) 16-35-40
Director: Ramiro Landaverde Chávez
Teaching and Education Research.

Centro de Investigación Cientifica y de Educación Superior de Ensenada, B.C.
Avenida Ruiz y Calle 17 No. 1703, Apartado postal No. 2732 C.P. 22800, 22830 Ensenada (Baja California)
Tel: +52(667) 4-45-01
Fax: +52(667) 4-48-80
Telex: 56-539
Director General: Mario Martínez García
Electronics and Telecommunication; Materials Physics; Oceanology; Marine Ecology; Seismology.

Centro de Investigación y Desarróllo de Tecnología Digital
Avenida del Parque No. 1310, Mesa de Otay, Apartado postal No. 152-E, 22510 Tijuana (Baja California)
Tel: +52(66) 23-13-44
Director: José María Montoya Flores
Digital Technology.

Centro de Investigación y de Estudios Superiores en Antropología Social
General Guadalupe Victoria No. 75, Apartado postal 22-048, 14000 México (D.F.)
Tel: +52(5) 5-73-69-83
Director General: Teresda Rojas Rabiela
Social Anthropology.

Centro Regional de Educación Normal de Aguascalientes
Avenida de los Maestros Km. 1.9, 20000 Aguascalientes (Aguascalientes)
Tel: +52(49) 13-49-31
Director: Rolando Bernal Acevedo
Teacher Training.

Centro Regional de Educación Normal de Artega
Domicílio Conocido, 50920 Arteaga (Michoacán)
Director: Juan García Moreno
Teacher Training.

Centro Regional de Educación Normal 'Benito Juárez'
Gral. Gonzalez y Dr. Agustin Torres, Graviotto s/n, Col. Doctores, 42090 Pachuca (Guerrero)
Tel: +52(771) 3-78-00
Director: José Cuatepotzo Costeira
Teacher Training.

Centro Regional de Educación Normal de Ciudad Guzman
Calz. Madero y Carranza s/n, Col. Ejidal, 49070 Ciudad Guzman (Jalisco)
Tel: +52(341) 2-03-98
Director: Juan Medina Ramírez
Teacher Training.

Centro Regional de Educación Normal 'Felipe Carrillo Puerto'ZX
Carretera Valladolid Km. 1.5, 77200 Felipe Carillo Puerto (Quintana Roo)
Directora: María del Rosario Gamboa Ceballos
Teacher Training.

Centro Regional de Educación Normal 'Lic. Adolfo López Mateos'
Ignacio Maya No. 85, 40000 Iguala (Guerrero)
Tel: +52(733) 2-03-75
Director: Jorge Bello Bobadilla
Teacher Training.

Centro Regional de Educación Normal 'Lic. Javier Rojo Gómez'
Avenida Costera s/n Municipio Othon P. Blanco, 77930 Bacalar (Quintana Roo)
Director: Humberto Lima Flores
Teacher Training.

Centro Regional de Educación Normal 'Marcelo Rubio Ruiz'
Salvatierra s/n, 23880 Loretto (Baja California Sur)
Tel: +52(683) 3-01-31
Director: Alvaro Aguilar Rosas
Teacher Training.

Centro Regional de Educación Normal de Oaxaca
Prolongación de la Calzada Porfirio Diaz s/n, 38040 Oaxaca (Oaxaca)
Tel: +52(951) 5-94-66
Director: Fernando Espinosa Cuevas
Teacher Training.

Centro Regional de Educación Normal 'Profra. Amina Madera Lauterio'
Domicílio Conocido, 78520 Cedral (San Luis Potosí)
Director: Jorge Mitre Anguiano
Teacher Training.

Centro Regional de Educación Normal 'Rafael Ramírez Castañeda'
Carretera Internacional Sur Km. 153, 85800 Navojoa (Sonora)
Tel: +52(642) 2-28-20
Director: Rogelio Rodríguez Sepúlveda
Teacher Training.

Centro Regional de Educación Normal de Río Grande
Carretera Costera s/n, 71000 Putla de Guerrero (Oaxaca)
Tel: +52(2) 15
Director: Leonel Toledo Toledo
Teacher Training.

Centro Regional de Educación Normal de Tuxpan
Carretera Barra Norte Km. 5.5, Tuxpan (Veracruz)
Tel: +52(783) 4-33-24
Director: Luis Cortés Ruiz
Teacher Training.

Centro Sindical de Estudios Superiores de la CTM, A.C.
Camelia 108 Fracc. Rancho Cortez, Apartado postal 134-C Sucursal C., 62050 Cuernavaca (Morelos)
Tel: +52(73) 13-07-00
Director: Guillermo Vargas Chávez
Labour Law, Administration, Economics.

Centro Universitario de Mazatlán
Calle Cruz No. 2, Paseo Olas Altas, Apartado postal 275, Mazatlán (Sinaloa)
Tel: +52(69) 81-73-04
Director: Hector Javier Díaz Zatarain
Public Accountancy; Business Administration.

Colegio de la Frontera Norte
Blvd. Abelardo L. Rodríguez No. 21 Zona del Río,
22320 Tijuana (Baja California)
Tel: +52(66) 30-00-50
Fax: +52(66) 84-20-33
President: Jorge Agustín Bustamante
*Regional Development; Industrial Economics;
Applied Economics; Population Studies.*

El Colegio de México
Camino al Ajusco 20, 10740 México (D.F.)
Tel: +52(5) 6-45-04-64
Fax: +52(5) 6-45-59-55
Telex: 1777585 colme
Director: Mario Ojeda Gómez
Founded: 1940
*International Relations; Public Administration;
Demography; Urban Development; Economy;
Asian and African Studies; Population Studies;
History; Linguistics; Spanish Literature;
Sociology.*

Colegio de Postgraduados
Montecillo, 56230 Chapingo (Estado de México)
Tel: +52(595) 4-57-23
Fax: +52(595) 5-07-12
Director General: Rafael Rodríguez Montessoro
*Botany; Economics; Edaphic Studies;
Entomology; Statistics; Rural Development;
Stockraising; Genetics.*

El Colegio de Sonora
Avenida Obregón No. 54, 83000 Hermosillo
(Sonora)
Tel: +52(62) 12-65-51
Fax: +52(62) 12-00-15
Rector: Gerardo Cornejo Murrieta
Social Sciences; Regional Studies.

Colegio Superior Agropecuario del Estado de Guerrero
Nicolás Bravo No. 2 Despacho 4, Apartado postal
Nos. 6 y 9, 40000 Iguala (Guerrero)
Tel: +52(733) 2-43-28
Director General: Julio Cesar López Uriza
Agriculture and Stockraising.

Conservatorio Nacional de Música
Avenida Presidente Mazarik No. 582, Polanco,
11560 México (D.F.)
Tel: +52(5) 520-10-22
Director: María Teresa Rodríguez y Rodríguez
Music.

Escuela de Arte Teatral
Piaza Angel, Atrás del Auditorio Nacional, 11510
México 18 (D.F.)
Tel: +52(5) 520-85-18
Director: Ricardo Ramírez Carnero
Drama.

Escuela de Ciencias de la Educación
Juan Escutia y M. del Lano, Col. Obrero, 64010
Monterrey (Nuevo León)
Tel: +52(83) 44-67-03
Directora: Argelia García Méndez
Educational Sciences.

Escuela de Dietetica y Nutrición del ISSTE
Avenida San Fernando 15, Col. Toriello Guerra
14050, Tlalpán (D.F.)
Tel: +52(5) 5-73-15-95
Directora: Luz Elena Pale Montero
Dietetics and Nutrition.

Escuela Nacional de Antropología e Historia
Periférico Sur y Calle Zapote, Col. Isidro Fabela,
14030 México (D.F.)
Tel: +52(5) 5-55-24-79
Directora: Gloria Artis Mercadet
Anthropology and History.

Escuela Nacional de Biblioteconomía y Archivonomía
Viaducto Miguel Alemán 155, México 13 (D.F.)
Tel: +52(5) 7-52-75-75
Director: Nahum Pérez Paz
Library Science and Archives.

Escuela Nacional de Capacitación Aduanera
Calz. Tlalpán 2775, Col. El Reloj, 04046 México
(D.F.)
Tel: +52(5) 6-84-31-09
Directora: Norma Saeb Camargo
Customs and Revenue.

Escuela Nacional de Conservación, Restauración y Museografía 'Manuel del Castillo Negrete'
Ex Convento de Churubusco Xicotencatl y
General Anava, Coyoacán (D.F.)
Tel: +52(5) 6-04-51-63
Director: Jaime Cama Villafranca
Conservation and Restauration, and Museology.

Escuela Nacional de Pintura, Escultura y Grabado 'La Esmeralda' del INBA
San Fernando 14, Col. Guerrero, 06300 México
(D.F.)
Tel: +52(5) 5-21-84-27
Director: José Zúñiga Delgado
Painting, Sculpture and Engraving.

Escuela Náutica Mercante 'Cap. de Alt. Antonio Gómez Maqueo'
Calz. Gabriel Leyva No. 2111, 82040 Mazatlán
(Sinaloa)
Tel: +52(69) 81-24-86
Director: Daniel Gustavo Izunsa Romano
Merchant Marine Engineering.

Escuela Náutica Mercante 'Fernando Siliceo'
Boulevard Avila Camacho s/n, 91700 Veracruz
(Veracruz)
Tel: +52(29) 31-33-36
Fax: +52(29) 31-08-73
Director: Humberto Roffiel Gutiérrez
Merchant Marine Engineering.

Escuela Náutica Mercante de Tampico
Boulevard López Mateos y Blvd. Fidel Velazquez,
89070 Tampico (Tamaulipas)
Tel: +52(12) 12-88-82
Fax: +52(12) 19-05-59
Telex: 14763 enmtme
Director: Ezequiel Súarez Ríos
Merchant Marine Engineering.

Escuela Normal de Aguascalientes
Héroe de Nacozari Sur Esq. con Avenida de la
Cruz, 20040 Aguascalientes (Aguascalientes)
Tel: +52(49) 15-15-74
Directora: Martha Elia Gallardo de Mora
Teacher Training.

Escuela Normal de Especialización del Distrito Federal
Campos Elíseos No. 467, Col. Polanco
Chapultepec, 11560 México (D.F.)
Tel: +52(5) 5-40-38-06
Director: Humberto Galeana Romano
Teacher Training (for the Handicapped).

Escuela Normal Estatal de Especialización de Aguascalientes
Avenid San Francisco de los Vivero No.101,
Fracc. Ojo Caliente, 20040 Aguascalientes
(Aguascalientes)
Tel: 52(49) 18-53-47
Directora: María Guadalupe González Macías
Teacher Training (for the Handicapped).

Escuela Normal 'Profr. Gregorio Torres Quintero'
Calle Niños Héroes No. 321, Col. Lazardo
Cárdenas, Apartado postal No. 187, 22930 San
Quintin (Baja California)
Tel: +52(666) 5-23-78
Director: Prisciliano Viera Llamas
Teacher Training.

Escuela Normal Regional de Especialización
Hildago y Aldáma, Saltillo (Coahuila)
Tel: +52(84) 12-71-29
Directora: Irma Valdés Ramos
Teacher Training (for the Handicapped).

Escuela Normal Rural 'Justo Sierra Mendez'
Domicílio Conocido, Cañada Darado Honda,
20320 Aguascalientes (Aguascalientes)
Director: Carlos Nájera Riviera
Teacher Training.

Escuela Normal Superior de Educación Física de Jalisco
Nueva Escocia No. 1535, Fracc. La Providencia,
Unidad Deportiva Revolución, Guadalajara
(Jalisco)
Tel: +52(3) 6-42-57-51
Director: Victor Miranda
Physical Education.

Escuela Normal Superior de Educación Fisica, Tabasco
H. Colegio Militar Esq. Velodromo, Ciudad
Deportiva, Villahermosa (Tabasco)
Tel: +52(931) 3-38-43
Director: Salvador Rodulfo Santoyo
Physical Education.

Escuela Normal Superior de Especialidades
Francisco Siles No. 1279, Fracc. Jardines Plaza
del Sol, 04500 Guadalajara (Jalisco)
Tel: +52(3) 6-22-52-7؟
Directora: Aurora Luevanos de Ceballos
Teacher Training (for the Handicapped).

Escuela Normal Superior del Estado de Baja California Sur
República y Altamirano, La Paz (Baja California
Sur)
Tel: +52(112) 2-04-90
Fax: +52(112) 5-20-35
Director: Enrique Estrada Lucero
Techer Training.

Escuela Normal Superior del Estado de Chiapas
Avenida 20 de Noviembre s/n, Col. Albania,
Tuxtla Gutíerrez (Chiapas)
Tel: +52(961) 2-68-76
Director: Camilo A. Nucamendi Albores
Teacher Training.

Escuela Normal Superior del Estado de Coahuila
Calle Aldáma Pte. 858, Saltillo (Coahuila)
Tel: +52(841) 3-65-39
Director: Francisco Raúl Hernández Carrillo
Teacher Training.

Escuela Normal Superior del Estado de México No. 1
Natalia Carrasco, 400 Col. Federal, 50070 Toluca
(Estado de México)
Tel: +52(72) 19-34-81
Director General: Camerino Lara Castillo
Teacher Training.

Escuela Normal Superior del Estado de México No. 2
Avenida Revolución y Avenida de Los Maestros,
55000 Ecatepec (Estado de México)
Director: Roberto Ruiz Llanos
Teacher Training.

UNIDAD A DISTANCIA NEUCALPAN
Camino Real a San Mateo No. 174, San Mateo
Nopala, Neucalpan de Juárez (Estado de México)
Tel: +52(5) 7-87-54-53
Director: Francisco Legorreta Baeza
Distance Education Unit.

Escuela Normal Superior del Estado de México No.3
Circuito Vial Jorge Jimenez Cantu s/n,
Atlacomulco (Estado de México)
Tel: +52(722) 2-00-01
Director General: Antonio Medrano Guadarrama
Teacher Training.

Escuela Normal Superior del Estado de México No. 4
Tizapa s/n, Chalco (Estado de México)
Tel: +52(597) 3-05-56
Director General: José Luis Abut Sánchez
Teacher Training.

Escuela Normal Superior del Estado 'Profr. Moises Saenz Garza'
Venustiano Carranza y Ruperto Martínez,
Apartado postal No. 2035, €4000 Monterrey
(Nuevo León)
Tel: +52(83) 43-64-40
Director General: Jesús García García
Teacher Training.

Escuela Normal Superior del Estado de Puebla
Calle 11 Sur No. 1102, 72000 Puebla (Puebla)
Tel: +52(22) 43-84-73
Director: Roberto Montiel Pérez
Teacher Training.

Escuela Normal Superior Federal de Aguascalientes
Boulevard Nazario Ortíz Garza s/n, 20170
Aguascalientes (Aguascalientes)
Tel: +52(49) 16-26-76
Directora: Raquel García Zapata
Teacher Training.

Escuela Normal Superior Federal para Cursos Intensivos en Veracruz
Carretera Jalapa-Veracruz Km. 4.5, Jalapa
(Veracruz)
Tel: +52(281) 8-42-05
Director: Uriel Alvarez Velázquez
Teacher Training (Intensive Courses).

Escuela Normal Superior de Guanajuato
Paseo de la Presa 76, Guanajuato (Guanajuato)
Tel: +52(473) 2-58-41
Director: Artemio Guzmán López
Teacher Training.

Escuela Normal Superior de Jalisco
Lisboa 488, Col. Sta. Elena Estadio, Guadalajara
(Jalisco)
Tel: +52(3) 6-24-54-01
Director: Alvaro Pelayo Pérez
Teacher Training.

Escuela Normal Superior de México 'Manuel Salazar' No. 201
Col. Ex-Hacienda 'El Rosario', 02430 México
(D.F.)
Tel: +52(5) 3-94-33-93
Director: Luis Medina Arteaga
Teacher Training.

Escuela Normal Superior de Nayarit
Ciudad de la Cultura 'Amado Nervo', Tepic
(Nayarit)
Tel: +52(321) 3-31-74
Director: Salvador Langarica Cabrera
Teacher Training.

Escuela Normal Superior de Santa Ana
Aldáma Sur Final, Santa Ana (Sonora)
Director: Marco Antonio Ortiz Nuñez
Teacher Training.

Escuela Normal Superior de Yucatán
Calle 59 No. 426, Mérida (Yucatán)
Tel: +52(99) 24-27-24
Director: Santiago Ricardo Gómez y Cámara
Teacher Training.

Escuela Normal Urbana Federal de Educadoras de Mexicali
Avenida San Valentin No. 2638, Col. Baja
California, 21130 Mexicali (Baja California)
Tel: +52(65) 53-86-70
Directora: Patricia Valdés Gonzales
Teacher Training.

Escuela Normal Urbana Federal 'Fronteriza'
Blvd. Benito Juárez s/n, 21360 Mexicali (Baja
California)
Tel: +52(65) 66-44-35
Director: Miguel Cruz Estrada
Teacher Training.

Escuela Normal Urbana Nocturna del Estado de Baja California
Río Culiacan y Francisco Márquez, Col.
Prohogar, Mexicali (Baja California)
Tel: +52(65) 68-14-95
Directora: Victoria Castro Gurrola
Teacher Training (Evening Courses).

Escuela Superior de Educación Física
Puerta 4 Cd. Deportiva, Col. Magdalena Mixuca,
08010 México (D.F.)
Tel: +52(5) 5-19-50-60
Director: Cipriano Barreto Amaro
Physical Education.

Escuela Superior de Música
Fernandez Leal No. 31, Col. Coyoacan, 04000
México (D.F.)
Tel: +52(5) 6-58-10-96
Directora: Leticia Alba Trejo
Music.

Escuela Superior de Música y Danza de Monterrey
Padre Mier No. 1720 Pte., Col. Obispado, 54000
Monterrey (Nuevo León)
Tel: +52(83) 48-42-65
Directora: María Isabel García Ortíz
Music and Dance.

Facultad Latinoamericana de Ciencias Sociales

Carretera Al Ajusco Km. 1.5 s/n, Col. Héroes de Padierna, 10740 México (D.F.)
Tel: +52(5) 5-68-62-87
Fax: +52(5) 5-68-63-21
Director: José Luis Barros Horcasitas
Social Sciences.

Instituto Campechano

Calle 10 No. 357 Centro, Campeche (Campeche)
Tel: +52(981) 129-75
Director General: Javier García González
Social Work; Tourism; Journalism and Communication Sciences; Artistic Education.

Instituto de Capacitación Magisterial del Estado de México

Blvd. Isidro Fabela No. 601, Toluca (Estado de México)
Tel: +52(721) 522-71
Director: José Luis Pérez Tovar
Customs.

Instituto de Ciencia y Artes de Chiapas

2a Avenida Norte y 3a Calle Ote., 29000 Tuxtla Gutíerrez (Chiapas)
Tel: +52(961) 258-92
Fax: +52(961) 138-73
Director General: Javier A. Molina Utrilla
Topographic Engineering; Biology; Psychology; Nutrition; Dentist.

Instituto de Ecología A.C.

Carretera a Coatepec Km. 2.5, Apartado postal No. 63, 91000 Jalapa (Veracruz)
Tel: +52(281) 860-00
Fax: +52(281) 869-10
Director General: Sergio Guevara Sada
Ecology.

Instituto de Educación Normal del Estado de Nayarit

Republica de Colombia y 12 de Octubre, Tepic (Nayarit)
Tel: +52(321) 331-73
Directora: Martha Rodríguez
Teacher Training.

Instituto Estatal para el Desarollo de la Seguridad en el Trabajo

Vialidad Toluca-Zinacantepec Km. 4.5, Apartado postal No. 899 (En Toluca), Zinancantepec (Estado de México)
Tel: +52(721) 322-57
Director General: Federico López de Alba
Workplace Security.

Instituto de Estudios Superiores de Chiapas

2a Avenida Norte Oriente No. 460, 29000 Tuxtla Gutierriez (Chiapas)
Tel: +52(961) 269-28
Rector: Frederico Luis. Salazar Narvaez
Business Administration; Public Accountancy; Administrative Data Processing; Law; Architecture; Animal Husbandry Admimistration; Construction Engineering.

Instituto Latinoamericano de la Comunicación Educativa

Calle del Puente No. 45, Col. Ejidos de Huipulco, 14380 México (D.F.)
Tel: +52(5) 671-70-65
Fax: +52(5) 594-96-83
Director General: Juan de Dios Rodríguez Cantón
Educational Communication.

Instituto Michoacano de Ciencias de la Educación 'José María Morelos'

Calzada Juárez 1600, Col. Villa Universidad, 58060 Morelia (Michoacán)
Tel: +52(43) 16-75-15
Fax: +52(43) 16-75-93
Director General: Alfredo Esquivel Avila
Founded: 1986
Educational Sciences.

Instituto Nacional de Astrofísica, Optica y Electronica

Domicílio Conocido, Tonantzintla, Apartados Pts. Nos. 51 y 216, 72000 Puebla (Puebla)
Tel: +52(22) 47-20-44
Fax: +52(22) 47-25-80
Director: Alfonso Serrano Pérez-Grovas
Astrophysics, Optics and Electronics.

Instituto Nacional de Bellas Artes

P. de la Reforma y Campo Marte s/n, Edif.'A' 2o. Piso, Atrás del Aud. Nac., Bosque de Chapultepec, 11580 México (D.F.)
Tel: +52(5) 280-54-74
Fax: +52(5) 280-48-65
Director General: Gerardo Estrada Rodríguez
Fine Arts.

Instituto Nacional de Perinatología

Montes Urales No. 800, Lomas de Virreyes, 11000 México (D.F.)
Tel: +52(5) 5-20-85-65
Director General: Samuel Karchmer K.
Perinatal Studies.

Instituto Politécnico Nacional

Avenida Juan de Dios Batiz s/n, Esq. Avenida Luis Enrique Erro, Col. Lindavista, 07738 México (D.F.)
Tel: +52(5) 7-54-41-21
Fax: +52(5) 7-54-45-32
Director General: Oscar Javier Joffre Velásquez
Mechanics and Electonics Engineering; Engineering and Architecture; Chemistry and Extractive Industries Engineering; Textile Engineering; Physics and Mathematics; Homeopathic Medicine; Tourism; Medicine; Biological Sciences; Economy; Commerce and Administration; Nursing and Medwifery.

CENTRO INTERDISCIPLINARIO DE CIENCIAS MARINAS DEL IPN
Playa el Conchalito s/n, Apartado postal Nos. 476 y 592, 23000 La Paz (Baja California Sur)
Tel: +52(112) 2-53-22
Director: Julian René Torres Villegas
Marine Sciences.

CENTRO INTERDISCIPLINARIO DE CIENCIAS DE LA SALUD DEL IPN
Carretera Xochimilco-Oaxtepec km. 39.5, Ex-Haciendadel Mayorazgo, Apartado postal No. 5, 12000 México (D.F.)
Tel: +52(5) 8-44-03-50
Director: Adrian Guillermo Quintero Gutiérrez

CENTRO DE INVESTIGACIÓN Y DE ESTUDIOS AVANZADOS DEL I.P.N.
Avenida Instituto Politécnico Nacional No.2508, Esq. Ticoman, Col. San Pedro Zacatenco, Apartado postal No. 14-740 C.P. 07000, 07360 México (D.F.)
Tel: +52(5) 5-86-27-70
Fax: +52(5) 7-54-87-07
Telex: 1772827 pptme
Director: Feliciano Sánchez Sinencio
D: Cellular Biology; Biochemistry; Biotechnology; Pharmacology and Toxicology; Physics; Genetics; Electrical Engineering; Mathematics; Pathology; Chemistry; Physiology, Biophysics and Neurosciences.

UNIDAD MERIDA
Antigua Carretera a Progresso Km. 6, Apartado postal No. 73 Cordemex, 97310 Mérida (Yucatán)
Tel: +52(99) 26-05-45
Director: Juan Luis Peña Chapa
Marine Biology; Applied Physics.

UNIDAD SALTILLO
Manuel Othon de Mendizabal, Col. Universidad, Apartado postal No. 663, Saltillo (Coahuila)
Director: Manuel Méndez Nonell

UNIDAD PROFESIONAL INTERDISIPLINARIA DE INGENIERA Y CIENCIAS SOCIALES Y ADMINISTRIVAS
Avenida Te No. 950, Col. Granjas México, 08400 México (D.F.)
Tel: +52(5) 6-57-14-70
Director: Ernesto Angeles Mejía
Industrial Engineering; Industrial Management; Computer Sciences; Engineering in Transport.

Instituto Superior de Ciencias de la Educación del Estado de México
Ex-Rancho Los Uribe, Santa Cruz Azcapotzaltongo, Apartado postal No. 295 Admon. Correos, Toluca (Estado de México)
Director: Ranulfo Vivero Castañeda
Education.

Instituto Superior de Educación Tecnológica Agropecuaria
Carretera Celaya-Juventino Rosas Roque Km. 8, Apartado postal No. 508, 38010 Celaya (Guanajuato)
Tel: +55(461) 1-63-61
Director: Rodolfo Casillas Nevares
Agriculture and Stockraising Technology.

Instituto Tecnológico de Acapulco
Carretera México-Acapulco Km. 274, Apartado postal 600, 39300 Acapulco (Guerrero)
Tel: +52(74) 87-39-63
Director: Amado Palomino Solórzano
Biochemistry; Electromechanic Engineering; Computer Engineering; Commercial Relations; Tourism Management; Architecture.

Instituto Tecnológico Agropecuario No. 1, Durango
Carretera Durango-México Km. 22, Apartado postal 393, 34000 Durango (Durango)
Tel: +52(181) 2-38-57
Director: Gerardo Edgar Vargas Mata
Agronomics Engineering; Agriculture and Stockraising Accountancy.

Instituto Tecnológico Agropecuario No. 2
Carretera Mérida-Motul Km. 16.3, Apartado postal 53-D, 97110 Mérida (Yucatán)
Tel: +52(99) 27-72-84
Director: Gilberto Barrera Candila
Agriculture and Stockraising.

Instituto Tecnológico Agropecuario No. 3
Daniel Soto No. 370, Esq. Sebastián Ortíz, Apartado postal 38, 68300 Tuxtepec (Oaxaca)
Tel: +52(287) 5-16-97
Director: Margarito Peralta Cruz
Agriculture and Stockraising.

Instituto Tecnológico Agropecuario No. 4
Km. 24.5 Carretera Tampico-Mante, Altamira (Tamaulipas)
Tel: +52(126) 4-05-45
Director: Oscar Ramírez Alvarado
Agriculture and Stockraising.

Instituto Tecnológico Agropecuario No. 5, Campeche
Ejido China, 24000 Campeche (Campeche)
Tel: +52(981) 6-11-50
Director: Julio César Chac Pérez
Agriculture and Stockraising.

Instituto Tecnológico Agropecuario No. 6, Huejutla de Reyes
Apartado postal 94, 43000 Huejutla de Reyes (Hidalgo)
Director: Salvador Vargas Cerón
Agriculture and Stockraising.

Instituto Tecnológico Agropecuario No. 7, Morelia
Carretera Morelia a Salamanca Km. 65, Cap. Francisco Jimenez No. 89, Apartado postal 39 'B', 58000 Morelia (Michoacán)
Tel: +52(43) 15-75-08
Director: Fidel Montaño Mendoza
Agriculture and Stockraising.

Instituto Tecnológico Agropecuario No. 8, San Pedro de Comitancillo
Centenario 61, Apartado postal No. 15, San Pedro Comitancillo (Oaxaca)
Director: Leandro Marcos Ramos
Agriculture and Stockraising.

Instituto Tecnológico Agropecuario No. 9, Miacatlán
Cerro de la Trilla, Apartado postal 18, 62600 Miacatlán (Morelos)
Director: Eleuterio Astorga Chaidez
Agriculture and Stockraising.

Instituto Tecnológico Agropecuario No. 10, Torreón
Km. 7.5 Carretera Torreón a San Pedro No. 638, Col. Navarro, Apartado postal No. 876, 27000 Torreón (Coahuila)
Tel: +52(17) 62-10-00
Director: Guadalupe Rodríguez Meza
Agriculture and Stockraising.

Instituto Tecnológico Agropecuario No. 13, Santiago Pinotepa National
Prolongación 6a Nte. s/n, Apartado postal No. 26, 71600 Santiago Pinotepa Nacional (Oaxaca)
Tel: +52(984) 3-23-77
Director: Rúben Piña Pérez
Agriculture and Stockraising.

Instituto Tecnológico Agropecuario No. 16 de Othon P. Blanco, Chetumal
km. 21.5 Carretera Chetumal, Escárcega Ejido Juan Saravia, 77000 Chetumal (Querétaro)
Director: Jésus Cerón Ruiz
Agricultural Engineering.

Instituto Tecnológico Agropecuario No. 18, Cd. Cardel
Domicilio Conocido, Ursulo Gavúu, Apartado postal No. 76, 91680 Cd. Cardel (Veracruz)
Tel: +52(296) 2-05-33
Fax: +52(296) 2-05-33
Director: Enrique Mercado Rodriguez
Agriculture and Stockraising.

Instituto Tecnológico Agropecuario No. 19, Tizimín
Apartado postal 79, 97700 Tizimín (Yucatán)
Tel: +52(986) 3-24-69
Director: Raúl Martín Fernández
Agriculture and Stockraising.

Instituto Tecnológico Agropecuario No. 20, Aguascalientes
Km. 18 Carretera Ags. S.L.P, 20270 Aguascalientes (Aguascalientes)
Tel: +52(49) 18-14-08
Director: Jaime Macías López
Agriculture and Stockraising.

Instituto Tecnológico Agropecuario No. 21, Valle de Yaqui
Block No. 611, Municipio de Bacum, 85000 Valle del Yaqui (Sonora)
Tel: +52(641) 3-00-28
Director: Valentín León Torres
Agriculture and Stockraising.

Instituto Tecnológico Agropecuario No. 22, Cd. Valles
Km. 2 de la Carretera Valles-Engenio Plan de Ayala, 79010 Cd. Valles (San Lui Potosí)
Tel: +52(138) 2-44-81
Agriculture and Stockraising.

Instituto Tecnológico Agropecuario No. 23, Sta. Cruz Xoxocotlan
Ex-Hacienda de Nazareno, Sta. Cruz Xoxocotlan (Oaxaca)
Tel: +52(951) 6-84-44
Director: Francisco Marini Zúñiga
Agriculture and Stockraising.

Instituto Tecnológico Agropecuario No. 24, Ciudad Cuauhtemoc
Calle Aldáma No. 554, Apartado postal No. 507, 31500 Ciudad Cuauhtemoc (Chihuahua)
Tel: +52(158) 1-17-07
Fax: +52(158) 2-39-54
Director: Serafín Luna Sánchez
Agriculture and Stockraising.

Instituto Tecnológico Agropecuario No. 25, Cd. Altamirano
Avenida Pungarabato Ote No. 22, Apartado postal No. 68, 40660 Cd. Altamirano (Guerrero)
Tel: +52(737) 2-12-13
Director: Jesús Salgado Norato
Agriculture and Stockraising.

Instituto Tecnológico Agropecuario No. 26, Tlacomulco
Km. 10 Carretera Etonque, sta. Cruz de las Flores a San Miguel Coyutlan, Municipio Tlacomulco de Zúñiga, 45640 Tlacomulco (Jalisco)
Director: José Luis López Pulido
Agriculture and Stockraising.

Instituto Tecnológico Agropecuario No. 27, Santiago Ixcuintla
Pozo de Ibarra, 63300 Santiago Ixcuintla (Nayarit)
Director: Francisco Javier Rivera Vielmas
Agriculture and Stockraising.

Instituto Tecnológico Agropecuario No. 28, Oeviltza Potlan
Prolongación de Zaragoza s/n Centro, Oeviltza Potlan (Tabasco)
Tel: +52(931) 3-61-50
Director: Julio Hernández Hernández
Agriculture and Stockraising.

Instituto Tecnológico Agropecuario No. 29, Ixtacuixtla
Km. 7.5 Carretera San Diego, Xocoyucan-San Martín Texmelucan, Ixtacuixtla (Tlaxcala)
Tel: +52(248) 4-28-19
Director: Alfonso Pimentel Cruz
Agriculture and Stockraising.

Instituto Tecnológico Agropecuario No. 31, Comitán
El Rosario Yocnajab, Apartado postal No. 57
Rancho J.B., Comitán (Chiapas)
Tel: +52(963) 2-38-04
Fax: +52(963) 2-00-51
Director: Jesús Eduardo León Tarín
Agriculture and Stockraising.

Instituto Tecnológico Agropecuario No. 32, Tecomatlan
Domicílio Conocido, 74870 Tecomatlan (Puebla)
Tel: +52(243) 6-06-63
Director: Gustavo Ortiz y Rivera
Agriculture and Stockraising.

Instituto Tecnológico de Aguascalientes
Avenida Tecnólogico y Avenida Lopez Mateos s/n, Apartado postal 263, 20000 Aguascalientes (Aguascalientes)
Tel: +52(49) 7-07-40
Fax: +52(49) 70-04-23
Director: Sergio Espinoza Gurrola
Industrial Engineering; Business Administration; Computer Sciences; Electronical Engineering; Chemical Engineering; Mechanical Engineering.

Instituto Tecnológico de Apizaco
Calz. Instituto Tecnológico s/n, Apartado postal 19, 90300 Apizaco (Tlaxcala)
Tel: +52(241) 7-27-38
Telex: 128857 itrcme
Director: Delfino Castañeda Sánchez
Civil Engineering; Industrial Engineering; Electromechanical Engineering; Business Administration; Computer Sciences.

Instituto Tecnológico de Campeche
Carretera Campeche-Escarcega Km. 9, Apartado postal 347, 24500 Campeche (Campeche)
Tel: +52(981) 2-00-33
Fax: +52(981) 2-02-24
Director: Ramón Agustín Bocos Patrón
Industrial Engineering; Mechanical Engineering; Chemical Engineering; Business Administration; Computer Sciences; Architecture.

Instituto Tecnológico de Cancun
Avenida Kabah Km. 3, Apartado postal No. 1790, 77500 Cancun (Quintana Roo)
Tel: +52(98) 84-97-08
Fax: +52(98) 84-97-08
Director: Guillermo Morales Santiago
Electromechanical Engineering; Industrial Fishing Engineering; Hotel Management; Accountancy; Computer Sciences.

Instituto Tecnológico de Celaya
Avenida Tecnológico y Antonio García Cubas s/n, Apartado postal 57, 38010 Celaya (Guanajuato)
Tel: +52(461) 3-93-12
Telex: 128857 itrcme
Director: Juan Sillero Pérez
Industrial Engineering; Biochemical Engineering; Computer Engineering; Business Administration; Electronical Engineering.

Instituto Tecnológico de Cerro Azul
Carretera Tuxpan-Tampico Km. 60, Apartado postal No. 118, 92510 Cerro Azul (Veracruz)
Tel: +52(785) 2-07-03
Fax: +52(785) 2-20-67
Director: Fidel Aguillón Hernández
Civil Engineering; Electromechanical Engineering; Computer Sciences; Accountancy.

Instituto Tecnológico de Chetumal
Avenida Insurgentes s/n Col. Centro, Ciudad Chetumal, Apartado postal 267, 77000 Chetumal (Quintana Roo)
Tel: +52(983) 2-10-19
Director: Juan Carlos Azueta Cárdenas
Industrial Engineering; Civil Engineering; Architecture; Business Administration; Accountancy; Computer Sciences; Biology.

Instituto Tecnológico de Chihuahua
Avenida Tecnológico 2909, Apartado postal 119, 31310 Chihuahua (Chihuaha)
Tel: +52(14) 13-74-74
Fax: +52(14) 13-51-87
Telex: 349682 itchme
Director: Manuel Gallardo Rodríguez
Industrial Engineering; Metalurgical Engineering; Electronical Engineering; Electromechanical Engineering; Commercial Relations.

Instituto Tecnológico de Chihuahua II
Bogoto No. 902 Fracc. Gloria, Chihuahua (Chihuahua)
Tel: +52(14) 81-01-98
Fax: +52(14) 81-04-52
Director: Luis Guillermo Floriano Gavaldón
Industrial Engineering; Computer Engineering; Business Relations; Computer Sciences.

Instituto Tecnológico de Chilpancengo
Carretera México-Acapulco Km. 274, Predio el Barrial, Apartado postal 343, 39090 Chilpancingo (Guerrero)
Tel: +52(747) 2-71-52
Director: Juan Manuel Rodríguez Vásquez
Data Processing; Computer Sciences; Civil Engineering.

Instituto Tecnológico de Ciudad Delicias
Carretera A. Rosetilla Km. 3.5, Apartado postal No. 1014, 33000 Chihuahua (Chihuahua)
Tel: +52(147) 2-76-75
Fax: +52(147) 2-91-13
Director: Carlos Cruz Vaca
Industrial Engineering; Electromechanical Engineering; Computer Sciences.

Instituto Tecnológico de Ciudad Guzmán
Carretera al Fresnito Km. 3, Apartado 150, 49100
Ciudad Guzmán (Jalisco)
Tel: +52(341) 3-23-04
Director: Antonio Enrique Leal Cruz
*Industrial Engineering; Electronical Engineering;
Mechanical Engineering; Business
Administration; Accountancy; Computer Sciences;
Business Relations.*

Instituto Tecnológico de Ciudad Juárez
Blvd. Tecnológico No. 1340, Apartado postal No.
2734, 32000 Ciudad Juárez (Chihuahua)
Tel: +52(16) 17-31-04
Fax: +52(16) 17-35-12
Telex: 333888 itrjme
Director: Humberto Carlos Morales Moreno
*Industrial Engineering; Electromechanical
Engineering; Mechanical Engineering;
Electronical Engineering; Computer Engineering;
Business Administration; Accountancy.*

Instituto Tecnológico de Ciudad Madero
Calle 1 de Mayo y Sor Juana Inés de la Cruz,
89440 Ciudad Madero (Tamaulipas)
Tel: +52(12) 15-21-53
Fax: +52(12) 15-63-39
Director: Juan Manuel Turrubiate Martínez
*Electrical Engineering; Geophysical Engineering;
Geology Engineering; Industrial Engineering;
Mechanical Engineering; Chemistry Engineering;
Computer Engineering; Electronical and
Communicational Engineering.*

Instituto Tecnológico de Ciudad Victoria
Boulevard Lic. Emilio Portes Gil y Camino a La
Libertad, Apartado postal 175, Ciudad Victoria
(Tamaulipas)
Tel: +52(131) 3-06-63
Fax: +52(131) 3-06-63
Director: Tomás Garza Wong
*Civil Engineering; Industrial Engineering;
Mechanical Engineering; Electronical
Engineering; Computer Sciences; Biology.*

Instituto Tecnológico de Colima
Avenida Tecnológico 1, Apartado postal No. 10,
28030 Villa de Alvorez (Colima)
Tel: +52(331) 2-63-93
Fax: +52(331) 4-06-83
Telex: 62234 intrme
Director: Victor Manuel Hermosillo Gaytan
*Biochemical Engineering; Computer Engineering;
Industrial Engineering; Business Administration;
Computer Sciences.*

Instituto Tecnológico de la Costa Grande
Calle La Riveira Manzana 30 Lote No. 1, Col. El
Limón, Apartado postal No. 234, Zihuatanejo
(Guerrero)
Tel: +52(753) 4-48-51
Fax: +52(753) 4-48-52
Director: Raúl Roberto Aguilar Rezza
*Electromechanical Engineering; Business
Administration; Accountancy; Computer Sciences.*

Instituto Tecnológico de Culiacán
Avenida Juan de Dios Bátiz y R. Corral, Col.
Guadalupe, Apartado postal 1273, Culiacán
(Sinaloa)
Tel: +52(67) 13-17-96
Telex: 665436 itrcme
Director: Francisco Javier Mozqueda Alarcón
*Industrial Engineering; Electrical Engineering;
Mechanical Engineering; Electronical
Engineering; Biochemical Engineering; Computer
Sciences.*

Instituto Tecnológico de Durango
Boulevard Felipe Pescador 1830, Apartado postal
465, 34080 Durango (Durango)
Tel: +52(181) 8-57-06
Fax: +52(181) 8-48-13
Telex: 66311 itrdme
Director: Jesús Ruvalcaba González
*Industrial Engineering; Biochemical Engineering;
Civil Engineering; Electronical Engineering;
Chemical Engineering; Industrial Engineering.*

Instituto Tecnológico Forestal de El Salto No. 1
Mesa del Tecnológico s/n, Apartado postal No. 2
El Salto, 34950 P. Nuevo (Durango)
Tel: +52(187) 6-02-39
Fax: +52(187) 6-02-40
Director: Fabián Fernández Sánchez
Forestry Engineering.

Instituto Tecnológico de Hermosillo
Avenida Tecnológico s/n, Apartado postal 518,
83170 Hermosillo (Sonora)
Tel: +52(62) 16-28-75
Fax: +52(62) 16-10-75
Telex: 58797
Director: Luis Armando Cheu Ramírez
*Industrial Engineering; Mechanical Engineering;
Electrical Engineering; Computer Sciences.*

Instituto Tecnológico de Hidalgo del Parral
Avenida Tecnológico No. 57, Apartado postal No.
216, 33850 Hidalgo del Parral (Chihuahua)
Tel: +52(152) 3-03-36
Fax: +52(152) 3-07-52
Director: Leonel Gildardo Loya Pacheco
*Industrial Engineering; Electromechanical
Engineering; Business Administration;
Accountancy.*

Instituto Tecnológico de Huatabampo
Avenida Juárez 33 Ote. Centro, Apartado postal
No. 16, Huatabampo (Sonora)
Tel: +52(642) 6-14-77
Fax: +52(642) 6-14-77
Director: José Antonio López Herrera
*Industrial Engineering; Computer Engineering;
Accountancy.*

Instituto Tecnológico del Istmo
Carretera Panamericana Km. 821.5, Apartado
postal 63, 70000 Juchitán de Zaragoza (Oaxaca)
Tel: +52(971) 1-10-42
Director: Herman Calderón Pineda
*Civil Engineering; Electromechanical
Engineering; Electrical Engineering; Industrial
Engineering; Mechanical Engineering;
Architecture; Computer Sciences; Accountancy.*

Instituto Tecnológico de Jiquilpán
Carretera Nacional Km. 202, Parque Pdte. Lazaro
Cárdenas, Apartado Postal No. 35, 59510
Jiquilpán (Michoacán)
Tel: +52(353) 3-02-37
Fax: +52(353) 3-11-26
Director: Arnoldo Solís Covarrubias
*Industrial Engineering; Biochemical Engineering;
Computer Sciences; Accountancy; Commercial
Relations.*

Instituto Tecnológico de la Laguna
Boulevard Revolución y Calz. Cuauhtemoc,
Apartado postal 681, 27000 Torreón (Coahuila)
Tel: +52(17) 13-72-53
Fax: +52(17) 13-09-70
Telex: 32834 itrlme
Director: Gabriel Fragoso Monarrez
*Industrial Engineering; Electronical Engineering;
Computer Engineering.*

Instituto Tecnológico de Lazaro Cárdenas
Domicílio Conocido, Apartado postal No. 228,
60950 Ciudad Lazaro Cárdenas (Michoacán)
Tel: +52(743) 7-19-77
Fax: +52(743) 7-19-77
*Electronical Engineering; Electromechanical
Engineering; Chemical Engineering; Computer
Engineering; Accountancy; Business
Administration.*

Instituto Tecnológico de León
Carretera a León-Silao, Avenida Tecnológico s/n
Fracc. Julián de Obregón, 37000 León
(Guanajuato)
Tel: +52(47) 11-41-86
Fax: +52(47) 11-20-72
Director: Angel Castro Cortés
*Industrial Engineering; Electromechanical
Engineering; Computer Engineering; Business
Administration; Computer Sciences.*

Instituto Tecnológico del Mar, Boca del Río
Km. 12 Carretera Internacional, Veracruz-México,
Vía Córdoba, 94290 Boca del Río (Veracruz)
Tel: +52(29) 86-01-89
Director: Carlos Sánchez Pereyra
Marine Technology.

Instituto Tecnológico del Mar en Campeche
Carretera Campeche-Champotón Km. 10,
Apartado postal No. 186, 24500 Campeche,
Campeche
Tel: +52(981) 2-00-89
Director: Humberto Lanz Cárdenas
Marine Technology.

Instituto Tecnológico del Mar, Mazatlán
Carretera Internacional Sur Urias Estero la
Tel: +52(69) 84-72-09
Director: Jorge Flores Olivares
Marine Technology.

Instituto Tecnológico del Mar, Quaymas
Carretera Varadero Nacional de Suiación, Casino
Naval, Sector Playitas, Apartado postal 742,
85480 Quaymas (Sonora)
Tel: +52(622) 2-06-50
Director: Joaquín Pérez Mellado
Fish Engineering; Maritime Engineering.

Instituto Tecnológico de Matamoros
Km. 6 Carretera Lauro Villar, 87490 Matamoros
(Tamaulipas)
Tel: +52(891) 4-09-52
Director: Oscar Javier Alonso Banda
*Civil Engineering; Electromechanical
Engineering; Industrial Engineering; Chemical
Engineering; Electronical Engineering; Public
Accountancy; Computer Sciences; Industrial
Management.*

Instituto Tecnológico de Mérida
Carretera Mérida-Progreso Km. 5, Apartado
postal 9-11 Chuburna, 97118 Mérida (Yucatán)
Tel: +52(99) 27-19-55
Telex: 753760 itrmme
Director: Carlos Sauri Duch
*Industrial Engineering; Biochemical Engineering;
Civil Engineering; Electronical Engineering;
Mechanical Engineering; Chemical Engineering;
Computer Engineering; Business Administration.*

Instituto Tecnológico de Mexicali
Avenida Instituto Tecnólólogico s/n, Col. P. Elías
Calles, Mexicali (Baja California)
Tel: +52(65) 61-85-22
Fax: +52(65) 61-90-07
Director: Ramón Armando Heredia Ruiz
*Electronical Engineering; Industrial Engineering;
Mechanical Engineering; Electrical Engineering;
Computer Sciences.*

Instituto Tecnológico de Minatitlán
Km. 27 Carretera Transístmica, Apartado postal
777, 96700 Minatitlán (Veracruz)
Tel: +52(922) 4-23-10
Fax: +52(922) 4-37-07
Telex: 78423
Director: Felix Polito López
*Electromechanical Engineering; Chemical
Engineering; Electronical Engineering;
Environmental Engineering; Business
Administration.*

Instituto Tecnológico de los Mochis

Blvd. Juan de Dios Bátiz y Prolongación 20 de
Noviembre, Apartado postal 766, 81200 Los
Mochis (Sinaloa)
Tel: +54(681) 8-32-89
Fax: +54(681) 5-03-26
Telex: 53205 itrlme
Director: Gustavo Apocada Lugo
*Biochemical Engineering; Chemical Engineering;
Industrial Engineering; Electronical Engineering;
Architecture; Public Accountancy; Business
Administration; Computer Sciences; Biology.*

Instituto Tecnológico de Morelia

Avenida Tecnológico 1500, Apartado postal 262,
58120 Morelia (Michoacan)
Tel: +52(43) 12-35-16
Fax: +52(43) 12-16-43
Director: Jorge Isaias López Chale
*Industrial Engineering; Electronical Engineering;
Computer Engineering; Biochemical Engineering;
Mechanical Engineering; Business
Administration; Computer Sciences.*

Instituto Tecnológico de la Paz

Blvd. Forsadores de Baja California Sur, Km. 3.5,
Apartado postal 243, 23050 La Paz (Baja
California Sur)
Tel: +52(112) 1-04-24
Fax: +52(112) 1-12-95
Telex: 52516 itrme
Director: Angel Rafael Quevedo Camacho
*Electromechanical Engineering; Computer
Engineering; Industrial Engineering; Biochemical
Engineering; Civil Engineering; Business
Administration; Accountancy; Computer Sciences.*

Unidad Pedagógica de Atlacomulco

Avenida Lic. Mario Colin Sanchez No. 5, 50450
Atlacomulco (Estado de México)
Tel: +52(722) 2-00-90
Director General: Antonio Medrano G.
Education.

PRIVATE INSTITUTIONS

Aeroscuela

Zona 'C' No. 5, Hangar 12 Terminal de la
Aviación General, Aeropuerto Internacional,
15620 México (D.F.)
Director General: Arturo Ureña C.
Aviation.

Arte, A.C. Escuela de Diseño

Belisario Domínguez No. 2202, Col. Obispado,
64000 Monterrey (Nuevo León)
Tel: +52(83) 46-20-42
Director: Jesús Javier Martínez A.
Design.

Asociación Satélite de Estudios Culturales Sor Juana A.C.

Colibri 6, Primera Sección de Lomas Verdes,
53120 Naucalpán de Juárez (Estado de México)
Tel: +52(5) 5-62-03-71
Directora: María del Pilar G.L.P. de Cordero
Human Sciences.

Avitec Escuela de Vuelo, S.A.

Lote 24 Terminal de la Aviación General,
Aeropuerto Internacional, 15620 México (D.F.)
Tel: +52(5) 5-58-09-01
Director: Raúl González
Aviation.

Centro de Arte Mexicano, A.C

Cascada 180, Pedregal San Angel, 01900 México
(D.F.)
Tel: +52(5) 5-68-32-44
Directora: Carmen Diaz de Turrent
History of Art.

Centro de Investigaciones en Optica, A.C

Loma del Pocito s/n, Col. Lomas del Campestre,
Apartado postal No. 948, 37000 León
(Guanajuato)
Tel: +52(471) 7-58-23
Director: Arquímedes Morales Romero
Optics Research.

Centro de Educación Profesional, S.C

Puebla 162 Col. Roma, 06700 México (D.F.)
Tel: +52(5) 2-07-50-48
Director General: Eduardo Solís Torres
Administration.

Centro Educativo Grupo Sol

Avenida Cuauhtemoc No. 60, 5o Piso, Col.
Doctores, 06720 México (D.F)
Tel: +52(5) 5-14-23-76
Telex: 1762292 dydme
Rector: Arturo Solís Torres
*Accountancy and Administration; Law; Computer
Sciences.*

Centro de Enseñanza Técnica y Superior

Calz, Cetys s/n, Apartado postal 3-797, Mexicali
(Baja California)
Tel: +52 65-0111
Fax: +52 65-0241
*Engineering; Business Administration and
Accountancy; Accountancy and Administration
(Ensenada); Engineering (Ensenada); Business
Administration and Accountancy; Vocational and
Technical Studies.*

UNIDAD TIJUANA
Avenida Gran Lago s/n, Fracc. El Lago, Apartado
postal No. 4012, Tijuana (Baja California)
Tel: +52(66) 25-32-00
Fax: +52(66) 25-39-51
Director General: Oscar Licona Nieto
*Accountancy and Administration; Psychology;
Engineering.*

Centro Escolar 'Benito Juárez'
5 de Febrero No. 443 Sur, Ciudad Obregón
(Sonora)
Tel: +52(641) 3-32-82
Director General: Frederico Pedraza Jiménez

Centro Escolar 'Miguel Alemán'
Calle 27 No. 150, Fracc. San Miguel, 97140
Mérida (Yucatán)
Tel: +52(99) 27-46-67
Director General: Rubén Avila Ruiz
Accountancy.

Centro de Estudios en Ciencias de la Comunicación
Xochicalco No. 678, Col.Vertiz-Narvarte, 03020
México (D.F.)
Tel: +52(5) 6-04-90-28
Rector: Raymundo Ampudia Malacara
Communication.

Centro de Estudios Superiores de Diseño de Monterrey
Cerro de las Mitras No. 2206, Col. Obispado,
Apartado postal No. 4074, 64010 Monterrey
(Nuevo León)
Tel: +52(83) 46-13-12
Fax: +52(83) 48-68-63
Rector: Eduardo Carranza García
Design.

Centro de Estudios Superiores de Guamuchil, S.C.
Silverio Trueba y Fernando Amilpa, Guamuchil
(Sinaloa)
Tel: +52(673) 2-34-02
Director General: Rafael Castro Juárez
Accountancy and Administration; Law.

Centro de Estudios Superiores de Ortodoncia, A.C.
Oso No. 127, Desp. 109 Col. del Valle, 03100
México (D.F.)
Tel: +52(5) 5-24-88-80
Director General: Adan Casasa Araújo
Ortodontology.

Centro de Estudios Superiores de San Angel
Morelos No. 7, Col. Tizapan-San Angel, 01090
México (D.F.)
Tel: +52(5) 6-83-19-20
Fax: +52(5) 6-83-19-20
Director General: Luz María Arteaga de Guerrero
Business Administration; Hotel Management.

Centro de Estudios Superiores de Tamaulipas, A.C.
Carretera Soto la Marina Km. 2, Apartado postal
No. 328, 87130 Ciudad Victoria (Tamaulipas)
Tel: +52(131) 2-67-02
Director General: José Maldonado García

Centro de Estudios Universitarios
Avenida Hidalgo Pte. 546, 64000 Monterrey
(Nuevo Leon)
Tel: +52(83) 42-50-25
Rector: Antonio Coello Valadés
*Law and Social Sciences; Engineering;
Psychology; Trade and Administration;
Agronomy; Pedagogy; Physical Education and
Recreation.*

Centro de Estudios Universitarios del Distrito Federal
Aguascalientes No. 157, Col. Hipodromo, 06100
México (D.F.)
Tel: +52(5) 5-74-07-73
Rector: Agustín Nuñez Sánchez
Economic and Administration; Social Sciences.

Centro de Estudios Universitarios de Xochicalco
San Francisco de Alcalá No. 1139,
Fraccionamento Misión, Ensenada (Baja
California Norte)
Tel: +52(667) 6-35-13
Fax: +52(667) 6-38-61
Rector: Hugo Gutiérrez de Alba
*Health Sciences; Engineering and Technology;
International Relations.*

Centro de Investigación en Alimentación y Desarrollo, A.C.
Carretera a la Victoria Km. 0.6, Apartado postal
No. 1735, Hermosillo (Sonora)
Tel: +52(62) 14-98-45
Fax: +52(62) 14-93-27
Director General: Inocencio Higuera Ciapara
Food Research.

Centro de Investigación y Docencia Económicas, A.C.
Carretera México-Toluca Km. 16.5, Col. Lomas
de Santa Fe, Apartado postal No. 10-883, 01210
México (D.F.)
Tel: +52(5) 5-70-37-02
Fax: +52(5) 5-70-37-02
Executive President: Carlos Bazdresch Parada
Economic Research and Teaching.

Centro Universitario Galilea
Avenida de la Convención Esq. Zacatecas, Int.
33, 20140 Aguascalientes (Aguascalientes)
Tel: +52(49) 14-75-92
Director: Alfonso María Alva Martínez

Centro Universitario Hispanoamericano
Avenida Cruz del Sol 3, Esq. Avenida Lopez
Mateos, Col. Santa Cruz del Monte, 53110 Cd.
Satelite (Estado de México)
Tel: +52(5) 8-74-55-22
Rector: Eduardo Antonio Ituarte Verduzco
*Business Administration; Public Accountancy;
Law; Tourism; Pedagogy; Informatics
Administration.*

Centro Universitario del Noreste, A.C.
Lic. Guillermo Martínez Domínguez 116, 87360 H
Matamoros (Tamaulipas)
Tel: +52(891) 3-88-35
Rector: Ricardo Díaz Garza
*Business Administration; Computer Sciences;
Psychology; Law; Architecture; Administration
Computer Sciences.*

Colegio Español de México
Artículo 123 No. 44, Col. Centro, 06050 México
(D.F.)
Tel: +52(5) 5-12-05-40
Director: David Gallegos Lozano
Public Accountancy; Administration.

PLANTEL GUADALAJARA
Avenida Libertad No. 1690, Sector Juárez,
Guadalajara (Jalisco)
Tel: +52(5) 6-25-78-94
Directora: Laura Solís Torres
Public Accountancy; Computer Sciences.

PLANTEL SANTO TOMAS
Avenida de los Maestros No. 75, Col. Santo
Tomás, 11340 México (D.F.)
Tel: +52(5) 5-41-05-44
Director: Nereo Castillo Medina
*Public Accountancy; Information Sciences; Fiscal
Law.*

Colegio 'Esparza'
13 Poniente No. 111, 72000 Puebla (Puebla)
Tel: +52(22) 46-55-23
Directora General: María Elena Torreblanca
Trujillo

Colegio Excelsior, A.C.
Washington No. 107 Pte, Monterrey (Nuevo León)
Tel: +52(83) 42-64-96
Directora: Margarita Ortiz Guerra
Education.

Colegio Hispanoamericano
Dr. Atl No. 199, Col. Santa María la Riveira,
06400 México (D.F.)
Tel: +52(5) 5-41-67-45
Director: Consuelo Zarza Bernal
Education.

El Colegio Mexiquense, A.C.
Avenida Prof. Carlos Hank Gonsáles y Hacienda
Rancho seco s/n, 57170 Nezahualcoyotl (Estado
de México)
Tel: +52(72) 18-00-56
Fax: +52(72) 18-03-58
Presidenta: María Teresa Jarquin Ortega
Social Sciences; Municipal Development.

El Colegio de Michoacán, A.C
Martínez de Navarrete No. 505, Fracc. las
Fuentes, Apartado postal No. 207, 59690 Zamora
(Michoacán)
Tel: +52(351) 506-09
Fax: +52(351) 553-07
Presidente: Brigitte Bohem de Lameiras
*Social Anthropology; History; Rural Studies;
Ethnic Studies; Social Sciences.*

Colegio Motolinia
Eduardo M. Vargas No. 931, Col. Moderna,
Irapuato (Guanajuato)
Tel: +52(462) 6-13-65
Director: María Guadalupe Sandoval Rodríguez
Education.

El Colegio de Puebla, A.C
11 Sur No. 1708-A, 1er Piso, Puebla (Puebla)
Tel: +52(22) 37-01-19
Presidente: Rodolfo Hidalgo Rojas
*Economic Geography; History; Sociology; Political
Studies.*

Colegio San Agustín, A.C.
Calle 58 No. 484, 97000 Mérida (Yucatán)
Tel: +52(99) 23-04-90
Director General: Jorge Enrique Sauma Novelo
Tourism.

Columbia College Panamericano
Xochicalco No. 195, Polanco, 11560 México (D.F.)
Tel: +52(5) 5-19-76-68
Director General: Agustin Carrera Alamilla

Complejo Educativo Hispanoamericano, A.C
Avenida Morelos 220, Col. Peñitas, 37180 León
(Guanajuato)
Tel: +52(471) 7-13-51
Fax: +52(471) 7-13-51
Director General: Patricia Aranda Orozco
Educational Sciences.

Escuela de Arquitectura
Calzada H. Colegio Militar Antiguo Colegio, La
Salle s/n, 31110 Chihuahua (Chihuahua)
Tel: +52(14) 11-09-19
Director: Gilberto Cedano Grijalva
Architecture.

Escuela Bancaria y Comercial
Paseo de la Reforma 202, 06600 México 6 (D.F.)
Tel: +52(5) 726-99-33
Director General: Javier Prieto Sierra
Banking and Commercial Studies.

Escuela de Comunicación Social
Riva Palacio No. 684 Nte, 80000 Culiacán
(Sinaloa)
Tel: +52(67) 13-58-29
Directora: María Teresa Zazueta y Zazueta
Social Communication.

Escuela de Educación Física 'Profr. Antonio Estopier E.'
Zaragoza 443 Norte, 35150 Cd. Lerdo (Durango)
Tel: +52(17) 14-95-08
Director: Antonio Ríos Fuentes
Physical Education.

Escuela Independiente de Psicología
Avenida Melchor Ocampo No. 1810, Col. Centro,
Chihuahua (Chihuahua)
Tel: +52(14) 15-71-86
Director: Jesús Gómez Chacón
Psychology.

Escuela de Ingeniería Municipal
Moeteruma No. 125, Col. San Pablo Tepletlapa
4620, México (D.F.)
Tel: +52(5) 6-77-26-42
Director General: Carlos Becker Perdomo
Engineering.

Escuela Libre de Derecho, Culiacán
Rosales No. 266 Pte, Culiacán (Sinaloa)
Tel: +52(67) 12-71-68
Director: Rául René Rosas Echavarría
Law.

Escuela Libre de Derecho, México
Arcos de Belen Esq. Vertiz, México 7 (D.F.)
Tel: +52(5) 5-88-02-11
Rector: Fausto Rico Alvarez
Law.

Escuela Libre de Homeopatia
Primera de Santa Lucía No. 6, 06200 México
(D.F.)
Tel: +52(5) 5-26-09-13
Director General: Raúl Tamayo Rodriguez
Homeopathy.

Escuela de Medicina Física y Rehabilitación
Avenida Observatorio y Esq. Sur 136, Col.
Tacubaya, México 18 (D.F.)
Tel: +52(5) 2-72-85-00
Director: Renato Donati Sánchez
Physiotheraphy and Rehabilitation.

Escuela Normal 'F.E.P.'
Sadi Carnot 44, 06470 México 4 (D.F.)
Tel: +52(5) 5-46-93-78
Directora General: Estela Iñiguez Amézquita
Teacher Training.

Escuela Normal 'Juana de Asbaje'
Dr. Verduzco 380 Sur, Zamora (Michoacán)
Tel: +52(351) 2-45-68
Directora General: Celia Díaz Becerril
Teacher Training.

Escuela Normal Superior Benavente
Calle 25 Oriente 9, 72000 Puebla (Puebla)
Tel: +52(22) 43-63-00
Director: Ricardo Preciado A.
Teacher Training.

Escuela Normal Superior de Celaya
Luis Velazco de Mendoza No. 225, Col.
Residencial, 38060 Celaya (Guanajuato)
Tel: +52(461) 2-30-05
Director: Javier A. Abarca Cancino
Teacher Training.

Escuela Normal Superior de Ciudad Madero, A.C.
Brasil y 5 de Mayo No. 406 Pte., 89400 Cd.
Madero (Tamaulipas)
Tel: +52(12) 15-91-80
Fax: +52(12) 12-67-02
Director: Oscar Hernández Gutiérrez
Teacher Training.

Escuela Normal Superior de Durango
Calle Pino Suárez 3000 Ote., Durango (Durango)
Tel: +52(181) 2-11-35
Director: Everardo García Balderas
Teacher Training.

Escuela Normal Superior del Estado 'José E. Madrane'
Calle Ramírez y 6a, Chihuahua (Chihuahua)
Tel: +54(14) 12-12-32
Director: Carlos Urquidi Gaytán
Teacher Training.

Escuela Normal Superior 'Fray Matias de Cordova y Ordoñez', A.C.
Calle Julio M. Corzo No. 16 'A', 29250 San
Cristobal de las Casas (Chiapas)
Tel: +52(967) 8-04-62
Director: Jorge Paniagua Herrera
Teacher Training.

Escuela Normal Superior de La Laguna
Blvd. Miguel Alemán Frente a la Termoeléctrica,
Gómez Palacio (Durango)
Tel: +52(17) 12-64-61
Director: Martín Rodolfo Silva Rosales
Teacher Training.

Escuela Normal Superior de la Laguna Cursos Intensivos
Blvd. Guadalupe Victoria s/n, Col. Sacramento,
27050 Gomez Palacio (Durango)
Director: Jesús Esquivel Martínez
Teacher Training.

Escuela Normal Superior 'Profr. Porfirio Parra'
Calle 24a Esq. con 10 de Mayo Nos. 1803 y 1805,
31020 Chihuahua (Chihuahua)
Tel: +52(14) 12-77-75
Director: Rogelio A. Quiroz de la Rosa
Teacher Training.

Escuela Normal Superior de Querétaro, A.C.
Domicílio Conocido, Colonia Vista Alegre, 76090
Querétaro (Querétaro)
Director: Horacio Sarmiento Galván
Teacher Training.

Escuela Normal Superior del Sur de Tamaulipas
Ayuntamiento y Nicolás Bravo, Col. Martock,
Tampico (Tamaulipas)
Tel: +52(121) 2-50-04
Directora: Esperanza Garza Rodríguez
Teacher Training.

Escuela Normal Superior de Tamaulipas, A.C.
Carretera Soto la Marina Km. 2, Apartado postal 338, Ciudad Victoria (Tamaulipas)
Tel: +52(131) 2-67-02
Directora: Josefina Barrón Olazarrán
Teacher Training.

Escuela Panamericana de Hotelería
Prolong. Martín Mendalde 1795, Col. Valle, 03100 México (D.F.)
Tel: +52(5) 5-34-84-21
Fax: +52(5) 34-84-22
Director General: David E. Freyer Manjarrez
Hotel Administration.

Escuela Particular Superior del Estado de Morelos
Avenida Palmas No. 13, Col. Bellavista, Apartado postal 1275, Cuernavaca (Morelos)
Tel: +52(73) 13-25-28
Director: Aurelio Sandoval Trahyn

Escuela de Periodismo 'Carlos Septien García'
Basilio Badillo 43 ler Piso, 06030 México 1 (D.F.)
Tel: +52(5) 5-10-49-00
Fax: +52(5) 5-18-55-65
Director: Manuel Pérez Miranda
Journalism.

Escuela Profesional de Comercio y Administración de León, A.C.
Independencia 1706, 37380 León (Guanajuato)
Tel: +52(471) 5-54-57
Director General: José de Jesús Zúñiga Morales
Commerce and Administration.

Escuela Profesional de Contabilidad y Administración 'Maestro José Calvo', A.C.
Avenida Cuauhtemoc 60, México 7 (D.F.)
Tel: +52(5) 5-88-37-11
Directora: Lilia Rocío Alvarado Lagunas
Accountancy and Administration.

Escuela Superior de Administración de Recursos Naturales
Blvd. Ortíz Mena s/n Col. Centro, 33800 Hidalgo del Parral (Chihuahua)
Tel: +52(152) 2-65-85
Directora: Silvia Manuela Vasquez Lazcano
National Resources Administration.

Escuela Superior de Comercio y Administración 'Colegio Guasave'
Domicílio Conocido, Colonia Ejidal, 81020 Guasave (Sinaloa)
Tel: +52(687) 2-17-70
Director: Pablo Valdés Domínguez
Commerce and Administration.

Escuela Superior de Comunicación Gráfica
Avenida División del Norte, 3102 Col. Altavista, 31320 Chihuahua (Chihuahua)
Tel: +52(14) 13-65-05
Director: Juan E. Ruiz Trujillo
Graphics.

Escuela Superior de Contaduría y Administración
Avenida Monterrey s/n, Col. Chapultepec, 26860 Nueva Rosita (Coahuila)
Tel: +52(861) 4-37-45
Director: Carlos Angel Garza Ramírez
Accountancy and Administration.

Escuela Superior de Educación Física de Orizaba
Poniente 7 No. 291, Orizaba (Veracruz)
Tel: +52(272) 5-17-58
Director: Victor Manuel Contreras Cuburo
Physical Education.

Escuela Superior de Medicina Veterinaria y Zootecnia, A.C.
Km. 125.5 Carretera Federal México, Puebla, Momoxpán, 72760 San Pedro Cholula (Puebla)
Tel: +52(22) 49-49-59
Director General: José Antonio Gómez Lince
Veterinary Medicine and Animal Husbandry.

Escuela Superior en Organización y Administración Agropecuaria
Bravo y Degollado, 27000 Torreón (Coahuila)
Tel: +52(17) 13-47-67
Director: Juan Alberto de la O. Alvarez
Agricultural and Stockraising Administration.

Escuela Superior de Pedagogía, A.C.
División del Norte No. 3102, Col. Altavista, Apartado postal No. 1576, 31320 Chihuahua (Chihuahua)
Tel: +52(14) 14-07-77
Director: Juan E. Ruiz Trujillo
Pedagogy.

Escuela Superior de Relaciones Industriales
Calz. Valle de Juárez 6922, Col. San Lorenzo, 32320 Col. Juárez (Chihuahua)
Tel: +52(161) 7-26-00
Director: Daniel García Coello
Industrial Relations.

Escuela de Trabajo Social de Tampico
Boulevard López Mateos 3401, Col. Santo Niño, Tampico (Tamaulipas)
Tel: +52(12) 15-63-11
Directora: Edith Martínez Vásquez
Social Work.

Escuela de Trabajo Social de Tijuana
Calz. de Guadalupe 6, Fraccionamiento, La Villa, La Mesa, Tijuana (Baja California)
Tel: +52(66) 86-89-11
Director: Alejandro Iñigo Soto
Social Work.

Facultad Libre de Derecho, A.C
Privada Liendo No. 712 Sur, Col. Obispado, 64010 Monterrey (Nuevo León)
Tel: +52(83) 47-18-15
Director: Arturo Salinas Martínez
Law.

Facultades Universitarias de Saltillo, A.C.
Hidalgo Norte 160, Saltillo (Coahuila)
Tel: +52(84) 13-91-50
Director: Juan Manuel Jiménez Valdés
Business Administration.

Instituciones Educativas 'Labastida', A.C.
José Vasconcelos No. 110 Ote., Col. del Valle,
66220 Garza García (Nuevo León)
Tel: +52(83) 56-99-30
Director: José Medardo Méndez

Instituto Activo de Mercandotécnia y Publicidad, S.C.
Guillermo Prieto No. 2, Col. San Rafael, 06470
México (D.F.)
Tel: +52(5) 5-35-66-03
Director: Jaime Garduño Garfias
Marketing; Computer Sciences; Tourism; Public Accountancy; Administration.

Instituto Allende
Calle Ancha de San Antonio No. 20, 37750 San
Miguel de Allende (Guanajuato)
Tel: +52(465) 201-90
Director: Stirling Dickinson

Instituto América
Calz. del Tepeyac No. 609, Col. Moderna, 37480
León (Guanajuato)
Tel: +52(471) 335-52
Directora: Ma. Conceptión Flores Montufar
Education.

Instituto Celayense
Paseo de Bajío y Magnolia Jardin de Celaya,
Apartado postal No. 473, 38080 Celaya
(Guanajuato)
Tel: +52(461) 343-85
Rector: Ramón Lemus Muñoz-Ledo
Psychology; Dentist; Design; Architecture; International Commerce.

Instituto de Ciencia y Cultura, A.C
Victoria Pte. No. 311, 25000 Saltillo (Coahuila)
Tel: +52(84) 14-02-12
Director General: Antonio Amavizca Melendrez
Business Administration; Industrial Relations; Biology.

Instituto de Ciencias y Estudios Superiores de Tamaulipas, A.C.
Calle Septima No. 706 entre Rayo y Victoria,
87300 H Matamoros (Tamaulipas)
Tel: +52(891) 334-49
Rector: Carlos L. Dorantes del Rosal
Psychology; Social Work; Business Administration; Public Accountancy; Tourism; Computer Science.

Instituto de Ciencias y Estudios Superiores de Tamaulipas, A.C.
Avenida Altamira, No. 418 Pte, Tampico
(Tamaulipas)
Tel: +52(12) 12-04-09
Directora: Lilí Cobos González
Health; Psychology; Computer Science; Social Work; Pedagogy.

Instituto de Ciencias Sociales, Económicas y Administrativas
Balderas No. 138, 1er Piso, Col. Centro, 06070
México (D.F.)
Tel: +52(5) 709-11-79
Rector: Alberto Ponce de Léon
Public Accountancy; Business Administration.

Instituto de Ciencias Sociales de Mérida, A.C.
Calle 26 x 27 No. 216, Col. García Gineres, 97070
Mérida (Yucatán)
Tel: +52(99) 23-11-34
Director General: José Luis Rivera Paz
Communication Sciences; Sociology; Education Sciences.

Instituto de Cultura Superior, A.C.
Prado Norte 664, Lomas de Chapultepec, 11000
México (D.F.)
Tel: +52(5) 540-27-92
Director General: Ricardo Mena Penna
Art History.

Instituto de Estudios Superiores de Tamaulipas
Blvd. Divisorio Tampilo-Altamira s/n Pte,
Apartado postal No. 257 Lentameicol, Altamira
(Tamaulipas)
Tel: +52(12) 28-01-68
Rector: David Efrain Gómez Fuentes
Psychology; Social Work; Business Administration.

Instituto de Enseñanza e Investigación Superior en Comercio Internacional
Monterrey 242, Col. Roma, 06760 México 7 (D.F.)
Tel: +52(5) 564-16-59
Director General: Juan Manuel Avila García
International Commerce.

Instituto de Estudios Profesionales para la Administración del Tiempo Libre
Avenida Ejército Nacional 253, Col. Anzures,
11300 México (D.F.)
Tel: +52(5) 531-05-74
Director: Antonio Bassols Zaleta
Administration (Free Time).

Instituto de Estudios Profesionales de Saltillo, A.C.
De la Fuente No. 352, 25000 Saltillo (Coahuila)
Tel: +52(841) 334-38
Coordinador General: Eleazar A. Valdes Ramos
Business Administration; Public Accountancy and Auditing.

Instituto de Estudios Superiores del Estado de México
Río Frío No. 7, Col. El Parque, Naucalpán de
Juárez (Estado de México)
Coordinadora General: Isabel Torre Blanca

Instituto de Estudios Superiores de Oaxaca
Camino Nacional No. 709, Santa Rosa, Centro,
Oaxaca (Oaxaca)
Tel: +52(951) 449-49
Director General: Luis Cortes Osorio
*Social Anthropology; Sciences and Techniques of
Communication; Psychology; Pedagogy.*

**Instituto de Estudios Superiores de Poza
Rica**
General O'Higins s/n, Poza Rica (Veracruz)
Tel: +52(782) 341-84
Director: Fernando Rojas Calderon

**Instituto de Estudios Superiores de
Turismo, S.C.**
Privada del Lago 40, Col. Américas Unidas,
03610 México (D.F.)
Tel: +52(5) 539-03-08
Director General: Miguel Mandujano Contreras
Tourism.

Instituto 'Guadalupe Victoria', A.C.
Estrella Polar Esq. con Avenida López Mateos,
20250 Aguascalientes (Aguascalientes)
Tel: +52(49) 17-26-65
Directora: Carmen Zermeño Cervantes
Education.

Instituto José Vasconcelos
Independencia No. 1603, Col. San Miguel, León
(Guanajuato)
Tel: +52(471) 279-22
Directora: Aurelia Gutiérrez R.
Education; Physical Education.

Instituto Leonardo Bravo
Ezequiel Montes 115, Col. San Rafael, 06470
México 4 (D.F.)
Tel: +52(5) 535-29-40
Director: Francisco Bravo Malpica
Public Accountancy and Auditing.

**Instituto Mantense de Estudios
Profesionales**
Calle Ocampo 212 Sur, 89800 Ciudad Mante
(Tamaulipas)
Tel: +52(123) 217-78
Director General: Joaquín Treviño Arizmendi
*Law; Business Administration; Public
Accountancy.*

Instituto Mayllen
A. Serdan No. 221 Centro, León (Guanajuato)
Tel: +52(471) 423-59
Directora: Eva Maria Rodríguez Islas
Education.

**Instituto de Mercandotécnia y Publicidad,
S.C.**
Chihuahua No. 225 Altos, Col. Roma, 06760
México (D.F.)
Tel: +52(5) 584-08-24
Directora Académica: Norma Lisette Chavez
Castellanos
Marketing and Publicity.

**Instituto de Mercandotécnia y Publicidad,
S.C.**
Calle 16 de Septiembre No. 4, Casi Esq.
Periférico, Col. El Parque Naucalpán, 53560
Naucalpán de Juárez, Estado de México
Tel: +52(5) 358-08-55
Director General: Reynaldo Ampudia Carrillo
Marketing and Publicity.

**Instituto Méxicano de la Audición y el
Lenguaje, A.C.**
Avenida Progreso 141-A Col. Escandón, 11800
México (D.F.)
Tel: +52(5) 277-64-44
Directora: Paz Villalobos de Berruecos
Speech Therapy and Language.

**Instituto Méxicano de Estudios Superiores,
S.C.**
Avenida Ocampo con Privada Rayon No. 245,
27500 Torreón (Coahuila)
Tel: +52(17) 12-32-54
Director: Juan Jose Bernal Gómez
Social Work; Nutrition.

Instituto 'Miguel Angel', A.C.
Iztacgihuatl No. 239, Col. Florida, 01030 México
(D.F.)
Tel: +52(5) 534-40-90
Directora: Leticia Barba Martin
Education.

Instituto Morelos
Golfo de Campeche No. 17, Col. Tacuba, 11410
México (D.F.)
Tel: +52(5) 527-32-24
Fax: +52(5)399-41-85
Directora General: Rosa Maria Peccorini
Education.

Instituto del Noreste
Angel Flores 247 Ote, Culiacán (Sinaloa)
Tel: +52(671) 272-63
Director: Guillermo Castro Ugalde

Instituto 'Nueva Galicia'
Hidalgo No.1083, 44680 Guadalajara (Jalisco)
Tel: +52(3) 6-25-21-02
Directora: Carlotta Blanco Couciño
Education.

**Instituto Panamericano de Alta Dirección de
Empresas**
Floresta No. 20, Col. San Rafael, 06470 México
(D.F.)
Tel: +52(5) 3-99-00-04
Director General: Sergio Raymund-Kedilhac
Business Administration.

Instituto Pedagógico Anglo Español
Sadi Carnot No. 13, Col. San Rafael, 06470
México (D.F.)
Tel: +52(5) 5-35-99-44
Directora: Ma. Guadalupe Pantoja Villegas
Anglo-Spanish Pedagogy.

Instituto Puebla
Priv. 26-A. Pte. No. 3315, Fracc. Valle Dorado,
72070 Puebla (Puebla)
Tel: +52(22) 48-65-45
Directora: Ma. Luisa Gutiérrez Burgos
Education.

Instituto Regiomontano
Fco. G. Sada y José Benitez, Col. Chepe Vera,
Apdo. Postal 492, 64000 Monterrey (Nuevo León)
Tel: +52(83) 46-09-34
Director General: Miguel Angel Alva Carpio
Education.

Instituto Superior de Arquitectura
Insurgentes Sur 1027-402, Col. Napoles, México
18 (D.F.)
Tel: +52(5) 5-98-47-00
Director General: Rafael Enríquez Colmeneros
Architecture.

Instituto Superior de Ciencias y Tecnología de La Láguna, A.C.
Héroes de Nacozari s/n, Col. Bellavista, 35050
Gómez Palacios (Durango)
Tel: +52(17) 14-16-36
Rector: Ramón María Nava González
Architecture; Civil Engineering; Graphic Design; Information Sciences; Industrial Design; Export Trade.

Instituto Superior de Cultura y Arte de Monterrey
Avenida San Jerónimo 201 Pte., 64640 Monterrey
(Nuevo León)
Tel: +52(83) 46-78-84
Directora General: Rosalía Manzano Sevilla
Culture and Art.

Instituto Superior de Docentes en Educación Especial
Playa Regatas No. 473, Col. Marte, 08830 México
(D.F.)
Tel: +52(5) 6-33-57-69
Director: Jorge Acosta Laguna
Teacher Training (for the Handicapped).

Instituto Superior de Estudios Comerciales
Mier y Pesado No. 227, Col. del Valle, 03100
México (D.F.)
Tel: +52(5) 5-36-14-40
Director: Adrían Mora Aguilar
Public Accountancy; Business Administration; Computer Sciences.

Instituto Superior de Interpretes y Traductores
Río Rhin 40, 06500 México 5 (D.F.)
Tel: +52(5) 5-66-77-22
Director General: Jacobo Chencinsky
Interpretation and Translation.

Instituto Superior de Odontología, A.C.
Rosales 3302 Hospital Central 2o Piso, 31000
Chihuahua (Chihuahua)
Tel: +52(14) 15-83-42
Director: Gabriel Jiménez Velasco
Odontology.

Instituto Tecnológico de la Construcción, A.C.
Colima 254 Col. Roma, 06700 México (D.F.)
Tel: +52(5) 5-25-21-46
Director General: José Antonio Aguirre Balcells
Construction.

Instituto Tecnológico de Estudios Contables y Administrativos
Viaducto Pte. Miguel Alemán 255, Col. Roma Sur,
06760 México 7 (D.F.)
Tel: +52(5) 2-64-85-20
Rector: Gonzalo Vivanco Florido
Accountancy and Administration.

Instituto Tecnológico y de Estudios Superiores de Monterrey
Avenida Eugenio Garza Sada 2501, Sucursal de
Correos J, Monterrey (Nuevo León)
Tel: +52(83) 58-21-33
Fax: +52(83) 58-25-32
Telex: 382975
Rector: Rafael Rangel Sostmann
Founded: 1943
Administration and Social Sciences; Agronomics and Food Technology; Sciences and Humanities; Engineering and Architecture; Health Sciences.

Instituto Tecnológico y de Estudios Superiores Potosino
Madero 335, Apartado postal 743, San Luis Potosí
(San Lui Potosí)
Tel: +52(481) 2-17-93
Director General: Tomás Dávalos Serrano
Accountancy; Tourism; Business Administration; Computer Sciences.

Instituto Tecnológico Méxicano
5 de Febrero No. 283, Esq. con Gutiérriez Najera,
Col. Obrera, 06800 México (D.F.)
Tel: +52(5) 7-40-39-99
Director General: Joaquina Gallardo Piña
Public Accountancy.

Instituto Tecnológico Universitario de México
Avenida Azcapotzalco 308, Col. Claveria, 02080
México (D.F.)
Tel: +52(5) 5-61-86-46
Director General: Salvador Rocha Segura
Public Accountancy; Administration.

Instituto Tepeyac de León
Tres Guerras Nos. 113 y 115, Zona Centro, León
(Guanajuato)
Tel: +52(471) 6-62-69
Directora General: Margarita Morales Manrique
Education.

Instituto Universitario de Ciencias de la Educación
Calle Colegio Salesiano 35, Col. Anáhuac,
México 3 (D.F.)
Tel: +52(5) 3-96-33-46
Rector: Roberto Guzmán Leal
Law; Administration; Accountancy; Pedagogy; Psychology; Sociology; Communication Sciences.

Instituto Universitario del Norte
Calle Bolívar 112, 31000 Chihuahua (Chihuahua)
Tel: +52(14) 15-81-15
Directora General: Elizabeth Nájera Castro
Education.

Liceo Profesional de Comercio y Administración, A.C.
Bravo y 7a No. 1501, 87300 H Matamoros (Tamaulipas)
Tel: +52(891) 3-08-15
Director: Alfredo Aldete Herrera
Commerce and Administration.

Unidad Escolar Particular 'Miguel Castulo Alatriste', A.C.
Corregidora No. 5, 74400 Izucar de Matamoros (Puebla)
Tel: +52(243) 6-04-30
Director: José Gerardo Crivelli
Education.

Universidad del Claustro de Sor Juana
Ex-Convento de San Jerónimo, Plaza de San Jerónimo 47, 06080 México 3 (D.F.)
Tel: +52(5) 7-09-40-26
Rector: Juan Manuel Silva Camarena
Human Sciences; Communication; Administration.

Universidad 'Isidro Fabela de Toluca' S.C
Gonzales y Pichardo No. 1219, Col. Granjas, 50120 Toluca (Estado de México)
Tel: +52(72) 17-41-08
Fax: +52(72) 17-32-04
Director General: Carlos Mercado Galan
Accountancy and Administration; Law; Computer Sciences; Psychology.

Universidad Vasco de Quiroga, A.C.
Prol. V. de Mendoza 1678, Col. Felix Ireta, 58070 Morelia (Michoacán)
Tel: +52(43) 14-13-35
Director General: Francisco Chavez Ponce
Business Administration; Public Accountancy and Auditor; Architecture; Psychology; Philosophy; Graphic Design; International Commerce; Computer Sciences; Sciences of Communication.

NATIONAL ACADEMIC BODIES

Secretariat for Public Education
[Secretaría de Educación Pública]
Argentina 28, Oficina 2, 06029 México, Distrito Federal
Tel: +52(5) 518-6136
Fax: +52(5) 510-4075
Secretary: José Angel Pescador Osuna

National Association of Universities and Institutions of Higher Education
[Asociación Nacional de Universidades e Institutos de Enseñanza Superior]
Insurgentes Sur 2133, San Angel, México, Distrito Federal
Tel: +52(5)-55-2755
Fax: +52(5) 550-4885
Executive Secretary-General: Juan Casillas G. de L.

Mexican National Commission for Unesco
[Comisión Nacional de los Estados Unidos Mexicanos para la Unesco]
Presidente Mazarik 526, Colonia Polancio, 11560 México (D.F.)
Tel: +52(5)280-6597
Fax: +52(5)280-7474
Presidente: José Angel Pescador Osuna, Secretary for Public Education
Secretaria General: Karen Kovaks

MOLDOVA

UNIVERSITIES

Bălti State University 'Alecu Russo'
[Universitatea de Stat 'Alecu Russo']
str. Puşkin 38, 279200 Bălţi
Tel: +3732 2-55-63
Fax: +3732 2-44-88
Rector: N. Filip (1994-96)
Prime-Rector: S. Băncilă
Founded: 1945
F: Philology; Romanic and Germanic Philology; Mechanics, Physics and Mathematics; Music Education; Psychopedagogy.

Comrat State University
[Universitatea de Stat din Comrat]
str. Galaţan 217, 278710 Comrat
Tel: +3732(2) 43-45
Fax: +3732(2) 43-45
Rector: D. Tanasoglo (1992-97)
Founded: 1991
F: Economy; Agriculture; National Culture.

Moldova Cooperative University
[Universitatea Cooperatist-Comercială din Moldova]
str. Gagarin 28, 277001 Chisinău
Tel: +3732(26) 06-43
Rector: T. Maleca (1993-98)
Pro-Rector, Didactic and Methodical Activity: S. Petrovici
International Relations: Pro-Rector, V. Colibaba
Founded: 1993
F: Management and Accounting; Marketing; Commerce; Instruction and Research.

Moldova Independent International University
[Universitatea Liberă Internaţională din Republica Moldova]
str. Stefan cel Mare 198, 277004 Chişinău
Tel: +3732(24) 25-75
Fax: +3732(24) 25-75
Rector: A. Galben (1992-97)
Prime-Vice-Rector: N. Gheorghită
International Relations: A. Barbăneagră
Founded: 1992

Moldova Medical State University 'N. Testemiţanu'
[Universitatea de Stat de Medicină 'N. Testemiţanu']
str. Stefan cel Mare 165, 277004 Chisină
Tel: +3732(23) 46-17
Fax: +3732(24) 23-44
Rector: L. Cobîleanschi (1986-95)
Prime-Vice-Rector, Didactic and Methodical Activity: V. Ghicavîi
Founded: 1945
F: General Medicine; Pediatrics; Preventive Medicine; Stomatology; Pharmacology.
C: Medicine.

*Moldova State University
[Universitatea de Stat din Moldova]
str. A. Mateevici 60, 277009 Chişinău
Tel: +3732(24) 00-41
Fax: +3732(24) 06-55
Rector: G. Rusnak (1993-95)
Pro-Rector: P. Chetrus
International Relations: Pro-Rector, Al. Stahii
Founded: 1946
F: Mathematics and Cybernetics; Physics; Chemistry; Biology and Soil Science; History, Philosophy, Psychology; Law; Theology; Journalism; Philology; Library Science; Romanic and Germanic Philology.
C: Computer.
D: Correspondence Courses.

Moldavian State Agricultural University
[Universitatea agrară de Stat din Moldova]
str. Miroesti 44, 277049 Chişinău
Tel: +3732(24) 64-22
Fax: +3732(24) 63-26
Pro-Rector: V. Podaru
International Relations: Pro-Rector, G. Gaber
Founded: 1932
F: Agriculture; Agriculture Mechanization and Electrification; Horticulture; Hydrotechnical Amelioration; Zootechnology; Agricultural Economics; Veterinary Medicine.
I: Recycling and Development.
C: Computer.

Moldova Technical University
[Universitatea Tehnică a Moldovei]
str. Stefan cel Mare 168, 277012 Chişinău
Tel: +3732 (23) 45-28
Fax: +3732 (23) 75-09
Rector: I. Bostan (1992-97)
Pro-Rector: P. Tudos
Founded: 1964
F: Energetics; Mechanics; Vehicle Construction; Electro-Physics; Radio-Electronics; Private and Civil Construction; Urban Construction and Architecture; Technology.

Pedagogical State University 'Ion Creangă'
[Universitatea Pedagogică de Stat 'Ion Creangă']
I. Creagnă 1, 277069 Chisinău
Tel: +3732 (62) 99-14
Rector: I. Guţu (1992-97)
Prime-Rector: N. Andronatii
International Relations: Pro-Rector, N. Banuh
Founded: 1940
F: Philology; History and Ethnopedagogy; Pedagogy; Psychology and Psychopedagogy; Recycling of Personnel; Fine Arts and Design Graphics.
C: Computer.

Tiraspol State University
[Universitatea de Stat din Tiraspol]
str. Iablocchin 5, 277012 Chisinău
Tel: +3732(63) 49-24
Rector: P. Tolocenco (1992-97)
Prime-Rector, Didactic Activity: I. Pancenco
International Relations: Pro-Rector, N. Ciobanu
Founded: 1930
F: Physics and Mathematics; Biology and Chemistry; Philology; Geography; Pedagogy.
D: Correspondence Courses.

OTHER INSTITUTIONS

Academia de Muzică 'G. Muzicescu'
str. A. Mateevici 87, 277014 Chişinău
Tel: +3732 22-43-44
Fax: +3732 23-23-88
Rector: C. Rusnac (1984-94)
Pro-Rector: S. Sîrcunova
Founded: 1919
Music.

National Police Academy 'Stefan cel Mare'
[Academia Naţională de Poliţie 'Stefan del Mare']
str. Doina 102, 277020 Chişinău
Tel: +3732 49-86-31
Rector: T. Roşca (1991-96)
Pro-Rector: D. Baltaga
Founded: 1990
Law.

Academia de Studii Economice din Moldova
str. Banulescu-Bodeni 61, 277225 Chişinău
Tel: +3732 22-41-28
Fax: +3732 22-77-24
Rector: P. Bran (1991-96)
Vice-Rector: V. Şoimaru
Founded: 1991
F: Management; Marketing; Accounting,
Informatics and Administration; Finance, Credit
and Coins; Cybernetics, Statistics and
Economical Information.
Ce: Computer.

Institul de Arte din Republica Moldova
str. A. Mateevici 111, 277012 Chişinău
Tel: +3732 24-04-97
Rector: V. Apostol (1992-97)
Pro-Rector, Didactic Activity: C. Crăciun
Founded: 1986
Pedagogy and Music; Theatre Arts; Fine Arts.

Institutul National de Educatie Fizică şi Sport
str. A. Doga 24/1, 277024 Chişinău
Tel: +3732 49-40-81
Rector: P. Telmaciev (1991-96)
Pro-Rector, Didactic Activity: V. Lupaşcu
Founded: 1991
Pedagogy; Recycling.

Institutul National de Instruire Continuă
str. Stefan cel Mare 200, 277004 Chişinău
Tel: +3732 62-73-72
Fax: +3732 62-58-49
Rector: T. Vascan (1993-98)
Pro-Rector, Didactic Activity: V. Gestetkii
Founded: 1991
D: Philological Sciences; Sociology and Human
Sciences; Science and Nature; Pre-school and
Primary Education; Methodical Instruction;
Construction and Design Technology; Projecting
and Implementation; Informatics and Computers;
Instruction for Market Economy; Handycrafts;
Psychopedagogics; Management.

NATIONAL ACADEMIC BODIES

Ministry of Education
[Ministerul Invătămantului]
1 Piaţa Marii Adunări Naţional, 277033 Chişinău
Tel: +3732 23-33-48
Minister: P. Gaugaş

Republic of Moldova National Commission for Unesco
c/o Ministry of Foreign Affairs, Department of
Mass Media and Culture, Piaţa Marii Adunări
Naţionale, 277012 Chişinău
Tel: +3732 23-36-86
Fax: +3732 23-36-09
Secretary-General: Constantin Rusnac
Executive Secretary: Victoria Marinat

MONACO

OTHER INSTITUTIONS

Monaco Business School (University of Southern Europe)
22, avenue Prince Héréditaire Albert, 98000
Monaco
Tel: +33 92-05-70-57
Fax: +33 92-05-28-30
Directeur général: François de Bruyne
Directeur administratif: Martine Grouselle
International Relations: Samir Nassif
Founded: 1986
Economics; Social Sciences; Political Science;
Diplomatic Science; Communication and
Journalism.

NATIONAL ACADEMIC BODIES

Office for National Education, Youth and Sports
[Direction de l'Education nationale, de la
Jeunesse et des Sports]
Avenue de l'Annonciade, 98000 Monaco
Tel: +33(93) 15-83-05
Fax: +33(93) 15-85-74
Directeur: Yvette Lambin-Berti
Adjoint au Directeur: Hélène Repaire
International Relations: Cécile Rivetta

Monaco National Commission for Unesco
[Commission nationale monégasque pour
l'Unesco]
8, rue Louis Notari, 98000 Monaco
Tel: +33(93) 93-15-83-09
Fax: +33(93) 50-66-94
Telex: 469942
Cable: gouvernement monaco
Président: René Novella
Secrétaire général: Rainier Rocchi
International Relations: Cécile Rivetta

MONGOLIA

UNIVERSITIES

*Mongolian State University
[Mongol Ulsyn Ikh Surguuli]
p.b. 377, Ulan Bator 11
Tel: +976 206-68
Rector: Daachaagiyn Dorj
Founded: 1942
F: Physics and Mathematics; Natural Sciences;
Social Sciences; Philology; Economics; Trade
Economics; Preparatory.
D: Evening and Correspondence Studies.

*Mongolian Technical University

P.O. 46, Box 520, Ulan Bator
Tel: +976 251-09
Rector: D. Badarch (1992-)
Founded: 1969, 1983, 1991
S: Geology and Mining; Mechanical and Technology Engineering; Electrical Engineering; Civil Engineering.
I: Telecommunication; Transport.
Ce: Foreign Language; General Education.

State Agricultural University Ulan Bator

Post Office 53, Ulan Bator
Founded: 1942
F: Agricultural Engineering; Veterinary Medicine; Animal Husbandry; Agricultural Economics.

State Medical University Ulan Bator

Post Office 48, Ulan Bator
Founded: 1942
F: Medicine; Pediatrics; Dentistry; Pharmacy; Hygiene; Therapy.

State Pedagogical University Ulan Bator

p.b. 48/103, Peace Street 2, Ulan Bator
Founded: 1951
F: Mongolian Language and Literature; Russian Language; Mathematics and Physics; Natural and Social Sciences; Art and Labour Studies; Physical Education; Teachers Retraining; External.

OTHER INSTITUTIONS

College of Commerce and Business

Ulan Bator
Tel: +976 21666
Founded: 1991
Commerce and Business.

College of Economics

Ulan Bator
Tel: +976 50378
Founded: 1991
Economics.

College of Railway Engineering

Ulan Bator
Tel: +976 715520
Founded: 1991
Railway Engineering.

Institute of Culture and Art

Ulan Bator
Tel: +976 28845
Founded: 1990
Culture and Art.

NATIONAL ACADEMIC BODIES

Ministry of Science and Education

Ulaanbaatar 46, Barilgachdyn Talbai 15, Ulan Bator
Tel: +976(800) 21539
Fax: +976(873) 150-7441
Minister: Nadmid Ulziikhutag

Mongolian National Commission for Unesco

Ministry of Foreign Affairs, Ulan Bator
Tel: +976 324-810
Telex: 245 gayam mh
Cable: mounesco ulan bator
Chairman: Jalbuugiin Choinkhor
Secretary-General: D. Tsakhilgaan

MOROCCO

UNIVERSITIES

University Ibn Zohr Agadir

[Université Ibn Zohr Agadir]
Agadir
Tel: +212(8) 22-70-17
Fax: +212(8) 22-72-60
Rector: Mustapha Dkhissi
Founded: 1989
F: Letters and Humanities.
I: Technology; Science.

Hassan II University Casablanca

[Université Hassan II Casablanca]
Zankat Tarik Ibnou Ziad, B.P. 9167, Mers-Sultan, Casablanca
Tel: +212(2) 27-37-37
Fax: +212(2) 27-61-50
Recteur: Abdelhamid Daoudi El Idrissi (1985-)
Founded: 1975
F: Law, Economics and Social Studies; Medicine and Pharmacy; Dental Medicine; Letters and Humanities (Aïn Chock); Sciences (Aïn Chock).
S: Advanced Electrical and Mechanical Engineering.
S: Technology.

Hassan II University Mohammedia

[Université Hassan II Mohammedia]
279 Cité Yassmina, P.O. Box: 150, Mohammedia
Tel: +212(3) 31-46-35
Fax: +212(3) 31-46-35
Rector: Mohamed Ferhat
Founded: 1992
F: Sciences (Ben M'Sik); Letters and Humanties (Ben M'Sik); Letters and Hamanities; Law, Economics and Social Studies; Science and Technology.

University Chouaib Doukkali El Jadida

[Université Chouaib Doukkali El Jadida]
2bis, Av. Mohamed Ben Larbi Alaoui, B.P. 9, 25000 El Jadida
Tel: +212(3) 34-44-48
Fax: +212(3) 34-44-49
Recteur: Ahmed Kerkour
Founded: 1989
F: Letters and Human Sciences; Sciences; Sciences and Technology (Settat).
I: Business Administration.

University Quaraouiyine Fès
[Université Quaraouiyine Fès]
Dhar El Mahraz, B.P. 60, Fès
Tel: +212(6) 41199
Telex: 31016
Founded: 1859, 1947
*F: Islamic Law; Arabic Language and Literature
(Marrakech); Theology and Philosophy (Tétouan);
Islamic Law (Agadir).*

University Sidi Mohammed Ben Abdallah Fès
[Université Sidi Mohammed Ben Abdallah Fès]
Boulevard des Almohades, B.P. 2626, Fès
Tel: +212(5) 62-55-85
Fax: +212(5) 62-24-01
Recteur: Jellal Amal
Secrétaire général: Mohamed Ferhane
Founded: 1975
*F: Law, Economics and Social Sciences; Letters
and Human Sciences; Science; Letters.
S: Technology.*

University Ibn Tofail Kenitra
[Université Ibn Tofail Kenitra]
P.O. Box: 242, Kenita
Tel: +212(7) 37-28-09
Fax: +212(07) 37-40-52
Recteur: Abdelouahed Belkeziz
Secrétaire général: Abdeljalil Lahlou
Founded: 1989
F: Letters and Humanities; Sciences.

University Cadi Ayyad Marrakech
[Université Cadi Ayyad Marrakech]
Avenue Prince My Abdellah, P.O. Box: 511,
Marrakesh
Tel: +212(4) 43-48-13
Fax: +212(4) 43-44-94
Telex: 74869
Rector: Mohamed Knidiri
Founded: 1975
*F: Letters and Humanities; Letters and
Humanities (Beni Mellal); Science; Science and
Technology; Science and Technology (Beni
Mellal); Law, Economics, and Social Sciences.
I: Technology (Safi).*

University Moulay Ismail Meknès
[Université Moulay Ismail Meknès]
1, Place Andalous, P.O. Box: 298, Meknes
Tel: +212(5) 52-63-78
Fax: +212(5) 52-73-14
Rector: Abdellatif Chadli
*F: Letters and Human Sciences; Law,
Economics and Social Studies; Sciences;
Scienceand Technology (Errachidia); Science and
Technology.
I: Technology.*

*Mohammed I University Oujda
[Jami'at Muhammad al-Awwal Oujda]
P.O. Box: 524, Oujda 60000
Tel: +212(6) 74-74-83
Fax: +212(6) 74-47-79
Recteur: Hassan Mekouar (1989-)
Secrétaire général: Abderrahman Houtch
Founded: 1978
*F: Letters and Hamanities; Law, Economics and
Social Sciences; Science.
I: Technology.*

*Mohammed V Agdal University Rabat
[Université Mohammed V Agdal/Jâmiât
Mohammed El Khâmiss Rabat]
3, rue Michlifen, Agdal, B.P. 554, Rabat, Chellah
Tel: +212(7) 67-13-24
Fax: +212(7) 67-14-01
Telex: recuniv 32603
Recteur: Abdellatif Benabdejalil
Secrétaire général: Abderrahmane Rida
Founded: 1957
*F: Letters and Humanities; Law, Economics and
Social Sciences; Sciences.
S: Engineering (Mohammadia).
I: Technology (Salé); Science.*

Mohammed V Souissi University Rabat
[Université Mohammed V Souissi/Jâmiât
Mohammed El Khâmiss Rabat]
3, Rue Idriss al-Akbar, P.O. Box: 8025, Hassan,
Rabat
Tel: +212(7) 70-71-98
Fax: +212(7) 70-61-88
Rector: Abdellah Meslout
Founded: 1992
*F: Medicine and Pharmacy; Dental Medicine;
Education Science.
S: Computer Science and Systems Analysis
(Advanced).
I: Studies and Research on Arabization;
Scientific Research (University); African Studies.*

University Abdelmalek Es-Saadi Tétouan
[Université Abdelmalek Es-Saadi Tétouan]
P.O. Box: 28, Martil, Tétouan
Tel: +212(9) 97-90-99
Fax: +212(9) 97-91-51
Rector: Saâd Daoudi
Founded: 1989
*F: Letters and Humanities; Sciences; Science
and Technology (Tangiers).
S: King Fahd Advanced Translation (Tangiers).
I: Businee Administration (Tangiers).*

OTHER INSTITUTIONS

Ecole des Sciences de l'Information
Avenue Maa Al Aïnaïne, Haut Agdal, Rabat
Tel: +212(7) 74913
Founded: 1975
Information Science.

Ecole Hassania des Travaux publics et des Communications
Km. 7, Route d'El Jadida, Casablanca
Tel: +212 230-7150
Founded: 1971
Public Work and Communication.

Ecole national forestière d'Ingénieurs
Tabriquet, B.P. 511, Salé
Tel: +212(7) 871-49
Founded: 1968
Forestry.

Ecole nationale d'Administration publique
1, avenue de la Victoire, Rabat
Tel: +212(7) 25I-68
Founded: 1948
Public Administration.

Ecole nationale d'Agriculture
Haj Kaddour, Route d'Ifrane, Meknès
Tel: +212(5) 22389
Telex: 41969
Founded: 1945
Agriculture.

Ecole nationale d'Architecture
Bab al Irfane, Haut Agdal, Rabat
Tel: +212(7) 22427
Founded: 1980
Architecture.

Ecole nationale de l'Industrie minérale
Rue Abderrahmen, El Ghafiki, Haut Agdal, Rabat
Tel: +212(7) 71360
Founded: 1972
Mineral Industries.

Ecole normale supérieure
Avenue Victor Hugo, B.P. 9172, Casablanca
Teacher Training.

Ecole normale supérieure
Kariat Bensouda Ahouaz-Ouad, Fès
Tel: +212(6) 383720
Teacher Training.

Ecole normale supérieure
Cité Mohammadia, B.P. 41S, Marrakech
Teacher Training.

Ecole normale supérieure
Hay Toulal, Meknès
Tel: +212(5) 31607
Teacher Training.

Ecole normale supérieure (Enseignement technique)
Avenue Maa Al Aïnaïne, Haut Agdal, Rabat
Teacher Training (Technical).

Ecole normale supérieure Takaddoum
Avenue Oued Akrach, Takaddoum, Rabat
Tel: +212(7) 50025
Teacher Training.

High Tech
Angle rue Fès-Meknès, Quartier de la Résidence, Rabat
Tel: +212(7) 33331
Founded: 1985
Technical Studies.

Institut agronomique et vétérinaire Hassan II
Avenue Maa Al Aïnaïne, Haut-Agdal, B.P. 6202, Rabat
Tel: +212(7) 71758
Telex: 32089
Founded: 1966
Agriculture; Veterinary Medicine.

Institut Dar-Al-Hadith Al-Hassania
2, rue Dahomi, Rabat
Tel: +212(7) 22587
Founded: 1964

Institut national d'Aménagement et Urbanisme
Avenue Maa Al Aïnaïne, Haut-Agdal, Rabat
Tel: +212(7) 73510
Founded: 1981
Town Planning and Development.

Institut national de l'Action sociale
Boulevard el Hariri, Tanger
Founded: 1983
Social Work.

Institut national des Postes et Télécommunications
Avenue Maa Al Aïnaïne, Haut Agdal, Rabat
Tel: +212(7) 73079
Founded: 1971
Telecommunications.

Institut national des Statistiques et d'Economie appliquée
Avenue Maa Al Aïnaïne, Haut Agdal, B.P. 6217, Rabat
Tel: +212(7) 70915
Telex: 32719
Founded: 1967
Statistics and Applied Economics.

Institut national d'Etudes Judiciaires
Avenue Beni Snassen, Haut Agdal-Souissi, Rabat
Tel: +212(7) 50285
Founded: 1970
Judicial Studies.

Institut royal de Formation des Cadres de la Jeunesse et des Sports
Belle-Vue, Avenue Ibn Sina, Haut Agdal, Rabat
Tel: +212(7) 72674
Founded: 1980
Cadres Training.

Institut supérieur de Commerce et d'Administration des Entreprises

Km. 9, 5 route de Nouasseur, Casablanca
Tel: +212 230-666
Telex: 22884
Founded: 1971
Commerce and Business Administration.

Institut supérieur de Journalisme

Avenue Maa Al Aïnaïne, Haut Agdal, Rabat
Tel: +212(7) 74913
Founded: 1970
Journalism.

Institut supérieur de Tourisme

13, avenue Allal Ben Abdellah, Tanger
Tel: 39429
Founded: 1972
Tourism.

Institut supérieur des Etudes maritimes

Km. 7, Route d'El Jadida, Casablanca
Tel: +212 364-4445
Founded: 1957
Maritime Studies.

NATIONAL ACADEMIC BODIES

Ministry of Education

[Ministère de l'Education nationale]
24, rue du Sénégal-Océan, B.P. 420, Rabat
Tel: +212(7) 77-19-76
Ministre: Mohamed Knidiri

Division for Equivalence of Diplomas

[Division de la Réglementation et des Equivalences de Diplômes]
Ministère de l'Education nationale, 24, rue du Sénégal-Océan, Rabat
Tel: +212(7) 74839
Telex: 31016 meps-mes

Moroccan National Commission for Unesco

[Commission nationale marocaine pour Unesco]
Ministère de l'Education nationale, 24, rue du Sénégal-Océan, B.P. 420, Rabat
Tel: +212(7) 77-12-21
Fax: +212(7) 77-90-29
Telex: 31016
Cable: commissionunesco b.p. 420 rabat
Président: Mohamed Knidiri, Ministre d'Education
Secrétaire général: M'Hand Meziane

MOZAMBIQUE

UNIVERSITIES

*University Eduardo Mondlane Maputo

[Universidade Eduardo Mondlane Maputo]
Praça 25 de Junho, Caixa postal 257, Maputo
Tel: +258(1) 427-851
Fax: +258(1) 426-426
Telex: 6-718 uem mo
Reitor: Narciso Matos
Founded: 1962, 1968, 1976

F: Law; Economics; Agricultural Sciences; Biology; Geology; Medicine; Veterinary Medicine; Mathematics; Arts; Physics; Electrical Engineering; Civil Engineering; Chemistry; Mechanical Engineering.
I: Scientific Research.
Ce: African Studies; Ecology; Communication Studies; Psychopedagogics.

OTHER INSTITUTIONS

Instituto Superior Pedagógico

Caixa postal 3276, Maputo
Tel: +258(1) 420-860
Fax: +258(1) 430-204
Telex: 6-635
Founded: 1986
Teacher Training.

NATIONAL ACADEMIC BODIES

Ministry of Education

[Ministero da Educaçao]
Caixa postal 34, Maputo
Tel: +258(1) 491-158
Minister: Aniceto Dos Muchangos

Mozambique National Commission for Unesco

45 rua Dr. Egas Moniz, Caixa pstal 3674, Maputo
Tel: +258(1) 491-766
Fax: +258(1) 491-766
Telex: 6812 mec mo
President: Graca Machel
Secretary-General: Ana Elisa de Santano Afonso

MYANMAR

UNIVERSITIES AND UNIVERSITY INSTITUTIONS

Institute of Agriculture Pyinmana

Ye Zin, Pyinmana
Founded: 1924, 1964
Agriculture.

Institute of Animal Husbandry and Veterinary Science Yangon

Yangon
Founded: 1964
Animal Husbandry and Veterinary Science.

Institute of Computer Science and Technology

Hline Campus, Hline P.O., Yangon
Tel: +95(1) 60630
Founded: 1988
Computer Science and Technology.

Institute of Dental Medicine Yangon
Schwedagon Padoga Road, Yangon
Tel: +95(1) 70866
Founded: 1964, 1974
Dentistry.

Institute of Economics Yangon
University P.O., Yangon 11041
Tel: +95(1) 30376
Founded: 1964
Economics; Applied Economics; Commerce;
Management Studies; Statistics.

Institute of Education Yangon
University P.O., Yangon
Tel: +95(1) 30919
Founded: 1930, 1946
Teacher Training.

Institute of Medicine Mandalay
Mandalay
Tel: +95(2) 22011
Founded: 1954, 1958, 1964
Medicine; Adult Education.

Institute of Medicine I Yangon
245 Myoma Road, Lanmadow P.O. 11131, Yangon
Founded: 1964
Medicine.

Institute of Medicine II Yangon
13 Mile Pyay Road, Mingaladon, Yangon
Tel: +95(1) 45501
Founded: 1964
Medicine.

Magwe Degree College
University Campus, Magwe
Tel: +95(63) 21030
Founded: 1958

Mawlamyine University
Taung Waing Road, Mawlamyine, Mon State
Tel: +95(32) 211-80
Rector: Hla Tun Aung
Secretary-General (Administration and Finance):
Saw Gipson
Founded: 1953, 1986
F: Myanmar; English; History; Geography;
Philosophy; Oriental Studies; Chemistry; Physics;
Zoology; Botany; Mathematics; Geology; Marine
Science.
Ce: Aquaculture Research; Zoology Research.

Myitkyina Degree College
University Campus, Myitkyina, Kachin State
Tel: +95(101) 21053
Founded: 1963
Arts; Science.

Taunggyi State College
Taunggyi, Shan State
Tel: +95(81) 21160
Founded: 1961
Arts; Science.

University of Mandalay
University P.O., Mandalay
Tel: +95(2) 212-11
Founded: 1958, 1964
Arts; Science.

University of Yangon
University P.O., Yangon
Tel: +95(1) 31144
Founded: 1920, 1946, 1964
Arts; Science.

Workers' College Yangon
273 Konthe Lan, Botahtaung P.O., Yangon
Tel: +95(1) 92825
Founded: 1964
Arts; Science.

Yangon Institute of Technology
Gyogon, Insein P.O., Yangon
Tel: +95(1) 40526
D: Mechanical Engineering; Civil Engineering;
Electrical Engineering; Chemical Engineering;
Mining Engineering; Petroleum Engineering;
Textile Engineering; Metallurgy; Architecture;
Geology.

OTHER INSTITUTIONS

Government Technical Institute
Insein
Founded: 1890
Technical Studies.

Government Technical Institute
Kalaw
Founded: 1968
Technical Studies.

Government Technical Institute
Mandalay
Founded: 1955
Technical Studies.

Institute for Foreign Languages
University Avenue, Yangon
Founded: 1963
Foreign Languages.

Institute of Para-Medical Sciences
General Hospital Compound, Yangon
Founded: 1964
Para-Medical Sciences.

State Agricultural Institute
Pyinmana
Founded: 1954
Agriculture.

State Agricultural Institute
Thaton
Founded: 1967
Agriculture.

State Teachers' Training School
Bogalay
Founded: 1970
Teacher Training.

State Teachers' Training College
Kanbe Yangon
Founded: 1947
Teacher Training.

State Teachers' Training School
Kyaukpyu
Founded: 1953
Teacher Training.

State Teachers' Training College
Mandalay
Founded: 1952
Teacher Training.

State Teachers' Training College
Mawlaymyine
Founded: 1953
Teacher Training.

State Teachers' Training School
Meiktila
Founded: 1953
Teacher Training.

State Teachers' Training School
Myaungmya
Founded: 1953
Teacher Training.

State Teachers' Training School
Myitkyina
Founded: 1962
Teacher Training.

State Teachers' Training School
Prome
Founded: 1968
Teacher Training.

State Teachers' Training School
Sagaing
Founded: 1968
Teacher Training.

State Teachers' Training School
Taunggyi
Founded: 1964
Teacher Training.

State Teachers' Training School
Thegon, Prome District
Founded: 1965
Teacher Training.

State Teachers' Training School
Thinkangyun, Yangon
Founded: 1969
Teacher Training.

State Teachers' Training School
Toungoo
Founded: 1967
Teacher Training.

NATIONAL ACADEMIC BODIES

Ministry of Education
Theinbyu Street, Yangon
Tel: 95(1) 86704
Fax: +95(1) 85480
Minister: Pei Thein

Myanmar National Commission for Unesco
Ministry of Educationon, Office of the Ministers,
Theinbyu Street, Yangon
Tel: +95(1) 86704
Chairman: PeiThein, Minister of Education
Secretary-General: U. Hang Tin

NAMIBIA

UNIVERSITIES

*University of Namibia
Private Bag 13301, Windhoek
Tel: +264(61) 307-9111
Fax: +264(61) 307-2413
Telex: (50) 908-7271
Vice-Chancellor: Peter H. Katjavivi (1992-)
Registrar: Zach J.N. Kazapua
Founded: 1981, 1992
*F: Agriculture (planned for 1995); Economics
and Management Sciences; Science; Education;
Humanities and Social Sciences; Law; Curriculum
Group of Management and Administration;
Medical and Health Sciences.*
*Ce: Visual and Perfoming Arts; External
Studies; Computing; Multidisciplinary Research.*

NATIONAL ACADEMIC BODIES

Ministry of Education and Culture
Private Bag 13186, Windhoek 9000
Tel: +264(61) 223-489
Fax: +264(61) 228-641
Minister: Nahas Angula

Namibia National Commission for Unesco
Ministry of Education and Culture, Private Bag
13186, Trosky Building, Windhoek 9000
Tel: +264(61) 29-33-127
Fax: +264(61) 231-037
Chairperson: Hon. Buddy Wentworth
Secretary-General: Ms. G. Tuli-Mevava
Nghiyoonanye

NEPAL

UNIVERSITIES

Mahendra Sanskrit University
Beljhundi, Dang
Tel: +977(1) 213-245
Rector: Puruswottam Bhattarai
Registrar: Madhav Raj Gautam
Founded: 1986
Sanskrit Studies.

*Tribhuvan University Kathmandu
[Tribhuvan Vishwavidyalaya Kathmandu]
Kirtipur, Kathmandu
Tel: +977(1) 225-433
Fax: +977(1) 226-964
Cable: Trivarsity
Vice-Chancellor: Kedar Bhakta Mathema
Registrar: Sudarshan Risal
Founded: 1958, 1971
*F: Humanities and Social Sciences;
Management and Public Administration; Law;
Education.*
*I: Science and Technology; Forestry;
Engineering; Agriculture and Animal Science;
Medicine.*
Research Ce: *Economic Development and
Administration (CEDA); Applied Science and
Technology (RECAST); Nepal and Asian Studies
(CNAS); Educational Innovation and Development
(CERID).*

NATIONAL ACADEMIC BODIES

Ministry of Education, Culture and Social Affairs
Kaiser Mahal, Kantipah, Kathmandu
Tel: +977(1) 418-782
Fax: +977(1) 412-460
Minister: Govinda Raj Joshi

Nepal National Commission for Unesco
Ministry of Education, Culture and Social Affairs,
Kaiser Mahal, Kantipah, Kathmandu
Tel: +977(1) 418-782
Fax: +977(1) 412-460
Cable: nepnatcom kathmandou
Chairman: Govinda Raj Joshi, Minister of
Education, Culture and Social Affairs
Secretary-General: Ishwar Prasad Upadhaya

NETHERLANDS

UNIVERSITIES AND UNIVERSITY INSTITUTIONS

Free University Amsterdam
[Vrije Universiteit Amsterdam]
P.O. Box 7161, 1007 MC Amsterdam
Tel: +31(20) 444-7777
Fax: +31(20) 444-5300
Telex: 11329 dpvvunl
Rector Magnificus: E. Boeker (1993-)
Administrative Director: D.M. Schut
Founded: 1880, 1905
*F: Theology; Law; Medicine; Dentistry;
Mathematics and Science; Arts; Economics and
Econometrics; Social Sciences; Philosophy; Earth
Sciences; Human Movement Sciences; Physics
and Astronomy; Chemistry; Biology; Psychology
and Pedagogics.*

*University of Amsterdam
[Universiteit van Amsterdam]
P.O.Box 19268, 1000 GG Amsterdam
Tel: +31(20) 525-2677
Fax: +31(20) 525-2136
E-Mail: hansdwđu.uva.nl
Telex: 16526 unasd nl
Rector Magnificus: P.W.M de Meijer (1988-96)
Secretary-General: R.H.T. Bleijerveld
Founded: 1632, 1876
*F: Theology; Law; Medicine; Mathematics and
Information Sciences; Letters; Economics and
Econometrics; Physics and Astronomy;
Chemistry; Biology; Psychology; Education;
Environmental Studies.*

Delft University of Technology
[Technische Universiteit Delft]
P.O. Box 5, 2600 AA Delft
Tel: +31(15) 789-111
Fax: +31(15) 786-522
Telex: 38151 butud nl
Rector Magnificus: P.A. Schenck (1988-)
Registrar: J.M. Bronneman
Founded: 1842, 1986
*F: Technical Mathematics and Informatics;
Philosophy and Technical Social Sciences; Civil
Engineering; Architecture, Urban Planning and
Housing; Mechanical Engineering and Marine
Technology; Mechanical Engineering; Chemical
Technology and Materials Science; Mining and
Petroleum Engineering; Applied Physics;
Aerospace Engineering; Industrial Design
Engineering; Geodetic Engineering.*
*I: Interfaculty Reactor; Delft Microelectronics
and Submicron Technology (DIMES).*

Eindhoven University of Technology
[Technische Universiteit Eindhoven]
Postbus 513, 5600 MB Eindhoven
Tel: +31(40) 479-111
Fax: +31(40) 445-187
Telex: 51163 tuehv nl.
Rector Magnificus: J.H. van Lint (1991-)
Secretary: H.P.J.M. Roumen
Founded: 1956, 1982
F: Philosophy and Social Sciences; Mathematics and Computer Sciences; Physics; Mechanical Engineering; Electrical Engineering; Chemical Engineering; Architecture, Building Construction, and Town Planning; Industrial Engineering.
I: Perception Research; Continuing Education; Eindhoven International (in preparation).
Ce: Computer.

University of Groningen
[Rijksuniversiteit Groningen]
Postbus 72, 9700 AB Groningen
Tel: +31(50) 639-111
Fax: +31(50) 635-380
Telex: 53410
President: E. Bleumink
Registrar: H.J.D. Bruins
Founded: 1614
F: Theology; Law; Medicine; Mathematics and Science; Arts; Economics; Social Sciences; Philosophy; Organization and Management; Spatial Sciences.
I: Nuclear Physics Accelerator; Astronomy; Biomolecular Sciences and Biotechnology; Clinical Cell Biology; Drugs Studies.
Ce: Materials Science; Ecological and Evolutionary Studies; Behavioural, Cognitive and Neuro Sciences; Traffic Research; Educational Research (Interuniversity); Law Administration and Society; Biomedical Technology; Classical, Oriental, Medieval, and Renaissance Studies; Theory and Methodology in the Social Sciences (Interuniversity).

*Institute of Social Studies The Hague
[Stichting Internationaal Instituut voor Sociale Studiën Den Haag]
Kortenaerkade 12, 2518 AX Den Haag
Tel: +31(70) 351-0100
Fax: +31(70) 354-9851
Telex: 31 491 nl
Cable: socinst
Rector: G. Lycklama À Nyeholt (1990-)
Managing Director: F. Koopman
Founded: 1952
D: Social Sciences; Research.

Open University Heerlen
[Open Universiteit Heerlen]
P.O. Box 2960, 6401 DL Heerlen
Tel: +31(45) 762-222
Fax: +31(45) 711-486
Telex: 56559
Rector: W.H. de Jen
Founded: 1982
F: Law; Economics; Business and Administration and Politics; Natural Sciences; Technology; Cultural Sciences; Social Sciences.

*Leiden University
[Rijksuniversiteit te Leiden]
P.O.Box 9500, 2300 RA Leiden
Tel: +31(71) 272-727
Fax: +31(71) 273-118
Telex: 39427 (burul nl)
President: C.P.C.M. Oomen
Secretary: W.L.C.H.M. van den Berg
Founded: 1575
F: Theology; Law; Medicine; Mathematical and Physical Sciences; Arts; Social Sciences; Philosophy; Pre- and Protohistory.
I: Radiopathology and Radiation Protection Research (Interuniversity).
Ce: Computer; Environmental Studies; Medical-Genetic of South-West Netherlands.

University of Limburg
[Rijksuniversiteit Limburg]
P.O. Box 616, 6200 MD Maastricht
Tel: +31(43) 882-222
Fax: (43) 252-195
Rector: H. Philipsen
Administrative Director: M.J.N. Verhulst-Bots
Founded: 1974, 1976
F: Medicine; Health Sciences; Law; Economics; General Sciences.
I: Coronary Diseases; Biomaterials (BIOPRIME) (in co-operation with Eindhoven Technical University); Innovation and Technology (MERIT); Transnational Juridical Studies (METRO).

*Catholic University of Nijmegen
[Katholieke Universiteit Nijmegen]
Comeniuslaan 4, P.O. Box 9102, 6500 HC Nijmegen
Tel: +31(80) 619-333
Fax: +31(80) 564-606
E-Mail: int.relationsüro.kun.nl (internet)
Telex: 48211 nm nl
Rector Magnificus: Theo J.M. Van Els (1990-)
Administrative Director: J.G.J.M Wennink
International Relations: J.G.J.M. Wennink
Founded: 1923
F: Theology; Literature and Arts; Law; Medicine; Mathematics and Informatics; Natural Sciences; Social Sciences; Philosophy; Administration and Policy Sciences.
Ce: Computer; Women's Studies.

*Erasmus University Rotterdam

[Erasmus Universiteit Rotterdam]
Burgemeester Oudlaan 50, Postbus 1738, 3000
DR Rotterdam
Tel: +31(10) 408-1111
Fax: +31(10) 452-0204
Telex: 24421
Rector: P.W.C. Akkermans (1993-)
Secretary: H.B. Patoir
Founded: 1973
F: Economics; Law; Medicine; Philosophy;
Social Sciences (Sub-Faculty); Societal History
and Study of the Arts (Sub-Faculty); Management.
S: Management.

*Catholic University of Tilburg

[Katholieke Universiteit Brabant te Tilburg]
P.O. 90153, 5000 LE Tilburg
Tel: +31(13) 669-111
Fax: +31(13) 663-019
Telex: 52426
Chancellor and Rector: L.F.W. de Klerk
Administrative Officer: J.J.A. van de Riet
International Relations: J.W.C.J.M. de Kort
Founded: 1927, 1938, 1963
F: Economics; Social and Behavioural Sciences;
Law; Philosophy; Arts; Theology.
I: Fiscal Research; Social Research;
Development Research; Economic Research;
Advanced Studies.
Ce: Economics Research.

University of Twente

[Universiteit Twente]
P.O. Box 217, 7500 AE Enschede
Tel: +31(53) 899-111
Fax: +31(53) 357-956
Telex: 44200
Rector: Th.J.A. Popma (1992-95)
Registrar: F.C. Verschoor
Founded: 1961, 1986
D: Philosophy of Science, Technology and
Society; Applied Mathematics; Mechanical
Engineering; Electrical Engineering; Management
Studies; Chemical Engineering; Applied Physics;
Public Administration; Applied Educational
Science; Computer Science.

*Utrecht University

[Universiteit te Utrecht]
Heidelberglaan 8, Postbus 80125, 3508 JC Utrecht
Tel: +31(30) 539-111
Fax: +31(30) 521-818
Telex: 40087
Rector Magnificus: J.A. van Ginkel (1990-)
Secretary: W. Kardux
Founded: 1636, 1992
F: Theology; Philosophy; Arts and Humanities;
Law; Social Sciences; Geographical Sciences;
Medicine; Veterinary Medicine; Mathematics and
Computer Science; Physics and Astronomy;
Chemistry; Pharmacy; Biology; Earth Sciences.
I: Theological and Religious Studies;
Netherlands Social and Economic Law Research;

Rudolf Magnus for Pharmacological Research;
Toxicology Research; Theoretical Physics;
Pharmaceutical Sciences; Language and Speech
Research (OTS); History and Culture Research
(OGC); Social Sciences (ISOR) (Interdisciplinary);
Geographical Research (IRO); Biomembrane
Research; Biophysical; Meteorology and Physical
Oceanography (IMOU); Developmental Biology;
Curriculum Development and Teacher Training
(IVLOS); Veterinarian Sciences.
Ce: Computer; Biomolecular Research (Bijvoet).

*Wageningen Agricultural University

[Landbouwuniversiteit Wageningen]
P.O.Box 9101, 6700 HB Wageningen
Tel: +31(8370) 88111
Fax: +31(8370) 84449
E-Mail: bg@rcl.wau.nl
Telex: 45854
Rector Magnificus: C.M. Karssen
Founded: 1876, 1918
F: Agricultural and Environmental Sciences.
I: Experimental Plant Sciences Research.
Ce: Climate Change Research; Environmental
Studies; International Courses.

OTHER INSTITUTIONS

Academie voor Eurythmie

Riouwstraat 1, 2585 GP 's-Gravenhage
Tel: +31(70) 355-0039
Fax: +31(70) 354-3330
Director: W. Barfod
Founded: 1986
Eurythmics.

Akademie Industriële Vormgeving Eindhoven

Postbus 2125, 5600 CC Eindhoven
Tel: +31(40) 122-425
Fax: +31(40) 126-015
President: J.L.Th.A. Lucassen
Founded: 1980
Industrial Design.

Agrarische Hogeschool Delft

Postbus 3190, 2601 DD Delft
Tel: +31(15) 150-215
Fax: +31(15) 150-299
President: Mrs. L.M.W. Pellaert
Administrative Officer: A. Boonekamp-Iterson
Founded: 1988
Agriculture.

Agrarische Hogeschool Den Bosch

Postbus 90108, 5200 MA 'S-Hertogenbosch
Tel: +31(73) 120-788
Fax: +31(73) 144-510
Director: A.F.Bomers
Founded: 1983
Agriculture.

AKI, Hogeschool voor Beeldend Kunstonderwÿs
Postbus 1440, 7500 BK Enschede
Tel: +31(53) 350-055
Fax: +31(53) 350-531
President: S. Huismans
Founded: 1980
Fine Arts.

Amsterdamse Hogeschool voor de Kunsten
Postbus 15079, 1001 MB Amsterdam
Tel: +31(20) 627-8232
Fax: +31(20) 622-9833
President: S.H. Piersma
Administrative Officer: P. de Haan
Founded: 1987
Architecture; Dance; Music; Museology; Theatre; Visual Arts (and Teacher Training).

Christelijke Agrarische Hogeschool
De Drieslag 1, 8251 JZ Dronten
Tel: +31(3210) 12824
Fax: +31(3210) 13040
President: G.W. van Dorp
Administrative Officer: A.J. Kok
Founded: 1986
Agriculture; Agriculture and Business Administration.

Christelÿke Hogeschool de Driestar
Postbus 368, 2800 AJ Gouda
Tel: +31(1820) 74700
Fax: +31(1820) 38449
Director: M. Houtman
Founded: 1980
Education.

Christelijke Hogeschool voor de Kunsten 'Constantijn Huygens'
Postbus 5012, 8260 GA Kampen
Tel: +31(5202) 95600
Fax: +31(5202) 95666
Director: E. Koenen
Founded: 1987
Drama; Music; Visual Arts (and Teacher Training).

Christelijke Hogeschool Noord-Nederland
Postbus 1298, 8900 CG Leeuwarden
Tel: +31(58) 330-330
Fax: +31(58) 330-401
President: H.E.Siegers
Administrative Officer: H. Bruins
Founded: 1987
Education; Hotel Management; Social Work.

Christelijke Hogeschool Rijn-Delfland
Postbus 64827, 2506 CE 's-Gravenhage
Tel: +31(70) 325-5637
Fax: +31(70) 368-3008
Director: A. van der Ende
Founded: 1987
Education; Social Work.

Christelijke Hogeschool De Vÿverberg-Felua
Postbus 80, 6710 BB Ede
Tel: +31(8380) 39750
Fax: +31(8380) 21396
President: M. Burggraaf
Founded: 1980
Education; Nursing; Social Work.

Christelijke Hogeschool Windesheim
Postbus 10090, 8000 GB Zwolle
Tel: +31(38) 699-911
Fax: +31(38) 659-277
President: R.A. Steenberger
Administrative Officer: E. Kuiper-van der Voorde
Founded: 1986
Economics and Business Administration; Education; Journalism; Nursing; Physical Education; Social Work; Technology.

Evangelische Hogeschool
Postbus 957, 3800 AZ Amersfoort
Tel: +31(33) 621-731
Fax: +31(33) 610-912
Director: J.A. van Delden
Founded: 1980
Journalism; Information.

Gerrit Rietveld Academie
F. Roeskestraat 96, 1076 ED Amsterdam
Tel: +31(20) 662-0406
Fax: +31(20) 673-2936
President: S.H. den Hartog
Founded: 1980
Visual Arts.

Gereformeerde Hogeschool voor Beroepsonderwijs
Postbus 10030, 8000 GA Zwolle
Tel: +31(38) 656-022
Fax: +31(38) 650-533
Director (Acting): J.Hoagland
Founded: 1980
Education; Nursing; Social Work.

Haagse Hogeschool
Postbus 13336, 2501 EH 's-Gravenhage
Tel: +31(70) 310-8888
Fax: +31(70) 365-2821
President: C. Boerman
Founded: 1987
Economics and Business; Economics, Business and Administration; Education; Home Economics; Laboratory Studies; Library Sciences; Nursing (and Teacher Training); Paramedicine; Physical Education; Social Work; Technology.

Hague Academy of International Law
Peace Palace Carnegieplein 2, 2517 KJ The Hague
Tel: +31(70) 346-9680
Telex: 32323 icj nl
Cable: acintlaw
International Law.

Hanzehogeschool, Hogeschool van Groningen

Postbus 30030, 9700 RM Groningen
Tel: +31(50) 684-684
Fax: +31(50) 138-924
President: B.J. den Ouden
Administrative Officer: F. Hoekman
Founded: 1986
*Economics and Business; Education;
Architecture; Home Economics; Music; Visual
Arts (and Teacher Training); Laboratory Studies;
Nautical Studies; Nursing (and Teacher
Training); Paramedicine; Social Work;
Technology.*

Hoger Onderwÿs Zuid Nederland, Hogeschool Eindhoven

Postbus 347, 5600 AH Eindhoven
Tel: +31(40) 605-911
Fax: +31(40) 444-242
President: J.M. Prins
Administrative Officer: J.M. de Kooning
Founded: 1986
*Economics and Business Administration;
Education; Drama; Laboratory Studies; Nursing;
Paramedicine; Social Work; Technology; Medical
Technology.*

Hoger Onderwÿs Zuid.Nederland Hogeschool Katholieke

Burg. Geuljanslaan 16, 6041 NB Roermond
Tel: +31(4750) 599-555
Fax: +31(4750) 17864
President: F.C.H. Slangen
Founded: 1990
*Education; Architecture; Dance; Music; Visual
Arts; Journalism; Physical Education; Social Work
(Roermond, Tilberg); Education ('s-
Hertogenbosch, Sittard).*

Hoger Onderwÿs Zuid-Nederland, Pedagogisch Technische Hogeschool

Postbus 826, 5600 AV Eindhoven
Tel: +31(40) 479-222
Fax: +31(40) 440-045
President: J.W.M.A. Houben
Founded: 1987
Education.

Hogeschool Alkmaar

Postbus 403, 1800 AK Alkmaar
Tel: +31(72) 183-456
Fax: +31(72) 183-666
President: G.M. van Wÿk
Administrative Officer: D. Holster
Founded: 1987
*Economics and Business Administration;
Education; Music; Laboratory Studies; Nursing;
Technology.*

Hogeschool van Amsterdam

Postbus 931, 1000 AX Amsterdam
Tel: +31(20) 570-2500
Fax: +31(20) 570-2510
President: S.M. Korteweg
Administrative Officer: M.H. ter Schegget
Founded: 1987
*Education; Library Science; Nautical Studies (and
Teacher Training); Nursing (and Teacher
Training); Paramedicine; Social Work;
Technology; Economics and Business
Administration.*

Hogeschool van Beeldende Kunsten, Muziek en Dans

Postbus 11670, 2502 AR 's-Gravenhage
Tel: +31(70) 381-4251
Fax: +31(70) 385-3941
President: C.M. Rehorst
Founded: 1990
Fine Art, Music and Dance.

Hogeschool Diedenoort

Postbus 203, 6700 AE Wageningen
Tel: +31(8370) 23200
Fax: +31(8370) 24200
President: F.J.M. Kalmthout
Administrative Officer: M.D.M Stadhouders
Founded: 1980
Home Economics.

Hogeschool Domstad, Katholicke Lerarenopleiding Basisonderwÿs

Postbus 2511, 3500 GM Utrecht
Tel: +31(30) 943-072
Fax: +31(30) 963-268
Director: P.M.M. Verleg
Founded: 1980
Teacher Training.

Hogeschool Drenthe

Postbus 2080, 7801 CB Emmen
Tel: +31(5910) 14080
Fax: +31(5910) 42882
President: W.M.van Beck
Administrative Officer: J.Janssen-Buÿs
Founded: 1987
*Economics and Business Administration;
Education; Laboratory Studies; Technology.*

Hogeschool voor Economie en Management

Postbus 2188, 3500 GD Utrecht
Tel: +31(30) 333-410
Fax: +31(30) 331-050
President: H. Noordhof
Administrative Officer: A.C. Kattekamp-Holten
Founded: 1980
Economic and Management.

Hogeschool voor Economisch en Administratief Onderwĳs Arnhem
Postbus 5171, 6802 ED Arnhem
Tel: +31(85) 539-111
Fax: +31(85) 455-660
President: J. de Koning
Administrative Officer: H.R. de Lange
Founded: 1980
Economic and Administration.

Hogeschool voor Economisch en Administratief Ond. Limburg
Postbus 5268, 6130 PG Sittard
Tel: +31(46) 510-641
Fax: +31(46) 529-180
President: L.J.A Heÿenrath
Founded: 1980
Economic and Administration.

Hogeschool voor Economische Studies Amsterdam
Postbus 295, 1000 Ag Amsterdam
Tel: +31(20) 523-6311
Fax: +31(20) 523-0077
President: W.A. Ysseldÿk
Administrative Officer: M.A.C van Dalen
Founded: 1980
Economic Studies.

Hogeschool for Economic Studies Rotterdam
[Hogeschool voor Economische Studies Rotterdam]
Postbus 4030, 3006 AA Rotterdam
Tel: +31(10) 452-4663
Fax: +31(10) 452-7051
President: J.W.L. Stubbe
Administrative Officer: J.G. Koehoorn
Founded: 1980
Economic Studies.

Hogeschool Edith Stein
M.A. de Ruyterstraat 3, 7556 CW Hengelo
Tel: +31(74) 916-286
Fax: +31(74) 916-779
Director: F.T. Beugens
Founded: 1980
Education.

Hogeschool Enschede
Postbus 70000, 7500 KB Enschede
Tel: +31(53) 871-111
Fax: +31(53) 350-588
President: A. Peters
Administrative Officer: G.H.A.M Lohuis
Founded: 1989
Economics and Business Administration; Education; Dance; Music; Nursing; Teacher Training; Paramedicine; Social Work; Technology.

Hogeschool Gelderland
Postbus 5375, 6802 AJ Arnhem
Tel: +31(85) 713-131
Fax: +31(85) 452-207
President: O.G. Brouwer
Administrative Officer: S.G.G. Markering
Founded: 1990
Education; Laboratory Studies; Paramedicine; Social Work; Technology.

Hogeschool Haarlem
Postbus 137, 2000 AC Haarlem
Tel: +31(23) 161-161
Fax: +31(23) 340-026
President: H. Vaessen
Administrative Officer: E. Meÿer
Founded: 1987
Economics and Business Administration; Education; Paramedicine; Social Work; Technology; Medical Technology.

Hogeschool Heerlen
Postbus 550, 6400 AN Heerlen
Tel: +31(45) 734-700
Fax: +31(45) 719-898
President: A.van Giessel
Administrative Officer: G.P.M.G. Kamps
Founded: 1987
Education; Home Economics; Laboratory Studies; Paramedicine; Technology.

Hogeschool 's-Hertogenbosch
Postbus 732, 5201 AS 's-Hertogenbosch
Tel: +31(73) 295-295
Fax: +31(73) 295-200
President: C.A.M.Tetteroo
Founded: 1987
Economics and Business Administration; Visual Arts; Social Work; Technology.

Hogeschool Holland
Postbus 261, 1110 AG Diemen
Tel: +31(20) 495-1111
Fax: +31(20) 699-4636
President: W.B. Rievelt
Administrative Officer: A.M. van Rossum
Founded: 1986
Economics and Business Administration; Education; Nursing and (Teacher Training).

Hogeschool De Horst, Opleiding voor Sociale Beroepen
Postbus 121, 3970 AC Driebergen
Tel: +31(3438) 15544
Fax: +31(3438) 15520
President: P. Beugels
Administrative Officer: de heer Ysseling
Founded: 1980
Social Work.

Hogeschool voor de Kunsten Arnhem
Onderlangs 9, 6812 CE Arnhem
Tel: +31(85) 535-635
Fax: +31(85) 535-678
Director: W.S. Hillenius
Founded: 1987
Architecture; Dance; Music; Theatre; Visual Arts Teacher Training.

Hogeschool voor de Kunsten Utrecht
Postbus 1520, 3500 BM Utrecht
Tel: +31(30) 332-256
Fax: +31(30) 332-096
President: B.Groenemeÿer
Administrative Officer: K.Devos
Founded: 1987
Drama; Music; Visual Arts (and Teacher Training).

Leidse Hogeschool
Gebouw Eurocentre, 6e verd, Plesmantaan 100, 2332 CB Leiden
Tel: +31(71) 171-121
Fax: +31(71) 154-041
President: A.J. Ouwerkerk
Founded: 1987
Education; Laboratory Studies; Nursing (and Teaching); Paramedicine; Social Work.

Hogeschool Maastricht
Postbus 414, 6200 AK Maastricht
Tel: +31(43) 466-600
Fax: +31(43) 466-609
President: J.J.T.E. Gÿsen
Administrative Officer: H.C.A.H. Delnooz
Founded: 1987
Hotel Management; Education; Architecture; Music; Theatre; Visual Arts (and Teacher Training); Library Science; Social Work; Translation.

Hogeschool Midden-Brabant
Postbus 1097, 5004 BB Tilburg
Tel: +31(13) 635-250
Fax: +31(13) 637-942
President: W.F.H Doors
Administrative Officer: J.C.de Jongh
Founded: 1987
Library Science; Technology.

Hogeschool of Central Netherlands
[Hogeschool Midden-Nederland]
Postbus 85150, 3508 AD Utrecht
Tel: +31(30) 585-300
Fax: +31(3) 521-562
President: H.A.P de Greef
Founded: 1987
Education; Journalism; Nursing (and Teaching); Paramedicine; Social Work.

Hogeschool voor Muziek en Theater Rotterdam
Pieter de Hoochweg 222, 3024 BJ Rotterdam
Tel: +31(10) 477-3750
Fax: +31(10) 476-8163
President: J. Floore
Administrative Officer: T.A.M.A. Bloemkolk
Founded: 1980
Music and Drama.

Hogeschool Nijmegen
Postbus 9029, 6500 JK Nijmegen
Tel: +31(80) 271-399
Fax: +31(80) 600-357
President: A.G.M. Mulder
Administrative Officer: W.J.van der Heÿden
Founded: 1987
Nursing; Nursing Teaching; Paramedicine; Social Work.

Hogeschool voor Opvoedkunst
Socrateslaan 22, A 3707 GL Zeist
Tel: (3404) 25463
Fax: (3404) 11440
Director: C.Eckart
Founded: 1980
Pedagogy.

Hogeschool Rotterdam en Omstreken
Postbus 25035, 3001 HA Rotterdam
Tel: +31(10) 436-1233
Fax: +31(10) 436-7033
President: C.D.J.Waal
Administrative Officer: H.A. Veenema
Founded: 1988
Education; Architecture; Visual Arts (and Teacher Training); Laboratory Studies; Nautical Studies; Nursing (and Teacher Training); Paramedicine; Social Work; Technology.

Hogeschool Sittard
Postbus 69, 6130 AB Sittard
Tel: +31(46) 591-212
Fax: +31(46) 513-941
President: W.G.J. Schmitz
Founded: 1987
Nursing; Social Work.

Hogeschool Utrecht
Postbus 573, 3500 AN Utrecht
Tel: +31(30) 308-108
Fax: +31(30) 333-073
President: G.L.E.M. Koopman
Founded: 1987
Economics and Business; Laboratory Studies; Nautical Studies; Technology.

Hogeschool Venlo
Postbus 141, 5900 AC Venlo
Tel: +31(77) 546-666
Fax: +31(77) 512-853
President: P.J.M. Thomeer
Founded: 1987
Economics and Business Administration; Education; Laboratory Studies; Technology.

Hogeschool West-Brabant
Postbus 90116, 4800 RA Breda
Tel: +31(76) 250-500
Fax: +31(76) 205-493
President(Acting): C. Datema
Administrative Assistant: A.M.J.M. Rijnen
Founded: 1986
*Economics and Business Administration;
Education; Visual Arts; Laboratory Studies;
Nursing (and Teacher Training); Paramedicine;
Social Work; Technology.*

Hogeschool Zeeland
Edisonweg 4, 4382 NW Vlissingen
Tel: +31(1184) 89000
Fax: +31(1184) 89200
President: A.P. van Antwerpen
Administrative Officer: F.J. Stols-Breure
Founded: 1987
*Economics and Business Administration;
Education; Laboratory Studies; Nursing;
Paramedicine; Technology.*

Hotelschool Den Haag, Hogeschool voor Bedrijfskunde
Brusselselaan 2, 2587 AH 's-Gravenhage
Tel: +31(70) 351-2481
Fax: +31(70) 351-2155
President: E.Th. Cassee
Administrative Officer: L.F. Uitzinger
Founded: 1980
Hotel Management.

Ichthus Hogeschool
Postbus 23145, 3001 KC Rotterdam
Tel: +31(10) 201-2880
Fax: +31(10) 411-5094
Director: J.A. Breur
Administrative Officer: R. Kleiker
Founded: 1987
*Economics and Business Administration;
Education; Social Work.*

Institute for Housing Studies
P.O. Box 20718, 3001 JA Rotterdam
Tel: +31(10) 402-1523
Telex: 24548 ihs nl
Founded: 1946
Housing Studies.

Interconfessionele PABO Amsterdam/Alkmaar
Postbus 90506, 1006 BM Amsterdam
Tel: +31(20) 613-7079
Director: J.F.J Verhallen
Founded: 1987
Education.

International Agricultural Centre
P.O. Box 88, 6700 AB Wageningen
Tel: +31(8370) 19040
Telex: 45888 intas nl
Founded: 1951
Agriculture.

Internationale Academie Fysiotherapie 'Thim van der Laan'
J.C. Maylaan 6, 3526 GV Utrecht
Tel: +31(30) 886-670
Fax: +31(30) 898-811
Director: T.F. van der Laan
Founded: 1991
Paramedicine.

Internationale Agrarische Hogeschool Larenstein
Postbus 9001, 6880 GB Velp
Tel: +31(85) 695-695
Fax: +31(85) 615-287
President: M.J. Hÿink
Founded: 1988
Agriculture.

International Institute for Aerospace Survey and Earth Sciences (ITC)
P.O. Box 6, 7500 Enschede
Tel: +31(53) 874-444
Telex: 44525 itc nl
Cable: aesur ensched
Founded: 1951
Aerospace Survey and Earth Science.

International Institute for Hydraulic and Environmental Engineering
P.O. Box 3015, 2601 DA Delft
Tel: +31(15) 783-648
Telex: 38099 ihe nl
Founded: 1957
Hydraulic and Environmental Engineering.

International Institute for Land Reclamation and Improvement
P.O. Box 45, 6700 AA Wageningen
Tel: +31(8370) 74-200
Telex: 45888 intas nl
Cable: intas, iac, wageningen
Founded: 1955
Land Reclamation and Improvement.

International Union of Local Authorities
P.O. 90646, 2509 LP The Hague
Tel: +31(70) 324-4032
Telex: 32504 inta iula
Cable: iula, the hague
Founded: 1964
Local Authorities Studies.

Iselinge Hogeschool voor Onderwÿsberoepen
Postbus 277, 7000 AG Doetinchem
Tel: +31(8340) 23406
Fax: +31(8340) 33990
Director: I.J.H. Rhebergen
Founded: 1980
Educational Training.

Katholieke PABO Zwolle
Ten Oeverstraat 68, 8012 EW Zwolle
Tel: +(38) 217-425
Fax: +31(38) 210-914
Director: A.J.M van de Velde
Founded: 1980
Education.

National Agricultural College Deventer
P.O. Box 7, 7400 AA Deventer
Tel: +31 22150
Telex: 49517 tgcon nl
Agriculture.

Nationale Hogeschool voor Toerisme en Verkeer
Grieglaan 4, 4837 CB Breda
Tel: +31(76) 659-312
Fax: +31(76) 100-069
President: P.C. Huilmand
Administrative Officer: W. van Straten
Founded: 1987
Tourism and Transport.

Netherlands International Institute for Management (RVB)
P.O. Box 143, 2600 AC Delft
Tel: +31(15) 569-394
Telex: 38323 rvb nl
Founded: 1955
Management.

Netherlands Universities Foundation for International Co-operation (NUFFIC)
P.O. Box 90734, 2509 LS The Hague
Tel: +31(70) 426-0260
Fax: +31(70) 426-0399
Telex: 33565 nufic nl
President: P.J.C. Van Dijk
Secretary: H.F. Vriesendorp
Founded: 1952
International Cooperation.

Nijenrode, The Netherlands School of Business
Straatweg 25, 3621 BG Breukelen
Tel: +31(3462) 912-111
Business.

Northern Hogeschool Leeuwarden
[Noordelijke Hogeschool Leeuwarden]
Postbus 63, 8900 AB Leeuwarden
Tel: +31(58) 961-555
Fax: +31(58) 131-021
President: F. Kuipers
Administrative Officer: A. Boudewÿn
Founded: 1987
*Economics and Business Administration;
Education; Drama; Music; Visual Arts; Laboratory
Studies; Nautical Studies; Nursing (and Teacher
Training); Paramedicine; Social Work;
Technology.*

PC Hogeschool Marnix Academie
Vogelsanglaan 1, 3571 ZM Utrecht
Tel: +31(30) 715-530
Fax: +31(30) 711-324
Director: P.F. Keus
Founded: 1980

Pedagogische Hogeschool 'De Kempel'
Deurnseweg 11, 5709 AH Helmond
Tel: +31(4920) 14400
Fax: +31(4920) 16360
Director: A.W. de Bruÿn
Founded: 1980
Pedagogy.

Pedagogische Hogeschool 'Hemelrijken'
Hemelrijken 106, A 5612 LH Eindhoven
Tel: +31(40) 436-507
Fax: (40) 461-880
President: F.C.M. Rokebrand
Founded: 1988
Pedagogy.

Philips' International Institute of Technological Studies
P.O. Box 218, 5600 MD Eindhoven
Tel: +31(40) 757-511
Founded: 1957
Technology Studies.

Radio Nederland Training Centre
P.O. Box 222, 1200 JG Hilversum
Tel: +31 16151
Telex: 43336 womr nl
Cable: mundivox hilversum

Rijkshogeschool IJselland
Postbus 501, 7400 AM Deventer
Tel: +31(5700) 36333
Fax: +31(5700) 25280
Director: A.C.M. van den Heuvel-Vis
Founded: 1986
*Economics and Business Administration;
Education; Home Economics; Library Science;
Nursing; Paramedicine; Social Work; Technology.*

RK Technische Hogeschool 'Rijswijk'
Lange Kleiweg 4, 2288 GK Rijswijk
Tel: +31(70) 340-1500
Fax: +31(70) 319-2406
Director: G.A.van Duÿse
Founded: 1980

Royal Tropical Institute Amsterdam
Mauritskade 63, 1092 AD Amsterdam
Tel: +31(20) 568-8477
Telex: 15080 kit nl
Cable: intropen amsterdam
Founded: 1960
Tropical Studies.

Stichting Amsterdamse Ballet Academie
Ferdinand Bolstraat 89, 1072 LD Amsterdam

STOAS Agrarische Pedagogische Hogeschool
Postbus 78, 6700 AB Wageningen
Tel: +31(8370) 23355
Fax: +31(8370) 24770
Director: H. van der Straten
Administrative Officer: J.A. Klop
Founded: 1988
Pedagogy.

Sweelinck Conservatorium Amsterdam
Postbus 78022, 1070 lp Amsterdam
Tel: +31(20) 664-7641
Fax: +31(20) 676-1506
Director: T. Hartsuiker
Founded: 1980
Music.

Van Hall Instituut
Postbus 1528, 8901 BV Leeuwarden
Tel: +31(58) 888-777
Fax: +31(58) 884-985
President: W.R. Simons
Founded: 1992
*Agriculture; Agriculture and Business
Administration; Agriculture and Food Technology.*

NATIONAL ACADEMIC BODIES

Netherlands Ministry of Education and Science, Department of University Education
[Ministerie van Onderwijs en Wetenschappen]
P.O. Box 25000, 2700 LZ Zoetermeer
Tel: +31(79) 531-911
Fax: +31(79) 531-953
Telex: 32636 minow nl

Association of Universities in the Netherlands
[Vereniging van Samenwerkende Nederlandse Universiteiten (VSNU)]
Postbus 19270, 3501 DG Utrecht
Tel: +31(30) 363-888
Fax: +31(30) 333-540
E-Mail: bestuur@vsnu nl
Chairman: W.C.M. van Lieshout
Director: F.E.H. van Eijkern

HBO-Raad Association of Dutch Polytechnics and Colleges
Prinsessegracht 21, Postbus 123, 2501 CC Den Hague
Tel: +31(70) 362-4951
Fax: +31(70) 365-5816

National Equivalence Information Centre NUFFIC
P.O. Box 90734, 2509 LS Den Haag
Tel: +31(70) 426-0260
Fax: +31(70) 426-0399
Telex: 33565 nufic nl

Netherlands Universities Foundation for International Co-operation (NUFFIC)
P.O. Box 90734, 2509 LS Den Haag
Tel: +31(70)426-0260
Fax: +31(70) 426-0399
President: P.J.C. van Dijk
Secretary: H.F. Vriesendorp
Founded: 1952

Rectors' Conference of the Netherlands
[Rectoren College]
P.O. Box 19270, 3501 DG Utrecht
Tel: +31(30) 363-888
Fax: +31(30) 333-540
Chairman: C. Datema
Secretary: Mona H.J. Coppens-Wijn
Founded: 1898

Netherlands National Commission for Unesco
Schenkkade 50, 2595 AR Den Haag
Tel: +31(70)364-4655
Fax: +31(70)364-9917
Telex: 32636 mino nl
Chairman: Gottfried J. Leibbrandt
Secretary-General: Dick Lageweg

NETHERLANDS ANTILLES

UNIVERSITIES

University of the Netherlands Antilles
[Universidat Nashonal di Antia Universiteit van de Nederlandse Antillen]
Jan Noorduynweg 111, P.O. Box 3059,
Willemstad, Curaçao
Tel: +599(9) 84422
Fax: +599(9) 85465
Telex: 1411 Una Na
Rector: V. Marcha
Secretaris: Harold F. Hollander
Founded: 1970, 1973, 1979
F: Law; Social Sciences and Economics; Engineering.
Ce: Computer.

NATIONAL ACADEMIC BODIES

Ministry of Education
Fort Amsterdam, Curaçao
Tel: +599(9) 630-481
Fax: +599(9) 613-770
Minister: Marta B. Dijkhoff

Netherlands Antilles National Commission for Unesco
Schouwburgweg 24-26, Curaçao
Tel: +599(9) 615-577
Fax: +599(9) 618-941
Chairman: Marta B. Dijkhoff, Minister of Education
Secretary-General: Frank Elstak

NEW CALEDONIA

UNIVERSITIES

University Centre of New Caledonia
[Centre universitaire de Nouvelle Calédonie]
B.P. 4477, Nouméa
Tel: +687 25-49-55
Fax: +687 25-48-29
Telex: 175
Directeur: M. Chauchat
Founded: 1987
D: Law; Humanities and Literature; Languages; Sciences; Biology.

OTHER INSTITUTIONS

Centre Régional Associé du C.N.A.M. (Centre des Arts et Métiers)
Chambre de Commerce et d'Industrie, de Nouvelle-Calédonie, 10, rue de Verdun, B.P. 3562, Nouméa
Tel: +687 28-37-07
Fax: +687 27-79-96
Founded: 1971

Institut Universitaire de Formation des Maîtres
Rue Georges Clémenceau, Noumea
Teacher Training.

NEW ZEALAND

UNIVERSITIES

*University of Auckland
Private Bag 92019, Auckland
Tel: +64(9) 373-7999
Fax: +64(9) 373-7407
Cable: university auckland
Vice-Chancellor: W.G.O. Carson (1995-)
Registrar: W.B. Nicoll
Founded: 1883
F: Architecture, Property and Planning; Arts; Commerce and Economics; Education; Engineering; Fine Arts; Medicine and Human Biology; Music; Science; Law.

University of Canterbury
Private Bag 4800, Christchurch
Tel: +64(3) 366-7001
Fax: +64(3) 384-2999
E-Mail: a.wildbore@regy.canterbuiy.ac.nz
Cable: university christchurch
Vice-Chancellor: A.D. Bronwnlie (1978-)
Registrar: A.W. Hayward
International Relations: A.C. Wildbore
Founded: 1873, 1957
F: Arts; Science; Engineering; Law; Commerce; Music and Fine Arts; Forestry.

Lincoln University
P.O. Box 94, Lincoln University, Canterbury
Tel: +64(3) 325-2811
Fax: +64(3) 325-2965
Vice-Chancellor: B.J. Ross (1985-)
Registrar: A.J. Sargison
International Relations: G. Ormandy
Founded: 1878, 1962, 1990
Goup: Animal and Veterinary Sciences.
D: Accounting and Valuation; Economics and Marketing; Entomology and Animal Ecology; Farm Management; Horticulture; Natural Resources Engineering; Parks, Recreation and Tourism; Plant Science; Soil Science; Wool Science; Landscape Architecture.
Ce: Computing and Biometrics; Mountain Lands; Molecular Biology; Resource Management; Maori Studies and Research.
Ut: Agribusiness and Economics Research; Plant Protection Research.

Massey University
Private Bag 11-222, Palmerston North
Tel: (6) 356-9099
Fax: (6) 350-5603
E-Mail: Datex: nz 30974 mas uni
Cable: massey university
Vice-Chancellor: T.N.M. Waters (1983-)
Assistant Vice-Chancellor and Registrar: W.J. Tither
Founded: 1963, 1964
F: Agriculture and Horticultural Sciences; Business Studies; Education; Humanities; Science; Social Sciences; Technology; Veterinary Sciences.
S: Aviation; Mathematical and Information Science.
I: Executive Development.

University of Otago
P.O. Box 56, Dunedin
Tel: +64(3) 479-1100
Fax: +64(3) 474-1607
Vice-Chancellor: G. Fogelberg (1994-)
Registrar: D.W. Girvan
International Relations: G. Parata
Founded: 1869
D: Commerce; Health Sciences; Humanities; Sciences.
L: Portobello Marine.

Victoria University of Wellington
P.O. Box 600, Wellington
Tel: +64(4) 472-1000
Fax: +64(4) 499-4601
E-Mail: registrar@vuw.ac.nz
Vice-Chancellor: L.C. Holborow (1987-)
Registrar: A.T.M. Neeson
International Relations: A.T.M. Neeson
Founded: 1899, 1962
F: Architecture; Arts; Commerce and Administration; Education; Law; Education; Science.

S: *Business and Government Management (Graduate).*
Ce: *Continuing Education; Antarctic Research; Industrial Relations; Stout Research; University Teaching Development; Building Performance Research.*
I: *Policy Studies; English Language; Criminology; Statistics and Operations Research.*
Ut: *Coastal Marine Research.*

University of Waikato
Private Bag 3105, Hamilton
Tel: +64(7) 856-2889
Fax: +64(7) 856-0135
E-Mail: username@waikato.ac.nz
Vice-Chancellor: B.C. Gould (1994-)
Assistant Vice-Chancellor and Registrar: J.J. Callaghan
International Relations: Director of Community and External Relations, D. Guy
Founded: 1964
S: *Humanities:; Computing and Mathematical Sciences; Law; Management Studies; Science and Technology; Social Sciences; Education.*
Ce: *Environmental and Resource Studies; Labour and Trade Union Studies; Maori Studies and Research; Science and Mathematics Education Research; Population Studies; Applied Statistics; Technology; Animal Behaviour and Welfare Research.*
I: *Language.*
Ut: *Antarctic Research; Thermophile and Microbial Biochemistry and Biotechnology.*

OTHER INSTITUTIONS

PUBLIC INSTITUTIONS

The Auckland Institute of Technology
Private Bag 92006, Auckland
Tel: +64(9) 307-9999
Fax: +64(9) 307-9983
E-Mail: jhinchcl@centre.ait.ac.nz
President: John Hinchcliff (1984-)
General Manager: J. Bakeman
Founded: 1895
F: *Commerce; Arts (City Campus); Maori Studies (City Campus); Science and Engineering (City Campus); Languages (City Campus); Health Studies (North Shore Campus).*

Ce: *International English; International Projects; Professional Development; Executive Education; External Studies.*

Central Institute of Technology
Somme Road, Heretaunga, Upper Hutt, Private Bag 39807, Wellington Mail Centre
Tel: +64(4) 527-6398
Fax: +64(4) 527-6359
E-Mail: postmastercommercial@cit.ac.nz
(1986-)
Registrar: R. Hamilton-Williams
Founded: 1960
F: *Engineering; Health Sciences; Information Technology; Health Sciences; Hospitality and Tourism Management; Management; Science.*

Centre for Higher Learning of Awanuiarangi
Apanui Education Centre, Domain Road, Private Bag, Whakatane
Tel: +64(7) 307-1467
Fax: +64(7) 307-1475
Chairperson, Establishemnt Committee: H.M. Mead (1992-)
Administrator (Acting): M. Te Pou
International Relations: Chairperson, Indigenous Studies Committee, R. Green
Founded: 1991
D: *Maori Studies; Indigenous Studies; Teacher Training; Maori Leadership; Iwi Development.*

Centre for Higher Learning of Ngati Raukawa, Ngatitoa and Te Atiawa Tribes
160 Tasman Road, P.O. Box 119, Otaki
Tel: +64(6) 364-5479
Fax: +64(6) 364-5415
Tumuaki: W. Winiata (1994-)
Administrator: H. Winiata
International Relations: Director, Maori Language Studies, P. Winiata
Founded: 1981
D: *Administration; Hapu Development; Language Studies; Matauranga Maori; Art and Design; Health Studies; Law and Philosophy.*

Christchurch Polytechnic
Coventry Street, P.O. Box 22-095, Christchurch 1
Tel: +64(3) 364-9015
Fax: +64(3) 364-9615
Director/Tumuaki: J.W. Scott (1994-97)
Associate Director: L. Brash
International Relations: Associate Director (International), R. Knowles
D: *Applied Business Management; Art and Design; Community Studies; Electrotechnology; Engineering; Food and Fashion; Languages; Media Studies; Nursing and Health Education; Office Technology and Travel; Science and Computing; Te Matautanga Maori; Building and Design.*

Manawatu Polytechnic

Centennial Drive, Private Bag 11-022, Palmerston North
Tel: +64(6) 356-7104
Fax: +64(6) 356-6110
Chief Executive: G.O. Moltzen (1980-)
Director, Corportate Services: P.L. McElroy
International Relations: Director, Programme Development, W.J. Korndörffer
Founded: 1971
F: Business; Community Arts and Social Sciences; Nursing and Health; Science and Industrial Technology.

Manukau Polytechnic

Newbury Street, P.O. Box 61-066, Otara, City of Manukau
Tel: +64(9) 274-6009
Fax: +64(9) 273-0701
Chief Executive: R.J. Willyams (1980-)
Director, Academic and Human Resources: E. Holmberg
International Relations: T. Reade
F: Arts; Business; Health Studies; Technology.

Nelson Polytechnic

P.O. Box 19, Nelson
Tel: +64(3) 546-9175
Fax: +64(3) 546-2440
E-Mail: jcretney@admin.nelpoly.ac.nz
Chief Executive: J.R. Cretney
Director, Corporate Services: Ms. E. Fijn
Founded: 1971

The Open Polytechnic of New Zealand

Wyndrum Avenue, Private Bag 31914, Lower Hutt.
Tel: +64(4) 566-6189
Fax: +64(4) 566-5633
E-Mail: butsho@mhs.topnz.ac.nz
Chief Executive/Principal: S. Butterfield (1989-)
Deputy Principal: P. Egan
International Relations: International Marketing Manager, J. Hawker
Founded: 1946
F: Commerce; General Studies; Technology.

Otago Polytechnic

Forth Street, Private Bag 1910, Dunedin
Tel: +64(3) 477-3014
Fax: +64(3) 477-5185
E-Mail: craigs@tekotago.ac.nz
Director: N. Idrus (1993-)
Registrar: C. Sargison
International Relations: Manager, International Education, H. Fleming

UNITEC Institute of Technology

Carrington Road, P.O. Box 92025, Auckland
Tel: +64(9) 849-4180
Fax: +64(9) 849-4375
Director: D.K. Armstrong
Technology.

The Waikato Polytechnic

Tristram Street, Private Bag HN 3036, Hamilton
Tel: +64(7) 834-8888
Fax: +64(7) 838-0707
Principal and Chief Executive Officer: P. Johnson (1982-)
Administration Manager: G. Gunn
Founded: 1968
S: Business; Communication Studies; Engineering and Primary Industries; Health Studies.

Wanganui Regional Community Polytechnic

Private Bag 3020, Wanganui
Tel: +64(6) 345-0997
Fax: +64(6) 345-2263
Chief Executive: S. Town (1994-)

Wellington Polytechnic

Wallace Street, Private Box 756, Wellington
Tel: +64(4) 385-0559
Fax: +64(4) 385-3868
Principal and Chief Executive Officer: R.W.F. Bubendorfer (1984-)
Executive Registrar: J. Oliver
International Relations: Executive Director, External Relations, P. Ashford
Founded: 1962
S: Business and Information Systems; Design; Engineering and Construction; Fashion and Food; Languages and Communication; Maori Studies; Nursing, Health and Environmental Science.

Whitecliffe College of Art and Design

136 Grafton Road, P.O. Box 8192, Symonds Street, Auckland
Tel: +64(9) 309-5970
Fax: +64(9) 302-2957
E-Mail: 100242.3101@compuserve.com
President: K. Wikiriwhi (1982-)
Dean of Faculty: J. Block
International Relations: Mrs. M. Pearce
Founded: 1982
Art and Design.

PRIVATE INSTITUTIONS

Asia Pacific International Institute (New Zealand) Ltd.

API Graduate School of Management, 303 Manukau Road, Epsom, P.O. Box 26-259, Auckland 3
Tel: +64(9) 631-0331
Fax: +64(9) 631-0330
President: H. Place (1994-)
Registrar: T. Munto-Keene
International Relations: G.H. Hines
Founded: 1989
Management (Graduate).

International Pacific College
57 Aokautere Drive, Private Bag 11-021,
Palmerston North
Tel: +64(6) 354-0922
Fax: +64(6) 354-0935
President/Chief Executive Officer: A. Ohtomo
(1993-)
Registrar: K. Gill
International Relations: K. Cunningham
Founded: 1990
*D: English as a Second Language; International
Relations; Information Systems; International
Business Studies; Japanese Studies;
Environmental Studies; Recreation Education.*

NATIONAL ACADEMIC BODIES

Department of Education
Government Buildings, Lambton Quay, Wellington
1
Tel: +64(4) 735-499
Cable: deped wellington

New Zealand Vice-Chancellors' Committee (NZVCC)
P.O. Box 11-915, Wellington
Tel: +64(4) 801-5086
Fax: +64(4) 801-5089
Chairman: B.J. Ross (1995-)
Executive Director: L.S. Taiaroa
Founded: 1962

The New Zealand Council for Educational Research (NZCER)
P.O. Box 3237, Wellington
Tel: +64(4) 3847939
Fax: +64(4) 3847933
E-Mail: anne.meade@vuw.ac.nz
Chair: C. Knight
Director: A. Meade
Founded: 1934

New Zealand Qualifications Authority
U-BIX Centre, 79 Taranaki STreet, P.O. Box 160,
Wellington 1
Tel: +64(4) 802-3000
Fax: +64(4) 802-3112
E-Mail: sarah@nzqa.govt.nz
Chief Executive: D. Hood (1990-)
Founded: 1990

New Zealand National Commission for Unesco
Ministry of Education, 45-47 Pipitea Street, P.O.
Box 1666, Wellington 1
Tel: +64(4) 499-1004
Fax: +64(4) 499-1090
Cable: unesco wellington
Chairperson: The Hon. Russell Marshall (1990-)
Secretary: ELizabeth L. Rose
Founded: 1947

NICARAGUA

UNIVERSITIES

*Central American University Managua
[Universidad Centroamericana Managua]
Apartado postal 69, Managua
Tel: +505(2) 70352
Fax: +505(2) 670106
E-Mail: ucanic@nicarao.apc.org
Rector: P. Xabier Gorostiaga, S.J. (1992-94)
Secretario General: Otilio Miranda, S.J.
Founded: 1960
*F: Business Administration; Law; Humanities;
Animal Husbandry and Agriculture; Foreign
Languages; Communication.
I: Foreign Commerce and Business
Management; Central American History
Research; Atlantic Coast Research; Nicaraguan
History Research.*

National University of Agriculture Managua
[Universidad Nacional Agraria]
Kilometro 12,5, Carretera Norte, Apartado postal
453, Managua
Tel: +505(2) 31619
Fax: +505(2) 31619
Rector: Noel E. Eumiga
Vice Rector: Elly Castellón
Founded: 1929, 1954
*F: Agronomy; Natural Resources and
Environment; Agricultural Education and Rural
Development; Animal Sciences.
D: Basic Sciences.*

National University of Engineering Managua
[Universidad Nacional de Ingeniería]
Apartado postal 5595, Managua
Tel: +505(2) 71650
Fax: +505(2) 673709
Rector: Edgar Herrera Zuñiga
Founded: 1983
*F: Basic Sciences; Construction Engineering
and Architecture; Industrial Engineering;
Technical Studies.*

National Autonomous University of Nicaragua
[Universidad Nacional Autónoma de Nicaragua
León]
León
Tel: +505 (311) 5013
Fax: +505 (311) 4970
Rector: Alejandro Serrrano Caldera
Founded: 1812, 1958
*F: Medicine; Dentistry; Chemistry Sciences;
Sciences; Law and Social Sciences; Education
Sciences.*

Polytechnical University of Nicaragua
[Universidad Politécnica de Nicaragua]
Apartado postal 3595, Managua
Tel: +505(2) 97740
Rector: Sergio Denis García Velásquez
Founded: 1968, 1976
S: Education; Administration, Commerce, and Finance; Nursing; Design; Statistics.

OTHER INSTITUTIONS

Escuela de Enfermería
Jinotepe-Carazo
Founded: 1984
Nursing.

Escuela de Enfermería
Puerto Cabezas
Founded: 1982
Nursing.

Escuela de Enfermería de la Trinidad
Estelí
Founded: 1982
Nursing.

Instituto Nacional Politécnico 'Ernest Thalmann'
Km. 47, salida carretera, a Nandaime, Jinotepe

Instituto Nacional Técnico Energético'Simón Bolívar'
Km. 7 carretera Norte 1 km. al Oeste, Managua
Energetics.

Instituto Nacional Técnico 'Heroes y Mártires'
Región Autónoma Atlántico Norte, Puerto Cabezas
Technical Studies.

Instituto Nacional Técnico Vocacional
Km. 8 carratera Norte 1 km. al Oeste, Managua
Vocational Technical Studies.

Instituto Politécnico 'La Salle'
Apartado postal 4, León
Tel: +505 2584
Founded: 1982

Instituto Técnico Aeronáutico
Managua
Founded: 1982
Aeronautical Technics.

Instituto Tecnológico Nacional
Salida Carretera a Malacatoya, Frente al Lago Cocibolca, Granada
Technology.

Instituto Tecnológico Nacional 'Cristóbal Colón'
Región Autónoma Atlántico Sur, Bluefields
Technology.

NATIONAL ACADEMIC BODIES

Ministry of Education
[Ministerio de Educación]
Managua
Tel: +505(2) 650-046
Fax: +505(2) 651-191
Minister: Humberto Belli Pereira

Nicaraguan Association of Institutions of Higher Education
[Asociación Nicaragüense de Instituciones de Educación Superior (ANIES)]
Universidad Nacional Autónoma de Nicaragua, León
Tel: +(505) 2612

Nicaragua National Commission for Unesco
Ministerio de Educación, Centro Cívico y Camilo Ortega Saavedraa, Managua
Tel: +505(2) 650-342
Fax: +505(2) 651-595
President: Humberto Belli Pereira, Minister of Education
Secretary-General: Juan Bautista Arrien Garcia

NIGER

UNIVERSITIES

Islamic University of Niger
[Université Islamique du Niger]
Say
Founded: 1987

University of Niamey
[Université de Niamey]
B.P. 237, Niamey
Tel: +227 732-713
Telex: 5258
Recteur: Yenivoyé Alhassané
Founded: 1971, 1973
F: Science; Letters and Human Sciences; Health Sciences; Agriculture and Animal Husbandry; Economics and Law; Education.
Research I: Mathematics; Human Sciences; Radioisotope.

OTHER INSTITUTIONS

Centre Agrhymet
Niamey

Ecole Africaine et Malgache de l'Aviation civile
B.P. 746, Niamey
Tel: +227 72-3661
Civil Aviation.

Ecole des Mines et de la Géologie
B.P. 732, Niamey
Tel: +227 733697/735100
Mining and Geology.

Ecole nationale d'Administration niveau supérieur
B.P. 542, Niamey
Tel: +227 72-2853
Administration.

Ecole nationale de la Santé publique niveau supérieur
B.P. 290, Niamey
Tel: +227 72-3001
Public Health.

NATIONAL ACADEMIC BODIES

Ministry of National Education
[Ministère de l'Education nationale]
B.P. 557, Niamey
Tel: +227 72-2620
Ministre: Garba Djibo

Nigerian National Commission for Unesco
[Commission nationale nigérienne pour l'Unesco]
Ministère de l'Education nationale, B.P. 557, Niamey
Tel: +227 72-2365
Telex: 5512 ni
Cable: mineducation niamey
Président: Garba Djibo, Minister of Education

NIGERIA

UNIVERSITIES AND TECHNICAL UNIVERSITIES

University of Agriculture of Abeokuta
P.M.B. 2240, Abeokuta, Ogun State
Tel: +234(39) 230-768
Fax: +234(39) 234-650
Telex: 24676
Cable: unaab ng
Vice-Chancellor: N.O. Adedipe
Registrar: C.A. Soboyejo
Founded: 1983, 1984, 1988
C: Agricultural Management, Rural Development, and Consumer Studies; Animal Science and Livestock Production; Environmental Resources Management; Natural Sciences and General Studies; Plant Science and Crop Production.

Ce: Research and Development; Agricultural Media Resources and Extension.

Abia State University
P.M.B. 2000, Uturu, Abia State
Tel: +234(88) 220330
Vice-Chancellor: G.M. Umezurike
Registrar: J.C. Ogike
Founded: 1981
C: Agriculture and Veterinary Medicine; Biological and Physical Sciences; Business Administration; Education.
F: Engineering and Environmental Studies; Humanities and Social Sciences; Legal Studies; Medicine and Health Sciences; Postgraduate Studies.
Ce: Igbo Studies.
I: Distance Education.

Abubakar Tafawa Balewa University of Technology
P.M.B. 0248, Bauchi, Bauchi State
Tel: +234(77) 42095
Vice-Chancellor: B.G. Bajoga
Registrar: M. Suleiman
Founded: 1980, 1988
S: Agriculture and Agricultural Technology; Engineering and Engineering Technology; Science and Scientific Education.
Ce: Industrial Studies; Computer.

University of Abuja
P.M.B. 117, Abuja, Federal Capital Territory
Tel: +234(9) 882 1380
Fax: +234(9) 882 1605
Cable: unibuja
Vice-Chancellor: I.B. Mohammed
Registrar (Acting): Mallam Y.H. Habi
Founded: 1988
F: Arts and Social Sciences; Education; Law; Science.

*Ahmadu Bello University
Zaria
Tel: +234 (69) 50691
Fax: +234 (69) 50022
Telex: 75244 con ng; 75241 zarabu ng
Cable: unibello, zaria
Vice-Chancellor: D.I. Saror (1991-)
Registrar (Acting): Alhaji Abdullahi Musa
Founded: 1962
F: Agriculture; Arts and Social Sciences; Education; Engineering; Environmental Design; Law; Medicine; Pharmaceutical Sciences; Science; Veterinary Medicine.
I: Education; Agricultural Research; Administration; Health.
S: Postgraduate; General and Remedial Studies.
Ce: Agricultural; Adult Education and Extension Services; Educational Technology; Islamic Legal Studies; Nigerian Cultural Studies; Energy Research and Training.

DIVISION OF AGRICULTURAL COLLEGES
Samaru, Zaria, Kaduna State
Tel: +234(69) 32581/5
Telex: 75252 wzza
Cable: unibello, zaria
Founded: 1971
Agriculture.

Federal University of Technology Akure
P.M.B. 704, Akure, Ondo State
Tel: +234(34) 200090-99
Fax: +234(34) 230450
Telex: 32492futatek ng
Cable: fedunitech, akure
Vice-Chancellor: A.A. Ilemobade
Registrar: B.A. Adebayo
Founded: 1991
*F: Agriculture and Agricultural Technology;
Engineering and Engineering Technology;
Environmental Technology; Science.*

Bayero University
P.M.B. 3011, Kano
Tel: +234(64) 666023
Telex: 77189 unibayero ng
Cable: unibayero, kano
Vice-Chancellor: M.S. Zahraddeen
Registrar: Y.A. Ibrahim
Founded: 1960, 1977
*F: Arts and Islamic Studies; Education; Law;
Medicine; Science; Social and Management
Sciences; Technology.*
S: General Studies.
Ce: Study of Nigerian Languages.

Bendel State University
P.M.B. 14, Ekpoma
Tel: +234(55) 98448
Telex: and
Cable: bendel varsity, ekpoma
Vice-Chancellor: A. Maduemezia
Registrar: E.A. Omonbude
Founded: 1981
*F: Arts and Social Sciences (Ekpoma);
Education (Abraka); Engineering and Technology
(Ekpoma); Environmental Design (Ekpoma); Law
(Ekpoma); Medical Sciences; Natural Sciences
(Ekpoma).*

ABRAKA CAMPUS
Tel: +234 54-66027
Founded: 1985

*University of Benin
Private Mail Bag 1154, Benin City
Tel: +234(52) 200250
Cable: uniben, benin
Vice-Chancellor: Grace A. Alele Williams
Registrar: R.A. Williams
Founded: 1970, 1972
*F: Agriculture; Arts; Education; Engineering;
Law; Science; Social Sciences.*
*S: Dentistry; Medicine; Pharmacy; Postgraduate
Studies.*
*I: Education; Public Administration and
Extension Services.*

University of Calabar
P.M.B. 1115, Calabar
Tel: +234 222-695
Telex: 65103 unical ng
Cable: unical, calabar
Vice-Chancellor: C.E. Effiong
Registrar: E.J. Akpan
Founded: 1975
*F: Agriculture; Arts; Education; Law; Science;
Social Sciences.*
*I: Education; Oceanography; Public Policy and
Administration.*
S: Graduate.

Enugu State University of Science and Technology
Independence Layout, P.M.B. 01660, Enugu
Tel: +234 331-244
Telex: 51440 asutech ng
Cable: unitech, enugu
Vice-Chancellor: J.O. Jonah
Registrar: F.C. Eze
Founded: 1991
*C: Engineering and Technology; Agricultural
Sciences (Abakaliki).*

*University of Ibadan
Ibadan
Tel: +234(22) 412668
Telex: campus 31128 ng
Cable: university ibadan
Vice-Chancellor: Allen Bankole Oladunmoye
Olukayode Oyediran
Registrar: I. Ekanem-Ita
Founded: 1948, 1962
*F: Agriculture and Forestry; Arts; Education;
Law; Pharmacy; Science; Social Sciences;
Technology; Veterinary Medicine.*
S: Postgraduate.
*C: Medicine; Basic Medicine Science; Clinic
Science and Dentistry.*
I: African Studies; Education; Child Health.

*University of Ilorin
P.M.B. 1515, Ilorin
Tel: ilorin (31)(main campus 221685-87)
Telex: 33144 unilon ng
Cable: unilorin
Vice-Chancellor: Adeoye Adeniyi
Registrar: A.O.A. Alao
Founded: 1975, 1977
*F: Agriculture; Arts; Business and Social
Sciences; Education; Engineering and
Technology; Health Sciences; Science.*
D: Postgraduate Studies.
Research I: Unilorin Sugar.

*University of Jos
P.M.B. 2084, Jos
Tel: +234(73) 53724
Telex: 81136 unijos ng
Cable: unijos, nigeria 2019
Vice-Chancellor: O.C. Onazim
Registrar (Acting): A.Y. Goshi
Founded: 1971, 1975

F: Arts; Education; Environmental Sciences;
Law; Medicine; Natural Sciences; Pharmaceutical
Sciences; Social Sciences.
S: Postgraduate Studies.
I: Education.

Lagos State University
Badagry Expressway, Ojo, P.M.B. 1087, Apapa,
Lagos
Tel: +234(1) 884096
Telex: 27899
Cable: lasu
Vice-Chancellor: Jadesola Akande
Registrar: J.A. Olusoga
Founded: 1983
F: Arts; Education; Engineering; Law; Science;
Social Sciences.

*University of Lagos
Lagos
Tel: +234(1) 821111
Fax: +234(1) 822644
Telex: 26983
Cable: university. lagos
Vice-Chancellor: N.O. Alao (1988-)
Registrar: A.A. Omotoso
Founded: 1962
F: Arts; Business Administration; Education;
Engineering; Environmental Sciences; Law;
Science; Social Sciences.
S: Postgraduate Studies; Basic Medical
Sciences; Clinical Sciences; Dentistry; Pharmacy.
C: Medicine.
Ce: Cultural Studies.
I: Correspondence and Open Studies; Child
Health and Primary Care; Education.

University of Maiduguri
P.M.B. 1069, Maiduguri, Borno State
Tel: +234(76) 231730
Telex: 82102 unimai ng
Cable: university maiduguri
Vice-Chancellor: N.M. Gadzama (1994-)
Founded: 1975
F: Agriculture; Arts; Education; Engineering;
Law; Science; Social and Management Studies;
Veterinary Medicine.
C: Medical Sciences.
S: Postgraduate.
D: General Studies.
P: Remedial Year; Diploma.
Ce: Arid Zone Studies; Trans-Saharan Studies.
Ut: Teacher Education.

University of Agriculture of Makurdi
P.M.B. 2373, Makurdi, Benue State
Tel: +234(44) 33205
Telex: 85304
Vice-Chancellor: F.S. Idachaba
Registrar: L.H.V. Tsumbu
Founded: 1988

C: Agricultural Economics and Extension;
Agricultural Engineering and Engineering
Technology; Agronomy; Animal Sciences and
Fisheries; Food Technology; Science, Agriculture
and Scientific Education.

Federal University of Technology Minna
P.M.B. 65, Minna
Tel: +234(66) 222397
Cable: futech minna
Vice-Chancellor: S.O. Adeyemi
Registrar: L.S. Ahmed
Founded: 1983
S: Agriculture and Agricultural Technology;
Engineering and Engineering Technology;
Environmental Technology; Science and Science
Education; Postgraduate.

*University of Nigeria
Nsukka, Anambra State
Tel: +234(42) 771911
Cable: nigersity nsukka
Vice-Chancellor: Oloka Udeala
Registrar: U.O. Umeh
Founded: 1960
F: Agriculture (Nsukka); Arts; Biological
Sciences; Business Administration (Enugu);
Education; Engineering; Environmental Studies;
Health Sciences and Technology; Law; Medical
Sciences and Dentistry; Pharmaceutical Sciences;
Physical Sciences; Social Sciences; Veterinary
Medicine.
S: Postgraduate Studies (Fac-based).
C: Medicine (Enugu).
I: African Studies (Hansberry); Education;
Development Studies.
D: Adult Education and Extramural Studies;
General Studies.
Ce: Rural Development and Cooperatives;
Energy Research and Development.

ENUGU CAMPUS
Enugu, Anambra State
Tel: +234 252-080
Cable: nigersity enugu

Obafemi Awolowo University
Ile-Ife
Tel: +234(36) 230290
Telex: 34261 oau ife nigeria
Cable: ifevarsity ile-ife, nigeria
Vice-Chancellor: T.A. Omole
Founded: 1961, 1987
F: Administration; Agriculture; Arts; Education;
Environmental Design and Management; Health
Sciences; Law; Pharmacy; Science; Social
Sciences; Technology.
S: Postgraduate.
I: Physical Education.

Ogun State University
P.M.B. 2002, Ago-Iwoye
Tel: +234(37) 390660
Cable: ogunvasity
Vice-Chancellor: T.O. Bamkole
Registrar: N.O. Sotoyinbo
Founded: 1982
F: Arts; Basic Medical Sciences; Clinic
Sciences; Education; Law; Science; Social and
Management Sciences.

*Ondo State University
P.M.B. 5363, Ado-Ekiti, Ondo State
Tel: +234(30) 240370
Cable: ondovarsity ado-ekiti
Vice-Chancellor: P.O. Bodunrin
Registrar: G.O. Adegbite
Founded: 1982, 1985
F: Arts; Education; Engineering; Science; Social
Sciences.

Federal University of Technology Owerri
P.M.B. 1526, Owerri, Imo State
Tel: +234(83) 230974
Cable: fedunitech, owerri
Vice-Chancellor: C.O.G. Obah
Registrar: T.I. Igwe
Founded: 1980
S: Agriculture and Agricultural Technology;
Engineering and Engineering Technology;
Management Technology; Postgraduate; Science.
Ce: Industrial Studies; Erosion Research;
Computer.

*University of Port Harcourt
P.M.B. 5323, Port Harcourt, Rivers State
Tel: +234(84) 334400
Telex: 61184 phuni ng
Cable: university pharcourt
Vice-Chancellor: K.A. Harrison
Registrar: O. Wonodi
Founded: 1975, 1977
F: Education; Engineering; Humanities;
Management Sciences; Sciences; Social
Sciences.
C: Health Sciences; Continuing Education.
S: Basic Studies.
I: Agricultural Research Development.
P: General Studies.

Rivers State University of Science and Technology
Private Mail Bag 5080, Port Harcourt
Tel: +234(84) 335823
Cable: riverstech port harcourt
Vice-Chancellor: A.I. Ahiauzu
Registrar: M.B. Mieyebo
Founded: 1980
F: Agriculture; Engineering; Environmental
Sciences; Law; Management Sciences; Science;
Technical and Scientific Education.
S: Postgraduate.

I: Agricultural Research and Training (Rivers);
Geosciences and Space Technology; Pollution
Studies; Foundation Studies.
Ce: Computer; Continuing Education.

Usmanu Danfodiyo University Sokoto
P.M.B. 2346, Sokoto
Tel: +234(60) 233221
Telex: 73134 udusok, nigeria
Cable: udusok, sokoto
Vice-Chancellor: A.A. Gwandu
Registrar: A. Usman
Founded: 1975, 1988
F: Agriculture; Arts and Islamic Studies;
Education and Extension Services; Law; Science;
Social Sciences and Administration; Veterinary
Science.
C: Health Sciences.
S: Postgraduate.

*University of Uyo
P.M.B. 1017, Uyo, Akwa Ibom State
Tel: +234(85) 202696
Fax: +234(85) 202694
Cable: Uniuyo
Vice-Chancellor: Fola Lasisi
Registrar: M.O. Dickson
Founded: 1983, 1991
F: Arts and Social Sciences; Education; Natural
and Applied Sciences; Agriculture; Business
Administration; Law; Social Sciences.
S: Postgraduate.
I: Education.
Ce: Development Studies; Cultural Studies.

Federal University of Technology Yola
P.M.B. 2076, Yola
Tel: +234(75) 25426
Vice-Chancellor: A.T. Sulaiman
Registrar (Acting): M. Aminu
Founded: 1981
S: Agriculture and Agricultural Technology;
Engineering and Engineering Technology;
Environmental Sciences; Science and
Technological Education.

OTHER INSTITUTIONS

Auchi Polytechnic
P.M.B. 13, Auchi, Bendel State
Tel: +234(57) 200-148
Founded: 1964

Benue Polytechnic Ugbokolo
Markurdi, Benue State
Founded: 1977

Calabar Polytechnic
P.M.B. 1110, Calabar, Cross River State
Tel: +234(87) 222-418
Founded: 1973

College of Arts, Science and Technology
Oko, Anambra State
Arts, Science and Trades.

College of Technology
P.M.B. 1036, Owerri, Imo State
Tel: +234(83) 230-974
Founded: 1975
Technology.

Federal Polytechnic
Ado-Ekiti, Ondo State
Tel: +234(34) 230-727
Founded: 1977

Federal Polytechnic
Bauchi State
Tel: +234(77) 42-562
Founded: 1977

Federal Polytechnic
Bida, Niger State
Tel: +234(66) 461-707
Founded: 1977

Federal Polytechnic
Idah, Benue State
Tel: +234 40
Founded: 1977

Federal Polytechnic
Ilaro, Ogun State
Tel: +234(39) 440-005
Founded: 1979

Federal Polytechnic
Mulsi, Gongola State
Founded: 1979

Federal Polytechnic
Nassarawa
Founded: 1982

Federal Polytechnic
Unwani Afikpo, Imo State
Tel: +234 54
Founded: 1982

Federal Polytechnic
Kaura Namoda, Sokoto State

Ibadan Polytechnic
P.M.B. 5063, Ibadan, Oyo State
Tel: +234(22) 410-255
Telex: 31222 polyib ng
Founded: 1960

Institute of Management and Technology
P.M.B. 1079, Enugu, Anambra State
Tel: +234 330-416
Founded: 1958
Management and Technology.

Kaduna Polytechnic
P.M.B. 2121, Kaduna, Kaduna State
Tel: +234(62) 211-551
Founded: 1968

Kano Institute of Higher Education
Kano State Polytechnic, P.M.B. 3481, Kano, Kano State
Founded: 1977

Katsina Polytechnic
P.M.B. 2052, Katsina, Kaduna State
Founded: 1973

Kwara State College of Technology
P.M.B. 1375, Ilorin, Kwara State
Tel: +234 221-441
Founded: 1972
Technology.

Lagos State College of Science and Technology
P.M.B. 1606, Ikeja, Lagos State
Tel: +234(1) 523-528
Founded: 1977
Science and Technology.

Murtala C.A.S. Technology
Makurdi, Benue State
Technology.

Ogun State Polytechnic
P.M.B. 2210, Abeokuta, Ogun State
Founded: 1978

Ondo State Polytechnic
Owo, Ondo State
Founded: 1980

Ozoro Polytechnic
Ozoro, Bendel State

Plateau State College of Technology
Barakin Ladi, P.M.B. 23, Jos, Plateau State
Technology.

Ramat Polytechnic
P.M.B. 1070, Maiduguri, Borno State
Tel: +234(76) 232-264
Founded: 1972

Sokoto State Polytechnic
P.M.B. 90, Birnin Kebbi, Sokoto State
Founded: 1976

The Polytechnic
Ogwashi-Uku, Bendel State

Yaba College of Technology
Yaba, Lagos State
Tel: +234(1) 800-160
Cable: tekinst
Founded: 1948
Technology.

NATIONAL ACADEMIC BODIES

Federal Ministry of Education, Science and Technology
Ahmadu Bellow Way, Victoria Island, Lagos
Tel: +234(1) 616-943
Fax: +234(1) 261-9904
Minister: Iyorchia Ayu

509

National Universities Commission
National Assembly Complex, Tafawa Balewa Square, Lagos
Tel: +234(1) 635-233
Founded: 1962

Committee of Vice-Chancellors
4 Idowu Taylor Street, Victoria Island, P.M.B. 12022, Lagos
Tel: +234(1) 612425/612465/611554
Telex: 23555 comvic ng
Cable: nivicom lagos
Chairman: Grace Alele Williams
Secretary: Henry Bandele Afolabi
Founded: 1962

National Standing Committee for the Evaluation of Foreign Qualifications
c/o Federal Ministry of Education, Science and Technology, Victoria Island, Lagos
Tel: +234(1) 12793

Nigerian National Commission for Unesco
Federal Ministry of Education, 14 Broad Street, 3rd Floor, PMB 2823, Lagos
Tel: +234(1) 263-6099
Fax: +234(1) 263-3104
Cable: seceducate lagos
President: Iyorchia Ayu, Minister of Education
Secretary-General: Y.M.O. Nwafor

NORWAY

UNIVERSITIES AND UNIVERSITY INSTITUTIONS

*University of Bergen
[Universitetet i Bergen]
Muséplass 1, 5020 Bergen
Tel: +47(55) 21-30-50
Fax: +47(55) 32-85-85
Telex: 42690 ubbnTeletex: 2421-441023 uibta
Rektor: Ole Didrik Lærum (1990-95)
Direktør: Kåre Rommetveit
Founded: 1948
F: Arts; Mathematics and Natural Sciences; Medicine; Social Sciences; Dentistry; Law; Psychology.
Ce: Development Studies; Environmental and Resource Studies; International Health; Middle East and Islamic Studies; Study of Science and Humanities.

*Norwegian College of Agriculture
[Norges landbrukshøgskole]
Box 5003, 1432 As
Tel: +47(2) 6494-75-00
Fax: +47(2) 6494-75-05
Telex: 77125 nihbi n
Rektor: Nils Kolstad
Directør: Kjell Ahsnis
Founded: 1859, 1972
D: Animal Husbandry; Food Technology; Mathematics and Natural Sciences; Plant

Production; Social Sciences; Agricultural Technology; Agricultural Vocational Education.
I: Forest Research; Plant Protection; Agricultural Engineering.

*Norwegian College of Economics and Business Administration
[Norges handelshøyskole]
Helleveien 30, 5035 Bergen-Sandviken
Tel: +47(55) 95-90-00
Fax: +47(55) 25-83-83
E-Mail: inf-ibmébet.nhh.no
Telex: 40642 nhh n
Rektor: Leif B. Methlie
Direktør: Geir Kjell Ardersland
Founded: 1936
D: Economics; General Studies; Extension.
Ce: Applied Research.

Norwegian College of Music
[Norges musikkhøgskole]
Postboks 5190, Majorstua, 0302 Oslo 3
Tel: +47(22) 46-40-55
Fax: +47(22) 46-70-74
Principal: Bjørn Boysen (1993-96)
Direktør: Sigmund Skrinde
Founded: 1973
Music.

Norwegian College of Veterinary Medicine
[Norges veterinærhøgskole]
Postboks 8146, DEP, 0033 Oslo 1
Tel: +47(22) 69-36-90
Fax: +47(22) 56-57-04
Rektor: Knut Karlberg (1993-95)
Direktør: Kjell Gjaevenes
Founded: 1935
Veterinary Medicine.

*Norwegian University of Sport and Physical Education
[Norges idrettshøgskole]
P.O. Box 40 Kringsjaa, 0807 Oslo 8
Tel: +(22) 18-56-00
Fax: +47(22) 23-42-20
Rektor: Per Wright (1993-96)
Secretary-General: Thor Volla
Founded: 1968
I: Sport; Biology and Sport Medicine; Social Sciences.

Oslo School of Architecture
[Arkitekthøgskolen i Oslo]
Postboks 6768, St. Olavsgt. 2-4, 0130 Oslo 1
Tel: +47(22) 20-83-16
Fax: +47(22) 11-19-70
Rektor: Odd Kjeld Østbye (1990-93)
Direktør: Inger Stray Lien
Founded: 1945, 1969
Architecture.

*University of Oslo
[Universitetet i Oslo]
P.O. 1072, 0316 Oslo
Tel: +47(22) 22-85-50-50
Fax: +47(22) 85-44-42
Telex: 72425 unios n
Cable: oslo 3
Rektor: Lucy Smith
Universitetsdirektør: Tor Saglie
International Relations: Sigrid Holtermann
Founded: 1811, 1939
*F: Theology; Law; Medicine; Liberal Arts;
Mathematics and Natural Sciences; Dentistry;
Social Sciences.*
D: Nursing.
Ce: Teacher Training and School Service.

*University of Tromsø
[Universitetet i Tromsø]
Breivika, 9037 Tromsø
Tel: +47(776) 44000
Fax: +47(776) 44760
Rektor: Ole D. Mjøs (1990-)
Direktør: Harald Overvaag
Founded: 1958
*S: Medicine; Law; Fisheries; Languages and
Literature.*
*I: Social Sciences; Biology and Geology;
Mathematics, Physics, and Chemistry;
Museology.*
D: Education.

*University of Trondheim
[Universitetet i Trondheim]
Kollegiet, Sverresqt. 15, 7000 Trondheim
Tel: +47(79) 59-50-00
Fax: +47(79) 59-68-93
Rektor: Karsten Jakobsen (1987-93)
Administrerende Direktør: Tor H. Johansen
Founded: 1968
I: Technology.
*C: Arts and Science; Museum of Natural History
and Archaeology.*
*D: Architecture; Mining and Metallurgy; Civil
Engineering; Mechanical Engineering; Electrical
and Computer Engineering; Chemistry; Physics
and Mathematics; Economics and Administration;
Naval Architecture and Marine Engineering.*
F: Arts; Sciences; Social Sciences.
I: Teacher Training.
D: Medicine; Archaeology; Natural History.

COLLEGE OF ARTS AND SCIENCE
[DEN ALLMENNVITENSKAPELIGE HOGSKOLEN]
7000 Trondheim
Founded: 1922
Arts and Science.

TECHNICAL UNIVERSITY
[NORGES TEKNISKE HOGSKOLE]
7000 Trondheim
Founded: 1900

OTHER INSTITUTIONS

PUBLIC INSTITUTIONS

Herens ingeniorhøgskole
Hvalsmoen, 3500 Honefoss
Engineering.

Høgskolen i Agder
Tordenskjoldsgt. 65, 4604 Kristiansand
Tel: +47(38) 07-95-00
Fax: +47(38) 07-95-01
Rektor: Knut Brautaseth
Høgskoledirektør: Oddvar Haugland
Founded: 1994
*C: Engineering; Nursing (Avendal); Nursing
(Kristiansand); Education (Kristiansand).*
Conservatory: Music.

Høgskolen i Akershus
Ringstabekkveien 105, 1340 Bekkestua
Tel: +47(67) 12-07-20
Fax: +47(67) 58-13-96
Rektor: Inger Johanne Nossum
Høgskoledirektør: Tor-Inge Dovland
Founded: 1994
*C: Welfare Nursing; Domestic Science
(Stabekk); Arts and Crafts Teaching (Blaker);
Vocational Subjects; Nursing (Lørenskog).*

Høgskolen i Ålesund
Fogd Greves vei 9, 6009 Alesund
Tel: +47(70) 13-74-30
Fax: +47(70) 13-74-48
Rektor: Per Ekelund
Høgskoledirektør: Oddvar Skarbø
Founded: 1994
*C: Fishery Technology (Møre og Romsdal);
Engineering (Møre og Romsdal); Nursing.*

Høgskolen i Bergen
Lars Hillesgt 34, 5008 Bergen
Tel: +47(55) 57-35-00
Fax: +47(55) 32-64-07
Rektor: Kari Blomi
Høgkoledirektør: Nils Maehle
Founded: 1994
*C: Social Work and Health Care Education;
Engineering; Education; Physiotherapy; Health
Care Education (Haukeland).*
Conservatory: Music.

Høgskolen i Bodø
8002 Bodø
Tel: +47(75) 51-72-00
Fax: +47(75) 51-74-57
Rektor: Inger-Johanne Pettersen
Founded: 1994
Education; Nursing (Nordland).

Høgskolen i Buskerud

Postboks 235, 3601 Kongsberg
Tel: +47(32) 86-95-00
Fax: +47(32) 86-95-16
Rektor: Widar Hvamb
Founded: 1994
*C: Nursing (Drammen); Engineering
(Kongsberg); Teachers of Commercial Subjects
(National).*

Høgskolen i Finnmark

Follumsvei, 9500 Alta
Tel: +47(78) 43-76-00
Fax: +47(78) 43-44-38
Rektor: Pål Markusson
Høgskoledirektør: Siri Margarethe Løksa
Founded: 1994
C: Education; Nursing.

Høgskolen i Gjøvik

Teknologiveien 22, 2800 Gjøvik
Tel: +47(61) 73548
Rektor: Fred Johansen
Høgskoledirektør: Johs. Kjosbakken
Founded: 1994
C: Engineering; Nursing (Oppland).

Høgskolen i Harstad

Postboks 2130 Kanebogen, 9401 Harstad
Tel: +47(77) 07-02-33
Fax: +47(77) 07-43-05
Rektor: Kristian Floer
Høgskoledirektør: Age Lamo
Founded: 1994

Høgskolen i Hedmark

2400 Elverum
Tel: +47(62) 42-99-00
Fax: +47(61) 17-06-07
Rektor: Kåre Rørhus
Høgskoledirektør: Berit Ramleth
Founded: 1994
C: Education; Education (Hamar); Nursing.

Høgskolen i Lillehammer

Postboks 1004, 2601 Lillehammer
Tel: +47(61) 28-80-00
Fax: +47(61) 26-07-50
Rector: Svein O. Haaland
Høgskoledirektør: Ivar Skeide
Founded: 1994

Høgskolen i Molde

Postboks 308, 6401 Molde
Tel: +47(71) 21-40-00
Fax: +47(71) 21-41-00
Rektor: Anders Dedekam
Høgskoledirektør: Kjell Bugge
Founded: 1994
C: Nursing.

Høgskolen i Narvik

Lodve Langegsgt 2, 8500 Narvik
Tel: +47(76) 94-41-30
Fax: +47(76) 94-57-26
Telex: 64446
Rektor: Ulf A. Halvorsen
Høgskoledirektør: Olav Soleng
Founded: 1994
C: Engineering; Nursing.

Høgskolen i Nesna

8700 Nesna
Tel: +47(75) 05-61-02
Fax: +47(75) 05-61-03
Rektor: Simon Bringeland
Founded: 1994
Education.

Høgskolen i Nord-Trøndelag

Pb.169, 7701 Steinkjer
Tel: +47(76) 81211
Rektor: Asbørjn Folkvord
Høgskoledirektør: Tor Frigaard

Høgskolen i Oslo

Wergelandsveien 27, 0167 Oslo
Tel: +47(22) 60-00-61
Fax: +47(22) 60-00-20
Rektor: Steinar Stjernø
Høgskoledirektør: Asulv Frøysnes
Founded: 1994
*C: Nursing; Nursing (Aker); Nursing (Ullevål);
Early Childhood Education; Public Administration
and Social Work; Journalism; Engineering;
Library and Information Science; Arts and Crafts
Teaching; Dispensing.*
Conservatory: Music (East Norwegian).

Høgskolen i Østfold

Remmen, 1783 Halden
Tel: +47(69) 18-07-11
Fax: +47(69) 18-44-45
Rektor: Gunnar Montelius
Høgskoledirektør: Wiktor Tvete
Founded: 1994
*C: Education; Engineering; Nursing; Welfare
Nursing.*

Sogn og Fjordane College

[Høgskolen i Sogn og Fjordane]
Postboks 133, 5801 Sogndal
Tel: +47(57) 67-60-00
Fax: (57) 67-61-00
Rektor: Jan Olav Fretland
Høgskoledirektør: Hans Jørgen Benningsbø
Founded: 1994
C: Education; Engineering; Nursing.

Høgskolen i Sør-Trøndelag College

7005 Trondheim
Tel: +47(73) 93-04-00
Fax: +47(73) 93-05-00
Rector: Ove Gustafsson
Høgsoledirektør: Torkill Løvli
Founded: 1994

C: Health Care Education; Engineering; Education; Economics and Business Administration; Social Work; Food and Drink Industry Techniques; Nursing.
Conservatory: Music.

Høgskolen i Stavanger
Postboks 2557, Ullandhaug, 4004 Stavanger
Tel: +47(51) 88-75-70
Fax: +47(51) 88-75-74
Rektor: Erik Leif Eriksen
Founded: 1994
C: Hotel Management; Social Work; Education; Nursing.
Conservatory: Music (Rogaland).

Høgskolen Stord/Augesund
5414 Rommetveit
Tel: +47(53) 49-13-00
Fax: +47(53) 41-04-77
Rektor: Torodd Lokna
Høgskoledivektør: Arild Karlsen
Founded: 1994
C: Nursing; Safety Engineering; Education.

Høgskolen i Telemark
Kjolnes ring 56, 3914 Porsgrunn
Tel: +47(35) 57-50-00
Fax: +47(35) 55-75-47
Rektor: Olav Hesjedal
Høgskoledirektør: Nils Røttingen
Founded: 1994
C: Engineering; Education; Nursing.

Høogskolen i Tromsø
9005 Tromsø
Tel: +47(77) 65-54-66
Fax: +47(77) 68-99-56
Rektor: Lisbeth Halse Ytreberg
Høgskoledirektør: Bjørn Skancke Hanssen
Founded: 1994
C: Education; Health Care Education; Maritime Studies.
Conservatory: Music (North Norwegian).

Høgskolen i Vestfold
Pb. 500, 3193 Horten
Tel: +47(33) 08-26-00
Fax: +47(33) 08-29-71
Rektor: Ingeborg Tveter Thoresen
Høgskoledirektør: Olav Refsdal
Founded: 1994
C: Education; Nursing.

Høgskolen i Volda
Postboks 500, 6101 Volda
Tel: +47(70) 07-51-00
Fax: +47(70) 07-50-51
Rektor: Sverre Måseidvåg
Høgskoledirektør: Jan Driveklepp
Founded: 1994
Education.

Samisk hogskole/Sami allaskuvla
Postboks 10, 9520 Kautokeino
Tel: +47(78) 48-68-88
Fax: +47(78) 48-68-78
Rektor: Jan Henry Keskitalo
Høgskoledirektor: Aslak Nils Sara
Founded: 1994

Statens balletthøgskole
Tjuvholmen Bygning B, 0250 Oslo 2
Tel: +47(22) 83-25-81
Fax: +47(22) 83-70-19
Rektor: Anne Borg (1991-95)
Founded: 1964
Ballet.

Statens håndverks-og kunstindustriskole
Ullevålsveien 5, 0165 Oslo 1
Tel: +47(22) 20-12-35
Fax: +47(22) 11-14-96
Rektor: Roar Høyland (1991-95)
Høgskoledirektør: Tor Dahlien
Founded: 1818
Handcrafts and Industrial Arts.

Statens høgskole for kunsthåndverk og design i Bergen
Stromsgt. 1, 5015 Bergen
Tel: +47(5) 31-22-14
Fax: +47(5) 32-67-56
Rektor: Nils Eger (1993-96)
Høgskoledirektør: Osmud Larsen
Art and Design.

Statens kunstakademi
St. Olavsgt. 12, 0166 Oslo 1
Tel: +47(22) 20-01-50
Fax: +47(22) 20-05-73
Rektor: Nils Ake Pettersson
Arts.

Statens operahøgskole
Tjuvholmen Bygning B, 0250 Oslo 2
Tel: +47(22) 83-23-77
Fax: +47(22) 83-70-19
Rektor: Kresimir Sipusch (1990-94)
Opera.

Statens teaterhøgskole
Vika, Postboks 1509, 0117 Oslo 1
Tel: +47(22) 83-00-10
Rektor: Sverre Rødahl (1992-96)
Theatre.

PRIVATE INSTITUTIONS

Bergen arkitektskole
Postboks 2650, 5026 Bergen
Tel: +47(55) 31-46-92
Fax: +47(55) 31-91-05
Architecture.

BI Stittelsen
Postboks 580, 1301 Sandvika
Tel: +47(67) 57-05-00
Fax: +47(67) 57-05-70

Diakonhjemets høgskolesenter
Postboks 184, Vindern, 0319 Oslo
Tel: +47(22) 45-19-45
Fax: +47(22) 45-19-50

Dronning Mauds Minne, Høgskole for for skolelarerutdanning
Th. Owesensgt. 18, 7044 Trondheim
Tel: +47(73) 51-24-77
Fax: +47(73) 51-24-87
Teacher Training (pre-school level).

Misjonshøgskolen
Misjonsveien 34, 4024 Stavanger
Tel: +47(51) 51-62-10
Fax: +47(51) 51-62-25
Founded: 1843

Norsk ljrerakademi for kristendomsstu dium og pedagogikk
Amalie Skrams vei 3, 5053 Bergen
Tel: +47(55) 32-56-50
Fax: +47(55) 31-02-57

Den norske Eurytmihøyskole
1512 Moss
Tel: +47(69) 27-39-45

Det Teologiske Menighetsfakultet
Gydas vei 4, 0363 Oslo
Tel: +47(22) 46-79-00
Fax: +47(22) 69-18-90
Founded: 1908
Theology.

NATIONAL ACADEMIC BODIES

The Royal Norwegian Ministry of Education, Research and Church Affairs
[Kirke, utdannings- og forskningsdepartementet]
Akersgt 42, P.O. Box 8119 Dep., 0032 Oslo
Tel: +47(22) 34-90-90
Fax: +47(22) 34-05-40
Telex: 17241 nsbp n
Minister: Gudmund Hernes

The Norwegian Council of Universities
[Det norske universitetsråd]
Harald Haarfagresgate 17, 5007 Bergen
Tel: +47(55) 90-27-37
Fax: +47(55) 90-27-48
Chairman: Inge Lonning
Secretary-General: Per Nyborg
Founded: 1977

Norwegian National Commission for Unesco
Klingenberggatan 5, P.O. Box 1507, Vika, 0117 Oslo 1
Tel: +47(22) 83-30-56
Fax: +47(22) 83-16-89
Telex: 71004
Cable: norunesco oslo
President: Ingrid Eide
Secretary-General: Mari Hareide

OMAN

UNIVERSITIES

*Sultan Qaboos University
Al Khoudh, P.O. Box 32500, Muscat
Tel: +968 513-333
Fax: +968 513-254
Telex: 5602 squ on
Cable: jam'iah
Vice-Chancellor: Yahya bin Mahfoudh Al-Mantheri
Secretary-General: Hammad H. Al-Ghafri
Founded: 1980
C: Education and Islamic Sciences; Engineering; Science; Agriculture; Medicine; Arts.
Ce: Computer; Language; Islamic Research; Education Research.

NATIONAL ACADEMIC BODIES

Ministry of Education
Muscat
Tel: +968 513-333
Fax: +968 513-413
Telex: 3369 tarbia on
Minister: Sayyid Soud Ibrahim bin Soud Al-Busaidi

Oman National Commission for Unesco
Ministry of Education, Muscat
Tel: +968 704-852
Fax: +968 705-659
Telex: 3369
Chairman: Sayyid Soud Ibrahim bin Soud Al-Busaidi, Minister of Education
Secretary-General: Ali Saleh Al-Mejainy

PAKISTAN

UNIVERSITIES AND TECHNICAL UNIVERSITIES

PUBLIC INSTITUTIONS

*Allama Iqbal Open University
Sector H-8, Islamabad
Tel: +92(51) 854-372
Fax: +92(51) 853-154
Cable: openuniversity, islamabad
Vice-Chancellor: Javed Iqbal Syed
Registrar: Hafeez Ullah
Founded: 1974, 1977

F: Basic and Applied Sciences; Education; Social Sciences and Humanities.
I: Educational Technology.
Ce: Research and Evaluation; Computer.

Azad Jammu and Kashmir University

Muzaffarabad, Azad Kashmir
Tel: +92(58) 4444
Fax: +92(58) 4717
Cable: university muzaffarabad
Vice-Chancellor: M. Sarwar Abbasi
Registrar: R. M. Azad Khan
Founded: 1980
F: Administrative Sciences; Agriculture; Arts; Engineering; Home Economics; Science; Textile Design.
I: Kashmir Studies; Islamic Studies; Geology.
Ce: Computer.

UNIVERSITY COLLEGE OF ADMINISTRATIVE SCIENCES
Kotli
Tel: +92 4067
Dean: Abdul Aziz Qureshi
Administration.

UNIVERSITY COLLEGE OF AGRICULTURE
Rawalakot
Tel: +92 2686
Dean: Fasahat Ali Khan
Agriculture.

UNIVERSITY COLLEGE OF ENGINEERING AND TECHNOLOGY
Mirpur
Dean: Manzoor Hussain
Engineering.

UNIVERSITY COLLEGE OF HOME ECONOMICS
Moirpur
Tel: +92 3681
Dean: Saeeda Jehan Ara Shah
Home Economics.

UNIVERSITY COLLEGE OF TEXTILE DESIGNING
Muzaffarabad
Tel: +92 2748
Dean: Zainab Butt Khan
Textile Designing.

Bahauddin Zakariya University

Multan, Punjab 60800
Tel: +92(61) 520-101
Fax: +92(61) 521-165
Cable: univzakaria
Vice-Chancellor: Khwaja Imtiaz Ali (1990-)
Registrar: M. Zafarullah
Founded: 1975, 1979
F: Arts and Social Sciences; Islamic Studies and Languages; Law, Commerce and Business Administration; Medicine, Dentistry, and Pharmacy; Science, Engineering, and Agriculture.
U: Agriculture.
C: Law (Gilani).

COLLEGE OF ENGINEERING AND TECHNOLOGY
Multan
Engineering.

University of Baluchistan

Sariab Road, Quetta, Baluchistan
Tel: +92(81) 440-323
Fax: +92(81) 440323
Cable: baluchistan university quetta
Vice-Chancellor: D.K. Riaz Baluch
Registrar: M.K. Bugti
Founded: 1970
F: Arts; Sciences; Pedgagogy.
D: Administrative Sciences; Botany; Chemistry; Commerce; Economics; Education; English; Fine Arts; Geography; Geology; History; International Relations; Islamic Studies; Library Science; Mass Communication; Mathematics; Pharmacy; Philosophy; Physics; Political Science; Psychology; Social Work; Sociology; Statistics; Urdu; Zoology.
I: Biochemistry.
Ce: English Language.

University of Agriculture, Faisalabad

Faisalabad, Punjab
Tel: (411) 259-1119
Fax: (411) 27846
Cable: agriversity, faisalabad
Vice-Chancellor: M. Rafiq Khan
Registrar: M. Akram
Founded: 1909, 1961
F: Agricultural Economics and Rural Sociology; Agricultural Engineering and Technology; Agriculture; Animal Husbandry; Sciences; Veterinary Science.

BARANI AGRICULTURAL COLLEGE
Rawalpindi
Agriculture.

COLLEGE OF VETERINARY SCIENCES
Lahore
Tel: +92(42) 259-11
Fax: +92(42) 278-46
Dean: Ala-ud-din
Veterinary Sciences.

PAKISTAN MEN'S CO-OPERATION TRAINING RESEARCH INSTITUTE
Chak-Faiz, Multan

Gomal University

Dera Ismail Khan, North West Frontier Province
Tel: +92(529) 9200
Fax: +92(529) 4673
Cable: university campus d.i. khan
Vice-Chancellor: M. I. Khattak
Registrar: Nawabzada Khan
Founded: 1974
F: Agriculture; Arts; Pharmacy; Sciences.

COLLEGE OF AGRICULTURE
Founded: 1980
Agriculture.

COLLEGE OF COMMERCE
Der Ismail Khan, North West Frontier Province
Tel: +92(529) 3772
Dean: M. Tariq Awan
Founded: 1974
Commerce.

UNIVERSITY LAW COLLEGE
Der Ismail Khan, North West Frontier Province
Tel: +92(529) 9258
Dean: Abdur Rashid
Founded: 1974
Law.

WENSAM COLLEGE
Der Ismail Khan, North West Frontier Province
Tel: +92(529) 3919
Dean: M. Akram Khan
Founded: 1979

Hamdard University

Madinat-al-Hikmat Muhammad Bin Qasim
Avenue, Karachi 74700
Tel: +92(21) 650-000
Fax: +92(21) 664-1766
Telex: 24529 hand pk
Founded: 1991
Education.

International Islamic University

P.O.B. 1243, Islamabad
Tel: +92(51) 850-751
Fax: +92(51) 853-360
Telex: 54068 iiu pk
Cable: al-jamia
President: H.H. Hassan
Vice-Presidents: A. Al-Assal; A.H. Siddiqui
Founded: 1980, 1985
*F: Arabic; Economics; Linguistics and
Languages; Shariah and Law.
I: Usul-ud-Din.*

Islamia University, Bahawalpur

Bahawalpur
Tel: +92(621) 80331
Fax: +92(621) 80372
Cable: islamia university
Vice-Chancellor: M.B. Sukhera (1993-)
Registrar: R.M. Arshad
Founded: 1975
*F: Science; Islamic Learning; Arts.
I: Desert Studies (Cholistan); Management
Sciences (in process of development).*

University of Karachi

University Road, Karachi 75270, Sindh
Tel: +92(21) 479-001
Fax: +92(21) 473-226
Cable: karachi university
Vice-Chancellor: A. Wahab
Registrar: S. Sikandar Mehdi
Founded: 1950
*F: Arts; Business Administration and
Commerce; Education; Islamic Studies; Law;
Medicine; Pharmacy; Science.*

*University of Engineering and Technology Lahore

Grand Trunk Road, Lahore 31, Punjab
Tel: +92(42) 339205
Fax: +92(42) 331875
Cable: univengtech lahore 31
Vice-Chancellor: Ikram ul Haq Dar
Registrar: M.A. Shah
Founded: 1950
*F: Architecture and Planning; Chemistry,
Mineral and Metallurgical Enginering; Civil
Engineering; Electrical Engineering; Mechanical
Enginering; Natural Sciences, Humanities, and
Islamic Studies.
I: Public Health Engineering and Research.*

University of Engineering and Technology

Taxila
Science and Technology.

Mehran University of Engineering and Technology Jamshoro

Jamshoro, Sind
Tel: +92 (221) 671-197
Fax: +92 (221) 671-633
Cable: muetjam
Vice-Chancellor: S.M.A. Shah (1993-)
Registrar: Nisar Ahmad Baloch
Founded: 1963, 1971
*Architecture and Town Planning; Natural
Sciences, Humanities, and Islamic Studies; Civil
Engineering.*

UNIVERSITY COLLEGE OF ENGINEERING AND TECHNOLOGY
Nawabshah
Tel: +92 2405
The Principal: Mahmood Memon
Engineering.

National University of Science and Technology

57 Margalla Road, Rawalpindi Canntt.
Fax: +92(51) 563-576
Rector: S.S. Hussain
Science and Technology.

N.E.D. University of Engineering and Technology Karachi

Karachi 75270
Tel: +92(21) 496-9261
Fax: +92(21) 496-1934
Cable: n.e.d. university of engineering and
technology, karachi
Vice-Chancellor: Muhammad Munir Hassan
Registrar: S. Ghulam Kadir Shah
Founded: 1922
*F: Engineering; Humanities, Architecture and
Planning; Science and Technology.*

North West Frontier Province Agricultural University
P.O. Pakistan Forest Institute, Peshawar, North West Frontier Province
Tel: +92(521) 402-309
Fax: +92(521) 840-147
Cable: agricultural university peshawar
Vice-Chancellor: S. Basit Ali Shah
Registrar: Ruhullah Khan
Founded: 1981
F: Animal Husbandry and Veterinary Sciences; Crop Production Sciences; Crop Protection Sciences; Nutritional Sciences; Rural Social Sciences.

North West Frontier Province University of Engineering and Technology
P.O.B. 814, Peshawar, North West Frontier Province
Tel: +92(521) 405-73
Fax: +92(521) 841-758
Telex: 52477 engup pk
Cable: nwfp university of engineering and technology, peshawar
Vice-Chancellor: Karim Khan
Registrar: Humayun Zia
Founded: 1980
F: Mining Engineering.
D: Civil Engineering; Mechanical Engineering; Electrical Engineering; Agricultural Engineering; Basic Sciences and Islamiat.
Board of Advanced Engineering Studies and Research.

University of Peshawar
Peshawar, North West Frontier Province
Tel: +92(521) 842-165
Fax: +92(521) 419-79
Cable: university peshawar
Vice-Chancellor: F.A. Durani
Registrar: Shakeel Ahmed
Founded: 1950
F: Arabic; Arts; Oriental Languages; Sciences; Islamic Studies; Medicine.

*University of the Punjab
Lahore, Punjab
Tel: +92(42) 354-4289
Fax: +92(42) 354-428
Cable: university lahore
Vice-Chancellor: Muhammad Safdar
Registrar: Muhammad Saad-ud-Din Butt
Founded: 1882
F: Arts; Commerce; Education; Engineering and Technology; Islamic and Oriental Learning; Pharmacy; Science; Medicine and Dentistry.
C: Commerce (Hailey); Oriental; University Law.
I: Business Administration; Chemical Engineering and Technology; Chemistry; Education and Research; Geology; Statistics.

HAILEY COLLEGE OF COMMERCE
Quaid-i-Azam
Tel: +92 586-3937
Principal: Nisar-ud-Din
Founded: 1927

ORIENTAL COLLEGE
Lahore
Tel: +92(42) 355-541
Chairman: Zulfiqar Ali Malik
Founded: 1970
Oriental Studies.

UNIVERSITY LAW COLLEGE
Quaid-i-Azam
Tel: +92 586-4213
Principal: M. A. Mannan
Founded: 1870
Law.

Quaid-I-Azam University Islamabad
P.O.B. 1090, Islamabad
Tel: +92(51) 214-801
Fax: +92(51) 821-397
Cable: quaid-i-azam university, islamabad
Vice-Chancellor: Nazir Romani
Registrar: A.F. Butt
Founded: 1965, 1976
F: Medicine; Natural Sciences; Social Sciences.
C: Computer.

Shah Abdul Latif University Khaipur
Khairpur, Sindh
Tel: +92(792) 449-13
Fax: +92(792) 3137
Cable: saluni
Vice-Chancellor: Abdul Hameed Memon
Registrar: Noorullah Malik
Founded: 1987
F: Science; Arts; Law; Sachal Chair; Women's Chair.
C: Indus Development and Research; Indus Script Research.

*University of Sindh
Jamshoro, Hyderabad 6, District Dadu, Sindh
Tel: +92(221) 671-2915
Fax: +92(221) 671-616
Cable: unisindh
Vice-Chancellor: G.A. Allana (1993-)
Registrar: M.S. Rajar
Founded: 1947
F: Arts; Commerce and Business Administration; Education; Islamic Studies; Law; Medicine; Natural Sciences; Social Sciences.

Sindh Agricultural University
Tandojam, District Hyderabad, Sindh 70060
Tel: +92(2233) 282
Fax: +92(2233) 654
Cable: sauni
Vice-Chancellor: Irshad Ali Soomro
Registrar: Mohammad Ali Chang
Founded: 1939, 1977

F: Agriculture and Social Sciences; Animal Husbandry and Veterinary Sciences; Agricultural Engineering; Crop Protection; Crop Production.
C: Z.A. Bhutto (Dokri).

PRIVATE INSTITUTIONS

Agha Khan University
Stadium Road, P.O. B. 3500, Karachi 74800
Tel: +92(21) 493-0051
Fax: +92(21) 493-4294
Telex: 23667 akhmc pk
President: Shams Kassen Lakha
Director-General: Levin Hilling
International Relations: Director, Professional Services, Nadeem M. Khan
Founded: 1983
F: Health Sciences.
Ce: Medical.

Lahore University of Management Sciences
103-C/2, Gulberg 111, Lahore 54660, Punjab
Tel: +92 581-1548
Fax: +92 572-2591
Telex: 44291 ums pk
Cable: legsba lahore
Vice-Chancellor: Syed Babar Ali
Senior Administrator/Treasurer: Pervez Hassan
Business Administration (Graduate).

NATIONAL ACADEMIC BODIES

Ministry of Education
Block 'D' Pakistan Secretariat, Islamabad
Tel: +92(51) 212-020
Fax: +92(51) 822-851
Mnister: Syed Khurshid Ahmad Shah

Vice-Chancellors' Committee of Pakistan
Allama Iqbal Open University, Sector H-8, Islamabad
Tel: +92(51) 854-897
Fax: +92(51) 853-154
Vice-Chancellor: Javed Iqbal Syed

Central Bureau of Education
Sector H9 Cultural Area, Islamabad
Tel: +92(51) 852-653
Director-General: Muhammad Qasim Mazhar

University Grants Commission
Sector H-9, Islamabad
Tel: +92(51) 851-862
Fax: +92(51) 256-057
Telex: 5591 ugc pk
Cable: unigrant
Chairman: Naseer A. Sheikh
Director-General: Hamayun Tajik
Founded: 1973

Pakistan National Commission for Unesco
Ministry of Education, 30 Unesco House, Sector H-8, Islamabad
Tel: +92(51) 857-730
Fax: +92(51) 855-561
Telex: 54424 pncu pk
Cable: education islamabad
Chairman: Syed Khurshid Amad Shah, Minister of Education
Secretary-General: Mian Abdul Qaseem

PALESTINE

UNIVERSITIES

*Al-Quds University/Jerusalem University
8 Nur Al-Din Street, East Jerusalem
Tel: (2) 274979
Fax: (2) 277166
President: Hatem I. Hussaini
Vice-President for Academic Affairs: Tawfiq Shakhshir
Founded: 1978, 1982
C: Sciences and Technology; Medical Professions and Nursing; Islamic Theology; Arts for Women.
Ce: Islamic Archaeology; Research and Development.

*An-Najah University
P.O. Box 7, Nablus (West Bank)
Tel: (53) 370042
Fax: (53) 377982
President: Bahjat Sabri
Registrar: Sadeq Anabtawi
Founded: 1977
F: Arts; Science; Economics and Administrative Sciences; Education; Engineering; Islamic Studies; Agriculture.
Ce: Rural Research.

*Bethlehem University
Rue des Frères, B.P. 9, Bethlehem (West Bank)
Tel: (2) 741241
Fax: (2) 744440
Telex: 26526 ndc il
President: Msgr. Raouf Najjar (1989-)
Vice-Chancellor: Ronald Gallagher, FSC
Founded: 1973
F: Arts; Science; Business Administration; Nursing; Education.
I: Hotel Management.

*Birzeit University
P.O. Box 14, Birzeit (West Bank)
Tel: (2) 957650
Fax: (2) 957656
E-Mail: baramkiirzeit.wariat.org
Telex: 23076 birzeit jo
President: Hanna Nasir (1972-)
Vice-President: Gabi Baramki
Founded: 1924, 1972

F: Arts; Science; Commerce and Economics; Engineering.
I: Archaeology (Palestinian).
D: Continuing Education.
P: Adult Literacy.
Ce: Community Health; Environmental and Occupational Health Sciences; Computer; Palestinian Research and Documentation.

Hebron University
[Jami'at Al Khalil]
P.O. Box 40, Hebron (West Bank)
Tel: (2) 963293
President: Khulqi Khanfar (1988-)
Founded: 1971, 1980
C: Islamic Law; Arts; Science; Agriculture.

Islamic University of Gaza
P.O. Box 108, Gaza
Tel: (51) 63554
President: M. Saker (1984-92)
Registrar: S. Salama
Founded: 1978
F: Arts; Sciences; Shari'a and Law; Daw'ao wa Usul al-Deen; Education; Commerce and Economics.

NATIONAL ACADEMIC BODIES

Palestinian Department of General and Higher Education
P.O. Box 926990, Amman, Jordan
Tel: 670113
Telex: 21411 al aqsa

PANAMA

UNIVERSITIES

Santa María La Antigua University Panamá
[Universidad Santa María La Antigua]
Apartado 6-1696, Estafeta El Dorado, Panamá 6
Tel: +507 361-868
Fax: +507 361-022
Rector: Stanley Muschett Ibarra
Secretario General: Narciso Arenas
Founded: 1965, 1973
D: Administration; Technology and Natural Sciences; Humanities, Religious Studies, and Social Sciences; Law and Political Science.
Ce: Promotion and Study of Urban Areas (CIPSU).

*University of Panamá
[Universidad de Panamá]
Ciudad Universitaria, Dr. Octavio Méndez Pereira, El Cangrejo-Estafeta Universitaria, Panamá 3
Tel: +507 636-133
Rector: Abdiel J. Adames (1987-)
Founded: 1935

F: Business Administration and Accountancy; Public Administration; Agriculture; Architecture; Natural Sciences and Pharmacy; Social Communication; Economics; Law and Political Science; Philosophy, Letters, and Education; Medicine; Dentistry.
I: Criminology Research; Earth Sciences; Education Administration Research.

University of Technology Panamá
[Universidad Tecnológica]
Panamá
Founded: 1984
F: Civil Engineering; Electrical Engineering; Mechanical Engineering; Computer Systems.
D: Natural and Social Sciences.

OTHER INSTITUTIONS

Escuela Náutica de Panamá
Apartado 5936, Panamá 2
Tel: +507 648-625
Maritime Studies.

Escuela Superior de Secretarias Ejecutivas Bilingües
Panamá
Founded: 1971
Executive Bilingual Secretarial Studies.

Instituto Superior de Enseñanza
Panamá
Founded: 1969
Teacher Training.

Instituto Superior de Turismo
Panamá
Founded: 1972
Tourism.

NATIONAL ACADEMIC BODIES

Ministry of Education
[Ministerio de Educación]
Apartado 2440, Panamá 3
Tel: +507 622-671
Fax: +507 629-087
Minister: Marco Antonio Alarcón

Panama National Commission for Cooperation with Unesco
[Comisión Nacional Panameña de Cooperación con la Unesco]
Ministerio de Educación, Apartado 2440, Panamá 3
Tel: +507 629-087
Cable: comision unesco mineduc panama
Presidente: Marco A. Alarcón, Minister of Education
Coordinadora: Etelvina Hernández

PAPUA NEW GUINEA

UNIVERSITIES

Papua New Guinea University of Technology
Private Mail Bag, Lae
Tel: +675(43) 4999
Fax: +675(45) 7667
Telex: ne42428
Cable: utech, lae
Vice-Chancellor: M. Baloiloi (1992-94)
Registrar: T. Chan
International Relations: Pro Vice-Chancellor, W.F. Tovirika
Founded: 1965, 1973
D: Accountancy and Business Administration; Agriculture; Architecture and Building; Civil Engineering; Electrical and Communications Studies; Mechanical Engineering; Mining Engineering; Forestry; Mathematics and Statistics; Applied Physics; Applied Sciences; Surveying and Land Studies; Language and Communication Studies.
C: Vudal University (Rabaul).

University of Papua New Guinea
P.O.Box 320
Tel: +675(26) 7200
Fax: +675(26) 7187
Telex: ne22366
Cable: university port moresby
Vice-Chancellor: J.T.W. Sukwianomb (1992-94)
Registrar: B. Naing
International Relations: Pro Vice-Chancellor, C. Nembou
Founded: 1966
F: Arts; Creative Arts; Education; Law; Medicine; Science; Health Sciences (Goroka).
I: Continuing and Distance Education; National Sports (Goroka).

OTHER INSTITUTIONS

Divine Word Institute
P.O. Box 483, Madang
Tel: +675(82) 2937
Fax: +675(82) 2812
President: J. Ommerborn, S.V.D. (1992-94)
Director of Academic Affairs/Registrar: R. Debrouwere
International Relations: J. Ommerborn, S.V.D., President
Founded: 1980
D: Business Studies; Communication Arts; Religious Studies; Liberal Arts.

Pacific Adventist College
Post Office, Private Mail Bag, Boroko, National Capital District
Tel: +675(28) 1112
Fax: +675(28) 1257
Principal: A.J. Sonter (1992-94)
Registrar: P.T. Alu
International Relations: W.J. Rieger, Academic Dean
Founded: 1984
D: Agriculture; Commerce; Education; Science and Mathematics; Theology; Extension Services.

NATIONAL ACADEMIC BODIES

Commission for Higher Education
P.O. Box 5117, Boroko
Fax: +675(25) 8386
Telex: 22193
Chairman: N. Tulaha (1991-98)
Deputy Chairman: R. San Mateo
Founded: 1983

Papua New Guinea National Commission for Unesco
Boroko
Tel: +675(27) 6111
Fax: +675(25) 4648
Telex: 22193 ne
Cable: eduoff moroko
Chairman: Jerry E. Tetaga
Director: Kila Ravusiro
Founded: 1982

PARAGUAY

UNIVERSITIES

Autonomous University of Paraguay
[Universidad Autónoma del Paraguay]
General Díaz y Colń, Asunción
Tel: +595(21) 441-924
Rector: Carlos Lahaye

Autonomous University of Asunción
[Universidad Autónoma de Asunción]
Oliva y Montevideo, Asunción
Tel: +595(21) 495-873
Rector: José de Jesús Ríos Torres

Catholic University
[Universidad Católica]
Independencia Nacional y Comuneros, Casilla 1718, Asunción
Tel: +595(21) 441-044
Fax: +595(21) 445-245
Rector: Juan Oscar Usher
Founded: 1960
F: Philosophy and Human Sciences; Law and Diplomatic Studies; Accountancy and Business Administration; Science and Technology; Science

and Letters (Villarrica, Encarnación, Concepción, Ciudad del Este, Pedro Juan Caballero).
I: Theology.
S: Nursing.

Columbian University of Paraguay
[Universidad Columbia del Paraguay]
Avenida España y Padre Cardozo, Asunción
Tel: +595(21) 490-813
Rector: Favio Rivas Araujo

Comunera University
[Universidad Comunera]
San José y Artigas, Asunción
Tel: +595(21) 23892
Rector: Adriano Irala Burgos

National University of Asunción
[Universidad Nacional de Asunción]
España 1098, Asunción
Tel: +595(21) 507-080
Rector: Luis H. Berganza
Founded: 1890, 1929
F: Law and Social Sciences; Philosophy; Medicine; Physics and Mathematics; Economics; Dentistry; Chemistry; Agriculture; Architecture; Veterinary Science; Polytechnic; Exact and Natural Sciences.
S: Library Science.
I: Social Work; Nursing, Midwifery, and Social Work; Geographical Sciences; Electronic Engineering; Languages.

National University of the East
[Universidad Nacional del Este]
Ciudad del Este, Alto Parana
Rector: Gilberto Ruiz Carballo

Private University of the East
[Universidad Privada del Este]
Ciudad Pte. Franco, Alto Parana
Tel: +595(61) 62898
Rector: Flores Faniña

University 'Americana'
[Universidad 'Americana']
Avenida Brasilia y Pte. 2do. Villamayor, 495, Asunción
Tel: +595(61) 291-633
Rector: Andrés Benko

University 'Bautista'
[Universidad 'Bautista']
Argentina y Pacheco, Asunción
Tel: +595(61) 600-121
Rector: Andrés Benko

University of the North
[Universidad del Norte]
22 de Septiembre y Mcal. Estigarribia, Asunción
Tel: +595(21) 201-024
Rector: Juan Manuel Marcos

OTHER INSTITUTIONS

Instituto Superior de Educación
Avenida Eusebio Ayala Km. 4.5, Asunción
Education.

NATIONAL ACADEMIC BODIES

Ministry of Education and Culture
[Ministerio de Educación y Culto]
Casilla de Correos 1080, Asunción
Tel: +595(21) 490-375
Fax: +595(21) 443-919
Ministro: Nicanor Duarte Frutos

Paraguay National Commission for Unesco
[Comisión Nacional Paraguaya de Cooperación con la Unesco]
Ministerio de Educación y Culto, Chile 864, Casilla de Correos 1080, Asunción
Tel: +595(21) 443-919
Fax: +595(21) 443-919
Cable: mineducation y culto chile 864 asuncion
President: Nicanor Duarte Frutos
Secretary-General: Basilia Miltos Arrúa

PERU

UNIVERSITIES AND TECHNICAL UNIVERSITIES

NATIONAL INSTITUTIONS

National University of 'San Cristóbal de Huamanga 'Ayacucho
[Universidad Nacional de 'San Cristóbal de Huamanga']
Portal Independencia 57, Apartado 120, Ayacucho, Ayacucho
Tel: +51 912-522
Fax: +51 912-510
Rector: Pedro Villena Hidalgo
Founded: 1677, 1959
P: Engineering; Social Sciences; Nursing and Midwifery; Education; Agriculture; Chemical Engineering; Mining Engineering; Law.

National University of Cajamarca
[Universidad Nacional de Cajamarca]
Correos Villa Universitaria, Cajamarca,
Cajamarca
Tel: +51(92) 2796
Fax: +51(92) 3356
Rector: César Paredes Canto (1989-94)
Vice-Rector Administrativo: Aurelio Martos Díaz
Founded: 1962
F: Agriculture and Forestry; Education;
Engineering; Health Sciences; Social Sciences;
Veterinary Medicine; Economics, Accountancy,
and Administration; Animal Husbandry.

National University of Callao
[Universidad Nacional del 'Callao']
Colina 310, Apartado 138, Callao, Callao
Tel: +51 96607
Rector: Nicanor Ninahuaman Mucha
Founded: 1966
P: Engineering; Accountancy; Economics.

National University of Central Peru
[Universidad Nacional del Centro del Perú]
Calle Real 160, Apartado 77, Huancayo, Junín
Tel: 233032
Telex: 6400 pe
Rector: Gustavo Ramírez Piza
Founded: 1959, 1961, 1969
P: Agriculture; Chemical Engineering; Forestry;
Animal Husbandry; Economics; Education and
Humanities; Social Services; Architecture;
Mechanical and Electrical Engineering; Food
Technology; Nursing; Administration; Electrical
Engineering; Metallurgical Engineering; Mining
Engineering; Sociology; Anthropology;
Accountancy.

National University 'Daniel Alcides Carrión' Cerro de Pasco
[Universidad Nacional 'Daniel Alcides Carrión'
Cerro de Pasco]
Edificio Estatal 4, Apartado 77, Cerro de Pasco,
Pasco
Tel: +51 2197
Rector: Norberto Gonzales Peralta
Founded: 1965, 1969
P: Education; Economics and Commerce;
Engineering; Animal Husbandry; Nursing;
Geology.

National University of Santa Chimboate
[Universidad Nacional de Santa]
Avenida Pacífico 508, Urb. Buenos Aires,
Chimbote, Ancash

National University of Education 'Enrique Guzmán y Valle' Chosica
[Universidad Nacional de Educación 'Enrique
Guzmán y Valle']
La Cantuta, Chosica, Lima
Tel: +51(14) 910052
Rector: Miliciades Hidalgo Cabrera
Founded: 1905, 1960

National University of San Antonio Abad Cuzco
[Universidad Nacional de San Antonio Abad]
Avenida de la Cultura s/n, Casilla 367-167,
Cuzco, Cuzco
Tel: +51 222271
Rector: Carlos Chacon Galindo
Founded: 1598, 1692, 1969
P: Economics; Commerce; Education;
Technology; Geology; Mining; Animal Husbandry.

National University 'José Faustino Sánchez Carrión' Huacho
[Universidad Nacional 'José Faustino Sánchez
Carrión']
Avenida Grau 592, Calle Colón 461, Huacho,
Lima
Tel: +51(14) 324-741
Rector: Severo Llanos Bayona
Founded: 1968
P: Industrial Engineering; Fisheries; Business
Administration; Accountancy; Sociology; Nursing;
Nutrition.

National University 'Hermilio Valdizán' Huánuco
[Universidad Nacional 'Hermilio Valdizán']
Dos de Mayo 680, Apartado 278, Huánuco,
Huánuco
Tel: +51 2341
Fax: +51 3360
Rector: Edgardo Torres Vera
Founded: 1964
P: Agriculture; Education; Economics and
Commerce; Nursing; Engineering.

National University 'Santiago Antúnez de Mayolo' Huaraz
[Universidad Nacional 'Santiago Antúnez de
Mayolo']
Avenida Centenario s/n, Apartado 70, Huaraz,
Ancash
Tel: +51(72) 1393
Fax: +51(72) 1393
Rector: José Narváez Soto
Founded: 1977
P: Mining; Civil Engineering; Agricultural
Engineering; Industrial Engineering.

National University of 'San Luis Gonzaga' Ica
[Universidad Nacional 'San Luis Gonzaga']
Jr. Cajamarca 194, Ica, Ica
Tel: +51(34) 233-201
Fax: +51(34) 226-036
Rector: Alejandro Encinas Fernández
Founded: 1955, 1961, 1969
F: Administration; Agriculture; Science;
Education; Law; Economics and Accountancy;
Nursing; Pharmacy and Biochemistry; Civil
Engineering; Mechanical and Electrical
Engineering; Minining and Metallurgy
Engineering; Chemical Engineering; Medicine;
Veterinary Medicine and Animal Husbandry;
Dentistry; Fisheries.

National University of the Peruvian Amazon Iquitos
[Universidad Nacional de la 'Amazonía Peruana']
Apartado 496, Iquitos, Loreto
Tel: +51(23) 5351
Fax: +51(23) 3657
Rector: José Rojas Vásquez
Founded: 1962, 1969
P: Engineering; Biology; Nursing; Education; Administration.

National University 'Pedro Ruíz Gallo' Lambayeque
[Universidad Nacional 'Pedro Ruíz Gallo']
Jr. 8 de Octubre 637, Casilla 557, Lambayeque, Lambayeque
Tel: +51 2080
Rector: Angel Diaz Celis
Founded: 1960, 1970
P: Biology; Law; Nursing; Engineering; Veterinary Medicine; Economics and Social Sciences.

National University of Agriculture Lima
[Universidad Nacional Agraria Lima]
Apartado 456, La Molina, Lima, Lima
Tel: +51(14)352-035
Cable: uniagraria
Rector: Alberto Fujimori F.
Founded: 1901, 1960
F: Science; Forestry; Economics and Planning; Food Technology; Agricultural Engineering; Agriculture; Fishery; Animal Husbandry.
Ce: Statistics and Data Processing.

National University of San Marcos Lima
[Universidad Nacional Mayor de San Marcos de Lima]
Avenida República de Chile 295, Lima, Lima
Tel: +51(14) 314-629
Rector: Antonio Cornejo Polar
Founded: 1551, 1861
P: Physics and Mathematics; Chemistry and Chemical Engineering; Engineering; Geology and Geological Engineering; Biological Sciences; Pharmacy and Biochemistry; Veterinary Medicine; Medicine; Dentistry; Social Sciences; Economics; Law and Political Science; Accountancy and Administrative Studies; Philosophy, Psychology, and Art; Linguistics, Philosophy, and Spanish Literature; Education; Metallurgical Engineering; Nutrition.

National University of Piura
[Universidad Nacional de Piura]
Prolongación Avenida Grau s/n, Piura, Piura
Tel: +51(14) 321-931
Rector: Arturo Davies Guaylupo
Founded: 1961, 1969
F: Agriculture; Administration; Accountancy and Finance; Physics and Mathematics; Social Sciences and Education; Economics; Industrial Engineering; Mining; Fishery; Medicine; Animal Husbandry.

National University of Pucallpa
[Universidad Nacional de Pucallpa]
Pucallpa, Ucayali
Tel: +51 16044
Founded: 1979
F: Forestry; Agriculture; Nursing.

National University of 'Altiplano' Puno
[Universidad Nacional del 'Altiplano']
Ciudad Universitaria, Apartado 291, Puno, Puno
Tel: +51 352-912
Telex: 54772
Rector: Victor Torres Esteves
Founded: 1856, 1961
F: Agriculture; Veterinary Medicine and Animal Husbandry; Economics; Accountancy and Administration; Health Sciences; Social Work; Social Sciences; Statistics; Mining Engineering; Law; Chemical Engineering; Education; Nursing.

National University of San Martín
[Universidad Nacional de San Martín]
Martínez de Compagñón 527, Tarapoto, San Martín
Rector: Dalín Encomenderos Dávalos
Founded: 1979
Agriculture and Forestry; Civil Engineering; Agricultural Engineering; Sciences and Humanities; Mother and Child Care.

National University of Engineering San Martín de Pores
[Universidad Nacional de Ingeniería]
Avenida Túpac Amaru s/n, Apartado 1301, San Martín de Porres, Lima
Tel: +51 811-035
Cable: Uni
Rector: José Ignacio López Soria
Founded: 1875, 1941, 1954
F: Architecture and Town Planning; Science; Economics and Social Sciences; Geological, Mining, and Metallurgical Engineering; Civil Engineering; Mechanical; Industrial and Systems Engineering; Sanitary Engineering; Petroleum Engineering; Environmental Engineering; Chemical and Manufacturing Engineering.

National University 'Federico Villarreal' San Miguel
[Universidad Nacional 'Federico Villarreal']
Calle Carlos González 285, San Miguel, Lima
Tel: +51 (14) 641-301
Fax: +51 (14) 644-370
Rector: Santiago Agurto Calvo
Founded: 1963
F: Architecture and Town Planning; Administration; Economics; Finance and Accountancy; Natural Sciences and Mathematics; Social Sciences; Co-operative Studies; Law and Political Science; Education and Human Sciences; Civil Engineering; Geographic Engineering; Industrial and Systems Engineering; Medicine; Oceanography, Fishery, and Food Technology; Dentistry; Psychology; Medical Technology.

National University 'Jorge Basadre Grohmann' Tacna

[Universidad Nacional 'Jorge Basadre Grohmann' Tacna]
Avenida Bolognesi con Pinto s/n, Casilla 316, Tacna, Tacna
Tel: +51 721-385
Rector: Mgr. Alberto Coayla Vilca
Founded: 1971
F: Administration; Accountancy and Finance; Mining; Metallurgy; Fishery; Midwifery; Agriculture; Food Technology; Education.

National University of Agriculture of 'La Selva' Tingo María

[Universidad Nacional Agraria de 'La Selva']
Apartado 156, Tingo María, Huánuco
Tel: +51 2341
Founded: 1964

National University 'La Libertad' Trujillo

[Universidad Nacional de 'La Libertad']
Independencia 431, Oficina 216, Casilla 315, Trujillo, La Libertad
Tel: +51(44) 243-721
Cable: diego de almagro 396
Rector: Carlos Chirinos Villaneueva
Founded: 1824, 1969
P: Economics; Science; Metallurgy; Law and Political Science; Social Sciences; Education; Engineering; Pharmacy and Biochemistry; Biology; Physics and Mathematics; Medical Sciences.

National University of Tumbes

[Universidad Nacional de Tumbes]
Bolognesi 218, Tumbes, Tumbes
Tel: +51 3081

PRIVATE INSTITUTIONS

Apurimac University

[Universidad Particular de Apurimac]
Apartado 140, Abancay, Apurimac
Founded: 1984
F: Agriculture; Accountancy; Law; Education; Nursing.

Catholic University of 'Santa María' Arequipa

[Universidad Católica de Santa María]
Avenida Santa Catalina 410, Casilla 1350, Arequipa, Arequipa
Tel: +51(54) 243-271
Fax: +51(54) 219-283
Founded: 1961, 1969
F: Social Communications; Accountancy; Law; Economics and Management; Nursing; Dentistry; Social Service; Education.

Chiclayo University

[Universidad Particular de Chiclayo]
Avenida Quinones 615, Urb. San Juan, Chiclayo, Lambayeque
Tel: +51(74) 227-806
Fax: +51(74) 240-638
Rector: Maximiliano Larrea Portilla
Secretario General: Juan Pablo Moreno Muro
Founded: 1985
F: Architecture; Health Studies; Communication Sciences; Education.
Research Ce: Information Sciences and Technology.

University 'Los Angeles' of Chimbote

[Universidad Particular 'Los Angeles' de Chimbote]
José Olaya 981, Chimbote, Ancash
Tel: +51 321-621

Andean University of Cusco

[Universidad Andina del Cusco]
Parque la Madre 186, Cusco, Cusco
Tel: +51 226-377

'Los Andes' Private University Huancayo

[Universidad Privada 'Los Andes']
Jr. Cusco 259, Huancayo, Junín
Tel: +51 234-480

University of Huánuco

[Universidad de Huánuco]
Jirón Constitución 650, Huánuco, Huánuco
Tel: +51 3154
Founded: 1989
F: Law and Political Sciences; Midwifery; Animal Husbandry.

Andean University 'Néstor Cácares Velásquez' Juliaca

[Universidad Andina 'Néstor Cácares Velásquez']
Carretera Km. 19, Apartado 4896, Juliaca, Puno
Tel: +51 540

University of Lima

[Universidad de Lima]
Avenida Javier Prado s/n, Monterrico, Lima 33, Lima
Tel: +51(14) 376-767
Fax: +51(14) 378-066
E-Mail: orpi@ulima.pe
Rector: Desiderio Blanco López (1989-94)
Secretario General: Antonino Espinosa Laña
Founded: 1962
F: Administration; Economics; Accountancy; Communication Sciences; Industrial Engineering; Metallurgy; Systems Engineering; Human Sciences; Law and Political Science.
P: General Studies; Education Administration.
I: Co-operative Studies; Philosophy Research; Economics and Social Research.
Ce: Accountancy Research; Social Communication Research; Study and Qualification, Mass Media; Legal Research; Industrial Production Research.

University 'Marcelino Champagnat' Lima
[Universidad 'Marcelino Champagnat' Lima]
Jr. Mártir Olaya 162, Lima, Lima
Tel: +51(14) 473-064
Founded: 1948, 1983
Education.

University of the Pacific Lima
[Universidad del Pacífico]
Avenida Salaverry 2020, Apartado 4683, Jesús María, Lima 11, Lima
Tel: +51(14) 712-277
Fax: +51(14) 706-121
Telex: 25650 pe cp shera
Cable: udelpa
Rector: Raimundo Villagrasa Novoa, S.J. (1989-94)
Secretario General: Carlos Gatti Murriel
Founded: 1962
F: Economics; Business Administration and Acccounting.
S: Graduate.
Ce: Management Development; Research.

Women's University of the Sacred Heart Lima
[Universidad Femenina del Sagrado Corazón Lima]
Avenida Los Frutales s/n, Monterrico, Lima, Lima
Tel: +51(14) 364-641
Rector: Gladys Buzzio Zamora
Founded: 1962
P: Architecture; Education; Sociology; Psychology and Humanities; Translation and Interpretation; General Studies.
Ce: Social and Educational Research.

University 'San Martín de Porres' Lima
[Universidad 'San Martín de Porres' Lima]
Calle Bolívar 348, Miraflores, Lima, Lima
Tel: +51(14) 442-905
Rector: Ricardo Nugent
Founded: 1962
P: Letters; Education.
I: Philosophy and Social Science; History; Geography.

Inca Private University 'Garcilaso de la Vega' Lince
[Universidad Particular Inca Garcilaso de la Vega]
Avenida Arequipa 1841, Lince, Lima
Tel: +51 711-421
Founded: 1964
P: Administration; Psychology; Sociology and Social Work; Accountancy; Economics; Education; Industrial Engineering; Political Science.

*Pontifical Catholic University of Peru
[Pontificia Universidad Católica del Perú]
Avenida Universitaria, s/n, San Miguel, Lima 32, Lima
Tel: +51(14) 622-540
Fax: +51(14) 611-785
E-Mail: postmast@pucp.pe
Rector: Hugo Sarabía Swett (1989-94)
Founded: 1917, 1942
F: Administrative Sciences; Social Sciences; Science and Engineering; Law; Education; Letters and Human Sciences; General Studies; Art; Social Work.
S: Social Service (Trujillo).
Ce: Language; Archaeology, Philosophy, History, Linguistics and Literature Research; Anthropology, Political Science, Economics, and Sociology Research.
I: Legal Research.

Inca Unión University Naña
[Universidad Unión Incaíca]
Villa Unión, Casilla 4896, Naña, Lima
Tel: +51 971-344
Fax: +5197-1333
Cable: incaunion, lima
Rector: Máximo Vicuña Arrieta
Secretario General: Carlos Bendezú Luna Victoria
Founded: 1919
F: Education and Social Sciences; Theology; Natural and Food Sciences; Accountancy and Administration; Health Sciences.

University of Piura
[Universidad de Piura]
Ciudad Universitaria San Eduardo, Apartado 3208, Piura, Piura
Tel: +51(74) 328-171
Fax: +51(74) 328-645
Rector: Antonio Mabres Torello
Founded: 1968
F: Engineering; Economics and Business Administration; Journalism; Science and Humanities.

*Peruvian University 'Cayetano Heredia' San Martín de Porres
[Universidad Peruana 'Cayetano Heredia']
Avenida Honorio Delgado 430, Urb. Ingeniería, San Martín de Porres, Lima
Tel: +51 820-252
Fax: +51 824-541
Rector: Roger Guerra-García Cueva (1989-94)
Vice-Rector Administrativo: Anibal Gastanaga Coll-Cardenas
Founded: 1961
F: Sciences and Philosophy; Medicine; Stomatology.
I: Tropical Medicine; High Altitude Studies; Population Studies; Gerontology; Genetics.

University 'Ricardo Palma' Surco

[Universidad 'Ricardo Palma' Surco]
Avenida Prolongación Benavides Gda. 54, Las
Gardenias, Surco, Lima
Tel: +51 459-035
Rector: Edmundo Velarde Laos
Founded: 1969
*F: Architecture and Town Planning; Psychology;
Biology; Engineering; Economics and Business
Administration; Modern Languages.*

University of Tacna

[Universidad de Tacna]
Opus Sacerdotale Cooperationis Hispano-
Americanae P.J. Vigil, Calle San Camilo 1000,
Tacna, Tacna
Tel: +51 725-343

NATIONAL ACADEMIC BODIES

Ministry of Education, Office of International Affairs

[Ministerio de Educación, Oficina de Asuntos
Internacionales]
Lima
Tel: +51(14) 281-209
Ministro: Jorge Trelles Montero

Rectors' National Assembly

[Asamblea Nacional de Rectores (ANR)]
Calle Aldabas 337, Las Gardenias, Lima 33
Tel: +51(14) 495-716
Fax: +51(14) 496-711
President: Javier Sata Nadal
Executive Secretary: Héctor Lújan Peralta
Founded: 1985

Peruvian Commission for Cooperation with Unesco

[Comisión Nacional Peruana de Cooperación con
la Unesco]
Van de Velde 160, San Borja Norte, Apo postal
4681, Lima
Tel: +51(14) 364-990
Fax: +51(14) 364-992
Telex: 25803
Presidente: Jorge Trelles Montero, Minister of
Education
Secretaria General: Judith Reyes Campana

PHILIPPINES

UNIVERSITIES

PUBLIC INSTITUTIONS

Benguet State University

La Trinidad, Benguet 2601
Tel: +63 43-22-401
President: Cipriano C. Consolacion (1993-99)
Administrative Officer: Estrella A. Ramos
Founded: 1956

*C: Agriculture; Forestry; Applied Engineering
and Technology; Veterinary Medicine; Arts and
Sciences; Education; Home Economics and
Technology.*
Research And Training Ce: *Northern Philippines
Root Crops.*
*I: Highland Farming Systems; Highland
Agro-Forest.*
Research I: *Highland Socio-Economic;
Horticulture Training.*

Bicol University

Legazpi City 4500
Tel: +63 4913-4932
Presidente: Lylia O. Sena (1993-98)
Administrative Officer: José A. Rico
Founded: 1969
*C: Engineering; Education; Agriculture;
Fisheries; Arts and Science; Nursing.
S: Arts and Trade; Graduate.
Ce: Research and Statistics; Extension.*

Bulacan State University

Malolos, Bulacan
President: Rosario Pimental (1990-96)

Cagayan State University

Tuguegarao, Cagayan
Prsesident: Armando B. Cortes (1989-95)
Founded: 1907
*Engineering; Arts and Science; Agricultural
Business; Education; Industrial Technology;
Technical Sciences.*

Central Luzon State University

Muñoz, Nueva Ecija 2320
Tel: +63 107 (PLDT)
Cable: clsu, muñoz, n.e.
President: Fortunato A. Battad
Administrative Officer: Ricardo C. Bernardo
Founded: 1907, 1950
*C: Agriculture; Arts and Sciences; Engineering;
Education; Inland Fisheries; Veterinary Medicine;
Business Administration; Home Economics.
I: Graduate Studies.*

Central Mindanao University

University Town, Musuan, Bukidnon 8710
President: Jaime G. Gellor (1993-99)
Founded: 1910, 1952, 1965
*C: Agriculture; Arts and Sciences; Education;
Engineering; Forestry; Home Economics;
Veterinary Medicine.
S: Graduate.*

Don Mariano Marcos Memorial State University

Bacnotan, La Union
President: Manuel T. Corpus (1989-95)
Founded: 1960
*Agriculture; Agronomy; Sciences; Business
Administration; Education; Home Technology;
Fishery; Hotel and Restaurant Management; Arts;
Law; Industrial Technology; Midwifery; Technical
Sciences.*

Iligan Institute of Technology-MSU Iligan City Campus

Tibanga, Iligan City 8801
Tel: +63 20800
President: Camar A. Umpa
Founded: 1946, 1957, 1968
C: *Engineering; Engineering Technology; Arts and Social Sciences; Science and Mathematics; Business Administration; Education; Instructional Staff Development.*
S: *Management Technology; Development Management; Physical Education; Graduate Studies.*
Coordination Ce: *Research and Development.*
D: *Ceramics.*

Isabela State University

Echague, Isabela
President: Rodolfo C. Nayga (1993-99)
Founded: 1926
S: *Arts and Sciences; Agricultural Industries; Vocational and Industrial Studies; Forestry; Engineering; Education; Home Technology; Technical Sciences.*

Mariano Marcos State University

Brgy. 16 Quiling Sur, Batac, Ilocos Norte 2906
Tel: +63(77) 792-31-91
Fax: +63(77) 792-31-31
Cable: unibatac
President: Elias L. Calacal (1993-99)
Secretary: Alegria T. Visaya
Founded: 1978
C: *Arts and Sciences; Agriculture and Forestry; Economics and Management; Nursing; Engineering and Technology; Education (secondary and elementary levels).*
I: *Technology; Sustainable Dryland Agriculture; Cotton Research Development.*
S: *Fisheries; Graduate.*
Ce: *Applied Research and Technology Transfer (Dingras); Applied Research and Technology Transfer (Paoay); National Research; Iloko Research and Information.*

*Mindanao State University

Marawi City
Tel: +63 222
Telex: MSU Manila Info Office Vasquez Street
Malate, Metro Manila
President: Emily M. Marohombsar (1993-99)
Founded: 1961
C: *Agriculture; Business Administration; Community Development and Public Administration; Education; Engineering; Fisheries; Forestry; Health Sciences; Hotel and Restaurant Management; Law; Medicine; Physical Education and Sports; Natural Science and Mathematics; Social Sciences and Humanities.*
S: *Graduate.*
I: *Fisheries Research and Development.*
Ce: *Arabic and Islamic Studies; Science Training.*

Pangasinan State University

Lingayen, Pangasinan 0706
Tel: +63 5252
President: Reynaldo P. Segui (1993-97)
Founded: 1950
C: *Education; Arts, Sciences and Technology; Agriculture; Agriculture (San Carlos City); Agriculture (Infanta); Arts and Technology; Fisheries; Engineering.*
S: *Graduate; Fisheries Research.*

Philippine Normal University

Taft Avenue and Ayala Boulevard, Ermita
Tel: +63(2) 47-53-14
Fax: +63(2) 40-48-85
President: Gloria G. Salandanan
Arts and Sciences; Education; Engineering.
Ce: *Language Study; Child Study; Health Education; Special Education.*
S: *Graduate.*

Polytechnic University of the Philippines

Anonas St., Sta. Mesa, Manila
Tel: +63(2) 61-67-75
Cable: Pup Manila
President: Zenaido A. Olonan (1992-98)
Vice-President for Administration and Finance: Dante G. Guevara
Founded: 1904, 1977
S: *Graduate.*
C: *Accountancy; Arts and Sciences; Business; Office Administration and Business Teacher Education; Computer Management and Information Technology; Languages and Mass Communications; Engineering; Economics and Politics; Hotel and Restaurant Management, Food Science and Technology; Physical Education.*
I: *Co-operatives; Center-Off Campus Development Endeavour; Pamantasang Bayan.*

Tarlac State University

Romulo Blvd., Tarlac, Tarlac
Tel: +63 2905
President: Alejandro M. Fernandez
Founded: 1919
Technology.

Technological University of the Philippines

Ayala Boulevard Corner San Marcelino Street, Ermita, Manila 2801
Tel: +63(2) 58-63-55
President: Frederick So.Pada (1988-94)
Founded: 1901, 1959, 1978
C: *Arts and Sciences; Industrial Education; Architecture and Fine Arts; Industrial Technology; Engineering.*
S: *Graduate.*

*University of the City of Manila

Intramuros, Manila
Tel: +63(2) 40-76-21
Fax: +63(2) 40-76-29
President: Benjamin G. Tayabas (1990-)
Vice-President for Administration: Edelita F. Reyes
Founded: 1963

C: Business Administration; Arts and Sciences; Engineering and Technology; Nursing; Education; Law; Medicine.
S: Graduate.
D: Sports, Physical Education and Recreation.

University of Eastern Philippines
University Town, Catarman, Northern Samar
President: Pedro D. Destura (1990-96)
Founded: 1964, 1951, 1957, 1964
C: Agriculture; Arts and Sciences; Business Administration; Engineering; Education; Veterinary Medicine.
S: Graduate.

University of Northern Philippines
Tamag, Vigan, Ilocos Sur 0401
Tel: +63 3093
President: Dorotea C. Filant (1993-97)
Founded: 1910, 1951, 1965
C: Arts and Sciences; Nursing; Engineering; Architecture; Criminology; Teacher Education; Business Administration.
I: Fine Arts; Social Work; Technical Education and Cottage Industries Development.
S: Graduate.

University of the Philippines System
Diliman, Quezon City 3004
Tel: +63(2) 96-15-72
Fax: +63(2) 98-67-80
Telex: 2231 up dil pu
Cable: univerphil
President: Emil G. Javier (1993-99)
Founded: 1908
Main Campus, Diliman.
C: Architecture; Arts and Sciences; Business Administration; Education; Engineering; Fine Arts; Science; Social Sciences and Philosophy; Home Economics; Law; Music; Public Administration; Agriculture; Arts and Sciences; Forestry; Veterinary Medicine; Dentistry; Medicine; Pharmacy; Arts and Sciences (Iloilo); Fisheries (Miagao); Arts and Sciences; Nursing; Development Economics and Management.
Ce: Asian; Statistics; Health Sciences (Manila).
S: Economics; Allied Medical Professions; Development Management; Graduate.
I: Tourism (Asian); Industrial Relations; Urban and Regional Planning; Islamic Studies; Library Science; Mass Communication; Population Studies; Social Work and Community Development; Physical Education and Sports; Plant Breeding; Agricultural Engineering and Technology; Human Ecology; Public Health.

COLLEGE AT LOS BAÑOS

BAGUIO COLLEGE
Baguio City

CEBU COLLEGE
Lahug, Cebu City

UNIVERSITY OF THE PHILIPPINES IN THE VISAYAS
Iloilo City

UNIVERSITY OF THE PHILIPPINES MANILA

COLLEGE OF TACLOBAN
Tacloban City

University of Southeastern Philippines
Barrio Obrero, Davao City
Tel: +63(82) 7-86-53
President: Edmundo B. Prantilla (1993-99)
Founded: 1979
C: Engineering; Education; Engineering and Technology; Industrial Technology; Arts and Sciences; Agriculture; Agribusiness; Forestry; Statistics.
S: Graduate.
D: Extension.

University of Southern Mindanao
Kabacan, North Cotabato 9311
Cable: Kabacan, North Cotabato
President: Kundo E. Pahm (1988-94)
Founded: 1952, 1978
C: Agriculture; Agribusiness; Arts and Sciences; Education; Engineering; Home Ecological Sciences; Industrial Technology; Technical Sciences.
Regional Training Ce: Rural Development.

West Visayas State University
Iloilo City
President: Bernabe B; Cocjin (1993-99)
Founded: 1924
Agriculture; Education; Nursing; Medicine; Forestry; Arts.

Western State University
Baliwasan, Zamboanga City
Tel: +63 3486
President: Erdulfo B. Fernando (1991-97)
Founded: 1918, 1955, 1961
C: Agriculture; Arts and Sciences; Home Economics and Nutrition; Education; Engineering; Science and Mathematics; Forestry; Law; Nursing; Social Work.
S: Graduate.
Ce: Research.

PRIVATE INSTITUTIONS

Adamson University
900 San Marcelino Street, Ermita, Manila 1000
Tel: +63(2) 50-20-11
President: Rolando S. Delgoza, C.M.
Founded: 1932, 1941
C: Liberal Arts and Science; Engineering; Education; Commerce and Business Administration; Pharmacy; Law; Sciences; Architecture.
Graduate S: Education and Chemistry.
I: Continuing and Professional Development.

Angeles University Foundation
MacArthur Highway, Angeles City 2017
Tel: +63(455) 2958
President: Emmanuel X. Angeles
Founded: 1962, 1971, 1977

C: Medicine; Nursing; Civil Engineering; Criminology; Business and Economics; Arts and Sciences; Education.
S: Graduate; Secretarial Studies.

Aquinas University Inc.
Rawis, Legazpi City 4901
President: Orlando Aceron, O.P.
Founded: 1948, 1965, 1969
C: Law; Engineering; Education; Arts and Sciences; Commerce; Nursing; Architecture and Fine Arts.
D: Business Administration; Religious Studies; Physical Education.
S: Graduate.
Ce: Computer; Regional Science Teaching; Socio-Economic Research; Regional Audio-Visual.

Araullo University
Bitas, Cabanatuan City 3100
Tel: +63 963-2215
President: Rolan C. Esteban (1987-)
Registrar: Raoul S. Esteban
Founded: 1950, 1953, 1983
C: Arts and Sciences; Commerce; Criminology; Education; Engineering; Law; Nutrition.
D: Graduate Studies.
Ce: Computer.

Arellano University
2600 Legarda, Sampaloc, Manila
Tel: +63(2) 60-74-41
President: Florentino Cayco, Jr.
Founded: 1938, 1947
C: Arts and Sciences; Education; Commerce; Law; Nursing.
Graduate S: Arts.

Ateneo de Davao University
E. Jacinto Street, Davao City 9501
Tel: +63(82) 7-33-49
Fax: +63 (82) 64116
President: Edmundo Martinez, S.J.
Founded: 1948, 1977
C: Arts and Sciences, Commerce, and Mass Communication; Law.
Graduate I: Education (Mindanao).
I: Small-scale Industries.
S: Graduate; Medicine; Engineering.
D: Accountancy; Business Administration; Humanities; Agriculture; Social Science; Natural Sciences; Religious Studies.

Ateneo de Manila University
Loyola Height, Quezon City, Manila
Tel: +63(2) 99-87-21
Fax: +63(2) 921-61-59
President: Bienvenido Nebres, S.J.
Executive Vice-President: Edmundo M. Martinez, S.J.
S: Arts and Sciences; Business Administration (Graduate).
C: Law.
Ce: Ateneo Computer Technology.
I: Philippine Culture.

Baguio Central University
18 Bonifacio Street, Baguio City
Tel: +63(74) 442-49-49
President: Margarita J. Fernández
Registrar: Clarita Botor
Founded: 1951
C: Education; Arts and Sciences; Engineering; Commerce and Accountancy.
S: Graduate.
I: Research, Evaluation, and Science.

Central Philippine University
Iloilo City 5000
Tel: +63(33) 7-34-71
Fax: +63(33) 7-34-70
Founded: 1905, 1953, 1969
C: Arts and Sciences; Agriculture; Commerce; Education; Engineering; Law; Nursing; Theology.
S: Graduate Studies.
Ce: Social Research.

*Centro Escolar University
9 Mendiola Street, San Miguel, Manila
Tel: +63(2) 742120-91
Cable: ceuniv
President: Lourdes T. Echauz
Registrar: Lucia D. Gonzales
Founded: 1907, 1952
C: Liberal Arts; Science; Accountancy, Commerce and Secretarial Studies; Dentistry; Education and Social Work; Medical Technology; Music; Nursing; Nutrition and Home Economics and Tourism; Optometry; Pharmacy.
S: Graduate.
D: Biological Science; Religion; Pilipino; Behavioural Sciences; Educational Technology; Humanities and Social Arts; English; Mathematics; Library Science; Physical Education; Social Science; Social Work.
Ce: Research and Statistics; Data Analysis.

*De La Salle University
2401 Taft Avenue, P.O Box 3819, Manila 1004
Tel: +63(2) 50-46-11
Fax: +63(2) 522-3661
Cable: delasal
President: Andrew Gonzalez, F.S.C. (1994-)
Administrative Officer: Benildo Feliciano, F.S.C.
Founded: 1911, 1975
C: Business and Economics; Computer Studies; Engineering; Liberal Arts; Science; Education; Medicine (Cavité).
Graduate S: Business and Economics.
Research Ce: Social Science.

Far Eastern University
Nicanor Reyes Street, Sampaloc Manila
Tel: +63(2) 741-3459
Fax: +63(2) 741-4833
President: Felixberto C. Sta. Maria (1989-)
Founded: 1928, 1933
I: Accountancy, Finance and Business Administration; Architecture and Fine Arts; Education; Law; Nursing; Technology; Graduate Studies; Arts and Sciences.

Feati University
Helios Street, Santa Cruz, Manila
Tel: +63(2) 48-59-51
President: Jose M. Segovia
Founded: 1946, 1947, 1959
I: Engineering and Technology; Liberal Arts and Education; Architecture; Commerce; Science; Vocational and Technical Sciences; Maritime Transport.
S: Graduate; Finance.

Foundation University
Dr.E. Meciano Road, Dumaguete City 6501
Tel: +63 3389
President: Aurora A. Mihoza (1991-)
Vice-President for Finance and Administration: Edmundo G. Sinco
Founded: 1949, 1969
C: Arts and Sciences; Law; Agriculture; Business and Economics; Education.
S: Graduate; Industrial Engineering.

Gregorio Araneta University Foundation Manila
Victoneta Park, Malabon, Metro Manila, Rizal
Tel: +63(2) 361-90-53
Fax: +63(2) 361-90-54
President: Manuel D. Punzal (1991-95)
Director for Administration: Cecilio A. Acasio
Founded: 1946, 1958, 1965
I: Agriculture and Forestry; Arts and Sciences; Education and Sports; Business and Agricultural Administration; Engineering; Veterinary Medicine; Graduate Studies and Applied Research.

Holy Angel University
Santo Rosario, 2009 Angeles City
Tel: +63(455) 241-30
President: Josefina G. Nepomuceno, O.S.B.
Founded: 1933, 1962, 1981
C: Arts and Sciences; Business Administration; Education; Engineering; Secretarial Studies.
Ce: Computer Studies.
D: Vocational/Technical.
S: Graduate.

Manila Central University
Epifanio de los Santos Avenue, Coloocan City
Tel: +63 35-10-71
Cable: mcu manila
President: Purificacion G. Tanchoco (1963-)
Founded: 1904, 1948
C: Arts and Sciences; Medicine; Dentistry; Optometry; Commerce; Pharmacy and Medical Technology; Nursing.
S: Midwifery.
D: Education (Graduate); Extension.

Manuel L. Quezon University
916 R. Hidalgo Street, Quiapo, Manila
Tel: +63(4) 742-42-01
Cable: mlqu manila
President: Amado C. Dizon
Founded: 1947, 1958

F: Law; Arts and Sciences; Education; Commerce; Engineering and Architecture; Criminology; Graduate Studies.

Manuel S. Enverga University Foundation
Ibabang Dupay, Lucena City 3901
Tel: +63(42) 71-25-41
President: Jose S. Loureles
Founded: 1947, 1968
C: Arts and Sciences; Commerce; Education; Engineering; Agriculture.
I: Applied Business.
S: Architecture; Graduate; Vocational Studies; Lifelong Education.

Misamis University
Mabini and Bonifacio Streets, Ozamiz City
Tel: +63 20431
President: Nestor M. Feliciano
Founded: 1929, 1931, 1955, 1977
C: Agriculture and Forestry; Commerce and Secretarial Studies; Arts and Sciences; Dentistry; Nursing and Midwifery; Engineering; Criminology; Education; Social Work and Community Development; Law.
I: Graduate Studies.
P: Community Extension.

*National University
551 M.F. Jhocson Street, Sampaloc, Manila
Tel: +63(2) 60-81-67
President: Jesus M. Jhocsonon
Founded: 1900, 1921
C: Commerce; Liberal Arts; Dentistry; Pharmacy; Education; Engineering; Law; Technical Sciences.
S: Arts and Architecture; Graduate.

Northwestern University of the Philippines
P. Burgos Street, Laoag City
President: Jose G. Castro
Founded: 1932

Notre Dame of Marbel University
Alunan Avenue, Koronadal, South Cotabato
Tel: +63218
Cable: marist marbel phil
Founded: 1946

Notre Dame University
Notre Dame Avenue, Cotabato City 9600
Tel: +63 21-43-12
President: Eliseo R. Mercado, Jr., O.M.I. (1992-)
Vice-President for Academic Affairs: Ofelia L. Durante
Founded: 1948, 1969
C: Arts and Sciences; Engineering; Law; Commerce; Nursing; Teacher; Community.
S: Graduate.
Ce: Socio-Economic Research.
D: Elementary Training.

Philippine Christian University
Dasmarinae, Cavite
Founded: 1946
Agricultural Technology; Business Administration; Education; Social Work.

*Philippine Christian University
1648 Taft Avenue and Corner Pedro Gil, Manila
Tel: +63(2) 57-24-35
Fax: +63(2) 57-24-35
President: Carlito S. Puno (1990-95)
Vice-President for Academic Affairs: Edna Flor M. de los Santos
Founded: 1947, 1976
C: Business Administration; Arts and Sciences and Social Work.
Ce: Commerce, Arts, Education and Allied Professions; Nursing and Allied Sciences; Secretarial and Vocational Technology; Computer Science; Institutional Research and Development.
D: Agricultural Technology; Accountancy.
Graduate S: Education (M.A.); Business and Management.

*Philippine Women's University
1743 Taft Avenue, Manila D-406
Tel: +63(2) 58-80-38
Fax: +63(2) 521-20-29
President: Jose Conrado Benitez
Founded: 1919, 1932
D: Education; Science and Technology; Business Industry; Allied Health Sciences and Social Development.
Ce: Computer; Lifelong Education.

Saint Louis University
P.O. Box 71, A Bonifacio Street, Baguio City 2600
Tel: +63(74) 442-30-43
President: Joseph Van den Daelen, CICM (1983-)
Registrar: Violeta C. Garcia
Founded: 1911, 1952, 1963
C: Law; Human Sciences; Accountancy and Commerce; Engineering and Architecture; Education; Natural Sciences; Medicine; Nursing.
Graduate S: Arts and Sciences.
Ce: Regional Science Teaching; Guidance and Counselling; Research and Extension Services.
I: Information and Computer Science; Physical Education; Small Scale Industries.

Saint Mary's University
Bayombong, Nueva Vizcaya
President: John Van Bawel, CICM
Founded: 1928

Saint Paul University
Mabini Street, Tuguegarao, Cagayan
Tel: +63(8822) 446-1863
President: Mary Angela Barrios, S.P.C.
Founded: 1907, 1982
C: Education; Arts and Sciences; Business and Administration; Nursing; Engineering; Nutrition and Dietetics.
S: Graduate.
D: Secretarial.

Silliman University
Hibbard Avenue, Dumaguete City 6501
Tel: +63 32-00
President: Quintin S. Doromal
Founded: 1901, 1938

C: Arts and Science; Education; Engineering; Nursing; Medical Technology; Social Work; Law; Business Administration; Agriculture.
S: Divinity; Mass Communications; Music and Fine Arts; Graduate.
D: Physical Education and Athletics.

Southwestern University
Villa Aznar, Urgello, Private Road, Cebu City
Tel: +63 96690
President: Alicia P. Cabatingan
Founded: 1946, 1959
C: Medicine; Dentistry; Medical Technology; Nursing; Pharmacy; Optometry; Law; Arts and Sciences; Commerce; Engineering; Education; Social Work; Veterinary Medicine; Physical Therapy.
S: Graduate.
I: Computer Sciences; Physical Education.
D: Agricultural Technology.

University of the Assumption
San Fernando, Pampanga 2001
Tel: +63 61-36-17
Cable: San Fernando, pamp. Phil
President: R.P. Ricardo T. Serrano
Founded: 1963, 1980
C: Education; Commerce; Architecture; Engineering; Nursing; Nutrition and Dietetics; Liberal Arts.
S: Graduate.

*University of Baguio
17 Gen Luna, Baguio City 2600
Tel: +63(74) 442-3071
Fax: +63(74) 442-6501
Cable: unibaguio
President: Virgilio C. Bautista
Founded: 1948, 1969
C: Arts and Sciences; Commerce; Criminology; Education; Engineering; Dentistry.
S: Graduate.

University of Bohol
Maria Clara Street, Tagbilaran, Bohol 6301
Tel: +63 3101 ITT
President: Ulysses B. Tirol
Founded: 1946, 1970
C: Law; Technology; Pharmacy; Nursing; Commerce and Business Administration; Teachers; Arts and Sciences; Forestry; Architecture; Criminology; Home Economics.
S: Graduate.

University of Cebu
Sanciangko Street Corner Osmena Blvd, Cebu City
Tel: +63 221-500
President: Samuel W. Go
Founded: 1964

University of the East Manila
Claro M. Recto Avenue, Manila
Tel: +63(2) 741-95-01
Cable: philcolcom
Founded: 1946, 1947, 1951

C: Arts and Sciences; Business Administration; Dentistry; Education; Engineering; Law; Medicine; Nursing.
S: Fine Arts; Graduate.
I: Technical Education; Computer.

University of the East Ramon-Magsaysay Memorial Medical Center
Aurora Boulevard, Quezon City
President: Franciso P. Dalupan
Founded: 1958
Dentistry.

University of Iloilo
Rizal Street, La Paz, Iloilo City
Founded: 1947, 1968
C: Education; Law; Liberal Arts; Science; Commerce; Criminology; Engineering; Agriculture; Nursing; Social Work.
S: Secretarial Studies.

University of the Immaculation Conception
Father Selga Street, Davao City
President: Ma. Rafaela Q. Singzon, R.V.M.
Founded: 1905

*University of Manila
546 M.V. de Los Santos Street, Manila 2806
Tel: +63(2) 741-36-50
Cable: Univman
President: Virgilio D. de los Santos
Founded: 1913, 1921
C: Law; Education; Business Administration; Liberal Arts; Criminology and Penology; Graduate Studies; Engineering; Sciences.

University of Mindanao
Bolton Street, Davao City
Tel: +63(82) 7-54-56
Fax: +63(82) 6-35-26
President: Dolores P. Torres
Vice-President for Academic Affairs: Paquita D. Gavino
Founded: 1946, 1963
C: Commerce; Criminology; Education; Engineering and Architecture; Forestry; Law; Arts and Sciences; Special and Career Development; Student Affairs.
S: Graduate.

University of Negros Occidental-Recoletos
P.O. Box, 214, Lizares Avenue, Bacolod City
Tel: +63(34) 2-50-36
Fax: +63(34) 2-50-36
Cable: Uno-Recoletos
President: Jose A. Rodriguez, O.A.R.
Founded: 1941, 1957
C: Law; Arts and Sciences; Engineering; Education; Criminology; Commerce; Medical Technology.
S: Graduate; Agriculture.

University of Northeastern Philippines
Iriga City
President: Ciriaco R. Alfelor
Founded: 1948

C: Arts; Architecture; Engineering; Law; Education; Commerce; Nursing; Criminology; Social Work.
S: Graduate.
I: Technology.

University of Nueva Caceres
Jaima Hernandez Avenue, Naga City 4721
Tel: +63 9287
Cable: Unc
President: Dolores H. Sison
Founded: 1948, 1954
C: Liberal Arts and Sciences; Engineering; Law; Commerce; Education; Nursing.
S: Graduate.

University of Pangasinan
Arellano-Bani Street, Dagupan City
Tel: +63(75) 38-50
President: Cesar T. Duque
Founded: 1925
C: Architecture; Commerce; Education; Engineering; Law; Liberal Arts; Medical Technology; Nursing; Secretarial Studies.
S: Graduate Studies.

University of Saint Anthony
San Miguel, Iriga City 4431
Tel: +63(403) 2401
President: Santiago D. Orgega, Jr.
Founded: 1947, 1963, 1973
C: Engineering; Commerce; Education; Nursing; Criminology; Arts and Sciences; Technical Vocational Studies,.
S: Graduate.

University of St. La Salle
La Salle Avenue, Bacolod City, Negros Occidental 6001
Tel: +63 20577
President: Rolando R. Dizon, F.S.C.
Founded: 1952, 1988
C: Arts and Science; Engineering; Commerce; Business Management; Education; Nursing.
S: Graduate.

University of San Agustín
General Luna Street, Iloilo City 5000
Tel: +63(33) 74841
President: R.P. Eusebio B. Berdon
Founded: 1904, 1953
C: Teacher; Commerce; Liberal Arts; Pharmacy and Medical Technology; Technology; Nursing.
S: Graduate; Law.
Conservatory: Music.

University of San Carlos
P. del Rosario Street, Cebu City 6000
Tel: +63 7-24-10
Fax: +63 32-543-41
Cable: steyl, cebu
President: Ernesto M. Lagura, S.V.D.
Registrar: Roberto Tratagotia
Founded: 1595, 1948

C: *Architecture and Fine Arts; Commerce; Engineering; Law; Arts and Sciences; Nursing; Pharmacy; Teacher.*
S: *Graduate.*
Ce: *Area Research and Training; Botany Research; Cebuano Studies; Marine Biology; Religious Education.*

University of San Jose-Recoletos
Corner Magallanes and P. Lopez Streets, Cebu City 6401
Tel: +63 5-38-02
Fax: +63 5-38-02
Cable: recoletos, cebu
President: Emeterio D. Bunao, O.A.R.
Founded: 1947, 1984
C: *Arts and Science; Law; Education; Engineering; Commerce.*
S: *Graduate.*
Ce: *Research, Planning and Scholarship; Instructional Media.*
I: *Management.*

*University of Santo Tomas
España Street, Sampalac, Manila 2806
Tel: +63(2) 731-31-01
Fax: +63(2) 732-74-86
Rector: Rolando V. De La Rosa, O.P. (1990-94)
Secretary-General: Maximo Marina, O.P.
Founded: 1611, 1947
F: *Philosophy, Theology and Canon Law; Medicine; Civil Law; Pharmacy; Arts and Letters; Engineering.*
C: *Education; Science; Commerce and Business Administration; Architecture and Fine Arts; Nursing.*
S: *Graduate.*
I: *Religion; Technology; Development Education.*
Ce: *Natural Sciences (Research); Social Research.*
Conservatory: *Music.*

University of Southern Philippines Foundation
Mabini Street, Cebu City
Tel: +63 72926
President: Ronald R. Duterte
Founded: 1927, 1933, 1949
C: *Liberal Arts and Sciences; Social Sciences; Engineering; Commerce; Education; Southern; Don Felix Montinola Memorial (Victorias).*
S: *Graduate.*

University of the Visayas
Colon Street, Cebu City 6401
Tel: +63 93812
Vice-President: Eduardo R. Gullas
Founded: 1919
C: *Medicine; Law; Engineering and Architecture; Arts and Sciences; Nursing; Pharmacy; Teacher; Commerce and Business Administration; Criminology.*
S: *Graduate; Marine Engineering.*

Virgen Milagrosa University Foundation
San Carlos City, Pangasinan
President: Martin P.Posadas
Founded: 1958

Wesleyan University-Philippines
Mabini Street, Cabantuan City
President: Gloria D. Lacson
Founded: 1946
Agriculture; Commerce; Engineering; Arts and Sciences; Nutrition; Nursing; Social Work; Education; Technical and Vocational Studies.

Xavier University
Corrales Avenue, Cagayan de Oro City 9000
Tel: +63(8822) 3742
Fax: +63(8822) 6069
President: Antonio S. Samson, S.J.
Founded: 1933, 1940, 1958
C: *Law; Medicine; Arts and Sciences; Commerce; Education; Engineering; Agriculture; Nursing.*
Ce: *Computer; Industrial Technology.*
S: *Graduate.*

OTHER INSTITUTIONS

PUBLIC INSTITUTIONS

Abra School of Arts and Trades
Santiago Street, Bangued, Abra
Founded: 1957
Arts and Trades.

Abra State Institute of Science and Technology
Langangilang, Abra
President: Imelda Buenafe
Founded: 1908
Science and Technology.

Aklan Agricultural College
Banga Aklan
Founded: 1918
Agriculture.

Aklan National College of Fisheries
New Washington, Aklan
Founded: 1949
Fisheries.

Antique College of Agriculture
Hamtic, Antique
Founded: 1952
Agriculture.

Antique National School
San Jose, Antique
Founded: 1976

Apolinario R. Apacible School of Fisheries
Nasugbu, Batangas
Founded: 1952
Fishery.

Bago City College
Bago City
Founded: 1980

Bais Developmental College
Bais City
Founded: 1980

Basilan State College
Santa Clara, Lamitan
Founded: 1966

Bataan National School of Arts and Trades
Balanga, Bataan
Founded: 1967
Arts and Trades.

Benguet School of Arts and Trades
Bokod, Benguet
Arts and Trades.

Bicol College of Arts and Trades
Peñafrancia Avenue, Naga City
Founded: 1911
Arts and Trades.

Biliran National Agricultural College
Biliran, Sub-Province
Founded: 1949
Agriculture.

Bohol Agricultural College
Zamora, Pilar, Bohol
Founded: 1912

Bohol School of Arts and Trades
Tagbilaran City
Tel: +63 32-88
Founded: 1907

Bohol School of Fisheries
Cogtong, Candijay, Bohol
Founded: 1959
Fisheries.

Bukidnon State College
Malaybalay, Bukidnon
Founded: 1924

Bulacan College of Arts and Trades
Malolos, Bulacan
Tel: +63 797-4114
Founded: 1957
Arts and Trade.

Bulacan National Agricultural School
San Ildefonso, Bulacan
Agriculture.

Calinog Agricultural and Industrial College
Calinog, Iloilo
Founded: 1959
Agriculture and Industry.

Camarines Sur Polytechnic College
Nabua, Camarines Sur
Founded: 1983

Camarines Sur State Agricultural College
Pili, Camarines Sur
Founded: 1954
Agriculture.

Canavid Agricultural College
Canavid, Eastern Samar
Founded: 1962
Agro-Industry.

Capiz Institute of Technology
Hemingway Street, Roxas City
Tel: +63 577
Founded: 1969
Technology.

Catanduanes Agricultural and Industrial College
Panganiban, Catanduanes
Founded: 1956
Agriculture; Industry.

Catanduanes College
Virac, Catanduanes
Founded: 1971

Cavite College of Arts and Trades
Rosario, Cavite
Founded: 1960
Arts and Trades.

Cavite College of Fisheries
Bucana, Naic, Cavite
Founded: 1960
Fisheries.

Cebu State College
Osmeña Boulevard, Cebu City
Founded: 1954

Central Luzon Polytechnic College
Cabanatuan City
Tel: +63 963-2621
Founded: 1964

Central Visayas Polytechnic College
Dumaguete City
Tel: +63 3072
Founded: 1910

Concepcion College of Fisheries
Concepcion, Iloilo
Founded: 1979

Cotabato City State Polytechnic College
Cotabato City
Founded: 1924

Cotabato Foundation College of Science and Technology
Dorolumna Magpet, North Cotabato
Founded: 1973
Science and Technology.

Dingle Agricultural and Technical College
Dingle, Iloilo
Founded: 1977
Agriculture and Technology.

Dipolog School of Fisheries
Dipolog City
Founded: 1960
Fisheries.

Don Honorio Ventura College of Arts and Trades
Bacolor, Pampanga
Founded: 1978
Art and Trade.

Don Severino Agricultural College
Indang, Cavite
Founded: 1964
Agriculture.

Dr. Emilio B. Espiñosa Sr. Memorial Agricultural College
Cabitan, Mandaon, Masbate
Founded: 1952
Agriculture.

Eastern Samar State College
Borongan, Eastern Samar
Founded: 1983

Eulogio "Amang" Rodriguez Institute of Science and Technology
Nagtahan, Manila
Tel: +63(2) 601366
Founded: 1945
Science and Technology.

Felipe J. Abrigo Memorial School of Arts and Trades
Buiuan, Eastern Samar
Founded: 1962
Art and Trade.

Hadji Butu School of Arts and Trades
Jolo, Sulu
Founded: 1928
Arts and Trades.

Ifugao State College of Agriculture and Forestry
Mayon Lamut, Ifugao
Founded: 1973
Agriculture and Industry.

Ilocos Sur Agricultural College
Sta. Maria, Ilocos Sur
Founded: 1922
Agriculture.

Iloilo State College of Fisheries
Tiwi Barotac Nuevo, Iloilo
Cable: iscof btac, nvo, phil
Founded: 1962
Fisheries.

Kalinga-Apayao School of Arts and Trades
Conner, Kalinga-Apayao
Founded: 1971
Arts and Trades.

Kalinga-Apayao State Polytechnic College

Kaloocan City Polytechnic College
General San Miguel Road, Sangandaan, Kaloocan City
Founded: 1971

La Carlota City College
La Carlota City
Founded: 1966

Laguna School of Arts and Trades
Santa Cruz, Laguna
Founded: 1984
Arts and Trades.

Laguna State Polytechnic College
Wawa East, Sinaloan Laguna
Founded: 1983

Lambunao Institute of Science and Technology
Lambunao, Iloilo
Founded: 1945
Science and Technology.

Lanao Agricultural College
Lumbatan, Lanao del Sur
Founded: 1963
Agriculture.

Lanao del Norte Agricultural College
Karomatan, Lanao del Norte
Founded: 1969
Agriculture.

Lanao National College of Arts and Trades
Marawi City, Lanao del Sur
Founded: 1920
Arts and Trades.

Laoang National Trade School
Laoang, Northern Samar
Founded: 1959
National Trade.

Lapak Agricultural School
Lapak, Siasi, Sulu
Agriculture.

Leyte Agro-Industrial School
Leyte, Leyte
Founded: 1971
Agro-Industry.

Leyte Institute of Technology
Salazar Street, Tacloban City
Tel: +63 321-2185
Founded: 1907
Technology.

535

Leyte National Agricultural College
Villaba, Leyte
Founded: 1960
Agriculture.

Leyte State College
Tacloban City
Tel: +63 321-2177
Founded: 1921

Los Baños College of Fisheries
Los Baños, Laguna
Founded: 1959
Fisheries.

Maigo School of Arts and Trades
Maigo, Lanao del Norte
Founded: 1948
Arts and Trades.

Marikina Institute of Sciences and Technology
Shoe Avenue, Sta. Elena, Marikina, Metro Manila
Tel: +63(2) 947-2130
Founded: 1969
Science and Technology.

Marinduque State College
Boac, Marinduque
Founded: 1954
Science and Technology.

Mindanao Polytechnic State College
Lapasan, Cagayan de Oro City
Tel: +63(8822) 38-40
Cable: dmmmpsc, cagayan deoro
Founded: 1927

Mindoro College of Agriculture and Technology
Victoria, Oriental Mindoro
Founded: 1962
Agriculture and Technology.

Misamis Oriental State College of Agriculture and Technology
Claveria, Misamis Oriental
Founded: 1963
Agriculture and Technology.

Naval Institute of Technology
Naval, Biliran Sub-Province
Founded: 1965
Technology.

Negros Occidental Agricultural College
Kabankalan, Negros Occidental
Founded: 1947
Agriculture.

Negros Occidental School of Fisheries
Enclaro, Binalbagan, Negros Occidental
Founded: 1961
Fisheries.

North Cotabato College of Arts and Trades
Kidapawan, North Cotabato
Founded: 1962
Arts and Trades.

Northern Iloilo Polytechnic State College
Estancia, Iloilo
Founded: 1965

Northern Mindanao State Institute of Science and Technology
Ampayon, Butuan City
Founded: 1946
Science and Technology.

Nueva Vizcaya State Institute of Technology
Bayombong, Nueva Vizcaya
Tel: +63 4-8-2
Founded: 1916
Technology.

Nueva Vizcaya State Polytechnic College
Bambang, Nueva Vizcaya
Founded: 1947

Occidental Mindoro National College
San Jose, Occidental Mindoro
Founded: 1983

Pablo Borbon Memorial Institute of Technology
Rizal Avenue, Batangas City
Tel: +63(33) 725-2138
Cable: pbmit, batangas city
Founded: 1963
Technology.

Paglaum State College
Talisay, Negros Occidental
Tel: +63 57-13
Founded: 1983

Palawan National Agricultural College
Aborlan, Palawan
Founded: 1963
Agriculture.

Palawan Schools of Arts and Trades
Cuyo, Palawan
Founded: 1958
Arts and Trades.

Palawan State College
Puerto Princesa City
Founded: 1972

Pampanga Agricultural College
Magalang, Pampanga
Founded: 1965
Agriculture.

Panay State Polytechnic College
Pontevedra, Capiz
Founded: 1980

Philippine Merchant Marine Academy
Fort Bonifacio, Metro Manila
Founded: 1967

Polytechnic State College of Antique
Sibalom, Antique
Cable: psca, sibalom, antique
Founded: 1976

Pototan College of Arts and Sciences
Pototan, Iloilo
Founded: 1983
Arts and Sciences.

Quirino State College
Diffun, Quirino
Founded: 1969

Ramon Magsaysay Polytechnic College
Iba, Zambales
Arts and Trades.

Rizal College of Agriculture and Technology
Sampaloc Tanay, Rizal
Tel: +63 79-20-24
Founded: 1974
Agriculture and Technology.

Rizal Technological and Polytechnic Institute
Morong, Rizal
Tel: +63 23-051
Founded: 1983
Technology.

Rizal Technological College
Boni Avenue, Mandaluyong, Metro Manila
Founded: 1969
Technology.

Romblon College of Fisheries and Forestry
San Agustin, Romblon
Fisheries; Forestry.

Romblon State College
Odiongan, Romblon
Founded: 1976

Ruperto K. Kangleon Agro-Fisheries Technical Institute
Bonton, Southern Leyte
Founded: 1967
Agro-Fishery Technology.

Roxas Memorial College of Arts and Trades
Andagao, Kalibo, Aklan
Founded: 1983
Arts and Trades.

Sabani Estate Agricultural College
Cabaldon, Nueva Ecija
Founded: 1960
Agriculture.

Samar National Agricultural School
San Jorge, Western Samar
Founded: 1954
Agriculture.

Samar State Polytechnic College
Catbalogan, Samar
Tel: +63 285
Founded: 1912

San Enrique Polytechnic College
San Enrique, Iloilo
Founded: 1983
Agriculture.

San Pablo City School of Arts and Trades
San Pablo City
Founded: 1965
Arts and Trades.

School for Philippine Craftsmen
Polangul, Albay
Founded: 1959
Crafts.

Sorsogon College of Arts and Trades
Sorsogon, Sorsogon
Founded: 1907
Arts and Trades.

Southern Iloilo Polytechnic College
Miagao, Iloilo

Southern Leyte School of Arts and Trades
Sogod, Southern Leyte
Founded: 1982
Arts and Trades.

Southern Luzon Polytechnic College
Lucban, Quezon
Tel: +63 278
Founded: 1968

Southern Samar Agricultural College
Salcedo, Eastern Samar
Founded: 1960
Agriculture.

Sulu State College
Jolo, Sulu
Founded: 1970

Surigao del Norte College of Agriculture and Technology
Magpayang, Mainit, Surigao del Norte
Founded: 1983
Agriculture and Technology.

Surigao del Sur Institute of Technology
Cantilan, Surigao del Sur
Founded: 1983
Technology.

Zamboanga City Polytechnic College
Justice R.T. Lim Boulevard, Zamboanga
Founded: 1912
Arts and Trades.

Tangub Agro-Industrial School
Labuyo, Tangub City
Cable: tanais, tangut city
Agro-Industry.

Tarlac College of Agriculture
Camiling, Tarlac
Founded: 1974
Agriculture.

Tawi-Tawi Regional Agricultural College
Bongao, Tawi-Tawi Sulu
Founded: 1963
Agriculture.

Tiburcio Tancinco Memorial Institute of Science and Technology
Calbayog City Samar
Tel: +63 4-71
Cable: timist, calbayog city
Founded: 1960
Science and Technology.

Visayas State College of Agriculture
Baybay, Leyte
Tel: +63 521-2027
Founded: 1924
Agriculture.

West Visayas State Colleges
La Paz, Iloilo City
Tel: +63(33) 7-49-05
Founded: 1924

Western Luzon Agricultural College
San Marcelino, Zambales
Founded: 1957
Agriculture.

Zamboanga State College of Marine Science and Technology
Zamboanga City
Tel: +63 3941
Founded: 1956
Marine Science and Technology.

Zamboanga del Norte Agricultural College
Tampilisian, Zamboanga del Norte
Founded: 1958
Agriculture.

Zamboanga del Sur Agricultural School
Dumingag, Zamboanga del Sur
Founded: 1954
Agriculture.

PRIVATE INSTITUTIONS

Abada College
Pinamalayan, Oriental Mindoro
Founded: 1950

Abra Valley College
Mckinley Street, Bangued, Abra
Tel: +63 2-0-8
Founded: 1948

Adelphi College
Lingayen, Pangasinan
Director: Jose L. Lopez, Jr.
Founded: 1945

Agno Valley College
Malasiqui, Pangasinan
President: Florentino F. Frias

Ago Medical and Educational Center
Rizal Street, Legaspi City
Tel: +63 41-36
Founded: 1975
Medicine; Education.

Agro-Industrial Foundation College of the Philippines
Bolton Unit, Bolton Riverside, Davao City
Founded: 1978
Agro-Industry.

Agusan Colleges
Butuan City
Founded: 1951

Agusan del Sur College
Bayugan, Agusan del Sur
Founded: 1966

Aklan College
Archbishop Reyes Street, Kalibo, Aklan
Founded: 1945

Aldersgate College
Solano, Nueva Vizcaya
Founded: 1965

AMA Computer College
5486, South Super Highway, Cor. Hen. M. Tinio Street, Makati, Metro Manila
Founded: 1980
Computer Science.

Andres Bonifacio College
College Park, Dipolog City
Founded: 1940

Andres Soriano College
Bislig, Surigao del Sur
Founded: 1952

Annunciation College
479 Magsaysay Avenue, Sorsogon, Sorsogon
Tel: +63 507
Founded: 1961

Annunciation College of Gubat
Gubat, Sorsogon
Founded: 1981

Asbury College
Anda, Pangasinan

Asian Institute for Distance Education
Makti Stock Exchange Building, Ayala Avenue, Makati, Metro Manila
Tel: +63(2) 851186
Founded: 1983
Distance Education.

ASEAN Institute of Arts
CCP Building, 117 Gamboa Street, Legaspi
Village, Makati, Metro Manila
Arts.

Asian Institute of Journalism
SCC Chevalier Building, 3892 R. Magsaysay
Boulevard, Santa Mesa, Manila
Founded: 1980
Journalism.

Asian Social Institute
1518 Leon Guinto Street, Malate, Manila
Tel: +63(2) 59-56-13
Telex: 40793 ohd pm

**Assembleyman Mariano Marcos Memorial
Foundation College**
Kiblawan, Davao del Sur
Founded: 1968

Assumption College
San Lorenzo Village, Makati, Metro Manila
Tel: +63(2) 817-9264
Founded: 1892

Assumption College of Nabunturan
Nabunturan, Davao del Norte
Founded: 1955

Ateneo de Naga
Ateneo Avenue, Naga City
Tel: +63 31-75
Founded: 1940

Ateneo de Zamboanga
La Purisima Street, Zamboanga City
Tel: +63 51-51
Founded: 1912

Baguio Colleges Foundation
Harrizon Street, Baguio City
Tel: +63(74) 442-3316
Founded: 1946

Balatan Institute
Balatan, Camarines Sur
Founded: 1959

Baliuag Colleges
Baliuag, Bulacan
Tel: +63 767-2045
Founded: 1925

Bataan Educational Institution
Orani, Bataan
Founded: 1977
Education.

Bataan Heroes Memorial College
Balanga, Bataan
Founded: 1979

Batac Junior College
Batac, Ilocos Norte

Bicol College
Daraga, Albay
Tel: +63 4613
Founded: 1941

Binalbagan Catholic College
Binalbagan, Negros Occidental
Founded: 1961

Brokenshire College
Brokenshire Heights, Davao City
Tel: +63(82) 7-56-36
Founded: 1954

Burias Academy
Claveria, Masbate
Founded: 1962

Butuan City Colleges
Butuan City
Founded: 1950

Butuan Doctors' College
Butuan City
Founded: 1971
Doctor Training.

Cabalum Western College
Iznart Street, Iloilo City
Tel: +63(33) 7-25-36
Founded: 1945

Cagayan Capitol College
Cagayan de Oro City
Founded: 1971

Cagayan Colleges Tuguegarao
Tuguegarao, Cagayan

Cagayan de Oro Colleges
Carmen, Cagayan de Oro City
Tel: +63(8822) 42-81
Founded: 1948

Calauag Central College
Calauag, Quezon
Founded: 1933

Camarines Norte College
Labo, Camarines Norte
Founded: 1947

Camarines Sur Institute
Goa, Camarines Sur
Founded: 1979

Camiling College
Camiling, Tarlac
Founded: 1946

Canossa Colleges
San Pablo City, Laguna
Tel: +63 24-80
Founded: 1955

Catanduanes State College
Virac, Catanduanes
Tel: +63 473

Cebu Aeronautical Technical School
Cebu City
Founded: 1953
Aeronautics.

Cebu Doctors' College
Osmeña Boulevard, Cebu City
Tel: +63 5-36-92
Founded: 1975
Medicine.

Cebu Eastern College
Leon Kilat Street, Cebu City
Founded: 1915

Cebu Institute of Technology
Natalio Bacalso Avenue, Cebu City
Founded: 1946
Technology.

Cebu Polytechnic School
D. Jakosalem Street, Cebu City
Founded: 1932

Cebu Roosevelt Memorial College
Bogo, Cebu
Founded: 1947

Center for Research and Communication
Pearl Drive, Pasig, Metro Manila
Tel: +63(2) 673-77-81
Telex: etp 65524 crcrp rn
Cable: metro manila
Founded: 1967
Research and Communication.

Central Colleges of the Philippines
52 Aurora Boulevard, Quezon City
Tel: +63 60-78-53
Founded: 1954

Central Institute of Technology
P. Paredes Quezon Boulevard, Sampaloc, Manila
Founded: 1945
Technology.

Central Institute of Technology
Burgos Street, Paniqui, Tarlac
Founded: 1945
Technology.

Central Luzon Doctor's Hospital Educational Institution
San Vicente, Tarlac
Founded: 1976
Hospital Education.

Central Lyceum of Catanduanes
Bato, Catanduanes

Central Maguindanao Institute
Buayan Datu Piang, Maguindanao
Founded: 1960

Central Mindanao College
Kidapawan, North Cotabato
Founded: 1946

Central Negros College
Severino Street, San Carlos City
Founded: 1951

Central Sulu College
Siasi, Sulu

Chiang Kai Shek College
1274 Padre Algue Street, Tondo, Manila
Tel: +63(2) 26-38-81
Founded: 1939

Chinese General Hospital College of Nursing
286 Blumentritt, Sta. Cruz, Manila
Founded: 1921
Nursing.

Christ the King College
Magsaysay Boulevard, Calbayog City
Founded: 1905

Christ the King College
Gingoog City
Founded: 1947

Claret College of Isabela
Isabela, Basilan Province
Founded: 1949

Colegio de la Immaculada Concepcion
45 Gorordo Avenue, Cebu City
Tel: +63 7-65-85
Cable: CIC. CEBU
Founded: 1880

Colegio de la Milagrosa
Sorsogon
Founded: 1937

Colegio de la Purisima Concepcion
1, Arzobispo Street, Roxas City
Founded: 1948

Colegio de Saint Rita
San Carlos City
Founded: 1932

Colegio de San Agustin
Bacolod City
Founded: 1962

Colegio de San Jose
Jaro, Iloilo City
Founded: 1872

Colegio de San Juan de Letran
Bucal, Calamba, Laguna
Tel: +63 545-1829
Founded: 1979

Colegio de Sta. Isabel
Naga City
Tel: +63 3100
Founded: 1968

Colegio del Sagrado Corazon de Jesus
Iloilo City
Tel: +63(33) 7-16-54

Colegio San Juan de Letran
151 Muralla Street, Intramuros, Manila
Tel: +63(2) 491236
Founded: 1620

College of Maasin
Maasin, Southern Leyte
Founded: 1924

College of the Holy Spirit
163 E. Mendiola Street, Manila
Tel: +63(2) 7410916
Founded: 1913

College of the Holy Spirit
Tarlac, Tarlac
Founded: 1939

College of the Republic
San Jose City
Founded: 1948

Columban College, Inc
1 Mt. Apo Street, East Tapinas, Olongapo City
Founded: 1961

Concord Technical Institute
Jakosalem España Street, Cebu City
Founded: 1956
Technology.

Concordia College
1739 Pedro Gil Street, Paco, Manila
Founded: 1947

COR Jesu College
Digos, Davao del Sur
Founded: 1959

Corrigidor College
Guimba, Nueva Ecija

Daniel B. Peña Memorial College Foundation
Tabaco, Albay
Founded: 1949

Davao Central College
Toril, Davao City
Tel: +63(82) 812-10
Founded: 1948

Davao Doctor's College
E. Quirino Avenue, Davao City
Tel: +63(82) 7-84-11
Founded: 1975
Doctor Training.

Davao Medical School Foundation
Bajada, Davao City
Tel: +63(82) 7-21-94
Cable: davaomedschool
Medicine.

De Los Santos College
201 E. Rodriguez Sr. Boulevard, Quezon City
Tel: +63 78-70-11
Founded: 1975

De Ocampo Memorial College
2921 Nagtahan Street Sta., Mesa, Manila
Tel: +63(2) 61-27-86

De Paul College
E. Lopez Street, Jaro, Iloilo City
Founded: 1948

Divina Pastora College
Gapan, Nueva Ecija
Founded: 1958

Divine Word College of Bangued
Rizal Street, Bangued Abra
Tel: +63 203
Cable: divine bangued
Founded: 1920

Divine Word College of Calapan
Oriental Mindoro
Cable: dwcc
Founded: 1946

Divine Word College of Laoag
Barangay 17, General Segurado Avenue, Laoag
City, Ilocos Norte
Founded: 1946

Divine Word College of Legazpi
Rizal Street, Legazpi City
Founded: 1961

Divine Word College of San Jose
San Jose, Occidental Mindoro
Founded: 1960

Divine Word College of Urdaneta
Urdaneta, Pangasinan
Founded: 1967

Divine Word College of Vigan
Vigan, Ilocos Sur
Founded: 1925

Dominican College
179, Blumetrit Street, San Juan, Metro Manila
Founded: 1924

Don Bosco Technical College
736 Kalentong Street, Mandaluyong Metro Manila
Tel: +63(2) 70-11-26
Founded: 1953
Technology.

Don Jose Ecleo Memorial Educational Foundation
San Jose, Dinagat, Surigao del Norte
Founded: 1981
Education.

Dr. Aurelio Mendoza Memorial College
Ipil, Zamboanga del Sur
Founded: 1958

Dr. Faustino Legaspi Uy College
Pilar Village, Almanza, Las Piñas, Metro Manila
Founded: 1975

Dr. Nicanor Reyes Memorial Colleges
Paniqui, Tarlac
Founded: 1950

Dr. Yanga's F. Balagtas College
McArthur Highway, Bocaue, Bulacan
Founded: 1950

Dumaguete Cathedral College
Dumaguete City
Tel: +63 36-59
Founded: 1959

Dynamic Computer Centrum
Legazpi City
Computer Science.

East Central College
B. Mendoza Street, San Fernando, Pampanga
Founded: 1945

East Negros Institute
Tanjay, Negros Oriental
Founded: 1947

Eastern Laguna College
J. Rizal Street, Paete, Laguna
Founded: 1947

Eastern Mindoro College
Bongabong, Oriental Mindoro
Founded: 1945

Eastern Quezon College
Ipil-Ipil Avenue, Gumaca, Quezon
Founded: 1947

Eastern Tayabas College
Lopez, Quezon
Founded: 1920

Elenton Mission College
Maitum, South Cotabato

Emilio Aguinaldo College
Bagong Bayan, Dasmariñas Cavite
Tel: +63 741-92-71
Founded: 1977

Emilio Aguinaldo College
918 U.N. Avenue, Ermita, Manila
Founded: 1973

Emilio Aguinaldo College of Medicine (Medical School Foundation)
Bayong Bayan, Desmariñas Cavite
Medicine.

Emmanuel College
Magsaysay Avenue, General Santos City
Founded: 1962

Eveland Junior College
San Mateo, Isabela
Founded: 1942

Fatima College of Camiguin
Mambajao, Camiguin
Founded: 1922

Fatima Medical Science Foundation, Inc.
120, McArthur Highway, Valenzuela, Metro Manila
Founded: 1979
Medical Science.

Fellowship Baptist College
Rizal Street, Kabankalan, Negros Occidental
Tel: +63 210
Founded: 1954

Fernandez Piano School
110 Bonifacio Street, Davao City
Piano Playing.

Filamer Christian College
Roxas City
Tel: +63 210-471
Founded: 1904

Franciscan College of the Immaculate Concepcion
Baybay Leyte, Inc., Baybay, Leyte
Tel: +63 6-4-5
Founded: 1948

Galang Medical Center College
1240, Batangas Street, Sta. Cruz, Manila
Medicine.

Garcia College of Technology
Kalibo, Aklan
Technology.

Gingoog Institute
Gingoog City
Founded: 1946

Golden Gate College
Batangas City
Founded: 1946

Good Samaritan College
Burgos Aveenue, Cabanatuan City
Founded: 1973

Good Shepherd's Fold Academy
Buenavista, Gumaras, Iloilo
Founded: 1965

Grace Mission College
Socorro, Oriental Mindoro
Founded: 1976

Great Plebian College
Plaridel Street, Alaminos, Pangasinan
Founded: 1947

Guagua National College
Guagua, Pampanga
Founded: 1918

Guzman Institute of Technology
509 Mendoza Street, Quiapo, Manila
Tel: +63(2) 47-48-06
Founded: 1947
Technology.

Harris Memorial College
1267, General Luña Street, Ermita, Manila
Founded: 1903

Harvardian Colleges
San Fernando, Pampanga
Founded: 1945

Heroes Memorial Colleges
Daet, Camarines Norte
Founded: 1947

Holy Cross of Bansalan College
Bansalan, Davao del Sur
Founded: 1959

Holy Cross of Davao College
Sta. Ana Avenue, Davao City
Founded: 1956

Holy Infant College
Tacloban City
Founded: 1924

Holy Rosary College
Tala, Caloocan, Metro Manila
Tel: +63(2) 905721
Founded: 1951

Holy Trinity College
Ginatilan, Cebu
Founded: 1945

Holy Trinity College
Puerto Princesa City, Palawan
Founded: 1940

Holy Trinity College
Domingo P. Fontivo Street, Bato, Camarines Sur
Founded: 1966

I.B. Calingasan Memorial Institution
Nasugbu, Batangas
Tel: +63 26-85-71
Founded: 1976

Iligan Capital College
Mahagahaz, Iligan City

Iloilo Doctors' College
West Avenue, Molo, Iloilo City
Tel: +63(33) 7-91-22
Founded: 1972
Medicine.

Immaculate Conception College
Balayan, Batangas
Founded: 1935

Immaculate Conception College
Fr. Selgas Street, Davao City
Founded: 1905

Immaculate Conception College
Ozamis City
Founded: 1933

Immaculate Conception College
Daraga, Albay
Founded: 1963

Imus Institute
Imus, Cavite
Tel: +63 435-2967
Founded: 1923

Isabela Colleges Foundation
Cauayan, Isabela
Founded: 1948

Jamiatul Philippine Al-Islamia
Amai Manabilang Street, Marawi City
Founded: 1955

John B. Lacson College Foundation-Iloilo
M.M. del Pilar Street, Molo, Iloilo City
Tel: +63(33) 77267
Founded: 1948

John B. Lacson Colleges Foundation-Bacolod
Tangub, Bacolod City
Founded: 1948

Jose Rizal College
80 Shaw Boulevard, Mandaluyong, Metro Manila
Founded: 1919

Kabankalan Catholic College
Kabankalan, Negros Occidental
Founded: 1927

King's College of Marbel
Koronadal, South Cotabato
Founded: 1959

Kolehiyo ng Mamamayan-San Isidro
Pili Camarines Sur

La Consolacion College
Bacolod City
Tel: +63(34) 2-10-64
Founded: 1919

La Consolacion College
La Carlota City
Founded: 1966

La Consolacion College
Mendiola Street, Manila

La Sallete of Santiago
Santiago, Isabela
Tel: +63 721-71-82
Cable: salamid, manila
Founded: 1951

Lacson College
2188, F.B. Harrison Street Pasay, Metro Manila
Founded: 1915

Laguna College
Zulueta Street, San Pablo City
Founded: 1923

Laguna College of Business and Arts
Calamba, Laguna
Founded: 1930
Business and Arts.

Laguna Northwestern Institute
192 Mabini Street, San Antonio, San Pedro, Laguna
Tel: +63 846-0738
Founded: 1978

Remedios T. Romualdez Medical Foundation
T. Claridero Street, Tacloban City
Founded: 1980
Medicine.

Learning Center of the Arts
San Pedro and Ladislava Villages, Buhangin, Davao City
Arts.

Leyte College
Tacloban City
Founded: 1945

Liceo de Cagayan
Cagayan de Oro City
Founded: 1954

Liceo de San Jacinto
Almonte Street, San Jacinto Masbate
Founded: 1981

Lipa City College
Lipa City, Batangas
Founded: 1947

Lisun Institute
Liloy, Zamboanga del Norte

Lorma College
San Fernando, La Union
Tel: +63 26-16
Founded: 1934

Lourdes College
Capistrano Street, Cagayan de Oro City
Tel: +63(8822) 36-83
Founded: 1928

Luna College
Tayug, Pangasinan
Founded: 1934

Luzon College
Perez Boulevard, Dagupan City
Tel: +63(75) 3010

Lyceum Northwestern
Tapuao, Dagupan City
Founded: 1969

Lyceum of Aparri
Aparri, Cagayan
Tel: +63(8822) 2-2075
Cable: lyceumparri
Founded: 1967

Lyceum of Batangas
Capital Site, Batangas City
Tel: +63(43) 725-3313
Founded: 1966

Lyceum of the Philippines
Intramuros, Manila
Tel: +63(2) 47-04-81
Founded: 1952

Mabini College
Daet, Camarines Norte
Tel: +63 23-70
Founded: 1924

Mabini Junior College
Talaga, Batangas
Founded: 1949

Magsaysay Memorial College
Isulan, Sultan Kudarat
Founded: 1965

Magsaysay Memorial College
Tacurong, Sultan Kudarat
Founded: 1962

Magsaysay Memorial College
San Narciso, Zambales
Founded: 1947

Mandawe Academy
Plaridel Street, Mandawe City
Founded: 1952

Manila Doctors College
667, United Nations Avenue, Ermita, Manila
Tel: +63(2) 50-30-11
Founded: 1975
Medicine.

Manuel V. Gallego Foundation College
Cabanatuan City Nueva Ecija
Tel: +63 963-3277
Founded: 1952

Mapua Institute of Technology
Muralla Street, Intramuros, Manila
Tel: +63(2) 40-25-46
Founded: 1928
Technology.

Marian College
Ipil, Zamboanga del Sur
Founded: 1958

Mariners' Polytechnic College Foundation
Baras, Canaman, Camarines Sur
Founded: 1974

Martinez Memorial College
198 A. Mabini Street, Kaloocan, Metro Manila
Tel: +63(2) 23-8861
Founded: 1962

Mary Chiles College
667 Gastambide, Sampaloc, Manila
Founded: 1930

Maryhill School of Theology
13th Street, Corner Gilmore, Quezon City
Founded: 1972
Theology.

Masbate College
Rosero Street, Masbate
Tel: +63 103
Cable: mascoin
Founded: 1964

Mater Dei College
Tubigon, Bohol
Founded: 1983

Mats College of Technology
R. Castillo Street, Agdao, Davao City
Founded: 1970
Technology.

Medical Center Lucena Educational Institution
Lucena City
Founded: 1973
Medicine.

Medina College
Ozamis City
Tel: +63 20036
Founded: 1963

Metro Manila College
966 Plaza Novaliches, Quezon City
Tel: +63(2) 90-18-55
Cable: mirenter, manila

Metropolitan Hospital School of Nursing
1357 Masangkay, Sta. Cruz, Manila
Founded: 1976
Nursing.

Mindanao Institute of Technology
Circuit Road, Rosary Heights, Cotabato City
Founded: 1982
Technology.

Mindanao Polytechnic College
General Santos City
Tel: +63 26-71
Founded: 1980

Mindanao School of Business Administration
Marawi City
Founded: 1979
Business Administration.

Misamis Institute of Technology
Pingol/Bañadero, Ozamis City
Founded: 1965
Technology.

Molave Institute
Molave, Zamboanga del Sur

Mount Apo Science Foundation College
Eden-Bayabas Toril, Davao City
Founded: 1960
Science.

Mount Carmel College
Baler Aurora, Quezon
Founded: 1948

Mount Carmel College
New Escalante, Negros Occidental
Founded: 1961

Mount Carmel School of Quezon City
48, N. Domingo Street, Quezon City

Mountain View College
Malaybalay, Bukidnon
Founded: 1953

Naga College
Peñafrancia Avenue, Naga City
Founded: 1947

Namei Polytechnic Institute
123 A. Mabini, Mandaluyong, Metro Manila
Tel: +63(2) 79-42-21

National College of Business and Arts
3394, V. Mapa Street, Sta. Mesa, Manila
Founded: 1982
Business and Arts.

National College of Business and Arts
Lepanto Cor. R. Papa Street, Sampaloc, Manila
Founded: 1967
Business and Arts.

National Radio School and Institute of Technology
1813, C.M. Recto Avenue, Manila
Tel: +63(2) 27-49-68
Founded: 1931
Technology.

National Teachers College
629 Nepomuceno Street, Quiapo, Manila
Tel: +63(2) 741-09-51
Founded: 1928
Teacher Training.

New Era College
Don Mariano Marcos Avenue, Diliman, Quezon City
Founded: 1975

North Negros College
Cadiz City, Negros del Norte
Founded: 1979

Northeastern College
Villasis, Santiago, Isabela
Tel: +63 6-5-9
Founded: 1941

Northern Bataan Institute
Dinalupihan, Bataan
Founded: 1945

Northern Cagayan Academy
Ballesteros, Cagayan
Founded: 1930

Northern Cebu College
Corner D. Rubio Street, Bogo, Cebu
Founded: 1932

Northern Christian College
General Ablan Avenue and Mabini Street, Laoag City
Tel: +63 22-00-521
Founded: 1946

Northwestern Visayan College
aklan
Founded: 1948

Notre Dame of Dadiangas College
Marist Avenue, General Santos City
Tel: +63 4351
Cable: marist dadiangas
Founded: 1953

Notre Dame of Jolo College
Jolo, Sulu
Founded: 1954

Notre Dame of Kidapawan College
Datu Ingkal Street, Kidapawan, Cotabato
Tel: +63 181
Founded: 1948

Notre Dame of Midsayap College
Midsayap, North Cotabato
Founded: 1960

Notre Dame of Tacurong College
Tacurong, Sultan Kudarat
Founded: 1950

Nueva Ecija College
Cagayan Valley Road, Cabanatuan City

Olivarez College
Sucat Road, Parañaque, Metro Manila
Founded: 1976

Osias Educational Foundation
Balaoan, La Union
Founded: 1947

Osias College
F. Tañedo Street, Tarlac
Founded: 1949

Osmena College
Masbate, Masbate
Founded: 1948

Our Lady of Fatima College
120 McArthur Highway, Valenzuela, Metro Manila
Founded: 1973

Our Lady of the Pillar's Institute
Cauayan, Isabela
Founded: 1956

Ovilla Technical College
38 Danao Street, Masbate
Founded: 1964
Technology.

Pacasum College
Marawi City

Palaris College
San Carlos City, Pangasinan
Founded: 1947

Palawan Polytechnic College
Manalo Extension, Puerto Princesa City
Founded: 1979

Pampanga Colleges
Macabebe, Pampanga
Founded: 1938

Pangasinan Memorial College
Lingayen, Pangasinan

Pangasinan Merchant Marine Academy
Perez Boulevard, Dagupan City
Founded: 1973
Marine Academy.

Pasig Catholic College
Plaza Rizal, Pasig, Metro Manila
Tel: +63(2) 682-2675
Founded: 1915

PATS School of Aeronautics
PATS Hanger, Domestic Airport, Pasay City, Metro Manila
Founded: 1969
Aeronautics.

Perpetual Help College of Laguna
Sto. Niño, Biña, Laguna

Perpetual Help College of Manila
1240 V. Concepcion Street, Sampaloc, Manila
Founded: 1968

Perpetual Help College of Rizal
Pamplona, Las Piña, Metro Manila
Tel: +63(2) 801-00-80
Founded: 1975

**Perpetual Help School of Laguna
(Foundation for Medicine and Health
Science)**
Biñan, Laguna
Founded: 1976
Medical and Health Science.

Philippine Advent College
Sindangan, Zamboanga del Norte

Philippine College of Criminology
641 Sales Street, Sta. Cruz, Manila
Founded: 1954
Criminology.

**Philippine College of Technological
Resources**
Maysan Road, Valenzuela, Metro Manila
Founded: 1980
Technological Resources.

Philippine Harvardian College
68, Almonte Street, Cotabato City
Tel: +63 2318
Founded: 1969

Philippine Maritime Institute
730 Roosevelt Avenue, Quezon City
Maritime Studies.

**Philippine School of Business
Administration**
826 R. Papa Street, Sampaloc, Manila
Tel: +63(2) 27-31-09
Founded: 1963
Business Administration.

**Philippine School of Business
Administration**
1029 Aurora Boulevard, Quezon City
Founded: 1980
Business Administration.

Philippine Statesman College
Cabanatuan City
Founded: 1947

Philippine Union College
Putking Kahoy, Silang, Cavite
Founded: 1917

Philippine Union College
Alicia, Isabela
Founded: 1983

Philippine Union College
Panicuason, Naga City
Cable: puc-nvc c/o tony's grocery igualdad, naga
city
Founded: 1965

Philippine Women's College
Juna Subdivision, Matina, Davao City
Founded: 1953

Pilar College
Zamboanga City

Pines City Educational Center
Maysaysay Avenue, Baguio City
Tel: +63(74) 43-08

Pius XII Catechetical Institute
Jaro, Iloilo City
Tel: +63(33) 72-339
Founded: 1959
Catechetical and Social Studies.

PMI College-Manila
419 David Street, Sta Cruz, Manila

PMI College-Bohol
Bohol, CPC Avenue, Tagbilaran City
Founded: 1973

PMMC Cabansay Foundation
Urdaneta, Pangasinan
Founded: 1961

Quezon City Medical Center and Colleges
960 Aurora Boulevard, Quezon City
Founded: 1971
Medicine.

Quezon Colleges of Southern Philippines
Tacurong, Sultan Kudarat
Founded: 1959

Quezon Memorial College
90Tomas Morato Avenue, Quezon City
Tel: +63 701-238
Founded: 1945

Ramon Magsaysay Memorial College
General Santos City
Founded: 1960

Recaredo Castillo College
Mangagoy, Bislig, Surigao del Sur

Regina Carmeli College
Barasoain, Malolos Bulacan
Founded: 1937

**Remedios Trinidad Romualdez Memorial
School**
S. Amorsolo Street, Makati, Metro Manila

Republic Central Colleges
Plaridel Street, Angeles City
Founded: 1946

Republic College
G. Alban Street, Guinobatan, Albay
Founded: 1947

Republican College
42, 18th Avenue, Murphy, Quezon City
Founded: 1949

R.G. de Castro College
Bulan, Sorsogon

Riverside College
Pablo O. Torre Sr. Street, Bacolod City
Tel: +63(34) 27031
Founded: 1954

Rizal Memorial Colleges
A. Bichon Sr. Street, Davao City
Founded: 1948

Rizal Memorial Institute
Gov. Carnicero Street, Dapita City
Founded: 1946

Roosevelt College
Sumulong Highway, Cainta, Rizal
Founded: 1933

Roosevelt College
Marikina, Metro Manila
Tel: +63(2) 947-70-66
Founded: 1962

Roxas College
Roxas, Oriental Mindoro
Founded: 1946

Sacred Heart College
Merchant Street, Lucena City
Founded: 1884

Sacred Heart College
Catbalogan, Samar
Founded: 1946

Sacred Heart School
Calamba, Misamis Occidental
Founded: 1947

Saint Gabriel College
G. Pastrana Street, Kalibo, Aklan
Tel: +63 3001
Founded: 1970

Saint John the Baptist College
Jimenez, Misamis Occidental
Founded: 1939

Saint Joseph College
Sindangan, Zamboanga del Norte
Founded: 1968

Saint Joseph Institute of Technology
Corners Montilla Boulevard and Rosales Streets,
Butuan City
Founded: 1971
Technology.

Saint Louis College
Carlatan, San Fernando, La Union
Founded: 1964

Saint Louis College of Tuguegarao
Tuguegarao, Cagayan
Tel: +63 446-1872
Founded: 1965

Saint Peter's College
Ormoc City
Tel: +63 2321
Founded: 1914

Saint Rita College
Plaza del Carmen, Quiapo, Manila
Founded: 1907

Saint Rita College
Dr. A. Santos Avenue, Sucat, Parañaque, Metro
Manila

Saint Vincent De Paul College
Mangagoy, Bislig, Surigao del Sur
Founded: 1983

Saint Vincent's College
Padre Ramon Street, Dipolog City
Founded: 1917

Samal Institute
Babak, Davao del Norte
Founded: 1948

Samar College
Catbalogan, Samar

San Antonio de Padua Institute
Pila, Laguna
Founded: 1979

San Carlos College
San Carlos City, Pangasinan
Founded: 1946

San Estanislao Kotska College
Manukan, Zamboanga del Norte
Founded: 1955

San Ildefonso College
Tanay, Rizal
Tel: +63 24-005
Founded: 1947

San Isidro College
Malaybalay, Bukidnon
Founded: 1949

San Jose College
San Nino Street, San Jose City
Founded: 1947

San Juan de Dios College
Roxas Boulevard, Pasay City
Tel: +63 831-97-31
Founded: 1913

San Nicolas College
Surigao City
Tel: +63 623
Founded: 1915

San Pablo Colleges
San Pablo City
Founded: 1947

San Pedro College
12 de Guzman Street, Davao City
Tel: +63(82) 6-44-61
Founded: 1956

San Sebastian College
Sablayan, Occidental Mindoro
Founded: 1957

San Sebastian College
Santa Cruz, Cavite
Founded: 1966

San Sebastian College
C.M. Recto Avenue, Quiapo, Manila
Founded: 1946

Santa Isabel College
210 Taft Avenue, Metro Manila
Founded: 1594

Scout Ramon Albano Memorial College
2407 T. Earnshaw Street, Gagalangin, Tondo,
Manila
Founded: 1956

Siena College
Del Monte Avenue, Quezon City
Founded: 1959

Silay Institute
Rizal Street, Silay City
Founded: 1925

SMC Agro-Tech
Dumalinao, Zamboanga del Sur.
Founded: 1969
Agro-Technology.

Southeastern College
Padada, Davao del Sur
Founded: 1951

Southeastern College
College Road, Pasay, Metro Manila
Tel: +63(2) 831-84-84
Founded: 1946

Southern Baptist College
M'lang, Cotabato
Cable: bapto, m'lang, RCPI
Founded: 1952

Southern Capital College
Washington Street, Oroquieta City
Founded: 1946

Southern Christian College
Midsayap, North Cotabato
Founded: 1949

Southern City College
Pilar Street, Zamboanga City
Tel: +63 3847
Founded: 1946

Southern Masbate Roosevelt College
Placer, Masbate
Founded: 1950

Southern Mindanao Colleges
Pagadian City

Southern Negros College
Binalbagan, Negros Occidental
Founded: 1947

Southern Philippines College
Julio Pacona Street, Cagayan de Oro City
Founded: 1981

St. Anthony College of Roxas City
San Roque Street, Roxas City
Founded: 1958

St. Anthony College of Technology
Mabalacat, Pampanga
Founded: 1945
Technology.

St. Anthony's College
San Jose, Antique
Founded: 1958

St. Augustine College
Dr. Gonzales Street, Baliwag, Bulacan
Founded: 1940

St. Bridget's College
M.H. del Pilar Street, Batangas City
Tel: +63(43) 725-2394
Founded: 1913

St. Columban College
Lingayen, Pangasinan

St. Columban College
Pagadian City
Tel: +63 202

St. Dominic College
Basco, Batanes

St. Ferdinand College
Ilagan, Isabela
Tel: +63 2-21-25

St. Francis Educational Institution
Allen, Northern Samar
Founded: 1946

St. Joseph College
Cavite City
Tel: +63 431-1937

St. Joseph College
Maasin, Southern Leyte
Tel: +63 631
Founded: 1928

St. Joseph's College
Borongan, Eastern Samar
Founded: 1949

St. Joseph's College
295, E. Rodriguez Sr. Boulevard, Quezon City
Founded: 1932

St. Jude Agro-Industrial College
Topas Nabua, Camarines Sur
Founded: 1965
Agro-Industry.

St. Jude College
Don Quijote Street, Sampaloc, Manila
Founded: 1968

St. Mary's College
Sta. Maria, Ilocos Sur
Founded: 1948

St. Mary's College
Bayombong, Nueva Vizcaya
Founded: 1928

St. Mary's College
SMC Tagum, Davao
Founded: 1948

St. Michael's College
Cantilan, Surigao del Sur

St. Michael's College
Quezon Avenue, Iligan City
Founded: 1915

St. Michael's College of Guagua
Guagua, Pampanga
Founded: 1941

St. Michael's College of Laguna
Biñan, Laguna
Founded: 1976

St. Paul College
Dumaguete City
Tel: +63 2959
Founded: 1904

St. Paul College
680, Pedro Gil Street, Malate, Manila
Founded: 1912

St. Paul College
Aurora Boulevard, Corner Gilmore Avenue,
Quezon City
Founded: 1946

St. Paul College
San Miguel, Bulacan
Founded: 1938

St. Paul College
Vigan, Ilocos Sur
Founded: 1905

St. Paul College of Iloilo
Iloilo City
Founded: 1946

St. Peter College
Balingasag, Misamis Oriental
Founded: 1950

St. Peter's College of Daliaon, Inc.
Toril, Davao City
Tel: +63(82) 84-71
Founded: 1948

St. Rita's College
Balingasag, Misamis Oriental
Founded: 1929

St. Scholastica's College
2560 Leon Guinto Street, Malate, Manila
Founded: 1906

St. Theresa College
Tandag, Surigao del Sur

St. Theresa's College
R. Aboitiz Street, Cebu City
Tel: +63 7-70-21
Founded: 1933

Sta. Catalina College
2660, Legarda Street, Sampaloc, Manila
Founded: 1946

Sta. Cruz Institute
Sta. Cruz, Marinduque
Founded: 1951

Stella Maris College
Oroquieta City
Founded: 1935

Sultan Kudarat Educational Institution
Tacurong, Sultan Kudarat
Founded: 1978
Liberal Arts; Nursing; Midwifery.

T. del Rosario Academy
Capitol Drive, Balanga, Bataan
Founded: 1950

Tabaco College
5, Tomas Cabeles Avenue, Tabaco, Albay
Tel: +63 334
Founded: 1982

Tanauan Institute
J.V. Pagaspas Street, Tanauan, Batangas.

Tayabas Western Academy
Candelaria, Quezon
Founded: 1928

Technological Institute of the Philippines
888, Gonzales Puyat Street, Quiapo, Manila
Tel: +63(2) 47-18-90
Founded: 1962
Technology.

Family College Foundation
1452 A. Mendoza Street, Sta. Cruz., Manila
Founded: 1961

Toledo Gullas College
Toledo City
Founded: 1947

Tomas Claudio Memorial College
Morong, Rizal
Tel: +63 23169
Founded: 1950

Toril Community Educational Institution
McArthur Highway, Crossing Bayabas, Toril,
Davao City
Founded: 1963

Trinity College
Cathedral Heights, Quezon City
Tel: +63 70-78-79
Founded: 1963

Unciano Paramedical College
V. Mapa Guadalcanal Street, Sta. Mesa, Manila
Founded: 1977
Paramedical Training.

Union Christian College
San Fernando, La Union
Founded: 1910

Union College
Mabini Street, Sta. Cruz, Laguna
Tel: +63 645-1083
Founded: 1947

United Doctors' Medical Center
6 Ramirez Street, Quezon City
Founded: 1975
Medicine.

University of Mindanao Panabo College
Panabo, Davao
Founded: 1953

Urios College
Corner Zamora and Francisco Streets, Butuan
City
Tel: +63 2040
Founded: 1900

Velez College
F. Ramos Street, Cebu City
Tel: +63 9-68-12
Founded: 1966

Veritas College of Irosin
Irosin, Sorsogon

Villaflores College
Legaspi Street, Negros Oriental
Founded: 1952

Visayan Maritime Academy
Sum-ag, Bacolod City
Maritime Studies.

Visaya's Data Computer College
RBL Building, Gatuslao Street, Bacolod City
Founded: 1969
Computer Science.

West Negros College
Burgos Street, Bacolod City
Tel: +63(34) 2-23-13
Founded: 1948

Western College
Naic, Cavite
Founded: 1945

Western Institute of Technology
Luna Street, La Paz, Iloilo City
Tel: +63(33) 7-42-13
Founded: 1953
Technology.

Western Leyte College
Bonifacio Street, Ormoc City
Tel: +63 2599
Founded: 1945

Western Philippine College
Batanagas City
Tel: +63(43) 725-3762
Founded: 1947

Zamboanga Arturo Eustaqiwo Foundation
Juan S. Alano Street, Zamboanga City
Tel: +63 41-35
Founded: 1948

Zaragosa College
Tayug, Pangasinan

NATIONAL ACADEMIC BODIES

Department of Education, Culture and Sports
University of Life Complex, Meralco Avenue,
Pasig, Metro Manila
Tel: +63(2) 632-0805
Fax: +63(2) 632-0805
Secretary: Ricardo T. Gloria

Philippine Association of Colleges and Universities (PACU)
244 Isabel Building, España Street, Manila
Founded: 1932

Philippine Association of State Universities and Colleges (PASUC)
PUP-Hasmin Hotel, Magsaysay Boulevard, Santa
Mesa, Manila
Tel: +63(2) 49-17-75
President: Frederick So. Pada
Executive Secretary: Alicia O. Asuncion
Founded: 1967

Catholic Educational Association of the Philippines (CEAP)
Zip Code 1007, 1175 United Nations Avenue,
Paco, P.O. Box 1214, Manila
Tel: +63(521) 74-68
President: Jose D. Ante, O.M.I.
Vice-President: Miguel Ma. Varela, S.J.

Association of Christian Schools and Colleges
1664 Taft Avenue, Manila
Tel: +63(2) 521-8154
President: Lino Q. Arquiza
General Secretary: Modesto G. Rico

Association of Catholic Universities of the Philippines (ACUP)
Room 106-B, UST Main Building, España, Manila
Tel: +63(2) 731-3139
President (Acting): Ronaldo V. de la Rosa, O.P.
Secretary-General (Acting): José Ma. B. Tinoko, O.P.
Founded: 1973

Unesco National Commission of the Philippines
Department of Foreign Affairs, PICC Building, CCP Complex, Roxas Boulevard, Manila
Tel: +63(2) 834-4818
Fax: +63(2) 831-8873
Telex: 40-257
Chairman: Roberto R.Romulo, Secretary of Foreign Affairs
Secretary-General: Lourdes R. Quisumbing

POLAND

UNIVERSITIES AND OTHER UNIVERSITY INSTITUTIONS

Academy of Medicine in Białystok
[Akademia Medyczna]
ul. Kilińskiego 1, 15-320 Białystok
Tel: +48(85) 217-05
Fax: +48(85) 249-07
Telex: 852200 am pl
Rektor: Jan Górski (1993-96)
Dyrektor Administracyjny: Elżbieta Kaufman-Suszko
Founded: 1950
F: Medicine; Pharmacy.
D: Stomatology; Medical Laboratory Science.

*Technical University of Białystok
[Politechnika Białostocka]
ul. Wiejska 45a, 15-351 Białystok
Tel: +48(85) 223-93
Fax: +48(85) 223-93
Telex: 852424 pb pl
Rektor: Tadeusz Citko (1993-96)
Dyrektor Administracyjny: Mirosław Milewski
Founded: 1949, 1974
F: Architecture; Civil and Environmental Engineering; Electrical Engineering; Mechanical Engineering.
I: Computer Science; Business Administration and Management.

Academy of Medicine in Bydgoszcz
[Akademia Medyczna]
ul. Jagiellońska 13/15, 85-067 Bydgoszcz
Tel: +48(52) 22-98-48
Fax: +48(52) 22-62-29
Telex: 562138 amb pl
Rektor: Józef Kałużny (1993-96)
Dyrektor Administracyjny: Witold Pac
International Relations: Prorektor, Ryszard Oliński
Founded: 1984
F: Medicine; Pharmacy.
D: Medical Laboratory Science.

Academy of Technology and Agriculture in Bydgoszcz
[Akademia Techniczno-Rolnicza]
ul. Ks. Kordeckiego 20, 85-025 Bydgoszcz
Tel: +48(52) 327-06
Fax: +48(52) 303-70
Telex: 562569 atr pl
Rektor: Jerzy Pączkowski (1993-96)
Dyrektor Administracyjny: Adam Reinke
Founded: 1951
F: Agriculture; Animal Husbandry; Civil Engineering; Chemical Engineering; Mechanical Engineering; Telecommunication and Electrical Engineering.

The Feliks Nowowiejski Academy of Music in Bydgoszcz
[Akademia Muzyczna im. Feliksa Nowowiejskiego]
ul. Słowackiego 7, 85-008 Bydgoszcz
Fax: +48(52) 21-17-54
Telex: t+48(52) 21-11-42
Rektor: Antoni Poszowski (1993-96)
Dyrektor Administracyjny: Tadeusz Zieliński
Founded: 1974

Higher Teacher Education School in Bydgoszcz
[Wyższa Szkoła Pedagogiczna]
ul. Chodkiewicza 30, 85-064 Bydgoszcz
Tel: +48(52) 41-47-73
Fax: +48(52) 41-35-33
Telex: 562573 wsp pl
Rektor: Andrzej Tchórzewski (1993-96)
Dyrektor Administracyjny: Zygfryd Dziemitko
Founded: 1969
F: Humanities; Mathematics and Technology; Education.

The Hugo Kołłątaj Agricultural Academy in Cracow
[Akademia Rolnicza]
Al. Mickiewicza 21, 31-120 Kraków
Tel: +48(12) 33-13-36
Fax: +48(12) 33-62-45
Telex: 322469 arpl
Rektor: Kazimierz Kosiniak-Kamysz (1993-96)
Dyrektor Administracyjny: Jan Sobociński
Founded: 1953

F: *Agriculture; Animal Science; Agricultural Technology and Power Engineering; Forestry; Horticulture; Agricultural Economics; Agricultural Trade and Cooperation.*

BRANCH AT RZESZÓW
[FILIA W RZESZOWIE]
ul. M. Ćwiklińskiej 2, 35-959 Rzeszów
Tel: +48(17) 412-55
Fax: +48(17) 541-23
Telex: (17) 0633367
Prorektor: Marek Zin (1993-96)
Founded: 1973
F: *Agricultural Economics; Agricultural Trade and Cooperation; Land Reclamation and Surveying.*

Academy of Economics in Cracow
[Akademia Ekonomiczna]
ul. Rakowiecka 27,b31-510, Kraków
Tel: +48(12) 21-21-82
Fax: +48(12) 21-05-36
Telex: 0325414 aek pl
Rektor: Jerzy Mikułowski-Pomorski (1993-96)
Dyrektor Administracyjny: Józef Tkacz
Founded: 1926
F: *Economics; Management.*
I: *Commodity Science.*

The Bronisław Czech Academy of Education in Cracow
[Akademia Wychowania Fizycznejo im. Bronisława Czecha]
ul. Jana Pawła II 78, 31-571 Kraków
Tel: +48(12) 48-50-05
Fax: +48(12) 48-17-08
Telex: 325-235 pl
Rektor: Janusz Zolebski (1993-96)
Dyrektor Administracyjny: Zenon Rogala
Founded: 1927
Education.

Jan Matejko Academy of Fine Arts in Cracow
[Akademia Sztuk Pięnych im. Jana Matejki]
Plac Matejki 13, 31-157 Kraków
Tel: +48(12) 22-24-50
Fax: +48(12) 22-65-66
Telex: 0325606 asp pl
Rektor: Włodzimierz Kunz (1993-96)
Dyrektor Administracyjny: Józef Jankowski
International Relations: Prorektor, Władysław Pluta
Founded: 1818
F: *Painting; Graphics; Sculpture; Interior Design; Industrial Design; Conservation of Art Objects.*

Higher Teacher Education School in Cracow
[Wyższa Szkoła Pedagogiczna im. Komisji Edukacji Narodowej]
ul. Podchorążych 2, 30-084 Kraków
Tel: +48(12) 37-38-46
Fax: +48(12) 37-22-43
Telex: 322444 wsp pl
Rektor: Feliks Kiryk (1993-96)
Dyrektor Administracyjny: Karol Grzybacz
Founded: 1946
F: *Geography and Biology; Humanities; Mathematics, Physics and Technology; Education.*

Jagiellonian University Cracow
[Uniwersytet Jagielloński]
ul. Gołębia 24, 31-007 Kraków
Tel: +48(12) 22-66-89
Fax: +48(12) 22-63-06
Telex: 0322297 uj pl
Rektor: Aleksander Koj (1987-)
International Relations: Prorektor, Marek Szymoński
Founded: 1364, 1942
F: *Biology and Earth Sciences; Chemistry; History; Law and Administration; Mathematics and Physics; Philology; Philosophy; Collegium Medicum; Medicine; Nursing; Pharmacy and Medical Laboratory Science.*
I: *Inventiveness and Protection of Intellectual Property; Polish Law, Culture Research.*
Ce: *Debts and Development; External Studies; Language; Physical Education; Research on the History and Culture of Polish Jewry; Social Self-Government Studies.*
Laboratories: *Physico-Chemical Analysis and Structural Research.*
Observatory.
U. for Lifelong Education.

The Stanisław Staszic University of Mining and Metallurgy Cracow
[Akademia Górniczo-Hutnicza im. Stanisława Staszica]
Al. Mickiewcza 30, 30-059 Kraków
Tel: +48(12) 33-49-98
Fax: +48(12) 33-10-14
E-Mail: sokol@plkagh11.bitnet
Telex: 0322203 agh pl
Rektor: Mirosław Handke (1993-96)
Dyrektor Administracyjny: Zbigniew Błażejowski
Founded: 1919, 1949
F: *Mining; Metallurgy; Electrical Engineering, Automation and Electronics; Mechanical Engineering and Automation; Geology, Geophysics and Environmental Protection; Mining Surveying and Environmental Engineering; Material Science and Ceramics; Foundry Engineering; Non-Ferrous Metals; Drilling and Oil-Gas Engineering; Management; Energochemistry of Coal and Physical Chemistry of Sorbents; Physics and Nuclear Techniques.*
I: *Mathematics; Social Sciences.*

Ce: Foreign Languages; Physical Training and Sport; Computer.

Academy of Music in Cracow
[Akademia Muzyczna]
ul. Starowiślna 3, 31-038 Kraków
Tel: +48(12) 22-32-50
Fax: +48(12) 22-23-43
Rektor: Marek Stachowski (1993-96)
Dyrektor Administracyjny: Ryszard Starzyk
International Relations: Prorektor, Adam Walaciński
Founded: 1888, 1945, 1979
Music.

Cracow University of Technology
[Politechnika Krakowska im. Tadeusza Kościuszki]
ul. Warszawska 24, 31-155 Kraków
Tel: +48(12) 33-57-73
Fax: +48(12) 33-57-73
Telex: 0322468 pk pl
Rektor: Józef Nizioł (1993-96)
Dyrektor Administracyjny: Jerzy Lachowicz
International Relations: Prorektor, Jacek Skrzypek
Founded: 1954, 1970
F: Architecture; Chemical Engineering and Technology; Civil Engineering; Electrical Engineering; Mechanical Engineering; Sanitary and Hydraulic Engineering.
I: Mathematics; Physics; Social and Economic Sciences.
Ce: Computer and Data Processing; Educational Technology; Modern Languages.

L. Solski Theatre Academy in Cracow
[Państwowa Wyższa Szkoła Teatralna im. L. Solskiego]
ul. Straszewskiego 21/22, 31-109 Kraków
Tel: +48(12) 22-18-55
Fax: +48(12) 67-16-27
Rektor: Jerzy Stuhr (1993-96)
Dyrektor Administracyjny: Franciszek Gałuszka
Founded: 1946
Acting; Stage Directing; Acting (Dramatic Acting and Mime) (Wrocław); Puppetry (Wrocław).

Higher Teacher Education School in Częstochowa
[Wyższa Szkoła Pedagogiczna]
ul. A. Waszyngtona 4/8, 42-201 Czestochowa
Tel: +48(34) 417-88
Fax: +48(34) 651-497
Telex: 037259 wsp pl
Rektor: Jozef Świątek (1993-96)
Dyrektor Administracyjny: Aleksander Gogulski
Founded: 1969
F: Languages and History; Mathematics and Natural Sciences; Education; Art Education.

*Technical University of Częstochowa
[Politechnika Częstochowska]
ul. Dąbrowskiego 69, 42-200 Częstochowa
Tel: +48(34) 61-25-80
Fax: +48(34) 61-23-85
Telex: 037341 metal pl
Rektor: Janusz Braszczyński (1993-96)
Dyrektor Administracyjny: Henryk Koźmiński
Founded: 1949, 1955
F: Mechanical Engineering; Metallurgy and Materials Engineering; Electrical Engineering; Civil and Environmental Engineering.
I: Social Sciences and Economics; Management.
Ce: Computer; Foreign Languages; Teacher Training of Technical Subjects; Physical Training and Sports.

School of Fine Arts in Gdańsk
[Wyższa Szkoła Sztuk Plastycznych]
ul. Targ Weglowy 6, 80-836 Gdańsk
Tel: +48(58) 31-44-40
Fax: +48(58) 31-22-00
Telex: 05-2289 wspf
Rektor: Stanisław Radwański (1993-96)
Dyrektor Administracyjny: Jerzy Jankowiak
Founded: 1945
Painting and Graphics; Sculpture; Interior and Industrial Design.

Academy of Medicine in Gdańsk
[Akademia Medyczna]
ul. Marii Curie-Skłodowskiej 3a, 80-210 Gdańsk
Tel: +48(58) 41-92-69
Fax: +48(58) 31-61-15
Telex: 0512997 a med pl
Rektor: Zdzisław Wajda (1993-96)
Dyrektor Administracyjny: Sławomir Bautembach
Founded: 1945
Medicine; Pharmacy; Stomatology.

S. Moniuszko Academy of Music in Gdańsk
[Akademia Muzyczna im S. Moniuszki]
ul. Łagiewniki 3, 80-847 Gdańsk
Tel: +48(58) 31-77-23
Fax: +48(58) 31-43-65
Rektor: Waldemar Wojtal (1993-96)
Dyrektor Administracyjny: Henryk Mączka
International Relations: Prorektor, Grażyna Fiedoruk-Sienkiewicz
Founded: 1947
Music.

J. Śniadecki Academy of Physical Education in Gdańsk
[Akademia Wychowania Fizycznego im. J. Śniadeckiego]
ul. Wiejska 1, 80-336 Gdańsk
Tel: +48(58) 52-17-69
Fax: +48(58) 52-17-69
Telex: 572-496 pl
Rektor: Zbigniew Mroczyński (1993-96)
Dyrektor Administracyjny: Jan Horbulewicz
Founded: 1969
Physical Education.

*Technical University of Gdańsk
[Politechnika Gdańska]
ul. Narutowicza 11/12, 80-952 Gdańsk
Tel: +48(58) 41-57-91
Fax: +48(58) 41-58-21
E-Mail: borg@sunrise.pg.gda.pl
Telex: 0512302 plg pl
Rektor: Edmund Wittbrodt (1993-96)
Dyrektor Administracyjny: Ewa Mazur
Founded: 1904
F: *Chemical Engineering; Civil Engineering;
Electrical Engineering; Electronics Engineering;
Mechanical Engineering; Architecture; Hydraulic
Engineering; Ocean Engineering and
Shipbuilding Technology; Technical Physics and
Applied Mathematics; Management and
Economics.*
I: *Social Sciences.*

University of Gdańsk
[Uniwersytet Gdański]
ul. Bażyńskiego 1a, 80-309, Gdańsk
Tel: +48(58) 52-46-41
Fax: +48(58) 52-22-12
E-Mail: rekug@halina.univ.gda.PL
Telex: 0512024 rekug pl
Rektor: Zbigniew Grzonka
Dyrektor Administracyjny: Jerzy Gwizdała
International Relations: Prorektor, Jan Burnewicz
Founded: 1970
F: *Chemistry; Linguistics and History;
Mathematics and Physics; Biology, Geography
and Oceanography; Law and Administration;
Management; Economics; Social Sciences.*

The Silesian Technical University in Gliwice
[Politechnika Śląska]
ul. Pstrowskiego 7, 44-100 Gliwice
Tel: +48(32) 31-23-49
Fax: +48(32) 31-80-85
E-Mail: :polslask@plwrtu11
Telex: 036304 pols pl
Rektor: Wilibald Winkler (1993-96)
Dyrektor Administracyjny: Wojciech
Wydrychiewicz
Founded: 1945
F: *Automatic Control, Electronics, and Computer
Sciences; Architecture; Civil Engineering;
Chemistry; Electrical Engineering; Mining and
Geology; Environmental Engineering;
Mathematics and Physics; Mechanical
Engineering; Energy and Mechanical
Engineering; Materials Science, Metallurgy,
Transport and Management.*
Ce: *Foreign Languages Teaching; Computer;
Physical Training and Sports.*

Merchant Marine Academy in Gydnia
[Wyższa Szkoła Morska]
ul. Morska 83, 81-225 Gdynia
Tel: +48(58) 20-75-12
Fax: +48(58) 20-67-01
Telex: 054568 wsm pl
Rektor: Józef Lisowski
Dyrektor Administracyjny: Jolanta Ewertowska
International Relations: Prorektor, Romuald
Cwilewicz
Founded: 1969
*Marine Engineering; Navigation; Marine
Electrical and Electronics Engineering; Maritime
Administration.*

**K. Adamiecki Academy of Economics in
Katowice**
[Akademia Ekonomiczna im. K. Adamieckiego]
ul. 1 Maja 50, 40-287 Katowice
Tel: +48(32) 58-67-86
Fax: +48(32)58-68-31
Telex: 0312455 ae pl
Rektor: Lucyna Frąckiewicz (1993-96)
Dyrektor Administracyjny: Włodzimierz Mitoraj
International Relations: Prorektor, Florian Kuźnik
Founded: 1936
Economics; Management.

Academy of Physical Education in Katowice
[Akademia Wychowania Fizycznego]
ul. Mikołowska 72a, 40-065 Katowice
Tel: +48(32) 51-70-70
Fax: +48(32) 51-68-68
Telex: 315581 awf pl
Rektor: Joachim Raczek (1993-96)
Dyrektor Administracyjny: Alfred Sosgórnik
Founded: 1970
Physical Education.

Silesian Academy of Medicine in Katowice
[Śląska Akademia Medyczna]
ul. Poniatowskiego 15, 40-952 Katowice
Tel: +48(32) 514-964
Fax: +48(32) 515-046
Telex: 315338 slam pl
Rektor: Władysław Pierzchała (1993-96)
Dyrektor Administracyjny: Adam Sataniewski
Founded: 1948
*Medicine; Pharmacy; Nursing; Stomatology;
Medical Laboratory Science.*

**K. Szymanowski Academy of Music in
Katowice**
[Akademia Muzyczna im K. Szymanowskiego]
ul. Zacisze 3, 40-025 Katowice
Tel: +48(32) 156-51-65
Fax: +48(32) 156-44-85
Rektor: Jan Wincenty Hawel (1993-96)
Dyrektor Administracyjny: Maria Nazarewicz
Founded: 1929
Music.

*University of Silesia in Katowice
[Uniwersytet Śląski w Katowicach]
ul. Bankowa 12, 40-007 Katowice
Tel: +48(32) 58-71-19
Fax: +48(32) 59-96-05
Telex: 0315584 usk pl
Rektor: Maksymilian Pazdan (1993-96)
Dyrektor Administracyjny: Jan Jelonek
International Relations: Prorektor, Marek Zrałek
Founded: 1968
*F: Mathematics, Physics, and Chemistry; Law
and Administration; Technology; Linguistics;
Social and Behavioural Sciences; Teacher
Education and Psychology; Biology and
Environmental Protection; Earth Sciences; Radio
and Television; Pedagogic and Artistic Education.
Ut: Foreign Language Teaching; Physical
Education.
Ce: French (The Alliance Française); English
Language; Business Language.
I: Scientific and Technical Information.
Branch U.: (Education, Cieszyn).*

BRANCH AT CIESZYN
[FILIA W CIESZYNIE]
ul. Bielska 62, 43-400 Cieszyn
Tel: +48(333) 20-93-32
Fax: +48(333) 21251
Telex: 038233
Prorektor: Kazimierz Ślęczka (1993-96)
Founded: 1971
Artistic Education.

The Jan Kochanowski Higher Teacher Education School in Kielce
[Wyższa Szkoła Pedagogiczna im. Jana Kochanowskiego]
ul. Żeromskiego 5, 25-369 Kielce
Tel: +48(41) 423-14
Fax: +48(41) 488-05
Telex: 613478 wsp pl
Rektor: Adam Kołątaj (1993-96)
Dyrektor Administracyjny: Stanisław Zych
Founded: 1969
*F: Humanities; Management and Administration;
Mathematics and Natural Sciences; Education I;
Education II (Piotrków Trybunalski).*

Technical University of Kielce
[Politechnika Świętokrzyska]
Al. Tysiąclecia Państwa Polskiego 7, 25-314 Kielce
Tel: +48(41) 24-100
Fax: +48(41) 41-684
Telex: 0613225 psbi pl
Rektor: Andrzej Neimitz (1993-96)
Dyrektor Administracyjny: Witold Zięba
Founded: 1951, 1965, 1974
*F: Civil Engineering; Electrical Engineering,
Automation and Computer Science; Mechanical
Engineering.*

Higher School of Engineering in Koszalin
[Wyższa Szkoła Inżynierska]
ul Racławicka 15/17, 75-620 Koszalin
Tel: +48(94) 260-20
Fax: +48(94) 259-63
Telex: 0532296 wsi pl
Rektor: Wojciech Kacalak (1993-96)
Dyrektor Administracyjny: Bogumił Grycner
Founded: 1968
*Civil and Environmental Engineering; Mechanical
Engineering; Foreign Languages Teacher
Training (English).*

L. Schiller School of Cinema, Television and Theatre in Łodź
[Wyższa Szkoła Filmowa, Telewizyjna i Teatralna im. L. Schillera]
ul. Targowa 61/63, 90-323 Łódź
Tel: +48(42) 74-35-38
Fax: +48(42) 74-81-39
Telex: 0884380 film plt
Rektor: Wojciech Jerzy Has (1993-96)
Dyrektor Administracyjny: Janisław Baranowski
International Relations: Prorektor, Jerzy Woźniak
Founded: 1948
Cinema, Television and Theatre.

The Władysław Strzemiński School of Fine and Applied Arts in Łódź
[Wyższa Szkoła Sztuk Plastycznych im. Władysława Strzemińskiego]
ul. Wojska Polskiego 121, 91-726 Łódź
Tel: +48(42) 55-32-00
Fax: +48(22) 57-68-82
Rektor: Jerzy Treliński (1993-96)
Dyrektor Administracyjny: Tomasz Nowakowski
Founded: 1945
*Graphics; Fashion and Textile Design; Industrial
Design; Art Education.*

Academy of Medicine in Łódź
[Akademia Medyczna]
Al. Kościuszki 4, 90-419 Łódź
Tel: +48(42) 32-21-13
Fax: +48(42) 32-23-47
Telex: 885410 amed pl
Rektor: Jan Berner (1993-96)
Dyrektor Administracyjny: Stanisław Zagdański
Founded: 1950
*Medicine; Pharmacy; Stomatology; Medical
Laboratory Science.*

Academy of Music in Łódź
[Akademia Muzyczna]
ul. Gdańska 32, 90-716 Łódź
Tel: +48(42) 33-86-59
Fax: +48(42) 32-67-40
Rektor: Bogdan Dowlasz (1993-96)
Dyrektor Administracyjny: Roman Baranowski
International Relations: Prorektor, Anna Wesołowska-Firlej
Founded: 1945
Music.

Technical University of Łódź
[Politechnika Łódzka]
u. Żwirki 36, 90-539 Łódź
Tel: +48(42) 36-74-77
Fax: +48(42) 36-85-22
Telex: 886136 polit pl
Rektor: Jan Krysiński (1993-96)
Dyrektor Administracyjny: Jerzy Prywer
International Relations: Prorektor, Janusz Turowski
Founded: 1945
F: Mechanical Engineering; Electrical Engineering and Electronics; Chemistry; Textile Engineering; Food Chemistry and Biotechnology; Civil Architecture, and Environmental Engineering; Technical Physics and Applied Mathematics; Process Engineering and Environmental Protection; Organization and Management; Machine Design (Bielsko-Biała); Textile Engineering and Environmental Protection (Bielsko-Biała).

BRANCH AT BIELSKO-BIAŁA
[FILIA W BIELSKU-BIAŁEJ]
ul. Willoma 2, 43-309 Bielsko-Biała
Tel: +48(30) 270-61
Telex: (30) 035246
Prorektor: Andrzej Włochowicz (1993-96)
Founded: 1968
Machine Design; Textile Engineering and Environmental Protection.

University of Łódź
[Uniwersytet Łódzki]
ul. Narutowicza 65, 90-131 Łódź
Tel: +48(42) 34-98-85
Fax: +48(42) 78-39-58
Telex: 886291 ulpl
Rektor: Michał Seweryński (1993-96)
Dyrektor Administracyjny: Wojciech Nowak
International Relations: Prorektor, Grzegorz Malinowski
Founded: 1945
F: Philosophy and History; Philology; Mathematics, Physics, and Chemistry; Biology and Earth Sciences; Law and Administration; Economics and Sociology; Educational Sciences.
Ce: Polish Language Tuition for Foreign Students; Foreign Languages; French Research and Studies.

Academy of Agriculture in Lublin
[Akademia Rolnicza]
ul. Akademicka 13, 20-934 Lublin
Tel: +48(81) 37-68-68
Fax: +48(81) 335-49
Telex: 0643176 ar pl
Rektor: Józef Nuryński (1993-96)
Dyrektor Administracyjny: Jerzy Tyczyński
Founded: 1955
F: Agriculture; Agricultural Technology; Animal Husbandry; Horticulture; Veterinary Medicine.

Academy of Medicine in Lublin
[Akademia Medyczna]
Al. Racławickie 1, 20-059 Lublin
Tel: +48(81) 246-33
Fax: +48(81) 289-03
Telex: 642345 am
Rektor: Marian Klamut (1993-96)
Dyrektor Administracyjny: Andrzej Niedzielski
Founded: 1950
Medicine; Pharmacy; Nursing; Stomatology.

*Catholic University of Lublin
[Katolicki Uniwersytet Lubelski]
Aleje Racławickie 14, 20-037 Lublin
Tel: +48(81) 304-26
Fax: +48(81) 304-33
E-Mail: kulzagr@plumcs11.bitnet
Telex: 0643233 kul pl
Rektor: Stanisław Wielgus (1992-95)
Dyrektor Administracyjny: Tadeusz Kądziołka
Founded: 1918, 1944
F: Humanities; Theology; Canon and Civil Law; Philosophy; Social Sciences.
I: Polish Migration and Immigrant Pastoral Care; Polish Church History; John Paul II; Higher Religious Education.

Maria Curie-Skłodowska University Lublin
[Uniwersytet Marii Curie-Skłodowskiej Lublin]
Pl. Marii Curie-Skłodowskiej 5, 20-031 Lublin
Tel: +48(81) 37-51-07
Fax: +48(81) 37-51-02
Telex: 0643223 umcs pl
Rektor: Kazimierz Goebel
Founded: 1944
F: Chemistry; Law and Administration; Humanities; Teacher Education and Psychology; Mathematics and Physics; Biology and Earth Sciences; Economics; Philosophy and Sociology.
I: Political Science; Art Education.
Branch University: (Rzeszów).

BRANCH AT RZESZÓW
[FILIA W RZESZOWIE]
ul. Grunwaldzka 13, 35-068 Rzeszów
Tel: +48(17) 352-76
Telex: (17) 063-3250
Prorektor: Zbigniew Sobolewski (1993-96)
Founded: 1969
F: Economics; Law and Administration.

Technical University of Lublin
[Politechnika Lubelska]
ul. Bernardyńska 13, 20-109 Lublin
Tel: +48(81) 226-12
Fax: +48(81) 273-64
Telex: 0642745 pl
Rektor: Iwo Pollo (1993-96)
Dyrektor Administracyjny: Bogdan Lebedowicz
Founded: 1953, 1977
F: Civil and Sanitary Engineering; Electrical Engineering; Mechanical Engineering; Management and Basic Problems of Technology.

D: Foreign Languages; Physical Training and
Sports.

The Michał Oczapowski Academy of Agriculture and Technology in Olsztyn
[Akademia Rolniczo-Techniczna]
ul. Oczapowskiego 2, 10-957 Olsztyn-Kortowo
Tel: +48(89) 23-39-26
Fax: +48(89) 27-39-08
Telex: 0522669 art pl
Rektor: Andrzej Hopfer (1993-96)
Dyrektor Administracyjny: Stanisław Szumera
Founded: 1950
F: Agriculture; Animal Husbandry; Civil
Engineering; Food Technology; Mechanics;
Surveying and Land Management; Veterinary
Medicine; Water Protection and Inland Fishery.

Higher Teacher School in Olsztyn
[Wyższa Szkoła Pedagogiczna]
ul. Głowackiego 17, 10-447 Olsztyn
Tel: +48(89) 27-26-15
Fax: +48(89) 27-66-74
Telex: 0526223 wsp pl
Rektor: Andrzej Staniszewski (1993-96)
Dyrektor Administracyjny: Wiesław Dudziński
International Relations: Prorektor, Andrzej
Skrzypek
Founded: 1969
F: Humanities; Mathematics; Education.

Higher School of Engineering in Opole
[Wyższa Szkola Inżynierska]
ul. Stanisława Mikołajczyka 5, 45-233 Opole
Tel: +48(77) 26-041 ext.254
Fax: +48(77) 26-724
Telex: 733876 wsi pl
Rektor: Piotr Wach (1993-96)
Dyrektor Administracyjny: Wiesław Henzler
Founded: 1966
F: Civil Engineering; Electrical Engineering;
Mechanical Engineering.

The Silesian Insurgents Higher Teacher Education School in Opole
[Wyższa Szkoła Pedagogiczna im. Powstańców
Śląskich]
ul. Oleska 48, 45-052 Opole
Tel: +48(77) 358-41 ext.253
Fax: +48(77) 358-87
Telex: 733810 wsp pl
Rektor: Jerzy Pośpiech (1993-96)
Dyrektor Administracyjny: Tadeusz Kampczyk
International Relations: Prorektor, Grzegorz Bryll
Founded: 1950
F: Humanities; Economics; Mathematics,
Physics and Chemistry.

*Academy of Agriculture Poznań
[Akademia Rolnicza]
ul. Wojska Polskiego 28, 60-637 Poznań
Tel: +48(61) 47-03-34
Fax: +48(61) 41-10-22
Telex: 0413322 Ar pl
Rektor: Ryszard Ganowicz (1993-96)
Dyrektor Administracyjny: Ludwik Młodziejowski
International Relations: Prorektor, Marek
Świtoński
Founded: 1951, 1972
F: Agriculture; Forestry; Animal Husbandry;
Wood Technology; Horticulture; Food Technology;
Land Reclamation and Environmental
Engineering.
Ce: Physical Education and Sports; Language
Teaching.
I: Social Sciences.

Academy of Economics in Poznań
[Akademia Ekonomiczna]
Al. Niepodległości 146/150, 60-967 Poznań
Tel: +48(61) 52-57-22
Fax: +48(61) 66-89-24
Telex: 0413390 ae pl
Rektor: Bohdan Gruchman (1993-96)
Dyrektor Administracyjny: Józef Krawczyk
International Relations: Romuald Zalewski
Founded: 1926
F: Economics; Management; Commodity
Science.

School of Fine Arts in Poznań
[Wyższa Szkoła Sztuk Plastycznych]
ul. Marcinkowskiego 29, 60-967 Poznań
Tel: +48(61) 55-25-21
Fax: +48(61) 52-23-09
Rektor: Wojciech Ryszard Muller (1993-96)
Dyrektor Administracyjny: Stanisław Słopień
Founded: 1946
Painting, Graphics and Sculpture; Interior Design
and Industrial Design; Art Education.

Academy of Medicine in Poznań
[Akademia Medyczna]
ul. Fredry 10, 60-701 Poznań
Tel: +48(61) 52-03-42
Fax: +48(61) 52-04-55
Telex: 0414321 ampl
Rektor: Janusz Gadzinowski (1993-96)
Dyrektor Administracyjny: Bogdan Poniedziałek
Founded: 1950
Medicine; Pharmacy; Stomatology; Medical
Laboratory Science.

I.J. Paderewski Academy of Music in Poznań
[Akademia Muzyczna im. I.J. Paderewskiego]
ul. Św. Marcina 87, 61-809 Poznań
Tel: +48(61) 52-35-02
Fax: +48(61) 52-21-50
Rektor: Mieczysław Koczorowski (1993-96)
Dyrektor Administracyjny: Piotr Jaborski
Founded: 1920
Music.

E. Piasecki Academy of Physical Education in Poznań
[Akademia Wychowania Fizycznego im. E. Piaseckiego]
ul. Królowej Jadwigi 27/39, 61-871 Poznań
Tel: +48(61) 52-67-67
Fax: +48(61) 33-00-87
Telex: 413230 awf pl
Rektor: Wiesław Osiński (1993-96)
Dyrektor Administracyjny: Włodzimierz Rataszewski
Founded: 1950
Physical Education.

*Technical University of Poznań
[Politechnika Poznańska]
ul. Marii Skłodowskiej-Curie 5, 61-542 Poznań
Tel: +48(61) 31-32-31
Fax: +48(61) 33-02-17
E-Mail: rector@poznan IV.tup.edu.pl
Telex: 0413250 polp pl
Rektor: Eugeniusz Mitkowski (1993-96)
Dyrektor Administracyjny: Mirosław Stroiński
Founded: 1919, 1955
F: Civil Engineering, Architecture and Environmental Engineering; Machine Building; Electrical Engineering; Working Machines and Vehicles; Chemical Technology.
I: Mathematics; Physics.

Adam Mickiewicz University of Poznań
[Uniwersytet im. Adama Mickiewicza w Poznaniu]
ul. Wieniawskiego 1, 61-712 Poznań
Tel: +48(61) 52-64-25
Fax: +48(61) 53-55-35
E-Mail: rectorof@plpuam11.bitnet
Telex: 0413260 uam pl
Rektor: Jerzy Fedorowski (1993-96)
Dyrektor Administracyjny: Stanisław Wachowiak
Founded: 1919
F: Biology; Modern Languages; History; Mathematics and Computer Science; Geography and Geology; Social Sciences; Law and Administration; Education; Physics; Chemistry; Polish and Classical Languages.
Ce: Open Studies; Arabic Culture; Experimental Biotechnology.
C: Language Teaching (English, German, French); Education and Arts (Kalisz).
I: Eastern Affairs.

Higher School of Engineering in Radom
[Wyższa Szkoła Inżynierska]
ul. Malczewskiego 29, 26-600 Radom
Tel: +48(48) 263-33
Fax: +48(48) 239-69
Telex: 067227 wsi
Rektor: Wiesław Wasilewski (1993-96)
Dyrektor Administracyjny: Marián Gos
International Relations: Prorektor, Andrzej Całczyński
Founded: 1974

F: Economics; Education and Teacher Training; Material Science and Footwear Technology; Mechanical Engineering; Transport.

Higher Teacher Education School in Rzeszów
[Wyższa Szkoła Pedagogiczna]
ul. Księcia Józefa Jałowego 24, 35-959 Rzeszów
Tel: +48(17) 396-36
Fax: +48(17) 324-22
Telex: 0633343 wsp pl
Rektor: Kazimierz Sowa (1993-96)
Dyrektor Administracyjny: Stanisław Dudziński
Founded: 1965
F: Languages; Mathematics and Physics; Education and Social Sciences.

Ignacy Łukaszewicz Technical University of Rzeszów
[Politechnika Rzeszowska im. Ignacego Łukaszewicza]
ul. Wincentego Pola 2, 35-021 Rzeszów
Tel: +48(17) 412-60
Fax: +48(17) 412-60
E-Mail: zfszyman @plkrcy11
Telex: 0632224 prz pl
Cable: inwsz
Rektor: Kazimierz Oczoś (1993-96)
Dyrektor: Janusz Bury
Founded: 1951, 1963, 1974
F: Civil and Environmental Engineering; Electrical Engineering; Machine Building and Aviation; Chemical Technology; Management and Marketing.
I: Mathematics and Physics; Foreign Languages; Human Sciences; Physical Education.

Higher Agriculture and Teacher Education School in Siedlce
[Wyższa Szkoła Rolniczo-Pedagogiczna]
ul. 3 Maja 54, 08-110 Siedlce
Tel: +48(25) 249-13
Fax: +48(25) 242-85
Telex: 84715 wsrp
Rektor: Lesław Szczerba (1993-96)
Dyrektor Administracyjny: Andrzej Tarasiuk
Founded: 1977
F: Agriculture; Chemistry and Mathematics; Humanities.

Higher Teacher Education School in Słupsk
[Wyższa Szkoła Pedagogiczna]
ul. Arciszewskiego 22, 76-200 Słupsk
Tel: +48(59) 294-44
Fax: +48(59) 242-75
Dyrektor: Stefan Rudnik (1994-96)
Dyrektor Administracyjny: Jan Szumski
Founded: 1969
F: Humanities; Mathematics and Natural Sciences; Education.

Agricultural Academy in Szczecin
[Akademia Rolnicza]
ul. Janosika 8, 71-424 Szczecin
Tel: +48(91) 22-02-60
Fax: +48(91) 23-24-17
Telex: 0425494 ar pl
Rektor: Marian Piech (1993-96)
Dyrektor Administracyjny: Stanisław Cąpała
International Relations: Prorektor, Mikolaj
Protasowicki
Founded: 1954
F: Agriculture; Economics and Organization of
Food Economy; Animal Husbandry; Marine
Fisheries and Food Technology.

Maritime Academy in Szczecin
[Wyzśza Szkoła Morska]
ul. Wały Chrobrego 1, 70-500 Szczecin
Tel: +48(91) 34-42-26
Fax: +48(91) 33-81-23
Telex: 0422585 wsm pl
Rektor: Aleksander Walczak (1993-96)
Dyrektor Administracyjny: Andrzej Durajczyk
International Relations: Prorektor, Adam Wolski
Founded: 1947
Marine Engineering; Marine Transport, Sea
Fisheries and Maritime Administration.

The Pomeranian Academy of Medicine in Szczecin
[Pomorska Akademia Medyczna]
ul. Rybacka 1, 70-204 Szczecin
Tel: +48(91) 336-303
Fax: +48(91) 336-303
Telex: 425677 pom pl
Rektor: Seweryn Wiechowski (1993-96)
Dyrektor Administracyjny: Jerzy Łuczak
Founded: 1948
Medicine; Stomatology.

*Szczecin University
[Uniwersytet Szczeciński]
ul.Korsarzy 1, 70-540 Szczecin
Tel: +48(91) 34-25-36
Fax: +48(91) 34-29-92
Telex: 0422719
Rektor: Hubert Bronk (1993-96)
Dyrektor Administracyjny: Eugeniusz Kisiel
Founded: 1968, 1973, 1985
F: Humanities; Economics; Mathematics and
Physics; Natural Sciences; Law and
Administration.
I: Physical Education; Transport and
Communication.
C: Foreign Languages.

Technical University of Szczecin
[Politechnika Szczecińska]
Al. Piastów 17, 70-310 Szczecin
Tel: +48(91) 34-67-51
Fax: +48(91) 34-73-26
Telex: 422141 ps pl
Rektor: Stefan Berczynski (1993-96)
Dyrektor Administracyjny: Franciszek Kamola
Founded: 1946, 1955
F: Civil Engineering and Architecture;
Mechanical Engineering; Chemical Engineering
and Technology; Electrical Engineering; Marine
Engineering.

Nicholas Copernicus University of Toruń
[Uniwersytet Mikołaja Kopernika w Toruniu]
ul. Gagarina 11, 87-100 Toruń
Tel: +48(56) 226-94
Fax: +48(56) 246-02
Telex: 0552412 umk pl
Rektor: Andrzej Jamiołkowski (1993-96)
Dyrektor Administracyjny: Stefan Nielek
International Relations: Prorektor, Michał
Rozwadowski
Founded: 1945
F: Humanities; Economics and Management;
Fine Arts; Law and Administration; Biology and
Earth Sciences; Mathematics and Computer
Science; Chemistry; Physics and Astronomy.

Warsaw Agricultural University
[Szkoła Główna Gospodarstwa Wiejskiego w
Warszawie]
ul. Nowoursynowska 166, 02-766 Warszawa
Tel: +48(22) 43-63-87
Fax: +48(22) 47-15-62
Telex: 816238 sggw pl
Rektor: Jan Górecki (1993-96)
Dyrektor Administracyjny: Władysław Skarżyński
International Relations: Prorektor, Włodzimierz
Kluciński
Founded: 1906
F: Agriculture; Agricultural Economics;
Agricultural and Forestry Engineering; Animal
Science; Food Technology; Forestry; Horticulture;
Human Nutrition and Home Economics; Land
Reclamation and Environmental Engineering;
Veterinary Medicine; Wood Technology.

Central School of Commerce in Warsaw
[Szkoła Główna Handlowa]
Al. Niepodległości 162, 02-554 Warszawa
Tel: +48(22) 49-51-95
Fax: +48(22) 49-53-12
Telex: 816031 sgpis pl
Rektor: Janina Jóźwiak (1993-96)
Dyrektor Administracyjny: Halina Adamiak
International Relations: Prorektor, Krzysztof
Rutkowski
Founded: 1915
F: Economics of Production; Finance and
Statistics; Foreign Trade; Home Trade; Social
Economics.

Academy of Fine Arts in Warsaw
[Akademia Sztuk Pięknych]
ul. Krakowskie Przedmieście 5, 00-068 Warszawa
Tel: +48(22) 26-19-72
Fax: +48(22) 26-21-14
Rektor: Adam Myjak (1993-96)
Dyrektor Administracyjny: Andrzej Gałązka
Founded: 1903
F: Painting; Graphics; Sculpture; Interior Design; Industrial Design; Conservation of Art Design.

Academy of Medicine in Warsaw
[Akademia Medyczna]
ul. Filtrowa 30, 02-032 Warszawa
Tel: +48(22) 25-19-04
Fax: +48(22) 25-73-00
Telex: 815403 ac med pl
Rektor: Tadeusz Tłoczko (1993-96)
Dyrektor Administracyjny: Jacek Zbikowski
International Relations: Prorektor, Andrzej Górski
Founded: 1950
Medicine; Pharmacy; Nursing; Stomatology; Medical Laboratory Science.

The Chopin State Academy of Music in Warsaw
[Akademia Muzyczna im F. Chopina]
ul Okólnik 2, 00-368 Warszawa
Tel: +48(22) 27-83-03
Fax: +48(22) 27-83-06
Rektor: Andrzej Chorosiński (1993-96)
Dyrektor Administracyjny: Zenon Cembalski
International Relations: Prorektor, Bogusław Kaczyński
Founded: 1810, 1979
Music.

The Józef Piłsudskig Academy of Physical Education in Warsaw
[Akademia Wychowania Fizycznego im. Jozefa Piłsudskego]
ul. Marymoncka 34, 01-813 Warszawa
Tel: +48(22) 34-08-13
Fax: +48(22) 34-76-65
Telex: 816213 awf pl
Rektor: Zbigniew Krawczyk (1993-96)
Dyrektor Administracyjny: Ryszard Wróblewski
Founded: 1929
Physical Education.

M. Grzegorzewska College of Special Education in Warsaw
[Wyższa Szkoła Pedagogiki Specjalnej im. M. Grzegorzewskiej]
ul. Szczęśliwicka 40, 02-353 Warszawa
Tel: +48(22) 659-59-54
Fax: +48(22) 22-71-34
Rektor: Kazimierz Pospiszyl (1993-96)
Dyrektor Administracyjny: Tadeusz Konrad
Founded: 1922
Special Education.

Warsaw University of Technology
[Politechnika Warszawska]
Plac Politechniki 1, 00-661 Warszawa
Tel: +48(2) 628-5985
Fax: +48(22) 29-29-62
Telex: 813307 pw pl
Rektor: Marek Dietrich (1993-96)
Dyrektor Administracyjny: Marek Lepa
Founded: 1826
F: Architecture; Chemistry; Electronics; Electrical Engineering; Technical Physics and Applied Mathematics; Surveying and Mapping; Civil Engineering; Environmental Engineering; Mechanical, Power, Aeronautical Engineering; Mechanical, Technological, and Automation Engineering; Fine Mechanics; Automobile and Heavy Machine Engineering; Civil Engineering and Agricultural Machines (Płock); Materials Science and Engineering.
I: Chemical and Process Engineering; Transport.

Aleksander Zelwerowicz State Theatre Academy in Warsaw
[Państwowa Wyższa Szkoła Teatralna im. Aleksandra Zelwerowicza]
ul. Miodowa 22/24, 00-246 Warszawa
Tel: +48(22) 31-69-25
Fax: +48(22) 635-74-14
Rektor: Andrzej Łapicki (1993-96)
Dyrektor Administracyjny: Tadeusz Wieczorek
International Relations: Prorektor, Aleksandra Górska
Founded: 1949
Acting; Stage Directing; Theatrical Knowledge; Puppetry (Białystok).

Catholic Theological Academy in Warsaw
[Akademia Teologii Katolickiej]
ul. Dewajtis 5, 01-653 Warszawa
Tel: +48(22) 39-52-45
Fax: +48(22) 39-52-45
Telex: 825-105 atk pl
Rektor: Jan Łach (1993-96)
Dyrektor Administracyjny: Andrzej Grochowski
International Relations: Prorektor, Edward Nieznanski
Founded: 1954
F: Christian Philosophy; Ecclesiastical Historical and Social Sciences; Canon; Theology.
I: Family Studies.

Christian Theological Academy in Warsaw
[Chrześcijanska Akademia Teologiczna]
ul. Miodowa 21, 00-246 Warszawa
Tel: +48(22) 31-95-97
Rektor: Wiktor Wysoczański (1993-96)
Dyrektor Administracyjny: Jerzy Machaj
Founded: 1945
Theology; Ecumenical Education and Catechism.

*University of Warsaw
[Uniwersytet Warszawski]
ul. Krakowskie Przedmieście 26/28, 00-325
Warszawa
Tel: +48(22) 26-18-47
Fax: +48(22) 26-75-20
E-Mail: fdl54@plearn.bitnet
Telex: 825439 uw pl
Rektor: Włodzimierz Siwinski (1993-96)
Dyrektor Admnistracyjny: Ryszard Szpakowski
International Relations: Pro:ektor, Jacek Hołówka
Founded: 1808, 1816, 1945
F: *Biology; Chemistry; Modern Languages;*
Russian Language and Applied Linguistics;
Polish Language; Journalism and Political
Sciences; Physics; Geology; History;
Mathematics, Computer Sciences, and
Mechanics; Philosophy and Sociology; Law and
Administration; Economics; Education;
Psychology; Geography and Regional Studies;
Management; Social Prevention, Socialization
and Social Problems; Humanities; Economics;
Education and Psychology; Law; Mathematics
and Natural Science.
Branch University: *(Bialystok).*

BRANCH AT BIAŁYSTOK
[FILIA W BIAŁYMSTOKU]
ul. Marii Curie-Skłodowskiej 14, 15-097 Białystok
Tel: +48(85) 228-46
Fax: +48(85) 277-32
Telex: (85) 852564
Prorektor: Władysław A. Serczyk
Founded: 1968
F: *Economics; Education and Psychology;*
Humanities; Law; Mathematics and Natural
Sciences.

Academy of Agriculture in Wrocław
[Akademia Rolnicza]
ul. Norwida 25, 50-375 Wrocław
Tel: +48(71) 205-101
Fax: +48(71) 229-576
Telex: 0715327 arw pl
Rektor: Jerzy Kowalski (1993-96)
Dyrektor Administracyjny: Marian Rybareczyk
International Relations: Prorektor, Stanisław
Krzywiecki
Founded: 1951
F: *Agriculture; Animal Husbandry; Food*
Technology; Land Reclamation and
Environmental Engineering; Veterinary Medicine.

The O. Lange Academy of Economics in Wrocław
[Akademia Ekonomiczna im. O. Langego]
ul. Komandorska 118/120, 53-345 Wrocław
Tel: +48(71) 67-12-36
Fax: +48(71) 67-27-78
Telex: 0712427aew pl
Rektor: Andrzej Baborski (1993-96)

Dyrektor Administracyjny: Władysław Pękala
International Relations: Prorektor, Krzysztof
Jajuga
Founded: 1946
F: *National Economy; Management and*
Computer Science; Industrial Engineering and
Economics; Regional Economics and Tourism
(Jelenia Góra).

State College of Fine Arts in Wrocław
[Państwowa Wyższa Szkoła Sztuk Plastycznych]
pl. Polski 3/4, 50-156 Wrocław
Tel: +48(71) 33-668
Fax: +48(71) 31-558
Telex: 0712306 pwss pl
Rektor: Konrad Jarodzki (1993-96)
Dyrektor Administracyjny: Wojciech Orzechowski
Founded: 1946
Painting, Graphics and Sculpture; Ceramics and
Glass; Interior and Industrial Design.

Academy of Medicine in Wrocław
[Akademia Medyczna]
ul Pasteura 1, 50-367 Wrocław
Tel: +48(71) 22-18-91
Fax: +48(71) 21-57-29
Telex: 715354 am pl
Rektor: Jerzy Czernik (1993-96)
Dyrektor Administracyjny: Andrzej Kaiser
Founded: 1950
F: *Medicine; Pharmacy; Nursing.*
D: *Stomatology; Medical Laboratory Science.*

K. Lipinski Academy of Music in Wrocław
[Akademia Muzyczna im K. Lipinskiego]
Pl.1 Maja 2, 50-043 Wrocław
Tel: +48(71) 55-90-56
Fax: +48(71) 55-90-56
Rektor: Marek Dyżewski (1993-96)
Dyrektor Administracyjny: Witold Prętki
Founded: 1948
Music.

Academy of Physical Education
[Akademia Wychowania Fizycznego]
ul. Banacha 11, 51-617 Wrocław
Tel: +48(71) 48-25-27
Fax: +48(71) 48-25-27
Telex: 0712103 awf pl
Rektor: Krzysztof Sobiech (1993-96)
Dyrektor Administracyjny: Ryszard Łossowski
Founded: 1950
Physical Education.

Technical University of Wrocław
[Politechnika Wrocławska]
Wybrzeze Stanisława Wyspiańskiego 27, 50-370
Wrocław
Tel: +48(71) 22-73-36
Fax: +48(71) 22-36-64
Telex: 0712254 pwr pl
Rektor: Andrzej Wiszniewski (1993-96)
Dyrektor Administracyjny: Andrzej Kaczkowski
Founded: 1945, 1968

F: *Architecture; Civil and Hydraulic Engineering; Chemistry; Electronics; Electrical Engineering; Mining Engineering; Sanitary Environmental Engineering; Computer Sciences and Management; Mechanical Engineering; Mechanical and Power Engineering; Basic Problems of Technology.*

BRANCH AT JELENIA GÓRA
[FILIA W JELENIEJ GÓRZE]
pl. Piastowski 27, 58-560 Jelenia-Góra
Tel: +48(75) 515-99
Prorektor: Zdzisław Kremens (1993-96)
Founded: 1976
F: *Electronics; Electrical Engineering; Computer Sciences and Management; Mechanical Engineering.*

BRANCH AT LEGNICA
[FILIA W LEGNICY]
ul. Batorego 8, 59-200 Legnica
Tel: +48(76) 223-79
Prorektor: Zdzisław Kremens (1993-96)
Founded: 1969
F: *Civil and Hydraulic Engineering; Electrical Engineering; Mining Engineering; Computer Sciences and Management; Mechanical Engineering.*

BRANCH AT WAŁBRZYCH
[FILIA W WAŁBRZYCHU]
ul. Armii Krajowej 78, 58-302 Wałbrzych
Tel: +48(74) 785-94
Prorektor: Zdzisław Kremens (1993-96)
Founded: 1969
F: *Civil and Hydraulic Engineering; Electrical Engineering; Mining Engineering; Computer Sciences and Management; Mechanical Engineering.*

*University of Wrocław
[Uniwersytet Wrocławski]
Plac Uniwersytecki 1, 50-137 Wrocław
Tel: +48(71) 40-22-12
Fax: +48(71) 40-28-00
Telex: 0712791uwr pl
Rektor: Wojciech Wrzesiński (1993-96)
Dyrektor Administracyjny: Zbigniew Sadowski
International Relations: Prorektor, Aleksandra Kubicz
Founded: 1702, 1811
F: *Languages; Social Sciences; History and Education; Law and Administration; Natural Sciences; Mathematics, Physics, and Chemistry.*

Higher School of Engineering in Zielona Góra
[Wyższa Szkoła Inżynierska]
ul. Podgórna 50, 65-246 Zielona Góra
Tel: +48(68) 703-82
Fax: +48(68) 39-44
Telex: 0432215 wsi pl
Rektor: Marian Miłek (1993-96)
Dyrektor Administracyjny: Andrzej Rybicki
Founded: 1965
F: *Civil Engineering; Electrical Engineering; Fundamental Problems of Engineering; Mechanical Engineering.*

The Tadeusz Kotarbiński Higher Teacher Education School in Zielona Góra
[Wyższa Szkoła Pedagogiczna im. Tadeusza Kotarbińskiego]
Al. Wojska Polskiego 69, 65-625 Zielona Góra
Tel: +48(68) 631-11
Fax: +48(68) 654-49
Telex: 0433467 wsp pl
Dyrektor: Jerzy K. Baksalary (1993-96)
Dyrektor Administracyjny: Elżbieta Polus
International Relations: Prorektor, Stefan Jan Kowalski
Founded: 1971
F: *Humanities; Mathematics, Physics and Technology; Education.*

NATIONAL ACADEMIC BODIES

Ministry of National Education
[Ministerstwo Edukacji Narodowej]
Al. Szucha 25, 00-513 Warszawa
Tel: +48(2) 628-0768
Fax: +48(2) 29-24-83
Minister: Aleksander Łuczak

Ministry of National Education, Department for International Cooperation
Al. Szucha 25, 00-513 Warszawa
Tel: +48(22) 29-72-31
Fax: +48(2) 628-85-61
Director: Jerzy Wisniewski

Central Council of Higher Education
[Rada Główna Szkolnictwa Wyzszego]
Al. Szucha 25, 00-513 Warszawa
Tel: +48(22) 29-72-31
President: Jerzy Osiowski
Director: Stefan Nawrocki

Polish Universities' Rectors' Conference
[Konferencja Rektorów Uniwersytetów]
ul. G. Narutowicza 65, 90131 Łódź
Tel: +48(42) 78-98-85
President: Michał Seweryński, Rector, Łódź University

Polish National Commission for Unesco
Palac Kultury i Nauki (7th floor), 00-901
Warszawa
Tel: +48(22) 20-33-62
Fax: +48(22) 20-33-62
Telex: 816025 pk pl
Cable: polunesco warsaw
Chairman: Jerzy Kłoczowski
Secretary-General: Wojciech Fałkowski

PORTUGAL

UNIVERSITIES AND UNIVERSITY INSTITUTIONS

PUBLIC INSTITUTIONS

University of Algarve
[Universidade do Algarve]
Estrada da Penha Cruz 26, 8000 Faro
Tel: +351(89) 803561
Fax: +351(89) 801575
Telex: 56168 ipfaro p
Reitor: Jacinto José Montalvão de Santos e Silva
Marques
Administrador: João Salavessa Belo
Founded: 1979
Ut: Horticulture and Fruit Production; Biology
and Fishery; Business Administration; Exact and
Human Sciences.
S: Technology (Higher); Education (Higher);
Business Hospitality and Tourism.

University of Aveiro
[Universidade de Aveiro]
Rua Dr. Mário Sacramento, 62, 3800 Aveiro
Tel: +351(34) 25085
Fax: +351(34) 28600
Telex: 37373 aveiro p
Reitor: Joaquim Renato Ferreira de Araújo
(1986-)
Administrador: Jorge Manuel Pereira Baptista
Lopes
Founded: 1973
D: Modern Languages and Culture; Education;
Mathematics; Physics; Chemistry; Earth Sciences;
Biology; Environmental Engineering; Electronics
and Telecommunications; Ceramics and Glass
Technology; Didactics; Art and Communication;
Management.

University of the Azores
[Universidade dos Açores]
Rua da Mãe de Deus, 9502 Ponta Delgada
Codex, S. Miguel, Açores
Tel: +651(96) 35360
Fax: +351(96) 35370
Telex: 82115 unipdl
Founded: 1976, 1980

D: History and Social Sciences; Modern
Languages and Literature; Education;
Mathematics and Computer Sciences; Earth
Sciences; Economics and Business
Administration; Ecology; Agriculture (Angra do
Heroísmo); Oceanography and Fishery (Horta).

University of 'Beira Interior'
[Universidade da Beira Interior]
Rua Marqués d'Avila e Bolama, 6200 Covilhã
Tel: +351(75) 25141/6
Fax: (75) 26198
Telex: 53733 ubi p
Reitor: Cañdido Manuel Passos Morgado
Secretário Geral: Correia Pinheiro
Founded: 1973, 1979, 1986
D: Textile Engineering; Business Administration;
Mathematics; Civil Engineering; Sociology,
Information, and Social Sciences; Chemical
Engineering; Physics; Paper Engineering;
Electromechanical Engineering.
Ce: Computer Sciences; Teaching and Learning
Resource; Study for Regional Development;
Study for Patrimony Protection.

*University of Coimbra
[Universidade de Coimbra]
Paço das Escolas, 3000 Coimbra
Tel: +351(39) 35448
Fax: (39) 25841
E-Mail: à ciuc 2. uc. rccn. pt
Telex: 52273 unicoi p
Reitor: Rui de Alarcão (1982-94)
Secretário Geral: Carlos Luzio Vaz
Founded: 1290, 1537, 1772
F: Arts; Law; Medicine; Science and
Technology; Pharmacy; Economics; Psychology
and Educational Studies.
Ce: History of Society and Culture; Classical
and Humanities Studies; Portuguese Literature;
Psychopedagogy; Juridical and Economic Studies
(Interdisciplinay); Ophthamology;
Gastroenterology.

University of Évora
[Universidade de Évora]
Largo dos Colegiais 2, 7001 Évora Codex
Tel: +351(66) 25572/3
Fax: +351(66) 20775
Telex: 18771 unievr p
Founded: 1972
D: Exact Sciences; Natural Sciences; Phytology;
Bionomics; Environmental Planning; Education;
Rural Engineering; Animal Husbandry and
Veterinary Medicine; Arts; Sociology; Ecology;
Agricultural Economics; Materials Technology.
Sec: Lifelong Education.

Higher Institute for Industrial and Business Science Lisbon
[Instituto Superior de Ciências do Trabalho e da Empresa]
Avenida das Forças Armadas, 1600 Lisboa
Tel: +351(1) 793-5000
Fax: +351(1) 764-710
Telex: 62542
Presidente: João Ferreira de Almeida
D: Managements Sciences; Sociology; Social Anthropology.
Sec: Economics; History; Social Psychology.
Ce: Anthropological Studies; Contemporary Portuguese History; African Studies.

Institute of Dentistry Lisbon
[Escola Superior de Medicina Dentária]
Avenida Prof. Gama Pinto, 1600 Lisboa
Dentistry.

*New University of Lisbon
[Universidade Nova de Lisboa]
Praça do Príncipe Real 26, 1200 Lisboa
Tel: +351(1) 346-7972
Fax: +351(1) 346-1924
Telex: 44733 unlrtr p
Reitor: Manuel S. Pinto Barbosa
Founded: 1973, 1977
F: Science and Technology; Social and Human Sciences; Economics; Medical Sciences.
I: African Studies; Hygiene and Tropical Medicine; Statistics and Information Management.

Open University Lisbon
[Universidade Aberta Lisboa]
Rua da Escola Politécnia 147, 1200 Lisboa
Tel: +351(1) 670810
Fax: +351(1) 673229
Telex: 616129 iped p
Founded: 1988

Technical University of Lisbon
[Universidade Técnica de Lisboa]
Alameda Santo António dos Capuchos 1, 1100 Lisboa
Tel: +351(1) 545434
Fax: +351(1) 556472
Telex: 62067 utl p
Reitor: António Simões Lopes (1985-)
Administrador: Pedro Meireles
Founded: 1930
F: Veterinary Medicine; Human Kinetics; Architecture.
Higher I: Agronomy; Social and Political Sciences; Economics and Management; Technology.

University of Lisbon
[Universidade de Lisboa]
Alameda da Universidade, 1699 Lisboa Codex
Tel: +351(1) 767624
Fax: +351(1) 793-3624
Telex: 63778 univu p
Reitor: Virgilio A. Meira Soares
Administrador: Maria José de Freitas
Founded: 1911
F: Arts; Law; Medicine; Science; Pharmacy; Psychology and Education; Fine Arts (in process of development); Dental Medicine (in process and development).
I: Social Sciences; Portuguese Language and Culture (for foreign students).

University of Madeira
[Universidade da Madeira]
Colégo dos Jesuítas, Praça do Municipio, 9000 Funchal, Madeira
Tel: +351(91) 36070
Fax: +351(91) 37143
Founded: 1982, 1988
D: Human Motivity; Computer Studies.
Ce: Teacher Training.

*University of Minho
[Universidade do Minho]
Largo do Paço, 4719 Braga Codex
Tel: +351(53) 612234
Fax: +351(53) 77936
Telex: 32135 uminho p
Reitor: Sérgio Machado dos Santos (1985-)
Administrador: José Frederico Aguilar Monteiro
Founded: 1974
S: Engineering; Economics and Management; Sciences.
I: Letters and Human Sciences; Social Sciences; Education.
Ce: Teacher Training (kindergarten and primary levels); Systems Engineering; History and Social Sciences; Environmental Sciences and Technology; Materials Science and Technology; Textile Technology; Civil Engineering; Economic and Social Development Studies; Educational Studies and Community Development; Portuguese Studies; Mathematics; Pure and Applied Chemistry.
Ut: Lifelong Education.

University of Porto
[Universidade do Porto]
Rua D. Manuel II, 4003 Porto Codex
Tel: +351(2) 699519
Fax: +351(2) 698736
Telex: 23121 unipor p
Reitor: Alberto M. Amaral (1985-)
Founded: 1803, 1837, 1913
F: Science; Medicine; Engineering; Architecture; Letters; Pharmacy; Economics; Psychology and Education.
I: Physical Education; Biomedical Sciences; Anthropology; Botanical; Geophysics; Zoology.
Ce: Nutrition and Food Technology; Computer.

University of Trás-os-Montes e Alto Douro
[Universidade de Trás-os-Montes e Alto Douro]
Quinta de Prados, 5000 Vila Real
Tel: +351(59) 25031
Fax: +351(59) 74480
Telex: 24436 utad p
Reitor: José Torres Pereira (1980-)
Administrador: Francisco Miguel Rodríguez
Founded: 1973, 1979, 1986
D: Biology; Economics and Sociology; Forestry; Mathematics and Physics; Pathology and Animal Health; Earth Sciences; Plant Protection; Crop Science and Rural Engineering; Animal Science; Educational Sciences; Food Technology; Engineering; Physics; Letters; Sport.
I: Agricultural and Agrobusiness Sciences and Technologies.

PRIVATE INSTITUTIONS

International University Lisbon
[Universidade Internacional Lisboa]
Estrada de Benfica 275, 1500 Lisboa
Tel: +351(1) 726-2234
Fax: +351(1) 726-7422
Rector: Ilídio Melo Peres do Amaral
Secretary-General: Henrique de Miranda Vasconcelos Martins de Carvalho
Founded: 1986
D: Law; Business Administration.
I: Co-ordination of Graduate Studies.
Ce: African Studies; Cultural Anthropology; Social Security Studies.

Luís de Camões Autonomous University of Lisbon
[Universidade Autónoma de Lisboa Luís de Camões]
Rua Sta. Marta 56, 1100 Lisboa
Tel: +351(1) 526-765
Founded: 1986
D: Law; Business Administration; Economics; Arts.

University Lusíada Lisbon
[Universidade Lusíada]
Rua da Junqueira 194, 1300 Lisboa
Tel: +351(1) 623-282
Founded: 1978, 1986
D: Law; History; Business Administration; Economics.

University 'Portucalense Infante D. Henrique' Porto
[Universidade Portucalense Infante D. Henrique]
Rua Rodrigues de Freitas 349, 4000 Porto
Tel: +351(2) 568-839
Fax: +351(2) 572-127
Telex: 20091 uportu
Reitor: Francisco da Costa Durão
Secretário Geral: Fernando Bayolo Pacheco de Amorim
Founded: 1986
D: Law; History; Business Administration; Economics; Mathematics; Computer Sciences; Extension.
I: History Research; Juridical Research; Archaeology Research; Property Conservation and Restoration; Finance; Informatics Systems Development.
Ce: Economic Studies; Pure and Applied Mathematics; Technology and Information Systems Research.

Catholic University of Portugal
[Universidade Católica Portuguesa]
Palma de Cima, 1600 Lisboa 4
Tel: +351(1) 726-5550
Fax: +351(1) 726-0546
Telex: 65094 unicap p
Reitor: José da Cruz Policarpo (1992-96)
Founded: 1967
F: Philosophy; Theology; Human Sciences; Economics; Law.
S: Biotechnology.
I: Social Research; Religious Sciences.
Ce: Informatics; European Studies; Applied Studies; Studies for Portuguese-Speaking Peoples and Portuguese Culture; Information Studies; Social-Pastoral Studies; Study for History of Religion; Study for Canon Law.

OTHER INSTITUTIONS

Escola de Tecnologias Artísticas de Coimbra
Rua Venâncio Rodrigues 7, 3000 Coimbra
Tel: +351(39) 25142
Founded: 1989
Arts.

Escola Náutica Infante D. Henrique
Avenida Engenheiro Boneville Franco, Paço de Arcos, 2780 Oeiras
Tel: +351(1) 443-0605
Fax: +351(1) 442-9546
Telex: 63679 enidh p
Marine Studies.

Escola Superior Artística do Porto
Rua Passeio das Virtudes 14, 4000 Porto
Tel: +351(2) 319-636
Founded: 1986
Arts.

Escola Superior de Artes e Design
Rua Conde Alto Mearim 383/385, 4450 Motosinhos
Tel: +351(2) 932-163
Founded: 1989
Arts and Design.

Escola Superior de Arts Decorativas
Largo das Portas do Sol 2, 1100 Lisboa
Tel: +351(1) 862-183
Fax: +351(1) 872-173
Founded: 1990
Decorative Arts.

Escola Superior de Belas-Artes de Lisboa
Largo da Biblioteca Pública, 1200 Lisboa
Tel: +351(1) 346-6148
Fax: +351(1) 342-7635
Founded: 1836
Fine Arts.

Escola Superior de Belas-Arts do Porto
Avenida Rodrigues de Freitas 265, 4300
Tel: +351(2) 565-488
Fax: +351(2) 567-036
Founded: 1881
Fine Arts.

Escola Superior de Educação de Fafe
Rua Montenegro, 4820 Fafe
Tel: +351(53) 493-606
Founded: 1988
Education.

Escola Superior de Educação de Joao de Deus
Avenida Alvares Cabral 69, 1200 Lisboa
Tel: +351(1) 677-357
Founded: 1988
Education.

Escola Superior de Educação de Paula Frassinetti
Rua Gil Vicente 138, 4000 Porto
Tel: +351(2) 480-799
Founded: 1988
Education.

Escola Superior de Educação de Santa Maria
Rua de Guerra Junqueira 597, 4100 Porto
Tel: +351(2) 692-838
Founded: 1988
Education.

Escola Superior de Educação de Torres Novas
2350 Torres Novas
Tel: +351(49) 24892
Founded: 1988
Education.

Escola Superior de Educaçao Jean Piaget Almada
Quinta da Arreinela de Cima, Centro Sul, 2800 Almada
Tel: +351(1) 295-6107
Education.

Escola Superior de Educação Jean Piaget Arcozelo
Lugar da Agreja, Arcozel, 4405 Valadares
Tel: +351(2) 762-5303
Founded: 1988
Education.

Escola Superior de Educadores de Infáncia Maria Ulrich
Rua do Jarmim à Estrela 16, 1300 Lisboa
Founded: 1988
Education (infant).

Escola Superior de Enfermagem da Guarda
Avenida Rainha D. Amélia, 6300 Guarda
Tel: +351(71) 22806
Nursing.

Escola Superior de Enfermagem de Angara do Heroísmo
Rua dos Melancólicos, 9700 Angra do Heroïsmo
Tel: +351(95) 26026
Nursing.

Escola Superior de Enfermagem de Artur Ravara
Alameda de Santo António dos Capuchos, 1100 Lisboa
Tel: +351(1) 554-532
Nursing.

Escola Superior de Enfermagem de Beija
Rua Dr António Fernando Covas Lima, 7800 Beija
Tel: +351(84) 26101
Nursing.

Escola Superior de Enfermagem de Bissaia Barreta
Quinta do Vales, 3000 Coimbra
Tel: (39) 814-871
Nursing.

Escola Superior de Enfermagem de Bragança
Avenida do Quartel, 5300 Bragança
Tel: +351(73) 22593
Nursing.

Escola Superior de Enfermagem de Calouste Gulbenkian
Rua da Escola de Enfermagem, 4700 Braga
Tel: +351(53) 613-437
Nursing.

Escola Superior de Enfermagem de Calouste Gulbenkian de Lisboa
Avenida Prof. Egas Moniz, 1600 Lisboa
Tel: +351(1) 793-2180
Nursing.

Escola Superior de Enfermagem de D. Ana Guedes
Estrada Interior da Circunvalação, 4100 Porto
Tel: +351(2) 680-383
Nursing.

Escola Superior de Enfermagem de Francisco Gentil
Rua Prof. Lima Bastos, 1093 Lisboa Codex
Tel: +351(1) 726-2440
Nursing.

Escola Superior de Enfermagem de Leiria
Rua da Fábrica, 2400 Leiria
Tel: +351(44) 33138
Nursing.

Escola Superior de Enfermagem de Ponta Delgada
Rua Dr. Armando Cortes Rodrigues, 9501 Ponta Delgada Codex
Tel: +351(96) 34148
Telex: 82 183
Nursing.

Escola Superior de Enfermagem de Portalegre
Rua de Santo António, 7300 Portalegre
Tel: +351(45) 23728
Nursing.

Escola Superior de Enfermagem de Santarém
Avenida Madre Andaluz, 2000 Santarém
Tel: +351(43) 236-349
Nursing.

Escola Superior de Enfermagem de Vila Real
Lordelo, 5000 Vila Real
Tel: +351(59) 24060
Nursing.

Escola Superior de Enfermagem de Viseu
Estrada da Circunvalaçâo, 3500 Viseu
Tel: +351(32) 25330
Nursing.

Escola Superior de Enfermagem do Dr. Angelo da Fonseca
Avenida Bissaio Barreto, 3000 Coimbra
Tel: +351(39) 36135

Escola Superior de Enfermagem do Dr. Lopes Dias
Largo do Hospital da Misrericórdia, 6001 Castelo Branco Codex
Tel: +351(72) 21402
Nursing.

Escola Superior de Enfermagem do Faro
Rua Teófilo Braga 19, 8000 Faro
Tel: +351(89) 25680
Nursing.

Escola Superior de Enfermagem do S. Joâo de Deus
Largo do Senhor da Pobreza, 7034 Évora
Tel: +351(66) 23347
Nursing.

Escola Superior de Enfermagem do Viana do Castelo
Avenida Conde da Carreira 11, 4900 Viana do Castelo
Tel: +351(58) 829-198
Nursing.

Escola Superior de Polícia
Rua l8 de Maio, 1300 Lisboa
Tel: +351(1) 640-926
Fax: +351(1) 363-3133
Police Studies.

Instituto de Novas Profissoes
Avenida Duque de Loulé 47, 1000 Lisboa
Tel: +351(1) 555-319
Fax: +351(1) 548-501
Founded: 1986
Professional Studies.

Instituto Erasmus de Ensino Superior
Rua Monte da Luz 16, 4100 Porto
Tel: +351(2) 679-389
Founded: 1990

Instituto Politécnico da Guarda
Rua Comandante Salvador do Nascimento, 6300 Guarda
Tel: +351(71) 21634
Fax: +351(71) 21690
Telex: 53549 ipgua p
Founded: 1979
Education; Administration.

Instituto Politécnico de Beja
Rua de Santo António, 1-A, 7800 Beja
Tel: +351(84) 29327
Fax: +351(84) 25771
Telex: 13584 ipbejap
Founded: 1979
Agriculture; Education.

Instituto Politécnico de Bragança
Quinta de Santa Apolónia, Apartado 38, 5300 Bragança
Tel: +351(73) 23082
Fax: +351(73) 25405
Founded: 1979
Agriculture; Education.

Instituto Politécnico de Castelo Branco
Rua Sâo Joâo de Deus 25-3, 6000 Castelo Branco
Tel: +351(72) 23394
Fax: +351(72) 31874
Telex: 27750
Founded: 1979
Agriculture; Education.

Instituto Politécnico de Faro
Quinta da Penha, Estrada da Penha, 8000 Faro
Tel: +351(89) 803561
Fax: +351(89) 801575
Telex: 56168 ipfaro p
Founded: 1979
Education; Hotel Administration and Tourism.

Instituto Politécnico de Leiria
Edifício Maringa, Apartado 579, 2404 Leiria
Tel: +351(44) 34773
Fax: +351(44) 28097
Founded: 1980
Arts and Design; Education; Technology and Management.

Instituto Politécnico de Lisboa
Campo dos Mártires da Pátria 2, 1100 Lisboa
Tel: +351(1) 547347
Fax: +351(1) 529625
Founded: 1979
*Social Communications; Dance; Education;
Theatre and Cinema; Accountances and
Administration; Engineering.*

Instituto Politécnico de Portalegre
Praça da República, Apartado 84, 7301
Portalegre Codex
Tel: +351(45) 26275
Fax: +351(45) 23353
Founded: 1980
Education; Technology and Management.

Instituto Politécnico de Santarém
Complexo Andaluz, Apartado 279, 2002 Santarém
Codex
Tel: +351(43) 27540
Fax: +351(43) 21384
Telex: 43003 ipsant p
Founded: 1979
Education; Technology.

Instituto Politécnico de Setúbal
Largo dos Defensores da República 1, 2900
Setúbal
Tel: +351(65) 35301
Fax: +351(65) 31110
Founded: 1979
Education; Technology.

Instituto Politécnico de Viana do Castelo
Rua de Escola Industrial e Comercial,
Nun'Alvares, Apartado 51, 4901 Viana do Castelo
Codex
Tel: +351(58) 829-063
Fax: +351(58) 829-065
Telex: 32941 ispam p
Founded: 1980
*Agriculture (Ponte de Lima); Education;
Technology.*

Instituto Politécnico de Viseu
Rua Maximiano Aragâo, 3500 Viseu
Tel: +351(32) 25528
Fax: +351(32) 25705
Founded: 1979
Education; Technology.

Instituto Politécnico do Coimbra
Apartado 3023, 3000 Coimbra
Tel: +351(39) 841-890
Fax: +351(39) 841-890
Founded: 1979
*Agriculture; Education; Accountancy;
Engineering.*

Instituto Politécnico do Porto
Rua Dr. Roberto Frias, 4200 Porto
Tel: +351(2) 491-140
Fax: +351(2) 480-772
Telex: 28506 esep p
Founded: 1979
*Education; Music; Accountancy and
Admininstration; Engineering.*

**Instituto Superior de Administração e
Gestao**
Avenida da Boavista 1043, 4100 Porto
Tel: +351(2) 667-235
Founded: 1987
Administration and Management.

**Instituto Superior de Administração e
Línguas**
Rua das Dificuldades 44-45, 9000 Funchal
Tel: +351(91) 25910
Fax: +351(91) 49540
Founded: 1989
Administration.

**Instituto Superior de Arts Plásticas da
Madeira**
Rua da Carrera 56, 900 Funchal
Tel: +351(91) 26209
Founded: 1982
Plastic Arts.

**Instituto Superior de Assistentes e
Intérpretes**
Rua António Pedro 24, 4000 Porto
Tel: +351(2) 316-465
Telex: 20166 isai p
Founded: 1986
Intepretation.

**Instituto Superior de Ciências da
Informaçáo e da Empresa**
Rua do Monte da Luz 12, 4100 Porto
Tel: +351(2) 676-556
Founded: 1989
Information Science; Business Admininstration.

**Instituto Superior de Ciências Dentárias de
Lisboa**
Rua de Xabregas 20, 1900 Lisboa
Tel: +351(1) 858-6533
Fax: +351(1) 858-4623
Founded: 1989
Dentistry.

**Instituto Superior de Ciências Dentárias do
Porto**
Rua de Sao Roque da Lameira 439, 4300 Porto
Tel: +351(2) 567-789
Founded: 1989
Dentistry.

Instituto Superior de Ciências Educativas
Serra da Aloreira, 2675 Odivelas
Tel: (1) 931-3972
Founded: 1988
Education.

Instituto Superior de Gestão
Estrada da Ameixoeira 112/116, 1700 Lisboa
Tel: +351(1) 759-0053
Fax: +351(1) 759-9788
Telex: 64524 isgens p
Founded: 1976
Management.

Instituto Superior de Humanidades e Tecnologias
Largo do Leao 9/10, 1000 Lisboa
Tel: +351(1) 530-744
Fax: +351(1) 346-0554
Telex: 40500
Founded: 1988
Human Sciences; Technology.

Instituto Superior de Línguas e Administração
Rua do Sacramento à Lapa 14-16, 1200 Lisboa
Tel: +351(1) 396-6677
Fax: +351(1) 396-6734
Telex: 65 501 isla p
Founded: 1986
Languages; Administration.

Instituto Superior de Matemática e Gestão
Largo do Leao 9, 1000 Lisboa
Tel: (1) 53 07 44
Fax: (1) 346 05 54
Telex: 40500
Founded: 1989
Mathematics.

Instituto Superior de Psicologia Aplicada
Rua Jardim do Tabaco 44, 1100 Lisboa
Tel: +351(1) 863-184
Fax: +351(1) 860-954
Founded: 1986
Applied Physics.

Instituto Superior de Serviço Social de Coimbra
Rua Oliveira Matos 17, 3000 Coimbra
Tel: +351(39) 24557
Founded: 1990
Social Sciences.

Instituto Superior de Serviço Social de Lisboa
Largo do Mitelo 1, 1100 Lisboa
Tel: +351(1) 570-710
Founded: 1989
Social Sciences.

Instituto Superior de Serviço Social do Porto
Avenida Rodrigues de Freitas 202, 4000 Porto
Tel: +351(2) 573-581
Founded: 1989
Social Sciences.

Instituto Superior de Tecnologias Avançadas
Avenida Eng. Arantes de Oliveira, Lote 13B, 1900 Lisboa
Tel: +351(1) 801-200
Fax: +351(1) 848-6063
Founded: 1989
Advanced Technology.

Instituto Superior Politécnico Internacional
Estrada de Benfica 275, 1500 Lisboa
Tel: +351(1) 726-2349
Fax: +351(1) 726-7422
Founded: 1988

Instituto Superior Tomaz Alcaide
Rua de S. Marçal 77, 1200 Lisboa
Tel: +351(1) 346-0554
Founded: 1989

NATIONAL ACADEMIC BODIES

Ministry of Education
[Ministério da Educação]
Avenida 5 de Outubro 107, 1051 Lisboa Codex
Tel: +351(1) 796-4915
Fax: +351(1) 793-8206
Telex: 18428
Minister: Maria Manuela Ferreira Leite

The Portuguese Conference of Rectors
[Conselho de Reitores das Universidades Portuguesas (CRUP)]
Largo do Paço, 4710 Braga Codes
Tel: +351(53) 612-234
Fax: +351(53) 616-936
Telex: 32135 u minho p
Chairman: Sérgio Machado dos Santos
Secretary: Daniel Luzia da Silva
Founded: 1979

Portuguese National Commission for Unesco
[Commissão Nacional par a Unesco]
Ministry of Foreign Affairs, Avenida Infante Santo 42, 1300 Lisboa
Tel: +351(1) 604-942
Fax: +351(1) 396-9064
Telex: 66886 cnulis p
Cable: cuneso c/clt nestrangeiros lisboa portugal
Chairman: Helena Vaz Da Silva
Executive Secretary: João Estévão Lopes Serrada

QATAR

UNIVERSITIES

*University of Qatar
P.O. Box 2713, Doha
Tel: +974 832-222
Fax: +974 835-111
Telex: 4630 unvsty dh
Cable: univqatar
President: Ibrahim Saleh Al Naimi (1994-)
Secretary-General: Abdul Rahman Hassan Al-Ibrahim
Founded: 1973, 1977
F: Education; Humanities and Social Sciences; Science; Islamic Studies; Engineering; Administrative Sciences and Economics; Technical Education.
Ut: English Language Teaching; Environmental Studies.
Ce: Computer; Scientific and Applied Research; Educational Research; Sirra and Sunna Research; Documentation and Humanities Research.

NATIONAL ACADEMIC BODIES

Ministry of Education
P.O. Box 80, Doha
Tel: +974 413-886
Telex: 4316 min ed dh
Minister: Abdulaziz Abdullah bin Turki

Qatar National Commission for Unesco
Ministry of Education, 22nd February Street, P.O. Box 9865, Doha
Tel: +974 861412
Fax: +974 820-911
Telex: 4672 mined dh
Cable: eduqatar doha
Chairman: Abdulaziz Abdullah bin Turki, Minister of Education
Secretary-General: Abdul Aziz Al-Ansari

REUNION

UNIVERSITIES

University of Réunion
[Université de La Réunion]
15, Avenue René Cassin, 97715 Saint-Denis Messag Cedex 9
Tel: +262 29-45-45
Fax: +262 29-17-00
Telex: 916645 Re
Président: Patrick Hervé (1993-)
Secrétaire général: Jöelle Zampini
Founded: 1825, 1926, 1950, 1971
F: Law, Economics, and Political Science; Letters and Human Sciences; Science.

I: Business Administration; Linguistics and Anthropology; Teacher Training.
Ce: Juridical Studies; Administration Studies; Economic and Social Studies and Research.

CENTRE FOR ADMINISTRATIVE STUDIES
[CENTRE D'ETUDES ADMINISTRATIVES]
2426 avenue de la Victoire, 97489 Saint-Denis Cedex
Tel: +262 21-21-20
Directeur: Jacques Colon
Administrative Studies.

INSTITUT OF BUSINESS ADMINISTRATION
[INSTITUT D'ADMINISTRATION DES ENTREPRISES]
17, rue Labourdonnais, 97400 Saint-Denis
Tel: +262 21-16-26
Fax: +262 21-48-56
Directeur: Michel Boyer
Business Administration.

INSTITUTE OF LINGUISTICS AND ANTHROPOLOGY
[INSTITUT DE LINGUISTIQUE ET D'ANTHROPOLOGIE]
24, Avenue de la Victoire, Saint-Denis
Tel: +262 29-45-45 (Poste 265)
Directeur: Christian Barat
Founded: 1977
Linguistics; Anthropology.

REGIONAL CENTRE FOR TERRITORIAL STUDIES
[CENTRE UNIVERSITAIRE RÉGIONAL D'ETUDES TERRITORIALES (C.U.R.E.T.)]
2426 avenue de la Victoire, 97489 Saint-Denis Cedex
Tel: +262 21-21-20
Directeur: Pierre Cregut
Territorial Studies.

JOINT SERVICE FOR LIFELONG TRAINING
[SERVICE COMMUN DE LA FORMATION PERMANENTE]
42, rue Général de Gaulle, 97400 Saint-Denis
Tel: +262 21-18-69
Fax: +262 41-25-05
Directeur: Guy Rapanoel
Lifelong Education.

JOINT SERVICE FOR TEACHER TRAINING
[SERVICE COMMUN DE LA FORMATION DES ENSEIGNANTS]
Allée des Aigues Marines, Bellepierre, 97487 Saint-Denis Cedex
Tel: +262 21-74-45
Fax: +262 41-79-20
Directeur: Albert Lopez
Teacher Training.

ROMANIA

UNIVERSITIES AND TECHNICAL UNIVERSITIES

University 'Areal Vlaicu' of Alba Iulia
[Universitatea '1 Decembrie' din Alba Iulia]
Strada Mihai Viteazul 12, Alba Iulia
Tel: +40(96) 811-512
Sciences.

University 'Areal Vlaicu' of Arad
[Universitatea 'Aureal Vlaicu' din Arad]
Bulevardul Revoluţiei 81, 2900 Arad
Tel: +40(96) 612-276
Fax: +40(96) 612-276
Rector: Gheorghe Halic (1990-)
Director: Silvia Hanganu
Founded: 1812, 1972, 1990
F: Engineering; Theology.

University of Bacău
[Universitatea din Bacău]
Calle Mărăşeşti 157, 5500 Bacău
Tel: +40(93) 14-2411
Fax: +40(93) 134-712
Founded: 1961
F: Philology and Sciences; Engineering.

*University of Baia Mare
[Universitatea den Baia Mare]
Stradă Victor Babeş 62a, 4800 Baia-Mare
Tel: +40(62) 422-778
Fax: +40(62) 422-173
Telex: 33343
Rektor: Eugen Pay
Secretar şef: Elisabeta Panţel
Founded: 1961, 1991
F: Mechanical Engineering; Mining; Philology and Sciences.
C: Technical.

University 'Transilvania' of Braşov
[Universitatea 'Transilvania' din Braşov]
29, boulevard Eroilor, 2200 Braşov
Tel: +40(92) 142-576
Fax: +40(92) 150-274
Founded: 1971, 1956, 1960
F: Mechanical Engineering; Technology and Machine Engineering; Forestry; Wood Technology.

*Technical Institute of Bucharest
[Institutul politehnic din Bucureşti]
Splaiul Independenţei 313, 77206 Bucureşti 6
Tel: +40(1) 312-0292
Fax: +40(1) 312-5365
Telex: 10252 ipolb
Rector: Gheorghe Zgura (1992-96)
Secrétar şef: Dumitru Catrina
Founded: 1867, 1965
F: Electrical Engineering; Automation and Computers; Electronics and Telecommunications; Mechanical Engineering; Machine Engineering Equipment and Precision Mechanics; Agricultural Engineering; Aerospace Construction; Material Science and Engineering; Transport Engineering; Chemical Engineering; Power Engineering.
D: Engineering Sciences (with training in English, French and German).

University of Agriculture Bucharest
[Universitatea de Stiinte Agricole din Bucureşti]
Bulevardul Mărăşti 59, 71329 Bucureşti
Tel: +40(1) 618-2230
Fax: +40(1) 312-5693
Founded: 1852, 1921, 1948
F: Agriculture.

*University of Bucharest
[Universitatea din Bucureşti]
64 bulevardul Mihail Kogălniceanu, 70609 Bucureşti
Tel: +40(1) 615-7187
Fax: +40(1) 613-1760
Rector: Emil Constantinescu (1992-96)
Secretarul Universităţii: Marius Ciurel
Founded: 1694, 1864, 1990
F: Mathematics; Physics; Chemistry; Biology; Law; Letters; Geology and Geophysics; Geography; Foreign Languages and Literatures; History; Human Sciences; Philosophy; Psychology, Education and Sociology; Journalism; Orthodox Theology; Baptist Theology.
Ce: Entrepreneurial Studies (International); American Studies; Japanese Studies; Hindu Studies; Long Distance Education; Transition Studies; Ecological Studies; Computer.

University of Medicine and Pharmacy 'Carol Davila' Bucharest
[Universitatea de Medicină si Farmacie 'Carol Davila' din Bucureşti]
Stradă Dionisie Lupu 37, 70183 Bucureşti
Tel: +40(1) 611-1708F+40(1) 637-2252
Founded: 1857, 1869, 1948
F: Medicine; Pediatrics; Dentistry; Pharmacy; Postgraduate Specialization.

Technical University of Cluj-Napoca
[Universitatea Tehnica din Cluj-Napoca]
Stradă Constantin Daicoviciu 15, 3400 Cluj-Napoca
Tel: +40(95) 1645-65
Fax: +40(95) 112-055
Rector: Viorel Handra-Luca (1992-)
Secrétar şef: Teodor Nilas
Founded: 1922, 1948, 1953
F: Civil Engineering; Control and Computer Engineering; Electrical Engineering; Electronics and Telecommunications; Manufacturing Technologies; Materials Science Engineering; Mechanical Engineering.

University of Agricultural Sciences Cluj-Napoca
[Universitatea de Stiinte Agricole din Cluj-Napoca]
Stradă Mănăştur 3, 3400 Cluj-Napoca
Tel: +40(95) 196-384
Fax: +40(95) 118-792
Founded: 1869, 1948
Agriculture.

University 'Babeş Bolyai' of Cluj-Napoca
[Universitatea 'Babeş Bolyai' din Cluj-Napoca]
Stradă Mihail Kogălniceanu 1, 3400 Cluj-Napoca
Tel: +40(95) 116-101
Fax: +40(95) 111-905
Rector: Ionel Haiduc (1992-94)
Secretar şef: Cornel Iures
Founded: 1959
F: Mathematics; Chemistry and Industrial
Chemistry; Biology, Geography, and Geology;
History and Philosophy; Letters; Law; Economics.
I: Physics.
Ce: Computer Ce.

University of Medicine and Pharmacy Cluj-Napoca
[Universitatea de Medicină şi Farmacie]
Stradă Emil Isac 13, 3400 Cluj-Napoca
Tel: +40(95) 116-585
Fax: +40(95) 117-257
Rector: Oliviu Pascu (1992-96)
Secretar şef: Ioan Chira
Founded: 1775, 1872, 1948
F: Medicine; Pharmacy; Dentistry.

University 'Ovidius' of Constanţa
[Universitatea 'Ovidius' din Constanţa]
Bulevardul Mamaia 124, 8700 Constanţa
Tel: +40(9) 161-4576
Fax: +40(9) 161-8372
Founded: 1961
F: Letters, History, Law, and Theology;
Mathematics and Economic Sciences; Medicine;
Natural Sciences; Engineering.

University of Craiova
[Universitatea din Craiova]
13 Str. Alex Ioan Cuza, 1100 Craiova
Tel: +40(94) 1145-48
Fax: +40(94) 111-668
Rector: Mircea Ivánescu
Founded: 1966
F: Sciences; Mathematics and Informatics;
Letters and History; Law; Economics; Medicine;
Mechanical Engineering; Electrotechnics;
Electromechanics; Automatics, Computers and
Electronics; Horticulture; Agriculture; Theology.

University 'Dunarea de Jos' of Galaţi
[Universitatea 'Dunarea de Jos' din Galaţi]
Strada Domneasca 47, 6200 Galaţi
Tel: +40(93) 414-112
Fax: +40(93) 412-328
Rector: Mihai Jâşcanu (1990-94)
Founded: 1948, 1974
F: Mechanical Engineering; Food Technology
and Fishery; Shipbuilding and Electrical
Engineering; Metallurgy; Letters and Sciences;
Economics and Juridical Science.

Farming University 'Ion Ionescu de la Brad' of Iaşi
[Universitatea 'Ion Ionescu de la Brad'din Iaşi]
Strada Mihail Sadoveanu 3, Iaşi
Tel: +40(98) 140-798
F: Agriculture; Horticulture; Animal Husbandry;
Veterinary Medicine.

Technical University 'Gh. Asachi' of Iaşi
[Universitatea Tehnica 'Gh. Asachi' din Iaşi]
Bulevardu Copou 22, 6600 Iaşi
Tel: +40(98) 140-160
Fax: +40) 147-923
Telex: 22216 ipol
Rector: Vitalie Belousov
Founded: 1912
F: Chemical Engineering; Civil Engineering and
Architecture; Electrical Engineering; Mechanical
Engineering; Control System and Computer
Engineering; Electronics and
Telecommunications; Hydrotechnical Engineering;
Science and Engineering of Materials;
Technology of Machine Building; Textiles and
Leather.

*University 'Alexandru Ion Cruza of Iaşi
[Universitatea 'Alexandru Ion Cruza' din Iaşi]
Bulevardul Copou 11, 6600 Iaşi
Tel: +40(98) 144-760
Fax: +40(98) 146-330
Telex: 22371 ccui r
Rector: Gheorghe Popa
Secrétar şef: Rodica Stegaru
Founded: 1860
F: Mathematics; Physics; Biology; Geography
and Geology; Law; History; Philosophy; Letters;
Economics; Informatics; Orthodox Theology;
Chemistry.
Ce: Computer.

University of Medicine and Pharmacy Iaşi
[Universitatea de Medicină si Farmacie 'Grigore
T. Popa' din Iaşi]
Stradă Universităţii 16, 6600 Iaşi
Tel: +40(98) 116-104
Fax: +40(98) 117-845
President: Carol Stanciu
Founded: 1879, 1948
Medicine; Dentistry; Pharmacy.

University of Oradea
[Universitatea din Oradea]
Strada Armatei Române 5, 3700 Oradea
Tel: +40(99) 132-830
Fax: +40(99) 132-789
Founded: 1963, 1990, 1991
F: Electrotechnical Engineering; Mechanical
Engineering; Sciences; Medicine; Economics and
Law; Orthodox Theology; Baptist Theology.

*Technical University of Petroşani
[Universitatea Tehnica din Petroşani]
Stradă Universităţii nr. 20, 2675 Petroşani
Tel: +40(93) 542-994
Fax: +40(93) 543-491
Telex: 72524 univ.p
Founded: 1948, 1952
F: Mining Engineering; Mining, Mechanical
Engineering and Installations.

University of Piteşti
[Universitatea din Piteśti]
Piaţa Vasile Milea, 1, 0300 Piteşti
Tel: +40(97) 622-289
Fax: +40(97) 622-289
Rector: Ioan Vucu
Secretar şef: Silvia Tufeanu
Founded: 1962, 1990
F: Socio-Humanistic Sciences; Mechanical
Engineering; Theology.
C: Technical.

University of Ploeşti
[Universitatea din Ploeşti]
Bulevardul Bucureşti 39, 2000 Ploeşti
Tel: (97) 173-172
Fax: (97) 171-974
President: Constantin Ionescu
Founded: 1973, 1992
F: Oil Chemistry and Technology; Oil Drilling
and Extraction; Petrochemical Technology;
Mechanical and Electrical Engineering; Philology
and Sciences.

University 'Eftimie Murgu' of Reşita
[Universitatea 'Eftimie Murgu' din Reşita]
Piaţa Traian Vui 1, Reşita
Tel: +40(96) 410-227
F: Engineering; Law and Economics.

University of Sibiu
[Universitatea din Sibiu]
Bulevardul Victoriei 5-7, 2700 Sibiu
Tel: +40(92) 4160
Founded: 1976
F: Engineering; Philology, History, and Law;
Sciences; Textiles and Food Processing
Technology; Theology; Medicine.

University 'Stefan cel Mare' of Suceava
[Universitatea 'Stefan cel Mare' din Suceava]
Stradă Universităţii 1, 5800 Suceava
Tel: +40(98) 716-147
Fax: +40(98) 716-967
Founded: 1963
F: Mechanical Engineering; Electrical
Engineering; Forestry; Philology and Sciences.

Technical University of Timişoara
[Universitatea Tehnica din Timişoara]
Piaţa Victoriei 2, 1900 Timişoara
Tel: +40(96) 134-713
Fax: +40(96) 133-721
Telex: 71347 iptrv r
Rector: Alexandru Nichici (1992-)
Secretar şef: Pavel Atim
Founded: 1920, 1970, 1991

F: Mechanical Engineering; Electronical
Engineering; Electronics and Communications;
Computer Sciences and Control Engineering;
Civil and Constructional Engineering;
Hydrotechnical Engineering; Chemical
Engineering; Agriculture Machinery.
F: Production Engineering (Hunedoara);
Production Engineering (Resita).

University of Agriculture of Timişoara
[Universitatea de Stiinte Agricole Agronomica a
Banatului din Timiśoara]
Calea Aradului 119, 1900 Timişoara
Tel: +40(96) 143-016
Fax: +40(96) 141-563
Founded: 1945, 1948
Agriculture; Experimental Didactics.

University of Medicine and Pharmacy of Timişoara
[Universitatea de Medicină si Farmacie din
Timişoara]
Piaţa Eftimie Murgu 2, 1900 Timişoara
Tel: +40(61) 304096
Founded: 1945
Medicine and Pharmacy.

University of Timişoara
[Universitatea din Timişoara]
Bulevardul Vasile Pîrvan 4, 1900 Timişoara
Tel: +40(96) 112-805
Fax: +40(96) 116-722
Rector: Eugen Todoran (1992-)
Secrétar şef: Gheorghe Velciov
Founded: 1948
F: Mathematics; Letters, Philosophy, History,
and Physical Education; Economics, Psychology,
and Law; Physics; Chemistry, Biology, and
Geography; Arts.
Ce: Solid State Physics Research; Chemistry
Research and Microproduction; Economics
Research.

University of Tirgovişte
[Universitatea din Tirgovişte]
Strada Domnească 236, Tirgovişte
Tel: +40(92) 611-210
Engineering; Sciences; Technology, Economics,
and Administration.

University 'Constantin Brâncuşi' of Tirgu Jiu
[Universitatea 'Constantin Brâncuşi' din Tirgu
Jiu]
Bulevardul Republicii 1, Tirgu Jiu
Tel: +40(92) 914-307
Engineering; Sciences.

Technical University of Tîrgu-Mureş
[Universitatea Tehnica din Tîrgu-Mureş]
Stradă Nicolae Iorga I, 4300 Tîrgu-Mureş
Tel: +40(95) 413-101
Fax: +40(95) 417-275
Secretar şef: Ioan Diaconescu
Founded: 1960

F: *Engineering.*
D: *Production and Research.*

University of Medicine and Pharmacy of Tîrgu Mureş
[Universitatea de Medicină si Farmacie din Tîrgu Mureş]
38 Stradă Gheorghe Marinescu, 4300 Tirgu-Mureş
Tel: +40(95) 415-551
Fax: +40(95) 430-804
Rector: Ion Pascu
Secretar şef: Gheorghe Serban
Founded: 1945
F: *Medicine; Pharmacy; Dentistry.*

OTHER INSTITUTIONS

Academeia de Teatru şi Film din Bucureţ
Strada Matei Voievod 75-77, Bucureţ
Tel: +40(1) 422-720
Founded: 1864
Theatre and Cinema.

Academia de Arta din Bucureşti
Strada General Budişteanu 19, Bucureşti
Tel: +40(1) 130-556
Founded: 1864
Art.

Academia de Arta Teatral din Tîrgu Mureş
Strada Köteles Samuel 6, Tîrgu Mureş
Tel: +40(954) 20794
Founded: 1948
Theatrical Arts.

Academia de Arte 'George Enescu' din Iaşi
Strada Cloşca 9, Iaşi
Tel: +40(98) 147-246
Founded: 1864
Art.

Academia de Arte Vizuale 'Ion Andreescu' din Cluj-Napoca
Strada Liberaţii 31, Cluj-Napoca
Tel: +40(95) 111-577
Founded: 1948
Visual Arts.

Academia de Muzică din Bucureşti
Strada Mamaia 124, Bucureşti
Tel: +40(1) 146-341
Music.

Academia de Muzică 'Gheorghe Dima' din Cluj-Napoca
Strada I.C. Bratianu 25, Cluj-Napoca
Tel: +40(951) 11241
Founded: 1919
Music.

Academia de Studii Economice din Bucureşti
Piaţa Romană 6, Bucureşti
Tel: +40(1) 110-610
Founded: 1913
Economics.

Academia Nationala de Educatie Fizică din Bucureşti
Strada Stefan Furtuna 140, Bucureşti
Tel: +40(1) 115-699
Founded: 1922
Physical Education.

Institutul Agronomic 'Ion Ionescu de la Brad' din Iaşi
Aleea Mihail Sadoveanu 3, Iaşi
Tel: +40(98) 140-798
Founded: 1918
Agriculture.

Institutul Agronomic 'Nicolae Balceşcu' din Bucureşti
Strada Mărăşti 140, Bucureşti
Tel: +40(1) 182-230
Founded: 1852
Agriculture.

Institutul de Arhitectură 'Ion Mincu' din Bucureşti
Strada Academiei 18-20, Bucureşti
Tel: +40(1) 138-080
Founded: 1904
Agriculture.

Institutul de Construcţii din Bucureşti
Bulevardul Lacul Tei 124, Bucureşti
Tel: +40(1) 877-030
Founded: 1946
Construction Engineering.

Institutul de Marina Civila din Constanţa
Strada Stirbei Voda 33, Constanţa
Tel: +40(91) 614-576
Civil Marine Studies.

Institutul de Petrol şi Gaze din Ploieşti
Bulevardul Bucureşti 39, Ploieşti
Tel: +40(97) 142-451
Founded: 1948
Petroleum and Gas Technology.

NATIONAL ACADEMIC BODIES

Ministry of Education
Str. Spiru Haret 12, 70738 Bucureşti
Tel: +40(1) 615-7430
Fax: +40(1) 615-7736
Minister: Liviu Maior

The National Rectors' Conference of Romania (NRC)
Bd. M. Kogalniceanu 64, 70609 Bucureşti
President: Emil Constantinescu, Rector, Universitatea din Bucureşti
Secretary-General: N. Cristescu, Universitatea din Bucureşti
Founded: 1990

National Commission of Romania for Unesco
Cehov 8, Bucureşti 71291
Tel: +40(1) 617-4249
Fax: +40(1) 312-7636
Chairman: Mihai Golu
Secretary-General: Mircea Ifrim

RUSSIAN FEDERATION

UNIVERSITIES AND OTHER UNIVERSITY INSTITUTIONS

Academy of Slavonic Culture
[Akademija Slavjanskoj Kul'tury]
ul. Krasnogo Majaka 4a, 113519 Moscow
Tel: +7(095) 314-42-32
Slavonic Culture.

Altaj Mountains State University
[Gorno-Altajskij Universitet]
ul. Lenina 1, 569700 Gorno-Altajsk
Tel: +7(385-041) 25-67

All-Russian Corresponding Institute for Railway Engineers
[Vserossijskij Zaočnyj Institut Inzenerov Železnodarožnogo Transporta]
ul. Časovaja 22/2, 125808 Moscow GSP-47
Tel: +7(095) 151-14-51
Fax: +7(095) 151-18-37
F: Transportation Economics and Management; Transportation; Automatics, Communication and Computer Engineering for Transport; Transportation Construction; Advanced Training; Foreign Students.

All-Russian Institute of Finance and Economics
[Vserossijskij Zaočnyj Finansovo-Ekonomičeskij Institut]
ul. Okeko Dundiča 23, 121807 Moscow GSP-2
Tel: +7(095) 144-86-19
Fax: +7(095) 144-85-59
Finance and Economics.

Altaj State Technical University
[Altajskij Gosudarstvennyj Tehničeskij Universitet]
pr Lenin 46, 656099 Barnaul
Tel: +7(385-22) 25-51-84
Fax: +7(385-22) 26-05-02
E-Mail: bvi@altpi.altai.su
Engineering.

Altaj State University
[Altajskij Gosudarstvennyj Universitet]
ul. Dimitrova 66, 656099 Barnaul
Tel: +7(3852) 22-18-07
Fax: +7(3852) 22-28-75
E-Mail: vup@mezon.altai.su
Founded: 1973
F: History; Philology; Economics; Law; Mathematics; Physics; Biology; Chemistry; Geography.
D: Journalism; Sociology.

Angara Institute of Technology
[Angarskij Tehnologičeskij Institut]
ul. Čajkovskogo 60, 665835 Angarsk, Irkutskaja Oblast
Tel: +7(395-18) 6-18-32
Fax: +7(395-18) 6-27-90
E-Mail: marina@anti.irkutsk.su
Engineering.

Arhangelsk Institute of Forestry Engineering
[Arhangel'skij Lesotehničeskij Institut]
nab. Severnoj Dviny, 163007 Arhangelsk
Tel: +7(818-0) 44-11-46
Fax: +7(818-0) 44-07-17
F: Mechanical Engineering; Forestry Engineering; Wood Machining Technology; Chemical Technology; Forestry; Heat Power Engineering; Economics; Correspondence Studies.

Baltic State Technical University
[Baltijskij Gosudarstvennyj Tehničeskij Universitet]
-ja Krasnoarmejskaja 1, 198005 Sankt-Peterburg
Tel: +7(812) 292-23-94
Technology.

Baškir State University
[Baškirskij Gosudarstvennyj Universitet]
ul. Frunze 32, 450074 Ufa
Tel: +7(3472) 22-63-70
Fax: +7(3472) 33-16-77
Telex: 162125 ptb su
Rektor: Raghib N. Guimayev
Founded: 1957
F: History; Philology; Mathematics; Physics; Geography; Biology; Chemistry; Roman-German Philology; Law; Economics.
I: Scientific Research; Technological.
D: Evening Studies; Correspondence Courses.

Bauman Moscow State Technical University
[Moskovskij Gosudarstvennyj Tehničeskij Universitet im. N.E.Baumana]
ul. 2-ja Baumanskaja 5, 107005 Moskva
Tel: +7(095) 261-17-43
Fax: +7(095) 267-98-93
E-Mail: postmaster@interd.bmgtu.msk.su
Founded: 1960
F: Materials and Technology; Radioelectronics and Laser Technology; Informatics and Control Systems; Special Machinery; Robotics and Complex Automation; Power Engineering; General Engineering Sciences.

Belgorod Institute of Building Materials Technology

[Belgorodskij Tehnologičeskij Institut Stroitel'nyh Materialov]
ul. Kostjukova 46, 308012 Belgorod
Tel: +7(072-22) 5-41-03
Fax: +7(072-22) 5-71-39
E-Mail: rekt@rprog.belgorod.su
F: *Building Materials Chemical Technology; Building Technology; Mechanical Equipment; Control Systems; Humanities; Correspondence and Part-Time Education; Advanced Training and Retraining.*

Blagoveščensk Polytechnical Institute

[Blagoveščenskij Politehničeskij Institut]
Ignat'evskoe šosse 21, 675027 Blagoveščensk, Amurskaja obl.
Tel: +7(416-22) 5-45-97

Bratsk Institute of Industry

[Bratskij Industrial'nyj Institut]
ul. Makarenko 40, 665928 Bratsk
Tel: +7(395-3) 37-03-22
Fax: +7(395-3) 37-21-02
Industrial Technology.

Brjansk Institute of Transport Engineering

[Brjanskij Institut Transportnogo Mašinostroenija]
Bulvar 50-letija Oktjabrja 7, 241035 Brjansk
Tel: +7(083-22) 56-29-39
Fax: +7(083-22) 56-05-33
E-Mail: postmasterĭtmenit.bryansk.su
Transport Engineering.

Brjansk Institute of Technology

[Brjanskij Tehnologičeskij Institut]
pr. Stanke Dimitrov 3, 241037 Brjansk
Tel: +7(083-22) 1-19-12
Fax: +7(083-22) 1-65-14
F: *Building Technology; Mechanical Engineering Technology; Forestry Engineering.*

Čelyabinsk State Technical University

[Čeljabinskij Gosudarstvennyj Tehničeskij Universitet]
pr. Lenina 76, 454080 Čeljabinsk
Tel: +7(351-2) 33-58-82
Fax: +7(351-2) 34-74-08
E-Mail: root@inform.granit.chel.su
F: *Automatics and Mechanical Engineering; Tractor Engineering; Architecture and Civil Engineering; Aerospace Engineering; Metallurgy; Mechanical Engineering Technology; Instrumentation Technology; Economics and Management; Power Engineering; Economics and Business Studies; Humanities.*

*Čelyabinsk State University

[Čeljabinskij Gosudarstvennyj Universitet]
ul. Bratjev Kaširinyh 129, 454136 Čeljabinsk
Tel: +7(351-2) 42-12-02
Fax: +7(351-2) 42-09-25
E-Mail: nig@cgu.chel.su
Cable: 124303 rebus
Rektor: Valentin D. Batukhtin (1987-97)
Vice-Rektor: Yurii Mikhailovich Kovaliov
Founded: 1976
F: *History; Philology; Mathematics; Economics; Physics and Technics; Chemistry; Law; Humanitarian.*
C: *Economics.*

Čerepoveck State Institute of Industry

[Čerepoveckij Gosudarstvennyj Industrialnyj Institut]
pr. Pobedy 12, 162600 Čerepoveck
Tel: +7(817-36) 5-25-89
Fax: +7(817-36) 5-92-97
F: *Economics and Humanities; Natural Sciences; Construction Technology; Mechanical Engineering and Metallurgy; Automatics and Control Systems; Correspondance and Part-time Education.*

Čita Polytechnical Institute

[Čitinckij Politehničeskij Institut]
ul. Alek-Zavodskaja 30, 672039 Chita
Tel: +7(302-22) 6-43-93
Fax: +7(302-22) 6-27-01

Čuvask State University

[Čuvašskij Gosudarstvennyj Universitet]
pr. Moskovskij 15, 428015 Čuvask Republic Čeboksary
Tel: +7(835-0) 24-03-79
Fax: +7(835-0) 42-80-90
Rektor: Lev Panteleymonovich Kurakov (1990-)
Administrative Officer: Yefremov Leonid Georgiyevich
Founded: 1967
F: *Electrical Engineering; History; Philology; Chuvash Philology and Culture; Medicine; Economics; Chemistry; Industrial Electrification and Automation; Physics and Mathematics; Mechanical Engineering; Civil Engineering; Law; Evening Studies.*

Dagestan State University

[Dagestanskij Gosudarstvennyj Universitet]
ul. Sovetskaja 8, 367025 Mahačkala, Respublika Dagestan
Tel: +7(872-00) 7-29-50
E-Mail: postmaster@ohecnit.dagestan.su
Founded: 1957
F: *History; Philosophy; Physics; Mathematics; Chemistry; Biology; Foreign Languages; Economics; Law; Commerce; Evening Studies; Correspondence Courses.*

Dagestan Polytechnical Institute
[Dagestanskij Politehničeskij Institut]
pr. Kalinina 70, 367015 Mahačkala, Respublika Dagestan
Tel: +7(872-00) 2-39-81

Don State Technical University
[Donskoj Gosudarstvennyj Tehničeskij Universitet]
Pl. Gagarina 1, 344010 Rostov-na-Donu
Tel: +7(8632) 38-15-80
F: Mechanical Engineering Technology; Engineering Design; Computer Science; Humanities.

East-Siberian Institute of Technology
[Vostočno-Sibirskij Tehnologičeskij Institut]
ul. Ključevskaja 40a, 670042 Respublika Buriata Ulan-Ude
Tel: +7(301-22) 7-23-39
Fax: +7(301-22) 7-32-74
E-Mail: root@techn.buriatia.su
Technology.

Ekaterinburg State Theatre Institute
[Ekaterinburgskij Gosudarstvennyj Teatral'nyj Institut]
GSP-636 ul. Vajnera 2, 620077 Ekaterinburg
Tel: +7(343-2) 51-36-90
Theatre.

Far Eastern Institute for Business Studies
[Dal'nevostočnyj Kommerčeskij Institut]
Prosp. Okeanskij 19, 690600 Vladivostok
Tel: +7(423-2) 26-50-89
Business Studies.

Far Eastern State Academy of Railway Communication
[Dal'nevostočnaja Gosudarstvennaja Akademija Putej Soobščenija]
ul. Seryševa 47, 680056 Habarovsk
Tel: +7(421-2) 35-95-00
Fax: +7(421-2) 34-08-08
F: Ground Transportation Systems; Telecommunication, Monitoring and Automatic Systems; Correspondence Education; Preliminary Studies; Foreign Students.
D: Electrical Power Engineering.

Far Eastern State Technical University
[Dal'nevostočnyj Gosudarstvennyj Tehničeskij Universitet]
ul. Puškinskaja 10, 690600 Vladivostok
Tel: +7(4232) 261-689
Fax: +(4232) 266-988
F: Architecture and Design; Mining Engineering; Humanities; Natural Sciences; Naval Engineering; Mechanical Engineering; Radioelectronics and Instrumentation Technology; Civil Engineering and Technical Ecology; Economics and Management; Electrical Engineering.

Far Eastern State University
[Dal'nevostočnyj Gosudarstvennyj Universitet]
ul. Suhanova 8, 690600 Vladivostok
Tel: +7 (423-2) 26-12-80
Fax: +7(423-2) 25-72-00/22-73-86
E-Mail: kurilov@kommercheskoe.dwgupmarine.su
Telex: 213218 tesu
Founded: 1923
F: Philology; Oriental Studies; Journalism; History; Law; Mathematics; Physics; Geophysics; Chemistry; Biology and Soil Science.
D: Evening Studies; Correspondence Courses.

Finance Academy
[Finansovaja Akademija]
pr. Leningradskij 49, 125468 Moskva
Tel: +7(095) 943-98-55
Fax: +7(095) 943-93-80
Finance.

Frunze Ivanovo Textile Institute
[Ivanovskij Tekstil'nyj Institut im. M.V. Frunze]
pr. F. Engel'sa 21, 153000 Ivanovo
Tel: +7(093-2) 32-8545
Fax: +7(093-2) 32-3950
F: Textile Technology; Economics and Design; Mechanical Engineering; Clothing Manufacture; Part-time Education; Correspondence Education; Advanced Training for Managers and Specialists.

Gorkij Institute of Literature
[Literaturnyj Institut im. A.M.Gor'kogo]
Tverskoj bul'var 25, 103104 Moskva
Tel: +7(095) 202-84-22
Fax: +7(095) 202-67-55
Literature.

Groznoj Institute of Oil Industry
[Groznenskij Neftjanoj Institut]
pr. Revoljucii 21, 364902 Groznyj
Tel: +7(871-2) 22-55-45
Oil Technology.

Gubkin State Academy of Gas and Oil
[Gosudarstvennaja Akademija Nefi i Gaza im. I.M. Gubkina]
pr. Leninskij 65, 117917 Moskva B-296
Tel: +7(095) 930-92-01
Fax: +7(095) 135-88-95
F: Economics, Management and Law; Computer Engineering and Automatics; Geology and Geophysics of Oil and Gas; Pipeline Systems Design, Construction and Maintenance; Oil and Gas Fields Exploitation; Chemical Technology and Ecology; Engineering Mechanics.

Higher School of Economics
[Vysšaja Škola Ekonomiki]
pr. ak. Saharova 12, 107078 Moscow
Tel: +7(095) 229-86-67
Fax: +7(095) 291-41-43
E-Mail: hse@glas.arc.org
Economics.

Iĕvsk State Technical University
[Iževskij Gosudarstvennyj Tehničeskij Universitet]
ul. Studenčeskaja 7, 426069 Iževsk
Tel: +7(341-2) 23-83-11
Fax: +7(341-2) 23-04-01

Institute of Asian and African Countries
[Institut Stran Azii i Afriki]
ul. Mohovaja 11, 103009 Moskva
Tel: +7(095) 203-64-76

Irkutsk Institute for Railway Engineers
[Irkutskij Institut Inženerov Železnodorožnogo Transporta]
ul. Černyševskogo 15, 664074 Irkutsk
Tel: +7(395-2) 28-27-12
F: Railway Construction; Railway Transportation Management; Electromechanics; General Engineering.

Irkutsk State Academy of Economics
[Irkutskaja Gosudarstvennaja Ekonomičeskaja Akademia]
ul. Lenina 2, 664015 Irkutsk
Tel: +7(3952) 34-10-57
F: Finance and Economics; Stocktaking and Economics; Industrial Economics and Business Studies; Personnel Management; Industrial Economics and Management; Economics and Management in Construction and Mining Engineering; Economics and Management in Transportation and Mechanical Engineering; Law; Information Systems.

Irkutsk State Technical University
[Irkutskij Gosudarstvennyj Tehničeskij Universitet]
ul. Lermontova 83, 664074 Irkutsk 74
Tel: +7(395-2) 43-05-74
F: Aircraft and Motor Car Engineering; Civil Engineering; Architecture; Geology and Minerals Prospecting; Mining Engineering; Cybernetics; Mechanical Engineering; Chemical Engineering and Metallurgy; Special Construction Works; Power Engineering.

*Irkutsk State University
[Irkutskij Gosudarstvennyj Universitet]
ul. K. Marksa 1, 664003 Irkutsk
Tel: +7(395-2) 33-34-53
Fax: +7(395-2) 33-22-38
Founded: 1918
F: Philology; Law; History; Mathematics; Physics; Chemistry; Soil Science; Geology; Geography; Psychology and Social Works.

Ivanovo Institute of Civil Engineering
[Ivanovskij Inženerno-Stroitel'nyj Institut]
ul. Marta 8, 153002 Ivanovo
Tel: +7(093-2) 32-97-55

Ivanovo State Academy of Chemical Technology
[Ivanovskaja Gosudarstvennaja Himikotehnologičeskaja Akademija]
Prosp. Fridriha Engel'sa 7, 153460 Ivanovo
Tel: +7(0932) 32-04-10
F: Solids and Rational Use of Natural Resources; Non-Organic Chemistry and Electrochemical Technology; Organic Chemistry and Technology; Chemical Engineering and Cybernetics; Humanities.

Ivanovo State University of Power Engineering
[Ivanovskij Gosudarstvennyj Energetičeskij Universitet]
ul. Rabfakovskaja 34, 153003 Ivanovo
Tel: +7(093-2) 32-72-43
Fax: +7(093-2) 38-57-01
E-Mail: Nuzdin@polutech.ivanovo.SU
F: Philology; History; Law; Economics; Roman-German Philology.

Ivanovo State University
[Ivanovskij Gosudarstvennyj Universitet]
ul. Ermaka 39, 153025 Ivanovo
Tel: +780932) 32-62-10
Founded: 1974
F: History; Law; Philology; Romanc-German Philology; Economics.

Jaroslavl Polytechnical Institute
[Jaroslavskij Politehničeskij Institut]
pr. Moskovskij 88, 150053 Jaroslavl'
Tel: +7(085-2) 44-15-19
Fax: +7(085-2) 44-07-29
F: Automobile Engineering; Architecture and Construction; Humanities; Mechanical Engineering; Chemical Technology.

Jaroslav' State University
[Jaroslavskij Gosudarstvennyj Universitet]
ul. Sovetskaja 14, 150000 Jaroslav'-Centr
Tel: F
Founded: 1970
Physics; Mathematics; Economics; Psychology and Biology; History and Law.

Jakutsk State University
[Jakutskij Gosudarstvennyj Universitet]
ul. Belinskogo 58, 677000 Yakutsk
Tel: +7(411-22) 6-33-44
Fax: +7(411-22) 6-26-39
E-Mail: yucjit@yucnit.infonet.yakutia.su
Founded: 1934, 1956
F: History and Law; Foreign Languages; Physics; Mathematics; Biology and Geography; Agriculture; Medicine; Engineering and Technology; Geology and Surveying; Philology; Teacher Training.

Kabardin-Balkarian University

[Kabardino-Balkarskij Gosudarstvennyj Universitet]
ul. Černyševskogo 173, 36004 Nal'čik
Tel: +7(866-22) 2-52-58
Fax: +7(866-22) 2-25-62
Founded: 1957
History; Physics; Applied Mathematics and Control Systems; Philology; Chemistry and Biology; Mechanical Engineering; Medicine; Physical Education and Sports; Law; Education Sciences; Economics; Kabardin and Balkarsk Philology; Roman and German Philology.

Kaliningrad State University

[Kaliningradskij Gosudarstvennyj Universitet]
ul. A. Nevskogo 14, 236040 Kaliningrad
Tel: +7(011-2) 46-59-17
Fax: +7(011-2) 46-58-13
E-Mail: uni@kalcnit.koenig.su
Founded: 1967
F: History; Physics; Philology; Mathematics; Economics and Law; Chemistry; Geography; Pedagogics; Engineering Teacher Training; Sports; Biology.

Kalmyk State University

[Kalmyckij Gosudarstvennyj Universitet]
ul. Puškina 11, 358000 Elista
Tel: +7(847-22) 5-34-31
Founded: 1970
F: Philology; Physics and Mathematics; Biology; Agriculture.

Kamsk Polytechnical Institute

[Kamskij Politehničeskij Institut]
pr. Mira 68/19, 423810 Naberežnye Čelny
Tel: +7(843-9) 53-73-96
Fax: +7(843-9) 53-73-11
Mechanical Engineering; Motor Cars Engineering; Civil Engineering; Mechanical Engineering Technology.

Karačaevo-Čerkessk Institute of Technology

[Karačaevo-Čerkesskij Tehnologičeskij Institut]
ul. Stavropol'skaja 36, 357100 Čerkessk
Karačaevo-Čerkesskaja Respublika
Tel: +7(865-71) 3-41-98
Technology.

Kazan Institute of Civil Engineering

[Kazanskij Inženerno Stroitel'nyj Institut]
ul. Zelenaja 1, 420043 Kazan'
Tel: +7(843-2) 36-25-32
Civil Engineering.

Kazan' Institute of Finance and Economics

[Kazanskij Finansovo-Ekonomičeskij Institut]
ul. Butlerova 4, 420012 Kazan'
Tel: +7(843-2) 32-40-36
Fax: +7(843-2) 38-30-54
Finance and Economics.

*Kazan' State University

[Kazanskij Gosudarstvennyj Universitet]
ul. Lenina 18, 420008 Kazan'
Tel: +7(8432) 38-09-94
E-Mail: univex@glas.arc.orc
Founded: 1804
F: History; Biology and Soil Science; Geography; Law; Geology; Mechanics and Mathematics; Physics; Computing Mathematics and Cybernetics; Tatar Philology and Eastern Languages; Journalism; Ecology; Economics; Chemistry; Philology.

Kazan' State University of Technology

[Kazanskij Gosudarstvennyj Tehnologičeskij Universitet]
ul. K. Marksa 68, 420015 Kazan'
Tel: +7(843-2) 36-75-42
Technology.

Kemerovo Institute of Food Science and Technology

[Kemerovskij Tehnologičeskij Institut Piščevoj Promyšlennosti]
bul. Stroitelej 47, 650060 Kemerovo
Tel: +7(384-2) 51-09-38
Food Science and Technology.

Kemerovo State University

[Kemerovskij Gosudarstvennyj Universitet]
ul. Krasnaja 6, 650043 Kemerovo
Tel: +7(384-2) 23-12-26
Fax: +7(384-2) 23-38-85
E-Mail: rector@kemgu.kemerovo.su
Telex: 215229 ptb
Founded: 1974
F: Economics; Philology; Roman-German Philology; History; Mathematics; Physics; Chemistry; Biology; Law.

Habarovsk Institute of Economics

[Habarovskij Institut Narodnovo Hozjajstva]
ul. Tihookeanskaja 134, 680042 Habarovsk
Tel: +7(421-0) 35-87-37
Fax: +7(421-0) 35-88-74
E-Mail: 614521 kine su
Economics.

Habarovsk State Technical University

[Habarovskij Gosudarstvennyj Tehničeskij Universitet]
ul. Tihookeanskaja 136, 680035 Habarovsk
Tel: +7(421-2) 35-83-16
Fax: +7(421-2) 35-80-20
E-Mail: postmaster@hpicnit.khabarovsk.su

Komsomol'sk-na-Amure Polytechnical Institute

[Komsomol'skij-na-Amure Politehničeskij Institut]
Prosp. Lenina 27, 681013 Komsomol'sk-na-Amure, Habarovskij Kraj
Tel: +7(421-72) 3-23-04
Fax: +7(421-72) 3-61-50
E-Mail: KnAPI@summit.khabarovsk.su
F: Aircraft and Naval Engineering; Civil Engineering; Mechanical Engineering; Electrical Engineering; Correspondence Studies; Market Economics; Studies of Foreign Students.

Kostroma Institute of Technology

[Kostromskoj Tehnologičeskij Institut]
ul. Dzeržinskogo 17, 156005 Kostroma
Tel: +7(0942) 57-48-14
Fax: +7(0942) 57-78-60
F: Industrial Economics; Forestry Engineering; Mechanical Engineering; Mechanical Engineering Technology; Technology.

Kovrov Institute of Technology

[Kovrovskij Tehnologičeskij Institut]
ul. Majakovskogo 19, 601910 Kovrov, Vladimirskaja obl.
Tel: +7(092-32) 3-21-60
Technology.

Krasnojarsk Institute of Civil Engeneering

[Krasnojarskij Inženerno-Stroitel'nyj Institut]
pr. Svobodnyj 82, 660041 Krasnojarsk
Tel: +7(391-2) 45-66-69
Fax: +7(391-2) 45-58-92
Civil Engineering.

Krasnojarsk Institute of Non-Ferrous Metals

[Krasnojarskij Institut Cvetnyh Metallov]
pr. im. gazety 'Krasnojarskij rabočij' 95, 660025 Krasnojarsk
Tel: +7(391-2) 34-78-82
Fax: +7(391-2) 34-63-11
Non-Ferrous Metals Techniques.

Krasnojarsk State Medical Institute

[Krasnojarskij Gosudarstvennyj Medicinskij Institut]
ul. Partizana Železnjaka 1, 660022 Krasnojarsk
Tel: +7(3912) 2749-24
Medicine; Pediatrics; Stomatology.

Krasnojarsk State Technical University

[Krasnojarskij Gosudarstvennyj Tehničeskij Universitet]
ul. Kirenskogo 26, 660074 Krasnojarsk
Tel: +7(391-2) 44-19-02
Fax: +7(391-2) 43-06-92
E-Mail: postmaster@krpicnit.krasnoyarsk.su

Krasnoyarsk State University

[Krasnojarskij Gosudarstvennyj Universitet]
pr. Svobodnyj 79, 660062 Krasnojarsk
Tel: +7(391-2) 45-53-05
Fax: +7(391-2) 45-64-68
E-Mail: postmaster@kgu.krasnoyarsk.su
Founded: 1970
F: Law; Mathematics; Physics; Biology and Chemistry; Evening Studies; Correspondence Courses.

Kuban State University

[Kubanskij Gosudarstvennyj Universitet]
ul. Karla Libknehta 149, 350640 Krasnodar
Tel: +7(861-2) 33-75-02
Fax: +7(861-2) 33-98-87
Founded: 1970
F: Philology; History; Mathematics; Physics; Biology; Chemistry; Geography; Roman and Germanic Philology; Law; Economics; Art and Graphic Art.

Kuban State University of Technology

[Kubanskij Gosudarstvennyj Tehnologičeskij Universitet]
ul. Moskovskaja 2, 350072 Krasnodar
Tel: +7(8612) 55-84-01
Fax: +7(8612) 57-65-92
F: Power Engineering, Oil and Gas Technology; Automatic Systems and Equipment for Food Production; Chemical Technology; Food Production Technology; Bakery Technology; Construction Engineering; Motor and Highway Engineering; Industrial Economics; Mechanics and Mechanical Engineering.

Kurgan Institute of Mechanical Engineering

[Kurganskij Mašinostroitel'nyj Institut]
pl. Lenina, 640669 Kurgan
Tel: +7(35222) 2-26-52
Fax: +7(35222) 2-20-51
E-Mail: postmaster@kmi.rcupi.e-burg.su
F: Natural Sciences; Automatics and Control Systems; Mechanical Engineering Technology; Motor Car and Traktor Engineering; History; Foreign Languages; Russian Language and Literature; Phisics and Mathematics; Biology and Chemistry; Physical Education and Sports.

Kursk Polytechnical Institute

[Kurskij Politehničeskij Institut]
ul. 50-let Oktjabrja 94, 305039 Kursk
Tel: +7(071-00) 2-57-43
Fax: +7(071-00) 2-12-08

Kuzbass State Technical University

[Kuzbasskij Gosudarstvennyj Tehničeskij Universitet]
ul. Vesennjaja 28, 650026 Kemerovo
Tel: +7(384-2) 23-33-80
Fax: +7(384-2) 23-08-08
E-Mail: gbd@kuzpi.kemerovo.su
F: Mining Engineering; Electical Engineering; Mine Construction; Mechanical Engineering; Chemical Technology; Engineering Economics.

Lipeck Polytechnical Institute
[Lipeckij Politehničeskij Institut]
ul. Moskovskaja 30, 398055 Lipeck
Tel: +7(074-2) 25-00-61
Fax: +7(074-2) 25-40-65
*F: Metallurgy; Automated Manufacturing
Processes; Civil Engineering; Transport
Engineering; Computer Science and Computer-
Aided Manufacturing; Applied Physics and
Technology; Business and Management.*

Lomonosov Moscow State Academy of Fine Chemical Technology
[Moskovskaja Gosudarstvennaja Akademija
Tonkoj Himičeskoj Tehnologii im.
M.V.Lomonosova]
pr. Vernadskogo 86, 117571 Moskva
Tel: +7(095) 437-35-27
Fax: +7(095) 430-79-83
E-Mail: postmaster@ivc mitht.msk.su
*F: Biotechnology and Organic Synthesis;
Polymer Chemistry,Phisics and Processing
Technology; Chemistry and Technology of Rare
Elements and Materials for Electronics; Natural
Sciences; Management, Economics and Ecology.
D: Humanities.*

*Lomonosov Moscow State University
[Moskovskij Gosudarstvennyj Universitet im M.B.
Lomonosova]
Leninskije Gory MGU, 119899 Moskva
Tel: +7(095) 939-36-10f
Fax: +7(095) 939-01-26
E-Mail: koroteev@compnet.msu.su
Founded: 1755
*F: Physics; Computer Mathematics and
Cybernetics; Chemistry; Mathematics and
Mechanics; Biology; Soil Science; Geography;
Geology; History; Philology; Law; Foreign
Language; Philosophy; Sociology; Economics;
Journalism; Psychology; Fundamental Medicine.*

Magnitogorsk Institute of Metallurgy and Mining Engineering
[Magnitogorskij Gorno-Metallurgičeskij Institut]
pr. Lenina 38, 455000 Magnitogorsk
Tel: +7(413-00) 32-12-87
Fax: +7(413-00) 32-28-86
E-Mail: mgmi@mgmi.chel.su
Metallurgy; Mining Engineering.

Majkop State University of Technology
[Majkopskij Gosudarstvennyj Tehnologičeskij
Universitet]
ul. Piervomajskaja 191, 352700 Majkop
Tel: +7(87722) 2-13-87
Technology.

Mari State University
[Marijskij Gosudarstvennyj Universitet]
pl. Lenina 1, 424001 Joškar-Ola, Marij El Republik
Tel: +7(83622) 6-32-16
Fax: +7(83622) 5-45-81
E-Mail: postmaster@margu.mari.su
Founded: 1972
*F: History and Philology; Physics and
Mathematics; Biology and Chemistry; Agriculture;
Economics; Correspondence Courses.*

Marijsk Polytechnical Institute
[Marijskij Politehničeskij Institut]
pl. Lenina 3, 424024 Joškar-Ola, Marij El
Tel: +7(83622) 9-68-69
Fax: +7(8362) 11-08-72
E-Mail: eldar@mpicnit.mari.su
*F: Industrial Economics; Forestry; Forestry
Engineering; Radio Engineering; Highway
Engineering; Civil Engineering.*

Mendeleev Russian University of Chemical Technology
[Rossijskij Himiko-Tehnologičeskij Universitet im.
D.I. Mendeleeva]
Miusskaja pl. 9, 125190 Moskva A-190
Tel: +7(095) 158-87-33
Fax: +7(095) 200-42-04
E-Mail: Sarkisov@mhti.msk.su
Telex: 411744 argon
*F: Non-Organic Materials Technology; Silicate
Chemical Technology; Polymer Chemical
Technology; Organic Materials Technology;
Engineering Physics and Chemistry; Chemical
Engineering Technology; Engineering Ecology.*

Moscow Institute of Architecture
[Moskovskij Arhitekturnyj Institut]
ul. Roždestvenka 11, 103754 Moskva
Tel: +7(095) 925-50-82
Fax: +7(095) 921-12-40
Architecture.

Moscow Institute of Arts and Art Industry
[Moskovskij Hudožestvenno-Promyšlennyj Institut]
ul. Volokolamskoje Šosse 9, 125080 Moskva
Tel: +7(095) 158-01-33
Fax: +7(095) 158-07-54
Arts and Art Industry.

Moscow Institute of Automobile Engineering (VTUZ-ZIL)
[Moskovskij Avtomobilestroitel'nyj Institut
(VTUZ-ZIL)]
Avtozavodskaja 16, 109280 Moskva
Tel: +7(095) 275-52-37
Fax: +7(095) 275-22-56
*Science; Automobile Engineering; Engineering;
Economics and Management.*

Moscow Institute of Economics and Statistics
[Moskovskij Ekonomiko-Statističeskij Institut]
ul. Nežinskaja 7, 119501 Moskva
F: Statistics; Economic Informatics; Economics and Management; Economic Cybernetics.

Moscow Institute of Instrumentation Technology
[Moskovskij Institut Priborostroenija]
ul. Stromynka 20, 107846 Moskva
Tel: +7(095) 268-01-01
Fax: +7(095) 268-00-60
E-Mail: ver@oktava.msk.su
F: Electronics, Computer Science and Engineering; Radioelectronics and Instrumentation Technology; Engineering Systems with Artificial Intellect; Materials Science and Technology; Humanities; Computer Science and Instrumentation (Serviev Posad); Automobile Engineering and Instrumentation Technology (Serpukhov); Information Technology and Computer-Integrated Manufacturing; Mechanical Engineering Technology (Khimki).

Moscow Institute-Internate for the Motor Disabled
[Moskovskij Institut-Internat dlja Invalidov s Narušeniem Oporno-Dvigatel'noj Sistemy]
ul. Losinoostrovskaja 49, 107150 Moskva
Tel: +7(095) 160-92-00
Fax: +7(095) 230-27-96
F: Applied Mathematics; Law; Economics; Foreign Languages.

Moscow Institute of Municipal Economics and Construction
[Moskovskij Institut Kommunal'nogo Hozjajstva i Stroitel'stva]
ul. Sr. Kalitnikovskaja 30, 109807 Moskva
Tel: +7(095) 278-32-05
Fax: +7(095) 278-15-10
E-Mail: kolkunov@mikhs.mik.su
F: Industrial and Civil Engineering; Urban and Highway Construction; Automated Systems; Technology; Engineering and Systems and Ecology; Industrial Economics and Management.

Moscow Institute of Physics and Technology
[Moskovskij Fiziko-Tehničeskij Institut]
Institutskij per. 9, Dolgoprudnyj 141700, Moskovskaja obl.
Tel: +7(095) 408-57-00
Fax: +7(095) 362-16-20
E-Mail: postmaster@mei.msk.su
F: Radio Engineering and Cybernetics; General and Applied Physics; Aerophysics and Space Research; Molecular and Chemical Physics; Physical and Quantum Electronics; Aeromechanics and Aircrafts; Management and Applied Mathematics; Physical and Power Problems; Physical and Chemical Biology.

*Moscow Institute of Power Engineering (Technical University)
[Moskovskij Energetičeskij Institut (Tehničeskij Universitet)]
ul. Krasnokazarmennaja 14, 105835 Moskva
Tel: +7(095) 362-56-45
Fax: +7(095) 362-16-20
E-Mail: postmaster@mei.msk.su
Telex: 411610 mei su
Rektor: I.M. Arlov
F: Industrial Heat Power Engineering; Heat Power Engineering; Power Engineering Industry; Power Physics; Electrical Power Engineering; Electromechanical Systems; Electronic Engineering; Computer Engineering and Automatics; Radio Engineering; Industrial and Transportation Automated Systems and Electrical Equipment.

Moscow Part-time Institute of Metallurgy
[Moskovskij Večernij Metallurgičeskij Institut]
Lefortovskij val 26, 112250 Moskva
Tel: +7(095) 362-00-95
Fax: +7(095) 361-14-43
F: Engineering; Industrial Economics; Metallurgy Automated Manufacturing Processes; Metallurgy and Metal Processing.

*Moscow State Academy of Agriculture
[Moskovskaja Sel'skohozjajstvennaja Akademija]
ul. Timirjazevskaja 49, 127550 Moskva
Tel: +7(095) 976-04-80
Fax: +(095) 488-52-22
Rektor: M.I. Sinyukov
Founded: 1865
F: Agronomy; Economics and Organization of Agriculture; Animal Husbandry; Horticulture and Viticulture; Agricultural Chemistry and Soil Science; Education (Agriculture); Agricultural Retraining; Professional Retraining.

Moscow State Academy of Automobile and Tractor Engineering
[Moskovskaja Gosudarstvennaja Akademija Avtomobilnogo i Traktornogo Mašinostroenija]
ul. B. Semenovskaja 38, 105839 Moskva
Tel: +7(095) 369-28-32
Fax: +7(095) 369-01-49
F: Automobile and Tractor Technology; Power Machine and Instrument Engineering; Mechanical Engineering; Automatics and Monitoring Systems; Design and Technology; Economics; Mechanical Engineering.

Moscow State Academy of Applied Biotechnology

[Moskovskaja Gosudarstvennaja Akademija Prikladnoj Biotehnologii]
ul. Talalihina 33, 109316 Moskva
Tel: +7(095) 276-19-10
Fax: +7(095) 276-14-23
E-Mail: postmaster@ibiot.msk.su
F: Applied Biotechnology; Bioengineering; Automated Biotechnological Systems; Refrigerating and Technology; Industrial Economics; Veterinary and Sanitation; Humanities; Advanced Training.

Moscow State Academy of Chemical Engineering

[Moskovskaja Gosudarstvennaja Akademija Himičeskogo Mašinostroenija]
ul. Staraja Basmannaja 21/4, 107884 Moskva
Tel: +7(095) 267-07-01
Fax: +7(095) 261-96-12
F: Chemical and Biological Engineering; Cryogenic Engineering; Chemical Apparatus Manufacturing; Chemical Engineering; Engineering Cybernetics and Automated Chemical Manufacturing Processes; Engineering; Humanities.

Moscow State Academy of Food Industry

[Moskovskaja Gosudarstvennaja Akademija Piščevyh Proizvodstv]
Volokolamskoe Šosse 11, 125080 Moskva
Tel: +7(095) 158-72-68
Fax: +7(095) 158-03-71
F: Biotechnology, Microbiological Technology and Food Processing Technology; Bakery Technology; Mechanical Engineering and Design; Industrial Economics; Cybernetics and Automated Food Manufacturing Processes.

Moscow State Academy of Geological Prospecting

[Moskovskaja Gosudarstvennaja Geologorazvedočnaja Akademija]
ul. Mikluho-Maklaja 23, 117873 Moskva
Tel: +7(095) 433-62-56
Fax: +7(095) 433-63-33
F: Geological Prospecting; Hydrogeology; Geophysics; Prospecting and Exploitation Technology; Advanced Training.

Moscow State Academy of Law

[Moskovskaja Gosudarstvennaja Juridičeskaja Akademija]
ul. Sadovaja-Kudrinskaja 9, 123286 Moskva
Tel: +7(095) 254-99-72
Fax: +7(095) 244-01-35
Law.

Moscow State Academy of Light Industry

[Moskovskaja Gosudarstvennaja Akademia Legkoj Promyšlennosti]
ul. Osipenko 33, 113806 Moskva
Tel: +7(095) 231-58-01
Fax: +7(095) 231-55-72
Light Industry.

Moscow State Academy of Printing Arts

[Moskovskaja Gosudarstvennaja Akademija Pečati]
ul. Prjanišnikova 2a, 127550 Moskva
Tel: +7(095) 976-40-77
Fax: +7(095) 976-03-41
Printing Arts.

Moscow State Academy of Water Transport

[Moskovskaja Gosudarstvennaja Akademija Vodnogo Transporta]
ul. Sudostroitel'naja 46, 115407 Moskva
Tel: +7(095) 116-30-88
Fax: +7(095) 118-31-11
F: Ships', Ports' and Hydrotechnical Structures Maintenance; Naval Engineering; Ports' Equipment and Robotics Systems; Engineering Economics; Correspondence Studies.

Moscow State Automobile and Road Technical University

pr. Leningradskij 64, 125829 Moskva
Tel: +7(095) 151-06-91
Fax: +7(095) 151-79-11
E-Mail: info@madi.mska.su
Rektor: Valentin N. Lukanin
International Relations: Kyazim H. Akmaev
F: Natural Sciences; Construction and Mechanical Engineering; Motor Transport; Building and Technological Machines; Energy and Environment; Highways and Aerodromes; Bridges and Transport Tunnels; Economics; Management; Humanities; Training for Foreign Students.
Research I: Energy and Environmental Problems; Controlling Systems and Traffic Safety; Mechanics; Technology of Machine Reparation; Social Economical Problems; Humanitarian; Natural Sciences.

Moscow State Aviation Institute (Technical University)

[Moskovskij Gosudarstvennyj Aviacionnyj Institut (Tehničeskij Universitet)]
Volokolamskoe Šosse 4, 125871 Moskva
Tel: +7(095) 158-13-73
Fax: +7(095) 158-29-17
E-Mail: aet@tk majnet.msk.su
F: Aircraft Engineering; Aircraft Engines; Control Systems, Informatics and Electrical Power Engineering; Aircraft Radio-Electronic Equipment; Economics and Management; Aerospace Engineering; Robotics and Intellectual Systems; Applied Mathematics and Physics; Applied Mechanics; Humanities.

Moscow State Correspondence Institute of Food Industries
[Moskovskij Gosudarstvennyj Zaočnyj Institut Piščevoj Promyšlennosti]
ul. Zemljanoj Val 73, 109803 Moskva
Tel: +7(095) 915-03-40
Fax: +7(095) 915-08-77
F: Bakery Engineering; Mechanical Engineering; Fishery and Biotechnology; Ecological Education (International).

Moscow State Institute of Electronics and Mathematics (Technical University)
[Moskovskij Gosudarstvennyj Institut Elektroniki i Matematiki (Techničeskij Universitet)]
B. 3-h Svjatitel'skij per. 3/12, 109028 Moskva
Tel: +7 (095)297-90-89
Fax: +7(095) 277-28-07
E-Mail: bin@miem.msk.su
F: Electronics; Informatics and Telecommunication; Automatics and Computer Engineering; Mathematics.

Moscow State Institute of Electronic Engineering (Technical University)
[Moskovskij Gosudarstvennyj Institut Elektronnoj Tehniki (Tehničeskij Universitet)]
ul. Solnečnaja Alleja, 103498 Moskva
Tel: +7(095) 531-27-36
Fax: +7(095) 530-22-33
E-Mail: infokom@mastak.msk.su
F: Cybernetics; Electronics and Computer Technology; Microtechnology; Electronic Engineering; Economics and Humanities.

Moscow State Institute of Physics and Engineering (Technical University)
[Moskovskij Gosudarstvennyj Inženerno-fizičeskij Institut (Tehničeskij Universitet)]
Kaširskoe šosse 31, 115409 Moskva
Tel: +7(095) 324-87-66
Fax: +7(095) 324-21-11
F: Electronics and Automatics; Cybernetics; Physics; Engineering Physics.

Moscow State Institute of Radio Engineering, Electronics and Automatics (Technical University)
[Moskovskij Institut Radiotehniki Elektroniki i Avtomatiki (Tehničeskij Universitet)]
pr. Vernadskogo 78, 117454 Moskva
Tel: +7(095) 433-00-44
Fax: +7(095) 434-86-65
F: Informatics; Cybernetics; Radio Engineering Systems; Electronics and Optoelectronic Engineering.

Moscow State Institute of Steel and Alloys (University of Technology)
[Moskovskij Gosudarstvennyj Institut Stali i Splavov(Tehnologičeskij Universitet)]
pr. Leninskij 4, 117936 Moskva
Tel: +7(095)237-22-22
Fax: +7(095)236-21-05
E-Mail: rita@misis.msk.su
Rector: A.G. Diljk
F: Ferrous Metals and Alloys Metallurgy; Technology; Physics and Chemistry; Semiconductor Materials and Instruments; Informatics and Economics; Metallurgy of Non-Ferrous Metals, Rare Metals.

*Moscow State Linguistic University
[Moskovskij Gosudarstvennyj Lingvističeskij Universitet]
ul. Ostoženka 38, 119837 Moskva
Tel: +7(095) 324-87-66
Fax: +7(095) 324-21-11
Rektor: M.K.Borodulina
F: Humanities; German Language; French Language.

Moscow State Open University
[Moskovskij Gosudarstvennyj Otkrytyj Universitet]
ul. Korčagina 22, 129805 Moskva
Tel: +7(095) 283-42-96
Fax: +7(095) 283-80-71

*Moscow State Pedagogical University
[Moskovskij Pedagogičeskij Gosudarstvennyj Universitet]
ul. M. Pirogovskaja 1, 119882 Moskva
Tel: +7(095) 246-01-23
Fax: +7(095) 248-01-62
Rektor: Victor L. Matrosov (1986-)
Prorektor: Michail L. Rodionov
Founded: 1872, 1989
F: Physics; Mathematics; Biology and Chemistry; Geography; Chemistry; History; Russian Language and Literature; Foreign Languages; Education (primary level); Education (pre-school level); Music and Singing; Graphic Arts; Pedagogics and Psychology; Education of the Handicapped; Industrial Pedagogy; Improvement of Public School Administration; Improvement of College Teaching; Sociology.

Moscow State Textile Academy
[Moskovskaja Gosudarstvennaja Tekstilnaja Akademija]
ul. Malaja Kaluzskaja 1, 112918 Moskva
Tel: +7(095) 954-46-82
Fax: +7(095) 952-14-40
F: Mechanical Engineering; Textile Engineering; Power and Mechanical Engineering; Chemical Technology; Industrial Economics; Applied Arts.

Moscow State University of Aviation Technology
[Moskovskij Gosudarstvennyj Aviacionnyj Tehnologičeskij Universitet]
ul. Petrovka 27, 103767 Moskva
Tel: +7 (095)200-40-06
Fax: +7(095) 200-67-64
E-Mail: vicr@asdi.msk.su
F: Aviation Technology; Aerospace Engineering; Radio Engineering and Electronics; Composite Materials Science and Technology; Applied Mathematics and Information Technology; Economics; International Education.

Moscow State University of Civil Engineering
[Moskovskij Gosudarstvennyj Stroitel'nyj Universitet]
Jaroslavskoe šosse 26, 129337 Moskva
Tel: 7+(095) 183-53-83
Fax: +7(095) 183-04-92
F: Industrial and Civil Engineering; Heat Power Construction; Hydrotechnical Construction; Urban Infrastructure Engineering; Construction Technology; Heat and Gas Supply and Ventilation; Water Supply and Sewerage; Construction Planning, Economics and Management.

Moscow State University of Forestry Engineering
[Moskovskij Gosudarstvennyj Universitet Lesa]
141001 Mytisci 1, Moskovskaja obl.
Tel: 582-45-78
Forestry Engineering.

Moscow State University of Geodesy and Cartography
[Moskovskij Gosudarstvennyj Universitet Geodezii i Kartografii]
Gorohovyj per. 4, 103064 Moskva K-64
Tel: +7(095) 261-31-52
Fax: +7(095) 267-46-81

Moscow State University of Mining Engineering
[Moskovskij Gosudarstvennyj Gornyj Universitet]
Leninskij pr. 6, 117935 Moskva
Tel: +7(095) 236-94-80
Fax: +7(095) 237-64-88
Mining Engineering.

Moscow State University of Railway Communication
[Moskovskij Gosudarstvennyj Universitet Putej Soobščenija]
ul. Obrazcova 15, 101475 Moskva
Tel: +7(095) 284-23-48
Fax: +7(095) 284-54-91
F: Railway Automatic Systems, Telemechanics and Communication; Industrial Economics; Mechanical Engineering; Bridges and Tunnels; Industrial and Civil Engineering; Railway Construction; Technical Cybernetics; Transport Management; Railway Electrification.

Moscow State University of Technology
[Moskovskij Gosudarstvennyj Tehnologičeskij Universitet (STANKIN)]
Vadkovskij per. 3a, 101472 Moskva
Tel: +7(095) 973-30-76
Fax: +7(095) 973-31-67
E-Mail: svl@compinf.zgrad.glas.apc.org
F: Mechanics and Control Systems; Technology; Information Technology; Automatic Systems for Metals Plastic Processing.

V.I.Muhinoj Saint-Petersburg Higher School of Arts and Art Industry
[Sankt-Peterburgskoe Vysshee Hudožestvenno-Promyšlennoe Učilišče im V.I.Muhinoj]
per. Soljanoj 13, 192028 Sankt-Peterburg
Tel: +7(812) 273-38-04
Fax: +7(812) 272-84-46
Arts and Art Industry.

Nižnij Novgorod Academy of Architecture and Civil Engineering
[Nižegorodskaja Gosudarstvennaja Arhitekturno-Stroitel'naya Akademija]
ul. Il'inskaja 65, 603600 Nižnij Novgorod
Tel: +7(8312) 34-04-05
Fax: +7(8312) 34-02-01
F: Architecture; Construction; Engineering and Ecology; Hydrotechnical Construction.

Nižnij Novgorod State Technical University
[Nižegorodskij Gosudarstvennyj Tehničeskij Universitet]
ul. Minina 24, 603600 Nižnij Novgorod
Tel: +7(8312) 36-23-25
Fax: + +7(8312) 36-94-75
E-Mail: koshelev@nnpi.nnov.su
F: Automobile Engineering; Electrical Engineering; Metallurgy; Physical Chemistry; Applied Physics; Radio Electronics and Engineering Cybernetics; Naval Engineering; Sociology and Economics; Mechnical Engineering and Automated Manufacturing Processes.

Nižnij Novgorod State University
[Nižegorodskij Gosudarstvennyj Universitet]
Prosp. Gagarina 23, 603600 Nižnij Novgorod
Tel: +7(8312) 65-79-23
Fax: +7(8312) 65-85-92
E-Mail: rector@nnucnit.nnov.su
Founded: 1920
F: Biology; History; Radio Physics; Economics; Law; Computational Mathematics and Cybernetics; Chemistry; Philology; Applied Physics and Microelectronics; Mechanics and Mathematics.

Norilsk Institute of Industry
[Noril'skij Industrial'nyj Institut]
ul. 50-letija Oktjabrja 7, 663310 Norilsk
Tel: +7 6-38-61
Fax: +7 6-54-79
Industrial Techniques.

North Caucasus Institute of Metallurgy and Mining Engineering
[Severo-Kavkazskij Gorno-Metallurgičeskij Institut]
ul. Nikolaeva 44, 362021 Severo-Osetinskaja Respublika Vladikavkaz
Tel: +7(867-22) 4-93-79
E-Mail: postmaster@skcnit.vladikavkaz.su
Metallurgy and Mining Engineering.

North-Western Polytechnical Institute for Correspondence Studies
[Severo-Zapadnyj Zaočnyj Politehničeskij Institut]
ul. Millionnaja 5, 191065 Sankt-Peterburg
Tel: +7(812) 312-28-22
Fax: +7(812) 311-60-16
F: Motor Car Engineering, Industrial Economics and Management; Informatics and Monitoring Systems; Mechanical Engineering; Radioelectronics; Substances and Materials Technology; Power Engineering.

Northern Ossetian State University
[Severo-Osetinskij Gosudarstvennyj Universitet]
ul. Vatutina 46, 362040 Severo-Osetinskaya Respublika Vladikavkaz
Tel: +7(867-22) 3-09-04
Fax: +7(867-22) 3-27-06
E-Mail: nusu@astak.msk.su
F: Geography; Foreign Languages; History; Mathematics; Ossetian Literature; Pedagogics and Primary Education; Management; Physics; Philology; Chemistry and Biology; Economics; Law.

Novgorod State University
[Novgorodskij Gosudarstvennyj Universitet]
ul. Sankt-Peterburgskaja 41, 173003 Novgorod
Tel: +7(816) 00-2-72-44
Fax: +7(816) 00-2-41-10
E-Mail: polin@npi.nov.su

Novočerkassk State Technical University
[Novočerkasskij Gosudarstvennyj Tehničeskij Universitet]
ul. Prosveščenija 132, 346400 Novočerkassk
Tel: +7(863-52) 2-33-44
Fax: +(863-52) 2-84-63
E-Mail: root@npi.microel.sensor.zgzad.su
F: Geology and Mining Engineering; Chemical Engineering; Civil Engineering; Power Engineering; Economics; Applied Robotics and Mechanical Engineeering; Systems Engineering and Robotics; Electrical Engineering.

Novosibirsk Institute of Architecture
[Novosibirskij Arhitekturnij Institut]
Krasnyj pr. 38, 630099 Novosibirsk
Tel: +7(383-2) 22-10-00
Fax: +7(383-2) 22-17-66
Architecture.

Novosibirsk Institute of Economics
[Novosibirskij Institut Narodnogo Hozjaistva]
ul. Kamenskaja 56, 630016 Novosibirsk 70
Tel: +7(383-2) 24-59-55
Fax: +7(383-2) 24-13-77
Economics.

Novosibirsk Institute of Geodesy, Surveying and Cartography
[Novosibirskij Institut Inženerov Geodezii, Aerofotosemki i Kartografii]
ul. Plahotnogo 10, 630108 Novosibirsk
Tel: +7(3822) 43-25-34
Fax: +7(3822) 43-39-37
E-Mail: postmaster.niigaik.nsk.su
F: Geodesy; Aerophotogeodesy; Optics.

Novosibirsk Institute for Water Transport
[Novosibirskij Institut Inzěnerov Vodnogo Transporta]
ul. Ščetinkina 33, 630099 Novosibirsk
Tel: +7(3832) 22-84-88
Water Transport Technology.

Novosibirsk Institute of Social Rehabilitation
[Novosibirskij Institut Sotsialnoj Reabilitatsii]
ul. Saratovskaya 24a, 630003 Novosibirsk
Tel: +7(383-2) 25-69-31
Social Reabilitation.

Novosibirsk State Academy of Construction
[Novosibirskaja Gosudarstvennaja Akademija Stroitel'stva]
ul. Leningradskaja 113, 630008 Novosibirsk
Tel: +7(383-2) 66-07-39
Fax: +7(383-2) 66-19-39
Construction Engineering.

Novosibirsk State Technical University
[Novosibirskij Gosudarstvennyj Tehničeskij Universitet]
pr. Karla Marksa 20, 630092 Novosibirsk
Tel: +7(3832) 46-50-01
Fax: +7(3832) 46-08-43
Telex: 614636 nstu su
F: Automated Electromechanical Systems; Electronic Engineering; Electrical Engineering; Electical Power Engineering; Business Studies; Automatics and Computer Engineering; Informatics; Automated Manufacturing Processes; Instrumentation Technology; Radio Engineering; Aircraft Engineering; Engineering Physics; Advanced Training; Humanities.

*Novosibirsk State University
[Novosibirskij Gosudarstvennyj Universitet]
ul. Pirogova 2, 630092 Novosibirsk
Tel: +7(383-2) 35-62-44
Fax: +7(383-2) 35-52-37
E-Mail: root@cnit.nsk.su
Telex: 133 146 tevus su
Founded: 1959
F: Mathematics and Applied Mathematics; Physics; Natural Sciences; Geology and Geophysics; Humanities; Economics.

Obninsk Institute of Nuclear Power Engineering
[Obninskij Institut Atomnoj Energetiki]
IATE, Studgorodok, 249020 Obninsk, Kalužskoj Region
Tel: +7(084-39) 7-08-22
Fax: +7(095) 255-22-25
E-Mail: ap12.fei.obnunsk.su
Nuclear Power Engineering.

Ogariev Mordovian State University
[Mordovskij Gosudarstvennyj Universitet im. N.P.Ogarieva]
ul. Bol'ševistskaja 68, 430000 Saransk
Tel: +7(834-22) 4-17-77
Founded: 1957
F: History; Geography; Philology; National Culture; Mathematics; Physics; Chemistry; Biology; Electronics; Civil Engineering; Law; Economics; Mechanization and Electrification of Agriculture; Agriculture; Medicine; Agricultural Economics.

Omsk Institute for Railway Engineering
[Omskij Institut Inženerov Železnodorožnogo Transporta]
pr. K. Marksa 35, 644046 Omsk
Tel: +7(381-2) 31-42-19
Electrical Transport; Mechanical Engineering; Electrical Engineering; Automatics and Telemechanics; Correspondence Studies; Advanced Training.

Omsk State Technical University
[Omskij Gosudarstvennyj Tehničeskij Universitet]
pr. Mira 11, 644050 Omsk
Tel: +7(381-2) 65-31-16
Fax: +7(381-2) 65-26-98

Omsk State University
[Omskij Gosudarstvennyj Universitet]
pr. Mira 55a, 644077 Omsk
Tel: +7(381-2) 64-25-87
Fax: +7(381-2) 66-60-60
E-Mail: e-mail@univer.omsk.su
Founded: 1974
F: Philology; History; Mathematics; Chemistry; Humanities; Physics.

Orel State Polytechnical Institute
[Orlovskij Gosudarstvennyj Politehničeskij Institut]
Naugorskoe šosse 29, 302020 Orel
Tel: +7(086-00) 4-58-37
Fax: +7(086-00) 4-66-84
F: Economics; Mechanical Engineering; Instrumentation Technology; Radioelectronics; Food and Light Industry; Advanced Studies.

Orenburg Polytechnical Institute
[Orenburgskij Politehničeskij Institut]
pr. Pobedy 13, 460352 Orenburg
Tel: +7(352-2) 47-67-70
Fax: +7(352-2) 72-33-95

Penza Higher Technical School
[Penzenskij Zavod-Vtuz pri Zavode Vyčislitel'nyh Elektkronnyh Mašin]
Bajdukova Proezd 1-a, 440605 Penza
Tel: +7(841-2) 62-34-41
Fax: +7(841-2) 55-95-40
Electro-Machine Techniques.

Penza Institute of Architecture and Construction
[Penzenskij Gosudarstvennyj Arhitekturno-Stroitelnyj Institut]
ul. G. Titova 28, 440028 Penza
Tel: +7(841-2) 62-07-77
Fax: +7(841-2) 62-04-10
Architecture; Construction Engineering.

Penza State Technical University
[Penzenskij Gosudarstvennyj Tehničeskij Universitet]
ul. Krasnaja 40, 440017 Penza
Tel: +7(841-2) 66-37-44
Fax: +7(841-2) 66-29-27

Perm State Technical University
[Permskij Gosudarstvennyj Tehničeskij Universitet]
Prosp. Komsomolskij 29a, 614600 Perm
Tel: +7(3422) 31-83-86
Fax: +7(3422) 32-42-69
E-Mail: zhm@ppicnit.perm.su
F: Humanities; Aerospace Engineering; Automobile and Highway Engineering; Mining Engineering; Mechanical Engineering Technology; Civil Engineering; Electrical Engineering; Chemical Technology; Physics and Mathematics.

Perm State University
[Permskij Gosudarstvennyj Universitet]
ul. Bukireva 15, 614600 Perm'
Tel: +7(342-2) 39-63-26
Fax: +7(342-2) 33-80-14
E-Mail: rector@pgu.perm.su
Telex: 134249 yantar su
Founded: 1817
F: History; Philology; Law; Economics; Mathematics and Applied Mathematics; Physics; Chemistry; Biology; Geology; Geography.
D: Evening Studies; Correspondence Courses.

Petrozavodsk State University
[Petrozavodskij Gosudarstvennyj Universitet]
pr. Lenina 33, 185640 Petrozavodsk
Tel: +7(814-00) 7-51-40
Fax: +7(814-00) 7-10-21
E-Mail: postmaster@pgu.karelia.su
Founded: 1940
F: History and Philology; Physics and Mathematics; Biology; Agriculture; Forestry and Wood Technology; Medicine; Building Construction.
D: Correspondence Courses.

Plehanov Russian Academy of Economics
[Rossijskaja Ekonomičeskaja Akademija im.G.V. Plehanova]
Stremjannyj per. 28/3, 113054 Moscow
Tel: +7(095) 237-92-47
Fax: +7(095) 237-92-54
F: General Economics; Industrial Economics; Finance and Credit; Engineering Technology; Commodity Studies; Economics Bybernetics; International Economics Relations.

Puschino State University
[Puščinskij Gosudarstvennyj Universitet]
pr. Nauki 3, 142292 Puščino, Moscow Region
Tel: +7(8462) 32-25-13
Fax: +7(8462) 32-48-64

Rjazan Academy of Radio Engineering
[Rjazanskaja Gosudarstvennaja Radiotehničeskaja Akademija]
ul. Gagarina 59/1, 390005 Rjazanskaja
Tel: +7(091-2) 72-18-44
Fax: +7(091-2) 72-22-15
E-Mail: vvrrti@rricnii.rjazan.su

Rjbinsk Institute of Aviation Technology
[Rybinskij Aviacionnyj Tehnologičeskij Institut]
ul. Puškina 53, 152934 Rybinsk Jaroslavskoj obl.
Tel: +7(085-5) 52-02-91
Fax: +7(085-5) 52-86-88
E-Mail: postmaster@ratj.jaroslavl.su
F: Aerospace Engineering; Aircraft Engineering; Radio Engineering, Electronics and Informatics; Advanced Training.

Robtsovsk Higher Technical School
[Rubcovskij Zavod-Vtuz pri PO 'Altajskij Traktornyj Zavod']
ul. Traktornaja 4, 658207 Rubtsovsk Altai Region
Tel: +7(385-57) 326-29
Fax: +7(385-57) 327-44
E-Mail: kurkow@rubltd.altai.su
Technology; Design.

Rostov Institute of Architecture
[Rostovskij Arhitekturnyj Institut]
pr. Budennovskij 39, 344082 Rostov-na-Donu
Tel: +7(863-2) 39-09-95
Fax: +7(863-2) 66-51-78
E-Mail: root@rai.rostov-na-donu.su

Rostov-upon-Don Institute of Economics
[Rostovskij-na-Donu Institut Narodnogo Hozjaistva]
ul. Sadovaja 69, 344007 Rostov-na-Donu
Tel: +7(863-2) 66-51-23
Fax: +7(863-2) 65-45-21

Rostov-upon-Don Institute of Mechanical Engineering Technology and Manufacturing Sciences
[Rostovskij-na-Donu Institut Avtomatizacii i Tehnologii Mašinostroenija]
pl. Strana Sovetov 2, 344023 Rostov-na-Donu
Tel: +7(863-2) 52-93-51
Fax: +7(863-2) 54-84-11

Rostov-upon-Don State Academy of Construction
[Rostovskaja-na-Donu Gosudarstvennaya Akademija Stroitel'stva]
ul. Socialističeskaja 162, 344022 Rostov-na-Donu
Tel: +7(863-2) 65-50-76
Fax: +7(863-2) 65-57-31

*Rostov State University
[Rostovskij Gosudarstvennyj Universitet]
ul. B.Sadovaja 105, 344006 Rostov-na-Donu GSP 711
Tel: +7(863-2) 65-31-58
Fax: +7(863-2) 64-52-55
E-Mail: rec@rsu.Rostov-na-Donu.su
Rektor: J.V.A. Žhdanov
Founded: 1915
F: Philology; History; Mathematics and Applied Mathematics; Law; Physics; Chemistry; Biology and Soil Science; Geology and Geography; Economics; Philosophy.
D: Evening Studies; Correspondence Courses.

Rostov State University of Railway Communication
[Rostovskij Gosudarstvennyj Universitet Putej Soobščenija]
pl. Narodnogo Opolčenija 2, 344006 Rostov-na-Donu
Tel: +7(863-2) 59-54-58
Fax: +7(863-2) 39-34-37
F: Automatics and Telemechanics; Transportation Management; Road-Building Machines; Power Engineering; Electromechanical Engineering; Construction; Humanities; Part-Time Studies; Correspondance Studies.

Russian Institute of Textile and Light Industry (Distance Learning)
[Rossijskij Zaočnyj Institut Tekstil'noj i Legkoj Promyšlennosti]
ul. Narodnogo Opolčenija 38 Korp 2, 123298 Moscow
Tel: +7(095) 943-63-62
Fax: +7(095) 943-63-62
F: Light Industry Technology; Electrical Engineering; Chemical Technolgy; Industrial Economics; Textile Technology; Moscow.

*Russian Peoples' Friendship University
[Rossijskij Universitet Družby Narodov]
ul. Mikluho-Maklaja 6, 117198 Moskva
Tel: +7(095) 434-53-00
Fax: +7(095) 433-15-11
E-Mail: filippov@udn.msk.su
Rektor: V.M. Filippov
F: Engineering; Physics, Mathematics and Natural Sciences; Medicine; Economics and Law; Agriculture; History and Philology; Preparatory; Russian Language Teaching; Ecology; Pre-University Studies.

Russian State Hydrometeorological Institiute
[Rossijskij Gosudarstvennij Gidrometerologičeskij Institut]
pr. Maloohtinskij 98, 195196 Saint-Petersburg
Tel: +7(812) 221-60-90
Fax: +7(812) 221-41-32
E-Mail: bouush@rgmi.spb.su
F: *Meteorology; Hydrology; Oceanology.*

Russian State Social Institute
[Rossijskij Gosudarstvennyj Social'nyj Institut]
ul. Losinoostrovskaja 34, 107150 Moscow
Tel: +7(095) 169-96-91
Fax: +7(095) 169-81-32
E-Mail: rgsi.unep@center.unicor.free.net
F: *Social Economics; Socilology; Social Work; Journalism; Law; Psychology; Advanced Training.*
Ce: *Education and Cultural Cooperation (International).*

Russian State University of Humantities
[Rossijskij Gosudarstvennyj Gumanitarnyj Universitet]
Miusskaja pl. 6, 125267 Moscow
Tel: +7(095) 250-62-11
Fax: +7(095) 250-51-09
E-Mail: afn@rggu.msk.su
F: *History and Archiving; Museum Studies; Management; Informatics; Economics; Philosophy; History and Philology; Theoretic and Applied Linguistics.*

Samara Institute of Architecture and Construction
[Samarskij Arhitekturno-Stroitelnyj Institut]
ul. Molodogvardejskaja 194, 443001 Samara
Tel: +7(846-2) 33-87-87
Fax: +7(846-2) 33-92-51
E-Mail: root@sbi.samara.su

Samara Institute of Economics
[Samarskij Ekonomičeskij Institut]
ul. Sovetskoj Armii 141, 443090 Samara
Tel: +7(846-2) 22-15-42
Fax: +7(846-2) 22-09-53

Samara State Aerospace University
[Samarskij Gosudarstvennyj Aerokosmičeskij Universitet]
Moskovskoe Šosse 34, 443086 Samara
Tel: +7(8462) 35-18-26
Fax: +7(8462) 35-18-36
E-Mail: soifer@space.samara.su
Telex: 214181 AIST SU
F: *Aircraft Engineering; Aircraft Engines; Metal Pressure Processing; Radio Engineering; Informatics.*
C: *Civil Aviation Engineers; Economics and Management.*

Samara State Technical University
[Samarskij Gosudarstvennyj Tehničeskij Universitet]
ul. Galaktionovskaja 141, 443010 Samara
Tel: +7(8462) 32-16-92
Fax: +7(8462) 32-42-35
F: *Automatics and Information Technology; Physics and Technology; Mechanical Engineering; Industrial Economics; Electrical Engineering; Heat Power Engineering; Mechanical Engineering Technology; Chemical Technology; Oil Technology.*

Samara State University
[Samarskij Gosudarstvennyj Universitet]
ul. Akademika Pavlova 1, 443011 Samara
Tel: +7(8462) 54-36-91
Fax: +7(8462) 34-54-17
E-Mail: root@univer.samara.su
Founded: 1970
F: *Philology; History; Law; Mechanics and Applied Mathematics; Physics; Chemistry and Biology.*
D: *Evening Studies; Correspondence Courses.*

Saint-Petersburg Electrotechnical University
[Sankt-Peterburgskij Elektrotehničeskij Universitet]
ul. Prof. Popova 5, 197376 Sankt-Peterburg
Tel: +7(812) 234-46-51
Fax: +7(812) 234-27-58
E-Mail: leti@sovamsu.sovusa.com
F: *Radio Engineering; Electronic Engineering; Automatics and Computer Engineering; Electrical Engineering and Automated Systems; Electrophysics; Naval Radio and Electrical Engineering and Automated Systems; Humanities; Advanced Training and Retraining.*
S: *Management.*

Saint-Petersburg Institute of Mechanical Engineering
[Sankt-Peterburgskij Institut Mašinostroenija (Vtuz LMZ)]
pr. Poljustrovskij 14, 195108 Sankt-Peterburg
Tel: +7(812) 540-01-54
Fax: +7(812) 541-20-87
Mechanical Engineering.

Saint-Petersburg Institute of Precise Mechanics and Optics
[Sankt-Peterburgskij Institut Točnoj Mehaniki i Optiki]
ul. Sablinskaja 14, 197101 Sankt-Peterburg
Tel: +7(812) 238-89-29
Fax: +7(812) 232-05-74
E-Mail: ngi@ipmo.spb.su
Telex: 121408 inlac su
F: *Humanities; Natural Sciences; Computer Technology and Monitering Systems; Optics; Engineering Physics.*

Saint-Petersburg State Academy of Aerospace Instrumentation

[Sankt-Peterburgskaja Gosudarstvennaya Akademija Aerokosmičeskogo Proborostroeniya]
ul. B.Morskaja 67, 190000 Sankt-Peterburg
Tel: +7(812) 312-09-37
Fax: +7(812) 315-77-78
E-Mail: liap@sovam.com
Telex: 121226 PUNA SU
F: *Devices and Automatical Air-Vehicles; Radio Engineering; Aircraft Electrical Devices and Control Systems; Computing and Radioelectronic Systems; General Engineering Sciences; Part-Time and Correspondence Studies; Engineer-Researcher Training; Humanities.*

Saint-Petersburg State Academy for Engineering Economics

[Sankt-Peterburgskaja Gosudarstvennaya Inženerno-Ekonomičeskaja Akademija]
ul. Marata 27, 191002 Sankt-Peterburg
Tel: +7(812) 112-06-33
Fax: +7(812) 112-06-07
Telex: 121345 ptb su ingecon
F: *Industrial Management; Informatics and Business Administration; Transportation Economics and Management; Chemical Industry Economics and Management; Humanitiies and General Sciences; Regional Economics and Management (Institute).*

Saint-Petersburg State Academy of Forestry Engineering

[Sankt-Peterburskaja Lesotehničeskaja Akademija]
Per. Institutskij 5, 194018 Sankt-Peterburg
Tel: +7(812) 550-08-19
Fax: +7(812) 550-08-15
Telex: 122374 posev
F: *Forestry; Forestry Engineering; Forestry Mechanical Engineering; Industrial Economics; Chemical Technology; Wood Machining Technology.*

Saint-Petersburg State Institute of Mining Engineering (Technical University)

[Sankt-Peterburgskij Gosudarstvennyj Gornyj Institut (Tehničeskij Universitet)]
21 linija 2, 199026 Sankt-Peterburg
Tel: +7(812) 218-86-81
Fax: +7(812) 218-54-63
Telex: 121494 lgip su
F: *Geological Prospecting; Geophysics; Mining Engineering; Mining Electrical Engineering; Engineering Economics; Metallurgy; Mining Surveying; Correspondance Studies; Mine Construction.*
Branch: *Vorkuta; Monchegorsk; Slantsy for Correspondance Studies; Inta for Correspondance Studies; Vorkuta for Correspondance Studies; Kostomuksha for Correspondance Studies.*

Saint-Petersburg State Institute of Technology (Technical University)

[Sankt-Peterburskij Gosudarstvennyj Tehnologičeskij Institut (Tehničeskij Universitet)]
pr. Moskovskij 26, 198013 Sankt-Peterburg
Tel: +7(812) 292-95-37
Fax: +7(812) 110-62-85
E-Mail: office@spti.spb.su
F: *Non-Organic Materials Chemical Technology; Chemical Engineering Technology; Engineering Cybernetics; Chemical Technology of Organic Substances and Microbiological Manufacturing Process; Engineering Physics and Chemical Engineering; Part-Time Studies; Chemistry and Computer Engineering (Advanced Training for Staff); High Technology (Advanced Training); Oil Chemical Technology (Advanced Training).*

Saint-Petersburg State Technical University

[Sankt-Peterburgskij Gosudarstvennyj Tehničeskij Universitet]
ul. Politehničeskaja 29, 195251 Sankt-Peterburg
Tel: +7(812) 247-16-16
Fax: +7(812) 552-66-86
E-Mail: arg@stu.spb.su
Rektor: Yuri Sergeevitch Vasiliev (1983-)
Founded: 1899
F: *Hydraulic Engineering; Electrical Engineering; Energetics and Power Engineering; Mechanical and Machine Engineering; Physical Mechanics; Physical Metallurgy; Economics and Management; Engineering Economics; Radio Engineering; Technical Cybernetics; Computer Engineering and RadioElectronics; Humanities; Electrical and Radio Engineering; Technology and Automated Manufacturing Systems; Foreign Students; Evening Studies; Correspondence Courses.*

Saint-Petersburg State Technical University of Marine Engineering

[Sankt-Peterburgskij Gosudarstvennyj Morskoj Tehničeskij Universitet]
ul. Locmanskaja 3, 190008 Sankt-Peterburg
Tel: +7(812) 114-07-61
Fax: +7(812) 113-81-09
E-Mail: rec@mtu-rec.spb.su
F: *Naval Architecture and Ocean Engineering; Marine Engineering and Automatics; Marine Electronics and Control Systems; Engineering Economics; General Engineering Training.*

*Saint-Petersburg State University

[Sankt-Petersburgskij Gosudarstvennyj Universitet]
Universitetskaja nab. 7/9, 199034 Sankt-Peterburg
Tel: +7(812) 218-76-31
Fax: +7(812) 218-54-79
E-Mail: hg.lgu.spb.su
Telex: 064121481 lsu su
Rektor: Ludmila Verbitskaja
Founded: 1819
F: *Mathematics and Mechanics; Physics; Applied Mathematics for Monitoring Processes;*

Chemistry; Biology and Soil Science; Geology; Geography and Geoecoloby; Economics; Law; History; Philsophy; Philology; East Studies; Journalism; Psychology; Sociology.
S: Management.

Saint-Petersburg State University of Architecture and Civil Engineering
[Sankt-Peterburgskij Gosudarstvennyj Arhitekturno-Stroitel'nyj Universitet]
ul. 2-aja Krasnoarmejskaja 4, 198005 Sankt-Peterburg
Tel: +7(812) 292-99-65
Fax: +7(812) 292-58-72
E-Mail: rector@spice.spb.su
Telex: (64) 121079 spice su
F: Architecture; Construction; Technical Sanitation; Motor Car and Highway Engineering.

Saint-Petersburg State University of Railway Communication
[Sankt-Peterburgskij Gosudarstvennyj Universitet Putej Soobščenija]
pr. Moskovskij 9, 190031 Sankt-Peterburg
Tel: +7(812) 310-25-21
Fax: +7(812) 315-26-21
F: Mechanical Engineering; Bridges and Tunnels; Construction; Transportation Management; Electromechanical Engineering; Electrical Engineering; Economics and Social Management; Part-Time Studies; Pre-University Studies; Foreign Students Studies.

Saint-Petersburg State University of Technology and Design
[Sankt-Peterburgskij Gosudarstvennyj Universitet Tehnologii i Dizajna]
ul. Bolšaja Morskaja 18, 191065 Sankt-Peterburg
Tel: +7(812) 315-08-93
Fax: +7(812) 311-95-84
F: Leather Foot-Wear Technology; Technology; Mechanical Engineering; Engineering Economics; Chemical Technology; Sewing Technology.

Saint-Petersburg State University of Vegetable Polymer Technology
[Sankt-Peterburgskij Gosudarstvennyj Tehnologičeskij Universitet Rastitel'nyh Polimerov]
ul. Ivana Černyh 4, 198095 Sankt-Peterburg
Tel: +7(812) 186-57-44
Fax: +7(812) 186-86-00
Vegetable Polymer Technology.

Saint-Petersburg University of Economics and Finance
[Sankt-Peterburgskij Universitet Ekonomiki i Finansov]
ul. Sadovaja 21, 191023 Sankt-Peterburg
Tel: +7(812) 310-38-23
Fax: +7(812) 110-56-74
E-Mail: rector@finec.spb.su
F: Economic Theory and Politics; Economics and Management; Business Studies; Finance, Credit and International Economic Relations; Personnel Management; Statistics, Stock-Taking and Economic Analysis; General Economics.

Saint-Petersburg Technological Institute of Refrigeration
[Sankt-Peterburskij Tehnologičeskij Institut Holodilnoj Promyšlennosti]
ul. Lomonosova 9, 191002 Sankt-Peterburg
Tel: +7(812) 315-36-17
Fax: +7(812) 315-05-35
E-Mail: boss geeref.spb.su
F: Refrigerating Engineering; Food Production Engineering; Technology; Cryogenic Engineering and Conditioning; Advanced Training; Correspondance Studies.

Saint-Petersburg University of Water Communication
[Sankt-Peterburgskij Universitet Vodnyh Kommunikacij]
ul. Dvinskaja 5/7, 198035 Sankt-Peterburg
Tel: +7(812) 251-12-21
Fax: +7(812) 251-76-20
Water Communication.

Samara Institute for Railway Engineers
[Samarskij Institut Inženerov Železnodorožnogo Transporta im.M.T.Elizarova]
per. 1-yj Bezymjannyj 18, 443066 Samara
Tel: +7(8462) 51-77-90
Fax: +7(8462) 51-77-90
F: Maintenence; Electrical Engineering; Electromechanics; Construction; Humanities; Correspondence Studies.

Saratov Institute of Law
[Saratovskij Gosudarstvennyj Juridičeskij Institut]
ul. Černyševskogo 104, 410720 Saratov
Tel: +7(845-2) 25-04-86
Fax: +7(845-2) 25-23-70
Law.

Saratov State Institute of Economics
[Saratovskij Gosudarstvennyj Ekonomičeskij Institut]
ul. Radiščeva 89, 410760 Saratov
Tel: +7(845-2)26-33-93
Economics.

Saratov State Technical University
[Saratovskij Gosudarstvennyj Tehničeskij Universitet]
ul. Politehničeskaja 77, 410016 Saratov
Tel: +7(845-2) 25-27-90
Fax: +7(845-2) 25-52-26

Saratov State University
[Saratovskij Gosudarstvennyj Universitet]
ul. Astrahanskaja 83, 410071 Saratov
Tel: +7(845-2) 24-16-96
Fax: +7(845-2) 24-04-46
E-Mail: schit.saratov.su
Telex: 241125 ATOLL
Founded: 1909
F: History; Philology; Mechanics and
Mathematics; Physics; Chemistry; Biology;
Geography; Geology.
Chair: Philosophy; Political Economy; Political
Sciences; Sociology; Pedagogy; Physical Training
and Sport; German Language; English and
French Languages.
D: Evening Studies; Correspondence Courses.

*Sečenov Moscow Medical Academy
[Moskovskaja Medicinskaja Akademija im. I.M.
Sečenova]
ul. Pirogovskaja 2/6, 119881 Moskva
Tel: +7(095) 248-31-22
Fax: +7(095)248-01-81
Rektor: Michail A. Paltsev
Founded: 1755
F: Medicine; Nursing; Pharmacy; Sanitation and
Hygiene.

Siberian Academy of Aerospace Engineering
[Sibirkaja Aerokosmičeskaja Akademija]
Pros. im. Gazetj
Tel: +7(391-2) 33-00-14
Fax: +7(391-2) 33-47-09
E-Mail: saa@stu.krasnojarsk.su
Telex: 288177 kurs su
Aerospace Engineering; Electrical Engineering;
Economics.

Siberian Institute of Automobile and Highway Engineering
[Sibirskij Avtomobil'no-Dorožnyj Institut]
pr. Mira 5, 644080 Omsk
Tel: +7(381-2) 65-22-18
Fax: +7(381-2) 65-03-23
Automobile and Highway Engineering.

Siberian State Academy of Railway Engineering
[Sibirskaja Gosudarstvennaja Akademija Putej
Soobščenija]
ul. D. Kovalčuk 191, 630023 Novosibirsk
Tel: +7(383-2) 28-74-70
Fax: +7(383-2) 28-74-02
F: Bridges and Transport Tunnels; Industrial
and Civil Engineering; Water Supply, Sewerage,
Rational Use and Protectionof Water Resources;
Railway Transportation Planning and
Management; Lifting and Hoisting Machines,
Construction and Track Equipment;
Transportation Economics and Management;
Construction Economics and Management; Social
Management; Russian Language.

Siberian State Medical University
[Sibirskij Gosudarstvennyj Medicinskij
Universitet]
ul. Moskovskij Trakt 2, 634050 Tomsk
Tel: +7(382-2) 23-03-37
Fax: +7(382-2) 23-33-09
Medicine.

Siberian Metallurgy Institute
Sibirskij Metallurgičeskij Institut
ul. Kirova 42, 654080 Novokuznetsk
Tel: +7(384-3) 46-35-02
Fax: +7(384-3) 45-57-92
Metallurgy.

Siberian Technological Institute
Sibirskij Tehnologičeskij Institut
pr. Mira 82, 660049 Krasnojarsk
Tel: +7(391-2) 27-02-21
Fax: +7(391-2) 27-44-40
E-Mail: buka@sibti.krasnojarsk.su
F: Humanities; Industrial Economics;
Preliminary Studies; Forestry Engineering;
Automatics and Robotics; Forestry; Mechanical
Engineering; Natural Resources Processing
Technology; Chemical Engineering Technology;
Wood Machining Technology.

Sochi Institute of Tourism Business and Hotel Management
[Sočinskij Institut Kurortnogo Dela i Turizma]
ul. Sovetskaja 26a, 354000 Sochi
Tel: +7(862-2) 99-97-92
Fax: +7(862-2) 99-97-90
Tourism Business and Hotel Management.

State Academy of Management
[Gosudarstvennaja Akademija Upravlenija]
pr. Rjazanskij 99, 109542 Moskva
Tel: +7(095) 371-13-22
Fax: +7(095) 174-62-81
F: Management in Mechanical Engineering
Industry; Management in Power Engineering;
Management in Chemical and Metallurgical
Industry; Transportation Management; Urban
Planning and Construction Management;
Economical Cybernetics; International Economic
Relations; Industrial Economics and
Management; Sociology; Russian-British.

State Jewish Academy
[Gosudarstvennaja Evrejskaja Akademija]
ul. B. Bronnaja 6, 103104 Moskva
Tel: +7(095) 202-45-30
Fax: +7(095) 121-25-37

Stavropol Polytechnical Institute
[Stavropol'skij Politehničeskij Institut]
pr. Kulakova 2, 355038 Stavropol
Tel: +7(865-22) 6-32-86
Fax: +7(865-22) 5-19-22

Syktyvkar State University
[Syktyvkarskij Gosudarstvennyj Universitet]
pr. Oktjabrskij 55, 167001 Komi Republic
Syktyvkar
Tel: +7(821-22) 3-72-86
Fax: +7(821-22) 3-18-88
E-Mail: postmaster@sucnit.komi.su
Founded: 1909
F: History and Philology; Physics and
Mathematics; Chemistry and Biology; Economics;
Humanities; Finno-Ugrian Languages.
D: Evening Studies; Correspondence Courses.

Taganrog State University of Radio Engineering
[Taganrogskij Gosudarstvennyj Radiotehničeskij
Universitet]
per. Nekrasovskij 44, 347928 Taganrog
Tel: +7(863-44) 6-50-67
Fax: +7(863-44) 6-50-19
E-Mail:
VGZakharevich@trincnit.rostov-na-donu.su
F: General Engineering; Computer Engineering
and Automated Systems; Radio Engineering;
Electronic Device Engineering.

Tambov State Technical University
[Tambovskij Gosudarstvennyj Tehničeskij
Universitet]
ul. Leningradskaja 1, 392620 Tambov
Tel: +7(075-2) 22-94-41
Fax: +7(075-2) 22-07-35
E-Mail: root@tixm.tambov.su

Tchecheno-Inguš State University
[Čečeno-Ingušskij Gosudarstvennyj Universitet]
ul. A.Šeripova 32, 364907 Groznyj
Tel: +7(871-2) 23-40-89
Founded: 1972
F: Philology; History; Economics; Biology and
Chemistry; Geography; Physics; Mathematics;
Romance and Germanic Philology.
D: Evening Studies; Medical Treatment Studies;
Correspondence Courses.
Ce: Problems of Psychological Communication
(All-Union).
L: Plants; Physical and Chemical Research of
Mercury; Radio Measurements.

Tjumen Institute of Civil Engineering
[Tjumenskij Inženerno-Stroitel'nyj Institut]
ul. Lunačarskogo 2, 625001 Tjumen'
Tel: +7(3452) 26-20-51
Fax: +7(3452) 26-10-10
Civil Engineering.

Tjumen Institute of Industry
[Tjumenskij Industrial'nyj Institut]
ul. Volodarskogo 38, 625000 Tjumen'
Tel: +7(3452) 25-08-61
Fax: +7(3452) 25-08-52
Institutional Technology.

Tjumen State University
[Tjumenskij Gosudarstvennyj Universitet]
ul. Semakova 10, 625003 Tjumen'
Tel: +7(3452) 26-19-30
Fax: +7(3452) 25-12-55
E-Mail: postmaster@tucunit.tyumen.su
Rektor: Gennadiy F. Kutsev (1992-)
Registrar: Tatyana Lysova
Founded: 1973
F: Philology; Romance and Germanic Philology;
Physics; Chemistry; Economics; Geography;
History; Biology; Mathematics; Law; Physical
Culture.
D: Preparatory.
Ce: Research.

Tol'jatti Polytechnical Institute
[Tol'jattinskij Politehničeskij Institut]
ul. Belorusskaja 14, 445667 Tol'jatti
Tel: +723-41-25
Telex: 21446 tlt su

Tomsk Polytechnical University
[Tomskij Politehničeskij Universitet]
pr. Lenina 30, 634004 Tomsk
Tel: +7(8322) 22-44-22
Fax: +7(8322) 22-46-07
E-Mail: tpu@tpu.tomsk.su
F: Physics and Technology; Electrical Physics;
Geological Prospecting, Oil and Gas Extraction;
Mechanical Engineering; Chemical Technology;
Heat Power Engineering; Automatics and
Electrical Mechanics; Automatics and Computer
Engineering; Automatics and Electrical Power.

Tomsk State Academy of Architecture and Civil Engineering
[Tomskaja Gosudarstvennaya Arhitekturno-
Stroitel'naja Akademija]
pl. Soljanaja 2, 634003 Tomsk
Tel: +7(3822) 75-33-43
Fax: +7(3822) 75-39-22
Architecture and Civil Engineering.

Tomsk State Academy of Radioelectronics and Monitoring Systems
[Tomskaja Gosudarstvennaja Akademija Sistemy
Upravlenija i Radioelektroniki]
pr. Lenina 40, 634050 Tomsk
Tel: +7(382-2) 22-32-27
Fax: +7(382-2) 22-32-62
E-Mail: office@tiasur.tomsk.su
Radioelectronics and Monitoring Systems.

Tomsk University
[Tomskij Gosudarstvennyj Universitet]
pr. Lenin 36, 634010 Tomsk
Tel: +7(3822) 23-44-65
Fax: +7(3822) 22-24-66
E-Mail: mng@tgu.tomsk.su
Founded: 1888
F: History; Philology; Law; Economics;
Mathematics and Mechanics; Applied
Mathematics; Physics; Radio-Physics; Physics

*and Technology; Chemistry; Biology and Soil
Science; Geology and Geography.*
D: *Evening Studies; Correspondence Courses.*

Tula State Technical University
[Tul'skij Gosudarstvennyj Tehničeskij Universitet]
pr. Lenina 92, 300600 Tula
Tel: +7(087-2) 25-53-57
Fax: +7(087-2) 33-21-91
E-Mail: postmaster@tulgtu.tula.su

Tupolev Kazan' State Technical University
[Kazanskij Gosudarstvennyj Tehničeskij
Universitet im. A.N. Tupoleva]
ul. K. Marksa 10, 420111 Kazan', Respublika
Tatarstan
Tel: +7(843-2) 32-69-10
F: *Aircraft Engineering; Aircraft Engines;
Automatics and Electronic Engineering;
Informatics and Technical Cybernetics; Radio
Engineering; Management and Business Studies;
Pre-University Studies; Advanced Training.*

Tver Polytechnical Institute
[Tverskoj Politehničeskij Institut]
nab. Afanasija Nikitina 22, 170026 Tver'
Tel: +7(082-22) 1-63-35
Fax: +7(082-22) 1-43-07
F: *Mechanical Engineering Technology;
Mechanical Engineering; Industrial and Civil
Engineering; Automated Control Systems;
Foreign Students.*

Tver State University
[Tverskoj Gosudarstvennyj Universitet]
ul. Željabova 33, 170000 Tver'
Tel: +7(082-22) 3-24-52
Fax: +7(082-22) 3-83-42
E-Mail: postmaster@tvegu.tver.su
Founded: 1971
*Mathematics; Physics; Chemistry; Biology;
Geology; History; Law; Russian Literature;
Foreign Languages; Pedagogics; Economics.*

Udmurt State University
[Udmurtskij Gosudarstvennyj Universitet]
ul. Krasnogerojskaja 71, 426037 Iževsk
Tel: +7(34-12) 75-16-10
Fax: +7(34-12) 78-70-10
E-Mail: adm@matsim.udmurtia.su
Telex: 255110 ptb su (box 103)
Rektor: Vitaly A. Zhuravljov (1987-92)
Registrar: Alexandre A. Kuznetsov
Founded: 1972
F: *History; Philology; Physics and Mathematics;
Biology and Chemistry; Economics and Law;
Romance and Germanic Philology; Art and
Graphic Art; Physical Education.*
I: *Ugro-Finnish History and Culture;
Mathematical Simulation.*

Ufa State Aviation Technical University
[Ufimskij Gosudarstvennyj Aviacionnyj
Tehničeskij Universitet]
ul. Marksa 12, 450025 Ufa, Respublika Baškirja
Tel: +7(34-72) 22-63-07
Fax: +7(34-72) 22-99-09
E-Mail: rector@ugatu.uaicnit.bashkiria.su
Aviation Technology.

**Ufa State University of Petroleum
Technology**
[Ufimskij Gosudarstvennyj Neftjanoj Tehničeskij
Universitet]
ul. Kosmonavtov 1, 450062 Ufa, Respublika
Baķirja
Tel: +7(34-72) 42-03-70
Fax: +7(34-72) 43-14-19
E-Mail: postmaster@uni.ifc.bashkiria.su
F: *Oil and Gas Mining; Pipe Line
Transportation; Management and Automated;
Chemical Technology and Biotechnology; Civil
Engineering; Geology and Geography.*
D: *Foreign Students; Correspondence Studies.*

Ukhta Institute of Industry
[Uhtinskij Industrial'nyj Institut]
ul. Pervomajskaja 13, 169400 Uhta
Tel: +7(82-1-47) 6-03-33
Fax: +7(82-1-47) 3-45-12
Industrial Studies.

Uljanovsk Polytechnical Institute
[Ul'janovskij Politehničeskij Institut]
ul. Severnyj Venec 32, 432700 Ul'janovsk
Tel: +7(84-22) 34-77-34
Fax: +7(84-22) 34-80-85
E-Mail: svs@nitpt.pti.simbirsk.su
F: *Radio Engineering; Power Engineering;
Construction; Mechanical Engineering; Aircraft
Engineering.*

**Ural Academy of Geology and Mining
Engineering**
[Ural'skaja Gosudarstvennaja Gorno-
Geologičeskaja Akademija]
ul. Kujbyševa 30, 620219 Ekaterinburg
Tel: +7(3452) 22-25-47
Fax: +7(3452) 22-27-08
Geology and Mining Engineering.

**Ural Electromechanical Institute for Railway
Engineers**
[Ural'skij Elektromehaničeskij Institut Inžnerov
Železnodorožnogo Transporta]
ul. Kolmogorova 66, 620079 Ekaterinburg
Tel: +7(3432) 58-30-36
Fax: +7(3432) 51-86-47
F: *Electromechanics; Electrical Engineering;
Mechanical Engineering; Transportation
Management; Civil Engineering.*

Ural Institute of Architecture and Arts
[Ural'skij Arhitekturno-Hudožestvennyj Institut]
ul. Libknehta 23, 620219 Ekaterinburg GSP-1089
Tel: +7(3432) 51-76-13
Fax: +7(3432) 58-98-10
E-Mail: rector@architekt.eburg.su
Architecture and Arts.

Ural Institute of Economics
[Ural'skij Institut Narodnogo Hozjaistva]
ul. 8 Marta 62, 620219 Ekaterinburg GSP-985
Tel: +7(3432) 22-02-46
Fax: +7(3432) 22-71-47
*F: Economics; Management and International
Economic Relations; Finance; Business Studies;
Engineering; Correspondence Studies.*

Urals State Academy of Forestry Engineering
[Ural'skaja Gosudarstvennaja Lesotehničeskaj
Akademija]
ul. Sibirskij trakt 37, 620032 Ekaterinburg
Tel: +7(34-32) 24-23-73
Fax: +7(34-32) 24-03-37
*F: Forestry Engineering; Economics and
Management; Forestry Mechnical engineering;
Chemical Technology; Wood Machining
Technology; Forestry.*

Ural State Academy of Law
[Ural'skaja Gosudarstvennaja Juridičeskaja
Akademija]
ul. Komsomol'skaja 21, 620066 Ekaterinburg
GSP-1038
Tel: +7(34-32) 44-43-63
Fax: +7(34-32) 44-50-34
E-Mail: postmaster@urura.rcupi.eburg.su
*F: Judge and Public Prosecutor Training;
Judical Inquiry; Administrative Law;
Correspondence Studies.*

Ural State Technical University
[Ural'skij Gosudarstvennyj Tehničeskij
Universitet]
Vtuzgorodok ul. Mira 19, 620002 Ekaterinburg K-2
Tel: +7(34-32) 44-03-62
Fax: +7(34-32) 44-16-24
E-Mail: rec@rec.rcupi.eburg.su
*F: Metallurgy; Chemical Technology; Silicate
Technology; Mechnics and Mechanical
Engineering; Electrical Engineering; Heat Power
Engineering; Radio Engineering; Civil
Engineering; Economics and Management;
Engineering Physics; Humanities; Physical
Education and Sport Science; Correspondence
Studies; Manager Training for Industry and
Construction.*

Ural State University
[Ural'skij Gosudarstvennyj Universitet]
pr. Lenina 51, 620083 Ekaterinburg
Tel: +7(3432) 55-75-12
Fax: +7(3432) 55-74-01
Founded: 1920

*F: History; Philosophy; Philology; Journalism;
Mathematics and Applied Mathematics; Physics;
Chemistry; Biology; Economy; Printing Shop for
Training Journalists; Statesmanship (Graduate).
I: Physics and Applied Mathematics; Russian
Culture.
L: Biorecultivation of Industrially Destroyed
Lands.*

Ural State University for Technical Teacher Training
[Ural'skij Gosudarstvennyj Professionalno-
Pedagogičeskij Universitet]
ul. Mašinostroitelej 11, 620012 Ekaterinburg
Tel: +7(3432) 31-04-36
Fax: +7(3432) 31-94-63
*F: Power Engineering; Mechanical Engineering;
Humanities.*

Vjatka State Technical University
[Vjatskij Gosudarstvennyj Tehničeskij Universitet]
ul. Moskovskaja 36, 610601 Vjatka
Tel: +7(8330) 62-65-71
Fax: +7(8330) 62-65-71
Technology.

Vladimir State Pedagogical University
[Vladimirskij Gosudarstvennyj Pedagogičeskij
Universitet]
pr. Stroitelej 11, 600024 Vladimir
Tel: +7(092-22) 7-26-21
Fax: +7(092-22) 3-63-02
*F: Russian Language and Literature; History;
Law; Natural Sciences and Geography; Physics
and Mathematics; Engineering Economics;
Foreign Languages; Music and Pedagogics;
Painting and Printmaking; Physical Education and
Sport Studies; Primary Education; Practical
Psychology.
D: Russian Language (for foreign students).*

Vladimir State Technical University
[Vladimirskij Gosudarstvennyj Tehničeskij
Universitet]
ul. Gor'kogo 87, 6000026 Vladimir
Tel: +7(092-22) 7-96-03
Fax: +7(092-22) 3-33-58
*F: Radio Engineering; Technical Cybernatics;
Motor Transport; Mechanical Engineering
Technology; Chemics Technology; Civil
Engineering.*

Volga Regional Institute of Radio Engineering, Informatics and Communication
[Povolžskij Institut Informatiki Radiotehniki i
Svjazi]
ul. L'va Tolstogo 23, 443099 Samara
Tel: +7(8462) 32-25-13
Fax: +7(8462) 32-48-64
Founded: 1940
*F: Engineering; Radiocommunication,
Broadcasting and Television; Automated and
Multichannel Electrical Communication.*

Volga State Academy of Water Transport
[Volžskaja Gosudarstvennaja Akademija Vodnogo Transporta]
ul. Nesterova 5, 603600 Nižnij Novgorod
Tel: +7(831-2) 36-17-56
Fax: +7(831-2) 32-17-91
Water Transport.

Vologda Polytechnical Institute
[Vologodskij Politehničeskij Institut]
ul. Lenina 15, 160008 Vologda
Tel: +1(817-22) 2-46-45
Fax: +1(817-22) 2-45-62
F: Civil Engineering; Electrical Power Engineering; Mechanical Engineering Technology; Engineering Ecology for Water Systems.

Volgograd Institute of Civil Engineering
[Volgogradskij Inženerno-Stroitel'nyj Institut]
ul. Akademičeskaja 1, 400074 Volgograd
Tel: +7(8442) 44-91-64
Fax: +7(8442) 44-09-33
E-Mail: postmaster@uisi.tsaritsyn.su
F: Civil Engineering; Architecture; Highway Engineering; Ecology for Civil Engineering; Automated Systems in Construction; Correspondence Studies; Advanced Training.

Volgograd State Technical University
[Volgogradskij Gosudarstvennyj Tehničeskij Universitet]
pr. Lenina 28, 400066 Volgograd
Tel: +7(8442) 34-00-76
Fax: +7(8442) 34-85-70
E-Mail: postmaster@vgti.tsaritsyn.su

Volgograd State University
[Volgogradskij Gosudarstvennyj Universitet]
ul. 2-ja Prodol'naja 30, 400062 Volgograd 62
Tel: +7(8442) 43-81-24
Fax: +7(8442) 43-87-86
Founded: 1978
D: Russian Language and Literature; Romance and German Language and Literature; History; Mathematics; Physics.

Voronež Institute of Forestry Engineering
[Voronežskij Lesotehničeskij Institut]
ul. Timirjazeva 8, 394613 Voronež
Tel: +7(0732) 52-84-11
Forestry Engineering.

Voronež Institute of Technology
[Voronežskij Tehnologičeskij Institut]
pr. Revoljucii 19, 394017 Voronež
Tel: +7(0732) 55-35-21
Fax: +7(0732) 55-42-67

Voronež State Academy of Architecture
[Voronežskaja Gosudarstvennaja Arhitekturno-Stroitel'naja Akademija]
ul. 20-Letija Oktjabrja 84, 394006 Voronež
Tel: +7(0732) 57-52-68
Fax: +7(0732) 57-59-05
Architecture.

Voronež State Technical University
[Voronežskij Gosudarstvennyj Tehničeskij Universitet]
Moskovskij per. 14, 394693 Voronež
Tel: +7(0732) 16-09-19

Voronež State University
[Voronežskij Gosudarstvennyj Universitet]
Universitetskaja pl. 1, 294693 Voronež
Tel: +7(0732) 55-65-83
Fax: +7(0732) 56-65-51
E-Mail: postmaster@vucnit.voronezh.su
Founded: 1919
F: History; Philology; Romance and Germanic Languages; Economics; Law; Mathematics and Applied Mathematics; Physics; Chemistry; Biology and Soil Science; Geology; Geography.

NATIONAL ACADEMIC BODIES

Ministry of Education
bul. Čistoprudnyj 6, 101856 Moskva
Tel: +7(095) 924-17-84
Fax: +7(095) 924-69-89
Minister: E. Tkacenko

State Committee for Higher Education
ul. Lusinovskaja 51, 113833 Moskva
Tel: +7(095) 237-97-63
Fax: +7(095) 236-01-71
E-Mail: root@com.rkcnit.msk.su
Chairman: Vladimir G. Kinelev
International Relations: Michael G. Myasnikov

Association of Universities
Moscow University, Main Building, Office 907-908, Leninskije Gory, 119899 Moskva
Tel: +7(095) 939-50-04
Fax: +7(095) 939-00-64

Interuniversity Centre for International Education Programmes (ICIEP)
ul. Petrovka 27, 103767 Moskva
Tel: +7(095) 200-40-06
Fax: +7(095) 200-67-643
Director: Sergej G. Kulik
Founded: 1993

Commission of the Russian Federation for Unesco
Ministry of Foreign Affairs, ul. Vozdvijenka 9, 121019 Moskva
Tel: +7(095) 290-08-53
Fax: +7(095) 202-10-83
Telex: 411587 mfaug su
Chairman: Boris G. Saltykov, Minister of Science and Technology
Deputy Secretaries-General: Vladimir L. Gaï; Boris V. Smirnov

RWANDA

UNIVERSITIES

Adventist University of Central Africa
[Université adventiste d'Afrique Centrale]
B.P. 118, Gisenyi
F: Theology; Sciences; Letters; Education;
Education and Administration.
Ce: Technical Research and Applied Sciences.

*National University of Rwanda
[Université nationale du Rwanda]
B.P. 56, Butare
Tel: +250 30302
Telex: 22 605 bte rw
Recteur: Maurice Ntahobari (1989-)
Secrétaire général: Charles Ntakirutinka
Founded: 1963
F: Letters (Ruhengeri); Applied Sciences;
Science (Ruhengeri); Economics, Social Sciences
and Management; Medicine; Law; Agriculture;
Education (Ruhengeri).
C: Modern Technology (Ruhengeri).
University Extension: (Kigali).

BUTARE CAMPUS
[CAMPUS DE BUTARE]
B.P.117, Butare
Tel: +250 30271
Fax: +250 30870
Founded: 1963

RUHENGERI CAMPUS
[CAMPUS DE RUHENGERI]
B.P.44, Ruhengeri
Founded: 1981

OTHER INSTITUTIONS

Institut Africain et Mauricien de Statistiques et d'Economie appliquée
B.P.1109, Kigali
Tel: +250 84989
Founded: 1976
Statistics; Economics.

Institut Saint Fidèle (Ecole supérieure de Gestion et d'Information)
B.P.210, Gisenyi
Tel: +250 40306
Founded: 1985
Management; Information Sciences.

Institut supérieur Catholique de Pédagogie appliquée
B.P.37, Ruhengeri
Founded: 1986
Applied Pedagogics.

Institut supérieur d'Agriculture et d'Elevage de Busogo
B.P.210, Ruhengeri
Tel: +250 46045
Founded: 1989
Agriculture; Stockraising.

Institut supérieur des Finances publiques
B.P.1514, Kigali
Tel: +250 72513
Founded: 1986
Public Finance.

NATIONAL ACADEMIC BODIES

Ministry of Higher Education, Scientifique Research and Culture
[Ministère de l'Enseignement supérieur, de la
Recherche scientifique et de la Culture]
B.P.624, Kigali
Tel: +250 82745
Fax: +250 82162
Ministre: Daniel Mbangura

Rwanda National Commission for Unesco
[Commission nationale rwandaise pour l'Unesco]
Ministère de l'Enseignement supérieur, de la
Recherche scientifique et de la Culture, B.P.624,
Kigali
Tel: +250 82028
Fax: +250 82162
Président p.i.: Jean de Dieu Damuhanda
Coordonnateur: Athanase Mugambira

SAUDI ARABIA

UNIVERSITIES

Al-Imam Mohammad Ibn Saud Islamic University Riyadh
[Jamiat Al-Imam Mohamed Ibn Saud Al-Islamiah]
P.O. Box 5701, Riyadh 11432
Tel: +966(1) 258-0000
Fax: +966(1) 259-0555
Telex: 407956
Cable: muhammadiah
Director: Muhamed Al Ajlan
Founded: 1974
F: Islamic Law; Arabic Language; Fundamentals
of the Religion; Social Sciences; Islamic D'awa
and Communication; Shari'a and Fundamentals
of the Religion (Qassim); Arabic and Social
Sciences (Qassim); Shari'a and Fundamentals of
the Religion (in the South); Arabic Language and
Social Sciences (in the South); Shari'a and
Islamic Studies (Al Ahsa).
Higher I: Islamic Call (Madinah Al
Munawwarah); Judiciary.

Islamic University Medinah
[Al-Jamiat Al Islamiah]
P.O. Box 170, Medinah
Tel: +966(4) 847-4045
Fax: +966(4) 822-4045
Telex: 470022 islamia
Cable: alislamia
Director: Abdullah Alubaid
Founded: 1961
F: Islamic Law; Islamic History; Theology;
Sunna; Arabic Language and Literature.

King Abdul-Aziz University
[Jamiat Al-Malik Abdul-Aziz]
P.O. Box 1540, Jeddah 21441
Tel: +966(2) 695-2011
Fax: +966(2) 640-5974
Telex: 602491 kauni sj
Cable: jameat abdulaziz
Director: Usamah Shubukshi
Founded: 1967, 1971
F: Economics and Administration.
Ce: Arts and Humanities; Science; Engineering;
Marine Sciences; Meteorology and Environmental
Studies; Medicine and Allied Sciences; Education
(Medina); Earth Sciences; Computer.

King Fahd University of Petroleum and Minerals
[Jamaah-Tul-Malik Fahd Lil-Betrol wal Ma'adin]
Dhahran 31261
Tel: +966(3) 860-2000
Fax: +966(3) 860-3332
Telex: 801060 kfupm sj
Cable: aljamaah
Rector: Bakr Abdulah Bakr
Founded: 1963, 1986
C: Sciences; Engineering Sciences and Applied
Engineering; Environmental Design; Industrial
Management; Computer Science and
Engineering; Graduate Studies.
Ce: Data Processing; English Language.
I: Research.

King Faisal University
[Jamiat Al-Malik Faisal]
P.O. Box 380, El-Hasa 31982
Tel: +966(3) 850-000
Fax: +966(3) 580-1243
Telex: 81629 faisal s.j. al-hasa
President: Mohammed S. Al-Qahtani
Founded: 1974
F: Agriculture and Food Sciences; Medicine and
Medical Sciences; Architecture and Planning;
Veterinary Medicine and Animal Resources
(Hofuf).
C: Education; Administrative Science and
Planning.

*King Saud University
[Jamiat Al-Malik Saud]
P.O. Box 2454, Riyadh 11451
Tel: +966(1) 467-0000
Fax: +966(1) 467-7580
Telex: 403490 ksu sj
President: Ahmed Mohammad Al-Dhobaib (1979-)
Founded: 1957
Ce: Arts; Education; Education (Abha);
Agriculture; Agriculture and Veterinary Medicine
(Al-Gaseem); Pharmacy; Medicine; Dentistry;
Science; Administration; Business Administration
and Economics (Al-Gaseem); Allied Medical
Sciences; Engineering; Medicine (Abha);
Computer Sciences and Information; Architecture
and Planning; for Women; Lifelong Education.
I: Arabic Language.

Umm Al-Qura University
[Jamiat Umm Al-Qura]
P.O. Box 407/715, Makkah 21441
Tel: +966(2) 556-5321
Fax: +966(2) 556-4560
Rector: Rashid alrajih
Founded: 1979
F: Islamic Law; Education; Applied Sciences
and Engineering; D'awa and Usul al-Din; English;
Education (Taif); Library Science (Taif).

NATIONAL ACADEMIC BODIES

Directorate General for the Development of Higher Education
Ministry of Higher Education, Riyadh
Tel: +966(1) 4410234
Fax: +966(1) 4419004
Telex: 400860 ali sj
Director: Abdul Aziz

Higher Education and Universities Council
Ministry of Higher Education, Riyadh 11153
Tel: +966(1) 441-5555
Fax: +966(1) 4419004
Cable: 400980 ali sj
Secretary-General: Muhammd Al Assalim

National Commission for Unesco
Ministry of Education, Riyadh
Tel: +966(1) 404-2888 (ext. 1485)
Fax: +966(1) 401-0992
Telex: 401673 saudinesco sj
Cable: saudinesco riyadh
Chairman: Abdulaziz A. Al-Khowaiter, Minister of
Education
Secretary-General: Ibrahim A. Alsheddi

SENEGAL

UNIVERSITIES

*University Cheikh Anta Diop of Dakar
[Université Cheikh Anta Diop de Dakar]
B.P. 5005, Dakar-Fann
Tel: +221 23-05-84
Fax: +221 25-28-83
Telex: 51262 sg
Cable: unndak sg
Recteur: Souleymane Niang (1986-)
Secrétaire général: Mbaye Niang
Founded: 1918, 1950, 1957
F: Law and Economics; Medicine and
Pharmacy; Science; Letters and Human Sciences.
I: African Studies; Social Pediatrics; Applied
Tropical Medicine; French; Mathematics
Research; Technology; Rights of Man and Peace;
Health and Development; Black Africa
(Fundamental).
S: Sciences and Veterinary Medicine; Library
Science and Documentation Studies; Teacher
Training; Technical and Professional Teacher
Training (E.N.S.E.T.P.).
Ce: Applied Linguistics; Information Sciences
and Techniques; Psychopathological Research.

CENTRE FOR APPLIED LINGUISTICS
[CENTRE DE LINGUISTIQUE APPLIQUÉE]
Dakar
Tel: +221 23-06-39
Directeur: Cherif Mbodj (1990-)
Secrétaire administratif: Jean François Fonseca
Founded: 1966
Applied Linguistics (French, English, National
Langages).

CENTRE FOR INFORMATION SCIENCES AND TECHNIQUES
[CENTRE D'ÉTUDES DES SCIENCES ET TECHNIQUES DE
L'INFORMATION]
Dakar
Tel: +221 23-03-66
Fax: +221 24-24-17
Telex: 61338 sg
Directeur: Birahim Moussa Gueye (1989-)
Founded: 1970
Journalism; Television; Radio; Photography.

CENTRE FOR PSYCHO-PATHOLOGICAL RESEARCH
[CENTRE DE RECHERCHE PSYCHO-PATHOLOGIE]
Founded: 1984
Psycho-pathological Research.

CENTRE FOR RENEWABLE ENERGIES STUDIES AND RESEARCH
[CENTRE D'ÉTUDES ET DE RECHERCHE SUR LES ÉNERGIES
RENOUVELABLES]
Route de Hann, Dakar
Tel: +221 32-14-14
Fax: +221 32-10-53
Directeur: Mansour Kane (1993-)
Chef des Services Administratifs: Seydou Samb
Founded: 1980
Renewable Studies and Research.

HIGHER UNIVERSITY SCHOOL OF TECHNOLOGY
[ECOLE NATIONALE SUPÉRIEURE UNIVERSITAIRE DE
TECHNOLOGIE]
B.P. 5085, Dakar
Tel: +221 25-08-79
Fax: +221 25-55-94
Directeur: Ahmadou Lamine Dia (1990-)
Founded: 1967
Management; Engineering; Computer Sciences.

INSTITUTE OF APPLIED NUCLEAR TECHNOLOGY
[INSTITUT DE TECHNOLOGIE NUCLÉAIRE APPLIQUÉE]
Dakar
Tel: +221 25-04-43
Founded: 1980
Applied Nuclear Technology.

INSTITUTE OF APPLIED TROPICAL MEDICINE
[INSTITUT DE MÉDECINE TROPICALE APLIQUÉE]
Dakar
Applied Tropical Medicine.

INSTITUTE OF BLACK AFRICAN STUDIES AND RESEARCH
[INSTITUT FONDAMENTAL D'AFRIQUE NOIRE CHEIKH ANTA
DIOP]
B.P. 206, Dakar
Tel: +221 25-00-90
Fax: +221 24-49-18
Directeur: Abdoulaye Bara Diop (1986-)
Human Sciences; Languages and Civilizations;
Biology and Geology; Animal Biology; Scientific
Information.

INSTITUTE OF FRENCH
[INSTITUT DE FRANÇAIS POUR LES ÉTUDIANTS]
Dakar
Directeur: Amadou Ly (1984-)
Chef des Services Administratifs: Papa Oumar
Niane
Founded: 1979
French.

INSTITUTE OF HEALTH AND DEVELOPMENT
[INSTITUT DE SANTÉ ET DE DÉVELOPPEMENT]
Dakar
Founded: 1964
Health and Development.

INSTITUTE FOR HUMAN RIGHTS AND PEACE
[INSTITUT DES DROITS DE L'HOMME ET DE LA PAIX]
Dakar
Tel: +221 24-14-12
Directeur: Bakary Traoré
Chef des Services Administratifs: Moussa Samb
Founded: 1983
Human Rights and Peace Studies.

INSTITUTE FOR MATHEMATICS OF PHYSICS AND
TECHNOLOGYRESEARCH
[INSTITUT DE RECHERCHE SUR L'ENSEIGNEMENT DE LA
MATHÉMATIQUE DE LA PHYSIQUE ET DE LA TECHNOLOGIE]
Dakar
Tel: +221 25-93-75
Directeur: Mamadou Sangharé
Founded: 1975
Mathematics of Physics, and Technology
(Research).

INSTITUTE OF SOCIAL PEDIATRICS
[INSTITUT DE PÉDIATRIE SOCIALE]
Avenue Cheikh Anta Diop, Dakar
Tel: +221 23-03-70
Directeur: Mounamadou Fall (1985-)
Founded: 1964
Social Pediatrics.

SCHOOL FOR LIBRARIANS, ARCHIVISTS AND
DOCUMENTATALISTS
[ECOLE DES BIBLIOTHÉCAIRES, ARCHIVISTES ET
DOCUMENTALISTES]
Dakar
Tel: +221 22-20-18
Directeur: Ousmane Sane (1987-)
Directeur des Etudes: Ibrahima Lo
Founded: 1967
Library Studies.

SCHOOL OF TEACHER TRAINING
[ECOLE NORMALE SUPÉRIEURE]
Avenue Bourguiba, B.P. 5036, Dakar-Fann
Tel: +221 24-22-42
Fax: +221 25-47-14
Directeur: Sega Seck Fall (1983-)
Chef des Services administratifs: Oumar Thiam
Founded: 1963
Teacher Training.

TEACHER TRAINING SCHOOL FOR TECHNICAL AND
PROFESSIONAL EDUCATION
[ECOLE NORMALE SUPÉRIEURE D'ENSEIGNEMENT TECHNIQUE
ET PROFESSIONNEL]
Camp Claudel, Dakar
Tel: +221 21-76-69
Fax: +221 21-70-51
Directeur: Oumar Sock (1990-)
Founded: 1979
Technical and Professional Studies.

University of Saint-Louis
[Université de Saint-Louis]
B.P. 234, Saint-Louis
Tel: +221 61-17-68
Fax: +221 61-18-84
Telex: 75 128 univ.sl/sg
Recteur: Ahmadou Lamine Ndiaye (1990-)
Secrtaire général: Adoulayé Diagne
Founded: 1990
Ut: *Legal Science; Economics and Management;
Applied Mathematics and Computer Sciences;
Letters and Human Sciences.*
Ce: *African Civilizations and Language Studies.*

OTHER INSTITUTIONS

Centre africain d'Etudes supérieures en Gestion
Boulevard Général de Gaulle, B.P. 3802, Dakar
Tel: +221 22-66-53
Founded: 1980
Management.

Centre de Formation et de Perfectionnement administratif
Boulevard Dial Diop, Dakar
Tel: +221 25-00-58
Fax: +221 24-87-44
(1992-)
Secrétaire général: Souleymane Bitey
Founded: 1965
Administration.

Centre de Perfectionnement en Langueanglaise
35, rue Jules Ferry, Dakar
Tel: +221 21-03-59
Directeur: Cheikh Talibouya Thiraré (1973-)
Directeur des Etudes: Farba Diouf
Founded: 1973
English.

Conservatoire national de Musique, de Danse et d'Arts dramatique
Dakar
Tel: +221 22-46-73
Directeur: Moustapha Ndiaye (1991-)
Secrétaire général: Horace Dacosta
Music; Dance; Drama.

Ecole Inter-Etats des Sciences et Médecine vétérinaire
Avenue Cheikh Anta Diop, Dakar
Tel: +221 25-66-92 +221 24-42-83
Telex: 51 403 inter vet
Directeur: François Adebayo Abiola (1994-)
Science; Veterinary Medicine.

Ecole nationale d'Administration et de Magistrature
Rua Dial Diop, Dakar
Tel: +221 25-00-58
Fax: +221 25-87-44
Founded: 1972
Administration; Magisterial Studies.

Ecole nationale des Beaux Arts
124/126, avenue A. Peytavin, Dakar
Directeur: Kalidou SY (1986-)
Directeur des Etudes: Samsidine Mane
Founded: 1979
Fine Arts.

Ecole nationale de Cadres ruraux
B.P. 41, Bambay
Tel: +221 73-60-60
Fax: +221 73-60-61
Directeur: Sidy Harou Camara (1987-)
Founded: 1960
Rural Studies.

Ecole nationale des Douanes
Avenue Carde-Rue René Ndiayé, Dakar
Tel: +221 21-28-79
Directeur: Mamado Sarré (1992-)
Founded: 1970
Customs.

Ecole nationale d'Economie appliquée
Avenue Cheikh A. Diop, Dakar
Tel: +221 24-79-28
Directeur: Samba Dioné (1989-)
Directeur des Etudes et des Stages: Réné Bassa
Founded: 1968
Applied Economics.

Ecole nationale de Formation maritime
Km. 4,5 Route de Rufisque, Dakar
Tel: +221 21-38-23
Maritime Studies.

Ecole nationale d'Horticulture Cambérène
Dakar
Tel: +221 35-78-21
Fax: +221 35-39-91
Directeur: Cheikh Baba Ndiaye
Directeur des Etudes: Mael Sylla
Horticulture.

Ecole nationale de Police et de la Formation pamanente
B.P. 5025, Dakar-Fann
Tel: +221 25-28-18
Fax: +221 24-25-57
Directeur: Thierno Gning
Directeur des Etudes: Réné Privot
Founded: 1954
Police Studies.

Ecole nationale des Postes et Télécommunications
Rue Ousmane Socé Diop, Rufisque
Tel: +221 36-00-29
Directeur: Babacar Touré (1994-)
Post and Telecommunications.

Ecole nationale supérieure de l'Agriculture
Thiès
Tel: +221 51-12-57
Fax: +221 51-15-51
Directeur: Moussa Fall
Directeur des Etudes: Aliou Coly
Agriculture.

Ecole normale supérieure d'Education artistique
124-126, avenue A. Peytavin, Dakar
Tel: +221 23-03-43
Fax: +221 22-16-38
Directeur: Kalidou Sy (1986-)
Directeur des Etudes: Samsidine Mane
Plastic Arts; Communication; Environmental Studies.

Ecole supérieure multi-états des Télécommunications
Dakar
Tel: +221 36-00-29
Directeur: Babacar Touré (1994-)
Founded: 1981
Telecommunications.

Institut national supérieur de l'Education populaire et du Sport
Stade Iba Mar Diop, Dakar
Tel: +221 23-33-84
Directeur: Gérald Diamé (1992-)
Directeur des Etudes: Michel Diouf
Founded: 1979
Education and Sport.

Institut Sénégalo-Britannique d'Enseignement de l'Anglais
Rue du 18 juin, B.P. 35, Dakar
Tel: +221 22-40-23
Directeur: Mamadou Kandji (1986-)
Secrétaire général: Fatimata Kane
Founded: 1976
English.

NATIONAL ACADEMIC BODIES

Ministry of National Education (Higher Education Division)
[Ministère de l'Education nationale (Direction de l'Enseignement supérieur)]
Dakar
Tel: +221 22-57-30
Telex: 3239 miensup sg

Senegal National Commission for Unesco
[Commission nationale du Sénégal pour l'Unesco]
Ministère de l'Education nationale, 97, rue Carnot x Bayeux, Dakar
Tel: +221 22-57-30
Fax: +221 21-89-30
Cable: comnat unesco mineducation dakar
Directeur: André Sonko, Minister of Education
Secrétaire général: Assane Hane

SIERRA LEONE

UNIVERSITIES

University of Sierra Leone
Private Mail Bag, Freetown
Tel: +232(22) 26859
Vice Chancellor: D.E. Babatunji Chaytor

COLLEGE OF MEDICINE AND ALLIED HEALTH SCIENCES
Private Mail Bag, Freetown
Tel: +232(22) 240-884
Principal: A.M. Taqi
Founded: 1988
Medicine; Allied Health Sciences.

FOURAH BAY COLLEGE
P.O. Box 87, Freetown
Tel: +232(22) 27260
Cable: fourahbay
Principal (Acting): V.E. Strasser-King
Founded: 1827, 1966
F: Arts; Economics and Social Studies; Engineering; Law; Pure and Applied Sciences. I: Adult Education and Extramural Studies; African Studies; Marine Biology and Oceanography; Population Studies.

NJALA UNIVERSITY COLLEGE
Private Mail Bag, Freetown
Tel: 4
Cable: njalun
Principal: H.M. Turay
Founded: 1964, 1966
F: Agriculture; Education; Environmental Sciences.

OTHER INSTITUTIONS

Bo Teachers' College
Private Mail Bag, Bo
Teacher Training.

Bunumbu Teachers' College
Private Mail Bag, Kenema
Teacher Training.

Freetown Teachers' College
Private Mail Bag, Freetown
Teacher Training.

Makeni Teachers' College
Private Mail Bag, Makeni
Teacher Training.

Milton Margai Teachers' College
Goderich
Teacher Training.

Technical Institute
Congo Cross, Freetown
Tel: 31368
Technical Studies.

NATIONAL ACADEMIC BODIES

Ministry of Education
New England, Freetown
Tel: +232 40560
Minister: Bassie Bangura

Sierra Leone National Commission for Unesco
Ministry of Education, New England, Freetown
Tel: +232 40560
Chairman: Bassie Bangura, Minister of Education
Secretary: D.S. Kai-Rogers

SINGAPORE

UNIVERSITIES

Nanyang Technological University
Nanyang Avenue, Singapore 2263
Tel: +65 791-1744
Fax: +65 791-1604
Cable: sinntu
President: Tao Soon Cham (1981-)
Registrar: Sing Wong Ling
International Relations: Hee Kiat Cheong, Director
Founded: 1981

S: Accountancy and Business; Applied Sciences; Civil and Structural Engineering; Electric and Electronic Engineering; Mechanical and Production Engineering; Communication Studies; Arts; Education; Physical Education; Science.
I: Gintic Manufacturing Technology.
Ce: Advanced Construction Studies; Transportation Studies; Applied Research in Education; Graphics and Imaging Technology; Enterpreneurship Development; Innovation; Network Technology Research; Chinese Language and Culture; Education Development.

National University of Singapore
10 Kent Ridge Crescent, Singapore 0511
Tel: +65 775-6666
Fax: +65 778-5281
E-Mail: ykisec:ulo:nus
Telex: rs33943 unispo
Cable: univspore, singapore
Vice-Chancellor: Lim Pin (1981-)
Registrar: Huan Tzu Hong
International Relations: E. Sukumar
Founded: 1980
F: Architecture and Building; Arts and Social Sciences; Business Administration; Dentistry; Engineering; Law; Medicine; Science.
I: Molecular and Cell Biology; Microelectronics; Systems Science.
Research Centres: National Supercomputing; Bioscience; Advanced Studies; Business and Development; Integrated Circuit Failure Analysis and Reliability; Management of Technology; Natural Product; Wireless Communication; Chinese Language; Magnetics Technology; Immunology (WHO).

OTHER INSTITUTIONS

Nanyang Polytechnic
Tiong Bahru Campus, Lower Delta Road, Singapore 0316
Tel: 2731183
Fax: 2732649
Principal and CEO: Lin Cheng Ton (1992-)
Registrar and Director of Academic Services: Chan Lee Mun
Founded: 1992
S: Business Management; Engineering; Health Sciences; Information Technology.
I: French-Singapore; German-Singapore; Japan-Singapore.

National Institute of Education
469 Bukit Timah Road, Singapore 1025
Tel: +65 469-5151
Fax: +65 469-5694
Cable: educator
Director: Leo Tan (1994-)
Head, Administration: Cheng Tee Sim
Founded: 1991

S: Arts; Education; Physical Education; Science.
Ce: Applied Research in Education.

Ngee Ann Polytechnic
535 Clementi Road, Singapore 2159
Tel: +65 466-6555
Fax: +65 468-7326
Telex: rs 39206 ianpol
Principal: Tan Gee Paw (1989-)
Registrar (Acting): Wang Foot Ti Chye
International Relations: Director, Industrial
Liaison Unit, David Tandy
Founded: 1963
D: Accountancy; Biotechnology; Building;
Business Studies; Electrical Engineering;
Electronic and Computer Engineering; Mass
Communication; Mechanical Engineering;
Shipbuilding and Offshore Engineering.
Ce: Computer Studies; Quality.
Ut: Film, Sound and Video.

Singapore Polytechnic
500 Dover Road, Singapore 0513
Tel: +65 772-1220
Fax: +65 772-1985
Principal: Khoo Kay Chai
Founded: 1954

NATIONAL ACADEMIC BODIES

Ministry of Education, Singapore
Kay Siang Road, Singapore 1024
Tel: +65 473-9111
Fax: +65 475-6128
The Permanent Secretary

SLOVAK REPUBLIC

UNIVERSITIES AND TECHNICAL UNIVERSITIES

Matej Bel University in Banská Bystrica
[Univerzita Mateja Bela v Banskej Bystrici]
Komenského 20, 974 01 Banská Bystrica
Tel: +42(88) 83223
Fax: +42(88) 33132
E-Mail: benkoěl.pdfbb.cs
Rector: Otto Tomeček (1994-97)
Registrar: Igor Naňo
International Relations: Vice-Rector, Peter Patúš
Founded: 1959
Humanities and Natural Sciences; Economics.

Comenius University in Bratislava
[Univerzita Komenského v Bratislave]
Šfříkovo nám. 6, 818 06 Bratislava
Tel: +42(7) 320740
Fax: +42(7) 361652
E-Mail: hudoba@cvt.stuba.sk
Rector: Jurj Švec (1992-97)
Registrar: Zora Zobríková
International Relations: Vice-Rector, Igor Brezina
Founded: 1919

F: Medicine; Medicine (Martin); Pharmacy; Law;
Arts; Natural Sciences; Mathematics and Physics;
Physical Education and Sports; Education;
Management; Theology (Catholic); Theology
(Evangelic).
I: Language and Academic Preparation (for
foreign students); Computer.

University of Economics in Bratislava
[Ekonomická univerzita v Bratislave]
Odbojárov 10, 832 20 Bratislava
Tel: +42(7) 63067
Fax: +42(7) 63045
Rector: Juraj Stern (1994-97)
Registrar: Milan Kačírek
International Relations: Vice-Rector, Zlatica
Ivanovičová
Founded: 1940
F: National Economy; Commerce; Economic
Informatics; Enterprise Management; Enterprise
Economics.

*Slovak Technical University in Bratislava
[Slovenská technická univerzita v Bratislave]
Nám. Slobody 17, 812 43 Bratislava
Tel: +42(7) 320-740
Fax: +42(7) 361-652
E-Mail: hudoba@cvt.stuba.sk
Rector: Igor Hudoba
Registrar: Helena Žideková
International Relations: Vice-Rector, Marian
Veselý
Founded: 1938, 1991
F: Electrical Engineering; Chemical Technology;
Civil Engineering; Architecture; Mechanical
Engineering; Materials Science and Technology
(Trnava); Professional Studies.

*P.J. Šafárik University in Košice
[Univerzita Pavla Josefa Šafárika v Košice]
Šrobárova 57, 041 80 Košice
Tel: +42(95) 622-2608
Fax: +42(95) 766-959
E-Mail: bukovsky@kosice.upjs.sk
Rector: Lev Bukovský (1992-97)
Kvestor: Jozef Lokša
Founded: 1954
F: Medicine; Law; Arts; Sciences; Education;
Theology (Greek Catholic); Theology (Orthodox).
I: Tourism and Hotel Management.

University of Veterinary Medicine in Košice
[Univerzita veterinárskeho lekárstvá v Košiciach]
Komenského 73, 041 81 Košice
Tel: +42(95) 30127
Fax: +42(95) 767-675
E-Mail: belan@ccsun.tuke.sk
Rector: Rudolf Cabadaj (1992-97)
Registrar: Rudolf Lukáč
International Relations: Vice-Rector, Marta
Prosbová
Founded: 1949
Veterinary Medicine.

Technical University in Košice
[Technická Univerzita v Košiciach]
Letmá ub. 9, 042 00 Košice
Tel: +42(95) 399-087
Fax: +42(95) 32748
E-Mail: rektor@ccsun.tuke.sk
Rector: I. Hrivňák
Registrar: Koloman Urban
International Relations: Vice-Rector, Tomáš Sabol
Founded: 1952
F: Mining Engineering; Metallurgy; Mechanical Engineering; Electrical Engineering; Civil Engineering; Professional Studies (Prešov); Economics.

Technical University in Zvolen
[Technická univerzita vo Zvolene]
T.G. Masarykova 24, 960 53 Žvolen
Tel: +42(855) 23271
Fax: +42(855) 20027
Rector: Štefan Śmelko (1994-97)
Registrar: Ladislav Naňo
International Relations: Vice-Rector, Stanislav Kurjatko
Founded: 1946
Forestry; Wood Technology; Ecology.

*University of Agriculture in Nitra
[Vysoká škola pol'nohospodárska v Nitra]
Tr. A. Hlinku 2, 949 76 Nitra
Tel: +42(87) 411-152
Fax: +42(87) 411-593
Rector: Ladislav Kabát (1994-97)
Registrar: Štefan Ballay
Founded: 1941
F: Operation and Economy; Agronomy; Mechanization.
Ce: Computer.

University of Trnava
[Trnavskúniverzita]
Hornopotočná, 917 24 Trnava
Tel: +42(805) 25283
Fax: +42(805) 21483
Rector: Anton Hajduk (1994-97)
Registrar: Jozef Vančo
Founded: 1992
Humanities; Education.

University of Transport and Communications in Žilina
[Vysoká škola dopravy a spožov v Žiline]
Moyzesova 20, 010 26 Žilina
Tel: +42(89) 623408
Fax: +42(89) 47702
E-Mail: zelem@uvt.utc.sk
Rector: Miroslav Kopecký (1994-97)
Registrar: Miloš Haščíc
International Relations: Vice-Rector, Milan Dado
Founded: 1953, 1980
F: Operation and Economics of Transport and Communications; Mechanical Engineering; Electrical Engineering; Civil Engineering; Management; Military.

OTHER INSTITUTIONS

Academia Istropolitana
Hanulova 5/8, P.O. Box 92, 840 02 Bratislava
Tel: +42(7) 785-069
Fax: +42(7) 785-341
E-Mail: direct@acadistr sk
Director: Alena Brunovská (1992-)
Registrar: Daniel Kovačič
Founded: 1990
Public Administration; Architectural and Urban Heritage Conservation; Environmental Planning and Management; Applied Economics.

Akadémia Policajného zboru SR v Bratislave
Sklabínská 1, 814 00 Bratislava
Tel: +42(7) 285-805
Fax: +42(7) 286-620
Rector: Pavol Baláž
Police Studies.

City University in Bratislava
Mudroůova 47, 811 04 Bratislava
Tel: +42(7) 316-735
Fax: +42(7) 316-735
E-Mail: morovic@cub.sanet.sk
President: Ján Morovič (1990-)
Secretary: Júlia Pazderová
International Relations: Dorota Ulalhová
Founded: 1990
Envionmental Studies; Accountancy; Marketing; Manager.

Vysoká škola pedagogická v Nitra
Tr.A. Hlinku 1, 949 74 Nitra
Tel: +42(87) 411-253
Fax: +42(87) 411-243
E-Mail: jga@unitra.cs
Rector: Peter Liba (1992-97)
Registrar: Jozef Pospíšil
International Relations: Vice-Rector, Jozef Gembarovič
Founded: 1959
Humanities; Natural Sciences; Education.

Vysoká skola vytvarnych umení v Bratislave
Hviezdoslavovo nám. 18, 814 37 Bratislava
Tel: +42(7) 332-431
Fax: +42(7) 332-340
Rector: Štefan Šlachta (1994-97)
Registrar: Jana Hriňová
International Relations: Vice-Rector, Imrich Vaško
Founded: 1949
Fine Arts and Design.

NATIONAL ACADEMIC BODIES

Ministry of Education and Science of the Slovak Republic
[Minsterstvo školstva a vedy Slovenskej Republiky]
Hlboká 2, 813 30 Bratislava
Tel: +42(7) 595-772
Fax: +42(7) 497-098
E-Mail: harach@msv.sanel.sk
Minister: Lubomír Harach (1994-)
Secretary-General: Štefan ciabák
International Relations: Vladimír Grieger
Founded: 1958

Centre for Equivalence of Certificates of Education
[Stredisko pre ekvivalenciu dokladov o vzdelaní]
Institute of Information and Prognoses of Education, Youth and Sports, Staré grunty 52, 842 44 Bratislava
Tel: +42(7) 726-521
Fax: +42(7) 726-180

Conference of Rectors of Higher Edcuation
[Konferencia rektotov vysokých škôl]
Hlboká 2, 813 30 Bratislava
Tel: +42(7) 321-594
Fax: +42(7) 363-836
President: Juraj Švec, Rector, Comenius University (1992-)

Foreign Relations Centre, Ministry of Education and Science
[Dom zahraničných stykov Ministerstva školstva a vedy Slovenskej republiky]
Hviezdoslavovo nám. 14, 813 29 Bratislava
Tel: +42(7) 333-2888
Fax: +42(7) 335-827

Government Accreditation Commission
[Akreditačná komisia vlády]
Hlboká 2, 813 30 Bratislava
Tel: +42(7) 433-141
Fax: +42(7) 498-989
E-Mail: urbanévin.fns.uniba.sk
President: Miroslav Urban (1990-)
Secretary: Michal Denci
Founded: 1990

Higher Education Council
[Rada vysokých škôl]
Starégrunty 52, 842 44 Bratislava
Tel: +42(7) 726-508
Fax: +42(7) 726-180
President: Milan Žalman (1990-)
Secretary: Jana Bocová
Founded: 1990

Slovak Academic Information Agency
[Slovenská akademická informačná agentúra]
Hviezdoslavovo nám. 14, P.O. Box 108, 810 00 Bratislava
Tel: +42(7) 333010
Fax: +42(7) 335827

Slovak Commission for Unesco
Stromová 1, 833 36 Bratislava
Tel: +42(7) 367-057
Fax: +42(7) 367-791
Chairman: Miroslav T. Bazány
Secretary-General: Miroslav Musil

SLOVENIA

UNIVERSITIES

*University of Ljubljana
[Univerza v Ljubljani]
Kongresni trg 12, 61000 Ljubljana
Tel: +386(125) 4117
Fax: +386(125) 4053
Rector: Miha Tišler
Secretary-General: Marjeta Vilfan
Founded: 1595, 1919
F: Arts and Science; Law; Economics; Social Sciences; Natural Sciences and Technology; Architecture, Civil Engineering and Geodesy; Electrical Engineering and Computer Sciences; Mechanical Engineering; Medicine; Biotechnology; Education; Theology; Sport; Veterinary Medicine.
A: Music; Theatre, Radio, Film and Television; Fine Arts.
UC: Naval and Maritime Transport Piran (Portorož); Social Work; Health Care.
C: Administration; Internal Affairs.
S: Higher Technical Safety.

*University of Maribor
[Univerza v Mariboru]
Krekova ul. 2, 62000 Maribor
Tel: +386(62) 212-281
Fax: +386(62) 23-541
E-Mail: university@uni-mb.si
Telex: 386 62 3334 tf mb si
Rector: Ludvik Toplak
Founded: 1975
F: Organizational Sciences (Kranj); Education.
S: Business Economics; Law.
C: Agriculture; Nursing Studies.

NATIONAL ACADEMIC BODIES

Ministry of Education and Sport
[Ministrstvo za Šolstvo in Šport]
Župančičevaa 6, 61000 Ljubljana
Tel: +386(61) 154-208
Fax: +386(61) 214-820
Minister: Slavko Gaber

Slovenian National Commission for Unesco
Minstry of Science and Technology, Slovenska
50, 61000 Ljabljana
Tel: +386(61) 131-1107
Fax: +386(61) 302-95
President: Peter Tancig
Secretary-General: Zofija Klemen-Krek

SOLOMON ISLANDS

UNIVERSITIES

University of the South Pacific Centre
P.O. Box 460, Honiara
Tel: +677 21307
Fax: +677 21287
Founded: 1970

OTHER INSTITUTIONS

College of Higher Education
P.O. Box G23, Honiara
Founded: 1969

Solomon Islands Training College
P.O. Box 1, Honiara
Founded: 1959

NATIONAL ACADEMIC BODIES

Ministry of Education, Higher Education and Cultural Affairs
P.O. Box G28, Honiara
Tel: +677 23900
Fax: +677 20485
Minister: Dennis C. Lulei

SOMALIA

UNIVERSITIES

Somali National University
[Jaamacadda Ummadda Soolaaliyeed]
P.O. Box 15, Mogadiscio
Tel: +252 25035
Founded: 1954, 1959, 1970
F: Law; Economics; Agriculture; Education; Veterinary Medicine; Medicine; Industrial Chemistry; Geology; Languages; Journalism; Engineering.

NATIONAL ACADEMIC BODIES

Ministry of Education and Culture
Mogadiscio

Somali National Commission for Unesco
Ministry of Education and Culture, P.O. Box 1182, Mogadiscio
Tel: +252 80204
Telex: 3696
Executive Secretary: Nurein Sheikh Abrar

SOUTH AFRICA (REPUBLIC OF)

UNIVERSITIES

University of Bophuthatswana
Private Bag X2046, Mafikeng, Bophuthatswana
Tel: +27(140) 89-2005
Fax: +27(140) 24-285
Founded: 1994
F: Architecture; Education; Health Science; Law; Management; Social Science.

*University of Cape Town
Private Bag, Rondebosch 7700
Tel: +27(21) 650-9111 (South Africa)
Fax: +27(21) 650-2138
E-Mail: aeshtařemner.uct.ac.za
Telex: 5-22208
Vice-Chancellor: S.J. Saunders (1981-)
Founded: 1829, 1873, 1916
F: Architecture; Arts; Commerce; Education; Engineering; Fine Arts; Law; Medicine; Music; Science; Social Science.
I: Energy Research; Child Health; Oceanography; Marine Law; Criminology; Advanced Studies in Philosophy; Molecular Biology; Photogrammetry and Remote Sensing; African Ornithology.
Ce: African Studies; Heart Disease and Immunology (Mining Research); Intergroup Studies; Extramural Studies.

University of Durban-Westville
Private Bag X64001, Durban 4001
Tel: +27(31) 820-9111
Fax: +27(31) 820-2383
Cable: inkol
Vice-Chancellor and Rector: J. Reddy
Founded: 1961, 1972
F: Arts; Commerce; Dentistry; Education;
Engineering; Health Science; Law; Science;
Theology.

University of Fort Hare
Private Bag X1314, Alice 5700, Ciskei
Tel: +27(404) 32-011
Fax: +27(404) 31-643
E-Mail: alecia@admin.ufh.ac.za
Telex: cx 242193
Vice-Chancellor and Rector (Acting): E.A. Ngara
Founded: 1916, 1970
F: Agriculture; Arts; Economics and
Administration; Education; Law; Science;
Theology.
D: External Studies; Agricultural and Rural
Development.
I: Management (FHIM) (Fort Hare).
Ce: Xhosa Literature; Academic Development.

Medical University of Southern Africa
Medunsa 0204, Transvaal
Tel: +27(12) 529-4111
Fax: +27(12) 58-2323
Telex: 3-2580 sa
Principal: E.T. Mokgokong
Founded: 1976
F: Basic Science; Dentistry; Medicine;
Veterinary Science.

University of Natal
King George V. Avenue, Durban 4001
Tel: +27(31) 816-9111
Fax: +27(31) 816-2214
E-Mail: trotter@admind.und.ac.za
Vice-Chancellor and Rector: B.M. Gourley
Founded: 1909, 1949
F: Agriculture; Architecture; Arts; Commerce;
Education; Engineering (Durban only); Law;
Medicine; Science; Social Science.

*University of the North
Private Bag X1106, Sovenga 0727
Tel: +27(1521) 68-9111
Fax: +27(1521) 67-0142
Telex: 331813 unin
Cable: unikol sovenga
Vice-Chancellor and Rector: N.S. Ndebele
Vice-Principal: G.M. Nkondo
F: Agriculture; Arts; Economics and
Administration; Education; Health Science; Law;
Science; Theology.
Ut: Aqiacimtire Research; Electron Microscope.

*University of the Orange Free State
+Universiteit van die Oranje-Vrystaat
P.O. Box 339, Bloemfontein 9300
Tel: +27(51) 401-9111
Fax: +27(51) 401-2117
Rektor en Vise-Kanselier (Rector and Vice-
Chancellor): F.P. Retief (1989-)
Vice-Rectors: C.D. Roode; E.G. Boonstra
Founded: 1855, 1904, 1950
F: Agriculture; Arts; Commerce; Education; Law;
Medicine; Social Science; Theology.

University of Port Elizabeth +Universiteit
Port Elizabeth
P.O. Box 1600, Port Elizabeth 6000
Tel: +27(41) 504-2911
Fax: +27(41) 504-2574
Telex: 74-7342sa
Vice-Chancellor: J.M. Kirsten (1994-)
Founded: 1964
F: Arts; Economics and Administration;
Education; Law; Science.
I: Science and Mathematics Education; Planning
Research; Coastal Research.
Ut: Uranium Chemistry Research.
Ce: Continuing Education.

Potchefstroom University for Christian
Higher Education
[Potchefstroomse Universiteit vir Christelike Hoër
Onderwys]
Private Bag, Potchefstroom 2520, Transvaal
Tel: +27(148) 99-9111
Fax: +27(148) 99-2799
E-Mail: regjr@puknet.puk.ac.za
Telex: 4-21363 sa
Cable: puk
Vice-Chancellor and Rector: C.J. Reinecke
Founded: 1869, 1921, 1951
F: Arts; Commerce; Education; Engineering;
Law; Pharmacy; Science; Theology.
I: Biokinetics; Leisure Studies; Linguistic and
Literary Research; Planning and Development;
Politics and African Studies; Provincial Press in
South Africa; Psychotherapy and Guidance;
Reformational Studies; Research in Children's
Literature; South African Music; Ecological
Research; Petrochemical Research; Industrial
Pharmacy; Pedology; Physiological Research;
Futures Studies; Management Development;
Manpower and Management Research.
Bureau: Lifelong Education.

University of Pretoria
[Universiteit van Pretoria]
Lynnwoodroad, Hillcrest, Pretoria 0083
Tel: +27(12) 420-9111
Fax: +27(12) 342-2712
E-Mail: hester@admin-1.up.ac.za
Telex: 322723
Cable: puniv
Visekanselier en Rektor: P. Smit
Viserektor: J.J. Stadler
Founded: 1908, 1910, 1930

SOUTH AFRICA

F: *Agriculture; Arts; Commerce; Dentistry; Education; Engineering; Law; Medicine; Science; Theology; Veterinary Science.*
I: *Strategic Studies; Sport Research and Training; Geological Research on the Bushveld Complex; Mammal Research; Seed Research (Margaretha Mes); Agricultural Extension (South African); Missiological Research; Study of Disease Phenomena Peculiar to Southern Africa (Hans Snyckers); Glaxo I. for Clinical Pharmacology; Pathology; Micro-Electronics (Carl and Emily Fuchs).*
Bureau: *Economic Policy and Analysis; Financial Analysis.*
Ce: *Stomatological Research.*

Rand Afrikaans University
[Randse Afrikaanse Universiteit]
P.O. Box 524, Auckland Park 2006
Tel: +27(11) 489-2911
Fax: +27(11) 489-2191
E-Mail: ath@rau 1.rau.ac.za
Telex: 4245426 sa
Cable: rauniv
Vice-Chancellor and Rector: C.F. Crouse (1987-)
Registrar: H.J. Kruger
Founded: 1966
F: *Arts; Economics and Administration; Education; Engineering; Law; Science.*
I: *Child and Adult Guidance; Energy Studies.*
Ce: *Islamic Studies.*

Rhodes University
P.O. Box 94, Grahamstown 6140
Tel: +27(461) 31-8111
Fax: +27(461) 25-049
E-Mail: registrar@kudu.ru.ac.za
Telex: 24-4219 sa
Cable: rhodescol
Vice-Chancellor and Principal: D.S. Henderson (1975-)
Registrar: K.S. Hunt
Founded: 1904, 1916, 1951
F: *Arts; Commerce; Divinity; Education; Law; Pharmacy; Science; Social Science.*
I: *Social and Economic Research; Study of English in Africa; Leather Industries Research - LIRI Technologies; Water Research; Ichthyology; Biopharmaceutics Research; Social and Individual Development in Africa.*

University of South Africa +Universiteit van Suid-Afrika
P.O. Box 392, Pretoria, Transvaal 0001
Tel: +27(12) 429-9111
Fax: +27(12) 429-2533
E-Mail: stockmh@alpha.unlsa.ac.za
Telex: 350068 sa
Rector: M. Wiechers (1994-)
Founded: 1873, 1916
F: *Arts; Economics and Administration; Education; Law; Science; Theology.*
I: *Behavioural Sciences; Continuing Education; Criminology; Educational Research; Foreign and*

Behavioural Sciences; Theological Research; Market Research.

University of Stellenbosch
[Universiteit van Stellenbosch]
Victoria Street, Stellenbosch 7600
Tel: +27(21) 808-9111
Fax: +27(21) 808-4499
E-Mail: ecdb@matles.sun.ac.za
Telex: 52-0383
Vice-Chancellor and Rector: A.H. Van Wyk (1993-)
Registrar: S. Kritzinger
Founded: 1866, 1918
F: *Agriculture; Arts; Commerce; Dentistry; Education; Engineering; Forestry; Law; Medicine; Science; Theology.*
I: *Industrial Engineering; Biotechnology; Electrical Engineering; Electronics; Cartographical Analysis; Polymer Science; Sport and Movement Studies; Theoretical Nuclear Physics; Applied Business Sciences; Applied Computer Sciences; Mathematics and Science; Structural Engineering; Futures Research.*
Buro: *Chemical Engineering; Economic Research; Medical and Dental Education; Systems Engineering; Bio-Engineering; Continuing Education.*
Ce: *Molecular and Cellular Biology; Robotics; Computer Applications on Language and Text of the Old Testament (Research).*
Ut: *Soviet Studies.*

University of Transkei +Universiteit van Transkei
Private Bag X1, Umtata, Transkei
Tel: +27(471) 31-22-67
Fax: +27(471) 23-884
Vice Chancellor: A.T. Moleah (1994-)
Founded: 1994
F: *Arts; Economics and Administration; Education; Law; Medicine; Science.*

University of Venda
Private Bag X2220, Sibasa, Venda
Tel: +27(159) 21-071
Fax: +27(159) 22-045
Telex: (15581) 331694
Vice Chancellor and Rector: G.M. Nkondo
Founded: 1983
F: *Agriculture; Arts; Economics and Administration; Education; Law; Science.*

Vista University
[Vista University/Vista Universiteit (Decentralized Campuses)]
Private Bag X634, Pretoria 0001
Tel: +27(12) 322-8967
Fax: +27(12) 320-0582
Vice-Chancellor and Rector: S.W.B. Engelbrecht
Founded: 1982
F: *Arts; Economics and Administration; Education; Science.*
D: *Accountancy; African Languages; Afrikaans; Business Economics; Commercial Law;*

609

Economics; Education; English; Geography;
History; Mathematics and Statistics; Psychology;
Sociology; Private Law; Public Administration;
Public Law.
Ut: Cognitive Studies.
Ce: Further Training.

University of the Western Cape
+ Universiteit van Wes-Kaapland
Private Bag X17, Bellville 7535
Tel: +27(21) 959-2911
Fax: +27(21) 959-3126
E-Mail: jsmith@admin.uwc.ac.za
Telex: sa 5226661
Cable: unibel sa
Vice-Chancellor and Rector: J.J.F. Durand (1994-)
Registrar: J.F. Smith
F: Arts; Dentistry; Economics and
Administration; Education; Law; Science;
Theology.
I: Social Development; Historical Research;
Counselling; Small Business Studies.
Ce: Research Development; Academic
Development; Adult Continuing Education; Gold
Fields Science and Mathematics Research.

University of the Witwatersrand
1 Jan Smuts Avenue, Johannesburg 2001
Tel: +27(11) 716-1111
Fax: +27(11) 716-8030
Telex: 42 27126
Cable: uniwits
Vice-Chancellor and Principal: R.W. Charlton
Founded: 1896, 1922
F: Architecture; Arts; Commerce; Dentistry;
Education; Engineering; Law; Management;
Medicine; Science; Portuguese Studies; Medical
Research; Dental Research; Geophysical
Research; African Studies; Palaeontological
Research.
Ce: Nuclear Sciences Research; Study of
Medical Education; Continuing Education;
Nuclear Sciences (Schonland Research).

University of Zululand + Universiteit van
Zululand
Private Bag X1001, Kwa-Dlangezwa 3886
Tel: +27(351) 93-911
Fax: +27(351) 93-130
Telex: 6-28081 sa
Cable: unizul
Vice-Chancellor and Rector: C.R.M. Dlamini
(1993-)
Founded: 1959, 1970
F: Arts; Commerce and Administration (Umlazi
Campus); Education (Umlazi Campus); Law;
Science; Theology.
D: Extramural Studies.
Ce: Nursing.

OTHER INSTITUTIONS

B.G. Alexander College of Nursing
P.Bag X43, Johannesburg 2000
Tel: +27(11) 488-3219
Fax: +27(11) 643-1036
Principal: Mrs. N.M. Veale
Registrar: Mrss. A. du Plessis
Founded: 1961
Nursing.

Boitumelo Hospital College
Private Bag, Kroonstad 9500
Tel: +27(562) 52113
Chief Nursing Service Manager: Miss E.J. van Zyl
Secretary: D.T. Robberts
Nursing.

Border Technikon
P.O. Box 1421, East London 5200
Tel: +27(403) 63-1491
Fax: +27(403) 63-2236
Rector: C.W. Poole

Cape Technikon
P.O. Box 652, Cape Town 8000
Tel: +27(21) 460-3911
Fax: +27(21) 461-7564
E-Mail: tshippey@maxwell.ctech.ac.za
Telex: 521666 sa
Cable: teccom
Rector: T.C. Shippey (1979-)
Registrar: J. Vanzyl
Founded: 1923
*Architecture and Building; Business Informatics;
Civil Engineering; Design; Electrical Engineering;
Life Sciences; Management; Mechanical
Engineering; Physical Sciences; Teacher
Education; Hotel and Catering Studies (Ganger
Bay).*

Cedara College of Agriculture
Private Bag X9059, Pietermaritzurg 3200
Tel: +27(331) 33371
Fax: +27(331) 431253
Principal: A. van Niekerk
Agriculture.

Elsenburg Agricultural College
Private Bag X5023, Elsenburg 7607
Tel: +27(21) 884-4620
Fax: +27(21) 884-4226
Principal (Acting): M.J. Paulse
Agriculture.

Fort Cox Agricultural College
P.O. Box 790, Alice 5700
Tel: +27(40462) X26
Principal: Z.M. Gebeda
Agriculture.

Frere Nursing College
Private Bag X9023, East London 5200
Tel: +27(431) 491-136
Fax: +27(431) 434-265
Head: MissP. Bellad-Ellis
Nursing.

Glen Agricultural College
Private Bag X01, Glen 9360
Tel: +27(5214) 2051
Fax: +27(5214) 2207
Telex: 267690 sa
Agriculture.

Grootfontein Agricultural College
Private Bag X529, Middelburg 5900
Tel: +27(4924) 21113
Fax: +27(4924) 24352
Principal: F.C. Hayward
Agriculture.

Highveld Region Agricultural College
Private Bag X804, Potchefstroom 2520
Tel: +27(148) 297-7111
Fax: +27(148) 297-7135
Principal: V. van der Westhuizen
Agriculture.

L.M. Mangope Agricultural College
Private Bag X532, Taung 8584
Tel: +27(1405) 41832
Fax: +27(1405) 41130
Principal: P.G.F. Coetzee
Agriculture.

Lowveld Agricultural College
Private Bag X11283, Nelspruit 1200
Tel: +27(1311) 53064
Fax: +27(1311) 55-1110
Principal: S.E. Terblanche
Agriculture.

M.L. Sultan Technikon
P.O. Box 1334, Durban 4000
Tel: +27(31) 308-5111
Cable: sulkon
Founded: 1946

Madzivhandila Agricultural College
Private Bag X2377 hohoyandou
Tel: +27(159) 21109
Fax: +27(159) 31414
Principal: E.F. Kolajo
Agriculture.

Mangosuthu Technikon
P.O. Box 12363, Jacobs 4026
Tel: +27(31) 907-1855
Fax: +27(31) 907-2892
Rector: A.J. Vos

Natal Technikon
P.O. Box 953, Durban 40001
Tel: +27(31) 225-2111
Fax: +27(31) 22-3405
Telex: 620187 sa
Cable: nattechnikon
Rector: A.L. du Preez (1983-)
Vice-Rector: Nico de Koker
International Relations: Antre du Preez
Founded: 1907
Applied Sciences; Arts; Commerce; Design; Engineering; Health Services.

Northern Transvaal Technikon
Private Bag X7, Pretoria North 0116
Tel: +27(1214) 80950
Fax: +27(1214) 80968
Telex: 323239 sa
Principal: C.S.K. Lenyai (1994-)
Vice-Principal: M.A. Mashego
International Relations: C.H.J. van der Westheizen
Founded: 1979
Economics and Manegement; Food and Health; Engineering; Teacher Training; Computer.

OFS Technikon
20 President Brand Street, Private Bag X20539, Bloemfontein 9300
Tel: +27(15) 407-3911
Fax: +27(15) 407-3199
E-Mail: cajvr@studm.tofs.ac.za
Rector: J.J. van Lill (1981-)
Registrar: J.J. Hamman
International Relations: H.S. Wolvaardt
Founded: 1981
Management; Engineering; Art and Design; Applied Sciences.

Otto du Plessis College of Nursing
Private Bag 7, Tygerberg 7505
Tel: +27(21) 938-4118
Fax: +27(21) 931-1451
The DirectorHead: Miss J.M. Viljoen
Assistant Administrative Officer: Mrs. A. Rust
Nursing.

Owen Sithole Agricultural College
Private Bag X20013, Empangeni 3830
Tel: +27(351) 95-1390
Principal: C.J. Oberholzer
Agriculture.

Peninsula Technikon
P.O. 1906, Bellville 7530
Tel: +27(21) 959-6911
Fax: +27(21) 951-5617
Rector: F.A. Sonn (1979-)
Vice-Rector, Administration: A.M. Slabbert
International Relations: Senior Vice-Rector, B. Fiwdji
S: Science; Mechanical and Electrical Engineering; Architecture, Building and Civil

Engineering; Business Studies; Education; Art, Design and Journalism.
Ce: *Continuing Education.*

Port Elizabeth Technikon

University Way, Summerstrand, Private Bag X6011, Port Elizabeth 6000
Tel: +27(41) 504-3911
Fax: +27(41) 53-3644
Telex: 243051 sa
Rector: H.C. Snyman (1988-)
Vice-Rector: D.B. Raix
International Relations: Vice-Rector, B.K. Wells
Founded: 1977
F: *Management; Commerce; Public Management; Computer Studies; Communication Studies; Applied Science; Electrical Engineering; Mechanical Engineering; Civil Engineering; Building; Architecture and Agriculture; Art and Design; Education; Forestry (Saavedld Campus).*

Pretoria Technikon

Private Bag X680, Pretoria 0001
Tel: +27(12) 326-1066
Fax: +27(12) 325-7387
Cable: techpret
Rector: D.J.J. Van Rensburg (1981-)
Vice-Rector: A.J.J. Van Rensburg
International Relations: Vice-Rector, Research and Strategic Initiative, H.H. Dürrheim
Founded: 1979
F: *Engineering; Information Sciences; Economic Sciences; Environmental Sciences; Arts; Natural Sciences.*
Ce: *Tatol Quality; Medical Orthotics and Prosthetics; Polymer Technology; Explovives Technology; Applied Chemistry; Language and Leadership Development; Food Service Management.*

SA (Teletuition) Technikon

Private Bag X6, Florida 1710
Tel: +27(11) 471-2000
Fax: +27(11) 471-2134
Rector: A.J.H. Buitendacht
Founded: 1980

Setlogelo Technikon

P.O. Box 1263, Rosslyn 0200
Tel: +27(1461) 32251
Fax: +27(1461) 32255
Rector: G. Wienand

Tompi Seleka Agricultural College

Private Bag X9619, Marble Hall 0450
Tel: +27(12020) 2025
Fax: +27(12020) 3478
Principal: C.M.K. Mannya
Agriculture.

Tsolo Agricultural College

Private Bag X1008 solo
Tel: +27(471) 311-897
Fax: +27(471) 311-898
Principal (Acting): Ramoketsi
Agriculture.

Vaal Triangle Technikon

Private Box X021, Vanderbijlpark 1900
Tel: +27(16) 885-2221
Fax: +27(16) 85-2103
Telex: 748014 sa
Rector: P.W. du Plessis (1966-)
Vice-Rector, Administration: J. de W. du Toit
International Relations: A.J. Kempen
Founded: 1972
S: *Accountancy; Applied Sciences; Art and Design; Computer Technology; Electrical Engineering; Food and Clothing; Management; Mechanical Engineering.*

Witwatersrand Technikon

P.O. Box 17011, Doornfontein 2028
Tel: +27(11) 406-2911
Fax: +27(11) 402-0475
Rector: C. Swanepoel (1991-96)
Registrar, Financial Management: D. Strauss
International Relations: J.L. Stead
Founded: 1968
F: *Art and Design; Business Management; Engineering; Health and Biotechnology; Mining and Metallurgy.*
Ce: *Career Development.*

NATIONAL ACADEMIC BODIES

Human Sciences Research Council

[Raad vir Geesteswetenskaplike Navorsing]
Private Bag X270, Pretoria 0001
Tel: +27(12) 202-9111
Fax: +27(12) 202-2892
E-Mail: ebm@gallup.hsrc.ac.za
Director: R. Stümpf
Founded: 1967

Committee of University Principals (CUP)

P.O. Box 27392, Sunnyside 0132
Tel: +27(12) 429-3168
Fax: +27(12) 429-3071
E-Mail: vrooys 1 alpha.unisa.ac.za
Chairman: C.J. Reinecke
Chief Director: J.W. Grobbelaar
Founded: 1955

Committee of Technikon Principals

Private Bag X680, Pretoria 0001
Tel: +27(12) 326-1066
Fax: +27(12) 325-7387
Executive Director: A.E. Strydom

Foundation for Research and Development

P.O. Box 2600, Pretoria 0001
Tel: +27(12) 841-3762
Fax: +27(12) 804-2679
E-Mail: joletta frd.ac.za
President: R.R. Arndt

Medical Research Council
P.O. Box 19070, Tygerberg 7505
Tel: +27(21) 938-0211
Fax: +27(21) 938-0201
E-Mail: owprozes eagle.mrc.ac.za
President: O.W. Prozesky

SPAIN

UNIVERSITIES

University of Alcalá de Henares
[Universidad de Alcalá de Henares]
Plaza de San Diego, s/n, 28801 Alcalá de
Henares, Madrid
Tel: +34(1) 889-0400
Fax: +34(1) 889-0667
Telex: 23896
Rector: Manuel Gala Muñoz
Vice-Rector (International Relations): Luis Beltrán
Founded: 1499, 1977
F: Science; Economics and Business
Administration; Law; Pharmacy; Philosophy and
Letters; Medicine.
S: Telecommunications Engineering; Teachers'
Training.
C: Nursing (Guadalajara); Education
(Guadalajara).
Ce: European Studies; American Studies;
Hispanic-American of Industrial Relations
(Madrid); Modern Languages.

University of Alicante
[Universidad de Alicante]
San Vicente del Raspeig, Alicante
Tel: +34(65) 661-150
Fax: +34(65) 668-867
Telex: 66616
Rector: Andrés Pedreño Muño
Secretario General: Juan José Díaz
Founded: 1968, 1979
F: Science; Philosophy and Letters; Medicine;
Law; Economics and Management.
Ce: Optics; Education; Nursing; Management;
Industrial Medicine; Social Work; Statistics.
I: Geography; Biology; Sociology.

*University of the Balearic Islands
[Universitat de les Illes Balears]
Son Lladó, Campus UIB, 07071 Palma de
Mallorca
Tel: +34(71) 295-200
Fax: +34(71) 754-445
Telex: 69121
Rector: Nadal Batle Nicolau (1982-)
Secretari General: Joan Oliver
Founded: 1978
D: Environmental Biology; Fundamental Biology
and Health Sciences; Educational Sciences;
History and Theory of the Arts; Mathematics and
Computer Science; Public Law; Economics and
Business Studies; Catalan Philology and General

Linguistics; Spanish and Modern Philology;
Philosophy; Physics; Chemistry; Psychology.
F: Private Law; Earth Sciences.
I: Research (IEA) (Catalan Philology and
Linguistics, Cognitive Sciences, Natural
Resources); Education (ICE); British.

*Autonomous University of Barcelona
[Universitat Autònoma de Barcelona]
Campus Universitari de Bellaterra, 08193
Bellaterra
Tel: +34(3) 581-1000
Fax: +34(3) 581-2000
E-Mail: g-ofinf@cc.uab.es
Telex: 52040
Rector: Josep M. Vallès Casadevall
Secretari General: Enric Cassany Cels
Founded: 1968
F: Medicine; Philosophy and Letters; Science;
Economics and Business Administration; Law;
Information Sciences; Veterinary Medicine;
Political Sciences and Sociology; Psychology;
Educational Sciences; Translation and
Interpretation.
Ce: Education (Bellaterra); Business
Administration (Sabadell); Computer Sciences
(Sabadell); Nursing 'Creu Roja' (Terrassa);
Nursing and Physiotherapy 'Gimbernat' (Santa
Coloma de Gramenet); Nursing (Manresa);
Nursing 'Osona' (Vic); Japanese Studies; Chinese
Studies; Nursing 'Sant Pau'; Nursing 'Vall
d'Hebrón'.
I: Musicology Research; Education Sciences;
Biology; Medieval Studies.

*University of Barcelona
[Universitat de Barcelona]
Gran Vía de les Corts Catalanes 585, 08007
Barcelona
Tel: +34(3) 318-4266
Fax: +34(3) 302-5947
Telex: 98871 unb
Rector: Antonio Caparros (1994-)
Gerente: Josep Roig Marti
Founded: 1450, 1873, 1985
D: Human and Social Sciences; Experimental
Sciences and Mathematics; Health Sciences;
Educational Sciences; Law, Economics, and
Social Sciences.
F: Philosophy; Geography and History;
Philology; Fine Arts; Law; Economics and
Business Administration; Biology; Chemistry;
Physics; Mathematics; Geology; Medicine;
Pharmacy; Dentistry; Psychology; Educational
Sciences.
Ce: Nursing; Business Administration;
Podology; Education.
I: Educational Sciences; Labour Studies;
Hispanic Studies; Oriental Studies; Andorran
Studies.
S: Modern Languages Studies; Gemmology
Studies.

University of Burgos
[Universidad de Burgos]
Burgos
Founded: 1994
Science; Food Technology; Law; Humanities;
Chemistry; Business Administration; Education;
Engineering.

University of Cádiz
[Universidad de Cádiz]
C/Ancha 16, Cádiz
Tel: +34(56) 223-808
Fax: +34(56) 226-809
Telex: 76197
Rector: José Luis Romero Palanco
Founded: 1979
F: Science; Medicine; Philosophy and Letters;
Law (Jérez de la Frontera).
Ce: Undergraduate (Law, Jérez de la Frontera);
Undergraduate (Chemistry, Philosophy and
Letters); Business Administration; Education;
Engineering; Nursing (Jérez de la Frontera);
Education (La Línea de la Concepción); Business
Administration (Jérez de la Frontera);
Engineering (Algeciras).

University Pompeu Fabra Barcelona
[Universitat Pompeu Fabra]
Marc Aureli 22-36, 08006 Barcelona
Tel: +34(3) 484-9800
Fax: +34(3) 484-9808
Rector: Enric Argullol i Murgadas
Secretario General: Monserrat Vives
Founded: 1990
F: Humanities; Law; Economics and Business
Studies; Social Sciences and Communication.
S: Translation and Interpretation; Business
Studies; Public Management and Administration.
I: History.

University Ramón Llull Barcelona
[Universitat Ramón Llull]
Comte de Salvatierra 8, 08006 Barcelona
Tel: +34(3) 415-4881
Fax: +34(3) 415-8726
Founded: 1990

*University of the Basque Country
[Universidad del País Vasco/Euskal Herriko
Unibertsitatea]
Apartado 1397, 48080 Bilbao (Vizcaya)
Tel: +34(4) 480-1068
Fax: +34(4) 480-1590
E-Mail: rvzrigoo lg.ehu.es
Telex: 32098 educi e
Rector: Juan José Goiriena de Gandarias
Founded: 1968, 1980
F: Economics and Business Administration
(Bilbao); Science (Bilbao); Medicine and Dentistry
(Bilbao); Chemistry (San Sebastián); Law (San
Sebastián); Computer Sciences (San Sebastián);
Fine Arts (Bilbao); Information Services (Bilbao);
Philology, Geography and History (Vitoria);
Philosophy and Education (San Sebastián).

S: Industrial Engineering and
Telecommunications (Bilbao); Architecture (San
Sebastián).
Ce: Undergraduate (Vitoria); Business
Administration (Bilbao); Nursing (Bilbao);
Engineering (Bilbao); Business Administration
(San Sebastián); Engineering (San Sebastián);
Engineering (Vitoria); Mining Engineering
(Bilbao); Education (Bilbao); Education (San
Sebastián); Education (Vitoria); International Law
(Vitoria); Lifelong Education.
I: Criminology; Public Economics; Epidemiology
and Heart Disease Prevention; Educational
Sciences.

*University of Cantabria
[Universidad de Cantabria]
Pabellón de Gobierno, Avenida de los Castros s/
n, 39005 Santander
Tel: +34(42) 201-222
Fax: +34(42) 201-103
Telex: 35861 educi e
Rector: Jaime Vinuesa Tejedor
Secretaria General: Beatriz Arizaga
Founded: 1972
F: Science; Medicine; Philosophy and Letters;
Law (Cantabria); Economics and Business
Administration.
S: Civil Engineering; Engineering (Polytechnic);
Marine Studies.
Ce: Education; Mining Engineering; Nursing;
Education (Torrelavega); Labour Relations.
I: Educational Sciences; Animal Husbandry;
Prehistory.

*University of Castilla-La Mancha
[Universidad de Castilla-La Mancha]
Calle Paloma 9, 1307 Ciudad Real
Tel: +34(26) 227-415
Fax: +34(26) 223-894
Telex: 48127 ucma e
Rector: Luis Arroyo Zapatero
Founded: 1982
F: Chemistry; Philosophy and Letters; Law
(Albacete); Fine Arts (Cuenca).
Ce: Undergraduate Ce. (Law, Letters, Cuenca);
Undergraduate Ce. (Law, Economics, Letters, and
Chemistry, Toledo); Agricultural Engineering
(Technical); Industrial Engineering (Technical,
Albacete); Architecture (Technical, Cuenca);
Agricultural Engineering; Education; Industrial
Engineering (Albacete, Almadén); Agricultural
Engineering (Albacete); Forestry (Albacete);
Computer Science (Albacete); Education
(Albacete, Cuenca, Guadalajara, Toledo); Nursing
(Albacete, Cuenca, Guadalajara); Mining
(Almadén); Electrical Engineering (Toledo).

Technical University of Cataluña
[Universidad Politécnica de Cataluña]
Avenida Dr. Gregorio Marañón s/n, Barcelona 26
Tel: +34(3) 249-3804
Telex: 52821
Founded: 1968, 1973

F: Computer Sciences; Economics; Business Administration.
S: Architecture; Architecture (El Vallés); Industrial Engineering; Industrial Engineering (Tarrasa); Telecommunications Engineering; Highway Engineering; Agricultural Engineering (Lérida).
I: Education; Textile Research; Petrochemistry; Transport Research; Cybernetics; Energetics.
Ce: Architecture (Technical); Industrial Engineering (Technical, Tarrasa); Industrial Engineering (Technical, Vilanueva y Geltrú); Polytechnic (Manresa); Polytechnic (Gerona); Agricultural Engineering (Technical, Lérida); Optometry (Tarrasa); Agricultural Engineering (Technical); Industrial Engineering (Technical); Knitting and Weaving; Telecommunications Engineering (Vilanueva y Geltrú); Industrial Engineering (Igualada); Industrial Engineering (Tarragona); Computer.

*Pontifical University Comillas
[Universidad Pontificia Comillas]
Alberto Aguilera 23, 28049 Madrid
Tel: +34(1) 734-3950
Fax: +34(1) 734-4570
E-Mail: spaøo182@applelink.apple.link
Telex: 2486569 G3
Rector: Manuel Gallego Diaz, S.J.
Secretario General: Ricardo Lobato García
Founded: 1892, 1901
F: Theology; Canon Law; Philosophy and Letters; Economics and Business Administration; Law.
S: Engineering.
I: Business Management; Home and Family Life; Modern Languages; Technological Research; Liberalism Research.
Ce: Industrial Engineering (Technical); Social Work; Lifelong Education; Computer Science; Nursing.

*University of Córdoba
[Universidad de Córdoba]
Alfonso XIII, 13, 14071 Córdoba
Tel: +34(57) 21-80-00
Fax: +34(57) 21-80-30
Telex: 76561 educi e
Rector: Amador Jover Moyano (1990-94)
Secretario General: Rafael Ayuso Muñoz
Founded: 1972
F: Veterinary Medicine; Medicine; Science; Philosophy and Letters; Law; Economics and Business.
C: Politechnic; Mining (Bélmez); Education; Education 'Sagrado Corazón'; Business Studies.
S: Nursing; Agricultural Engineering (Technical).
I: Education; Criminology (Andalusian Interuniversity); Advanced Social Studies; Andalusian History; Rural Sociology and Studies; Chemistry; Sustainable Agriculture; Animal Husbandry.

*University of Deusto
[Universidad de Deusto]
Avenida de las Universidades, Apartado 1, 48080 Bilbao
Tel: +34(4) 445-4004
Fax: +34(4) 445-7854
Rector: R.P. Jesus Ma. Eguiluz Ortuzar, S.J.
Founded: 1886, 1963
F: Law; Philosophy and Arts; Theology; Economics and Business Administration; Economics and Business Administration (San Sebastián); Political Science and Sociology; Philosophy and Education; Computer Science.
I: Business Administration (International); Education; Modern Languages; Religious Studies; Pastoral Studies; Basque Studies; European Studies; Co-operative Studies.
S: Juridical Studies; Tourism.

*University of Extremadura
[Universidad de Extremadura]
Avenida Elvas s/n, Badajoz
Tel: +34(24) 274-800; (Cáceres)+34(27) 212-000
Fax: +34(24) 272-983; (Cáceres)+34(27) 211-268
E-Mail: sbcc@ccue.unex.es
Telex: 28638
Rector: César Chaparro Gómez (1991-)
Registrar: Angel López Piñeiro
Founded: 1973
F: Law (Cáceres); Philosophy and Letters (Cáceres); Veterinary Medicine (Cáceres); Medicine; Science; Economics and Business Administration.
Ce: ndustrial Engineering (Technical); Agricultural Engineering (Technical); Business Administration (Cáceres); Polytechnic (Cáceres); Polytechnic (Mérida); Nursing (Cáceres); Nursing; Nursing; Nursing (Mérida); Nursing (Plasencia); Business Administration; Business Administration (Plasencia); Agricultural Engineering (Technical, Almendralejo); Education (Cáceres); Education; Education (Almendralejo).

University of Gerona
[Universidad de Gerona]
Gerona
F: Letters; Law and Economics Sciences; Experimental and Health Sciences; Educational Sciences.
S: Engineering (Technical).

*University of Granada
[Universidad de Granada]
Hospital Real, Avenida del Hospicio s/n, Granada
Tel: +34(58) 243-063
Fax: +34(58) 243-066
Rector: Lorenzo Morilla Cueva (1992-)
Founded: 1531
F: Law; Medicine; Pharmacy; Philosophy and Letters; Science; Fine Arts.
Ce: Undergraduate (Science, Philosophy and Letters, Almería); Undergraduate (Science, Philosophy and Letters, Jaén); Business Administration; Translation and Interpretation;

Nursing; Library Science; Business Administration (Almería); Business Administration (Melilla); Business Administration (Jaén); Architecture (Technical); Engineering (Technical, Jaén); Engineering (Technical, Linares); Education; Education (Almería); Education (Ceuta); Education (Jaén); Education (Melilla).

Hispano-American University of 'Santa María de la Rábida' Huelva
[Universidad Hispanoamericana 'Santa María de la Rábida']
Huelva

University of La Laguna
[Universidad de La Laguna]
La Laguna, Tenerife, Canarias
Tel: +34(22) 603-000
Fax: +34(22) 259-628
Telex: 93137 educi e
Rector: Marisa Tejedor
Founded: 18th, 1927
F: Law; Chemistry; Philology; Medicine and Surgery; Mathematics; Biology; Pharmacy; Economics and Business Administration; Fine Arts; Geography and History; Philosophy and Education.
I: Education; Astrophysics; Linguistics; Organic Chemistry; Regional Development; Political and Social Sciences; Business Administration.
Ce: Business Administration (Santa Cruz de Tenerife); Business Administration (Las Palmas); Nursing; Nursing; Nursing (Las Palmas); Education; Education (Las Palmas); Education (Santa Cruz de Tenerife).

University of La Rioja
[Universidad de La Rioja]
La Rioja
Human and Social Sciences; Scientific and Technical Studies.

International University 'Pérez Galdós' Las Palmas
[Universidad Internacional 'Pérez Galdós']
Las Palmas de Gran Canaria
Founded: 1962

University of Las Palmas
[Universidad de Las Palmas]
Alfonso XIII, 2, 35003 Las Palmas, Gran Canaria
Tel: +34(28) 451-003
Fax: +34(28) 451-006
Telex: 95238
Rector: Francisco Rubio Royo
Secretario General: Gonzalo Pérez Melián
Founded: 1979
F: Veterinary Medicine; Informatics.
S: Architecture; Industrial Engineering; Telecommunications Engineering (Technical).
Ce: Polytechnic.; Architecture; Marine Sciences.
I: Physical Education.

C: Business Studies; Nursing; Technical Engineering; Translation and Interpretation; Education.

University of León
[Universidad de León]
Carretera de Santander s/n, León
Tel: +34(87) 291-000
Fax: +34(87) 291-614
Telex: 89892
Founded: 1979
F: Biology; Veterinary Medicine; Law; Philosophy and Letters.
Ce: Undergraduate (Philosophy and Letters, Law); Business Administration; Nursing; Social Work; Engineering (Technical); Education; Education (Ponferrada).

University of Lérida
[Universidad de Lérida]
Lérida
Founded: 1991
F: Letters; Law and Economics Sciences; Medicine.
S: Nursing; Agricultural Engineering (Technical); Polytechnic (Industrial, Management Computer Science, and Systems Computer Science Engineering).

Autonomous University of Madrid
[Universidad Autónoma de Madrid]
Ciudad Universitaria de Cantoblanco, 28049 Madrid
Tel: +34(1) 734-0100
Telex: 27810 educi e
Rector: Raul Villar
Founded: 1968
F: Philosophy and Letters; Law; Science; Medicine; Economics and Business Administration; Psychology.
Ce: Undergraduate (Science, Economics and Business Administration, Cuenca); Undergraduate (Law, Philosophy and Letters, Cuenca); Undergraduate (Medicine, Cuenca); Education; Education (Cuenca); Education (Segovia).

*Complutense University of Madrid
[Universidad Complutense de Madrid]
Pabellón de Gobierno, Ciudad Universitaria, Madrid 3
Tel: +34(1) 549-0256
Fax: +34(1) 394-3437
Telex: 41857 ucsi e
Rector: D. Gustavo Villapalos Salas (1987-94)
Secretario General: Teodoro González Ballesteros
Founded: 7th, 1499, 1836
F: Philosophy and Educational Sciences; Geography and History; Philology; Mathematics; Physics; Chemistry; Geology; Biology; Law; Medicine; Pharmacy; Veterinary Science; Economics and Management; Political Science

and Sociology; Information Science; Psychology; Fine Arts; Odontology.
C: Undergraduate (4) (Philology, Geography and History, Psychology, Chemistry, Biology, Medicine, Pharmacy, Law, Economics and Business, Information Sciences).
S: Statistics; Business Administration; Optometry; Nursing, Physiotherapy, and Podology; Social Work; Education (4) (primary level); Development of Teaching.
I: Environmental Sciences; Embryology; Applied Magnetism; Forensic Anatomy; Astronomy and Geodesy; Educational Sciences; Criminology; Modern Languages and Translation; Statistics and Operations Research; Human Rights; Drug Dependence; Comparative Law; Meat Science and Technology; Human Resources; Industrial Pharmacy; Feminist Research; Radio.
Ce: European Documentation.

International University 'Menéndez Pelayo' Madrid

[Universidad Internacional 'Menéndez Pelayo']
Calle Isaac Peral 23, 28040 Madrid
Tel: +34(1) 592-0600
Fax: +34(1) 543-0897
Rector: Ernest Lluch
Founded: 1932, 1945
D: Comparative Politics (Research); Economics and Energy Resources (Research); Development and Social Change (Research); Humanities (Research); European Community Law (Research); Experimental Science (Research); Social History (Research); Art and Communication (Research).
I: Educational Research.

*National University for Distance Education Madrid

[Universidad Nacional de Educación a Distancia]
Ciudad Universitaria, s/n. Pabellón de Gobierno, 28040 Madrid
Tel: +34(1) 398-6525
Fax: +34(1) 398-6036
Telex: 45256
Rector: Mariano Artés Gómez (1987-95)
Secretario General: Jesús Ávila Rey
Founded: 1972
F: Law; Economics and Business Studies; Philosophy and Pedagogy; Sciences; Psychology; Philology; Geography and History.
Ce: Industrial Engineering (Technical).
I: Educational Sciences.

*Technical University of Madrid

[Universidad Politécnica de Madrid]
Avenida Ramiro de Maeztu 7, Ciudad Universitaria, 28040 Madrid
Tel: +34(1) 336-6000
Fax: +34(1) 336-6173
Telex: 23780 upmad e
Rector: Rafael Portaencasa Baeza (1980-94)
Secretario General: José Manuel Herrero Marzal
Founded: 1972

S: Architecture; Aeronautical Engineering; Agricultural Engineering; Civil Engineering; Industrial Engineering; Mining; Naval Engineering; Telecommunications; Forestry Engineering; Informatics; Telecommunications Engineering (Technical); Surveying (Technical); Aeronatical Engineering (Technical); Agriculture (Technical); Architecture (Technical); Forestry (Technical); Industrial Engineering; Civil Engineering; Computer Sciences (Technical).
I: Further Education and Industrial; Educational Sciences; Renewable Energy.

University of Málaga

[Universidad de Málaga]
Plaza del Ejido, Málaga 52
Tel: +34(52) 131-000
Fax: +34(52) 263-858
Telex: 77173
Founded: 1972
F: Science; Economics and Business Administration; Philosophy and Letters; Medicine; Law.
Ce: Business Administration; Computer Sciences; Nursing; Nursing (Ronda); Engineering (Technical); Education; Education (Antequera).

University of Murcia

[Universidad de Murcia]
Calle Santo Cristo, 1 Murcia
Tel: +34(68) 217-278
Fax: +34(68) 221-569
Telex: 67058
Founded: 1915
F: Law; Philosophy and Education; Science; Medicine; Economics and Business Administration; Veterinary Medicine.
Ce: Computer Sciences; Nursing; Nursing (Cartagena); Business Administration; Business Administration (Cartagena); Engineering (Technical, Cartagena); Education.

*University of Navarra

[Universidad de Navarra]
Campus Universitario, 31080 Pamplona
Tel: +34(48) 252-700
Fax: +34(48) 173-650
E-Mail: allano@rector.unav.es
Telex: 37917 unav e
Rector: Alejandro Llano
Founded: 1952, 1960
F: Law; Philosophy and Letters; Canon Law; Medicine; Pharmacy; Science; Theology; Journalism; Economics and Management; Philosophy.
S: Industrial Engineering Technology; Architecture; Library Science; Laboratory Technology; Internal Medicine.
I: Education; Liberal Arts; Secretarial Studies and Administration; Business Administration; Spanish Language and Culture (for foreign students); Church History; Modern Languages; Applied Sciences; Science for the Family.

Ce: *Nursing; Physiology Research; European Documentation; Applied PharmacobiologyResearch; Social Responsibility of Private Enterprise; Industrial Research (Guipúzcoa); Computer Technology Ce.; Modern History Research.*

*University of Oviedo
[Universidad de Oviedo]
San Francisco 1-3-5, Oviedo
Tel: +34(91) 510-4058
Fax: +34(91) 522-7126
Telex: 87322 educi e
Rector: Santiago Gascón Muñoz
Founded: 1604
F: *Medicine; Philosophy and Education; Law; Economics and Business Administration; Philology; Geography and History; Chemistry; Biology; Geology.*
S: *Industrial Engineering; Mining.*
I: *Education; Management.*
Ce: *Mining (Technical); Business Administration (Gijón); Business Administration (Oviedo); Industrial Engineering (Technical); Nursing; Education; Computer Science; Computer Science (Gijón).*

Pontifical University of Salamanca
[Universidad Pontificia de Salamanca]
Compañía 5, 37008, Salamanca
Tel: +34(23) 215-209
Fax: +34(23) 213-450
Rector: José Manuel Sánchez
Secretario General: Marceliano Arranz Rodrigo
Founded: 1940
F: *Theology; Canon Law; Philosophy; Trilingual Biblical Philology; Education; Psychology; Political and Social Sciences; Informatics.*
S: *Speech Studies; Language Psychology; Family Studies; Education.*
I: *European Studies of Human Rights; Pastoral Studies; Catechetical Studies; Infant Clinical Psychology; Spanish Language and Culture; History of Theology; Biblical Archaeology.*
Ce: *Oriental and Oecumenical Studies.*

*University of Salamanca
[Universidad de Salamanca]
Patio de Escuelas 1, 37008 Salamanca
Tel: +34(23) 214-518
Fax: +34(23) 294-502
Telex: 26828 educi e
Rector: Julio Fermoso García
Secretario General: Antonio Morales Moya
Founded: 1218
F: *Philology; Geography and History; Philosophy and Educational Sciences; Law; Fine Arts; Science; Chemistry; Biology; Medicine; Pharmacy; Economic Sciences.*
Ce: *Business Administration; Nursing; Social Sciences; Library Science; Education (Zamora); Education (Ávila); Education (Ávila); Social Graduates; Industrial Engineering.*

S: *Polytechnic.*
I: *Educational Sciences.*

*University of Santiago de Compostela
[Universidad de Santiago de Compostela]
Palacio de San Jerónimo, Plaza del Obradoiro, Santiago de Compostela, La Coruña 15705
Tel: +34(81) 583-800
Fax: +34(81) 588-522
Telex: 86013
Rector: Ramón Villares Paz (1992-)
Secretario General: Enrique Jiménez Gómez
Founded: 1495
F: *Philosophy and Educational Sciences; Biology; Economics and Business; Law; Pharmacy; Philology; Physics; Geography and History; Mathematics; Medicine; Chemistry; Veterinary Science; Political and Social Science; Journalism; Psychology; Sciences (Lugo).*
Ce: *Undergraduate (Hispanic Philology, Germanic Philology, and Romance Languages, Lugo); Nursing; Optics and Optometry; Teacher Training; Labour Relations;; Social Studies; Business Studies (Lugo); Nursing (Lugo); Teacher Training (Lugo); Agricultural Technology (Lugo); Forestry (Lugo).*
I: *Galician Language; Galician Development; Agricultural Engineering (Lugo); Educational Sciences; Criminology; Mathematics; Neurology; Industrial Pharmacy; Ceramics; Industrial Law; Legal Medicine.*

University of Saragossa
[Universidad de Zaragoza]
Plaza de San Francisco s/n, 50009 Zaragoza
Tel: +34(76) 354-100
Fax: +34(76) 350-558
Telex: 58064 educi e
Rector: Juan José Badiola (1992-)
Founded: 1474, 1583
F: *Arts; Law; Science; Economics and Business Administration; Medicine; Veterinary Medicine; Engineering.*
Ce: *Undergraduate (Medicine, Philosophy and Letters, Huesca); Undergraduate (Science, Philosophy and Letters, Logroño); Undergraduate (Science, Philosophy and Letters, Teruel); Business Administration; Engineering (Technical); Polytechnic; Nursing; Business Administration (Logroño); Business Administration (Pamplona); Education; Education (Huesca); Education (Logroño); Education (Pamplona); Education (Soria); Social Studies.*
I: *Educational Sciences; Languages.*

University of Seville
[Universidad de Sevilla]
Calle San Fernando 4, Sevilla
Tel: +34(5) 421-8600
Fax: +34(5) 421-1294
Telex: 72161
Rector: Manuel Medina Precioso (1992-)
F: *Philosophy and Education; Economics and Business Administration; Science; Law; Fine Arts;*

Medicine; Geography and History; Philology; Biology; Pharmacy; Physics; Mathematics; Chemistry; Geology (La Rábida).
Ce: Undergraduate; Business Administration; Architecture (Technical); Engineering (Technical); Nursing; Nursing (Huelva); Nursing (La Rábida); Engineering (Technical, La Rábida); Education; Education (Huelva).

University of Tarragona-Reus
[Universidad de Tarragona-Reus]
Tarragona-Reus
F: Letters; Chemistry; Law and Economics Sciences; Medicine and Health Sciences; Educational Sciences.
S: Engineering (Technical).
Ce: Oenology.

Polytechnic University of Valencia
[Universidad Politécnica de Valencia]
Camino de Vera s/n, 46071 Valencia
Tel: +34(6) 360-3600
Fax: +34(6) 360-4208
Telex: 62808 upva e
Rector: Justo Nieto Nieto (1989-94)
Secretario General: Luis Segura Gomis
Founded: 1968, 1971
S: Agriculture; Architecture; Civil Engineering; Industrial Engineering; Telecommunications.
F: Computer Science; Fine Arts.
I: Hydrology; Biomechanics; Education; Construction.
Ce: Architecture; Industrial Engineering (Technical); Industrial Engineering (Technical, Alcoy); Agricultural Engineering (Technical); Agricultural Engineering (Technical, Orihuela); Technical Studies; Computer Sciences; Topography and Public Works.

University of Valencia
[Universidad de Valencia]
Calle Nave 2, Valencia 3
Tel: +34(6) 321-7380
Fax: +34(6) 386-4117
Telex: 64298
Founded: 1500
F: Law; Physics; Science (Alicante); Medicine; Psychology; Philosophy and Education; Philosophy and Letters (Alicante); Economics and Business Administration; Geography and History; Philology; Chemistry; Mathematics; Biology; Pharmacy.
Ce: Undergraduate (Pharmacy, Law); Undergraduate (Castellón de la Plana); Business Administration; Physiotherapy; Nursing; Nursing (Castellón de la Plana); Education; Education (Castellón de la Plana); Education (Cheste).

*University of Valladolid
[Universidad de Valladolid]
Plaza Santa Cruz 8, 47002 Valladolid
Tel: +34(83) 423-000
Fax: +34(83) 423-234
Telex: 26357
Rector: F. Javier Alavarez Guisasola
Secretario General: Jesús María Palomares Ibañez
Founded: 1293
F: Law; Science; Arts and Philology; Medicine; Economics and Business Administration; Law; Food Science and Technology; Architecture; Industrial Engineering; Telecommunications Engineering.
Ce: Business Administration; Industrial Engineering (Technical); Nursing; Business Administration (Burgos); Industrial Engineering (Burgos); Agricultural Engineering (Palencia); Education; Education (Burgos); Education (Palencia); Agricultural Education (Soria); Social Affairs; Physiotherapy; Social Work.
I: Educational Sciences; Atmosphere Studies.

OTHER INSTITUTIONS

Academia Universitaria de Derecho
Burgos
Founded: 1956
Law.

Escuela Superior de Administración y Dirección de Empresas
Avenida de Pedralbes 60-62, 08034 Barcelona
Tel: +34(3) 203-7800
Founded: 1958
Administration and Business Management.

Escuela Superior de Relaciones Públicas
Barcelona
Founded: 1969
Public Relations.

Escuela Superior Empresarial Agrícola
Casillas s/n, Córdoba
Tel: +34(57) 296-133
Founded: 1964
Agricultural Management.

Estudios Universitarios y Tecnicos de Guipúzcoa
Paseo del Urumea, San Sebastián
Tel: +34(43) 273-100
Founded: 1956

Facultad de Ciencias Económicas y Empresariales
Paseo de Mundaiz s/n, 20012 San Sebastián
Tel: +34(43) 273-100
Founded: 1956
Economics and Business.

Instituto Católico de Artes e Industrias
Calle de Alberto Aguilera 23, Madrid 15
Arts and Industries.

Instituto Católico de Dirección de Empresas
23 Calle Alberto Aguilera, Madrid
Founded: 1960
Business Management.

Instituto Químico de Sarriá
Barcelona 17
Tel: +34(3) 203-8900
Founded: 1916
Chemistry.

NATIONAL ACADEMIC BODIES

Ministry of Education and Culture
[Ministerio de Educación y Ciencia]
Calle Alcalá 34, Madrid 14
Tel: +34(1) 532-1300
Fax: +34(1) 522-9256
Ministro: Gustavo Suarez Pertierra

Council of Universities
[Consejo de Universidades]
Ciudad Universitaria s/n, 28040 Madrid
Tel: +34(1) 449-7437
Founded: 1983

Conference of Rectors of State Universities
[Conferencia de Rectores de Universidades del Estado]
Universidad de Sevilla, San Fernanelo 4, 41071 Sevilla
Tel: +34(54) 422-1204
Fax: +34(54) 421-1204
Presidente: Javier Pérez-Royo

Section for the Recognition of Foreign Studies
[Sección de Convalidaciones de Estudios Extranjeros]
Ministerio de Educación y Ciencia, Calle Cartagena 83, Madrid 14
Tel: +34(1) 532-1300

Spanish National Commission for Cooperation with Unesco
[Comisión Nacional Española de Cooperación con la Unesco]
Escuela Diplomática, Paseo de Juan XXIII 5, 28040 Madrid
Tel: +34(1) 513-9639
Fax: +34(1) 535-1433
Presidente: D. Luís Ramallo
Secretario General: Manuel Benavides López-Escobar

SRI LANKA

UNIVERSITIES

Buddhist and Pali University of Sri Lanka
214 Bauddhaloka Mawatha, Colombo 7
Tel: +94(1) 580-609
Fax: +94(1) 580-610
Vice-Chancellor: Ven. Akuratiye Nanda (1994-)
Registrar: W.D. Tissera
Founded: 1982
Pali and Buddhist Studies.

Eastern University Chenkalady
Chenkalady
Tel: +94(65) 2473
Fax: +94(65) 2302
Cable: eastern university, chenkalady
Vice-Chancellor: S. Sandanam
Registrar: C. Nadarajah
Founded: 1981, 1986
F: Agriculture; Arts and Culture; Commerce and Management; Science.
Ut: English Language Teaching; Computer.

*University of Colombo
College House, P.O. Box 1490, Cumaratunga Munidasa Mawatha, Colombo 3
Tel: +94(1) 581-835
Fax: +94(1) 583-810
Telex: 22039
Cable: university
Vice-Chancellor: G.L. Peiris
Registrar: H.M.N. Warakaulle
Founded: 1921, 1942, 1972
F: Arts; Education; Graduate Studies; Law; Medicine; Sciences.
I: Computer Technology; Indigenous Medicine; Workers Education; Postgraduate Medicine.

INSTITUTE OF COMPUTER TECHNOLOGY
Founded: 1987
Computer Technology.

INSTITUTE OF INDIGENOUS MEDICINE
Bandaranayake Place, Rajagiriya
Founded: 1980
Indigenour Medicine.

INSTITUTE OF WORKERS' EDUCATION
Founded: 1980
Workers' Education.

POSTGRADUATE INSTITUTE OF MEDICINE
Founded: 1981
Medicine (postgraduate).

University of Jaffna
Thirunelvely, Jaffna
Tel: +94(21) 22481
Cable: university, jaffna
Vice-Chancellor: A. Thurairajah
Registrar: K. Parameswaran
Founded: 1974
F: Arts; Medicine; Science; Agriculture; Civil Engineering.

University of Kelaniya
Kelaniya
Tel: +94(1) 521-397
Cable: university, kelaniya, sri lanka
Vice-Chancellor: K. Dharmasena (1993-)
Registrar: N.B. Amarasinghe
Founded: 1959, 1972
F: Humanities; Medicine; Science; Social Sciences.
I: Aesthetic Studies; Archaeology (postgraduate); Pali and Buddhist Studies (postgraduate).

INSTITUTE OF AESTHETIC STUDIES
Founded: 1980
Aesthetic Studies.

POSTGRADUATE INSTITUTE OF PALI AND BUDDHIST STUDIES
Founded: 1980
Pali and Buddhist Studies (postgraduate).

POSTGRADUATE INSTITUTE OF ARCHAEOLOGY
Founded: 1986
Archaeology.

University of Moratuwa
Katubedda, Moratuwa
Tel: +94(1) 505-301
Fax: +94(1) 507-622
Cable: ceycoltec
Vice-Chancellor: G.T.F. de Silva
Registrar: K.C.F. Silva
Founded: 1966, 1972, 1978
F: Architecture; Engineering.

Open University of Sri Lanka
P.O. Box 21, Nawala, Nugegoda
Tel: +94(1) 853-777
Fax: +94(1) 436-858
E-Mail: postmast@ou.ac.lk
Cable: open university
Vice-Chancellor: D.S. Wijeyesekera
Registrar: N.W.S.W.S. de Silva
Founded: 1980
F: Humanities and Social Sciences; Engineering Technology; Natural Sciences.

University of Peradeniya
Peradeniya
Tel: +94(8) 88051
Fax: +94(8) 88151
Vice-Chancellor: J.M. Gunadasa
Registrar: D.M.W. Dissanayake
Founded: 1942, 1972, 1978
F: Agriculture; Arts; Dental Science; Engineering; Medicine; Science; Veterinary Science.
I: Agriculture (postgraduate).
Ut: Agricultural Education; English Language Teaching; Engineering Education; Medical Education; Science Education.

POSTGRADUATE INSTITUTE OF AGRICULTURE
Founded: 1980
Agriculture.

University of Ruhuna
Matara
Tel: +94(41) 2681
Fax: +94(41) 2683
Cable: university of ruhuna, sri lanka, matara
Vice-Chancellor: Niriellage Chandrasiri
Registrar: K.A. Ratnatilake
Founded: 1978, 1979, 1984
F: Agriculture; Humanities and Social Sciences; Medicine; Science.

University of Sri Jayewardenepura
Gangodawila, Nugegoda
Tel: +94(85) 2695
Fax: +94(85) 2604
Cable: unisjay sri lanka
Vice-Chancellor: W.B. Dorakumbura
Registrar: M. Abeywardene
Founded: 1959, 1972
F: Applied Science; Arts; Management Studies and Commerce; Medical Sciences.

POSTGRADUATE INSTITUTE OF MANAGEMENT
Founded: 1986
Management (postgraduate).

NATIONAL ACADEMIC BODIES

Ministry of Education, Higher Education and Cultural Affairs
Colombo 1a
Tel: +94(1) 564-809
Fax: +94(1) 565-889
Minister: The Hon. W.J.M. Lokubandara

Committee of Vice-Chancellors and Directors (CVCD)
c/o Open University of Sri Lanka, Nawala Road, Nugugoda
Tel: +94(55) 3615
Fax: +94(55) 463-858
Chairman: N. Chandrasiri, Vice-Chancellor, University of Ruhana

University Grants Commission
University of Peradeniya, 20 Ward Place, Colombo 7
Tel: +64(1) 595-301
Founded: 1978

Sri Lanka National Commission for Unesco
Ministry of Education, Higher Education and Cultura, Colombo 1
Tel: +94(1) 864-809
Fax: +94(1) 865-889
Chairman: The Hon. W.J.M. Lokubandara, Minister of Education, Higher Education and Culture
Secretary-General: Bogoda Appuhamilage Premaratne

SUDAN

UNIVERSITIES

Atbara University
[Jameat Atbara]
P.P.Box 1843, Khartoum
Tel: +249(11) 84149
Vice-Chancellor: Mohamed Elhassan Sinada (1993-)
F: Education; Engineering.

Bahr-Elghazal University
[Jameat Bahr Alghazal]
Waw Town
Vice Chancellor: Mossis Moshar (1991-)
President: Lotan Wool Wool
International Relations: Mossis Moshar
Founded: 1991
F: Education; Veterinary Sciences; Medicine; Pharmacy; griculture and Environmental Studies; Law; Economic and Social Studies.

Dongola University
[Jameat Dongola]
Khartoum
Tel: +249(11) 84214
Vice-Chancellor: Hassan El-Saori
Founded: 1990
F: Arts; Agriculture.

El-Azhari University
[Jameat El-Azhari]
Omdurman
Vice-Chancellor: Ahmed Abdel-Rahman El-Agib
Founded: 1993
F: Medicine and Health Sciences; Engineering and Industrial Technology; Food, Agriculture and Vital Technology; Education; Politics and Strategical Studies.

El-Dalang University
[Jameat El-Dalang]
El-Dalang
Tel: +249(11) 84214
Vice-Chancellor: Ibrahim Mukhtar (1993-)
Founded: 1990
F: Education.

El-Gadarif University
[Jameat El-Gadarif]
El-Gadarif
Tel: +249(11) 84214
Vice-Chancellor: Mohamed Bakheet Gailani (1994-)
Founded: 1990
F: Economics and Administration; Agriculture and Natural Resources.

El-Mahadi University
[Jameat El-Mahadi]
El-Mahadi
Tel: +249(11) 84204
Vice-Chancellor: Mohamed El Hassan Abu Shanab (1994-)
Founded: 1993

El-Nelien University, Khartoum
[Jameat El-Nelien]
P.O. Box 1055, Khartoum
Tel: +249(11) 80055
Vice-Chancellor: Ibraheem Elameen Hajar (1993-)
F: Arts; Law; Commerce; Sciences; Statistics.

El-Obied University
[Jameat El-Obied]
P.O. Box 517, El-Obied
Tel: +249(11) 2157
Telex: 600I
Vice-Chancellor: Al-Taj Fadlalla Abdel-Rahim (1994-)
International Relations: Al-Taj Fadlalla Abdel-Rahim
Founded: 1990
F: Medicine; Natural Resources.

High Institute for Banking Studies
[El-Maahad El-Ali Lerasat El-Masrafia]
Jama'A Street, Box 1880 Khartoum
Tel: +249(11) 70-564
Fax: 249(11) 80-913
Director: El-Hadi Abdel-Samad (1993-)
Founded: 1993
D: Research and Economics; Accounting; Computer; Management Studies; Law and Islamic Studies.

International University of Africa
[Jameat Africa Al-Alamia]
P.O. Box 2469, Khartoum
Tel: +249(11) 224430
Telex: 22706 badr
Vice-Chancellor: Mohamed Abdel-Rahim
Deputy Vice-Chancellor: Mahgoub Mohamed El-Hussain
Founded: 1986
F: Education and Humanities; Sharia and Islamic Studies; Pure and Applied Sciences.
S: Institute for Computer Sciences.
Ce: Research and Translation; Arabic Language; Islamic African.

*Omdurman Islamic University
P.O. Box 382, Omdurman
Tel: +249(11) 84355
Telex: sdo iufm 22527
Vice-Chancellor: Ali AhmedBabiker
Founded: 1912, 1924, 1965, 1975
F: Islamic Principles; Al-Dawa Al-Islamia; Sharia' and Law; Arts; Medicine and Health Sciences; Engineering and Education Sciences; Sciences; Arabic Language; Agriculture; Pharmacy; Postgraduate Studies and Scientific Research; Further Education.

Red Sea University
[Jameat Al-Bahar Al-Ahmar]
Port Sudan/Kassala
Tel: +249(11) 84-214
Vice-Chancellor: Mohamed Hassan Sinada
(1994-)
Founded: 1990
F: Marine and Fisheries; Engineering; Earth
Sciences; Sea Transport Studies.

Shandi University
[Jameat Shandi]
Shandi P.O. Box 1843, Khartoum
Tel: +249(11) 84214
Vice-Chancellor: Ali Abdel Rahman (1994-)
F: Medicine; Hygiene; Nursing; Sharia'and Law.

Sinar University
[Jameat Sinar]
Sinar
Tel: +249(11) 84214
Vice-Chancellor: Faisal Abdella Alhij (1993-)
Founded: 1993
F: Agriculture and Natural Resources.

Sudan University for Science and Technology
[Jameat El Sudan l'Leloom wal Technology]
P.O. Box 407, Khartoum
Tel: +249(11) 72508
Founded: 1950, 1967, 1975
F: Engineering; Education; Sciences;
Commerce; Physical Education; Agriculture;
Vocational Studies; Fine and Applied Arts;
Further Education; Music and Drama;
Radiography and Radiotherapy.

University of Gezira
P.O. Box 30, Wad Medani, 2667 Khartoum
Tel: +249(11) 72062
Telex: 22115
Vice-Chancellor: Mobarak Mohamed Ali El-
Magzoob (1994-)
Founded: 1975
F: Medical Sciences; Economics and Rural
Development; Pharmacy; Agriculture Sciences;
Animal Production; Education; Science and
Technology.
C: Agriculture and Natural Resources.

*University of Juba
P.O. Box 321/1, Juba
Tel: +249 451-351
Cable: Juvarsity Juba
Vice-Chancellor: Mohamed Ahmed Ali El Shiekh
Founded: 1975
Ce: Natural Resources; Social and
Environmental Studies; Medicine; Education;
Adult Education.

*University of Khartoum
[Jameat El-Khartoum]
P.O. Box 321, Khartoum
Vice-Chancellor: Hashim Mohamed Elhadi (1994-)
Founded: 1951, 1956

F: Agriculture; Arts; Economics and Social
Studies; Engineering and Architecture; Law;
Medicine; Pharmacy; Science; Veterinary
Science; Education; Hygiene; Postgraduate
Studies.
S: Extra Mural Studies; Mathematical.
Ce: African and Asian Studies; Development
Studies and Research Ce.

University of Quraan and Islamic Studies, Omdurman
[Jameat El-Quraan El-Kareem Wa El-Iloom
El-Islamia]
P.B. 1459, Omdurman
Tel: +249(11) 84612
Vice-Chancellor: Ahmed Ali El-Iman (1991-)
Founded: 1990
F: Holy Quraan; Sharia'and Law; Dawa and
Media; Arabic Language; Education Sciences.
C: Girls.

Upper Nile University
[Jameat Ali Alneel]
P.O. 1660, Khartoum
Tel: +249(11) 222174
Vice-Chancellor: Awad Abu-Zaid (1991-)
Founded: 1991
F: Natural Resources and Environmental
Studies; Medicine and Health Studies; Education;
Engineering and Technical Studies.

OTHER INSTITUTIONS

Africa University College
Alreiad Street No.12.P.O. Box 3493, Khartoum
Tel: +249(11) 224090
(1991-)
Founded: 1976
Div: Accounting and Management; Home
Economics and Social Development of Women.

Ahfad University College for Women
P.O. Box 167, Omdurman
Tel: +249(11) 53363
President: Yourif Badry (1966-)
Founded: 1966
S: Home Economics and Community Care;
Psychology and Infant Education; Medicine;
Administrative; Education and Rural
Development.

College of Aviation Sciences
Azhari Street Bahri P.O. Box, Khartoum
Tel: +249(11) 613-163
Telex: 24212 Satco Asd
Vice-Chancellor: Wageea-Alla Soliman Wageea-
Alla (1991-)
Secretary General: Mohammed Alsafy Hassan
Alzain
Founded: 1976
Aviation Studies; Commerce.

College of Medical Laboratory Sciences
P.O. Box 11081, Khartoum
Tel: +249(11) 78377
Director: Alsir Abu-Groon (1993-)
Founded: 1966
Medical Laboratory Sciences.

Computerman College for Computer Studies
P.O. Box 3173, Khartoum
Tel: +249(11) 40296
Telex: 24288
Rector: Abu-Bakr Mustafa Mohamed Khair (1991-)
Founded: 1991
Computer Engineering and Sciences.

East Nile College
[Koliat Shark Elmeel]
P.O. Box 1087, Omdurman
Tel: +249(11) 50631
Director: Altahi Mohamed Ali (1991-)
Secretary-General: Altigani Ahmed Abu Algasim
Founded: 1991
F: Education; Medicine and Health Sciences;
Engineering and Energy.

Elnasr Technical College
P.O. Box 744, Omdurman
Tel: +249(11) 54469
President: Mohamed Kamal Badr (1990-)
Founded: 1990
P: Commerce; Banking; Architecture; Building.

Institute of Optometry and Visual Science
P.O. Box 9007, Khartoum
Tel: +249(11) 73055
Director: Hashim Abdalla Mangail
Founded: 1954
Optometry and Visual Sciences.

Islamic Institution of Translation
Central P.O. Box 44755, Khartoum
Vice-Chancellor: Abdel-Hadi Tameem (1989-)
Founded: 1954
Translations.

Khartoum College for Applied Studies
P.O. Box 3887, Khartoum
Tel: +249(11) 223135
President: Abdalla Mohi-Aldeen Algenaid (1990-)
Academic Secretary: Mohamed Kamal Albakri
Founded: 1990
D: Architectural Drawing and Decoration;
Management.

Khartoum Nursing College
P.O. Box 1063, Khartoum
Tel: +249(11) 71812
Director: Ahmed Abdel Azeez (1992-)
Founded: 1956
Nursing.

Omdurman Alalia University College
P.O. Box 786, Omdurman
Vice Chancellor: Abdel Rahman Abuzeid (1986-)
International Relations: bdalla Kareem Aldeen
Founded: 1986

P: Administrative Sciences; Arabic Language;
Computer Studies; Documentation and Sciences;
English Language; Environmental Studies;
Executive Secretarial Studies; Mathematics and
Physics; Laboratory Techniques; Sudanese and
General Studies.
Ce: Design.

Sudan University College for Girls (SUC)
Building No.8 Block 17 P.O. Box 1176, Ryadh
Town Khartoum
Tel: +249(11) 224265
Fax: +249(11) 77844
Telex: 22657 VTCO SD
Director: Fadwa Abd El Rahman Ali Taha (1990-)
Founded: 1990
P: Business Administration; Language and
Translation; Computer Sciences; Nutrition and
Food Sciences; Economics and Social Sciences;
Mass Communication Media.

Wad Madani Ahlia College
P.O. Box 6, Wad Madani
Director: Ameen Mohamed Ahmed (1992-)
Founded: 1992
Home Economics; Business Administration.

NATIONAL ACADEMIC BODIES

Ministry of Higher Education and Research
P.O. Box 2081, Khartoum
Tel: +249(11) 79 312
Telex: 223-442
Minister: Ibrahim Ahmed Omer

National Council for Higher Education
P.O. Box 2081, Khartoum
Tel: +249(11) 79970
Fax: +249(11) 79312
President: Ibrahim Ahmed Omer (1989-)
Founded: 1972

National Council of Scientific Research
P.O. Box 2404, Khartoum
Tel: +249(11) 78513
Fax: +249(11) 24911
Telex: 22342 Elmisd
Cable: huhuts
President: Faisal Taj El Deen Abu Shama
Secretary-General: Soliman Gabir
Founded: 1970

Sudanese National Commission for Unesco
Ministry of Education 13, 17th Street, P.O. Box
2324, Khartoum East
Tel: +249(11) 79888
Fax: +249(11) 76030
Telex: 22051sd esm
Chairman: Ibrahim Ahmed Omer, Minister of
Education
Secretary-General: Mubarak Yahia Abass

SURINAME

UNIVERSITIES

University of Suriname
[Anton de Kom Universiteti van Suriname]
Leysweg 26, Paramaribo
Tel: +597 60410
Telex: Adekus 311 Sn
Cable: Unisur
Founded: 1968, 1983
F: Medicine; Social Sciences; Technology.

NATIONAL ACADEMIC BODIES

Ministry of Education, Science and Culture
P.O.Box 3017, Paramaribo
Tel: +597 61865
Minister: Gerard Hiwat

Suriname National Commission for Unesco
Ministry of Education, Science and Culture,
P.O.Box 3017, Paramaribo
Tel: +597 401-108
Fax: +597 495-083
Telex: 376 minow sn
Chairman: Gerard Hiwat, Minister of Education,
Science and Culture
Secretary-General: W. Wong Loi Sing

SWAZILAND

UNIVERSITIES

University of Swaziland
Private Bag 4, Kwaluseni
Tel: +268 84011
Fax: +268 85276
Telex: 2087 wd
Cable: uniswa, swaziland
Vice-Chancellor: Lydia P. Makhubu
Registrar: C.W.S. Sukati
Founded: 1976, 1982
*F: Agriculture; Education; Humanities; Science;
Social Science; Commerce.*
Ut: Social Studies Research.
I: Educational Research.

LUYENGO CAMPUS
P/Bag, Luyengo

NAZARENE TRAINING COLLEGE
P.O.Box 14, Manzini
Tel: +268 52211
Founded: 1933

NGWANE TRAINING COLLEGE
P.O.Box 474, Nhlangaro
Founded: 1982

WILLIAM PITCHER COLLEGE
P.O.Box 87, Manzini
Tel: +268 52081
Founded: 1962

OTHER INSTITUTIONS

Institute of Development Management
P.O.Box 1534, Mbabane
Founded: 1979
Development Management.

Institute of Health Sciences
P.O.Box 396, Mbabane
Tel: 22171
Founded: 1980
Health Sciences.

Lutheran Farmer Training Centre
P/Bag, Piggs Peak
Farming.

Mananga Agricultural Management Centre
P.O.Box 86, Tjaneni
Tel: +268 31133
Founded: 1972
Agricultural Management.

Mlalatini Development Centre
P.O.Box 547, Mbabane
Founded: 1970
Development Studies.

Nazarene Nursing College
P.O.14, Manzini
Tel: +268 52211
Founded: 1968
Nursing.

Swaziland College of Technology
P.O.Box 69, Mbabane
Tel: +268 42681
Founded: 1974
Technology.

**Swaziland Institute of Management and
Public Administration**
P.O.Box 495, Mbabane
Tel: +268 42981
Management; Public Administration.

NATIONAL ACADEMIC BODIES

Ministry of Education
P.O.Box 39, Mbabane
Tel: +268 42491
Fax: +268 43880
Minister: Prince Khuzulwandle Dlamini

Swaziland National Commission for Unesco
Ministry of Education, P.O.Box 39, Mbabane
Tel: +268 42491
Fax: +268 43880
Telex: 2293 wd
Chairman: Myekeni Vilakazi
Secretary-General: Dorothy Littler

SWEDEN

UNIVERSITIES AND UNIVERSITY INSTITUTIONS

Chalmers University of Technology Göteborg
[Chalmers tekniska högskola Göteborg]
41296 Göteborg
Tel: +46(31) 772-10-00
Fax: +46(31) 772-38-72
Telex: 2369 chalbib s
Rektor: Anders Sjöberg (1989-)
Administrativ chef: Stig Ekman
International Relations: Folke Hjalmers
Founded: 1829, 1937, 1994
S: Mathematics and Computing Sciences; Physics and Engineering Physics; Chemical Engineering; Electrical and Computer Engineering; Mechanical Engineering and Vehicle Engineering; Civil Engineering; Architecture; Technology Management and Economics; Environmental science.
C: Applied Engineering and Maritime Studies.

University of Göteborg
[Göteborgs universitet]
Vasaparken, 41124 Göteborg
Tel: +46(31) 773-10-00
Fax: +46(31) 773-46-60
Rektor: Jan Ling (1992-98)
Akadenisekreterare: Silas Gastsofsson
International Relations: Ingela Elofsson
Founded: 1891, 1954
F: Medicine; Odontology; Arts and Fine Arts; Social Sciences; Mathematics and Natural Sciences.

Linköping University
[Linköping Universitet]
581-83 Linköping
Tel: +46(13) 281-000
Fax: +46(13) 281-002
Telex: 509 66 unlin
Rektor: Sven Erlander (1983-)
Administrativ chef: Curt Karlsson
International Relations: Margareta Sandewall
Founded: 1967, 1970, 1975
F: Education; Humanities and Social Sciences; Health Sciences.
I: Tema Research; Technology.
Ce: Computer (National).
D: In-Service Education of Teaching Staff.

Luleå University
[Högskolan i Luleå]
Högskolområdet, Porsön, 97187 Luleå
Tel: +46(920) 91000
Fax: +46(920) 97288
Rektor: Ingegerd Palmér (1979-91)
Högskoledirektör: Staffan Sarbäck
International Relations: Harald Herbertssor
Founded: 1971, 1977
S: Engineering; Education; Music; Business.

*Lund University
[Lunds universitet]
Box 117, 221 00 Lund
Tel: +46(46) 107-000
Fax: +46(46) 104-720
Telex: 33533 luniver s
Rektor: Boel Flodgren (1992-98)
Universitetsdirektör: Peter Honeth
International Relations: Bengt Nilsson
Founded: 1666, 1977
F: Liberal Arts; Law; Medicine; Social and Political Sciences; Mathematics and Natural Sciences; Dentistry (Malmö); Technology and Engineering.
S: Education (Malmö); Music and Theatre (Malmö).
Ce: Women's Studies.
P: East and South-East Asian Studies; Middle East and North Africa Studies.
I: Human Rights and Humanitarian Law (Raoul Wallenberg); Economics and Management.
Committee: Habitat and Development Studies.
L: Electron Accelerator; Wallenberg (Medicine and Natural Sciences Research I.).

Karolinska Institute Stockholm
[Karolinska institutet Stockholm]
Solnavägen 1, 17177 Stockholm
Tel: +46(8) 7286400
Fax: +46(8) 318406
Cable: Karolinst
Rektor: Bengt Samuelsson (1983-)
Förvaltningschef: Lars Ekholm
International Relations: Marianne Svennilson
Founded: 1810, 1977
F: Medicine; Dentistry.
S: Physiotherapy; Speech Theraphy; Psychotherapy.

Royal Institute of Technology Stockholm
[Kungliga tekniska högskolan Stockholm]
100 44 Stockholm
Tel: (8) 790-60-00
Fax: (8) 790-65-00
Telex: 11421 kehs
Cable: technology
President: Janne Carlsson
Högskoledirektör (Registrar): Jan Nygren
International Relations: Lennart Johansson
Founded: 1827, 1876, 1977
S: Physics; Mechanical Engineering; Applied Mechanics and Vehicle Technology; Electrical Engineering; Civil Engineering; Chemical

Engineering; Metallurgy and Materials
Technology; Architecture; Surveying; Computer
Sciences and Engineering.
I: Microelectronics; Optical Research;
Production Engineering Research; Technical
Audiology.
Ce: Design and Production Technology;
Computional Mathematics and Mechanics
(C2M2); Consortium for Materials Technology/
Oxidic Overlayers; Environmental Sciences;
Electric Power Research; International Technical
and Educational Co-ooperation (CITEC).
L: Computer Vision Graphics.

Stockholm Institute of Education
[Lärarhögskolan i Stockholm]
Box 34 103, 100 26 Stockholm
Tel: +46(08) 737-5500
Fax: +46(08) 737-5501
Rektor: Bengt Börjeson
Administrativ chef: Borgit Ahlberg
International Relations: Conny Andersson
Founded: 1956
*Education; Physical Education; Nursing; Music;
Art.*

Stockholm School of Economics
[Handelshögskolan i Stockholm]
Sveavägen 65, Box 6501, 113 83 Stockholm
Tel: +46(8) 736-90-00
Fax: +46(8) 318-186
E-Mail: admbmf@hhs.bitnet
Telex: 16514
Cable: Schoolecon
President: Staffan Burenstam Linder (1986-)
Administrativ chef: Per-Jonas Eliaeson
Founded: 1909
D: Economics; Business Administration;
Finance; International Economics and Geography;
Law; Economic Statistics; Finance.
Ut: Professional Communication Skills.
I: Economic Research; International Business;
Management of Innovation and Technology;
Soviet and East European Economics; Japanese
Studies.

*Stockholm University
[Stockholms universitet]
Universitetsvägen 10, 106 91 Stockholm
Tel: +46(8) 162-000
Fax: +46(8) 153-693
Telex: 8105199 univers
Cable: university Stockholm
Rektor: Gustaf Lindencrona (1994-)
Universitetsdirektör: Leif Lindfors
International Relations: Jonas Engberg
Founded: 1878, 1977
F: Humanities; Law; Social Sciences; Natural
Sciences.
Ce: Baltic Studies; Study of Child Culture;
Research in International Migration and Ethnic
Relations; Women Research Workers; Pacific
Asia Studies; Marine Research; Research on
Bilingualism.

I: English-Speaking Students; Latin American
Studies; Social Research; Interpretation and
Translation Studies.
Ut: Sign Language Interpretation.
L: Wallenberg (Environmental Chemistry,
Organic Chemistry, Genetic and Cellular
Toxicology).

Swedish University of Agricultural Sciences
[Sveriges lantbruksuniversitet]
750 07 Uppsala
Tel: +46(18) 671-000
Fax: +46(18) 300-337
Telex: 76949 agruni s
Rektor: Thomas Rosswall (1994-2000)
Universitetsdirektör: Asa Elfström
F: Agriculture; Forestry; Veterinary Medicine.
I: Veterinary Medicine.

Umeå University
[Umeå universitet]
901-87, Umeå
Tel: +46(90) 165-000
Fax: +46(90) 165-488
Telex: 54005 univume
Rektor: Sigbrit Franke-Wikberg (1992-98)
Universitetsdirektör: Rune Axelsson
International Relations: Ake G. Svensson
Founded: 1965
F: Dentistry; Medicine; Mathematics and Natural
Sciences; Social Sciences; Arts.
Sec: Education.
D: Population Studies.
Ce: Interdisciplinary Studies; Marine Research
Ce.; Women's Studies; Environmental Science;
Computer.

*Uppsala University
[Uppsala universitet]
P.O. Box 256, 751 05 Uppsala
Tel: +46(18) 182-500
Fax: +46(18) 182-000
E-Mail: j.andersson@uadm.uu.se
Telex: 76024 univups s
Rektor: Stig Strömholm (1989-95)
Universitetsdirektör: Johnny Andersson
International Relations: Lars Fransson
Founded: 1477, 1595
F: Theology; Law; Medicine; Pharmacy; Arts;
Social Sciences; Science and Technology.
S: Teacher Training; Domestic Sciences.

OTHER INSTITUTIONS

Danshögskolan
Box 27043, 102 51 Stockholm
Tel: +46(8) 666-3600
Fax: +46(8) 667-7963
Rektor: Lena Malmsjä (1976-96)
Administrativ chef: Gunnel Gustafsson
International Relations: Gun Román
Founded: 1963
Dance.

Dramatiska Institutet
Box 27090, 102 51 Stockholm
Tel: +46(8) 665-1300
Fax: +46(8) 662-1484
Rektor: Kjell Greda (1992-97)
Administrativ chef: Staffan Sjöberg
International Relations: Eva Steneby
Drama.

Grafiska institutet och Institutet för högre kommunikations-och reklamutbildning
Box 27094, 102 51 Stockholm
Tel: +46(8) 783-2720
Fax: +46(8) 783-2721
Rektor: Chirs Ottander
International Relations: Chris Ottander
Communication Studies (graduate).

Högskolan i Borås
Box 874, 501 15 Borås
Tel: +46(33) 164-000
Fax: +46(33) 164-003
E-Mail: int.office@hb.se
Rektor: Anders Fransson (1990-95)
Administrativ chef: Ulf Grahm
International Relations: Larin Linde
S: Library and Information Science.
D: Business Administration and Computer Science; Education; Engineering Sciences; Textiles and Clothing.

University College of Falun/Borlänge
[Högskolan i Falun/Borlänge]
Box 1992, 79119 Falun
Tel: +46(23) 54500
International Relations: Bengt Nybelius

Högskolan i Gävle/Sandviken
Box 1992, 79119 Gävle
Tel: +46(26) 648-500
Fax: +46(26) 648-686
Rektor: irgitta Stymne Administrativ chef: Lars Hansson
International Relations: Kristina Haesert
Founded: 1977
D: Technology; Mathematics, Natural Sciences and Computer Sciences; Business Administration; Humanities and Social Sciences; Teacher Training.

Högskolan på Gotland
Cramégatan 3, 62157 Visby
Tel: +46(498) 299-900
Fax: +46(498) 299-962
Rektor: Lars Magnus Lahne
International Relations: Caroline Nygren
Founded: 1988

Högskolan i Halmstad
Box 823, 30118 Halmstad
Tel: +46(35) 153-100
Fax: +46(35) 186-192
E-Mail: sven-ove johansser@re.hh.se
Rektor: Sven-Ove Johanssen (1993-95)
Administrativ chef: Jan Arvidsson
International Relations: Bengt Dahlqvist
Founded: 1983

Högskolan i Jönköping
Box 1026, 551 11 Jönköping
Tel: +46(36) 157-700
Fax: +46(36) 157-718
E-Mail: info@hj.se
Rektor: Clas Wahlbin (1994-)
International Relations: Johan Wiklund
Founded: 1977
S: International Business; Engineering; Education and Communication.

Högskolan i Kalmar
Box 905, 391 29 Kalmar
Tel: +46(480) 446-000
Fax: +46(480) 18298
Rektor: Dan Isacson (1977-95)
International Relations: Kristina Albertsson
Founded: 1977
Tourism and Business Administration; Teacher Training; Communication and Media Studies; Engineering; Arts; Interdisciplinary Study in Science; Maritime Studies; Further Education for Journalists.

Högskolan i Karlskrona/Ronneby
Box 37179, Karlskrona
Tel: +46(455) 78000
Fax: +46(455) 78097
Rektor: Per Eriksson (1989-95)
Administrativ chef: Sven-Ove Nilsson
International Relations: Göran Christenson
Founded: 1989
D: Mechanical Engineering; Telecommunications and Mathematics; Humanities; Physical Planning and Building Construction; Signal Processing (Ronnely); Computer Science and Business Administration (Ronnely).

Högskolan i Karlstad
Box 9501, 650 09 Karlstad
Tel: +46(54) 838-000
Fax: +46(54) 838-450
Rektor: Christina Ullenius (1977-94)
Administrativ chef: Bo-Hidén
International Relations: Michael Cooper
D: Humanities; Social Sciences; Education and Psychology; Economics and Business Studies; Mathematics, Statistics and Computer Science; Natural Sciences; Engineering and Technology.
Ce: Service Research.

Högskolan i Kristianstad
Box 59, 291 21 Kristianstad
Tel: +46(44) 183-000
Fax: +46(44) 12965
E-Mail: eva.anderssos@info.hkn.se
Rektor: Kaj Björk (1977-94)
Administrativ chef: Lars Lindahl
International Relations: Eva Andersson
D: Business Administration; Education; Humanities and Social Sciences; Mathematics and Natural Sciences; Technology.

Högskolan i Örebro
Box 923, 701 30 Örebro
Tel: +46(19) 301-000
Fax: +46(19) 301-465
E-Mail: registrator@hoe.se
Rektor: Ingemar Lind
International Relations: Caroline Runéus
D: Humanities; Social Sciences; Business
Administration, Computer Science, Economics
and Statistics; Teacher Training; Sport and
Health; Technology and Natural Science; Music
Education; Domestic Science.

Högskolan i Skövde
Box 408, 541 28 Skövde
Tel: +46(500) 464-600
Fax: +46(500) 416-325
E-Mail: magnus.karlsson@sta.his.se
Rektor: Lars-Erich Johansson (1986-94)
Administrativ chef: Ted Hullberg
International Relations: Magnus Karlsson
Founded: 1977
D: Business Economics and Statistics;
Technology; Computer Science; Languages; Art
and the Media.

Högskolan i Trollhättan/Uddevalla
Box 936, 46129 Trollhättan
Tel: +46(520) 475-000
Fax: +46(520) 475-199
Rektor: Olof Blomqvist
Administrativ chef: Rolf Johansson
International Relations: Bodd Järnerot
Founded: 1990
D: Technology; Economics and Computer
Science; Education and Humanities.

Högskolan i Växjö
Box 35195, Växjö
Tel: +46(470) 68500
Fax: +46(470) 83217
Telex: 52301 hivsfc s
Rektor: Hans Wieslander
International Relations: John Glarner

Konstfack
Box 27116, 102 52 Stockholm
Tel: +46(8) 450-4100
Fax: +46(8) 783-0563
Rektor: Inez Svensson (1990-)
Administrativ chef: Bertil Metzger
International Relations: Isa Kling
Arts, Crafs and Design.

Kungliga Konsthögskolan
Box 16317, Stockholm
Tel: +46(8) 614-4000
Fax: +46(8) 211-399
Rektor: Olle Kåks (1987-99)
Administrativ chef: Eva Borgström
International Relations: Björn Bergman
Founded: 1735
Painting; Sculpture; Graphic Arts; Video;
Architecture.

Kungliga Musikhögskolan
Valhallavägen 103-109, P.O. Box 27711, 115 91
Stockholm
Tel: +46(8) 161-800
Fax: +46(8) 664-1424
Rektor: Göran Malmgren
International Relations: Claes Pehrsson
Music.

Mälardalens Högskola
Box 883, 72123 Västerås
Tel: +46(21) 101-300
Fax: +46(21) 101-440
E-Mail: goeran.huss@mdh.se
Rektor: Lillemor Kim (1985-95)
Administrativ chef: Gunnel Gustafsson
International Relations: Göran Huss
Founded: 1977
TD; Economics and Administrative Data
Processing; Systems and Electric Engineering
and Electrotechnology; Energy; Humanities;
Mechanical Engineering; Real-Time Computer
Systems.

Mitthögskolan
Box 85170, Sundsvall
Tel: +46(60) 188-600
Fax: +46(60) 188-700
E-Mail: kaari marklund
Rektor: Kari Marklund (1994-)
Administritiv chef: Lars Gunnar Nilsson
International Relations: Agneta Liljesham-Cerruta
Founded: 1977
D: Media and Communication; Social Sciences;
Science and Engineering; Science and
Engineering (Härnäsand); Engineering
(Härnäsand); Natural and Social Sciences;
Behavioural Sciences; Humanities and Liberal
Arts; Social Sciences (Östessund); Social Work
(Östessund); Tourism (Östessund); Informatics
(Östessund); Science and Engineering
(Östessund).

Operahögskolan i Stockholm
Strandvägen 82, 115 27 Stockholm
Tel: +46(8) 144-785
Fax: +46(8) 667-0050
Rektor: Jonny Blanc (1994-)
International Relations: Erik Ljungqvist
Opera.

Teaterhögskolan i Stockholm
Box 20044, 104 60 Stockholm
Tel: +46(8) 641-2160
Fax: +46(8) 702-9580
Rektor: Fred Hjelm (1994-)
Administrativ chef: Benny Jonsson
International Relations: Brigitta Prejborn
Founded: 1787
Theatre Studies.

NATIONAL ACADEMIC BODIES

Office of the University Chanceller
[Kanslersämbetet]
Box 7575, 10393 Stockholm
Tel: +46(8) 453-4210
Fax: +46(8) 453-4230
Universitetskansler: Stig Hagström

Swedish Rectors' Conference (SAR)
Uppsala universitet, Box256, 75105 Uppsala
Tel: +46(18) 182-500
Fax: +46(18) 181-640
Cable: univups-s76024
Ordförande (Chairman): Stig Strömholm
General-Sekreterare: Lennart Ståhle
Founded: 1966

National Agency for Higher Education
[Verket för högskoleservice (VHS)]
Box 7851, 10399, tockholm
Tel: +46(8) 453-5000
Fax: +46(8) 453-5050
Chancellor: Anitra Steen (1992-)
International Relations: Torsten Kälvemark

National Academic Recognition Information Centre
National Agency for Higher Education, P.O. Box 7851, 10399 Stockholm
Tel: +46(8) 453-5000
Fax: +46(8) 453-5140
E-Mail: marianne.hildebrand@vhs.se

Swedish Institute
[Svenska institutet]
Hamngalan 27, P.O. Box 7434, S-10391 Stockholm
Tel: +46(8) 789-2000
Fax: +46(8) 207-248
Telex: 10025
Cable: swedins
Direktör: Per Sörbom (1993-98)
Administrativ chef: Mats Backström
Founded: 1945

Swedish National Commission for Unesco
Ministry of Education and Cultural Affairs, Drottninggatan, 16 103 33 Stockholm
Tel: +46(8) 763-1000
Fax: +46(8) 723-1192
Cable: unescosweden stockholm
Chairman: Göran Lövdahl
Secretary-General: Anders Falk

SWITZERLAND

UNIVERSITIES AND TECHNICAL UNIVERSITIES

University of Basle
[Universität Basel]
Petersplatz 1, 4003 Basel
Tel: +41(61) 267-31-11
Fax: +41(61) 267-30-35
Rektor: Luzius Wildhaber (1992-94)
Leiter der Universitätsverwaltung: Mathias Stauffacher
Founded: 1460
F: *Protestan Theology; Law; Medicine; Philosophy and History; Philosophy and Natural Sciences.*
I: *Physical Education; Remedial Education and Psychology; Tropical Medicine; Gerontology.*
Ce: *Computer.*

University of Berne
[Universität Bern]
Hochschulstrasse 4, 3012 Bern
Tel: +41(31) 631-82-54
Fax: +41(31) 631-39-39
Rektor: Andreas Ludi (1991-95)
Secretary-General: Peter Mürner
Founded: 1528, 1834
F: *Protestant Theology; Catholic Theology; Law and Economics; Medicine; Veterinary Medicine; Philosophy; Science.*
S: *Teacher Training.*

University of Fribourg
[Université de Fribourg]
Miséricorde, 1700 Fribourg
Tel: +41(37) 21-92-31
Fax: +41(37) 21-97-03
Recteur: Hans Meier (1991-95)
Dierstchef: Fernand Python
Founded: 1889
F: *Catholic Theology; Law, Social Sciences, and Economics; Letters; Sciences.*
I: *Moral Theology; Pastoral Theology; Oecumenical Studies; Missiology; Economics and Social Sciences; Automation Research; Ecclesiastical Law; Social and Political Sciences (International); Education; Orthopaedic Education; Physical Education; Psychology; Eastern European Studies; Mediaeval Studies; Journalism and Social Communication; English; French; German.*

*University of Geneva
[Université de Genève]
24, rue du Général-Dufourt, 1211 Genève 4
Tel: +41(22) 705-71-11
Fax: +41(22) 320-29-27
E-Mail: INTERNET:(unige.ch)
Telex: unich 423801
Recteur: Luc Weber (1991-95)
Directeur administratif: Daniel Collet
Secrétaire général: André Vifian
Founded: 1559, 1873

F: Science; Letters; Economics and Social Sciences; Law; Medicine; Protestant Theology; Psychology and Education.
S: Architecture; Translation and Interpretation; Physical Education; French Language and Culture.
I: International Studies; Oecumenical Studies; European Studies; Development Studies; Reformation History; Numeric Research in Material Physics (Romand).
Ce: Ancient Near Eastern Studies; Computer Sciences; Human Ecology and Environmental Sciences; Energy Studies; Industrial Medicine Ecology.
A: The Environment.
University for Mature Students.

*Federal Institute of Technology of Lausanne

[École polytechnique fédérale de Lausanne]
Les Terrasses 15, CE (Ecublens), 1015 Lausanne
Tel: +41(21) 693-21-01
Fax: +41(21) 693-21-24
Telex: 454478 epfv ch
Cable: epfl
Président: Jean-Claude Baeloux (1994-2000)
Directeur administratif: Pierre Immer
Founded: 1853, 1890, 1946, 1969
D: Rural Engineering; Civil Engineering; Mechanical Engineering; Microtechnics; Physics; Electrical Engineering; Computer Science; Chemistry; Mathematics; Architecture; Materials Testing; Special Mathematics; Education and Didactics.
I: Metallurgy; Microscopy Electronics.
Ce: Language; Plasma Research; Computer.

*University of Lausanne

[Université de Lausanne]
Dorigny, 1015 Lausanne
Tel: +41(21) 692-42-50
Fax: +41(21) 692-42-44
Telex: 455110 Unil
Recteur: Eric Junod (1995-99)
Directeur administratif: Jean-Paul Dépraz
Founded: 1537, 1890
F: Protestant Theology; Law; Medicine; Letters; Science; Political and Social Sciences.
S: Commercial Studies; Modern French; Pharmacy.
I: Criminology and Police Science; Public Administration.

University of Lucerne

[Hochschule Luzern]
Pfistergasse 20, Postfach 7967, 6000 Luzern 7
Tel: +41(41) 24-55-10
Fax: +41(41) 24-55-05
Rektor: Hans Jürgen Münk (1994-95)
Administrator: Marhus Vogler
Founded: 1970, 1993
F: Theology; Humanities.

University of Neuchâtel

[Université de Neuchâtel]
Avenue du Ier-Mars 26, 2000 Neuchâtel
Tel: +41(38) 25-38-51
Fax: +41(38) 25-18-32
Recteur: Denis Maillat (1991-95)
Secrétaire général: Pierre Barraud
Founded: 1838, 1909
F: Letters; Science; Law and Economics; Protestant Theology.
I: Sociology and Political Science; Ethnology; History; Physics; Botany; Geography; Zoology; Geology; Chemistry; Microtechnology; Structural Metallurgy; Mathematics; Theology Research; Linguistics.
Ce: Applied Linguistics; Hydrogeology; Franco-Swiss Studies; Dialectology and the Study of Regional French; Semiological Research; Computer.
L: Language and Spoken Word Processing.
University for Mature Students.

University of St. Gallen for Business Administration, Economics, Law and Social Sciences

[Hochschule St. Gallen für Wirtschafts-, Rechts- und Sozialwissenschaften]
Dufourstrasse 50, 9000 St. Gallen
Tel: +41(71) 30-21-11
Fax: +41(71) 22-83-55
E-Mail: Eugsterli
Rektor: Georges Fischer (1994-97)
Verwaltungsdirektor: Hans-Ruedi Troxler
Founded: 1898
D: Business Administration; Economics and Economic Geography; Law; Cultural Sciences.
Ce: Futurology.

*Swiss Federal Institute of Technology +Eidgenössische Technische Hochschule Zürich +École polytechnique fédérale Zurich +Politecnico federale Svizzero Zurigo

Rämistrasse 101, ETH-Zentrum, 8092 Zürich
Tel: +41(1) 256-20-57
Fax: +41(1) 262-10-05
Telex: 816 039 pdeth ch
Präsident: Jakob Nüesch (1994-95)
Rektor: Hans von Gunten
Generalsekretär: Peter Kottusch
Founded: 1855
D: Architecture; Civil Engineering; Mechanical Engineering; Electrical Engineering; Computer Sciences; Materials Science; Chemistry; Industrial and Production Engineering; Pharmacy; Forestry; Agriculture; Rural Engineering and Surveying; Mathematics and Physics; Environmental Sciences; Earth Sciences; Training of Physical Education and Sports Teachers; Humanities and Social Sciences.
I: Paul Scherrer (Würenlingen, Villigen); Forest, Snow and Landscape Research (Birmensdorf);

Water Resources and Water Pollution Control
(Dübendorf).
L: Materials Testing and Research (Dübendorf).

*University of Zürich
[Universität Zürich]
Rämistrasse 71, 8006 Zürich
Tel: +41(1) 257-11-11
Fax: +41(1) 257-23-04
Telex: uniz ch 817260
Rektor: Hans Heinrich Schmid (1992-96)
Universitätssekretär: Hanspeter Meister
Founded: 1523, 1833
F: Protestant Theology; Law; Medicine;
Veterinary Medicine; Philosophy I (Letters);
Philosophy II (Sciences); Economics.
University for Mature Students.

NATIONAL ACADEMIC BODIES

Federal Office of Education and Science
[Bundesamt für Bildung und Wissenschaft/Office
fédéral de l'Education et de la Science]
Postfach 5675, Wildhainweg 9, 3001 Bern
Tel: +41(31) 322-96-91
Fax: +41(31) 322-78-54
Direktor: Gerhard Schuwey

Group for Science and Research
[Gruppe für Wissenschaft und Forschung/
Groupement de la Science et de la Recherche]
Inselgasse 1, 3003 Bern
Tel: +41(31) 322-68-99
Fax: +41(31) 322-64-92
Direktor: Heinrich Ursprung

Central Office of the Swiss Universities
[Schweizerische Zentralstelle für
Hochschulwesen/Office central universitaire
Suisse]
Seidenweg 68, 3012 Bern
Tel: +41(31) 302-23-50
Fax: +41(31) 302-68-11
Director: Rudolf Nägeli
Founded: 1920

Swiss Rectors' Conference
[Schweizerische Hochschulrektorenkonferenz/
Conférence des Recteurs des Universités
Suisses]
Seidenweg 68, 3012 Bern
Tel: +41(31) 302-83-41
Fax: +41(31) 302-68-11
President: Luc Weber
Secretary-General: Rudolf Naegell
Founded: 1904

National Union of Swiss Students
[Verband der Schweizerischen
Studentinnenschaften (VSS)/Union nationale des
étudiant/es de Suisse (UNES)]
Schanzenstrasse 1, 3008 Bern
Tel: +41(31) 382-11-71
Fax: +41(31) 382-11-76
Präsident: Gallus Rieger

Society of Swiss Students
[Schweizerischer Studentenverein (StV)/Société
des étudiants Suisses (SES)]
Alte Simplonstrasse 10, 3900 Brig
Tel: +41(28) 23-62-00
Fax: +41(28) 23-62-00

Swiss Association of University Professors
[Vereinigung Schweizerisher Hochschuldozenten
(VSH)/Association Suisse des Professeurs
d'Universités (APU)]
Altwiesenstrasse 1, 8116 Wurenlos
Tel: +41(31) 257-37-11
Fax: +41(31) 364-03-66
Präsidentin: Heidi Schelbert-Syfrig

Swiss National Fund for Scientific Research
[Schweizerischer Nationalfonds zur Förderung
der wissenschaftlichen Forschung/Fond national
Suisse de la Recherche scientifique]
Wildhainweg 20, Postfach 8232, 3001 Bern
Tel: +41(31) 308-22-22
Fax: +41(31) 301-30-09
Generalsekretär: Hans Peter Hertig

Swiss University Conference
[Schweizerische Hochschulkonferenz (SHK)/
Conférence universitaire Suisse (CUS)]
Wildhainweg 21, 3012 Bern
Tel: +41(31) 302-55-33
Fax: +41(31) 302-17-92
Chairman: Hans Rudolf Striebel
Secretary-General: Nivardo Ischi

Swiss National Commission for Unesco
[Commission nationale Suisse pour l' Unesco]
Département fédéral des Affaires étrangères,
Gutenbergstrasse 44, 3003 Bern
Tel: +41(31) 322-65-50
Fax: +41(31) 322-33-11
Telex: 911440
Cable: affetra berne pour commission unesco
Présidente: Doris Morf
Secrtaire général: Berhard Theurillat

SYRIA

UNIVERSITIES

Higher Institute of Political Sciences
Al-Tall, Damascus
Tel: +963 741110
Rector: Majed Shaddoud (1991-)
Senior Administrative Officer: Omar Al-Abdallah
International Relations: Omar Al-Abdallah
Founded: 1976
Political Studies; International Relations;
Economics and Administration.

University of Aleppo
[Gami't Alep]
Aleppo
Tel: +963(21) 236130
Fax: +963(21) 229148
Telex: aluniv 331018 sy
President: Mohammed Ali Hourie (1979-)
Vice-President: Abdul Rahman Ibrik
International Relations: Vice-President, Tajeddin Dia
Founded: 1946, 1960
F: Medicine; Economics; Letters; Agriculture I; Agriculture II; Science; Dentistry; Law; Civil Engineering; Architecture; Mechanical Engineering; Electrical Engineering.
I: History of Arabic Science.
Ce: Agriculture Research; Computer; Languages (English, French, Russian, Spanish, German, Arabic); Audio-visual.
S: Nursing.
Ut: Professional Work (Engineering, Chemistry, Physics, Agriculture, and Economics).

*Al-Baath University
[Gami't Alba'ath]
P.O. Box 77, Homs
Tel: +963(31) 431440
Fax: +963(31) 431847
Telex: 441133
President: Abdul Majid Sheikh Hussein (1979-)
Secretary-General: Kassem Hammoud
Founded: 1979
F: Arts and Humanities; Dentistry; Veterinary Medicine; Science; Chemical and Petroleum Engineering; Civil Engineering and Architecture; Architecture; Agriculture.

*University of Damascus
[Gami't Dimašq]
Damascus
Tel: +963(11) 215100
Fax: +963(11) 236010
Telex: hamak 411971
President: Abdul-Ghani Maa Bared (1994-)
Secretary-General: Fayez Tubaji
International Relations: Abbass Sondouk
Founded: 1903, 1923
F: Letters; Law; Economics and Commerce; Science; Medicine; Dentistry; Pharmacy; Civil Engineering; Mechanical and Electrical Engineering; Education; Islamic Studies; Fine Arts; Agriculture; Architecture.
S: Nursing.

Tishreen University
[Gami't Tichreen]
P.O. Box 2230, Lattakia
Tel: +963 416311
Fax: +963 418504
Telex: tiuniv 451084 sy
Founded: 1971, 1976
F: Sciences; Agriculture; Arts and Humanities; Civil Engineering; Electrical and Mechanical

Engineering; Medicine; Dentistry; Architecture; Economics; Pharmacy.
I: Agriculture; Engineering; Medicine; Commerce; Languages.
Ce: Marine Research; Computer.
S: Nursing.

NATIONAL ACADEMIC BODIES

Ministry of Higher Education
P.O. Box 9355, Damascus
Tel: +963(11) 330-700
Fax: +963(11) 332-7719
Telex: 412170 mhe sy
Minister: Saliha Sounkor (1992-)
Executive Director: Mouafak Jalanbo
International Relations: Dalal Al-Shatti

Council of Higher Education
P.O. Box 9355, Damascus
Tel: +963(11) 223-9298
Fax: +963(11) 223-9298
Secretary-General: Badih Kaaied (1989-)
Founded: 1975

Syrian National Commission for Unesco
Ministry of Education, P.O. Box 9355, Damascus
Tel: +963(11) 44-702
Fax: +963(11) 420-435
Telex: 412-559
Chairman: Mohamed Ghassan Halabi, Minister of Education
Secretary-General: Hassan Al-Hamwi

TAIWAN

UNIVERSITIES AND COLLEGES

PUBLIC INSTITUTIONS

National Central University
38, Wu Chuan Li, Chung-Li, Taoyuan 32054
Tel: +866(3) 422-7151
Founded: 1968
C: Liberal Arts; Science; Engineering.
S: Management.
Ce: Space and Remote Sensing Research; Computer.

National Cheng Kung University
1, Ta-Hsueh Road, Tainan 70101
Tel: +886(6) 275-7575
Fax: +886(6) 236-8660
President: Jer Ru Maa
Founded: 1931, 1971
C: Liberal Arts; Sciences; Engineering; Management; Medicine.
S: Vocational Technical (evening courses); Evening.

National Chengchi University
64, Chih-Nan road, Sec. 2, Taipei 11623
Tel: +886(2) 939-3091
Fax: +886(2) 939-8043
Cable: Nccu
President: King-Yuh Chang
Founded: 1927, 1929, 1945
I: International Relations.
C: Foreign Languages.
*Ce: Law; Liberal Arts and Science; Commerce;
Public and Business Administration;
Communication Studies; Computer; Foreign
Language; Election Study.*

National Chiao Tung University-College
1001, Ta-Hsueh Road, Hsinchu 30050
Tel: +886(35) 712-121
Fax: +886(35) 714-031
Cable: Chiaota Hsinchu
Founded: 1957, 1967
*I: Electronics; Management Science; Computer
Sciences; Transport Engineering; Applied
Mathematics.*

National Chung-Cheng University
160, San Hsing, Ming Hsiung, Chia Yi 62117
Tel: +886(5) 272-0411
Fax: +886(5) 272-0400
E-Mail: username@ccunix.ccu.edu.tw
President: Ching-Jiang Lin
Founded: 1989
*C: Liberal Arts; Science; Social Sciences;
Engineering; Management.*
*Ce: Language and Literature (Research);
History and Culture (Research); Social
Development (Researchy Systems, Equality of
Education Opportunity); Cognitive Science
(Research); Automation; Environmental
Technology (Research).*

National Chung Hsing University, Taichung
250, Kuokuang Road, Taichung 40227
Tel: +886(42) 287-3181
Fax: +886(42) 873-702
Cable: 6593 taichung, taiwan
Founded: 1919, 1961
*C: Agriculture; Law and Commerce; Science
and Engineering; Liberal Arts.*
*S: Law and Commerce (Evening); Liberal Arts
and Business Administration (Evening).*
*Ce: Data Processing (Taipei); Audio-visual;
Computer.*

National Chung Hsing University, Taipei
69, Chien Kuo North Rd., Sec. 2, Taipei 10489
Tel: +886(2) 502-1520
Founded: 1919

National College of Physical Education
250, Wen Hua 1st Road, Kweishan, Taoyuan
Tel: +886(3) 328-3201
Founded: 1987
Physical Education.

National Open University
172, Chung Cheng Road, Lu Chow, Taipei 24702
Tel: +886(2) 282-9355
Founded: 1966
*D: Business; Humanities; Social Sciences;
Production and Programming.*

National Taiwan Normal University
162, East Hoping Road, Section 1, Taipei 10610
Tel: +886(2) 362-5101
Fax: +886(2) 392-2784
President: Shangyung Liang (1984-)
Secretary-General: Hsiping Wang
Founded: 1946, 1955
*C: Education; Arts; Science; Fine and Applied
Arts.*
Ce: In-service Teachers' Education.
D: Extension.

National Taiwan University
1, Roosevelt Road, Sec. 4, Taipei 10764
Tel: +886(2) 363-0231
President: Wei-jao Chen
Founded: 1945
*C: Liberal Arts; Science; Law; Medicine;
Engineering; Agriculture.*
Ce: Computer; Language.
Evening D.

National Tsing Hua University
101, Kuang-Fu Road, Sec. 2, Hsinchu 30043
Tel: +886(35) 715-130
Fax: +886(35) 710-776
Cable: tsinghua
Founded: 1911, 1925, 1955
*C: Science; Engineering; Nuclear Science;
Humanities and Social Sciences.*
I: Linguistics.
Ce: Computer.

National Institute of the Arts
1, Hsueh-Yuan Rd., Peitou, Taipei 11221
Tel: +886(2) 896-1000
President: You-Yu Bao
Founded: 1982
Graduate S: Theatre; Music.
D: Music; Fine Arts; Theatre; Dance.
Ce: Traditional Arts Research.

National Taiwan Institute of Technology
Section 4, 43 Keelung Road, Taipei
Tel: +66(2) 733-3141
Fax: +66(2) 733-1044
Founded: 1974
S: Graduate.
*D: Industrial Management; Electronics
Engineering; Mechanical Engineering; Textile
Engineering; Construction Engineering; Chemical
Engineering; Electrical Engineering; Business
Administration; Information Management;
Humanities.*
*Ce: Construction Technology; Automation and
Control System; Materials Research; Research in*

Technological and Vocational Education; Computer.
P: Continuing Education.

National Taiwan Ocean University
2, Peining Road, Keelung 20224
Tel: +886(2) 462-2192
Fax: +886(2) 462-0724
President: Chuntsung Wang (1990-)
Dean of Academic Affairs: Chingshyong Wu
Founded: 1953, 1979
D: Marine Transportation; Marine Engineering; Nautical Technology; Marine Engineering and Technology; Fisheries; Marine Food Science; Shipping and Transportation Management; Harbour and River Engineering; Naval Architecture; Oceanography; Electronic Engineering; Aquaculture.
I: Maritime Science; Maritime Law Study; Marine Biology.

National Yang Ming Medical College
155, Li-Nong Street, Sec. 2, Peitou, Taipei 11221
Tel: +886(2) 821-2300
Fax: +886(2) 826-4051
Founded: 1975
S: Medicine; Dentistry; Medical Technology.
Graduate I: Neurosciences; Microbiology and Immunology; Biochemistry; Biomedical Engineering; Physiology; Pharmacology; Public Health; Clinical Medicine; Anatomical Sciences; Genetics.

National Kaohsiung Normal University
116, Ho-ping First Road, Kaohsiung 80264
Tel: +886(7) 7751-7161
Fax: +886(7) 721-1857
President: Chen-ku Hwang
Secretary-General: Song Lin Wu
Founded: 1969, 1989
D: Chinese; English; Mathematics; Industrial Arts Education; Physics; Education; Chemistry.
Graduate I: Chinese Literature and Language; Education; English Education; Mathematics Education; Industrial Arts and Technology Education.
D: Extension Studies; Special Education.
Ce: Computer; Audio-Visual Education; Special Education; Science Education; Research and Development in Humanities Education; Adult Education Research.

National Sun Yat-Sen University
70, Lien-Hai Rd., Kaohsiung 80424
Tel: +886(7) 531-6170
Founded: 1980

National Taiwan College of Education
1, Chin-Teh Rd., Pai Sha Village, Changhua 50058
Tel: +886(47) 723-2105
Founded: 1971, 1980
D: Guidance and Counselling; Language Education; Special Education; Industrial

Education; Business Education; Mathematics; Physics; Biology; Chemistry.
I: In-service Training for Teachers.

National Pingtung Polytechnic Institute
1, Hsueh-Fu Rd., Nei Pu, Pingtung
Tel: +886(8) 770-3202

National Yunlin Institute of Technology
123, Universtity Rd., Sec. 3, Touliu, Yunlin
Tel: +886(5) 534-2601

National Chiayi Teachers College
85, Wen Lung, Ming-Hsiung, Chiayi
Tel: +886(5) 226-3411
Founded: 1957, 1966, 1987
D: Elementary Education; Literature and Language Education; Social Studies Education; Mathematics and Science Education; Early Childhood Education.

National Taiwan Hsin-Chu Teachers' College
521, Nan Dah Road, Hsin-Chu 30033
Tel: +886(35) 213-132
Fax: +886(35) 231-380
President: Han-Chiang Chen
Secretary-General: Wan-Mei Chen
Founded: 1940, 1965, 1987
D: Elementary Education; Languages and Literature; Social Studies; Music Education; Science Education; Early Childhood Education.
P: Art Education.

National Hualien Teachers College
123, Hua-Hsi, Hualien 79037
Tel: +886(38) 227-106
Founded: 1947, 1987
Teacher Training.

National Pingtung Teachers College
1, Lin-Sen Road, Pingtung 90070
Tel: +886(8) 722-6141
Founded: 1940, 1987
Teacher Training.

National Taichung Teachers College
140, Min-shen Road, Taichung 40302
Tel: +886(4) 226-3181
Founded: 1923, 1987
Teacher Training.

National Tainan Teachers College
33, Shu-Lin St., Sec. 2, Tainan 70010
Tel: +886(6) 211-3111
Founded: 1898, 1987
Teacher Training.

National Taipei Teachers College
134, Ho Ping East Rd., Sec. 2, Taipei 10659
Tel: +886(2) 732-1104
Founded: 1896, 1987
Teacher Training.

National Taitung Teachers College
684, Chunghua Rd., Sec. 1, Taitung
Tel: +886(89) 318-855
Founded: 1848, 1987
Teacher Training.

Taipei Municipal Teachers College
1, Ai Kuo West Road, Taipei 10001
Tel: +886(2) 311-3040
Founded: 1945, 1987
Teacher Training.

PRIVATE INSTITUTIONS

Chang Gung Medical College
259, Wen Hua 1st Rd., Kwei-Shan, Taoyuan
Tel: +886(3) 328-3016
Fax: (3) 328-3031
Chancellor: Delon Wu
Secretary-General: J.T. Shih
Founded: 1987
S: Medicine; Medical Technology; Nursing.

Chang Jung College of Management
75-80, Village of Tatan, Kwayjen, Tainan
Tel: +886(3) 278-0123
Management.

China Medical College
91, Hsieh-Shih Road, Taichung 40421
Tel: +886(4) 205-3366
Founded: 1958
S: Medicine; Chinese Medicine; Pharmacy; Public Health; Dentistry; Nursing; Medical Technology.

Chung-Hua Polytechnic Institute
30, Tung-Hsiang, Hsinchu
Tel: +886(35) 374-281

Chung Shan Medical and Dental College
113, Tachien St., Sec. 2, Taichung
Tel: +886(4) 389-6190
Founded: 1960, 1977
S: Medicine; Dentistry; Nursing; Medical Technology; Nutrition.

Chung Yuan Christian University
22, Pu-Jen Li, Chung-Li, Tao Yuan 32023
Tel: +886(3) 456-3171
Fax: +886(3) 456-3160
President: Shiu-Hau Yin
Founded: 1955, 1980
C: Science; Engineering; Business Administration.
Ce: Computer.
Evening D.

Da-Yeh Institute of Technology
12, Shan-Jeau Rd., Sec. 1, Ta Tsun, Changhua
Tel: +886(4) 852-8469
Technology.

Fu Jen Catholic University
510, Hsin-Chuang RD., Hsin Chuang, Taipei 24205
Tel: +886(2) 903-1111
Fax: +886(2) 903-5524
Founded: 1963
C: Arts and Letters; Science and Engineering; Foreign Languages; Law; Business Administration; Theology; Liberal Arts; Fine Arts.
I: East Asia Spiritual Studies.
Ce: Mandarin Language.
D: Evening Studies.

Huafan College of Humanities and Technology
1, Hua-Fan Rd., Shihtin, Taipei
Tel: +886(2) 663-2102
Humanities; Technology.

Kaohsiung Medical College
100, Shih-Chuan 1st Road, Kaohsiung 80780
Tel: +886(7) 312-1101
Cable: kaomedco
Founded: 1954
S: Medicine; Dentistry; Pharmacy; Nursing; Technology for Medical Sciences.
Graduate I: Medicine; Pharmacy.

Kaohsiung Polytechnic Institute
1, Hsueh-Cheng Rd., Sec. 1, Ta-Hsu, Kaohsiung
Tel: +886(7) 656-3711

Ming Chuan College
250, Chung Shan North Rd., Sec. 5, Taipei
Tel: +886(2) 882-4564

Providence University
200, Chung Chi Road, Sa Lu, Taichung Hsien 43309
Tel: +886(4) 631-1150
Founded: 1957, 1963
D: Chinese Literature; Western Language and Literature; Business Administration; Mathematics; Chemistry; Nutrition and Food Technology; Information Sciences.
Evening S.

Shih Chien College
3, Ta-Chi St., Lane 62, Taipei
Tel: +886(2) 503-8151

Soochow University
70, Lin-Hsi Road, Shih Lin, Taipei 11102
Tel: +886(2) 881-9471
Founded: 1900, 1950
C: Arts; Science; Law; Commerce.
Graduate S: Chinese Literature; Law; Economics; Accountancy.
Extension D.
Evening S.

Taipei Medical College
250, Wu Hsing Street, Taipei 10502
Tel: +886(2) 736-1661
Fax: +886(2) 736-6485
President: Chung-Hong Hu
Registrar: Chien-Hu Chen
Founded: 1960

S: Medicine; Dentistry; Pharmacy; Medical Technology; Nursing; Nutrition and Health Sciences; Pharmacy (Evening Studies); Public Health.
Graduate I: Pharmacognosy Science; Pharmaceutical Sciences.

Tamkang University
151, Yingchuan Road, Tamsui, Taipei 25137
Tel: +886(2) 621-5656
President: Yung-shan Lin (1992-)
Founded: 1950, 1958, 1980
C: Liberal Arts; Science; Engineering; Commerce; Management; Evening.
S: Graduate Studies.
Ce: Area Studies.
D: Public Service.

Tatung Institute of Technology
40, Chung Shan N. Road, Sec. 3, Taipei 10451
Tel: +886(2) 592-5252
Fax: +886(2) 592-1813
Telex: 11348 Tatung
D: Mechanical Engineering; Electrical Engineering; Business Administration; Industrial Design; Chemical Engineering.
Graduate S: Electrical Engineering; Mechanical Engineering; Business Administration.

Tunghai University
181, Taichung Harbor Rd., Sec. 3, Taichung 40704
Tel: +886(4) 359-0200
Fax: +886(4) 359-0361
President: Ta-Nien Yuan
Chief Secretary: Tung-sheng Liu
Founded: 1955
C: Arts; Science; Agriculture; Engineering; Management; Law.
D: Evening.
Ce: Chinese Language; Environmental Research; Environmental Planning and Landscape Research.

University of Chinese Culture
55, Hwa Kang Rd., Yang Ming Shan, Taipei 11114
Tel: +886(2) 861-0511
Fax: +886(2) 861-053
President: Louis J.W. Jeng
Founded: 1962, 1980
C: Letters; Journalism and Communication; Science; Engineering; Business Administration; Agriculture; Arts; Foreign Languages.
Graduate S.
Evening D.

The World College of Journalism and Communications
1, Mu-Cha Rd., Lane 17, Sec. 1, Wen San, Taipei
Tel: +886(2) 936-8225
Journalism and Communication.

Yuan-Ze Institute of Technology
135, Yuan-Tung Rd., Chung-Li, Taoyuan 32026
Tel: +886(3) 463-8800
Technology.

NATIONAL ACADEMIC BODIES

Ministry of Education
5 South Chung Shan Road, Taipei
Telex: 10894 chiapu

TAJIKISTAN

UNIVERSITIES

*Tajik State University
[Tadžikskij Gosudarstvennyj Universitet]
Prosp. Rudaky 17, 734025 Dušanbe
Tel: +7(3772) 22-77-11
Fax: +7(3772) 23-37-03
Rector: F.T. Tahirov
Founded: 1948
F: History; Tajik Philology; Accountancy and Economics; Finance and Credit; Russian Language and Literature; Oriental Languages; Law; Economics and Planning; Physics; Mathematics and Applied Mathematics; Chemistry; Biology; Geology; Radiochemistry of Rare and Scattered Elements Research; Problems of Coordinating Chemistry and Ecology Research.
Research L: Physics of Polymer Strength; Automated Teaching Systems; Introduction and Acclimatization of Plants; Peptids; Biotechnology; Fermentology; Sociological Studies; Archaeology, Ethnography and Folklore of Tajikistan.
Ce: Information and Computer.
D: Evening Studies; Correspondence Courses.

OTHER INSTITUTIONS

Tadzikskij Gosudarstvennyj Institut Iskusstv
Ul. Zdanova 73a, 734032 Dusanbe
Music.

Tadzikskij Gosudarstvennyj Medicinskij Institut
Prosp. V.I. Lenina 139, 734003 Dusanbe
Medicine.

Tadzikskij Politehniceskij Institut
Prosp. Kujbyseva 10a, 734042 Dusanbe
Tel: +7(3772) 22-35-11

Tadzikskij Sel'skohozjajstvennyj Institut
Prosp. Lenina 146, 734056 Dusanbe
Tel: +7(3772) 24-53-41
Agriculture.

NATIONAL ACADEMIC BODIES

Ministry of Education
Dusanbe
Tel: +7(3772) 232-664
Fax: +7(3772) 232-664
Minister: B. Dodhoudoeva

TANZANIA

UNIVERSITIES

*University of Dar es Salaam
P.O. Box 35091, Dar es Salaam
Tel: +255(51) 435-00
Fax: +255(51) 430-78
Telex: 41561 univip tanzania
Cable: university dar es salaam
Vice-Chancellor: M.L. Luhanga
Chief Administrative Officer: D.J. Mkude
Founded: 1961
F: Arts and Social Sciences; Commerce and Management; Education; Engineering; Law; Science.
I: Development Studies; Resource Assessment; Marine Sciences (Zanzibar); Production Innovation Research; Kiswahili Research.

MUHIMBILI UNIVERSITY COLLEGE OF HEALTH SCIENCES
P.O. Box 65001, Dar es Salaam
Tel: +255(51) 461-63
Principal: S.Y. Maselle
Registrar: R.A. Lema
Founded: 1991
Health Sciences.

Sokoine University of Agriculture
P.O. Box 3000, Chuo Kikuu, Morogoro
Tel: +255(51) 3511
Telex: 55308 univmotz
Cable: uniagric, morogoro
Vice-Chancellor: A.B. Lwoga
Registrar: F.O.K. Mgongo
Founded: 1984
F: Agriculture; Forestry; Veterinary Medicine.
D: Veterinary Medicine and Public Health; Veterinary Surgery, Obstetrics and Reproduction; Veterinary Physiology, Biochemistry, Pharmacology and Toxicology; Veterinary Anatomy; Veterinary Pathology.

OTHER INSTITUTIONS

Ardhi Institute
P.O. Box 35176, Dar es Salaam
Tel: +255(51) 491-12
Founded: 1974

College of Business Education
P.O. Box 1968, Dar es Salaam
Tel: +255(51) 310-56
Founded: 1965
Business Administration.

Co-operative College
P.O. Box 474, Moshi
Tel: +255 2228
Founded: 1963

Dar es Salaam Technical College
P.O. Box 2958, Dar es Salaam
Tel: +255(51) 28-331
Founded: 1957
Technical Studies.

Institute of Development Management
P.O. Box 1, Morogoro
Tel: +255 2401
Founded: 1970
Development Management.

Institute of Finance Management
P.O. Box 3918, Dar es Salaam
Tel: +255(51) 271-71
Founded: 1972
Finance Management.

National Institute of Transport
P.O. Box 705, Dar es Salaam
Tel: +255(51) 483-28
Transport Studies.

National Social Welfare Training Institute
P.O. Box 3375, Dar es Salaam
Tel: +255(51) 440-19
Social Welfare.

Nyegezi Social Training Institute
P.O. Box 307, Mwanza
Tel: +255 2645
Founded: 1960
Social Work.

Open University of Tanzania
P.O. Box 9213, Dar es Salaam
Tel: +255(51) 24844
Fax: +255(51) 68948
Vice-Chancellor: G.R.V. Mmari
Founded: 1992
F: Arts and Social Sciences; Education; Science, Technology and Environmental Sciences.

NATIONAL ACADEMIC BODIES

Ministry of Science, Technology and Higher Education
P.O. Box 2645, Dar es Salaam
Tel: +255(51) 46-169
Fax: +255(51) 46-167
Minister: Benjamin W. Mkapa

Unesco National Commission of the United Republic of Tanzania
Jengo la Umoja wa Vijana, Morogoro Road, P.O. Box 20384, Dar es Salaam
Tel: +255(51) 46-167
Fax: +255(51) 46-167
Chairman: Benjamin W. Mkapa, Minister of Science, Technology and Higher Education
Secretary-General: Niwako E. Mnzava

THAILAND

UNIVERSITIES AND UNIVERSITY INSTITUTIONS

STATE INSTITUTIONS

Burapha University
Bangsaen, Chonburi
Tel: +66(38) 384-047
Fax: +66(38) 382-351
President: Purachai Piumsombun
F: Education; Science; Nursing; Human and Social Sciences.

Chiang Mai University
Huay Kaew Road, Changwat Chiang Mai 50002
Tel: +66(53) 221-699
Fax: +66(53) 217-143
Telex: 43553 unichim th
President: Kasem Watanachai
Founded: 1964
F: Humanities; Social Sciences; Science; Education; Medicine; Dentistry; Nursing; Pharmacy; Medical Technology; Agriculture; Engineering; Associated Medical Sciences; Fine Arts.
S: Graduate.
I: Science and Technology Research and Development; Health Sciences (Research); Social Research.

*Chulalongkorn University
Phyathai Road, Bangkok 10330
Tel: +66(2) 215-0871
Fax: +66(2) 215-4804
Telex: 20217 unichul th
President: Charas Suwanwela (1989-92)
Vice-President: Dasni Punyashthiti
Founded: 1902, 1911, 1916
F: Arts; Architecture; Commerce and Accountancy; Dentistry; Economics; Education; Engineering; Law; Medicine; Pharmaceutical Science; Political Science; Science; Veterinary Science; Communication Arts; Fine and Applied Arts; Allied Health Science; Nursing.
I: Population Studies; Social Research; Health Research; Environmental Research; Asian Studies; Metallurgy and Materials Science Research; Biotechnology and Genetic Engineering; Computer Services; Sasin Business Administration (Graduate); Language; Merchant

Marine; Energy Research; Aquatic Resources Research; Thai Studies.
S: Graduate.
C: Petroleum and Petrochemical.
Ce: Scientific and Technological Research Equipment.

SASIN GRADUATE INSTITUTE OF BUSINESS ADMINISTRATION

THE THAI RED CROSS COLLEGE OF NURSING
Bangkok 10500

Kasetsart University
50 Phaholyothin Road, Bangkhen, Bangkok 10900
Tel: +66(2) 579-0113
Fax: +66(2) 579-8781
Telex: 21957 recoftc th
Cable: unikase 10900
President: Kamphol Adulavidhaya (1992-94)
Vice-President for Administration: Boonsom Suwachirat
Founded: 1917, 1928, 1943
F: Agriculture; Forestry; Economics and Business Administration; Fishery; Veterinary Medicine; Engineering; Agro-Industry; Humanities; Science; Education; Social Sciences.
S: Graduate.
I: Research and Development; Food Research and Product Development; Office of Computer Service; Suwanvajokkasikit Animal Research and Development; Research and Development for Agriculture System Under Adverse Condition; Inseechandrasatitya for Crop Research and Development.
Ce: Regional Community Forestry Training; National Agricultural Extension and Training; National Agricultural Machinery; National Biological Control Research; Tropical Vegetable Research; Dairy Research and Development.
L: Greenhouse Complex (Central); Central Scientific Equipment.
Office for Extension and Training.
National Agricultural and Agro-Industrial Product Improvement Complex.

KAMPHAENGSAEN CAMPUS
Nakhon Pathom 73140
Tel: +66 579-2293

Khon Kaen University
123 Friendship Highway, Khon Kaen 40002
Tel: +66(43) 241-331
Fax: +66(43) 243-216
Telex: 55303 unikhon th
President: Nopadol Tongsopit
Founded: 1964
F: Agriculture; Engineering; Education; Science; Nursing; Medicine; Humanities and Social Sciences; Associated Medical Sciences; Public Health; Dentistry; Pharmaceutical Sciences; Technology; Veterinary Science; Architecture.
I: Research and Development.
Ce: Instructional Resources; Computer.

*King Mongkut's Institute of Technology Ladkrabang

Chalongkrung Road, Ladkrabang District, Bangkok 10520
Tel: +66(2) 326-9080
Fax: +66(2) 326-7333
E-Mail: parash@crsc.kmitl.ac.th
Telex: 84967 insmong th
Rector: Pairash Thajchayapong
Vice-Rector for Administration: Wilaiwan Wonyodpun
Founded: 1960, 1971, 1986
F: Architecture; Engineering; Industrial Education; Agricultural Technology; Science; Graduate Studies.
Ce: Computer Research and Service; Electronic Research.

King Mongkut's Institute of Technology North Bangkok

1518 Pibulsongkram Road, Khet Dusit, Bangkok 10800
Tel: +66(2) 585-8541-8
Fax: +66(2) 587-4350
Founded: 1960, 1971, 1986
F: Engineering; Industrial Education and Science; Applied Science.
S: Graduate.
I: Technical Education Development.
C: Industrial Technology.

King Mongkut's Institute of Technology Thonburi

91 Suksawat 48 Road, Khwaeng Bangmod, Khet Ratburana, Bangkok 10140
Tel: +66(2) 427-0039
Fax: +66(2) 427-9860
President: Haris Sutabutr (1992-94)
Founded: 1960, 1971, 1986
F: Engineering; Industrial Education; Science.
S: Energy and Materials.
I: Pilot Plant Development and Training.
Ce: Continuing Education; Computer; Operation for Research and Development; Scientific Instruments for Standards and Industry.

Maejo Institute of Agricultural Technology

Tambol Nong Han, Amphoe Sansai, Chiang Mai 50290
Tel: +66(53) 244858
Fax: +66(53) 244-861
Telex: 43553 unichim th
Cable: insmajo
President: Ahnon Tiangtrong (1989-92)
Vice-President (Administration): Suporn Ketvaraporn
Founded: 1934, 1975
F: Agricultural Production; Agricultural Business.
S: Graduate.
Office: Agricultural Research and Extension.

Mahidol University

198/2 Trok Wat Saowakhon, Bang Yikan, Bangkok I0700
Tel: +66(2) 433-0140
Fax: +66(2) 433-7083
Telex: 84770 unimahi th
Cable: unimahi
President: Pradit Chareonthaitawee
Founded: 1889, 1969
F: Medicine (Siriraj Hospital); Public Health; Medical Technology; Tropical Medicine; Science; Medicine (Ramathibodi Hospital); Dentistry; Pharmacy; Social Sciences and Humanities; Nursing; Environment and Resource Studies; Graduate Studies; Engineering.
I: Population and Social Research; Nutrition; Language and Culture for Rural Development; Sciences and Technology for Development; Health Development (ASEAN).
Ce: Computer; National Laboratory Animal.

CENTRE FOR THE PRODUCTION AND DEVELOPMENT OF PUBLIC HEALTH MEDIA

SUNG HOEN RURAL HEALTH TRAINING AND RESEARCH CENTRE

Naresuan University

Muang District, Phitsanulok 65000
Tel: +66(55) 258-921
Fax: +66(55) 252-930
President: Sujin Jinahyon
F: Education; Science; Human and Social Sciences.

National Institute of Development Administration Bangkok

Sukhapibal 2 Road, Bangkok 10240
Tel: +66(2) 377-7400-19
Fax: +66(2) 375-8802
Telex: nida bangkok 10240
Cable: insnida bangkok 10240
President: Purachai Piumsombun
Founded: 1955, 1966
S: Public Administration; Business Administration; Development Economics; Applied Statistics.
Ce: Development Administration Research; Training; Language; Research; Information Systems Education.
P: Social Development (Graduate).

Prince of Songkla University

Hatyai Campus, tambon Kho Hong, Hat Yai, Songkhla 90110
Tel: +66(74) 235-800-9
Fax: +66(74) 231-376
President: Siripongse Sribhibhadh (1991-)
Vice-President: Vicharm Panich

F: Science; Engineering; Education; Humanities and Social Sciences; Management Sciences; Natural Resources; Pharmaceutical Sciences; Nursing and Midwifery; Dentistry; Science and Technology; Medicine.
S: Graduate.
D: Extension.
Ce: Computer.

HAT YAI CAMPUS
Tambon Khorhong, Hat Yai, Songkhla 90110

PATTANI CAMPUS
Tambon Roosameelae, Pattani Province 94000

Ramkhamhaeng University (Open University)
Ramkhamhaeng Road, Huamark, Bangkapi, Bangkok 10240
Tel: +66(2) 318-0867
Fax: +66(2) 318-0917
President: Chousak Sirinil
Founded: 1971
F: Law; Business Administration; Humanities; Education; Science; Political Science; Economics.

Silpakorn University
Na Phralan Road, Bangkok 10200
Tel: +66(2) 221-7760
Fax: +66(2) 225-7258
Telex: Unisilp
President: Khaisri Sri-Aroon
Founded: 1934, 1943
F: Painting, Sculpture and Graphic Arts; Architecture; Decorative Arts; Archaeology; Arts; Education; Science; Pharmacy; Industrial Technology.
S: Graduate.
I: Research and Development; Western Thai Culture; Art.
Ut: Institutional Research.
Ce: Computer.

SANAMCHANDRA PALACE CAMPUS
Nakhon Pathom Province 73120

Sri Nakharinwirot University (SWU)
Sukumvit Rd. Soi 23, Prakhanong, Bangkok 10110
Tel: +66(2) 258-0310-3
Fax: +66(2) 258-4006
President: Chatri Muangnapoe
Vice-President for Administrative Affairs: Somkid Boonraung
Founded: 1954, 1974
F: Education; Science; Social Science; Humanities; Physical Education; Technology; Medicine; Engineering.
S: Graduate.
I: Behavioural Science (Research); ISAN Art and Culture Research; Southern Thai Studies.
Ce: Computer.

BANGKHEN CAMPUS
Changwattana Road, Bangkhen, Bangkok 10220
Tel: +66 521-1578

BANGKOK COLLEGE OF NURSING, SONGKHLA CAMPUS
Muang District, Songkhla 90000
Tel: +66(74) 311-711

MAHA SARAKHAM CAMPUS
Muang District, Maha Sarakham 44000
Tel: +66(43) 711-180

PALASUKSA CAMPUS
Rama I Road, Bangkok 10330

PATHUMWAN CAMPUS
Henri Dunant Road, Pathumwan District, Bangkok 10500
Tel: +66 251-2915

PRASARNMIT CAMPUS
Soi 23, Sukhumvit Road, Bangkok 10110
Tel: +66(2) 258-0310
Fax: +66(2) 258-3996

Sukhothai Thammathirat Open University
9/9 Moo 9, Tambon Bangpood, Changwatana Road, Pakkred, Nonthaburi 11120
Tel: +66(2) 576-0030-3
Fax: +66(2) 573-5890
Telex: 72353 unisuko th
Cable: unisuko th
President: Ahnon Thiangtrong
Vice-President for Academic Affairs: Wisan Pantuna
Founded: 1978
S: Educational Studies; Liberal Arts; Management Science; Law; Economics; Health Science; Home Economics; Agriculture Extension and Co-operatives; Political Science; Communication Arts.

Suranaree Technology University
Maung District, Nakhonrathcharima
Tel: +66(44) 245-843
Fax: +66(44) 254-843
Technology.

*Thammasat University
2 Prachan Road, Thaprachan, Bangkok 10200
Tel: +66(2) 224-4869
Fax: +66(2) 224-8099
Telex: 72132 tamsat th
President: Noranit Setabutr
Founded: 1934, 1952
F: Law; Commerce and Accountancy; Economics; Social Administration; Liberal Arts; Journalism and Mass Communication; Sociology and Anthropology; Science and Technology; Political Science; Engineering.
I: Continuing Education and Social Service; Thai Khadi Research; Human Resources; East Asian Studies; Language.
Ce: Information Processing and Education and Development; Graduate Volunteers'.

RANGSIT CAMPUS
Pathum Thani 12120
Tel: +66(2) 516-0020-39
Fax: +66(2) 516-0976
Telex: 72433

Ubon Ratchathani University

Warin-Det Udom Rd., Warinchamrap, Ubon
Ratchathani 34190
Tel: +66(45) 244-282
Fax: +66(45) 244-282
President: Somchit Vodseranee (1991-94)
Administrative Vice-President: Aik Watana
Founded: 1987, 1990
F: Agriculture; Engineering; Science.
I: Languages and Culture.

PRIVATE INSTITUTIONS

*Asian Institute of Technology

P.O. Box 2754, Bangkok 10501
Tel: +66(2) 516-0110-44
Fax: +66(2) 516-2126
E-Mail: pres@rccvax.ait.ac.th
Telex: 84276 th
Cable: ait bangkok
President: Alastair M. North (1983-)
*D: Agricultural and Food Technology; Computer
Technology; Energy Technology; Human
Settlements Development; Environmental
Engineering; Geotechnical and Transport
Engineeering; Industrial Engineering and
Management; Structural Engineering and
Construction; Water Resources Engineering.*
S: Management.
*Ce: Language; Regional Computer; Asian
Disaster Preparedness; Continuing Education;
Regional Research and Development.*
*P: Agricultural Land and Water Development;
Interdisciplinary Natural Resources Development
Management.*
Telecommunications Project.

Assumption University

682 Soi Ramkhambaeng 24, Hua Mark, Bangkapi,
Bangkok 10240
Tel: +66(2) 314-0456
Fax: +66(2) 318-0125
Telex: 87468 abac th
President: Prathip M. Komolmas
Founded: 1972

Bangkok University

40/4 Rama 4 Road, Phra Khanong, Bangkok
10110
Tel: +66(2) 249-5132-4
Fax: +66(2) 249-6274
Founded: 1962, 1982
*S: Accountancy; Business Administration;
Communication Arts; Economics; Humanities;
Law; Computer Sciences; Business
Administration (Graduate); Evening.*

Hua-Chiew University

121 Anantanak Road, Pomprab District, Bangkok
10100
Tel: +66(2) 223-1351
Fax: +66(2) 226-5827
President: Kunnikar Tanprasert
Founded: 1981

Dhurakijpundit University

110 Prachachuen Road, Don Muang, Bangkok
10210
Tel: +66(2) 580-0050
Fax: +66(2) 589-9606
Cable: sudhi
President: Sawai Sudhipitak (1968-)
Vice-President for Administrative Affairs: Lertlak
S. Burusphat
Founded: 1968, 1984
*F: Business Administration; Accountancy;
Economics; Law; Humanities; Communication
Arts.*
S: Graduate.

Payap University Chaiang Mai

P.O. 101, Chiang Mai 50000
Tel: +66(53) 241-255
Fax: +66(53) 241-983
Cable: papayuniv
President: Amnuay Tapingkae (1977-)
Founded: 1974, 1984
*F: Humanities; Science Social Sciences;
Nursing; Theology; Business Administration;
Accountancy and Finance.*
S: Graduate.
I: Payap Research and Development.

Siam University

[Mahawitthayalai Siam]
235 Phetkasem Road, Phasicharoen, Bangkok
10160
Tel: +66(2) 457-0068
Fax: +66(2) 457-3982
President: Pornchai Mongkhonvanit (1984-)
Vice-President for Academic Affairs: Niphon
Kanthasewi
Founded: 1965, 1986
*F: Liberal Arts; Business Administration;
Engineering; Communications' Arts; Law;
Science.*
S: Graduate.
Ce: Language; Research.

South-East Asia University

19/1 Phetkasem Road, Nong-Khaem, Bangkok
10160
Tel: +66(2) 421-1347
Fax: +66(2) 421-0390
President: Suchon Hamant
Founded: 1973

Sripatum University
[Vitayalai Sripatum]
61 Phahonyotin Road, Bangkhen, Bangkok 10900
Tel: +66(2) 561-1036-40
Fax: +66(2) 561-1721
President: Rutchaneeporn Pookayaporn
Founded: 1970
F: Business Administration; Law; Polytechnic.

*University of the Thai Chamber of Commerce Bangkok
126/1 Vipavadee Rangsit Road, Samsen Nai,
Phayathai, Bangkok 10400
Tel: +66(2) 276-1040
Fax: +66(2) 276-2126
President: Krikkiat Phipatseritham
Founded: 1970
F: Accountancy; Business Administration; Economics; Human Sciences; Science; Communication Arts; Engineering.
S: Graduate Studies.
Ce: Research.

OTHER INSTITUTIONS

Ayutthya Teachers' College
Ayutthya 13000
Founded: 1936
Teacher Training.

Bansomdet Chao Pheaya Teachers' College
Thonburi, Bangkok 10600
Founded: 1923
Teacher Training.

Bundit Phitsanulok College
601 Phraongkhaw Road, Muang District,
Phitsanulok 65000
Tel: +66(55) 251-397
Telex: 46253 th
Founded: 1986

Bundit Sakonnakhon College
50/11 Tambon Thatnaweng, Muang District,
Sakonnakhon 47000
Tel: +66(42) 711-880
Fax: +66(42) 713-237
President: Nivat Jangsuk
Founded: 1987

Buriram Teachers' College
Buriram 3100
Founded: 1930
Teacher Training.

Chachoengsao Teachers' College
Chachoengsao 24000
Founded: 1940
Teacher Training.

Chantharakasem Teachers' College
Bangkhen, Bangkok 10900
Founded: 1941
Teacher Training.

Chiangmai Teachers' College
Chiangmai 5000
Founded: 1924
Teacher Training.

Christian College
124 Silom Road, Bangrak, Bangkok 10500
Tel: +66(2) 235-1000
Fax: +66(2) 236-2911
President: Janjira Wongkhomthong
Founded: 1983

Institute of Social Technology
43/111 Raminthra Road, Bangkhen, Bangkok 10220
Tel: +66(2) 552-3502-5
Fax: +66(2) 552-3511
President: Saeng Sanguanruang
Founded: 1970
Social Technology.

Institute of Technology and Vocational Education
339 Samsen Road, Thewes, Bangkok 10300
Founded: 1977
Technology and Vocational Education.

BANGKOK TECHNICAL CAMPUS
Linchee Road, Tung-Mahamec, Bangkok 10120
Tel: +66(2) 286-3843

BANGPHRA AGRICULTURAL CAMPUS
Sriracha Province 20210
Tel: +66(38) 311-808

CHAKRAPONGPHUVANART CAMPUS
Wipavadeerangsit Road, Bangkok
Tel: +66(2) 277-9124

DRAMATIC ARTS COLLEGE
Rashini Road, Bangkok 10120
Tel: +66(2) 224-1408

NAKORN-SRITHAMMARAT AGRICULTURAL CAMPUS
Nakorn-Srithammarat 80110
Tel: +66(75) 411-144

Kamphaengpet Teachers' College
Kamphaengpet 62000
Founded: 1973
Teacher Training.

Kanchanaburi Teachers' College
Kanchanaburi 71000
Founded: 1973
Treacher Training.

Kasembundit College
99/101 Soi Akhanay, Phatanakarn Road, Bangkok 10250
Tel: +66(2) 321-6930-9
Fax: +66(2) 321-4444
President: Vallop Suwandee
Founded: 1987

Lampang Teachers' College
Lampang 52000
Founded: 1972
Teacher Training.

Loei Teachers' College
Loei 42000
Founded: 1973
Teacher Training.

Mahanakorn Colleges
51 Moo1, Chuem Sampan Road, Nong-Chok,
Bangkok 10530
Tel: +66(2) 543-1070-1
President: Sittichai Poolaiyandom

Mahasarakham Teachers' College
Mahasarakham 44000
Tel: +66(43) 711-452
Founded: 1930
Teacher Training.

Mission College
430 Phitsanulok Road, Dusit, Bangkok 10300
Tel: +66(2) 281-1422
Fax: +66(2) 280-0441
Telex: 67273 mission th
President: Salinee Navamaratna
Founded: 1986

Muban Chombung Teachers' College
Ratchaburli 70150
Founded: 1954

Nakhornsawan Teachers' College
Nakhornsawan 60000
Founded: 1922
Teacher Training.

Nakorn Si Thammarat Teachers' College
Nakorn Si Thammarat 80000
Tel: +66 356-544
Founded: 1957
Teacher Training.

Nakornpathom Teachers' College
Nakornpathom 73000
Tel: +66 241-019
Founded: 1934
Teacher Training.

Nakornratchasima Teachers' College
Nakornratchasima 30000
Tel: +66 242-158
Founded: 1914
Teacher Training.

North-Eastern College
199/19 Mitraphab Road, Muang District, Khon
Kaen 40000
Tel: +66(43) 222-959
Fax: +66(43) 222-960
President: Pairat Wanapan
Founded: 1988

Phakklang College
932/1 Moo 9, Asia Road, Tambon
Nakhonsawantok, Muang District, Nakhonsawan
60000
Tel: +66(56) 221-690
Fax: +66(56) 221-690
President: Praphan Dhammasrion
Founded: 1986

Phetchabun Teachers' College
Phetchabun 67000
Founded: 1973
Teacher Training.

Phetchaburi Teachers' College
Phetchaburi 76000
Founded: 1926
Teacher Training.

Phibunsongkram Teachers' College
Pitsanuloke
Founded: 1923

Phuket Teachers' College
Phuket 83000
Founded: 1972

Pohchang Campus
Treepatch Road, Bangkok 10120
Tel: 66(2) 221-4468

Pranakhorn Teachers' College
Bangkhen, Bangkok 10900
Founded: 1892

Ramphaiphanni Teachers' College
Chanthaburi 22000
Founded: 1972

Rangsit University
Muang District, Pathum Thani 12000
Tel: +66(2) 533-9020
Fax: +66(2) 533-9470
President: Authit Ourairat
Founded: 1985

Saengtham College
20 Phetkasem Road, Sampran, Nakhon Pathom
73110
Tel: +66(34) 420-1626
President: Virasak Vanarotsuvit
Founded: 1975

Saint John College
124/1-2 Vibhavadi, Rungsi Road, Bangkok 10900
Tel: +66(2) 512-2271-5
Fax: +66(2) 513-0770
President: Samai Chinnapha

Saint Louis Nursing College
215/4 South Sathorn Road, Bangkok 10120
Tel: +66(2) 212-4604-7
President: Bunsom Martin
Founded: 1985
Nursing.

Sakonnakhon Teachers' College
Sakonnakhon 47000
Founded: 1964

Siam Bundit College
Ronachaicharynyut Road, Muang District, Roi Et
45000
Tel: +66(42) 512-653
President: Suchon Hamant
Founded: 1985

Songkhla Teachers' College
Songkhla 90000
Founded: 1919

Srisophon College
Moo 2 Mamong-songton, Muang District, Nakhon
Si Thammarat 80000
Tel: +66(75) 356-000
President: Sasithorn Sophon
Founded: 1984

Suansunantha Teachers' College
Dusit 10300
Founded: 1937

Suandusit Teachers' College
Dusit 10300
Tel: +66 241-0769
Founded: 1934

Suratthani Teachers' College
Suratthani 84000
Founded: 1973

Surin Teachers' College
Surin 32000
Founded: 1973

Thepsatri Teachers' College
Lopburi 15000
Tel: +66 411-029
Founded: 1920

Thewes Campus
339 Samsen Road, Bangkok 10310
Tel: +66(2) 282-8737

Thonburi Teachers' College
Thonburi, Bangkok 10600
Founded: 1953

Ubonratchathani Teachers' College
Ubonratchathani 34000
Founded: 1942

Udonthani Teachers' College
Udonthani 41000
Founded: 1923

Uttaradit Teachers' College
Uttaradit 53000
Founded: 1936

Vongchavalitkul College
700 Muang District, Nakhorn Ratchasima 30000
Tel: +66(44) 255-523
Fax: +66(44) 256-833
President: Pranee Vongchavalitkul
Founded: 1984

Yala Teachers' College
Yala 95000
Tel: +66(73) 21-2443
Founded: 1927

Yonok College
12 Prasanmaitri Road, Laupang 52000
Tel: +66(54) 226-950-6
Fax: +66(54) 226-957
President: Nirund Jivasantikorn
Founded: 1988

NATIONAL ACADEMIC BODIES

Ministry of Education
Rajdamneon Avenue, Bangkok 10300
Tel: +66(2) 280-0306
Fax: +66(2) 281-0953
Cable: minoedu bangkok 10300
Minister: Samphan Thongsamak

Ministry of University Affairs
328 Si Ayutthaya Road, Bangkok 10400
Fax: +66 245-8636
Telex: 76210 minunia th

**Council of Universities' Presidents of
Thailand**
Old Administrative Building, Chulangkorn
University, Patumwan, Bangkok 10330
Tel: +66(2) 215-0871
Fax: +66(2) 216-1259
Chairman: Kaisri Sri-aroon

**Association of Thai Private Higher
Education Institutions**
328 Si Ayutthaya Road, Phayathai, Bangkok
10400
Tel: +66(2) 245-8548
Fax: +66(2) 245-9327
Chairman: Dhanu Kulachol

Thailand National Commission for Unesco
External Relations Division, Ministry of
Education, Rajdamneon Nok Avenue, Bangkok
10300
Tel: +66(2) 281-6370
Fax: +66(2) 281-0953
Cable: thainatcom education ministry bangkok
Chairman: Samphan Thongsamak, Minister of
Education
Secretary-General: Surat Silpa-Anan

TOGO

UNIVERSITIES

*University of Bénin
[Université du Bénin]
B.P. 1515, Lomé
Tel: +228(21) 35-00
Telex: ubto 5258
Recteur: Komlavi Fofoli Francisco Seddoh
Secrétaire géneral: Abalo Tabo
Founded: 1962, 1970
*F: Letters and Human Sciences; Medicine;
Science; Economics and Management.*
*Higher S: Agriculture (ESA); Engineering (ENSI);
Secretarial Studies (ESSD).*
S: Medical Assistants.
*I: Technology of Management (IUT); Educational
Sciences.*
Ce: Informatics and Computer Sciences.

OTHER INSTITUTIONS

Ecole normale supérieure
B.P. 7, Atakpame
Founded: 1968
Teacher Training.

NATIONAL ACADEMIC BODIES

Ministry of Education and Scientific Research
[Ministère de l'Education nationale et de la
Recherche scientifique]
Direction des Affaires académiques, B.P. 515,
Lomé
Tel: +228(21) 48-44
Fax: +228(21) 16-41
Ministre: Komlavi F. Seddoh

Togo National Commission for Unesco
[Commission nationale de la République
togolaise pour l'Unesco]
Ministère de l'Education nationale, et de la
Recherche scientifique, B.P. 3226, Lomé
Tel: +228(21) 61-54
Fax: +228(21) 61-54
Telex: 5322
Président: Komlavi Seddoh, Ministre de
l'Education
Secrétaire général: Sambiani Sakardja Lare

TONGA

UNIVERSITIES

University of the South Pacific Centre
P.O. Box 278, Nuku'alofa
Tel: +676 21-955
Director: S.N. Fiefia
Founded: 1971

OTHER INSTITUTIONS

Atenisi Institute
P.O. Box 220, Nuku'alofa
Founded: 1966

Institute of Rural Development
Private Bag, Nuku'alofa
Tel: +676 21-955
Founded: 1981
Rural Development.

Maritime Polytechnical Institute
P.O. Box 485, Nuku'alofa
Tel: +676 22-667
Founded: 1985
Maritime Studies.

Teachers' College
P.O. Box 123, Nuku'alofa
Founded: 1944
Teacher Training.

NATIONAL ACADEMIC BODIES

Ministry of Education
P.O. Box 61, Nuku'alofa
Tel: +676 21-511
Minister: Langi Kavaliku

Tonga National Commission for Unesco
Ministry of Education, P.O. Box 61, Nuku'alofa
Tel: +676 21-511
President: Langi Kavaliku, Minister of Education
Secretary-General (Acting): Lucy Mafi

TRINIDAD AND TOBAGO

UNIVERSITIES

University of the West Indies St. Augustine
St. Augustine
Tel: P.B.X. +1809(66) 31359
Fax: +1809(66) 39684
Telex: 24520 uwiwg
Cable: stomata
Pro-Vice-Chancellor and Principal: G.M. Richards
Founded: 1960
*F: Agriculture; Arts and General Studies;
Education; Engineering; Law and Council of
Legal Education; Medical Sciences (Mount Hope);
Natural Sciences; Social Science.*

NATIONAL ACADEMIC BODIES

Ministry of Education
Alexandra Street, St. Clair, Port-of-Spain,
Trinidad
Tel: +1809(62) 21815
Fax: +1809(62) 87818
Minister: Augustus Ramrekersingh

Committee on the Recognition of Degrees (CORD)
National Institute of Higher Education, 20 Victoria Avenue, Port-of-Spain
Tel: +1809 625-4145
Fax: +1809 625-4161
E-Mail: president@n.i.h.e.r.s.t. gortt.
President: Maureen Manchouck (1990-)
Accreditation Specialist: Althea Laurence
Founded: 1994

Trinidad and Tobago National Commission for Unesco
Ministry of Education, 8 Elizabeth Street, St. Clair, Port-of-Spain, Trinidad
Tel: +1809 62-20939
Fax: +1809 62-31658 (undevpri port of spain, att. unesco natcom)
Cable: unescom port of spain
Chairman: Selwyn Ryan
Secretary-General: Sandra Gift

TUNISIA

UNIVERSITIES

Ezzitouna University Tunis
[Université Ezzitouna Tunis]
20, rue Asrubal, Tunis
Tel: +216(1) 788-424
Fax: +216(1) 789-686
Recteur: Abdelmajid Ben Hamda

HIGHER INSTITUTE OF ISLAMIC CIVILIZATION STUDIES
[INSTITUT SUPÉRIEUR DE LA CIVILISATION ISLAMIQUE]
4, Rue Abou Zakaria El Hafsi, Montfleury-Tunis
Tel: +216(1) 256-199
Directeur: Mohsen El Abed
Secrétaire général: Said Tazagdenti
Islamic Civilization Studies.

HIGHER INSTITUTE OF RELIGIOUS SCIENCES
[INSTITUT SUPÉRIEUR DES SCIENCES RELIGIEUSES]
Maakal Ezzaim, Tunis
Tel: +216(1) 569-233
Directeur: Jelloul Jeribi
Secrétaire général: Rodha Khemmassi
Religious Sciences.

HIGHER INSTITUTE OF THEOLOGY
[INSTITUT SUPÉRIEUR DE THÉOLOGIE]
4, Rue Abou Zakaria El Fasi, Montfleury-Tunis
Tel: +216(1) 257-038
Directeur: Saafi Hammenda
Secrétaire général: Habib Felfel
Theology.

University of Sfax (South)
[Université de Sfax (Sud)]
Route de l'Aéroport km 1, Sfax 3029
Tel: +216(4) 240-678
Fax: +216(4) 240-913
Prsident: Mohamed Hedi Ktari (1987-)
Secrétaire général: Mohsen Ben Mansour
International Relations: Salma Zouari Bouattour
Founded: 1986
F: Economics and Management; Medicine; Sciences; Letters and Human Sciences; Law.

CENTRE FOR BIOTECHNOLOGY
[CENTRE DE BIOTECHNOLOGIE DE SFAX]
Route de Soukra km 4, 3038 Sfax
Tel: +216(5) 274-110
Fax: +216(5) 275-970
E-Mail: ellouz@cbs.rnrt.tn
Directeur: Radhouane Ellouze (1987-)
Founded: 1987
Biotechnology.

HIGHER INSTITUTE OF ENGINEERING, GABÈS
[INSTITUT SUPÉRIEUR TECHNIQUE DE GABÈS]
Cité El Manara, 6011 Gabès
Tel: +216(5) 280-651
Fax: +216(5) 280-041
Directeur: Slah Ramdhane
Secrétaire général: Samia Bel Haj
Engineering.

HIGHER INSTITUTE OF SPORTS AND PHYSICAL EDUCATION
[INSTITUT SUPÉRIEUR DU SPORT ET DE L'EDUCATION PHYSIQUE DE SFAX]
Route de l'Aérodrome Km. 4, 3023 Sfax
Tel: +216(4) 278-502
Directeur: Zouhir Hmama
International Relations: Abdelkarim Haj Taieb
Founded: 1989
Sports and Physical Education.

HIGHER SCHOOL OF HEALTH AND SCIENCE AND TECHNIQUES, SFAX
[ECOLE SUPÉRIEURE DES SCIENCES ET TECHNIQUES DE LA SANTÉ DE SFAX]
Route El Ain Km. 0,5 B.PN, 1099 3018 Sfax
Tel: +216(4) 246-971
Fax: +216(4) 246-821
Directeur: Ahmed Rekik (1990-)
Secrétaire général: Ali Marzouk
Founded: 1989
Health Science and Techniques.

INSTITUTE OF INDUSTRIES AND MINING ENGINEERING
[INSTITUT SUPÉRIEUR DES INDUSTRIES ET DES MINES DE GAFSA]
Cité de la Jeunesse, 2119 Gafsa
Tel: +216(6) 224-382
Fax: +216(6) 225-521
Directeur: Essaid Laatar (1988-)
Secrétaire général: Ali Bousaha
Founded: 1981
Industries and Mining Engineering.

INSTITUTE OF OLIVE PRODUCTION, SFAX
[INSTITUT DE L'OLIVIER DE SFAX]
Route de l'Aerodrome km. 1.5, 3029 Sfax
Tel: +216(4) 241-589
Fax: +216(4) 241-033
Directeur: Taib Jardak (1990-)
Founded: 1981
Olive Production.

NATIONAL SCHOOL OF ENGINEERING, GABES
[ECOLE NATIONALE D'INGÉNIEURS DE GABÈS]
Route de Médenine, 6029 Gabès
Tel: +216(5) 272-391
Fax: +216(5) 275-190
Directeur: Mohieddine Aloui
Secrétaire général: Belgacem Rajah
International Relations: Mahmoud Bouabdallah
*Manufacturing Process; Electrical Engineering;
Civil Works; Physics; Chemistry; Computing;
Mining Industry.*

NATIONAL SCHOOL OF ENGINEERING, SFAX
[ECOLE NATIONALE D'INGÉNIEURS DE SFAX]
Route de la Soukra Km. 4, 3038 Sfax
Tel: +216(4) 274-090
Fax: +216(41) 275-595
Directeur: Hamed Ben Dhia (1993-96)
Secrétaire général: Moncef Ksontini
International Relations: Boubaker Elleuch
Founded: 1983
*Electrical Engineering; Physics; Chemistry;
Biology; Geology; Mathematics; Mechanics.*

PREPARATORY INSTITUTE FOR ENGINEERING STUDIES, GABES
[INSTITUT PREPARATOIRE AUX ETUDES D'ING 7ENIEURS DE
GABES]
Route de Medenine, 6029 Gabes
Tel: +216(5) 272-391
Fax: +216(5) 275-180
Directeur: Mohyeddine Aloui (1992-)
Secrétaire général: Belgacem Rajah
Founded: 1992
Engineering Studies.

PREPARATORY INSTITUTE FOR ENGINEERING STUDIES, SFAX
[INSTITUT PRÉPARATOIRE AUX ETUDES D'INGÉNIEURS DE
SFAX]
Route Menzel Chaker km 0.5, 3003 Sfax
Tel: +216(4) 241-733
Fax: +216(4) 246-347
Directeur: Youssef Mlik (1993-)
Secrétaire général: Béchir Moakhar
Founded: 1993
Engineering Studies.

University of the Centre, Sousse

[Université du Centre Sousse]
43, avenue Mohamed Karoui, B.P. 526, Sousse
4002
Tel: +216(3) 235-582
Fax: +216(3) 234-014
Président: Lazhar Bouony
Secrétaire général: Salem Ben Amor
Founded: 1986

*F: Medicine; Law, Economics and Political
Science; Letters (Kairouan); Science; Medicine
(Monastir); Dentistry; Pharmacy.*
I: Preparatory Engineering Studies (Monastir).

CENTRE FOR ISLAMIC STUDIES
[CENTRE DES ETUDES ISLAMIQUES]
Rue Beit el Hikma, El Mansoura, Kairouan
Tel: +216(7) 224-844
Fax: +216(7) 222-669
Directeur: Hassine Boulbaba
Founded: 1989
Islamic Studies.

HIGHER SCHOOL OF HEALTH SCIENCES AND TECHNIQUES
[ECOLE SUPÉRIEURE DES SCIENCES ET TECHNIQUES DE LA
SANTÉ]
Rue Ibn Sina, 5000 Monastir
Tel: +216(3) 462-477
Fax: +216(3) 464-599
Directeur: Habib Sabbah
Secrétaire général: Lamjed Saad
Founded: 1990
Health Sciences and Techniques.

HIGHER SCHOOL OF HORTICULTURE, CHOTT MARIEM
[ECOLE SUPÉRIEURE D'HORTICULTURE DE CHOTT MARIEM]
Chott Mariem 4042
Tel: +216(3) 248-275
Fax: +216(3) 248-275
Directeur: Ridha Tira
Secrétaire général: Ridha Rouis
Founded: 1976
Horticulture.

HIGHER INSTITUTE OF TEXTILE INDUSTRIES, KASR HELAL
[INSTITUT SUPÉRIEUR DES INDUSTRIES TEXTILES DE KASR
HELAL]
Avenue El Haj Ali Soua, 5070 Ksar Helal
Tel: +216(3) 475-900
Fax: +216(1) 475-163
Directeur: Mohamed Gorsane
Secrétaire général: Amara Harzallah
Textile Industries.

MERCHANT MARINE SCHOOL
[ECOLE DE LA MARINE MARCHANDE DE SOUSSE]
12, rue Abdallah Ibn Zoubeir, Sousse
Tel: +216(3) 226-365
Fax: +216(3) 224-923
Directeur: Moncef Souguir
Secrétaire général: Alaya Ayache
Founded: 1976
Merchant Marine.

NATIONAL CENTRE FOR AQUACULTURE
[CENTRE NATIONAL D'AQUACULTURE]
Route de Khnis, 5000 Monastir
Tel: +216(3) 462-867
Directeur: Ismail Bellagha
Founded: 1985
Aquaculture.

NATIONAL SCHOOL OF ENGINEERING, MONASTIR
[ECOLE NATIONALE D'INGÉNIEURS DE MONASTIR]
Route de Kairouan, 5000 Monastir
Tel: +216(3) 464-703
Fax: +216(3) 461-900
Telex: (3) 430816
Directeur: Mohamed El Baker Rammah
Secrétaire général: Mahmoud Sghaier
Founded: 1987
D: *Mechanical Engineering; Electrical Engineering; Textile Engineering.*

PREPARATORY INSTITUTE FOR ENGINEERING STUDIES, MONASTIR
[INSTITUT PRÉPARATOIRE AUX ETUDES D'INGÉNIEURS DE MONASTIR]
Tel: +216(3) 463-705
Directeur: Mohamed Raker Rammah
Founded: 1990
Engineering Studies.

*University of Letters, Arts and Human Sciences (Tunis I)
[Université des Lettres, des Arts et des Sciences humaines (Tunis I)]
23, rue Asdrubal, Lafayette, 1002 Tunis
Tel: +216(1) 788-068
Fax: +216(1) 786-776
Président: Abdelkader Mehiri (1988-)
Secrétaire général: Hassine Aleya
Founded: 1988
F: *Human and Social Sciences; Letters (Mannouba).*

BOURGUIBA INSTITUTE OF MODERN LANGUAGES
[INSTITUT BOURGUIBA DES LANGUES VIVANTES]
47, avenue de la Liberté, Tunis 1008
Tel: +216(1) 780-389
Directeur: Houcine El Oued (1993-)
Secrétaire général: Saadi Ben Bechir
Founded: 1964
D: *Arabic; French; English.*

CENTRE OF ECONOMIC AND SOCIAL STUDIES AND RESEARCH
[CENTRE D'ETUDES ET DES RECHERCHES ÉCONOMIQUES ET SOCIALES (CERES)]
23 Rue d'Espagne, 1000 Tunis
Tel: +216(1) 242-994
Fax: +216(1) 343-237
Directeur: Hechmi Labaied (1990-)
Secrétaire général: Taoufik Khenfir
Founded: 1962
Sociology; Psychology; History; Geography; Development; Arabic Language.

HIGHER INSTITUTE OF CULTURAL ANIMATION
[INSTITUT SUPÉRIEUR DE L'ANIMATION CULTURELLE (ISAC)]
26 Rue Mikhaïl Nouaïma, El Omrane, 1005 Tunis
Tel: +216(1) 284-765
Directeur: Tahar Labib
Secrétaire Général: Rafik Fadhlaoui
Founded: 1982
Cultural Animation.

HIGHER INSTITUTE OF DOCUMENTATION
[INSTITUT SUPÉRIEUR DE DOCUMENTATION]
10 rue Kébibia, 1002 Tunis
Tel: +216(1) 791-329
Fax: +216(1) 794-117
Directeur: Khélifa Chater (1981-)
Secrétaire général: Abdelkader Sfar
Founded: 1981
Documentation.

HIGHER INSTITUTE OF DRAMATIC ART
[INSTITUT SUPÉRIEUR D'ART DRAMATIQUE]
Rue Danton, Tunis
Tel: +216(1) 782-574
Directeur: Boubaker Khelouj (1992-)
Directeur des Etudes: Mohamed Abaza
Founded: 1982
Dramatic Art.

HIGHER INSTITUTE OF EDUCATION AND FURTHER EDUCATION
[INSTITUT SUPÉRIEUR DE L'EDUCATION ET DE LA FORMATION CONTINUE]
Rue de la Liberté, 2000 Le Bardo
Tel: +216(1) 264-727
Fax: +216(1) 568-954
Directeur: Mehdi Abdeljaoued (1988-)
Secrétaire général: Bechir Kachoukh
Founded: 1982
D: *Arabic Language and Letters; Foreign Languages; Human Sciences; Education; Mathematics; Physical Sciences and Techniques; Natural Sciences.*

HIGHER INSTITUTE OF MUSIC
[INSTITUT SUPÉRIEUR DE MUSIQUE DE TUNIS]
23 Rue Asdrubal, 1002 Lafayette
Tel: +216(1) 245-575
Fax: +216 341-639
Directeur: Mahmoud Guetat (1982-)
Founded: 1982
Music.

HIGHER INSTITUTE OF NATIONAL MOVEMENT HISTORY
[INSTITUT SUPÉRIEUR DE L'HISTOIRE DU MOUVEMENT NATIONAL]
11 Rue du Tolede el Manar I, 2092 Tunis
Tel: +216(1) 881-263
Fax: +216(1) 881-263
Directeur: Ammar Mahjoubi (1990-)
Founded: 1990
National Movement History.

HIGHER INSTITUTE OF PRESS AND INFORMATION SCIENCE
[INSTITUT SUPÉRIEUR DE PRESSE ET SCIENCES DE L'INFORMATION]
7, Impasse Bachrouch, Mont-Fleury, Tunis
Tel: +216(1) 492-341
Fax: +216(1) 351-900
Directeur: Ridha Methnani (1990-)
Secrétaire général: Ahmed Hajji
Founded: 1967
Press; Information Science.

HIGHER INSTITUTE OF YOUTH
[INSTITUT SUPÉRIEUR DE LA JEUNESSE DE BIR EL BEY]
2050 Bir El Bey
Tel: +216(1) 430-244
Fax: +216(1) 430-606
Directeur: Khelil Guezguez (1993-)
Secrétaire général: Azzouz Ben Amara
Founded: 1968
Youth Studies.

NATIONAL CENTRE OF SCIENTIFIC DOCUMENTATION
[CENTRE NATIONAL UNIVERSITAIRE DE DOCUMENTATION]
1 Avenue de France, 1000 Tunis
Tel: +216(1) 258-603
Fax: +216(1) 354-216
Directeur: Fatma Chammem (1980-)
Founded: 1980
Documentation.

NATIONAL INSTITUTE OF HERITAGE
[INSTITUT NATIONAL DU PATRIMOINE]
4 Place Chateau-Musée, Bab Manara, Tunis
Tel: +216(1) 261-693
Fax: +216(1) 562-452
Directeur: Abdelaziz Doulatli
Founded: 1957
Heritage Studies.

University of Sciences, Techniques and Medicine (Tunis II)

[Université des Sciences, des Techniques et de Médecine (Tunis II)]
29, rue Asdrubal, 1002 le Belvédére, Tunis
Tel: +216(1) 789-312
Fax: +216(1) 789-312
Recteur: Ali Bousnina
Secrétaire général: Mustapha Ouerghimi
F: Mathematics, Physics and Natural Sciences; Science (Bizerte); Medicine.

BORJ EL AMRI SCHOOL OF CIVIL AVIATION AND METEOROLOGY
[ECOLE DE L'AVIATION CIVILE ET DE LA MÉTÉOROLOGIE DE BORJ ET AMRI]
1142 Aérodrome de Borj el Amri, Route de Mejez El Bab
Tel: +216(1) 540-837
Directeur: Mohamed Touil
Civil Aviation and Meteorology.

EL KHAWARIZMI COMPUTER CENTRE
[CENTRE DE CALCUL EL KHAWARIZMI]
Campus Universitaire, 1060 Tunis
Tel: +216(1) 514-740
Directeur: Moncef Chekir
Founded: 1976
Computer Studies.

HIGHER INSTITUTE OF SPORTS AND PHYSICAL EDUCATION
[INSTITUT SUPÉRIEUR DES SPORTS ET DE L'EDUCATION PHYSIQUE DE KASR SAÏD]
Kasr Saïd, 2027 La Manouba
Tel: +216(1) 512-528
Directeur: Taoufit Haouet
Secrétaire général: Mohamed Louahchi
Sports and Physical Education.

HIGHER SCHOOL OF AGRICULTURE, KEF
[ECOLE SUPÉRIEURE D'AGRICULTURE DU KEF]
7119 Le Kef
Tel: +216(8) 221-117
Directeur: Amor El Yahiaoui
Founded: 1976
Agriculture.

HIGHER SCHOOL OF AGRICULTURE, MATEUR
[ECOLE SUPÉRIEURE D'AGRICULTURE DE MATEUR]
7030 Mateur
Tel: +216(2) 465-290
Directeur: Mohamed Ber Hamonda
Secrétaire général: Tahar Mazlout
Agriculture.

HIGHER SCHOOL OF AGRICULTURE, MOGRANE
[ECOLE SUPÉRIEURE D'AGRICULTURE DE MOGRANE]
1121 Mograne-Zaghouan
Tel: +216(2) 675-043
Directeur: Habib Amamon
Scrétaire général: Mohamed Lamine Ben Khond
Founded: 1974
Agriculture.

HIGHER SCHOOL OF FOOD TECHNOLOGY
[ECOLE SUPÉRIEURE DES INDUSTRIES ALIMENTAIRES DE TUNIS]
58, rue Alain Savary, Cité El Khadrha, 1003 Tunis
Tel: +216(1) 285-526
Directeur: Abdel Hafidh Nafti
Secrétaire général: Jalel Abdeljaoued
Food Technology.

HIGHER SCHOOL OF HEALTH SCIENCES AND TECHNOLOGY
[ECOLE SUPÉRIEURE DES SCIENCES ET TECHNIQUES DE LA SANTÉ]
1007 Jabbari, La Rabta, Tunis
Tel: +216(1) 262-455
Fax: +216(1) 570-062
Directeur: Khemaies Nagati
Secrétaire général: Chedli B 7eji
Founded: 1990
Health Sciences and Technology.

HIGHER SCHOOL OF POSTS AND TELECOMMUNICATIONS
[ECOLE SUPÉRIEURE DES POSTES ET DES TÉLÉCOMMUNICATIONS DE TUNIS]
Route de Raoued Km. 3,5, 2080 Ariana
Tel: +216(1) 762-499
Directeur: Bouallégue Ammar
Secrétaire général: Salah Guez Guez
Founded: 1974
Posts and Telecommunications.

HIGHER SCHOOL OF RURAL ENGINEERING, MEJEZ EL BAB
[ECOLE SUPÉRIEURE D'INGÉNIEURS DE L'EQUIPEMENT RURAL DE MEJEZ EL BAB]
Route du Kef Km. 4,5, 9070 Mejez El Bab
Tel: +216(8) 460-422
Directeur: Ali Guarbi
Secrétaire général: Hechmi Abdelmalek
Founded: 1976
Rural Engineering.

HIGHER SCHOOL OF SCIENCE AND TECHNIQUES, TUNIS
[ECOLE NORMALE SUPÉRIEURE DES SCIENCES ET TECHNIQUES DE TUNIS]
5, Avenue Taha Hussein Montflury, 1008 Tunis
Tel: +216(1) 491-272
Directeur: Slahedine Gherissi
Secrétaire général: Nouredine Ben Ammar
D: Physics and Chemistry; Mathematics and Computer Studies; Civil Engineering; Electrical Engineering; Mechanical Engineering.

INSTITUTE FOR THE ADVANCEMENT OF THE DISABLED
[INSTITUT DE PROMOTION DES HANDICAPÉS]
Rue Yabran Khalil Yabran, 2010 Manouba
Tel: +216(1) 510-588
(1990-)
Advancement of the Disabled.

INSTITUTE OF FORESTRY, TABARKA
[INSTITUT SYLVO-PASTORAL DE TABARKA]
8110 Tabarka
Tel: +216(8) 644-542
Directeur: Ali Aloui
Founded: 1970
Forestry.

INSTITUTE OF SPORTS AND PHYSICAL EDUCATION, KEF
[INSTITUT DU SPORT ET DE L'EDUCATION PHYSIQUE DU KEF]
Cité Eddyr, Le Kef 7100
Tel: +216(1) 222-873
Founded: 1976
Sports and Physical Education.

LA MARSA PREPARATORY INSTITUTE OF SCIENTIFIC AND TECHNICAL STUDIES
[INSTITUT PRÉPARATOIRE AUX ETUDES SCIENTIFIQUES ET TECHNIQUES DE LA MARSA]
La Marsa, Tunis
Tel: +216(1) 741-964
Fax: +216(1) 746-551
Directeur: Mohamed Jaona
Secrétaire général: Trabelsi Nebiha
Founded: 1992
Scientific and Technical Studies.

NABEUL PREPARTORY INSTITUTE OF ENGINEERING
[INSTITUT PRÉPARATOIRE AUX ETUDES D'INGÉNIEURS DE NABEUL]
Merrazka, 8000 Nabeul
Tel: +216(1) 220-091
Directeur: Moncef Haddad
Secrétaire général: Mahamed Moncef Hadj Selem
Founded: 1986
Engineering.

NATIONAL AGRICULTURAL INSTITUTE OF TUNIS
[INSTITUT NATIONAL AGRONOMIQUE DE TUNISIE]
43, avenue Charles Nicolle Le Belvédère, Cité El Mahrajene, Belv 7ed 6re, 1002 Tonis
Tel: +216(1) 289-166
Directeur: Mohamed Habib Ben Hamouda
Secrétaire général: Tahar Jemmali
Founded: 1898
Agriculture.

NATIONAL HIGHER INSTITUTE OF TECHNOLOGY
[INSTITUT SUPÉRIEUR TECHNIQUE DE NABEUL]
Merazka, 8000 Nabeul
Tel: +216(2) 220-035
Directeur: Bechir Hadj Sassi
Secrétaire général: Faygal Ammar
Civil Engineering; Electrotechnics; Electrical Maintenance.

NATIONAL INSTITUTE OF OFFICE AUTOMATION AND MICROCOMPUTER SCIENCE
[INSTITUT NATIONAL DE BUREAUTIQUE ET DE MICROINFORMATIQUE]
18bis Rue de l'Inde, 1002 unis
Tel: +216(1) 794-476
Fax: +216(1) 792-084
Directeur: Tahar Hafayedh
Secrétaire général: Hosni El Ouni
Founded: 1983
Office Automation and Computer Science.

NATIONAL SCHOOL OF COMPUTER SCIENCES
[ECOLE NATIONALE DES SCIENCES DE L'INFORMATIQUE]
Rue 8000 Quartier Montplaisir, 2049 L'Ariana
Tel: +216(1) 780-394
Fax: +216(1) 785-659
Directeur: Frank Kamoun
Secrétaire général: Hassen Lazrag
Computer Science.

NATIONAL SCHOOL OF ENGINEERING
[ECOLE NATIONALE D'INGÉNIEURS DE TUNIS]
Campus Universitaire, 1060 Tunis
Tel: +216(1) 514-700
Fax: +216(1) 510-729
Directeur: Mustapha Resbes
Secrétaire général: Allagué Naceur
Engineering.

NATIONAL SCHOOL OF VETERINARY MEDICINE, SIDI THABET
[ECOLE NATIONALE DE MÉDECINE VÉTÉRINAIRE DE SIDI THABET]
Sidi Thabet 2020
Tel: +216(1) 552-460
Directeur: Mohamed Kilani
Founded: 1915
Veterinary Medicine.

POLYTECHNIC SCHOOL OF TUNISIA
[ECOLE POLYTECHNIQUE DE TUNISIE]
La Marsa
Tel: +216(1) 741-964
Fax: +216(1) 746-551
Founded: 1994
D: Signals and Systems; Mechanics and Structure; Scientific Economics and Management.

TECHNOLOGICAL INSTITUTE OF ART, ARCHITECTURE AND
TOWN PLANNING
[INSTITUT TECHNOLOGIQUE D'ART, D'ARCHITECTURE ET
D'URBANISME]
Route de l'Armée nationale, 1005
El-Omrane-Tunis
Tel: +216(1) 564-928
Fax: +216(1) 568-291
Directeur: Amor Khodja
Secrétaire général: Salem Missaoui
Founded: 1972
Art, Architecture and Town Planning.

University of Law, Economics and Management (Tunis III)
[Université de Droit, d'Economie et de Gestion
(Tunis III)]
29 Rue Asdrubal, Lafayette, 1002 Tunis
Tel: +216(1) 787-502
Fax: +216(1) 788-768
Président: Hendaoui Afif (1991-)
Secrétaire général: Hakimi Sihem
Founded: 1987
*F: Law and .Political Science; Economics;
Juridical Studies, and Political and Social
Sciences.*

HIGHER INSTITUTE OF ACCOUNTANCY, TUNIS
[INSTITUT SUPÉRIEUR DE COMPTABILITÉ DE TUNIS]
Rue des Entrepreneurs Z.I. Aéroport, Tunis
Carthage 2035
Tel: +216(1) 701-018
Fax: +216(1) 701-270
Directeur: Abdelmajid Abouda
Secrétaire général: Noureddine Harrathi
Founded: 1988
Accountancy.

HIGHER INSTITUTE OF MANAGEMENT
[INSTITUT SUPÉRIEUR DE GESTION DE TUNIS]
45, rue de la Liberté, Cité Bouchoucha, La Bardo,
Tunis
Tel: +216(1) 260-378
Fax: +216(1) 568-767
Directeur: Ahmed Ben Hamouda (1991-94)
Secrétaire général: Oueslati Naceur
International Relations: Ahmed Ben Hamouda
Founded: 1969
Management.

HIGHER SCHOOL OF COMMERCE, TUNIS
[ECOLE SUPÉRIEURE DE COMMERCE DE TUNIS]
Rue des Entrepreneurs, Zone Industrielle
Aéroport, 2035 Tunis
Tel: +216(1) 704-667
Fax: +216(1) 704-667
Directeur: Abderrazek Zouari (1991-94)
Secrétaire général: Yousef Charfeddine
Founded: 1987
*Banking Management; Hospital Management;
Tourism Management; International Trade.*

NATIONAL INSTITUTE OF LABOUR AND SOCIAL STUDIES, TUNIS
[INSTITUT NATIONAL DU TRAVAIL ET DES ETUDES SOCIALES
DE TUNIS]
5, rue Elyès Le Belvedère, Tunis
Tel: +216(1) 286-854
Fax: +216(1) 783-461
Directeur: Hatem Kotrane
Secrétaire générale: Hayer Bouhnek-Guiza
Founded: 1975
Labour and Social Studies.

NATIONAL ACADEMIC BODIES

Ministry of Education and Sciences
[Ministère de l'Education, l'Enseignement
supérieur et de la Recherche scientifique]
Tunis
Tel: +261(1) 786-300
Fax: +261(1) 786-711
Telex: 13870 minsup tn
Ministre: Ahmed Friia (1994-)
Secrétaire général: Mohamed Ayadi

Tunisian National Commission for Unesco
[Commission nationale tunisienne pour l'Unesco]
Ministère de l'Education, de l'Enseignement
supérieur et de la Recherche scientifique, 22, rue
d'Angleterre B.P., 1000 R.P. Tunis
Tel: +261(1) 258-290
Fax: +216(1) 331-014
Telex: mednat 13004 (att. commission unesco)
Président: Ahmed Friia, Minister of Education
Secrétaire général: Mongi Chemli

TURKEY

UNIVERSITIES AND TECHNICAL UNIVERSITIES

Abant Izzet Baysal University
[Abant Izzet Baysal Üniversitesi]
14300 Bolu
Tel: +90(374) 253-45-03
Fax: +90(374) 253-45-06
Rektör: Kemal Güçlüol
Genel Sekreter: I. Hakki Ülker
International Relations: Kemal Güçlüol
Founded: 1992
*F: Economics and Business Administration;
Education; Science and Literature; Technical
Education (Düzce).*
I: Social Science; Exact Sciences.
*Higher S: Vocational Education (Bolu, Düce,
Gerede, Akçakoca).*

Adnan Menderes University
[Adnan Menderes Üniversitesi]
Gazi Bulvari 39, 09010 Aydin
Tel: +90(256) 214-66-8081
Fax: +90(256) 225-32-40
Rektör: Cezmi Öncüer
Genel Sekreter: Ertan Serdar
International Relations: Cezmi Öncüer
Founded: 1992

F: Agriculture; Economics and Business Administratiion (Nazilli); Veterinary Medicine; Science and Literature; Medicine.
I: Exact Sciences; Social Sciences.
Higher S: Vocational Education.

Afyon Kocatepe University
[Afyon Kocatepe Üniversitesi]
Ordu Bulvari, 03200 Afyon
Tel: +90(272) 212-08-81
Fax: +90(272) 214-12-11
Rektör: Şehabettin Yiğitbaşi
Genel Sekreter: Özkan Yüksel
International Relations: Şehabettin Yiğitbaşi
Founded: 1992
F: Technical Education; Science and Literature; Education; Engineering.
I: Social Science.
Higher S: Vocational Education (Afyon, Bolvadin, Sandikli, Dinar, Emirdağ, Şuhut, Uşak, Banaz, Eşme, Karahalli).

*Aegean University
[Ege Üniversitesi]
Bornova, 35040 Izmir
Tel: +90(232) 388-10-19
Fax: +90(232) 339-90-90
Rektör: Refet Saygili (1982-92)
Genel Sekreter: Abdürrahim Incekara
International Relations: Refet Saygili
Founded: 1955, 1982
F: Medicine; Agriculture; Exact Sciences; Dentistry; Literature; Engineering; Pharmacy; Economics and Business Administration; Press and Publication Studies; Water Production.
I: Social Sciences; Exact Sciences; Health Sciences; Solar Energy; Nuclear Sciences; Turkish Language.
Higher S: Nursing; Physical Education and Sporti; Vocational Education (Ege, Çeşme, Izmir, Bornova).
Conservatory of Turkish Music.

Akdeniz University
[Akdeniz Üniversitesi]
PK.510, 07003 Campus Antalya
Tel: +90(242) 227-59-81
Fax: +90(242) 227-55-40
Rektör: Tuncer Karpuzoğlu
Genel Sekreter: Hüseyin Cahit Oğuz
International Relations: Tuncer Karpuzoğlu
Founded: 1982
F: Agriculture; Science and Literature; Economics and Business Administration; Medicine.
I: Health Sciences; Exact Sciences; Social Sciences.
Higher S: Physical Education and Sport; Tourism and Hotel Management; Vocational Education (Antalya, Elmali).

Anadolu (Anatolia) University
[Anadolu Üniversitesi]
Yunusemre Kampüsu, 26470 Eskisehir
Tel: +90(222) 335-34-53
Fax: +90(222) 335-36-16
E-Mail: (EARN Node ID'S) Tranavm1, tranavm2
Telex: 35147 esak tr
Rektör: Akar Öcal
Genel Sekreter: Ali Riza Önder
International Relations: Akar Öcan
Founded: 1973, 1982
F: Engineering and Architecture; Pharmacy; Economics; Science; Education; Correspondence Studies; Economics and Business Administration; Fine Arts; Communication Sciences; Literature; Administration; Law.
I: Social Sciences; Exact Sciences; Health Science Education; Economy of Communication; Communication Research for the Handicapped; Space Sciences; Fine Arts.
Higher S: Civil Defence; Tourism and Hotel Management; Physical Education and Sports; Vocational Education (Bilecik, Eskişehir, Bozüyük).
State Conservatory.

*Ankara University
[Ankara Üniversitesi]
Tandoğan Meydani, 06100 Ankara
Tel: +90(312) 223-4361
Fax: +90(312) 223-6370
Telex: tr irb 42045
Rektör: Günal Akbay
Genel Sekreter: Yavuz Okan
International Relations: Günal Akbay
Founded: 1946, 1982
F: Languages, History and Geography; Dentistry; Pharmacy; Educational Sciences; Exact Sciences; Law; Political Science; Medicine; Theology; Veterinary Medicine; Agriculture; Communication Sciences.
I: Health Sciences; Turkish Republic History; Exact Sciences; Forensic Medicine; Social Sciences; Educational Sciences.
Higher S: Justice; Midwifery and Health Sciences; Home Economics; Physical Education and Sports; Vocational Education (Ankara, Kastamonu, Çankiri, Kalecik, Dikimevi).

*Atatürk University
[Atatürk Üniversitesi]
Atatürk Üniverstesi Rektörlüğü, 2505 Erzurum
Tel: +90(442) 218-4209
Fax: +90(442) 218-7140
Rektör: Erol Oral
Genel Sekreter: Yaşar Gök
Founded: 1957, 1982
F: Dentistry; Law (Erzincan); Science and Literature; Medicine; Agriculture; Theology; Education; Education (Erzincan); Education (Ağri); Fine Arts; Economics and Administration; Engineering.

I: Fine Arts; Exact Sciences; Social Sciences; Medical Sciences; Research on Turkish Language and Literature.
Higher S: Nursing; Physical Education and Sports; Vocational Education (Erzurum, Erzincan, Bayburt).

Balikesir University
[Balikesir Üniversitesi]
10100 Balikesir
Tel: +90(266) 245-96-50
Fax: +90(266) 245-96-63
Rektör: Asim Yücel
Genel Sekreter: Cengiz Aydemir
International Relations: Asim Yücel
Founded: 1992
F: Education (Necatibey); Engineering and Architecture; Science and Literature; Economics and Business Administratione.
I: Exact Sciences; Social Sciences.
Higher S: Tourism and Hotel Management; Vocational Education (Balikesir, Bandirma, Ayvalik, Havran Burhaniye, Sağlik).

Bilkent University
[Bilkent Üniversitesi]
P.O. Box 8, 06533 Bilkent/Ankara
Tel: +90(312) 266-41-20
Fax: +90(312) 266-41-27
Telex: 443 98 tcsm tr
Rector: Ali Doğramaci
Genel Sekreter: Ümit Berkman
International Relations: Ali Doğramaci
Founded: 1984
F: Art, Design and Architecture; Business Administration; Economics, Administrative, and Social Sciences; Engineering; Humanities and Industry; Music and Performing Arts; Science.
I: Economic and Social Sciences; Engineering and Exact Sciences; Fine Arts; Music and Performing Arts; World Systems, Economies, and Strategic Research.
S: Applied Languages; English Language; Tourism and Hotel Management.
Higher S: Vocational Education.

*Boğaziçi (Bosphorous) University
[Boğaziçi Üniversitesi]
80815 Bebek/Istanbul
Tel: +90(212) 265-14-86
Fax: +90(212) 265-63-57
Telex: 26411 boun tr
Rektör: Üstün Ergüder
Genel Sekreter: Metin Balci
International Relations: Üstün Ergüder
Founded: 1863, 1971
F: Economic and Administrative Sciences; Engineering; Science and Literature; Education; Economics and Business Administration; Engineering.
I: Turkish Republic History; Environment Sciences; Biomedical Engineering; Earthquake Research; Exact Sciences; Social Sciences.

Higher S: Foreign Languages; Vocational Education.

Çanakkale (Eighteenth March) University
[Çanakkale Onsekiz Mart Üniversitesi]
17100 Canakkale
Tel: +90(286) 212-88-16
Fax: +90(286) 212-88-15
Rektör: Mete Tunçoku
Genel Sekreter: Ramazan Eren
International Relations: Mete Tunçoku
Founded: 1992
F: Education; Science and Literature.
I: Exact Sciences; Social Sciences.
Higher S: Tourism and Hotel Management; Vocational Education (Çanakkale, Biga).

Celal Bayar University
[Celal Bayar Üniversitesi]
45040 Manisa
Tel: +90(236) 237-29-28
Fax: +90(236) 237-24-42
Rektör: Ümit Doğay Arinç
Genel Sekreter: Necmettin Yalçin
International Relations: Ümit Doğay
Founded: 1992
F: Economics and Business Administration; Engineering; Science and Literature.
I: Physical Education and Sports; Tobacco Studies.
Higher S: Vocational Education (Alaşehir).

*Çukurova University
[Çukurova Üniversitesi]
01330 Balcali/Adana
Tel: +90(322) 338-65-52
Fax: +90(322) 338-69-45
Telex: 629 35 çtüb tr
Rektör: Can Özşahinoğlu
Genel Sekreter: A. Adnan Tibet
International Relations: Can Özşahinoğlu
Founded: 1969, 1973
F; Agriculture; Medicine; Science and Literature; Engineering and Architecture; Education; Economics and Business Administration; Fisheries; Theology.
I: Exact Sciences; Social Sciences; Health Sciences.
Higher S: Vocational Education (Ceyhan, Osmaniye, Adana, Kozan).

*Cumhuriyet (Republic) University
[Cumhuriyet Üniversitesi]
58140 Sivas
Tel: +90(346) 266-15-93
Fax: +90(346) 226-15-13
Telex: 15167
Rektör: Asim Gültekin
Genel Sekreter: Ateş Gültekin
International Relations: Asim Gültekin
Founded: 1974, 1982
F: Medicine; Science and Literature; Engineering.

I: Health Sciences; Exact Sciences; Social Sciences.
Higher S: Nursing; Vocational Education (Sivas, Divriği).

*Dicle (Tigris) University
[Dicle Üniversitesi]
21280 Diyarbakir
Tel: +90(412) 248-82-02
Fax: +90(412) 248-82-16
Rektör: Sedat Aritürk
Genel Sekreter: Mehmet Tekdöş
International Relations: Sedat Aritürk
Founded: 1966, 1973, 1982
F: Medicine; Dentistry; Law; Science and Literature; Engineering and Architecture; Agriculture; Education; Education (Siirt); Veterinary Medicine.
I: Exact Sciences; Health Sciences; Social Sciences.
Higher S: Vocational Education (Batman, Diyarbakir, Mardin, Çermik, Bismil).

Dokuz Eylül (Ninth September) University
[Dokuz Eylül Üniversitesi]
Cumhuriyet Bul. 144, 35210 Alsancak/Izmir
Tel: +90(232) 421-40-80
Fax: +90(232) 422-09-78
Telex: 52407 dbte tr
Rektor: Namik Çevik
Genel Sekreter: Ismail Hakki Karataş
International Relations: Namik Çevik
Founded: 1982
F: Medicine; Education (Buca); Engineering; Fine Arts; Architecture; Law; Theology; Management.
S: Tourism and Hotel Administration.
I: Ataturk's Principles and Turkish Republic History; Marine Sciences; Educational Sciences; Exact Sciences; Social Sciences; Health Sciences; Oncology.
Higher S: Justice; Marine Administration and Management; Theology; Health Services, Physical Therapy and Rehabilitation; Vocational Education (Izmir, Torbali).
Conservatory.

Dumlupinar University
[Dumlupinar Üniversitesi]
43100 Çamlibahçe/Kütahya
Tel: +90(274) 224-42-85
Fax: +90(274) 224-42-88
Rektor: Ömer Riza Akgün
Genel Sekreter: Paşa Yildiz
International Relations: Ömer Riza Akgün
Founded: 1992
F: Economics and Administration; Science and Literature; Engineering; Economics and Administration (Bilecik); Technical Education.
S: Tourism and Hotel Administration.
I: Exact Sciences; Social Sciences.
Higher S: Vocational Education (Kütahya, Tavşanli, Gediz).

Erciyes University
[Erciyes Üniversitesi]
Talas Yolu, Kayseri
Tel: +90(352) 437-49-22
Fax: +90(352) 437-49-37
Rektör: Mehmet Şahin
Genel Sekreter: Mümin Ertürk
International Relations: Mehmet Şahin
Founded: 1978, 1982
F: Science and Literature; Medicine; Engineering; Theology; Economics and Business Administration; Fine Arts; Architecture.
I: Social Sciences; Health Sciences; Exact Sciences.
Higher S: Tourism and Hotel Management (Nevşehir); Vocational Education (Nevşehir, Kocasinan, Kayseri, Yozgat).

Firat (Euphrates) University
[Firat Üniversitesi]
23119 Elâziğ
Tel: +90(424) 212-85-10
Fax: +90(424) 212-27-17
Telex: 236 45 38 efut
Rektör: Eyüp G. Ispir
Genel Sekreter: Gazi Özcan
International Relations: Eyüp G. Ispir
Founded: 1975, 1982
F: Science and Literature; Engineering; Medicine; Technical Education; Veterinary Science; Water Products.
I: Health Sciences; Exact Sciences; Social Sciences.
Higher S.: Vocational Education (Elaziğ, Muş, Tunceli, Bingöl, Keban).

Galatasary University
[Galatasary Üniversitesi]
Çirağan Cad., Yildiz Mah.9, Ortaköy/Istanbul
Tel: +90(212) 259-55-57
Fax: +90(212) 259-20-85-17
Rektör: Yildizhan Yayla
International Relations: Yildizhan Yayla
Founded: 1992
F: Science and Literature; Engineering and Technology; Law; Economics and Business Administration; Communication.
I: Social Sciences; Exact Sciences.

*Gazi University Ankara
[Gazi Üniversitesi]
Bandirma Sok, Teknikokullar, Ankara 06500
Tel: +90(312) 213-4244
Fax: +90(312) 221-3200
Rektör: Enver Hasanoğlu
Genel Sekreter: Satilmiş Erdal
International Relations: Enver Hasanoğlu
Founded: 1982
F: Architecture and Engineering; Science and Literature; Dentistry; Economics and Business Administration; Education; Medicine; Pharmacy; Technical Education; Theology (Çorum); Vocational Education; Communication; Industrial

TURKEY

Arts; Tourism and Commerce; Non-formal
(External) Vocational Training.
Higher I: Physical Training and Sports.
Higher S: Title Deed and Cadastrial Studies;
Public Finance Studies; Health Services Studies;
Vocational Education (Kiralan, Çorum, Keçiören,
Kastamonu).

Gaziantep University
[Gaziantep Üniversitesi]
27310 Gaziantep
Tel: +90(342) 360-10-10
Fax: +90(342) 360-10-13
Telex: 691 46 gaum tr
Rektör: Uğur Büget
Genel Sekreter: Çevik Çakmur
International Relations: Uğur Büget
Founded: 1987
F: Engineering; Medicine; Science and
Literature; Economics and Business
Administration.
I: Exact Sciences; Health Sciences; Social
Sciences.
Higher S: Vocational Education (Gaziantep,
Kilis).
Music Conservatory.

Gaziosmanpaşa University
[Gaziosmanpaşa Üniversitesi]
60110 Tokat
Tel: +90(356) 214-30-49
Fax: +90(356) 214-14-86
Rektör: M. Kemal Özsoy
Genel Sekreter: Osman Alkaç
International Relations: Kemal Özsoy
Founded: 1992
F: Agriculture; Science and Literature.
I: Exact Sciences; Social Sciences.
Higher S: Vocational Education (Tokat, Niksar,
Zile, Erbaa).

Gebze Technological Institute
[Gebze Yüksek Teknoloji Enstitüsü]
Gebzeldak
Tel: +90(212) 257-50-31
Fax: +90(212) 257-50-31
Rektör: Ahmet Ayhan
International Relations: Ahmet Ayhan
Founded: 1992
F: Science; Engineering; Architecture;
Management; Teacher Education.
I: Engineering and Exact Sciences.

*Hacettepe University
[Hacettepe Üniversitesi]
Hacettepe Parki, 06100 Ankara
Tel: +90(312) 311-00-65
Fax: +90(312) 310-55-52
Telex: 422 37htk tr
Rektör: A. Yüksel Bozer
Genel Sekreter: M. Erdem Takçi
International Relations: Yüksel Bozer.
Founded: 1206, 1967

F: Medicine; Pharmacy; Dentistry; Economics
and Business Administration; Education;
Engineering; Fine Arts; Literature; Science;
Engineering; History of Art; Child Health; Exact
Sciences; Neurology and Psychiatrics; Psychiatry
and Neurology; Sciences; Nuclear Science
(Beytepe); Social Sciences (Beytepe); Turkish
Republic History (Beytepe); Population Research;
Nuclear Science; Oncology; Health Sciences;
Social Sciences; Fine Arts; Turkish Research.
S: Foreign Languages (Beytepe).
Higher S: Home Economics; Physical Therapy
and Rehabilitation; Nursing; Health Services;
Foreign Languages; Vocational Education
(Ankara).
Ankara State Conservatory: (Beytepe).

Harran University
[Harran Üniversitesi]
63200 Şanliurfa
Tel: +90(414) 312-81-41
Fax: +90(414) 312-81-44
Rektör: Servet Armağan
Genel Sekreter: Ismail Benek
International Relations: Servet Armağan
Founded: 1992
F: Theology; Agriculture; Engineering; Medicine.
I: Exact Sciences; Social Sciences.
Higher S: Vocational Education.

Inönü University
[Inönü Üniversitesi]
44100 Malatya
Tel: +90(422) 341-00-27
Fax: (422) 341-0034
Telex: 661 40 inon tr
Rektör: Mehmet Yücesoy
Genel Sekreter: Zekeriya Çalişkan
International Relations: Mehmet Yücesoy
Founded: 1975, 1982
F: Science and Literature; Education;
Economics and Business Administration;
Medicine; Theology; Engineering.
I: Social Sciences; Exact Sciences; Health
Sciences.
Higher S: Vocational Education (Malatya,
Adiyaman, Arapkir).

*Istanbul Technical University
[Istanbul Teknik Üniversitesi]
Ayazağa Campus, 80626 Maslak-Istanbul
Tel: +90(212) 285-3333
Fax: +90(212) 285-6610
E-Mail: rksaglam@tritu.bitnet
Telex: 28186 Itü tr .
Rektör: Reşat Baykal
Genel Sekreter: Nevzat Özkök
International Relations: Reşat Baykal
Founded: 1944, 1982
F: Civil Engineering; Engineering (Sakarya);
Architecture; Mechanical Engineering; Aerospace
Engineering; Electrical Engineering and
Electronics; Mining Engineering; Science and
Letters; Marine Architecture; Chemical

656

Engineering and Metallurgy; Management
Studies.
I: Nuclear Energy; Sciences and Technology;
Social Sciences.
D: Languages and Turkish Republic History;
Fine Arts; Physical Education.
Higher S: Vocational Education (Düzce, Sakary).
Conservatory of Turkish Music.

Izmir Technological Institute
[Izmir Yüksek Teknoloji Enstitüsü]
Anafartalar Cad. 904, 35230 Izmir
Tel: +90(232) 441-99-00
Fax: +90(232) 441-95-96
Rektör: Erdal Saygin
International Relations: Erdal Saygin
Founded: 1992
F: Science; Engineering; Architecture.
I: Engineering and Exact Sciences.

*Istanbul University
[Istanbul Üniversitesi]
Beyazit, 34452 Istanbul
Tel: +90(212) 513-4187
Fax: +90(212) 520-5473
Telex: 229 62 isur tr
Rektör: Bülent Berkarda
Genel Sekreter: Hüseyin Çavuşoğlu
International Relations: Bülent Berkarda
Founded: 1453, 1933, 1946
F: Medicine; Medicine (Cerrahpaşa); Law;
Literature; Science; Economics; Forestry;
Pharmacy; Dentistry; Engineering; Business
Administration; Veterinary Science; Political
Science; Communication; Water Products;
Theology.
I: Cardiology; Exact Sciences; Social Sciences;
Health Sciences; Child Health; Forensic
Medicine; Oncology; Marine Sciences and
Geography; Atatürk's Principles and Turkish
Republic History; Türkiyat (Turkology); Neurology;
Lung Diseases.
Higher S: Nursing; Journalism; Marine
Products; Justice; Vocational Education (Şişli,
Bakirköy).
Ce: Experimental Medicine Research and
Application (DETAM).
Istanbul University Conservatory.

Kafkas University
[Kafkas Üniversitesi]
36040 Kars
Tel: +90(474) 223-75-64
Fax: +90(474) 223-38-99
Rektör: Nihat Bayşu
Genel Sekreter: Ismail Alabulut
International Relations: Nihat Bayşu
Founded: 1992
F: Veterinary Medicine; Science and Literature;
Forestry (Artvin).
I: Health Sciences; Exact Sciences.
Higher S: Physical Education and Sport;
Vocational Education.

Kahramanmaraş Sütçü Imam University
[Kahramanmaraş Sütçü Imam Üniversitesi]
46060 Kahramanmaraş
Tel: +90(344) 223-74-05
Fax: +90(344) 223-74-09
Rektör: Yusuf Vanli
Genel Sekreter: Salih Ayhan
International Relations: Yusuf Vanli
Founded: 1992
F: Agriculture; Science and Literature; Forestry;
Economics and Business Administration; Exact
Sciences; Social Sciences.
Higher S: Vocational Education
(Kahramanmaraş, Elbistan, Göksun).

*Karadeniz University of Technology
[Karadeniz Teknik Üniversitesi]
6108 Trabzon
Tel: +90(462) 325-3152
Fax: +90(325) 325-3205
Telex: 067-83110
Rector: A. Aydin Dumanoğlu
Genel Sekreter: Turgut Seymen Sekban
International Relations: Aydin Dumanoğlu
Founded: 1963, 1982
F; Architecture and Engineering; Medicine;
Science and Literature; Forestry; Education
(Fatih, Giresun); Economics and Business
Administration; Economics and Business
Administration (Ünye); Marine Sciences
(Sürmene); Theology (Rize); Water Products
(Rize); Engineering (Gümüşhane).
I: Exact Sciences; Health Sciences; Social
Sciences.
Higher S: Vocational Education (Rize,
Gümüşhane, Giresun, Trabzon, Artvin).

Kirikkale University
[Kirikkale Üniversitesi]
711002 Kirakkale
Tel: +90(318) 224-69-07
Fax: +90(318) 224-46-83
Rektör: Beşir Atalay
Genel Sekreter: Halil Şaliş
International Relations: Beşir Atalay
Founded: 1992
F: Science and Literature; Engineering;
Economics and Business Administration.
I: Exact Sciences; Social Sciences.
Higher S: Vocational Education
(Kahramanmaraş, Elbistan, Göksun).

Koç University
[Koç Üniversitesi]
80860 Istinye/Istanbul
Tel: +90(212) 277-57-68
Fax: +90(212) 229-36-02
Rektör: Seha M. Tiniç
Genel Sekreter: Ferdin Hoyi
International Relations: Seha M. Tiniç
Founded: 1993
F: Exact and Human Sciences; Economics and
Business Administration.
I: Administration; English Language.

Kocaeli University
[Kocaeli Üniversitesi]
Anit Park Tani Pk. 318, 41300 Izmit
Tel: +90(262) 321-59-68
Fax: +90(262) 321-59-68
Rektör: Atif Ural
Genel Sekreter: Ömer Yalçin
International Relations: Atif Ural
Founded: 1992
F: Engineering; Science and Literature;
Technical Education; Economics and Business
Administration.
I: Exact Sciences; Social Sciences.

Marmara University
[Marmara Üniversitesi]
Sultanahmet, 34413 Istanbul
Tel: +90(212) 518-48-03
Fax: +91(212) 518-16-15
Telex: 31143 odfo tr
Rektor: Ömer Faruk Batirel
Sekreter Genel: Altan Kitapçi
International Relations: Ömer Faruk Batirel
Founded: 1883, 1959, 1982
F: Science and Literature; Law; Education;
Technical Education; Administrative Economics
and Sciences; Dentistry; Pharmacy; Medicine;
Engineering; Theology; Fine Arts; Commerce.
I: Exact Sciences; Health Sciences; Social
Sciences; Banking and Insurance; European
Community Studies; Turkic Studies; Neurology;
Middle East and Islamic Countries Studies;
Education; Gastroenterology; Fine Arts.
Higher S: Vocational Education.

Mersin University
[Mersin Üniversitesi]
33070 Mersin
Tel: +90(324) 336-80-10
Fax: +90(324) 336-80-15
Rektör: Vurul Ülkü
Genel Sekreter: Mithat Barim
International Relations: Vurul Ülkü
Founded: 1992
F: Science and Literature; Engineering; Fine
Arts; Economics and Business Administration.
I: Exact Sciences; Social Sciences.
Higher S: Tourism and Hotel Management;
Vocational Education (Tarsus, Mut,Mersin,
Gülnar).

*Middle East Technical University Ankara
[Orta Dogu Teknik Üniversitesi]
Inönü Bulvaru, 06531 Ankara
Tel: +90(312) 210-11-00
Fax: +90(312) 210-11-05
E-Mail: halkilis@trmetu.bitnet
Telex: 42761 odtk tr
Rektör (President): Süha Sevük (1992-)
Genel Sekreter: Mehmet Çalişkan
Founded: 1956, 1959
F: Economics and Business Administration;
Architecture; Science and Literature; Education;
Engineering.

I: Exact Sciences; Marine Sciences; Social
Sciences.
Higher S: Foreign Languages; Vocational
Education.

Mimar Sinan University
[Mimar Sinan Üniversitesi]
Findikli-Istanbul
Tel: +90 (212) 293-37-60
Fax: +90(212) 244-03-98
Telex: 24723 msu tr
Rektör: Gündüz Gökçe
Genel Sekreter: Sabit Ayasbeyoğlu
International Relations: Gündüz Gökçe
Founded: 1883, 1926, 1982
F: Fine Arts; Science and Literature;
Architecture.
I: Social Sciences; Exact Sciences.
Higher S: Vocational Education (Tarsus, Mut,
Mersin, Gülnar).
Conservatory.

Muğla University
[Muğla Universitesi]
48170 Muğla
Tel: +90(252) 223-82-47
Fax: +90(252) 223-80-01
Rektör: Ethen Ruhu Fiğlali
Genel Sekreter: Isa Özkul
International Relations: Ethem Ruhu Fiğli
Founded: 1992
F: Science and Literature; Economics and
Business Administration.
I: Social Sciences; Exact Sciences.
Higher S: Vocational Education.

Mustafa Kemal University
[Mustafa Kemal Universitesi]
31040 Antakya
Tel: +90(326) 216-06-72
Fax: +90(326) 216-06-70
Rektör: Haluk Ipek
Genel Sekreter: Nurettin Çağlar
International Relations: Haluk Ipek
Founded: 1992
F: Education; Engineering and Architecture;
Economics and Business Administration;
Agriculture.
Higher S: Vocational Education (Antakya,
Iskenderun, Dörtyol).

Niğde University
[Niğde Universitesi]
51200 Niğde
Tel: +90(388) 232-38-74
Fax: +90(388) 232-24-23
Rektör: Oktay Yazgan
Genel Sekreter: Güngör Çolak
International Relations: Oktay Yazgan
Founded: 1992
F: Education; Engineering and Architecture;
Economics and Business Administration;
Economics and Business Administration
(Aksaray); Science and Literature.

I: Exact Sciences; Social Sciences.
Higher S: *Vocational Education (Niğde, Zübeyde Hanim, Bor, Aksaray).*

*Ondokuz Mayis (Nineteenth May) University Samsun

[Ondokuz Mayis Üniversitesi]
Kurupelit, Samsun 55139
Tel: +90(362) 457-58-70
Fax: +90(362) 457-60-91
Telex: 82022 som tr
Rektör: Naci Gúrses
International Relations: Naci Gürses
Founded: 1975, 1982
F: *Agriculture; Medicine; Education; Education (Amasya); Science and Literature; Theology; Water Products; Dentistry.*
I: Health Sciences; Exact Sciences; Social Sciences.
Higher S: *Vocational Education (Samsun, Bafra, Ordu, Sihop, Havza, Amasya, Merzifon).*

Osmangazi University

[Osmangazi Universitesi]
26480 Meşelik/Eskişehir
Tel: +90(222) 239-71-48
Fax: +90(222) 239-54-00
Rektör: Esat Erenoğlu
International Relations: Oktay Yazgan
Founded: 1993
F: *Medicine; Science and Literature; Economics and Business Administration; Engineering and Architecture.*
I: Exact Sciences; Social Sciences; Metallurgy; Health Sciences.
Higher S: *Vocational Education.*

Pamukkale University

[Pamukkale Universitesi]
20020 Incilipinar/Denizli
Tel: +90(258) 264-14-40
Fax: +90(258) 263-00-88
Rektör: Arif Akşit
Genel Sekreter: Metin Bulut
International Relations: Arif Akşit
Founded: 1992
F: *Engineering; Education; Economics and Business Administration.*
I: Exact Sciences; Social Sciences; Health Sciences.
Higher S: *Vocational Education.*

Sakarya University

[Sakarya Üniversitesi]
54040 Sakarya
Tel: +90(264) 343-12-70
Fax: +90(264) 343-12-75
Rektör: Ramazan Evren
Genel Sekreter: Zübeyir Yilmiz
International Relations: Ramazan Evren
Founded: 1992
F: *Theology; Science and Literature; Economics and Business Administration; Engineering; Technical Education.*

I: Exact Sciences; Social Sciences.
Higher S: *Vocational Education.*

Selçuk University

[Selçuk Üniversitesi]
Meram Yeni Yol, 42151 Konya
Tel: +90(332) 352-09-91
Fax: +90(332) 352-09-98
Rektör: Halil Cin
Genel Sekreter: Rifat Karaman
International Relations: Halil Cin
Founded: 1975, 1982
F: *Agriculture; Engineering and Architecture; Science and Literature; Education; Law; Medicine; Theology; Veterinary Science; Dentistry; Economics and Business Administration; Economics and Business Administration (Karaman); Vocational Education; Communication.*
I: Social Sciences; Exact Sciences; Health Sciences; Turkic Language and Literature.
Higher S: *Vocational Education (Ereğli, Karaman, Seydişehir, Beyşehir, Akşehir, Ermenek, Hadim, Sarayönü, Ilgin, Silifke Taşucu, Kadinhani).*

Süleyman Demirel University

[Süleyman Demirel Universitesi]
32200 Isparta
Tel: +90(246) 237-08-50
Fax: +90(246) 237-04-31
Rektör: Hasan Gürbüz
Genel Sekreter: Ahmet Tevfik Köse
International Relations: Hasan Gürbüz
Founded: 1992
F: *Theology; Science and Literature; Medicine; Economics and Business Administration; Engineering and Architecture; Education; Water Products.*
I: Exact Sciences; Social Sciences; Health Sciences.
Higher S: *Vocational Education (Isparta, Burdur, Yalvaç).*

Trakya University

[Trakya Üniversitesi]
22030 Edirne
Tel: +90(284) 235-82-17
Fax: +90(284) 235-72-74
Rektör: Poyraz Ülger
Genel Sekreter: Suat Sucuoğlu
International Relations: Poyraz Ülger
Founded: 1977, 1982
F: *Agriculture (Tekirdag); Engineering and Architecture; Engineering (Çorlu); Science and Literature; Medicine; Economics and Business Administration.*
I: Social Sciences; Sciences; Health Sciences; Exact Sciences.
Higher S: *Vocational Education (Edirne, Tekirdağ, Kirklareli, Çorlu, Keşan, Şarköy, Hayrabolu, Lüleburgaz, Malkara).*
Conservatory.

*Uludag University
[Uludag Üniversitesi]
Görkle Kampusü, Görükle, 16096 Bursa
Tel: +90(224) 442-80-01
Fax: +90(224) 442-80-12
Telex: 322 25 burn tr
Rektör: Ayhan Kizil (1992-96)
Genel Sekreter: Suna Gökirmak
International Relations: Ayhan Kizil
Founded: 1975, 1982
*F: Agriculture; Medicine; Education; Science
and Literature; Economics and Business
Administration Sciences; Theology; Engineering
and Architecture; Veterinary Medicine.
I: Exact Sciences; Social Sciences; Health
Sciences.
Higher S: Vocational Education.*

Yildiz Technical University
[Yildiz Teknik Üniversitesi]
80750 Beşiktaş/Istanbul
Tel: +90(212) 261-20-02
Fax: +90(212) 261-42-84
Rektör: Turgut Uzel
Genel Sekreter: Atilla Salt
International Relations: Turgut Uzel
Founded: 1911, 1937, 1969, 1982
*F: Architecture; Electrical and Electronic
Engineering; Construction; Economics and
Business Administration; Chemistry and
Metallurgy; Mechanics.
I: Social Sciences; Exact Sciences.
Higher S: Vocational Education.*

*Yüzüncü Yil (Centennial) University
[Yüzüncü Yil Üniversitesi]
65080 Van
Tel: +90(432) 225-10-10
Fax: +90(432) 225-10-09
Rektör: Seyet Mehmet Şen
Genel Sekreter: Salih Mercan
International Relations: Seyit Mehmet Şen
Founded: 1982
*F: Science and Literature; Veterinary Medicine;
Agriculture; Education; Theology; Medicine.
I: Social Sciences; Exact Sciences; Health
Sciences.
Higher S: Vocational Education (Van, Hakkari,
Bitlis, Erciş, Tatvan, Adilcevaz, Ahlat).*

Zonguldak Karaelmaz University
[Zonguldak Karaelmaz Üniversitesi]
67100 Zonguldak
Tel: +90(372) 257-40-14
Fax: +90(372) 257-50-78
Rektör: Ramazan Özen
Genel Sekreter: Amuhittin Koca
International Relations: Ramazan Özen
Founded: 1992
*F: Engineering; Science and Literature (Devrek);
Forestry (Bartin); Teacher Education (Karabük).
I: Exact Sciences.*

*Higher S: Vocational Education (Zonguldak,
Alapli, Safranbolu, Sağlik).*

NATIONAL ACADEMIC BODIES

Ministry of National Education
General Directorate of Higher Education,
Education Abroad and External Relations, Ankara
Tel: +90(312) 418-21-89
General Director: Aydoğan Ataünal

Higher Education Council
[Yükset Ögretim Kurulu]
Bilkent, Ankara
Tel: +90(312) 266-47-31
President: Mehmet Sağlam
Secretary-General: Attila Konaç
Founded: 1981

Committee of Turkish University Rectors
[Türk Üniversite Rektörleri Komitesi]
Yüksek Ögretim Kurulu, Bilkent, Ankara
Tel: +90(41) 22-5316
Telex: 42839
President: Ihsan Doğramaci
International Relations: Ergün Togröl
Founded: 1967

Turkish National Commission for Unesco
7 Göreme Sokak, Kavaklidere, 06680 Ankara
Tel: +90(4) 426-5894
Fax: +90(4) 427-2064
Telex: 46585 unes tr
Chairman: Olus Arik

TURKMENISTAN

UNIVERSITIES

*Turkmen University
[Turkmenskij Gosudarstvennyj Universitet]
Prosp. Lenina 31, 744014 Ašhaabad
Tel: +7 5-11-59
Rektor: O.N. Muradov
Founded: 1950
*F: Economics; History; Law; Turkmen Philology;
Russian Philology; Mathematics; Physics; Biology
and Geography; Physical Education; Foreign
Languages; Evening Studies.
D: Correspondence Courses.*

OTHER INSTITUTIONS

Ashabadskij Institut Narodnogo Hozjajstva
Ul. Hudajberdyeva 46, 744004 Ashabad
Fine and Applied Arts.

**Turkmenskij Gosudarstvennyj Medicinskij
Institut**
Ul. Saumjana 58, 744000 Ashabad 19
Medicine.

Turkmenskij Gosudarstvennyj Pedagogiceskij Institut Iskusstv
Prosp. V.I. Lenina 3, 744007 Ashabad
Education.

Turkmenskij Politehniceskij Institut
Ul. Kotovskogo 1, 744025 Ashabad 8
Tel: +7 9-37-10

Turkmenskij Sel'-skohozjajstvennyj Institut
Ul. Pervomajskaja 62, 744000 Ashabad
Tel: +7 4-25-22
Agriculture.

NATIONAL ACADEMIC BODIES

Academy of Sciences of Turkmenistan
Ul. Gogol 15, 744000 Ashabad
Tel: +7(3632) 295-427
Fax: +7(3632) 253-716
Director, Desert Research Institute: Agadjan G. Babaev

Turkmen National Commmision for Unesco
Ministry of Foreign Affairs, Magtymguly 83, 744000 Ashabad
Tel: +7(3632) 251-411
Fax: +7(3632) 251-463
Chairman: B. Shikhmuradov, Deputy Prime Minister
Secretary: M. Charyyev

UGANDA

UNIVERSITIES

PUBLIC INSTITUTIONS

Makerere University
P.O. Box 7062, Kampala
Tel: +256(41) 532-752
Telex: 61351
Vice-Chancellor: William Senteza-Kajubi
Academic Registrar: B. Onyango
Founded: 1922, 1949, 1975
F: Agriculture and Forestry; Arts; Commerce; Education; Fine and Industrial Arts; Law; Medicine; Sciences; Social Sciences; Technology; Veterinary Medicine.

Mbarara University of Science and Technology
P.O. Box 1410, Mbarara
Tel: +256(485) 20782
Fax: +256(485)21373
Cable: must uga
Vice-Chancellor: F.I.B. Kayanja
Registrar: S.B. Bazirake
Founded: 1989

F: Medicine.
I: Tropical Forest Conservation.

PRIVATE INSTITUTIONS

Islamic University in Uganda
P.O. Box 2555, Mbale
Tel: +156(45) 3061
Fax: +256(45) 3544
Telex: 66176 isluniv ug
Vice-Chancellor and Rector (Acting): Ally Kirunda-Kivejinja
Secretary: A.K. Segendo

Martyrs University
Nkozi Hill

Uganda Christian University
Ndejje

OTHER INSTITUTIONS

Institute of Teacher Education
P.O. Box 1, Kampala

NATIONAL ACADEMIC BODIES

Ministry of Education and Sports
Crested Towers, Hannington Road, P.O. Box 7063, Kampala
Tel: +256(41) 234-440
Fax: +256(41) 244-394
Minister: Nuwe Amanye-Mushega

Uganda National Examinations Board
P.O. Box 7066, Kampala

Uganda National Commission for Unesco
Ministry of Education, Crested Towers, Hannington Road, P.O. Box 4962, Kampala
Tel: +256(41) 259-713
Fax: +256(41) 244-394
Telex: 61298 unesco ug
Chairman: Nuwe Amanye-Mushega, Minister of Education
Secretary-General: Anastasia Nakkazi

UKRAINE

UNIVERSITIES

Chernovtsy University
[Černovickij Gosudarstvennyj Universitet]
Ul. Kocjubinskogo 2, 274012 Černovcy
Founded: 1875

F: History; Philology; Mathematics; Physics; Chemistry; Biology; Geography; Foreign Languages.
D: Evening Studies; Correspondence Courses.

Dniepropetrovsk University
[Dnepropetrovskij Gosudarstvennyj Universitet]
Prosp. Gagarina 72, 320625 Dnepropetrovsk 10
Tel: +7 3-16-71
F: History; Philosophy; Mathematics and Applied Mathematics; Physics; Physics and Technology; Chemistry; Biology; Economics; Radio-Physics; General Studies.
D: Evening Studies.

Donets University
[Doneckij Gosudarstvennyj Universitet]
Universitetskaja ul. 24, 340055 Doneck
Tel: +7 33-00-28
Founded: 1965
F: Law; History; Philology; Languages; Physics; Mathematics; Chemistry; Biology; Economics.
D: Evening Studies; Correspondence Courses.

International Science and Technology University
Pros. Pobeda 37, Bldg.13, 252110, Kiev
Tel: +7(044)244-6479
Fax: +7(044) 274-932
President: Y. Bugai
Electronic and Electrical Engineering; Computer Systems; Business; Science and Methology; Mechanical Engineering.

*Kharkov University
[Har'kovskij Gosudarstvennyj Universitet]
Pl. Dzeržinskogo 4, 310077 Har'kov
Tel: +7 45-73-75
Rektor: Ivan E. Tarapov
Founded: 1805
F: History; Mathematics and Mechanics; Physics; Chemistry; Biology; Geology and Geography; Economics; Foreign Languages; Philology; Radio-Physics; Technical Physics; Foreign Students (Preparatory).
I: Chemical Research; Biological Research.
D: Evening Studies; Correspondence Courses.

*Kiev 'Taras Scevchenko' University
[Kyius'kyi Universytet IM. Tarasa Shevchenka]
Volodymyrs'ka 60, 252017 Kiyiv
Tel: +7 220-86-91
Fax: +7 224-61-66
Rektor: V.V. Skopenko (1985-)
Founded: 1834
F: Philology; History; Philosophy; Law; Economics; Foreign Philology; Journalism; Mathematics and Applied Mathematics; Cybernetics; Physics; Radio-Physics; Chemistry; Biology; Geography; Geology; History; Foreign Students (Preparatory).
I: International Relations (Ukrainian); Physiology (Research); Teachers of Social Sciences (Refresher).
D: Physical Training.

Ce: Calculus.
Observatory.

L'vov University
[L'vovskij Gosudarstvennyj Universitet]
Ul. Universitetskaja 1, 290602 L'vov
Tel: +7 72-20-68
Founded: 1661, 1817, 1851, 1919
F: History; Philology; Journalism; Law; Economics; Mathematics; Mechanics and Applied Mathematics; Physics; Chemistry; Geology; Biology; Geography; Foreign Languages.
D: Correspondence Courses; Evening Studies.
Observatory: Astronomical.
Station: Magnetics; Mountain Biological.
L: Radio-Biological; Geo-Chemical and Radio Metrical Prospection.

Odessa University
[Odesskij Gosudarstvennyj Universitet]
Ul. Petra Velikogo 2, 270057 Odessa
Tel: +7 235-254
Fax: +7 232-236 su trade
Rektor: Igor Petrovitch Zelinsky
Founded: 1865
F: History; Law; Philology; Romance and Germanic Philology; Mathematics and Applied Mathematics; Physics; Chemistry; Biology; Geology and Geography.
D: Evening Studies; Correspondence Courses.
Scientific Research I: Physics.

Simferopol University
[Simferopol'skij Gosudarstvennyj Universitet]
Ul. Jaltinskaja 4, 333036 Simferopol'
Tel: +7 3-22-80
Founded: 1972
F: History; Philology; Romance and Germanic Philology; Geography; Natural Sciences; Physics; Mathematics.
D: Evening Studies; Correspondence Courses.

Uzhgorod University
[Užgorodskij Gosudarstvennyj Universitet]
Ul. M. Gor'kogo 46, 294000 Užgorod
Tel: +7 3-42-02
Founded: 1945, 1953
F: History; Romance and German Philology; Mathematics; Physics; Chemistry; Biology; Medicine; General Technological Studies.
D: Evening Studies; Correspondence Courses.

Zaporozhe University
[Zaporozskij Gosudarstvennys Universitet]
Ul. Žukovskogo 66, 330600 Zaporože
Tel: +7 64-29-30
F: Philology; Foreign Languages; History; Physics and Mathematics; Physical Education.

OTHER INSTITUTIONS

Belocerkovskij Sel'skohozjajstvennyj Institut
Ul. M. Svobody 8/1, 256400 Belaja Cerkov, Kievskoj obl.
Tel: +7 5-12-88
Agriculture.

Cernovickij Gosudarstvennyj Medicinskij Institut
Pl. Teatral'naja 2, 274000 Cernovcy
Medicine.

Dneprodzerzinskij Industrial'nyj Institut
Ul. Dneprostroevskaja 2, 322618 Dneprodzerzinsk
Tel: +7 3-21-23
Industrial Engineering.

Dnepropetrovskij Gornyj Institut
Prosp. Karla Marksa 19, 320600 Dnepropetrovsk
Tel: +7 45-43-44
Mining.

Dnepropetrovskij Himiko-Tehnologiceskij Institut
Prosp. Gagarina 8, 320640 Dnepropetrovsk
Tel: +7 45-32-91
Chemico-Technology.

Dnepropetrovskij Institut Inzenerov Zeleznodoroznogo Transporta
Ul. Akademika Lazarjana 2, 320629-GSP Dnepropetrovsk 10
Tel: +7 3-13-12
Transport.

Dnepropetrovskij Inzenerno-Stroitel'nyj Institut
Ul. Cernysevskogo 24-a, Dnepropetrovsk
Tel: +7 46-73-57
Civil Engineering.

Dnepropetrovskij Medicinskij Institut
Ul. Dzerzinskogo 9, 320044 Dnepropetrovsk
Medicine.

Dnepropetrovskij Metallurgiceskij Institut
Prosp. Gagarina 4, 320095 Dnepropetrovsk
Tel: +7 45-31-56
Metallurgy.

Dnepropetrovskij Sel'skohozjajstvennyj Institut
Ul. Vorosilova 25, 320638 Dnepropetrovsk
Tel: +7 44-81-32
Agriculture.

Doneckaja Gosudarstvennaja Konservatorija
Ul. Artema 44, 340086 Doneck
Music.

Doneckij Gosudarstvennyj Medicinskij Institut
Prosp. Il'ica 16, 340098 Doneck
Medicine.

Doneckij Institut Sovetskoj Torgovli
Ul. Scorsa 31, 340050 Doneck 50
Commerce.

Doneckij Politehniceskij Institut
Ul. Artema 58, 340000 Doneck, Ukrainskaja SSR
Tel: +7 91-08-89

Har'kovskij Aviacionnyj Institut
Ul. bkalova 17, 310084 Har'kov 84
Tel: +7 44-23-13
Aviation.

Har'kovskij Avtomobil'no-Doroznyj Institut
Ul. Petrovskogo 25, 310078 Har'kov
Tel: +7 42-30-29
Automobile Technology.

Har'kovskij Farmacevticeskij Institut
Ul. Puskinskaja 53, 310024 Har'kov 24
Pharmacy.

Har'kovskij Gosudarstvennyj Institut Iskusstv
Pl. Soretskoj Ukrainy 11/13, 310003 Har'kov
Arts.

Har'kovskij Institut Inzenerov Gorodskogo Hozjajstva
Ul. Revoljucii 12, 310002 Har'kov
Tel: +7 47-00-88
Economics.

Har'kovskij Institut Inzenerov Zeleznodoroznogo Transporta
Pl. Fejerbaha 7, 310050 Har'kov 50
Tel: +7 22-22-82
Railways.

Har'kovskij Institut Mechanizacii Elektrifikacii Sel'skogo Hozjajstva
Ul. Artema 44, 310078 Har'kov
Tel: +7 22-37-86
Mechanization and Electrification of Agriculture.

Har'kovskij Institut Obscestvennogo Pitanija
Ul. Klocovskaja 333, 310051 Har'kov 51
Catering.

Har'kovskij Institut Radioelektroniki
Prosp. Leninskija 14, 310141 Har'kov
Tel: +7 43-30-53
Radioelectronics.

Har'kovskij Inzenerno-Ekonomiceskij Institut
Prosp. Lenina 9a, 310141 Har'kov
Economic Engineering.

Har'kovskij Juridiceskij Institut
Ul. Puskinskaja 77, 310024 Har'kov
Law.

Har'kovskij Medicinskij Institut
Prosp. V.I. Lenina 4, 310022 Har'kov
Medicine.

Har'kovskij Politehniceskij Institut
Ul. Frunze 21, 310002 Har'kov 2
Tel: +7 47-80-68
Technology.

Har'kovskij Zooveterinarnyj Institut
p/o 'Malaja Danilovka' Dergacevskij r-n, 312050 Har'kovskaja obl.
Tel: +7 32-00-03
Animal Husbandry.

Hersonskij Industrial'nyj Institut
Bereslavskoe sosse 24, 325008 Herson
Tel: +7 5-47-11
Industrial Studies.

Hersonskij Sel'skohozjajstvennyj Institut
Ul. Rosa Luxemburg 23, 325006 Herson 6
Tel: +7 2-64-71
Agriculture.

Hmel'nickij Tehnologiceskij Institut Bytovogo Obsluzivanija
Ul. Institutskaja 11, 280016 Hmel'nickij
Tel: +7 2-37-55
Technology.

Ivano-Frankovskij Institut Nefti i Gaza
Ul. Karpatskaja 15, 284018 Ivano-Frankovsk
Tel: +7 4-22-18
Petroleum and Gas Technology.

Ivano-Frankovskij Medicinskij Institut
Ul. Galickaja 2, 284000 Ivano-Frankovsk
Medicine.

Kamenec-Podol'skij Sel'skohozjajstvennyj Institut
Ul. Sevcenko 13, 281900 Kamenec-Podol'skij, Chmielnickoj obl.
Tel: +7 52-18
Agriculture.

Kievskaja Gosudarstvennaja Konservatorija
Ul. Karla Marksa 1/3, 252001 Kiev
Music.

Kievskij Avtomobil'no-Doroznyj
Ul.Suvorova 1, 252601 Kiev
Tel: +7 93-82-03
Highway Engineering.

Kievskij Gosudarstvennyj Hudozestvennyj Institut
Ul. Smirnova-Lastockina 20, 252053 Kiev
Art.

Kievskij Institut Inzenerov Grazdanskoj Aviacii
Prosp. Kosmonavta Komorova 1, 252058 Kiev
Tel: +7 43-31-41
Aviation Engineering.

Kievskij Institut Narodnogo Hozjajstva
Prosp. Pobeby 54/1, 252057 Kiev
Economics.

Kievskij Inzenerno-Stroitel'nyj Institut
Prosp. Vozduhoflotskij 31, 252180 Kiev
Tel: +7 267-71-20
Agricultural Engineering.

Kievskij Medicinskij Institut
Bul. Tarasa Sevcenko 13, 252004 Kiev
Medicine.

Kievskij Politehniceskij Institut
Prosp. Pobedy 37, 252056 Kiev
Tel: +7 441-93-03

Kievskij Tehnologiceskij Institut Legkoj Promyslennosti
Ul. Nemirovica-Dancenko 2, 252601 Kiev 11
Tel: +7 97-75-12
Light Industrial Technology.

Kievskij Tehnologiceskij Institut Piscevoj Promyslennosti
Ul. Vladimirskaja 68, 252017 Kiev
Tel: +7 220-64-00
Food Technology.

Kievskij Torgogo-Ekonomiceskij Institut
Ul. Kioto 19, 252156 Kiev
Commerce.

Kijevskij Gosudarstvennyj Institut Teatral'nogo Iskusstva
Ul. Jaroslavov Val 40, 252034 Kiev
Theatre.

Kirovogradskij Institut Sel'skohozjajstvennogo Masnostroenija
Prosp. Pravdy 70a, 316017 Kirovograd
Tel: +7 9-34-64
Agricultural Engineering.

Kirovogradskoe Vyssee Letnoje Ucilisce Grazdanskoj Aviacii
Ul. Dobrovoljskogo 1, 316005 Kirovograd Obl.
Tel: +7 2-38-64
Civil Aviation.

Kirovskij Sel'skohozjajstvennyj Institut
Prosp.Oktjabr'skij 133, 610039 Kirov obl.
Tel: +7 2-97-19
Agriculture.

Kommunarskij Gorno-Metallurgiceskij Institut
Prosp. Leninskij 16, 349104 Kommunarsk Vorosilovgradskoj obl.
Tel: +7 2-01-61
Metallurgy.

Kramatorskij Industrial'nyj Institut
Ul. Skadinova 76, 343916 Kramatorsk
Tel: +7 5-90-97
Industrial Studies.

Krivorozskij Gornorudnyj Institut
Ul. XXII Parts'ezda 11, 324030 Krivoj Rog, Dnepropetrovsk
Tel: +7 71-46-04
Mining.

L'vovskaja Gosudarstvennaja Konservatorija
Ul. Bojko 5, 290005 L'vov
Music.

L'vovskij Gosudarstvennyj Institut Prikladnogo i Dekorativnogo Iskusstva
Ul. Goncarova 38, 290011 L'vov
Applied and Decorative Arts.

L'vovskij Lesotehniceskij Institut
Ul. Puskina 103, 290032 L'vov
Tel: +7 35-24-11
Forestry and Wood Technology.

L'vovskij Medicinskij Institut
Ul. Pekarskaja 69, 290010 L'vov
Medicine.

L'vovskij Politehniceskij Institut
Ul. Mira 12, 290646 L'vov
Tel: +7 72-47-33

L'vovskij Sel'skohozjajstvennyj Institut
292040 Nesterskogo r-na Dubljany, L'vovskoj obl.
Tel: +7 79-33-45
Agriculture.

L'vovskij Torgovo-Ekonomiceskij Institut
Ul. Ckalova 10, 290008 L'vov
Commerce.

L'vovskij Zooveterinarnyj Institut
Ul. Pekarskaja 50, 290601 L'vov
Tel: +7 72-30-23
Animal Husbandry.

Makeevskij Inzenerno-Stroitel'nyj Institut
Pos. Dzerzinskogo, 339023, Makeevka, Doneckoj obl., Ukrainskaja SSR
Tel: +7 90-29-38
Agricultural Engineering.

Nikolaevskij Korablestroitel'nyj Institut
Ul. Geroev Stalingrada 5, 327001 Nikolaev
Tel: +7 35-91-48
Shipbuilding.

Odesskaja Gosudarstvennaja Konservatorija
Ul. Ostrovidova 63, 270000 Odessa
Music.

Odesskaja Gosudarstvennaja Morskaja Akademija
Ul. Mecnikova 34, 270029 Odessa
Tel: +7 3-35-28
Marine Engineering.

Odesskij Gidrometeorologiceskij Institut
Ul. Lwowskaja 15, 270016 Odessa
Tel: +7 22-49-83
Meteorology and Hydrology.

Odesskij Institut Narodnogo Hozjajstva
Ul. Sovetskoj Armii 8, 270100 Odessa
Economics.

Odesskij Institut Nizkotemperaturnoj Tehniki i Energetiki
Ul. Petra Velikogo 1/3, 270000 Odessa
Tel: +7 23-22-20
Energy and Energetics.

Odesskij Inzenerno-Stroitel'nyj Institut
Ul. Didrihsona 4, 270029 Odessa
Tel: +7 23-33-42
Agricultural Engineering.

Odesskij Medicinskij Institut
Per. Narimana Narimanova 2, 270100 Odessa
Medicine.

Odesskij Politehniceskij Institut
Prosp. T.G. Sevcenko 1, 270044 Odessa
Tel: +7 22-19-92

Odesskij Sel'skohozjajstvennyj Institut
Ul. Sverdlova 99, 270039 Odessa 39
Tel: +7 22-37-23
Agriculture.

Odesskij Tehnologiceskij Institut Piscevoj Promyslennosti
Ul. Sverdlova 112, 270039 Odessa
Tel: +7 25-32-84
Food Technology.

Odesskoe Vyssee Inzenernoe Morskoe Ucilisce
Ul. Didrihsona 8, 270029 Odessa 29
Tel: +7 3-40-88
Marine Engineering.

Orenburgskij Sel'skohozjajstvennyj Institut
Ul. Celjuskincev 18, 460795 Orenburg
Tel: +7 7-52-30
Agriculture.

Poltavskij Inzenerno-Stroitel'nyj Institut
Prosp. Pervomajskij 24, 314601 Poltava
Tel: +7 7-33-27
Civil Engineering.

Poltavskij Kooperativnyj Institut
Ul. Kovalja 3, 314601 Poltava
Cooperative Commerce.

Poltavskij Medicinskij-Stomatologiceskij Institut
Ul. Sevcenko 23, 314024 Poltava
Medicine; Dentistry.

Poltavskij Sel'skohozjajstvennyj Institut
Ul. Skovorody 1/3, 314003 Poltava
Tel: +7 7-34-46
Agriculture.

Sevastopol'skij Priborostroitel'nyj Institut
Studgorodok, 335053 Sevastopol'
Tel: +7 24-14-24
Precision Engineering.

Ternopol'skij Finansovo-Ekonomiceskij Institut
Pl. Pobedy 3, 282004 Ternopol'
Finance and Economics.

Ternopol'skij Medicinskij Institut
Pl. Svobody 6, 282001 Ternopol'
Medicine.

Ukrainskaja Sel'skohozjajstvennaja Akademija
Ul. Geroev Oborony 15, 252041 Kiev
Tel: +7 63-51-75
Agriculture.

Ukrainskij Institut Inzenerov Vodnogo Hozjajstva
Ul. Leninskja 11, 266000 Rovno
Tel: +7 2-10-86
Water Utilization.

Ukrainskij Poligraficeskij Institut
Ul. Pidgolosko 19, 290006 L'vov
Tel: +7 22-78-62
Planting Technology.

Ukrainskij Zaocnyj Politehniceskij Institut
Ul. Universitetskaja 16, 310003 Har'kov
Tel: +7 22-43-03

Umanskij Sel'skohozjajstvennyj Institut
p/o 'Sofievka', 258900 Uman', Cerkasskoj obl.
Tel: +7 5-25-58
Agriculture.

Vinnickij Medicinskij Institut
Ul. Pirogova 54, 286018 Vinnica
Medicine.

Vorosilovgradskij Masinostroitel'nyj Institut
Kvartal Molodeznij 20a, 348034 Vorossilovgrad
Tel: +7 6-23-90
Machine Engineering.

Vorosilovgradskij Medicinskij Institut
Ul. 50-let Oborony Luganska, 348045
Vorosilovgrad
Medicine.

Vorosilovgradskij Sel'skohozjajstvennyj Institut
348008 Vorosilovgrad 8
Tel: +7 5-20-40
Agriculture.

Zaporozskii Masinostroitel'nyj Institut
Ul. Zukovskogo 64, Zaporoz'e
Tel: +7 64-25-06
Machine Technology.

Zaporozskij Industrial'nyj Institut
Prosp. Leninskij 226, 330600 Zaporoz'e
Tel: +7 2-72-21
Industrial Studies.

Zaporozskij Medicinskij Institut
Ul. Majakovskogo 26, 330074 Zaporoze
Medicine.

Zdanovskij Metallurgiceskij Institut
Prosp. Respubliki 7, 341000 Zdanov, Doneckoj
obl.
Tel: +7 34-30-97
Metallurgy.

Zitomirskij Sel'skohozjajstvennyj Institut
Ul. 50-letija Oktjabrja 9, 262001 Zitomir
Tel: +7 7-44-71
Agriculture.

NATIONAL ACADEMIC BODIES

Ministry of Education
Av. Peremogi 10, 252135, Kiev.135
Tel: +7(044) 216-2442
Fax: +7(044) 274-1049
Minister: Petro Talanchuk

Ukrainian National Commission for Unesco
Mykhailivska Square 1, 252018, Kiev
Tel: +7(044) 293-4233
Fax: +7(044) 226-3169
Telex: 131373 rubin su
Cable: unescocom kiev
Chairman: Mykola P. Makarevych
Secretary-General: Volodymyr F. Skofenko

UNITED ARAB EMIRATES

UNIVERSITIES

*United Arab Emirates University
[Jameat Alemarat Al Arabia Al Mutaheda]
P.O. Box 15551, Al-Ain
Tel: +971(3) 660-200
Fax: +971(3) 645-277
Telex: 33521 jameah em
Chancellor: Sheikh Nahyan bin Mubarak Al
Nahyan (1990-)
Secretary-General: Shabeeb M. Al Marzooqi
Founded: 1976
*F: Arts; Science; Education; Economics and
Administrative Sciences; Shari'a and Law;
Agricultural Sciences; Engineering; Medicine and
Health Sciences.*
*Ce: Educational and Psychological Research,
Development, and Services; History and Folklore
Research; Desert and Marine Environmental
Research; Administrative, Financial, and
Economics Research; Remote Sensing;
Technology and Energy Research; Language;
Basic University Education.*

NATIONAL ACADEMIC BODIES

Ministry of Education and Youth
P.O. Box 295, Abu Dhabi
Tel: +971(2) 343-933
Fax: +971(2) 351-164
Minister: Hamad Abdul Rahman Al-Madfa

United Arab Emirates National Commission for Unesco
Ministry of Education and Youth, P.O. Box 295, Abu Dhabi
Tel: +971(2) 343-933
Chairman: Hamad Abdul Rahman Al-Madfa, Minister ofEducation and Youth
Secretary-General: Dhayn Jumaa Ahmad

UNITED KINGDOM

UNIVERSITIES AND UNIVERSITY COLLEGES

University of Aberdeen
Aberdeen, Scotland AB9 1FX
Tel: +44(1224) 272-000
Fax: +44(1224) 487-048
Telex: 73458
Cable: aberdeen university
Principal and Vice-Chancellor: J.M. Irvine
Founded: 1860, 1889
F: Arts and Divinity; Biological Sciences; Clinical Medicine; Economics and Social Sciences; Engineering, Mathematics and Physical Sciences; Law.

University of Abertay Dundee
Bell Street, Dundee, Scotland DD1 1MG
Principal: Bernard King
Founded: 1994

Anglia Polytechnic University
Victoria Road South, Chelmsford, Essex, England CM1 1LL
Tel: +44(1245) 493-131
Fax: +44(1245) 490-835
Vice-Chancellor: Mike Salmon
Senior Pro Vice-Chancellor: Robin Smith
Founded: 1991
S: Business.
F: Built Environment, Science and Technology; Humanities, Arts and Education; Health and Social Work.
Ce: European Research and Development; Total Quality Research and Development; Employment Relations; Higher Education Management; Health and Social Work Research.
Ut: Science and Technology.
Group: Population, Housing and Research.

Aston University
Aston Triangle, Birmingham, England 4 7ET
Tel: +44(121) 359-3611
Fax: +44(121) 359-7358
Telex: 336997 uniast g
Vice-Chancellor: Sir Frederick Crawford
Founded: 1895, 1951, 1966
F: Engineering and Applied Sciences; Management and Modern Languages; Science.

University of Bath
Claverton Down, Bath, England BA2 7AY
Tel: +44(1225) 826-826
Fax: +44(1225) 625-08
Telex: 449097 uobath g
Vice-Chancellor: V.D. Vanderlinde
Founded: 1894, 1966, 1971
S: Architecture and Building Engineering; Biological Sciences; Chemistry; Education; Chemical Engineering; Electrical Engineering; Mechanical Engineering; Management; Materials Science; Mathematical Sciences; Postgraduate Medicine; Modern Languages and International Studies; Pharmacy and Pharmacology; Physics; Social Sciences.

Queen's University of Belfast
Belfast, Northern Ireland BT7 INN
Tel: +44(1232) 245-133
Fax: +44(1232) 247-895
Telex: 74487 qubadm
Cable: university, belfast, northern ireland
President and Vice-Chancellor: G.S.G. Beveridge
Founded: 1845
F: Agriculture and Food Science; Arts; Economics and Social Sciences; Education; Engineering; Law; Medicine; Science; Theology.

University of Birmingham
Edgbaston, Birmingham, England BI5 2TT
Tel: +44(121) 414-3344
Fax: +44(121) 414-3971
Vice-Chancellor and Principal: Sir Michael Thompson
Registrar and Secretary: D.R. Holmes
Founded: 1880
F: Arts; Commerce and Social Sciences; Education and Continuing Studies; Engineering; Law; Medicine and Dentistry; Science.

University of Central England in Birmingham
Perry Barr, Birmingham, England B42 2SU
Tel: +44(121) 331-5000
Fax: +44(121) 356-2875
Telex: 33409 cbpoly g
Director: P.C. Knight
Registrar: M. Penlington
Founded: 1992
I: Art and Design.
F: Built Environment; Computing and Information Studies; Education and Teacher Training; Engineering and Computer Technology; Health and Social Sciences.

Bournemouth University
Poole House, Talbot Campus, Fern Barrow, Poole, Dorset BH12 5BB
Tel: +44(1202) 524-111
Fax: +44(1202) 513-293
Vice-Chancellor: Gillian Slater (1994-)
Academic Secretary: B. Chamberlain
Founded: 1976, 1990, 1992

D: Applied Computing and Electronics; Conservation Sciences; Finance and Law; Management Systems; Marketing, Advertising and Public Relations; Media Production; Product Design and Manufacture; Service Industries.
S: Business.
I: Health Services.
Ce: National for Computer Animation.

University of Bradford
Richmond Road, Bradford, England BD7 1DP
Tel: +44(1274) 733-466
Fax: +44(1274) 305-340
Telex: 51309 unibfd g
Cable: unibfd g
Vice-Chancellor and Principal: David Johns (1989-)
Registrar and Secretary: Don W. Granger
Founded: 1882, 1957, 1966
B of ST: Engineering; Social Sciences; Natural and Applied Sciences.
Ce: Continuing Education; Management; Development and Project Planning; Interdisciplinary Research (IRC) in Polymer Sciences and Technology; West Yorkshire Research on Women (WYCROW).
Ut: European Briefing; Clinical Oncology; Clinical Epidemiology; Food Policy Research; Haematology Research; Plastic Surgery and Burns Research (St Luke's Hospital); Biomaterials Research; Research on European/ Latin American Relations (RUELAR); Baltic Research; Balkan Research; Disaster Prevention and Limitation; Technological Management; Cancer Medicine Research; Pharmacy Practice Research; Work and Gender Research; Christian Urban Resources; Microcomputer Music Research; Research in Education.

University of Brighton
Mithras House, Lewes Road, Moulsecomb, Brighton, England BN2 4AT
Tel: +44(1273) 600-900
Fax: +44(1273) 694-062
Director: D. Watson
Registrar: P.J. Reynolds
Founded: 1970, 1992
F: Art, Design and Humanities; Education, Sport and Leisure; Engineering and Environmental Studies; Health; Information Technology.
S: Brighton Business.

University of Bristol
Senate House, Tyndall Avenue, Bristol, England BS8 1TH
Tel: +44(1179) 303-030
Fax: +44(1179) 251-424
Telex: 445938 bsuniv g
Cable: university, bristol bs8 1th
Vice-Chancellor: Sir John Kingman
Secretary: J.H.M. Parry
Founded: 1876, 1893
F: Arts; Science; Law; Medicine; Engineering; Social Sciences.
D: Continuing Education.

University of the West of England at Bristol
Coldharbour Lane, Frenchay, Bristol, England BS16 1QY
Tel: +44(1179) 656-261
Fax: +44(1179) 763-972
Vice-Chancellor: Alfred C. Morris
Founded: 1969, 1992
S: Bristol Business.
D: Art, Media and Design.
F: Science, Engineering, Mathematics and Computing; Education and Community Studies; Languages and Law; Built Environment; Humanities, Health and Social Science.

Brunel University
Kingston Lane, Uxbridge, Middlesex, England UB8 3PH
Tel: +44(1895) 274-000
Fax: +44(1895) 232-806
Telex: 261173 g
Vice-Chancellor and Principal: M.J.H. Sterling
Secretary-General and Registrar: D. Neave
Founded: 1957, 1962, 1966
F: Education and Design; Social Sciences; Technology; Science.
D: Biology/Biochemistry; Chemistry; Computer Science; Mathematics and Statistics; Materials Technology; Physics; Education; Industrial Design; Electrical Engineering and Electronics; Manufacturing and Engineering Systems; Mechanical Engineering; Economics; Government; Human Sciences; Law.
I: Brunel Bioengineering; Brunel Power Systems.
Ce: Wolfson for Materials Processing; Research into Innovation, Culture and Technology.

University of Buckingham
Buckingham, England MK18 1EG
Tel: +44(1280) 814-080
Fax: +44(1280) 822-245
Vice-Chancellor: The Rt. Hon. Sir Richard Luce
Secretary and Registrar: M.E. Lavis
Founded: 1973
S: Accounting, Business and Economics; Humanities; Law; Sciences.

*University of Cambridge
University Registry, The Old Schools, Trinity Lane, Cambridge, England CB2 ITN
Tel: +44(1223) 332-200
Fax: +44(1223) 332-332
Telex: 81240 camspl g
Vice-Chancellor: Sir David Williams
Registrary: S.G. Fleet
Founded: 1318, 1570
F: Architecture and History of Arts; Classics; Divinity; English; Modern and Mediaeval Languages; Music; Oriental Studies; Economics and Politics; Education; History; Law; Philosophy; Social and Political Sciences; Engineering; Earth Sciences and Geography; Mathematics; Physics and Chemistry; Archaeology and Anthropology; Biology 'A' (Botany and Zoology); Biology 'B'

(Anatomy, Biochemistry and Pathology); Clinical Medicine.
D: *Chemical Engineering; Clinical Veterinary Medicine; History and Philosophy of Science; Land Economy.*
L: *Computer and Computing Service.*

CHRIST'S COLLEGE
Cambridge, England CB2 3BU
Tel: +44(1223) 334-900
Fax: +44(1223) 334-967
Master: Sir Hans Kornberg
Founded: 1448, 1505

CHURCHILL COLLEGE
Cambridge, England CB3 0DS
Tel: +44(1223) 336-000
Fax: +44(1223) 336-177
Master: A.N. Broers
Founded: 1960

CLARE COLLEGE
Cambridge, England CB2 ITL
Tel: +44(1223) 333-200
Fax: +44(1223) 333-219
Master: R.C.O. Matthews
Founded: 1326, 1339

CLARE HALL
Cambridge, England CB3 9AL
Tel: +44(1223) 332-360
Fax: +44(1223) 332-333
President: D.A. Low
Founded: 1966

CORPUS CHRISTI COLLEGE
Cambridge, England CB2 1RH
Tel: +44(1223) 338-000
Fax: +44(1223) 338-061
Master: M.W. McCrum
Founded: 1352

DARWIN COLLEGE
Cambridge, England CB3 9EU
Tel: +44(1223) 335-660
Fax: +44(1223) 335-667
Master: G.E.R. Lloyd
Founded: 1964

DOWNING COLLEGE
Cambridge, England CB2 1DQ
Tel: +44(1223) 334-800
Fax: +44(1223) 467-934
Master: P. Mathias
Founded: 1800

EMMANUEL COLLEGE
Cambridge, England CB2 3AP
Tel: +44(1223) 334-200
Fax: +44(1223) 334-426
Master: Lord St. John of Fawsley
Founded: 1584

FITZWILLIAM COLLEGE
Cambridge, England CB3 0DG
Tel: +44(123) 332-000
Fax: +44(123) 464-162
Master: A.W. Cuthbert
Founded: 1869

GIRTON COLLEGE
Cambridge, England CB3 0JG
Tel: +44(1223) 338-999
Fax: +44(1223) 338-896
Mistress: Juliet Campbell
Bursar: Charles Larkum
Founded: 1869, 1869, 1978

GONVILLE AND CAIUS COLLEGE
Cambridge, England CB2 1TA
Tel: +44(1223) 332-400
Master: P. Gray
Founded: 1348

HOMERTON COLLEGE
Cambridge, England CB2 2PH
Tel: +44(1223) 411-141
Fax: +44(1223) 411-622
Principal: Kate B. Pretty
Founded: 1848, 1977

HUGHES HALL
Cambridge, England CB1 2EW
Tel: +44(1223) 334-893
President: T.D. Hawkins
Founded: 1885, 1985

JESUS COLLEGE
Cambridge, England CB5 8BL
Tel: +44(1223) 686-11
Fax: +44(1223) 324-910
Master: Lord Renfrew
Founded: 1496

KING'S COLLEGE
Cambridge, England CB2 1ST
Tel: +44(1223) 350-411
Fax: +44(1223) 314-019
Provost: P.P.P. Bateson
Founded: 1441, 1861

LUCY CAVENDISH COLLEGIATE SOCIETY
Lady Margaret Road, Cambridge, England CB3 0BU
Tel: +44(1223) 332-190
President: Baroness Perry (1993-)

MAGDALENE COLLEGE
Cambridge, England CB3 0AG
Tel: +44(1223) 332-100
Fax: +44(1223) 636-37
Master: Sir David Calcutt
Founded: 1542

NEW HALL
Cambridge, England CB3 0DF
Tel: +44(1223) 351-721
Fax: +44(1223) 352-941
President: Valerie Pearl
Founded: 1018

NEWNHAM COLLEGE
Sidgwick Avenue, Cambridge, England CB3 9DF
Tel: +44(1223) 335-700
Fax: +44(1223) 359-155
Principal: Onora O'Neill (1992-)
Bursar: Michael Payne
Founded: 1871, 1948

PEMBROKE COLLEGE
Cambridge, England CB2 1RF
Tel: +44(1223) 338-100
Fax: +44(1223) 338-163
Master: Lord Adrian
Founded: 1347

PETERHOUSE
Cambridge, England CB2 1RD
Tel: +44(1223) 338-200
Fax: +44(1223) 337-578
Master: Henry Chadwick (1987-93)
Senior Tutor: P. Pattenden
Founded: 1287

QUEEN'S COLLEGE
Cambridge, England CB3 9ET
Tel: +44(1223) 335-511
Fax: +44(1223) 335-522
President: J.C. Polkinghorne
Senior Tutor: J.T. Green
Founded: 1448, 1475

ROBINSON COLLEGE
Cambridge, England CB3 9AN
Tel: +44(1223) 311-431
Fax: +44(1223) 351-794
Warden: Lord Lewis
Founded: 1977

St. CATHARINE'S COLLEGE
Cambridge, England CB2 1RL
Tel: +44(1223) 338-300
Fax: +44(1223) 338-340
Founded: 1473

St. EDMUND'S COLLEGE
Cambridge, England CB3 0BN
Tel: +44(1223) 350-398
Master: R.M. Laws
Founded: 1896, 1975

St. JOHN'S COLLEGE
Cambridge, England CB2 1TP
Tel: +44(1223) 338-600
Fax: +44(1223) 337-720
Master: R.A. Hinde
Founded: 1511

SELWYN COLLEGE
Cambridge, England CB3 9DQ
Tel: +44(1223)-335-846
Fax: +44(1223) 335-537
Master: Sir Alan Cook
Founded: 1596

SIDNEY SUSSEX COLLEGE
Cambridge, England CB2 3HU
Tel: +44(1223) 338-800
Fax: +44(1223) 338-884
Master: D.H. Northcote

TRINITY COLLEGE
Cambridge, England CB2 1TQ
Tel: +44(1223) 338-400
Fax: +44(1223) 338-564
Master: Sir Michael Atiyah
Founded: 1546

TRINITY HALL
Cambridge, England CB2 1TJ
Tel: +44(1223) 352-500
Fax: +44(1223) 332-537
Master: Sir John Lyons
Founded: 1350

WOLFSON COLLEGE
Cambridge, England CB3 9BB
Tel: +44(1223) 335-900
Fax: +44(1223) 335-908
President: Gordon Johnson
Founded: 1973, 1977

City University
Northhampton Square, London, England EC1V 0HB
Tel: +44(171) 253-43997
Fax: +44(171) 250-0837
Vice-Chancellor and Principal: R.N. Franklin
Academic Registrar: A.H. Seville
S: Business; Engineering; Informatics; Mathematics, Actuarial Sciences, and Statistics.

Coventry University
Priory Street, Coventry, England CV1 5FB
Tel: +44(1203) 631-313
Fax: +44(1203) 838-793
Vice-Chancellor and Chief Executive: M. Goldstein
Founded: 1970, 1992
F: Art and Design; Engineering; Applied Sciences; Social, Biological and Health Sciences; Business.

Cranfield Institute of Technology
Cranfield, Bedford, England MK43 0AL
Tel: (1234) 750-111
Fax: (1234) 750-875
Telex: 820722 citech g
Vice-Chancellor: F.R. Hartley
Secretary and Registrar: J.K. Pettifer
Founded: 1946, 1969
F: Agricultural Engineering, Food Production and Rural Land Use; Defence Science Technology and Management; Engineering; Management and Administration; Manufacturing Technology and Production Management; Science and Technology.
C: Silsoe Agricultural Engineering, Food Production and Rural Land Use.

University of Derby
Kedleston Road, Derby, England DE22 1GB
Tel: +44(1332) 471-81
Fax: +44(1332) 294-861
Vice-Chancellor: R.W. Waterhouse

Dundee Institute of Technology
Bell Street, Dundee, Scotland DD1 1HG
Tel: +44(1382) 308-000
Fax: +44(1382) 308-877
Principal: B. King
Technology.

University of Dundee

Dundee, Scotland DD1 4HN
Tel: +44(1382) 231-81
Fax: +44(1382) 201-604
Telex: 76293
Cable: dundee university
Principal and Vice-Chancellor: Ian J.
Graham-Bryce
Secretary: R. Seaton
Founded: 1881, 1897, 1897, 1967
F: *Science and Engineering; Law; Medicine and Dentistry; Arts and Social Sciences; Environmental Studies.*
Ut: *Language; Concrete Technology; Protein Phosphorylation.*
L: *Laparoscopic Skills.*
Ce: *Biomedical Research; Microcomputer; Petroleum and Mineral Law and Policy.*

University of Durham

Old Shire Hall, Durham, England DH1 3HP
Tel: +44(191) 374-2000
Fax: +44(191) 374-3740
Telex: 537351 durlib g
Vice-Chancellor and Warden: E.A. Ebsworth
Registrar and Secretary: J.C.F. Hayward
Founded: 1832
F: *Arts; Science; Social Sciences.*

University of East Anglia

Norwich, England NR4 7TJ
Tel: +44(1603) 561-61
Fax: +44(1603) 585-53
Telex: 975197
Cable: ueanor norwich
Vice-Chancellor: D.C. Burke
Founded: 1964
S: *Art History and Music; Biological Sciences; Chemical Sciences; Development Studies; Economic and Social Studies; Education; English and American Studies; Environmental Sciences; Information Systems; Law; Mathematics and Physics; Modern Languages and European History.*

*University of East London

Romford Road, Stratford, London, England E15 4LZ
Tel: +44(181) 590-7722
Fax: +44(181) 590-7799
Vice-Chancellor: F.W. Gould
Founded: 1970, 1992
D: *Accounting and Finance; Applied Economic Studies; Architecture; Art and Design; Biochemistry; Business Studies; Civil Engineering; Continuing Education; Cultural Studies; Education Studies; Electrical and Electronic Engineering; Environmental Sciences; Estate Management; Health and Rehabilitation; Innovation Studies; Land Surveying; Law; Management Studies; Manufacturing Systems; Mathematical Sciences; Physics and Computing; Physiology and Pharmacology; Psychology; Sociology.*

University of Edinburgh

Old College, South Bridge, Edinburgh, Scotland EH8 9YL
Tel: +44(131) 650-1000
Fax: +44(131) 667-7938
Telex: 727442 unived g
Principal and Vice-Chancellor: Stuart Sutherland
Secretary: Martin Lowe
Founded: 1580
F: *Arts; Science and Engineering; Law; Medicine and Dentistry; Divinity; Music; Social Sciences; Veterinary Medicine.*
Ce: *Social Sciences Research; Study of Christianity in the Non-Western World.*
S: *Scottish Studies.*
I: *Europa.*

University of Essex

Wivenhoe Park, Colchester, Essex, England CO4 3SQ
Tel: +44(1206) 873-333
Fax: +44(1206) 873-598
Telex: 98440 (unilib G)
Cable: university colchester
Vice-Chancellor: Ron Johnston
Registrar and Secretary: E. Newcomb
Founded: 1961
S: *Comparative Studies; Law; Mathematical and Computer Sciences; Science and Engineering; Social Sciences.*

University of Exeter

Northcote House, The Queen's Drive, Exeter, England EX4 4QJ
Tel: +44(1392) 263-263
Fax: +44(1392) 263-108
Telex: 42894
Cable: university exeter
Vice-Chancellor: Sir Geoffrey Holland
Registrar and Secretary: Ian H.C. Powell
Founded: 1922, 1955
F: *Arts; Science; Law; Social Sciences; Education.*
S: *Engineering.*
Ce: *Complementary Health Studies; Earth Resources; Management Studies; Police and Criminal Justice Studies; English Language.*
I: *Population Studies Research.*

University of Glamorgan

Llantwit Road, Treforest Pontypridd, Mid-Glamorgan, Wales CF37 7DL
Tel: +44(1443) 480-480
Fax: +44(1443) 480-558
Vice-Chancellor: Adrian Webb
Founded: 1913, 1956, 1970
F: *Environment Studies; Technology Studies; Professional Studies.*

Glasgow Caledonian University

Cowcaddens Road, Glasgow, Scotland G4 0BA
Tel: +44(141) 331-30
Fax: +44(141) 331-3005
Vice-Chancellor: Stan Mason
Founded: 1971, 1985, 1993
F: Business, Management and Social Sciences; Health, Science, Engineering and Construction.

University of Glasgow

Glasgow, Scotland G12 8QQ
Tel: +44(141) 339-8855
Fax: +44(141) 330-4808
Telex: 777070 unigla
Rector: Johnny Ball
Registrar: J.M. Black
Founded: 1451, 1858
F: Arts; Divinity; Engineering; Law and Financial Studies; Medicine; Science; Social Sciences; Veterinary Medicine.

University of Greenwich

Southwood House, Avery Hill Road, London, England SE9 2HB
Tel: +44(181) 316-8000
Fax: +44(181) 316-8876
Vice-Chancellor: D. Fussey
Founded: 1992
F: Technology; Built Environment; Science; Business, Social Sciences and Humanities; Education.

Heriot-Watt University

Riccarton, Edinburgh, Scotland EH14 4AS
Tel: +44(131) 449-5111
Fax: +44(131) 449-5153
Vice-Chancellor: A.G.J. MacFarlane
Secretary: P.L. Wilson
Founded: 1821, 1966
F: Arts and Design; Engineering; Economics and Social Studies; Science; Environmental Studies; Textiles.
I: Education; Technology Management; Computer-Based Learning; Offshore Engineering.
Ce: Continuing Education; The Esmée Fairbairn Research; International Mathematical Sciences.

Hertfordshire University

P.O. Box 109, Hatfield, Hertfordshire, England AL10 9AB
Tel: +44(1707) 279-000
Fax: +44(1707) 279-670
Telex: 262413 hertis g
Vice-Chancellor: N.K. Buxton
Founded: 1952, 1969, 1992
S: Business; Engineering; Health and Human Sciences; Information Sciences; Natural Sciences.

University of Huddersfield

Queensgate, Huddersfield, England HD1 3DH
Tel: +44(1484) 422-288
Fax: +44(1484) 516-151
Vice-Chancellor and Rector: Sir William Taylor (1994-)
Founded: 1970, 1974, 1992
F: Arts; Business; Education; Engineering; Sciences.

University of Hull

Hull, England HU6 7RX
Tel: +44(1482) 463-11
Fax: +44(1482) 465-936
Telex: (482) 465936
Vice-Chancellor: D.N. Dilks
Founded: 1927, 1954
S: Arts; Chemistry; Economic Studies; Education; Engineering and Computing; European Languages and Cultures; Geographical and Earth Resources; Humanities; Law; Life Sciences; Management; Mathematics; Social and Political Sciences.
Ce: South East Asian Studies.
I: Estuarine and Coastal Studies; Nursing Studies.
Ut: European Community Research.

University of Humberside

Cottingham Road, Hull, North Humberside, England HU6 7RT
Tel: +44(1482) 440-550
Fax: +44(1482) 440-846
Vice-Chancellor and Rector: Roger P. King
Founded: 1983, 1991, 1992
S: Art, Architecture, and Design; Food, Fisheries, and Environmental Studies; Humberside Business; Social and Professional Studies; Art, Architecture, and Design Research; Food, Fisheries, and Environmental Studies; Humberside Business (Research); Social and Professional Studies.

Keele University

Keele, Staffordshire, England ST5 5BG
Tel: +44(1782) 621-111
Fax: +44(1782) 613-847
Telex: 36113 unklib g
Vice-Chancellor: B.E.F. Fender
Registrar and Director of Administration: D. Cohen
Founded: 1949, 1962
S: Biological Sciences and Postgraduate Medicine; Earth Sciences; History and American Studies; Human Development; Humanities; Information Sciences and Mathematics; Law; Management and Economics; Physical Science and Engineering; Political and Social Sciences.

University of Kent at Canterbury

The Registry, Canterbury, Kent, England CT2 7NZ
Tel: +44(1227) 764-000
Fax: +44(1227) 452-196
Telex: 965449 ukclib g
Vice-Chancellor: Robert Sibson
Registrar: T.J. Mead
Founded: 1964
F: Humanities; Natural Sciences; Social
Sciences; Information Technology.
S: Continuing Education; Business; European
and Modern Language Studies.
Ut: Personal Social Services Research; Channel
Tunnel Research; Applied Statistics Research;
History, Philosophy and Social Relations of
Science; Urban and Regional Studies; Space
Sciences.
I: Social and Applied Psychology; Conservation
and Ecology (Durrell); Mathematics and
Statistics; Social Research.
Ce: Health Service Studies; Applied Psychology
of Social Care.
Group: Optics.

Kingston University

River House, 53 37 High Street, Kingston-upon-
Thames, Surrey, England KT1 1LQ
Tel: +44(181) 547-2000
Fax: +44(181) 547-1277
Vice-Chancellor and Chief Executive: Robert C.
Smith
Founded: 1970, 1992
F: Art and Design; Human Sciences; Business
and Law; Education; Technology; Science.

University of Central Lancashire

Preston, Lancashire, England PR1 2HE
Tel: +44(1772) 201-201
Fax: +44(1772) 262-830
Rector: B.G. Booth
Founded: 1828, 1973, 1992
S: Business.
F: Cultural, Legal and Social Studies; Design
and Technology; Health; Science.
P: Combined Honours.

University of Lancaster

University House, Lancaster, England LA1 4YW
Tel: +44(1524) 652-01
Fax: +44(1524) 638-06
E-Mail: lancaster.ac.uk
Telex: 65111
Vice-Chancellor: H.J. Hanham (1985-)
Secretary: G.M. Cockburn
B. of St: Engineering, Computing and
Mathematical Sciences; Physics and Materials;
Business and Management; Social Sciences;
Humanities; Teacher Training and Education.
I: Environmental and Biological Sciences;
English Language Education.
Ce: Study of Cultural Values; Study of
Environmental Change; Women's Studies;
Engineering Design.
S: Independent Studies.

Leeds Metropolitan University

Calverley Street, Leeds, England LS1 3HE
Tel: +44(1532) 832-600
Fax: +44(1532) 833-117
Vice-Chancellor: Brian Roper (1994-)
Founded: 1970, 1992
S: Business; Environment.
F: Cultural and Education Studies; Health and
Social Care Studies; Information and Engineering
Systems.

De Montfort University Leicester

The Gateway, Leicester, England LE1 9 BH
Tel: +44(1162) 551-551
Fax: +44(1162) 471-690
Vice-Chancellor and Chief Executive: K. Barker
Founded: 1969, 1992
D: Performing Arts; Architecture; Building
Surveying; Land Management; Graphics; Fashion
and Textile Design and Technology; Mechanical
Production and Engineering; Economics;
Electronic and Electrical Engineering; Accounting
and Finance; Human Resource Management;
Marketing and Business Policy; Management;
Public Policy and Managerial Studies; Law;
Professional Legal Study; Mathematical Sciences;
Computing Science; Information Systems;
Chemistry; Applied Physics; Pharmacy; Applied
Biology and Biotechnology; Speech Pathology;
Health and Community Studies; Fine Art;
Humanities.
Ce: Postgraduate Teacher Education.

*University of Leicester

University Road, Leicester, England LE1 7RH
Tel: +44(1162) 522-522
Fax: +44(1162) 522-200
Telex: 341198
Vice-Chancellor: K.J.R. Edwards
Executive Pro-Vice Chancellor and Registrar: C.
Bernbaum
Founded: 1918, 1957
F: Arts; Science; Social Sciences; Law;
Medicine.
S: Education.
D: Adult Education.

*University of Liverpool

P.O. Box 147, Liverpool, England L69 3BX
Tel: +44(51) 794-2000
Fax: +44(51) 708-6502
Telex: 627095 unilpl g
Vice-Chancellor: P.N. Love (1992-)
Registrar: M.D. Carr
Founded: 1881, 1884
F: Arts; Science; Medicine; Law; Engineering;
Veterinary Science; Social and Environmental
Studies; Education.
I: Public Administration and Management; Irish
Studies; Latin American Studies; Human Ageing;
Popular Music.
Ce: Interdisciplinary Research in Surface
Science.

C: Chester.
L: Oceanographic (Proudman).

Liverpool John Moores University

2 Rodney Street, Liverpool, England L3 5UX
Tel: +44(151) 231-2121
Fax: +44(151) 709-0172
Vice-Chancellor and Chief Executive: T. Toyne
Founded: 1970, 1992
S: Arts, Media and Design; Built Environment; Business; Education and Community Studies; Engineering and Technology Management; Health Sciences; Social Science; Information Science and Technology; Law, Social Work and Social Policy; Natural Sciences; Nursing and Midwifery.

London Guildhall University

117-119 Houndsditch, London, England EC3A 7BU
Tel: +44(171) 283-1030
Fax: +44(171) 623-2858
Provost: Roderick Floud
Deputy Provost: Elizabeth Reid
Founded: 1970, 1992
F: Arts, Design and Manufacture; Business; Life, Social and Communication Sciences.

*University of London

Senate House, Malet Street, London, England WC1E 7HU
Tel: +44(171) 636-8000
Fax: +44(171) 636-0373
Telex: 269400 senlib g
Vice-Chancellor: S.R. Sutherland
Principal: P. Holwell
Founded: 1836
F: Arts; Economics; Education; Engineering; Laws; Medicine; Music; Science; Theology.

BIRKBECK COLLEGE
Malet Street, London, England WC1E 7HX
Tel: +44(171) 580-6622
Fax: +44(171) 631-6270
Cable: birkbeck college, london
Master: The Baroness Blackstone of Stoke Newington
Registrar: B.A. Harwood
F: Arts; Science; Economics.

BRITISH INSTITUTE IN PARIS
II rue de Constantine, 75340 Paris Cedex 07 (France)
Tel: +33(1) 4555-7199 (Paris)
Fax: +33(1) 4550-3155 (Paris)
Director: Cristophe L. Campos
Secretary-General: Kenneth Freeman
Founded: 1894, 1927, 1969
D: English as a Foreign Language; French Language, Literature and Civilization.
Ce: Franco-British Studies.
Ut: Distance Course.

THE BRITISH POSTGRADUATE MEDICAL FEDERATION
33 Millman Street, London, England WC1N 3EJ
Tel: +44(171) 831-6222
Fax: +44(171) 831-7599
Director: M. Green
Secretary: Jane M. Jones
Founded: 1945
F: Medicine.

CHARING CROSS AND WESTMINSTER MEDICAL SCHOOL
St. Dunstan's Road, London, England W6 8RP
Tel: +44(181) 748-2040
Fax: +44(181) 846-7222
Dean: J.E.H. Pendower (1989-93)
School Secretary: G.K. Buckley
Founded: 1984
F: Medicine.

COURTAULD INSTITUTE OF ART
Somerset House, Strand, London, England WC2R 0RN
Tel: +44(171) 872-0220
Director: C.M. Kauffmann
Registrar and Secretary: J.A. Hearnshaw
Founded: 1932, 1891, 1988

GOLDSMITHS' COLLEGE
Lewisham Way, New Cross, London, England SE14 6NW
Tel: +44(181) 692-7171
Fax: +44(181) 469-0516
Cable: goldsmiths' college london
Warden: A. Rutherford
Academic Registrar: Mary A. Barrie
F: Arts; Education; Social and Mathematical Sciences.

HEYTHROP COLLEGE
Kensington Square, London, England W8 5HQ
Tel: +44(171) 795-6600
Fax: +44(171) 795-4200
Principal: B.A. Callaghan, S.J.
Secretary and Registrar: Edward O'Connor
Founded: 1926, 1970, 1971
D: Biblical Studies; Christian Doctrine; Church History; Philosophy; Pastoral Studies.
I: Spirituality.

IMPERIAL COLLEGE OF SCIENCE, TECHNOLOGY AND MEDICINE
South Kensington, London, England SW7 2AZ
Tel: +44(171) 589-5111
Fax: +44(171) 584-7596
Rector: Sir Ronald Oxburgh (1993-)
Registrar: P.E. Mee
Founded: 1907
C: Science; City and Guilds.
S: Mines; Medical (St Mary's Hospital).

INSTITUTE OF ADVANCED LEGAL STUDIES
17 Russell Square, London, England WC1B 5DR
Tel: +44(171) 637-1731
Fax: +44(171) 436-8824
Director: T.C. Daintith
Administrative Secretary: D.E. Phillips
Founded: 1947
Legal Research.

INSTITUTE OF CLASSICAL STUDIES
31-34 Gordon Square, London, England WC1H
0PY
Tel: +44(171) 387-7696
Founded: 1979

INSTITUTE OF COMMONWEALTH STUDIES
27-28 Russell Square, London, England WC1B
5DS
Tel: +44(171) 580-5876
Fax: +44(171) 255-2160
Director: Shula E. Marks
Founded: 1949

INSTITUTE OF EDUCATION
20 Bedford Way, London, England WC1H 0AL
Tel: +44(171) 580-1122
Fax: +44(171) 612-6126
Cable: institute of education london wc1
Director: Sir Peter Newsam
Secretary and Registrar: D.J. Warren
Founded: 1902, 1987
*Ce: Higher Education Studies; Multicultural
Education; Post Sixteen Education; Research and
Education on Gender.*

INSTITUTE OF GERMANIC STUDIES
29 Russell Square, London, England WC1B 5DP
Tel: +44(171) 580-2711
Fax: +44(171) 436-3497
Cable: germanic institute, russell square london
Honorary Director: M.W. Swales (1989-93)
Deputy Director: J.L. Flood
Founded: 1949
Germanic Studies.

INSTITUTE OF HISTORICAL RESEARCH INCLUDING INSTITUTE
OF UNITED STATES STUDIES
Senate House, Malet Street, London, England
WC1E 7HU
Tel: +44(171) 636-0272
Director: P.K. O'Brien
Founded: 1987

INSTITUTE OF LATIN AMERICAN STUDIES
31 Tavistock Square, London, England WC1H 9HA
Tel: +44(171) 387-5671
Fax: +44(171) 387-5024
Founded: 1965

JEWS' COLLEGE
44A Albert Road, London, England NW4 2SJ
Tel: +44(181) 203-6427
Principal: Rabbi Dr. I. Jacobs
Academic Registrar: C.A. Fierstone
Jewish Studies.

KING'S COLLEGE LONDON
Cornwall House Annex, Waterloo Road, London,
England E1 8TX
Tel: +44(171) 636-5454
Fax: +44(171) 836-1799
Principal: Arthur Lucas (1993-)
Secretary: W.C. Slade
Founded: 1829
*S: Education; Humanities; Law; Life, Basic
Medical and Health Sciences; Medicine and
Dentistry; Physical Sciences and Engineering.*

LONDON BUSINESS SCHOOL
Sussex Place, Regent's Park, London, England
NW1 4SA
Tel: +44(171) 262-5050
Fax: +44(171) 724-7875
Telex: 27461
Cable: lonbiskol
Principal: G.S. Bain
Founded: 1965, 1986
*Marketing; Strategic and International
Management; Accounting; Economics.*
*Ce: Business Strategy; Design Management;
Economic Forecasting; Marketing and
Communications.*
*I: Finance and Accounting; Organisational
Research.*
E.S.R.C: Technology Project.

THE LONDON HOSPITAL MEDICAL COLLEGE
Turner Street, London, England E1 2AD
Tel: +44(171) 377-7000
Fax: +44(171) 377-7677
Chairman: D.J. Dickinson
Registrar: H.A.J. Butter
Founded: 1785, 1900
F: Medicine.

THE LONDON SCHOOL OF ECONOMICS AND POLITICAL
SCIENCE
Houghton Street, London, England WC2A 2AE
Tel: +44(171) 405-7686
Fax: +44(171) 242-0392
Telex: 24655 lselon g
Director: J.M. Ashworth
Academic Registrar: J.A. Bursey
Founded: 1895, 1900
*D: Accounting and Finance; Anthropology;
Economic History; Economics; Geography;
Government; Industrial Relations; International
History; International Relations; Law; Philosophy,
Logic and Scientific Method; Social Psychology;
Social Science and Administration; Sociology;
Statistical and Mathematical Sciences.*
C: Language Studies.

THE LONDON SCHOOL OF HYGIENE AND TROPICAL MEDICINE
Keppel Street, London, England WC1E 7HT
Tel: +44(171) 636-8636
Fax: +44(171) 436-5389
Telex: 8953474
Dean: R.G.A Feachem
Secretary and Registrar: B.K. Gooch
Founded: 1924
D: Clinical Sciences; Medical Parasitology; Epidemiology and Population Sciences; Public Health and Policy.

QUEEN MARY AND WESTFIELD COLLEGE
Mile End Road, London, England E1 4NS
Tel: +44(17 1) 975-5555
Fax: +44(171) 975-5500
Telex: 893750
Principal: Graham J. Zellick (1990-)
Academic Secretary: D.B.T. Jaynes
Founded: 1989
F: Arts; Laws; Engineering; Basic Medical Science; Informatics and Mathematical Sciences; Physical and Biological Sciences; Social Studies.

ROYAL ACADEMY OF MUSIC
Prince Consort Road, London, England W7 2BS
Tel: +44(171) 935-5461
Fax: +44(171) 487-3342
Principal: Sir David Lumsden
Founded: 1822, 1830

ROYAL COLLEGE OF MUSIC
Prince Consort Road, London, England SW7 2BS
Tel: +44(171) 589-3643
Fax: +44(171) 589-7740
Director: Michael Gough Matthews
Founded: 1883

ROYAL FREE HOSPITAL SCHOOL OF MEDICINE
Rowland Hill Street, London, England NW3 2PF
Tel: +44(171) 794-0500
Dean: A.J. Zuckerman
Secretary: B.A. Blatch
Founded: 1874
F: Medicine.

ROYAL HOLLOWAY COLLEGE
Egham Hill, Egham, Surrey, England W20 0EX
Tel: +44(171) 784-434455
Fax: +44(171) 784-437520
Telex: 935504 (library)
Cable: royal holloway college, egham
Principal: N.W. Gowar
Academic Registrar: M.A. Miller
Founded: 1985
F: Arts and Music; Science.

ROYAL POSTGRADUATE MEDICAL SCHOOL
Hammersmith Hospital, Du Cane Road, London, England W12 0HF
Tel: +44(181) 743-2030
Fax: +44(181) 740-3203
Cable: postgradmed london w12
Chairman of the Council: L. Banks
Secretary: N.J. Gershon
Founded: 1931
F: Medicine.

ROYAL VETERINARY COLLEGE
Royal College Street, London, England NW1 0TU
Tel: +44(171) 387-2898
Cable: veternosis, london nw1
Principal: L.E. Lanyon
Secretary: D.W. Gordon
Founded: 1791
F: Medicine.

St. BARTHOLOMEW'S HOSPITAL MEDICAL COLLEGE
West Smithfield, London, England EC1A 7BE
Tel: +44(171) 982-6060
Fax: +44(171) 796-3753
Cable: bart's medical college london
President: Lord Raynor of Crowborough
Academic Registrar: T. Webb
Founded: 1662
F: Medicine.

St. GEORGE'S HOSPITAL MEDICAL SCHOOL
Cranmer Terrace, Tooting, London, England SW17 0RE
Tel: +44(181) 672-9944
Fax: +44(181) 672-6940
Chairman of the Council: H.S. Axton
Academic Registrar: G. Jones
Founded: 1751
F: Medicine.

SCHOOL OF ORIENTAL AND AFRICAN STUDIES
Thornhaugh Street, Russell Square, London, England WC1H 0XG
Tel: +44(171) 637-2388
Fax: +44(171) 436-3844
Telex: 262433 w 6876
Cable: soasul london wc 1
Director: M.D. McWilliam
Registrar: T. Harvey
Founded: 1916
D: Languages and Cultures of Africa; Languages and Cultures of the Far East; Languages and Cultures of South East Asia and the Islands; Anthropology and Archaeology; Economics; Geography; History; Indology and Modern Languages and Literatures of South Asia; Law; Phonetics and Linguistics; Political Studies.

SCHOOL OF PHARMACY
29-39 Brunswick Square, London, England WC1N 1AX
Tel: +44(171) 753-5800
Fax: +44(171) 278-0622
Chairman of Council: Sir Graham Wilkins
Registrar: Jacqueline Barr
Founded: 1842, 1952
F: Medicine.

SCHOOL OF SLAVONIC AND EAST EUROPEAN STUDIES
Senate House, Malet Street, London, England
WC1E 7HU
Tel: +44(171) 637-4934
Fax: +44(171) 436-8916
Director: Michael Branch
Clerk to the Council: Philip Robinson
Founded: 1915
*D: Russian Language and Literature; History;
East European Languages and Literatures; Social
Sciences.*

TRINITY COLLEGE OF MUSIC
Mandeville Place, London, England W1M 6AQ
Tel: +44(171) 935-5773
Fax: +44(171) 487-5717
Principal: Philip Jones
Founded: 1872

UNITED MEDICAL AND DENTAL SCHOOLS OF GUY'S AND St.
THOMAS'S HOSPITALS
London Bridge (Guy's); Lambeth Palace Road (St.
Thomas's, London, England SE1 9RT (Guy's); SE1
7EH (St. Thomas's)
Tel: +44(171) 955-5000 (Guy's); +44(171) 928-
9292 (St. Thomas's)
Fax: +44(171) 407-0082 (Guy's) +44(171) 928-
7964 (St. Thomas's)
Principal: I.R. Cameron
Registrar: A.W. Baker
Founded: 1982
F: Medicine.
S: Dentistry.
I: Dermatology.

UNIVERSITY COLLEGE LONDON
Gower Street, London, England WC1E 6BT
Tel: +44(171) 387-7050
Fax: +44(171) 387-8057
Cable: university college london
Provost: D. Roberts
Registrar: M. Butcher
Founded: 1826
*F: Arts; Laws; Clinical Sciences; Engineering;
Life Sciences; Mathematical and Physical
Sciences; Built Environment.*
Ce: Language.

WARBURG INSTITUTE
Woburn Square, London, England WC1H 0AB
Tel: +44(171) 580-9663
Fax: +44(171) 436-2852
Director: Nicholas Mann
Secretary and Registrar: Anita Pollard
Founded: 1921
Historical Studies.

WYE COLLEGE
Ashford, Kent, England TN25 5AH
Tel: +44(1233) 812401
Fax: +44(1233) 813320
Telex: 9401 7832 wyec g
Cable: college, wye
Principal: J.H.D. Prescott
Registrar: C.H. Martindale
Founded: 1447, 1893, 1948, 1945
F: Science.

Loughborough University of Technology
Loughborough, England LE11 3TU
Tel: +44(1509) 263-171
Fax: +44(1509) 610-813
Telex: 34319
Cable: technology, loughborough
Vice-Chancellor: D.E.N. Davies
Registrar: D.E. Fletcher
Founded: 1952, 1966
*S: Education and Humanities; Engineering;
Human and Environment Studies; Pure and
Applied Science.*

The University of Luton
Park Square, Luton, Bedfordshire, England LU1
3JUU
Tel: +44(1582) 341-11
Fax: +44(1582) 486-260
Vice-Chancellor: A.J. Wood
Registrar: Steve Kendall
Founded: 1993
*F: Applied Sciences; Business; Design and
Technology; Health Care and Social Studies;
Humanities; Management.*

The Manchester Metropolitan University
All Saints Building, Oxford Road, Manchester,
England M15 6BH
Tel: +44(161) 247-2000
Fax: +44(161) 236-7383
Vice-Chancellor: Sir Kenneth Green (1981-)
Academic Registrar: J.D.M.
Karczewski-Slowikowski
Founded: 1970, 1992
*F: Arts and Design; Community Studies and
Education; Hollings; Humanities, Law and Social
Science; Management and Business; Science and
Engineering.*
I: Advanced Studies; Popular Culture.
Ut: Social Information Technology.
*Ce: Archival Polymeric Materials; Atmospheric
Research and Information; Mass Spectronomy;
Arts for Health; Analytical.*

University of Manchester Institute of Science and Technology (UMIST)
P.O. Box 88, Sackville Street, Manchester,
England M60 1QD
Tel: +44(161) 236-3311
Fax: +44(161) 228-7040
Telex: 666094
Cable: technology manchester
Principal: H.C.A. Hankins

Secretary and Registrar: P.C.C. Stephenson
Founded: 1824, 1956, 1966
D: *Biochemistry and Applied Molecular Biology; Building Engineering; Chemical Engineering; Chemistry; Civil and Structural Engineering; Computation; Corrosion and Protection; Electrical Engineering and Electronics; Instrumentation and Analytical Science; Language and Linguistics; Management; Mechanical Engineering; Materials Science; Optometry and Vision Sciences; Paper Science; Pure and Applied Physics; Textiles; Total Technology.*

Victoria University of Manchester
Oxford Road, Manchester, England M13 9PL
Tel: +44(161) 275-2000
Fax: +44(161) 273-8715
Telex: 666517 uniman
Vice-Chancellor: M.B. Harris (1992-)
Registrar: K.E. Kithen
Founded: 1851, 1880
F: *Arts; Science; Law; Medicine and Dentistry; Theology; Economics and Social Studies; Education; Technology (U. of Manchester, I. of Science and Technology-UMIST: See above); Business Administration.*
S: *Biological Science.*

*Middlesex University
Trent Park, Bramley Road, London, England N14 4XS
Tel: +44(181) 362-5000
Fax: +44(181) 365-1772
Telex: 8954762 midpol g
Vice-Chancellor: David Melville
Corporate Services Director: W.M. Bradley
Founded: 1992
F: *Art and Design; Business Studies and Management; Education and Performing Arts; Engineering; Science and Mathematics; Humanities and Social Science.*

Napier University
10 Colinton Road, Edinburgh, Scotland EH10 5DT
Tel: +44(131) 444-2266
Fax: +44(131) 455-7209
Principal and Vice-Chancellor: John Mavor (1994-)
Founded: 1964, 1992
F: *Humanities; Professional Studies; Faculty of Science; Technology.*

University of Newcastle upon Tyne
Newcastle upon Tyne, England NE1 7RU
Tel: +44(191) 223-26000
Fax: +44(191) 261-1182
Telex: 53654 uninew g
Cable: university newcastle upon tyne england
Vice-Chancellor: J.R.G. Wright
Registrar: D.E.T. Nicholson
Founded: 19th, 1963
F: *Agricultural and Biological Sciences; Arts; Dentistry; Education; Engineering; Law; Medicine; Science; Social and Environmental Sciences.*

North London University
166-220 Holloway Road, London, England N7 8DB
Tel: +44(171) 607-2789
Fax: +44(171) 753-5166
Vice-Chancellor: Brian Roper (1994-)
Founded: 1971, 1992
F: *Business; Environmental and Social Studies; Humanities and Teacher Education; Science, Computing and Engineering.*

University of Northumbria at Newcastle
Ellison Building, Ellison Place, Newcastle upon Tyne, England NE1 8ST
Tel: +44(191) 232-6002
Fax: +44(191) 235-8017
Vice-Chancellor and Chief Executive: Laing Barden
Secretary and Registrar: Richard A. Bott
Founded: 1969, 1992
F: *Arts and Design; Social Sciences; Engineering, Science and Technology.*
S: *Business.*

University of Nottingham
University Park, Nottingham, England NG7 2RD
Tel: +44(1159) 515-151
Fax: +44(1159) 513-666
Telex: 37346 uninot g
Cable: university nottingham
Vice-Chancellor: C.M. Campbell
Registrar: G.E. Chandler
Founded: 1881, 1948
F: *Agricultural and Food Sciences; Arts; Education; Engineering; Law and Social Sciences; Medicine; Science.*

Nottingham Trent University
Burton Street, Nottingham, England NG1 4BU
Tel: +44(1159) 418-418
Fax: +44(1159) 484-266
Telex: 377534 polnot g.
Director and Chief Executive: R. Cowell
Academic Registrar: A.E. Foster
Founded: 1970, 1992
F: *Art and Design; Business; Education Studies; Engineering; Environmental Studies; Law, Economics and Social Sciences; Humanities; Science.*

Open University
Walton Hall, Milton Keynes, England MK7 6AA
Tel: +44(1908) 740-66
Fax: +44(1908) 625-3744
E-Mail: janet (username)@uk.ac.open.acs.vax
Telex: 825061
Cable: openuniv walton
Vice-Chancellor: John S. Daniel (1990-95)
Secretary: D. Joe Clinch
Founded: 1969
F: *Arts; Mathematics; Science; Social Sciences; Technology.*
I: *Educational Technology.*
S: *Management Studies; Health, Welfare and Community Education; Educational Studies.*

Ce: Modern Languages.
Group: Brain and Behaviour Research;
Computer-assisted Learning Research.
L: Human Cognition Research.
Course: Petrogenesis.

Oxford Brookes University
Gipsy Lane, Headington, Oxford, England OX3 0BP
Tel: +44(1865) 741-111
Fax: +44(1865) 819-073
Director: C. Booth
Founded: 1970, 1976, 1992
D: Architecture; Biological and Molecular Sciences; Business; Civil Engineering Building and Cartography; Computing and Mathematical Sciences; Education; Engineering; Estate Management; Geology; Health Care Studies; Hotel and Catering Management; Humanities; Modern Languages; Modular Course; Planning; Social Studies; Visual Art, Music and Publishing.

*University of Oxford
University Offices, Wellington Square, Oxford, England OX1 2JD
Tel: +44(1865) 270-000
Fax: +44(1865) 270-708
Telex: 83147 via oxuniv
Cable: university offices, oxford
Vice-Chancellor: Peter North
Registrar: A.J. Dorey
Founded: 12th
F: Anthropology and Geography; Biological Sciences; Clinical Medicine; Education; English Language and Literature; Fine Art; Law; Literae Humaniores; Mathematical Sciences; Medieval and Modern Languages; Modern History; Music; Oriental Studies; Physical Sciences; Physiological Sciences; Psychological Studies; Social Studies; Theology.

ALL SOULS COLLEGE
Oxford, England OX1 4AL
Tel: +44(1865) 279-379
Fax: +44(1865) 279-299
Warden: Sir Patrick Neill
Founded: 1438

BALLIOL COLLEGE
Oxford, England OX1 3BJ
Tel: +44(1865) 277-777
Fax: +44(1865) 277-803
Master: Colin Lucas
Founded: 1268

BRASENOSE COLLEGE
Oxford, England OX1 4AJ
Tel: +44(1865) 277-830
Fax: +44(1865) 277-822
Principal: The Rt. Hon. Lord Windlesham
Founded: 1509

CAMPION HALL
Oxford, England OX1 1QS
Tel: +44(1865) 200-861
Master: Rev. J.A. Munitiz
Founded: 1896, 1918

CHRIST CHURCH
Oxford, England OX1 1DP
Tel: +44(1865) 276-150
Fax: +44(1865) 794-199
Dean: Very Rev. J.H. Drury
Founded: 1546

CORPUS CHRISTI COLLEGE
Oxford, England OX1 4JF
Tel: +44(1865) 276-700
Fax: +44(1865) 793-121
President: Keith Thomas
Bursar: B.C. Ruck Keene
Founded: 1517

EXETER COLLEGE
Oxford, England OX1 3DP
Tel: +44(1865) 279-600
Fax: +44(1865) 279-630
Rector: Marilyn Butler
Founded: 1314

GREEN COLLEGE
Oxford, England OX2 6HG
Tel: +44(1865) 274-700
Fax: +44(1865) 274-796
Warden: Sir Crispin Tickell
Senior Bursar: G.T. Warner
Founded: 1979

GREYFRIARS HALL
Oxford, England OX4 1SB
Tel: +44(1865) 243-694
Warden: Maurice W.T. Sheehan (1990-)
Senior Tutor: Stephen Innes
Founded: 1910, 1957

HERTFORD COLLEGE
Oxford, England OX I 3BW
Tel: +44(1865) 279-400
Principal: Sir Christopher Zeeman
Founded: 1740, 1874

JESUS COLLEGE
Oxford, England OX1 3DW
Tel: +44(1865) 299-700
Fax: +44(1865) 279-687
Principal: P.M. North
Founded: 1571

KEBLE COLLEGE
Oxford, England OX1 3PG
Tel: +44(1865) 272-727
Fax: +44(1865) 272-705
Warden: Averil Cameron
Founded: 1868, 1870

KELLOGG COLLEGE
1 Wellington Square, Oxford, England OX1 2JA
Tel: +44(865) 270-360
President: G.P. Thomas
Founded: 1990

LADY MARGARET HALL
Oxford, England OX2 6QA
Tel: +44(1865) 274-300
Fax: +44(1865) 511-069
Principal: D.M. Stewart
Founded: 1962

LINACRE COLLEGE
Oxford, England OX1 3JA
Tel: +44(1865) 271-650
Fax: +44(1865) 271-668
Principal: Sir Bryan Cartledge

LINCOLN COLLEGE
Oxford, England OX1 3DR
Tel: +44(1865) 279-800
Fax: +44(1865) 279-802
Rector: Sir Maurice Shock
Founded: 1427

MAGDALEN COLLEGE
Oxford, England OX1 4AU
Tel: +44(1865) 276-000
Fax: +44(1865) 276-103
President: A.D. Smith
Founded: 1458

MANCHESTER COLLEGE
Oxford, England OX1 3TD
Tel: +44(865) 271-006
Principal: Rev. R. Waller
Founded: 1786, 1990

MANSFIELD COLLEGE
Oxford, England OX1 3TF
Tel: +44(1865) 270-999
Fax: +44(1865) 270-970
Principal: D.J. Trevelyan
Founded: 1886, 1955

MERTON COLLEGE
Oxford, England OX1 4JD
Tel: +44(1865) 276-310
Fax: +44(1865) 276-361
Warden: J.M. Roberts
Domestic and Finance Bursar: C.R. Webb
Founded: 1264

NEW COLLEGE
Oxford, England OX1 3BN
Tel: +44(1865) 279-555
Fax: +44(1865) 279-590
Warden: H. McGregor
Founded: 1379

NUFFIELD COLLEGE
Oxford, England OX1 1NF
Tel: +44(1865) 278-500
Fax: +44(1865) 278-621
Warden: Sir David Cox
Founded: 1937, 1958

ORIEL COLLEGE
Oxford, England OX1 4EW
Tel: +44(1865) 276-555
Fax: +44(1865) 791-823
Provost: Rev. E.W. Nicholson
Founded:

PEMBROKE COLLEGE
Oxford, England OX1 1DW
Tel: +44(1865) 276-444
Fax: +44(1865) 276-418
Master: Sir Roger G. Bannister

THE QUEEN'S COLLEGE
Oxford, England OX1 4AW
Tel: +44(1865) 279-120
Fax: +44(1865) 790-819
Provost: J. Moffatt
Founded: 1340

REGENT'S PARK COLLEGE
Oxford, England OX1 2LB
Tel: +44(1865) 598-87
Principal: Rev. P.S. Fiddes
Founded: 1810, 1957

St. ANNE'S COLLEGE
Oxford, England OX2 6HS
Tel: +44(1865) 274-800
Principal: Ruth L. Deech
Founded: 1879, 1952

St. ANTONY'S COLLEGE
Oxford, England OX2 6JF
Tel: +44(1865) 596-51
Fax: +44(1865) 310-518
Warden: Sir Ralf Dahrendorf
Founded: 1950

St. BENET'S HALL
Oxford, England OX1 3LN
Tel: +44(1865) 515-006
Master: Rev. H. Wansbrough
Founded: 1897, 1918

St. CATHERINE'S COLLEGE
Oxford, England OX1 3UJ
Tel: +44(1865) 271-700
Fax: +44(1865) 271-768
Master: Lord Plant of Highfield
Founded: 1962

St. CROSS COLLEGE
Oxford, England OX1 3LZ
Tel: +44(1865) 278-490
Master: R.C. Repp
Founded: 1965

St. EDMUND HALL
Oxford, England OX1 4AR
Tel: +44(1865) 279-000
Fax: +44(1865) 279-090
Principal: J.C.B. Gosling
Founded: 1278

St. HILDA'S COLLEGE
Oxford, England OX4 1DY
Tel: +44(1865) 276-884
Fax: +44(1865) 276-816
Principal: Elizabeth Llewellyn Smith (1990-)
Secretary: Margaret Lintern-Ball
Founded: 1893

St. HUGH'S COLLEGE
Oxford, England OX2 6LE
Tel: +44(1865) 274-900
Fax: +44(1865) 274-912
Principal: D. Wood
Founded: 1886, 1926

St. JOHN'S COLLEGE
Oxford, England OX1 3JP
Tel: +44(1865) 277-300
Fax: +44(1865) 277-435
President: W. Hayes
Founded: 1555

St. PETER'S COLLEGE
Oxford, England OX1 2DL
Tel: +44(1865) 278-900
Fax: +44(1865) 278-855
Master: J.P. Barron
Founded: 1929, 1961

SOMERVILLE COLLEGE
Oxford, England OX2 6HD
Tel: +44(1865) 270-600
Fax: +44(1865) 270-616
Principal: Catherine E. Pestel
Founded: 1879

TRINITY COLLEGE
Oxford, England OX1 3BH
Tel: +44(1865) 279-900
Fax: +44(1865) 279-911
President: Sir John Birgh

UNIVERSITY COLLEGE
Oxford, England OX1 4BH
Tel: +44(1865) 276-602
Fax: +44(1865) 276-675
Master: W.J. Albery
Founded: 1249

WADHAM COLLEGE
Oxford, England OX1 3PN
Tel: +44(1865) 277-900
Fax: +44(1865) 277-937
Founded: 1612

WOLFSON COLLEGE
Oxford, England OX2 6UD
Tel: +44(1865) 274-100
Fax: +44(1865) 274-125
President: Sir Raymond Hoffenberg
Founded: 1966

WORCESTER COLLEGE
Oxford, England OX12 2HB
Tel: +44(1865) 278-3000
Fax: +44(1865) 278-387
Provost: Dick Smethurst
Founded: 1283, 1714

University of Paisley

High Street, Paisley, Scotland PA1 2BE
Tel: +44(141) 848-3000
Fax: +44(141) 887-0812
Principal and Vice Chancellor: Professor R.W. Shaw (1987-)
Registrar and Deputy Secretary: D. Rigg
Founded: 1897, 1992
F: Information, Social and Management Sciences; Engineering; Science and Technology.
Ce: Computer; Alcohol Studies; Technology and Business; Microelectronics Educational

Development; The Quality; Environmental and Waste Management.

University of Plymouth

Drake Circus, Plymouth, Devon, England PL4 8AA
Tel: +44(1752) 600-600
Fax: +44(1752) 232-293
Vice-Chancellor: R.J. Bull
Founded: 1970, 1989, 1992
F: Arts and Design; Science; Human Sciences; Technology; Agriculture.

University of Portsmouth

University House, Winston Churchill Avenue, Portsmouth, England PO1 2UP
Tel: +44(1705) 827-681
Fax: +44(1705) 843-319
Vice-Chancellor: Neil Merritt
Founded: 1870, 1992
F: Business, Economics and Management; Engineering; Environmental Studies; Humanities and Social Sciences; Faculty of Science.

University of Reading

Whiteknights, P.O. Box 217, Reading, England RG6 2AH
Tel: +44(1734) 875-123
Fax: +44(1734) 314-404
Telex: 847813
Vice-Chancellor: Roger Williams
Registrar: D.C.R. Frampton
Founded: 1892, 1898, 1902, 1926
F: Science; Agriculture and Food; Letters and Social Sciences; Urban and Regional Studies; Education and Community Studies.
I: Sedimentology Postgraduate Research; AFRC Food Research, Reading Laboratory.

The Robert Gordon University

Schoolhill, Aberdeen, Scotland AB9 1FR
Tel: +44(1224) 633-611
Fax: +44(1224) 634-377
Principal: David A. Kennedy
Secretary: David C. Caldwell
Founded: 1910, 1992
F: Design; Health and Food; Management; Science and Technology.
S: Art (Gray's); Architecture (Scott Sutherland); Surveying; Food and Consumer Studies; Health and Social Work; Pharmacy; Business; Librarianship and Information Studies; Applied Sciences; Electronic and Electrical Engineering; Computer and Mathematical Sciences; Mechanical and Offshore Engineering; Public Administration and Law.
D: Nursing; Occupational Therapy; Physiotherapy; Radiography.
Ut: Educational Development; Paper Technology; Hyperbaric Research; Research and Development.

Royal College of Art
Kensington Gore, London, England SW7 2EU
Tel: +44(171) 584-5020
Fax: +44(171) 225-1487
Rector: Anthony Jones (1992-)
Registrar: Alan Selby
Founded: 1837, 1896, 1967
F: Fine Arts; Design for Manufacture; Design for Communication; Humanities.

University of St. Andrews
College Gate, North Street, St. Andrews, Scotland KY16 9AJ
Tel: +44(1334) 761-61
Fax: +44(1334) 758-51
Telex: 9312110846 s ag
Cable: university st. andrews
Principal and Vice-Chancellor: Struther Arnott
Secretary: David J. Corner
Founded: 1411
F: Arts; Divinity; Science.

University of Salford
Salford, England M5 4WT
Tel: +44(161) 745-5000
Fax: +44(161) 745-5885
Telex: 668680
Vice-Chancellor: T.M. Husband
Registrar: S.R. Bosworth
Founded: 1896, 1967
F: Engineering; Science; Social Sciences and Arts.

Sheffield Hallam University
Pond Street, Sheffield, England S1 1WB
Tel: +44(1142) 720-911
Fax: +44(1142) 758-019
Telex: 54680 shpoly g
Principal and Vice-Chancellor: J. Stoddart
Founded: 1969, 1992
S: Computing and Management Sciences; Construction; Cultural Studies; Education; Engineering; Engineering Information Technology; Financial Studies and Law; Health and Community Studies; Leisure and Food Management; Science.

University of Sheffield
P.O. Box 594, Firth Court, Western Bank, Sheffield, England S10 2UH
Tel: +44(1142) 768-555
Fax: +44(1142) 739-826 group 3
Telex: 547216 ugshef g
Cable: university sheffield
Vice-Chancellor: G.G. Roberts
Registrar and Secretary: J.S. Padley
Founded: 1897, 1905
F: Arts; Architecture; Education; Engineering; Law; Medicine; Pure Science; Social Sciences.
Ce: Development and Planning Studies; English Cultural Tradition and Language; Human Nutrition; Palynology Studies; Statistical Education; Policy Studies.

ut: Social Services Research; Artificial Intelligence Vision Research; Medical Care Research; Social and Applied Psychology; Comparative Plant Ecology (NERC); Structural Integrity Research.
I: Robert Hill (photosynthesis in plants and micro-organism); Folklore Studies in Britain and Canada; Biomolecular Research (Krebs).

South Bank University
Borough Road, London, England SE1 0AA
Tel: +44(171) 928-8989
Fax: +44(171) 261-9115
Vice-Chancellor and Chief Executive: G. Bernbaum (1993-)
Founded: 1970, 1992
F: Built Environment; Engineering; Management and Policy Studies; Science.

University of Southampton
Highfield, Southampton, England SO9 5NH
Tel: +44(1703) 595-000
Fax: +44(1703) 593-037
Telex: 47661
Cable: university of southampton
Vice-Chancellor: Howard Newby
Secretary and Registrar: J.F.D. Lauwerys
Founded: 1902, 1952
F: Arts; Educational Studies; Engineering and Applied Sciences; Law; Mathematical Studies; Medicine; Science; Social Sciences.

Staffordshire University
Beaconside, Stafford, England ST18 0AD
Tel: +44(1782) 744-531
Fax: +44(1782) 744-035
Director: K.B. Thompson
Founded: 1970, 1992
F: Art and Design; Business, Humanities and Social Sciences; Computing, Engineering and Science.

University of Stirling
Stirling, Scotland FK9 4LA
Tel: +44(1786) 731-71
Fax: +44(1786) 630-00
Telex: 77557 stuniv g
Cable: stirling university
Principal and Vice-Chancellor: A. Miller
Founded: 1967
F: Arts; Human Sciences; Management; Natural Sciences.

University of Strathclyde
McCance Building, 16 Richmond Street, Glasgow, Scotland G1 1XQ
Tel: +44(141) 552-4400
Fax: +44(141) 552-0775
Telex: 77472
Principal and Vice-Chancellor: John P. Arbuthnott
Secretary: Peter W.A. West
Founded: 1796, 1964
F: Arts; Engineering; Business; Science; Education (Subject to government approval of an application for merger with Jordanhill College of Education).

University of Sunderland
Langham Tower, Ryhope Road, Sunderland,
England SR2 7EE
Tel: +44(191) 515-2000
Fax: +44(191) 510-2423
Telex: 537339 seeds g
Vice-Chancellor: Anne M. Wright
Founded: 1969, 1992
*F: Arts and Social Studies; Business,
Management and Education; Science;
Technology.*

University of Surrey
Guildford, Surrey, England GU2 5XH
Tel: +44(1483) 300-800
Fax: +44(1483) 300-803
Telex: 859331
Vice-Chancellor: A. Kelly
Secretary and Registrar: H.W.B. Davies
Founded: 1891, 1956
F: Engineering; Human Studies; Science.
I: Industrial and Environmental Health (Robens).
Ce: Satellite Engineering and Research.

*University of Sussex
Sussex House, Falmer, Brighton, England BN1
9RH
Tel: +44(1273) 606-755
Fax: +44(1273) 678-335
Telex: 877159 unisex
Cable: university, brighton
Vice-Chancellor: Gordon Conway (1992-)
Registrar and Secretary: Geoffrey Lockwood
Founded: 1961
*S: African and Asian Studies; Biological
Sciences; Cultural and Community Studies;
Engineering; English and American Studies;
European Studies; Mathematical and Physical
Sciences; Chemical and Molecular Sciences;
Social Sciences; Cognitive Sciences.*
*I: Continuing and Professional Education;
Development Studies.*
Ut: Science Policy Research.
*Ce: Medical Research (Trafford); Neuroscience
(Sussex).*

University of Teesside
Borough Road, Middlesborough, Cleveland,
England TS1 3BA
Tel: +44(1642) 218-121
Fax: +44(1642) 342-067
Telex: 587537 teplib g
Vice-Chancellor: D. Fraser
Founded: 1929, 1970, 1992
*S: Business; Computing and Mathematics;
Health, Social and Policy Studies; Science and
Technology.*

Thames Valley University
St. Mary's Road, Ealing, London, England W5
5RF
Tel: +44(181) 579-5000
Fax: +44(181) 566-1353
Director: Mike Fitzgerald
Founded: 1991, 1992

*F: Accounting, Law and Economics; Business
and Information Studies; Health Care Studies
(Queen Charlotte's); Hospitality Studies;
Humanities and Languages; Technology.*
S: Business.

*University of Ulster
University House, Cromore Road, Coleraine, Co.
Londonderry, Northern Ireland BT52 1SA
Tel: +44(1265) 441-41
Fax: +44(1265) 575-28
Telex: 747597
Vice-Chancellor: T.A. Smith (1991-)
Secretary: J.A. Hunter
Founded: 1984
*F: Arts and Design; Business and Management
(including Ulster Business S.); Education;
Humanities; Science and Technology; Social
Sciences and Health Sciences; Informatics.*
D: Adult and Continuing Education.
*Ce: (NI)Biomedical Sciences Research; Study
of Conflict; Energy Research; Health and Social
Research; Policy Research; Engineering
Composites; Research on Women.*

University of Wales
University Registry, King Edward VII Avenue,
Cathays Park, Cardiff, Wales CF1 3NS
Tel: +44(1222) 382-656
Fax: +44(1222) 396-040
Cable: university registry, cardiff
Vice-Chancellor: Kenneth Morgan (1993-)
Registrar: M.A.R. Kemp
Founded: 1893
*F: Architecture; Education; Engineering;
Medicine; Music; Rural Science; Theology or
Divinity.*

UNIVERSITY COLLEGE OF WALES, ABERYSTWYTH
P.O. Box 2, Aberystwyth, Dyfed, Wales SY23 2AX
Tel: +44(1970) 623-111
Fax: +44(1970) 611-446
Telex: 35181 aby ucw 9
Cable: university college of wales, aberystwyth
Principal: K.O. Morgan
Registrar and Secretary: D.G. Jones
Founded: 1872
*F: Arts; Economics and Social Studies;
Education; Law; Science.*

UNIVERSITY COLLEGE OF NORTH WALES, BANGOR
Bangor, Gwynedd, Wales LL57 2DG
Tel: +44(1248) 351-151
Fax: +44(1248) 370-451
Telex: 61100 ucnwsl g
Cable: unicol, bangor
Principal: E. Sunderland
Secretary and Registrar: G.R. Thomas
Founded: 1884
F: Arts; Science; Theology.

St. DAVID'S UNIVERSITY COLLEGE, LAMPETER
Lampeter, Dyfed, Wales SA48 7ED
Tel: +44(1570) 422-351
Fax: +44(1570) 423-423
Telex: 48475
Principal: K.G. Robbins
Registrar and Secretary: A.M.S. Kenwright
Founded: 1822
F: Arts; Theology.

UNIVERSITY COLLEGE OF SWANSEA
Singleton Park, Swansea, Wales SA2 8PP
Tel: +44(1792) 205-678
Fax: +44(1792) 295-618
E-Mail: @uk.ac.swan.vax
Cable: swansea university college
Principal: R. Williams
Registrar: V.J. Carney
Founded: 1920
F: Arts; Science; Economics and Social Studies; Educational Studies; Engineering.
S: European Business Management.

UNIVERSITY OF WALES COLLEGE OF CARDIFF
P.O. Box 920, Cardiff, Wales CF1 3XP
Tel: +44(1222) 874-000
Fax: +44(1222) 874-478
Telex: 498635
Principal: E.B. Smith
Registrar: M.J. Bruton
Founded: 1988
F: Business Studies and Law; Engineering and Environmental Design; Health and Life Sciences; Humanities and Social Studies; Physical Sciences.

UNIVERSITY OF WALES COLLEGE OF MEDICINE
Heath Park, Cardiff, Wales CF4 4XN
Tel: +44(1222) 747-747
Fax: +44(1222) 762-208
Telex: 498696
Provost: Sir Herbert Duthie
Registrar and Secretary: A.W. Roberts
Founded: 1931, 1992
F: Clinical Studies; Nursing Studies; Postgraduate Studies.
S: Dental.

*University of Warwick
Coventry, England CV4 7AL
Tel: +44(1203) 523-630
Fax: +44(1203) 461-606
Telex: 317472
Vice-Chancellor: Sir Brian Follett (1993-)
Registrar: M.L. Shattock
Founded: 1965
F: Arts; Educational Studies; Social Studies; Science.

University of Westminster
309 Regent Street, London, England W1R 8AL
Tel: +44(171) 911-5000
Fax: +44(171) 911-5103
Rector: Terence E. Burlin
Founded: 1970, 1992
F: Engineering and Science; Environment; Law, Languages and Communication; Business, Management and Social Studies.

University of Wolverhampton
Wulfruna Street, Wolverhampton, England WV1 1SB
Tel: +44(1902) 321-000
Fax: +44(1902) 322-632
E-Mail: dir@sysc.wolverhampton.ac.uk
Director/Vice-Chancellor: M.J. Harrisson
Assistant Director (Administration): G.R. Brooks
Founded: 1969, 1992
F: Business, Law and European Studies; Science and Technology; Education; Arts, Design and Social Studies.
Ce: Business Research; Audit Research (CITICORP); Education Research.

University of York
Heslington, York, England YO1 5DD
Tel: +44(1904) 430-000
Fax: +44(1904) 433-433
Telex: 57933 yorkul
Cable: university york
Vice-Chancellor: S.B. Saul (1979-93).
Registrar: David Foster
Founded: 1963
D: Archaeology; Biology; Chemistry; Computer Science; Economics; Education; Electronics; English; History; Language and Linguistic Science; Mathematics; Music; Philosophy; Physics; Politics; Psychology; Social Policy; Sociology.
I: Historical Research (Borthwick); Advanced Architectural Studies; Research into the Social Sciences.

OTHER INSTITUTIONS

Anglo-European College of Chiropractic
Parkwood Road, Bournemouth, Hampshire, England Bh5 2DF
Tel: +44(1202) 431-021
Fax: 44(1202) 417-352
Principal: B.N. Kilger
Chiropractic.

Bangor Normal College
Bangor, Gwynedd, England LL57 2PX
Tel: +44(1248) 370-171
Fax: +44(1248) 370-461
Principal: H. Gareth Ff Roberts
Arts, Design and Media Studies; Business Professions; Catering, Recreation and Tourism; Education/Teacher Training; The Environment: Past, Present and Future; Humanities; Modern Languages; Science, Techology and Engineering; Social and Health Studies.

Bedford College of Higher Education
Cauldwell Street, Bedford, England MK42 9AH
Tel: +44(1234) 345-151
Fax: +44(1234) 342-674
Chief Executive: P. Mansell
Arts, Design and Media Studies; Business Professions; Catering, Recreation and Tourism; Education/Teacher Training; The Environment: Past, Present and Future; Humanities; Modern Languages; Science, Technology and Engineering; Social and Health Studies.

Bishop Grosseteste College
Lincoln, England LN1 3DY
Tel: +44(1522) 527-47
Fax: +44(1522) 530-243
Principal: Leonard Marsh
Education/Teacher Training; Business Professions.

Bolton Institute of Higher Education
Deane Road, Bolton, Lancs, England BL3 5AB
Tel: +44(1204) 28851
Fax: +44(1204) 21920
Principal: R. Oxtoby
Arts, Design and Media Studies; Built Environment; Business Professions; Catering, Recreation and Tourism; Education/Teacher Training; The Environment: Past, Present and Future; Humanities; Modern Languages; Science, Technology and Engineering; Social and Health Studies.

The Buckinghamshire College
Queen Alexandra Road, High Wycombe, Buckinghamshire, England HP11 3JZ
Tel: +44(1494) 522-141
Fax: +44(1494) 438-123
Director: P.B. Monford
Arts, Design and Media Studies; Built Environment; Business Professions; Catering, Recreation and Tourism; Education/Teacher Training; The Environment: Past, Present and Future; Science, Technology and Engineering; Social and Health Studies.

Canterbury Christ Church College
North Holmes Road, Canterbury, Kent, England CT1 1QU
Tel: +44(1227) 782-200
Fax: +44(1227) 470-422
Principal: M. Berry
Arts, Design and Media Studies; Business Professions; Catering, Recreation and Tourism; Education/Teacher Training; The Environment: Past, Present and Future; Humanities; Modern Languages; Science, Technology and Engineering; Social and Health Studies.

Cardiff Institute of Higher Education
P.O. Box 377, Llandaff Centre, Western Avenue, Cardiff, Wales CF5 2SG
Tel: +44(1222) 551-111
Fax: +44(1222) 576-951
Arts, Design and Media Studies; Built Environment; Business Professions; Catering, Recreation and Tourism; Education/Teacher Training; The Environment: Past, Present and Future; Humanities; Modern Languages; Science, Technology and Engineering; Social and Health Studies.

Central School of Speech and Drama
Embassy Theatre, 64 Eton Avenue, London, England NW3 3HY
Tel: +44(171) 722-8183
Fax: +44(171) 586-1665
Principal/Chief Executive: R. Fowler
Speech and Drama.

Cheltenham and Gloucester College of Higher Education
P.O. Box 220, The Park Campus, Cheltenham, Gloucestshire, England GL50 2QF
Tel: +44(1242) 532-701
Fax: +44(1242) 532-879
Director: J. Trotter
Arts, Design and Media Studies; Built Environment; Business Professions; Catering, Recreation and Tourism; Education/Teacher Training; The Environment: Past, Present and Future; Humanities; Modern Languages; Science, Technology and Engineering; Social and Health Studies.

Chester College of Higher Education
Cheyney Road, Chester, England CH1 4BJ
Tel: +44(1244) 375-444
Fax: +44(1244) 373-379
Principal: E.V. Binks
Arts, Design and Media Studies; Built Environment; Education/Teacher Training; The Environment: Past, Present and Future; Humanities; Modern Languages; Science, Technology and Engineering; Social and Health Studies.

City College, Norwich
Ipswich Road, Norwich, Norfolk, England NR2 2LJ
Tel: +44(1603) 663-402
Fax: +44(1603) 760-326
Principal: Chief Executive: Caroline Neville
Business Professions; Catering, Recreation and Tourism; Education/Teacher Training; The Environment: Past, Present and Future; Humanities; Science, Technology and Engineering; Social and Health Studies.

College of Guidance Studies
College Road, Hextable, Swanley, Kent, England BR8 7RN
Tel: +44(1322) 664-407
Fax: +44(1322) 613-265
Principal: A.K. Sommerville
Guidance Studies.

The College of St. Mark and St. John
Derriforth Road, Plymouth, Devon, England PL6 8BH
Tel: +44(1752) 777-188
Fax: +44(1752) 761-128
Principal: J. Anderson
Arts, Design and Media Studies; Catering, Recreation and Tourism; Education/Teacher Training; The Environment: Past, Present and Future; Humanities; Science, Technology and Engineering; Social and Health Studies.

Cumbria College of Art and Disign
Brampton Road, Carlisle, Cumbria, England CA3 9AY
Tel: 44(1228) 25333
Fax: 44(1228) 514-491
Principal: David Vaughan
Art and Design.

Dartington College of Arts
Totnes, Devon, England Q9 6EJ
Tel: +44(1803) 862-224
Fax: +44(1803) 863-569
Principal: K. Thompson
Arts.

Edge Hill College of Higher Education
St. Helens Road, Ormskirk, Lancashire, England L39 4QP
Tel: +44(1695) 584-234
Fax: +44(1695) 577-137
Chief Executive: John Cater
Arts, Design and Media Studies; Business Professions; Education/Teacher Training; The Environment: Past, Present and Future; Humanities; Modern Languages; Science, Technology and Engineering; Social and Health Studies.

Edinburgh College of Art
Lauriston Place, Edinburgh, Scotland EH3 9DF
Tel: +44(131) 229-9311
Fax: +44(131) 229-0089
Director: Alistar J. Rowan
Founded: 1907
Art and Design; Architecture.

Enniskillen Agricultural College
Enniskillen, Co. Fermanagh, N. Ireland
Tel: +44(1365) 323-101
Fax: +44(1365) 324-722
Director: A. Mallon
International Relations: Kenneth Johnstone
Founded: 1967
Agriculture.

Falmouth School of Art and Design
Woodlane, Falmouth, Cornwall, England TR11 4RA
Tel: +44(1326) 211-077
Fax: +44(1326) 211-205
Principal: A.G. Livingston
Art and Design.

Glasgow School of Art
167 Renfrew Street, Glasgow, Scotland G3 6RQ
Tel: +44(141) 353-4500
Fax: +44(141) 353-4528
Director: D. Cameron
International Relations: Jackie Main
Founded: 1845
Fine Art and Design; Architecture.

Greenmount College of Agriculture and Horticulture
Antrim, N. Ireland BT41 4PU
Tel: +44(18494) 62114
Fax: +44(18494) 28201
Director: R.J. McClenaghan
Founded: 1912
Architecture; Horticulture.

Gwent College of Higher Education
College Crescent, Caerlon, Newport, Gwent, Wales NP5 1XJ
Tel: +44(1633) 432-000
Fax: +44(1633) 432-002
Principal: K.J. Overshott
Arts, Design and Media Studies; Built Environment; Business Professions; Education/ Teacher Training; The Environment: Past, Present and Future; Humanities; Science, Technology and Engineering; Social and Health Studies.

Harper Adams Agricultural College
Edgmond, Newport, Shropshire, England TF10 8NB
Tel: +44(1952) 820-820
Fax: +44(1952) 814-783
Principal/Chief Executive: A.G. Harris
Agriculture.

Hartpury College, Gloucestershire
Hartpury House, Hartpury, Gloucester, England GL19 3BE
Tel: +44(1452) 700-283
Fax: +44(1452) 700-629
Director: M. Wharton
Founded: 1948
Agriculture; Animal Care; Equestrian Studies; Horticulture; Conservation.

Homerton College
Cambridge, England CB2 2PH
Tel: +44(1223) 411-141
Fax: +44(1223) 413-727
Principal: K.B. Pretty
Education/Teacher Training.

Jewel and Esk Valley College
24 Milton Road East, Edinburgh, Scotland EH15 2PP
Tel: +44(131) 669-8461
Fax: +44(131) 657-2276
Director: J. Lisgo
International Relations: M. Somerville
Engineering and Building; Business and Computing.

Kent Institute of Art and Design
Oakwood Park, Maidstone, Kent, England ME16 8AG
Tel: +44(1622) 691-471
Fax: +44(1622) 688-077
Director: P. Williams
Art and Design.

King Alfred's College
Sparkford Road, Winchester, Hants, England SO22 4NR
Tel: +44(1962) 827-221
Fax: +44(1962) 879-033
Principal/Chief Executive: J. Dickinson
Arts, Design and Media Studies; Business Professions; Catering, Recreation and Tourism; Education/Teacher Training; The Environment: Past, Present and Future; Humanities; Modern Languages; Social and Health Studies.

*La Sainte Union College (LSU) of Higher Education
The Avenue, Southampton, England SO17 1BG
Tel: +44(1703) 228-761
Fax: +44(1703) 230-944
Principal: Anand C. Chitnis
Founded: 1904
F: Science; Humanities; Education.

Liverpool Institute of Higher Education
P.O. Box 6, Stand Park Road, Liverpool, England L16 9JD
Tel: +44(151) 737-3477
Fax: +44(151) 737-3100
Rector: J. Burke
Arts, Design and Media Studies; Eduation/ Teacher Training; The Environment: Past, Present and Future; Humanities; Modern Languages; Science, Technology and Engineering; Social and Health Studies.

Loughry College of Agriculture and Food Technology
Cookstown, Co. Tyrone, N. Ireland BT80 9AA
Tel: +44(16487) 62491
Fax: +44(16487) 61043
Director: R.C. Stevenson
Founded: 1949
Agriculture and Food Technology.

The London Institute
65 Davies Street, London, England W1Y 2DA
Tel: +44(171) 514-6000
Fax: +44(171) 514-6212
Rector: J. McKenzie
Arts, Design and Media Studies; Built Environment; Business Professions; Catering, Recreation and Tourism; Education/Teacher Training; The Environment: Past, Present and Future; Humanities; Modern Languages; Science, Technology and Engineering; Social and Health Studies.

Myerscough College EC
Myerscough Hall Bilsborrow, Preston, Lancashire, England PR3 0RY
Tel: +44(1995) 640-611
Fax: +44(1995) 640-842
Director: A. Fox
International Relations: B. Davies
Founded: 1894
Agriculture and Horticulture.

Nene College
Moulton Park, Northampton, England NN2 7AL
Tel: +44(1604) 716-462
Fax: +44(1604) 712-413
Director: S.M. Gaskell
Arts, Design and Media Studies; Built Environment; Business Professions; Catering, Recreation and Tourism; Education/Teacher Training; The Environment: Past, Present and Future; Humanities; Modern Languages; Science, Technology and Engineering; Social and Health Studies.

Newman College
Genners Lane, Bartley Green, Birmingham, England B32 3NT
Tel: +44(121) 476-1181
Fax: +44(121) 476-1196
Principal: J.S. Cuming
Arts, Design and Media Studies; Catering, Recreation and Tourism; Education/Teacher Training; The Environment: Past, Present and Future; Humanities; Science, Technology and Engineering.

North East Wales Institute of Higher Education
Plas Coch, Mold Road, Wrexham, Clwyd, Wales LL11 2AW
Tel: +44(1978) 290-666
Fax: +44(1978) 290-008
Principal/Chief Executive: J.O. Williams
Arts, Design and Media Studies; Built Environment; Business Professions; Education/ Teacher Training; The Environment: Past, Present and Future; Humanities; Science, Technology and Engineering; Social and Health Studies.

Queen Margaret College
Clerwood Terrace, Edinburgh, Scotland EH12 8TS
Tel: +44(131) 317-3000
Fax: +44(131) 317-3256
Principal: D. Leach

Ravensbourne College of Design and Communication
Walden Road, Chislehurst, Kent, England BR7 5SN
Tel: +44(181) 468-7071
Fax: +44(181) 295-0728
Director: N.J. Frewing

Bretton Hall College of the University of Leeds
West Bretton, Wakefield, West Yorkshire, England WF4 4LG
Tel: +44(1924) 830-261
Fax: +44(1924) 830-521
Principal/Chief Executive: M. Berry
Arts, Design and Media Studies; Education/ Teacher Training; The Environment: Past, Present and Future; Humanities; Social and Health Studies.

Roehampton Institute
Senate House, Roehampton Lane, London, England SW15 5PU
Tel: +44(181) 392-3101
Fax: +44(181) 392-3029
Rector: S.C. Holt
Arts, Design and Media Studies; Business Professions; Catering, Recreation and Tourism; Education/Teacher Training; The Environment: Past, Present and Future; Humanities; Modern Laguages; Science, Technology and Engineering; Social and Health Studies.

Rose Bruford College of Speech and Drama
Lamorbey Park, Sidcup, Kent, England DA15 9DF
Tel: +44(181) 300-3024
Fax: +44(181) 308-0542
Principal: R. Ely
Speech and Drama.

The Royal Scottish Academy of Music and Drama
St. George's Place, Glasgow, Scotland G2 1BS
Tel: +44(141) 332-4101
Fax: +44(141) 332-8901
Director: P. Ledger
Founded: 1847
Music; Drama.

The Scottish Agricultural College
Auchincruive Nr. Ayr, Scotland KA6 5HW
Tel: +44(1292) 520-331
Fax: +44(1292) 521-119
Director: P.C. Thomas
International Relations: D. Grant
Founded: 1899
Conservation; Rural Resources; Agriculture; Horticulture; Drama.

Seale-Hayne College
Newton Abbot, Devon, England TQ12 6NQ
Tel: +44(1626) 325-606
Fax: +44(1626) 325-605
Dean: F. Harper
Agriculture; Food Technology; Land Use.

Shuttleworth Agricultural College
Old Warden Park, Cranfield University, Biggleswade,Bedfordshire, England SG18 9DX
Tel: +44(1767) 627-441
Fax: +44(1767) 627-561
Director: R.W. Radley
Founded: 1988
Agriculture.

Silsoe College
Cranfield University, Bedford, England HK45 4D7
Tel: +44(1525) 860-428
Fax: +44(1525) 861-994
Director: R.W. Radley
Founded: 1975
Agriculture.

South Devon College
Newton Road, Torquay, Devon, England TQ2 5BY
Tel: +44(1803) 386-480
Fax: +44(1803) 386-483
Principal: T.R. Keen
Arts, Design and Media Studies; Built Environment; Business Professions; Catering, Recreation and Tourism; Social and Health Studies.

Southampton Institute of Higher Education
East Park Terrace, Southampton, Hants, England SO9 4WW
Tel: +44(1703) 319-216
Fax: +44(1703) 235-620
Director: D.G. Leyland
Arts, Design and Media Studies; Built Environment; Business Professions; Catering, Recreation and Tourism; The Environment: Past, Present and Future; Science, Technology and Engineering; Social and Health Studies.

St Martin's College
Lancaster, England LA1 3JD
Tel: +44(1524) 63446
Fax: +44(1524) 847-693
Principal: D. Edynbry
Arts, Design and Media Studies; Business Professions; Catering, Recreation and Tourism; Education/Teacher Training; The Environment: Past, Present and Future; Humanities; Science, Technology and Engineering; Social and Health Studies.

St. Mary's College
Waldegrave Road, Strawberry Hill, Twickenham, Middlesex, England TW1 4SX
Tel: +44(181) 892-0051
Fax: +44(181) 744-2080
Principal: A. Naylor
Arts, Design and Media Studies; Education/ Teacher Training; The Environment: Past, Present and Future; Humanities; Science, Technology and Engineering; Social and Health Studies.

Swansea Institute of Higher Education

Townhill Road, Swansea, West Glamorgan, Wales
SA2 0UT
Tel: +44(1792) 481-000
Fax: +44(1792) 208-683
Principal/Chief Executive: G. Stockdale
*Arts, Design and Media Studies; Built
Environment; Business Professions; Catering,
Recreation and Tourism; Education/Teacher
Training; The Environment: Past, Present and
Future; Humanities; Modern Languges; Science,
Technology and Engineering; Social and Health
Studies.*

Trinity and All Saints College

Brownberrie Lane, Horsforth, Leeds, England
LS18 5HD
Tel: +44(1132) 837-100
Fax: +44(1132) 837-200
Principal: G.L. Turnbull
*Arts, Design and Media Studies; Built
Environment; Business Professions; Catering,
Recreation and Tourism; Education/Teacher
Training; The Environment: Past, Present and
Future; Humanities; Modern Languages; Science,
Technology and Engineering; Social and Health
Studies.*

Trinity College

Carmarthen, Dyfed, Wales SA31 3EP
Tel: +44(1267) 237-971
Fax: +44(1267) 230-933
Principal: D.C. Jones-Davies
*Arts, Design and Media Studies; Education/
Teacher Training; The Environment: Past,
Present and Future; Humanities; Modern
Languages; Science, Technology and
Engineering; Social and Health Studies.*

University College Scarborough, North Riding College

Filey Road, Scarborough, Nork Yorkshire,
England YO11 3AZ
Tel: +44(1723) 362-392
Fax: +44(1723) 370-815
Principal and Chief Executive: R. Withers
*Arts, Design and Media Studies; Business
Professions; Education/Teacher Training; The
Environment: Past, Present and Future;
Humanities; Science, Technology and
Engineering.*

University College of Ripon and York St. John

Lord Mayor's Walk, York, England YO3 7EX
Tel: +44(1904) 656-771
Fax: +44(1904) 670-622
Principal: G.P. McGregor
*Arts, Design and Media Studies; Education/
Teacher Training; The Environment: Past,
Present and Future; Humanities; Modern
Languages; Science, Technology and
Engineering; Social and Health Studies.*

University College Salford

Frederick Road, Salford, England M6 6PU
Tel: +44(161) 7453-238
Fax: +44(161) 708-2088
Principal: T.J. Squires
*Arts, Design and Media Studies; Built
Environment; Business Professions; Catering,
Recreation and Tourism; Education/Teacher
Training; The Environment: Past, Present and
Future; Humanities; Modern Languages; Science,
Technology and Engineering; Social and Health
Studies.*

Warrington Collegiate Institute

Winwick Road Campus, Warrington, Lancashire,
England WA2 8QA
Tel: +44(1925) 814-343
Fax: +44(1925) 816-077
Principal/Chief Executive: Bill Bestwick

Welsh Agricultural College

Llanbadarn Fawr, Aberystwyth, Dyfed, Wales
SY23 3AL
Tel: +44(1970) 624-471
Fax: +44(1970) 611-264
Director: J. Warries
Founded: 1971
Agriculture.

West London Institute of Higher Education

Lancster House, Borough Road, Isleworth,
Middlesex, England TW7 7DU
Tel: +44(181) 568-8741
Fax: +44(11) 758-1285
Principal: J.E. Kane
*Arts, Design and Media Studies; Business
Professions; Catering, Recreation and Tourism;
Education/Teacher Training; The Environment:
Past, Present and Future; Science, Technology
and Engineering; Social and Health Studies.*

West Surrey College of Art and Design

The Hart, Farnham, Surrey, England GU9 7DS
Tel: +44(1252) 732-201
Fax: +44(1252) 717-539
Director: N.J. Taylor
Art and Design.

West Sussex Institute of Higher Education

College Lane, Chichester, West Sussex, England
PO19 4PE
Tel: +44(1243) 787-911
Fax: +44(1243) 536-011
Director: J.F. Wyatt
*Arts, Design and Media Studies; Catering,
Recreation and Tourism; Edcuation/Teacher
Training; The Environment: Past, Present and
Future; Humanities; Science, Technology and
Engineering; Social and Health Studies.*

Westhill College
Weoley Park Road, Selly Oak, Birmingham,
England B29 6LL
Tel: +44(121) 472-7245
Fax: +44(121) 472-1796
Principal: J. Priestley
*Arts, Design and Media Studies; Catering,
Recreation and Tourism; Education/Teacher
Training; The Environment: Past, Present and
Future; Humanities; Science, Technology and
Engineering; Social and Health Studies.*

Westminster College
Oxford, England OX2 9AT
Tel: +44(1865) 247-644
Fax: +44(1865) 251-847
Principal: K.B. Wilson
*Arts, Design and Media Studies; Education/
Teacher Training; The Environment: Past,
Present and Future; Humanities; Modern
Languages; Science, Technology and
Engineering.*

Wimbledon School of Art
Merton Hall Road, Wimbledon, London, England
SW19 3QA
Tel: +44(181) 540-0231
Fax: +44(181) 543-1750
Principal: C. Painter
Art.

Winchester School of Art
Park Avenue, Winchester, Hampshire, England
SO23 8DL
Tel: +44(1962) 842-500
Fax: +44(1962) 842-496
Principal: M. Sadler-Forster
Art.

Worcester College of Higher Education
Henwick Grove, Worcester, England WR2 6AJ
Tel: +44(1905) 748-080
Fax: +44(1905) 422-539
Principal: D. Urwin
*Arts, Design and Media Studies; Catering,
Recreation and Tourism; Education/Teacher
Training; The Environment: Past, Present and
Future; Humanities; Sceince, Technology and
Engineering; Social and Health Studies.*

Writtle College of Agriculture
Lordship Road, Writtle, Chelmsford, Essex,
England CM1 3RR
Tel: 44(1245) 420-705
Fax: 44(1245) 420-456
Principal: M.D. Adler
Agriculture.

NATIONAL ACADEMIC BODIES

Department for Education and Science
Sanctuary Building, Great Smith Street, London,
England SW1P 3BT
Tel: +44(171) 934-9033
Fax: +44(171) 934-9082
Telex: 2317

Committee of Vice-Chancellors and Principals of the Universities of the United Kingdom (CVCP)
29 Tavistock Square, London WC1H 9EZ
Tel: +44(171) 387-9231
Fax: +44(171)388-8649
Chairman: Kenneth Edwards (1993-95)
Secretary: T.U. Burgner
Founded: 1918

Higher Education Funding Council for England (HEFCE)
Northavon House, Coldharbour Lane, Bristol,
England BS3 1NG
Tel: +44(1179) 317-317
Fax: +44(1179) 317-203
Chairman: Brandon Gough
Chief Executive: Brian Fender
Founded: 1992

Standing Conference of Principals of University Sector Colleges (SCOP)
P.O. Box 190, Cheltenham, England GL50 3SJ
Tel: +44(1242) 225-925
Fax: +44(1242) 263-554
Chairman: Jim Burke
Executive Secretary: T.J. Cox

Association of University Teachers (AUT)
United House, 1 Pembridge Road, London W11
3HJ
Tel: +44(171) 221-4370
President: Alan Waton
General Secretary: David Triesman
Founded: 1919

The British Council
10 Spring Gardens, London, England SW1A 2BN
Tel: +44(171) 930-8466
Fax: +44(171) 839-6347
Telex: 8952201
Chairman: David Orr
Director-General: Richard Francis
Founded: 1934

The Carnegie Trust for the Universities of Scotland
The Merchant's Hall, 22 Hanover Street,
Edinburgh, Scotland EH2 2EN
Tel: +44(131) 220-1217
Chairman: Lewis Robertson
Secretary and Treasurer: J.T. Coppock
Founded: 1902

Central Bureau for Educational Visits and Exchanges (CBEVE)
Seymour Mews House, Seymour Mews, London,
England W1H 9PE
Tel: +44(171) 486-5101
Fax: +44(171) 935-5741
Chaiman: Anthony Carter
Director: Tony Male
Founded: 1948

The Commonwealth Foundation (CF)

Marlborough House, Pall Mall, London SW1Y 5HY
Tel: +44(171) 930-3783
Fax: +44(171) 839-8157
Telex: 27678
Chairman: Robert Stanfield
Director: 'Inoke Faletau
Founded: 1966

National Academic Recognition Information Centre (NARIC)

The British Council (Education Division), Medlok Street, Manchester, England M15 4PR
Tel: +44(161) 957-7000
Fax: +44(161) 957-7111
Telex: 8952201 bricon g
Director: Katherine Stewart

Overseas Development Administration

Eland House, Stag Place, London, England SW1E 5DH
Tel: +44(171) 273-3000
Fax: +44(171) 213-6749

Society for Research into Higher Education (SRHE)

344-354 Gray's Inn Road, London, England WC1X 8BP
Fax: +44(171) 833-1012
President: Herman Bondi
Director: Cynthia Iliffe
Founded: 1964

United States-United Kingdom Educational Commission (Fulbright Commission)

6 Porter Street, London, England W1M 2HR
Tel: +44(171) 486-7697
Fax: +44(171) 224-4567
Founded: 1948

Universities and Colleges Admission Service (UCAS)

P.O. Box 28, Cheltenham, England GL50 3SA
Tel: +44(1242) 222-444
Fax: +44(1242) 221-622
Telex: 43662
General Secretary: P.A. Oakley
Founded: 1993

Voluntary Service Overseas (VSO)

317 Putney Bridge Road, Putney, London, England SW15 2PN
Tel: +44(181) 780-2266
Fax: +44(181) 780-1326
Director: David Green
Founded: 1958

UNITED STATES OF AMERICA

UNIVERSITIES AND COLLEGES AWARDING DOCTORATES

PUBLIC INSTITUTIONS

Arizona State University

Tempe, Arizona 85287
Tel: +1(602) 965-9011
Fax: +1(602) 965-1608
President: Lattie F. Coor
Provost and Senior Vice-President: Milton D. Glick
Founded: 1885, 1958
C: Architecture and Environmental Design; Business; Education; Engineering and Applied Sciences; Fine Arts; Law; Liberal Arts and Sciences; Nursing; Public Programmes.
Div: Curriculum and Instruction; Educational Leadership and Policy Studies; Psychology in Education.
S: Accountancy; Agribusiness and Environmental Resources; Architecture; Art; Design; Engineering; Health Administration and Policy; Justice Studies; Music; Public Affairs; Technology; Journalism and Communication (Walter Cronkite); Social Work.

Auburn University

Auburn, Alabama 36849-3501
Tel: +1(205) 844-4000
Fax: +1(205) 844-6179
Telex: 5106002392 fishery
President: William V. Muse
Vice President of Academic Affairs: Jack E. Blackburn
Founded: 1856, 1872
C: Liberal Arts; Veterinary Medicine; Science and Mathematics; Agriculture; Business; Engineering; Education.
S: Architecture; Human Sciences; Pharmacy; Nursing; Forestry.
Ce: Advanced Technology; Alabama Microelectronics Science and Technology; Auburn Utilities Research; Arts and Humanities; International Commerce; Management and Executive Development; On Aging; Economic Development I.
I: Latin-American Studies; International DFT for Aquaculture; Leach Nuclear Science Ce.; For Asphalt Technology; Pulp and Paper Research and Educational Ce.; Small Business Development Ce.; Water Resources Research I.; Mass Spectrometry Ce.

Ball State University

2000 University Avenue, Muncie, Indiana 47306
Tel: +1(317) 289-1241
Fax: +1(317) 285-1624
President: John Worthen
Provost and Vice-President for Academic Affairs: D. Warren Vander Hill
Founded: 1918

C: *Architecture and Planning; Business; Teacher's C.; Fine and Applied Arts; Sciences and Humanistics.*
S: *Physical Education and Athleticsc; Music; Nursing; University C.*
Ce: *Middletown Studies; Social Science Research Ce.; Energy Research, Education and Service; Entrepreneurial Studies.*

Bowling Green State University
Bowling Green, Ohio 43403-0001
Tel: +1(419) 372-2531
President: Paul J. Olscamp
Founded: 1910, 1929, 1935
Vice-President of Academic Affairs.
C: *Arts and Sciences; Business Administration; Education and Allied Professions; Health and Human Services; Musical Arts; Technology; Firelands C.*
S: *Art; Mass Communication; Health, Physical Education and Recreation; Nursing.*

California State University, Los Angeles
5151 State University Drive, Los Angeles, California 90032
Tel: +1(213) 343-3000
Fax: +1(213) 343-2670
President: James M. Rosser
Provost and Vice-President for Academic Affairs: Mary Elizabeth Shutler
Founded: 1947, 1972
S: *Arts and Letters; Business and Economics; Education; Engineering and Technology; Health and Human Services; Natural and Social Sciences.*

Central Michigan University
Warriner Hall, Mount Pleasant, Michigan 48859
Tel: +1(517) 774-4000
Fax: +1(517) 774-3537
E-Mail: bitnet: userid @ cmuvm.bitnet
Telex: +1(650) 349-6763
President: Leonard E. Plachta (1992-93)
Provost: Robert G. Franke
Founded: 1892, 1959
C: *Arts and Sciences; Business and Administration; Health and Human Services; Extended Learning.*

City University of New York (CUNY) System
535 East 80th Street, New York, N.Y. 10021
Tel: +1(212) 794-5728
Fax: +1(212) 794-5590
Chancellor: W. Ann Reynolds
Deputy Chancellor: Laurence F. Mucciolo
Founded: 1926

City University of New York, Brooklyn College
2900Bedford Avenue and Avenue H, Brooklyn, N.Y. 11210-2889
Tel: +1(718) 951-5000
President: Vernon E. Lattin
Provost: Christoph M. Kimmich
Founded: 1901
Liberal Arts; Education; Sciences; Music.

City University of New York Graduate School and University Center
33 West 42nd Street, New York, N.Y. 10036
Tel: +1(212) 642-1600
Fax: +1(212) 642-2642
President: Frances Degan Horowitz
Provost: Geoffrey Marshall
Founded: 1961, 1972
Liberal Arts and Sciences.

Clemson University
201 Sikes Hall, Clemson, South Carolina 29634
Tel: +1(803) 656-3311
Fax: +1(803) 656-4676
Telex: 981694 clemson sc
President: Constantine W.(Deno) Curris (1994-)
Provost: J. Charles Jennett
Founded: 1889, 1964
C: *Liberal Arts; Agricultural Sciences; Sciences; Engineering; Forest and Recreation Resources; Architecture; Education; Nursing; Commerce and Industry.*
Ce: *National Drop Out Prevention.*
I: *Wildlife and Environmental Toxicology; Forest Science (Belle W. Baruch).*

Cleveland State University
Euclid Avenue at East 24th Street, Cleveland, Ohio 44115
Tel: (216) 687-2000
Fax: (216) 687-9366
Telex: 8104218252 csu clv
President: Claire A. Van Ummersen
Provost (Acting): Richard McArdle
Founded: 1964
C: *Arts and Sciences; Business Administration (James J. Nancey); Education; Engineering (Fen); Law (Cleveland-Marshall); Urban Affairs (Maxine Goodman Levin); Town-Planning Affairs.*
Ce: *Urban.*
D: *Continuing Education; Special Studies; Black Studies.*
P: *Women's Comprehensive.*
Ce: *Labour-Management Relations; Advanced Manufacturing; World Trade Education.*

The College of William and Mary
Williamsburg, Virginia 23187-8795
Tel: +1(804) 221-4000
Fax: +1(804) 221-2749
President: Timothy J. Sullivan
Vice-President of Administration and Finance: William F. Merck
Founded: 1693
F: *Arts and Sciences.*
S: *Business Administration; Education; Law (Marshall-Whythe); Marine Science.*
L: *Population Ecology.*
I: *Early American History and Culture; Virginia I. of Marine Science; For the Bill of Rights.*

Colorado School of Mines

1500 Illinois, Golden, Colorado 80401
Tel: +1(303) 273-3000
Fax: +1(303) 273-3278
Telex: 9109340190 csm ui
President: George S. Ansell (1984-)
Vice-President for Academic Affairs: Frank
Schowengerdt
Founded: 1874
*D: Chemical Engineering and Petroleum
Refining; Chemistry and Geochemistry; Mineral
Economics; Metallurgical and Materials
Engineering; Engineering; Environmental Science
and Engineering; Geology and Geological
Engineering; Geophysical Engineering;
Mathematical and Computer Sciences
Department; Mining Engineering; Petroleum
Engineering; Physics.*
*I: Excavation Engineering and Earth Mechanics;
Energy Resources Studies; Fuels and High
Altitude Engine Research; Extractive Metallurgy
(W.J. Kroll).*
*Ce: Potential Field Studies; Advanced Ceramics;
Wave Phenomena; Mining and Mineral
Resources Research; Advanced Steel Processing
and Products Research Ce.; Welding and Joining
Research; Hydrates and Other Solids;
International Ground Water Modelling.*

Colorado State University

Fort Collins, Colorado 80523
Tel: +1(303) 491-1101
Fax: +1(303) 491-0501
E-Mail: INTERNET
Telex: 452014 icard
President: Albert C. Yates
Provost: Eleanor Gilfoyle
Founded: 1870
*C: Applied Human Science; Agriculture
Sciences; Business; Engineering; Veterinary
Medicine and Biomedical Sciences; Natural
Sciences; Natural Resources; Liberal Arts.*

East Carolina University

East Fifth Street, Greenville, North Carolina
27858-4353
Tel: +1(919) 757-6131
Fax: +1(919) 757-4155
Chancellor: Richard R. Eakin
Vice Chancellor for Academic Affairs: Marlene
Springer
Founded: 1907, 1951, 1967
C: Arts and Sciences.
*S: Business; Education; Art; Human
Environmental Sciences; Nursing; Music;
Medicine; Industry and Technology; Social Work;
Allied Health Sciences.*
Ce: BB and T Leadership Development.
*I: Coastal and Marine Resources; Regional
Development.*

East Tennessee State University

Johnson City, Tennessee 37614
Tel: +1(615) 929-4112
Fax: +1(615) 929-4004
President (Interim): Roy S. Nicks (1992-93)
Vice-President of Administration and
Development: Richard A. Manahan
Founded: 1911, 1943, 1963
*C: Arts and Sciences; Applied Science and
Technology; Business; Education; Medicine
(James H. Quillen); Nursing; Public and Allied
Health.*

East Texas State University

ET Station, Commerce, Texas 75429
Tel: +1(903) 886-5081
Fax: +1(903) 886-5888
President: Stephen R. Hensley (1994-)
Vice-President for Academic Affairs: Donna
Arlton
Founded: 1889, 1965
*S: Liberal and Fine Arts; Arts and Sciences;
Business and Technology; Education.*

Florida Agricultural and Mechanical University

Tallahassee, Florida 32307
Tel: (904) 599-3000
Fax: (904) 561-2152
President: Frederick S. Humphries
Vice-President for Academic Affairs: Richard A.
Hogg
Founded: 1887, 1953
*S: Architecture; General Studies; Allied Health
Sciences; Journalism, Media and Graphic Arts;
Business and Industry; Nursing.*
*C: Arts and Sciences; Education; Engineering;
Engineering Sciences, Technology and
Agriculture; Pharmacy and Pharmaceutical
Studies.*
*D: Graduate Studies, Research and Continuing
Education.*

Florida Atlantic University

500 N.W. 20th Street, Boca Raton, Florida
33431-0991
Tel: +1(407) 367-3000
Fax: +1(407) 367-2777
President: Anthony James Catanese
Provost and Vice-President: Leonard Berry
Founded: 1961
*C: Arts and Humanities (Schmidt); Engineering;
Business; Education; Nursing; Science; Social
Science; Liberal Arts; Urban and Public Affairs.*
S: Accounting; Public Administration.

Florida International University

University Park, Miami, Florida 33199
Tel: +1(305) 554-2000
Fax: +1(305) 348-2994
President: Modesto Maidique
Provost/Vice-President (Academic Affairs): James
A. Mau
Founded: 1965

S: Health; Business; Engineering; Education; Nursing; Hospital Management; Public Affairs and Social Services; International Affairs; Arts and Sciences; Accountancy; Computer Sciences; Design; Engineering and Design; Journalism and Mass Communication.

Florida State University
Tallahassee, Florida 32306-1037
Tel: +1(904) 644-2525
Fax: +1(904) 644-9936
President: Dale W. Lick (1994-)
Provost: Robert B. Glidden
Founded: 1851
C: Arts and Sciences; FAMU/FSU Engineering; Communication and Communication Disorders; Social Sciences; Law; Engineering; Business; Education; Human Sciences; Library and Information Studies.
S: Motion Picture, Television and Recording Artso10ean:; Music; Theatre; Visual Arts and Dance; Nursing; Social Work; Criminology and Criminal Justice.
I: Geophysical Fluid Dynamics; Supercomputer Computations Research; I. of Aging; Florida-France Linkage; Molecular Biophysics; Business, Research and Service; Learning Systems.
Ce: Study of Population; Professional Development and Public Service; Intensive English Studies; Yugoslav-American Studies, Research and Exchanges; Florida-Costa Rica; Middle East Studies; African American Culture.

George Mason University
4400 University Drive, Fairfax, Virginia 22030-444
Tel: +1(703) 993-1000
Fax: +1(703) 993-3849
President: George W. Johnson
Provost: Frederick Rossini
Founded: 1957
C: Arts and Sciences.
S: Law; Education (Graduate); Business Administration; Information Technology and Engineering; Nursing.

Georgia Institute of Technology
225 North Avenue, Northwest Atlanta, Georgia 30332
Tel: +1(404) 894-2000
Fax: +1(404) 894-5520
Telex: 542507 gtrc oca atl
President: Gerald W. Clough (1994-)
Executive Vice President: Michael E. Thomas
Founded: 1885, 1948
C: Engineering; Architecture; Management; Sciences; Computing; C. of Management, Policy, and International Affairs (Ivan Allen).
I: Georgia Tech Research.

Georgia State University
University Plaza, Atlanta, Georgia 30303
Tel: +1(404) 651-2000
Fax: +1(404) 651-2013
E-Mail: admses@gsuvmi.bitnet
President: Carl V. Patton (1992-)
Provost: Thomas J. La Belle
Founded: 1913, 1947, 1969
C: Arts and Sciences; Business Administration; Education; Health Sciences; Law; Public Administration and Urban Studies.
I: I. of Personnel and Employment Relations (W.T. Beebe).
D: Developmental Studies.
S: S. of Hospitality (Cecile B. Day); Administration; Nursing; Accountancy; Allied Health Professions; Art and Design; Music.
Ce: Applied Research in Anthropology; High Resolution Astronomy; Hydrogeology; Interdisciplinary Parent-Infant Resource; Business and Economic Education; Mature Consumer Studies; Professional Education; Risk Management and Insurance Research; Study of Regulated Industry; Economic Forecasting; International Ce. for Enterpreneurship; Policy Research; Real Estate and Land Economics (Research for); Small Business Development; Cross-Cultural Education; Educational Research; Sports and Exercise; Human Resource Development; Family Education; Health Sciences; Legal Studies of Financial Institutions; Gerontology; Urban Policy Research; For the Study of Adult Literacy.

Grambling State University
100 Main Street, P.O. Drawer 607, Grambling, Louisiana 71245
Tel: +1(318) 274-2000
Fax: +1(318) 274-2398
President: Harold W. Lundy
Vice-President for Academic Affairs: Joyce Verret
Founded: 1901
C: Liberal Arts; Business; Education; Nursing.
S: Science and Technology; Social Work.

Idaho State University
741 South 7th Avenue, Pocatello, Idaho 83209
Tel: +1(208) 236-0211
Fax: +1(208) 236-4000
President: Richard L. Bowen
Vice-President for Academic Affairs: Michael Gallagher
Founded: 1901, 1947, 1963
C: Arts and Sciences; Business; Education; Engineering; Health-Related Professions; Pharmacy.
S: Applied Technology.

Illinois State University
North and School Street, Normal, Illinois
61761-6901
Tel: +1(309) 438-2111
Fax: +1(309) 438-2768
President: Thomas P. Wallace
Provost: David Strand
Founded: 1857
C: *Applied Science and Technology; Arts and
Sciences; Business; Education; Fine Arts.*

Indiana State University
Terre Haute, Indiana 47809
Tel: +1(812) 237-6311
Fax: +1(812) 237-4292
President: John W. Moore
Vice-President for Academic Affairs: Richard
M.Wells
Founded: 1857
C: *Arts and Sciences.*
S: *Business; Education; Health, Physical
Education and Recreation; Nursing; Technology.*

*Indiana University at Bloomington
International Admissions, 300 North Jordan
Avenue, Bloomington, Indiana 47405
Tel: +1(812) 855-4848
Fax: +1(812) 855-8990
Telex: 272279
Cable: inovers
President: Curt Simic
Director of Admissions: Robert Magee
Founded: 1820
C: *Arts and Sciences; Music; Optometry; Public
and Environmental Affairs; Social Work.*
S: *Fine Arts; Medecine; Business; Education;
Health, Physical Education, and Recreation;
Journalism; Law; Library and Information
Sciences.*
I: *Applied Mathematics and Scientific
Computing; The Kinsey I. for Sex Research;
Howard Hughes Medical; Early Music.*
Ce: *Nuclear Theory Ce. (Cyclotron).*
P: *Medical Sciences; Ce. for Latin American
and Caribbean Studies.*

Indiana University-Purdue University at Indianapolis
355 North Lansing, Indianapolis, Indiana 46202
Tel: +1(317) 274-5555
President: Curt Simic
Vice-President/Chancellor: Gerald L. Bepko
Founded: 1969
S: *Medicine; Dentistry; Nursing; Law; Social
Service; Arts (Herron); Liberal Arts; Engineering
and Technology; Sciences; Education; Business;
Optometry; Public and Environmental Affairs;
Journalism; Physical Education.*

Indiana University of Pennsylvania
Sutton Hall, Indiana, Pennsylvania 15705
Tel: +1(412) 357-2100
Fax: +1(412) 357-2685
President: Lawrence K. Pettit
Provost: Mark Staszkiewicz
Founded: 1875
C: *Business; Education; Fine Arts; Human
Ecology and Health Sciences; Natural Sciences
and Mathematics; Humanities and Social
Sciences.*

Iowa State University of Science and Technology
Ames, Iowa 50011
Tel: +1(515) 294-4111
Fax: +1(515) 294-0565
Telex: 283359
President: Martin C. Jischke
Provost: John J. Kozak
Founded: 1858
C: *Liberal Arts and Sciences; Agriculture;
Business; Design; Education; Engineering; Family
and Consumer Sciences; Veterinary Medicine.*

Kansas State University
1700 Anderson Avenue, Manhattan, Kansas
66506-9909
Tel: +1(913) 532-6250
Fax: +1(913) 532-5632
President: John Wefald (1986-93)
Provost: James R. Coffman
Founded: 1863
C: *Agriculture; Arts and Sciences; Architecture
and Design; Business Administration; Education;
Engineering; Human Ecology; Technology;
Veterinary Medicine.*
S: *Journalism and Mass Communication (A.Q.
Miller).*

Kent State University
P.O. Box 51980, Kent, Ohio 44242-0001
Tel: +1(216) 672-2121
Fax: +1(216) 672-3281
E-Mail: bitnet, internet
President: Carol A. Cartwright (1991-)
Provost: Myron S. Henry
Founded: 1910, 1935
C: *Arts and Sciences; Business Administration;
Education; Fine and Professional Arts.*
S: *Library and Information Science; Physical
Education, Recreation, and Dance; Nursing;
Family and Consumer Studies; Journalism and
Mass Communication; Music; Speech Pathology
and Audiology; Technology; Theater; Fashion
Design and Merchandizing (Shannon Rodgers/
Jerry Silverman); Education (Graduate);
Management (Graduate Schools); Architecture
and Envirnmental Design; Art; Biomedical
Sciences; Communication Studies.*
I: *Liquid Crystal; African-American Affairs;
Applied Linguistics; Computational Mathematics;
Water Resources; Bibliography and Editing.*

Ce: Applied Psychology; Health Promotion through Education; International and Comparative Ps.; Peaceful Change; Public Administration and Public Policy; Study of World Musics; Pan-African Culture; Child Development; Gerontology Ce.; Reading and Writing Development.
L: NATO and EC Studies (Lynman L. Lemnitzer).

Lamar University
4400 M.L. King, Jr. Parkway, P.O. Box 10001-LUS, Beaumont, Texas 77705
Tel: +1(409) 880-7011
Fax: +1(409) 880-8404
President: Rex L. Cottle
Executive Vice-President (Academic and Student Affairs): Beheruz N. Sethna
Founded: 1923, 1949, 1971
C: Business; Education and Human Development; Engineering; Fine Arts and Communication; Arts and Sciences.
I: Technology.
Ce: Gulf Coast Hazardous Substance Research.

Louisiana State University and Agricultural and Mechanical College
Baton Rouge, Louisiana 70803
Tel: +1(504) 388-3202
Fax: +1(504) 388-6400
Chancellor: William E. Vavis (1989-)
Provost: Ronald Haden
Founded: 1853, 1870
C: Agriculture; Arts and Sciences; Business Administration; Basic Sciences; Design; Education; Engineering; General; Music; Veterinary Medicine.
S: Mass Communication (Manship); Architecture; Art; Forestry, Wildlife, and Fisheries; Human Ecology; Landscape Architecture; Library and Information Science; Social Work; Vocational Education.
I: Recyclable Materials; Biodynamics; Mutagenesis; Entrepreneurship; Louisiana Real Estate Research; Public Administration; Basin Research; Coastal Ecology; Environmental Studies; Louisiana Mining and Minerals Resources Research; Wetland Biogeochemistry.
Ce: French and Francophone Studies; Life Course and Population Studies; Southern Regional Climate; Hazardous Waste Research; Louisiana Transportation Research; Louisiana Water Resources Research; Coastal, Energy and Environmental Resources; Energy Studies; Nuclear Science; Advanced Microstructures and Devices (J. Bennett Sr.); Law (Paul M. Herbert).

Louisiana State University Medical Center
433 Bolivar Street, New Orleans, Louisiana 70112-2223
Tel: +1(504) 568-4808
Fax: +1(504) 568-7399
Chancellor: Perry G. Rigby
Vice-Chancellor, Academic Affairs: Marilyn L. Zimny

Founded: 1931
S: Medicine (New Orleans); Medicine (Shreveport); Graduate Studies; Dentistry; Allied Health Professions; Nursing.

Louisiana Tech University
Box 3168 Tech Station, Ruston, Louisiana 71272
Tel: +1(318) 257-0211
Fax: +1(318) 257-2928
President: Daniel D. Reneau (1987-)
Vice-President for Academic Affairs: Ken Rea
Founded: 1894
C: Arts and Sciences; Administration and Business; Education; Engineering; Human Ecology; Life Sciences.
S: Forestry; Performing Arts; Professional Accountancy.
I: Micromanufacturing; Wildlife and Environmental Toxicology.
Ce: Trenchless Technology; Rehabilitation Science and Biomedical Engineering.

Medical College of Georgia
Augusta, Georgia 30912
Tel: +1(706) 721-0211
President: Francis J. Tedesco
Vice-President for Academic Affairs: Barry D. Goldstein
Founded: 1828
Allied Health Sciences; Dentistry; Graduate Studies; Medicine; Nursing.

Medical College of Ohio
3000 Arlington Avenue, P.O. Box 10008, Toledo, Ohio 43699-0008
Tel: +1(419) 381-4172
Fax: +1(419) 385-6351
President: Richard D. Ruppert (1977-)
Vice-President for Academic Affairs: Richard F. Leighton
Founded: 1964
S: Medicine; Nursing; Allied Health.

Medical University of South Carolina
171 Ashley Avenue, Charleston, South Carolina 29425
Tel: +1(803) 792-2300
Fax: +1(803) 792-8558
President: James B. Edwards (1982-)
Provost: W. Marcus Newberry
Founded: 1824, 1913
C: Medicine; Dental Medicine; Health Related Professions; Nursing; Pharmacy; Graduate Studies.

Miami University
East High Street, Oxford, Ohio 45056
Tel: +1(513) 529-1809
Fax: +1(513) 529-3841
President: Paul G. Riser
Provost/Executive Vice-President fo Academic Affairs: Ronald J. Henry
C: Arts and Sciences.

S: *Applied Sciences; Business Administration; Fine Arts; Education and Allied Professions; Interdisciplinary Studies.*
I: *Environmental Sciences.*
Ce: *Management Development; Labour-Management Co-operation; Warehousing Research; Pension and Retirement Research; Entrepreneurship (Tom Page); Business (Miami).*

*Michigan State University
East Langsing, Michigan 48824-1046
Tel: +1(517) 355-1855
Telex: 5106019207 natsupcyclab
President: M. Peter McPherson (1993-)
Provost: Lo Anna Kimsey Simon
Founded: 1855
C: *Arts and Letters; Business and Management (Eli Broad); Education; Engineering; Osteopathic Medicine; Natural Sciences; Social Science; Veterinary Medicine; Human Medicine; Agriculture and Natural Resources; Nursing; Communication Arts and Sciences; James Madison; Human Ecology.*
S: *Criminal Justice; Hotel, Restaurant, and Institutional Management; Journalism; Labors and Industrial Relations; Music; Packaging; Social Work.*
Ce: *African Studies; Asian Studies; Canadian Studies; Cancer; Action in Science and Technology at MSU; Advanced Study of International Development; Cartographic Research and Spatial Analysis; Ethics and Humanities in the Life Sciences; Fundamental Materials Research; Latin American and Caribbean Studies; Study of Active Oxygen in Biology and Medicine; Urban Affairs; Research on Teacher Education; Russian and East European Studies; National Science and Technology for Microbial Ecology.*

Michigan Technological University
1400 Townside Drive, Houghton, Michigan 49931-1295
Tel: +1(906) 487-1885
Fax: +1(906) 487-2398
President: Curtis J. Tompkins
Provost: Fredrick J. Dobney
Founded: 1885, 1964
C: *Sciences and Arts; Business and Engineering Administration; Engineering.*
S: *Forestry and Wood Products; Technology.*

Middle Tennessee State University
Murfreesboro, Tennessee 37132
Tel: +1(615) 898-2300
Fax: +1(605) 898-5538
President: James E. Walker
Vice-President for Academic Affairs: E. James Hindman
Founded: 1911
C: *Liberal Arts; Basic and Applied Sciences; Business; Education; Mass Communication.*

Mississippi State University
Mississippi State, Mississippi 39762
Tel: +1(601) 325-2323
Fax: +1(601) 325-8028
E-Mail: Easylink 62007813 esl ud
President: Donald W. Zacharias
Provost: Willie L. McDaniel
Founded: 1878, 1932, 1958
C: *Arts and Sciences; Business and Industry; Education; Engineering; Agriculture and Home Economics; Architecture; Veterinary Medicine.*
S: *Accountancy; Forest Resources.*

Montana State University
Bozeman, Massachusetts 59717
Tel: +1(406) 994-0211
Fax: +1(406) 994-2893
President: Michael P. Malone (1991-)
Provost: Mark A. Emmert
Founded: 1893, 1965
C: *Agriculture; Arts and Architecture; Business; Education, Health and Human Development; Engineering; Letters and Science; Nursing.*
Ce: *Engineering Research (CIMPE).*

Morgan State University
Cold Spring La-Hillen Road, Baltimore, Maryland 21239
Tel: +1(410) 319-3333
Fax: +1(410) 319-3698
President: Earl S. Richardson
Vice-President for Finance and Management: Abraham Moore
Founded: 1867, 1939, 1975
C: *Arts and Sciences.*
S: *Business and Management; Engineering; Education and Urban Affairs.*
I: *Architecture and Planning.*

New Jersey Institute of Technology
University Heights, Newark, New Jersey 07102-9938
Tel: +1(201) 596-3000
Fax: +1(201) 643-3934
President: Saul K. Fenster
Provost: Gary Thomas
Founded: 1881
C: *Architecture; Engineering; Science and Liberal Arts.*
S: *Industrial Management.*

New Mexico Institute of Mining and Technology
Campus Station, Socorro, New Mexico 87801
Tel: +1(505) 835-5011
Fax: +1(505) 835-6329
President: Laurence H. Lattman
Vice-President for Academic Affairs: Carl H. Popp
Founded: 1989
Bureau: *Mines and Mineral Resources.*
Ce: *New Mexico Petroleum Recovery Research.*

New Mexico State University
P.O. Box 30001, Las Cruces, New Mexico 88003
Tel: (505) 646-0111
Fax: (505) 646-6334
President: James E. Halligan
Executive Vice-President: William B. Conroy
Founded: 1888
C: Arts and Sciences; Business Administration
and Economics; Education; Engineering; Human
and Community Services; Agriculture and Home
Economics.

North Carolina State University
Raleigh, North Carolina 27695
Tel: +1(919) 515-2011
Fax: +1(919) 515-3787
Chancellor: Larry K. Monteith (1990-)
Provost/Vice-Chancellor: Phillip J. Stiles
Founded: 1887
C: Agriculture and Life Sciences; Education and
Psychology; Engineering; Forest Resources;
Humanities and Social Science; Management;
Physical and Mathematical Sciences; Textiles.
S: Design; Veterinary Medicine.

North Dakota State University
Office of International Support Services, P.O. Box
5582, Fargo, North Dakota 58105
Tel: +1(701) 237-8011
Fax: +1(701) 237-7050
President: Bruce Bergland (1994-)
Vice-President of Academic Affairs: Sharon
Wallace
Founded: 1890
C: Agriculture; Business Administration;
Electrical and Mechanical Engineering, and
Architecture; Human Development and Education;
Humanities and Social Science; Pharmacy;
Science and Mathematics; NDSU Extension
Service.

Northeast Louisiana University
700 University Avenue, Monroe, Louisiana
71209-0001
Tel: +1(318) 342-1000
Fax: +1(318) 342-5161
President: Lawson L. Swearingen, Jr.
Provost: Arlen R. Zander
Founded: 1931
C: Business Administration; Education;
Pharmacy.
S: Liberal Arts; Pure and Applied Sciences;
Allied Health Sciences; Communication;
Construction; Music; Nursing.

Northeastern University
360 Huntington Avenue, Boston, Massachusetts
02115
Tel: +1(617) 373-2000
President: John A. Curry (1989-)
Registrar: Edmund J. Mullen
Founded: 1896, 1909
C: Arts and Sciences; Pharmacy and Health
Sciences (Boove); Business Administration;

Computer Science; Criminal Justice; Engineering;
Nursing.
S: Journalism (Part-time); Professional
Accounting (Graduate); Law; Engineering
Technology.
I: African American; Chemical Analysis and
Materials (Barnett).
Ce: Applied Social Research; Cardiovascular
Health and Exercise; Electromagnetics Research;
Electron Microscopy; Study of Sport in Society;
Vertebrate Studies; Marine Science.

Northern Arizona University
NAU Box 4092, Flagstaff, Arizona 86011
Tel: (602) 523-9011
Fax: (602) 523-4230
President: Patsy Reed (1993-)
Registrar: Kris McCulsky
Founded: 1899
C: Arts and Sciences; Business Administration;
Creative and Communication Arts; Engineering
and Technology; Social and Behavioural
Sciences; Health Professions.
S: Forestry; Hotel and Restaurant Management;
Art and Design; communication; Performing Arts.
Ce: Excellence in Education.

Northern Illinois University
De Kalb, Illinois 60115-2864
Tel: +1(815) 753-1000
Fax: +1(815) 753-0198
Telex: 981417
President: John E. LaTourette
Vice-President and Provost (Acting): J. Carroll
Moody
Founded: 1895
C: Business; Education; Professional Studies;
Visual and Performing Arts; Engineering and
Engineering Technology; Liberal Arts and
Sciences; Law.

Oakland University
Rochester, Michigan 48309-4401
Tel: +1(313) 370-2100
Fax: +1(313) 370-2286
President: Sandra Packard
Vice-President for Academic Affairs: Gary D.
Russi
Founded: 1957, 1963
C: Arts and Sciences.
S: Engineering; Education and Human Services;
Business Administration; Nursing; Health
Sciences.

The Ohio State University
1800 Cannon Drive, Columbus, Ohio 43210
Tel: +1(614) 292-2424
Fax: +1(614) 292-1231
President: E. Gordon Gee
Senior Vice-President for Academic Affairs: Joan
N. Huber
Founded: 1870
C: Agriculture; Biological Sciences; Business;
Dentistry; Education; Human Ecology;

Humanities; Law; Mathematical and Physical Sciences; Medicine; Nursing; Optometry; Pharmacy; Social and Behavioural Sciences; Social Work; Arts; Veterinary Medicine; Engineering.
S: Allied Medical Professions; Architecture; Health, Physical Education and Recreation; Journalism; Music; Natural Resources; Public Policy and Management.

*Ohio University
108 Cutler Hall, Athens, Ohio 45701-2979
Tel: +1(614) 593-10000
Fax: +1(614) 593-4229
President: Charles J. Ping (1994-)
Provost: David Stewart
Founded: 1804
C: Arts and Sciences; Business Administration; Communication; Education; Engineering and Technology; Fine Arts; Health and Human Services; Osteopathic Medicine.
S: Applied Behavioural Sciences and Educational Leadership; Art; communication System Management; Curriculum and Instruction; Dance; Film; Health and Sport Sciences; Hearing and Speech Sciences; Music; Nursing; Theater; Visual Communication; Telecommunications; Human and Consumer Science; Interpersonal Communication; Journalism; Physical Therapy.
Ce: International Studies.

Oklahoma State University
Main Campus, Stillwater, Oklahoma 74078
Tel: +1(405) 744-5000
Fax: +1(405) 744-8871
President: James E. Halligan (1994-)
Provost: Ray M. Bowen
Founded: 1890, 1957
C: Arts and Sciences; Agriculture Sciences and Natural Resources; Business Administration; Education; Engineering, Architecture and Technology; Human and Environmental Sciences; Osteopathic Medicine (Tulsa); Veterinary Medicine.
S: Accounting; Architecture; Chemical Engineering; Civil and Envirnmental Engineering; Electrical and Computer Engineering; Health, Physical Education and Leisure; Hotel of Restaurant Administration; Industrial Engineering and Management; Journalism and Broadcasting; Occuptional and Adult Education.

Old Dominion University
5215 Old Hampton Boulevard, Norfolk, Virginia 23529
Tel: +1(804) 683-3000
Fax: +1(804) 683-4505
Telex: 823428 old dom nfk
President: James V. Koch
Provost: Jo Ann Gora
C: Health and Sciences; Business and Public Administration; Education; Engineering and Technology; Arts and Letters; Sciences.

Oregon Health Sciences University
3181 S.W. Sam Jackson Park Road, Portland, Oregon 97201
Tel: +1(503) 494-8311
Fax: +1(503) 494-5738
President: Peter O. Kohler
Vice-President, Academic Affairs: Jesley Hallick
Founded: 1974, 1981
S: Dentistry; Medicine; Nursing.

Oregon State University
Corvallis, Oregon 97331
Tel: +1(503) 754-0123
Fax: +1(503) 737-2400
President: John V. Byrne
Registrar: Barbara Balz
Founded: 1858, 1868, 1920, 1961
C: Agricultural Sciences; Business; Education; Engineering; Forestry; Health and Human Performance; Home Economics and Education; Liberal Arts; Oceanic and Atmospheric sciences; Pharmacy; Science; Veterinary Medicine.

*The Pennsylvania State University
System Administration, 201 Old Main, University Park, Pennsylvania 16802
Tel: +1(814) 865-4700
Telex: 5106703532 pn st bs adm
President: Joab L. Thomas (1990-)
Provost: John A. Brighton
Founded: 1855
C: Agricultural Sciences; Arts and Architecture; Business Administration; Earth and Mineral Sciences; Education; Engineering; Health and Human Development; Liberal Arts; Sciences; Medicine; Erie Behrend; Harrisburg Capital.
S: Communications; Forest Resources; Hotol, Restaurant and Recreation Management; Music; Nursing; Visual Arts.
I: Biotechnology; Environmental Resources Research; Arts and Humanistic Studies; Policy Research and Evaluation; Pennsylvania Transportation.
Ce: Australia-New Zealand Studies; Applied Behavioural Science; Particle Science and Engineering; Study of Higher Education.
L: Animal Resources P.; Materials Research; Applied Research.

Pennsylvania State University-Milton S. Hershey Medical Center
500 University Drive, P.O. Box 850, Hershey, Pennsylvania 17033
Tel: +1(717) 531-8521
Fax: +1(717) 531-7557
Senior Vice-President and Dean: C. McCollister Evarts
Director of Student Affairs: Edward E. Mills
Founded: 1964
Medicine.

Pennsylvania State University at Harrisburg Capital College
U.S. Route 230, Middletown, Pennsylvania
17057-4898
Tel: +1(717) 948-6000
Fax: +1(717) 948-6008
Provost/Dean: Ruth Leventhal
Registrar: David S. Bender
Founded: 1966
S: Science, Engineering and Technology; Business Administration.
D: Behavioral Sciences and Education; Humanities; Public Affairs; Business Administration.

Portland State University
P.O. Box 751, Portland, Oregon 97207-0751
Tel: +(503) 725-3000
Fax: +1(503) 725-4882
President: Judith A. Ramaley
Provost: Michael F. Reardon
Founded: 1946
C: Liberal Arts and Sciences.
S: Urban and Public Affairs; Fine and Performing Arts; Business Administration; Education; Social Work (Graduate); Engineering and Applied Science; Extended Studies.
I: Human Services (Regional Research); Aging.
Ce: Urban Studies; Population Research and Census.
P: Systems Science.

Princeton University
Princeton, New Jersey 08544-0015
Tel: (609) 258-3000
Fax: (609) 258-1294
President: Harold T. Shapiro
Provost: Stephen Goldfeld
Founded: 1746, 1748
S: Engineering and Applied Science; Public and International Affairs (Woodrow wilson); Architecture and Urban Planning (Raph Lerner).

*Purdue University
West Lafayette, Indiana 47907
Tel: +1(317) 494-7875
Fax: +1(317) 494-6609
E-Mail: Easylink 62005934 esl ud
Telex: 4930593 pherlui
President: Steven C. Beering
Founded: 1869
S: Agriculture; Consumer and Family Sciences; Education; Engineering; Liberal Arts; Management; Pharmacy, Nursing and Health; Science; Technology; Veterinary Medicine; Aeronautical and Astronautical Engineering; Chemical Engineering; Civil Engineering; Electrical Engineering; Industrial Engineering; Materials Engineering; Mechanical Engineering; Nuclear Engineering.

Rutgers, The State University of New Jersey - New Brunswick
P.O. Box 2101, New Brunswick, New Jersey
08903-2101
Tel: +1(908) 932-1766
Fax: +1(908) 932-8060
President: Francis L. Lawrence (1990-)
Vice-President for Academic Affairs: Joseph Seneca
Founded: 1766
C: Engineering; Pharmacy; Douglass (Liberal Arts); Livingston; Arts (Mason Gross); Rutgers; Business.
S: Communication, Information and Library Studies; Social Work.
Graduate S: Education; New Brunswich; Applied Professional.
I: American Affordable Housing; Animal Behaviour; Criminological Research; Environmental and Occupational Health Science; Jazz Studies; Politics (Eagleton); Journalism Resources; Management and Labour Relations; Research on Women; Women's Leadership; Marine and Coastal Sciences; Engineered Materials; Biostatistics.
Ce: Advanced Biotechnology and Medicine; Advanced Food Technology; Agricultural Molecular Biology; Alcohol Studies; Applied Psychology; Biorational Research; State Constitutional Studies; Business Innovation; Computer Aids for Industrial Technology; Ceramic Research; Coastal and Environmental Studies; Cognitive Science; International Conflict Resolution and Peace Studies; Conflict Resolution and Negotiation; Critical Analysis of Contemporary Culture; Controlled Drug Delivery Research; Urban Policy Research; Culture and Politics of Democracy (Walt Whitmant); Discrete Mathematics and Theoretical Computer Science; History of Electrical Engineering; Fisheries and Aquaculture Technology Extension; Hazardous Substance Management (Research); Historical Analysis; International Faculty and Studies Services; Labour Education; Learning Resources; Management Development; Mathematical Sciences Research; Television and Radio Media; Molecular and Behavioural Neuroscience; Operations Research; Packaging Engineering; Paul Robeson Cultural; Plastics and Recycling Research; Public Productivity (National); Public Interest Policy; Social Science Research; Urban Policy Research; Women's Global Leadership; Adelphia Research.

Rutgers, The State University of New Jersey-Newark
249 University Avenue, Newark, New Jersey
07102
Tel: +1(201) 648-1766
Provost: Norman Samuels (1985-)
Registrar: Miguel Estremera
Founded: 1892

C: *Arts and Sciences; Nursing.*
S: *Graduate; Law; Criminal Justice.*

Sam Houston State University
Sam Houston Avenue, Huntsville, Texas 77341
Tel: (409) 294-1111
Fax: (409) 294-1465
President: Martin J. Annisman (1989-)
Registrar: Robert L. Dunning
Founded: 1879
C: *Arts and Sciences; Business Administration; Education; Criminology Justice; Criminal Justice.*

San Diego State University, California State Universities
San Diego, California 92182
Tel: +1(619) 594-5209
Fax: +1(619) 594-5200
President: Thomas B. Day (1977-)
Vice-President, Academic Affairs: Ronald H. Hopkins
Founded: 1897, 1921, 1971
C: *Arts and Letters; Sciences; Professional Studies and Fine Arts; Business Administration; Education; Engineering; Health Services.*
S: *Public Health (Graduate); Accountancy; Social Work; Family Studies and Consumer Sciences; Nursing; Public Administration and Urban Sciences; Teacher Education.*
Ce: *Aging (University); International Business Education and Research; Research in Mathematics and Science Education.*
I: *Molecular Biology.*

San Francisco State University
1600 Holloway Avenue, San Francisco, California 94132
Tel: +1(415) 338-1111
Fax: +1(415) 338-2514
President: Robert A. Corrigan
Vice-President for Academic Affairs: Marilyn J. Boyer
Founded: 1899, 1974
S: *Behavioural and Social Sciences; Business; Creative Arts; Education; Ethnic Studies; Health, Physical Education, Recreation and Leisure Studies; Humanities; Science.*

South Dakota School of Mines and Technology
501 E. St. Joseph Street, Rapid City, South Dakota 57701-3995
Tel: +1(605) 394-2511
Fax: +1(605) 394-6131
President: Richard J. Gowen (1987-)
Vice-President for Academic Affairs: William C. Hughes
Founded: 1885
D: *Chemistry and Chemical Engineering; Civil Engineering; Electrical Engineering; Geology and Geological Engineering; Industrial Engineering; Mechanical Engineering; Metallurgical Engineering; Mining Engineering; Mathematics and Computer Science; Physics.*

South Dakota State University
Box 2201, Brookings, South Dakota 57007
Tel: +1(605) 688-4151
Fax: +1(605) 688-5822
President: Rober T. Wagner
Vice-President of Academic Affairs: Carol J. Peterson
Founded: 1881, 1907, 1964
C: *Arts and Sciences; Education and Counselling; Engineering; Home Economics; Nursing; Pharmacy; Agriculture and Biological Sciences.*

Southern Illinois University at Carbondale
Carbondale, Illinois 62901
Tel: +(618) 453-2121
Fax: +(618) 453-3000
E-Mail: Easylink 62017444 esl ud
Telex: 9106686894 sdsu bkng
President: John C. Guyon (1986-)
Vice-President, Academic Affairs: Benjamin Shepherd
Founded: 1869
C: *Liberal Arts; Education; Technical Careers; Business Administration; Communications and Fine Arts; Engineering and Technology; Science.*
S: *Agriculture; Law; Medicine; Accountancy; Arts and Design; Journalism; Music; Social Work.*
Ce: *International Business Education; Coal Extraction and Utilization Research; Materials Technology; Archaeological Research and Cultural Research Management.*

Southern Illinois University at Edwardsville
Edwardsville, Illinois 62026-1001
Tel: +1(618) 692-2000
President: Earl E. Lazerson (1993-)
Provost: David J. Werner
Founded: 1957
S: *Business; Education; Fine Arts and Communication; Humanities; Engineering; Social Sciences; Nursing; Medicine; Sciences; Dental Medicine.*

Southern University-Baton Rouge
Southern Post Office, Baton Rouge, Louisiana 70813
Tel: +1(504) 771-4500
Fax: +1(504) 771-2026
President: Marvin L. Yates (1991-)
Director, Office of Planning and Institutional Research: Robert A. Johnson
Founded: 1880
C: *Arts and Humanities; Agriculture; Architecture; Business; Education; Sciences; Engineering; Public Policy; Nursing.*
S: *Accountancy.*
Ce: *Energy and Environmental Studies; Social Research; Small Farm Research; Continuing Education (Ville Platte); Law.*
Div: *Technology; I; Special Education.*

State University of New York System (SUNY)
State University Plaza, Albany, New York 12246
Tel: +1(518) 443-5555
Fax: +1(518) 443-5677
E-Mail: Easylink 62437800 esl ud
Chancellor: Bruce Johnstone
Provost: Joseph Burke

State University of New York at Albany
1400 Washington Avenue, Albany, N.Y. 12222
Tel: +1(518) 442-3300
President: Vincent O'Leary
Executive Vice-President for Academic Affairs:
Warren Ilchman
Founded: 1844
*C: Human Sciences and Fine Arts; Sciences and
Mathematics.
S: Business; Criminal Justice; Education;
Library Science; Public Affairs; Social Sciences
and Behavioural Sciences; Social Welfare;
Information Sciences; Public Commerce.*

State University of New York at Binghamton
P.O. Box 6000, Binghamton, N.Y. 13902-6000
Tel: +1(607) 777-2000
Fax: +1(607) 777-4000
President: Lois B. DeFleur
Provost: Mary Ann Swain
Founded: 1846
*C: Arts and Sciences (Harpur); Education and
Human Developement; Physical Education.
S: Nursing; Technology; Management;
Engineering Applied Sciences and Technology
(Thomas J.Watson).*

State University of New York at Buffalo
Capen Hall, Buffalo, N.Y. 14260
Tel: +1(716) 645-2000
Fax: +1(716) 645-2895
Telex: +1(910) 250-8396
President: William R. Greiner (1991-)
Provost: Aaron N. Bloch
Founded: 1846, 1962
*F: Natural Sciences and Mathematics; Social
Sciences; Arts and Letters.
S: Architecture and Planning; Dental Medicine;
Graduate S. of Education; Engineering and
Applied Sciences; Rosewell Park G.D.; Health
Related Professions; Information and Library
Studies; Law; Management; Medicine and
Biomedical Sciences; Nursing; Pharmacy; Social
Work.*

State University of New York at Stony Brook
Nicolls Road, Stony Brook, N.Y. 11794-0701
Tel: +1(516) 689-6000
Fax: +1(516) 632-6252
Telex: 5102287767 sunnyadmin stlk
President: Shirley Strum Kenny III (1994-)
Provost: Tilden Edelstein
Founded: 1957, 1962

*D: Sociall and Behavioural Sciences;
Humanities and Fine Arts; Physical Sciences and
Mathematics.
C: Engineering and Applied Sciences;
Management and Policy (W. Averell Hariman);
Biological Sciences.
S: Continuing Education; Medicine; Dentistry;
Social Work; Nursing; Allied Health Professions
(Social Welfare).
I: Mathematical Sciences; Pattern Recognition;
Terrestrial and Planetary Atmospheres;
Theoretical Physics; Mineral Physics I.
Ce: Biotechnology; Mar0ne Sciences Research;
Exchange and Innovation in Education; Regional
Policy Studies; Science, Mathematics and
Technology Education; Health Sciences; Public
Management (W. Averell Harriman).*

State University of New York Health Science Center at Brooklyn
450 Clarkson Avenue, Brooklyn, New York, N.Y. 11203
Tel: +1(718) 270-1000
Fax: +1(718) 270-3378
President: Donald J. Scherl
Senior Vice President for Administration and
Finance: Wan Lisnitzer
Founded: 1860
*C: Nursing; Health Related Professions;
Medicine.*

State University of New York Health Science Center at Syracuse
750 East Adams Street, Syracuse, N.Y. 13210
Tel: +1(315) 464-4570
Fax: +1(315) 464-8823
President: Gregory L. Eastwood
Provost: Donald C. Goodman
Founded: 1834
*Medicine; Nursing; Health and Related
Professions.*

State University of New York College of Environmental Science and Forestry
Syracuse, N.Y. 13210-2779
Tel: +1(315) 470-6500
Fax: +1(315) 470-6779
President: Ross S. Whaley
Provost/Vice-President for Academic Affaires
Founded: 1911
Forestry; Landscape Design; Engineering.

State University of New York College of Optometry
100 East 24th Street, New York, N.Y. 10010
Tel: +1(212) 780-4900
Fax: +1(212) 780-5094
E-Mail: optom@sntbksal (bitnet)
President: Alder N. Haffner
Vice-President for Administration: David Bower
Founded: 1971
Optometry; Graduate P.

Stephen F. Austin State University
1936 North Street, Box 6078 SFA Station,
Nacogdoches, Texas 75962-6078
Tel: +1(409) 568-2011
Fax: +1(409) 568-2202
President: Daniel D. Angel
Vice-President for Academics Affairs: Janelle
C.Ashley
Founded: 1923
*S: Applied Arts and Sciences; Business
Administration; Education; Fine Arts; Forestry;
Liberal Arts; Sciences and Mathematics.*

Temple University
Broad Street and Montgomery Avenue,
Philadelphia, Pennsylvania 19122-1803
Tel: +1(215) 204-7000
President: Peter J. Liacouras
Provost: James W. England
Founded: 1884
*C: Arts and Sciences; Education; Engineering,
Computer Sciences and Architecture; Health,
Physical Education, Recreation, and Dance;
Allied Health Professions; Music (Esther Boyer).
S: Business and Management; Medicine;
Communications and Theatre; Business Law;
Dentistry; Pharmacy; Social Administration; Art
(Tyler,Amler Campus).
D: Landscape Architecture and Horticulture
(Ambler Campus).*

Tennessee State University
3500 John A. Merritt Boulevard, Nashville,
Tennessee 37209-1561
Tel: +1(615) 320-3131
Fax: +1(615)32-3114
President: James A. Hefner
Vice-President of Academic Affairs: Arhtur
Washington
Founded: 1912
*S: Arts and Sciences; Agriculture and Home
Economics; Education; Engineering and
Technology; Business; Allied Health Professions;
Nursing.*

Tennessee Technological University
Dixie Avenue and McGee Boulevard, Cookville,
Tennessee 38505
Tel: +1(615) 372-3101
Fax: +1(615) 372-3898
President: Angelo A. Volpe
Vice-President for Academic Affairs: Marvin W.
Barker
Founded: 1915
*C: Arts and Sciences; Agriculture and Home
Economics; Education; Engineering.
S: Agriculture; Home Economics; Business
Administration; Nursing.
Ce: Water; Electric Power; Manufacturing.*

Texas A&M University
Campus Box 215, Kingsville, Texas 78363-8202
Tel: +1(512) 595-2111
Fax: +1(512) 595-3107
President: Manuel L. Ibanez
Vice-President for Academic Affairs: Robert O.
Kirby
Founded: 1925, 1967, 1989
*C: Arts and Sciences; Business Administration;
Education; Engineering.
Ce: Continuing Education; Citrus (Lower Rio
Grande Valley).*

Texas A&M University
College Station, Texas 77843-1246
Tel: +1(409) 845-3211
Fax: +1(409) 845-5027
President: Ray M.Bowen (1994-)
Provost: E. Dean Gage
Founded: 1876, 1963
*C: Liberal Arts; Architecture; Business
Administration; Education; Engineering;
Geosciences and Maritime Studies; Medicine;
Science; Veterinary Medicine; Agriculture and
Life Sciences.*

Texas Southern University
3100 Cleburne Avenue, Houston, Texas 77004
Tel: +1(713) 527-7011
Fax: +1(173) 639-1092
President: William Harris (1993-)
Vice-President for Academic Affairs
Founded: 1947
*C: Arts and Sciences; Science and Technology.
S: Technology; Business; Education; Law;
Management; Pharmacy and Health Sciences.*

Texas Tech University
Box 45015, Lubbock, Texas 79409-5015
Tel: +1(806) 742-2011
Fax: +1(806) 743-2138
Telex: 5106012483 tiec tx tech
President: Robert W. Lawless
Provost: Donald R. Haragan
Founded: 1926
*S: Law; Arts and Sciences.
C: Agriculture Sciences; Business
Administration; Education; Engineering; Home
Economics; Architecture; International Ce. for
Arid and Semi-Arid Land Studies; International
Ce. for Textile Research and Development.
I: Biotechnology; Disaster Research.*

Texas Tech University Health Sciences Center
Box 42013, 124 Administration Building, Lubbock,
Texas 79430
Tel: +1(806) 743-3111
Fax: +1(806) 742-2138
President: Robert W. Lawless
Executive Vice-President/Provost: Bernhard T.
Mittemeyer
Founded: 1969
S: Allied Health; Medicine; Nursing.

Texas Woman's University
Box 23925, Denton, Texas 76204-1925
Tel: +1(817) 898-2000
Fax: +1(817) 898-3198
President: Shirley S. Chater (1986-)
Vice-President for Academic Affairs: Patricia
A.Sullivan
Founded: 1901, 1905, 1934, 1957
*C: Arts and Sciences; Education and Human
Ecology; Health Sciences; Nursing.*
*S: Occupational Therapy; Physical Therapy;
Library and Information Studies.*
I: Health Sciences.

The University of Akron
302 Buchtel Common, Akron, Ohio 44325-0001
Tel: +1(216) 972-7100
Fax: +1(216) 972-6990
President: Peggy Gordon Elliott (1992-)
Provost: Mark S. Alukurn
Founded: 1870, 1926
*C: Arts and Sciences (Buchtel); Business
Administration; Fine and Applied Arts; Education;
Engineering; Nursing; Polymer Science and
Polymer Engineering.*
I: Polymer Science; Applied Politics (Bliss).
S: Law.

University of Alabama
University Boulevard, P.O. Box 870132,
Tuscaloosa, Alabama 35487-0132
Tel: +1(205) 348-6010
Fax: +1(205) 348-6544
President: E. Roger Sayers
Provost: James E. Taaffe
Founded: 1820
*C: Arts and Sciences; Commerce and Business
Administration; Community Health Sciences;
Education; Engineering; Human Environmental
Sciences; Nursing (Capstone).*
*S: Graduate; Communication; Law; Library and
Information Studies; Social Work.*

University of Alabama at Birmingham
UAB Station, Birmingham, Alabama 35294
Tel: +1(205) 934-4011
President: Charles A. McCallum (1993-)
Vice-President for Financial Affairs
Founded: 1966
*S: Medicine; Dentistry; Optometry; Nursing;
Health Related Professions; Business; Education;
Engineering; Arts and Humanities; Natural
Sciences and Mathematics; Public Health; Social
and Behavioral Sciences.*

University of Alabama in Huntsville
Huntsville, Alabama 35899
Tel: +1(205) 895-6120
Fax: +1(205) 895-6073
President: Frank A. Franz
Provost: John K. Yost
Founded: 1950, 1969
*C: Administrative Science; Engineering; Liberal
Arts; Nursing; Sciences.*

S: Primary Medical Care.
*Ce: Microgravity and Materials Research;
Applied Optics; Space Plasma and Aeronomic
Research.*

University of Alaska Fairbanks
101 Bunnell Building, Tanana Drive, Fairbanks,
Alaska 99775-0660
Tel: +1(907) 474-7521
Fax: +1(907) 474-7225
Chancellor: Joan K. Wadlow
Chancellor: Janice M. Reynolds
Founded: 1917, 1935
C: Liberal Arts; Natural Sciences; Rural Alaska.
*S: Agriculture and Land Resources
Management; Career and Continuing Education;
Engineering; Fisheries and Ocean Sciences;
Management; Mineral Engineering.*

University of Arizona
Tucson, Arizona 85721
Tel: +1(602) 621-2211
Fax: +1(602) 621-9118
President: Manuel T. Pacheco
Senior Vice-President for Academic Affairs
Founded: 1885
*C: Agriculture; Architecture; Arts and Sciences;
Business and Public Administration; Education;
Engineering and Mines; Law; Medicine; Nursing;
Pharmacy.*
F: Fine Arts; Humanities; Sciences.
*S: Library Science (Graduate); Family and
Consumer Resources; Health and Related
Prosessions; Music; Public Administration and
Policy; Renewable Natural Resources; Social and
Behavioural Sciences.*

University of Arkansas at Little Rock
2801 South University Avenue, Little Rock,
Arkansas 72204-3000
Tel: +1(501) 569-3000
Fax: +1(501) 569-8915
Chancellor: Charles E. Hathaway (1993-)
Provost: Joel Anderson
Founded: 1927, 1957, 1969
*C: Arts, Humanities, and Social Sciences;
Business Administration; Education; Professional
and Public Affairs; Science and Engineering
Technology.*
S: Graduate; Law.

University of Arkansas for Medical Sciences
4301 West Markham Street, Little Rock, Arkansas
72205
Tel: +1(501) 686-5000
Fax: +1(501) 686-5905
Chancellor: Henry P. Ward
Vice-Chancellor for Institutional Advancement:
Larry Bone
Founded: 1879
*C: Medicine; Nursing; Pharmacy; Social
Sciences; Service; Health.*

*University of California
Office of the President, 300 Lakeside Drive,
Oakland, California 94612-3550
Tel: +1(510) 987-0700
Fax: +1(510) 987-0328
President: David Pierpont Gardner (1992-)
Vice-President (Administration): Ronald W. Brady
Founded: 1868

University of California, Berkeley
Berkeley, California 94720
Tel: +1(510) 642-6000
Fax: +1(415) 643-8245
Chancellor: Chang-Lin Tien
Founded: 1855, 1952
*C: Letters and Sciences; Chemistry;
Engineering; Environmental Design; Natural
Resources.*
*S: Law (Boalt Hall); Business Administration
(Walter A. Haas); Optometry; Education;
Journalism (Graduate); Library and Information
Studies; Public Health; Public Policy (Graduate);
Social Welfare.*

University of California, Davis
Davis, California 95616
Tel: (916) 752-1011
Fax: (916) 752-6363
Telex: 5310785
Chancellor: Larry N. Vanderhoef (1994-)
Registrar: Evelyn Babey
Founded: 1905
*C: Agriculture and Environmental Sciences;
Letters and Sciences; Engineering.*
*S: Law; Medicine; Veterinary Medicine;
Management (Graduate).*
D: Biological Sciences.

University of California, Irvine
Campus Drive, Irvine, California 92717-1425
Tel: +1(714) 856-5011
Fax: +1(714) 856-5451
Chancellor: Laurel L. Wilkening
Executive Vice-Chancellor: L. Dennis Smith
Founded: 1965
C: Medicine.
*S: Biological Sciences; Fine Arts; Humanities;
Physical Sciences; Social Sciences; Management
(Graduate).*

*University of California, Los Angeles (UCLA)
405 Hilgard Avenue, Los Angeles, California
90024
Tel: +1(310) 825-4321
Fax: +1(310) 206-6030
Chancellor: Charles E. Young (1968-)
Executive Vice-Chancellor: Andrea L. Rich
Founded: 1919
C: Letters and Science.
*S: Architecture (Graduate); Arts; Education
(Graduate); Engineering and Applied Science;
Law; Library and Information Science (Graduate);
Management (Anderson Graduate); Social*

*Welfare; Theatre, Film, and Television; Dentistry;
Medicine; Nursing; Public Health.*
*I: Dental Research; Molecular Biology; Plasma
and Fusion Research; Geophysics and Planetary
Physics; Social Science Research; Archaeology;
Brain Research; Biological Imaging (Crump);
Jules Stein Eye; Industrial Relations.*
*Ce: 17th and 18th Century Studies; Medieval
and Renaissance Studies; Study of Comparative
Folklore and Mythology; Study of Women; Mental
Retardation Research; American Indian Studies;
Asian American Studies; Afro-American Studies;
Chicano Studies Research; Latin American;
Russian and East European Studies; Coleman
African Studies; Near Eastern Studies (Von
Grunebaum).*

University of California, Riverside
900 University Avenue, Riverside, California
92521
Tel: +1(909) 787-1012
Fax: +1(909) 787-3866
Chancellor: Raymond L. Orbach
Registrar: James Sandoval
Founded: 1954
*Natural and Agricultural Sciences; Humanities
and Social Sciences; Engineering; Management
and Education (Graduate).*

*University of California, San Diego
9500 Gilman Drive, La Jolla, California 92093
Tel: +1(619) 534-2230
Fax: +1(619) 534-2230
Chancellor: Richard C. Atkinson
Registrar: Ronald J. Bowker
Founded: 1903, 1912, 1925, 1960
*Div: Engineering; Arts and Humanities; Natural
Sciences; Social Sciences.*
*S: International Relations and Pacific Studies
(Graduate); Architecture; Medicine; International
Relations and Pacific Studies (Graduate).*
I: Oceanography (Scripps).

University of California, San Francisco
500 Parnassus Avenue, San Francisco, California
94143
Tel: +1(415) 476-9000
Fax: +1(415) 467-8001
Chancellor: Joseph B. Martin (1993-)
Senior Vice-Chancellor of Academic Affairs:
David Ramsey
Founded: 1864, 1970
S: Dentistry; Pharmacy; Medicine; Nursing.

*University of California, Santa Barbara
Santa Barbara, California 93106
Tel: +1(805) 893-8000
Fax: +1(805) 893-8016
Chancellor: Barbara S. Uehling
Registrar: Charles W. McKinney
Founded: 1909, 1958
*C: Engineering; Letters and Sciences;
Education; Creative Studies.*

705

University of California, Santa Cruz
1156 High Street, Santa Cruz, California 95064
Tel: +(408) 459-0111
Fax: +1(408) 429-0146
E-Mail: internet, bitnet, uucp, decnet. (Contact
(408) 459-4693)
Telex: 9107607936
Cable: (800) 325-6000
Chancellor: Karl S. Pister (1991-)
Executive Vice-Chancellor: R. Michael Tanner
Founded: 1965
*Div: Arts; Humanities; Natural Sciences; Social
Science.*
*I: Marine Sciences; Nuclear Science; Particle
Physics; Tectonics.*

University of Central Florida
4000 Central Florida Boulevard, Orlando, Florida
32816
Tel: +1(407) 823-2000
President: John C. Hitt (1992-)
Registrar: John F. Bush
Founded: 1963, 1968, 1978
*C: Arts and Sciences; Business Administration;
Education; Engineering; Health and Public
Affairs.*
*Ce: Research in Electro-Optics and Lasers
(CREOL); Florida Solar Energy (FSEC).*
I: Simulation and Training (IST).

University of Florida
328 Tigert Hall, Gainesville, Florida 32611-2073
Tel: +1(904) 392-3261
Fax: +1(904) 392-8774
E-Mail: bitnet
President: John V. Lombardi (1990-)
Vice-Provost/Vice-President: Gene W. Hemp
Founded: 1853, 1906
*C: Liberal Arts and Sciences; Health and
Human Performance; Veterinary Medicine;
Architecture; Health Related Professions;
Business Administration; Medicine; Dentistry;
Law; Journalism and Communications; Nursing;
Fine Arts; Engineering; Pharmacy; Education.*
*S: Building Construction; Forest Resources and
Conservation; Accounting (Fisher).*
*Ce: Latin American Studies; Gerontological
Studies; Aeronomy and Other Atmospheric
Sciences; Applied Mathematics; Aquatic Plants;
Freedom of Information (Brechner); Business
Ethics, Education and Research; Consumer
Research; Florida Water Resources Research;
International Economics and Business Studies;
Wetlands.*

University of Cincinnati
Clifton Avenue, Cincinnati, Ohio 45221
Tel: +1(513) 556-6000
Fax: +1(513) 556-2340
President: Joseph A. Steger
University Registrar: Lynn M. Barber
Founded: 1819, 1870
*C: Arts and Sciences (McMicken); Engineering;
Education; Business Administration; Medicine;*

*Law; Nursing and Health; Design; Pharmacy;
Conservatory of Music; University; Design,
Architecture, art and Planning.*
*S: Social Work; Architecture and Interior
Design; Planning; Art.*

University of Colorado at Boulder
Boulder, Colorado 80309
Tel: +1(303) 492-1411
Fax: +1(303) 492-5105
President: Judith E.N. Alkino
Chancellor: James N. Corbridge
Founded: 1876
*C: Environmental Design; Business and
Administration; Arts and Sciences; Engineering;
Music.*
S: Education; Journalism; Law.

University of Colorado at Colorado Springs
1420 Austin Bluffs Parkway, P.O. Box 7150,
Colorado Springs, Colorado 80933-7150
Tel: +1(719) 593-3000
Fax: +1(719) 593-3362
Chancellor: Linda Bunnell Jones
Vice-Chancellor for Academic Affairs: Merrill J.
Lessley
Founded: 1965, 1972
*C: Business; Engineering and Applied Science;
Letters, Arts and Sciences.*
S: Public Affairs (Graduate); Education.

University of Colorado at Denver
1250 14th Street, Denver, Colorado 80217-3364
Tel: +1(303) 556-2400
Fax: +1(303) 556-3377
Chancellor: John Beuchner (1989-)
Executive Vice-Chancellor: Bruce W. Bergland
Founded: 1861
*C: Business Administration; Engineering and
Applied Science; Liberal Arts and Sciences;
Education; Public Affairs; Architecture and
Planning.*
*Ce: Health Ethics and Policy; Applied
Psychology; Research in Applied Language;
Community Development; Environmental
Sciences; Study of Racism and Ethnic Violence;
Urban Transportation Studies; Improvement of
Public Management, and for Public-Private Sector
Co-operation; Study of Indigenous Law and
Politics (4th World); Research in Rhetoric.*
*I: Aging (National Leadership); International
Business; National Veterans Training.*

University of Colorado Health Sciences Center
4200 East Ninth Avenue, Denver, Colorado 80262
Tel: +1(303) 399-1211
Fax: +1(303) 270-5969
Chancellor: Vincent A. Fulginiti
Registrar: Judith L. Boss
Founded: 1882, 1979
Dentistry; Nursing; Medicine.

University of Connecticut
Storrs, Connecticut 06269
Tel: +1(203) 486-2000
E-Mail: BITNET
President: Harry J. Hartley (1990-)
Provost: Thomas J. Tighe
Founded: 1909, 1961
C: Liberal Arts and Sciences; Agriculture and
Natural Resources.
S: Allied Health; Business Administration;
Education; Engineering; Fine Arts; Family
Studies; Nursing; Pharmacy; Law; Social Work;
Dental Medicine.

University of Connecticut Health Center
263 Farmington Avenue, Farmington, Connecticut
06030
Tel: +1(203) 679-2000
Fax: +(203) 679-2518
Executive Director: Leslie S. Cutler
Registrar: Pat Brothwell
S: Dental Medicine; Medicine.

University of Delaware
Newark, Delaware 19716
Tel: +1(302) 831-2000
Fax: +1(302) 831-8000
E-Mail: Easylink: 62035616 esl ud
Telex: 709985 ccm univdel ud
President: David Roselle
Senior Vice-President for Administration: David
Hollowell
Founded: 1921
C: Agricultural Sciences; Arts and Sciences;
Business and Economics; Education;
Engineering; Human Resources; Nursing;
Physical Education, Athletics and Recreation;
Marine Studies; Urban Affairs and Public Policy.
S: Life Health Sciences.
I: Energy Conversion; Bartol Research.
Ce: Composite Materials; Catalytic Science and
Technology; Agriculture Research and Education;
Beneficial Insect Introduction Research; Applied
Demography and Survey Research; Energy and
Urban Policy Research; Drug and Alcohol
Studies; Historic Architecture and Engineering;
Science and Culture; Teaching Effectiveness;
Water Resources.

The University of Georgia
Athens, Georgia 30602
Tel: +1(706) 542-3000
Fax: +1(706) 542-9492
President: Stephen R. Portch (1994-)
Vice-President for Academic Affairs: William F.
ProKasy
Founded: 1785
C: Agricultural and Environmental Sciences;
Arts and Sciences; Business; Family and
Consumer Sciences; Education; Journalism;
Pharmacy.
S: Environmental Design; Forest Resources;
Law; Veterinary Medicine; Social Work;

Accounting (J.M. Tull); Health and Human
Performance; Music.
Div: Adult Business and Vocational Education.

*University of Hawaii at Manoa
2444 Dole Street, Honolulu, Hawaii 96822
Tel: +1(808) 956-8111
President: Albert J. Simone
Vice-President for Academic Affairs: Paul. C.
Yuen
Founded: 1907
C: Arts and Humanities; Business
Administration; Education; Engineering; Tropical
Agriculture and Human Resources; Language,
Linguistics and Literature.
S: Architecture; Law (John A. Burns); Natural
Sciences; Social Sciences; Hawaiian, Asian and
Pacific Studies; Law; Library Studies and
Information; Nursing; Ocean, Earth Science and
Technology; Public Health; Social Work; Travel
Industry Management; Medicine.

University of Houston
4800 Calhoun Boulevard, Houston, Texas
77204-2162
Tel: +1(713) 743-1000
Fax: +1(713) 743-8837
President (Acting): James Pickering
Provost: Glenn Aumann
Founded: 1927, 1934, 1963
C: Architecture; Business Administration;
Education; Hotel and Restaurant Management
(Conrad N. Hilton); Engineering (Cullen);
Humanities; Law; Natural Sciences and
Mathematics; Optometry; Pharmacy; Social
Sciences; Technology.
S: Social Work (Graduate); Communication;
Music.

University of Idaho
Moscow, Idaho 83843-4140
Tel: +1(208) 885-6757
Fax: +1(208) 885-6111
President: Elisabeth A. Zinser
Provost: Thomas Bell
Founded: 1890
C: Agriculture; Arts and Architecture; Business
and Economics; Education; Engineering; Forestry,
Wildlife, and Range Sciences; Law; Letters and
Science; Mines and Earth Resources.

*University of Illinois
364 Henry Administration Building, 506 South
Wright Street, Urbana, Illinois 61801
Tel: +1(217) 333-1000
Fax: +1(217) 333-3072
President: Stanley O. Ikenberry
Vice-President for Academic Affairs: Robert. W.
Resek

UNIVERSITY OF ILLINOIS AT CHICAGO
601 S. Morgan, Chicago, Illinois 60680
Tel: +1(312) 996-3000
Fax: +1(312) 413-3393
Chancellor: James J. Stukel
Vice-Chancellor for Academic Affairs: David C. Broski
Founded: 1982
C: Architecture, Art and Urban Planning; Associated Health Professions; Business Administration; Education; Engineering; Kinesiology; Liberal Arts and Sciences; Nursing; Pharmacy; Social Work (Jane Addams); Medicine (Rockford); Medicine (Peoria); Nursing (Rockford); Nursing (Quad Cities); Dentistry.
S: Architecture; Art and Design; Public Health; Urban Planning.
I: Humanities; Study of Developmental Disabilities; Labour and Industrial Relations.
Ce: Research in Law and Justice; Urban Economic Development; Urban Educational Research and Development; Energy Resources; Gerontology; Social Policy and Research (Jane Addams); Neighbourhood and Community Improvement (Anthalie P. Voorhees); Research Resources; Urban Transportation.

UNIVERSITY OF ILLINOIS AT URBANA-CHAMPAIGN
506 S. Wright, Champaign, Illinois 6182001
Tel: +1(217) 333-1000
Fax: +1(217) 333-9758
Chancellor: Michael J. Aiken
Vice-Chancellor for Academic Affairs: Theodore L. Brown
Founded: 1867
C: Liberal Arts and Science; Education; Agriculture; Veterinary Medicine; Engineering; Law; Commerce and Business Administration; Fine and Applied Arts; Applied Life Studies; Communications.
S: Architecture; Art and Design; Music; Social Work; Library and Information Science (Graduate); Chemical Sciences; Human Resources and Family Studies.
I: Aviation; Labour and Industrial Relations; Advanced Science and Technology (Beckman); Competitive Manufacturing; Research on Human Development; Environmental Studies.
Ce: Russian and East European Studies; East Asian and Pacific Studies; Latin American and Caribbean Studies; African Studies; Cement Composite Materials; Study of Reading; Supercomputing Research and Development; Advanced Construction Technology; Compound Semiconductor Microelectronics; Supercomputing Applications (National); Air Conditioning and Refrigeration; Manufacturing Research; Complex Systems Research; Writing Studies; Science and Technology for Superconductivity; Magnetic Resonance Technology for Basic Biological Research.
P: P. for the Study of Cultural Values and Ethics; Women's Studies; Arms Control,

Disarmament, and International Security; Ancient Technologies and Archaeological Materials (Campus); History, Philosophy, and Sociology of Science.
Ut: Criticism and Interpretive Theory.

University of Iowa
Iowa City, Iowa 52242
Tel: +1(319) 335-3500
Fax: +1(319) 335-2951
Telex: 5106011952 esl ui
President: Hunter R. Rawlings III
Vice-President for Student Affairs: Peter E. Nathan
Founded: 1847, 1855
C: Liberal Arts; Education; Medicine; Engineering; Pharmacy; Business Administration; Law; Nursing.
S: Dentistry; Art and Art History; Music.
I: Hydraulic Research.
Ce: Laser Science and Engineering; Cardiovascular Research; International Rural and Environmental Health; Global and Regional Environmental Research; Computer Aided Designs.

University of Kansas
Lawrence, Kansas 66045
Tel: +1(913) 864-2700
Chancellor: Gene A. Budig
Executive Vice-Chancellor: Edward L. Meyen
Founded: 1881, 1952
C: Liberal Arts and Sciences.
S: Allied Health; Architecture and Urban Design; Business; Education; Engineering; Fine Arts and Design; Journalism and Mass Communication; Nursing; Pharmacy; Social Welfare; Law.
Ce: Medical (Kansas City).

University of Kentucky
206 Administration Building, Lexington, Kentucky 40506-0032
Tel: +1(606) 257-9000
Fax: +1(606) 257-4000
E-Mail: Easylink: 62953355esl ud
Telex: 204009 uk commsvc lex
President: Charles T. Wethington, Jr.
Vice-President for Administration: Donald B. Clapp
Founded: 1865
C: Education; Medicine; Dentistry; Engineering; Pharmacy; Business and Economics; Agriculture; Law; Nursing; Allied Health Professions; Communications; Arts and Sciences.
S: Social Work; Architecture; Human Environmental Sciences; Library Sciences (Information); Fine Arts; Graduate.
I: Tobacco and Health Research; Mining and Minerals Research.
Ce: Aging; Rural Health; McDowell Network; Computational Sciences; Applied Energy Research; Livestock Diagnostic and Disease Control; Kentucky Geological Survey; Kentucky

Transportation; Mineral Law; Biomedical
Engineering; Toxicology.

University of Louisville
Louisville, Kentucky 40292-0001
Tel: +1(502) 588-5555
Fax: +1(502) 588-5682
President: Donald C. Swain (1981-92)
Provost: Wallace Mann Jr.
Founded: 1798, 1837, 1846
C: Arts and Sciences; Health and Social
Sciences.
S: Business and Public Administration;
Dentistry; Education; Law; Medicine; Music;
Nursing; Speed Scientific (Engineering).

*University of Maine
Orono, Maine 04469-5703
Tel: +1(207) 581-1110
President: Frederick E. Hutchinson (1993-)
Vice-President for Academic Affairs: Julia
Watkins
Founded: 1862, 1897
C: Applied Sciences and Agriculture; Arts and
Humanities; Business Administration; Education;
Engineering; Forest Resources; Sciences; Social
and Behavioural Sciences; Natural Resource.
S: Engineering Technology; Human
Development; Human Development; Nursing;
Social Work.
D: Continuing Education.

University of Southern Maine
96 Falmouth Street, Portland, Maine 04103
Tel: +1(207) 780-4141
Fax: +1(207) 780-4933
President: Richard L. Patenaude
Provost: John Deegan, Jr.
Founded: 1878
C: Arts and Sciences.
S: Law; Business and Economics Management;
Education; Nursing; Applied Sciences.

University of Maryland at Baltimore
520 West Lombard Street, Baltimore, Maryland
21201-1627
Tel: +1(410) 706-7004
Fax: +1(410) 706-5483
President: Errol L.
Vice-President for Academic Affairs: Cheryl T.
Samuels
Founded: 1807
Dentistry; Law; Medicine; Nursing; Pharmacy;
Social Work.

University of Maryland at College Park
College Park, Maryland 20742
Tel: +1(301) 405-1000
Fax: +1(301) 314-9560
President: William E. Kirwan (1989-)
Vice-President for Administration Affairs: Charles
Sturtz
Founded: 1859, 1920
C: Agriculture; Architecture; Arts and
Humanities; Behavioural and Social Science;

Business and Management; Computer,
Mathematical and Physical Sciences; Education;
Engineering; Health and Human Performance;
Human Ecology; Journalism; Library and
Information Services; Life Sciences.
S: Public Affairs.
Ce: Aging; Systems Research; Engineering
Research; Renaissance Baroque Studies.

University of Maryland Eastern Shore
Backbone Road, Princess Anne, Maryland 21853
Tel: +1(410) 651-2200
Fax: +1(410) 651-6105
President: William P. Hytche (1975-93)
Vice-President for Academic Affairs: Edward V.
Ellis
Founded: 1886, 1926, 1970
D: Agriculture; Business Economics; Education;
English/Languages; Fine Arts; Hotel/Restaurant
Management; Human Ecology; Mathematics/
Computer Science; Natural Sciences; Physical
Education; Physical Therapy; Social Sciences;
Technology.
I: Crustacean Ecology and Mariculture; Small
Farm Research; Soybean Research.
Ce: Excellence; Excellence in Teaching and
Learning; Plant and Microbial Biotechnology.

University of Maryland Graduate School, Baltimore
5401 Wildens Avenue, Baltimore, Maryland 21228
Tel: +1(410) 455-2537
Fax: +1(410) 455-1092
Dean: JoAnna Boughman
Founded: 1988
Health and Human Services; Social and
Behavioural Sciences; Computer Science, and
Engineering; Policy Sciences; Basic Biological
and Physical Science.

University of Massachusetts at Amherst
Amherst, Massachusetts 01003
Tel: +1(413) 545-0111
Fax: +1(413) 545-2328
Telex: 948633 camp ctr htl
Chancellor: David K. Scott (1990-)
Provost: Glen Gordon
Founded: 1863, 1991
S: Agriculture; Public Health; Engineering;
Physical Education; Education; Management; Arts
and Sciences.
F: Humanities and Fine Arts; Social and
Behavioural Sciences; Food and Natural
Resources; Natural Sciences and Mathematics.
D: Nursing.
I: Scientific Reasoning; North American Trade
and Economics; Environmental; Social and
Demographic Research (Massachusetts);
Advanced Study of Humanities; Social and
Demographic Research.
Ce: Labour Relations and Research.

University of Massachusetts at Boston
100 Morrissey Boulevard, Boston, Massachusetts
02125-3393
Tel: +1(617) 287-5000
Fax: +1(617) 265-7173
Chancellor: Sherry H. Penney (1988-)
Provost: Fuad M. Safwat
Founded: 1964
C: Arts and Sciences; Management and
Business Administration; Public and Community
Service; Nursing; Education (Graduate).
I: Public Affairs (John W. McCormack);
Gerontology; Urban Harbours; Study of Black
Culture (William Monroe Trotter); Latino
Community Development and Public Policy
(Mauriciao Gaston); Learning and Teaching.
D: Human Performance and Fitness.
Ce: Study of War and Social Consequences
(William Joiner); Survey Research; Environmental
Sciences, Policy, Management and Education
(Harbour and Coastal).

University of Massachusetts at Lowell
1 University Avenue, Lowell, Massachusetts
01854
Tel: +1(508) 934-4000
President: William T. Hogan
Vice-Chancellor for Academic Affairs: Robert J.
Foy
Founded: 1894, 1991
C: Arts and Sciences; Engineering; Fine Arts;
Health Professions; Management; Education.

University of Massachusetts Medical Center at Worcester
55 Lake Avenue North, Worcester, Massachusetts
01655
Tel: +1(508) 856-0011
Fax: +1(508) 856-5648
Chancellor: Aaron Lazare
Provost: Michael A. Bratt
Founded: 1962
S: Medicine; Nursing; Biomedical Sciences.

University of Medicine and Dentistry of New Jersey
30 Bergen Street, Newark, New Jersey
07107-3000
Tel: +1(201) 982-4300
Fax: +1(201) 982-4429
President: Stanley S. Bergen, Jr.
Senior Vice-President for Administration and
Finance: Freederick J. Hammond
Founded: 1970
Biological Sciences.
S: Health Professions; New Jersey Dental; New
Jersey Medical; Osteopathic Medicine;
Biomedical Sciences (Graduate); Robert Wood
Johnson.

The University of Memphis
Memphis, Tennessee 38152
Tel: +1(901) 678-2000
Fax: +1(901) 678-5065 (President)
Telex: 53915 msu bookstr mfs
President: V. Lane Rawlins (1991-)
Provost: Ivan Legg
Founded: 1912, 1957
C: Arts and Sciences; Business; Education;
Engineering; Communications and Fine Arts;
Accountancy.
S: Law; Nursing.
I: Engineering Research; Governmental Studies
and Research.
Ce: Electron Microscopy; Environmental and
Energy Education; Humanities (Marcus W. Orr);
Manpower Studies; Research on Women; Study
of Higher Education; Regional Economic
Development; Speech and Hearing; Earthquake
Research and Information.

University of Nebraska-Lincoln
14th and R, Lincoln, Nebraska 68588
Tel: +1(402) 472-7211
Fax: +1(402) 472-2410
E-Mail: stafo42@unl.edu
Telex: unl comm lcn 484340
Chancellor: Graham B. Spanier (1991-)
Director of Admissions: John Beacon
C: Architecture; Arts and Sciences; Business
Administration; Engineering and Technology;
Home Economics; Agricultural Sciences and
Natural Resources; Journalism; Law; Teachers'.
Ce: Advanced Land Management Information
Technologies; Biotechnology; Electro-Optics;
Engine Technology; Laser Analytical Studies;
Materials Research and Analysis; Microelectronic
and Optical Materials Research; Nontraditional
Manufacturing Research; Sustainable Agricultural
Systems; Technology Management and Decision
Science.

University of Michigan
Ann Arbor, Michigan 48109
Tel: +1(313) 764-1817
Fax: +1(313) 936-0775
E-Mail: Easylink: 62488920 esl ud
Telex: 4993064 u of m aa
President: James J. Duderstadt (1988-)
Provost: Gilbert R. Whitaker, Jr.
Founded: 1817
C: Literature, Science and Arts; Architecture
and Urban Planning; Pharmacy; Engineering.
S: Law; Natural Resources and Environment;
Music; Medicine; Nursing; Dentistry; Business
Administration; Social Work; Public Health;
Education; Art; Information and Library Science;
Graduate Studies (Horace H. Rackham).
I: Social Research; Gerontology; Public Policy
Studies; Humanities.
Ce: Research on Economic Development;
Research on Learning and Teaching; African and
Afro-American Studies; Chinese Studies;

Japanese Studies; Mid-East and North African Studies; Russian and European Studies; South and Southeast Asian Studies; Great Lakes and Aquatic Sciences; Human Growth and Development; International Business Education; International; Population Planning and International Health; Population Studies.

*University of Minnesota, Twin Cities Campus
100 Church Street South East, Minneapolis, Minnesota 55455-6309
Tel: +1(612) 625-5000
Fax: +1(612) 624-6868
E-Mail: Easylink: 62023179 esl ud
Telex: 9102503489
President: Nils Hasselmo
Vice-President for Academic Affairs: Ettore F. Infante
Founded: 1851
C: Liberal Arts; Education; Veterinary Medicine; Human Ecology; Natural Resources; Pharmacy; Agriculture; Biological Sciences.
S: Nursing; Law; Medicine; Dentistry; Architecture and Landscape Architecture; Public Health; Management (Curtis L. Carson); Journlism and Mass Communication; Kinesiology and Leisure Studies; Mathematics; Physica and Astronomy; Social work; Statistics.
I: Public Affairs; Technology.

University of Mississippi
University, Mississippi 38677
Tel: +1(601) 232-7226
Fax: +1(601) 232-7010
Chancellor: R. Gerald Turner (1984-)
Vice-Chancellor for Academic Affairs: H. Ray Hoops
Founded: 1844
C: Liberal Arts.
S: Business Administration; Education; Engineering; Pharmacy; Law; Accountancy.
I: Pharmaceutical Sciences (Research); Mississippi Mineral Resources; Physical Acoustics (National); Computational Hydroscience and Engineering; Women's Studies (Sarah Isom); Telecommunications; Study of Southern Culture.

University of Mississippi Medical Center
2500 North State Street, Jackson, Mississippi 39216
Tel: +1(601) 984-1100
Fax: +1(601) 984-1013
Founded: 1955
S: Nursing; Dentistry; Medicine; Allied Health Professions; Health Related Professions.

University of Missouri-Columbia
130 Jesse Hall, Columbia, Missouri 65211
Tel: +1(314) 882-2121
Chancellor (Acting): Charles A. Kiesler
Provost: Gerald Brouder
Founded: 1839

C: Agriculture, Food and Natural Resources; Arts and Sciences; Business and Public Administration; Education; Engineering; Veterinary Medicine; Human and Environmental Sciences.
S: Journalism; Law; Library and Informational Science; Medicine; Nursing; Fine Arts; Accountancy; Health of Related Professions; Social Work; Business; Natural Resources.

University of Missouri-Kansas City
5100 Rockhill Road, Kansas City, Missouri 64110
Tel: +1(816) 235-1000
Fax: +1(816) 235-1717
Chancellor/Provost: Eleanor Brantley Schwartz
Registrar: Wilson Berry
Founded: 1870, 1964
C: Arts and Sciences.
S: Business and Public Administration (Henry W. Bloch); Dentistry; Education; Law; Pharmacy; Nursing; Medicine; Biology Sciences.
Conservatory: Music.

University of Missouri-Rolla
Rolla, Missouri 65401-0249
Tel: +1(314) 341-4111
Fax: +1(314) 341-6306
Chancellor: John T. Park
Vice-Chancellor: Walter Gajda
C: Arts and Sciences.
S: Mines and Metallurgy; Engineering.
Ce: Rock Mechanics and Explosives Research; Materials Research (Graduate); Intelligent Systems.

University of Missouri-Saint Louis
8001 Natural Bridge Road, Saint Louis, Missouri 63121-4499
Tel: +1(314) 553-5000
Fax: +1(314) 553-5378
Telex: 4948232 naussstl
Chancellor: Blanche M. Touhill
Vice-Chancellor for Academic Affairs: Roosevelt Wright, Jr.
Founded: 1963, 1839
C: Arts and Sciences.
S: Business Education; Optometry; Nursing; Education; Business Administration.
Ce: International Studies; Molecular Electronics; Busines and Industrial Studies; Cornea and Contact Lens Research; Public Policy Research; Science and Technology; Tropical Ecology (International); Economic Education.

University of Montana
Missoula, Montana 59812
Tel: +1(406) 243-0211
Fax: +1(406) 243-2797
President: George M. Dennison
Provost: Robert L. Kindrick
Founded: 1893
C: Arts and Sciences.
S: Fine Arts; Business Administration; Education; Forestry; Journalism; Law; Pharmacy and Allied Health Sciences.

University of Nebraska Medical Center
600 South 42nd Street, Omaha, Nebraska 68198
Tel: +1(402) 559-4000
Fax: +1(402) 559-5844
Chancellor: Carol Aschenbrener
Vice-Chancellor for Academic Affairs: William O. Berndt
Founded: 1869, 1902, 1968
C: Dentistry; Medicine; Pharmacy; Nursing.

University of Nebraska at Omaha
60th and Dodge Street, Omaha, Nebraska 68182
Tel: +1(402) 554-2200
Fax: +1(402) 554-3555
Chancellor: Delbert Weber
Vice-Chancellor for Academic Affairs: Otto F. Bauer
Founded: 1908, 1968
Ce: Arts and Sciences; Business Administration; Education; Engineering and Technology; Continuing Studies; Home Economics; Public Affairs and Community Service; Fine Arts; Social Work; Health, Physical Education and Recreation.

University of Nevada-Las Vegas
4505 Maryland Parkway, Las Vegas, Nevada 89154
Tel: +1(702) 895-3011
Fax: +1(702) 739-3850
President: Robert C. Maxson
Provost: John C. Unrue
Founded: 1951
C: Business and Economics; Hotel Administration; Education; Health Sciences; Moberam Arts; Science and Mathematics; Engineering (Howanrd R. Hughes); Human Performance and Development.

University of Nevada-Reno
9th and North Virginia Street, Reno, Nevada 89577-0002
Tel: +1(702) 784-1110
Fax: +1(702) 784-1300
President: Joseph N. Crowley
Founded: 1874
C: Agriculture; Arts and Sciences; Education; Engineering; Human and Community Sciences; Business Administration.
S: Mines (Mackay); Medicine; Nursing (Orvis); Journalism.

University of New Hampshire
Durham, New Hampshire 03824
Tel: +1(603) 862-1234
Fax: +1(603) 862-3060
E-Mail: internet
President: Dale F. Nitzschke
Vice-President for Finance and Administration: Fred Schnur
Founded: 1866, 1923
C: Liberal Arts; Life Sciences and Agriculture; Engineering and Physical Sciences.

S: Business and Economics (Whittemore); Health and Human Services; Applied Science (Thompson).
I: Study of Earth, Oceans and Space.

University of New Mexico
Albuquerque, New Mexico 87131-2039
Tel: +1(505) 277-0111
Fax: +1(505) 277-5965
President: Richard E. Peck
Provost: Mary Sure Cleman
Founded: 1889
C: Arts and Sciences; Ecucation; Engineering; Fine Arts; Nursing; Pharmacy.
S: Architecture and Planning; Law; Management (Anderson); Medicine.

University of New Orleans
Lakefront, New Orleans, Louisiana 70148
Tel: +1(504) 286-6000
Fax: +1(504) 286-7393
Chancellor: Gregory M. St. L. O'Brien
Provost: Louis V. Paradise
Founded: 1956
C: Liberal Arts; Business Administration; Sciences; Urban and Public Affairs; Education; Engineering; Metropolitan (for Adults).

University of North Carolina at Chapel Hill
Chapel Hill, North Carolina 27599-1100
Tel: +1(919) 962-2211
Fax: +1(919) 962-5604
Chancellor: Paul Hardin
Registrar: David G. Lanier
Founded: 1789
C: Arts and Sciences and General C.; Business (Kenan-Flagler); Education; Journalism; Law; Information and Library Science; Social Work; Dentistry; Medicine; Nursing; Pharmacy; Public Health.
I: Government.

University of North Carolina at Greensboro
1000 Spring Garden Street, Greensboro, North Carolina 27412-5001
Tel: +1(919) 334-5000
Fax: +1(919) 334-5926
Chancellor: William Edward Moran
Registrar: James R. Kaiser
Founded: 1891, 1919, 1931, 1963
C: Arts and Sciences; S; Business and Economics (Joseph M. Bryan); Education; Health and Human Performance; Human Environmental Sciences; Music; Nursing.

University of North Dakota
Grand Forks, North Dakota 58202
Tel: +1(701) 777-2011
Fax: +1(701) 777-3650
E-Mail: Easylink: 62049688 esl ud
Telex: 332537 underc
President: Kendall L. Baker (1992-)
Vice-President for Academic Affairs: Gene Kemper
Founded: 1883

C: Arts and Sciences; Business and Public
Administration; Engineering and Mines; Nursing;
Fine Arts; Human Resources Development.
S: Law; Medicine.
Ce: Energy and Environmental Research;
Teaching and Learning; Aerospace Sciences.

University of North Texas
Denton, Texas 76203-3737
Tel: +1(817) 565-2000
Fax: +1(817) 565-4913
Chancellor: Alfred F. Hurley
Provost: Blaine A. Brownwell
Founded: 1890, 1988
C: Arts and Sciences; Business Administration;
Music; Education.
S: Library and Information Sciences; Community
Service; Merchandising and Hospitality
Management.

University of Northern Colorado
Greeley, Colorado 80639
Tel: +1(303) 351-1890
Fax: +1(303) 351-1890
E-Mail: jray@gold.univnorthCO.edu@vaxf
President: Herman D. Lujan (1991-)
Senior Vice-President: Stephen T. Hulbert
Founded: 1889, 1970
C: Arts and Sciences; Education; Business
Administration; Health and Human Sciences;
Visual and Performing Arts.
S: Nursing; Library Science; Kinesiology; Music.
Ce: Mathematics and Science Teaching;
Research on Teaching and Learning; Research in
Music Teaching and Learning.

University of Northern Iowa
1222 W. 27th Street, Cedar Falls, Iowa 50614-0033
Tel: +1(319) 273-3509
Fax: +1(319) 273-3509
E-Mail: internet
President: Constantine Curris (1983-)
Registrar: Philip L. Patton
Founded: 1876, 1909, 1961, 1967
C: Business Administration; Education;
Humanities and Fine Arts; Natural Sciences;
Social and Behavioural Sciences.
S: Health, Physical Education and Leisure
Services; Music.
I: Decision-Making; Educational Leadership;
Environmental Education; Ce; Social and
Behavioural Research; Study of Adolescence;
Applied Research in Metal Casting; Iowa Waste
Reduction; Accounting Education; Economic
Education; Small Business Development; Early
Development Education (Regents); Recycling and
Reuse Technology Transfer; Enhancement of
Teaching.

University of Oklahoma
600 Parrington Oval, Norman, Oklahoma 73019
Tel: +1(405) 325-0311
Fax: +1(405) 325-7605
Telex: 9108306521 ou purch norm
President: David L. Boren (1994-)
Provost/Senior Vice-President: James F. Kimpel
Founded: 1890
C: Arts and Sciences; Education; Law; Fine
Arts; Liberal Studies; Architecture; Business
Administration; Engineering; Geosciences;
Medicine (Tulsa); Electrical Engineering.
S: Accounting; Aerospace and Mechnical
Engineering; Art; Chemical Engineering and
Materials; Civil Engineering and Environmental
Science; Drama; Geology and Geophysics;
Industrial Engineering; Journalism and Mass
Communication; Meteorology; Library and
Information Studies; Music; Social Work;
Petroleum and Geological Engineering.
Ce: Health Sciences (Oklahoma City).

University of Oklahoma Health Sciences
P.O. Box 26901, Oklahoma City, Oklahoma 73190
Tel: +1(405) 271-4000
Fax: +1(405) 271-3151
Provost/Senior Vice-President: Jay H. Stein
Vice-Provost for Academic Affairs: O. Ray Kling
Founded: 1842
C: Allied Health; Dentistry; Medicine; Nursing;
Public Health; Pharmacy; Medicine.

University of Oregon
Eugene, Oregon 97403-1242
Tel: +1(503) 346-3111
Fax: +1(503) 346-3660
Telex: 5105970354 u of o lib eug u
President: Myles Brand (1989-)
Vice-President for Administration: Dan Williams
Founded: 1876
C: Arts and Sciences; Business Administration;
Education; Human Development and
Performance.
S: Journalism; Architecture and Allied Arts;
Law; Music.
I: Advanced Science and Technology; Chemical
Physics; Cognitive and Decision Sciences;
Molecular Biology; Theoretical Science; Materials
Science; Marine Biology (Oregon); Neuroscience.
Ce: Asian and Pacific Studies; Housing
Innovation; Study of Women in Society; Study of
Work, Economy, and Community; Humanities;
Solar Energy.

University of Pittsburgh
4200 Fifth Avenue, Pittsburgh, Pennsylvania
15260
Tel: +1(412) 624-4141
Chancellor: J. Dennis O'Connor
Registrar: Samuel D. Conte
Founded: 1787
C: Arts and Sciences; General Studies.
S: Business (Joseph M. Katz Graduate); Public
and International Affairs (Graduate); Public

Health (Graduate); Social Work; Dental Medicine; Education; Engineering; Health and Rehabilitation Sciences; Law; Library and Information; Medicine; Nursing; Pharmacy.

*University of Puerto Rico Rio Pedras
[Universidad de Puerto Rico, Recinto de Rio Pedras]
Ponce de Leon Avenue, Stop 38, Rio Pedras, Puerto Rico 00931
Tel: +1(809) 764-0000
Fax: +1(809) 764-8799
Chancellor: Manuel G. Tejera
Dean of Administration: Pedro Bonilla Torres
Founded: 1903
C: *General Studies; Law; Business Administration; Pharmacy; Education; Humanities; Home Economics; Space Studies; Natural Science.*
S: *Architecture and Environmental Design; Public Studies; Public Health; Social Sciences; Library and Information Science; Planning; City and Regional Planning; Mass Communication; Public Administration.*
Ce: *Social Research; History Research; Education Research.*
P: *Business Administration.*

University of Puerto Rico Mayaguez Campus
Box 5000, Mayaguez, Puerto Rico 00681
Tel: +1(809) 832-4040
Fax: +1(809) 834-3031
Chancellor: Alejandro Ruiz-Acevedo
Dean of Academic Affairs: Jorge A. Cruz-Emeric
Founded: 1911
C: *Arts and Sciences; Engineering; Agriculture; Business Administration.*

University of Puerto Rico Medical Sciences Campus
P.O. Box 365067, San Juan, Puerto Rico 00936-5067
Tel: +1(809) 758-2525
Fax: +1(809) 767-0755
Chancellor: Franciscott H. Oquendo
Dean of Academic Affairs: Delva Camacho
Founded: 1912
C: *Allied Health Professions.*
S: *Medicine; Dentistry; Nursing; Pharmacy; Public Health.*

University of Rhode Island
22 Davis Hall, Lower College Road, Kingston, Rhode Island 02881-0807
Tel: +1(401) 792-1000
Fax: +1(401) 789-3878
Chancellor: Robert L. Carothers
Provost: M. Beverly Swan
Founded: 1888, 1951
C: *Arts and Sciences; Engineering; Human Science and Services; Resource Development;*

Nursing; Pharmacy; Continuing Education; Business Administration.
S: *Library and Information Studies; Oceanography (Graduate).*

University of South Alabama
Mobile, Alabama 36688
Tel: +1(205) 460-6101
Fax: +1(205) 460-7205
President: Frederick P. Whiddon (1963-)
Senior Vice-President for Academic Affairs: Charles W. Connell
Founded: 1963
C: *Arts and Sciences; Business and Management Studies; Education; Engineering; Allied Health Professions; Medicine; Nursing.*
S: *Continuing Education and Special Ps.; Computer and Information Sciences.*

*University of South Carolina
Columbia, South Carolina 29208
Tel: +1(803) 777-7000
Fax: +1(803) 777-9480
President: John M. Palms
Executive Vice-President for Academic Affairs/ Provost: James C. Moeser
Founded: 1801
C: *Science and Mathematics; Business Administration; Education; Engineering; Humanities and Social Sciences; Journalism and Mass Communications; Pharmacy; Nursing; Applied Professional Sciences; Criminal Justice; Library and Information Science; Social Work.*
S: *Public Health; Law; Medicine; Music.*

University of South Dakota
414 East Clark Street, Vermillion, South Dakota 57069-2390
Tel: +1(605) 677-5011
Fax: +1(605) 677-5073
E-Mail: Easylink: 62860888 esl ud
President: Betty Turner Asher
Vice President for Academic Affairs: Stephen Hazlett
Founded: 1862
C: *Arts and Sciences; Business; Education; Fine Arts; Medicine; Law.*

*University of South Florida
4202 Fowler Avenue, Tampa, Florida 33620
Tel: +1(813) 974-2011
President: Francis T. Borkowski (1993-)
Executive Vice-President: Albert C. Hartley
Founded: 1956
C: *Arts and Sciences; Education; Public Health; Business Administration; Engineering; Nursing; Medicine; Fine Arts.*
S: *Library and Information Sciences.*
I: *Mental Health; Oceanography; International Language; Research in Art.*

University of Southern Mississippi
Southern Station, Box 5167, Hattiesburg,
Mississippi 39406-5167
Tel: +1(601) 266-7011
Fax: +1(601) 266-5735
E-Mail: tomlinson@usmmcp6
President: Aubrey Keith Lucas (1975-)
Vice-President of Academic Affairs: G. David
Huffman
Founded: 1910, 1962
*C: Liberal Arts; Health and Human Sciences;
Science and Technology.
S: Business Administration; Education and
Psychology; Nursing; Fine Arts; Social Work;
Library Services; Home Economics;
Communication; Engineering Technology; Human
Performance and Recreation; Music;
Accountancy.
I: English Language (Second language for
University entrance)).
Ce: Marine Science.*

University of Southwestern Louisiana
200 East University Avenue, Lafayette, Louisiana
70504
Tel: +1(318) 231-6000
Fax: +1(318) 231-6195
President: Ray P. Authement
Vice-President for Academic Affairs
Founded: 1898
*C: Education; Engineering; Arts, Humanities and
Behavioural Sciences; Agriculture;
Communications; Biology, Mathematics and
Physical Sciences; Sciences; Nursing; Business
Education; Health; Applied Life Sciences; General
Studies.
S: Medicine; Art and Architecture; Human
Resources; Music.*

University of Tennessee at Knoxville
Cumberland Avenue, Knoxville, Tennessee
37996-0150
Tel: +1(615) 974-1000
Fax: +1(615) 974-8546
Chancellor: William T. Snyder
Vice-Chancellor for Academic Affairs: John
Peters
Founded: 1794
*C: Liberal Arts; Agricultural Science and
Natural Resources; Veterinary Medicine;
Education; Engineering; Law; Human Ecology;
Business Administration; Communications;
Nursing.
S: Architecture and Planning; Library and
Information Sciences (Graduate); Social Work
(Graduate).
I: Agriculture.*

University of Tennessee at Memphis
800 Madison Avenue, Memphis, Tennessee 38163
Tel: +1(901) 528-5500
Fax: +1(901) 577-8640
Chancellor: William R. Rice
Vice-Chancellor for Administration: Raymend H.
Colson
Founded: 1911
*C: Allied Health Sciences; Dentistry; Nursing;
Pharmacy.
S: Medical Sciences; Medicine.*

University of Tennessee Space Institute
B.H. Goethert Parkway, Tullahoma, Tennessee
37388-8897
Tel: +1(615) 455-0631
Fax: +1(615) 454-2354
Vice-President and CAO: Wesley L. Harris (1990-)
Dean for Academic Affairs: K.C. Reddy
Founded: 1964
*P: Aerospace Engineering; Applied
Mathematics; Aviation Systems; Chemical
Engineering; Computer Science.
Research Ce: Laser Applications; Space
Transportation and Applied Research.*

University of Texas at Arlington
800 South Cooper, Arlington, Texas 76019-0125
Tel: +1(817) 273-2011
Fax: +1(817) 794-5656
Telex: 5106012493 tiec tx arlton
President: Ryan C. Amacher (1992-)
Vice-President for Academic Affairs: W.A. Baker
Founded: 1895
*S: Liberal Arts; Engineering; Sciences;
Architecture; Social Work; Nursing; Business
Administration.
I: Town-Planning Studies; Technology Transfer
(Environmental); Urban and Public Affairs;
Automation and Robotics Research.
Ce: Advance Electronic Devices.*

University of Texas at Austin
University Station, Austin, Texas 78712
Tel: +1(512) 471-3434
Fax: +1(512) 471-8102
Telex: 5106012493 tiec tx arlton
President: Robert M. Berdahl
Executive Vice-President/Provost: Gerhand J.
Fonken
Founded: 1881, 1967
*C: Liberal Arts; Business Administration;
Communication; Education; Engineering; Fine
Arts; Pharmacy.
S: Natural Sciences; Nursing; Social Work; Law;
Library and Information Science (Graduate);
Public Affairs (Lyndon B. Johnson); Architecture.*

The University of Texas at Dallas
P.O. Box 830688, Richardson, Texas 75083-0688
Tel: +1(214) 690-2111
Fax: +1(214) 690-2237
E-Mail: @utdallas
President: Franklyn G. Jenifer (1994-)
Director of Records and Registration: Jean S. Stuart
Founded: 1962
S: Eric Jonsson S. of Engineering and Computer Science (Eric Jonsson); Arts and Humanities; Natural Sciences and Mathematics; Social Sciences; General Studies; Human Development; Management; Graduate Studies.
Ce: Communication Disorders (Callier); Development Studies (Bruton); Applied Optics; Genetic Technology; Lithospheric Studies; Quantum Electronics; Applied Research; Translation Studies; Research in Teaching and Learning; International Accounting Development; Communications and Learning; Engineering Mathematics.

University of Texas at El Paso
El Paso, Texas 79968-0512
Tel: +1(915) 747-5000
Fax: +1(915) 747-5068
Telex: 5106012490 tiec txelpaso
President: Diana Natalicio (1988-)
Vice-President for Academic Affairs: John Bruhn
Founded: 1913, 1967
C: Education; Business Administration; Engineering; Sciences; Liberal Arts; Nursing and Allied Health.
Ce: Academic Development (Pre-collegiate English, Writing, and Mathematics); Inter-American and Border Studies; International Resources Management; Minorities (Comprehensive Regional); Excellence (Materials Research).

University of Texas at San Antonio
6900 N. Loop 1604 West, San Antonio, Texas 78249
Tel: +1(210) 691-4011
Fax: +1(210) 691-4187
President: Samuel A. Kirkpatrick
Vice-President for Academic Affairs: James F. Gaertner
Founded: 1969
C: Social and Behavioural Sciences; Business; Fine Arts and Humanities; Sciences and Engineering.

University of Texas Southwestern Medical Center at Dallas
5323 Harry Hines Boulevard, Dallas, Texas 75235-9012
Tel: +1(214) 688-3111
President: Kern Wildenthal
Dean, Medical School: William B. Neaves
Founded: 1943
Allied Health Professions; Biomedical Science; Medicine.

University of Texas Health Science Center at Houston
1100 Bolconbe Boulevard, P.O. Box 20036, Houston, Texas 77225
Tel: +1(713) 792-2121
Fax: +1(713) 792-4986
President: M. David Low
Executive Vice-President for Research and Academic Affairs: Thomas F. Burks
Founded: 1905
S: Allied Health Sciences; Biomedical Science (Graduate); Dentistry Hygiene; Dentistry; Medicine; Nursing; Public Health.

The University of Texas Health Science Center at San Antonio
7703 Floyd Curl Drive, San Antonio, Texas 78284
Tel: +1(512) 567-7000
Fax: +1(512) 567-2047
E-Mail: Easylink: 62912195 esl ud
President: John P. Howe, III
Executive Vice-President for Administration and Business Affairs: Robert B. Price
Founded: 1956
S: Allied Health Profession; Biomedical Sciences; Medicine; Dentistry; Nursing.

The University of Texas Medical Branch at Galveston
300 University Boulevard, Galveston, Texas 77555-1215
Tel: +1(409) 772-1011
Fax: +1(409) 772-5064
President: Thomas N. James
Executive Vice-President: E.J. Pederson
Founded: 1881
S: Medicine; Biomedical Sciences (Graduate); Allied Health Sciences; Nursing.

University of Toledo
2801 W. Bancroft Avenue, Toledo, Ohio 43606-3398
Tel: +(419) 537-4242
Fax: +1(419) 537-4940
Telex: 8104421633 u of t lib
President: Frank E. Horton (1989-)
Vice-President for Academic Affairs (Acting): Judy G. Hample
Founded: 1872
C: Education; Engineering; Law; Arts and Sciences; Pharmacy; Technology; Business Administration.

University of Utah
Salt Lake City, Utah 84112-9804
Tel: +1(801) 581-7200
Fax: +1(801) 581-7880
President: Arthur K. Smith
Registrar: Ralph Boren
Founded: 1850
C: Engineering; Fine Arts; Health; Humanities; Law; Mines and Earth Sciences; Nursing; Pharmacy; Science; Social and Behavioural Science.

S: Architecture (Graduate); Business (David Eules); Education (Graduate); Medicine; Social Work (Graduate).

University of Vermont
Burlington, Vermont 05405-0160
Tel: +1(802) 656-3480
Fax: +1(802) 658-8611
President (Acting): Thomas Salmon (1991-)
Provost (Acting): Robert B. Low
Founded: 1791
C: Agriculture and Life Sciences; Arts and Sciences; Education and Social Services; Engineering and Mathematics; Medicine.
S: Allied Health Sciences; Business Administration; Natural Resources; Nursing.

University of Virginia
Charlottesville, Virginia 22906-9011
Tel: +1(804) 924-0311
Fax: +1(804) 924-3792
Telex: 9102500352 facartsci uq
President: John T. Casteen III
Senior Vice-President and Chief Financial Officer: Leonard W. Sandridge
Founded: 1819
C: Arts and Sciences.
S: Law; Education; Engineering and Applied Sciences; Medicine; Architecture; Nursing; Graduate Business Administration (Colgate Darden); Commerce.

University of Washington
Seattle, Washington 98195
Tel: +1(206) 543-5010
Fax: +1(206) 543-0801
President: William P. Gerberding
Provost: L.L. Wilkening
Founded: 1861
C: Architecture and Urban Planning; Arts and Sciences; Education; Engineering; Ocean and Fishery Sciences; Forest Resources.
S: Pharmacy; Oceanography; Business Administration; Dentistry; Law; Medicine; Nursing; Social Work; Public Health and Community Medicine; Public Affairs; International Studies (Henry M. Jackson); Art; Communication; Drama; Library and Information Science; Music.

University of Wisconsin-Madison
500 Lincoln Drive, Madison, Wisconsin 53706-1380
Tel: +1(608) 262-1234
Fax: +1(608) 262-0123
Chancellor: David Ward
Vice-Chancellor for Academic Affairs: Richard Barrows
Founded: 1848
C: Agricultural and Life Sciences; Engineering; Letters and Science.
S: Business; Education; Law; Medical S.; Nursing; Pharmacy; Veterinary Medicine; Journalism and Mass Communication; Library

and Information Systems; Music; Natural Resources; Social Work.
I: Environmental Studies.
Ce: Family Resources and Consumer Sciences.

University of Wisconsin-Milwaukee
P.O. Box 749, Milwaukee, Wisconsin 53201
Tel: +1(414) 229-1122
Fax: +1(414) 229-6329
Chancellor: John H. Schroeder,Jr (1992-)
Vice-Chancellor: Kenneth Watters
Founded: 1956
S: Allied Health Professions; Architecture and Urban Planning; Business Administration; Education; Engineering and Applied Science; Fine Arts; Letters and Sciences; Nursing; Social Welfare; Library and Information Science.
I: Race and Ethnicity.
Ce: Architecture and Urban Planning; Great Lake Studies; Latin America; Mathematics and Science Education Research; Nursing Research and Evaluation; Quality, Productivity and Economic Development; Twentieth Century Studies; Urban Transportation Studies; Women's Studies; Management Research; Urban Research.

University of Wyoming
Box 3434 University Station, Laramie, Wyoming 82071
Tel: +1(307) 766-1122
Fax: +1(307) 766-2271
Telex: 9103808784 atmos
President: Terry P. Roark
Provost: Albert K. Karnig
Founded: 1886
C: Education; Engineering; Law; Arts and Sciences; Agriculture; Health Science; Business; Education (Adult and Postsecondary Levels); Education (Educational Leadership).
S: Extended Studies; Human Medicine; Nursing; Pharmacy; Physical and Health Education.
I: Enhanced Oil Recovery.
Ce: Animal Science Livestock Research; Wyoming Water Resources; UW - National Park Service Research.
L: Environmental Simulation; Jelm Mountain Observatory; Red Buttes Environmental Biology.

Utah State University
Logan, Utah 84322
Tel: +1(801) 750-1000
Fax: +1(801) 750-3900
President: George H. Emert (1992-)
Provost: Karen W. Morse
Founded: 1889
C: Agriculture; Business; Education; Engineering; Family Life; Humanities, Arts and Social Sciences; Natural Resources; Science; Life-Span Learning.
S: Accountancy.
Ce: Space Engineering; Atmospheric and Space Science.

Virginia Commonwealth University
901 West Franklin Street, P.O. Box 2512,
Richmond, Virginia 23284-2512
Tel: +1(804) 367-0100
President: Eugene P. Trani
Provost: Grace E. Harris
Founded: 1838
C: Humanities and Sciences.
S: Arts; Business; Community and Public Affairs; Education; Social Work; Allied Health Professions; Basic Health Sciences; Dentistry; Medicine; Nursing; Pharmacy; Mass Comunication.

Virginia Polytechnic Institute and State University
Blacksburg, Virginia 24061-0202
Tel: +1(703) 231-6000
Fax: +1(703) 231-7826
President: James D. McComas (1993-)
Provost: E. Fred Carlisle
Founded: 1872, 1944, 1970
C: Arts and Sciences; Agriculture and Life Sciences; Architecture and Urban Studies; Business (Pamplin); Education; Engineering; Human Resources; Veterinary Medicine.
Ce: Public Administration and Policy.

Washington State University
Pullman, Washington 99164
Tel: +1(509) 335-3564
Fax: +1(509) 335-3421
Telex: 5107741099 coll ag pman
President: Samuel H. Smith
Provost: Thomas George
C: Education; Engineering and Architecture; Economics and Business; Agriculture and Home Economics; Pharmacy; Veterinary Medicine; Liberal Arts and Sciences.
S: Music and Theatre Arts.
Ce: Social and Economic Research; Agricultural Research; Visualization, Analysis and Design in the Molecular Sciences; International Marketing; Small Business Development; Nursing Education (Intercollegiate).

Wayne State University
5050 Cass Avenue, Detroit, Michigan 48202
Tel: (313) 577-2424
Fax: (313) 577-8098
President: David Adamany
Provost: Marilyn N. Williamson
Founded: 1933
C: Education; Engineering; Liberal Arts; Nursing; Pharmacy and Allied Health Professions; Medicine; Urban, Labour and Metropolitan Affairs.
S: Social Work; Law; Business Administration; Fine and Performing Arts.

West Virginia University
Morgantown, West Virginia 26506-6001
Tel: (304) 293-0111
President: Neil S. Bucklew
Provost: Nancy Lohmann
Founded: 1867
C: Arts and Sciences; Agriculture and Forestry; Business and Economics; Creative Arts; Engineering; Human Resources and Education; Law; Mineral and Energy Resources.
S: Dentistry; Medicine; Journalism (Perley Isaac Reed); Nursing; Pharmacy; Physical Education; Social Work.

Western Michigan University
1201 Oliver Street, Kalamazoo, Michigan 49008-3899
Tel: (616) 387-1000
Fax: (616) 387-0958
President: Diether H. Haenicke (1985-)
Provost: Nancy S. Barrett
Founded: 1903, 1957
C: Arts and Sciences; Business (Haworth); Education; Engineering and Applied Sciences; Fine Arts; Health and Human Services.
S: Music; Public Affairs and Administration; Social Work.
I: Medieval Studies; Paper and Printing Science and Engineering; Water Sciences.
Ce: Electron Microscopy; Enabling Technology.

Wichita State University
1845 Noth Fairmount, Wichita, Kansas 67260-1595
Tel: +1(316) 689-3456
Fax: +1(316) 689-3528
President: Eugene Morgan Hughes
Vice-President for Academic Affairs: John E. Dreifort
Founded: 1895
C: Liberal Arts and Sciences (Fairmount); Business (W. Frank Burton); Education; Engineering; Fine Arts; Health Professions.
S: Communication (Elliott); Accountancy; Art and Design; Music; Performing Arts.

Youngstown State University
410 Wick Avenue, Youngstown, Ohio 44555
Tel: +1(216) 742-3000
Fax: +1(216) 742-3499
President: Leslie H. Cochran (1992-)
Provost: James Scanlon
Founded: 1908, 1967
C: Arts and Sciences; Business Administration (Warren P. Williamson); Education; Engineering and Technology (William Rayen); Fine and Performing Arts; Applied Science and Technology; Health and Human Services.

PRIVATE INSTITUTIONS

Abilene Christian University
ACU Station Box 8197, Abilene, Texas 79699
Tel: +1(915) 674-2000
Fax: +1(915) 674-2202
President: Royce Money (1990-)
Vice-President: Gary McCaleb
Founded: 1906
C: Arts and Sciences; Biblical and Family Studies; Business Administration.
I: Intensive English; Fathering; Marriage and Family.
Ce: Study of Aging; Adolescent Studies; Christian Leadership; New Testament Language and Literature.

Adelphi University
South Avenue, Garden City, New York, N.Y. 11530
Tel: +1(516) 877-3000
Fax: +1(516) 741-7537
President: Peter Diamandopoulos
Provost: Igor Webb
Founded: 1896, 1963
S: Advanced Psychological Studies; Arts and Sciences; Nursing; Social Work; Business; Education.
Ce: Psychological Services.

Albany College of Pharmacy
106 New Scotland Avenue, Albany, N.Y. 12208
Tel: +1(518) 445-7200
Fax: +1(518) 445-7202
President: Kenneth W. Miller
Registrar: Janis Fiske
Founded: 1881
C: Pharmacy.

Albany Medical College
47 New Scotland Avenue, Albany, N.Y. 12208
Tel: +1(518) 262-5253
Fax: +1(518) 262-5029
Dean: Anthony Tartaglia
Director of Admissions/Registrar: Sara Kremer
Founded: 1839
S: Medicine.

Alfred Adler Institute
618 South Michigan Avenue, Chicago, Illinois 60605
Tel: +1(312) 294-7100
President: Randall L. Thompson
Founded: 1952
Psychology.

Alfred University
26 North Main Street, Alfred, N.Y. 14802
Tel: +1(607) 871-2111
Fax: +1(607) 871-2339
President: Edward G. Coll, Jr.
Provost: W. Richard Ott
Founded: 1836, 1857
C: Liberal Arts and Sciences; Business Administration; Engineering and Professional Studies; Professional Studies; Ceramics.
S: Art and Design; Ceramic Engineering and Sciences.

American Conservatory of Music
16 N. Wabash, Suite 1850, Chicago, Illinois 60602
Tel: +1(312) 263-4161
Fax: +1(312) 263-5832
President: Theodora Schulze (1991-)
Dean: Marvin Ziporyn
Founded: 1886
Music.

The American University
4400 Massachusetts Avenue, N.W., Washington, D.C. 20016
Tel: +1(202) 885-1000
President: Elliot Milstein (1994-)
Provost: Ann Ferren
Founded: 1893
C: Arts and Sciences; Business Administration; Law; Education.
S: Communications; Public Affairs; International Service.

Andrews University
Berrien Springs, Michigan 49104
Tel: +1(616) 471-7771
Fax: +1(616) 471-9751
President: W. Richard Lesher
Provost: Arthur O. Coetzee
Founded: 1874, 1960
C: Arts and Sciences; Technology.
S: Business; Education.

Antioch University
795 Livermore Street, Yellow Springs, Ohio 45387
Tel: +1(513) 767-7331
Fax: +1(513) 767-1891
President: James Crowfoot (1994-)
Executive Vice-President of Financial Affairs: Phyllis J. Williams
Founded: 1852
D: Natural Sciences; Social and Behavioural Sciences; Humanities; Arts.

Ashland University
401 College Avenue, Ashland, Ohio 44805
Tel: +1(419) 289-4142
Fax: +1(419) 289-5333
President: William Benz
Registrar: Richard J. Obrecht
Founded: 1878, 1989
S: Arts and Humanities; Nursing; Business Administration; Business Administration and Economics; Education and Related Professions; Sciences.

Baltimore Hebrew College
5800 Park Heights Avenue, Baltimore, Maryland 21215
Tel: +1(301) 578-6900
Fax: +1(301) 578-6940
President: Norma F. Furst
Registrar: Zelda Rachbach
Founded: 1919
Judaic and Hebraic Studies.

Barry University
11300 Northeast Second Avenue, Miami Shores, Florida 33161
Tel: +1(305) 899-3000
Fax: +1(305) 899-3054
President: Sister Jeanne O'Laughlin, O.P.
Vice Pesident for Academic Affairs: J. Patrick Lee
Founded: 1940, 1981
C: Arts and Sciences; Adult and Continuing Education; Business; Nursing; Education; Natural and Health Sciences; Podiatric Medicine; Sports and Leisure Sciences.
S: Social Work.

Bastyr College
144 NE 54th Street, Seattle, Washington 98105
Tel: +1(206) 523-9585
Fax: +1(206) 527-4763
President: Joseph E. Pizzorno, Jr.
Executiva Vice-President: Keith Asplin
Founded: 1978
Naturopathic Medicine.

*Baylor College of Medicine
Room 143A, Houston, Texas 77030
Tel: +1(713) 798-4846
Fax: +1(713) 798-5555
President: William T. Butler
Executive Vice-President: Bobby R. Alford
Founded: 1903, 1969
S: Medicine.

Baylor University
Waco, Texas 76798
Tel: +1(817) 755-1011
Fax: +1(817) 755-3843
President: H.H. Reynolds
Vice-President: James Netherton
Founded: 1845
C: Arts and Sciences.
S: Law; Business; Education; Music; Nursing; Dentistry.
Ce: Medicine.

American International College
1000 State Street, Springfield, Massachusetts 01109-3189
Tel: +1(413) 737-7000
Fax: +1(413) 737-2803
President: Harry J. Courniotes (1969-)
Vice-President for Academic Affairs: Charles F. Maher
Founded: 1885
S: Arts and Sciences; Business Administration; Psychology and Education; Nursing.

Biola University
13800 Biola Avenue, La Mirada, California 90639-0001
Tel: +1(310) 903-6000
Fax: +1(310) 903-4748
President: Clyde Cook
Senior Vice-President: Sherwood Lingenfelter
Founded: 1908, 1980
S: Arts and Sciences; Psychology; Theology (Talbot); Intercultural Studies.

Boston College
University Heights, Chestnut Hill, Massachusetts 02167
Tel: +1(617) 552-8000
Fax: +1(617) 552-8828
President: Donald Monan, S.J.
Registrar: Louise M. Lonabocker
Founded: 1863
C: Arts and Sciences; Arts, Sciences and Business Administration (Evening Courses).
S: Education; Law; Social Work; Management; Nursing.
I: Religious Education and Pastoral Ministry.

*Boston University
881 Commonwealth Avenue, Boston, Massachusetts 02115
Tel: +1(617) 353-2000
Fax: +1(617) 353-2053
President: John Silber
Executive Vice-President and Provost: Jon Westling
Founded: 1939, 1867, 1869
C: Liberal Arts; General Studies; Communication; Engineering.
S: Arts; Education.
S: Management; Metropolitan C.; Sargent C. of Allied Health Professions; Public Health; Medicine; Social Work; Theology; Broadcasting and Film; Mass Communication and Public Relations; Theater Arts; Visual Arts; Journalism; Dentistry; Law.

Brandeis University
415 South Street, Waltham, Massachusetts 02254-9110
Tel: +1(617) 736-2000
Fax: +1(617) 736-8699
President: Samuel O. Thier (1994-)
Provost: Jehuda Reinharz
Founded: 1947
C: Arts and Sciences.
S: Advanced Studies in Social Welfare (Florence Heller).
D: Creative Arts; Humanities; Science; Social Science.

Brigham Young University
Provo, Utah 84602
Tel: +1(801) 378-1211
Fax: +1(801) 378-5278
President: Rex E. Lee (1989-93)
Provost: Bruce C. Hafen
Founded: 1875, 1903
C: Biology and Agriculture; Education; Engineering and Technology; Family, Home and Social Science; Fine Arts and Communications; Humanities; Nursing; Physical and Mathematical Sciences; Physical Education; Religious Education.
S: Management (Willard and Alice); Law (J. Reuben Clark).
Ce: American Western Studies (Charles Redd).

Brown University
Providence, Rhode Island 02912
Tel: +1(401) 863-1000
Fax: +1(401) 863-3700
Telex: 952095 brntlxctr pvd
President: Vartan Gregorian
Provost: Frank Rothman
Founded: 1764
C: Arts and Sciences.
S: Medicine.
D: Engineering; Applied Mathematics; Biology and Medecine.
Ce: Advanced Materials Research; Alcohol and Addiction Studies; Biomedical Ethics; Study of Languages; Latin American Studies; Modern Culture and Media; Old World Archaeology and Art; For Teaching and Research on Women; Study of Race and Ethnicity in America.

Bryn Mawr College
101 N. Merion Avenue, Bryn Mawr, Pennsylvania 19010-2899
Tel: +1(215) 526-5000
Fax: +1(215) 526-7450
President: Mary Patterson McPherson
Provost: Judith Shapiro
Founded: 1885
S: Arts and Sciences; Social Work and Social Research.

California Institute of Integral Studies
765 Ashbury Street, San Pasedena, California 94117
Tel: +1(415) 753-6100
President: Robert McDermott
Registrar: Marsha Pool
Organizational Develoment and Transformation; Social and Cultural Anthropology; Philosophy and Religion.

California Institute of Technology
1201 East California Boulevard, Pasadena, California 91125
Tel: +1(818) 395-6811
Fax: +1(818) 795-1547
President: Thomas E. Everhart
Provost: Paul C. Jennings
Founded: 1891, 1913, 1920
Chemistry and Chemical Engineering; Engineering and Applied Science; Geological and Planetary Sciences; Humanities and Social Sciences; Physics, Mathematics and Astronomy.

California School of Professional Psychology-Berkeley/Alameda
1900 Addison Street, Alameda, California 94501
Tel: +1(510) 523-2300
Fax: +1(510) 521-3678
Chancellor: Katsujuki Sakamoto
Registrar: Karin Nystrom
Founded: 1969
Psychology.

California School of Professional Psychology-Fresno
1350 M Street, Fresno, California 93721
Tel: +1(209) 486-8420
Fax: +1(209) 486-0734
Chancellor: Mary Kenkel
Registrar: Linda Witt
Founded: 1969
A: Psychology.

California School of Professional Psychology-Los Angeles
Alhambra, California 91803-1360
Tel: +1(818) 284-2777
Fax: +1(818) 284-0550
Chancellor: Lisa Porché-Burke
Registrar: Rosemary Abend
Founded: 1969
Psychology.

California School of Professional Psychology-San Diego
6212 Ferris Square, San Diego, California 92121-3250
Tel: +1(619) 452-1664
Fax: +1(619) 558-2279
Chancellor: Raymond Trybus
Registrar: Erin Maynard
Founded: 1969
Psychology.

Campbell University
Buie's Creek, North Carolina 27506
Tel: +1(919) 873-1200
Fax: +1(919) 893-9850
President: Norman A. Wiggins
Registrar: Jerry M. Wallace
Founded: 1887, 1979
S: Arts and Sciences; Law; Pharmacy; Business (Lundy-Fetterman); Education.

Caribbean Center for Advanced Studies
Apartado 41246 Manillas Station, San Juan, Puerto Rico 00902-3711
Tel: +1(809) 725-6500
Fax: +1(809) 721-7187
President: Salvador Santiago-Negron
Academic Dean: Maria A. Rodriguez
Founded: 1966
Arts and Sciences.

Carnegie Mellon University
5000 Forbes Avenue, Pittsburgh, Pennsylvania 15213
Tel: +1(412) 268-2000
Fax: +1(412) 268-5249
President: Robert Mehrabian (1990-)
Vice-President for Business Affairs: Patrick J. Keating
Founded: 1900, 1912, 1967
C: Humanities and Social Sciences; Fine Arts; Sciences.
S: Graduate S. of Industrial Administration.
I: Technology (Carnegie); Public Policy and Management (H. John Heinz).

Ce: Advanced Deformation Processing Research; Dependable Systems; Energy and Environmental Studies; Engineered Materials; Entrepreneurial Development; Excellence in Optical Data Processing; Iron and Steelmaking Research; Risk Perception and Communication; Solid Waste Management; Environmental I.; Building Performance and Diagnostics; Decisions Systems Research I.; Urban Sytems I.; L. for Computational Linguistics; Stastical Ce. for Quality Improvement; Ce. for the Study of Writing; Ce. for History and Policy; Research I.; Software Engineering I.

Case Western Reserve University
10900 Euclid Avenue, Cleveland, Ohio 44106
Tel: +1(216) 368-2000
President: Agnar Pytte (1987-)
Provost: Richard A. Zdanis
Founded: 1826
C: Arts and Sciences.
S: Applied Social Sciences (Mandel); Dentistry; Engineering Sciences; Law; Management; Medicine; Nursing (Frances Payne Bolton); Bio-Architectonics Ce.
Ce: Cancer Research; Electrochemical Sciences; Ce. for Adolescent Health; Applied Polymer Research; Automation and Intelligent Systems Research; Biomedical Ethics; International Health; Molecular and Microstructures of Composites; Professional Ethics; Regional Economic Issues; Commercial Development of Space; Urban Poverty and Social Change; Aging and Health; Electronics Design; Health Systems Management; Law-Medicine; Nonprofit Organizatons (Mandel); Canada-U.S. Law.

The Catholic University of America
620 Michigan Avenue, N.E., Washington, D.C. 20064
Tel: +1(202) 319-5000
Fax: +1(202) 319-5579
President: Brother Patrick Ellis, F.S.C. (1992-)
Executive Vice-President: Rosemary Donley, S.C.
Founded: 1889
S: Arts and Sciences; Library and Information Sciences; Philosophy; Engineering and Architecture; Law (Columbus); Music (Benjamin T. Rome); Nursing; Social Service; Religious Studies; Architecture and Planning.
C: University.
I: Life Cycle; Biomolecular Studies.
Ce: Advanced Training in Cell and Molecular Biology.
L: Vitreous State.

Chicago School of Professional Psychology
806 South Plymouth Court, Chicago, Illinois 60605
Tel: +1(312) 786-9443
Fax: +1(312) 786-9611
President: Jeffrey C. Grip
Registrar: C.R. Toft
Founded: 1979
Psychology.

The Claremont Graduate School
150 E. Tenth Street, Claremont, California 91711
Tel: +1(906) 621-8000
Fax: +1(906) 621-8390
President: John D. Maguire
Vice-President for Academic Affairs: Murray M. Schwartz
Founded: 1925, 1971
Arts and Sciences.

Clark University
950 Main Street, Worcester, Massachusetts 01610-1477
Tel: +1(508) 793-7780
Fax: +1(508) 793-7711
E-Mail: internet
President: Richard P. Traina
Provost: Fern L. Johnson
Founded: 1887
C: Management (Graduate); Professional and Continuing Education.
I: George Perkins Marsh; Economic Studies.
Ce: European Ce. for Urban Education.
L: Cartographic Technology and Geographic Analysis.

Clarkson University
Potsdam, N.Y. 13699
Tel: +1(315) 268-6400
Fax: +1(315) 268-2319
President: Richard H. Gallacher
Executive Vice-President: R. Thomas Williamson
Founded: 1896
F: Liberal Studies.
S: Engineering; Science; Management.

Cleveland Institute of Music
11021 East Boulevard, Cleveland, Ohio 44106-1776
Tel: +1(216) 791-5000
Fax: +1(216) 791-3063
President: David Cerone
Registrar: Robert McAllister
Founded:
A: Music.

Columbia University in the City of New York
212 Hamilton Hall, New York, N.Y. 10027
Tel: +1(212) 854-1754
Fax: +1(212) 932-0418
President: George E. Rupp
Provost: Johnathan R. Cole
Founded: 1754, 1784, 1912
C: Physicians and Surgeons; Business; General Studies; Columbia.
S: Engineering and Applied Science; Architecture, Planning and Preservation; Arts; Arts and Sciences; Dental and Oral Surgery; International and Public Affairs; Journalism; Law; Medicine; Nursing; Public Health; Social Work.

Columbia University Teachers College

525 West 120th Street, New York, N.Y. 10027
Tel: +1(212) 678-3000
Fax: +1(212) 678-4048
President: P. Michael Timpane
Dean: Judith B. Brandenburg
Founded: 1887
D: *Philosophy, the Social Sciences and
Education; Psychology and Education;
Educational Institutions and Programs;
Instruction; Health Services, Sciences, and
Education.*

Cornell University

Ithaca, N.Y. 14853
Tel: +1(607) 255-2000
Fax: +1(607) 255-7116
Telex: 6713054 corneluw
President: Hunter R. Rawlings, III (1994-)
Registrar (Acting): Ronald Loomis
Founded: 1865
C: *Agriculture and Life Sciences; Human
Ecology; Veterinary Medecine; Industrial and
Labour Relations; Arts and Sciences;
Architecture, Arts and Planning; Engineering;
Medical (New York); Education.*
S: *Hotel Administration; Law.*
S: *Medical Sciences (Graduate, New York);
Management (Graduate, Johnson).*
Ce: *High Energy Synchrotron Studies; Theory
and Simulation in Science and Engineering;
National Astronomy and Ionosphere; Africana
Studies and Research.*
I: *Mathematical Sciences.*
L: *Nuclear Studies (Floyd R. Newman).*
P: *East Asia; South Asia; Southeast Asia; Latin
American Studies; Western Societies.*

Creighton University

Omaha, Nebraska 68178-0001
Tel: +1(402) 280-2700
Fax: +1(402) 280-2244
Telex: 438119 creighton
President: Michael G. Morrison
Vice-President for Academic Affairs: John W.
Carlson
Founded: 1878
C: *Arts and Sciences; Business Administration;
Education.*
S: *Boyne School of Dental Science; Law;
Medicine; Pharmacy and Allied Health
Professions; Nursing; University C. and Summer
Sessions.*

*Dartmouth College

Hanover, New Hampshire 03755
Tel: +1(603) 646-1110
Fax: +1(603) 646-2850
President: James Oliver Freedman
Provost: John Walter Strohbehn
Founded: 1769
F: *Arts and Sciences.*
S: *Medical; Engineering (Thayer); Business
Administration (Amos Tuck).*

DePaul University

25, East Jackson Boulevard, Chicago, Illinois
60604
Tel: +1(312) 362-8000
Fax: +1(312) 362-5322
President: John T. Richardson
Provost: Gladys Styles
Founded: 1898, 1907
C: *Commerce; Liberal Arts and Sciences; Law.*
S: *Education; Theatre; Music; Accountancy; New
Learning.*

Drake University

2507 University Avenue, Des Moines, Iowa
50311-4505
Tel: +1(515) 271-2011
Fax: +1(515) 271-3977
President: Michael R. Ferrari
Provost: Barbara Gitenstein
Founded: 1881
C: *Arts and Sciences; Pharmacy and Health
Sciences; Business and Public Administration.*
S: *Journalism and Mass Communication;
Education; Law.*

Drew University

Madison Avenue, Madison, New Jersey 07940
Tel: +1(201) 408-3000
Fax: +1(201) 408-3939
President: Thomas H. Kean
Vice-President for Academic Affairs: Eric Gould
Founded: 1867
C: *Arts and Sciences.*
S: *Theology.*

Drexel University

32 and Chestnut Streets, Philadelphia,
Pennsylvania 19104
Tel: +1(215) 895-2000
Fax: +1(215) 895-1414
President: Richard D. Breslin
Provost: Dennis G. Brown
Founded: 1891, 1970
C: *Arts and Sciences; Information Studies;
Engineering; Business Administration; Design
Arts (Nesbit).*
I: *Biomedical Engineering and Science Institute;
Environmental Studies Institute.*

Duke University

Durham, North Carolina 27708-0586
Tel: +1(919) 684-8111
Fax: +1(919) 684-3200
President: Nannerl O. Keohane (1993-)
Provost: Thomas A. Langford
Founded: 1838, 1924
C: *Arts and Sciences (Trinity); Nursing.*
S: *Engineering; Law; Medicine; Environment;
Fuqua S. of Business; Divinity.*

Duquesne University
600 Forbes Avenue, Pittsburgh, Pennsylvania 15282
Tel: +1(412) 396-6000
Fax: +1(412) 434-5656
President: John E. Murray, Jr.
Provost and Vice-President for Academic Affairs: Michael Weber
Founded: 1878, 1960
C: Liberal Arts and Sciences.
S: Business Administration (A.J. Palumbo); Education; Health Sciences (John G. Rangos); Music; Nursing; Pharmacy; Law.

Emory University
1380 South Oxford Road N.E., Atlanta, Georgia 30322
Tel: +1(404) 727-6123
Fax: +1(404) 727-2613
President: William M. Chace (1994-)
Vice-President for Academic Affairs: Billy E. Fry
Founded: 1836
C: Liberal Arts.
S: Business; Dentistry; Law; Medicine; Nursing (Nell Hodgson Woodruff); Theology (Candler); Public Health.
Ce: Ethics in Public Policy and the Professions; Yerkes Regional Primate Research; The Carter; Aquinas Theology; Educational Studies; Latin American Studies; Soviet, Post-Soviet, and East European Studies.
Div: Allied Health Professions; Religion.

Fairleigh Dickinson University, Teaneck-Hackensack Campus
1000 River Road, Teaneck, New Jersey 07666
Tel: +1(201) 692-2000
Fax: +1(201) 460-5467
President: Francis J. Mertz
Vice-President for Academic Affairs: Geoffrey S. Weinman
Founded: 1942, 1956
C: Business Administration (Samuel J. Silberman); Education (Peter Sammartino).

Fielding Institute
2112 Santa Barbara Street, Santa Barbara, California 93105
Tel: +1(805) 687-1099
Fax: +1(805) 687-4590
President: Donald J. MacIntyre
Director for Institutional Advancement: Michael Stuck
Founded: 1974
Clinical Psychology; Human and Organization Development.

Florida Institute of Technology
150 W. University Boulevard, Melbourne, Florida 32901-6988
Tel: +1(407) 768-8000
Fax: +1(407) 984-8461
Telex: 9103509068 fit iver
President: Lynn E. Weaver

Vice-President, Academic Affairs: Andrew W. Revay
Founded: 1958
Science and Liberal Arts.
C: Engineering.
S: Business; Aeronautics; Psychology.
I: Aging and Therapeutic Research (Claude Perrer).
L: Microelectronics.
Ce: Electronics Manufacturability; Space Science Research; Spaceflight Engineering; Geo-Space Environmental Research; Medical Genetics; Indian River Marine Science Research; Waste Utilization (Research); Computational Fluid Dynamics; Energy Alternatives (Research).

Fordham University
East Fordham Road, Bronx, New York, N.Y. 10458-5191
Tel: +1(718) 817-1000
Fax: +1(718) 817-4925
President: Joseph A. O'Hare, S.J.
Vice-President for Administration: Brian J. Byrne
Founded: 1841, 1907
C: Business Administration (Rose Hill); Lincoln Ce.
S: Arts and Sciences (Rose Hill); General Studies (Rose Hill); Religion and Religious Education (Rose Hill); Law (Lincoln Ce.); Graduate S. of Social Service (Lincoln Ce.); Graduate S. of Education (Lincoln Ce.); Graduate S. of Business Administration (Lincoln Ce.(Joseph A. Martino)); Graduate Ce. (Tarrytown).

Gallaudet University
800 Florida Avenue, Nebraska, Washington, D.C. 20002-3625
Tel: +1(202) 651-5000
Fax: +1(202) 651-5463
President: I. King Jordan
Registrar: Carolyn Willis
Founded: 1856, 1954, 1986
C: Continuing Education; Arts and Sciences.
S: Communication; Education and Human Services; Management; Preparatory Studies.

George Fox College
414 N. Meridian, Newberg, Oregon 97132
Tel: +1(503) 538-8383
Fax: +1(503) 537-3830
President: Edward F. Stevens (1983-93)
Vice-President for Financial Affairs: Donald Millage
Founded: 1891
C: Professional Studies.
S: Humanities; Natural and Behavioural Sciences.

*The George Washington University
Washington, D.C. 20052
Tel: +1(202) 994-1000
Fax: +1(202) 994-0458
President: Stephen J. Trachtenberg

Vice-President for Academic Affairs: Roderick Stuart French
Founded: 1821, 1873, 1904
S: *Columbian C. and Graduate S. of Arts and Sciences; Business and Public Management; Education and Human Development; Engineering and Applied Science; International Affairs (Elliott); Medicine and Health Sciences.*
Ce: *National Law.*
D: *Continuing Education.*

Georgetown University

37th and O Street, N.W., Washington, D.C. 20057
Tel: +1(202) 687-5055
President: Leo J. O'Donovan
Registrar: Patrick A. Heelan
Founded: 1901
C: *Arts and Sciences.*
S: *Nursing; Foreign Service (Edmund A. Walsh); Languages and Linguistics; Business Administration; Of Continuing Education; Law; Medecine.*

Golden Gate University

536 Mission Street, San Francisco, California 94105
Tel: +1(415) 442-7000
Fax: +1(415) 495-2671
Telex: 6502754174 mci un
President: Thomas M. Stauffer (1992-)
Vice-President: Tony Branch
Founded: 1901
C: *Arts and Sciences; Business Administration; Accountancy.*
S: *Law; Business; Finance; Public Administration; Taxation; Technology Management; Health Services Management; International Management; Operations Management.*

Gonzaga University

East 502 Boone, Spokane, Washington 99258
Tel: +1(509) 328-4220
Fax: +1(509) 484-2818
E-Mail: bitnet, internet
President: Bernard J. Coughlin, S.J. (1974-)
Academic Vice-President: Patrick J. Ford, S.J.
Founded: 1887
C: *Arts and Sciences.*
S: *Business Administration; Education; Engineering; Professional Studies; Law.*
A: *Educational Studies.*
Ce: *Indian Education.*

Harvard University

Cambridge, Massachusetts 02138
Tel: +1(617) 495-1000
Fax: +1(617) 495-0500
Telex: 325660 las pau
President: Neil Rudenstine (1991-)
Vice-President for Finance: Robert Scott
Founded: 1636
F: *Arts and Sciences.*

S: *ExtensionS.; Business Administration (Graduate); Dental Medicine; Design; Education; Law; Public Health; Divinity; Medical; Government (Kennedy).*
Ce: *International Affairs; European Studies.*
C: *Harvard; Radcliffe.*
I: *Harvard I. for International Development.*
D: *Applied Sciences; Medical Sciences.*

Hofstra University

Hempstead, Long Island, N.Y. 11550-1090
Tel: +1(516) 463-6600
Fax: +1(516) 564-4296
President: James M. Stuart
Provost: Herman A. Berliner
Founded: 1935, 1939, 1963
S: *Business; Law; Education; New.*
C: *Liberal Arts and Sciences; Continuing Education.*

*Howard University

2400 Sixth Street, N.W., Washington, D.C. 20059
Tel: +1(202) 636-6100
President: Franklun G. Jenifer
Vice-President for Academic Affairs: Joyce Ladner
Founded: 1867
C: *Dentistry; Arts and Sciences; Liberal Arts; Medicine; Pharmacy and Pharmacal Sciences; Fine Arts; Allied Health Sciences; Nursing.*
S: *Social Work; Arts and Sciences (Graduate); Engineering; Law; Architecture and Planning; Communications; Divinity; Education; Business and Public Administration.*

Illinois Institute of Technology

3300 South Federal Street, Chicago, Illinois 60616
Tel: +1(312) 567-3000
President: Lewis Collens
Provost: Darsh Wasan
Founded: 1940
C: *Engineering and Science (Armour); Liberal Arts (Lewis C.); Law (Chicago-Kent C.); Architecture.*
I: *Design; IIT Research (IITRI).*
S: *Business (Stuart).*

Inter-American University of Puerto Rico, Metropolitan Campus

P.O. Box 1293, Hato Rey, Puerto Rico 00919
Tel: +1(809) 250-1912
Fax: +1(809) 250-0782
Chancellor: Manuel J. Fernos
Dean of Studies: Zoraida Santiago
Founded: 1960
C: *Arts, Sciences, and Education; Economics; Nursing; Science and Technology; Behavioural Sciences; Humanities; Medicine; Technology.*
D: *Education; Humanistic Studies; Social and Behavioural Sciences.*

The Johns Hopkins University

3400 North Charles Street, Baltimore, Maryland 21218
Tel: +1(410) 516-8000
President: William C. Richardson
Provost: Joseph Cooper
Founded: 1876
S: Arts and Sciences; Engineering (A.W.C. Whiting); Medicine; Hygiene and Public Health; Nursing; Continuing Studies; Paul H. Nitze of Advanced International Studies (Washington); Peabody Conservatory of Music.

The Juilliard School

40 Lincoln Center Plaza, New York, N.Y. 10023-4590
Tel: +1(212) 799-5000
Fax: +1(212) 724-2363
President: Joseph Lo. Polisi (1984-)
Director of Admissions: Carole J. Everett
Founded: 1905, 1924, 1968
Performing Arts.

Lehigh University

Bethlehem, Pennsylvania 18015-3094
Tel: +1(215) 758-3000
Fax: +1(215) 691-5420
Telex: 7106701086 lehigh univ ud
President: James R. Davis
Vice-President for Academic and Student Affairs: Michael J. McGovern
Founded: 1865
C: Arts and Sciences; Business and Economics; Engineering.
S: Education and Applied Sciences; Arts and Sciences; Business and Economics; Engineering.
S: Education.

Life College

1269 Barclay Circle, Marietta, Georgia 30060
Tel: +1(404) 424-0554
Fax: +1(404) 429-8359
President: Sid E. Williams
Vice-President of Academics: Ronald J. Hash
Founded: 1974
Chiropractic Studies.

Loma Linda University

Loma Linda, California 92350
Tel: +1(909) 824-4300
Fax: +1(909) 824-4577
Telex: 676482 intlh loml
President: Lyn Behrens
Vice-President for Academic Research Affairs: Ian M. Fraser
Founded: 1905

S: Dentistry; Allied Health Professions; Medicine; Public Health; Nursing; Graduate; F; Religion.

Long Island University, Brooklyn Campus

University Plaza, Brooklyn, New York, N.Y. 11201-9926
Tel: +(718) 488-1000
President: David J. Steinberg
Vice-President for Academic Affairs: Walter S. Jones
Founded: 1926
C: Pharmacy and Health Sciences (Arnold and Marie Schwartz); Liberal Arts and Sciences (Richard L. Conolly).
S: Health Professions; Education; Business, Public Administration, and Information Sciences; Nursing.

Long Island University, C.W. Post Campus

Northern Boulevard, Route 25A, Brookville, N.Y. 11548
Tel: +1(516) 299-0200
Fax: +1(516) 626-0694
President: David J. Steinberg
Vice-President for Academic Affairs: Walter Jones
Founded: 1954
C: Liberal Arts and Sciences; Management.
S: Health Professions; Visual and Performing Arts; Library and Information Science (Palmer); Education.
Ce: Academic Resource; Business Research; Aging; Writing.

Loyola University of Chicago

820 North Michigan Avenue, Chicago, Illinois 60611
Tel: +1(312) 915-6000
Fax: +1(312) 915-7003
E-Mail: BITNET-INTERNET
President: Raymond C. Baumhaet
Executive Vice-President: Ronald W. Walker
Founded: 1870
C: Mundelein; Arts and Sciences.
S: Business Administration; Dentistry; Law; Medicine; Nursing; Social Work; Education; Graduate.
I: Industrial Relations; Pastoral Studies.

Maharishi International University

Office of Admissions, 1000 North Fourth Street, DB 1155, Fairfield, Iowa 52557-1155
Tel: +1(515) 472-1000
Fax: +1(515) 472-1189
President: Bevan Morris
Registrar: Kristine Wood
Founded: 1971
C: Arts and Sciences.

Manhattan School of Music
120 Claremont Avenue, New York, N.Y.
10027-4698
Tel: +1(212) 749-2802
Fax: +1(212) 749-5471
President: Peter C. Simon (1992-)
Dean of Faculty and Performance: Richard E.
Adams
Founded: 1917
Music.

Marquette University
615 North 11th Street, Milwaukee, Wisconsin
53233
Tel: +1(414) 288-7223
Fax: +1(414) 288-3300
President: Albert Diulio, S.J. (1990-)
Executive Vice-President: William Leahy, S.J.
Founded: 1881
*C: Arts and Sciences; Business Administration;
Engineering; Communication, Journalism, and
Performing Arts; Nursing; Medical L. Technology;
Education.*
S: Dentistry; Law.
*I: Biomedical Research; Democracy and Public
Values (Bradley); Family Studies.*
*Ce: Applied Economic Analysis; Energy Studies;
International Studies; Addiction Studies;
Advanced Manufacturing; Geriatric Education.*
P: Physical Therapy.

Massachusetts College of Pharmacy and Allied Health Sciences
179 Longwood Avenue, Boston, Massachusetts
02115
Tel: +1(617) 732-2800
Fax: +1(617) 723-2801
President: Louis P. Jeffrey
Vice-President for Academic Affairs: Benjamin R.
Hershenson
Founded: 1823, 1979
Pharmacy.

Massachusetts Institute of Technology (MIT)
77 Massachusetts Avenue, Cambridge,
Massachusetts 02139
Tel: +1(617) 253-1000
Fax: +1(617) 253-8000
E-Mail: Bitnet, Internet
Telex: 174194 mit com
President: Charles M. Vest
Executive Vice-President: William R. Dickson
Founded: 1861
*S: Architecture and Planning; Engineering;
Humanities and Social Sciences; Management
(Sloan); Science.*
*C: Health Sciences, Technology and
Management (Whitaker).*
*Ce: Biotechnology Process Engineering;
Advanced Engineering Studies; Cancer Research;
Cognitive Science; Environmental Health
Sciences; International Studies; Materials
Science and Engineering; Space Research;
Technology, Policy and Industrial Development;*

*Transportation Studies; Clinical Research;
Materials Processing; Plasma Fusion; Operations
Research.*
*L: Energy; Francis Bitter National Magnet;
Artificial Intelligence; Haystack Observatory;
Electromagnetic and Electronic Systems;
Computer Science; Information and Decision
Systems; Manufacturing and Productivity; Nuclear
Science; Lincoln; Media; Nuclear Reactor;
Electronics (Research); Spectroscopy.*
D: Comparative Medicine.

Medical College of Pennsylvania
3300 Henry Avenue, Philadelphia, Pennsylvania
19129
Tel: +1(215) 842-6000
Fax: +1(215) 843-4074
President: D. Walter Cohen
Executive Vice-President: Leonard L. Ross
Founded: 1850, 1970
Medicine.

Medical College of Wisconsin
8701 Watertown Plank Road, Milwaukee,
Wisconsin 53226
Tel: +1(414) 257-8296
Fax: +1(414) 257-0449
President: Michael Bolger
Executive Vice-President: Richard A. Cooper
Founded: 1913
Health Professions.

Meharry Medical College
1005 D.B. Todd Boulevard, Nashville, Tennessee
37208
Tel: +1(615) 327-6111
Fax: +1(615) 372-6540
President: John E. Maupin (1994-)
Executive Vice-President: Walter L. Strong
Founded: 1876
Div: Biomedical Sciences.
S: Dentistry; Medicine.

Mercer University
1400 Coleman Avenue, Macon, Georgia
31207-0001
Tel: +1(612) 752-2700
Fax: +1(612) 752-2108
President: R. Kirby Godsey
Executive Vice-President: Horace Flemming
Founded: 1833, 1838
C: Liberal Arts; University.
*S: Law (Walter F. George); Business and
Economics (Eugene W. Stetson); Engineering;
Medicine; Pharmacy.*

Middlebury College
Middlebury, Vermont 05753
Tel: (802) 388-3711
Fax: (802) 388-9646
President: John M. McCardell
Provost and Academic Vice-President: Eward C.
Knox
Founded: 1800

C: Sciences; Humanities.
S: Languages.

Mount Sinai School of Medicine
One Gustave L. Levy Place, New York, N.Y. 10029
Tel: +1(212) 241-6500
Fax: +1(212) 996-9764
President: John W. Rowe
Senior Vice-President for Business Finance:
Rober Wertheim
Founded: 1963
Graduate S: Biological Sciences.

National University
4141 Camino Del Rio South, San Diego,
California 92108-4194
Tel: +1(619) 563-7100
Fax: +1(619) 563-7391
President: Jerry C. Lee
Vice-President for Administration: Murray C.
Cook
Founded: 1971
C: Arts and Sciences; Education and Human
Services; Management of Technology.
D: Business; Law.

New England Conservatory of Music
290 Huntington Avenue, Boston, Massachusetts
02115
Tel: +1(617) 262-1120
Fax: +1(617) 262-0500
President: Laurence Lesser
Founded: 1867
Music.

New School for Social Research
66 West 12th Street, New York, N.Y. 10011
Tel: +1(212) 741-5600
Fax: +1(212) 691-7172
President: Johathan F. Fanton
Provost: Judith B. Walzer
Founded: 1919
F: Political and Social Science (Graduate).
D: Adult.
C: Eugene Lang; Music (Mannes).
S: Management and Urban Policy (Graduate);
Design (Parsons).

New York Medical College
Sunshine Cottage, Valhalla, N.Y. 10595
Tel: +1(914) 993-4000
Fax: +1(914) 993-4145
President: Rev. Harry C. Barrett
Registrar: Barbara Wines
Founded: 1860
C: Medical.
Graduate S: Basic Medical Sciences; Health
Sciences.
Ce: Medical Research.

*New York University
70 Washington Square South, New York, N.Y.
10012
Tel: +1(212) 995-4500
Fax: +1(212) 988-4100
President: L. Jay Oliva (1991-)
Deputy Chancellor: Sylvia Baeuch
Founded: 1901
C: Arts and Sciences; Dentistry.
S: Arts and Sciences (Graduate); Business
(Leonard N. Stern); Health, Education, Nursing
and Arts Professions; Arts; Social Work; Public
Service (Wagner Graduate); Medicine; Law;
Continuing Education.
I: American Language; Fine Arts; Mathematics
(Courant).
Div: Alternative and Individualized Study
(Gallatin).

Northwestern University
633 Clark Street, Evanston, Illinois 60208
Tel: +1(708) 491-3741
Fax: +1(708) 491-7973
President: Henry S. Bienen (1994-)
Provost: David H. Cohen
Founded: 1851
C: Arts and Sciences; Music.
S: Education and Social Policy; Journalism
(Medill); Speech; Engineering and Applied
Science (Robert R. McCormick); Management
(Kellogg); Law; Medical; Dentistry.

Nova University
3301 College Avenue, Fort Lauderdale, Florida
33314
Tel: +1(305) 475-7360
Fax: +1(305) 476-1999
President: Stephen Feldman
Vice-President for Academic Affairs: Ovid C.
Lewis
Founded: 1964
C: Arts and Sciences.
P: Liberal and Professional Studies; Career
Development Study.
Ce: Comuters and Information Sciences;
Psychological Studies; Law; Ocenographic.

Oral Roberts University
7777 South Lewis Avenue, Tulsa, Oklahoma
74171
Tel: +1(918) 495-6161
Fax: +1(918) 495-6033
President: Richard Roberts
Provost: Carl H. Hamilton
Founded: 1963
S: Arts and Sciences; Business; Education;
Nursing (Anna Vaugh); Theology and Missions.

Oregon Graduate Institute of Science and Technology
19600 N.W. Von Neuman Drive, Beaverton, Oregon 97006-1000
Tel: +1(503) 690-1121
Fax: +1(503) 690-1029
President: Dwight A. Sangrey
Vice-President of Finance and Administration: Ross M. Hall
Founded: 1963
D: Computer Science and Engineering; Chemical and Biological Sciences; Electrical Engineering and Applied Physics; D. of Environmental Science and Engineering; D. of Materials Science and Engineering; Ce. for Groundwater Research; Ce. for Global Change Research; Ce. for Semiconductor Materials, Devices and Applications; Ce. for Spoken Language Understanding.

Pace University
One Pace Plaza, New York, N.Y. 10038
Tel: +1(212) 346-1200
Fax: +1(212) 346-1933
President: Patricia O. Ewers (1990-)
Executive Vice-President (Finance and Administration): Paul Magali
Founded: 1906
S: Arts and Sciences (Dyson); Business (Administration (Lubin)); Education; Nursing (Lienhard); Law; Computer Science and Information Systems.

Pacific Graduate School of Psychology
935 East Meadow Drive, Palo Alto, California 94303
Tel: +1(415) 494-7477
Fax: +1(415) 856-6734
President: Allen Calvin (1984-)
Vice-President for Enrolment Management: Rick Kaplowitz
Founded: 1975
Clinical Psychology.

Pacific University
2043 College Way, Forest Grove, Oregon 97116
Tel: +1(503) 357-6151
Fax: +1(503) 359-2242
President: Robert F. Duvall
Provost: Donald S. Rushmer
Founded: 1842, 1915
C: Arts and Sciences; Optometry.
S: Professional Psychology; Occupational Therapy.

Pepperdine University
24255 Pacific Coast Highway, Malibu, California 90263
Tel: +1(310) 456-4000
Fax: +1(310) 456-4758
President: David K. Davenport (1985-)
Executive Vice-President: Andrew Benton
Founded: 1937, 1970
C: Letters, Arts, and Sciences (Seaver).

S: Business and Management; Education and Psychology (Graduate); Law.

Philadelphia College of Pharmacy and Science
600 South Forty Third Street, Philadelphia, Pennsylvania 19104-4495
Tel: +1(215) 596-8800
Fax: +1(215) 895-1100
President: Allen Misher
Vice-President of Academic Affairs: Philip P. Gerbino
Founded: 1821
C: Arts and Sciences; Humanities.
S: Pharmacy.
D: Mathematics and Physics; Social Sciences; Biological Sciences; Pharmacology and Toxicology; Health Sciences.

*Polytechnic University
6 Metrotech Center, Brooklyn, New York, N.Y. 11201-2999
Tel: +1(718) 260-3600
Fax: +1(718) 260-3136
President: George Bugliarello
Provost: Jvan T. Frisch
Founded: 1854, 1889, 1983
S: Engineering; Management; Electrical Engineering and Comuter Science.

Polytechnic University, Farmingdale Campus
Route 110, Farmingdale, N.Y. 11735-3995
Tel: +1(516) 755-4300
Fax: +1(516) 755-4404
Founded: 1854
Arts and Sciences.

Providence College
Eaton Street and River Avenue, Providence, Rhode Island 02918
Tel: +1(401) 865-1000
Fax: +1(401) 865-2057
President: John F. Cunningham, O.P.
Executive Vice-President: James F. Quigiey
Founded: 1854, 1920, 1960
Art; Music; Nursing; Social Work; Teacher Education.

Rensselaer Polytechnic Institute
110 8th Street, Troy, N.Y. 12180-3590
Tel: +1(518) 276-6000
Fax: +1(518) 518-4072
Telex: 6716050 rpi trou
President: R. Byron Pipes (1993-)
Provost: James D. Meindl
Founded: 1824
S: Architecture; Engineering; Humanities and Social Sciences; Management; Science.
Ce: Integrated Electronics (CIE); Manufacturing Productivity and Technology Transfer (CMPTT); Rennselaer Design Research; Services Sector Research and Education (CSSRE); Advanced Technology (CAT) in Automation and Robotics (New York State); Science and Technology Policy

(CSTP); Northeast Manufacturing Technology (To Assist Small to Medium-sized Manufacturing Firms in the Adoption of Advanced Manufacturing Technologies); Entrepreneurship of New Technological Ventures (CENTV); Biophysics; Scientific Computation Research; Composite Materials and Structures (CCMS); Lighting Research; Architectural Research; Glass Science and Technology; Intelligent Robotic Systems for Space Exploration (CIRSSE) (NASA); Bioseparation Research; Rotorcraft Technology; Innovation in Undergraduate Education; Multiphase Research; Earthquake Engineering.
P: High Temperature Technology.
I: Fresh Water.
L: Image Processing.

Rice University

6100 S. Main, Post Office Box 1892, Houston, Texas 77251
Tel: +1(713) 527-8101
Fax: +1(713) 523-4117
President: Malcolm Gillis
Registrar: James G. Williamson
Founded: 1891, 1960
S: Humanities; Natural Sciences (Wiess); Engineering (George R. Brown); Social Sciences; Architecture; Music (Shepherd); Administration (Jesse H. Jones).

Rochester Institute of Technology

1 Lomb Memorial Drive, Rochester, N.Y. 14623-0887
Tel: +1(716) 475-2400
Fax: +1(716) 475-7049
President: albert J. Simone
Provost: Thomas R. Plough
Founded: 1823, 1944
C: Applied Science and Technology; Continuing Education; Engineering; Fine and Applied Arts; Graphic Arts and Photography; Liberal Arts; Science; Business; Imaging Arts and Science.
S: American Crafts; Art and Design; Computer Science and Information Technology; Engineering Technology; Food, Hotel and Travel Management; Photographic Arts and Science; Painting Management Science.
I: Deaf (National Technical).

The Rockefeller University

1230 York Avenue, New York, N.Y. 10021-6399
Tel: +1(212) 327-8000
Fax: +1(212) 327-7974
President: Torsten Wiesel
Executive Vice-President: Frederick Bohen
Founded: 1901, 1954, 1965
Basic Research in the Natural and Physical Sciences; Life Sciences; Rockefeller University Hospital; Field Research (Millbrook, New York).

Rush University

1653 West Congress Parkway, Chicago, Illinois 60612
Tel: +1(312) 942-5099
Fax: +1(312) 942-2219
President: Leo M. Henikoff
Senior Vice-President: Donald R. Oder
Founded: 1969, 1972
C: Health Sciences; Nursing; Medical (Rush).

St. John's University

Grand Central and Utopia Parkways, Jamaica, N.Y. 11439
Tel: +1(718) 990-6161
President: Donald J. Harrington
Executive Vice-President: Andrew J. Bartilucci
Founded: 1870, 1933, 1954
C: Business Administration; Pharmacy and Allied Health Professions; Libral Arts and Sciences; Liberal Arts and Vocational Education (St. Vincent's).
S: Law; Education and Human Services.

Saint Louis University

221 North Grand Boulevard, Saint Louis, Missouri 63103
Tel: +1(314) 658-2222
Fax: +1(314) 658-3874
President: Lawrence H. Biondi, S.J.
Provost: Alice B. Hayes
Founded: 1818, 1820, 1832
C: Arts and Sciences; Philosophy and Letters; Parks.
S: Business and Administration; Nursing; Allied Health Professions; Social Service; Law; Medicine; Public Health.

Salve Regina University

100 Ochre Point Avenue, Newport, Rhode Island 02840-4192
Tel: +1(401) 847-6650
Fax: +1(401) 847-6650 ext. 2990
President: M. Lucille Mckillep, RSU (1994-)
Academic Vice-President: Christopher M. Kiernan
Founded: 1934
Arts and Sciences; Graduate.

Santa Clara University

500 El Camino Real, Santa Clara, California 95053
Tel: +1(408) 554-4764
Fax: +1(408) 554-2700
President: Paul L. Locatelli, S.J.
Academic Vice-President: Stephen A. Privett
Founded: 1851, 1912
C: Arts and Sciences.
S: Engineering; Business and Administration (Leavey); Law.
D: Counselling Psychology and Education.

Saybrook Institute
1550 Sutter Street, San Francisco, California 94109
Tel: +1(415) 441-5034
Fax: +1(415) 441-7556
President: J. Bruce Francis (1991-)
Dean of Students: Don Cooper
Founded: 1971, 1982
Psychology; Human Science.

Seattle University
17th and East Columbia, Seattle, Washington 98122
Tel: +1(206) 296-6000
Fax: +1(206) 296-2163
President: William J. Sullivan
Provost: John D. Eshelman, S.J.
Founded: 1891
C: Arts and Sciences.
S: Business and Economics (Albers); Education; Nursing; Science and Engineering.
I: Theological Studies.

Seton Hall University
400 South Orange Avenue, South Orange, New Jersey 07079-2691
Tel: (201) 761-9000
Fax: (201) 761-9788
Chancellor/President: Thomas R. Peterson, O.P.
Provost: Bernhard W. Scholz
Founded: 1856
C: Arts and Sciences; Education and Human Sciences; Law; Nursing; University (for Adult Students).
S: Business (W. Paul Stillman); Medical Education (Graduate); Theology.

Simmons College
300 The Fenway, Boston, Massachusetts 02115
Tel: +1(617) 738-2000
Fax: +1(617) 738-2099
President: William J. Holmes
Registrar: Donna Dolan
Founded: 1899
C: Arts and Sciences.
S: Management (Graduate); Sciences; Humanities; Social and Professional Sciences; Library Science; Social Work; Health Studies (Graduate).

Smith College
Northampton, Massachusetts 01063
Tel: +1(413) 584-2700
Fax: +1(413) 584-2174
President: Ruth Simmons (1994-)
Registrar: Patricia O'Neil
Founded: 1871
C: Liberal Arts.
S: Social Work.
P: Ada Comstock Scholars (for Women beyond traditional College age).

Southern Methodist University
Dallas, Texas 75275
Tel: +1(214) 678-2000
Fax: +1(214) 678-4138
Telex: 5106017197 smu geo ug
President: A. Kenneth Pye
Vice-President for Business and Finance/ Treasurer: Elizabeth C. Williams
Founded: 1911
S: Human Sciences and Science; Arts (Meadows); Business Administration (Edwin L. Cox); Law; Theology (Perkins); Engineering and Applied Sciences.

Spalding University
851 S. Fourth Street, Louisville, Kentucky 40203
Tel: +1(502) 585-9911
Fax: +1(502) 581-0108
President: Thomas R. Oates (1994-)
Provost: M. Janice Murphy
Founded: 1814
C: Arts and Sciences; Health Sciences; Business; Social Work; Psychology and Social Work.
S: Education; Nursing and Health Sciences; Pastoral Ministry P.

Springfield College
263 Alden Street, Springfield, Massachusetts 01109
Tel: +1(413) 787-3000
Fax: +1(413) 748-3746
President: Randolph W. Bromery
Registrar: D.W. Wuerthele, Jr.
Founded: 1885
S: Human Services.

Stanford University
Stanford, California 94305-2060
Tel: +1(415) 723-2300
President: Gerhard Casper
Provost: Condollezza Rice
Founded: 1885
S: Business (Graduate); Earth Sciences; Education; Engineering; Humanities and Sciences; Law; Medicine.
Ce: Stanford Linear Accelerator.

Stevens Institute of Technology
Castle Point in the Hudson, Hoboken, New Jersey 07030
Tel: +1(201) 216-5000
Fax: +1(201) 216-8341
President: Harold J. Raveche
Vice-President for Business and Finance: Robert Fernandez
Founded: 1870
Sciences and Engineering.

*Syracuse University
Syracuse, N.Y. 13244
Tel: +1(315) 443-1870
Fax: +1(315) 443-1819
Chancellor and President: Kenneth A. Shaw
Registrar: Peter DeBlois
Founded: 1870

S: *Art and Design; Music; Architecture; Computer and Information Science; Citizenship and Public Affairs (Maxwell); Information Studies; Management; Social Work; Education; Sciences and Mathematics.*
C: *Arts and Sciences; Engineering and Computer Science (L.C. Smith); Human Development; Law; Nursing; Visual and Performing Arts; Public Communications (Newhouse).*

Tennessee Temple University
1815 Union Avenue, Chattanooga, Tennessee 37404
Tel: +1(615) 493-4100
Fax: +1(615) 493-4497
President: L.W. Nichols
Vice-President of Academic Affairs: Lexie O.Wiggins
Founded: 1946
Arts and Sciences.

Texas Christian University
2800 South University Drive, Fort Worth, Texas 76129
Tel: +1(817) 921-7000
Fax: +1(817) 921-9333
E-Mail: Easylink 62028475 esl ud
Chancellor: William E. Tucker
Provost: William H. Koehler
Founded: 1873
C: *Arts and Sciences (Addran); Nursing (Harris).*
S: *Business (M.J. Neeley); Education; Fine Arts and Communication; Divinity (Brite).*
I: *Behavioural Research.*

*Thomas Jefferson University
1020 Walnut Street, Philadelphia, Pennsylvania 19107
Tel: +1(215) 955-6000
Fax: +1(215) 923-6690
President: Paul C. Brucker
Dean for Academic Affairs: Joseph S. Gonnella
Founded: 1824, 1969
C: *Biology and Medicine; Allied Health Sciences.*

*Tufts University
Medford, Massachusetts 02155
Tel: +1(617) 628-5000
President: John A. DiBaggio (1992-)
Executive Vice-President: Steven S. Manos
Founded: 1852
C: *Liberal Arts and Sciences; Engineering.*
S: *Arts and Sciences; Law and Diplomacy; Nutrition; Graduate Biomedical Sciences; Medicine; Dental Medicine; Veterinary Medicine; Occupational Therapy.*
Ce: *Lincoln Filene; Environmental Management.*

Tulane University
6823 St. Charles Avenue, New Orleans, Louisiana 70118
Tel: +1(504) 865-5000
President: Eamon M. Kelly
Provost: James F. Kilroy
Founded: 1834
C: *Arts and Sciences.*
S: *Business (Freeman); Engineering; Architecture; Law; Medicine; Public Health and Tropical Medicine; Social Work.*

United States International University
10455 Pomerado Road, San Diego, California 92131-1799
Tel: +1(619) 271-4300
Fax: +1(619) 693-8562
President: Garry D. Hays (1992-)
Registrar: Joyce K. Lunt
Founded: 1952
C: *Arts and Sciences; Business Administration.*
S: *Hotel, Restaurant and Tourism; Human Behaviour; Education.*
I: *Stress Management; Strategic Management.*

United States Sports Academy
One Academy Drive, Daphne, Alabama 36526
Tel: +1(205) 626-1149
Fax: +1(205) 626-3874
President: Thomas Rosandich
Vice-Chancellor: Albert G. Applin
Founded: 1972
C: *Sport Management; Sports Medicine.*
D: *Sport Coaching; Sport Research; Sport Fitness.*

University of Arkansas at Fayetteville
Administration Building, Maple Street, Fayetteville, Arkansas 72701
Tel: +1(501) 575-2000
Fax: +1(501) 575-7575
Chancellor: Daniel E. Ferritor
Vice-Chancellor for Academic Affairs: Donald O. Pederson
Founded 1971
C: *Arts and Sciences (J. William Fullbright); Agriculture and Home Economics; Business Administration; Education; Engineering.*
S: *Architecture; Law.*

University of Bridgeport
126 Park Avenue, Bridgeport, Connecticut 06601
Tel: +1(203) 576-4000
Fax: +1(203) 576-4653
E-Mail: email: admit@cse.bridgeport.edu
President: Edwin Eigel, Jr.
Vice-President for Academic Affairs: G. Lansing Blackshaw
Founded: 1927
C: *Arts and Sciences; Business; Engineering; Professional Studies; Chiropractic.*

University of Chicago

5801 South Ellis Avenue, Chicago, Illinois 60637
Tel: +1(312) 702-1234
Fax: +1(312) 702-0934
President: Hugo F. Sonnensche (1993-)
Registrar: Maxine H. Sullivan
Founded: 1857
Div: *Biological Sciences; Humanities; Physical Sciences; Social Sciences.*
S: *Business; Divinity; Law; Medicine; Social Service Administration.*

University of Dallas

1845 East Northgate Drive, Irving, Texas 75062-4799
Tel: +1(214) 721-5000
Fax: +1(214) 721-5017
President: Robert F. Sasseen
Vice-President for Administration: George H. Herbst
Founded: 1955
C: *Liberal Arts (Graduate).*
S: *Management (Graduate).*
P: *Liberal Arts Program (Braniff).*

University of Dayton

300 College Park Avenue, Dayton, Ohio 45469
Tel: +1(513) 229-1000
Fax: +1(513) 229-4000
Telex: 411262805649
President: Raymond L. Fitz, S.M. (1979-)
Senior Vice-President for Administration: Bernard J. Ploeger, S.M.
Founded: 1850
C: *Arts and Sciences.*
S: *Business Administration; Education; Engineering; Law.*
I: *Research.*

University of Denver

2199 South University Boulevard, Denver, Colorado 80208-0132
Tel: +1(303) 871-2000
Fax: +1(303) 871-4000
Chancellor: Daniel L. Ritchie
Provost: William Zaranka
F: *Arts and Humanities; Social Sciences; Natural Sciences, Mathematics, and Engineering.*
S: *International Studies (Graduate); Social Work (Graduate); Music (Lamont); Accountancy; Art; Hospitality Management and Tourism; Professional.*
C: *Business Administration; Law.*

University of Detroit Mercy

4001 West McNichols, Detroit, Michigan 48221
Tel: +1(313) 993-1000
Fax: +1(313) 993-1011
President: Maureen A. Fay, O.P.
Registrar: Gerald Cavanagh, S.J.
Founded: 1877, 1911
C: *Liberal Arts; Health Sciences; Engineering and Science; Architecture; Education and Human Services; Business Administration.*

S: *Law; Dentistry; Nursing.*
I: *Development and Transfer of Technology.*

*University of Hartford

200 Bloomfield Avenue, West Hartford, Connecticut 06117
Tel: +1(203) 768-4100
Fax: +1(203) 768-4070
Telex: 9102505313 u of h ug
President: Humphrey Tonkin
Senior Vice-President for Academic Affairs: Jonathan Lawson
Founded: 1877, 1957
C: *Arts and Sciences; Basic Studies; Education, Nursing and Health Professions; Engineering; Technology (Ward); Women (Ward C.).*
S: *Hartford Art; Business and Public Administration (Barney); Health Professions.*
I: *Social Research.*
Ce: *Engineering Applications.*

University of Health Sciences-The Chicago Medical School

3333 Green Bay Road, North Chicago, Illinois 60064
Tel: +1(708) 578-3000
Fax: +1(708) 578-3401
President: Herman M. Finch
Registrar: Linda Norstrom
Medicine; Health Sciences; Graduate Postdoctoral Studies.

University of La Verne

1950 Third Street, La Verne, California 91750
Tel: +1(909) 593-3511
Fax: +1(909) 593-0965
President: Stephen C. Morgan
Vice-President for Academic Affairs: William A. Cook
Founded: 1891, 1977
C: *Arts and Sciences; Law; S; Organizational Leadership; Business and Economics.*

University of Miami

Carol Gables, Florida 33124
Tel: +1(305) 284-2211
President: Edward T. Foote II
Provost: Luis Glaser
C: *Arts and Sciences; Engineering.*
S: *Business Administration; Education; Architecture; Law; Medicine; Music; Nursing; Continuing Studies; Marine and Atmospheric Sciences (S. Rosenstial); International Studies (Graduate); Communication.*

University of New England

11 Hillsbeach Road, Biddeford, Maine 04005-9526
Tel: +1(207) 283-0171
Fax: +1(207) 282-6379
President: Thomas Hedles Reynolds
Founded: 1939
C: *Arts and Sciences; Osteopathic Medicine; Social Work.*

University of New Haven

300 Orange Avenue, West Haven, Connecticut
06516
Tel: +1(203) 932-7000
President: Lawrence J. DeNardis (1991-)
Provost: James W. Vebelacker
Founded: 1920
S: Arts and Sciences; Business; Engineering; Hotel, Restaurant and Tourism Administration; Public Safety and Professional Studies.

*University of Notre Dame

Notre Dame, Indiana 46556
Tel: +1(219) 631-5000
Fax: +1(219) 631-6252
President: Edward A. Malloy, C.S.C.
Executive Vice-President: E. William Beauchamp, C.S.C.
Founded: 1842
C: Arts and Letters; Business Administration; Engineering; Science; Architecture.
S: Law.
Ce: Environmental Research.

University of the Pacific

3601 Pacific Avenue, Stockton, California 95211
Tel: +1(209) 946-2011
Fax: +1(209) 946-2652
President: Bill L. Atchley
Academic Vice-President: Jeo Subbiondo
Founded: 1851
C: Business and Public Administration; Education; Engineering; International Studies; Liberal Arts; Music; Pharmacy.
S: Dentistry; Law (McGeorge).

*University of Pennsylvania

34th and Spruce Street, Philadelphia,
Pennsylvania 19104
Tel: +1(215) 898-5000
Fax: +1(215) 898-5756
Telex: twx 7106700328 u of pa pha
President: Claire Fagin (1993-)
Executive Vice-President: Janet Hale
Founded: 1740
S: Arts and Sciences; Education; Communication; Dentistry; Law; Fine Arts; Business; Engineering and Applied Science; Nursing; Social Work; Veterinary Medicine; Medicine.
I: Diplomacy and Foreign Affairs (Anspach); Research in Cognitive Science; Management and International Studies (Lauder); Plant Science.
Ce: International Health and Development Communication; Analytic Research in Economics and Social Science (CARESS); Cultural Studies; Economic Studies in Technology; Family and Household Economics; Italian Studies; Middle East; Population Studies; Russian and East European Studies; Study of Black Literature and Culture; Study of Organizational Innovations; Artificial Intelligence.

University of Rochester

Rochester, N.Y. 14627-0001
Tel: +1(716) 275-2121
Fax: +1(716) 275-0359
President: G. Dennis O'Brien (1993-)
Provost: Brian J. Thompson
Founded: 1850
C: Art and Sciences; Engineering and Applied Science.
S: Medicine and Dentistry; Music (Eastman); Nursing; Management (Graduate); Education and Human Development (Graduate); Business Administration (William E. Simon Graduate).

University of St. Thomas

3800 Montrose Boulevard, Houston, Texas 77006
Tel: +1(713) 522-7911
Fax: +1(713) 525-2161
Chancellor: Joseph M. McFadden
Executive Vice-Chancellor for Academic Affairs:
Lee J. Williams
Founded: 1947
S: Arts and Sciences; Nursing; Business; Education; International Studies.

University of St. Thomas

2115 Summit Avenue, St. Paul, Minnesota 55105
Tel: +1(612) 962-5000
Fax: +1(612) 962-6360
President: Dennis Dease
Provost: Charles Keffer
Founded: 1885, 1894, 1991
C: Day; New.
S: Education, Professional Psychology and Social Work (Graduate); Technology (Graduate); Business (Graduate); Divinity; Arts and Sciences (Graduate).

University of San Diego

Alcala Park, San Diego, California 92110-2492
Tel: +1(619) 260-4600
Fax: +1(619) 260-4697
President: Author E. Hughes
Provost: Sister Sally Furay
Founded: 1949
C: Arts and Sciences.
S: Business Administration; Education; Nursing; Law.

*University of San Francisco

2130 Fulton Street, Ignatian Heights, San
Francisco, California 94117-1080
Tel: +1(415) 666-6886
Fax: +1(415) 386-1074
Telex: 9103722298 usfenroll
President: John P. Shlegel, S.J.
Provost and Academic Vice-President: John W.
Clark, S.J.
Founded: 1855
C: Arts and Sciences; Business Administration; Professional Studies.
S: Nursing; Law; Education.
I: Chinese-Western Cultural History (Ricci).
Ce: Pacific Rim Studies.

University of the South

735 University Avenue, Sewanee, Tennessee
37375-1000
Tel: +1(615) 598-1000
Fax: +1(615) 598-1145
Vice-Chancellor and President: Samuel Ruthven
Williamson
Provost: Frederick Hailey Croom
Founded: 1857
F: *Arts and Sciences.*
Graduate S: *Theology.*

University of Southern California

University Park, Los Angeles, California 90089
Tel: +1(213) 740-2311
Fax: +1(213) 740-7254
E-Mail: internet, bitnet, nsfnet
Telex: 4720490 usc lsa
President: Steven B. Sample (1991-)
Registrar: Kenneth L. Servis
Founded: 1956
C: *Letters, Arts and Sciences.*
Div: *Humanities; Natural Science and Mathematics; Social Sciences and Communication.*
S: *Architecture; Accounting; Business Administration; Cinema-Television; Communication (Annenberg); Dentistry; Education; Engineering; Fine Arts; Gerontology (Leonard Davis); Medicine; Music; Pharmacy; Public Administration; Social Work; Theatre; Urban and Regional Planning.*
I: *Safety and Systems Management; Information Sciences I.; Signal and Image Processing; Loker Hydrocarbon Research; Gerontology Research; Social Sciences Research; Politics (Jesse M. Unruh); Public-Private Partnership.*
Ce: *Law; Laser Studies; Applied Mathematical Sciences; Earth Sciences; Andrus Older Adult; Multilingual, Multicultural Research.*

University of Tulsa

600 South College Avenue, Tulsa, Oklahoma
74104-3189
Tel: +1(918) 631-2000
Fax: +1(918) 631-2033
President: Robert H. Donaldson
Provost: George H. Gilpin, Jr.
Founded: 1984, 1980
C: *Arts and Sciences (Henry Kendall); Business Administration; Engineering and Applied Sciences; Law; Nursing; Continuing Education.*

Vanderbilt University

2309 West End Avenue, Nashville, Tennessee
37240
Tel: +1(615) 322-7311
Fax: +1(615) 343-5555
Chancellor: Joe B. Wyatt
Provost (Acting): Thomas Burish
Founded: 1873
C: *Arts and Sciences; Education and Human Development (Peabody).*

S: *Music (Blair); Divinity; Engineering; Law; Management (Owen Graduate); Medicine; Nursing.*
I: *Public Policy Studies.*
Ce: *Research on Education and Human Development (John F. Kennedy); Free Electron Lazer; Humanities (Robert Penn Warren); Arthritis and Lupus; Cancer; Clinical and Research Ethics; Clinical Research; Diabetes Research and Training; Molecular Toxicology; Nephrology; Pharmacology and Drug Toxicology; Reproductive Biology Research; Molecular and Atomic Studies at Surfaces; Biomedical Engineering and Computing; Intelligent Systems; Materials Tribology; Microgravity Research and Applications; Transportation Systems.*

Villanova University

Lancaster Pike, Villanova, Pennsylvania 19085
Tel: +1(215) 645-4500
Fax: +1(215) 645-4500 ext. 7599
President: Edmund J. Dobbin
Vice-President for Academic Affairs: Lawrence
Gallen, O.S.A.
Founded: 1842
C: *Engineering; Liberal Arts and Sciences; Commerce and Finance; Nursing; Law.*

Wake Forest University

Box 7205, Reynolds Station, Winston-Salem,
North Carolina 27109
Tel: +1(919) 759-5000
Fax: +1(919) 759-6074
President: Thomas K. Hearn, Jr. (1983-)
Vice-President for Administration and Planning:
John P. Anderson
Founded: 1834, 1967
C: *Arts and Sciences.*
S: *Business and Accountancy; Law; Management (Babcock Graduate); Arts and Sciences (Graduate); Medicine (Bowman Gray).*

Washington University

One Brookings Drive, St. Louis, Missouri 63130
Tel: (314) 935-5000
Fax: (314) 935-4290
Chancellor: William H. Danforth (1971-)
Provost: Edward S. Macias
Founded: 1853
C: *Arts and Sciences; Engineering and Applied Sciences; Business and Public Administration (John M. Olin); Architecture; Fine Arts; Law (Graduate).*
S: *Social Work (George Warren Brown); Medicine.*
Div: *Cell Biology and Physiology.*
Ce: *Study of American Business; Air Pollution Impact and Trend Analysis; Studies of Higher Brain Function (McDonnell); Study of History of Freedom; Cellular and Molecular Neurobiology (McDonnell).*
I: *Biomedical Computing; Technology (Sever).*

Wesleyan University

Middletown, Connecticut 06459-0290
Tel: +1(203) 347-9411
Fax: +1(203) 344-7957
E-Mail: bitnet, internet
President: William M. Chase
Vice-President for Academic Affairs: Joanne V. Creighton
Founded: 1831
C: Arts and Sciences.
Ce: Afro-American Studies; Arts; Humanities.

Widener University

One University Place, Chester, Pennsylvania 19013-5792
Tel: +1(215) 499-4000
Fax: +1(215) 876-9751
President: Robert J. Bruce
Provost: Lawrence P. Buck
Founded: 1821
C: Arts and Sciences.
S: Engineering; Hotel and Restaurant Management; Management; Nursing; Law.
I: Graduate Clinical Psychology.
Ce: Social Work Education; Education.

Willamette University

900 State Street, Salem, Oregon 97301
Tel: +1(503) 370-6300
Fax: +1(503) 370-6148
E-Mail: @willamette.edu
President: Jerry E. Hudson (1980-)
Registrar: Paul J. Olsen
C: Liberal Arts; Law.
S: Management (Atkinson Graduate).

Worcester Polytechnic Institute

100 Institute Road, Worcester, Massachusetts 01609
Tel: +1(508) 831-5000
Fax: +1(508) 831-5753
President: Jon C. Strauss
Provost: Diran Apelian
Engineering and Sciences.

Wright Institute

2728 Durant Avenue, Berkeley, California 94704
Tel: +1(510) 841-9230
President: Peter Dybwad
Dean: Andrea Morrison
Founded: 1969
Psychology.

Yale University

New Haven, Connecticut 06520
Tel: +1(203) 432-1900
President: Richard C. Levin
Provost: Judith Rodin
Founded: 1701, 1887
C (Yale): Arts and Sciences.
S: Medicine; Divinity; Law; Art; Music; Forestry and Environmental Studies; Architecture; Nursing; Drama; Organization and Management; Arts and Sciences.

Yeshiva University

500 West 185th Street, New York, N.Y. 10033-3299
Tel: +1(212) 960-5400
Fax: +1(212) 960-0055
Telex: 220883
President: Norman Lamm
Senior Vice-President: Israel Miller
Founded: 1886
C: Yeshiva (for Men); Psychology (Ferkauf Graduate); Hebraic Studies (Isaac Breuer); For Women (Stern); Business (Sy Syms); Higher Jewish Studies (Harry Fischel); Law (Benjamin N. Cardozo); Medicine (Albert Einstein); Social Work (Wurzweiler).
I: Jewish Education and Administration (David J. Azrieli Graduate).
Div: Biological Sciences; Medical Sciences (Sue Golding Graduate).

UNIVERSITIES AND COLLEGES WITH GRADUATE SCHOOLS

PUBLIC INSTITUTIONS

Adams State University

208 Edgemont Boulevard, Alamosa, Colorado 81102
Tel: +1(719) 589-7011
Fax: +1(719) 589-7522
President: William M. Fulkerson
Vice-President for Academic Affairs: Gary G. Peer
Founded: 1921, 1945
S: Arts and letters; Business; Education and Behavioural Science; Science, Mathematics, and Technology.

Alabama Agricultural and Mechanical University

4107 Meridian Street, P.O. Box 1347, Normal, Alabama 35672-0785
Tel: +1(205) 851-5244
Fax: +1(205) 851-9747
President: David B. Henson
Vice-President for Academic Affairs: Virginia Caples
Founded: 1875, 1969
S: Agriculture and Home Economics; Arts; Business; Education; Engineering and Technology.

Alabama State University

915 Jackson Street, Montgomery, Alabama 3610-0271
Tel: +1(205) 293-4100
Fax: +1(205) 269-2107
President: C.C. Baker (1994-)
Vice-President for Academic Affairs: Roosevelt Steptoe
Founded: 1874, 1929, 1969

C: Education; Business Administration; Arts and Sciences.
S: Music.

Albany State College
504 College Drive, Albany, Georgia 31705
Tel: +1(912) 430-4600
President: Billy C. Black
Vice-President for Academic Affairs: Ernest Benson
Founded: 1903, 1917, 1943
S: Arts and Sciences; Business; Education; Nursing and Allied Health.

Alcorn State University
Lorman, Mississippi 39096
Tel: +1(601) 877-6100
Fax: +1(601) 877-2975
President: Walter Washington
Vice-President: Rudolph E. Waters
Founded: 1871, 1974
Div: Arts and Sciences; Business; Education; Agriculture; Nursing.

Angelo State University
2601 West Avenue, North, San Angelo, Texas 76909
Tel: +1(915) 942-2041
Fax: +1(915) 942-2038
President: Lloyd D. Vincent
Vice-President for Academic Affairs: Bernard T. Young
Founded: 1928, 1965, 1969
C: Liberal and Fine Arts; Professional Studies; Sciences.

Appalachian State University
Boone, North Carolina 28608
Tel: (704) 262-2000
Fax: (704) 262-2511
Telex: 888370 app state univ
Chancellor: John E. Thomas
Registrar: Brooks McLeod
Founded: 1899
C: Arts and Sciences; Fine and Applied Arts; Education; Business; Music.

Arkansas State University
P.O. Box 2910, State University, Arkansas 72467
Tel: +1(501) 972-2100
Fax: +1(501) 972-3818
E-Mail: quapaw.astate.edu
President: John Mangieri
Vice-President for Academic Affairs: Robert Hoskins
Founded: 1909, 1967
S: Arts and Sciences; Business; Education; Fine Arts; Communication; Nursing and Health Professions; Agriculture.

Arkansas Tech University
Russellville, Arkansas 72801-2222
Tel: +1(501) 968-0389
Fax: +1(501) 968-0883
President: Robert C. Brown
Registrar: Ronald D. Harrell
Founded: 1909, 1925, 1976
C: Education; Systems Sciences; Physical Sciences.
S: Business; Liberal and Fine Arts.

Armstrong State College
11935 Abercorn Street, Savannah, Georgia 31419-1997
Tel: +1(912) 927-5211
Fax: +1(912) 927-5209
President: Robert A. Burnett
Vice-President: Frank A. Butler
Founded: 1935, 1964
C: Arts, Sciences, and Education; Communication Studies; Health Sciences.
S: Allied Health Professions.

Arthur D. Little Management Education Institute
35 Acorn Park, Cambridge, Massachusetts 02140-2390
Tel: +1(617) 498-4200
Fax: +1(617) 498-7100
President: Alfred E. Wechsler
Admissions Director/Registrar: Judith H. Feancis
Founded: 1972
Business and Management.

Auburn University at Montgomery
7300 University Drive, Montgomery, Alabama 36117-3596
Tel: +1(205) 244-3000
Fax: +1(205) 244-3762
Chancellor: James O. Williams (1980-)
Assistant to the Chancellor: Joe L. Boyer
Founded: 1967
S: Liberal Arts; Business; Education; Sciences; Nursing.

Augusta College
2500 Walton Way, Augusta, Georgia 30904-2200
Tel: +1(706) 737-1400
Fax: +1(706) 737-1774
President: Martha Farmer
Vice-President for Academic Affairs: Bill E. Bompart
Founded: 1925, 1958
S: Arts, Sciences, and Education; Business; Education.

Austin Peay State University
601 College Street, Clarksville, Tennessee 37044
Tel: +1(615) 648-7011
Fax: +1(615) 648-7475
President: Oscar Page
Vice-President for Academic Affairs
Founded: 1927, 1967

C: Arts and Sciences; Business; Education and Human Service.
Ce: Fort Campbell.

Bemidji State University
1500 Birchmount Drive N.E., Bemidji, Minnesota 56601
Tel: +1(218) 755-2000
Fax: +1(218) 755-4048
President: Linda Baer (1994-)
Registrar: David Carlson
Founded: 1919
C: Arts and Letters; Professional Studies; Social and Natural Sciences.

Black Hills State University
1200 University Avenue, Spearfish, South Dakota 57799-9502
Tel: +1(605) 642-6011
Fax: +1(605) 642-6090
President: Clifford M. Trump
Vice-President for Academic Affairs: Larry M. Landis
Founded: 1881, 1885, 1989
C: Arts and Humanities; Education and Human Resources Development; Business and Public Affairs; Applied Science and Technology.
Ce: Advancement and Study of Tourism; Business and Entrepreneurship; American Indian Studies.

Bloomsburg University of Pennsylvania
Bloomsburg, Pennsylvania 17815
Tel: +1(717) 389-4000
Fax: +1(717) 389-3700
President: Jessica Sledge Kozloff (1994-)
Provost: Betty Allamong
C: Arts and Sciences; Business; Professional Studies.
S: Education.

Boise State University
1910 University Drive, oise, Idaho 83725
Tel: +1(208) 385-1156
Fax: +1(208) 385-3779
President: Charles Ruch
Founded: 1932, 1974
C: Arts and Sciences; Business; Education; Health Sciences.
S: Social Sciences and Public Affairs; Vocational/Technical Education.

Bowie State University
14000 Jericho Park Road, Bowie, Maryland 20715
Tel: +1(301) 464-7814
Fax: +1(301) 464-9350
President: Nathanael Pollard, Jr.
Provost: John Dill
Founded: 1865, 1963, 1989
Div: Behavioural Sciences and Human Services; Business, Economics, and Public Administration; Communications; Education and Physical Education; History, Politics and International Studies; Humanities and Fine Arts; Natural Sciences, Mathematics and Computer Science; Nursing.

Bridgewater State College
Bridgewater, Massachusetts 02325-0001
Tel: +1(508) 697-1200
Fax: +1(508) 697-1707
President: Adrian Tinsley (1989-)
Registrar: Dennis Bicknell
Founded: 1840, 1968
S: Arts and Sciences; Education; Graduate.
Ce: Applied Research in Teaching (CART).

California Polytechnic State University-San Luis Obispo, California State University
San Luis Obispo, California 93407
Tel: +1(805) 756-1111
Fax: +1(805) 756-5292
President: Warren J. Baker
Vice-President for Academic Affairs: Robert Koob
Founded: 1901
C: Liberal Arts; Agriculture; Business; Science and Mathematics; Architecture and Environmental Design; Engineering.
S: Teacher Education.
Ce: Practical Politics.

California State Polytechnic University-Pomona
3801 West Temple Avenue, Pomona, California 91768-4109
Tel: +1(909) 869-7659
Fax: +1(909) 869-2292
President: Bob H. Suzuki (1991-93)
Registrar: Patricia A. Kurisko
Founded: 1938
C: Agriculture; Arts; Business Administration; Engineering; Environmental Design; Sciences.
S: Education; Hotel and Restaurant Management.
Ce: Continuing Education (Kellogg West).

California State University-Bakersfield
9001 Stockdale Highway, Bakersfield, California 93311-1099
Tel: +1(805) 664-2011
Fax: +1(805) 664-3188
President: Thomas A. Arciniega
Academic Vice-President: Fred Dorer
Founded: 1965
S: Arts and Sciences; Business and Public Administration; Education.

California State University-Chico
Chico, California 95929-0720
Tel: +1(916) 898-6324
Fax: +1(916) 898-6116
President: Manuel A. Esteban (1993-)
Provost: William Stephens
Founded: 1889
C: Agriculture and Human Environmental Sciences; Business; Communication; Education; Engineering, Computer Science and Technology; Humanities and Fine Arts; Natural Sciences; Behavioural and Social Studies.
I: Liberal and Interdisciplinary Studies.
Ce: International Studies.

California State University-Dominguez Hill

1000 East Victoria Street, Carson, California
90747
Tel: +1(310) 516-3300
Fax: +1(310) 516-3449
President: Robert C. Detweiler
Executive Vice-President: Amer El-Ahraf
Founded: 1960, 1977
*C: Humanities and Fine Arts; Science,
Mathematics and Technology; Social and
Behavioural Sciences; Education; Management.*

California State University-Fresno

5241 N. Maple, Fresno, California 93740-0048
Tel: (209) 278-4240
Fax: (209) 278-4715
E-Mail: Easylink: 62025757 esl ud
Telex: 5106001919 csuf ag
President: John D. Welty
Director, Admissions, Records and Evaluations:
Richard Backer
*S: Social Sciences; Arts and Humanities;
Natural Sciences; Education and Human
Development; Agriculture Sciences; Business;
Engineering; Health and Social Work.*
C: Education; Humanities.

California State University-Fullerton

P.O. Box 34080, Fullerton, California 92634
Tel: +1(714) 773-2011
Fax: +1(714) 773-2649
President: Milton A. Gordon (1990-)
Director of Administration and Records: James
Blackburn
Founded: 1957, 1960, 1972
*S: Arts; Business Administration and
Economics; Communications; Engineering and
Computer Science; Human Development and
Community Service; Humanities and Social
Sciences; Natural Science and Mathematics.*
Ce: Desert Studies.

California State University-Hayward

25800 Carlos Bee Boulevard, Hayward, California
94542-3074
Tel: +1(510) 881-3000
Fax: +1(510) 881-7484
President: Norma S. Rees (1990-)
Provost: Frank Martino
Founded: 1959, 1972
*C: Arts, Letters and Social Sciences; Business
and Economics; Education; Science.*

California State University-Long Beach

1250 Bellflower Boulevard, Long Beach,
California 90840-0119
Tel: +1(310) 985-4111
Fax: +1(310) 985-5584
President: Karl W.E. Anatol (1994-)
ProvostRegistrar: Karl Anatol: Nova Mclaughlin
Founded: 1949
*C: Health and Human Services; Education;
Engineering; Arts; Humanities and Social and
Behavioural Sciences; Natural Sciences.*

S: Business Administration.
*I: American Language; Science and
Mathematical Education; Parasitology.*
*Ce: Brain Hemisphere Research Ce.; Criminal
Justice Research and Training; Career Studies;
Educational Research and Services; International
Education.*

California State University-Northridge

18111 Nordhoff Street, Northridge, California
91330
Tel: +1(818) 885-1200
Fax: +1(818) 885-4545
President: Blenda J.Wilson
Vice-President for Academic Affairs: Donald
Bianchi
Founded: 1956, 1972
*S: Arts; Business Administration and
Economics; Communication, Health and Home
Service; Education; Engineering and Computer
Science; Humanities; Science and Mathematics;
Social and Behavioural Sciences.*

*California State University-Sacramento

6000 J. Street, Sacramento, California 95819-6048
Tel: +1(916) 278-6011
Fax: +1(916) 278-6664
E-Mail: dongerth@csus.edu
President: Donald R. Gerth
Vice-President for Academic Affairs: Jolen
Koester
Founded: 1947
*S: Arts and Sciences; Business Administration;
Education; Engineering and Computer Science;
Health and Human Services.*
I: Real Estate and Land Use.
*Ce: Economic Education; Social Research;
Management Services; Assistive Device;
California Studies.*
Bureau: Business Service.

California State University-San Bernardino

5500 University Parkway, San Bernardino,
California 92407-2397
Tel: +1(909) 880-5000
Fax: +1(909) 880-5903
President: Anthony H. Evans (1982-)
Vice-President for Academic Affairs: Dennis L.
Hefner
Founded: 1960, 1984
*S: Business and Public Administration;
Education; Humanities; Natural Sciences; Social
and Behavioural Sciences.*
*I: Applied Research and Policy Analysis;
Science Education.*

California State University-San Marcos

San Marcos, California 92096
Tel: +1(619) 752-4000
Fax: +1(619) 752-4030
President: Bill W. Stacy
Executive Vice-President: Richard R. Rush
Founded: 1990

California State University-Stanislaus

800 West Monte Vista Avenue, Turlock, California 95380
Tel: +1(209) 667-3122
Fax: +1(209) 667-3333
President: Marvalene Hughes (1994-)
Provost: Horace A. Judson
Founded: 1957, 1985
C: *Arts, Letters, and Sciences; Business.*
S: *Education.*

California University of Pennsylvania

Third Street, California, Pennsylvania 15419-1394
Tel: +1(412) 938-4000
President: John P. Watkins
Vice-President for Academic Affairs: Nancy Z. Nelson
Founded: 1852, 1865, 1983
S: *Liberal Arts; Education; Science and Technology.*

Castleton State College

Castleton, Vermont 05735
Tel: +1(802) 468-5611
Fax: +1(802) 468-5237
President: Martha K. Farmer (1994-)
Registrar: Patrick Hampton
Founded: 1787, 1867, 1962
Arts and Sciences.

Central Connecticut State University

1615 Stanley Street, New Britain, Connecticut 06050-4010
Tel: +1(203) 827-7000
Fax: +1(203) 827-7200
E-Mail: Internet
Telex: 9102505958
President: John W. Shumaker
Vice-President for Finance and Administration: Stephen O. Mitchell
Founded: 1849, 1959, 1983
S: *Arts and Sciences; Business; Technology; Education and Professional Studies.*
I: *Business Studies; European and American Studies; Asian and American Studies.*

Central Missouri State University

Office of Admissions, Warrensburg, Missouri 64093
Tel: +1(816) 543-4111
Fax: +1(816) 747-7813
President: Ed Elliott (1985-)
Provost: William Bloodworth
Founded: 1870, 1919, 1972
C: *Arts and Sciences; Applied Science and Technology; Business and Economics; Education and Human Services; Library Services.*
Ce: *Business and Economics Research; Family Studies; Technology and Small Business Development; English Language.*
I: *Gerontology; Small Business.*

Central Washington University

Ellensburg, Washington 98926
Tel: +1(509) 963-1111
Fax: +1(509) 963-1241
President: Ivory V. Nelson
Provost: Donald Schliesman
Founded: 1980, 1977
C: *Letters, Arts and Sciences.*
S: *Business and Economics; Professional Studies.*

Chadron State College

Tenth and Main, Chadron, Nebraska 69337
Tel: +1(308) 432-4451
Fax: +1(308) 432-6464
E-Mail: Easylink 62009587 esl ud
President: Samuel H. Rankin
Provost (Acting): Merlyn Gramberg
Founded: 1911, 1964
S: *Liberal Arts; Education and Physical Education; Natural Sciences and Mathematics; Business and Applied Science.*

Cheyney University of Pennsylvania

Cheyney and Creek Roads, Cheyney, Pennsylvania 19319
Tel: +1(215) 399-2000
Fax: +1(215) 548-7056
President: Douglas Covington
Vice-President for Academic Affairs: Eugene Roystere
Founded: 1837, 1921, 1959, 1982
Business Administration, Education and Professional Services, Educational Administration, English, Guidance and Counselling, Health/Physical Education/ Recreation, Humanities, Mathematics/Computer Science, Science/Allied Health, Social and Behavioural Sciences, Technology and Engineering.

Chicago State University

95th and King Drive, Chicago, Illinois 60628
Tel: +1(312) 995-2000
Fax: +1(312) 995-3762
President: Dolores E. Cross (1990-)
Provost: Chernoh Sesay
Founded: 1867
C: *Arts and Sciences; Business; Nursing and Allied Health Professionals; Education; Allied Health.*

City University of New York Baruch College

17 Lexington Avenue, New York, N.Y. 10010
Tel: +1(212) 447-3000
Fax: +1(212) 387-1090
President: Mathew Goldstein
Provost for Academic Affairs: Lois Cronholm
Founded: 1919
S: *Liberal Arts and Sciences; Business; Education.*

City University of New York-City College
138th Street and Convent Avenue, New York, N.Y. 10031
Tel: +1(212) 650-7000
Fax: +1(212) 650-7340
President (Acting): Augusta Sousa Kappner
Executive Vice-President: Donald Jordan
Founded: 1847, 1961
S: Education; Engineering; Architecture; Social Sciences; Sciences; Nursing; Biomedical Education (Sophie Davis).
Div: Arts (Leonard Davis Center); Humanities.

City University of New York-Hunter College
695 Park Avenue, New York, N.Y. 10021
Tel: +1(212) 772-4000
Fax: +1(212) 772-4554
President: Paul LeClerc
Provost: Laura Strauminglier
Founded: 1870, 1961
Div: Education; Humanities and Arts; Sciences and Mathematics; Social Sciences.
S: Nursing; Health Sciences.

City University of New York-John Jay College of Criminal Justice
445 West 59th Street, New York, N.Y. 10019
Tel: +1(212) 237-8000
Fax: +1(212) 237-8901
President: Gerald Lynch
Provost/Academic Vice-President: Brasil Wilson
Founded: 1964, 1966
F: Liberal Arts; Professional Studies.

City University of New York-Lehman College
250 Bedford Park Boulevard West, Bronx, New York, N.Y. 10468-1589
Tel: +1(718) 960-8000
Fax: +1(718) 584-1765
President: Ricardo R. Fernandez
Provost: Rosanne Willie
Founded: 1931, 1968
Div: Arts and Humanities; Natural and Social Sciences; Professional Studies; Nursing.

City University of New York-Queens College
65-30 Kissena Boulevard, Flushing, N.Y. 11367-1597
Tel: +1(718) 997-5000
Fax: +1(718) 793-8044
President: Shirley Strum Kenny (1985-)
Vice-President of Administration: Donald Meyer
Founded: 1937
S: Arts and Humanities; Mathematics and Natural Science; Education; Social Sciences; Asian American Ce.; Music (Aaron Copland); Library and Information Studies (Graduate).
Ce: Biology of Natural Systems; Improvement of Education; Jewish Studies; Labour and Urban Ps. Research and Analysis; New American Workforce; Environmental Teaching and Research.

Clarion University of Pennsylvania
Clarion, Pennsylvania 16214
Tel: +1(814) 226-2000
Fax: +1(814) 226-1826
President: Diane L. Reinhard
Founded: 1867, 1887, 1983
Arts and Sciences; Business Administration; Communication, Computer Information Sciences and Library Science; Nursing.

College of Charleston
66 George Street, Charleston, South Carolina 29424
Tel: +1(803) 792-5500
Fax: +1(803) 792-5505
President: Alexander M. Sanders Jr.
Provost: Convad Festa
Founded: 1770, 1970
I: Public Affairs and Policy Studies.

The College of Staten Island of the City of New York
130 Stuyvesant Place, Staten Island, New York, N.Y. 10314-6600
Tel: +1(718) 982-2000
Fax: +1(718) 982-2404
President: Edmond L. Volpe
Provost: Felix Cardegna
Founded: 1976
Div: Humanities and Social Sciences; Science and Technology.
Ce: Developmental Neuroscience and Developmental Disabilities; Environmental Science; Immigrant and Population Studies.

Columbus College
3600 Algonquin Drive, Columbus, Georgia 3190-2079
Tel: +1(706) 568-2001
Fax: +1(706) 568-2123
President: Frank D. Brown (1988-)
Assistant to the President for Institutional Advancement: Lon Marlow
Founded: 1958
S: Arts and Letters; Business; Education; Science.

Coppin State College, University of Maryland
2500 West North Avenue, Baltimore, Maryland 21216-3698
Tel: +1(401) 383-5535
Fax: +1(401) 333-5369
President: Calvin W. Burnett
Vice-President for Academic Affairs: Sidney Krorne
Founded: 1900, 1930, 1967
Div: Nursing; arts and Sciences; Continuing Education; Education.

Corpus Christi State University
6300 Ocean Drive, Corpus Christi, Texas 78412
Tel: +1(512) 991-6810
Fax: +1(512) 993-4204
President: Robert R. Furgason
Provost: Tito Guerrero III
Founded: 1973
*C: Arts and Humanities; Business
Administration; Education; Sciences and
Technology.*
S: National Oil Spill Control.
I: Surveying and Sciences (Blucher).

Delaware State College
1200 North DuPont Highway, Dover, Delaware
19901
Tel: +1(302) 739-4924
Fax: +1(302) 739-2856
President: William B. Delauder
Vice-President for Academic Affair: Henry Tisdale
Founded: 1891, 1892
Arts and Sciences.

Delta State University
Cleveland, Mississippi 38733
Tel: +1(601) 846-3000
Fax: +1(601) 846-4016
President: Forest Kent Wyatt (1975-)
Registrar: James Donald Cooper
Founded: 1924, 1974
*S: Arts and Sciences; Business; Education;
Nursing.*

East Central University
Ada, Oklahoma 74820
Tel: +1(405) 332-8000
Fax: +1(405) 521-6516
President: Bill S. Cole
Registrar: Palma Armstrong
Founded: 1909, 1985
*Div: Arts and Letters; Health, Physical
Education and Recreation; Social Sciences.*
*S: Business; Education and Psychology;
Mathematics and Sciences.*

East Stroudsburg University
East Stroudsburg, Pennsylvania 18301-2999
Tel: +1(717) 424-3211
Fax: +1(717) 424-3478
President: James E. Gilbert
Registrar: Elizabeth Buzzelli
Founded: 1893, 1926, 1982
*S: Arts, Sciences, and Education; Health
Sciences and Physical Education; Professional
Studies.*

East Texas State University at Texarkana
2600 North Robison Road, Texarkana, Texas
75505-0518
Tel: +1(903) 838-6514
Fax: +1(903) 832-8890
President: John F. Moss
Registrar: Pat Black
Founded: 1971
*Div: Arts and Sciences; Teaching Professions;
Business Administration.*

Eastern Connecticut State University
83 Windham Street, Connecticut 06226
Tel: +1(203) 456-2231
Fax: +1(203) 456-5400
President: David G. Carter
Vice-President for Administrative Affairs: Roy H.
Merroli
Founded: 1889
*S: Arts and Sciences; Personnel Administration;
Professional Studies/Graduate Studies;
Continuing Education.*
*Ce: Connecticut Studies (David M. Roth);
Educational Excellence; Chase Free Enterprise
(David T.); Small Business Development (Greater
Windham).*

Eastern Illinois University
600 Lincoln Street, Charleston, Illinois 61920-3099
Tel: +1(217) 581-5000
Fax: +1(217) 581-2722
President: David L. Jorns (1992-)
Registrar: John Conley
Founded: 1895
*C: Liberal Arts and Sciences; Applied Sciences;
Business (Lumpkin); Education; Fine Arts; Health,
Physical Education and Recreation.*
S: Home Economics; Technology.

Eastern Kentucky University
203 Jones Building, Richmond, Kentucky
40475-3101
Tel: +1(606) 622-2106
Fax: +1(606) 622-1020
President: Handley Funderburk, Jr.
Founded: 1906, 1966
*C: Arts and Sciences; Applied Arts and
Technology; Business; Education; Allied Health
and Nursing; Law Enforcement; Mathematics;
Arts and Humanities; Physical Education; Health,
Physical Education, Recreation and Athletics;
Social and Behavioural Sciences.*

Eastern Michigan University
Ypsilanti, Michigan 48197
Tel: +1(313) 487-1849
Fax: +1(313) 481-1095
President: William Shelton (1989-)
Founded: 1849
*C: Arts and Sciences; Industry and Technology;
Education; Business; Health, Physical Education
and Recreation; Health and Human Services;
Technology.*
*I: Community and Regional Development; Study
of Children and Families.*

Eastern Montana College
1500 North 30th Street, Billings, Montana 59101
Tel: +1(406) 657-2011
Fax: +1(406) 657-2051
President: Bruce H. Carpenter
Administrative Vice-President: Terrie Iverson
Founded: 1927
*S: Arts and Sciences; Business and Economics;
Education and Human Services.*

Eastern New Mexico University
Portales, New Mexico 88130
Tel: +1(505) 562-1011
Fax: +1(505) 367-3668
President: Everett Frost (1992-)
Vice-President for Academic Affairs: Dorothy Allen
Founded: 1927
C: Liberal Arts and Sciences; Education and Technology; Business; Fine Arts.
D: Technology.
S: Education; Health and Physical Education; Music.

Eastern Oregon State College
1410 L Avenue, La Grange, Oregon 97850-2899
Tel: +1(503) 962-3672
Fax: +1(503) 962-3493
President: David Gilbert
Dean of Student Service: Richard Stenard
Founded: 1929
S: Education; Arts and Sciences; Administration Studies; Nursing; School of Agriculture.

Eastern Washington University
Cheney, Washington 99004-2496
Tel: +1(509) 359-6200
Fax: +1(509) 359-6927
President: Marshall E. Drummond
Founded: 1890, 1977
C: Letters and Social Sciences; Education and Human Development; Health, Social and Public Services.
S: Fine Arts; Business Administration; Mathematics and Technloogy; Science.

Edinboro University of Pennsylvania
Edinboro, Pennsylvania 16444
Tel: +1(814) 732-2000
Fax: +1(814) 732-2420
President: Foster F. Diebold (1979-)
Associate Dean of Records and Registration: Gerald Kiel
Founded: 1857
S: Education; Liberal Arts; Science, Management and Technology.

Elmira College
Park Place, Elmira, N.Y. 14901
Tel: +1(607) 735-1800
Fax: +1(607) 735-1701
President: Thomas K. Meier
Founded: 1855
Div: Business and Economics; Creative Arts; Humanities; Mathematics and Natural Sciences; Professional Studies; Social and Behavioral Sciences.

Emporia State University
1200 Commercial Street, Emporia, Kansas 66801-5087
Tel: +1(316) 341-1200
Fax: +1(316) 341-5073
President: Robert E. Glennen (1984-)
Registrar: Bill H. Schulte
Founded: 1863, 1923, 1977
C: Liberal Arts and Sciences; Teachers.
S: Business; Library and Information Management; Graduate Studies and Research.
I: Educational Exellence (Jones); Business and Economic Development.

Evergreen State College
Olympia, Washington 98505
Tel: +1(206) 866-6000
Fax: +1(206) 866-6823
President: Jone Jervis
Executive Vice-President: T.L. Purce
Founded: 1967
Arts and Sciences.

Fashion Institute of New York
117 West 27th Street, New York, N.Y. 10001-5992
Tel: +1(212) 760-7675
Fax: +1(212) 594-9413
President: Allan F. Hershfield
Director of Registration and Records: Young-Jakim
Founded: 1944
Div: Liberal Arts; Art and Design; Business and Technology.

Fayetteville State University
1200 Murchinson Road, Fayetteville, North Carolina 28301-4298
Tel: +1(919) 486-1111
Fax: +1(919) 486-6024
Chancellor: Lloyd B. Hackley
Registrar: Michael Hearon
Founded: 1867, 1869
C: Arts and Sciences.
S: Education; Business and Economics.

Ferris State University
901 S. State, Big Rapids, Michigan 49307
Tel: +1(616) 592-2000
Fax: +1(616) 592-3545
President: Helen Popovich (1989-)
Vice-President of Academic Affairs (Acting): Isabel Barnes
Founded: 1884
C: Arts and Sciences; Allied Health Sciences; Business; Education; Optometry; Pharmacy; Technology.
Ce: Occupational Education.

Fitchburg State College
160 Pearl Street, Fitchburg, Massachusetts 01420-2697
Tel: +1(508) 345-2151
Fax: +1(508) 343-8603
President: Vincent J. Mara
Vice-President for Academic Affairs: Fran Nowotny
Founded: 1894, 1967
Arts and Sciences.

Fort Hays State College
Hays, Kansas 67601
Tel: +1(913) 628-4000
Fax: +1(913) 628-4096
President: Edward H.Hammond
Provost: Rodolgo Arevalo
Founded: 1902, 1977
C: Arts and Sciences; Business; Health and Life Sciences; Education.

Fort Valley State College
1005 State College Drive, Fort Valley, Georgia 31030-3298
Tel: +1(912) 825-4211
Fax: +1(912) 825-4394
President: Oscar L. Prater (1990-)
Registrar: Edward T. Graening
Founded: 1895
S: Agriculture, Home Economics and Allied Ps.; Arts and Sciences; Education, Graduate and Special Academic Ps.

Framingham State College
State Street, Framingham, Massachusetts 01701-9101
Tel: +1(508) 620-1220
Fax: +1(508) 626-4592
President: Paul F. Weller
Registrar: Dudley R. Marsh
Founded: 1839, 1968
Arts and Sciences.

Francis Marion University
Highway 301 North, P.O. Box 100547, Florence, South Carolina 29501-0547
Tel: +1(803) 661-1362
Fax: +1(803) 661-1165
President: Lee A. Vickers (1994-)
Registrar: Frances L. Elmore
Founded: 1970
Business; Education.

Frostburg State University
Frostburg, Maryland 21532
Tel: +1(301) 689-4000
Fax: +(301) 689-4737
President: Catherine Gira (1991-)
Vice-President for Academic Affairs (Acting): Kenneth Stewart
Founded: 1898
S: Arts and Humanities; Business; Natural and Social Sciences; Education.

Georgia College
231 West Hancock Street, Middledgeville, Georgia 31061
Tel: +1(912) 453-5004
Fax: +1(912) 454-2510
President: Edwin G. Speir, Jr. (1980-)
Vice-President for Academic Affairs: Ralph W. Hemphill
Founded: 1889, 1971
S: Arts and Sciences; Education; Business (J. Whitney Bunting); Nursing.

Ce: Central Georgia Research and Development.

Georgia Southern University
Highway 301, South, Statesboro, Georgia 30460
Tel: +1(912) 681-5008
Fax: +1(912) 681-5611
President: Nicholas L. Henry
Registrar: Mike Deal
Founded: 1906, 1959, 1990
Arts, Sciences, and Education; Business; Health Sciences; Nursing; Technology.

Georgia Southwestern University
800 Wheatley Street, Americus, Georgia 31709-4693
Tel: +1(912) 928-1279
Fax: +1(912) 928-1630
President: William H. Capitan
Registrar: Linda A. Tennant
Founded: 1906, 1926, 1932
Arts, Sciences, and Education.

Glassboro State College
Route 322, Glassboro, New Jersey 08028
Tel: +1(609) 863-5000
Fax: +1(609) 863-5188
President: Herman C. James
Founded: 1921, 1923, 1966
Liberal Arts.

Governors State University
Stunkel Road, Universtity Park, Illinois 60466
Tel: +1(708) 534-5000
Fax: +1(708) 534-8399
President: Paula Wolff
Provost: Carolyn Conrad
Founded: 1969
C: Arts and Sciences; Education; Health Professions; Business and Public Administration.

Grand Valley State University
1 Campus Drive, Allendale, Michigan 49401
Tel: +1(616) 895-6611
Fax: +1(616) 895-3214
President: Arend D. Lubbers (1968-)
Provost: Glenn A. Niemeyer
Founded: 1960
D: Arts and Humanities; Science and Mathematics; Social Science.
S: Business (Seidman); Nursing (Russell B. Kirkhof); Communications; Criminal Justice; Education; Engineering; Health Sciences; Public Administration; Social Work.
I: Water Resources.

Henderson State University
1100 Henderson Street, Arkadelphia, Arkansas 71999-0001
Tel: +1(501) 246-5511
Fax: +1(501) 246-3199
President: Charles D. Dunn
Vice-President for Academic Affairs: Joe T. Clark
Founded: 1890

C: *Arts and Sciences (Ellis).*
S: *Business; Education.*

Humboldt State University
130 Siemens Hall, Arcata, California 95521-8299
Tel: +1(707) 826-3011
Fax: +1(707) 826-555
President: Alistair W. McCrone
Founded: 1913, 1935, 1972, 1974
C: *Arts and Humanities; Natural Resources and Science; Behavioural and and Social Sciences; Professional Studies.*

Indiana University at Kokomo
2300 South Washington Street, Kokomo, Indiana 46904-9003
Tel: +1(317) 453-2000
Fax: +1(317) 455-9276
Chancellor: Emita B. Hill (1991-)
Registrar: Lois Hathaway
Founded: 1945
C: *Arts and Sciences; Business and Economics.*

Indiana University Northwest
3400 Broadway, Gary, Indiana 46408
Tel: +1(219) 980-6500
Fax: +1(219) 980-6670
Chancellor: Hilda Richards (1993-)
Vice-Chancellor for Academic Affairs: Lioyd A. Rowe
Founded: 1922, 1936
Div: *Arts and Sciences; Business and Economie; Education; Nursing; Allied Health Sciences; Continuing Studies; Dental Auxiliary Education; Labor Studies; Public and Environmental Affairs and Political Science.*

Indiana University at South Bend
1700 Mishawaka Avenue, South Bend, Indiana 46634
Tel: +1(219) 237-4111
Fax: +1(219) 237-4599
Chancellor: H. Daniel Cohen
Vice-Chancellor for Academic Affairs: Lester C. Lamon
Founded: 1940, 1968
Div: *Liberal Arts and Sciences; Business and Economics; Education; Music; Public and Environmental Affairs; Arts.*
S: *Nursing; Library and Information Sciences.*

Indiana University Southeast
4201 Grand Line Road, New Albany, Indiana 47150
Tel: +1(812) 945-2731
Fax: +1(812) 945-2731
Chancellor: Leon Rand
Vice-Chancellor for Academic Affairs: Gilbert W. Atnip
Founded: 1941, 1968
Div: *Humanities; Social Sciences; Business and Economics; Nursing; Education; Continuing Studies.*

Indiana University-Purdue University at Fort Wayne
4201 Grand Line Road, Fortwayne, Indiana 46805-1499
Tel: +1(219) 481-6100
Fax: +1(219) 481-6880
Chancellor: Joanne B. Lantz
Vice-Chancellor for Academic Affairs: Michael A. Wartell
Founded: 1941, 1968
S: *Arts, Sciences and Education; Business and Management Sciences; Nursing; Engineering and Technology; Education; Fine and Performing Arts; Health Sciences.*

Jackson State University
1440 J.R. Lynch Street, Jackson, Mississippi 39217
Tel: +1(601) 968-2121
Fax: +1(601) 968-2358
President: James E. Lyons, Sr. (1992-)
Vice-President for Academic Affairs: Everette L. Witherspoon
Founded: 1877
S: *Business and Economics; Liberal Arts; Science and Technology; Education.*

Jacksonville State University
700 Pelham Road North, Jacksonville, Alabama 36265-9982
Tel: +1(205) 782-5781
Fax: +1(205) 782-5291
President: Harold J. McGee
Vice-President for Academic Affairs: W. David Watts
Founded: 1883, 1967
C: *Commerce and Business Administration; Criminal Justice; Letters and Sciences.*
S: *Education; Nursing; Fine Arts and Communication.*

James Madison University
Harrisonburg, Virginia 22807
Tel: +1(703) 568-6211
President: Ronald E. Carrier
Vice-President for Academic Affairs: Bethany S. Obest
Founded: 1908, 1938, 1977
C: *Fine Arts and Communication; Business; Health and Human Services; Letters and Sciences; Education and Psychology; Integrated Science and Technology.*
S: *Accounting.*

Jersey City State College
2039 Kennedy Boulevard, Jersey City, New Jersey 07305-1597
Tel: +1(201) 200-2000
Fax: +1(201) 200-2072
President: Carlos Hernández
Academic Vice-President: Larry Carter
Founded: 1927
C: *Arts, Sciences and Education.*
Ce: *Professional Studies and Education.*

Johnson State College
Johnson, Vermont 05656
Tel: +1(802) 635-2356
Fax: +1(802) 635-9745
President: Robert Haln
Dean of Academic Affairs: Vincent Crockenberg
Founded: 1828, 1961
Div: Humanities; Mathematics; Education; Fine and Performing Arts; Behavioural Sciences; English; Business and Economics.

Kean College of New Jersey
Morris Avenue, Union, New Jersey 07083
Tel: +1(908) 527-2000
Fax: +1(908) 355-5143
President: Elsa Gomez
Vice-President for Academic Affairs: Louanne Kennedy
Founded: 1855
S: Business, Government and Technology; Education; Liberal Arts; Natural Sciences, Mathematics and Nursing.

Keene State College
229 Main Street, Keene, New Hampshire 03431-4183
Tel: +1(603) 357-5833 toll free-800-833-4800
Fax: ++1(603) 358-2257
E-Mail: Internet via UNH
President: Judith Sturnick (1994-)
Registrar: Susan Sulke
Founded: 1909
Div: Professional Studies; Arts and Humanities; Science.

Kennesaw State College
P.O. Box, Marietta, Georgia 30061
Tel: +1(404) 423-6000
Fax: +1(404) 423-6433
President: Betty Siegel (1981-)
Registrar: Bill Hamrick
Founded: 1963
S: Arts and Behavioural Sciences; Business Administration; Education; Science and Allied Health.

Kentucky State University
East Main Street, Frankfort, Kentucky 40601
Tel: +1(502) 227-6000
Fax: +1(502) 227-6490
President: Mary L. Smith
Registrar: Lyman Dale
Founded: 1886, 1972
C: Leadership Studies.
S: Business; Public Affairs.

Kutztown University
Kutztown, Pennsylvania 19530
Tel: +1(215) 683-4000
Fax: +1(215) 683-4010
President: David McFarland
Provost: Richard J. Collings
Founded: 1866, 1983
C: Liberal Arts and Sciences; Education; Visual and Performing Arts; Business.

Lake Superior State University
1000 College Drive, Sault Ste. Marie, Michigan 49783
Tel: +1(906) 632-6815
Fax: +1(906) 635-2111
President: Robert D. Arbuckle
Provost: Frederick Gilliard
Founded: 1946, 1987
Arts, Sciences, and Education.

Lander University
Stanley Avenue, Greenwood, South Carolina 29649-2099
Tel: +1(803) 229-8400
Fax: +1(803) 229-8890
President: William C. Moran
Registrar: R. Thomas Nelson, III
Founded: 1872
C: Arts and Sciences.
S: Business.

Laredo State University
1 West End Laredo Street, Laredo, Texas 78040-9960
Tel: +1(512) 722-8001
Fax: +1(512) 726-3405
President: Leo Sayavedra
Special Assistant to the President: Mary Trevino
Founded: 1970
S: Education, Arts and Sciences; International Trade and Business Administration.

Lincoln University Missouri
820 Chestnut, Jefferson City, Missouri 65102
Tel: +1(314) 681-6074
Fax: +1(314) 681-5511
President: Wendell G. Rayburn
Vice-President for Academic Affairs: John Taylor
Founded: 1866
C: Arts, Sciences and Education; Business and Economics; Agriculture, Applied Sciences and Technology.
Ce: Co-operative Research.

Lincoln University Pennsylvania
Old Route 1, Lincoln University, Pennsylvania 19352
Tel: +1(215) 932-8300
Fax: +1(215) 932-4586
President: Niara Sudarkasa
Vice-President for Academic Affairs: Richard C. Winchester
Founded: 1854, 1972
Arts and Sciences.

Livingston University
Highway 11 North, Livingston, Alabama 35470
Tel: +1(205) 652-9661
Fax: +1(205) 652-9661, ext. 482
President: Asa N. Green
Vice-President for Business Affairs: T. Raiford Noland
Founded: 1835
C: Business and Commerce; Education; General Studies.

Lock Haven University of Pennsylvania
North Fairview Street, Lock Haven, Pennsylvania
17745-2390
Tel: +1(717) 893-2011
Fax: +1(717) 893-2432
President: Craig D. Willis
Provost/Vice-President for Academic Affairs:
Mary Pursell
Founded: 1870, 1983
*C: Arts and Sciences; Education and Human
Services.*

Long Island University - Southampton Campus
239 Montauk Highway, Southampton, N.Y. 11968
Tel: +1(516) 283-4000
Fax: +1(516) 283-4081
President: David Steinberg (1985-)
Provost: Timothy Bishop
Founded: 1963

Longwood College
High Street, Farmville, Virginia 23909
Tel: +1(804) 395-2000
Fax: +1(804) 395-2635
President: William F. Dorrill
Vice-President for Academic Affairs: Darryl G.
Poole
Founded: 1839, 1949
C: Arts and Sciences.
*S: Business and Economics; Education and
Human Services.*

Louisiana State University in Shreveport
One University Place, Shreveport, Louisiana
71115
Tel: +1(318) 797-5000
Fax: +1(318) 797-5180
Chancellor: John R. Darling
Registrar: Kathleen G. Plante
Founded: 1965
*C: Business Administration; Education;
Sciences; Liberal Arts.*

Lyndon State College
Vail Hill, Lyndonville, Vermont 05851
Tel: +1(802) 626-9371
Fax: +1(802)-626-9770
President: Peggy R. Williams
Dean of Academic Affairs: Rex Mayers
Founded: 1911, 1962
C: Arts and Sciences.

Maine Maritime Academy
Castine, Maine 04420
Tel: +1(207) 326-4311
Fax: +1(207) 326-2218
President: Ken Curtis
Academic Dean: Al Higgins
Founded: 1941
C: Marine Engineering; Ocean Studies.

Mankato State University
South Road and Ellis Avenue, Mankato,
Minnesota 56002-8400
Tel: +1(507) 389-2463
Fax: +1(507) 389-5859
President: Richard R. Rush (1992-)
Vice-President for Academic Affairs: Richard
Crofts
Founded: 1868
*C: Arts and Humanities; Business; Education;
Health and Human Performance; Physics,
Engineering and Technology; Natural Sciences,
Mathematics and Home Economics; Social and
Behavioural Sciences.*
C: Nursing.

Mansfield University
Mansfield, Pennsylvania 16933
Tel: +1(717) 662-4000
Fax: +1(717) 662-4995
President: Rod C. Kelchner (1984-)
Provost: George H. Mullen
Founded: 1857, 1862, 1863
*Div: Art; Biology; Business Administration;
Chemistry; Communication and Theatre;
Computer Sciences; Criminal Justice; Education;
English; Foreign Languages; Geography and
Geology; Health Science; History; Mathematics;
Music; Physics; Politics and Economics;
Psychology; Social Work, Anthropology, and
Sociology.*

Marshall University
400 Hal Greer Boulevard, Huntington, West
Virginia 25755
Tel: +1(304) 696-3170
Fax: +1(304) 696-3333
President: J. Wade Gilley
Registrar: Robert Eddins
Founded: 1837, 1961
S: Medicine; Nursing; Journalism.
*C: Liberal Arts; Business; Education; Sciences;
Fine Arts; Community and Technical.*
*Ce: Higher Education for Learning Problems;
Research and Economic Development.*

Mary Washington College
1301 College Avenue, Fredericksburg, Virginia
22401-5358
Tel: +1(703) 899-4100
Fax: +1(703) 899-4373
President: William M. Anderson
Registrar: Nancy O Carter
Founded: 1908, 1972
S: Arts and Sciences.

Massachusetts College of Art
621 Huntington Avenue, Boston, Massachusetts
02115
Tel: +1(617) 232-1555
Fax: +1(617) 232-0050
President: William O'Neil
Senior Vice-President for Academic Affairs: Betty
Buchsbaum
Founded: 1873
C: Arts and Sciences.

McNeese State University
4100 Ryan Street, Lake Charles, Louisiana 70609
Tel: +1(318) 475-5000
Fax: +1(318) 475-5012
President: Robert D. Hebert
Registrar: Linda Finley
Founded: 1939, 1970
*C: Education; Liberal Arts; Science; Business;
Engineering and Technology; Nursing.*

Metropolitan State College
1006 Eleventh Street, P.O. Box 173362, Denver,
Colorado 80217-3362
Tel: +1(303) 556-3018
President: Sheila Kaplan
Provost: David W. Williams
Founded: 1963, 1965
S: Business; Letters, Arts and Sciences.
Ce: Education.

Metropolitan State University
700 East Seventh Street, St. Paul, Minnesota
55106-5000
Tel: +1(612) 772-7777
Fax: +1(612) 772-7632
President: Richard Green (1993-)
Vice-Prsident for Academic Affairs: A. Nancy
Avakian
Founded: 1971, 1975
*Libera Studies; Business and Management
Studies.*

Midwestern State University
3400 Taft Boulevard, Wichita Falls, Texas 76308
Tel: +1(817) 689-4000
Fax: +1(817) 689-4302
President: Louis J. Rodriguez
Registrar: Billye J. Tims
Founded: 1922, 1975
Liberal Arts.

Millersville University of Pennsylvania
P.O. Box 1002, Millersville, Pennsylvania
17551-0302
Tel: +1(717) 872-3011
Fax: +1(717) 872-3968
President: Joseph A. Caputo (1981-)
Registrar: Mariano Gonzalez
Founded: 1855, 1962, 1983
*S: Education; Humanities and Social Sciences;
Science and Mathematics.*

Minot State University
500 University Avenue, West Minot, North Dakota
58707
Tel: +1(701) 857-3000
Fax: +1(701) 839-6933
President: Erik Schaar
Vice-President for Business Affairs: Larry D. Eide
*C: Arts and Sciences; Business; Education
Human Services; Nursing.*

Mississippi Valley State University
Itta Bena, Mississippi 38941
Tel: +1(601) 254-9041
Fax: +1(601) 254-6709
President: William W. Sutton (1988-)
Vice-President for Administration: Roy C. Hudson
Founded: 1946
*C: Business Administration; Education; English
and Speech Communication; Fine Arts; Health,
Physical Education and Recreation; Industrial
Technology; Natural Sciences and Environmental
Health; Social Science.*

Montana College of Mineral Science and Technology
West Park Street, Butte, Montana 59701-8997
Tel: +1(406) 496-4258
Fax: +1(406) 496-4133
President: Lindsay Norman, Jr
Registrar: Douglas A. Drew
Founded: 1965, 1893
*C: Arts and Sciences; Mining; Industrial
Engineering.*

Moorhead State University
104 7th Avenue South, Moorhead, Minnesota
56563
Tel: +1(218) 236-2011
Fax: +1(218) 236-2168
President: Roland E. Barden (1994-)
Vice-President for Administrative Affairs: John
McCune
Founded: 1885, 1921, 1975
*Div: Business, Industry and Applied Ps.; Natural
and Social Sciences; Arts and Humanities;
Education and Regional Services.*

Murray State University
15th and Main, Murray, Kentucky 42071
Tel: +1(502) 762-3011
Fax: +1(502) 762-3413
President: Kern Alexander (1994-)
Provost: James L. Booth
Founded: 1922, 1966
*C: Education; Public Affairs; Humanistic Studies;
Fine Arts and Communication.*
*S: Arts, Sciences and Education; Industrial
Technology; Business.*

New Mexico Highlands University
Las Vegas, New Mexico 87701
Tel: +1(505) 454-3000
Fax: +1(505) 454-0026
President: Gilbert Sanchez (1985-)

Vice-President for Academic Affairs: Gilbert
Rivera
Founded: 1893
S: *Liberal Arts and Fine Arts; Science and
Technology; Professional Studies.*

Nicholls State University
Highway 1, P.O. Box 2004, Thibodaux, Louisiana
70310
Tel: +1(504) 446-8111
Fax: +1(504) 448-4929
Telex: 9102503719 nichols ud
President: Donald D. Ayo
Executive Director of Enrolment Services: Walker
M. Allen
Founded: 1948
C: *Arts and Sciences; Education; Business
Administration; Life Sciences and Technology.*

Norfolk State University
2401 Corprew Avenue, Norfolk, Virginia 23504
Tel: +1(804) 683-8600
Fax: +1(804) 683-9435
President: Harrison B. Wilson
Vice-President for Academic Affairs: Jesse C.
Levis
Founded: 1935, 1979
C: *Arts, Sciences and Education; Social Work;
Technology; Business; Health Related
Professions and Natural Sciences; Social
Science.*
S: *Arts and Letters; Education.*

North Adams State College
Church Street, North Adams, Massachusetts
01247
Tel: +1(413) 664-4511
Fax: +1(413) 663-3033
President: Thomas D. Aceto
Vice-President for Academic Affairs: Raymond J.
Rodrigues
Founded: 1894, 1968
C: *Arts and Sciences.*

North Carolina Agricultural and Technical State University
1601 East Market Street, Greensboro, North
Carolina 27411
Tel: +1(919) 334-7500
Fax: +1(919) 334-7082
Telex: 5106007089 intlag pro ncat
Chancellor: Edward B. Fort
Vice-Chancellor for Academic Affairs: Edward J.
Hayes
Founded: 1894, 1968
C: *Arts and Sciences.*
S: *Business and Economics; Education;
Engineering; Nursing; Technology; Agriculture.*

North Carolina Central University
1801 Fayetteville Street, Durham, North Carolina
27707
Tel: +1(919) 560-6100
Fax: +1(919) 560-5014
Chancellor: Julius L. Chambers (1992-)
Provost: Mickey L. Burnim
Founded: 1900, 1972
C: *Arts and Sciences.*
S: *Business; Law; Library and Information;
Education.*

North Carolina School of the Arts
200 Waughtown Street, P.O. Box 12189, Winston-
Salem, North Carolina 27117-2189
Tel: +1(919) 770-3399
Fax: +1(919) 770-3375
Chancellor: Alexander C. Ewing
Vice-Chancellor for Arts and Academic
Programs: William A. Pruitt
Founded: 1963
Div: *General Studies.*
S: *Design and Production; Drama; Music;
Dance; Filmmaking.*

North Georgia College
Dahlonega, Georgia 30597
Tel: +1(706) 864-1400
Fax: +1(404) 864-1756
President: Delmas J. Allen
Registrar: Gary R. Steffey
Founded: 1872
Arts and Sciences.

Northeast Missouri State University
205 McClain Hall, Kirkville, Missouri 63501-9980
Tel: +1(816) 785-4000
Fax: +1(816) 785-4181
President: Russell G. Warren
Vice-President of Academic Affairs: W. Jack
Magruder
Founded: 1867, 1972
Div: *Businessand Accountancy; Education; Fine
Arts; Human Potential and Performance;
Language and Literature; Mathematics and
Computer Science; Nursing; Science; Social
Science.*

Northeastern Illinois University
5500 North St. Louis Avenue, Chicago, Illinois
60625-4699
Tel: +1(312) 583-4050
Fax: +1(312) 794-6243
President: Gordon Lamb
Provost: Salme H. Steinberg
Founded: 1867, 1971
C: *Arts and Sciences; Business and
Management; Education.*

Northeastern Ohio Universities, College of Medicine
4209 State Route 44, Rootstown, Ohio 44272-0095
Tel: +1(216) 325-2511
Fax: +1(216) 325-7943
President/Dean: Robert S. Blacklow
Executive Associate Dean: Ralph E. Berggren, MD
Founded: 1973
Div: Basic Medical Sciences; Clinical Sciences; Community Health Sciences.

Northeastern State University
Tahlequah, Oklahoma 74464-7099
Tel: +1(918) 456-5511
Fax: +1(918) 458-2193
President: W. Roger Webb
Vice-President for Academic Affairs: Alton Williams
Founded: 1973
C: Arts and Letters; Optometry; Business; Education; Natural Science and Mathematics; Social Sciences.
D: Health, Physical Education and Safety; Nursing; Technology.

Northern Kentucky University
Highland Heights, Kentucky 41099
Tel: +1(606) 572-5100
Fax: +1(606) 572-5566
President: Leon E. Boothe (1983-)
Provost: Paul L. Gaston
Founded: 1968
C: Arts and Sciences; Business; Professional Studies; Law Salmon P. Chasse.

Northern Michigan University
610 Cohodas Administrative Center, Marquette, Michigan 49855
Tel: +1(906) 227-1000
Fax: +1(906) 227-2204
President: William E. Vandament
Academic Vice-President: Phillip L. Benkema
Founded: 1899, 1963
C: Technology and Applied Sciences; Arts and Sciences; Business (Walker L. Cisler); Education; Nursing and Allied and Applied Sciences.
S: Behavioural Sciences, Human Services and Education.

Northern Montana College
P.O. Box 751, Havre, Montana 59501
Tel: +1(406) 265-3700
Fax: +1(406) 265-3777
President: William A. Daehling
Vice-President for Academic Affairs: Karen R. LaRoe
Founded: 1913, 1931
C: Arts, Sciences and Education; Technology and Professional Studies.

Northern State University
1200 South Jay Street, Aberdeen, South Dakota 57401
Tel: +1(605) 622-3011
Fax: +1(605) 622-3022
E-Mail: Easylink: 62830276 esl ud
President: John M. Huchinson
Executive Vice-President: Thomas O. Flickema
Founded: 1901
C: Arts and Sciences.
S: Fine Arts; Education; Business.
Ce: International Business.

Northwest Missouri State University
800 University Drive, Maryville, Missouri 64468-6001
Tel: +1(816) 562-1212
Fax: +1(816) 562-1900
President: L. Hubbard
Vice-President for Academic Affairs: Robert Cuberstor
Founded: 1905, 1972
C: Arts and Humanities; Business, Government and Computer Science; Education.

Northwestern Oklahoma State University
Oklahoma Boulevard, Alva, Oklahoma 73717-9898
Tel: +1(405) 327-1700
Fax: +1(405) 327-1881
President: Joe J. Struckle
Registrar: Shirley Murron
Founded: 1897, 1974
C: Arts and Sciences.

Northwestern State University of Louisiana
College Avenue, Natchitoches, Louisiana 71497
Tel: +1(318) 357-6361
Fax: +1(318) 357-4223
President: Robert Alost
Founded: 1884
Div: Business; Nursing; Education; Sciences and Mathematics; Research.

Penn State Erie Behrend College
Station Road, Erie, Pennsylvania 16563
Tel: +1(814) 898-6000
Fax: +1(814) 898-6461
Provost: John M. Lilley
Registrar: Robert Schenker
Founded: 1926
S: Business.

Pennsylvania State University Great Valley
Malvern, Pennsylvania 19355
Tel: +1(215) 889-1300
Fax: +1(215) 889-1334
Executive Officer: Lawrence S. Cote
Registrar: Mary Shoffner
Founded: 1963

Pittsburg State University
1701 South Broadway, Pittsburg, Kansas 66762
Tel: +1(316) 231-7000
Fax: +1(316) 232-7515
President: Donald Wilson
Vice-President for Academic Affairs: Robert K. Ratzlaff
Founded: 1903, 1978
S: Arts, Sciences, and Education; Technology and Applied Science; Business and Economics.

Plymouth State College
Plymouth, New Hampshire 03246
Tel: +1(603) 536-5000
Fax: +1(603) 535-2654
President: Theodora J. Kalikow (1993-)
Dean: Sally Boland
Founded: 1871, 1963
S: Business.

Prairie View Agricultural and Mechanical University
3rd Street, P.O. Box 188, Prairie View, Texas 77446
Tel: +1(409) 857-3311
Fax: +1(409) 857-3928
President: Julius W. Becton, Jr.
Executive Assistant to the President: Walter W. Redd
Founded: 1876
C: Business; Nursing; Education; Engineering and Architecture; Applied Sciences and Engineering Technology; Arts and Sciences; Benjamin Banneker Honors.

Purdue University Calumet
2233 171st Street, Hammond, Indiana 46323-2094
Tel: +1(219) 989-2400
Fax: +1(219) 989-2581
Chancellor: James Yakel
Vice-Chancellor for Academic Affairs: Sandra M. Singer
Founded: 1946, 1878
S: Liberal Arts and Sciences; Professional Studies.

Purdue University, North Central Campus
Westville, Indiana 46391
Tel: +1(219) 785-5200
Fax: +1(219) 785-5355
Chancellor: Dale W. Alspaugh
Vice-Chancellor for Academic Services: W. Patrick Leonard
Founded: 1943
Social Sciences; Arts, Sciences and Education; Engineering; Nursing; Physics; Biochemical Studies.

Radford University
Radford, Virginia 24142
Tel: +1(703) 831-6000
Fax: +1(703) 831-5970
President: Donald D. Delmon (1972-)
Executive Assistant to President: Charles Wood Jr
Founded: 1910, 1979
C: Arts and Sciences; Business and Economics; Education and Human Development; Nursing and Health Services; Visual and Performing Arts.

Rhode Island College
600 Mount Pleasant Avenue, Providence, Rhode Island 02908
Tel: +1(401) 456-8000
Fax: +1(401) 456-8379
President: John Nazarian
Founded: 1854, 1820, 1960
S: Social Work; Educationand Human Development; Arts and Sciences.

Rutgers, The State University of New Jersey-Camden
406 Penn, Camden, New Jersey 08102
Tel: +1(609) 225-1766
Fax: +1(609) 757-6495
Provost: Walter K. Gordon
Registrar: Terry L. Richartz
Founded: 1950
C: Arts and Sciences; University (evening studies).
S: Business; Law; Graduate.

Saginaw Valley State University
2250 Pierce Road, University Center, Michigan 48710
Tel: +1(517) 790-4000
Fax: +1(517) 790-1314
President: Eric R. Gilbertson
Vice-President for Academic Affairs: Robert S.P. Yien
C: Arts and Behavioural Sciences; Business and Management; Education; Engineering Technology; Nursing and Allied Health Sciences.

St. Cloud State University
720 Fourth Avenue South, St. Cloud, Minnesota 56301-4498
Tel: +1(612) 255-2243
Fax: +1(612) 255-4873
President: Brendan J. McDonald
C: Business; Education; Science and Technology; Social Sciences; Fine Arts and Humanities.

Salem State College
352 Lafayette Street, Salem, Massachusetts 01970
Tel: +1(508) 741-6000
Fax: +1(508) 741-6126
President: Nancy D. Harrington
Founded: 1854, 1932, 1960, 1963
C: Arts and Sciences.
S: Business; Human Services.

Salisbury State University
1101 Camden Avenue, Salisbury, Maryland
21801-6837
Tel: +1(410) 543-6000
Fax: +1(410) 543-6068
President: Thomas E. Bellavance
Vice-President for Administration: Joseph K.
Gilbert
Founded: 1554
*S: Liberal Arts (Fulton); Business (Perdue);
Education and Professional Studies; Nursing and
Health Sciences; Science and Technology
(Henson).*
*Ce: Professional Development; Economic
Education; Teaching Peace; European American
Business I.; Image Processing and Remote
Sensing.*

San Jose State University
One Washington Square, San Jose, California
95192-0002
Tel: +1(408) 924-1000
Fax: +1(408) 924-1018
President: Robert L. Caret (1994-)
Academic Vice-President: Arlene Okerlund
Founded: 1857, 1974
*C: Humanities and Arts; Applied Arts and
Sciences; Business; Education; Engineering;
Science; Sociology; Social Work.*

Sangamon State University
Shepherd Road, Springfield, Illinois 62794-9243
Tel: +1(217) 786-6600
Fax: +1(217) 786-7188
President: Naomi B. Lynn
Vice-President for Academic Affairs (Acting): A.
Wayne Penn
Founded: 1969
*C: Liberal Arts and Sciences; Management and
Business; Human Services and Health; Politics;
Public Affairs and Administration.*

Savannah State College
P.O. Box 20449, Savannah, Georgia 31404
Tel: +1(912) 356-2186
Fax: +1(912) 356-2874
President: Annette K. Brock
Registrar: Robert Ray
*S: Business; Humanities and Social Sciences;
Sociology; Sciences and Technology.*

Shippensburg University of Pennsylvania
Shippensburg, Pennsylvania 17257
Tel: +1(717) 532-9121
Fax: +1(717) 532-1273
President: Anthony F. Ceddia
Provost/Vice-President for Academic Affairs:
Yoan C. Fenton
Founded: 1871
C: Arts and Sciences.
S: Education and Human Services; Business.

Slippery Rock University of Pennsylvania
Slippery Rock, Pennsylvania 16057
Tel: +1(412) 738-0512
Fax: +1(412) 738-2098
President: Robert N. Aebersold
Provost: Charles Foust
Founded: 1889, 1983
S: Arts and Sciences.

Sonoma State University
East Cotati Avenue, Rohnert Park, California
94928-3609
Tel: +1(707) 664-2880
Fax: +1(707) 664-2505
President: Ruben Armiñana
Vice-President for Academic Affairs (Acting):
Donald J. Farish
Founded: 1960, 1978
*S: Arts and Humanities; Business and
Economics; Education; Natural Sciences; Social
Sciences; Liberal Arts (Hutchins).*

Southern Connecticut State University
501 Crescent Street, New Haven, Connecticut
06515
Tel: +1(203) 397-4000
Fax: +1(203) 397-4207
President: Michael J. Adanti
Vice-President for Academic Affairs: Anthony
Pinciaro
Founded: 1893, 1959
*S: Arts and Sciences; Education; Graduate
Studies and Continuing Education; Business;
Library Science and Instructional Technology;
Professional Studies.*

South Carolina State College
300 College Street, N.E., Orangeburg, South
Carolina 29117
Tel: (803) 536-7000
Fax: (803) 533-3622
President: Albert E. Smith
Founded: 1896, 1954
*S. of Arts and Sciences; S. of Home Economics;
S. of Education; S. of Industrial Education; S. of
Engineering Technology; S. of Business.*

Southeast Missouri State University
One University Plaza, Cape Girardeau, Missouri
63701
Tel: +1(314) 651-2000
Fax: +1(314) 651-5061
President: Kala Stroup
Registrar: Fred Snider
Founded: 1873
*C: Liberal Arts; Business Administration;
Education; Health and Human Services; Science
and Technology.*
I: Gerontology.
*Ce: Child Study; SEMO Eldercare; Faulkner
Studies; Regional History; Earthquake Studies;
Science and Mathematics Education (Linda M.
Godwin); Teaching and Learning; Writing.*

Southeastern Louisiana University

100 W. Dakota Street, Hammond, Louisiana 70401
Tel: +1(504) 549-3880
Fax: +1(504) 549-5095
E-Mail: internet
President: G. Warren Smith (1986-)
Provost: Roy Saigo
Founded: 1925, 1970
C: Arts and Sciences; Business.
Div: Education; Nursing.

Southeastern Oklahoma State University

Station A, Durant, Oklahoma 74701
Tel: +1(405) 924-0121
Fax: +1(405) 924-0758
President: Larry Williams
Vice-President for Academic Affairs: Joe A. Wiley
Founded: 1895, 1974
C: Education and Behavioural Studies; Business; Liberal Arts.
S: Arts and Letters; Science and Technology.

Southern Arkansas University

Magnolia, Arkansas 71753
Tel: +1(501) 235-4000
Fax: +1(501) 235-5005
President: Steven G. Gamble
Vice-President for Academic Affairs: James F. Lovell
Founded: 1909, 1951, 1976
S: Liberal and Performing Arts; Business and Communication; Education; Science and Technology.

Southern College of Technology

1100 South Marietta Parkway, Marietta, Georgia 30060-2896
Tel: +1(404) 528-7281
President: Stephen R. Cheshier
Vice-President for Academic Affairs: Harris T. Travis
Founded: 1948, 1970
Arts and Sciences.

Southern Oregon State College

1250 Siskiyou Boulevard, Ashland, Oregon 97520
Tel: +1(503) 552-7672
Fax: +1(503) 552-6337
President: Joseph Cox
Provost: Stephen Reno
Founded: 1926, 1986
S: Arts and Letters; Business; Nursing and Health; Sciences; Social Science and Education.

Southern University at New Orleans

6400 Press Drive, New Orleans, Louisiana 70124
Tel: +1(504) 286-5000
Fax: +1(504) 286-5131
Chancellor: Robert B. Gex (1989-)
Vice-Chancellor for Academic Affairs: Melinda Bartlus
Founded: 1959
C: Business; Engineering; Education; Science; Arts and Social Sciences.
S: Social Work.

Southern Utah University

351 West Center Street, Cedar City, Utah 84720
Tel: +1(801) 586-7700
Fax: +1(801) 586-5475
President: Gerald R. Sherratt
Provost: Terry D. Alger
Founded: 1897, 1987
Arts and Letters.

Southwest Missouri State University

901 South National, Springfield, Missouri 65804
Tel: +1(417) 836-5517
Fax: +1(417) 836-6777
President: Marshall Gordon
Registrar: Jeannine McGinnis
Founded: 1905, 1972
S: Arts and Humanities; Education; Science and Technology; Business; Psychology; Health and Applied Science; Science and Mathematics.

Southwest Texas State University

601 University Drive, San Marcos, Texas 78666-4615
Tel: +1(512) 245-2111
Fax: +1(512) 245-2033
Rector: Jerome H. Supple
Executive Vice-President: Michael Abbott
Founded: 1899
General Studies; Liberal Arts; Applied Arts and Technology; Education; Science; Business; Health Profession; Fine Arts and Communication.

Southwestern Oklahoma State University

100 Campus Drive, Weatherford, Oklahoma 73096-3098
Tel: +1(405) 772-6611
Fax: +1(405) 774-3795
President: Joe Anna Hibler (1991-)
Executive Vice-President: John Hays
Founded: 1901
S: Arts and Sciences; Education; Business; Health Sciences; Pharmacy.

State University of New York (SUNY) College at Brockport

Brockport, N.Y. 14420
Tel: +1(716) 395-2211
Fax: +1(716) 395-2246
President: John Van de Wetering
Vice-President for College Relations and Development: John Stoller
Founded: 1867
S: Letters and Sciences; Professions; Arts and Performance.

State University of New York College at Cortland

P.O. Box 2000, Cortland, N.Y. 13045
Tel: +1(607) 753-2011
Fax: +1(607) 753-5999
President: James S. Clark (1979-)
Registrar: Laurence M. Webster
Founded: 1868, 1948, 1962
S: Arts and Science; Professional Studies.

State University of New York College at Fredonia
Central Avenue, Fredonia, New York 14063
Tel: +1(716) 673-3111
Fax: +1(716) 673-3397
President: Donald A. MacPhee
Vice-President for Academic Affairs: David T. Hess
Founded: 1826, 1948
C: Arts and Sciences; Education; Humanities; Natural Sciences; Sociology.
S: Music.

State University of New York College at Geneseo
1 College Circle, Geneseo, N.Y. 14454
Tel: +1(716) 245-5211
Fax: +1(716) 245-5005
President: Carol C. Harter (1989-)
Provost: Donald S. Spencer
Founded: 1867
C: Arts and Sciences.
S: Business; Education.

State University of New York College at New Palz
32 South Mannheim Boulevard, New Palz, N.Y. 12561-2449
Tel: +1(914) 257-3200
Fax: +1(914) 257-3009
President: Alice Chandler
Vice-President for Academic Affairs: William W. Vasse
Founded: 1828
C: Liberal Arts and Sciences; Education; Fine and Performing Arts.
S: Engineering and Business Administration.

State University of New York College at Oneonta
Oneonta, N.Y. 13820-40151
Tel: +1(607) 434-3500
Fax: +1(607) 436-2107
President: Alan B. Donovan
Provost: Walter Vom Saal
Founded: 1887, 1961
Div: Liberal Studies; Professional Studies.

State University of New York College at Oswego
Oswego, N.Y. 13126
Tel: (315) 341-2500
Fax: (315) 341-2916
President: Stephen L. Weber
Provost, Academic Vice-President: Jane A. Milley
Founded: 1861, 1962
C: Arts and Sciences.
S: Education; Business.
Ce: State University Research (SURCO).
D: Continuing Education, Public Service, and Summer Sessions.

State University of New York College at Plattsburgh
Plattsburgh, N.Y. 12901
Tel: +1(518) 564-2000
Fax: +1(518) 564-7827
President: Charles Warren
Senior Business Officer: John R. Homburger
Founded: 1889, 1942, 1948
F: Arts and Sciences; General and Professional Studies.
S: Business and Economics.

State University of New York College at Potsdam
Pierrepont Avenue, Potsdam, N.Y. 13676
Tel: +1(315) 267-2000
Fax: +1(315) 267-2496
President: William Merwin
Provost: Janet Dudley-Eschbach
Founded: 1816
C: Arts and Sciences; Music; Professional Studies.

State University of New York College at Purchase
735 Anderson Hill Road, Purchase, N.Y. 10577-1400
Tel: +1(914) 251-6000
Fax: +1(914) 251-6075
President: Sheldon Grebstein (1981-)
Founded: 1967
C: Letters and Sciences; Dance; Music; Theatre Arts and Film; Visual Arts.

State University of New York Empire State College
One Union Avenue, Saratoga Springs, N.Y. 12866-4391
Tel: +1(518) 587-2100
Fax: +1(518) 587-5448
President: James W. Hall
Vice-President for Academic Affairs: Jane Altes
Founded: 1972
C: Arts and Sciences.

State University of New York Institute of Technology at Utica/Rome
Marcy Campus, P.O. Box 3050, Utica, N.Y. 13504-3050
Tel: +1(315) 792-7100
Fax: +1(315) 792-7222
President: Peter J. Cayan (1982-93)
Vice-President for Administration: John Falcone
Founded: 1966
S: Arts and Sciences; Business and Public Management; Information Systems and Engineering Technology; Nursing.

State University of New York Maritime College
Throgs Neck, Bronx, New York, N.Y. 10465
Tel: +1(718) 409-7200
Fax: +1(718) 469-7392
President: Floyd H. Miller
Vice-President for Academic Affairs: Howard L. English Jr
Founded: 1874
C: Science; Humanities; Marine Transportation; Engineering; Naval Science.

Sul Ross State University
Alpine, Texas 79832
Tel: +1(915) 837-8011
Fax: +1(915) 837-8334
President: R. Victor Morgan
Vice-President for Business Affairs: Mickey Havens
Founded: 1917, 1969
S: Arts and Sciences; Professional Studies.
Ce: Uvalde Study.

Tarleton State University
Tarleton Station, Stephenville, Texas 76402
Tel: +1(817) 968-9000
Fax: +1(817) 968-9920
President: Dennis McCabe
Provost: Robert C. Fain
Founded: 1899, 1973
C: Arts and Sciences; Agriculture and Technology; Business Administration; Education and Fine Arts; Graduate Studies.

Texas College of Osteopathic Medicine
3500 Camp Bowie Boulevard, Forth Worth, Texas 76107
Tel: +1(817) 735-2000
Fax: +1(817) 735-2486
President: David M. Richards
Founded: 1966
Osteopathic Medicine.

Texas-Wesleyan University
1201 Wesleyan, Fort Worth, Texas 76105
Tel: +1(817) 735-2000
Fax: +1(817) 735-2486
Telex: 493-2916
President: David M. Richards
Registrar: Betty Belton
Founded: 1890
S: Sciences and Humanities; Business; Fine Arts; Education; Law.

Towson State University
Towsontown Boulevard and Osler Drive, Towson, Maryland 21204
Tel: +1(410) 830-2000
President: Hoke L. Smith
Provost: Robert Caret
Founded: 1866
C: Liberal Arts; Education; Natural Sciences and Mathematics; Fine Arts and Communications;

Allied Health Sciences and Physical Education; Continuing Studies.
S: Business and Economics; Graduate.
Ce: Applied Skills in Education.
I: Teaching and Research on Women; Campus Violence Prevention; Area Resource and Development; Suburban and Regional Studies.

Trenton State College
Hillwood Lakes, CN4700, Trenton, New Jersey 08650-4700
Tel: +1(609) 771-1855
Fax: +1(609) 771-3067
President: Harold W. Eickhoff
Vice-President for Administration and Finance: Peter L. Mills
Founded: 1855
S: Arts, Science and Humanities; Business; Technology; Nursing; Education.

Troy State University
University Avenue, Troy, Alabama 36082
Tel: +1(205) 670-3000
Fax: +1(205) 670-3774
Chancellor: Jack Hawkins, Jr.
Provost: Larry Lovik
Founded: 1887
C: Arts and Sciences; Education; Business; Journalism; Nursing.
S: Fine Arts.

Troy State University at Dothan
P.O. Box 8368, Dothan, Alabama 36304
Tel: +1(205) 983-6556
Fax: +1(205) 683-6322
President: Thomas Harrison
Executive Vice-President: Frank Lovrich
Founded: 1961
C: Arts and Sciences.
S: Business; Education.

Troy State University in Montgomery
P.O. Drawer 4419, Montgomery, Alabama 36103-4419
Tel: +1(205) 834-1400
Fax: +1(205) 241-9505
President: Glenda S. Mc. Gaha
President: Martha L. Johnson
Founded: 1965
C: Arts and Sciences.

Tusculum College
P.O. Box 5097, Greenville, Tennessee 37743
Tel: +1(615) 636-7300
Fax: +1(615) 638-7166
President: Robert E. Knott (1990-)
Vice-President: John E. Mays
Founded: 1794, 1868, 1912
Arts; Education; Applied Organizational Management.

University of Alaska Southeast Juneau Campus
11120 Glacier Highway, Juneau, Alaska 99801
Tel: +1(907) 465-6457
Fax: +1(907) 465-6365
E-Mail: Easylink 620 45293 esl ud
Chancellor: Marshal Lind
Director, Administrative Services: Carol Griffin
Founded: 1956, 1972
Div: Business and Public Administration; Education, Liberal Arts and Science.
S: Vocational/Technical Education (Regional).

University of Alaska Anchorage Campus
3211 Providence Drive, Anchorage, Alaska 99508
Tel: +1(907) 786-1800
Fax: +1(907) 526-1720
President: Donald Behrend
Provost: Beverly Beeton
Founded: 1970
C: Arts and Sciences.
S: Business and Public Administration; Education; Nursing and Health Sciences; Engineering; Career and Vocational Education.

University of Baltimore
1420 North Charles Street, Baltimore, Maryland 21201-5779
Tel: +1(410) 837-4200
Fax: +1(410) 539-3714
President: H. Mebane Turner
Registrar: Valarie Powell-Baldwin
Founded: 1925, 1970, 1988
C: Liberal Arts; Business.
S: Law.

University of California, Hastings College of Law
200 McAllister Street, San Francisco, California 94102-4978
Tel: +1(415) 565-4600
Fax: +1(415) 565-4865
Dean: Frank T. Read
Chief Financial Officer: Joan Majerus
Founded: 1878
Law.

University of Central Arkansas
201 Donaghey Avenue, Conway, Arkansas 72035
Tel: +1(501) 450-5000
Fax: +1(501) 329-2403
President: Winfred Thompson (1988-)
Vice-President for Academic Affairs: William Berry
Founded: 1908
C: Sciences and Humanities; Business Administration; Education; Health and Applied Sciences.

University of Central Oklahoma
100 North University Drive, Edmond, Oklahoma 73034-0172
Tel: +1(405) 341-2980
Fax: +1(405) 341-4964
President: George Nigh (1992-)
Director of Admissions: Suzanne Martin
Founded: 1890, 1971
C: Liberal Arts; Business Administration; Education; Mathematics and Sciences.

University of the District of Columbia
4200 Connecticut Avenue N.W., Washington, D.C. 20008
Tel: +1(202) 282-7300
Fax: +1(202) 282-3681
President: Tilden J. LeMelle (1991-)
Provost: Julius J. Nimmons Jr
Founded: 1977
C: Liberal and Fine Arts; Business and Public Management; Life Sciences; Education and Human Ecology; Physical Science, Engineering and Technology.

University of Guam
Uog Station, Mangilao, Guam 96923
Tel: +1(671) 734-2177
Fax: +1(671) 734-2296
President: Wilfred P. Leon Guerrero
Academic Vice-President: John C. Salas
Founded: 1952
C: Arts and Sciences; Agriculture and Life Sciences; Business and Public Administration; Education.

University of Houston-Clear Lake
2700 Bay Area Boulevard, Houston, Texas 77059
Tel: +1(713) 283-7600
Fax: +1(713) 283-2010
President: Glenn A. Goerke
Provost: Edward Hugetz
Founded: 1971
S: Business and Public Administration; Natural and Applied Sciences; Human Sciences and Humanities.
I: Computing and Information Systems.
Ce: Regional Technology Transfer; Conflict Analysis and Management; Advanced Management; Economic Development and Research.

University of Houston-Victoria
506 East Red River, Victoria, Texas 77901
Tel: +1(512) 576-3151
Fax: +1(512) 572-8463
President: Lesta Van Der Wert Turches
Provost/Vice-President for Academic Affairs: Larry Robinson
Founded: 1973
C: Arts and Sciences; Education; Business Administration.

University of Michigan-Dearborn
4901 Evergreen Road, Dearborn, Michigan 48128
Tel: +1(313) 593-5000
Fax: +1(313) 593-5452
E-Mail: um.cc.umich.edu
Chancellor (Acting): James C. Renick
Registrar: Linda Brown
Founded: 1959, 1971
C: Arts, Sciences and Letters; Management; Education; Engineering.
Ce: Armenian Research and Publication.

University of Michigan-Flint
Flint, Michigan 48502-2186
Tel: +1(313) 762-3000
Fax: +1(313) 762-3687
Chancellor: Charlie Nelms (1994-)
Provost: Victor K. Wong
Founded: 1956, 1971
C: Arts, Sciences and Education; Health Professions and Studies.
F: Management; Nursing.

University of Minnesota-Duluth
10 University Drive, Duluth, Minnesota 55812
Tel: +1(218) 726-8000
Fax: +1(218) 726-8994
Chancellor: Kathryn Martin (1994-)
Vice-President for Academic Administration: Sandra Featherman
Founded: 1947
C: Liberal Arts; Education; Science and Engineering.
S: Medicine; Social Development; Business and Economics; Fine Arts.

University of Montevallo
Montevallo, Alabama 35115-6001
Tel: +1(205) 665-6000
Fax: +1(205) 665-6003
President: Robert M. Mc Chesney
Provost/Vice-President for Academic Affairs: Wayne Seelbach
Founded: 1896, 1969
C: Arts and Science; Business; Education; Fine Arts.

University of Nebraska at Kearney
905 West 25th Street, Kearney, Nebraska 68849-0601
Tel: +1(308) 236-8441
Fax: +1(308) 234-8665
Chancellor: William R. Nester
Vice-Chancellor for Academic Affairs: Gene Koepke
Founded: 1903
C: Business and Technology; Education; Fine Arts and Humanities; Natural and Social Sciences.

University of North Alabama
University Station, Florence, Alabama 35632-0001
Tel: +1(205) 760-4100
Fax: +1(205) 760-4329
President: Robert L. Potts (1990-)
Provost: Joseph C. Thomas
Founded: 1830, 1974
S: Arts and Sciences; Business; Education; Nursing.
Ce: Education Research and Inservice; Environmental, Energy, and Science Education; Geographic Research; Endangered Species Research; Small Business Development; Wellness Research and Service.

University of North Carolina at Asheville
One University Heights, Asheville, North Carolina 28804-3299
Tel: +1(704) 251-6600
Fax: +1(704) 251-6385
Chancellor: Patsy B. Reed (1994-)
Vice-Chancellor for Academic Affairs: Lauren R. Wilson
Founded: 1927
C: Liberal Arts.
P: Adult Education.
I: Environmental Quality.
Ce: Mössbauer Data Effect; Creative Retirement; Southern Highlands Research; Jewish Studies.

University of North Carolina at Charlotte
University City Boulevard, Charlotte, North Carolina 28223
Tel: +1(704) 547-2000
Fax: +1(704) 547-2144
Chancellor: James H. Woodward
Vice-Chancellor for Academic Affairs: Philip L. Dubois
Founded: 1946
C: Architecture; Arts and Sciences; Business Administration; Education and Allied Professions; Engineering; Nursing.

University of North Carolina, Pembroke State University
Pembroke, North Carolina 28372
Tel: +1(919) 521-6000
Fax: +1(919) 521-3877
Chancellor: Joseph B. Oxendine (1989-)
Vice-Chancellor of Academic Affairs: Charles R. Jenkins
Founded: 1887
Div: American Indian Studies; Art; Biology; Business Administration; Communicative Arts; Education; Health, Physical Education and Recreation; History; Mathematics and Computer Science; Music; Nursing; Physical Science; Psychology; Political Science; Sociology, Social Work and Criminal Justice.

University of North Carolina at Wilmington
601 South College Road, Wilmington, North
Carolina 28403
Tel: +1(919) 395-3000
Chancellor: James R. Leutze
Registrar: Ronald Whittaker
Founded: 1947
C: Arts and Sciences.
S: Business Administration; Education; Nursing.

University of North Florida
4567 St. Johns Bluff Road, South, Jacksonville,
Florida 32224-2645
Tel: +1(904) 646-2666
Fax: +1(904) 646-2505
E-Mail: unf1vm
President: Adam W. Herbert (1989-)
Vice-President for Academic Affairs: Kenneth E.
Martin
Founded: 1972
C: Arts and Sciences; Business Administration;
Computer Sciences and Engineering; Education
and Human Services; Health.
I: Education.

University of Southern Colorado
2200 Bonforte Boulevard, Pueblo, Colorado 81001
Tel: +1(719) 549-2100
Fax: +1(719) 549-2938
President: Robert C. Shirley
Provost: Bruce Grube
Founded: 1933, 1963, 1978
C: Applied Science and Engineering
Technology; Humanities and Social Sciences;
Science and Mathematics.
S: Business.
Ce: Teaching and Learning.

University of Southern Indiana
8600 University Boulevard, Evansville, Indiana
47712
Tel: +1(812) 464-8600
Fax: +1(812) 464-1960
President: David L. Rice
Senior Vice-President: Byron C. Wright
Founded: 1965, 1985
S: Business; Education and Human Services;
Liberal Arts; Nursing and Health Professions;
Science and Engineering Technology.

University of Tennessee at Martin
Martin, Tennessee 38238
Tel: +1(901) 587-7000
Fax: +1(901) 587-7019
Chancellor: Margaret N. Perry
Registrar: Emily Knudsen
Founded: 1927, 1953, 1967
S: Arts and Sciences; Agriculture and Home
Economics; Business Administration; Education;
Engineering and Engineering Technology.

University of Texas of the Permain Basin
4901 East University Boulevard, Odessa, Texas
79762-0001
Tel: +1(915) 367-2011
Fax: +1(915) 367-2115
President: Charles A. Sorber
Founded: 1969
Div: Behavioral Science and Kinesiology;
Business; Education; Humanities and Fine Arts;
Science and Engineering.

University of Texas at Tyler
3900 University Boulevard, Tyler, Texas 75799
Tel: +1(903) 566-7000
Fax: +1(903) 566-8368
Chancellor: George F. Hamm
Vice-President for Academic Affairs: Gerald L.
Morris
Founded: 1973, 1975, 1979
S: Liberal Arts; Education and Psychology;
Business Administration; Science and
Mathematics.

University of the Virgin Islands
Charlotte Amalie, St. Thomas, Virgin Islands
00802-9999
Tel: +1(809) 776-9200
Fax: +1(809) 776-2399
President: Orville Kean
Registrar: Anya C. Sebastien
Founded: 1962
C: Arts and Sciences.

The University of West Florida
11000 University Parkway, Pensacola, Florida
32514-5750
Tel: +1(904) 474-2000
Fax: +1(904) 474-2096
President: Morris L. Marx (1988-)
Vice-President for Administrative Affairs: John
Martin
Founded: 1963
C: Education; Science and Technology;
Business; Arts and Social Science.
I: Archaeology; Coastal and Estuarine
Research.

University of Wisconsin-Eau Claire
105 Garfield Avenue, Eau Claire, Wisconsin
54702-4004
Tel: +1(715) 836-2637
Fax: +1(715) 836-2380
Chancellor: Larry Schnack
Registrar: Laura Patterson
Founded: 1916, 1971
S: Arts and Sciences; Business; Education;
Nursing.

University of Wisconsin-Green Bay
2420 Nicolet Drive, Green Bay, Wisconsin
54311-7001
Tel: +1(414) 465-2000
Fax: +1(414) 465-2032
Chancellor: David Outcalt (1993-)
Registrar: Sally Mancoske
Founded: 1965

C: Professional Studies; Arts and Sciences;
Humanities and Social Sciences.
Ce: Business Development; History and Social
Change; Public Affairs.
I: Land and Water Studies.

University of Wisconsin-La Crosse
1725 State Street, La Crosse, Wisconsin 54601
Tel: (608) 785-8000
Fax: (608) 785-8909
Chancellor: Judith L. Kuipers
Provost: Julius Erlenbach
Founded: 1905, 1976
C: Arts, Letters and Sciences; Physical
Education; Health and Recreation; Business
Administration.
I: Health and Human Services.

University of Wisconsin-Oshkosh
800 Algoma Boulevard, Oshkosh, Wisconsin
54901
Tel: +1(414) 424-1234
Fax: +1(414) 424-7317
Chancellor: John E. Kerrigan (1990-)
Registrar: Roger Herold
Founded: 1989
C: Education and Human Services; Nursing;
Business Administration; Letters and Science.

University of Wisconsin-Parkside
Box 2000, Kenosha, Wixconsin 53141-2000
Tel: +1(414) 595-2345
Fax: +1(414) 595-2630
Chancellor: Sheila Kaplan (1994-)
Provost: John Stockwell
Founded: 1965
S: Business Administration; Education; Liberal
Arts; Sciences and Technology.

University of Wisconsin-Platteville
One University Plaza, Platteville, Wisconsin
53818-3099
Tel: +1(608) 342-1491
Fax: +1(608) 342-1232
President: Robert G. Culbertson
Provost: Ralph W. Curtis
Founded: 1886, 1971
S: Arts and Sciences; Agriculture; Business,
Industry and Communication; Education;
Engineering.

University of Wisconsin-River Falls
River Falls, Wisconsin 54022
Tel: +1(715) 425-3911
Fax: +1(715) 425-3304
Chancellor: Gary Thibodeau
Assistant Chancellor of Administration and
Finance: Virgil Nylander
Founded: 1874
C: Arts and Sciences; Agriculture; Education.

University of Wisconsin-Stevens Point
2100 Main Street, Stevens Point, Wisconsin
54481-3897
Tel: +1(715) 346-0123
Fax: +1(715) 346-2561
Chancellor: Keith R. Sanders
Provost: Howard Thoyre
Founded: 1893, 1971
C: Letters and Science; Fine Arts and
Communication; Natural Resources; Professional
Studies; Education; Business; Home Economics;
Communication.

University of Wisconsin-Stout
Menomonie, Wisconsin 54751
Tel: +1(715) 232-1122
Fax: +1(715) 232-1416
Chancellor: Charles W. Sorensen (1988-92)
Assistant Chancellor for Administrative Services:
Jan Womack
Founded: 1891
S: Industry and Technology; Home Economics;
Liberal Studies; Education and Human Services.
Ce: Archives and Area Research; Design
Research; Research and Training.

University of Wisconsin-Superior
1800 Grand Avenue, Superior, Wisconsin
54800-2898
Tel: +1(715) 394-8101
Fax: +1(715) 394-8107
Chancellor: Betty J. Youngblood
Assistant Chancellor: Richard Carter
Founded: 1893
C: Business and Economics; Education; Fine
and Applied Arts; Humanities and Social
Sciences; Sciences and Mathematics.
I: Lake Superior Research.

University of Wisconsin-Whitewater
800 West Main Street, Whitewater, Wisconsin
53190-1790
Tel: +1(414) 472-1234
Fax: +1(414) 472-1518
Chancellor: H. Gaylon Greenhill
Vice-Chancellor: Kay Schallenkamp
Founded: 1868, 1971
S: Letters and Sciences; Business and
Economy; Education; Arts.

Valdosta State University
1500 North Patterson Street, Valdosta, Georgia
31698
Tel: +1(912) 333-5800
Fax: +1(912) 333-7400
President: Hugh C. Bailey
Registrar: Arthur L. Bostock, Jr.
Founded: 1906
C: Arts and Sciences.
S: Education; Business Administration.
D: Nursing; Fine Arts.

Virginia State University
Petersburg, Virginia 23803
Tel: +1(804) 524-5000
Fax: +1(804) 524-6506
President: Eddie N. Moore, Jr.
S: Humanities and Social Sciences; Education; Business; Contining Education; Agricultural Applied Sciences; Natural Sciences.

Washburn University of Topeka
17th and College Streets, Topeka, Kansas 66621
Tel: +1(913) 231-1089
Fax: +1(913) 231-2780
E-Mail: zztate@acc.w.u.acc.edu
President: Hugh Thompson
Vice-President for Academic Affairs: Wayne M. Sheley
Founded: 1865
C: Arts, Sciences, and Education.
S: Law; Business; Nursing; Applied Science.
Ce: Continuing Education.

Wayne State College
Wayne, Nebraska 68787
Tel: +1(402) 375-7000
President: Donald Mash
Vice-President for Administration and Finance: Andrew Soll
Founded: 1891, 1909
Div: Applied Science; Business.
F: Mathematics and Science.
D: Social Sciences; Education; Fine Arts; Human Performance and Leisure Studies; Humanities.

Weber State University
3750 Harrison Boulevard, Ogden, Utah 84408-omit
Tel: +1(801) 626-6000
Fax: +1(801) 626-8875
President: Paul H. Thompson (1889-)
Provost: Robert B. Smith
S: Arts and Sciences; Health Science; Education.
C: Business and Economic; Sciences; Social and Behavioral Sciences; rts and Humanities; Applied Science and Technology.

West Chester University of Pennsylvania
University Avenue and High Street, West Chester, Pennsylvania 19383
Tel: +1(215) 436-1000
President: Madeleine Wing Adler
Provost: Stanley Yarosewick
Founded: 1871, 1960, 1983
C: Arts and Letters.
S: Business; Education; Health and Physical Recreation; Music; Health Sciences.

West Georgia College
1600 Maple Street, Carrollton, Georgia 30118-0001
Tel: +1(404) 836-6500
Fax: +1(404) 836-6720
President: Maurice K. Townsend (1975-)
Vice-President and Dean of Faculties: Don N. Smith
Founded: 1933
C: Arts and Sciences; Business; Education.

West Texas State University
2505 Fourth Avenue, Canyon, Texas 79016-0001
Tel: +1(806) 656-2100
Fax: +1(806) 656-2126
President: Barry B. Thompson (1909-)
Registrar: Linda Elliott
Founded: 1909, 1963
C: Arts, Sciences, and Education; Education and Social Sciences.
S: Business; Agriculture, Nursing and Natural Sciences; Nursing; Fine Arts and Humanities.

West Virginia Graduate College
Institute, West Virginia 25112
Tel: +1(304) 766-2000
Fax: +1(304) 766-1942
President: Dennis P. Prisk
Vice-President for Institutional Advancement: Kemp W. Winfree
Founded: 1972
S: Business; Education, Human Services and Humanities; Engineering and Science.

West Virginia Institute of Technology
210 Old Main, Montgomery, West Virginia 25136
Tel: +1(304) 442-3071
Fax: +1(304) 442-3059
President: John P. Carrier (1992-)
Registrar: Robert P. School
Founded: 1895
C: Engineering (Leonard C. Nelson); Business and Economics; Arts and Sciences; Community and Technical C.

West Virginia School of Osteopathic Medicine
400 North Lee Street, Lewisburg, West Virginia 24901
Tel: +1(304) 645-6270
President: Olen E. Jones, Jr.
Dean for Academic Affairs: James Stookey
Founded: 1972
Osteopathic Medicine.

Western Carolina University
Cullowhee, North Carolina 28723
Tel: +1(706) 227-7211
Fax: +1(704) 227-7202
Chancellor: Myron L. Coulter
Vice-Chancellor for Academic Affairs: John H. Wakeley
Founded: 1889, 1972
C: Arts and Sciences.

S: Business; Education and Psychology; Applied Sciences and Technology.
Ce: Mountain Heritage; Mountain Aquaculture Research.

Western Connecticut State University
181 White Street, Danbury, Connecticut 06810
Tel: +1(203) 797-4347
Fax: +1(203) 731-2804
President: James R. Roach
Vice-President for Academic Affairs: Philip J.Steinkraues
Founded: 1903
C: Arts, Sciences and Education; Business; Public Administration.
S: Professional Studies.

Western Illinois University
900 West Adams Street, Macomb, Illinois 61455
Tel: (309) 295-1414
Fax: (309) 298-2400
President: Ralph H. Wagoner (1993-)
Registrar: Alan Deroos
Founded: 1899, 1947, 1957
S: Arts and Sciences; Business; Education; Health and Physical Recreation; Applied Sciences; Fine Arts.

Western Kentucky University
1526 Center Street, Bowling Green, Kentucky 42101-3576
Tel: +1(502) 745-0111
Fax: +1(502) 745-5387
E-Mail: BITNET
President: Thomas C. Meredith (1988-)
Vice-President for Academic Affairs: Robert V. Haynes
Founded: 1906, 1966
C: Arts, Humanities and Social Sciences; Science, Technology and Health; Business Administration; Education and Behavioural Sciences.
I: Economic Development.

Western Montana College
710 South Atlantic Street, Dillon, Montana 59725-3598
Tel: +1(406) 683-7011
Fax: +1(406) 683-7493
Provost: Sheila Mac. Stearns
Registrar: Fred Buys
Founded: 1893, 1965
Anthropology and Psychology; Business; English; History; Industrial Arts; Physical Education; Music; Mathematics.

Western New Mexico University
1000 College Avenue, Silver City, New Mexico 88062
Tel: +1(505) 538-4238
Fax: +1(505) 538-6155
President: John E. Counts (1993-)
Vice-President for Academic Affairs: Cecilia Cervantes
Founded: 1893, 1863

C: Arts, Sciences and Education; Business; Social Sciences.
S: Sciences and Mathematics.

Western Washington University
516 High Street, Bellingham, Washington 98225
Tel: +1(206) 650-3000
Fax: +1(206) 650-3022
President: Ronald L. Delorme
Vice-President of Business and Financial Affairs: George A. Pierce
Founded: 1893, 1937, 1961, 1977
C: Arts and Sciences; Environmental Studies; Business and Economics; Education; Fine and Performing Arts; Fairhaven.

Westfield State College
Western Avenue, Westfield, Massachusetts 01086
Tel: +1(413) 568-3311
Fax: +1(413) 562-3613
President: Ronald L. Applbaum
Senior Vice-President for Academic Affairs: William H. Lopes
Founded: 1838
Arts and Sciences; Human Resources.

William Paterson College of New Jersey-8420
300 Pompton Road, Wayne, New Jersey 07470
Tel: +1(201) 595-2000
Fax: +1(201) 595-2460
President: Arnold Speert (1985-)
Vice-President for Academic Affairs: Eleanor Smith
Founded: 1855
S: Arts and Communication; Education; Humanities, Management and Social Science; Science and Health.

Winona State University
8th and Johnston Streets, Winona, Minnesota 55987-5838
Tel: (507) 457-5000
Fax: (507) 457-5586
E-Mail: 62860939 esl ud
President: Darrell Krueger (1989-)
Comptroller: Fred Naas
Founded: 1858
C: Liberal Arts; Business; Science and Engineering; Nursing and Health Sciences; Education.

Winston-Salem State University
601 Martin Luther King, Jr., Drive, Winston-Salem, North Carolina 27110
Tel: +1(919) 750-2000
Fax: +1(919) 750-2953
President: Cleon F. Thompson, Jr. (1985-)
Registrar: William Cain
Founded: 1892, 1972
D: Arts and Sciences; Business and Economics; Education; Nursing and Allied Health.
Ce: Continuing Education and Graduate; Computer (Virginia K. Newell); Computer (Rayford A. Means); Microelectronics.

Winthrop University
701 Oakland Avenue, Rock Hill, South Carolina
29733
Tel: +1(803) 323-2211
Fax: +1(803) 328-2855
President: Anthony DiGiorgio
Vice-President for Academic Affairs: Patricia P.
Cormier
Founded: 1886, 1992
*S: Business Administration; Education; Home
Economics; Music; Sciences; Arts and Sciences;
Visual and Performing Arts.*

Worcester State College
486 Chandler Street, Worcester, Massachusetts
01602-2597
Tel: +1(508) 793-8000
Fax: +1(508) 793-8191
Chief Executive Officer: Kalyan K. Ghosh
Vice-President for Administration and Finance:
Robert Malone
Founded: 1874, 1960
C: Arts and Sciences.

PRIVATE INSTITUTIONS

Alaska Pacific University
4101 University Drive, Anchorage, Alaska 99508
Tel: +1(907) 561-1266
Fax: +1(907) 542-4276
President: Douglas M. North (1994-)
Provost: Rodney W. Kilcup
Founded: 1957, 1978
*Div: Education and Psychology; Environmental
Science and Mathematics; Humanities, Arts and
Communication; Management; Social Science,
Philosophy and Religion.
I: English Language.*

Albany Law School of Union University
80 New Scotland Avenue, Albany, N.Y. 12208
Tel: +1(518) 445-2315
Fax: +1(518) 445-2315
President: John T. Baker
Dean: John C. Welsh
Founded: 1851
S: Law.

Albertson College of Idaho
2112 Cleveland Boulevard, Caldwell, Idaho
83605-9990
Tel: +1(208) 459-5500
Fax: +1(208) 454-2077
President: Robert L. Hendren, Jr.
Vice-President of Academic Affairs: Nancy C.
Haylewood
Founded: 1891
Liberal Arts.

Allegheny College
North Main Street, Meadville, Pennsylvania 16335
Tel: +1(814) 332-3100
Fax: +1(814) 337-0988
President: Daniel F. Sulivan
Provost: Andrew T. Ford
Founded: 1815
Arts and Sciences.

Allentown College of St. Francis de Sales
2755 Station Avenue, Center Valley, Pennsylvania
18034-9568
Tel: +1(215) 282-1100
Fax: +1(215) 282-2254
President: Daniel G. Gambet S., O.S.F.S. (1978-)
Vice-President for Administration: Michael J.
Thompson
Founded: 1962
C: Liberal Arts.

Amber University
Eastgate Drive, Garland, Texas 75041
Tel: +1(214) 279-6511
Fax: +1(214) 279-9773
President: Douglas W. Warner
Vice-President for Academic Services/Director for
Admissions for Records: Algia Allen
Founded: 1971
*Business and Management; Computer and
Information Sciences.*

The American College
270 Bryn Mawr Avenue, Bryn Mawr,
Pennsylvania 19010
Tel: +1(215) 526-1000
Fax: +1(215) 526-1310
President: Samuel H. Weese
Vice-President for Academics: Gary K. Stone
Founded: 1927
*S: Financial Sciences; Management (Richard D.
Irwin).*

American Conservatory Theater
450 Geary Street, San Francisco, California 94108
Tel: +1(415) 749-2200
Fax: +1(415) 771-4859
Director: Susan Stauter
Registrar: Jack F. Sharrar
Founded: 1965
Drama.

American Film Institute Center for Advanced Film and Television Studies
2021 North Western Avenue, Los Angeles,
California 90027
Tel: +1(213) 856-7628
Fax: +1(213) 467-4578
Director: Jean Firstenberg
Registrar: Rod Merl
Founded: 1967
Cinema.

American Graduate School of International Management
Thunderbird Campus, Glendale, Arizona 85306
Tel: +1(602) 978-7011
Fax: +1(602) 978-8238
President: Roy A. Herberger, Jr.
Vice-President for Academic Affairs: David Ricks
Founded: 1946, 1973
Personnel Studies; Commerce.

Anderson University
1100 East Fifth Street, Anderson, Indiana 46012
Tel: +1(317) 649-9071
Fax: +1(317) 641-3851
President: James L. Edwards
Registrar: Michael Collette
Founded: 1917, 1929
C: Arts and Sciences.
S: Theology; Arts, Culture, and Religion; Theoretical and Applied Sciences; Business; Music and Art; Science and Humanities; Social and Professional Studies.

Anna Maria College
Sunset Lane, Paxton, Massachusetts 01612-1198
Tel: +1(508) 849-3300
Fax: +1(508) 756-2970
President: Sister Bernadette Madore
Registrar: Sister Rollande Quintal
Founded: 1946
Arts, Sciences, and Education.

Antioch School for Adult and Experiental Learning
800 Livermore Street, Yellow Springs, Ohio 45387
Tel: +1(513) 767-6321
Fax: +1(513) 767-6461
President: Alan E. Guskin
Registrar: Judith Denny Kumler
Founded: 1988
Adult and Experiental Learning.

Antioch Souther California/Los Angeles
13274 Fiji Way, Marina del Rey, California 90292
Tel: +1(310) 578-1080
Fax: +1(310) 822-4824
President: Alan E. Guskin
Registrar: Stephen Leiter
Founded: 1972

Antioch Souther California/Santa Barbara
801 Garden Street, Santa Barbara, California 93101
Tel: +1(805) 962-8179
Fax: +1(805) 962-4786
President: Alan E. Guskin
Registrar: Marion Taylor
Founded: 1972

Antioch University Seattle
2607 Second Avenue, Seattle, Washignton 98121-1211
Tel: +1(206) 441-5352
Fax: +1(206) 441-3307
President: Alan E. Guskin
Registrar: Katie Kelso
Founded: 1975

Aquinas College
1607 Robinson Road, S.E., Grand Rapids, Michigan 49506
Tel: +1(616) 459-8281
Fax: +1(616) 459-2563
President: R. Paul Nelson
Registrar: Lois B. Kalman
Arts and Sciences.

Armstrong University
2222 Harold Way, Berkeley, California 94704
Tel: +1(510) 848-2500
Fax: +1(415) 848-9438
President/Chief Executive Officer: Ronald R. Hoold
Dean of Students and Instruction: Rufus Williams
Founded: 1918, 1923, 1970
S: Business Administration; Law; Education; Accounting.

Art Center Collegeof Design
1700 Lida Street, Pasadena, California 91103
Tel: +1(818) 584-5000
Fax: +1(818) 405-9104
President: David R. Brown
Vice-President, Administration: Margaret Brucato
Founded: 1930, 1965
Fine and Applied Arts; Architecture and Environmental Design.

Assumption College
500 Salisbury Street, P.O. Box 15005, Worcester, Massachusetts 01615-0005
Tel: +1(508) 752-5615
Fax: +1(508) 756-1780
President: Joseph H. Hagen
Dean of Academic Affairs: Richard E. Lamoureux, A.A.
Founded: 1904, 1968
Biological Sciences; Business and Management; Communications; Computer and Information Sciences; Engineering; Fine and Applied Arts; Foreign Languages; Health Professions; Letters; Mathematics; Physical Sciences; Psychology; Social Sciences; Theology.

Athenaeum of Ohio
6616 Beechmont Avenue, Cincinatti, Ohio 45230-2006
Tel: +1(513) 231-2223
Fax: +1(513) 231-3254
President: Rev. Robert J. Mooney
Academic Dean: Terrence D. Callan
Founded: 1929, 1980
C: Liberal Arts.
S: Theology.

Audrey Cohen College
345 Hudson Street, New York, New York 10014
Tel: +1(212) 989-2002
Fax: +1(212) 627-5104
President: Audrey C. Cohen
Registrar: Rejeswari Murty
Founded: 1964

Augsburg College
731 21st Avenue South, Minneapolis, Minnesota 55454
Tel: +1(612) 330-1000
Fax: +1(612) 330-1649
President: Charles S. Anderson
Registrar: Paul Simmons
Founded: 1869, 1963
Arts and Sciences.

Augustana College
29th and South Summit, Sioux Falls, South Dakota 57197
Tel: +1(605) 336-0770
Fax: +1(605) 336-5299
E-Mail: internet: 192.103.41.1.; or: inst.augie.edu
President: Ralph H. Wagoner (1992-)
Vice-President for Academic Services: Gary D. Olson
Founded: 1860
Div: Humanities; Social Science; Natural Science.

Aurora University
347 South Gladstone, Aurora, Illinois 60506
Tel: +1(708) 892-6431
Fax: +1(708) 844-5463
President: Thomas H. Zarle
Vice-President for Academic: Douglass Steeples
Founded: 1893, 1985
C: Liberal Arts and Sciences.
S: Business and Professional Studies; Nursing and Health; Social Work.

Austin College
900 North Grand Avenue, Sherman, Texas 75091-1177
Tel: +1(903) 813-2000
Fax: +1(903) 813-3199
President: Harry E. Smith
Vice-President for Academic Affairs: David W. Jordan
Div: Humanities; Sciences; Social Sciences.

Averett College
420 West Main Street, Danville, Virginia 24541
Tel: +1(804) 791-5600
Fax: +1(804) 799-0658
President: Frank R. Campbell
Provost: Malcom W. Huckabee
Arts and Sciences.

Avila College
11901 Wornall Road, Kansas City, Missouri 64145-99990
Tel: +1(816) 942-8400
Fax: +1(816) 942-3362
President: Larry Kramer (1985-)
Vice-President and Dean for Academic Affairs: Sr. Marie Joan Harris
Founded: 1916
D: Humanities; Business; Education and Psychology; Social Sciences; Nursing.

Azusa Pacific University
901 East Alosta Street, Azusa, California 91702-7000
Tel: +1(818) 815-6000
Fax: +1(818) 969-7180
President: Richard E. Felix
Provost: A.J. Anglin
Founded: 1899, 1981
C: Liberal Arts and Sciences.
S: Business and Management; Education and Behavioural Studies; Music; Nursing; Theology.

Babson College
Babson Park, Massachusetts 02157
Tel: +1(617) 235-1200
Fax: +1(617) 239-5614
Telex: 948069
President: William F. Glavin
Founded: 1858
C: Business Administration; Education.
S: Management.

Baker University
Baldwin City, Kansas 66006
Tel: +1(913) 594-6451
Fax: +1(913) 594-6721
President: Daniel M. Lembert
Provost: J. Keith Keeling
Liberal Arts.

Baldwin-Wallace College
275 Eastland Road, Berea, Ohio 44017-2088
Tel: +1(216) 826-2900
Fax: +1(216) 826-2329
President: Neal Malicky
Vice-President for Academic Affairs: Mark Collier
Founded: 1845, 1855, 1913
Arts and Sciences.

Bank Street College of Education
610 West 112th Street, New York, N.Y. 10025
Tel: +1(212) 875-4400
Fax: +1(212) 875-4759
President: Joseph Shenker
Founded: 1916, 1950
Education; Administration.

Baptist Bible College
Springfield, Missouri 65803
Tel: +1(417) 867-9811
Founded: 1850

Baptist Bible College of Pennsylvania
Clarks Summit, Pennsylvania 18411
Tel: +1(717) 587-1172
Fax: +1(717) 586-1753
President: Milo Thompson
Registrar: Benjamin McGrew
Founded: 1858

Bard College
Annandale-on-Hudson, N.Y. 12504
Tel: +1(914) 758-6822
Fax: (914) 758-4294
President: Leon Botstein (1975-)
Dean: Stuart Levine
Founded: 1860

C: *Liberal Arts and Sciences.*
I: *Economics (Jerome).*
S: *Environmental Studies (Graduate); Arts (Milton Avery Graduate).*

Bard Graduate Center for Studies in the Decorative Arts
18 West 86th Street, New York, New York 10024
Tel: +1(212) 721-4245
Fax: +1(212) 721-7774
Director: Susan Weber Soros
Academic Dean: Derek E. Ostergard
Decorative Arts.

Bayamon Central University
P.O. Box 1725, Bayamon, Puerto Rico 00960-1725
Tel: +1(809) 786-3030
Fax: +1(809) 740-2200
President: Vincent A.M. Van Rooij, O.P.
Academic Dean: Delfina Fernandez
Founded: 1861
C: *Commerce and Business Administration; Humanities; Science; Education.*

Baylor College of Dentistry
3302 Gaston Avenue, Dallas, Texas 75246-2098
Tel: +1(214) 828-8100
Fax: +1(214) 828-8446
President and Dean: Dominick P. DePaola (1990-)
Executive Vice-President: James S. Cole
Founded: 1905, 1918, 1971
Dentistry.

Beaver College
Easton and Church Roads, Glenside, Pennsylvania 19038-3295
Tel: +1(215) 572-2900
Fax: +1(215) 572-0240
President: Bette E. Landman
Vice-President for Academic Affairs: Michael Berger
Founded: 1853, 1907, 1972
Arts and Sciences.

Bellarmine College
2001 Newburg Road, Louisville, Kentucky 40205-0671
Tel: +1(502) 452-8000
Fax: +1(502) 452-8033
President: Joseph J. McGowan, Jr. (1990-)
Vice-President for Academic Affairs: David B. House
Founded: 1950, 1968
C: *Arts and Science.*
S: *Business (W. Fielding Rubel); Nursing (Allan and Donna Lansing).*

Belmont University
1900 Belmont Boulevard, Nashville, Tennessee 37212-3737
Tel: +1(615) 383-7001
Fax: +1(615) 385-6446
President: William E. Troutt
Provost: Jerry Warren
Founded: 1951, 1991
S: *Sciences; Business; Humanities and Education; Music; Nursing; Religion.*

Beloit College
700 College Street, Beloit, Wisconsin 53511
Tel: +1(608) 363-2000
Fax: +1(608) 363-2717
E-Mail: internet -ëloit-edu
President: Victor E. Ferrall, Jr. (1991-)
Vice-President for Academic Affairs: Parker G. Marden
Founded: 1846
D: *Natural Sciences and Mathematics; Social Science; Arts and Humanities; Interdisciplinary Studies.*

Bennington College
Bennington, Vermont 05201
Tel: +1(802) 442-5401
Fax: +1(802) 442-6164
President: Elizabeth Coleman
Registrar: Gertrude Syverstad
Founded: 1925
Arts and Sciences.

Bentley College
175 Forest Street, Waltham, Massachusetts 02154-4705
Tel: +1(617) 891-2000
Fax: +1(617) 891-2569
Telex: (910) 240-0945
President: Joseph M. Cronin
Vice-President for Academic Affairs: Philip Friedmen
Founded: 1917, 1961, 1971
C: *Business; Arts and Sciences.*

Berry College
Mount Berry, Georgia 30149-0159
Tel: +1(706) 232-5374
Fax: +1(706) 236-2248
President: Gloria M. Shatto
Vice-President: L. Doyle Mathis
Founded: 1902, 1926, 1930
Arts and Sciences.

Beth-el College of Nursing
2790 North Acadmy Blvd, Colorado Springs, Colorado 8097
Tel: +1(719) 475-5170
Fax: +1(719) 475-5198
President: Carl Schoffstall
Director of Student Affairs: Marilyn J. Atwood
Founded: 1904
Nursing.

Beth Hamedrash Shaarei Yosher Institute
4102-10 Sixteenth Avenue, Brooklyn, New York 11204
Tel: +1(718) 854-2290
Founded: 1962

Beth Medrash Gohova Gohova
617 Sixth Street, Lakewood, New Jersey 8701
Tel: +1(908) 367-1060
Founded: 1943

Bethel College
1001 W. McKinley, Mishawaka, Indiana 46545
Tel: +1(219) 259-8511
Fax: +1(219) 257-3326
President: Norman Bridges (1989-)
Vice-President for Academic Services: Michael
Holtgren
Founded: 1947
D: Business; Education and Social Sciences;
Fine Arts; Language and Literature; Natural
Sciences; Nursing; Religion and Philosophy.

Birmingham-Southern College
900 Arkadelphia Road, Birmingham, Alabama
35254
Tel: +1(205) 226-4600
Fax: +1(205) 226-4627
President: Neal R. Berte (1975-)
Vice-President for Academic Affairs: H. Irvin
Penfield
Founded: 1856
D: Fine and Performing Arts; Humanities; Social
and Behavioural Science; Mathematics;
Education; Business and Economics.

The Boston Conservatory
8 The Fenway, Boston, Massachusetts 00215
Tel: +1(617) 536-6340
Fax: +1(617) 536-3176
President: William A. Seymour (1980-92)
Director of Enrolment: Allison Ball
Founded: 1867
D: Music; Dance; Musical Theatre.

Bradley University
1501 West Bradley Avenue, Peoria, Illinois 61625
Tel: +1(309) 676-7611
Fax: +1(309) 677-2827
President: John R. Brazil
Vice-President for Academic Affairs: Kalman
Goldberg
Founded: 1897, 1946
C: Liberal Arts and Sciences; Business
Administration; Communications and Fine Arts;
Education and Health Sciences; Engineering and
Technology.

Brenau Professional College
One Centennial Circle, Gainesville, Georgia
30501-3697
Tel: +1(404) 534-6200
Fax: +1(404) 534-6114
President: John S. Burd
Vice-President for Academic Affairs: Charles L.
Andrews
Founded: 1878, 1900
Div: Business; Education; Fine Arts; Humanities;
Mathematics and Sciences.

Brenau University
Gaivesville, Georgia 30501-3697
Tel: +1(404) 534-534-6299
Fax: +1(404) 534-6114
President: John S. Burd
Registrar: Nellie Hoenes
Founded: 1878

C: Professional Studies.
S: Nursing.

Bristol University
2409 Volunteer Parkway, Bristol, Tennessee
37620
Tel: +1(615) 968-1442
President: Craven Sumerell
Registrar: Sonia Craig
Founded: 1895
S: Business.

Brooklyn Law School
250 Joralemon Street, Brooklyn, New York, N.Y.
11201
Tel: +1(718) 625-2200
Fax: +1(718) 797-1403
Dean: David G. Trager
Treasurer: Jack C. Rosen
Founded: 1901
S: Law.

Brooks Institute of Photography
801 Alston Road, Santa Barbara, California 93108
Tel: +1(805) 966-3888
Fax: +1(805) 564-1675
President: Ernest H. Brooks (1975-)
Vice-President: Doug Murray
Founded: 1945
Photography; Motion Picture and Video.

Bucknell University
Lewisburg, Pennsylvania 17837
Tel: +1(717) 523-1271
Fax: +1(717) 524-3760
President: Gary A. Sojka (1984-)
Vice-President for Academic Affairs: Larry D.
Shinn
Founded: 1846
C: Arts and Sciences; Engineering.

Butler University
4600 Sunset Avenue, Indianopolis, Indiana 46208
Tel: +1(317) 283-8000
Fax: +1(317) 283-9519
President: Geoffrey Bannister
Founded: 1850, 1855, 1877
C: Fine Arts; Business Administration;
Education; Pharmacy; Liberal Arts and Sciences.

Cabrini College
610 King of Prussia Road, Radnor, Pennsylvania
19087-3499
Tel: +1(215) 971-8100
Fax: +1(215) 971-8204
President: Antoinette Ladavola
Founded: 1957
Arts and Sciences.

California Baptist College

8432 Magnolia Avenue, Riverside, California
92504
Tel: +1(714) 689-5771
Fax: +1(714) 351-1808
President: Russell R. Tuck
Academic Dean: Stephen P. Carleton
Founded: 1950
Arts and Sciences.

California College of Arts and Crafts

5212 Broadway, Oakland, California 94618
Tel: +1(510) 653-8118
Fax: +1(510) 655-3541
President: Neil Hoffman (1985-)
Vice-President for Administration: Kate Cranwell
Founded: 1907
D: Fine Arts; Architecture; Design; Humanities and Science.

California College for Health Sciences

222 West 24th Street, National City, California
91950
Tel: +1(619) 477-4800
Fax: +1(619) 477-4360
President: Kenneth B. Scheiderman
Registrar: Gina Ehito
Founded: 1977
Health Sciences.

California College of Podiatric Medicine

P.O. Box 7855, Rincon Annex, San Francisco,
California 94120
Tel: +1(415) 292-0407
Fax: +1(415) 292-0439
President: Richard A. Lanham, Jr.
Dean for Academic Affairs: Lawrence M. Oloff
Founded: 1891, 1913, 1920
C: Podiatry; Administration.

California Family Study Center

5433 Laurel Canyon Boulevard, North Hollywood,
California 91607
Tel: +1(818) 509-5969
Fax: +1(818) 762-6547
President: Edwin S. Cox
Founded: 1971
Family Studies.

California Institute of the Arts

24700 McBean Parkway, Valencia, California
91355
Tel: +1(805) 255-1050
Fax: +1(805) 254-8352
President: Steven D. Lavine
Registrar: Beverly O'Neill
Founded: 1961
S: Art and Design; Dance; Film and Video; Music; Theatre.

California Lutheran University

60 West Olsen Road, Thousand Oaks, California
91360
Tel: +1(805) 492-2411
Fax: +1(805) 492-8513
President: Luther S. Luedtke
Registrar: Alan Scott
Founded: 1959
Arts and Sciences.

California Western School of Law

350 Cedar Street, San Diego, California 92101
Tel: +1(619) 239-0391
Fax: +1(619) 696-9999
President: Michael H. Dessent
Registrar: Diane Shragg
Founded: 1958, 1975
Law.

Calvin College

Grand Rapids, Michigan 4956
Tel: +1(616) 957-6000
Fax: +1(616) 957-8551
President: Athony J. Diekema
Provost: Gordon L. Van Harn
Founded: 1876
D: Language, Literature and Art; Social Sciences; Natural Sciences and Mathematics; Contextual Disciplines.

Cambridge College

15 Mifflin Plac, Cambridge, Massachusetts 02138
Tel: +1(617) 492-5108
President: Eileen M. Brown
Registrar: Cecelia Cull
Founded: 1971
Counselling Psychology; Education; Integrated Studies and Management.

Canisius College

2001 Main Street, Buffalo, N.Y. 14208-1098
Tel: +1(716) 883-7000
Fax: +1(716) 888-2525
E-Mail: bitnet
President: James M. Demske, S.J. (1966-)
Vice-President for Academic Affairs: Joan
Connell
C: Arts and Sciences.
S: Business (Richard J. Wehle).

Capital University

2199 East Main Street, Columbus, Ohio 43209
Tel: +1(614) 236-6011
Fax: +1(614) 236-6490
President: Josiah Blackmore
Provost: Harry Jebsen, Jr.
Founded: 1850
C: Arts and Sciences.
S: Nursing; Capital Law; Administration.
Conservatory of Music.

Cardinal Stritch College
6801 N. Yates Road, Milwaukee, Wisconsin 53217
Tel: +1(414) 352-5400
Fax: +1(414) 351-7516
President: Sister Mary Lea Schneider (1991-)
Senior Vice-President: Robert Flahive
Founded: 1937, 1946
D: Arts and Sciences; Education Division; Business and Management.
Ce: Reading and Learning.

Carlow College
333 Fifth Avenue, Pittsburgh, Pennsylvania 15213
Tel: +1(412) 578-6000
Fax: +1(412) 578-6019
President: Grace Ann (1988-)
Founded: 1929, 1970
D: Business Management; Education; Humanities; Natural Sciences; Nursing; Social Sciences.
P: Continuing Education; Women's Studies.

Carson-Newman College
1646 Russell Avenue, Jefferson City, Tennessee 37760
Tel: +1(615) 471-3223
Fax: +1(615) 471-3502
President: Cordell Maddox (1977-)
Vice-President of Academic Affairs: Michael V. Carter
Founded: 1851
D: Business; Applied Human Sciences; Fine Arts; Natural Sciences and Mathematics; Social Sciences; Education; Humanities.

Carthage College
2001 Alford Drive, Kenosha, Wisconsin 53141
Tel: +1(414) 551-8500
Fax: +1(414) 551-6208
President: F. Gregory Campbell
Registrar: Ruth A. Johnson
Founded: 1847
C: Arts and Sciences; Education; Fine Arts; Humanities; Natural Science; Social Sciences.

Centenary College of Louisiana
2911 Centenary Boulevard, Shreveport, Louisiana 71134
Tel: +1(318) 869-5011
Fax: +1(318) 869-5026
President: Kenneth L. Schwab
Provost: Robert P. Bareikis
Arts and Sciences; Business; Music.

Center for Advanced Studies of Puerto Rico and the Caribbean
Cristo Street 52, Viejo San Juan, Puerto Rico 00901
Tel: +1(809) 723-4481
Executive Director: Ricardo E. Alegria
Founded: 1968, 1977
Area Studies.

Central University of the Caribbean
[Universidad Central del Caribe]
Bayamon, Puerto Rico 00960-6032
Tel: +1(809) 798-3001
Fax: +1(809) 798-6836
President: Raul A. Marcial Rojas
Founded: 1976
Medicine; Biomedical Sciences; Radiological Technology.

Centrode Estudios Avanzados de Puerto Rico y El Caribe
Old San Juan, Puerto Rico 00904
Tel: +1(809) 723-4481
Fax: +1(809) 723-4481
Executive Director: Ricardo Alegria
Admissions Officer: Amalia Alsina
Founded: 1974

Chaminade University of Honolulu
3140 Waialae Avenue, Honolulu, Hawaii 96816-1578
Tel: +1(808) 735-4711
Fax: +1(808) 735-4870
President: Kent M. Keith
Vice-President for Academic Affairs: Loretta D. Petrie
Founded: 1955, 1977
S: Business Administration; Humanities and Fine Arts; Science and Mathematics; Social Sciences.

Chapman University
333 North Glassell Street, Orange, California 92666
Tel: +1(714) 997-6815
President: James L. Doti
Senior Vice-President and Provost: Havvy L. Hamilton
Founded: 1861, 1934, 1991
Arts and Sciences.

Chestnut Hill College
Germantown and Northwestern Avenues, Philadelphia, Pennsylvania 19118-2695
Tel: +1(215) 248-7000
Fax: +1(215) 248-7056
President: Carol J. Vale, S.S.J.
Executive Director of Finance: Sr. Elaine Cullen
Founded: 1871, 1924, 1938
Arts, Sciences, and Education.

Chicago College of Osteopathic Medicine
555 31st Street, Downers Grove, Illinois 60515-1235
Tel: +1(708) 515-6060
Fax: +1(708) 971-6097
President: Jack B. Kinsinger (1987-)
Dean for Academic Affairs: Leonard Mennen
Founded: 1900
C: Osteopathic Medicine; Pharmacy; Allied Health Professions.

City University
335 116th Avenue S E, Bellevue, Washington 98004
Tel: +1(206) 643-2000
Fax: +1(206) 637-9689
President: Michael A. Pastore
Registrar: Robert A. Van Woert
Founded: 1973
Business Communications; Data Processing; Health Professions; Computer and Information; Management; Accounting; General Education; Education; Leadership (Seattle).

Clarke College
1550 Clarke Drive, Dubuque, Iowa 52001
Tel: +1(319) 588-6300
Fax: +1(319) 588-6789
President: Catherine Dunn, B.V.M.
Vice-President for Academic Affairs: Gertrude Ann Sullivan, B.V.M.
Founded: 1843, 1901, 1928
Arts and Sciences.

Cleveland Chiropractic College, Los Angeles
590 North Vermont Avenue, Los Angeles, California 90004
Tel: +1(213) 660-6166
Fax: +1(213) 660-5387
President: Carl S. Cleveland III
Executive Vice-President: Matthew M. Givvad
Founded: 1908, 1928
Chiropractic Studies.

Cleveland Chiropractic College, Kansas City
6401 Rockhill Road, Kansas City, Missouri 64131
Tel: +1(816) 333-8230
Fax: +1(816) 361-0272
President: Carl S. Cleveland III
Executive Vice-President: Dwight F. Gerred
Founded: 1922, 1924
Chiropractic Studies.

Coe College
Cedar Rapids, Iowa 52402-5092
Tel: +1(319) 399-8000
Fax: +1(319) 399-8748
President: John E. Brown (1982-)
Vice-President for Academic Affairs: James R. Phifer
Founded: 1849
Liberal Arts.

Coleman College
7380 Parkway Drive, Le Mesa, Californnia 91942-1532
Tel: +1(619) 465-3990
Fax: +(619) 463-0162
President: Michael J. Flood
Vice-President: Robert Davis
Founded: 1963
Arts and Sciences.

Colgate University
Hamilton, N.Y. 13346
Tel: +1(315) 824-1000
Fax: +1(315) 824-7798
President: Neil R. Grabois
Dean of Faculty/Provost: Brece W. Selleck
Founded: 1819
Div: Humanities; Natural Sciences and Mathematics; Social Sciences.

College of the Atlantic
105 Eden Street, Bar Harbor, Maine 04609
Tel: +1(207) 288-5015
Fax: +1(207) 288-2328
President: Louis Rabineau (1985-)
Administrative Dean: Melville P. Côté
Founded: 1969
C: Environmental Sciences, Human Ecology, and Arts and Design.

College of Great Falls
1301 20th Street South, Great Falls, Montana 59404
Tel: +1(406) 761-8210
Fax: +1(406) 761-8210
President: Frederick W. Gilliard
Academic Vice-President: Tirmothy O'Hare
Founded: 1732, 1949, 1952
Business and Natural Sciences; Humanities; Human Services.

College of Insurance
101 Murray Street, New York, N.Y. 10007
Tel: +1(212) 962-4111
Fax: +1(212) 964-3381
President: Ellen Thrower
Vice-President for Administration of Finance: Susan M. Cochran
Founded: 1947
Insurance Studies.

College Misericordia
Lake Street, Dallas, Pennsylvania 18612-1098
Tel: +1(717) 674-6400
Fax: +1(717) 675-2441
President: Caral A. Jobe
Registrar: Paula Wilkes
Founded: 1924
Arts, Sciences, and Education.

College of Mount St. Joseph
5701 Delhi Road, Cincinnati, Ohio 45233-1670
Tel: +1(513) 244-4200
Fax: +1(513) 244-4222
President: Francis Marie Thrailkill, O.S.U. (1986-)
Academic Dean: George Banziger
Founded: 1920
D: Art; Behavioural Sciences; Biology; Business Administration; Chemistry and Nutritional Sciences; Education; Humanities; Mathematics; Music; Nursing; Religious and Pastoral Studies. Ce: Social Work; Gerontology; Institutional Research.

College of New Rochelle
29 Castle Place, New Rochelle, N.Y. 10805-2308
Tel: +1(914) 632-5300
Fax: +1(914) 654-5554
President: Sister Dorothy A. Kelly
Founded: 1904, 1910
S: Arts and Sciences; New Resources; Nursing; Graduate.

College of Notre Dame
500 Ralston Avenue, Belmont, California 94002
Tel: +1(415) 593-1601
Fax: +1(415) 637-0493
President: Margaret A. Huber (1994-)
Registrar: Mark Goldstein
Founded: 1851, 1916
Div: Behavioural Social Sciences; Business Administration; Humanities; Natural Sciences and Mathematics; Visual and Performing Arts.

College of Notre Dame of Maryland
4701 North Charles Street, Baltimore, Maryland 21210
Tel: +1(410) 435-0100
Fax: +1(410) 435-5937
President: Sister Rosemarie Nassif
Registrar: Donald Dean
Founded: 1873
Arts and Sciences.

College of Osteopathic Medicine of the Pacific
College Plaza, Pomona, California 91766-1889
Tel: +1(909) 469-5335
Fax: +1(909) 629-7255
President: Philip Pumerantz
Registrar: Beverly Guidry
Founded: 1977
Osteopathic Medicine.

College of St. Catherine
2004 Randolph Avenue, St. Paul, Minnesota 55105
Tel: +1(612) 690-6000
Fax: (612) 690-6024
President: Anita Pawpusch
Academic Dean: Marilou Eldred
Founded: 1905
C: Arts and Sciences.

College of St. Francis
500 North Wilcox Street, Joliet, Illinois 60435
Tel: +1(815) 740-3360
Fax: +1(815) 740-4285
President: John C. Orr
Founded: 1920, 1930
S: Arts and Sciences.

College of St. Joseph
Clement Road, Rutland, Vermont 05701
Tel: +1(802) 773-5900
Fax: +1(802) 773-5900
President: Frank G. Miglorie, Jr.
Registrar: Patricia Miglorie
Founded: 1954, 1986
Arts and Sciences; Business; Education.

College of Saint Rose
432 Western Avenue, Albany, N.Y. 12203
Tel: +1(518) 454-5111
Fax: +1(518) 458-5447
President: Louis C. Vaccaro
Registrar: Judith Icelly
Founded: 1920
Arts and Humanities; Business; Education; Mathematics/Science.

The College of St. Scholastica
1200 Kenwood Avenue, Duluth, Minnesota 55811
Tel: +1(218) 723-6000
Fax: +1(218) 723-6278
President: Daniel H. Pilon (1981-)
Senior Vice-President: Mary Odile Cahoon
Founded: 1912
Div: Behavioural Arts and Sciences; Health Sciences; Humanities; Natural Sciences.

College of Santa Fe
St. Michael's Drive, Santa Fe, New Mexico 87501
Tel: +1(505) 473-6011
Fax: +1(505) 473-6127
President: James E. Fries
Registrar: Marianne Kuste
Founded: 1859, 1974
Business Administration; Humanities; Nursing; Performing Arts; Science and Mathematics; Social Science/Education; Visual Arts.

Colorado College
14 E. Cache la Poudre Street, Colorado Springs, Colorado 80903
Tel: +1(719) 634-4180
Fax: +1(389) 634-4180
President: Kathryn Mohrman
Registrar: Margaret Van Horn
Founded: 1847
S: Arts and Sciences.

Columbia College Chicago
600 South Michigan Avenue, Chicago, Illinois 60605
Tel: +1(312) 663-1600
Fax: +1(312) 986-8825
President: John B. Duff (1992-)
Provost and Executive Vice-President: Bert Gall
Founded: 1890, 1964
I: Science Education and Science Communication.

Columbia College South Carolina
1301 Columbia College Drive, Columbia, South Carolina 29203
Tel: +1(803) 786-3012
Fax: +1(803) 786-3771
President: Peter T. Mitchell
Registrar: Frances Owens
Founded: 1854, 1904
Liberal Arts.

Concordia University Illinois
7400 Augusta Street, River Forest, Illinois
60305-1499
Tel: +1(708) 771-8300
Fax: +1(708) 209-3176
President: Eugene Krentz (1983-92)
Registrar: Gary Wenzel
Founded: 1864
C: Education; Arts and Sciences.

Concordia College Nebraska
800 North Columbia Avenue, Seward, Nebraska
68434
Tel: +1(402) 643-3651
Fax: +1(402) 649-4073
President: Orville C. Walz
Vice-President for Academic Affairs: George C.
Heider
Founded: 1894
*Div: Education; Social Science; Humanities;
Music; Health and Physical Education; Science,
Mathematics and Business; Theology.
I: Aging and the Family (Lutheran); Rural
Ministry.*

Concordia University Wisconsin
12800 North Lake Shore Drive, Mequon,
Wisconsin 53092-7699
Tel: +1(414) 243-5700
Fax: +1(414) 243-4351
President: R. John Buuck (1979-)
Vice-President of Admission: William Ebel
Founded: 1881, 1989
*S: Arts and Sciences; Business and Legal
Studies; Human Services; Graduate Studies;
Adult and Continuing Education.*

Connecticut College
270 Mohegan Avenue, New London, Connecticut
06320
Tel: +1(203) 447-1911
Fax: +1(203) 447-7809
President: Claire Gaudiani
Provost: Steve Lomis
Founded: 1911
*C: Arts and Sciences.
Div: Continuing Education; Education; Nursing.*

Converse College
500 East Main Street, Spartanburg, South
Carolina 29302
Tel: +1(803) 596-9000
Fax: +1(803) 596-9158
President: Ellen Wood Hall
Vice-President for Academic Affairs/Dean:
Thomas R. McDaniel
Founded: 1889
Arts and Sciences; Music.

**The Cooper Union for the Advancement of
Science and Art**
Cooper Square, New York, N.Y. 10003-7183
Tel: +1(212) 254-4343
Fax: +1(212) 353-4347
President: John Jay Iselin
Provost: Edward Colker
Founded: 1859
*C: Arts; Architecture; Engineering; Humanities
and Social Sciences.*

Cranbrook Academy of Art
500 Lone Pine Road, Bloomfield Hills, Michigan
48303-0801
Tel: +1(313) 645-3300
Fax: +1(313) 646-0046
President: Roy Slade
Registrar: Lucille Harper
Founded: 1932
Art.

Cumberland College
Box 6191, College Station, Williamsburg,
Kentucky 40769-1317
Tel: +1(606) 549-2200
Fax: +1(606) 549-2200
President: James H. Taylor
Founded: 1889, 1913
Arts and Sciences.

Cumberland University
S. Greenwood Street, Lebanon, Tennessee 37087
Tel: +1(615) 444-2562
Fax: +1(615) 444-2569
President: Ray Phillips (1990-91)
Registrar: C. William Mc Kee
Founded: 1866
*Div: Business; Social Science; Nursing;
Education.*

Curry College
1071 Blue Hill Avenue, Milton, Massachusetts
02186
Tel: +(617) 333-0500
Fax: +1(617) 367-0320
E-Mail: Easylink 62958046 esl ud
President: Catherine Ingold (1992-)
Registrar: Allan C.M. Greenberg
Founded: 1879
C: Arts and Sciences.

Curtis Institute of Music
1726 Locust Street, Philadelphia, Pennsylvania
19103
Tel: +1(215) 893-5252
Fax: +1(215) 893-0194
Director: Gary Graffman
Registrar: Elaine Katz
Founded: 1924
Music.

Dallas Baptist University

777 West Kiest Boulevard, Dallas, Texas
75211-9288
Tel: +1(214) 331-8311
Fax: +1(214) 333-5115
President: Gary R. Cook
Vice-President for Academic Affairs: Edouard H.
Pauley
Founded: 1898, 1965, 1968
*C: Business; Fine Arts; Humanities and Social
Sciences; Natural Sciences and Mathematics;
Nursing; Education and Learning Resources.*

David Lipscomb University

Granny White Pike, Nashville, Tennessee
37204-3951
Tel: +1(615) 269-1000
Fax: +1(615) 269-1796
President: Harold Hazelip
Vice-President for Academic Affairs: James T.
Arnett
Liberal Arts.

Detroit College of Law

5462 East Elizabeth Street, Detroit, Michigan
48201
Tel: +1(313) 226-0100
Fax: +1(313) 965-5097
President: Arthur J. Lombard
Registrar: Charles List
Founded: 1891
Law.

The Dickinson School of Law

150 South College Street, Carlisle, Pennsylvania
17013
Tel: +1(717) 243-4611
Fax: +1(717) 243-4443
President: Dale F. Shughart (1963-)
Dean: John A. Maher
Founded: 1834
Law.

Dominican College of San Rafael

50 Acacia Avenue, San Rafael, California
94901-8008
Tel: +1(415) 457-4440
Fax: +1(415) 485-3205
President: Joseph R. Fink (1988-)
Vice-President for Administration and Fiscal
Affairs: Jeff Bialik
Founded: 1890
I: Pacific Basin Affairs.
S: Nursing.

Dowling College

Idle Hour Boulevard, Oakdale, Long Island, New
York 11769-1999
Tel: +1(516) 244-3000
Fax: +1(516) 589-6644
President: Victor P. Meskill
Provost: Albert E. Donor
Founded: 1955

*S: Aviation and Transportation; Arts and
Sciences; Business Administration; Education.*
C: Aeronautics.

Drury College

900 N. Benton, Springfield, Missouri 65802
Tel: +1(417) 865-8731
Fax: +1(417) 865-6502
President: John Moore, Jr (1983-)
Vice-President for Academic Affairs and Dean:
Stephen Good
Founded: 1873
*Div: Behavioural Sciences; History and Political
Science; Education; Languages and Literature;
Communication; Mathematics; Theatre; Art and
Art History; Physics; Chemistry; Biology; Music.*
*S: Architecture (Hammons); Business
Administration and Economics (Breech).*
*Ce: Study of Free Competitive Enterprise and
Economic Education.*

D'Youville College

320 Porter Avenue, Buffalo, N.Y. 14201
Tel: +1(716) 881-7600
Fax: +1(716) 881-7790
President: Sister Denise A. Roche
Director of Admissions: Ronald H. Dannecker
Founded: 1908
*Div: Nursing; Liberal Arts; Mathematics and
Natural Sciences; Rehabilitation Sciences;
Business; Education.*

Earlham College

701 National Road West, Richmond, Indiana
47374
Tel: (317) 983-1200
Fax: (317) 983-1304
President: Richard R. Wood
Founded: 1847, 1859
Arts and Sciences; Religion ((Earlham)).

Eastern College

10 Fairview Drive, St. Davids, Pennsylvania
19087-5800
Tel: +1(215) 341-5810
Fax: +1(215) 341-1375
President: Roberta Hestenes
Registrar: Diana H. Bacci
Founded: 1932, 1952
C: Arts and Sciences.

Eastern Nazarene College

23 E. Elm Avenue, Quincy, Massachusetts
02170-2999
Tel: +1(617) 773-6350
Fax: +1(617) 773-6324
President: Kent Hill (1992-)
Registrar: Myrna Giberson
Founded: 1918
C: Liberal Arts.

Edgewood College
855 Woodrow, Madison, Wisconsin 53711
Tel: +1(608) 257-4861
Fax: +1(608) 257-1455
President: James Ebben
Academic Dean: Judith Wimmer
Founded: 1927, 1942
C: Arts, Sciences and Education.

Elon College
101 Haggard Avenue, Elon College, North
Carolina 27244
Tel: +1(910) 584-9711
Fax: +1(910) 584-3986
President: James Fred Young
Senior Vice-President and Provost: Warren L.
Board
Arts and Sciences.

Embry-Riddle Aeronautical University
Daytona Beach, Florida 32114-3900
Tel: +1(904) 226-6000
Fax: +1(904) 226-6299
President: Steven M. Sliwa
Vice-President of Administration: Robert Jost
Founded: 1926
*C: Aeronautical Science; Aviation Technology;
Engineering; Engineering Technology; Aviation
Computer Science; Physical Sciences;
Mathematics; Humanities and Social Sciences;
Flight Technology; Engineering Technology;
Aviation Business Administraton.*

Emerson College
100 Beacon Street, Boston, Massachusetts 02116
Tel: +1(617) 578-8500
Fax: +1(617) 578-8579
President: Jacqueline W. Liebergott
Registrar: Neil Davin
Founded: 1926
Communication Arts and Sciences.

Emmanuel College
400 The Fenway, Boston, Massachusetts 02115
Tel: +1(617) 277-9440
Fax: +1(617) 735-9877
President: Sister Janet Eisner, S.N.D.
Dean of Academic Affairs: Sr. Patricia Johnson
Founded: 1919
Arts and Sciences.

Fairfield University
North Benson Road, Fairfield, Connecticut 06430
Tel: +1(203) 254-4000
Fax: +1(203) 254-4060
President: Aloysius P. Kelley, S.J.
Vice-President for Administration: William Miles
Founded: 1942
C: Arts and Sciences.
*S: Business; Nursing; Continuing Education;
Education and Allied Professions (Graduate).*

Fisk University
1000 17th Avenue North, Nashville, Tennessee
37208-3051
Tel: +1(615) 329-8500
Fax: +1(615) 329-8715
President: Henry Ponder
Executive Vice-President: George Neely, Jr.
Founded: 1865, 1867
Arts and Sciences.

Florida Southern College
111 Lake Hollingsworth Drive, Lakeland, Florida
33801-5698
Tel: +1(813) 680-4111
Fax: +1(813) 680-4126
President: Robert A. Davis (1994-)
Director of Records: Sally Thissen
Founded: 1855, 1906
Arts and Sciences. -

Fontbonne College
6800 Wydown Boulevard, St. Louis, Missouri
63105
Tel: +1(314) 862-3456
Fax: +1(314) 889-1451
President: Meneve Dunham
Registrar: Jean Miner
Founded: 1917
Arts and Sciences.

Franciscan School of Theology
1712 Euclid Avenue, Berkeley, California 94709
Tel: +1(510) 848-5232
President: William M. Cieslak
Registrar: Paschal Hocum
Founded: 1968
Theology.

Franciscan University of Steubenville
Steubenville, Ohio 43952
Tel: +1(614) 283-3771
Fax: +1(614) 283-6442
President: Michael Scanlan, T.O.R. (1974-)
Executive Vice-President and Treasurer: John W.
Green
Founded: 1946
C: Liberal Arts.

Freed-Hardeman University
158 East Main Street, Henderson, Tennessee
38340
Tel: +1(901) 989-6000
Fax: +1(901) 989-6065
President: Milton R. Sewell (1990-92)
Executive Vice-President for Academic Affairs:
B.J. Naylor
Founded: 1869
*S: Arts and Sciences; Biblical Studies;
Business; Education.*

Fresno Pacific College
1717 South Chestnut Avenue, Fresno, California
93702
Tel: +1(209) 453-2000
Fax: +1(209) 453-2007
President: Richard Kriegbaum
Academic Vice-President: Gerald Winkleman
Founded: 1944
Arts and Sciences.

Friends University
2100 University, Wichita, Kansas 67213
Tel: +1(316) 261-5800
Fax: +1(316) 263-1092
President: Biff Green
Vice-President for Academic Affairs: Bob Dove
Founded: 1898
*C: Arts and Sciences; Business; Continuing
Education.*

Furman University
3300 Poinsett Highway, Greenville, South
Carolina 29613
Tel: +1(803) 294-2000
Fax: +1(803) 294-3001
E-Mail: BITNET: @frmnvaxi
President: David E. Shi (1994-)
Vice-President for Business Affairs: R. Wayne
Weaver
Founded: 1826, 1850
Liberal Arts.

Gannon University
University Square, Erie, Pennsylvania 16451
Tel: +1(814) 871-7000
Fax: +1(814) 459-0996
President: Msgr. David Rubino
Registrar: Marilyn Moore
Founded: 1933, 1979
*C: Business Administration; Education;
Humanities; Science and Engineering; Health
Sciences (Villa Mavia).*

Geneva College
3200 College Avenue, Beaver Falls, Pennsylvania
16010
Tel: (412) 847-6506
Fax: (412) 847-5017
Founded: 1848
Liberal Arts.

Gardner Webb University
Boiling Springs, North Carolina 28017
Tel: +1(704) 434-2361
Fax: +1(704) 434-6246
President: M. Christopher White
Vice-President: A. Frank Bonner
Founded: 1905
*C: Business Administration; Teacher Education;
Nursing; Natural Science; Mathematics; Foreign
Languages; English; Religion and Philosophy;
Communication Studies; Fine Arts; Physical
Education; Social Science; Psychology.
S: Management (Broyhill).*

Georgetown College
400 East College Street, Georgetown, Kentucky
40324-1696
Tel: +1(502) 863-8000
Fax: +1(502) 868-8891
President: William H. Crouch Jr. (1991-)
Executive Vice-President: Thomas Benberg
Founded: 1829
*Div: Education; Fine Arts; Language and
Literature; Natural Science; Social Science.*

Georgian Court College
900 Lakewood Avenue, Lakewood, New Jersey
08701-2697
Tel: +1(908) 364-2200
Fax: +1(908) 367-3920
President: Sister Barbara Williams
Registrar: Sister Cecelia Fox
Founded: 1908
C: Arts and Sciences.

GMI Engineering and Management Institute
1700 West Third Avenue, Flint, Michigan
48504-4898
Tel: +1(313) 762-9500
Fax: +1(313) 762-9807
President: James E.A. John
Provost: John D. Lorenz
Founded: 1919, 1932, 1982
Engineering and Management.

Goddard College
Plainfield, Vermont 05667
Tel: +1(802) 454-8311
Fax: +1(802) 454-8017
President: Richard E. Greene (1994-)
Dean for Academic Affairs: Paul Garstki
Founded: 1863, 1938
Arts and Sciences.

Goucher College
1021 Dulaney Valle Road, Baltimore, Maryland
21204
Tel: +1(401) 337-6000
Fax: +1(401) 337-6123
President: Rhoda M. Dorsey (1994-)
Vice-President/Academic Dean: Robert Welch
Founded: 1885, 1910
Arts and Sciences.

Grand Rapids Baptist College
1001 East Beltline N.E., Grand Rapids, Michigan
49505
Tel: +1(800) 968-4722
Fax: +1(616) 949-0875
President: Rex M.Rogers
Registrar: Jennifer Westrate
Founded: 1941, 1972
C: Arts and Sciences.

Gratz College
Old York Road and Melrose Avenue, Melrose Park, Pennsylvania 19126
Tel: +1(215) 635-7300
Fax: +1(215) 635-7320
President: Gary S. Schiff
Dean of Academic Affairs: Marsha Bryan Edelman
Founded: 1895
Jewish, Hebraic, and Middle East Studies.

Gwynedd-Mercy College
Sumneytown Pike, Gwynedd Valley, Pennsylvania 19437
Tel: +1(215) 646-7300
Fax: +1(215) 641-5596
President: Isabelle Keiss (1991-)
Vice-President for Academic Affairs: Thomas Young
Founded: 1948
Div: Allied Health; Behavioural and Social Sciences; Business Administration; Computer Science; Education; Humanities; Language, Literature, and Fine Arts; Natural Science; Nursing; Graduate Education; Graduate Nursing; Sociology and Social Work.

Hamline University
1536 Hewitt Avenue, St. Paul, Minnesota 55104-1284
Tel: +1(612) 641-2800
Fax: +1(612) 641-2956
President: Larry G. Osnes (1988-)
Vice-President for Finance: Peter Lilienthal
Founded: 1854
C: Liberal Arts.
S: Law.

Hampton University
East Queen Street, Hampton, Virginia 23668
Tel: +1(804) 727-5000
Fax: +1(804) 727-5746
President: William R. Harvey
Vice-President for Academic Affairs: Elnora Daniel
Founded: 1868, 1922, 1930
Arts and Sciences.

Hardin-Simmons University
2200 Hickory Street, Abilene, Texas 79698-0001
Tel: +1(915) 670-1000
Fax: +1(915) 677-8351
President: Lanny Hall
Vice-President for Academic Affairs: W. Craig Turner
Founded: 1891
C: Arts and Sciences.

S: Education; Religion; Economics and Business Administration; Theology; Music; Nursing.

Harding University
Searcy, Arkansas 72149
Tel: +1(501) 279-4000
Fax: +1(501) 279-4865
President: David Burks
Registrar: Ren Finley
Founded: 1919, 1924, 1979
C: Arts and Sciences; Bible and Religion.
S: Business; Education; Nursing.

Harding University Graduate School of Religion
1000 Cherry Road, Memphis, Tennessee 38117
Tel: +1(901) 761-1352
Fax: +1(901) 761-1358
President: Bill Flatt (1987-)
Executive Director/Dean: Edward P. Myers
Founded: 1958
Theology.

Hartford Graduate Center
Windsor Street, Hartford, Connecticut 06120-2991
Tel: +1(203) 548-2400
Fax: +1(203) 548-7817
President: Worth Loomis
Dean of Student Affairs: Rebecca M. Danchak
Founded: 1955
S: Engineering and Science; Management.

Harvey Mudd College
301 E. 12th Street, Claremount, California 91711
Tel: +1(909) 621-8000
Fax: +1(909) 621-8360
President: Henry E. Riggs
Dean: Sheldon Wettack
Founded: 1955
C: Sciences and Engineering.

Hawaii Pacific University
1166 Fort Street, Honolulu, Hawaii 96813
Tel: +1(808) 544-0200
Fax: +1(808) 544-1136
President: Chatt C. Wright
Senior Vice-President: L. Jim Hochberg Sr.
Founded: 1965, 1990
S: Business Administration; Nursing.

Hebrew College
43 Hawes Street, Brookline, Massachusetts 02146
Tel: +1(617) 232-8710
Fax: +1(617) 734-9769
President: David M. Gordis
Provost: Barry Mesch
Founded: 1921, 1969
Arts and Sciences.

Heritage College
3240 Fort Road, Toppenish, Washington 98948
Tel: +1(509) 865-2244
Fax: +1(509) 865-4469
President: Kathleen Ross (1982-)
Vice-President for Academic Affairs: Espirtu
Dempsey
Founded: 1907, 1982
D: *Arts and Letters; Business and
Administration; Undergraduate Education;
Graduate Education; Psychology; Science and
Mathematics; Social Science and Public
Administraiton.*

Hollins College
7916 Williamson Road, Roanoke, Virginia 24020
Tel: +1(703) 362-6000
Fax: +1(703) 362-6642
President: Jane Margaret O'Brien (1991-)
Vice-President for Academic Affairs: Roger W.
Bowen
Founded: 1842
C: *Liberal Arts.*

Holy Apostles College
33 Prospect Hill Road, Cromwell, Connecticut
06416
Tel: +1(203) 632-3010
Fax: +1(203) 632-3007
President: Francis J. Lescoe
Founded: 1956, 1970, 1972
*Humanities and Social Sciences; Liberal/General
Studies; Philosophy; Religion; Social Sciences.*

Holy Names College
500 Mountain Boulevard, Oakland, California
94619-1699
Tel: +1(510) 436-1000
Fax: +1(510) 436-1199
President: Mary Alice Muellerleile (1992-)
Dean of Academic Affairs: Judie Gaffin-Wexler
Founded: 1868
D: *Fine and Performing Arts; Business and
Social Sciences; Humanities; Mathematics and
Science.*
I: *Culture and Creation Spirituality.*

Hood College
Rosemont Avenue, Frederick, Maryland 21701
Tel: (301) 663-3131
Fax: (301) 694-7653
President: Martha E. Church
Founded: 1893, 1913
Arts and Sciences.

Houston Baptist University
7502 Fondren Road, Houston, Texas 77074-3298
Tel: +1(713) 774-7661
Fax: +1(713) 995-3209
President: E. Douglas Hodo
Vice-President for Academic Affairs: Don Looser
Founded: 1960
Arts, Sciences, and Education.
C: *Business and Economics; Nursing; Fine Arts;
Humanities; Education and Behavioural Sciences;
Science and Mathematics.*

Huntington College
2303 College Avenue, Huntington, Indiana 46750
Tel: +1(219) 356-6000
Fax: +1(219) 356-9448
President: G. Blaire Dowden
Vice-President and Dean
C: *Arts and Sciences.*
S: *Gchristian Ministries (Graduate).*

Husson College
One College Circle, Bangor, Maine 04401
Tel: +1(207) 947-1121
Fax: +1(207) 947-6024
President: William H. Beardsley
Registrar: Donna Townsenal
Founded: 1898, 1947
*Business and Professional Studies; Education;
Nursing.*

Illinois Benedictine College
5700 College Road, Lisle, Illinois 60532-0900
Tel: +1(708) 960-1500
Fax: +1(708) 960-1126
President: Richard C. Becker
Vice-President for Administration and Finance:
Robert Head
Founded: 1887, 1971
Arts and Sciences.

Illinois College of Optometry
3241 South Michigan Avenue, Chicago, Illinois
60616
Tel: +1(312) 225-1700
Fax: +1(312) 225-1724
President: Boyd B. Banwell
Vice-President for Academic Affairs: David A.
Greenberg
Founded: 1872, 1955
Optometry.

Immaculata College
Immaculata, Pennsylvania 19345-0900
Tel: +1(215) 647-4400
Fax: +1(215) 251-1668
President: Sister Marie Roseanne Bonfini
Vice-President for Academic Affairs: Sister
Kathleen McKee
Founded: 1920
Arts and Sciences.

Incarnate Word College
4301 Broadway, San Antonio, Texas 78209-6397
Tel: +1(210) 829-6000
Fax: +1(210) 829-2101
President: Louis J. Agnese, Jr.
Vice-President for Academic Affairs: Sr. Helena
Monahan
Founded: 1881, 1904, 1909
Arts and Sciences.

Inter-American University of Puerto Rico, San German Campus
Call Box 5100, San German, Puerto Rico 00683
Tel: +1(809) 264-1912
Fax: +1(809)892-6350
Chancellor: Agnes Mojica
Registrar: Carmen Juan de Carmona
Founded: 1912
Arts and Sciences.

Iona College
715 North Avenue, New Rochelle, N.Y. 10801
Tel: +1(914) 633-2000
Fax: +1(914) 633-2020
President: John Driscoll, CFC (1971-)
Provost: John Gallagher
Founded: 1940, 1989
S: Business (Hagan); Arts and Science; General Studies.

Ithaca College
953 Danby Road, Ithaca, N.Y. 14850
Tel: +1(607) 274-3013
Fax: +1(607) 274-1366
President: James J. Whalen
Provost: Thomas Longin
Founded: 1892
S: Business Administration; Health Sciences and Human Performance (Roy H. Park); Communications; Humanities and Sciences; Music.

Jacksonville University
2800 University Boulevard, North, Jacksonville, Florida 32211
Tel: +1(904) 744-3950
Fax: +1(904) 744-0101
President: James J. Brady
Vice-President for Academic Affairs: Yess S. Robertson
Founded: 1943, 1956
Arts, Sciences; Business Administration; Fine Arts.

John Carroll University
20700 North Park Boulevard, University Heights, Cleveland, Ohio 44118
Tel: +1(216) 397-1886
Fax: +1(216) 397-4256
President: Michael J. Lavelle, S.J. (1988-)
Executive and Academic Vice-President: Vincent M. Cook, S.J.
Founded: 1886
C: Arts and Science.
S: S. of Business.

John F. Kennedy University
12 Altarind Road, Orinda, California 94563
Tel: +1(510) 254-0200
Fax: +1(510) 254-6964
President: Charles E. Glasser
Registrar: Sandra L. Lee
Founded: 1964
S: Professional Psychology (Graduate); Study of Human Consciousness (Graduate); Management; Liberal Arts; Law; Holistic Studies (Graduate).

John Marshall Law School
315 South Plymouth Court, Chicago, Illinois 60604
Tel: +1(312) 427-2737
Fax: +1(312) 427-8307
President: Gerald Lynch
Registrar: Jane D. Oswald
Founded: 1899
Law.

Keller Graduate School of Management
10 South Riverside Plaza, Chicago, Illinois 60602
Tel: +1(312) 454-0880
Fax: +1(312) 454-6013
President: Ronald L. Taylor
Vice-President for Academic Affairs: Patrick L. Mayers
Founded: 1973, 1975
Management.

Lagrange College
601 Broad Street, Lagrange, Georgia 30240-2999
Tel: +1(706) 882-2911
Fax: +1(706) 884-6567
President: Walter Y. Murphy (1980-92)
Dean of Academic Affairs: Frank James
Founded: 1831
Div: Business Administration and Economics; Education; Humanities and Fine Arts; Nursing; Natural Sciences and Mathematics; Social and Behavioural Sciences.

LaSalle University
20th Street and Olney Avenue, Philadelphia, Pennsylvania 19141
Tel: +1(215) 951-1000
Fax: +1(215) 951-1086
President: Joseph Burke (1992-97)
Provost: Daniel Pantaleo
Founded: 1863
C: Arts and Sciences.
S: Business Administration.

Lake Erie College
391 West Washington Street, Painesville, Ohio 44077-3389
Tel: +1(216) 352-3361
Fax: +1(216) 352-3533
President: Hall Laydon (1992-)
Dean: Albert Kretz
Founded: 1856
Liberal Arts.

Lake Forest College
Lake Forest, Illinois 60045
Tel: +1(708) 234-3100
Fax: +1(708) 234-6487
President: David Spadafova
Registrar: Ruthane I. Bopp
Founded: 1857, 1865, 1965
Arts and Sciences.

Lake Forest Graduate School of Management
Sheridan and Maplewood Roads, Lake Forest, Illinois 60045
Tel: +1(708) 234-5005
Fax: +1(708) 295-3656
President: Raymond E. Britt, Jr.
Registrar: Carolyn Goggin
Founded: 1846, 1972, 1985
Management Studies.

La Roche College
900 Babcock Boulevard, Pittsburgh, Pennsylvania 15237
Tel: +1(412) 367-9300
Fax: +1(412) 367-9277
President: Msgr. William Kerr
Executive Vice-President: Carolyn Winschel
Founded: 1963
Liberal Arts.

Lawrence Technological University
21000 West Ten Mile Road, Southfield, Michigan 48075
Tel: +1(313) 356-0200 ext. 3005
Fax: +1(313) 356-0200
E-Mail: bitnet
President: Richard E. Marburger (1965-)
Provost: Robert W. Ellis
Founded: 1932
C: Architecture and Design; Arts and Science; Engineering; Management.

Lebanon Valley College of Pennsylvania
101 North College Avenue, Annville, Pennsylvania 17003
Tel: +1(717) 867-6100
Fax: +1(717) 867-6124
President: John Synodinos (1988-)
Registrar: Karen Best
Founded: 1866
Liberal Arts and Sciences.

Lenoir-Rhyne College
Avenue at 8th Street, N.E., Hickory, North Carolina 28603
Tel: +1(704) 328-7300
Fax: +1(704) 328-7368
President: Ryan A. LaHurd (1994-)
Dean of Academic Affairs: Robert Spuller
Founded: 1891, 1923
Arts and Sciences.

Lesley College
29 Everett Street, Cambridge, Massachusetts 02138
Tel: +1(617) 868-9600
Fax: +1(617) 661-8788
President: Margaret McKenna (1986-92)
Vice-President: Robert Trow
Founded: 1909, 1943
Management.

Lewis and Clark College
0615 S.W. Palatine Hill Road, Portland, Oregon 97219
Tel: +1(503) 768-7000
Fax: (503) 768-7333
President: Michael Mooney
Vice-President for Academic Affairs: Evan T. Williams
Founded: 1867, 1942
C: Arts and Sciences.
S: Law (Northwestern); Professional Studies (Graduate).
I: Study of American Language and Culture.

Lewis University
Route 53, Romeoville, Illinois 60441
Tel: +1(815) 838-0500
Fax: +1(815) 838-9456
President: James Gaffney, F.S.C.
Vice-President for Academic Affairs: Henry W. Smorynski
Founded: 1934, 1937, 1949
C: Arts and Sciences; Business; Nursing.

Liberty University
3765 Candlers Mountain Road, Lynchburg, Virginia 24506-8001
Tel: +1(804) 582-2000
Fax: +1(804) 582-2017
President: A. Pierre Guillermin
Provost: Earl Mills
Founded: 1971, 1985
C: Arts and Sciences; Business and Government Affairs.
S: Communication; Education; Lifelong Learning; Religion.

Life Chiropractic College West
2005 Via Barrett, San Lorenzo, California 94580
Tel: +1(510) 276-9013
Fax: +1(510) 276-4893
President: Gerard W. Clum
Director of Finance: Reza Badiee
Founded: 1976
Chiropractic Studies.

Lincoln Memorial University
Cumberland Gap Parkway, Harrogate, Tennessee 37752-0901
Tel: +1(615) 869-3611
Fax: +1(615) 869-4825
President: Scott D. Miller
Vice-President for Academic Affairs: Ralph Evans
Founded: 1897
Liberal Arts.

Lindenwood College
First Capitol Highway and Kings Highway, St. Charles, Missouri 63301
Tel: +1(314) 949-2000
Fax: +1(314) 949-4910
President: Dennis C. Spellmann
Registrar: Jeanne Murabito
Founded: 1827, 1983
Arts and Sciences.

Linfield College
900 South Baker Street, McMinnville, Oregon
97128
Tel: +1(503) 472-4121 Ext. 279
Fax: +1(503) 472-9528
President: Vivian A. Bull
Vice-President of Academic Affairs: Kenneth P.
Goodrich
Founded: 1849, 1922
S: Nursing.

Loras College
1450 Alta Vista Street, Dubuque, Iowa 52004-0178
Tel: +1(319) 588-7100
Fax: +1(319) 588-7964
President: James Barta
Registrar: G.B. Noonan
Founded: 1839, 1939
C: Arts and Sciences.

Loyola College in Maryland
4501 North Charles Street, Baltimore, Maryland
21210-2699
Tel: +1(410) 617-2000
Fax: +1(304) 323-2768
Special Assistant to President: timothy Brown, SJ
(1993-)
Registrar: Rita L. Steiner
Founded: 1852
C: Arts and Sciences.
S: Business and Management (Sellinger).

Loyola Marymount University
7101 West 80th Street, Los Angeles, California
90045
Tel: +1(310) 338-2700
Fax: +1(310) 338-2732
Vice-President: Joseph C. Jabbra
Founded: 1914
*C: Liberal Arts; Fine Arts and Communications;
Business Administration; Sciences and
Engineering.*
S: Law.

Loyola University, New Orleans
6363 St. Charles Avenue, New Orleans, Louisiana
70118
Tel: +1(504) 865-2011
President: James C. Carter, S.J.
Vice-President for Academic Affairs: David C.
Danahar
Founded: 1912
*C: Arts and Sciences; Business Administration;
Law; Music.*

Lynchburg College
1501 Lakeside Drive, Lynchburg, Virginia
24501-3199
Tel: +1(804) 522-8100
Fax: +1(804) 522-0658
President: Charles D. Warren Jr.
Registrar: Jay Webb
Founded: 1903, 1919
C: Business.
S: Education and Haman Development.

Madonna University
36600 Schoolcraft Road, Livonia, Michigan
48150-1173
Tel: +1(313) 591-5000
Fax: +1(313) 591-0156
President: Mary Francilene
Academic Vice-President: Sr. Rose Marie
Founded: 1937, 1947
C: Arts and Sciences.

Manchester College
604 College Avenue, North Manchester, Indiana
46962
Tel: +1(219) 982-5000
Fax: +1(219) 982-6868
President: Edgar C. Butterbaugle (1994-)
Registrar: Jean Ann Tribolet
Founded: 1889, 1902
C: Arts and Sciences.

Manhattan College
Manhattan College Parkway, Riverdale, N.Y.
10471
Tel: +1(718) 920-0100
Fax: +1(718) 548-1008
President: Thomas J. Scanlan
Provost: Walter G. Emge
Founded: 1853
*S: Arts and Sciences; Engineering; Business;
Education and Human Services.*

Manhattanville College
125 Purchase Street, Purchase, N.Y. 10577
Tel: +1(914) 694-2200
Fax: +1(914) 694-2386
President: Marcia A. Savage
Provost: James B. Bryan
Founded: 1841
S: Arts and Sciences.

Marietta College
215 Fifth Street, Marietta, Ohio 45750-4000
Tel: +1(614) 376-4643
Fax: +1(614) 376-4896
President: Patrick D. McDonough (1989-)
Provost: Rew A. Godow, Jr.
Founded: 1835
*Div: Fine Arts and Communication; Social and
Behavioural Sciences; Science and Engineering.*
I: European Studies; Asian Studies.

Marist College
83 North Road, Poughkeepsie, N.Y. 12601-1387
Tel: +1(914) 575-3000
Fax: +1(914) 471-6213
President: Dennis J. Murrray (1980-92)
Executive Vice-President: Mark Sullivan
Founded: 1946
*Div: Humanities; Marketing and Computer
Science; Physical Sciences; Behavioural and
Social Science; Management Studies;
Communications and the Arts.*

Mary Baldwin College
Staunton, Virginia 24401
Tel: +1(703) 887-7000
Fax: +1(703) 886-5561
President: Cynthia H. Tyson (1985-93)
Dean: James Lott
Founded: 1842
*Art, Business, Computer Science, Biology,
Chemistry, Health Care Administration,
Economics, Political Science, Sociology,
Psychology, Philosophy, Languages, English
Literature, Social Work, Medical Technology.*

Marygrove College
8425 West McNichols Road, Detroit, Michigan
48221-2599
Tel: +1(313) 862-8000
Fax: +1(313) 864-6670
President: John E. Shay, Jr
Executive Vice-President: Andrea Lee
Founded: 1905, 1925
S: Arts and Sciences.

The Maryland Institute, College of Art
1300 Mt. Royal Avenue, Baltimore, Maryland
21217
Tel: +1(410) 669-9200
Fax: +1(410) 669-9206
President: Fred Lazarus IV (1980-)
Vice-President for Academic Affairs: Barbara
Price
Founded: 1826
*S: Visual Arts; Painting (Hoffberger);
Photography (Graduate); Arts (Mont Royal);
Sculpture (Rinenart).*

Marylhurst College
P.O. Box 261, Marylhurst, Oregon 97036
Tel: +1(503) 636-8141
Fax: +1(503) 636-9526
President: Nancy Wilgenbusch
Vice-President for Academic Affairs: Denis
Lawrence
Founded: 1859, 1930
C: Arts and Sciences; Management; Education.

Marymount University
2807 North Glebe Road, Arlington, Virginia
22207-4299
Tel: +1(703) 522-5600
Fax: +1(703) 284-1685
President: M. Majella Berg
Executive Vice-President: Gymard Gallegher
Founded: 1950, 1986
C: Arts and Sciences.
*S: Business Administration; Education and
Human Services; Nursing.*

Maryville University of St. Louis
13550 Conway Road, St. Louis, Missouri
63141-7299
Tel: +1(314) 576-9300
Fax: +1(314) 542-9085
President: Keith H. Lovin
Vice-President for Academic Affairs
Founded: 1872

C: Arts and Sciences.
S: Business.

Marywood College
2300 Adams Avenue, Scranton, Pennsylvania
18509
Tel: +1(717) 348-6211
Fax: +1(717) 348-1817
President: Sister Mary Reap, I.H.M. (1988-)
Vice-President for Academic Affairs: Sister
Patricia Ann Matthews, I.H.M.
Founded: 1915, 1964
*S: Arts and Sciences (Graduate); Social Work;
Continuing Education.*

Memphis College of Art
1930 Poplar Avenue, Overlon Purk, Memphis,
Tennessee 38104
Tel: +1(901) 726-4085
Fax: +1(901) 726-9371
President: Jeffrey Nesin (1990-92)
Vice-President: Phillip Morris
Founded: 1936
*D: Fine Arts; Design Arts; Computer Art;
Decorative Design.*

Mercer University
1400 Coleman Avenue, Macon, Georgia
31207-0001
Tel: +1(912) 752-2700
Fax: +1(912) 752-2108
President: R. Kirby Godsey
Vice-President for Academic Affairs: Horace
Fleming
Founded: 1833, 1838
C: Liberal Arts.
*S: Law; Medicine; Pharmacy; Business and
Economics; Engineering.*

Mercer University Southern School of Pharmacy, Cecil B. Day Campus
3001 Mercer University Drive, Atlanta, Georgia
30341
Tel: +1(404) 986-3000
Fax: +1(404) 986-3150
President: R. Kirby Godsey
Registrar: Phyllis C. Hancock
Founded: 1903, 1959
*S: Arts and Sciences (Stetson); Business and
Economics; Pharmacy.*

Mercy College
555 Broadway, Dobbs Ferry, N.Y. 10522
Tel: +1(914) 693-4500
Fax: +1(914) 693-9455
President: Jay Sexter (1992-)
Provost: Carol A. Moore
Founded: 1950
*Div: Accounting; Business Administration; Civic
and Cultural Studies; Law, Criminal Justice and
Safety Administration; Literature, Language and
Communication; Mathematics and Computer
Science; Natural Science and Veterinary
Technology; Nursing; Psychology, Sociology,
Behavioural Science and Social Work.*

Mercyhurst College
501 East 38th Street, Erie, Pennsylvania 16546
Tel: +1(814) 824-2000
Fax: +1(814) 824-2438
President: William P. Garvey
Academic Dean: Michael J. McQuilen
Founded: 1926
C: Arts, Sciences and Education.

Meredith College
3800 Hillsborough Street, Raleigh, North Carolina
27607-5298
Tel: +1(919) 829-8600
Fax: +1(919) 829-2828
President: John E. Weems (1972-)
Vice-President and Dean: C. Allen Burris
Founded: 1891, 1909
Liberal Arts.

MGH Institute of Health Professions
101 Merimac St., Boston, Massachusetts 02114
Tel: +1(617) 726-3140
Fax: +1(617) 726-3716
President: Patrick E. McCarthy
Vice-President of Administration: Thomas C.
Anderson
Founded: 1971, 1975
Health Professions.

Milligan College
P.O. Box 52, Milligan College, Tennessee 37682
Tel: +1(615) 461-8700
Fax: +1(615) 461-8755
President: Marshall J. Leggett (1982-)
Registrar: Sue H. Skidmore
Founded: 1866, 1881
Liberal Arts.

Mills College
5000 MacArthur Boulevard, Oakland, California
94613
Tel: +1(510) 430-2255
Fax: +1(510) 430-3314
President: Janet Holmgren McKay
Arts, Sciences and Education
Founded: 1852, 1911
C: Arts, Sciences and Education.

Millsaps College
1701 North State Street, Jackson, Mississippi
39210
Tel: +1(601) 974-1000
President: George M. Harmon
Founded: 1890
*C: Arts, Sciences, Education and Occupational
Studies.*
S: Management (Else).

Milwaukee School of Engineering
1025 North Broadway, Milwaukee, Wisconsin
53202-3109
Tel: +1(800) 332-6763
Fax: +1(14) 277-7186
President: Hermann Viets (1991-)
Senior Vice-President for Academic Affairs:
Thomas W. Davis
Founded: 1903

*Div: Architectural Engineering, and Building
Construction; Business and Management
Systems; Electrical Engineering and Computer
Science; General Studies; Mathematics;
Mechanical Engineering; Physics and Chemistry.*
I: Biomedical Research; Fluid Power.
Ce: Applied Technology.

Mississippi College
P.O. Box 4086, Clinton, Mississippi 39058
Tel: +1(601) 925-3000
Fax: +1(601) 925-3804
President: Lewis Nobles
Vice-Prsident for Academic Affairs: Charles E.
Martin
C: Arts and Sciences.
*S: Education; Nursing; Law; Business
Administration.*

Mississippi University for Women
P.O. Box W-1602, College Street, Columbus,
Mississippi 39701
Tel: +1(601) 329-7450
Fax: +1(601) 329-7297
President: Clyda S. Rent
Vice-President for Academic Affairs: Thomas
Richarson
*S: Arts and Sciences; Human Sciences;
Sciences and Mathematics; Nursing; Home
Economics; Education; Fine Arts and Performing
Arts; Business and Economics; Communications;
Health and Physical Recreation.*

Monmouth College
Cedar Avenue, West Long Branch, New Jersey
07764-1898
Tel: +1(908) 571-3400
Fax: +1(201) 571-3570
President: Rebecca Stafford (1980-)
Senior Vice-President for Finance and
Administration: Richard N. Schwartz
Founded: 1933
*S: Business Administration; Information
Sciences and Technology; Arts and Sciences
(The Wayne D. McMurray).*
Ce: Professional Development.

Montclair State College
Valley Road and Normal Avenue, Upper
Montclair, New Jersey 07043-1624
Tel: +1(201) 893-4000
Fax: +1(201) 893-5455
President: Irvin D. Reid
Provost: Richard A. Lynde
Founded: 1908, 1958
*S: Mathematics and Sciences; Human Sciences;
Professional Studies; Fine Arts and Performing
Arts; Business and Administration.*

The Monterey Institute of International Studies
425 Van Buren Street, Monterey, California 93940
Tel: +1(408) 647-4100
Fax: +1(408) 647-4199
President: Robert G. Gard, Jr
Academic Dean: Glynn Wood
Founded: 1955
Div: Translation and Interpretation; International Management; International Policy Studies and Public Administration; Language Studies.

Moody Bible Institute
820 North LaSalle Boulevard, Chicago, Illinois 60610-3284
Tel: +1(312) 329-4000
President: Joseph Stowell
Senior Vice-President/Dean of Education: Howard A. Whaley
Founded: 1886
Communication; Engineering; Physics; Religion.

Moravian College
10200 Main Street, Bethlehem, Pennsylvania 18018
Tel: +1(215) 861-1516
Fax: +1(215) 861-3919
President: Roger H. Martin (1986-92)
Dean and Vice-President for Academic Affairs: Martha Reid
Founded: 1745
Arts; Science; Music; Business Administration.

Morehead State University
University Boulvard, Morehead, Kentucky 40351
Tel: +1(606) 783-2221
Fax: +1(606) 783-2678
President: Ronald Eaglin
Executive Vice-President for Academic Affairs: John Philley
Founded: 1922, 1966
C: Business and Economics; Educational and Behavioural Sciences; Humanities; Science and Technology.

Morningside College
1501 Morningside Avenue, Sioux City, Iowa 51106-1751
Tel: +1(712) 274-5000
Fax: +1(712) 274-5101
President: Jerry Israel (1978-)
Vice-President for Academic Affairs (Acting): Carolyn Rants
Founded: 1894
Div: Fine Arts; Humanities; Natural and Mathematical Sciences, and Nursing Education; Economics and Business Administration; Behavioural Science and Human Development.

Mount Holyoke College
South Hadley, Massachusetts 01075
Tel: +1(413) 538-2000
Fax: +1(413) 538-2409
President: Elizabeth T. Kennan
Provost: Peter Berek
Founded: 1837
C: Arts, Sciences, and Education.

Mount Marty College
1105 West 8th Street, Yankton, South Dakota 57078-3724
Tel: +1(605) 668-1011
Fax: +1(605) 668-1357
President: Jacquelyn Ernster
Vice-President for Academic Affairs: William Nevious
Founded: 1936
C: Arts.

Mount Mary College
2900 North Menomonee River Parkway, Milwaukee, Wisconsin 53222
Tel: +1(414) 258-4810
Fax: +1(414) 256-1205
President: Ruth Hollenbach
Academic Dean: Sr. Theresa Lamy
Founded: 1877, 1929
C: Arts and Sciences.

Mount Saint Mary College
330 Powell Avenue, Newburgh, N.Y. 12550
Tel: +1(914) 561-0800
Fax: +1(914) 562-6762
President: Ann Sakac (1977-92)
Vice-President for Academic Affairs: Agnes Boyle
Founded: 1931, 1959
D: Arts and Letters; Business; Education; Mathematics and Computer Science; Natural Science; Nursing; Philosophy and Religion; Social Science.

Mount Saint Mary's College California
12001 Chalon Road, Los Angeles, California 90049
Tel: +1(310) 476-2237
Fax: +1(310) 476-9296
President: Karen M. Kennelly (1989-92)
Academic Vice-President: Jacqueline Doud
Founded: 1925
C: Arts and Sciences.

Mount Saint Mary's College Maryland
Emmitsburg, Maryland 21727
Tel: +1(301) 447-6122
Fax: +1(301) 447-5755
President: James N.Loughran, S.J (1994-)
Provost: John W. Camphell
Founded: 1808
S: Liberal Arts.

Mount Vernon Nazarene College
800 Martinsburg Road, Mount Vernon, Ohio
43050-9500
Tel: +1(414) 397-1244
Fax: +1(414) 397-2769
President: E. Lebron Fairbanks (1989-93)
Vice-President for Finance and Management:
Richard Raymond
Founded: 1968

Multnomah School of the Bible
8435 Northeast Glisan Street, Portland, Oregon
97220
Tel: +1(503) 255-0332
Fax: +1(503) 254-4268
President: Joseph C. Aldrich
Senior Vice-President for Finance and
Management: Paul Griffin
Founded: 1936
C: Theology.

The Naropa Institute
2130 Arapahoe Avenue, Boulder, Colorado 80302
Tel: +1(303) 444-0202
Fax: +1(303) 444-0410
President: John Whitehouse Cobb (1985-)
Vice-President for Academic Affairs: Pearl Olson
Founded: 1974
Div: Buddhist/Religious Studies; Contemplative
Education; Contemplative Pyschology;
Contemplative Psychotherapy; Environmental
Studies; Gerontology and Long-term Care;
Interarts; Somatic Psychology; Transpersonal
Psychology; Writing and Poetics.

National College of Chiropractic
200 East Roosevelt Road, Lombard, Illinois 60148
Tel: +1(708) 629-2000
Fax: +1(708) 628-6554
President: James F. Winterstein
Vice-President for Educational Affairs: Richard
Gilmore
Founded: 1906, 1920
Chiropractic Studies.

Nazareth College of Rochester
4245 East Avenue, Rochester, N.Y. 14618-3790
Tel: +1(716) 586-2525
Fax: +1(716) 586-2452
President: Rose Marie Beston
Vice-President for Academic Affairs: Dennis Silva
Founded: 1924, 1973
C: Arts and Sciences.

Neumann College
Convent and Concord Roads, Aston,
Pennsylvania 19104
Tel: +1(215) 459-0905
Fax: +1(215) 459-1370
President: Nan B. Hechenberger
Vice-President for Academic Affairs: Rosalie
Mirenda
Founded: 1965, 1980
S: Liberal Arts.

New College of California
50 Fell Street, San Francisco, California 94102
Tel: +1(415) 241-1300
Fax: +1(415) 626-5171
President: Peter Gabel (1985-)
Registrar: Gina Barnett
Founded: 1971
S: Humanities; Public Interest Law; Psychology
(Graduate).

New England College
7 Main Street, Henniker, New Hampshire
03242-3293
Tel: +1(603) 428-2211
Fax: +1(603) 428-7230
President: William R. O'Connell, Jr
Vice-President for Academic Affairs: Tamar
Maroh
Founded: 1946
C: Arts and Sciences; Engineering.

New England School of Law
154 Stuart Street, Boston, Massachusetts 02116
Tel: +1(617) 451-0010
Fax: +1(617) 422-7333
Dean: John F. O'Brien
Registrar: Pamela Jorgensen
Founded: 2907
C: Law.

New Hampshire College
2500 North River Road, Manchester, New
Hampshire 03106-1045
Tel: +1(603) 668-2211
Fax: +1(603) 645-9665
President: Richard Gustafson
Vice-President for Academic Affairs (Acting):
Richard A. Gustafson
Founded: 1932, 1969
C: Business; Human Services.

New York Chiropractic College
255 Valentine's Lane, Seneca falls, N.Y.
13148-0800
Tel: +1(315) 548-3000
Fax: (315) 568-3015
President: Kenneth Padgett
Founded: 1919, 1977
Chiropractic Studies.

New York College of Podiatric Medicine
53 East 124th Street, New York, N.Y. 10035
Tel: +1(212) 410-8000
President: Louis Levine
Founded: 1912
Podiatric Medicine.

New York Institute of Technology
Northern Boulevard, Old Westbury, N.Y.
11568-8000
Tel: +1(516) 686-7516
Fax: +1(516) 626-6830
President: Mathew Schure (1981-)
Vice-President for Academic Affairs: King V.
Cheek
Founded: 1955, 1960

S: Architecture and Fine Arts.
C: Education; Engineering and Technology; Liberal Arts, Sciences and Media; Management; Osteopathic Medicine (New York).

New York Law School
57 Worth Street, New York, N.Y. 10013
Tel: (212) 431-2100
Fax: (212) 431-2847
President: James F. Simon
Founded: 1891
Law.

Niagara University
Niagara Falls, N.Y. 14109
Tel: +1(716) 285-1212
Fax: +1(716) 286-8355
President: Brian J. O'Connell
Executive Vice-President: Vincent J.O'Malley, C.M
Founded: 1856, 1883
C: Arts and Sciences; Business Administration; Nursing.
S: Education.

Nichols College
Center Road, Dudley, Massachusetts 01571-5000
Tel: +1(508) 943-1560
Fax: +1(508) 943-1560 ext. 102
President: Lowell C. Smith (1978-92)
Business Manager: Kenneth E. Grant
Founded: 1815, 1971
Div: Business Administration, Liberal Arts, and Public Administration; Continuing Education.

North Central College
30 North Brainard Street, Naperville, Illinois 60566-7063
Tel: +1(708) 420-3400
Fax: +1(708) 420-4234
President: Harold R. Wilde
Vice-President for Academic Affairs: William G. Berberet
Founded: 1861
Div: Arts and Letters; Economics and Business; Human Thought and Behaviour; Science; Continuing Education.

Northrop University
5800 West Arbor Vitae Street, Inglewood, California 90306
Tel: +1(310) 337-4413
President: John R. Beljan
Founded: 1942, 1975
C: Arts, Sciences and Education; Engineering; Computer Sciences; Law; Aerospace Engineering.

Northwest Christian College
828 East Eleventh Avenue, Eugene, Oregon 97401
Tel: +1(503) 343-1641
Fax: +1(503) 343-9159
President: James E. Womack
Academic Dean: Song NaiRhee
Founded: 1895, 1908, 1934
C: Arts and Sciences.

Northwest Nazarene College
623 Holly Street, Nampa, Idaho 83686
Tel: +1(208) 467-8011
Fax: +1(208) 467-8360
President: Gilbert Ford
Vice-President for Academic Affairs (Acting): Lilburn Wesche
Founded: 1913, 1917
C: Arts and Sciences.

Northwestern College of Chiropractic
2501 West 84th Street, Bloomington, Minnesota 55431
Tel: +1(612) 888-4777
Fax: +1(612) 888-6713
President: Donald Cassata
Vice-President for Academic Affairs: Charles W. Jones
Founded: 1941
Chiropractic Studies.

Norwich University
Northfield, Vermont 05663
Tel: +1(802) 485-2000
Fax: +1(802) 485-2580
President: Richard Schneider
Vice-President for Academic Affairs: Robert J. Wittman
Founded: 1819
Liberal Arts.

Notre Dame College
2321 Elm Street, Manchester, New Hampshire 03104
Tel: +1(603) 669-4298
Fax: +1(603) 644-8316
President: Carol Descoteaux, CSC
Vice-President for Academic Affairs: Vernon Lindguist
Founded: 1950
C: Arts and Sciences.

Nyack College
1 South Boulevard, Nyack, New York 10960
Tel: +1(914) 358-1710
Fax: +1(914) 358-1751
President: David E. Schroeder (1988-)
Dean (Acting): Ronald W. Ruegsegger
Founded: 1882
Liberal Arts.

Oberlin College
Oberlin, Ohio 44074
Tel: +1(216) 775-8121
Fax: +1(216)775-8886
President: S. Frederick Starr
Registrar: Lori Gumpf
Founded: 1833, 1850
C: Arts and Sciences; Conservatory of Music.

Occidental College
1600 Campus Road, Los Angeles, California 90041
Tel: +1(213) 259-2500
Fax: +1(213) 259-2907
President: John B. Slaughter
Vice-President for Business and Finance: Carl B.Vance
Founded: 1987
C: Arts and Sciences.

Oglethorpe University
4484 Peachtree Road, N.E., Atlanta, Georgia 30319
Tel: +1(404) 261-1441
Fax: +1(404) 364-8500
President: Donald S. Stanton
Executive Vice-President: John B. Knott III
Founded: 1835, 1964, 1971
C: Arts and Sciences.

Ohio College of Podiatric Medicine
10515 Carnegie Avenue, Cleveland, Ohio 44106
Tel: (216) 231-3300
Fax: (216) 231-0453
President: Thomas V. Melilo
Executive Vice-President: David R. Nicolanti
Founded: 1916
Podiatric Medicine.

Ohio Northern University
525 South Main Street, Ada, Ohio 45810
Tel: +1(419) 772-2000
Fax: +1(419) 772-1932
E-Mail: internet: info@onu. edu
President: DeBow Freed (1979-)
Vice-President for Academic Affairs: Anne Lippert
Founded: 1871, 1885, 1903
C: Arts and Sciences; Business Administration; Engineering; Pharmacy and Allied Health Sciences; Law.
I: Parmacy-Law I; Small Business I.

Oklahoma City University
2501 North Blackwelder, Oklahoma City, Oklahoma 73106-1402
Tel: +1(405) 521-5000
Fax: +1(405) 521-5264
President: Jerald C. Walker
Vice-President for Academic Affairs: Frank Pfaff
Founded: 1907, 1924
C: Arts and Sciences (Petree).
S: Sciences; Law; Business; Music; Nursing; Religion and Church Relations.

Olivet College
Olivet, Michigan 49076
Tel: +1(616) 749-7000
Fax: +1(616) 749-7121
President: Gretchen Kreuter
Academic Vice-President: B. Lee Cooper
Founded: 1844
C: Arts, Sciences, and Education.

Olivet Nazarene College
Kankakee, Illinois 60901
Tel: +1(815) 939-5011
Fax: +1(815) 939-0153
President: John C. Bowlingtt
Vice-President for Academic Affairs: Gary Streit
Founded: 1907, 1940
C: Arts and Sciences.

Orlando College
5500 Diplomat Circle, Orlando, Florida 32810
Tel: +1(407) 628-5870
Fax: +1(407) 628-1344
President: Ouida Kirby
Registrar: Leslie Diggs
Founded: 1918, 1953, 1982
Business and Management; Computer and Information Sciences.

Otis Art Institute of Parson's School of Design
2401 Wilshire Boulevard, Los Angeles, California 90057
Tel: +1(213) 251-0500
Fax: +1(213) 480-0059
President: Roger Workman
Registrar: Dorthea Hamilton-John
Founded: 1918, 1947
Arts and Design.

Ouachita Baptist University
410 Ouachita Street, Arkadelphia, Arkansas 71998
Tel: +1(501) 245-5000
Fax: +1(501) 245-5500
President: Ben Elrod
Vice-President for Academic Affairs: Mike Arrington
Founded: 1886
C: Arts and Sciences.
S: Music; Business.

Our Lady of Holy Cross College
4123 Woodland Drive, New Orleans, Louisiana 70131
Tel: +1(504) 394-7744
Fax: +1(504) 391-2421
President: Thomas E. Chambers
Dean of Academic Affairs: Gerald F. Deluca
Founded: 1916
C: Arts and Sciences.

Our Lady of the Lake University
411 S.W. 24th Street, San Antonio, Texas 4689
Tel: +1(210) 434-6711
Fax: +1(512) 436-0824
President: Sister Elizabeth Ann Sueltenfuss
Executive Vice-President: Robert E. Gibbons
Founded: 1911
C: Arts and Sciences.
S: Education and Clinical Studies; Social Work (Worden); Counselling Psychology; Business Administration; Communication and Learning Disorders.

Pace University-Pleasantville/Briarcliff
Bedford Road, Pleasantville, N.Y. 10570.
Tel: +1(914) 769-3200
President: Frank Falcone
Founded: 1963
Computer Science; Nursing.

Pacific Christian College
2500 East Nutwood Avenue, Fullerton, California
92631
Tel: +1(714) 879-3901
Fax: +1(714) 526-0231
President: E. Le Roy Lawson
Dean: Gerald C. Tiffin
Founded: 1928
C: Sciences.
*Div: Social Sciences; Arts and Science; Bible;
Church Growth.*

Pacific Lutheran University
South 121st and Park Avenue, Tacoma,
Washington 98447-0003
Tel: +1(206) 531-6900
Fax: +1(206) 535-8320
President: Loren J. Anderson
Provost: J. Robert Wills
Founded: 1890, 1960
*S: Business Administration; Education; Arts;
Nursing; Physics; Physical Education.*
*Div: Humanities; Natural Science; Social
Sciences.*

Pacific Oaks College
5 Westmoreland Place, Pasadena, California
91103
Tel: +1(818) 397-1300
Fax: +1(818) 397-1356
President: Katherine Gabel
Dean: Laila Aaen
Founded: 1961
C: Arts and Sciences.
S: Human Development.

Pacific Union College
Angwin, California 94508
Tel: +1(707) 965-6336
Fax: +1(707) 965-6432
President: Malcolm Maxwell (1983-)
Academic Dean: Charles Bell
Founded: 1882
C: Optometry.
S: Professional Psychology; Liberal Arts.

Park College
8700 River Park Drive, Parkville, Missouri 64152
Tel: +1(816) 741-2000
Fax: +1(816) 746-6423
President: Donald Breckon
Vice-President for Administration: Paul Rounds
Founded: 1875
C: Arts and Sciences; Public Affairs (Graduate).

Parsons School of Design
66 Fifth Avenue, New York, N.Y. 10011
Tel: +1(212) 229-8910
Fax: +1(212) 229-8975
Dean: Charles Olton (1988-)
Founded: 1896
*Fashion Design; Design Marketing; Illustration;
Communication; Photography; Fine Arts; Product
Design; Interior Design; Environmental Design.*

Pennsylvania College of Optometry
1200 West Godfrey Avenue, Philadelphia,
Pennsylvania 19141
Tel: +1(215) 276-6200
Fax: +1(215) 276-6081
President: Thomas L. Lewis
Registrar: Virginia G. Kennedy
Founded: 1919, 1964
Optometry.

Pennsylvania College of Podiatric Medicine
8th and Race Streets, Philadelphia, Pennsylvania
19107
Tel: +1(215) 629-0300
Fax: +1(215) 629-1622
President: James E. Bates
Vice-President for Fiscal Affairs: Dennis M.
Donohue
Founded: 1963
Podiatric Medicine.

Philadelphia College of Bible
200 Manor Avenue, Langhorne, Pennsylvania
19047-2990
Tel: +1(215) 752-5800
Fax: +1(215) 752-5812
President: W. Sherrill Babb (1979-93)
Vice-President of Academic Affairs: Wesley R.
Willis
Founded: 1913
Bible Studies; Education.

Philadelphia College of Osteopathic Medicine
4150 City Avenue, Philadelphia, Pennsylvania
19131
Tel: +1(215) 871-1000
Fax: +1(215) 871-2822
President: Leonard H. Finkelstein
Director of Admissions: Carol A. Fox
Founded: 1899
Osteopathic Medicine.

Philadelphia College of Textiles and Science
School House Lane and Henry Avenue,
Philadelphia, Pennsylvania 19144
Tel: +1(215) 951-2700
Fax: +1(215) 951-2615
President: James P. Gallagher
Vice-President for Academic Affairs: Richard A.
Nigro
Founded: 1844, 1941, 1960
C: Arts and Sciences.
S: Business Administration; Textiles.

Phillips University
100 South University Avenue, Enid, Oklahoma 73701
Tel: +1(405) 237-4433
Fax: +1(405) 237-1607
President: Robert D. Peck (1994-)
Vice-President, International Programes and Student Development: Walter B. Shaw
Founded: 1906
Div: Philosophy, History and Religion; Social Science; Fine Arts; Science; Business; Language and Communication.

Point Loma Nazarene College
3900 Lomaland Road, San Diego, California 92106
Tel: +1(619) 221-2200
Fax: +1(619) 221-2579
President: Jim Bond (1984-)
Vice-President for Academic Affairs: Val Christensen
Founded: 1902

Point Park College
201 Wood Street, Pittsburgh, Pennsylvania 15222-1984
Tel: +1(412) 391-4100
Fax: +1(412) 391-1980
Telex: 314426 point park col
President: J. Mathew Simon (1986-)
Vice-President and Dean (Acting): James O. Prescott
Founded: 1960, 1966
Div: Business, Accounting and Computer Science; Education and Community Services; Fine, Applied and Performing Arts; Government and International Studies; International Business and Management; Humanities and Human Sciences; Journalism and Communications; Natural Science and Engineering Technology.

Polytechnic University, Westchester Campus
Hawthorne, N.Y. 10532
Tel: +1(914) 347-6940
Fax: +1(914) 347-6939
Director: Kathleen V. MacDonald
Dean of Admissions: Ellen Hartigan
Graduate Studies.

Ponce School of Medicine
P.O. Box 7004, Ponce, Puerto Rico 00732
Tel: +1(809) 840-2511
Fax: +1(809) 844-3685
President: Luis F. Sala
Dean of Academic Affairs: Ana Padro
Founded: 1976
Medicine; Biomedical Sciences.

Pontifical Catholic University of Puerto Rico
Las Americas Avenue, Station 6, Ponce, Puerto Rico 00732
Tel: +1(809) 841-2000
Fax: +1(809) 840-4295
President: Rev. Fr. Tosello Giangiacomo
Vice-President for Academic Affairs: Lillian Ramos
Founded: 1948, 1949

C: Arts and Humanities; Business Administration; Education; Sciences; Law.
S: Medical Technology.

Pratt Institute
200 Willoughby Avenue, Brooklyn, N.Y. 11025
Tel: +1(718) 636-3600
Fax: +1(718) 622-6174
President: Warren F. Llchman (1993-)
Provost: Richard Barsam
Founded: 1887
S: Arts and Design; Architecture; Library and Information Sciences; Arts and Sciences.

Queens College
1900 Selwyn Avenue, Charlotte, North Carolina 28274-0001
Tel: +1(704) 337-2200
Fax: +1(704) 337-2517
E-Mail: Easylink: 62025524esl ud
President: Billy O. Wireman
Vice-President for Academic Affairs: Joyce H. Snealy
Founded: 1857, 1930, 1987
C: Arts and Sciences.

Quincy University
1800 College Avenue, Quincy, Illinois 62301
Tel: +1(217) 222-8020
Fax: +1(217) 228-5354
President: James F. Toal
Academic Dean: Gary Carter
Founded: 1846
C: Arts and Sciences.

Quinnipiac College
Mount Carmel Avenue, Hamden, Connecticut 06518
Tel: +1(203) 281-8600
Fax: +1(203) 248-4703
President: John L. Lahey
Founded: 1929
C: Liberal Arts; Business; Natural Sciences; Professional Training.

Reed College
3203 S.E. Woodstock Boulevard, Portland, Oregon 97202-8199
Tel: +1(503) 771-1112
Fax: +1(503) 777-7769
President: Stephen Koblik
Dean: Linda H. Mantel
Founded: 1909
Arts and Sciences.

Regis University
3333 Regis Boulevard, Denver, Colorado 80221-1099
Tel: +1(303) 458-4100
Fax: +1(303) 458-4102
President: Michael J. Sheeran, S.J.
Director of Admissions: Robert Blust
Founded: 1877
C: Liberal Arts.

*S: Professional Studies; Health Care
Professions.*

Rhode Island School of Design
2 College Street, Providence, Rhode Island
02903-2784
Tel: +1(401) 354-6100
Fax: +1(401) 454-6320
President: Lois A. Jazzuro
International Relations: Provost, Hardu Keck
Founded: 1877
*A: Architecture; Arts and Design; Fine Arts;
Liberal Arts; Museum Studies.*

Rhodes College
2000 North Parkway, Memphis, Tennessee 38112
Tel: +1(901) 726-3000
Fax: +1(901) 726-3718
Registrar: Glen Munson (1973-)
Executive Vice-President: David L. Harlow
Founded: 1912, 1855, 1875, 1984
C: Arts and Science; Special Studies.

Rider College
2083 Lawrenceville Road, Lawrenceville, New
Jersey 08648-3099
Tel: +1(609) 896-5000
Fax: +1(609) 896-8029
President: J. Barton Luedeke
International Relations: Helen Stewart, Vice-
President for Academic Affairs/Provost
Founded: 1865, 1921
*S: Liberal Arts and Sciences; Business
Administration; Education.*

Rivier College
420 South Main Street, Nashua, New Hampshire
03060
Tel: +1(603) 888-1311
Fax: +1(603) 888-6447
President: Jeanne Perreault
Founded: 1933
Nursing.

Robert Morris College
Narrows Run Road, Coraopolis, Pennsylvania
15108
Tel: +1(412) 262-8200
Fax: +1(412) 262-5958
President: Edward A. Nicholson
International Relations: Jo-Ann Sipple, Vice-
President for Academic Affairs
Founded: 1921, 1969
*Applied Sciences and Education;
Communications and Informations Systems;
Management.*

Rockford College
5050 East State Street, Rockford, Illinois
61108-2393
Tel: +1(815) 226-4000
Fax: +1(815) 226-4119
President: Bill Shields
International Relations: Joann Herren, Registrar
Founded: 1846, 1892
Arts and Sciences.

Rockhurst College
1100 Rockhurst Road, Kansas City, Missouri
64110
Tel: +1(816) 926-4000
Fax: +1(816) 926-4666
President: Thomas J. Savage, S.J.
International Relations: Nancis Tonjis, Registrar
Founded: 1910
Arts and Sciences; Management.

Rollins College
100 Holt Avenue, Winter Park, Florida 32789-4499
Tel: +1(407) 646-2000
Fax: +1(407) 646-2600
President: Rita Bornstein
International Relations: Charles Edmondson,
Provost
Founded: 1885
C: Arts and Sciences; Business.

Roosevelt University
430 South Michigan Avenue, Chicago, Illinois
60605-1394
Tel: +1(312) 341-3500
Fax: +1(312) 341-3657 ext. 3800
President: Theodore L. Gross
Provost: Robert J. Graham
Founded: 1945
*C: Continuing Education; Arts and Sciences;
Business Administration; Music; Education.*

Rosary College
7900 West Division Street, River Forest, Illinois
60305
Tel: +1(708) 366-2490
Fax: +1(708) 366-5360
President: Jean Murray
Founded: 1848, 1918
*S: Business; Library and Information Science;
Education.*

Rose-Hulman Institute of Technology
5500 Wabash Avenue, Terre Haute, Indiana 47803
Tel: +1(812) 877-1511
Fax: +1(812) 877-3198
President: Samuel F. Hulbert
Vice-President for Academic Affairs: James R.
Eifert
Founded: 1874
*Div: Applied Optics; Chemistry; Chemical
Engineering; Civil Engineering; Computer
Engineering; Computer Science; Economics;
Electrical Engineering; Mathematics; Mechanical
Engineering; Physics.*

Rosemont College
1400 Montgomery Avenue, Rosemont,
Pennsylvania 19010-1699
Tel: +1(215) 527-0200
Fax: +1(215) 527-0341
President: Ofelia Garcia (1991-93)
Dean: David Harnett
Founded: 1921
*Div: Arts; Business; English, Theatre and
Classics; Foreign Language and Literature;
Humanities; Natural Sciences and Mathematics;
Social Science.*

Russell Sage College
45 Ferry Street, Troy, N.Y. 12180
Tel: +1(518) 270-2000
Fax: +1(518) 271-4545
President: Sara S. Chapman
Founded: 1916
C: Arts and Sciences.

Sacred Heart University
5151 Park Avenue, Fairfield, Connecticut
06432-1000
Tel: +1(203) 365-7609
Fax: +1(203) 371-7999
President: Anthony J. Cernera
Vice-President for Academic Affairs: Thomas
Trebon
*C: Arts and Sciences; Business Administration;
Humanities; Social Sciences; Mathematics.*

St. Ambrose University
518 West Locust Street, Davenport, Iowa 52803
Tel: +1(319) 383-8888
Fax: +1(319) 383-8791
President: Edward Rogalski (1988-)
Provost: Don Moeller
Founded: 1882
*C: Arts and Sciences; Human Services;
Business.
I: Industrial Engineering.*

St. Bonaventure University
Route 417, St. Bonaventure, N.Y. 14778
Tel: +1(716) 375-2000
Fax: +1(716) 375-2005
President: Alice Gallin, O.S.U.
Vice-President for Academic Affairs: Edouard
Eckert
Founded: 1882
*S: Arts and Sciences; Business Administration;
Education.*

St. Edward's University
3001 S. Congress Avenue, Austin, Texas 78704
Tel: +1(512) 448-8400
Fax: +1(512) 448-8492
President: Patricia A. Hayes
Vice-President and Academic Dean: Donna M.
Jurick
Founded: 1885
*S: Behavioural and Social Sciences; Business
Administration; Education; Humanities; Natural
Sciences.*

St. Francis College
Loretto, Pennsylvania 15940
Tel: +1(814) 472-3000
Fax: +1(814) 472-3044
President: Christian R. Oravec, T.U.R.
Vice-President for Academic Affairs: Kathleen
Owens
Founded: 1847
*C: Arts and Sciences.
S: Industrial Relations.*

St. John's College Maryland
P.O. Box 2800, Annapolis, Maryland 21404
Tel: +1(410) 263-2371
Fax: +1(301) 263-4828
President: Christopher B. Nelson (1991-)
Vice-President of Academic Affairs: Eva T.H.
Brann
Founded: 1696
Liberal Arts.

St. John's College New Mexico
1160 Camino Cenz Blanca, Santa Fe, New
Mexico 87501
Tel: +1(505) 982-3691
Fax: +1(505) 989-9269
President: John Agresto
Registrar: Diane Trudell
Founded: 1964
C: Liberal Arts and Sciences.

St. John Fisher College
3690 East Avenue, Rochester, N.Y. 14618
Tel: +1(716) 385-8000
Fax: +1(716) 385-8129
President: William L. Pickett (1987-)
Academic Vice-President (Acting): Mary Pat
Seurkamp
Founded: 1948
*Div: Accounting; Anthropology; Biology;
Chemistry; Communication/Journalism;
Economics; Education; English; Gerontology;
History; Management; Mathematics; Modern
Languages and Classical Studies; Nursing;
Philosophy; Physics; Political Science;
Psychology; Religious Studies; Sociology.*

St. John's University
Collegeville, Minnesota 56321
Tel: +1(612) 363-2011
Fax: +1(612) 363-2504
President: Dietrich Reinhart, O.S.B.
Registrar: David Lyndgaard
Founded: 1857
*C: Arts and Sciences; Theology.
S: Political Science and Economics.*

Saint Joseph College
1678 Asylum Avenue, West Hartford, Connecticut
06117
Tel: +1(203) 232-4571
Fax: +1(203) 233-5695
President: Winifred E. Coleman (1991-)
Provost: Martin D. Snyder
Founded: 1925, 1935
Div: Education; Natural Science; Nursing;
Humanities; Social Science.

St. Joseph's College
Po. Box 850, Rensselaer, Indiana 47978-0408
Tel: +1(219) 866-6000
Fax: +1(219) 866-4497
President: Albert J. Shannon
Registrar: Edward Habrowski
Founded: 1889
C: Liberal Arts.

Saint Joseph's University
5600 City Avenue, Philadelphia, Pennsylvania
19131
Tel: +1(215) 660-1000
Fax: +1(215) 473-0001
E-Mail: internet: sju.edu
President: Nicholas S. Rashford, S.J. (1986-)
Provost: Vincent A. McCarthy
Founded: 1851
C: Arts and Sciences; Business and
Administration.

St. Lawrence University
Romoda Drive, Canton, N.Y. 13617-1445
Tel: +1(315) 379-5011
Fax: +1(315) 379-5502
President: Patti McGill Peterson
Registrar: Janet J. Flight
Founded: 1856
C: Arts and Sciences.

St. Louis College of Pharmacy
4588 Parkview Place, St. Louis, Missouri 63110
Tel: +1(314) 367-8700
Fax: +1(314) 367-2784
President: Thomas F. Patton (1994-)
Vice-President for Academic Affairs: Robert E.
Smith
Founded: 1864
Pharmacy.

St. Louis Conservatory of Music
560 Trinity Avenue, St. Louis, Missouri 63130
Tel: +1(314) 863-3033
President: Theodore C. Hansen
Founded: 1923
C: Music.

St. Martin's College
5300 Pacific Avenue, S.E. Lacey, Washington
98503
Tel: +1(206) 491-4700
Fax: +1(206) 459-4124
President: David Spangler
Founded: 1895
Div: Humanities; Social Science; Education;
Science; Engineering; Business and Economics.

St. Mary-of-the-Woods College
St. Mary-of-the-Woods, Indiana 47876
Tel: +1(812) 535-5151
Fax: +1(812) 535-4613
President: Sister Barbara Doherty
Registrar: Susan Meier
Founded: 1841, 1909
Arts and Sciences.

St. Mary's College of Minnesota
700 Terrace Heights, Winona, Minnesota
55987-1399
Tel: +1(507) 452-4430
Fax: +1(507) 457-1633
President: Brother Louis DeThomasis (1984-)
Executive Vice-President: Anthony Piscitiello
Founded: 1912
S: Humanities and Sciences; Business,
Computer Science, and Media Communications;
Fine and Performing Arts; Education.

St. Mary's College of California
P.O. Box 4800, Moraga, California 94575
Tel: +1(510) 631-4000
Fax: +1(510) 376-8497
President: Bro. Mel Anderson
Registrar: Barbara Lakin
Founded: 1863, 1938
S: Liberal Arts; Business Administration and
Economics; Education; Science.

St. Mary's University of San Antonio
Camino Santa Maria, San Antonio, Texas
78228-8507
Tel: +1(210) 436-3011
Fax: +1(210) 436-3500
President: Rev. John J. Moder
Registrar: Bro. Richard Dix
Founded: 1852, 1923
S: Business Administration; Law; Science
Engineering and Technology; Humanities and
Social Science.

St. Michael's College
Box 7, Winooski Park, Colchester, Vermont 05439
Tel: +1(802) 654-2000
Fax: +1(802) 655-4079
E-Mail: stratford@smcvax
Telex: 510 299 0013 vtsmc
President: Paul J. Reiss (1985-)
Vice-President for Academic Affairs: David
LaMarche
Founded: 1904
Div: Classical Studies and Humanities; English
Literature; Fine Arts; History and American
Studies; Modern Languages; Philosophy;
Religious Studies; Economics and Geography;
Political Science; Psychology; Sociology and
Anthropology; Biology; Chemistry; Computer
Science; Mathematics; Physics.

St. Norbert College
100 Grant Street, De Pere, Wisconsin 54115
Tel: +1(414) 337-3181
Fax: +1(414) 337-4073
President: Thomas A. Manion (1983-)
Vice-President for Academic Affairs/Dean: Robert
L. Horn
Founded: 1898
*Div: Humanities and Fine Arts; Natural
Sciences; Social Sciences.*
Ce: International Ce. (St. Norbert College).

St. Peter's College
2641 Kennedy Boulevard, Jersey City, New
Jersey 07306
Tel: (201) 915-9000
Fax: (201) 451-0036
President: Daniel A. Degnan
Registrar: Joan Z. Shields
Founded: 1872
C: Arts and Sciences; Education; Nursing.

St. Thomas University
16400 N.W. 32nd Avenue, Miami, Florida 33054
Tel: +1(305) 625-6000
Fax: +1(305) 628-6510
President: Edward Mc Carthy (1994-)
Vice-President of Academic Affairs: Norma
Goonen
Founded: 1961
*S: Business Administration; Arts and Sciences;
Law.*
*Div: Physical Sciences and Mathematics;
Religious Studies and Philosophy; Social
Sciences; Sports Administration and
Tourism/Hospitality.*

St. Thomas Aquinas College
Route 340, Sparkill, N.Y. 10976
Tel: +1(914) 359-9500
Fax: +1(914) 359-8136
President: Donald T. McNelis
Vice-President for Academic Affairs: Peter
O'Connor
Founded: 1952
Arts and Sciences.

Saint Xavier University
3700 West 103rd Street, Chicago, Illinois 60655
Tel: +1(312) 298-3000
Fax: +1(312) 779-9061
President: Ronald O. Champagne
Founded: 1847, 1956
C: Education; Nursing; Management (Graham).

Salem-Teikyo University
223 West Main Street, Salem, West Virginia 26426
Tel: +1(304) 782-5011
Fax: +1(304) 782-5395
President: Ronald E. Ohl
Provost: Wayne H. England
Founded: 1989

*Div: Education; English as a Second Language;
Humanities and Social Sciences; Japanese
Studies; Management Studies; Natural Science
and Mathematics; Physical Education and Sports;
Technology Studies.*

Samford University
800 Lakeshore Drive, Birmingham, Alabama
35229
Tel: +1(205) 870-2011
Fax: +1(205) 870-2654
President: Thomas E. Corts
Registrar: Martha Ann Cox
Founded: 1841, 1965
C: Arts and Sciences.
*S: Law (Cumberland); Business; Education;
Music; Pharmacy; Nursing (Ida V. Moffet); Divinity
(Beeson).*

San Francisco Art Institute
800 Chestnut Street, San Francisco, California
94133-2299
Tel: +1(415) 771-7020
Fax: +1(415) 749-4590
President: William O. Barrett
Vice-President for Academic Affairs: Keith
Morrison
Founded: 1871, 1961
Art.

San Francisco Conservatory of Music
1201 Ortega Street, San Francisco, California
94122
Tel: +1(415) 564-8086
Fax: +1(415) 759-3499
President: Colin Mordoch (1991-)
Director of Student Services: Collen Katzowitz
Founded: 1917
Music.

Sarah Lawrence College
Bronxville, N.Y. 10708
Tel: +1(914) 337-0700
Fax: +1(914) 395-2668
President: Alice Stone Ilchman
Registrar: Mary Driscoll
Founded: 1926, 1947
Arts and Sciences.

Savannah College of Art and Design
342 Bull Street, P.O. Box 4146, Savannah,
Georgia 31402-3146
Tel: +1(912) 238-2400
Fax: +1(912) 238-2436
President: Richard G. Rowan
Executive Vice-President: Nancy H. Weber
Founded: 1978
C: Art and Design.

The School of the Art Institute of Chicago
37 South Wabash, Chicago, Illinois 60603
Tel: +1(312) 899-5100
President: Peter Brown
Registrar: Elizabeth Hoover
Founded: 1866, 1879
S: Art.

School for International Training

Kipling Road, Brattlebord, Vermont 05301
Tel: +1(802) 257-7751
Fax: +1(802) 254-6674
President: Neal Mangham (1991-)
Assistant DirectorRegistrar: Linda Gobbo: Mary Henderson
Founded: 1964
Div: International Management; Language Teacher Education; Global Issues.

School of the Museum of Fine Arts

230 The Fenway, Boston, Massachusetts 02115
Tel: +1(617) 267-6100
Fax: +1(617) 424-6271
Dean: Bruce K. MacDonald
Dean: Deborah Dluhy
S: Fine Arts.

School of Visual Arts New York

209 East 23rd Street, New York, N.Y. 10010-3994
Tel: +1(212) 679-7350
Fax: +1(212) 725-3587
President: David Rhodes
Registrar: Cynthia Benolken
Founded: 1947, 1956
Div: Art Education; Art Therapy; Film; Fine Arts; Humanities and Sciences; Interior Design; Illustration and Cartooning; Graphic Design and Advertising; Photography.

Seattle Pacific University

3307 Third Avenue West, Seattle, Washington 98119
Tel: +1(206) 281-2050
Fax: +1(206) 281-2500
President: E. Arthur (Woody) Self (1994-)
Assistant to the President: Marjorie R. Johnson
Founded: 1891
S: Business and Economics; Education; Fine and Performing Arts; Health Sciences; Humanities; Natural and Mathematical Sciences; Physical Education and Athletics; Religion; Social and Behavioural Sciences.

Shenandoah University

1460 University Drive, Winchester, Virginia 22601
Tel: +1(703) 665-4500
Fax: +1(703) 665-4627
President: James A. Davis
Registrar: Paul G. Wiley II
Founded: 1875
S: Arts and Sciences; Conservatory of Music; Business; Health Professions; Nursing and Health Professions (Eleanor Wade Custer).

Shorter College

315 Shorter Avenue, Rome, Georgia 30165-4298
Tel: +1(404) 291-2121
Fax: +1(404) 236-1515
President: Larry Mc. Swain (1992-)
Vice-President for Administration Affairs: Wayne Dempsey
Founded: 1873

Div: Business; Communication Arts; Education; Fine Arts; Humanities; Mathematics and Computer Science; Natural Sciences; Religion and Philosophy; Social Science.

Siena Heights College

1247 East Siena Heights Drive, Adrian, Michigan 49221
Tel: +1(517) 263-0731
Fax: +1(517) 265-3380
President: Richard B. Artman (1994-)
Registrar: Robert Parker
Founded: 1893, 1939
C: Arts and Sciences.

Silver Lake College

2406 S. Alverno Road, Manitowoc, Wisconsin 54220-9319
Tel: +1(414) 684-4691
Fax: +1(414) 684-7082
President: Sister Barbara Belinske (1987-)
Academic Dean: Catherine Gilles
Founded: 1935
Div: Arts and Sciences; Business Administration.

Simpson College

2211 College View Drive, Redding, California 96003-8606
Tel: +1(916) 224-5600
Fax: +1(916) 224-5608
President: James Grant
Dean of Academic Affairs: Gordon Browr
Founded: 1921, 1971
C: Arts and Sciences.

Sioux Falls College

1501 South Prairie Avenue, Sioux Falls, South Dakota 57105
Tel: +1(605) 331-5000
Fax: +1(605) 331-6615
President: Thomas F. Johnson (1988-)
Provost: Richard Mayer
Founded: 1883, 1960
Div: Business Administration; Mass Communication; Education, and Health and Physical Education; Religion, English, and Foreign Languages; Music; Sciences; Social Science, Social Work, Psychology, History, and Political Science.

South Texas College of Law

1303 South Jacinto Street, Houston, Texas 77002-7000
Tel: +1(713) 659-8040
Fax: +1(713) 659-3807
President: William L. Wilks
Founded: 1923
Law.

Southeastern Bible College
3001 Highway 280 East, Birmingham, Alabama
35243
Tel: +1(205) 969-0880
Fax: +1(205) 969-0880
President: John D. Talley (1988-)
Registrar: Jean Judge
Founded: 1935
*S: General Education (Liberal Arts); Pastoral
Theology; Education; World Missions; Church
Music; External Studies.*

Southeastern University
501 Eye Street, S.W., Washington, D.C. 20024
Tel: +1(202) 488-8162
Fax: +1(202) 488-8093
President: W. Robert Higgins
Registrar and Director of Financial Aid: Irwin
Alexis
Founded: 1879
S: Arts and Sciences.

Southern Baptist University
1601 South Springfield, Bolivar, Missouri 65613
Tel: +1(417) 326-5281
Fax: +1(417) 326-1514
President (Acting): Wayne Gott
Founded: 1878
C: Business.
*S: Arts and Sciences; Education and Human
Studies; Fine Arts; Theology.*

Southern California College
55 Fair Drive, Costa Mesa, California 95626
Tel: +1(714) 556-3610
Fax: +1(714) 957-9317
President: Wayne E. Kraiss
Vice-President for Academic Affairs: Lewis
Wilson
Arts and Sciences.

Southern California College of Chiropractic
8420 Beverly Road, Pico Rivera, California 90660
Tel: +1(310) 692-0331
Fax: +1(310) 692-2505
President: William Ralph Boone (1991-)
Dean of Admissions (Acting): Vivian Makiyama
Founded: 1972, 1974
*Div: Basic Sciences; Associated Studies;
Chiropractic Philosophy; Chiropractic Art and
Science; Chiropractic Practice; Research.*

Southern California College of Optometry
2575 Yorba Linda Boulevard, Fullerton, California
92631
Tel: +1(714) 870-7226
Fax: +1(714) 526-3907
President: Richard L. Hopping
Registrar: Lisa Russo
Founded: 1904
Optometry.

Southern California Institute of Architecture
5454 Beethoven Street, Los Angeles, California
90066
Tel: (310) 574-11-23
Director: Michael Rotondi (1986-)
Founded: 1972
Architecture.

Southern College of Optometry
1245 Madison Avenue, Memphis, Tennessee
38104
Tel: +1(901) 722-3200
President: William E. Cochran
Vice-President for Academic Affairs: Douglas
H.Poorman
Founded: 1932
Optometry.

Southern Nazarene University
6729 Northwest 39th Expressway, Bethany,
Oklahoma 73008-2694
Tel: +1(405) 789-6400
Fax: +1(405) 491-6381
President: Loren P. Gresham
Registrar: Gary L. Lance
Founded: 1899, 1986
*C: Ministry and Humanities (Bethany);
Professional and Social Studies (Breese); Health
and Sciences.*
S: Business; Education; Nursing; Music.

Southwestern University School of Law
675 South Westmorland Avenue, Los Angeles,
California 90005-3992
Tel: +1(213) 738-6700
Fax: +1(213) 383-1688
Dean: Leigh H. Taylor
Registrar: Karen Kaeni
Founded: 1911, 1913
Law.

Spertus College of Judaica
618 South Michigan Avenue, Chicago, Illinois
60605
Tel: +1(312) 922-9012
Fax: +1(312) 922-6406
President: Howard A. Sulkin
Registrar: Lisa Burnstein
Founded: 1925, 1970
Foreign Languages; Theology; Public Affairs.

Spring Hill College
4000 Dauphin Street, Mobile, Alabama 36608
Tel: +1(205) 460-2011
Fax: +1(205) 460-2095
President: William J. Rewak
Academic Vice-President: S.J. Kenneth N.
Hamilton, Jr.
Founded: 1830
Arts and Sciences; Foreign Languages.

Stetson University
421 North Woodland Boulevard, Deland, Florida
32720-3781
Tel: +1(904) 822-7000
Fax: +1(904) 822-8832
President: H. Douglas Lee
Founded: 1883, 1889
C: Arts and Sciences; Law.
S: Music; Business and Administration.

Strayer College
025 15th Street, N.W., Washington, D.C. 20005
Tel: +1(202) 408-2400
Fax: +1(202) 289-1831
President: Ron K. Bailey
Academic Dean: Younes P. Benab
Founded: 1898, 1904, 1970
Business Studies.

Suffolk University
41 Temple Street, Beachon Hill, Boston,
Massachusetts 02114-02108
Tel: +1(617) 573-8000
Fax: +1(617) 573-8353
President: David J. Sargent (1989-)
Vice-President/Treasurer: Frank Flannery
Founded: 1906
C: Liberal Arts and Sciences.
S: Management; Law.

Swarthmore College
Chester Road and College Avenue, Swarthmore,
Pennsylvania 19081-1397
Tel: +1(215) 328-8000
Fax: +1(215) 328-8673
President: Alfred H. Bloom
Provost: Jennie Keith
Founded: 1864
S: Arts and Sciences.

Tampa College
3319 West Hillsborough Avenue, Tampa, Florida
33614
Tel: +1(813) 879-6000
Fax: +1(813) 871-2483
President: David Zorn
Dean of Industrial: Daniel Palladino
Founded: 1890, 1962
Business and Management Studies.

Texas Chiropractic College
5912 Spencer Highway, Pasadena, Texas 77505
Tel: +1(713) 487-1170
Fax: +1(713) 487-0329 ext. 242
President: S.M. Elliott
Registrar: Anne Mc. Lane
Founded: 1908, 1925
Chiropractic Studies.

Thomas College
West River Road, Waterville, Maine 04901-5097
Tel: +1(207) 873-0771
Fax: +1(207) 877-0114
President: George R. Spann
Vice-President and Dean: Richard L. Begin
Founded: 1894

Div: Liberal Arts.
C: Business; Teacher Education.

Tiffin University
155 Miami Street, Tiffin, Ohio 44883
Tel: +1(419) 447-6442
Fax: +1(419) 447-9605
President: George Kidd, Jr. (1981-)
Registrar: Alice Nichols
Founded: 1888
Div: Business; Criminal Justice.

Treveca Nazarene College
333 Mufreesboro Road, Nashville, Tennessee
37210-4411
Tel: +1(615) 248-1200
Fax: +1(615) 248-7728
President: Millar Reed
Registrar: Martha Eby
Founded: 1901, 1935
C: Arts, Sciences, and Education.

Trinity College Connecticut
300 Summit Street, Hartford, Connecticut 06106
Tel: +1(203) 297-2000
Fax: +1(203) 297-2257
President: Evan S. Dobelle (1994-)
Registrar: Nancy Birch Wagner
Founded: 1823, 1845
C: Arts and Sciences.

Trinity College Washington
125 Michigan Avenue, N.E., Washington, D.C.
20017-1094
Tel: +1(202) 939-5000
Fax: +1(202) 939-5134
President: Patricia A. McGuire
Registrar: Patricia V. Mitchell
Founded: 1897
C: Arts and Sciences.

Trinity University
715 Stadium Drive, San Antonio, Texas 78212
Tel: +1(210) 736-7011
Fax: +1(210) 736-8164
President: Ronald Calgaard (1979-)
Vice-President for Academic Affairs: Edward Roy
Founded: 1869
Div: Science, Mathematics, and Engineering;
Behavioural and Administrative Studies;
Humanities and the Arts.

Tuskegee University
Old Montgomery Raod, Tuskegee Institute,
Alabama 36088
Tel: +1(205) 727-8011
Fax: +1(205) 727-8451
President: Thomas P. Rosandich
Provost: William L. Lester
Founded: 1881, 1937
S: Agriculture and Home Economics; Arts and
Sciences; Business; Education; Engineering and
Architecture; Nursing and Allied Health;
Veterinary Medicine.

Union College Kentucky
College Street, Barbourville, Kentucky 40906
Tel: +1(606) 546-4151
Fax: +1(606) 546-2215
President: Jack C. Phillips
Vice-President for Academic Affairs: Paul S.
Moore
Founded: 1879
C: Arts, Science and Education.

Union College New York
Union Street, Schenectady, N.Y. 12308
Tel: +1(518) 388-6000
President: Roger H.Hull
Registrar/Director of Academic Service: Dwight
Wolf
Founded: 1795, 1945
Div: Engineering; Arts.
I: Management Institute (Graduate).

University of Charleston
2300 MacCorkle Avenue S.E., Charleston, West
Virginia 25304-1099
Tel: +1(304) 357-4800
Fax: +1(304) 357-4715
President: Edwin H. Welch (1989-)
Vice-President: Robert L. Frey
Founded: 1888, 1901, 1947, 1978
C: Arts and Sciences; Health Sciences;
Business.
S: Art and Design; Music and Fine Arts.

University of Dubuque
2000 University Avenue, Dubuque, Iowa
52001-5099
Tel: +1(319) 589-3000
Fax: +1(319) 589-3682
President: John J. Agria
Registrar: Donald J. Corliss
Founded: 1852
C: Liberal Arts.

University of Evansville
1800 Lincoln Avenue, Evansville, Indiana 47722
Tel: +1(812) 479-2000
Fax: +1(812) 479-2320
Telex: 8103530525 meadag evs
President: James S. Vinson
Registrar: Paul Aucoin
Founded: 1854, 1967
C: Arts and Sciences.
S: Business Administration; Education; Nursing
and Health Sciences.
Ce.

University of Health Sciences
2105 Independence Boulevard, Kansas City,
Missouri 64124-2395
Tel: +1(816) 283-2000
Fax: +1(816) 283-2303
President: John P. Perrin
Vice-President for Academic Affairs: Anthony J.
Silvagni
Founded: 1916
Osteopathy.

University of Indianapolis
1400 E. Hanna Avenue, Indianapolis, Indiana
46227-3697
Tel: +1(317) 788-3368
Fax: +1(317) 788-3300
President: G. Benjamin Lantz, Jr. (1988-)
Vice-President and Provost: Lynn R. Youngblood
Founded: 1902
C: Arts and Sciences.
S: Business; Education; Physical Thearapy
(Graduate); Nursing.

University of Judaism-Lee College
15600 Mulholland Drive, Los Angeles, California
90077
Tel: +1(310) 476-9777
Fax: +1(310) 471-1278
President: Rabbi Robert Wexler
Registrar: Jill Lasker
Founded: 1947
C: Education.
S: Graduate Studies.

University of Mary
7500 University Drive, Bismarck, North Dakota
58504
Tel: +1(701) 255-7500
Fax: +1(701) 255-7687
President: Thomas Welder
Registrar: James Cash
Founded: 1955
C: Arts and Sciences; Nursing; Law; Medicine.

University of Mary Hardin-Baylor
Box 399, UMHB Station, Belton, Texas 76513
Tel: +1(817) 939-8642
Fax: +1(817) 939-4535
President: Jerry G.Bawcom
Vice-President for Academic Affairs: Dennis Dillin
Founded: 1845, 1866, 1924, 1978
C: Arts, Sciences and Education; Fine Arts;
Business; Nursing.

University of Phoenix
4615 E. Elwood P.O Box 52076, Phoenix, Arizona
85072-9382
Tel: +1(602) 966-9577
Fax: +1(602) 829-9030
President: William H. Gibbs (1987-)
Executive Vice-President: Todd Nelson
Founded: 1976
P: Business and Management; Educational.
I: Health Care Professions; Computer
Information Systems.
Div: Institutional Research.

University of Portland
5000 North Willamette Boulevard, Portland,
Oregon 97203-5798
Tel: +1(503) 283-7911
Fax: +1(503) 283-7110
President: David Tyson, CSC
Academic Vice-President: Charles D. Sherrer,
CSC
Founded: 1901, 1935

Arts and Sciences; Business Administration;
Education; Engineering; Nursing.

University of Puget Sound
1500 North Warner Street, Tacoma, Washington
98416
Tel: +1(206) 756-3100
Fax: +1(206) 756-3500
President: Susan Resneck Pierce
Dean: Thomas A. Davis
Founded: 1888, 1972
S: Law; Business and Public Administration;
Education; Music; Occupational Therapy; Physical
Therapy.

University of Redlands
1200 East Colton Avenue, P.O. Box 3080,
Redlands, California 92373-0999
Tel: +1(714) 793-2121
Fax: +1(714) 793-2029
President: James R. Appleton
Vice-President for Finance and Administration:
Phil Doolittle
Founded: 1907
C: Arts and Sciences.
S: Music.
Ce: Lifelong Learning; Individualized Learning.

University of Richmond
Richmond, Virginia 23173
Tel: +1(804) 289-8640
Fax: +1(804) 287-6003
President: Richard L. Morrill (1988-92)
Provost: Zeddie P. Bowen
Founded: 1830, 1840, 1920
S: Arts and Sciences; Business; Leadership
Studies (Jepson); Law (T.C. Williams).
C: University (Applied Studies in Human
Resources Management, Humanities and Social
Sciences Information, Processing Systems, Legal
Assistant Studies).

University of Scranton
Linden and Monroe, Scranton, Pennsylvania
18510-4622
Tel: +1(717) 941-7400
Fax: +1(717) 941-6351
E-Mail: (Internet) panuskaj1@lion.ucs.uofs.edu
President: J.A. Panuska
Provost: Richard Passon
Founded: 1888, 1942
C: Arts and Sciences; Health, Education and
Human Resources.
S: Management.
Ce: Eastern Christian Studies; Professional
Development and Training.

University of Tampa
401 West Kennedy Boulevard, Tampa, Florida
33606-1490
Tel: +1(813) 253-3333
Fax: +1(813) 254-4955

President: David G. Ruffer
Provost/Vice-President for Academic Affairs:
Thomas J. Hegarty
Founded: 1931, 1933
C: Business; Liberal Arts and Sciences.

University of Tennessee at Chattanooga
615 McCallie Avenue, Chattanooga, Tennessee
37403
Tel: +1(615) 755-4111
Fax: +1(615) 756-5559
E-Mail: 620 47076 esl ud
Telex: 558494 utbookstor cta
President: David G. Ruffer
Registrar: Eugene Cropsey
Founded: 1886
C: Arts and Sciences; Business Administration;
Education; Engineering; Nursing; Health and
Human Services.

University of Turabo
[Universidad del Turabo]
P.O. Box 3030, Turabo, Puerto Rico 00658
Tel: +1(809) 743-7979
Chancellor: Claudio R. Prieto
Founded: 1872
S: Arts and Sciences.

University of West Los Angeles
1155 Arbor Vitae Street, Inglewood, California
90301-2902
Tel: +1(310) 215-3339
Fax: +1(310) 313-2124
President: Bernard S. Jefferson
Director of Development: Dennis McIntyre
Founded: 1966
S: Law; Paralegal Studies.

Upsala College
345 Prospect Street, East Orange, New Jersey
07019-1186
Tel: +1(201) 266-7000
Fax: +1(201) 678-8837
President: Robert Karsten (1989-)
Provost: Warren H. Funk
Founded: 1893
Liberal Arts.

Ursuline College
2550 Lander Road, Pepper Pike, Ohio 44124
Tel: +1(216) 449-4200
Fax: +1(216) 449-3180
President: Anne Marie M. Diederich, O.S.U.
Registrar: Anne Marie Siclare
Founded: 1872
C: Arts and Sciences; Nursing.

Valparaiso University
Valparaiso, Indiana 46383-6493
Tel: (219) 464-5000
Fax: (219) 464-5381
E-Mail: Easylink: 62048380 esl ud/Internet:
b.galow@exodus.valpo.edu/Bitnet:
v.galow@valpo.bitnet
President: Alan F. Harre (1988-)
Provost: Roy A. Austensen
Founded: 1859

C: *Education, Graduate Studies and Continuing Education; Engineering; Business Administration; Arts and Sciences; Nursing.*
S: *Law.*

Vandercook College of Music
3209 Street Michigan Avenue, Chicago, Illinois 60616-3886
Tel: (312) 225-6288 tall free-800-448-2655
Fax: (312) 225-5211
President: Roseanne Rosenthal (1989-)
Dean: Joseph W. Searle, Jr.
Founded: 1909
Music Education.

Vassar College
Raymond Avenue, Poughkeepsie, N.Y. 12601
Tel: +1(914) 437-7000
Fax: +1(914) 437-7187
President: Frances D. Fergusson (1986-)
Dean of the Faculty: Nancy Schrom Dye
Founded: 1861
Liberal Arts.

Vermont Law School
Chelsea Street, South Royalton, Vermont 05068
Tel: +1(802) 763-8303 toll free-800-227-1395
Fax: +1(802) 763-7159
Dean: Maximilian W. Kempner
Registrar: Nina L. Thomas
Law.

Wagner College
631 Howard Avenue, Staten Island, N.Y. 10301
Tel: +1(718) 390-3100
Fax: +1(718) 390-3467
President: Norman Smith (1988-)
Vice-President for Academic Affairs: Linda Basch
Biological Sciences; Computer Science; Economics; Business Education; Psychology; History; Humanities; Political Science; Mathematics; Nursing; Performing and Visual Arts; Sociology; Physical Sciences; Graduate S.

Walla Walla College
204 South College Avenue, College Place, Washington 99324-1198
Tel: +1(509) 527-2327
Fax: +1(509) 527-2253
President: Niels-Erik Andreasen (1990-)
Vice-President for Academic Administration: John C. Brunt
Founded: 1892
C: *Arts and Sciences.*
S: *Nursing; Theology; Engineering.*

Walsh College of Accountances and Business Administration
P.O. Box 7006, Troy, Michigan 48007-7006
Tel: +1(313) 689-8282
Fax: +1(313) 689-9066
President: David A. Spencer
Vice-President/Dean/Chief Academic Officier: Thomas Courneya
Founded: 1922
Business; Professional Accountancy; Finance; Management; Taxation.

Warner Pacific College
2219 S.E. 68th Avenue, Portland, Oregon 97215
Tel: +1(503) 775-4366 toll free-800-582-7885
Fax: +1(503) 775-8853
President: Marshall K. Christensen
Executive Vice-President: Arthur M. Kelly
Founded: 1937, 1959
Arts and Sciences.

Warren Wilson College
701 Warren Wilson Road, Asheville, North Carolina 28778
Tel: +1(704) 298-3325 toll free-800-934-3536
Fax: +1(704) 299-4841
President: Douglas M. Orr, Jr.
Registrar: Christa Bridgman
Founded: 1894, 1965
C: *Arts and Sciences.*

Washington College
300 Washington Avenue, Chestertown, Maryland 21620-1197
Tel: +1(410) 778-2800 toll free-800-422-1782
Fax: +1(410) 778-7850
E-Mail: u1782@applelink.apple.com
President: Charles H. Trout
Senior Vice-President for Management and Finance: Gene A. Hessey
Founded: 1782
C: *Arts and Sciences.*

Washington and Lee University
Lexington, Virginia 24450
Tel: +1(703) 463-8400
Fax: +1(703) 463-8945
President: John Delane Wilson (1983-)
Registrar: D. Scott Dittman
Founded: 1794, 1871
The College.
S: *Commerce, Economics and Politics; Law.*

Wayland Baptist University
1900 West Seventh Street, Plainview, Texas 79072
Tel: +1(806) 296-5521
Fax: +1(806) 296-4580
President: Wallace E. Davis, Jr.
Vice-President for Academic and Student Affairs: Weldon Beckner
Founded: 1908, 1917
S: *Arts and Sciences.*

Waynesburg College
51 W. College Street, Waynesburg, Pennsylvania 15370
Tel: +1(412) 627-8191
Fax: +1(412) 627-6416
President: Timothy R. Thyreen (1990-)
Registrar: Ronald Coltrane
Div: *Nursing; Business; Chemistry and Engineering; English; Biology; Education; Fine Arts; History, Science, Philosophy, and Religion; Sports Medicine; Psychology.*

Webster University

470 East Lockwood Avenue, Saint Louis, Missouri
63119-3194
Tel: +1(314) 968-6900
Fax: +1(314) 968-7112
President: Richard S. Myers (1994-)
Registrar: Lucy Ruth Rawe
Founded: 1915, 1924, 1983
C: Arts and Sciences.

West Coast University

440 Shatto Place, Los Angeles, California
90020-1765
Tel: +1(213) 487-4433 toll free-800-248-4928
Fax: +1(213) 380-4362
President: Robert M.L. Baker (1989-)
Registrar: Roger A. Miller
Founded: 1909
*C: Business and Management; Arts and
Science; Engineering and Computer Science.*

West Virginia Wesleyan College

Meade Street and College Avenue, Buckhannon,
West Virginia 26201
Tel: +1(304) 473-8000 toll free-800-522-9933(in
state)/800-722-9933(out of state)
Fax: +1(304) 473-8187
President: Thomas B. Courtice (1986-)
Dean: G. Thomas Mann
Founded: 1972
C: Liberal Arts.

Western International University

9215 North Black Canyon Highway, Phoenix,
Arizona 85021
Tel: +1(602) 943-2311
Fax: +1(602) 371-8637
Chief Executive Officer: Robert S. Webber
Registrar: Gloria Deschler
Founded: 1978
*C: Arts and Sciences; Business; General
Studies.*

Western Maryland College

2 College Hill, Westminster, Maryland 21157-4390
Tel: +1(410) 848-7000
Fax: +1(410) 857-2729
President: Robert H. Chambers, III
Vice-President for Academic Affairs: David B.
Seligman
Founded: 1867
C: Arts, Sciences and Education.

Western New England College

1215 Wilbraham Road, Springfield, Massachusetts
01119
Tel: +1(413) 782-3111
Fax: +1(413) 782-1746
President: Beverly W. Miller (1981-)
Vice-President for Academic Affairs: Rex P.
Stevens
Founded: 1919, 1951

*S: Business; Engineering; Arts and Sciences;
Law.*
D: Continuing Education.

Western States Chiropractic College

2900 N.E. 132nd Avenue, Portland, Oregon 97230
Tel: +1(503) 256-3180 toll free-800-641-5641
Fax: +1(503) 256-4021
President: William H. Dallas
Vice-President for Academic Affairs: Steven
Oliver
Chiropractic Studies.

Westminster Choir College

Princeton, New Jersey 08540
Tel: +1(609) 921-7100 toll free-800-962-4647
Fax: +1(609) 921-8829
President: J. Barton Luedeke
Dean: Allen Crowell
Founded: 1926
Arts and Sciences; Music.

Westminster College

1840 South 1300 East, Salt Lake City, Utah
Tel: +1(801) 484-7651 toll free-800-748-4753
Fax: +1(801) 466-6916
President: Charles Dick
Executive Vice-President and Treasurer: Stephen
R. Morgan
*S: Business (Gone); Arts and Science; Nursing
and Health Sciences.*

Wheeling Jesuit College

316 Washington Avenue, Wheeling, West Virginia
26003-6233
Tel: +1(304) 243-2000 toll free-800-624-6992
Fax: +1(304) 243-2243
President: Thomas S. Acker, S.J.
Academic Dean: Normand J. Paulhus
Founded: 1954
S: Arts and Sciences.
*Div: Adult Studies (Evening Studies); Business
(Graduate); Religion (Graduate).*

Wheelock College

200 The Riverway, Boston, Massachusetts 02215
Tel: +1(617) 734-5200
President: General N. Tirozzi (1994-)
Academic Dean: Marjorie Bakken
Founded: 1888, 1941
Liberal Arts; Professional Studies.

Whittier College

13406 E. Philadelphia Street, P.O. Box 634,
Whittier, California 90608
Tel: +1(310) 907-4200
Fax: +1(310) 698-4067
President: James L. Ash Jr
Dean of Faculty/Vice-President for Academic
Affairs: Lisa Rossbacher
Founded: 1887
C: Arts and Sciences; Law.

Whitworth College

West 300 Hawthorne Road, Spokane, Washington
99251-0002
Tel: +1(509) 466-1000
Fax: +1(509) 466-3221
President: William P. Robinson
Provost: Icenneth Shipps
Founded: 1890
C: Arts and Sciences.

Wilkes University

184 South River Street, Wilkes-Barre,
Pennsylvania 18766
Tel: +1(717) 824-4651
Fax: +1(717) 824-2245
President: Christopher N. Breiseth (1984-)
Vice-President for Academic Affairs: J. Michael
Lennon
*S: Liberal Arts and Human Sciences; Business,
Society and Public Policy; Science and
Engineering.*

William Carey College

498 Tuscan Avenue, Hattiesburg, Mississippi
39401-5499
Tel: +1(601) 582-5051
Fax: +1(601) 582-6454
President: James W. Edwards
Registrar: Sarah G. Burris
Founded: 1906, 1954
S: Arts and Sciences; Nursing; Music; Business.

William Mitchell School of Law

875 Summit Avenue, St. Paul, Minnesota 55105
Tel: +1(612) 227-9171
Fax: +1(612) 290-6414
President: James Hogg
Vice-President/Treasurer: Bruce Hutchins
Founded: 1900
Law.

Williams College

Main Street, Williamstown, Massachusetts 01267
Tel: +1(413) 597-3131
Fax: +1(413) 458-2158
E-Mail: Bitnet; Internet
Telex: 469735 economics ci
President: Francis Oakley (1985-)
Registrar: Charles R. Toomajian Jr
Founded: 1793
C: Arts and Sciences.
*Ce: Development Economics; Humanities and
Social Sciences.*

Wilmington College

320 DuPont Highway, New Castle, Delaware
19720
Tel: +1(302) 328-9401
Fax: +1(302) 328-9442
President: Audrey K. Doberstein
Registrar: Patricia Jennings
Founded: 1965
*S: Arts and Sciences; Behavioural and Applied
Sciences.*

Wingate College

Campus Box 3059, Wingate, North Carolina
28174-31060
Tel: +1(704) 233-8000
Fax: +1(704) 233-8125
President: Jerry McGee (1992-)
Registrar: Barbara Cox
Founded: 1896
*D: Humanities; Fine Arts; Science and
Mathematics; Natural and Social Sciences, and
Mathematics.*
S: Business; Education.

Wittenberg University

P.O. Box 720, Springfield, Ohio 45501-0720
Tel: +1(513) 327-6231 toll free-800-677-7558
Fax: +1(513) 327-6340
President: William A. Kinnison
Provost: Sammye C.Oreer
Founded: 1842, 1959
C: Arts and Sciences.

Woodbury University

7500 Glenoaks Boulevard, Burbank, California
91510-7846
Tel: +1(818) 767-0888
Fax: +1(818) 504-9320
President: Paul E. Sago (1990-)
Vice-President, Business Affairs and Controller:
Lowell K. Bokelman
Founded: 1874, 1960
*D: Architecture; Fashion Design; Interior
Design; Graphic Design; Business; Computer
Information Systems; Fashion Marketing.*

Xavier University of Louisiana

7325 Palmetto Street, New Orleans, Louisiana
70125
Tel: +1(504) 486-7411
Fax: +1(504) 482-2801
President: Norman C. Francis
Executive Vice-President: Anthony M. Rachal Jr
Founded: 1915
C: Arts and Sciences; Pharmacy.

Xavier University Ohio

3800 Victory Parkway, Cincinnati, Ohio
45207-5311
Tel: +1(513) 745-3000
Fax: +1(513) 745-1954
President: James E. Hoff
Registrar: David M. Sauter
Founded: 1831
*C: Arts and Sciences; Business Administration;
Social Sciences.*
*Ce: Management and Professional Development
(Training and Consultation to Business
Community); Xavier Entrepreneurial.*

York College of Pennsylvania
Country Club Road, York, Pennsylavania
17405-7199
Tel: +1(717) 846-7788
Fax: +1(717) 849-1607
President: George Waldner
Registrar: Rebecca Link
Founded: 1887, 1968
Arts and Sciences.

UNIVERSITIES AND COLLEGES WITHOUT GRADUATE SCHOOLS

PUBLIC INSTITUTIONS

Athens State College
301 Beaty Street, Athens, Alabama 35611
Tel: +1(205) 232-1800
Fax: +1(205) 233-8164
President: Jerry F. Bartlett
Assistant to the President: Susan Parker
Founded: 1822

Bluefield State College
900 Pulaski Street, Bluefield, West Virginia 24701
Tel: +1(304) 327-4000
Fax: +1(304) 325-7747
President: Leonard C. Nelson
Director of Admissions: Ralph Patsel
Founded: 1895

California Maritime Academy
P.O. Box 1392, Vallejo, California 94590
Tel: +1(707) 648-4200
Fax: +1(707) 648-4204
President: Mary E. Lyons
Business Manager: Jill Johns
Founded: 1929
Maritime Studies.

Cameron University
2800 Gore Boulevard, Lawton, Oklahoma 73505
Tel: +1(405) 581-2000
Fax: +1(405) 581-2421
President: Don Davis
Founded: 1909
Business; Education and Behavioural Sciences; Fine Arts; Liberal Arts; Science, Mathematics, and Technology.

Central State University
Wilberforce, Ohio 45384
Tel: +1(513) 376-6011
Fax: +1(513) 376-6530
E-Mail: 620 25183 esl ud
President: Arthur E. Thomas
Registrar: Anita Marbury
Founded: 1887
C: Arts and Sciences; Business Administration; Education.

Charter Oak College
270 Farmington Avenue, Suite 171, Farmington, Connecticut 06032-1934
Tel: +1(203) 677-0076
Fax: +1(203) 677-5147
President: Merle W. Harris
Director of Administration: Helen Giliberto
Founded: 1973

Christopher Newport College
50 Shoe Lane, Newport News, Virginia 23606
Tel: +(804) 594-7000
Fax: +1(804) 594-7713
President: Anthony Santoro
Senior Administrative Officer: Robert A. Netter
Arts and Humanities; Business and Economics; Social Science and Professional Studies.

City University of New York-Medgar Evers College
1150 Bedford Avenue, Brooklyn, New York
11225-2298
Tel: +1(718) 270-4900
Fax: +1(718) 270-5126
President: Edisen O. Jackson
Provost: Dominic Nwasike
Founded: 1969

City University of New York-New York City Technical College
300 Jay Street, Brooklyn, New York 11201
Tel: +1(718) 260-5000
Fax: +1(718) 855-2933
President: Charles W. Merideth
Provost: Emilie Cozzi
D: Business and Communications; Engineering Technology Technology; Health and Human Services; Liberal Arts and General Education; Science.

CITY UNIVERSITIES OF NEW YORK-YORK COLLEGE
94-20 Guy R. Brewer Boulevard, Jamaica, New York 11451
Tel: +1(718) 262-2000
Fax: +1(718) 262-2730
President: Josephine D. Davis
Founded: 1966

Concord College
Vermillion Street, P.O. Box 1000, Athens, West Virginia 24712-1000
Tel: +1(304) 384-3115
Fax: +1(304) 384-9044
President: Jerry L. Beasley
Registrar: Ray A. Mull
Founded: 1872
D: Business and Economics; Education, Library Science, and Physical Education; Fine Arts; Languages and Literature; Natural and Literature; Social Sciences.

Conservatory of Music of Puerto Rico

Minillas Station, G.P.O. 41227, Santurce, Puerto Rico 00940-1227
Tel: +1(809) 751-0160
President: Amilcar Rivera
Dean of Studies: Cecilia Talauera
Founded: 1959

Dakota State University

North Washington Avenue, Madison, South Dakota 57042
Tel: +1(605) 256-5111
Fax: +1(605) 256-5136
E-Mail: 620 11182 els ud
President: Jerald Tunheim
Provost: David E. Cook
Founded: 1881
C: Business and Information Systems; Liberal Arts; Natural Sciences.
S: Education.

Dickinson State University

Dickinson, North Dakota 58601-4896
Tel: +1(701) 227-2507
Fax: +1(701) 227-2006
President: Albert A. Watrel
Registrar: Marshall R. Melbye
Founded: 1918
S: Applied Sciences and Technology; Arts and Sciences; Business and Administration; Education, Health, Physical Education, and Recreation.

Elizabeth City State University

Parkview Drive, Elizabeth City, North Carolina 27909
Tel: +1(919) 335-4000
Fax: +1(919) 335-3493
E-Mail: 620 24524 esl ud
President: Jimmy R. Jenkins
Vice-Chancellor (Academic Affairs): Helen M. Caldwell
Founded: 1891

Fairmont State College

Locust Avenue, Fairmont, West Virginia 26554
Tel: +1(304) 367-4000
Fax: +1(304) 366-4870
President: Robert J. Dillman
Vice-President (Academic Affairs): H. Dean Peters
Founded: 1865

Fort Lewis College

Durango, Colorado 81301-3999
Tel: +1(303) 247-7010
Fax: +1(303) 247-7310
President: Joel M. Jones
Registrar: Susan Smith
Founded: 1911
S: Arts and Sciences; Business Administration; Education.

Glenville State College

200 High Street, Glenville, West Virginia 26351-9990
Tel: +1(304) 462-7361
Fax: +1(304) 462-7610
President: William K. Simmons
Vice-President (Academic Affairs): James L. Peterson
Founded: 1872

Indiana University East

2325 Chester Boulevard, Richmond, Indiana 47374
Tel: +1(317) 973-8200
Fax: +1(317) 973-8315
Chancellor: Charlie Nelms
Registrar: Karla Telfer
Founded: 1971

Langston University

P.O. Box 907, Langston, Oklahoma 73050
Tel: +1(405) 466-2231
Fax: +1(405) 466-3461
E-Mail: 620 09383 esl ud
President: Ernest L. Holloway
Registrar: Margie Allen Bonner
Founded: 1897
D: Applied Sciences; Arts and Sciences.
S: Business; Education and Behavioural Sciences; Nursing and Health Professions.

Lewis Clark State College

8th Avenue and 6th Street, Lewiston, Idaho 83501-2698
Tel: +1(208) 799-5272
Fax: +1(208) 799-2831
President: Lee A. Vickers
Registrar: Jean Sass
Founded: 1894
S: Liberal Arts and Sciences; Professional Studies; Technology.

Massachusetts Maritime Academy
P.O. Box D, Buzzards Bay, Massachusetts 02532
Tel: +1(508) 759-5761
Fax: +1(508) 759-4116
Telex: 5101012536 oiti ma usa
President: Christine Griffin
Treasurer: Michael A. Joyce
Founded: 1891

Mayville State University
330 3rd Street, Mayville, North Dakota 58257-1299
Tel: +1(701) 786-2301
Fax: +1(701) 786-4748
Telex: 384386 mys mavl ud
President: Ellen Chaffee
Senior Administrative Officer: Mary K. Iverson
Founded: 1889

Mesa State College
P.O. Box 2647, Grand Junction, Colorado 81502
Tel: +1(303) 248-1020
Fax: +1(303) 248-1903
President: Ray N. Kieft
Registrar: Rich Baca
Founded: 1925
*S: Business; Hummanities and Fine Arts;
Industry and Technology; Natural Science and
Mathematics; Nursing and Allied Health; Social
and Behavioral Science.*

Miami University-Hamilton Campus
1601 Peck Boulevard, Hamilton, Ohio 45011
Tel: +1(513) 863-8833
Fax: +1(513) 863-1655
President: Harriet V. Taylor
: Roberta Lathram
Founded: 1968

Missouri Southern State College
Newmand and Duquesne Roads, Joplin, Missouri
64801-1595
Tel: +1(417) 625-9300
Fax: +1(417) 625-3121
President: Julio Leon
Registrar: Eugene C. Mouser
Founded: 1937
*S: Arts and Sciences; Business; Educations and
Psychology; Technology.*

Missouri Western State College
4525 Downs Drive, Saint Joseph, Missouri
64507-2294
Tel: +1(816) 271-4200
Fax: +1(816) 271-4574
President: Janet Gorman Murphy
Registrar: Bob Hines
Founded: 1915
Liberal Arts and Sciences; Professional Studies.

New College of the University of South Florida
Sarasota, Florida 34243
Tel: +1(813) 359-4200
Fax: +1(813) 359-4298
Dean and Warden: Gordon E. Michalson Jr.
Director of Records and Registration: Nancy Ferraro
Founded: 1960

Oglala Lakota College
Box 351, Kyle, South Dakota 57752
Tel: +1(605) 455-2321
President: Elgin Bad Wound
Registrar: Walean Herman
Founded: 1970

Ohio University-Portsmouth Resident Credit Center
Portsmouth, Ohio 45662
Tel: +1(614) 354-6446
Fax: +1(614) 353-3879
Director: Eric Cunningham
Coordinator of Admissions: Gail H. Thornton
Founded: 1975

Ohio State University: Lima Campus
4240 Campus Drive, Lima, Ohio 45804
Tel: +1(419) 221-1641
Fax: +1(419) 221-1658
Dean/Director (Acting): Violet I. Meek
Associate Director (Fiscal Affairs): Howard Reed
Founded: 1960

Ohio State University: Mansfield Campus
1680 University Drive, Mansfield, Ohio 44906
Tel: +1(419) 755-4011
Fax: +1(419) 755-4241
Dean/Director: John O. Riedl Jr.
Assistant Director: Rodger C. Smith
Founded: 1958

Ohio State University: Marion Campus
1465 Mount Vernon Avenue, Marion, Ohio 43302
Tel: +1(614) 389-6786
Fax: +1(614) 389-6786 ext 6258
Dean/Director: Dominic Dottavio
Business Manager: Patty Ionno
Founded: 1957

Ohio State University: Newark Campus
University Drive, Newark, Ohio 43055
Tel: +1(614) 366-3321
Fax: +(614) 366-5047
Dean/Director: Julius S. Greenstein
Registrar: Kyle Morgan
Founded: 1957

Ohio University-Eastern
45425 National Road, St. Clairsville, Ohio 43950
Tel: +1(614) 695-1720
Fax: +1(614) 695-1720
Dean: James Newton
Assistant Dean: Richard G. McMann
Founded: 1957

Ohio University-Chillicothe
571 West 5th Street, P.O. Box 629, Chillicothe,
Ohio 45601
Tel: +1(614) 774-7200
Fax: +1(614) 774-7268
Dean: Delbert Meyer
Director of Student Services: Richard Whitney
Founded: 1946

Ohio University-Southern Campus
Ironton, Ohio 45638
Tel: +1(614) 533-4600
Fax: +1(614) 533-4632
Dean: Bill Dingus
Assistant Dean: Eric Cunningham
Founded: 1956

Ohio University-Zanesville
1425 Newark Road, Zanesville, Ohio 43701
Tel: +1(614) 453-0762
Fax: +1(614) 453-6161
Dean: Craig D. Laubenthal
Senior Administrative Officer: John Kelbley
Founded: 1946

Oklahoma Panhandle State University
Goodwell, Oklahoma 73939
Tel: +1(405) 349-2611
Fax: +1(405) 349-2302
President: Ray Brown
Registrar: Emma Shultz
Founded: 1909
*S: Agriculture; Business; Education; Liberal
Arts; Mathematics and Science.*

Oregon Institute of Technology
Campus Drive, Klamath Falls, Oregon 97601-8801
Tel: +1(503) 885-1000
Fax: +1(503) 885-1115
President: Lawrence J. Wolf
Registrar: Russell Lyon
Founded: 1947
Technology.

Ramapo College of New Jersey
505 Ramapo Valley Road, Mahwah, New Jersey
07430
Tel: +1(201) 529-7500
Fax: +1(201) 529-7508
President: Robert A. Scott
Registrar: Cynthia Finch
Founded: 1969
*S: Administration and Business; American/
International Studies; Contemporary Arts; Social
Science and Human Services; Theoretical and
Applied Science.*

Saint Mary's College of Maryland
Saint Mary's City, Maryland 20686
Tel: +1(800) 492-7181
Fax: +1(301) 862-0999
President: Edward T. Lewis
Executive Vice-President for Administration: John
D. Underwood
Founded: 1840

Shepherd College
Shepherdstown, West Virginia 25443
Tel: +1(304) 876-2511
Fax: +1(304) 876-3101
President: Michael P. Riccards
Registrar: Ruth Campbell
Founded: 1871

Southwest State University
Marshall, Minnesota 56258
Tel: +(507) 537-7021
Fax: +1(800) 642-0684
E-Mail: 628 60389 esl ud
President: Oliver Ford III
Registrar: Phil Coltart
Founded: 1963

State University of New York-College of Agriculture and Technology at Cobleskill
Cobleskill, New York 12043
Tel: +1(518) 234-5011
Fax: +1(518) 234-5333
President: Kenneth E. Wing
Registrar: Anna Bautochka
Founded: 1916
*D: Agriculture; Business; Early Childhood
Education; Food Service and Hospitality; Liberal
Arts and Sciences Administration.*

State University of New York-College of Technology at Farmingdale
Farmingdale, New York 11735
Tel: +1(516) 420-2000
Fax: +1(516) 420-2753
President: Frank A. Cipriani
Registrar: Marvin D. Feutz
Founded: 1912
*S: Arts and Sciences; Business; Engineering
Technologies; Health Sciences and Human
Services.*

State University of New York-College at Old Westbury
Box 210, Old Westbury, New York 11568
Tel: +1(516) 876-3209
President: L. Eudora Pettigrew
Registrar: Patricia Smith
Founded: 1965

Texas A & M University at Galveston
51st on Pelican Island, P.O. Box 1675, Galveston,
Texas 77553
Tel: +1(409) 740-4400
Fax: +1(409) 740-4407
Campus Dean: David J. Schmidly
Director of Admissions: Su-Zan Harper
Founded: 1962
Maritime Studies.

Thomas A. Edison State College
101 West State Street, CN545 Trenton, New
Jersey 08608-1176
Tel: +1(609) 984-1100
Fax: +1(609) 984-1193
President: George A. Pruitt
Registrar: Jack Phillips
Founded: 1972

United States Coast Guard Academy
New London, Connecticut 06320-4195
Tel: +1(203) 444-8444
Fax: +1(203) 444-8288
Superintendent: Paul E. Versaw
Registrar: G. Phillip Boeding
Founded: 1876

United States Merchant Marine Academy
Steamboat Road, Kings Point, New York 11024
Tel: +1(516) 773-5000
Fax: +1(800) 732-6287
Superintendent: P.L. Krinsky
Registrar: Janet F. Palmer
Founded: 1943
Merchant Marine Studies.

University of Arkansas at Pine Bluff
North Cedar Street, Pine Bluff, Arkansas
71601-2799
Tel: +1(501) 543-8000
Fax: +1(501) 543-2021
Chancellor: Lawrence A. Davis Jr.
Vice-Chancellor (Academic Affairs): Mary E.
Benjamin
Founded: 1873
D: Continuing Education.
*S: Agriculture and Home Economics; Education;
Science and Technology.*

University of Arkansas at Monticello
Box 3596, Monticello, Arkansas 71655
Tel: +1(501) 367-6811
Fax: +1(501) 460-1321
Chancellor: Fred J. Taylor
Registrar: Janet Danley
Founded: 1909

University of Connecticut at Hartford
200 Bloomfield Avenue, West Hartford,
Connecticut 06117
Tel: +1(203) 241-4832
Fax: +1(203) 241-4822
Telex: 883997 ips intl
Director: Russell F. Farnen
Registrar: Carolyn Butler
Founded: 1946

University of Connecticut at Waterbury
Waterbury, Connecticut 06710-2288
Tel: +1(203) 596-4080
Fax: +1(203) 754-8540
Director: Cleveland Donald Jr.
Registrar: Angela Brightly
Founded: 1946

University of Connecticut at Avery Point
1084 Shennecosset Road, Groton, Connecticut
06340-6097
Tel: +1(203) 446-1020
Fax: +1(203) 445-3498
Director of Avery Point Campus: James L. Baird
Registrar: Mary Harrison
Founded: 1967

University of Hawaii at Hilo
Hilo, Hawaii 96720
Tel: +1(808) 933-3311
Fax: +1(808) 933-3622
Senior Vice-President and Chancellor: Edward J.
Kormondy
Coordinator for Records and Registration: Patrick
T. Omori
Founded: 1970
C: Agriculture; Arts and Sciences.

University of Hawaii-West Oahu College
96-043 Ike, Pearl City, Hawaii 96782
Tel: +1(808) 456-5921
Fax: +1(808) 456-5208
Chancellor: Eward J. Kormondy
Dean of Student Services: Stella Asahara
Founded: 1976

University of Houston Downtown
One Main Street, Houston, Texas 77002
Tel: +1(713) 221-8000
Fax: +1(713) 221-8064
President: George Magner
Registrar: Ann McDonald
Founded: 1974
*C: Humanities and Social Sciences; Sciences
and Technology.*

University of Maine at Augusta
University Heights, Augusta, Maine 04330-9410
Tel: +(1207) 621-3000
Fax: +1(207) 621-3405
President: George P. Connick
Registrar: Ann Corbett
Founded: 1965

University of Maine at Farmington
86 Main Street, Farmington, Maine 04938
Tel: +1(207) 778-7000
Fax: +1(207) 778-7247
President: Michael J. Orendulf
Registrar: Hazel Doak
Founded: 1864

University of Maine at Fort Kent
25 Pleasant Street, Fort Kent, Maine 04743-1292
Tel: +1(207) 834-3162
Fax: +(207) 834-3144
President: Richard G. Dumont
Registrar: Donald M. Raymond
Founded: 1878

University of Maine at Presque Isle
181 Main Presque Isle, Maine 04769
Tel: +1(207) 764-0311
Fax: +1(207) 764-0311
President: W. Michael Easton
Registrar: Sharon Roix
Founded: 1903

University of Maryland-University College
University Boulevard at Adelphi Road, College
Park, Maryland 20742-1628
Tel: +1(301) 985-7000
Fax: +1(301) 985-7364
E-Mail: 629 29200 esl ud
President: T. Benjamin Massey
Registrar: Mary Jane Cramer
Founded: 1947

University of Minnesota at Morris
Morris, Minnesota 56267
Tel: +1(612) 589-2211
Fax: +1(612) 589-381
E-Mail: 628 60901 els ud
Chancellor: David C. Johnson
Registrar: Ruth Thielke
Founded: 1959

University of Pittsburgh at Greensburg
Greensburg, Pennsylvania 15601
Tel: +1(412) 837-7040
Fax: +1(412) 836-9901
President: George F. Chambers
Registar: Carol Calloway
Founded: 1963

University of Pittsburgh at Johnstown
Johnstown, Pennsylvania 15904
Tel: +1(814) 269-7000
Fax: +1(814) 269-2096
President: Frank H. Blackington III
Registrar: Josoph Kissell
Founded: 1927

University of Pittsburgh at Bradford
ampus Drive, Bradford, Pennsylvania 16701
Tel: +1(814) 362-7500
Fax: +1(814) 362-7684
President: Richard E. McDowell
Registrar: Saguna Nayak
Founded: 1963

University of Puerto Rico, Arecibo Technological University College
P.O. Box 4010, Arecibo, Puerto Rico 00613
Tel: +1(809) 878-2830
Fax: +1(809) 880-4972
Telex: 1080641
Director/Dean: Zaida Perez
Registrar: Delvis Tarrado
Founded: 1967

University of Puerto Rico, Bayamà7on Technological University College
Bayamón, Puerto Rico 00959-1919
Tel: +1(809) 786-2885
Fax: +1(809) 798-1595
Director/Dean: Aida Canals de Bird
Registrar: Rafael Rosado
Founded: 1971

University of Puerto Rico Cayey University College
Barcelo Avenue, Cayey, Puerto Rico 00737
Tel: +1(809) 738-2161
Fax: +1(809) 738-8039
Chancellor: Margarita Benitez
Registar: Luis T. De la Cruz
Founded: 1967

University of Puerto Rico Humachao University College
CUH Station, Box 428, Humacao, Puerto Rico 00791
Tel: (809) 850-0000
Fax: (809) 852-4638
Chancellor: Félix Castrodad
Registrar: Olfa Gonzaález
Founded: 1962
C: Administrative Sciences; Arts; Sciences.

University of Puerto Rico, Ponce Technological University College
P.O. Box 7186, Ponce, Puerto Rico 00732
Tel: +1(809) 844-8181
Fax: +1(809) 840-8108
Dean/Director: Pedro E. Laboy
Registrar: Jaime Atiles
Founded: 1970

University of Science and Arts of Oklahoma
Chickasha, Oklahoma 73018-0001
Tel: +1(405) 224-3140
Fax: +1(405) 521-6244
President: Roy Troutt
Vice-President (Academic Affairs): John Feaver
Founded: 1908

University of South Carolina at Spartanburg
Spartanburg, South Carolina 29303
Tel: +1(803) 599-2000
Fax: +1(803) 599-2375
Chancellor: Olin B. Sansbury, Jr
Registrar: Eric S. Jolly
Founded: 1967
S: Nursing (Mary Black); Business Administration and Economics; Education; Humanities and Sciences.

University of South Carolina at Aiken
171 University Parkway, Aiken, South Carolina 29801
Tel: +1(803) 648-6851
Fax: +1(803) 641-3362
Chancellor: Robert E. Alexander
Registrar: Vivan Grice
Founded: 1961
C: Humanities and Social Sciences; Sciences.
S: Business Administration and Economics; Education; Nursing.

Valley City State University
Valley City, North Dakota 58072
Tel: +1(701) 845-7102
Fax: +1(701) 845-7245
President: Charles B. House Jr.
Registrar: Carl Peter
Founded: 1890

West Liberty State College
West Liberty, West Virginia 26074
Tel: +1(304) 336-5000
Fax: +1(304) 336-8285
President: Clyde D. Campbell
Registrar: Nelson Cain
Founded: 1837
S: *Business Administration; Education and Human Resources; Liberal Arts; Natural Sciences, Health Professions, and Mathematics.*

West Virginia State College
Institute, West Virginia 25112
Tel: +1(304) 766-3000
Fax: +1(304) 768-9842
President: Hazo W. Carter
Director for Admissions and Registration: John L. Fuller
Founded: 1891

PRIVATE INSTITUTIONS

Academy of Art College
79 New Montgomery Street, San Francisco, California 94105
Tel: +1(415) 274-2200
President: Andrew Jameson
Chief Financial Officer: Martha Lozano
Founded: 1929
Art.

Academy of the New Church
P.O. Box 278, Bryn Athyn, Pennsylvania 19009-0278
Tel: +1(215) 938-2543
Fax: +1(215) 938-2616
President: Rev. Daniel W. Goodenough
Dean of the College: Brian L. Schnarr
Founded: 1876
Theological Studies.

Agnes Scott College
East College Avenue, Decatur, Georgia 30030
Tel: +1(404) 371-6000
Fax: +1(404) 371-6177
President: Ruth A. Schmidt
Registrar: Mary K. Jarbok
Founded: 1889

Alaska Bible College
Box 289, Glennallen, Alaska 99588
Tel: +1(907) 822-3201
Fax: +1(907) 822-3290
President: Gary J. Ridley
Chief Officer for Academic Affairs: Steven Hostetter
Founded: 1966

Albertus Magnus College
700 Prospect Street, New Haven, Connecticut 06511-1189
Tel: +1(203) 773-8550
Fax: +1(203) 773-3117
President: Julia M. McNamara
Registrar: Gail Buccino
Founded: 1925

Albion College
611 East Porter Street, Albion, Michigan 49224-1899
Tel: +1(517) 629-1000
Fax: +1(517) 629-0509
President: Melvin L. Vulgamore
Provost: Margaret W. Curtis
Founded: 1835

Albright College
Box 15234, Reading, Pennsylvania 19612
Tel: +1(215) 921-2381
Fax: +1(215) 921-7530
President: Ellen S. Hurwitz
Vice-President (Academic Affairs): James Pitts
Founded: 1856

Alderson-Broaddus College
Philippi, West Virginia 26416
Tel: +1(304) 457-1700
Fax: +1(304) 457-6239
President: W. Christian Sizemore
Academic Dean: Robert V.Digman
Founded: 1871

Alice Lloyd College
Pippa Passes, Kentucky 41844
Tel: +1(606) 368-2101
Fax: +1(606) 368-2125
President: Fred Mullinax
Registrar: Thelmarie Thornsberry
Founded: 1923

Allen University
1530 Harden Street, Columbia, South Carolina 29204
Tel: +1(803) 254-4165
President: Collie Coleman
Director of Financial Services: William Love
Founded: 1870

Alma College
614 West Superior Street, Alma, Michigan 48801-1599
Tel: +1(517) 463-7111
Fax: +1(517) 463-7277
President: Alan J. Stone
Provost: Ann Stuart
Founded: 1886

Alvernia College
Reading, Pennsylvania 19607-1799
Tel: +1(215) 777-5411
Fax: +1(215) 777-6632
President: Daniel N. DeLucca
Vice-President (Academic Affairs): Richard Reed
Founded: 1958

Alverno College
3401 South 39 Street, PO Box 343922 Milwaukee,
Wisconsin 53234-3922
Tel: +1(414) 382-6004
Fax: +1(414) 382-6354
President: Joel Read
Registrar: Marianne Foote
Founded: 1887
D: Arts and Humanities; Behavioral Sciences;
Business and Management; Education; Fine Arts;
Natural Sciences; Nursing.

American Armenian International College
1950 Third Street, La Vern, California 91750
Tel: +1(714) 593-3511
Fax: +1(714) 593-0879
President: Garbis Der Yeghiayan
Coordinator of Academic Services
Founded: 1976

American College for the Applied Arts
3330 Peachtree Road, NE, Atlanta, Geogia 30326
Tel: +1(404) 231-9000
Fax: +1(404) 231-9000
President: Rafael A. Lago
Registrar: Sydney Sattler
Founded: 1977
Applied Arts.

American College for the Applied Arts
1651 Westwood Boulevard, Los Angeles,
California 90024
Tel: +1(310) 470-2000
Fax: +(310) 477-8640
President: Vicki McCarrell
Dean for Academic Affairs: Edi Lovenz
Founded: 1982
Applied Arts.

American Indian Bible College
10020 North 15th Avenue, Phoenix, Arizona 85021
Tel: +1(602) 944-3335
Fax: +1(602) 943-8299
President: David J. Moore
Academic Dean: Judith Mattes
Founded: 1957

American Technical Institute
P.O. Box 8, Brunswick, Teneessee 38014
Tel: +1(901) 382-5857
Fax: +(901) 385-7627
President: D.W. Jones
Records Clerk: Sharon Bryant
Founded: 1982

American University of Puerto Rico
Box 2037, Bayamon, Puerto Rico 00960-2037
Tel: +1(809) 798-2040
Fax: +1(809) 785-7377
President: Juan B. Nazario-Negron
Vice-President (Academic Affairs): Jose Jaime
Rivera
Founded: 1963

Amherst College
Amherst, Massachusetts 01002
Tel: +1(413) 542-2000
Fax: +1(413) 542-8103
President: Peter R. Pouncey
Senior Administrative Affairs: Ronald C.
Rosbottom
Founded: 1821

Anderson College
Anderson, South Carolina 29621
Tel: +1(803) 231-2000
Fax: +(803) 231-2004
President: Mark L. Hopkins
Registrar: William Childress
Founded: 1911

Appalachian Bible College
Bradley, West Virginia 25818
Tel: +1(304) 877-6428
Fax: +1(304) 877-6423
President: Daniel L. Anderson
Academic Dean: Douglas K. Winn
Founded: 1950

Arizona College of the Bible
2045 West Northern Avenue, Phoenix, Arizona
85021
Tel: +1(602) 995-2670
President: Robert W. Benton
Vice-President (Academic Affairs): John D.
Bechtle
Founded: 1971

Arkansas Baptist College
1600 Bishop Street, Little Rock, Arkansas 72202
Tel: +1(501) 374-7856
President: William T. Keaton
Dean of Academic Affairs: Mary R. Jarrett
Founded: 1884

Arkansas College
2300 Highland Road, P.O. Box 2317, Batesville,
Arkansas 72503
Tel: +1(501) 793-9813
Fax: +1(501) 698-4622
President: John V. Griffith
Registrar: Frances B. Rodgers
Founded: 1872

Arlington Baptist College
3001 West Division, Arlington, Texas 76012-3425
Tel: +1(817) 461-8741
Fax: +1(817) 274-1138
President: Rev. David Bryant
Registrar: Helen Sullivan
Founded: 1939

Art Academy of Cincinnati
Cincinnati, Ohio 45202
Tel: +1(513) 721-5205
Fax: +1(513) 562-8778
Director: Roger Williams
Registrar: Tersa Campbell
Founded: 1887
Art.

Art Academy of Boston
Boston, Massachusetts
Tel: +1(617) 262-1223
Fax: +1(617) 437-1226
President: Stan Trecker
Registrar: William Tisdale
Founded: 1912
Art.

Art Institute of Southern California
2222 Lagua Canyond Road
Tel: +1(714) 497-3309
Fax: +1(714) 497-4399
President: John W. Lottes
Registrar: Susanna Wilkinson
Founded: 1962
Art.

Asbury College
201 North Lexington Avenue, Wilmore, Kentucky
40390
Tel: +1(606) 858-3511
Fax: +1(606) 858-3921
President: David Gyerston
Registrar: Timothy Thomas
Founded: 1890

Atlanta Christian College
2605 Ben Hill Road, East Point, Georgia 30344
Tel: +1(404) 761-8861
President: Edwin Groover
Registrar: Lisa Sellers
Founded: 1937

Atlanta College of Art
Atlanta, Georgia 30309
Tel: +1(404) 898-1164
Fax: +1(404) 898-9577
President: Ellen L. Mayer
Registrar: Kate Flower
Founded: 1928
Art.

Atlantic Union College
South Lancaster, Massachusetts 01561
Tel: +1(508) 368-2000
Fax: +1(508) 368-2015
President: Lawrence T. Geraty
Academic Dean: Carol M. Allen
Founded: 1882

Augustana College
Rock Islan, Illinois 61201
Tel: +1(404) 898-1164
Fax: +1(404) 898-9577
President: Thomas Tredway
Director of Records: Michael Kirn
Founded: 1860

Baker College of Cadillac
Cadillac, Mishigan 49601
Tel: +1(616) 775-8458
Founded: 1986

Baker College of Flint
Flint, Michigan 48507-5508
Tel: +1(313) 766-4000
Fax: +1(313) 766-4049
President: Julianne T. Princinsky (1994-)
Registrar: David Johnston
Founded: 1911

Baker College of Muskegon
Muskegon, Michigan 49442
Tel: +1(616) 726-4904
Fax: +1(616) 728-1414
President: Robert D. Jewell
Registrar: Judy Cowden
Founded: 1888

Baker College of Owosso
1020 South Washington Street, Owosso, Michigan
48867
Tel: +1(517) 723-5251
Fax: +1(517) 723-3355
President: Rick Amidon
Director of Admissions: Bruce Lundeen
Founded: 1984

Barat College
700 East Westleigh Road, Lake Forest, Illinois
60045-3297
Tel: +1(708) 234-3000
Fax: +1(708) 615-5000
President: Lucy S. Morros
Vice-President (Finance and Administration):
Judy Moore
Founded: 1858

Barber-Scotia College
145 Cabarrus Avenue, Concord, North Carolina
28025
Tel: +1(704) 786-5171
Fax: +1(704) 784-3817
President: Joel O. Nwagbaraocha
Registrar: Marian Thompson
Founded: 1867

Barnard College
New York, New York 10027-6598
Tel: +1(212) 854-5262
Fax: +1(212) 854-7491
President: Ellen V. Futter
Registrar: Constance A. Brown
Founded: 1889

Bartlesville Wesleyan College
2201 Silverlake Road, Bartlesville, Oklahoma
74006-6299
Tel: +1(918) 333-6151
Fax: +1(918) 335-6210
President: Paul R. Mills
Registrar: Beulah Hooker
Founded: 1909

Barton College
Wilson, North, Carolina 27893
Tel: +1(919) 399-6300
Fax: +1(919) 237-4957
President: James B. Hemby
Vice-President for Institution: F. Mark Davis
Founded: 1902

Bassist College
2000 Southwest 5th Avenue, Portland, Oregon
97201
Tel: +1(503) 228-6528
Fax: +1(503) 228-4227
President: Donald Bassist
Registrar: christina Billinton
Founded: 1962

Bates College
Lewiston, Maine 04240
Tel: +1(207) 786-6255
Fax: (207) 786-6123
President: Donald W. Harward
Dean of Faculty: Marthar A. Crunkleton
Founded: 1855

Belhaven College
1500 Peachtree Street, Jackson, Mississippi
39202-1789
Tel: +1(601) 968-5940
Fax: +1(601) 968-9998
President: Newton Wilson
Registrar: Carol B. Busbee
Founded: 1883

Bellevue College
Galvin Road at Harvell Drive, Bellevue, Nebraska
68005-3039
Tel: +1(402) 291-8100
Fax: (402) 293-2020
President: John B. Muller
Founded: 1965

Bellin College of Nursing
929 Cass Street, P.O. Box, Green Bay, Wisconsin
54305-3400
Tel: +1(414) 433-3560
Fax: +1(414) 433-7416
President/Chief Executive Officer: Joyce A.
McCollum
Financial Aid Director/Registrar: Mary Ann
Ruben
Founded: 1909

Belmont Abbey College
Belmont, North Carolina 28012
Tel: +1(704) 825-6700
Fax: +1(704) 825-6743
President: Joseph Brosnan
Vice-President (Academic Affairs): Artin
Arslanian
Founded: 1876

Benedict College
Harden and Blanding Streets, Columbia, South
Carolina 29204
Tel: +1(803) 256-4220
Fax: +1(803) 253-5065
President: Ruby W. Watts
Registrar: Angelois Smalls
Founded: 1870
D: Business; Humanities; Mathematics; Social
and Behavioral Science.

Benedictine College
2nd and Division, Atchison, Kansas 66002
Tel: +1(913) 367-5340
Fax: +1(913) 367-6102
President: Thomas O. James
Dean: Sr. Georgia McGarry
Founded: 1859

Bennett College
900 East Washington Street, Greensboro, North
Carolina 27401-3239
Tel: +1(919) 273-4431
Fax: +1(919) 378-0511
President: Gloria Scott
Vice-President (Academic Affairs): Chalotte
Alston
Founded: 1873

Berea College
Berea, Kentucky 40404
Tel: +1(606) 986-9341
Fax: +1(606) 986-4506
President: John B. Stephson
Special Assistant to the President: Phyllis Hughes
Founded: 1855

Berean College of the Assemblied of God
Springfield, Missouri 65802
Tel: +1(417) 862-2781
Fax: +1(417) 862-8558
President: Zenas J. Bicket
Registrar: Steven Kersting
Founded: 1948

Berklee College of Music
Boston, Massachusetts 02215
Tel: +1(617) 266-1400
Fax: +1(617) 247-6878
President: Lee Eliot Beck
Registrar: Plul Morimoto
Founded: 1945

Beth Jacob Hebrew Teacher College
1212-23 Elm Avenue, Brooklyn, New York 11230
Tel: +1(718) 339-4747
Founded: 1956

Bethany College of the Asemblies of God
Scotts Valley, California 95066
Tel: +1(408) 438-3800
Fax: +1(408) 438-1821
President: Rev. Tom Duncan
Vice-President for Academic Affairs: Jimmy
Brewer
Founded: 1919

Bethany College
Lindsborg, Kansas 67456
Tel: +1(913) 227-3311
Fax: +1(913) 227-2860
President: Joel Mckean
Academic Dean: Vance Eckstrom
Founded: 1881

Bethany College
Bethany, West Virginia 26032-9989
Tel: +1(304) 829-7000
Fax: +1(304) 829-7108
President: D. Duane Cummins
Director of Development: Elizabeth B. Vannelle
Founded: 1840

Bethel College
McKenzie, Tennessee 38201
Tel: +1(901) 352-1000
Fax: +1(901) 352-1008
President: Bill J. Elkins
Registrar: Shirley Martin
Founded: 1842

Bethel College
3900 Bethel Drive, St. Paul, Minnesota 55112
Tel: +1(612) 638-6400
Fax: +1(612) 638-6001
President: George K. Brushaber
Executive Vice-President (Administration and Finance): Sherm Swenson
Founded: 1871

Bethel College
Northe Newton, Kansas 67114
Tel: +1(316) 283-2500
Fax: +1(316) 284-5286
President: John E. Zehr
Registrar: Rodney Frey
Founded: 1887

Bethune-Cookman College
640 2nd Avenue, Daytona, Beach Florida 32115
Tel: +1(904) 255-1401
Fax: +1(904) 257-7027
President: Oswald P. Bronson Sr.
Vice-President (Academic Affairs): Ann D. Taylor
Founded: 1904

Blackburn College
700 College Avenue, Carlinville, Illinois 62626
Tel: +1(217) 854-3231
Fax: +1(217) 854-3713
President: Miriam R. Pride
Director of Registration and Records: Mary Cosner
Founded: 1837

Blessing-Rieman College of Nursing
Broadway at 11th Street, PO Box C3, Quincy, Illinois 62305-3117
Tel: +1(217) 223-5811
Fax: +1(217) 223-6400
Dean/Chief Executive Officer: Rita Zaborowska
Chairperson of Academic Affairs: Beth Kenney
Founded: 1885

Bloomfield College
1 Park Place, Bloomfield, New Jersey 07003
Tel: +1(201) 748-9000
Fax: +1(201) 743-3998
President: John F. Noonan
Vice-President (Academic Affairs): Maureen C. Graut
Founded: 1868

Blue Mountain College
P.O. Box 338, Blue Mountain, Mississippi 38610-9509
Tel: +1(601) 685-4771
President: E. Harold Fisher
Registrar: Annie Hendricks
Founded: 1873

Bluefield College
Bluefield, Virginia 24605
Tel: +1(703) 326-3682
Fax: +1(703) 326-4288
President: Roy A. Dobyns
Registrar: Carrie Camden
Founded: 1922

Bluffton College
College Avenue, Bluffton, Ohio 45817-1196
Tel: +1(419) 358-3000
President: Elmer Neufeld
Registrar: Linda Suter
Founded: 1899

Boise Bible College
8695 Marigold Street, Boise, Idaho 83714
Tel: +1(208) 376-7731
Fax: +1(208) 376-7743
President: Charles A. Crane
Business Manager: Gloria Baimbridge
Founded: 1945

Boricua College
3755 Broadway, New York, New York 10032
Tel: +1(212) 694-1000
Fax: +1(212) 694-1015
President: Victor G. Alicea
Director for Registration and Assessment: Rosa Silva
Founded: 1974

Boston Architecture Center
320 Newbury Street, Boston, Massachusettes 02115
Tel: +1(617) 536-3170
Fax: +1(617) 536-5829
President: George B. Terrien
Registrar: Mark Poklemba
Founded: 1889

Bowdoin College
Brunswick, Maine 04011
Tel: +1(207) 725-3000
Fax: +1(207) 725-3123
President: Robert H. Edwards
Registrar: Sarah Bernard
Founded: 1794

Bradford College
320 South Main Street, Bradford, Massachusetts
01835
Tel: +1(508) 372-7161
Fax: +1(508) 521-0480
President: Joseph Short
Secretary to the President: Eileen Welch
Founded: 1803

Brescia College
120 West 7th Street, Owensboro, Kentucky
42301-3023
Tel: +1(502) 685-3131
Fax: +1(502) 486-4266
President: Ruth Gehres
Vice-President (Academic Affairs): Jo Ann Mark
Founded: 1950

Brewton-Parker College
Mt. Vernon, Georgia 30445
Tel: +1(912) 583-2241
Fax: +1(912) 583-4498
President: Y. Lynn Holmes
Registrar: Carol Boyd
Founded: 1904

Briar Cliff College
3303 Rebecca Street, Sioux City, Iowa 51104
Tel: +1(712) 279-5321
Fax: +1(712) 279-5410
President: Sr. Margaret Wick
Registrar: Jenny Quinn
Founded: 1930

Bridgeport Engineering Institute
P.O. Box 6459, Bridgeport, Connecticut
06430-9990
Tel: +1(203) 259-5717
Fax: +1(203) 259-9372
President: William M. Krummel
Registrar: Patricia Meehan
Founded: 1924

Bridgewater College
Bridgewater, Virginia 22812
Tel: +1(703) 828-2501
Fax: +1(703) 828-2160
President: Wayne F. Geisert
Assistant to the President: Marlene C. Goley
Founded: 1880

Brigham Young University Hawaii Campus
550220 Kulanui Street, Laie Oahu, Hawai 96762
Tel: +1(808) 293-3211
Fax: +1(808) 293-3645
Telex: 4993759 byutelcom
President: Alton L. Wade
Registrar: Vernelle Lakatani
Founded: 1955

Bryant College
450 Douglas Pike, Smithfield, Rhode Island 02917
Tel: +1(401) 232-6000
Fax: +1(401) 232-6319
President: William E. Trueheart
Executive Vice-President: Walter B. Roettger
Founded: 1863

Buena Vista College
Storm Lake, Iowa 50588
Tel: +1(712) 749-2351
Fax: +1(712) 749-2037
President: Keith G.Briscoe
Registrar: Susan Alger
Founded: 1891
*S: Business (Harold Walter Sieben);
Communication and Arts; Science; Education;
Social Scinece, Philosophy and Religion.*

Burlington College
95 North Avenue, Burlington, Vermont 05401-8477
Tel: +1(802) 862-9616
President: Steward Lacasce
Registrar: Ann Reading
Founded: 1972

Caldwell College
Ryerson Avenue, Caldwell, New Jersey
07006-6195
Tel: +1(201) 228-4424
President: Sr. Vivien Jennings
Academic Dean: Sr. Patrice Werner
Founded: 1939

Calumet College of St. Joseph
2400 New York Avenue, Whiting, Indiana 46394
Tel: +1(219) 473-7770
Fax: +1(219) 473-4259
President: Dennis C. Rittenmeyer
Dean of Academic and Student Affairs: Nancy
Harvey
Founded: 1951

Calvary Bible College
15800 Calvary Road, Kansas City, Missouri
64147-1341
Tel: +1(816) 322-0110
Fax: +1(816) 331-4474
President: Donald A. Urey
Registrar: David Richards
Founded: 1932

Campbellsville College
200 College Street, West Campbellsville,
Kentucky 42718-2799
Tel: +1(502) 465-8158
Fax: +1(502) 789-5020
President: Kenneth W. Winters
Treasurer: Tonya A. Penick
Founded: 1906

Capitol College
13301 Springfield Road, Laurel, Maryland 20708
Tel: +1(301) 953-0060
Fax: +1(301) 953-3876
President: G. William Troxler
Founded: 1964

Caribbean University College
Box 493, Bayamon, Puerto Rico 00960-0493
Tel: +1(809) 780-0070
Fax: +1(809) 785-0101
President: Angel E. Juan-Ortega
Registrar: Luy M. Torres
Founded: 1969

Carleton College
1 North College Street, Northfield, Minnesota
55057
Tel: +1(507) 663-4000
Fax: +1(507) 663-4204
President: Stephen R. Lewis, Jr.
Dean of the College: Elizabeth McKinsey
Founded: 1866

Carrol College of Montana
Helena, Montana 59625
Tel: +1(406) 447-4384
Fax: +1(406) 442-9291
President: Matthew Quinn
Registrar: Mary Pat Dutton
Founded: 1909

Carroll College
100 Northeast Avenue, Waukesha, Wisconsin
53186
Tel: +1(414) 547-1211
Fax: +1(414) 524-7139
President: Frank Falcone
Provost: Gary W. Stevens
Founded: 1846

Cedar Crest College
College Drive and Hamilton Street, Allentown,
Pennsylvania 18104
Tel: +1(215) 437-4471
Fax: +1(215) 437-5955
President: Dorothy G. Blaney
Registrar (Acting): Barbara Hegel
Founded: 1867

Cedarville College
251 North Main Street, Box 601, Cedarville, Ohio
45314-0601
Tel: +1(513) 766-2211
Fax: +1(513) 766-2760
President: Paul H. Dixon
Academic Vice-President: Duane Wood
Founded: 1887

Centenary College
400 Jefferson Street, Hackettstown, New Jersey
07840
Tel: +1(908) 852-1400
Fax: +(908) 892-3454
President: Stephanie M. Bennett-Smith
Vice-President (Finance): Yane Faulkner
Founded: 1867

Center of Creative Studies-College of Art and Design
Detroit, Michigan 48202-4034
Tel: +1(313) 872-3118
Fax: +1(313) 872-8377
President: Josephine Kelsey
Registrar: Kathy Grenda
Founded: 1926

Center for Humanistic Studies
Detroit, Michigan 48202-3802
Tel: +1(313) 875-7440
Fax: +1(313) 875-7442
President: Clark Moustakas
Registrar: Patricia Hagan
Founded: 1980
Humanistic Studies.

Central Baptist College
Conway, Arkansas 72032
Tel: +1(501) 329-6872
Fax: +1(501) 329-2941
President: Charles Attebery
Registrar/Admissions Office Recruiter: Gary
McAllister
Founded: 1952

Central Bible College
3000 North Grant Avenue, Springfield, Missouri
65803
Tel: +1(417) 833-2551
Fax: +1(417) 833-5141
President: H. Maurice Lednicky
Director of Admissions and Records: Eunice
Bruegman
Founded: 1922

Central Christian College of the Bible
P.O. Box 70, Moberly, Missouri 65270-1997
Tel: +1(816) 263-3900
Fax: +1(816) 263-3936
President: Lloyd M. Pelfrey
Registrar: Cheryl Ratzlaff
Founded: 1957

Central Methodist College
441 Central Methodist College, Church Street,
Fayette, Missouri 65248
Tel: +1(816) 248-3391
Fax: +1(816) 248-2287
President: Joe A. Howell
Registrar: Kathryn Winegard
Founded: 1854
Conservatory of Music.

Central University of Iowa
812 University, Pella, Iowa 50219
Tel: +1(515) 628-9000
Fax: +1(515) 628-5316
President: William M. Wiebenga
Dean of the College: Winfield H. Bearce
Founded: 1853

Central Wesleyan College
Central, South Carolina 29630-1020
Tel: +1(803) 639-2453
Fax: +1(803) 639-0826
President: John M. Newby
Academic Vice-President/Dean: Stephen Calhoon
Founded: 1906

Centre College
West Walnut Street, Danville, Kentucky 40422
Tel: +1(606) 238-5200
Fax: +1(606) 238-5507
President: Michael F. Adams
Executive Assistant to the President: Jackie
Kohler
Founded: 1819

Charles R. Drew University
Los Angeles, California 90059
Tel: +1(213) 563-4987

Chatham College
Woodland Road, Pittsburgh, Pennsylvania 15232
Tel: +1(412) 365-1100
Fax: +1(412) 365-1505
E-Mail: 627 78580 esl ud
President: Esther L. Barazzone
Executive Assistant to the President: Mary A.
Sheehan
Founded: 1869

Christendom College
Front Royal, Virginia 22630
Tel: +1(703) 636-2900
Fax: +1(703) 636-1655
President: Timothy D'Donnell
Business Office Manager: Judy Costello
Founded: 1977

Christian Brothers College
650 East Parkway South, Memphis, Tennessee
38104-5581
Tel: +1(901) 722-0200
Fax: +1(901) 722-0494
President: Br. Stanislaus Sobczyk
Registrar: Barbara Havey
Founded: 1871
S: Arts; Business Administration; Engineering;
Sciences.

Christian Heritage College
2100 Greenfield Drive, El Cajon, California 92019
Tel: +1(619) 441-2200
Fax: +1(619) 440-0209
President: David Jeremiah
Registrar: Paul Berry
Founded: 1970

Cincinnati College of Mortuary Science
2220 Victory Parkway, Cincinnati, Ohio
45207-1033
Tel: +1(513) 745-3631
President: Dan Flory
Registrar: Patsy Leon
Founded: 1882
Mortuary Science.

Circleville Bible College
1476 Lancaster Pike, PO Box 458 Circleville, Ohio
43113
Tel: +1(614) 474-8896
Fax: +1(614) 477-7755
President: David Van Hoose
Registrar: Lorraine Huffman
Founded: 1948

Claflin College
College Avenue N.E., Orangeburg, South
Carolina 29115
Tel: +1(803) 534-2710
Fax: +1(803) 531-2860
President: Oscar A. Rogers, Jr.
Vice-President (Academic Affairs): Douglas
Johnson
Founded: 1869

Claremont McKenna College
500 East 9th Street, Claremont, California 91711
Tel: +1(714) 621-8000
Fax: +1(714) 621-8249
President: Jack L. Stark
Registrar: Joke Johnson
Founded: 1946

Clark Atlanta University
240 Chestnut Street S.W., Atlanta, Georgia 30314
Tel: +1(404) 880-8000
Fax: +1(404) 880-8222
President: Thomas Cole Jr.
Executive Assistant to the President: Gloria
James
Founded: 1879
S: Arts and Sciences; Business Administration;
Education; Library and Information Studies;
Social Work.

Clearwater Christian College
Clearwater, Florida 34619-4595
Tel: +1(813) 726-1153
Fax: +1(813) 726-8597
President: George D. Youstra
Registrar: Ralph Hayes
Founded: 1966

Cleary College
2170 Washtenaw Avenue, Ypsilanti, Michigan
48197
Tel: +1(313) 483-4400
Fax: +1(313) 483-0090
President: Thomas Sullivan
Vice-President of Admininstration and Finance:
Nancy Tracy
Founded: 1883

Cleveland Institute of Art
11141 East Boulevard, Cleveland, Ohio 44106
Tel: +1(216) 421-7400
Fax: +1(216) 421-7438
President: Robert Mayer
Registrar: Karen Hudy
Founded: 1882

Cogswell Polytechnical College

10420 Bubb Road, Cupertino, California 95014
Tel: +1(408) 252-5550
Fax: +1(408) 253-2413
Chancellor (Acting): Garland P. Peed III
Academic Dean: Gabriella Sechi
Founded: 1887

Cogswell College North

10626 Northeast 37th Circle, Kirkland, Washington
98033
Tel: +1(206) 822-3137
President: J.W. Sutton
Registrar: Jacqueline Juras
Founded: 1979

Coker College

College Avenue, Hartsville, South Carolina 29550
Tel: +1(803) 383-8000
Fax: +1(803) 383-8197
President: James D. Daniels
Assistant to the President: Vicki Eaddy
Founded: 1908

Colby College

Mayflower Hill Drive, Waterville, Maine 04901
Tel: +1(207) 872-3000
Fax: +1(207) 872-3555
President: William R. Cotter
Vice-President (Academic Affairs): Robert P.
McArthur
Founded: 1813

Colby-Sawyer College

100 Main Street, New London, New Hampshire
03257
Tel: +1(603) 526-2010
Fax: +1(603) 526-2135
President: Peggy Stock
Registrar: Jo Ann Jarvis
Founded: 1837

College of Aeronautics

La Guardia Airport, Flushing, New York 11371
Tel: +1(718) 429-6600
Fax: +1(718) 429-0256
President: Richard B. Goetze
Treasurer: Suzanne M. Campbell
Founded: 1932
Aeronautics.

College of Mount St. Vincent

Riverdale Avenue and West 263rd Street,
Riverdale, New York 10471
Tel: +1(718) 405-3200
Fax: +1(718) 601-6392
President: Mary C. Stuart
Academic Vice-President: Kathleen P. Knowles
Founded: 1847

College of St. Benedict

37 South College Avenue, St. Joseph, Minnesota
56374
Tel: +1(612) 363-5011
Fax: +1(612) 363-6099
President: Sr. Colman O'Connell
Vice-President for Finance: Sr. Miriam Ardolf
Founded: 1887

College of St. Elizabeth

Morristown, New Jersey 07960-6989
Tel: +1(201) 292-6300
President: Sr. Jacqueline Burns
Dean of Studies: Sr. Jeanne Marie Gilligan
Founded: 1899

College of St. Mary

1901 South 72nd Street, Omaha, Nebraska 68124
Tel: +1(402) 399-2400
Fax: +1(402) 399-2341
President: Kenneth Nielson
Senior Vice-President: Margaret J. Munnelly
Founded: 1923

College of the Southwest

Lovington Highway, Hobbs, New Mexico
88240-9986
Tel: +1(505) 392-6561
President: Joan M. Tueker
Director of Educational Services: Glenna M.
Ohaver
Founded: 1962

College of Wooster

Wooster, Ohio 44691
Tel: +1(216) 263-2000
Fax: +1(216) 263-2427
President: Henry J. Copeland
Executive Assistant to the President: Deborah
Hilty
Founded: 1866

Colorado Christian University

180 South Garrison Street, Lakewood, Colorado
80226
Tel: +1(303) 238-5386
Fax: +1(303) 233-2735
President: Ronald Schmidt
Director of Admissions: Anna DiTorrice
Founded: 1914

Colorado Technical College

4435 -No.Chestnut Street, Colorado Springs,
Colorado 80907
Tel: +1(719) 598-0200
Fax: +1(719) 598-3740
President: David D. O'Donnell
Registrar: John Zingg
Founded: 1965

Columbia College
10th and Roger Streets, Columbia, Missouri
65216
Tel: +1(314) 875-8700
Fax: +1(314) 875-8765
President: Donald B. Ruthenberg
Registrar: Marilyn Whiteheed
Founded: 1851

Columbia College
925 North La Brea Avenue, Hollywood, California
90038
Tel: +1(213) 851-0550
Fax: +1(213) 851-6401
President: Allan Rossman
Secretary/Treasurer: Dianne McDonald
Founded: 1952

Columbia Union College
7600 Flower Avenue, Takoma Park, Maryland
20912
Tel: +1(301) 270-9200
President: Charles Scriven
Vice-President (Academic Administration): Sara
Karkkainen Terian
Founded: 1904

Columbus College of Art and Design
47 North Washington Avenue, Columbus, Ohio
43215-1758
Tel: +1(614) 224-9101
Fax: +1(614) 222-4040
President: Joseph V. Canzani
Vice-President: Mary T. Kinney
Founded: 1879

Concordia College
4090 Geddes Road, Ann Arbor, Michigan
48105-2797
Tel: +1(313) 995-7300
Fax: +1(313) 995-4610
President: James M. Koerschen
Registrar: Mark L. Joyce
Founded: 1963

Concordia College
171 White Plains Road, Bronxville, New York
10708-1998
Tel: +1(914) 337-9300
Fax: +1(914) 395-4500
President: Ralph C. Schultz
Business Manager: Bruce Mumm
Founded: 1881

Concordia College
Moorhead, Minnesota 56562
Tel: +1(218) 299-4000
Fax: +1(218) 299-3947
E-Mail: 628 60193 esl ud
Telex: 9102500321 concordia moor uc.
President: Paul J. Dovre
Vice-President (Planning and Development):
Linda J. Brown
Founded: 1891

Concordia College
Hamline and Marshall Avenues, St. Paul,
Minnesota 55104
Tel: +1(612) 641-8278
Fax: +1(612) 659-0207
President: Robert Holst
Executive Vice-President: Kay Madson
Founded: 1893

Concordia College
2811 N.E. Holman Street, Portland, Oregon 97211
Tel: +1(503) 288-9371
Fax: +1(503) 280-8518
President: Charles E. Schlimpert
Executive Vice-President: Stephen Braun
Founded: 1905

Concordia Lutheran College
3400 Interstate 35N., Austin, Texas 78705
Tel: +1(512) 452-7661
Fax: +1(512) 459-8517
President: Ray F. Martens
Academic Dean: Edna Aguirre Rehbein
Founded: 1926

Conway School of Landscape Design
Conway, Massachusetts 01341
Tel: +1(413) 369-4044
Administrative Director: Mollie Babize
Academic Director: Donald L. Walker Jr.
Founded: 1972

Corcoran School of Art
17th and New York Avenue N.W., Washington,
D.C. 20006-4899
Tel: +1(202) 628-9484
Fax: +1(202) 628-3186
President: David C. Levy
Vice-President (Development and Public Affairs):
Susan Rosen Baum
Founded: 1890

Cornell College
Mount Vernon, Iowa 52314-1098
Tel: +1(319) 895-4000
Fax: +1(319) 895-5237
President: David G. Marker
Registrar: Mary Lynn Rettig
Founded: 1853

Cornish College of the Arts
710 East Roy, Seattle, Washington 98102-4696
Tel: +1(206) 323-1400
Fax: +1(206) 323-1574
President: Robert N. Funk
Registrar: Adrienne Bolyard
Founded: 1915

Culver-Stockton College
College Hill, Canton, Missouri 63435-1299
Tel: +1(314) 288-5221
Fax: +1(314) 288-3984
President: Edwin B. Strong Jr.
Registrar: Margaret S. King
Founded: 1853
D: Applied Arts and Sciences; Fine Arts; Humanities; Natural and Mathematical Sciences; Social and Behavioral Sciences.

Cumberland University
Lebanon, Tennessee 37087-3554
Tel: +1(615) 444-2562
Fax: +1(615) 444-2569
President: Ray C. Phillips
Registrar: C. William Mckee
Founded: 1842

Daemen College
4380 Main Street, Amherst, New York 14226
Tel: +1(716) 839-3600
Fax: +1(716) 839-8516
President: Robert S. Marshall
Registrar: Paulette A. Anzelone
Founded: 1947

Dakota Wesleyan University
Mitchell, South Dakota 57301-9983
Tel: +1(605) 995-2600
Fax: +1(605) 995-2699
President: James B. Beddow
Executive Vice-President: Neal C. Eddy
Founded: 1885

Dallas Christian College
2700 Christian Parkway, Dallas, Texas 75234
Tel: +1(214) 241-3371
Fax: +1(214) 241-8021
President: Gene R. Shepherd
Business Manager: Annette Esclavon
Founded: 1950

Dana College
2848 College Drive, Blair, Nebraska 68008-1099
Tel: +1(402) 426-9000
Fax: +1(402) 426-7332
President: Myrvin Christopherson
Registrar: Nancy Penna
Founded: 1884

Daniel Webster College
University Drive, Nashua, New Hampshire 03063
Tel: +1(603) 883-3356
Fax: +1(603) 882-8505
President: Hannah M. McCarthy
Vice-President (Academic Affairs): Gerald R. Fairbairn
Founded: 1965

Davenport College of Business
415 East Fulton Street, Grand Rapids, Michigan 49503
Tel: +1(616) 451-3511
Fax: +1(616) 732-1144
President: Donald W. Maine
Executive Vice-President: Roger G. Vanderlaan
Founded: 1866

Davidson College
Davidson, North Carolina 28036
Tel: +1(704) 892-2000
Fax: +1(704) 892-2005
President: John W. KuyKendall
Vice-President (Academic Affairs): Robert C. Williams
Founded: 1837

Davis and Elkins College
Sycamore Street, Elkins, West Virginia 26241
Tel: +1(304) 636-1900
Fax: +1(304) 636-2521
President: Dorothy I. MacConkey
Registrar: Margaret Wyatt
Founded: 1904

Deaconess College of Nursing
6150 Oakland Avenue, St. Louis, Missouri 63139
Tel: +1(314) 768-3044
Fax: +1(313) 768-3136
President: Elizabeth Krekonan
Director: Janet Barrett
Founded: 1889

Defiance College
701 North Clinton Street, Defiance, Ohio 43512
Tel: +1(419) 784-4010
Fax: +1(419) 784-0426
President: Marvin J. Ludwig
Vice-President (Academic Affairs): Maureen L. Evans
Founded: 1850

Delaware Valley College
Route 202, Doylestown, Pennsylvania 18901-2697
Tel: +1(215) 345-1500
Fax: +1(215) 345-5277
President: George F. West
Registrar: Robert P. Moran
Founded: 1896

Denison University
Granville, Ohio 43023
Tel: +1(614) 587-0810
Fax: +1(614) 587-6417
President: Michele Tolela Myers
Provost: Charles J. Morris
Founded: 1831

Detroit College of Business
4801 Oakman Boulevard, Dearborn, Michigan 48126
Tel: +1(313) 581-4400
Fax: +1(313) 581-6822
President: James Mendola
Vice-President (Academic Affairs): John Kushner
Founded: 1962

DeVry Institute of Technology
901 Corpotate Center Drive, Pomona, California
91768-2642
Tel: +1(909) 622-8866
Fax: +1(213) 692-6272
President: David G. Moore
Dean (Academic Affairs): Rose Marie Dishman
Founded: 1983

DeVry Institute of Technology
250 North Arcadia Avenue, Decatour, Georgia
30030
Tel: +1(404) 292-7900
Fax: +1(404) 292-2321
President: Ronald Bush
Registrar: Nancy Wassmer
Founded: 1969

DeVry Institute of Technology
3300 North Campbell Avenue, Chicago, Illinois
60618
Tel: +1(312) 929-8500
Fax: +1(312) 348-1780
President: Arthur Stunnard
Registrar: Elizabeth Lukasiewicz
Founded: 1931
P: Business; Electronics.

DeVry Institute of Technology
2000 South Finley Road, Addison, Illinois
60101-6106
Tel: +1(708) 953-1300
Fax: +1(708) 953-1236
President: Jerry R. Dill
Registrar: Tricia Zelis
Founded: 1982

DeVry Institute of Technology
11224 Holmes Road, Kansas City, Missouri 64131
Tel: +1(816) 941-0430
Fax: +1(816) 941-0896
President: Charles R. Levalley
Registrar: Kena Zumalt
Founded: 1931

DeVry Institute of Technology
1350 Alum Creek Drive, Columbus, Ohio
43209-2705
Tel: +1(614) 253-7291
Fax: +(614) 252-4108
President: Richard A. Czereniak
Registrar: Jacke Carle
Founded: 1952

DeVry Institute of Technology
4250 Beltline Road, Irving, Texas 75038-2440
Tel: +1(214) 929-6777
Fax: +1(214) 659-1748
President: Francis V. Cannon
Dean (Academic Affairs): Timothy Staley
Founded: 1969

DeVry Institute of Technology
2149 West Dunlop Avenue, Phoenix, Arizona
85021
Tel: +1(602) 870-9222
Fax: +1(602) 870-1209
President: James A. Dugan
Registrar: Bette Stanfield
Founded: 1967

Dickinson College
P.O. Box 1773, Carlisle, Pennsylvania 17013-2896
Tel: +1(717) 243-5121
Fax: +1(717) 245-1899
President: Lee Fritshler
Registrar: Ronald E. Doernbach
Founded: 1773

Dillard University
2601 Gentilly Boulevard, New Orleans, Louisiana
70122-3097
Tel: +1(504) 283-8822
President: Samuel DuBois Cook
Registrar: Anthony A. Osei
Founded: 1869

Doane College
Crete, Nebraska 68333
Tel: +1(402) 826-2161
Fax: +1(402) 826-8600
President: Fred D. Brown
Registrar: Paula Valenta
Founded: 1872

Dominican College of Blauvelt
10 Western Highway, Orangeburg, New York
10962
Tel: +1(914) 359-7800
Fax: +1(914) 359-2313
President: Sr. Kathleen Sullivan
Registrar: Sr. Noel Dwyer
Founded: 1952

Dordt College
498 4th Avenue Northeast, Sioux Center, Iowa
51250-1697
Tel: +1(712) 722-3771
Fax: +1(712) 722-1198
President: John B. Hulst
Registrar: Douglas Eckardt
Founded: 1955

Dr. Martin Luther College
1884 College Heights, New Ulm, Minnesota
56073-3300
Tel: +1(507) 354-8221
Fax: +1(507) 354-8225
President: John C. Lawrenz
Registrar: Robert J. Stoltz
Founded: 1884

Dyke College
112 Prospect Avenue, Cleveland, Ohio 44115
Tel: +1(216) 696-9000
Fax: +1(216) 696-6430
President: John C. Corfias
Executive Vice-President: John J. Koral
Founded: 1848

East Coast Bible College
6900 Wilkinson Boulevard, Charlotte, North
Carolina 28214
Tel: +1(704) 394-2307
Fax: +1(704) 393-3689
President: Ronald D. Martin
Registrar: Linda Allen
Founded: 1976

East Texas Baptist University
1209 North Grove Street, Marshall, Texas
75670-1498
Tel: +1(903) 935-7963
Fax: +1(903) 938-1705
President: Bob E. Riley
Registrar: David P. Mohn
Founded: 1912

Eastern Christian College
P.O. Box 629, Bel Air, Maryland 21014
Tel: +1(410) 734-7727
President: Robin Underhill
Registrar: Lois Harris
Founded: 1946

Eastern Mennonite College
Harrisonburg, Virginia 22801
Tel: +1(703) 432-4000
Fax: +1(703) 432-4444
President: Joseph L. Lapp
Vice-President: Lee F. Snyder
Founded: 1917

East-West University
816 South Michigan Avenue, Chicago, Illinois
60605
Tel: +1(312) 939-0111
Fax: +1(312) 939-0083
Chancellor: M. Wasi Khan
Academic Dean: Peter Afriyie
Founded: 1978

Eckerd College
4200 54th Avenue, St. Petersburg, Florida 33733
Tel: +1(813) 867-1166
Fax: +1(813) 866-2304
President: Peter H. Armacost
Registrar: K. Russell Kennedy
Founded: 1958

Edward Waters College
1658 Kings Road, Jacksonville, Florida 32209
Tel: +1(904) 355-3030
Fax: +1(904) 366-2544
President: Jesse L. Burns
Vice-President/Dean: Gretchen Lockett
Founded: 1866

Electronic Data Processing College of Puerto Rico
PO Box 1923035, Suan Juan, Puerto Rico
00919-2303
Tel: +1(809) 765-3560
Fax: +1(809) 765-2650
President: Anibal Nieves
Registrar: Gloria Nieves
Founded: 1968

Elizabethtown College
College Avenue, Elizabethtown, Pennsylvania
17022-2298
Tel: +1(717) 361-1000
President: Gerhard E. Spiegler
Registrar: Martha A. Eppley
Founded: 1899

Elmhurst College
190 Prospect, Elmhurst, Illinois 60126-3296
Tel: +1(708) 617-3500
Fax: +1(708) 617-3245
President: Ivan E. Frick
Director (Registration and Records): Lawrence J.
Borgione
Founded: 1871

Emmanuel College School of Christian Ministries
P.O. Box 129, Franklin Springs, Georgia 30639
Tel: +1(706) 245-7226
Fax: +1(706) 245-4424
President: David Hopkins
Records Secretary: Debra F. Grizzle
Founded: 1919

Emmaus Bible College
2570 Ashbury Road, Dubuque, Iowa 52001
Tel: +1(319) 588-8000
Fax: +1(319) 588-1216
President: Daniel H. Smith
Executive Vice-President: Joseph Cumming
Founded: 1941

Emory & Henry College
Ambrister Drive, Emory, Virginia 24327
Tel: +1(703) 944-3121
Fax: +1(703) 944-4438
President: Thomas R. Morris
Registrar: Joy W. Dunbar
Founded: 1836

Erskine College
Due West, South Carolina 29639
Tel: +1(803) 379-2131
Fax: +1(803) 379-8759
President: James W. Strobel
Registrar: Julie A. Smith
Founded: 1839

Eugene Bible College
2155 Bailey Hill Road, Eugene, Oregon 97405
Tel: +1(503) 485-1780
Fax: +1(503) 343-5801
President: Jeffrey E. Farmer
Director of Academic Affairs: Clayton Crymes
Founded: 1925

Eureka College
300 East College Avenue, Eureka, Illinois
61530-0128
Tel: +1(309) 467-3721
Fax: +1(309) 467-6386
President: George A. Hearne
Chief Fiscal Officer: Genevia Sager
Founded: 1855

Evangel College
1111 North Glenstone, Springfield, Missouri 65802
Tel: +1(417) 865-2811
Fax: +1(417) 865-9599
President: Robert H. Spence
Vice-President (Academic Affairs): Glenn Bernet
Founded: 1955

Faulkner University
15345 Atlanta Highway, Montgomery, Alabama
36109-3398
Tel: +1(205) 272-5820
Fax: +1(205) 260-6268
President: Billy D. Hilyer
Vice-President (Finance): Wilma Phillips
Founded: 1942
*Arts and Science (Alabama Christian); Business
and Adult Professional Education (Harris); Law
(Jones).*

Felician College
260 South Main Street, Lodi, New Jersey 07644
Tel: +1(201) 778-1190
Fax: +1(201) 778-4111
President: Sr. Theresa Martin
Registrar: June Finn
Founded: 1942

Ferrum College
Box 22, Ferrum, Virginia 24088
Tel: +1(703) 365-2121
Fax: +1(703) 365-4203
President: Jerry M. Boone
Registrar: Margaret Clark
Founded: 1913

Flagler College
P.O. Box 1027, Saint Augustine, Florida 32085
Tel: +1(904) 829-6481
Fax: +1(904) 826-0094
President: William L. Proctor
Registrar: Kenneth Russom
Founded: 1968

Florida Bible College
1701 North Peinciana Boulevard, Kissimmee,
Florida 34758
Tel: +1(407) 933-4500
President: Paul C. Goodnight
Administrative Assistant: Ann Wasielewski
Founded: 1962

Florida Christian College
1011 Bill Beck Boulevard, P.O. Box 1579
Kissimmee, Florida 34744
Tel: +1(407) 847-8966
Fax: +1(407) 847-8966
President: Wayne Lowen
Academic Dean: J.R. Buchanan
Founded: 1976

Florida Memorial College
15800 Florida Memorial Colleges Avenue, Miami,
Florida 33054
Tel: +1(305) 626-3600
Fax: +1(305) 626-3769
President: Albert E. Smith
Registrar: Celestine Bouchard
Founded: 1879

Fort Lauderdale College
1401 East Broward Boulevard, Fort Lauderdale,
Florida 33304
Tel: +1(305) 568-1600
Fax: +1(305) 568-2008
President: William P. Bedard
Academic Dean: Dorothy Moore
Founded: 1940

Franklin College of Indiana
501 East Monroe Street, Franklin, Indiana
46131-2598
Tel: +1(317) 738-8000
Fax: +1(317) 736-6030
President: William Bryan Martin
Senior Administrative Officer: Cherie R. Hatlem
Founded: 1834

Franklin Pierce College
College Road, PO Box 60 Rindge, New
Hampshire 03461-0060
Tel: +1(603) 899-4000
Fax: +1(603) 899-6448
President: Walter Peterson
Registrar: Hazel Schelper
Founded: 1962

Franklin University
201 South Grant Avenue, Columbus, Ohio 43215
Tel: +1(614) 341-6237
Fax: +1(614) 221-7723
President: Paul J. Otte
Vice-President (Institutional Advancement):
Cynthia Hill
Founded: 1902
*C: Arts and Social Sciences; Business and
Technology.*

Freed-Hardeman College
158 East Main Street, Henderson, Tennessee
38340
Tel: +1(901) 989-6000
Fax: +1(901) 989-6065
President: Milton R. Sewell
Registrar: Larry R. Oldham
Founded: 1869
*D: Fine Arts; History and Political Science;
Mathematical and Computer Science.
S: Biblical Studies; Business; Education.*

Gettysburg College
North Washington Street, Gettysburg,
Pennsylvania 17325-1486
Tel: +1(717) 337-6000
Fax: +1(717) 337-6008
President: Gordon A. Haaland
Director of Development: Ann H. Neitzel
Founded: 1832

God's Bible School and College
1810 Young Street, Cincinnati, Ohio 45210
Tel: +1(513) 721-7944
President: Bence C. Miller
Registrar: Jauren Juslis
Founded: 1900

Goldey Beacom College
4701 Limestone Road, Wilmington, Delaware
19808-0551
Tel: +1(302) 998-8814
President: William R. Baldt
Vice-President (Financial Affairs): Phyllis R. Baldt
Founded: 1886

Gordon College
255 Grapevine Road, Wenham, Massachusetts
01984
Tel: +1(508) 927-2300
Fax: +(508) 921-1398
President: R. Judson Carlberg
Registrar: Judy Gaede
Founded: 1889

Goshen College
1700 South Main Street, Goshen, Indiana 46526
Tel: +1(219) 535-7000
Fax: +1(219) 535-7660
E-Mail: 620 11224 esl ud
President: Victor Stoltzfus
Business Manager: Mardene Kelley
Founded: 1894

Grace Bible College
P.O. Box 910, Grand Rapids, Michigan 49509
Tel: +1(616) 538-2330
President: Bruce Kemper
Business Manager: James Molenkamp
Founded: 1945

Grace College of the Bible
1515 South 10th Street, Omaha, Nebraska 68108
Tel: +1(402) 449-2800
Fax: +1(402) 341-9587
President: Neal F. McBride
Registrar: Bill Beard
Founded: 1943

Graceland College
Lamoni, Iowa 50140
Tel: +1(515) 784-5000
Fax: +1(515) 784-5480
President: William T. Higdon
Registrar: M. Joyce Lighthill
Founded: 1895

Grand Canyon University
3300 West Camelback Road, Phoenix, Arizona
85017
Tel: +1(602) 249-3300
Fax: +1(602) 589-2861
President: Bill Williams
Provost: Martha Taylor-Thomas
Founded: 1949
C: Business; Communications and Fine Arts; Education; Liberal Arts and Sciences; Nursing (Samaritan).

Grand View College
1200 Grandview Avenue, Des Moines, Iowa
50316-1599
Tel: +1(515) 263-2800
Fax: +1(515) 263-6095
President: Arthur E. Puotien
Vice-President and Dean for Academic Affairs:
Ronald L. Taylor
Founded: 1896

Grantham College of Engineering
34641 Grantham Colleges Road, Slidell,
Louisiana 70460
Tel: +1(504) 649-4191
Fax: +1(504) 649-4183
President: Donald Grantham
Director of Student Services: Mark P. Dean
Founded: 1951

Great Lakes Christian College
6211 West Willow Highway, Box 40060, Lansing,
Michigan 48917
Tel: +1(517) 321-0242
Fax: +1(517) 321-5902
Director of Admissions: Nancy L. Hooper
Registrar: James R. Estep Jr.
Founded: 1949

Green Mountain College
16 College Street, Poultney, Vermont 05764
Tel: +1(802) 287-9313
Fax: +(802) 287-9313 (ext 340)
President: James M. Pollock
Registrar: Suzanne Perry
Founded: 1834

Greensboro College
815 West Market Street, Greensboro, North
Carolina 27401-1875
Tel: +1(919) 272-7102
Fax: +1(919) 271-2237
President: Craven E. Williams
Registrar: Susan Morris
Founded: 1838

Greenville College
315 East College Avenue, Greenville, Illinois
62246-0159
Tel: +1(618) 664-1840
Fax: +1(618) 664-4084
President: Robert E. Smith
Registrar: Debra Miller
Founded: 1892

Grinnell College
P.O. Box 805, Grinnell, Iowa 50112-0810
Tel: +1(515) 269-4000
Fax: +1(515) 269-3408
President: Pamela A. Ferguson
Dean: Charles L. Duke
Founded: 1846

Grove City College
Grove City, Pennsylvania 16127-2104
Tel: +1(412) 458-2000
Fax: +1(412) 458-2190
President: Jerry H. Combee
Vice-President (Academic Affairs): Garthe Runion
Founded: 1876

Guilford College
5800 West Friendly Avenue, Greensboro, North
Carolina 27410
Tel: +1(910) 316-2000
Fax: +1(910) 316-2951
President: William R. Rogers
Registrar: Cathy O. West
Founded: 1837

Gustavus Adolphus College
St. Peter, Minnesota 56082
Tel: +1(507) 933-8000
Fax: +1(507) 933-7041
President: Axel D. Steueer
Dean: Elizabeth Baer
Founded: 1862

Hamilton College
Clinton, New York 13323
Tel: +1(315) 859-4011
Fax: +1(315) 859-4991
President: Harry C. Payne
Registrar: Jennifer Potter Hayes
Founded: 1812

Hampden-Sydney College
Hampden-Sydney, Virginia 23943
Tel: +1(804) 223-6000
Fax: +1(804) 223-7629
President: Samuel Wilson
Registrar: Florence Watson
Founded: 1776

Hampshire College
West Street, Amherst, Massachusetts 01002
Tel: +1(413) 549-4600
Fax: +1(413) 549-0707
President: Gregory S. Prince Jr.
Vice-President: Penina M. Glazer
Founded: 1965

S: Communications and Cognitive Science;
Humanities and Arts; Natural Science; Social
Sciences.

Hannibal-Lagrange College
2800 Palmyra Road, Hannibal, Missouri 63401
Tel: +1(314) 221-3675
Fax: +1(314) 221-6594
President: Paul Brown
Academic Dean: Beverly Simpson
Founded: 1858

Hanover College
Hanover, Indiana 47243
Tel: +1(812) 866-7000
Fax: +1(812) 866-2164
President: Russell L. Nichols
Dean: Charles L. Flynn Jr.
Founded: 1827

Harrington Institute of Interior Design
410 South Michigan Avenue, Chicago, Illinois
60605-1496
Tel: +1(312) 939-4975
Fax: +1(312) 939-8005
President: Robert C. Marks
Director of Education: Nancy C. Los
Founded: 1931

Harris-Stowe State College
3026 Laclede Avenue, St. Louis, Missouri 63103
Tel: +1(314) 340-3366
Fax: +1(314) 340-3399
President: Henry Givens Jr.
Registrar: Mary K. Jones
Founded: 1857

Hartwick College
West Street, Oneonta, New York 13820
Tel: +1(607) 431-4200
Fax: (607) 431-4318
President: Richard A. Detweiler
Registrar: Nancy P. Hulse
Founded: 1797

Hastings College
7th Street and Turner Avenue, Hastings,
Nebraska 68902
Tel: +1(402) 463-2402
Fax: +1(402) 463-3002
President: Thomas J. Reeves
Vice-President: Phillip L. Dudley Jr.
Founded: 1882

Haverford College
Haverford, Pennsylvania 19041-1392
Tel: +1(610) 896-1000
Fax: +1(610) 896-1224
President: Tom G. Kessinger
Provost: Bruce Partridge
Founded: 1833

Heidelberg College
310 East Market Street, Tiffin, Ohio 44883
Tel: +1(419) 448-2000
Fax: +1(419) 448-2124
E-Mail: 620 44719 esl ud
Telex: 241519 heid berg tifn
President: William C. Cassell
Vice-President (Administration): Jeannine Curns
Founded: 1850

Hendrix College
Conway, Arkansas 72032-3080
Tel: +1(501) 329-6811
Fax: +1(501) 450-1200
President: Ann H. Die
Dean: John Churchill
Founded: 1876

High Point University
University Station, 933 Montlieu Avenue, High
Point, North Carolina 27262-3598
Tel: +1(910) 841-9000
Fax: +1(910) 841-5123
President: Jacob C. Martinson Jr.
Dean (Academic Affairs): E. Vance Davis
Founded: 1924
Business (Earl N. Phillips).

Hillsdale College
33 East College, Hillsdale, Michigan 49242
Tel: +1(517) 437-7341
Fax: +1(517) 437-0190
President: George C. Roche III
Registrar: Kay Cosgrove
Founded: 1844

Hillsdale Free Will Baptist College
P.O. Box 7208, Moore, Oklahoma 73153-1208
Tel: +1(405) 794-6661
President: Jim Shepherd
Vice-President (Academic Affairs): Timothy Eaton
Founded: 1959

Hiram College
Hiram, Ohio 44234
Tel: +1(216) 569-3211
Fax: +1(216) 569-5494
Telex: 9103805429 hiram college
President: G. Benjamin Oliver
Vice-President/Dean: Vivian P. Makosky
Founded: 1850

Hobart College
337 Pulteney Street, Geneva, New York 14456
Tel: +1(315) 781-3300
Fax: +1(315) 781-3303
President: Richard H. Hersh
Provost: Sheila K. Bennett
Founded: 1822

Hobe Sound Bible College
P.O. Box 1065, Hobe Sound, Florida 33475
Tel: +1(407) 546-5534
Fax: +1(407) 546-9379
President: Robert E. Whitaker
Registrar: Carol Rosa
Founded: 1960

Holy Family College
Grant and Frankford Avenues, Philadelphia,
Pennsylvania 19114-2094
Tel: +1(215) 637-7700
Fax: +1(215) 632-8067
President: Sr. Francesca Onley
Registrar: Sr. M. Euphronia Plucinska
Founded: 1954

Hope College
137 East 12th Street, Holland, Michigan
49422-9000
Tel: +1(616) 392-5111
Fax: +1(616) 394-7922
President: John H. Jacobson Jr.
Registrar: Jon Huisken
Founded: 1862

Houghton College
One Willard Avenue, Houghton, New York 14744
Tel: +1(716) 567-9200
Fax: +1(716) 567-9570
President: Daniel R. Chamberlain
Registrar: Margery Avery
Founded: 1883
Music.

Howard Payne University
1000 Fisk Avenue, Brownwood, Texas 76801
Tel: +1(915) 646-2502
Fax: +1(915) 643-7835
President: Don Newbury
Registrar: Don Jackson
Founded: 1889
C: Arts and Sciences.
S: Business and Administration; Christianity;
Education; Music; Social Sciences.

Humphreys College
6650 Inglewood Avenue, Stockston, California
95207
Tel: +1(209) 478-0800
Fax: +1(209) 478-8721
President: Robert G. Humphreys
Registrar: Lisa Hernandez
Founded: 1896
Law.

Huntingdon College
1500 East Fairview Avenue, Montgomery,
Alabama 36106-2148
Tel: +1(205) 265-0511
Fax: +1(205) 264-2951
President: Wanda Bigham
Senior Administrative Officer: Marian
Morgenstern
Founded: 1854

Huron College
333 9th Street SW, Huron, South Dakota 57350
Tel: +1(605) 352-8721
Fax: +1(605) 352-7421
Assistant to President: Sandy Aymar
Registrar: Peggy Mann
Founded: 1883

Huston-Tillotson College
1820 East 8th Street, Austin, Texas 78702
Tel: +1(512) 476-7421
Fax: +1(512) 474-0762
President: Joseph T. McMillan Jr.
Vice-President (Academic Affairs): Lenora D. Waters
Founded: 1875

Illinois College
1101 West College Avenue, Jacksonville, Illinois 62650-2299
Tel: +1(217) 245-3000
Fax: +1(217) 245-3034
President: Richard Pfau
Vice-President (Academic Affairs): John L. Nies
Founded: 1829

Illinois School of Professional Psychology
220 South State Street/1 Quincy Court, Chicago, Illinois 60604
Tel: +1(312) 341-6500
Fax: +1(312) 922-1730
President: Harry O'Donnell
Business Officer: Carol Hemphill
Founded: 1976

Illinois Wesleyan University
210 East University Street, Bloomington, Illinois 61712-61702
Tel: +1(309) 556-1000
Fax: +1(309) 556-3411
President: Minor Myers Jr.
Provost: Janet M. McNew
Founded: 1850
S: Art and Fine Arts; Music; Nursing; Theatre Arts.

Inter-American University of Puerto Rico: Aguadilla Regional College
Aguadilla, Puerto Rico 00605
Tel: +1(809) 891-0925
Fax: +1(809) 882-3620
Chancellor: Hilda Bacó
Dean of Academic Affairs: Sylvia Aldebol
Founded: 1957

Inter-American University of Puerto Rico: Arecibo Regional College
Arecibo, Puerto Rico 00613
Tel: +1(809) 878-5475
Fax: +1(809) 880-1624
Chancellor: Zaida Vega
Dean of Studies: Mérida Mercado
Founded: 1957
Nursing.

Inter-American University of Puerto Rico: Barranquitas Regional College
Barranquitas, Puerto Rico 00618
Tel: +1(809) 857-3600
Fax: +1(809) 857-2284
Chancellor: Vidal Rivera
Dean (Academic Affairs): Irene Fernandez Aponte
Founded: 1957

Inter-American University of Puerto Rico: Fajardo Regional College
Fajardo, Puerto Rico 00738
Tel: +1(809) 863-2390
Fax: +(809) 860-3470
Chancellor: Yolanda Robles Garcia
Dean (Academic Affairs): Martiza Santana
Founded: 1965

International Bible College
P.O. Box IBC, Florence, Alabama 35630
Tel: +1(205) 766-6610
Fax: +1(205) 760-0981
President: Dennis Jones
Senior Vice-President: Basil Overton
Founded: 1971

Iowa Wesleyan College
North Main, Mount Pleasant, Iowa 52641
Tel: +1(319) 385-8021
Fax: +1(319) 385-6296
President: Robert J. Prins
Vice-President (Academic Affairs): Vance Yoder
Founded: 1842

ITT Technical Institute
4919 Coldwater Road, Fort Wayne, Indiana 462825
Tel: +1(219) 484-4107
President: Jack B. Cozad
Director of Education: Willie Vaughn
Founded: 1967

ITT Technical Institute
9511 Angola Court, Indianapolis, Indiana 46268
Tel: +1(317) 875-8640
Fax: +1(317) 875-8641
Director: Larry L. Graphman
Finance Manager: Michele Hurst
Founded: 1966

ITT Technical Institute
6035 North East, 78th Court, Portland, Oregon 97218
Tel: +1(503) 255-6500
Fax: +1(503) 255-6135
Director: James Horner
Director of Education: Galen Rose
Founded: 1971

Jamestown College
Jamestown, North Dakota 58405
Tel: +1(701) 252-3467
Fax: +1(701) 253-4318
Telex: 9103808869
President: James Walker
Registrar: Alice Kachel
Founded: 1883

Jarvis Christian College
P.O. Drawer G, Hawkins, Texas 75765-9989
Tel: +1(903) 769-5700
Fax: +1(903) 769-4842
President: Sebetha Jenkins
Registrar: Gwendolyn Robinson
Founded: 1912

John Brown University
Siloam Springs, Arkansas 72761
Tel: +1(501) 524-3131
Fax: +1(501) 524-9548
President: John E. Brown III
Registrar: Lee Demarias
Founded: 1919

John Wesley College
2314 North Centennial, High Point, North Carolina
27265-3197
Tel: +1(919) 889-2262
President: Brian C. Donley
Registrar: Steve Somers
Founded: 1932

Johnson and Wales University
8 Abbott Park Road, Providence, Rhode Island
02903-3776
Tel: +1(401) 456-1000
Fax: +1(401) 455-2880
President: John A. Yena
Vice-President (Academic Affairs): Richard Kosh
Founded: 1914
C: Business; Culinary Administration.
S: Management; Professional Technology.

Johnson Bible College
Knoxville, Tennessee 37998
Tel: +1(615) 573-4517
Fax: +1(615) 579-2336
President: David L. Eubanks
Registrar: Joel F. Rood
Founded: 1893

Johnson Cay. Smith University
100 Beatties Ford Road, Charlotte, North Carolina
28216
Tel: +1(704) 378-1000
Fax: +(704) 372-5746
President: Robert L. Albright
Vice-President (Academic Affairs): Maxine Moore
Founded: 1867

Jones College
5353 Arlington Expressway, Jacksonville, Florida
32211-5588
Tel: (904) 743-1122
Fax: +1(904) 743-4446
President: Dorothy D. Jones
Executive Vice-President: Judy Lima
Founded: 1918

Jordan College
Cedar Springs, Michigan 49319
Tel: +1(616) 696-1180
Fax: +1(616) 696-3790
President: Lexie K. Coxon
Executive Vice-President: Bruce Robinson
Founded: 1967

Judson College
1151 North State Street, Elgin, Illinois 60123
Tel: +1(708) 695-2500
Fax: +1(708) 695-0712
President: James D. Didier
Registrar: Brenda Atkinson
Founded: 1963

Judson College
Marion, Alabama 36756
Tel: +1(205) 683-6161
Fax: +1(205) 683-6675
President: David E. Potts
Registrar: Martha Williams
Founded: 1838

Juniata College
1700 Moore Street, Huntingdon, Pennsylvania
16652-2119
Tel: +1(814) 643-4310
Fax: +1(814) 643-3620
President: Robert W. Neff
Assistant to the President: Joanne M. Park
Founded: 1876

Kalamazoo College
1200 Academy Street, Kalamazoo, Michigan
49006
Tel: +1(616) 337-7000
Fax: +1(616) 337-7251
President: Lawrence Bryan
Registrar: Eileen Harrison
Founded: 1833

Kansas City Art Institute
Kansas City, Missouri 64111
Tel: +1(816) 561-4852
Fax: +1(816) 561-6404
President: Beatrice Rivas Sanchez
Registrar: Katherine Harlan
Founded: 1885

Kansas Newman College
3100 McCormick Avenue, Wichita, Kansas 67213
Tel: +1(316) 942-4291
Fax: +1(316) 942-4483
President: Sr. Tarcisia Roths
Registrar: Shirley Rueb
Founded: 1933

Kansas Wesleyan University
100 East Claflin, Salina, Kansas 67401-6196
Tel: +1(913) 827-5541
Fax: +1(913) 827-0927
President: Marshall P. Stanton
Registrar: Richard Keist
Founded: 1886

Kendall College
2408 Orrington Avenue, Evanston, Illinois 60201
Tel: +1(708) 866-1300
Fax: +1(708) 866-1320
President: Thomas J. Kerr IV
Vice-President (Academic Affairs): Gregg Lacy
Founded: 1934

Kentucky Christian College
Grayson, Kentucky 41143-1199
Tel: +1(606) 474-6613
Fax: +1(606) 474-3155
President: Keith P. Keeran
Registrar: Donna Jones
Founded: 1919

Kentucky Wesleyan College
3000 Frederica Street, PO Box 1039 Owensboro,
Kentucky 42301-1039
Tel: +1(502) 926-3111
Fax: +1(502) 926-3196
President: Paul W. Hartman
Registrar: Scott E. Kramer
Founded: 1858

Kenyon College
Gambier, Ohio 43022-9623
Tel: +1(614) 427-5000
President: Philip H. Jordan Jr.
Registrar: Richard L. Switzer
Founded: 1824

Keuka College
Keuka Park, New York 14478
Tel: +1(315) 536-4411
Fax: +1(315) 536-5216
President: Arthur F. Kirk Jr.
Registrar: Linda B. Feischman
Founded: 1890
*D: Basic and Applied Social Sciences; Business
and Management; Humanities and Fine Arts;
Occupational Therapy; Nursing; Natural Sciences,
Mathematics, and Physical Education.*

King College
1350 King College Road, East State Street Bristol,
Tennessee 37620-2699
Tel: +1(615) 968-1187
Fax: +1(615) 968-4456
President: Richard Stanslaw
Registrar: Thomas Daniel
Founded: 1867

King's College
Loge Road, Briarcliff Manor, New York 10510
Tel: +1(914) 941-7200
Fax: +1(914) 944-5636
President: Friedhelm K. Radandt
Registrar: Nancy Best
Founded: 1938

King's College
133 North River Street, Wilkes-Barre,
Pennsylvania 18711-801
Tel: +1(717) 826-5900
Fax: +1(717) 825-9049
President: Rev. James Kackennier, CSC
Senior Administrative Officer: George J.
Machinchick
Founded: 1946
*Arts and Sciences; Business (William G.
McGowan).*

Knox College
Galesburg, Illinois 61401
Tel: +1(309) 343-0112
Fax: +1(309) 343-8921
President: Frederick C. Nahm
Registrar: Harry J. Neumiller Jr.
Founded: 1837

Knoxville College
901 College Street N.W., Knoxville, Tennessee
37921
Tel: +1(615) 524-6500
Fax: +1(615) 524-6686
President: John B. Turner
Registrar: Brenda Rector
Founded: 1875

Laboratory Institute of Merchandising
12 East 53rd Street, New York, New York
10022-5268
Tel: +1(212) 752-1530
Fax: +1(212) 832-6708
President: Adrian G. Marcuse
Vice-President (Administration and Finance): Jon
Kenler
Founded: 1939

Lafayette College
Easton, Pennsylvania 18042-1798
Tel: +1(215) 250-5000
Fax: +1(215) 250-5127
President: Robert I. Rotberg
Executive Assistant to the President: Philip G.
Schroeder
Founded: 1826

Lakeland College
P.O. Box 359, Sheboygan, Wisconsin 53082-0359
Tel: +1(414) 565-2111
Fax: +1(414) 565-1206
President: David R. Black
Provost: Keith G. Striggow
Founded: 1862

Lambuth College
Lambuth Boulevard, Jackson, Tennessee 38301
Tel: +1(901) 425-2500
Fax: +1(901) 423-1990
President: Thomas F. Boyd
Dean of Records: Dan L. Huneycutt
Founded: 1843

Lancaster Bible College
901 Eden Road, Lancaster, Pennsylvania 17601
Tel: +1(717) 569-7071
Fax: +1(717) 560-8213
President: Gilbert A. Peterson
Registrar: Gilbert G. Gregory
Founded: 1933

Lane College
545 Lane Avenue, Jackson, Tennessee 38301
Tel: +1(901) 426-7500
Fax: +1(901) 427-3987
President: Wesley C. McClure
Registrar: George L. Thacker
Founded: 1882

Lawrence University
P.O. Box 599, Appleton, Wisconsin 54912
Tel: +1(414) 832-7000
Fax: +1(414) 832-6606
President: Richard Warch
Senior Administrative Officer: Donald C.
Rosenthal
Founded: 1847
Conservatory of Music.

Le Moyne College
Le Moyne Heights, Syracuse, New York 13214
Tel: +1(315) 445-4100
Fax: +1(315) 445-4540
President: Rev. Kevin G. O'Connell
Registrar: Dorothy A. Namishia
Founded: 1946

Le Moyne-Owen College
807 Walker Avenue, Memphis, Tennessee 38126
Tel: +1(901) 774-9090
Fax: +1(901) 942-7810
President: Doris W. Weathers
Registrar: Sara Buford
Founded: 1862

LeTourneau University
2300 South Mobberly Avenue, Longview, Texas
75607-7001
Tel: +1(903) 753-0231
Fax: +1(903) 237-2730
E-Mail: 620 06181 esl ud
President: Alvin O. Austin
Director of Registration and Records: Delinda
Hall
Founded: 1946

Lee College
Ecoee Street, Cleveland, Tennessee 37311
Tel: +1(615) 472-2111
Fax: +1(615) 478-7041
President: Paul Conn
Registrar: Veva L. Rose
Founded: 1918

Lesley College
29 Everett Street, Cambridge, Massachusetts
02138
Tel: +1(617) 868-9600
Fax: +1(617) 661-8788
President: Margaret A. McKenna
Registrar: Kim Kantz
Founded: 1909

Life Chiropractic College
1269 Barclay Circle, Marietta, Georgia 30060
Tel: +1(404) 424-0554
Fax: +1(404) 429-8359
E-Mail: 629 12799 esl ud
President: Sid E. Williams
Vice-President of Academics: Ronald J. Hash
Founded: 1974

Limestone College
1115 College Drive, Gaffney, South Carolina
29340
Tel: +1(803) 489-7151
Fax: +1(803) 487-8706
President: Walt Griffin
Registrar: Ralph Smith
Founded: 1845

Lincoln University
281 Masonic Avenue, San Francisc, California
94118
Tel: +1(415) 221-1212
Fax: +1(415) 387-9730
President: Clarence W. Rippel
Registrar: Pete Bogue
Founded: 1919
Undergraduate Studies.

Lindenwood College
St. Charles, Missouri 63301
Tel: +1(314) 949-2000
Fax: +1(314) 949-4910
President: Dennis Spellmann
Registrar: Jeanne Murabito
Founded: 1827

Lindsey Wilson College
Columbia, Kentucky 42728
Tel: (502) 384-2126
Fax: (502) 384-8200
President: John B. Begley
Registrar: Sue Coomer
Founded: 1903

Linfield College
Mc Minville, Oregon 97128
Tel: +1(503) 472-4121
Fax: +1(503) 472-9528
President: Vivian A. Bull
Registrar: Kenneth G. Williams
Founded: 1849
Nursing.

Livingstone College
701 West Monroe Street, Salisbury, North
Carolina 28144
Tel: +1(704) 638-5500
Fax: +1(704) 638-5522
President: Bernard W. Franklin
Registrar: Wendy Jackson
Founded: 1879

Louisiana College
1140 College Drive, Pineville, Louisiana 71359
Tel: +1(318) 487-7011
Fax: +1(318) 487-7191
President: Robert L. Lynn
Registrar: Alan Mobley
Founded: 1906

Lourdes College
6832 Convent Boulevard, Sylvania, Ohio 43560
Tel: +1(419) 885-3211
Fax: +1(419) 882-3987
President: Sr. Ann Francis Klimkowski
Registrar: Timothy Kusner
Founded: 1958

Lubbock Christian University
5601 West 19th Street, Lubbock, Texas 79407
Tel: +1(806) 796-8800
Fax: +1(806) 796-8917
President: Ken Jones
Registrar: John Castleman
Founded: 1957

Luther College
Decorah, Iowa 52101
Tel: +1(319) 387-2000
Fax: +1(319) 387-1658
President: H. George Anderson
Senior Administrative Officer: Mary Klimesh
Founded: 1861

Lutheran Bible Institute of Seattle
Providence Heights, Issaquah, Washington 98027
Tel: +1(206) 392-0400
Fax: +1(206) 392-0404
President: Trygve Skarsten
Registrar: Judy Odegaard
Founded: 1944

Lycoming College
700 College Place, Williamsport, Pennsylvania
17701-5192
Tel: +1(717) 321-4000
Fax: +1(717) 321-4337
President: James E. Douthat
Registrar: Jeanne Wagner
Founded: 1812

Macalester College
1600 Grand Avenue, St. Paul, Minnesota
55105-1899
Tel: +1(612) 696-6000
Fax: +1(612) 696-6689
President: Robert M. Gavin Jr.
Registrar: Daniel J. Balik
Founded: 1874

MacMurray College
447 East College Avenue, Jacksonville, Illinois
62650
Tel: +1(217) 479-7000
Fax: +1(217) 245-5214
President: Edward J. Mitchell
Registrar: Muriel K. Smith
Founded: 1846

Malone College
75 25th Street N.W., Canton, Ohio 44709
Tel: +1(216) 471-8100
Fax: +1(216) 454-6977
President: E. Arthur Self
Registrar: Gary L. Phelps
Founded: 1892

Manhattan Christian College
1415 Anderson, Manhattan, Kansas 66502
Tel: +1(913) 539-3571
Fax: +1(913) 539-0832
President: Kenneth Cable
Vice-President (Academic Affairs): Dennis Glenn
Founded: 1927

Marian College
3200 Cold Spring Road, Indianapolis, Indiana
46222
Tel: +1(317) 929-0213
Fax: +1(317) 929-0263
President: Daniel A. Felicetti
Registrar: John A. Hill
Founded: 1851

Marian College of Fond du Lac
45 South National Avenue, Fond du Lac,
Wisconsin 54935-4699
Tel: +1(414) 923-7600
Fax: +1(414) 923-7154
President: Matthew G. Flanigan
Registrar: Patrica McGregor
Founded: 1936

Mars Hill College
Mars Hill, North Carolina 28754
Tel: +1(704) 689-1201
Fax: +1(704) 689-1478
President: Fred B. Bentlay
Registrar: Edith Whitt
Founded: 1856

Martin University
2171 Avondale Place, P.O. Box 18567,
Indianapolis, Indiana 46218
Tel: +1(317) 543-3235
Fax: +1(317) 543-3257
President: Rev. Boniface Hardin
Registrar: Ella Love
Founded: 1977

Marymount College
100 Marymount Avenue, Tarrytown, New York
10591-3796
Tel: +1(914) 631-3200
Fax: +1(914) 631-8586
President: Brigid Dviscoll, RSHM
Registrar: Elizabeth Battle
Founded: 1907

Marymount Manhattan College
221 East 71st Street, New York, New York 10021
Tel: +1(212) 517-0400
Fax: +1(212) 517-0413
President: Regina Peruggi
Registrar: Diane Williams
Founded: 1936

Maryville College
Maryville, Tennessee 37801
Tel: +1(615) 981-8000
Fax: +1(615) 983-0581
President: Gerald W. Gibson
Registrar: Martha Hess
Founded: 1819

Massachusetts School of Professional Psychology
221 Rivermoor, Boston, Massachusetts 02132
Tel: +1(617) 327-6777
Fax: +1(617) 327-4447
President: Bruce J. Weiss
Registrar: Jocelyn Shepard
Founded: 1974

Master's College and Seminary
21726 West Placerita Canyon Road, Newhall,
California 91322
Tel: (805) 259-3540
Fax: (805) 254-1998
President: John F. MacArthur Jr.
Vice-President (Academic Affairs): John P. Stead
Founded: 1927

Mayo Medical School
200 First Street S.W., Rochester, Minnesota 55905
Tel: +1(507) 284-3671
Fax: +1(507) 284-2634
E-Mail: 629 12176 esl ud
Director for Education: Richard M. Weinshilbaum
Dean: Burton A. Sandok
Founded: 1971

McKendree College
701 College Road, Lebanon, Illinois 62254-9990
Tel: +1(618) 537-4481
Fax: +1(618) 537-6529
President: Gerrit J. TenBrink
Registrar: Elva Hines
Founded: 1828

McMurry College
14th and Sayles, Abilene, Texas 79697
Tel: +1(915) 691-6200
Fax: +1(915) 691-6599
President: Robert E. Shimp
Registrar: Bobbye Fry
Founded: 1923

McPherson College
1600 East Euclid Street, P.O. Box 1402,
McPherson, Kansas 67460
Tel: +1(316) 241-0731
Fax: +1(316) 241-0731
President: Paul W. Hoffman
Registrar: Karlene Tyler
Founded: 1887

Medaille College
18 Agassiz Circle, Buffalo, New York 14214
Tel: +1(716) 884-3281
Fax: +(716) 884-0291
President: Kevin I. Sullivan
Registrar: Kathleen Lazar
Founded: 1875

Menlo College
1000 El Camino Real, Atherton, California 94027
Tel: +1(415) 323-6141
Fax: +1(415) 324-4937
President: John R. Berthold
Registrar: Louis D. Riccardi Jr.
Founded: 1927
Business Administration.

Mennonite College of Nursing
804 North East Street, Bloomington, Illinois 61701
Tel: +1(309) 829-0715
Fax: +1(309) 829-0715
President: Kathleen A. Hogan
Director of Admissions: Watkins
Founded: 1919

Mercer University
1400 Coleman Avenue, Macon, Georgia 31207
Tel: +1(912) 752-2700
Fax: +1(912) 752-2108
President: R. Kirby Godsey
Registrar: Martha F. Reynolds
Founded: 1833
Liberal Arts; Business Economics (Eugene W. Stetson); Engineering; Medicine; Pharmacy; Law (Walter F. George).

Merrimack College
315 Turnpike Street, North Andover,
Massachusetts 01845
Tel: +(508) 837-5000
Fax: +1(508) 837-5222
President: Rev. John E. Deegan, OSA
Registrar: Shirley A. Smith
Founded: 1947
Business Administration; Continuing Education; Sciences and Engineering.

Messiah College
Grantham, Pennsylvania 17027
Tel: +1(717) 766-2511
Fax: +1(717) 691-6025
President: D. Ray Hostetter
Senior Administrative Officer: Jean Cooker
Founded: 1909

Methodist College
5400 Ramsey Street, Fayetteville, North Carolina
28311
Tel: +1(919) 630-7000
Fax: +1(919) 630-2123
President: M. Elton Hendricks
Registrar: Charles O. Plummer
Founded: 1956

Michigan Christian College
800 West Avon Road, Rochester Hills, Michigan
48307
Tel: +1(313) 651-5800
Fax: +1(313) 650-6060
President: Kenneth Johnson
Registrar: Lynne Stewart
Founded: 1959

Mid-American Bible College
3500 Southwest 119th Street, Oklahoma City,
Oklahoma 73170
Tel: +1(405) 691-3800
Fax: +1(405) 485-3961
President: Rev. Forrest Robinson
Registrar: Larry Higgins
Founded: 1953

Mid-American Nazarene College
2030 College Way, P.O. Box 1776, Olathe, Kansas
66062-1899
Tel: +1(913) 782-3750
Fax: +1(913) 791-3290
President: Richard Spindle
Registrar: N. James Main
Founded: 1966

Mid-Continent Baptist Bible College
Route 2, P.O. Box 7010, Mayfield, Kentucky
42066-0357
Tel: +1(502) 247-8521
President: LaVerne Butler
Registrar: Yvonne Yates
Founded: 1949

Midland Lutheran College
900 North Clarkson, Fremont, Nebraska
68025-4395
Tel: +1(402) 721-5480
Fax: +1(402) 721-0250
President: Carl L. Hansen
Registrar: Tim Ebner
Founded: 1883

Miles Colleges
Birmingham, Alabama 35208
Tel: +1(205) 923-2771
Fax: +1(205) 923-9292
President: Albert J.H. Sloan II
Registrar: Norma J. Kindall
Founded: 1905

Milligan College
Milligan College, Tennessee 37682
Tel: +1(615) 461-8700
Fax: +1(615) 461-8755
President: Marshall J. Leggett
Senior Administrative Officer: Sue H. SKidmore
Founded: 1866

Millikin University
1184 West Main Street, Decatur, Illinois 62522
Tel: +1(217) 424-6211
Fax: +1(217) 424-3993
President: Curtis L. McCray
Registrar: Walter Wessel
Founded: 1901
Arts and Sciences; Fine Acts; Music; Nursing;
Business (Tabor).

Milwaukee Institute of Art and Design
273 East Erie Street, Milwaukee, Wisconsin 53202
Tel: +1(414)276-7889
Fax: +1(414) 291-8077
President: Terrence J. Coffman
Registrar: Mary Strupp
Founded: 1974

Minneapolis College of Art and Design
133 East 25th Street, Minneapolis, Minnesota
55404
Tel: +1(612) 870-3161
Fax: +1(612) 874-3700
President: John Slorp
Senior Administrative Officer: Ingrid Perry-Houts
Founded: 1886

Minnesota Bible College
920 Mayowood Road Southwest, Rochester,
Minnesota 55902-2275
Tel: +1(507) 288-4563
Fax: +1(507) 288-9046
President: Donald R. Lloyd
Registrar: Melinda Sargent
Founded: 1913

Missouri Baptist College
12542 Conway Road, Saint Louis, Missouri
63141-8698
Tel: +1(314) 434-1115
Fax: +1(314) 434-7594
President: Thomas S. Field
Director of Records: Katheen McCaffrey
Founded: 1963

Missouri Valley College
500 East College, Marshall, Missouri 65340
Tel: +1(816) 886-6924
Fax: +1(816) 886-9818
President: Earl J. Reeves
Registrar: Clyde Willims
Founded: 1889

Molloy College
1000 Hempstead Avenue, Rockville Centre, New York 11570-1199
Tel: +1(516) 678-5000
Fax: +1(516) 678-5321
President: Janet A. Fitzgerald, OP
Registrar: James O'Reilly
Founded: 1955

Monmouth College
700 East Broadway, Monmouth, Illinois 61462
Tel: +1(309) 457-2311
Fax: +1(309) 457-2141
President: Bruce Haywood
Registrar: Erhard Saettler
Founded: 1853

Montreat-Anderson College
Montreat, North Carolina 28757
Tel: +1(704) 669-8011
Fax: +1(704) 669-9554
President: William W. Hurt
Registrar: M. Jac Whatley
Founded: 1916

Moore College of Art and Design
20th and the Parkway, Philadelphia, Pennsylvania 19103
Tel: +1(215) 568-4515
Fax: +1(215) 568-8017
President: Mary-Linda Merriam
Registrar: Virginia Kesting
Founded: 1844

Morehouse College
830 Westview Drive S.W., Atlanta, Georgia 30314
Tel: +1(404) 681-2800
Fax: +1(404) 659-6536
President: Leroy Keith Jr.
Senior Administrative Officer: William Dease
Founded: 1867

Morris Brown College
634 Martin L. King, Jr. Drive, Atlanta, Georgia 30314
Tel: +1(404) 220-0270
Fax: +1(404) 659-4315
President: Herman B. Smith
Registrar: Lucille S. Williams
Founded: 1881

Morris College
North Main Street, Sumter, South Carolina 29150-3599
Tel: +1(803) 775-9371
Fax: +1(803) 773-3687
President: Luns C. Richardson
Admissions and Records Officer: Queen W. Spann
Founded: 1908

Mount Ida College
777 Dedham Street, Newton Centre, Massachusetts 02159
Tel: +1(617) 969-7000
Fax: +1(617) 969-6993
President: Bryan E. Carlson
Senior Administrative Officer: Peter Newport
Founded: 1899
S: Design and Merchandising (Chamber Layne); Electricity (Coyne); Mortary Science; Animal Science; Business; Education; Liberal Arts; Science and Allied Health.

Mount Mercy College
1330 Elmhurst Drive N.E., Cedar Rapids, Iowa 52402-4797
Tel: +1(319) 363-8213
Fax: +1(319) 363-5270
President: Thomas R. Feld
Registrar: Mary L. Rettig
Founded: 1928

Mount Olive College
Mount Olive, North Carolina 28365
Tel: +1(919) 658-2502
Fax: +1(919) 658-8934
President: W. Burkette Raper
Registrar: Jack W. Overcash
Founded: 1951

Mount Saint Clare College
400 N. Bluff Boulevard, Clinton, Iowa 52732
Tel: +1(319) 242-4023
Fax: +1(319) 242-2003
President: James J. Ross
Registrar: MaryLou Mallicoat
Founded: 1918

Mount Senario College
1500 College Avenue West, Ladysmith, Wisconsin 54848
Tel: (715) 532-5511
Fax: (715) 532-7690
President: John N. Cable
Registrar: Judy Berger
Founded: 1962

Mount Union College
1972 Clark Avenue, Alliance, Ohio 44601
Tel: +1(216) 821-5320
Fax: +1(216) 821-0425
President: Harold M. Kolenbrander
Registrar: Stuart Terrass
Founded: 1846

Mount Vernon College
2100 Foxhall Road N.W., Washington, D.C. 20007
Tel: +1(202) 625-0400
Fax: +1(202) 338-1089
President: LucyAnn Geiselman
Registrar: Libby Sears
Founded: 1875

Muhlenberg College
24th and Chew Streets, Allentown, Pennsylvania 18104
Tel: +1(215) 821-3100
Fax: (215) 821-3234
President: Authur R. Taylor
Registrar: Eileen Kern
Founded: 1848

Muskingum College
College Drive, New Concord, Ohio 43762-1199
Tel: +1(614) 826-8211
Fax: +1(614) 826-8404
President: Samuel W. Speck Jr.
Registrar: Russell Brown
Founded: 1837

NAES College
2838 West Peterson Avenue, Chicago, Illinois 60659
Tel: +1(312) 761-5000
Fax: +1(312) 761-3808
President: Faith Smith
Dean/Vice-President (Academic Affairs): Robert V. Dumont Jr.
Founded: 1974

National College
321 Kansas City Street, P.O. Box 1780, Rapid City, South Dakota 57709
Tel: +1(605) 394-4800
Fax: +1(605) 394-4871
President: Harold R. Stone
Registrar: Mary Borella
Founded: 1941

National College of Chiropractic
200 East Roosevelt Road, Lombard, Illinois 60148-6118
Tel: +1(708) 629-2000
Fax: +1(708) 628-6554
President: J. F. Winterstein
Registrar: Cheryl Stowell
Founded: 1906

National College-St. Paul Campus
1380 Energy Lane, St. Paul, Minnesota 55108
Tel: +1(612) 644-1265
Founded: 1975

National Technological University
Fort Collins, Colorado 80526
Tel: +1(303) 495-6400
Fax: +1(303) 484-0668
President: Lionel V. Baldwin
Director of Admissions: Eileen Morce

Nazarene Bible College
P.O. Box 17549, Colorado Springs, Colorado 80935
Tel: +1(719) 596-5110
Fax: +1(719) 550-9437
President: Jerry D. Lambert
Registrar: Ron Attig
Founded: 1967

Nebraska Christian College
1800 Syracuse, Norfolk, Nebraska 68701
Tel: +1(402) 371-5960
Fax: +1(402) 371-5967
President: Ray D. Stites
Registrar: Richard E. Brown
Founded: 1944

Nebraska Wesleyan University
5000 St. Paul Avenue, Lincoln, Nebraska 68504
Tel: +1(402) 466-2371
Fax: +1(402) 465-2179
President: John W. White Jr.
Registrar: Patricia Hall
Founded: 1887

New England College of Optometry
424 Beacon Street, Boston, Massachusetts 02115
Tel: +1(617) 266-2030
Fax: +1(617) 424-9202
President: Larry R. Clausen
Registrar: Glenda Underwood
Founded: 1894

New York School of Interior Design
155 East 56th Street, New York, New York 10022
Tel: +1(212) 753-5365
Fax: +1(212) 753-2034
President: Paul Heyer
Academic Dean: Chris Welsh
Founded: 1916

Newberry College
2100 College, Newberry, South Carolina 29108
Tel: +1(803) 276-5010
Fax: +1(803) 321-5232
President: Peter L. French (1994-)
Registrar: Carol Bickley
Founded: 1856

North Carolina Wesleyan College
3400 Wesleyan Boulevard, Rocky Mount, North Carolina 27804
Tel: +1(919) 985-5100
Fax: +1(919) 977-3701
President: Leslie H. Garner Jr.
Registrar: C. Clifton Sullivan
Founded: 1956

North Central Bible College
910 Elliot Avenue South, Minneapolis, Minnesota 55404
Tel: +1(612) 332-3491
Fax: +1(612) 343-4778
President: Don H. Argue
Director of Admissions and Records: Dan Neary
Founded: 1930

North Park College and Theological Seminary
5125 North Spaulding Avenue, Chicago, Illinois 60625
Tel: +1(312) 583-2700
Fax: +1(312) 583-0858
President: David G. Horner
Vice-President (Administration and Finance): Carl E. Balsam
Founded: 1891

Northland College
1411 Ellis Avenue, Ashland, Wisconsin 54806-3999
Tel: +(715) 682-1699
Fax: +1(715) 682-1308
President: Robert Rue Parsonage
Registrar: Rick Guild
Founded: 1892

Northwest College of the Assemblies of God
P.O. Box 579, Kirkland, Washington 98083
Tel: +1(206) 822-8266
Fax: +1(206) 827-0148
President: Rev. Dennis Davis
Registrar: Jacqualyn Randolph
Founded: 1934

Northwestern College
101 9th Street, Orange City, Iowa 51041-1996
Tel: +1(712) 737-4821
Fax: +1(712) 737-8847
President: James E. Bultman
Registrar: Paula Evenhuis
Founded: 1882

Northwestern College
3003 North Snelling Avenue, St. Paul, Minnesota 55113-1598
Tel: +1(612) 631-5100
Fax: +1(612) 631-5269
President: Donald Erickesen
Registrar: Donald Carliss
Founded: 1902

Notre Dame College of Ohio
4545 College Road, South Eclid, Ohio 44121
Tel: +1(216) 381-1680
Fax: +1(216) 381-1680 ext. 301
President: Sr. Marla Loehr, SND
Registrar: Tina L. Coleman
Founded: 1922

Oakwood College
Oakwood Road, P.O. Box 107, Huntsville, Alabama 35896
Tel: +1(205) 726-7000
Fax: +1(205) 726-7409
President: Benjamin F. Reaves
Vice-President for Finance: Dennis Keith
Founded: 1896

Ohio Dominican College
1216 Sunbury Road, Columbus, Ohio 43219
Tel: +1(614) 253-2741
Fax: +1(614) 252-0776
President: Sr. Mary Andrew Matesich
Registrar: Shirley C. Nucklos
Founded: 1911

Ohio Northern University
525 South Main Street, Ada, Ohio 45810
Tel: +1(419) 772-2000
Fax: +1(419) 772-1932
President: DeBow Freed
Registrar: Richard Carpenter
Founded: 1871
C: Law (Claude W. Petit); Business Administration; Arts and Sciences (Getty); Pharmacy and Allied Health; Engineering Sciences (Smull).

Ohio Valley College
450 College Parkway, Parkersburg, West Virginia 26101
Tel: +1(304) 485-7384
Fax: +1(304) 485-8382
President: E. Keith Stotts
Executive Vice-President: Robert W. Stephens Jr.
Founded: 1960

Ohio Wesleyan University
Sandusky Street, Delaware, Ohio 43015
Tel: +1(614) 368-2000
Fax: +1(614) 368-3314
President: David L. Warren
Provost: William C. Louthan
Founded: 1842

Oklahoma Baptist University
500 West University, Shawnee, Oklahoma 74801
Tel: +1(405) 275-2850
Fax: +1(405) 878-2069
President: Bob R. Agee
Registrar: Peggy J. Askins
Founded: 1910
Fine Arts; Business; Christian Service; Nursing.

Oklahoma Christian University of Science and Arts
Route 1, Box 141, Oklahoma City, Oklahoma 73136
Tel: +1(405) 425-5000
Fax: +1(405) 425-5316
President: J. Terry Johnson
Executive Vice-President: R. Stafford North
Founded: 1950

O'More College of Design
423 South Margin Street, Franklin, Tennessee 37065
Tel: +1(615) 794-4254
President/Chief Executive Officer: Eloise O'More
Executive Vice-President: Roy O'More, V
Founded: 1970

Ottawa University
10th and Cedar Streets, Ottawa, Kansas
66067-3399
Tel: +1(913) 242-5200
Fax: +1(913) 242-7429
President: Harald D. Germer
Registrar: Peter G. Sandstrom
Founded: 1865

Otterbein College
College and Grove Streets, Westerville, Ohio
43081
Tel: +1(614) 890-3000
Fax: +1(614) 890-1200
President: C. Brent De Vore
Vice-President (Business Affairs): Stephen Storck
Founded: 1847

Ozark Christian College
1111 North Main Street, Joplin, Missouri 64801
Tel: +1(417) 624-2518
Fax: +1(417) 624-0090
President: Kenneth Idleman
Registrar: Jennifer McMillin
Founded: 1942

Pacific Coast Baptist Bible College
1100 South Valley Center, San Dimas, California
91773
Tel: +1(909) 599-6843
Founded: 1967

Pacific Northwest College of Art, Oregon Art Institute
1219 Southwest Park Avenue, Portland, Oregon
97205
Tel: +1(503) 226-4391
Fax: +1(503) 226-4842
Director: Sally C. Lawrence
Registrar: Jenifer Dekalb
Founded: 1909
Art.

Paier College of Art, Inc.
20 Gorham Avenue, Hamde, Connecticut 06511
Tel: +1(203) 777-3851
President: Edward T. Paier
Director of Student Records: Maureen Derose
Founded: 1946
Art.

Paine College
1235 15th Street, Augusta, Georgia 30910-3182
Tel: +1(706) 821-8200
Fax: +1(706) 821-8293
President: Julius S. Scott Jr.
Registrar: W. Amos Evans
Founded: 1882

Palm Beach Atlantic College
1101 South Olive Avenue, West Palm Beach,
Florida 33416-4708
Tel: +1(407) 650-7700
Fax: +1(407) 835-4342
President: Paul R. Corts
Director of Academic Records and
Advisement(Acting): Geneane Kelley-Miller
Founded: 1968
Business (Rinker).

Palmer College of Chiropractic
1000 Bradley Street, Davenport, Iowa 52803-5287
Tel: +1(319) 326-9600
Fax: +1(319) 326-9897
President: Donald P. Kern
Registrar: Howard Silverstein
Founded: 1895
Chiropractic Studies.

Palmer College of Chiropractic-West
San Jose, California 95134
Tel: +1(408) 983-4000
Fax: +1(408) 983-4010
President: Peter Martin
Registrar: Kim Lee
Founded: 1978
Chiropractic Studies.

Patten College
2433 Coolidge Avenue, Oakland, California 94601
Tel: +1(510) 533-8306
Fax: +1(510) 534-8564
President: Priscilla C. Benham
Registrar: Sandra Lentz
Founded: 1944

Paul Quinn College
1020 Elm Street, Dallas, Texas 75241
Tel: +1(214) 376-1000
Fax: +1(214) 371-1016
President: Lee E. Monroe
Coordinator of Records and Registration: J.D.
Hurd
Founded: 1872

Pennsylvania College of Optometry
1200 West Godfrey Avenue, Philadelphia,
Pennsylvania 19141
Tel: +1(215) 276-6200
Fax: +1(215) 276-6081
President: Thomas L. Lewis
Registrar: Virginia G. Kennedy
Founded: 1919
Optometry.

Pfeiffer College
Misenheimer, North Carolina 28109-0960
Tel: +1(704) 463-1360
Fax: +1(704) 463-1363
President: Zane E. Eargle
Registrar: Larry Durrett
Founded: 1885

Philander Smith College
812 West 13th Street, Little Rock, Arkansas 72202
Tel: +1(501) 375-9845
Fax: +1(501) 370-5278
President: Myer L. Titus
Director of Admissions and Records: Picola Smith
Founded: 1877

Piedmont Bible College
716 Franklin Street, Winston-Salem, North Carolina 27101-5197
Tel: +1(919) 725-8344
Fax: +1(919) 725-5522
President: Howard L. Wilburn
Registrar: Delores Fulton
Founded: 1847

Piedmont College
165 Central Avenue, Demorest, Georgia 30535
Tel: +1(706) 778-3000
Fax: +1(706) 776-2811
President: John F. Elger
Registrar: Carol Parker
Founded: 1897

Pikeville College
Sycamore Street, Pikeville, Kentucky 41501-1194
Tel: +1(606) 432-9200
Fax: +1(606) 432-9372
President: William Owens
Director of Academic Records: Barbara A. Strickler
Founded: 1889

Pillsbury Baptist Bible College
315 South Grove, Owatonna, Minnesota 55060
Tel: +1(507) 451-2710
Fax: +1(507) 451-6459
President: Alan L. Potter
Academic Dean: Paul Ague Jr.
Founded: 1957

Pine Manor College
400 Heath Street, Chestnut Hill, Massachusetts 02167
Tel: +1(617) 731-7000
Fax: +1(617) 731-7199
President: Rosemary Ashby
Registrar: David Aalto
Founded: 1911

Pitzer College
1150 North Mills Avenue, Claremont, California 91711-6110
Tel: +1(909) 621-8000
Fax: +1(909) 621-8521
President: Marilyn C. Massey
Registrar: Victor Egitto
Founded: 1963

Pomona College
333 North College Way, Claremont, California 91711
Tel: +1(909) 621-8000
Fax: +1(909) 621-8403
President: Peter W. Stanley
Registrar: Monica Augustin
Founded: 1887

Presbyterian College
South Broad Street, Clinton, South Carolina 29325
Tel: +1(803) 833-2820
Fax: +1(803) 833-8481
President: Kenneth B. Orr
Senior Vice-President (Academic Affairs): J. William Moncrief
Founded: 1880

Prescott College
220 Grove Avenue, Prescott, Arizona 86301
Tel: +1(602) 776-5180
Fax: +1(602) 776-5137
President: Douglas M. North
Registrar: Marsha Poole
Founded: 1966

Principia College
Elsah, Illinois 62028
Tel: +1(618) 374-2131
Fax: +1(618) 374-5122
President: David E. Pfeifer
Registrar: Daphne Selbert
Founded: 1910

Pugat Sound Christian College
410 Fourth Avenue North, Edmonds, Washington 98020-3171
Tel: +1(206) 775-8686
President: Glen R. Basey
Registrar: Delores Scarbrough
Founded: 1950

Randolph-Macon College
P.O. Box 5005, Ashland, Virginia 23005-5505
Tel: +1(804) 789-8372
Fax: +1(804) 752-7231
President: Ladell Payne
Registrar: Robert L. Hopkins Jr.
Founded: 1830

Randolph-Macon Women's College
2500 Rivermont Avenue, Lynchburg, Virginia 24503
Tel: +1(804) 947-8000
Fax: +1(804) 947-8138
President: Lindkoch Lorimer
Registrar: Ruth L. Tergesen
Founded: 1891

Reformed Bible College
1869 Robinson Road Southeast, Grand Rapids, Michigan 49506-9749
Tel: +1(616) 363-2050
Fax: +1(616) 363-9771
President: Edwin D. Roels
Registrar: Connie J. Scheurwater
Founded: 1940

Regis College
Weston, Massachusetts 02193
Tel: +1(617) 893-1820
Fax: +1(617) 899-4725
President: Sr. Sheila Megley, RSM
Registrar: Sr. Patricia McDonough, CSJ
Founded: 1927

Research College of Nursing-Rockhurst College
5225 Troast Avenue, Kansas City, Missouri 64132
Tel: +1(816) 276-4700
Fax: +1(816) 276-4387
President: Nancy O. DeBasio
Director of Student Affairs: Graham Houston
Founded: 1980
Nursing.

Ringling School of Art and Design
1191 27th Street, Sarasota, Florida 34234
Tel: +1(813) 351-4614
Fax: +1(813) 359-7517
President: Arland F. Christ-Janer
Registrar: Bettina Beer
Founded: 1931
Art and Design.

Ripon College
300 Seward Street, P.O. Box 248, Ripon, Wisconsin 54971-0248
Tel: +1(414) 748-8102
Fax: +1(414) 748-7243
President: William R. Stott Jr.
Registrar: Michele A. Wittler
Founded: 1851

Roanoke Bible College
P.O. Box 387, Elizabeth City, North Carolina 27909
Tel: +1(919) 338-5191
Fax: +1(919) 338-0801
President: William A. Griffin
Registrar: Joan U. Sawyer
Founded: 1948

Roanoke College
Salem, Virginia 24153
Tel: +1(703) 375-2500
President: David M. Gring
Registrar: Lean R. Russell
Founded: 1842

Roberts Wesleyan College
2301 Westside Drive, Rochester, New York 14624
Tel: +1(716) 594-6000
Fax: +1(716) 594-6371
President: William C. Crothers
Senior Vice-President/Provost: Wayne McCown
Founded: 1866

Rocky Mountain College
1511 Poly Drive, Billings, Montana 59102
Tel: +1(406) 657-1000
Fax: +1(406) 259-9751
President: Arthur H. DeRosier Jr.
Registrar: James R. Taylor
Founded: 1878

Roger Williams University
Ferry Road, Bristol, Rhode Island 02809
Tel: (401) 253-1040
Fax: (401) 254-0490
President (Acting): Malcalm H. Forbes
Registrar: Robert Fetterhoff
Founded: 1948
Architecture; Business; Continuing Education; Engineering; Fine and Performing Arts; Humanities; Science and Mathematics; Social Science.

Rust College
150 Rust Avenue, Holly Springs, Mississippi 38635
Tel: +1(601) 252-8000
Fax: +1(601) 252-6107
President: David L. Beckey
Registrar: Clarence Smith
Founded: 1866

Saint Leo College
Route 52, Saint Leo, Florida 33574
Tel: +1(904) 588-8200
Fax: +1(904) 588-8350
President: Msgr. Frank Mouch
Registrar: Fred Colby
Founded: 1889

Saint Louis University: Parks College of Saint Louis University
Cahokia, Illinois 62206
Tel: +1(618) 337-7500
Fax: +1(618) 332-6802
Associate Vice-President and Dean: Margaret J. Baty
Registrar: Anita Zieren-Amptman
Founded: 1927

Saint Mary's College
Orchard Lake and Commerce Roads, Orchard Lake, Michigan 48324
Tel: +1(313) 682-1885
Fax: +1(313) 683-0402
President: Edward D. Meyer
Registrar: Sr. Evelyn Kruskamp
Founded: 1885

Saint Paul's College
406 Windsor Avenue, Lawrenceville, Virginia 23868-1299
Tel: +1(804) 848-3111
Fax: +1(804) 848-0403
President: Thomas M. Law
Director for Registration and Records: Jugurtha Y. Byrd
Founded: 1888

Salem College
South Church Street, Winston-Salem, North Carolina 27108
Tel: +1(919) 721-2600
Fax: +1(919) 721-2832
President: Julianne Still Thrift
Registrar: Todd L. Fag
Founded: 1772

Samuel Merritt College of Nursing
370 Hawthorne Avenue, Oakland, California 94609
Tel: +1(510) 420-6011
Fax: +1(510) 420-6025
President: Sharon Diaz
Registrar: Lee Coble
Founded: 1909
Nursing.

San Jose Christian College
790 South 12th Street, P.O. Box 1090, San Jose,
California 95112
Tel: +1(408) 293-9058
Fax: +1(408) 293-7352
President: Bryce Jessup
Registrar: Bonnie Sloan
Founded: 1939

Schreiner College
Highway 27, Kerrville, Texas 78028
Tel: +1(210) 896-5411
Fax: +1(512) 896-3232
President: Sam M. Junkin
Registrar: Darlene Bannister
Founded: 1923

Scripps College
1030 North Columbia, Claremont, California
91711-3948
Tel: +1(909) 621-8000
Fax: +1(909) 621-8323
President: Nancy Y. Bekavae
Registrar: Carol Entler
Founded: 1926

Selma University
Selma, Alabama 36701
Tel: +1(205) 872-2533
Fax: +1(205) 872-7746
President: Willie L. Muse (1994-)
Registrar: Estella Baynes
Founded: 1878

Seton Hill College
Seton Hill Drive, Greensburg, Pennsylvania 15601
Tel: +1(412) 834-2200
Fax: +1(412) 830-4611
President: JoAnne W. Boyle
Registrar: Barbara C. Hinkle
Founded: 1883

Shaw University
118 East South Street, Raleigh, North Carolina
27601
Tel: +1(919) 546-8200
Fax: +1(919) 546-8301
President: Talbert O. Shaw
Director (Records and Registration): Rudolph
Williams
Founded: 1865

Sheldon Jackson College
801 Lincoln, Sitka, Alaska 99835
Tel: +1(907) 747-5221
Fax: +1(907) 747-5212
President: Lowell Tornquist
Vice-President for Administration: John H. Smith
Founded: 1878

Sherman College of Straight Chiropratic
Spartanburg, South Carolina 29304
Tel: +1(803) 578-8770
Fax: +1(803) 599-7145
President: T.A. Gelardi
Registrar: Julie Clayton
Founded: 1973
Chiropractic Studies.

Shimer College
P.O. Box A500, Waukegon, Illinois 60079-0500
Tel: +1(708) 623-8400
Fax: +1(708) 249-7171
President: Don P. Moon
Registrar: Kate Soule
Founded: 1853

Siena College
Route 9, Loudonville, New York 12211-1462
Tel: +1(518) 783-2300
Fax: +1(518) 783-4293
President: Fr. William McConville, ODM
Registrar: James Serbalik
Founded: 1937

Sierra Nevada College
Incline Village, Nevada 89450-4269
Tel: +1(702) 831-1314
Fax: +1(702) 831-1347
President: Mark Hurtubise
Registrar: Catherine Mitchell-Adams
Founded: 1969

Simon's Rock College of Bard
Alford Road, Great Barrington, Massachusetts
01230-9702
Tel: +1(413) 528-0771
Fax: +1(413) 528-7365
President: Leon Botstein
Registrar: Laura K. Martin
Founded: 1964

Sinte Gleska College
Box 490, Rosebud, South Dakota 57570
Tel: +1(605) 747-2263
President: Lionel Bordeaux
Vice-President: Cheryl Crazy Bull
Founded: 1970

Skidmore College
North Broadway, Saratoga Springs, New York
12866-0851
Tel: +1(518) 584-5000
Fax: +1(518) 584-3023
President: David H. Porter
Registrar: Ann L. Henderson
Founded: 1903

Sojourner-Douglass College
500 North Carolina Street, Baltimore, Maryland 21205
Tel: +1(410) 276-0306
Fax: +1(410) 675-1810
President: Charles W. Simmons
Registrar: Louise Taylor
Founded: 1980

Southeastern Baptist College
4229 Highway 15th North, Laurel, Mississipp 39440
Tel: +1(601) 426-6346
President: A.M. Wilson
Academic Dean: Medrick Savell
Founded: 1949

Southeastern College of the Assemblies of God
1000 Longfellow Boulevard, Lakeland, Florida 33801
Tel: +1(813) 665-4404
Fax: +1(813) 666-8103
President: James Hennesy
Vice-President (Academic Affairs): John Higgins
Founded: 1935

Southern College of Seventh-Day Adventists
P.O. Box 370, Collegedale, Tennessee 37315
Tel: +1(615) 238-2111
Fax: +1(615) 238-3001
President: Donald R. Sahby
Vice-President/Academic Administrator: Floyd Greenleaf
Founded: 1892

Southern Vermont College
Monument Road, Bennington, Vermont 05201
Tel: +1(802) 442-5427
Fax: +1(802) 442-5529
President: William A. Glasser
Registrar: Laurie Cubit
Founded: 1926

Southwestern Adventist College
Keene, Texas 76059
Tel: +1(817) 645-3921
Fax: +1(817) 556-4744
President: Marvin E. Anderson
Academic Vice-President: W.G. Nelson
Founded: 1894

Southwestern Assemblies of God College
1200 Sycamore, Waxahachie, Texas 75165
Tel: +1(214) 937-4010
Fax: +1(214) 923-0488
President: Delmer Guynes
Registrar: Greg Dufrene
Founded: 1927

Southwestern Christian College
P.O. Box 10, Terrell, Texas 75160
Tel: +1(214) 524-3341
Fax: +1(214) 263-7133
President: Jack Evans
Dean of the College: Zoa Ann Turner
Founded: 1949

Southwestern College
2625 East Cactus Road, Phoenix, Arizona 85032
Tel: +1(602) 992-6101
Fax: +1(602) 414-2159
President: Donald Engram
Vice-President (Administration): Arnold J. Doerksen
Founded: 1960

Southwestern College
Winfield, Kansas 67156-2499
Tel: +1(316) 221-4150
Fax: +1(316) 221-8224
President: Rev. Carl E. Martin
Vice-President (Business Affairs): David Galliart
Founded: 1885

Southwestern College of Christian Ministries
P.O. Box 340, Bethany, Oklahoma 73008
Tel: +1(405) 789-7661
Fax: +1(405) 789-7669 ext.132
President: Rev. Ronald Q. Moore
Dean of Academics: Douglas Jernigan
Founded: 1946

Southwestern University
University Avenue, Georgetown, Texas 78626
Tel: +1(512) 863-6511
Fax: +1(512) 863-5788
President: Roy B. Shilling Jr.
Registrar: George Brightwell
Founded: 1840
Arts and Sciences (Brown); Fine Arts.

Southwestern University School of Law
675 South Westmoreland Avenue, Los Angeles, California 90005
Tel: +1(213) 738-6700
Fax: +1(213) 383-1688
President: Leigh H. Taylor
Registrar: Karen Kaeni
Founded: 1911

Spelman College
350 Spelman Lane, Southwest, Atlanta, Georgia 30314
Tel: +1(404) 681-3643
Fax: +1(404) 688-2857
President: Johnnetta B. Cole
Registrar: Fred Buddy
Founded: 1881

Spring Arbor College
106 East Main, Spring Arbor, Michigan 49283
Tel: +1(517) 750-1200
Fax: +1(517) 750-2108
President: M. Allen Carden
Registrar: Darlene Mefford
Founded: 1873

St. Andrews Presbyterian College
Laurinburg, North Carolina 28352
Tel: +1(919) 277-5000
Fax: +1(919) 277-5020
President: Thomas L. Reuschling
Vice-President (Academic Affairs): Lawrence E. Schulz
Founded: 1958

St. Anselm College
Manchester, New Hampshire 03102
Tel: +1(603) 641-7000
Fax: +1(603) 641-7116
President: Rev. Jonathan DeFelice
Registrar: Rev. Augustine G. Kelly
Founded: 1889

St. Augustine's College
1315 Oakwood Avenue, Raleigh, North Carolina 27610-2298
Tel: +1(919) 516-4000
Fax: +1(919) 828-0817
President: Prezell R. Robinson
Registrar: Marshall Harvey
Founded: 1867

St. Francis College
180 Remsen Street, Brooklyn Heights, New York 11201
Tel: +1(718) 522-2300
Fax: +1(718) 522-1274
President: Br. Donald Sullivan
Registrar: Robert Schaefer
Founded: 1884

St. Joseph's College
Whites Bridge Road, North Windham, Maine 04062-1198
Tel: +1(207) 892-6766
Fax: +1(207) 892-7746
President: Loring E. Hart
Registrar: Sr. Elizabeth Dorsey
Founded: 1912

St. Joseph's College
245 Clinton Avenue, Brooklyn, New York 11205-3688
Tel: +1(718) 636-6800
President: Sr. George Aquin O'Connor
Registrar: Barbara Janusz
Founded: 1916

St. Joseph's College Suffolk Campus
155 Roe Boulevard, Patchogue, New York 11772
Tel: +1(516) 447-3200
President: Sr. George Aquin O'Connor
Registrar: Sr. Rose Catherine Stevens
Founded: 1916

St. Louis Christian College
1360 Grandview Drive, Florissant, Missouri 63033
Tel: +1(314) 837-6777
President: Thomas W. McGee
Dean of Students/Registrar: Christine Cable
Founded: 1956

St. Mary College
4100 South 4th Street Trafficway, Leavenworth, Kansas 66048-5082
Tel: +1(913) 682-5151
Fax: +1(913) 682-2406
President: Peter Clifford
Registrar: Sr. Dorothy Harvat
Founded: 1923

St. Mary's College
Notre Dame, Indiana 46556
Tel: +1(219) 284-4000
Fax: +1(219) 284-4716
President: William A. Hickey
Registrar: Sr. Francesca Kennedy
Founded: 1844

St. Olaf College
Northfield, Minnesota 55057-1098
Tel: +1(507) 646-2222
Fax: +1(507) 646-3549
E-Mail: 62835910 esl ud
President: Melvin George
Registrar: John Treon
Founded: 1874

St. Vincent College
Latrobe, Pennsylvania 15650
Tel: +1(412) 539-9761
Fax: +1(412) 537-4554
E-Mail: 620 09333 esl ud
President: Rev. John F. Murtha
Registrar: Br. Nathan Cochran
Founded: 1846

Stephens College
1200 East Broadway, Columbia, Missouri 65215-0001
Tel: +1(314) 442-2211
Fax: +1(314) 876-7248
President: Patsy H. Sampson
Assistant Dean/Registrar: Bobby Burk
Founded: 1833

Sterling College
Sterling, Kansas 67579
Tel: +1(316) 278-2173
Fax: +1(316) 278-3188
President: Roger Parrott
Registrar/Administrative Dean: Frances N. Calderwood
Founded: 1887

Stillman College
P.O. Drawer 1430, Tuscaloosa, Alabama 35403-9990
Tel: +1(205) 349-4240
Fax: +1(205) 349-4252
President: Cordell Wynn
Director of Admissions: Barbara Smith
Founded: 1876

Stonehill College
320 Washington Street, North Easton,
Massachusetts 02357
Tel: +1(508) 238-1081
Fax: +1(508) 230-3732
President: Rev. Bartley MacPhaidin
Associate Dean (Academic Services): Linda
I.Sullivan
Founded: 1948

Susquehanna University
University Avenue, Selinsgrove, Pennsylvania
17870-1001
Tel: +1(717) 374-0101
Fax: +1(717) 372-2745
Director: Joel L. Cunningham
Registrar: Alex G.H. Smith
Founded: 1858
*S: Arts and Sciences; Fine Arts and
Communications; Business (Sigmund Weis).*

Sweet Briar College
Sweet Briar, Virginia 24595
Tel: +1(804) 381-6100
Fax: +1(804) 381-6173
Director: Barbara A. Hill
Dean of the College: George H. Lenz
Founded: 1901

Tabor College
400 South Jefferson, Hillsboro, Kansas 67063
Tel: +1(316) 947-3121
Fax: +1(316) 947-2607
Director: LeVon Balzer
Registrar: Deanne Duerksen
Founded: 1908

Talladega College
627 West Battle Street, Talladega, Alabama 35160
Tel: +1(205) 362-0206
Fax: +1(205) 362-2268
President: Joseph B. Johnson
Registrar: Floretta J. Dortch
Founded: 1867

Taylor University
Reade Avenue, Upland, Indiana 46989-1001
Tel: +1(317) 998-2751
Fax: +1(317) 998-5569
Director: Jay L. Kestler
Registrar: Barbar Davenport
Founded: 1846

Tennessee Wesleyan College
College Street, P.O. Box 40, Athens, Tennessee
37371-0040
Tel: +1(615) 745-7504
Director: James E. Cheek
Registrar: Lydia Norfleet
Founded: 1857

Texas College
2404 North Grand Avenue, Tyler, Texas 75712
Tel: +1(903) 593-8311
Fax: +1(903) 592-2342
Director: A.C. Mitchell Patton
Registrar: Sandra Smith-Jiles
Founded: 1894

Texas Lutheran College
1000 West Court Street, Seguin, Texas 78155
Tel: +1(210) 372-8000
Fax: +1(210) 372-8096
President: Charles H. Oestreich
Registrar: Milroy R. Jaroszewski
Founded: 1891

Thiel College
75 College Avenue, Greenville, Pennsylvania
16125
Tel: +1(412) 589-2000
Fax: +1(412) 589-2860
President: C. Carlyle Haaland
Registrar: Mark McGrath
Founded: 1866

Thomas Aquinas College
10000 North Ojai Road, San Paula, California
93060-9980
Tel: +1(805) 525-4417
Fax: +1(805) 525-0620
President: Thomas E. Dillon
Dean of Academic Affairs: Kevin D. Kollbeck
Founded: 1971

Thomas More College
Crestview Hills, Kentucky 41017
Tel: +1(606) 341-5800
Fax: +1(606) 344-3345
President: Rev. William F. Cleves
Registrar: Patsy Kenner
Founded: 1921

Tiffin University
155 Miami Street, Tiffin, Ohio 44883
Tel: +1(419) 447-6442
Fax: +1(419) 447-9605
President: George Kidd Jr.
Registrar: Alice Nichols
Founded: 1888

Toccoa Falls College
Toccoa Falls, Georgia 30598
Tel: +1(706) 886-6831
Fax: +1(706) 886-0210
President: Paul L. Alford
Registrar: Kelly Vickers
Founded: 1907

Tougaloo College
Tougaloo, Mississippi 39174
Tel: +1(601) 977-7700
Fax: +1(601) 977-7739
President: Adib A. Shakir
Executive Vice-President: John Glover
Founded: 1869

Touro College
27-33 West 23rd Street, New York 10001
Tel: +1(212) 463-0400
Fax: +1(212) 779-2344
President: Bernard Lander
Registrar: Edward Schabes
Founded: 1970
Health Sciences (Barry Z. Levine); General Studies; Judaic Studies; Law (Jacob D. Fuschsberg).

Transylvania University
300 North Broadway, Lexington, Kentucky 40508-1797
Tel: +1(606) 233-8300
Fax: +1(606) 233-8797
President: Charles L. Sheaver
Registrar: James M. Mills
Founded: 1780

Trinity Bible College
50 South 6th, Ellendale, North Dakota 58436-7150
Tel: +1(701) 349-3621
Fax: +1(701) 349-5443
President: Ray Trask
Director of Records: Denise White
Founded: 1948

Trinity Christian College
6601 West College Drive, Palos Heights, Illinois 60463
Tel: +1(708) 597-3000
Fax: +1(708) 385-5665
E-Mail: 629 85736 esl ud
President: Kenneth B. Bootsma
Registrar: Ron Oosting
Founded: 1959

Trinity College
208 Colchester Avenue, Burlington, Vermont 05401
Tel: +1(802) 658-0337
Fax: +1(802) 658-5446
E-Mail: 629 05061 esl ud
President: Sr. Janice Ryan
Registrar: Alice Rouleau
Founded: 1925

Trinity College
2077 Half Day Road, Deerfield, Illinois 60015-1284
Tel: +1(708) 948-8980
Fax: +1(708) 317-7090
President: Kenneth M. Meyer
Executive Vice-President: Milo Lundell
Founded: 1897

Tri-State University
South Darling Street, Angola, Indiana 46703
Tel: +1(219) 665-4100
Fax: +1(219) 665-4292
President: R. John Rynolds
Registrar (Acting): Debbie Helmsing
Founded: 1884
Arts and Sciences; Business; Engineering.

Tusculum College
P.O. Box 49, Greenville, Tennessee 37743-9997
Tel: +1(615) 636-7300
Fax: +1(615) 638-7166
President: Robert E. Knott
Registrar: Nancy Thompson
Founded: 1794

Union College
3800 South 48th Street, Lincoln, Nebraska 68506
Tel: +1(402) 488-2331
Fax: +1(402) 486-2895
President: John Kerbs
Registrar: LeVerne Bissel
Founded: 1891

Union University
Highway 45 By-Pass, Jackson, Tennessee 38305
Tel: +1(901) 668-1818
Fax: +1(901) 664-9358
President: Hyran E. Barefoot
Registrar: Jane Nichols
Founded: 1823
Business Administration; Education and Human Services; Nursing.

Unity College
RR78 Quaker Hill Road, Unity, Maine 04988
Tel: +1(207) 948-3131
Fax: +1(207) 948-5626
President: Wilson G. Hess
Registrar: Holly Hein
Founded: 1965

Universidad Central del Caribea Escuela de Medicina de Cayey
José R. Oliver Street, Bayamon, Puerto Rico 00960-6032
Tel: +1(809) 798-3001
Fax: +1(809) 798-6836
President/Dean: Paul A. Marcial Rojas
Registrar: Yolanda Arzuaga
Founded: 1976

Universidad Metropolitana
Rio Pedras, Puerto Rico 00928
Tel: +1(809) 766-1717
Fax: +1(809) 766-1717 (ext. 511)
Chancellor: Rene L. Labarca Bonnet
Registrar: Sandra M. Colorado
Founded: 1980

Universidad Politécnica de Puerto Rico
Hato Rey, Puerto Rico 00919
Tel: +1(809) 754-8000
Fax: +1(809) 763-8919
President: Ernesto Vazquez-Barquet
Registrar: Adalias Maldonado
Founded: 1966

University of the Ozarks
415 College Avenue, Clarksville, Arkansas
72830-2880
Tel: +1(501) 754-3839
Fax: +1(501) 754-3839 (ext. 355)
President: Gene Stephenson
Registrar: Linda Fitzgerald
Founded: 1834

**University of the State of New York,
Regents College Degrees**
1450 Western Avenue, Cultural Education Center,
Room 5D45, Albany, New York 12230
Tel: +1(518) 474-3703
Fax: +1(518) 485-7520
President: C. Wayne Williams
Dean (Records and Enrolment Services): Louise
Koroluk
Founded: 1970

University of Virginia Clinch Valley College
College Avenue, Wise, Virginia 24293
Tel: +1(703) 328-0100
Fax: +1(703) 328-0115
Chancellor: L. Jay Lemons
Registrar: Sheila Cox Combs
Founded: 1954

Upper Iowa University
Box 1857, Fayette, Iowa 52142
Tel: +1(319) 425-5200
Fax: +1(319) 425-5271
President: James R. Rocheleau
Registrar: Gerge V. Capell
Founded: 1857

Urbana University
College Way, Urbana, Ohio 43078-2091
Tel: +1(513) 652-1301
Fax: +1(513) 652-3835
President: Francis E. Hazard
Registrar: Kathleen Yoder
Founded: 1850

Ursinus College
Collegeville, Pennsylvania 19426
Tel: +1(215) 489-4111
Fax: +1(215) 489-0627
President: Richard P. Richter
Registrar: Barbara A. Boris
Founded: 1869

Utica College of Syracuse University
1600 Burnstone Road, Utica, N.Y. 13502-4892
Tel: +1(315) 792-3111
Fax: +1(315) 792-3292
President: Michael Simpson
Vice-President: Thomas G. Brown
Founded: 1946
Arts and Sciences.

Valley Forge Christian College
Charlestown Road, Phoenixville, Pennsylvania
19460
Tel: +1(215) 935-0450
Fax: +1(215) 935-9353
President: Wesley W. Smith
Registrar: Darla Miller
Founded: 1938

Vennard College
University Park, Iowa 52595
Tel: +1(515) 673-8391
Fax: +1(515) 673-8365
President: Blake Neff
Vice-President/Academic Dean: Theodore Batson
Founded: 1910

Vermont Law School
Chelsea Street, P.O. Box 96, South Royalton,
Vermont 05068
Tel: +1(802) 763-8303
Fax: +1(802) 763-7159
Dean: Maximilian W. Kempner
Registrar: Nina L. Thomas
Founded: 1972

Villa Julie College
Stevenson, Maryland 21153
Tel: +1(410) 486-7000
Fax: +1(410) 486-3552
President: Carolyn Manuszak
Registrar: Teri Weston
Founded: 1952

Virginia Intermont College
Moore and Harmeling Streets, Bristol, Virginia
24201-4298
Tel: +1(703) 669-6101
Fax: +1(703) 669-5763
President: Gary M. Poulton
Registrar: Virginia L. Canter
Founded: 1884

Virginia Union University
1500 North Lombardy Street, Richmond, Virginia
23220-1170
Tel: +1(804) 257-5600
Fax: +1(804) 257-5818
President: S. Dallas Simmons
Registrar: Janice Bailey
Founded: 1865
Theology; Business Administration.

Virginia Wesleyan College
Wesleyan Drive, Norfolk, Virginia 23502-5599
Tel: +1(804) 455-3200
Fax: +1(804) 466-8526
President: William T. Greer Jr.
Registrar: Barbara S. Adams
Founded: 1961

Viterbo College
815 South 9th Street, La Crosse, Wisconsin
54601-4797
Tel: +1(608) 791-0040
Fax: +1(608) 791-0367
President: William J. Medland
Registrar: Janet Linderbaum
Founded: 1890

Voorhees College
1411 Voorhees Road, Denmark, South Carolina
29042
Tel: +1(803) 793-3351
Fax: +1(803) 793-4584
President: Leonard E. Dawson
Vice-President for Business Affairs: Eddie D.
Montgomery
Founded: 1897

Wabash College
P.O. Box 352, 301 West Wabash, Crawfordsville,
Indiana 47933-0352
Tel: +1(317) 362-1400
Fax: +1(317) 364-4295
President: Andrew T. Ford
Registrar: Lester L. Hearson
Founded: 1832

Warner Southern College
5301 Highway 27 South, Lake Wales, Florida
33853
Tel: +1(813) 638-1426
Fax: +1(813) 638-1472
President: Gregory V. Hall
Registrar: Jan Robillard
Founded: 1968

Wartburg College
222 9th Street Northwest, Waverly, Iowa 50677
Tel: +1(319) 352-8200
Fax: +1(319) 352-8514
Telex: 592866 wartburg wg ud
President: Robert Vogel
Registrar: Edith Waldstein
Founded: 1852

Webb Institute of Naval Architecture
Crescent Beach Road, Glen Cove, New York
11542
Tel: +1(516) 671-2213
Fax: +1(516) 674-9838
President: James J. Conti
Director of Admissions: William G. Murray
Founded: 1889

Wellesley College
Wellesley, Massachusetts 02181
Tel: +1(617) 283-1000
Fax: +1(617) 283-3639
President (Acting): Luella G. Goldberg
Registrar: Maggy Daly
Founded: 1870

Wentworth Institute of Technology
550 Huntington Avenue, Boston, Massachusetts
02115-5998
Tel: +1(617) 442-9010
Fax: +1(617) 442-2852
President: John F. Domelen
Registrar: Alan T. Whittemore
Founded: 1904

Wesley College
450 North State Street, Dover, Delaware 19901
Tel: +1(302) 736-2300
Fax: +1(302) 736-2301
President: Reed M. Stewart
Registrar: June Johnson
Founded: 1873

Wesleyan College
4760 Forsyth Road, Macon, Georgia 31297-4299
Tel: +1(912) 477-1110
Fax: +1(912) 477-7572
President: Robert K. Ackerman
Registrar: Patricia Hardeman
Founded: 1836

West Suburban College of Nursing
Erie at Austin, Oak Park, Illinois 60302
Tel: +1(708) 383-6200 ext. 6530
Fax: +1(708) 383-8783
Provost: Pamela Chally
Registrar: Ruth Rehwaldt
Founded: 1982
Nursing.

Westbrook College
716 Stevens Avenue, Portland, Maine 04103
Tel: +1(207) 797-7261
Fax: +1(207) 797-7225
President: William D. Andrews
Registrar: Susan S. Stanton
Founded: 1831

Western Baptist College
5000 Deer Park Drive S.E., Salem, Oregon
97301-9392
Tel: +1(503) 581-8600
Fax: +1(503) 585-4316
President: David F. Miller
Registrar: Rita Wright
Founded: 1935

Western State University College of Law of San Diego
1333 Front Street, San Diego, California 92110
Tel: +1(619) 297-9700
Fax: +1(619) 294-4713
President: John C. Monks
Founded: 1969

Western State University College of Law Orange County
111 N. State College Boulevard, Fullerton, California 92631
Tel: +1(714) 738-1000
Fax: +1(714) 871-4806
President: John C. Monks
Registrar: John E. Nichols
Founded: 1966

Westminster College
Fulton, Missouri 65251-1299
Tel: +1(314) 642-3361
Fax: +1(314) 642-6356
President: James F. Traer
Registrar: Phyllis Masek
Founded: 1851

Westmont College
955 La Paz Road, Santa Barbara, California 93108
Tel: +1(805) 565-6000
Fax: +1(805) 565-6234
President: David K. Winter
Registrar: William Wright
Founded: 1940

Wheaton College
Norton, Massachusetts 02766
Tel: +1(508) 285-7722
Fax: +1(508) 285-2908
President: Dale Rogers Marshall
Registrar: Patricia Santilli
Founded: 1834

Whitman College
345 Boyer Avenue, Walla Walla, Washington 99362
Tel: +1(509) 527-5111
Fax: +1(509) 527-5859
President: Charles Anderson
Dean of Faculty: David M. Deal
Founded: 1859

Wilberforce University
Wilberforce, Ohio 45384
Tel: +1(513) 376-2911
Fax: +1(513) 376-5793
President: John L. Henderson
Registrar: Roderick Rowland
Founded: 1856

Wiley College
711 Rosborough Spring Road, Marshall, Texas 75670
Tel: +1(214) 927-3300
Fax: +1(903) 938-8100
President: David L. Beckley
Registrar: Susie A. Robinson
Founded: 1873

William Jewell College
Liberty, Missouri 64068
Tel: +1(816) 781-7700
Fax: +1(816) 781-3164
President: J. Gordon Kingsley
Registrar: Elaine Barnes
Founded: 1849

William Penn College
Oskaloosa, Iowa 52577
Tel: +1(515) 673-1001
Fax: +1(515) 673-1396
President: John D. Wagoner
Registrar: Rita Vos
Founded: 1873

William Smith College
Geneva, New York 14456
Tel: +1(315) 789-3467
Fax: +1(315) 781-3303
President: Richard H. Hersh
Registrar: Peter Sarratori
Founded: 1908

William Tyndale College
35700 West 12 Mile Road, Farmington Falls, Michigan 48331
Tel: +1(313) 553-7200
Fax: +1(313) 553-5963
President: James C. McHann Jr.
Registrar: Pauline Grunden
Founded: 1945

William Woods College
Fulton, Missouri 65251
Tel: +1(314) 642-2251
Fax: +1(314) 642-5834
President: Jahnae Barnett
Registrar: Bonnie Shiverdecker
Founded: 1870

Wilmington College
Pyle Center, Box 1185, Wilmington, Ohio 45177
Tel: +(513) 382-6661
Fax: +1(513) 382-7077
President: Neil Thorburn
Director of Academic Records: Karen Garman
Founded: 1870

Wilson College
Philadelphia Avenue, Chambersburg, Pennsylvania 17201-9986
Tel: +1(717) 264-4141
Fax: +1(717) 264-1578
President: Gwendolyn E. Jensen
Registrar: Alice L. Leighty
Founded: 1869

Wisconsin Lutheran College
Milwaukee, Wisconsin 53226
Tel: +1(414) 774-8620
Fax: +1(414) 774-9367
President: Gary J. Greenfield
Registrar: Rev. Roger Fleming
Founded: 1973

Wofford College
429 North Church Street, Spartanburg, South
Carolina 29303-3663
Tel: +1(803) 597-4000
Fax: +1(803) 597-4219
President: Joab M. Lesesne
Registrar: Lucy B. Quinn
Founded: 1854

NATIONAL ACADEMIC BODIES

United States Department of Education
The Secretary of Education, U.S. Department of
Education, 400 Maryland Avenue, S.W., FOB-6,
Washington, D.C. 20202
Tel: +1(202) 732-3000
Founded: 1980

American Council on Education (ACE)
1 Dupont Circle, Suite 800, Washington, D.C.
20036
Tel: +1(202) 939-9300
Fax: +1(202) 833-4760
President: Robert H. Atwell

African-American Institute (AAI)
833 United Nations Plaza, New York, N.Y. 10017
Telex: 666565 aframny +
Tel: +1(212) 949-5666
Fax: +1(212) 682-6174
President: Vivian Lowery Derryck
Founded: 1953

**American Association of Community and
Junior Colleges (AACJC)**
One Dupont Circle, N.W. Suite 410, Washington,
D.C. 20036
Tel: +1(202) 728-0200
Fax: +1(202) 833-2467
President: David Pierce
Founded: 1920

American Association for Higher Education
One Dupont Circle, Suite 360, Washington, D.C.
20036
Tel: +1(202) 293-6440
Fax: +1(202) 293-0073
President: Russell Edgerton

**American Association of State Colleges and
Universities (AASCU)**
One Dupont Circle, Suite 700, Washington, D.C.
20036
Tel: +1(202) 293-7070
Fax: +1(202) 296-5819
President: James Appleberry
Director of Public Information: Gay Clyburn
Founded: 1951

Association of American Universities (AAU)
One Dupont Circle, N.W., Suite 730, Washington,
D.C. 20036
Tel: +1(202) 466-5030
Fax: +1(202) 296-4438
President: Cornelius J. Pings
Founded: 1900

Career Colleges Association
950 1st. St. N.E., Suite 900, Washington, D.C.
20002
Tel: +1(202) 336-6700
President: John G. Pucciano
Founded: 1962

**The Carnegie Foundation for the
Advancement of Teaching (CFAT)**
5 Ivy Lane, Princeton, New Jersey 08540
Tel: +1(609) 452-1780
Fax: +1(609) 520-1712
President: Ernest L. Boyer
Treasurer: David Walters
Founded: 1905

College Board
45 Columbus Avenue, New York, New York
10023-6992
Tel: +1(212) 713-8000
Fax: +1(212) 713-8282
President: Donald M. Stewart

**Council on International Educational
Exchange (CIEE)**
205 East 42nd Street, New York, New York 10017
Tel: +1(212) 661-1414
Fax: +1(212) 972-3231
Telex: 423227/6730395
Cable: costudents
President: Stevan K. Trooboff
Founded: 1947

Institute of International Education (IIE)
809 United Nations Plaza, New York, N.Y. 10017
Tel: +1(212) 883-8200
Fax: +1(212) 984-5452
Telex: trt175977
Cable: intered
President: Richard M. Krasno
Founded: 1919

**National Association of International
Educators**
1875 Connecticut Avenue, N.W., Suite 1000,
Washington, D.C. 20009-5728
Tel: +1(202) 462-4811
Fax: +1(202) 667-3419
E-Mail: NAFSA@VTVM2
Executive Vice-President: Naomi F. Collins

**National Association of State Universities
and Land-Grant Colleges**
1 Dupont Circle, N.W., Suite 710, Washington,
D.C. 20036
Tel: +1(202) 778-0818
Fax: +1(202) 296-6456
President: Robert L. Clodius
Founded: 1887

National Council for Higher Education (NCHE)
NEA/Affiliate Services, 1201 16th Street, N.W.,
Washington, D.C. 20036
Tel: +1(202) 822-7110
Fax: (202) 822-7624
Higher Education Coordinator: Christine Maitland
Organization Specialist: Chris Maitland

National Education Association (NEA)
1201 16th Street, N.W., Washington, D.C. 20036
Tel: +1(202) 822-7110
Fax: +1(202) 822-7624
President: Christine Maitland
Executive Director: Higher Education Coordinator

Peace Corps of the United States of America
1990 K Street, N.W., Washington, D.C. 20526
Tel: +1(202) 606-3970
Fax: +1(202) 606-3110
Director: Paul D. Coverdell
Founded: 1961

URUGUAY

UNIVERSITIES

PUBLIC INSTITUTIONS

University of the Republic Montevideo
[Universidad de la República]
Avenida 18 de Julio 1968, 2o piso, Montevideo
Tel: +598(2) 40-92-01
Fax: +598(2) 48-03-03
Telex: Udelar uy 26692
Rector: Jorge Brovetto Cruz
Founded: 1833
*F: Social Sciences; Agronomy; Architecture;
Economics; Sciences; Engineering; Medicine;
Dentistry; Chemistry; Veterinary Medicine;
Humanities and Pedagogics; Law.
I: Social Sciences; Psychology.
S: Librarianship and Related Sciences; Social
Service; Music; Fine Arts.
Ce: Mathematics; Research and Postgraduate.*

PRIVATE INSTITUTIONS

Catholic University of Uruguay 'Dámaso A. Larrañaga'
[Universidad Católica del Uruguay 'Dámaso A.
Larrañaga']
Avenida 8 de Octubre 2738, Montevideo
Tel: +598(2) 80-35-15
Fax: +598(2) 80-27-17
Rector: José Luis Mendizabal, S.J. (1993-)
Founded: 1954, 1984
*F: Philosophy and Letters; Human Sciences and
Theology; Social Sciences and Economics; Law.*

*I: Religious Sciences; Juridical Sciences;
Philosophy and Ethics; Social Sciences.*

ORT Institute of Technology
[Instituto Tecnológica ORT]
Avenida España 2633, 11300 Montevideo
Tel: +598(2) 77-18-06
Fax: +598(2) 78-88-10
Rector: Jorge A. Grünberg
Founded: 1943, 1980, 1988
*S: Computer Sciences; Electronics and
Telecommunications; Management and
International Studies.
Ce: Computer; Graphic Design; Marketing
Research; Human Resources Research;
Environmental Management Research.*

OTHER INSTITUTIONS

Universidad del Trabajo de Uruguay
Calle San Salvador 1674, Montevideo
Tel: +598(2) 48-50-94
Fax: +598(2) 49-82-38
Director General: Eduardo Burghi
Founded: 1942
Arts and Crafts.

NATIONAL ACADEMIC BODIES

Ministry of Education and Culture
[Ministerio de la Educación y la Culture]
Reconquista 535, Montevideo
Tel: +598(2) 96-11-74
Fax: +598(2) 96-26-32
Ministro: Antonio Mercader

Uruguay National Commission for Unesco
[Comisión Nacional del Uruguay para la Unesco]
Ministerio de Educación y la Cultura,
Reconquista 532, Montevideo
Tel: +598(2) 95-29-63
Fax: +598(2) 95-98-83
Telex: 23133 uy
Presidente: Pablo Landoni Couture
Secretario General: Martin Sarthou

UZBEKISTAN

UNIVERSITIES

Nukus University
[Nukusskij Gosudarstvennyj Universitet]
Ul. Universitetskaja 1, 742012 Nukus
Tel: +(7) 32372
*F: Languages; History; Romance and Germanic
Philology; Natural Sciences; Agriculture;
Economics.*

Samarkand University
[Samarkandskij Gosudarstvennyj Universitet]
Bul. Gor'kogo 15, 703004 Samarkand
Tel: +(7) 52626
Founded: 1927, 1933
F: Law; History; Geography; Uzbek and Tadjcic
Philology; Foreign Languages; Mechanics and
Mathematics; Physics; Chemistry; Biology.
D: Evening Studies; Correspondence Courses.

Taškent Technical State University
[Taěntskij Gosudarstvennyj Tehniceskij
Universitet]
Ul. Navoi 13, 700011 Taškent
Tel: +7(3712) 41-13-12

*Taškent University
[Taškentskij Gosudarstvennyj Universitet]
Vuzgorodok, 700095 Taškent
Tel: +7(3712) 460224
Founded: 1920
F: History; Philology; Journalism; Romance and
Germanic Philology; Oriental Studies; Law;
Mathematics; Applied Mathematics; Physics;
Chemistry; Biology and Soil Science; Geology;
Geography.
D: Evening Studies; Correspondence Courses.

OTHER INSTITUTIONS

Andizanskij Gosudarstvennyj Medicinskij Institut
Prosp. Navoi 136, 710000 Andizan
Medicine.

Andizanskij Institut Hlopkovodstva
Selo Kuigan-jar, Andizanokoro r-na, 711520
Andizankaja obl.
Tel: +(7) 4-54-34
Agriculture (Cotton).

Buharskij Tehnologiceskij Institut Pisevoj i Legkoj Promyslenosti
Prosp. Leninskogo Komsomola 15, 705017
Buhara
Tel: +(7) 3-04-02
Food Technology; Light Engineering.

Samarkandskij Arhitekturno-Stroitel'nyj Institut
Ul. Ljaljazar 70, 703047 Samarkand 47
Tel: +(7) 3-20-25
Architecture; Civil Engineering.

Samarkandskij Gosudarstvennyj Medicinskij Institut
Ul. Frunze 18, 703000 Samarkand
Medicine.

Samarkandskij Kooperativnyj Institut
Ul. Kommunisticeskaja 41, 703000 Samarkand
Cooperative Commerce.

Samarkandskij Sel'skohozjajstvennyj Institut
Ul. Karla Marksa 77, 703003 Samarkand
Tel: +(7) 4-33-20
Agriculture.

Sredneaziatskij Medicinskij Pediatriceskij Institut
Ul. Cermet 103, 700140 Taškent
Pediatrics.

Taškenstskij Institut Inzenerov Zeleznodoroznogo Transporta
Ul. Oboronnaja 1, 700045 Taškent L-45
Tel: +7(3712) 91-14-40
Railway Engineering.

Taškentskaja Gosudarstvennaja Konservatorija
Ul. Puskinskaja 31, 700000 Taškent
Music.

Taškentskij Avtomobil'no-Doroznyj Institut
Ul. Karla Marksa 32, 700047 Taškent
Tel: +7(3712) 33-08-27
Automobile Technology.

Taškentskij Elektrotehniceskij Institut Svjazi
Ul. Engel'sa 108, 700000 Taškent
Tel: +7(3712) 35-09-34
Electrical Engineering.

Taškentskij Farmacevtičeskij Institut
Ul. Kafanowa 35, 700015 Taškent
Pharmacy.

Taškentskij Gosudarstvennyj Medicinskij Institut
Ul. Karla Marksa 103, 700033 Taškent
Medicine.

Taškentskij Institut Inzenerov Irrigacii i Mechanizacii Sel'skogo Hozjajstva
Ul. Kary Nijazova 39, 700000 Taškent
Tel: +7(3712) 33-46-85
Irrigation Machanization.

Taškentskij Institut Narodnogo Hozjajstva
Ul. Almazar 183, 700063 Taškent 63
Economics.

Taškentskij Institut Tekstil'noj i Legkoj Promyslennosti
Ul. Gorbunova 5, 700100 Taškent
Tel: +7(3712) 53-06-06
Textiles.

Taškentskij Sel'skohozjajstvennyj Institut
Sel'hozinstitut, 700183 Taskent
Tel: +7(3712) 33-46-85
Agriculture.

Taškentskij Gosudarstvennyj Teatrol'nohudožestvennyj Institut Iskusstva
Ul. Germana Lopatina 77, 700031 Taškent 31
Drama; Fine Arts.

NATIONAL ACADEMIC BODIES

Ministry of Higher and Secondary Special Education
Moustakillik Maiidoni 5, Taškent
Tel: +7(3712) 394-214
Fax: +(3712) 391-173
Minister: Djura G. Iuldashev

VENEZUELA

UNIVERSITIES

PUBLIC INSTITUTIONS

National Experimental University of the Western Plaines 'Ezequiel Zamora', Barinas
[Universidad Nacional Experimental de los Llanos Occidentales 'Ezequiel Zamora', Barinas]
Avenida 23 de Enero, Alto Barubas, Barinas (Estado Barinas)
Tel: +58(73) 33-15-11
Telex: 73171 venez-v
Founded: 1975
Agriculture and Marine Sciences (Barinas, Guanares, San Carlos, San Fernando de Apure); Education; Engineering, Architecture and Technology (San Carlos); Social Sciences (Barinas, San Fernando de Apure).

Central Western University 'Lisandro Alvaredo' Barquisimeto
[Universidad Centro Occidental 'Lisandro Alvaredo']
Carrera 19 entre Calle 8 y 9, Barquisimeto (Estado Lara)
Tel: +58(51) 51-00-11
Founded: 1962
Sciences; Engineering, Architecture and Technology; Agriculture and Marine Sciences (Barquisimeto, Carora, Tocuyo); Health Sciences; Social Sciences.

National Experimental Politechnic University 'Antonio José de Sucre' Barquisimeto
[Universidad Nacional Experimental Politécnica 'Antonio José de Sucre']
Avenida Corpahuaico, Entre Avenida Rotaria y La Salle, Parque Tecnológico, Barquisimeto (Estado Lara)
Tel: +58(51) 422-209
Fax: +58(51) 423-532
Rector: Iván Olaizola D'Alessandro
Vice-Rector Secretario: Ramón Vielma
Founded: 1979
Industrial Engineering; Mechanical Engineering; Systems Engineering.

National Experimental University 'Rafael María Baralt'
[Universidad Nacional Experimental 'Rafael María Baralt']
Avenida El Rosario, Esquina El Muelle, Cabimas (Estado Zulia)
Tel: +58(64) 43-745
Engineering, Architecture and Technology: Education; Social Sciences.

University of Carabobo
[Universidad de Carabobo]
Avenida Bolivar Norte, Apartado postal 129, Valencia (Estado Carabobo)
Tel: +58(41) 21-6104
Telex: 41478 ucrvlv
Founded: 1833, 1883, 1958
Sciences; Health Sciences (Valencia, Maracay); Engineering, Architecture and Technology; Education; Social Sciences (Valencia, Maracay).

Experimental University of Education 'Libertador' Caracas
[Universidad Pedagógica Experimental Libertador]
Avenida Sucre, Catia Parque del Oeste, Apartado 2939, Caracas
Tel: +58(2) 837-511
Fax: +58(2) 755-6456
Rectora: Duilia Govea de Carpio
Founded: 1983
Teacher Training (Caracas, Maracay, Barquisimeto, Maturín, Aragua, Táchira); Education Research.

*Central University of Venezuela Caracas
[Universidad Central de Venezuela]
Ciudad Universitaria, Los Chaguaramas, Caracas 1050
Tel: +58(2) 619-811F + 58(2) 662-2486
Telex: 29482 revcv
Rector: Edmundo Chirinos
Founded: 1696, 1725
F: Architecture; Political Science and Law; Agriculture; Science; Veterinary Science; Medicine; Economics and Social Sciences; Pharmacy; Education and Humanities; Engineering; Dentistry.
D: Lifelong Education.

*National Experimental University 'Simón Rodríguez', Caracas
[Universidad Nacional Experimental 'Simón Rodríguez']
Avenida Intercommunal, Calle 14 Los Jardines del Valle, ElValle, Caracas
Tel: +58(2) 681-16-18
Rector: Elizabeth Y. de Caldera
Founded: 1974
Education; Social Sciences; Engineering.

National Open University Caracas
[Universidad Nacional Abierta Caracas]
Avenida Los Calvani (antes Avenida Gamboa
No.18), San Bernardino, Caracas
Tel: +58(2) 574-13-22
Fax: +58(2) 574-30-86
Telex: 26111
Rector: Gustavo Luis Carrera
Secretario: Milton Granados P.
Founded: 1975
*Courses: Mathematics; Engineering; Education;
Administration.*

National Experimental University 'Francisco de Miranda', Coro
[Universidad Nacional Experimental 'Francisco
de Miranda']
Calle Norte, Edf. Rosalla, Coro (Estado Falcón)
Tel: +58(68) 51-21-56
Telex: 56184 ufm
Founded: 1977
*Engineering, Architecture and Technology;
Education; Agriculture and Marine Sciences;
Health Sciences.*

University of the East, Cumana
[Universidad de Oriente]
Apartado postal 245, Cumaná (Estado Sucre)
Tel: +58(93) 51-53-68
Cable: Univorient
Rector: Pedro Augusto Beauperthuy
Founded: 1958
*Engineering, Architecture and Technology;
Science; Health Sciences; Social Sciences;
Agricultural Engineering (Monagas); Animal
Husbandry (Monagas); Geology and Mining
(Bolívar); Engineering (Anzoátequi).*

National Experimental University of the Eastern Coast of Lake Maracaibo
[Universidad Nacional Experimental de la Costa
Oriental del Largo de Maracaibo]
Maracaibo (Zulia)
Founded: 1982

University of the Andes, Mérida
[Universidad de los Andes]
Avenida 3, Plaza Bolívar, Mérida (Estado Mérida)
Tel: +58(74) 40-11-11
Telex: 74137 ulameve
Founded: 1785, 1810, 1832
*Basic Science; Engineering, Architecture and
Technology; Agriculture and Marine Sciences
(Mérida, Trujillo); Health Sciences; Education
(Mérida, Tachira, Trujilla); Social Sciences
(Mérida, Tachira); Humanities, Letters and Arts.*

National Experimental University of Guayana, Puerto Ordaz
[Universidad Nacional Experimental de Guayana]
Edif. General de Seguros, Av. Las Américas,
Puerto Ordaz (Estado Bolívar)
Tel: +58(86) 22-79-31
Fax: +58(86) 22-56-73
Telex: 86543

Rector: Aline Lampe Joubert
Secretario: Ingrid Hernández Mantellini
Founded: 1982, 1986
*S: Professional Studies; Forestry Industry;
Education; Industrial Engineering; Computer
Engineering; Business Administration and Public
Accounting.
D: Technological Research; Educational
Research; Anthropological Research.*

National Experimental University 'Romulo Gallegos', San Juan de los Morros
[Universidad Nacional Experimental 'Romulo
Gallegos']
Avenida Los Llanos, San Juan de los Morros
(Estado Guarico)
Tel: +58(46) 31-12-723
Rector: Sebastián Viale-Rigo
Founded: 1977
*Agricultural and Animal Sciences; Health
Sciences; Education.*

University 'Simón Bolívar'
[Universidad Simón Bolívar]
Valles de Sartenejas, Baruta (Estado Miranda)
Tel: +58(2) 939-056
Fax: +58(2) 979-7064
Telex: 21910
Rector: Freddy Malpica Pérez
Founded: 1967, 1970
*Basic Sciences: Engineering, Architecture and
Technology; Social Sciences (Litoral).*

National Experimental University of Táchira
[Universidad Nacional Experimental del Táchira]
Apartado 436, Paramillo, San Cristóbal (Estado
Táchira)
Tel: +58(76) 56-44-22
Telex: 76196
Founded: 1974
*Engineering, Architecture and Technology;
Agriculture and Animal Husbandry.*

University of Zulia
[Universidad del Zulia]
Apartado postal 526, Maracaibo 4011 (Estado
Zulia)
Tel: +58(61) 51-20-77
Telex: 62172
Rector: Angel Lombardi
Founded: 1891, 1904, 1946
*Education (Maracaibo, Cabimas); Humanities,
Letters and Arts; Health Sciences; Social
Sciences; Engineering, Architecture and
Technology (Maracaibo, Cabimas).*

PRIVATE INSTITUTIONS

Bicentenary University of Aragua
[Universidad Bicentenaria de Aragua]
Avenida Intercommunal Santiago Mariño, Cruce
con Avenida Universidad Bicententenaria de
Aragua, San Joaquin de Turmero (Estado
Aragua)
Tel: +58(43) 54-42-10
Fax: +58(43) 54-66-36
Founded: 1986
*Engineering, Architecture and Technology; Social
Sciences.*

Northeast University 'Gran Mariscal de Ayacucho', Barcelona
[Universidad Nororiental 'Gran Mariscal de
Ayacucho']
Avenida Cajigal 18-154, Barcelona (Estado
Anzoategui)
Tel: +58(81) 77-50-55
Founded: 1987
*Engineering, Architecture and Technology; Health
Sciences; Agriculture and Marine Sciences.*

University 'Fermín Toro' Barquisimeto
[Universidad 'Fermín Toro']
Avenida 20 entre 10 y 11, Edificio 6 Oficina 6-2,
Barquisimeto (Estado Lara)
Tel: +58(51) 62-344
Founded: 1975, 1979
*Engineering, Architecture and Technology; Social
Sciences.*

University Yacambu, Cabudare
[Universidad Yacambu]
Avenida Intercomunal Barquisimeto-La Campiña,
Cabudare (Estado Lara)
Tel: +58(51) 63-49-87
Fax: +58(51) 51-57-32
Founded: 1989
*Engineering, Architecture and Technology; Social
Sciences; Agriculture and Marine Sciences.*

Catholic University 'Andrés Bello', Caracas
[Universidad Católica 'Andrés Bello']
La Vega, Montalbán, Caracas
Tel: +58(2) 44-29-511
Founded: 1953
*Engineering, Architecture and Technology;
Education (Caracas, Los Teques); Humanities,
Letters and Arts.*

University New Sparta, Caracas
[Universidad Nueva Esparta]
Avenida Sur 7, Los Naranjos, El Cafetal, Caracas
Tel: +58(2) 98-52-936
Fax: +58(2) 98-71-412
President: Gladys Carmona De Marcano
Rector: Antonio Navas
Founded: 1954, 1989
*Engineering, Architecture and Technology; Social
Sciences; Design and Business Administration;
Tourism Business Administration.*

University 'Santa María', Caracas
[Universidad 'Santa María', Caracas]
Avenida Páez, Frente Plaza Madariaga, Urb. El
Paraíso, Caracas
Tel: +58(2) 483-51-33
Founded: 1953
*Engineering, Architecture and Technology; Social
Sciences; Health Sciences.*

University 'Cecilio Acosta', Maracaibo
[Universidad 'Cecilio Acosta']
Urb. La Paz, Etapa II, Edif. Sede Instituto Niños
Cantores del Zulia, Maracaibo (Estado Zulia)
Tel: +58(61) 89-165
Founded: 1983
*Education; Humanities, Letters and Arts; Social
Sciences.*

University 'Rafael Belloso Chacín', Maracaibo
[Universidad 'Rafael Belloso Chacín']
Cruce con la Avenida Guajira, Circunvalación 2
frente a la Plaza de Toros, Maracaibo (Estado
Zulia)
Tel: +58(61) 41-04-59
Founded: 1982, 1979
*Engineering, Architecture and Technology; Social
Sciences.*

University 'Rafael Urdaneta' Maracaibo
[Universidad Rafael Urdaneta]
La Retirada, Iada Noroeste de La Rinconada y
Country Club, Apartado 614, Maracaibo (Estado
Zulia)
Tel: +58(61) 92-26-59
Founded: 1973
*Engineering, Architecture and Technology;
Agriculture and Marine Sciences; Social
Sciences.*

University 'José María Vargas'
[Universidad 'José María Vargas']
Avenida Sucre, Torre Sucre, Urb. Los Dos
Caminos, Caracas
Fax: +58(2) 285-08-07
Founded: 1983
*Engineering, Architecture and Technology;
Humanities, Letters and Arts; Education; Social
Sciences.*

University of the South Lake 'Jesús María Semprum'
[Universidad Sur del Lago 'Jesús María
Semprum']
Hacienda La Glorieta, Santa Barbara (Estado
Zulia)
Tel: +58(75) 98-10-36
Founded: 1982
Agriculture and Marine Sciences.

Catholic University of Táchira
[Universidad Católica del Táchira]
Apartado 366, San Cristóbal (Estado Táchira)
Tel: +58(76) 44-68-44
Telex: 76499
Founded: 1962, 1982
Education; Humanities, Letters and Arts; Social Sciences.

Technological University of the Central Region
[Universidad Tecnológica del Centro]
Via Areguita, 2 Km. de la Carretera Nacional,
Guacara (Estado Carabobo)
Tel: +58(45) 71-87-34
Rector: César Peña Vigas
Secretario General: Héctor Manuel Tamayo
Founded: 1979
Engineering, Architecture and Technology; Social Sciences.

OTHER INSTITUTIONS

Colegio Universitario de Administración y Mercado
Avenida Díaz Moreno 111-63, Valencia (Estado Carabobo
Tel: +58(41) 66-50-40
Founded: 1990
Social Sciences; Engineering, Architecture and Technology; Education.

Colegio Universitario de Caracas
Avenida Libertador Cruce con Calle Adrián Rodríguez, Caracas
Tel: +58(2) 263-55-58
Education; Engineering, Architecture and Technology; Social Sciences.

Colegio Universitario 'Dr. Rafael Belloso Chacín'
Calle 77 Esquina Avenida 3H, Maracaibo (Estado Zulia)
Tel: +58(61) 91-12-52
Founded: 1982
Engineering, Architecture and Technology; Social Sciences.

Colegio Universitario de Enfermería Gobernación del Distrito Federal
Avenida San Martín, Edif. Lotería de Caracas, San Martín (Caracas)
Tel: +58 462-93-67
Founded: 1987
Nursing.

Colegio Universitario de Enfermería de La Cruz Roja de Venezuela
Avenida Andrés Bello 4, Caracas
Tel: +58(2) 571-47-13
Founded: 1988
Nursing.

Colegio Universitario Francisco de Mirandas
Esquina de Mijares, Parroquia Altagracia, Caracas
Tel: +58(2) 81-43-49
Founded: 1974
Social Sciences.

Colegio Universitario de Los Teques 'Cecilio Acosta'
Avenida Ali Primera, Los Teques (Estado Miranda)
Tel: +58(32) 44-195
Founded: 1972
Engineering, Architecture and Technology; Health Sciences; Education; Social Sciences.

Colegio Universitario Monseñor de Talavera
Calle Los Granados, Entre Avenida Eugenio Mendoza y Avenida, Caracas
Tel: +58(2) 33-99-66
Founded: 1975
Engineering, Architecture and Technology; Education; Social Sciences.

Colegio Universitario de Psicopedagogía
Avenida San Gabriel 45, Urb. El Avila, Caracas
Tel: +58(2) 74-19-94
Founded: 1977
Psychopedagogy.

Colegio Universitario de Rehabilitación
Avenida La Guayanita, Bella Vista, Caracas 102
Tel: +58(2) 49-47-67
Founded: 1965
Rahabilitation Techniques.

Instituto de Estudios Superiores de Artes Plásticas 'Armando Reverón'
Calle Principal de Caño Amarillo, Quinta Santa Inés, Caracas
Tel: +58(2) 481-06-23
Founded: 1991
Humanities, Letters and Arts.

Instituto de Nuevas Profesiones
Avenida Romulo Gallegos, Caracas
Tel: +58(2) 234-15-37
Engineering, Architecture and Technology.

Instituto Universitario de la Audición y el Lenguaje
Avenida Araure cruce con Calle Cuchivero, Urb. El Marqués, Municipio Petare, Caracas
Tel: +58(2) 242-04-39
Founded: 1979
Health Sciences (Speech Therapy); Education.

Instituto Universitario 'Avepane'
Avenida La Guarita, Calle el Martillo, Urb. La Trinidad, Caracas
Tel: +58(2) 93-08-25
Founded: 1971
Education.

Instituto Universitario de Barlovento
Edif. Sede Del IUJEL, Calle 78, 17-129, Higuerote,
Estado Miranda
Tel: +58(34) 23-11-71
Founded: 1990
*Social Sciences; Agriculture and Marine
Sciences.*

Instituto Universitario de Estudios Musicales
Avenida El Ejército, Calle Sanabria 5-3, El
Paraíso, Caracas
Tel: +58(2) 481-14-41
Founded: 1982
Humanities, Letters and Arts (Music).

Instituto Universitario Experimental de Tecnología y Agricultura Simón Bolívar
Vía a Mijaguas a 3 Kms. de Ciudad Bolivia,
Pedraza (Estado Barinas)
Tel: +58(73) 91-038
Founded: 1986
Agriculture and Marine Sciences.

Instituto Universitario de La Frontera
Calle 9 entre Carreras 17 y 18 No. 16-78, Barrio
Obrero, San Cristobál (Estado Táchira)
Tel: +58(76) 56-11-11
Founded: 1988
*Engineering, Architecture and Technology (San
Cristobál, Mérida); Social Sciences (San
Cristobál, Mérida); Agriculture and Marine
Sciences (San Cristobál, Mérida).*

Instituto Universitario de Mercadotecnia
Edificio Cediaz, Planta Principal, Avenida
Casanova, Sabana Grande, Caracas
Tel: +58(2) 762-46-31
Founded: 1973
Social Sciences (Marketing).

Instituto Universitario Nacional de Estudios Penitenciarios
Avenida Páez Sector Puente Hierro, Frente a
Villa Zoila El Paraíso, Caracas
Tel: +58(2) 545-15-82
Founded: 1990
Social Sciences (Penitentiary Administration).

Instituto Universitario Nueva Esparta
Reducto a Glorieta 73, Caracas
Tel: +58(2) 987-20-55
Founded: 1973
*Engineering, Architecture and Technology; Social
Sciences.*

Instituto Universitario Pedagógico Monseñor Rafael Arias Blanco
Sector UD-5, Detrás del Bloque 23, Urb. La
Hacienda, Caracas
Tel: +58(2) 431-12-43
Founded: 1977
Education.

Instituto Universitario de Policía Científica
Avenida Neveri con Monte Sacro., Frente la
Plaza Auyantepuy, Colinas de Bello Monte,
Caracas
Tel: +58(2) 752-16-39
Founded: 1973
Police Studies.

Instituto Universitario Politécnico de las Fuerzas Armadas
Oficina ASOBIES, Km. 5, Autopista Coche
Tejerías, El Valle, Caracas
Tel: +58(2) 681-76-03
Founded: 1974
*Engineering, Architecture and Technology; Health
Sciences.*

Instituto Universitario de Relaciones Públicas
Avenida Sur 3 Miseria a Pinto, Parróquía Santa
Rosalía, Caracas
Tel: +58(2) 545-31-28
Founded: 1972
Social Sciences (Public Relations).

Instituto Universitario de Seguros
Calle Santa Luisa, Colinas de la California,
Caracas
Tel: +58(2) 257-09-29
Founded: 1972
Social Sciences (Insurance).

Instituto Universitario de Teatro
Avenida Norte 4, Caja de Agua Al Cuño 48,
Altagracia, Caracas
Tel: +58(2) 481-50-74
Founded: 1991
Humanities, Letters and Arts (Theatre).

Instituto Universitario de Tecnología de Administración y Hacienda Pública
Torre Pomarroso, Boulevard de Catia, Estación
Metro Plaza Sucre, Caracas
Tel: +58(2) 872-00-84
Founded: 1977
Social Sciences.

Instituto Universitario de Tecnología de Administración Industrial
Centro Comercial Charo, Avenida Mérida con
Calle Urpín, Anaco (Estado Anzoátegui)
Tel: +58(82) 24-43-03
Founded: 1990
*Engineering, Architecture and Technology; Social
Sciences (Anaco, Puerto La Cruz).*

Instituto Universitario de Tecnología Agroindustrial Región Los Andes
Antiguo Parque Exposición 'Teotimo Depablos',
San Cristóbal (Estado Táchira)
Tel: +58(76) 26-290
Founded: 1971
*Engineering, Architecture and Technology;
Agriculture and Marine Sciences.*

Instituto Universitario de Tecnología Agropecuaria Fundación La Salle de Ciencias Naturales
Avenida Bolívar 20-1219, San Carlos (Estado Cojedes)
Tel: +58(58) 33-36-54
Agriculture and Marine Sciences; Social Sciences.

Instituto Universitario de Tecnología Alonso Gamero
Avenida Libertador, Parque Los Orumos, Coro (Estado Falcón)
Tel: +58(68) 51-21-34
Founded: 1971
Engineering, Technology and Architecture; Agriculture and Marine Sciences; Social Sciences.

Instituo Universitario de Tecnología 'Américo Vespucio'
Avenida Principal de Los Chorros, Caracas
Tel: +58(2) 254-98-76
Founded: 1988
Engineering, Architecture and Technology; Social Sciences.

Instituto Universitario de Tecnología Andres Eloy Blanco
Final Avenida La Salle con Avenida Los, Horcones, Pueblo Nuevo, Barquisimeto (Estado Lara)
Tel: +58(51) 42-44-33
Founded: 1982
Education; Engineering, Architecture and Technology; Social Sciences.

Instituto Universitario de Tecnología 'Antonio José de Sucre'
Calle 9 Edif. Alam. Urbanización La Urbina, Caracas
Tel: +58(2) 242-70-16
Founded: 1972
Engineering, Architecture and Technology; Social Sciences (Caracas, Barcelona, Barquisimeto, Barinas, Maracaibo, Maracay, Mérida, Puerto ordaz, San Cristóbal, San Felipe).

Instituto Universitaro de Tecnología Bomberil
Avenida Lecuna, Esquina El Rosario, Cuartel Central de Bomberos 'Victoriano Jordán P.', Caracas
Tel: +58(2) 541-46-87
Founded: 1989
Engineering, Architecture and Technology.

Instituto Universitario de Tecnología de Cabimas
Calle La Estrella, Sector Amparo, Cabimas (Estado Zulia)
Tel: +58(64) 43-013
Founded: 1986
Engineering, Architecture and Technology; Social Sciences.

Instituto Universitario de Tecnología Caripito
Sector Bello Monte, La Sabena, Caripito (Estado Monagas)
Tel: +58(91) 71-345
Founded: 1988
Engineering, Architecture and Technology; Health Sciences.

Instituto Universitario de Tecnología de Cumaná
Carretera Cumaná, Cumanacoa Km. 4, Cumaná (Estado Sucre)
Tel: +58(93) 66-38-08
Founded: 1971
Engineering, Architecture and Technology; Agriculture and Marine Sciences.

Instituto Universitario de Tecnología 'Don Rómulo Betancourt'
San Luis, Avenida La Feria, frente al Gimnasio Cuberto, Valera (Estado Trujillo)
Tel: +58(71) 21-31-14
Founded: 1978
Engineering, Architecture and Technology; Social Sciences.

Instituto Universitario de Tecnología 'Dr. Delfin Mendoza'
Avenida Orinoco, Frente al Caño Mánamo, Tucupita (Estado Delta Amacuro)
Tel: +58(87) 21-810
Founded: 1989
Agriculture and Marine Sciences; Health Sciences; Education; Social Sciences.

Instituto Universitario de Tecnología de Ejido
Via Manzano, Frente al Geriátrico Ricardo Sergent, Ejido (Estado Mérida)
Tel: +58(74) 92-07-46
Founded: 1981
Engineering, Architecture and Technology; Agriculture and Marine Sciences; Social Sciences.

Instituto Universitario de Tecnología de El Tigre José Antonio Anzoátegui
Carretera Salida, El Tigre-Ciudad Bolívar Km. 4 (Estado Anzoátegui)
Tel: +58(83) 35-39-01
Founded: 1977
Engineering, Architecture and Technology; Agriculture and Marine Sciences; Social Sciences.

Instituto Universitario de Tecnología Eustacio Guevara
Avenida Circunvalación Sur., Via Payara, Acarigua (Estado Portuguesa)
Tel: +58(55) 47-130
Founded: 1978
Agriculture and Marine Sciences; Social Sciences.

Instituto Universitario de Tecnología Industrial
Urb. Trigal Sur 3era, Sección Final Calle Los Mijaos con Avenida 14A, Valencia (Estado Carabobo)
Tel: +58(41) 42-80-50
Founded: 1978
Engineering, Architecture and Technology; Social Sciences.

Instituto Universitario de Tecnología Isaac Newton
Avenida Constitución con Calle Mariño, Edif. IUTIN, Maracay (Estado Aragua)
Tel: +58(43) 45-24-24
Founded: 1983
Engineering, Architecture and Technology; Education; Social Sciences.

Instituto Universitario de Tecnología Jacinto Navarro Vallenilla
Valle de Canchunchú, Via El Pilar, Carúpano (Estado Sucre)
Tel: +58(94) 31-17-67
Founded: 1986
Engineering, Architecture and Technology; Agriculture and Marine Sciences; Social Sciences.

Instituto Universitario de Tecnología Juan Pablo Pérez Alfonso
Avenida Urdaneta cruce con Avenida Cedeño, Valencia (Estado Carabobo)
Tel: +58(41) 84-033
Founded: 1989
Engineering, Architecture and Technology; Health Sciences; Social Sciences.

Instituto Universitario de Tecnología de La Victoria
Avenida Universidad, La Victoria (Estado Aragua)
Tel: +58(44) 22-27-53
Founded: 1976

Instituto Universitario de Tecnología de Los Llanos
Avenida Circunvalación, Parque Tecnológico, Urb. Guamachal, Valle de La Pascua (Estado Guarico)
Tel: +58(35) 34-299
Founded: 1973
Engineering, Architecture and Technology; Social Sciences; Agriculture and Marine Sciences.

Instituto Universitario de Tecnología del Mar
Fundación La Salle de Ciencias Naturales, Punta de Piedras (Estado Nueva Esparta)
Tel: +58(95) 98-173
Founded: 1977
Engineering, Architecture and Technology; Agriculture and Marine Sciences; Social Sciences.

Instituto Universitario de Tecnología de Maracaibo
Avenida 85 Urb. La Floresta, Sect. La Limpia, Maracaibo (Estado Zulia)
Tel: +58(61) 54-61-75
Founded: 1986
Engineering, Architecture and Technology; Social Sciences; Agriculture and Marine Sciences.

Instituto Universitario de Tecnología Pedro Emilio Coll
Avenida 17 con Calle 72, 72-16, Maracaibo (Estado Zulia)
Tel: +58(61) 51-34-47
Founded: 1982
Engineering, Architecture and Technology; Social Sciences.

Instituto Universitario de Tecnología de Puerto Cabello
Avenida Bolívar 31-17 Urb., Rancho Grande, Puerto Cabello (Estado Carabobo)
Tel: +58(42) 61-36-11
Founded: 1976
Engineering, Architecture and Technology.

Instituto Universitario de Tecnología Readic
Avenida Libertador, Edif. Readic Diagonal al Muelle, Maracaibo (Estado Zulia)
Tel: +58(61) 22-63-31
Founded: 1990
Engineering, Architecture and Technology; Social Sciences.

Instituto Universitario de Tecnología 'Rodolfo Loero Arismendi'
Final Avenida Caurimare, Quinta Villa Claret y Hortensia, Urb. Colinas de Bello Monte, Caracas
Tel: +58(2) 751-39-42
Founded: 1978
Engineering, Architecture and Technology; Social Sciences.

Instituto Universitario de Tecnología de Valencia
Avenida Cuatricentenario, Complejo Educacional, La Manguita Vía Guatáparo, Valencia (Estado Carabobo)
Tel: +58(41) 23-09-98
Founded: 1976
Engineering, Architecture and Technology.

Instituto Universitario de Tecnología Venezuela
Avenida Universidad Edif. La Metropolitána, Caracas
Tel: +58(2) 573-42-79
Founded: 1983
Engineering, Architecture and Technology; Social Sciences.

Instituto Universitario de Tecnología de Yaracuy
Avenida Alberto Ravell cruce con Avenida José
Antonio Páez, San Felipe (Estado Yaracuy)
Tel: +58(54) 31-31-68
Founded: 1974
*Agriculture and Marine Sciences; Health
Sciences.*

Instituto Universitario Tecnológico de Seguridad Industrial
Sector Los Arales, Vía San Diego, Valencia
(Estado Carabobo)
Tel: +58(41) 37-73-53
Founded: 1979
*Engineering, Architecture and Technology
(Industrial Security).*

Instituto Universitario YMCA 'Lope Mendoza'
Avenida Guicaipuro, San Bernardino, Caracas
Tel: +58(2) 52-08-91
Founded: 1983
Social Sciences.

NATIONAL ACADEMIC BODIES

Ministry of Education
[Ministerio de Educación]
Edificio Sede, Esquina de Salas, Caracas
Tel: +58(2) 557-62-459
Fax: +58(2) 563-84-88
Ministro: Elizabeth Caldera

National Council of Universities
[Consejo Nacional de Universidades]
Avenida La Salle, Torre Capriles, Plaza
Venezuela, Caracas
Tel: +58(2) 782-71-31
Fax: +58(2) 781-85-85
Chairman: Gustavo Roosen
Director: José Antonio Pimentel
Founded: 1946

Venezuelan National Commission for Unesco
[Comisión Nacional Venezolana de Coopéración
con la Unesco]
Ministerio de Relaciones Exteriores, Casa
Amarilla, Caracas
Tel: +58(2) 862-54-70
Fax: +58(2) 832-319
Telex: 22721

VIET NAM

UNIVERSITIES

Agricultural University of Bac Thai
[Truòng Dai hoc Nong Nghiep III Bac Thai]
Xa Thinh Dan, Thai Ngueyn, Bac Thai
Tel: +84 564
Founded: 1969

University of Tay Nguyen Buonmathuot
[Truong Dai Hoc Tay Nguyen]
Km 4, Route 14, Buonmathuot, Dak Lak Province
Tel: +84 522-90
Director: Y Ngong Nie Kdam
Deputy Director: Nguyen Khac Chien
Founded: 1977
*F: Fundamental Sciences; Agricultural Sciences;
Forestry; Medical Science.*
*Ce: Applied Computer Sciences; Forestry and
Agriculture.*

University of Can-Tho
[Trùong Dai hoc Câ-Thó]
30 Thang 4 Street, Can-Tho (Cantho Province)
Tel: +84 202-37
Telex: 812539 mekyno vt
Rektor: Tran Phuoc Duong (1989-92)
Vice-Rector: Le The Dong
Founded: 1966
*F: Mathematics and Physics; Chemistry and
Biology; Letters; Foreign Languages; History and
Geography; Agronomy; Water Management and
Land Reclamation; Food Processing Technology;
Animal Husbandry and Veterinary Medicine;
Fishery; Agricultural Economics; Agricultural
Engineering; Medicine.*
*D: Leninist Marxist; Educational Psychology;
Physical Training and Sports.*
*Ce: Biotechnology Research and Development;
Mekong Delta Farming System Research and
Development; Renewable Energy Research;
Electronics and Information Science; Foreign
Languages; Shrimp-Artemia Research and
Development.*
Station: Hoa An Acid Sulfate Soil Experiments.

University of Da Lat
[Trùong Dai hoc Da Lat]
Da Lat, Lam Dong
Tel: +84 7294

University of Technology of Da Nang
[Truóng Dai hoc Bách Khoa Da Nang]
Quant Nam, Da Nang
Tel: +84(51) 2906
Engineering.

Agricultural University of Hànôi
[Trùong Dai hoc Nông nghiêp I Hànôi]
Chau Quy, Gia Lam, Hànôi
Founded: 1956
*F: Agriculture; Animal Husbandry and
Veterinary Medicine; Agricultural Engineering.*

National Economics University Hànôi
[Trùong Dai hoc Kinh tê Quoc Dan]
Duòng Giai Phong, Quan Hai Ba, Hànôi
Rector: Công Tiên Dao
Founded: 1956
*F: Industrial Economics; Agricultural Economics;
Labour Economics; Planning; Statistics.*

Technical University of Hanoi
[Truòng Dai hoc Bách Khoa Hànôi]
Dai Co Viêt, Hànôi
Tel: +84(4) 262-006
Founded: 1955
F: Building Engineering; Electrical Engineering; Electronics; Industrial Chemistry; Food Technology; Metallurgy; Industrial Thermodynamics; Textile Engineering; Industrial Management; Physics and Mathematics.
I: Applied Mechanics and Physics.
Ce: Audio-Visual Languages; Lifelong Education.

Water Resources University Hànôi
[Trùong Dai hoc Thuy loi]
Dong Da, Hànôi
Tel: +84(4) 263-774
Founded: 1947, 1959, 1960
F: Hydraulic Engineering; Electrical Engineering.

Economics University of Hô Chí Minh City
[Trùong Dai hoc Kinh tê Hô Chí Minh]
17 Pham Ngoc Thac, Q, Hô Chí Minh
Tel: +84(8) 234-08
Founded: 1976

Ho Chi Minh City Polytechnic
[Trùong Dai hoc Bách Khoa Thành phó Hô Chí Minh]
268, rue Lý Thùong Kiêt, Q. 10, Hò Chí Minh
Tel: +84(8) 504-84
Telex: 8555 dhbk hcm
Founded: 1957, 1976
F: Correspondence Courses.
S: Mechanical Engineering; Electrical Engineering; Chemistry Engineering; Civil Engineering; Applied Geology; Basic Sciences; Water Resources Engineering; In-Service Training.
Ce: Computer; Essential Oils and Pharmaceuticals; Thermal Power and Renewable Energy; New Materials; Abrasive Powder; Silicate Materials; Polymer and Plastic; Water Supply and Environmemtal Sanitation; Foreign Languages.

Ho Chi Minh Open University
Hò Chín Minh
President: Van Phuong
Founded: 1990
Architecture; Biotechnology; Business; Computer Science; Journalism; Foreign Languages; Law; Music and Art; Computer; Essential Oils and Pharmaceuticals; Rural Development; Social Psychology; Southeast Asian Studies; Women's Studies.

University of Agriculture and Forestry Hò Chí Minh City
[Truòng Dai hoc Nông Làm Thành phó Hò Chí Minh]
Dai Hoc Nòng Làm, Thu Duc, Thành Phó Hò Chí Minh
Tel: +84(8) 966-780
Fax: +84(8) 231-541
Rector: Doàn Văn Diên (1990-94)
Director of International Programmes: Luu Trong Hiêu
Founded: 1985
F: Agriculture; Forestry; Animal Science and Veterinary Medicine; Agricultural Economics; Farm Machinery; Basic Sciences.
D: Fishery.
Ce: Sericulture; Foreign Language.

University of Ho Chi Minh City
[Viên Dai hoc Hô Chí Minh]
3, Công-Trùong Chien-Sï, Hô Chí Minh
Tel: +84(8) 531-93
Rector: Ngoc Giao Nguyen
Founded: 1954
F: Letters and Human Sciences; Exact and Natural Sciences.

Agricultural University of Huê
[Trùong Dai hoc Nong Nghiep II Huê]
24 Phung Hung, Huê
Tel: +84 2535
Founded: 1976

University of Huê
[Vien Dai hoc Huê]
3, Le Loi, Huê
Tel: +84 3290
Rector: Thanh Nguyen
Founded: 1957
F: Letters; Science; Law and Economics.

Vietnam National Institute of Open Learning and Distance Education
Nha B-101 Phuong Bach Khoa, Quan Hai Ba Trung, Hànôi
Director: Nyuyen Kim Truy
Founded: 1957
F: Education, Training and Retraining; Foreign Languages (English, Japanese, French, Chinese); Vocational Training.
Ce: Information; Business Management Training; Social Sciences; Technique and Technology; Internal Combustion Engine Repair; Domestic Electrical Equipment Repair.

Vietnam National University
Thùong Dinh, Dong Da, Hànôi
Tel: +84(4) 244-615
Rector: Nguyen Van Dao
Founded: 1956, 1994
C: General Education; Natural Sciences; Social Sciences and Humanities; Education; Foreign Languages.

OTHER INSTITUTIONS

Nhac Viên Hànôi
O Cho Dua, Hànôi
Tel: +84(4) 42-54969
Founded: 1965
Music.

Nhac Viên Hô Chí Minh
112 Nguyen Du, Q1, Hô Chí Minh
Tel: +84(8) 22748
Founded: 1976
Music.

Trùong Cao dang My thuât công nghiêp
O Cho Dua Dong Da, Hànôi
Tel: +84(4) 42-57364
Founded: 1965
Industrial Arts.

Trùong Dai hoc Duoc Hànôi
13 Le Than Ton, Hànôi
Tel: +84(4) 42-54539
Founded: 1964
Pharmacy.

Trùong Dai hoc Giao thông vân tai
Cau Giay, Hànôi
Tel: +84(4) 42-43311
Founded: 1962
Transport and Communications.

Trùong Dai hoc Kien truc Hànôi
Thanh Xuan, Dong Da, Hànôi
Tel: +84(4) 42-44364
Founded: 1965
Architecture.

Trùong Dai hoc Kien truc Hô Chí Minh
196 Nguyen Thi Minh Khai, Q3, Hô Chí Minh
Tel: +84(8) 22748
Founded: 1976
Architecture.

Trùong Dai hoc Mo Dia chât
Co Nhue, Tu Liem, Hànôi
Founded: 1966
Geology and Mineral Resources.

Trùong Dai hoc My thuât Hànôi
42 Yet kien, Hànôi
Tel: +84(4) 42-57598
Founded: 1957
Fine Arts.

Trùong Dai hoc My thuât Hô Chí Minh
5 Phan Dang Luu, Hô Chí Minh
Founded: 1976
Fine Arts.

Trùong Dai hoc Ngoai Thuong
Lang, Dong Da, Hànôi
Tel: +84(4) 42-43349
Founded: 1965
Foreign Trade.

Trùong Dai hoc Phap ly Hànôi
Duong Lang, Hànôi
Tel: +84(4) 42-43226
Founded: 1975
Law.

Trùong Dai hoc San Khan Dieh Anh
Mai Dich, Tu Liem, Hànôi
Tel: +84(4) 42-43397
Founded: 1976
Theatre and Cinema.

Trùong Dai hoc Su pham Huê
Thua Thien, Huê
Tel: +84 2132
Founded: 1976
Teacher Training.

Trùong Dai hoc Su pham ky Thuat
1-3 Hoang Dieu, Thu Dieu, Thu Duc, Hô Chí Minh
Tel: +84(8) 98641
Founded: 1976
Technical Teacher Training.

Trùong Dai hoc Su pham Ngoai ngu
Cau giay, Tu liem, Hànôi
Tel: +84(4) 42-43356
Founded: 1967
Foreign Languages Teacher Training.

Trùong Dai hoc Su pham Quy Nhon
Binh Dinh, Quy Nhon
Tel: +84 2156
Founded: 1978
Teacher Training.

Trùong Dai hoc Su pham thanh phô Hô Chí Minh
280 An Duong Vuong, Hô Chí Minh
Tel: +84(8) 52020
Founded: 1976
Teacher Training.

Trùong Dai hoc Su pham Viêt Bac
Thai Nguyen, Viêt Bac
Tel: +84 731
Founded: 1966
Teacher Training.

Trùong Dai hoc Su pham Vinh
Nghe Tinh, Vinh
Tel: +84 01 (ext. 4852)
Founded: 1959
Teacher Training.

Trùong Dai hoc Thuong nghiêp
Mai Dich, Tu Liem, Hànôi
Tel: +84(4) 42-432019
Founded: 1965
Commerce.

Trùong Dai hoc van Hoa
103 De La Thanh, Hànôi
Tel: +84(4) 42-55486
Founded: 1977
Culture.

Trùong Dai hoc Xây dung
Duong Giai Phong, Quan Hai Ba, Hànôi
Tel: +84(4) 42-5637
Founded: 1966
Civil Engineering.

Trùong Dai hoc y Duoc Hô Chí Minh
217 Hong Bang, Q5, Hô Chí Minh
Tel: +84(8) 52304
Founded: 1976
Medicine and Pharmacy.

Trùong Dai hoc y Hànôi
Khuong Thuong, Dong Da, Hànôi
Tel: +84(4) 42-63798
Founded: 1955
Medicine.

Trùong Dai hoc y Huê
Thua Thien, Huê
Tel: +84 2173
Founded: 1976
Medicine.

Trùong Dai hoc y Thai Binh
Thai Nguyen, Thai Binh
Tel: +84 704
Founded: 1968
Medicine.

Trùong Dai y Bac Thai
Thai Nguyen, Bac Thai
Tel: +84 588
Founded: 1968
Medicine.

NATIONAL ACADEMIC BODIES

Ministry of Education
49 Dai Co Viêt, Hànôi
Tel: +84(4) 255-441
Fax: +84(4) 252-220
Minister: Tzâr Hông Quân

Vietnamese National Commission for Unesco
8, Khuc Hao Street, Hànôi
Tel: +84(4) 230-697
Fax: +84(4) 230-702
Telex: 411516 nzvt
Cable: ubaunesco hanoi
Chairman: Nguyen Dy Nien
Secretary-General: Le Kinh Tai

WESTERN SAMOA

UNIVERSITIES

The National University of Samoa
[Le Iunivesite Aoao o Samoa]
P.O. box 5768, Apia
Tel: +685 20072
Fax: +685 20938
Cable: ia ao samoa
Vice-Chancellor: Tau'lli Uili (1987-)
Registrar: Faale Tumaalii
Founded: 1984
F: Arts; Science.
L: Computer Training.

University of the South Pacific School of Agriculture
Alafua Campus, Private Mail Bag, Apia
Tel: +685 21671
Fax: +685 22933
Telex: 251 usp sx
Pro Vice-Chancellor: W.A. Pattie
Campus Secretary: Aca Nagatalevu
Founded: 1977
D: Livestock Studies; Agricultural Economics; Crops; Soils.
I: Research, Extension and Training in Agriculture (IRETA).

NATIONAL ACADEMIC BODIES

Department of Education
P.O. Box 201, Apia

YEMEN

UNIVERSITIES

University of Aden
P.O. Box 7039, Al-Mansoor
Tel: +967 82434
Rector: Salim Omer Bukair
Founded: 1975
F: Education; Agriculture; Economics and Administration; Medicine; Technology; Law; Education (Aden, Mukalla, Zingibar).

Sana'a University
P.O. Box 1247, Sana'a
Tel: +967 200514
President: Abdul Aziz S. Al Maghaleh
Founded: 1970
F: Science; Arts; Law and Islamic Law; Commerce and Economics; Education; Medicine; Engineering.
Ce: Languages.

NATIONAL ACADEMIC BODIES

Ministry of Education
P.O.Box 12642, Sana'a
Tel: +967(1) 274-553
Fax: +967(1) 274-558
Telex: 31190
Minister: Abou Baker Al Karbi

Yemeni National Commission for Unesco
Bustan Alkheir, 26 Sep. Street, P.O. Box 12642,
Sana'a
Tel: +967(1) 274-553
Fax: +967(1) 274-156
Telex: 3190 ncesc ye
Chairman: Abou Baker Al Karbi, Minister of
Education
Secretary-General: Ahmed Mohammed Hashim

YUGOSLAVIA

UNIVERSITIES

*University of the Arts Belgrade
[Univerzitet Umetnosti u Beogradu]
Kosancicev venac 29, 11 000 Beograd
Tel: +381(11) 625-166
Fax: +381(11) 629-785
E-Mail: epmfsolåyubgss21.EARN
Rektor: Darinka Matić-Marović
Founded: 1957, 1973
*F: Music; Fine Arts; Applied Arts and Design;
Dramatic Arts.*
I: Theatre, Film, Radio, and Television.

*University of Belgrade
[Univerzitet u Beogradu]
Studentski trg broj 1, 11000 Beograd
Tel: +381(11) 635-153
Rektor: Rajko Vracar
Founded: 1808, 1838, 1863, 1905
*F: Architecture; Veterinary Medicine; Civil
Engineering; Economics; Electrical Engineering;
Mechanical Engineering; Medicine; Agriculture;
Law; Natural Sciences and Mathematics; Mining
and Geology; Technology (Bor); Transport
Engineering; Dentistry; Technology and
Metallurgy; Pharmacy; Philosophy; Physical
Education; Philology; Forestry; Political Science;
Organizational Sciences; Defectology; National
Defence.*
*I: Biological Research; Nuclear Research;
Social Sciences; Physics Research; Chemistry,
Technology, and Metallurgy; Nuclear Energy.*
*Ce: Multidisciplinary Studies; Social Sciences
(International).*

University of Kragujevac
[Univerzitet 'Svetozar Marković' u Kragujevcu]
Trg Avnoja 1, 34 000 Kragujevac
Tel: +381(34) 65-424
Fax: +381(34) 64-500
Founded: 1976
*F: Mechanical Engineering; Economics; Natural
Sciences and Mathematics; Law; Medicine;
Agriculture (Čačku); Technical (Čačku);
Mechanical Engineering (Kraljevo).*
I: Fruit Research (Čačak); Small Grains.

University of Niš
[Univerzitet u Nišu]
Trg bratstva i jedinstva 2, 18 000 Niš
Tel: +381(18) 25-544
Rector: Branimir Djordjević
Founded: 1965
*F: Electronic Engineering; Civil Engineering;
Mechanical Engineering; Medicine; Work
Protection; Technology; Philosophy; Economics;
Law.*
Ce: Lifelong Education.

University of Novi Sad
[Univerzitet u Nova Sadu]
Veljka Vlahovića 3, 21 000 Novi Sad
Tel: +381(21) 611-422
Fax: +381(21) 611-725
Founded: 1960
*F: Agriculture; Natural Sciences and
Mathematics; Economics; Technical Sciences;
Medicine; Law; Technology; Philosophy;
Education (Zrenjanin); Physical Education;
Technical Studies (Zrenjanin).*
A: Arts.

University of Podgorica
[Univerzitet 'Veljko Vlahović' u Podgorica]
Cetinski put 6b, 81000 Podgorica
Tel: +381(81) 52-981
Founded: 1974
*F: Economics; Law; Electrical Engineering;
Mechanical Engineering; Metallurgy; Philosophy
(Nikšić); Maritime (Kotor); Civil Engineering; Fine
Arts (Cetinje); Natural Science.*
*I: History; Agriculture; Biomedicine; Foreign
Languages; Technical Research.*
A: Music.

*University of Priština
[Univerzitet Kosova u Priština]
Vidovdanska b.b., 38 000 Priština, Kosova
Tel: +381 24-970
Fax: +381 27-628
Rector: Ejup Statovci
Founded: 1970
*F: Law; Economics; Medicine; Philology;
Philosophy; Electrotechnics; Machinery; Civil
Engineering and Architecture; Natural Science
and Mathematics; Arts; Physical Culture;
Agriculture; Mining and Metallurgy (Kosovska
Mitrovica).*

Higher S: Economics (Pejë); Technical Studies (Mitrovicë të Titos-Titova Mitrovica, Ferizaj-Uroševac); Pedagogy (Priština, Gjilan, Prizren, Gjakovë).

NATIONAL ACADEMIC BODIES

Federal Ministry of Education and Culture
Palata Federacije, 11 070 Nov Beograd
Tel: +381(11) 222-3943
Fax: +381(11) 602-391
Minister: Slavko Gordić
Founded: 1957

Yougoslav Commission for Cooperation with Unesco
Palata Federacije, 11 070 Beograd
Tel: +381(11) 222-3943
Fax: +381(11) 602-391
Telex: 11448
Cable: jugounesco beograd
President: Punisa Pavlović

ZAIRE

UNIVERSITIES

University of Kinshasa
[Université de Kinshasa]
B.P. 127, Kinshasa XI
Tel: +243(12) 30-123
Telex: 982 23 068
Founded: 1949, 1971, 1981
F: Medicine; Pharmacy; Law; Engineering; Science; Economics.

University of Kisangani
[Université de Kisangani]
B.P. 2012, Kisangani, Haut Zaïre
Tel: +243(12) 2152
Telex: 19
Founded: 1963, 1971, 1981
F: Sciences; Education and Psychology; Medicine; Social, Administrative, and Political Sciences.
I: Applied Social Sciences.
Ce: Development Research.

University of Lubumbashi
[Université de Lubumbashi]
B.P. 1825, Lubumbashi (Shaba)
Tel: +243(22) 5403/
Recteur: Musinde Khanga (1993-)
Founded: 1955, 1971, 1981
F: Letters; Veterinary Medicine; Social, Political, and Administrative Sciences; Polytechnic; Science.

OTHER INSTITUTIONS

Académie des Beaux-Arts
B.P. 8249, Kinshasa
Tel: +243(12) 68476
Fine Arts.

Institut de Formation des Cadres de l'Enseignement primaire
B.P. 711, Kisangani
Founded: 1971
Teacher Training (primary level).

Institut des Bâtiments et des Travaux publics
B.P. 4731, Kinshasa
Founded: 1961
Public Works.

Institut National des Arts
B.P. 8332, Kinshasa
Founded: 1971
Art.

Institut pédagogique national
B.P. 8815, Kinshasa-Binza
Founded: 1961
Teacher Training.

Institut supérieur d'Arts et Métiers
B.P. 15.198, Kinshasa-Gombe
Founded: 1968
Arts and Crafts.

Institut supérieur de Commerce
B.P. 16.596, Kinshasa
Founded: 1964
Commerce.

Institut supérieur de Commerce
B.P. 2012, Kisangani
Founded: 1971
Commerce.

Institut supérieur de Statistique
B.P. 2471, Lubumbashi
Founded: 1967
Statistics.

Institut supérieur des Techniques appliquées
B.P. 6593, Kinshasa
Tel: +243(12) 23592
Founded: 1971
Applied Techniques.

Institut supérieur des Techniques de l'Information
B.P. 14.998, Kinshasa
Tel: +243(12) 25117
Founded: 1971
Computer Science.

Institut supérieur des Techniques médicales
B.P. 774, Kinshasa
Founded: 1971
Medical Techniques.

Institut supérieur d'Etudes agronomiques de Bengamisa
B.P. 202, Kisangani
Founded: 1968
Bengamisa Agronomy.

Institut supérieur d'Etudes agronomiques de Mondongo
B.P. 60, Lisala
Founded: 1972
Mondongo Agronomy.

Institut supérieur d'Etudes sociales
B.P. 2849, Bukavu
Founded: 1971
Social Studies.

Institut supérieur d'Etudes sociales
B.P. 1575, Lubumbashi
Founded: 1971
Social Studies.

Institut supérieur pédagogique
B.P. 854, Bukavu
Founded: 1964
Teacher Training.

Institut supérieur pédagogique
B.P. 340, Bunia
Founded: 1968
Teacher Training.

Institut supérieur pédagogique
B.P. 282, Kananga
Founded: 1966
Teacher Training.

Institut supérieur pédagogique
B.P. 258
Founded: 1966
Teacher Training.

Institut supérieur pédagogique
B.P. 3580, Kinshasa-Gombe
Founded: 1961
Teacher Training.

Institut supérieur pédagogique
B.P. 1514, Kisangani
Founded: 1967
Teacher Training.

Institut supérieur pédagogique
B.P. 1796, Lubumbashi
Founded: 1959
Teacher Training.

Institut supérieur pédagogique
B.P. 116, Mbandaka
Founded: 1971
Teacher Training.

Institut supérieur pédagogique
B.P. 127, Mbanza-Ngungu
Founded: 1971
Teacher Training.

Institut supérieur pédagogique
B.P. 682, Mbuji-Mayi
Founded: 1968
Teacher Training.

Institut supérieur pédagogique technique
B.P. 3287, Kinshasa-Gombe
Founded: 1976
Teacher Training (Technical).

Institut supérieur pédagogique technique
B.P. 75, Likasi
Founded: 1971
Teacher Training (Technical).

NATIONAL ACADEMIC BODIES

Ministry of Primary, Secondary, and Professional Education
[Ministère de l'Enseignement primaire, secondaire et professionnel]
B.P. 14 Kinshasa/Gombe
Tel: +243(12) 33304
Ministre: Sekimonyo Wa Magango

Zaire National Commission for Unesco
[Commission nationale zaïroise pour l'Unesco]
B.P. 14, Kinshasa/Gombe
Tel: +243(12) 3304
Fax: +(871) 150-3261
Président: Sekimonyo Wa Magango, Ministre de l'Education
Secrétaire permanente: Ebale Belotsi Ikete

ZAMBIA

UNIVERSITIES

Copperbelt University
P.O. Box 21692, Kitwe
Tel: +260(1) 212-066
Fax: +260(1) 212-469
Telex: cbu za 53270 kitwe
Cable: cbu kitwe
Vice-Chancellor: G.K. Simwinga (1993-)
Registrar (Acting): A.S. Munyemba
Founded: 1987
S: Business; Environmental Studies; Technology; Wood Science.

*University of Zambia
P.O. Box 32379, Lusaka
Tel: +260(1) 213-221
Fax: +260(1) 253-952
Telex: za 44370
Cable: unza
Vice-Chancellor: Andrew A. Siwela
Registrar (Acting): F.S. Muyunda
Founded: 1965
S: Agricultural Sciences; Education; Engineering; Humanities and Social Sciences; Law; Medicine; Mines; Natural Sciences; Veterinary Medicine; Postgraduate Studies.
I: African Studies; Human Relations.
Ce: Computer; Arts; Continuing Education.

Bureau: *Rural Development Studies; Education Research.*
Ut: *Technology Development and Advisory; In-Service Training.*

LUANSHYA TECHNICAL AND VOCATIONAL TEACHERS' COLLEGE
P.O. Box 90199, Lyanshya
Founded: 1975
Teacher Training (Technical and Vocational).

OTHER INSTITUTIONS

Evelyn Hone-College of Applied Arts and Commerce
P.O. Box 30029, Lusaka
Tel: +260(1) 211-557
Founded: 1963
Applied Arts and Commerce.

Natural Resources Development College
P.O. Box CH99, Lusaka
Founded: 1965
Natural Resources.

Northern Technical College
Millar Road, P.O. Box KJ 250093, Ndola
Tel: +260(2) 86211
Founded: 1964
Technology.

Zambia Air Services Training Institute
P.O. Box CH 198, Lusaka
Tel: +260(1) 271-087
Founded: 1970
Air Services Training.

Zambia Institute of Technology
P.O. Box 21993, Kitwe
Tel: +260 212-243
Founded: 1973
Technology.

NATIONAL ACADEMIC BODIES

Ministry of Education
P.O. Box 50093, Lusaka
Tel: +260(1) 227-636
Fax: +260(1) 222-396
Minister: Alfeyo S. Hambayi

Department for Technical Education and Vocational Training
Birdcage Walk, Private Bag RW 16, Lusaka
Tel: +260(1) 212-716
Cable: zamtec

Zambia National Commission for Unesco
Ministry of Education, P.O. Box 50619, Lusaka
Tel: +260(1) 254-954
Fax: +260(1) 254-954
Chairman: Alfeyo Hambanyi, Minister of Education
Director: W.M. Kaiba

ZIMBABWE

UNIVERSITIES

Africa University
P.O. Box 1320, Mutare
Tel: +263(120) 61611
Vice-Chancellor: J.W.Z. Kurewa (1992-)
Registrar: C.M. Mafarachisi
Founded: 1992
Agriculture and Natural Resources; Theology.

*University of Zimbabwe
P.O. Box MP 167, Mount Pleasant, Harare
Tel: +263(4) 303-211
Fax: +263(4) 732-828
Telex: 26580 univz zw
Cable: university harare
Vice-Chancellor: G.L. Chavunduka (1993-)
Registrar: R.M. Zinyemba
Founded: 1955, 1980
F: *Agriculture; Arts; Commerce; Education; Engineering; Law; Medicine; Science; Social Studies; Veterinary Science.*
I: *Environmental Studies.*

National University of Science and Technology Bulawayo
P.O. Box 346, Bulawayo
Tel: +263(9) 76833
Fax: +263(9) 76804
Vice-Chancellor: P.M. Makhurane (1990-)
Registrar: M.T. Kariwo
Founded: 1991
F: *Engineering Industrial Technology; Applied Science; Commerce; Environmental Sciences; Communication and Information Science; Architecture and Quantity Surveying; Art, Social Studies and Education; Sports Science.*
Ce: *Research and Development.*

OTHER INSTITUTIONS

Bulawayo Technical College
P.O. Box 1392, Bulawayo
Tel: +263(9) 63181
Fax: +263(9) 71165
Director: A. Maboyi Ngube (1990-)
Executive Director: E.R. Nxumalo
Founded: 1961
Hotel and Catering; Engineering; Business and Secretarial Studies; Graphic and Design; Science and Technology; Adult and Continuing Education.

Harare Polytechnic
Causeway, P.O. Box 8074, Harare
Tel: +263(4) 705-951
Director: A. Mandimika (1988-)
Registrar: M.M. Nyahunqzui
Founded: 1927
Mass Communication; Printing; Engineering; Business and Secretarial Studies; Science and Technology; Graphic and Design; Rubber and Plastics Technology; Adult and Continuing Education.

NATIONAL ACADEMIC BODIES

Ministry of Higher Education
Old Mutual Centre, Union Avenue, P.O. Box UA 275, Harare

Tel: +263(4) 700-791
Fax: +263(4) 728-730
Cable: education
Minister: I.S.G. Mudenge (1992-)
Permanent Secretary: J.J. Chitauro
Founded: 1988

National Council for Higher Education
P.O. Box UA 94, Union Avenue, Harare
Tel: +263(4) 796-441
Fax: +263(4) 728-730
Minister: I.S.G. Mudenge (1992-)
Executive Secretary: H.V. Moyana
Founded: 1991

APPENDIX

IAU-INTERNATIONAL ASSOCIATION OF UNIVERSITIES
LIST OF PUBLICATIONS

PERIODICALS

+*Higher Education Policy*
Quarterly Journal
ISSN 0279-4631

MONOGRAPHS: *Issues in Higher Education*
IAU & Pergamon Press
• *Higher Education Policy: An International
Comparative Perspective*
Goedegebuure, Leo et al (eds.)
1993, 348 p.
ISBN 0-08-042-393-0
• *Government and Higher Education
Relationships Across Three Continents:
The Winds of Change*
Neave, Guy & Frans A. van Vught (eds.)

1993, 316 p
ISBN 0-08-042391-4
• *Revitalizing Higher Education*
Salmi, Jamil & Adriaan M. Verspoor (eds.)
1994, 421 p.
ISBN 0-08-041948-8
• *East Asian Higher Education: Traditions
and Transformations*
Yee, Albert H. (ed.)
1995, 213 p.
ISBN 0-08-042385X

REFERENCE WORKS

*International Handbook of Universities
Thirteenth Edition, 1993, x + 1304 pages
ISBN 92-9002-154-3
**World List of Universities and Other
Institutions of Higher Education*
Twentieth Edition, 1995, xii + 876 pages
ISBN 92-9002-159-4
*Universality, Diversity, Interdependence: IAU
1950–1990* (A Commemorative Essay)
Georges Daillant
1990. 209 pages
ISBN 92-9002-153-5
*Collection of Agreements Concerning the
Equivalence of University Qualifications*

1954–1961
Reprinted 1966. vii + 655 pages
ISBN 92-9002-013-X
Reissued 1977 (7 microfiches)
First Supplement to Collection of Agreements
1977. iv + 279 pages (3 microfiches)
ISBN 92-9002-031-8
Second Supplement to Collection of Agreements
1983. iv + 527 pages (6 microfiches).
ISBN 92-9002-039-3
*Documents Concerning the Equivalence of
University Qualifications*
1957. 280 loose leaves (microfilm).

PAPERS OF THE INTERNATIONAL ASSOCIATION OF UNIVERSITIES

International University Co-operation
1969. xvi + 161 pages.
ISBN 92-9002-115-2
*The University and the Needs of Contemporary
Society*
1970. xv + 81 pages.
ISBN 92-9002-116-0
*Problems of Integrated Higher Education – An
International Case Study of the*

Gesamthochschule
1972. 85 pages.
ISBN 92-9002-120-9
*The Social Responsibility of the University in
Asian Countries – Obligations and
Opportunities*
1973. 124 pages.
ISBN 92-9002-122-5
A Critical Approach to Inter-University

+ May be ordered from   Kogan Page, 120 Pentonville Road, London, United Kingdom N1 9JN.
Tel: +44(171) 278-0433. Fax: +44(171) 837-6348. (As from 1996: Elsevier-Pergamon, see below).

* May be ordered from: Macmillan Direct, Houndmills, Basingstoke, United Kingdom RG21
6XS. Tel: +44(1256) 817-245. Fax: +44(1256) 28339, ou Stockton Press, 345 Park Avenue South, 10th
Floor, New York, NY 10010–1707. Tel: +1(800) 221-2123. Fax: +1(212) 689-9711 (Orders from USA
and Canada).

• May be ordered from: Elsevier-Pergamon, The Boulevard, Langford Lane, Oxford, United
Kingdom OX5 1GB. Tel: +44(1865) 794-141. Fax: +44(1865) 843-591.

Co-operation
1974. 138 pages.
ISBN 92-9002-124-1
Differing Types of Higher Education
1977. 86 pages.
ISBN 92-9002-130-6
The Right to Education and Access to Higher Education
1978. 107 pages.
ISBN 92-9002-132-2
The Role of the University in Developing Countries: Its Responsibility Towards the Natural and Cultural Environment
1979. 95 pages.
ISBN 92-9002-133-0
Contemporary Scientific and Technical

Changes: their Impact on the Humanities in University Education
1983. 80 pages.
ISBN 92-9002-140-3
The Future of University Education
1983. 86 pages.
ISBN 92-9002-242-6
Universities and Regional Development
1985. 47 pages.
ISBN 92-9002-144-6
International University Co-operation, a Critical Analysis: Failures, Successes and Perspectives
1989. 103 pages.
ISBN 92-9002-150-0

STUDIES AND REPORTS

The Staffing of Higher Education
1960. 169 pages.
ISBN 92-9002-106-3
Some Economic Aspects of Educational Development in Europe
1961. 144 pages.
ISBN 92-9002-108-X
Formal Programmes of International Co-operation between University Institutions
1960. 39 pages in 4° (published by Unesco).
Report of a Meeting of Heads of African Institutions of Higher Education, Khartoum, 16–19 September 1963.
1964. 107 pages.
ISBN 92-9002-109-8
Report of the International Conference of Universities. Nice. December 1950
1951. 162 pages.
Report of Proceedings. Second General Conference of the International Association of Universities, Istanbul, September 1955
1956. 232 pages.
ISBN 92-9002-101-2
Report of Proceedings. Third General Conference of the International Association of Universities, Mexico. September 1960
1961. 224 Pages.
ISBN 92-9002-107-1
Report of the Fourth General Conference of the International Association of Universities. Tokyo, 31 August – 6 September 1965
1966. 264 pages.
ISBN 92-9002-112-8
Report of the Fifth General Conference of the International Association of Universities. Montreal, 30 August – 5 September, 1970
1971. 291 pages.
ISBN 92-9002-118-7
Report of the Sixth General Conference of the International Association of Universities, Moscow, 19–25 August 1975
1977. 309 pages.
ISBN 92-9002-127-6
Report of the Seventh General Conference of the

International Association of Universities, Manila, 25–30 August 1980
1981. 322 pages.
ISBN 92-9002-137-3
Report of the Eighth General Conference of the International Association of Universities, Los Angeles, 12–17 August 1985
1986. 203 pages.
ISBN 92-9002-146-2
Report of the Ninth General Conference of the International Association of Universities, Helsinki, 5–11 August 1990
1991.
ISBN 92-9002-155-1
Report of the Tenth General Conference of the International Association of Universities, New Delhi, 6-9 February 1995
(in preparation)
Administrative Reports of the International Association of Universities
1951–1954
1955. 40 pages.
ISBN 92–9002-100-4
1955–1959
1960. 58 pages.
ISBN 92-9002-105-5
1960–1964
1965. 129 pages.
ISBN 92-9002-111-X
1965–1969
1970. 117 pages.
ISBN 92-9002-117-9
1970–1974
1975. 113 pages.
ISBN 92-9002-125-X
1975–1979
1980. 104 pages.
ISBN 92-9002-136-5
1980–1984
1985. 78 pages.
ISBN 92-9002-145-4
1985–1989
1990. 83 pages.
ISBN 92-9002-152-7

JOINT UNESCO-IAU RESEARCH PROGRAMME IN HIGHER EDUCATION
(published jointly by Unesco and IAU)

The International Study of University Admissions:
Vol. I: *Access to Higher Education,*
by Frank Bowles. 1963. 212 pages.
Bound: ISBN 92-3-100574-X
Paper: ISBN 92-3-100575-8
Vol. II: National Studies
1965. 648 pages.
ISBN 92-3-100608-8
Higher Education and Development in South-East Asia:
Summary Report
1965. 94 pages.
ISBN 92-3-100543-X
Higher Education and Development in South-East Asia:
Vol. I: *Director's Report,*
by Howard Hayden
1967. 508 pages.
ISBN 92-3-100651-7
Vol. II: *Country Profiles*
1967. 615 pages.
ISBN 92-3-100650-9
Vol. III: Part 1. *High-level manpower for development,*
by Guy Hunter

1967. 184 pages.
ISBN 92-3-100649-5
Part 2. *Language policy and higher education,*
by Richard Noss
1967. 216 pages.
ISBN 92-3-100648-7
Teaching and Learning: An Introduction to New Methods and Resources in Higher Education,
by N. MacKenzie, M. Eraut, H.C. Jones
1970. 209 pages.
ISBN 92-3-100798-X
Second edition, revised. 1976. 224 pages.
ISBN 92-3-100798-X
Lifelong Education and University Resources
(eight case studies)
1978. 193 pages.
ISBN 92-3-101397-1
New Trends and New Responsibilities for Universities in Latin America
1980. 96 pages.
ISBN 92-3-101830-2
Universities and Environmental Education
1986. 127 pages.
ISBN 92-3-102364-0

AIU-ASSOCIATION INTERNATIONALE DES UNIVERSITES PUBLICATIONS

PERIODIQUES

+Higher Education Policy
  Revue trimestrielle
  ISSN 027

MONOGRAPHIES: *Issues in Higher Education*
  IAU & Pergamon Press
• *Higher Education Policy: An International
  Comparative Perspective*
  Goedegebuure, Leo et al (eds.)
  1993, 348 p.
  ISBN 0-08-042-393-0
• *Government and Higher Education Relationship
  Across Three Continents:
  The Winds of Change*
  Neave, Guy & Frans A. van Vught (eds.)

1993, 316 p.
ISBN 0-08-042391-4
• *Revitalizing Higher Education*
  Salmi, Jamil & Adriaan M. Verspoor (eds.)
  1994, 421 p.
  ISBN 0-08-041948-8
• *East Asian Higher Education: Traditions and
  Transformations*
  Yee, Albert H. (ed.)
  1995, 213 p.
  ISBN 0-08-042385X

OUVRAGES DE REFERENCE

International Handbook of Universities
  Treizième édition, 1993, x + 1304 pages
  ISBN 92-9002-154-3
*World List of Universities and Other Institutions
  of Higher Education*
  Vingtième édition, 1995, xii + 876 pages
  ISBN 92-9002-159-4
*Universality, Diversity, Interdependance: IAU
  1950-1990 (A Commemorative Essay)*
  Georges Daillant
  1990. 209 pages
  ISBN 92-9002-153-5
*Recueil d'accords concernant l'équivalence des
  titres universitaires*

1954–1961
Réimprimé en 1966. vii + 655 pages
ISBN 92-9002-013-X
Réédité en 1977 (7 microfiches)
Premier supplément aux Recueils d'accords
  1977. iv + 279 pages (3 microfiches)
  ISBN 92-9002-031-8
Second supplément aux Recueils d'accords
  1983. iv + 527 pages (6 microfiches)
  ISBN 92-9002-039-3
*Documentation concernant les équivalences
  des titres universitaires*
  1957. 280 fiches (sur microfilm).

CAHIERS DE L'ASSOCIATION INTERNATIONALE DES UNIVERSITES

La coopération universitaire internationale
  1969. xvi + 173 pages.
  ISBN 92-9002-215-9
*L'université et les besoins de la société
  contemporaine*
  1970. xv + 83 pages.
  ISBN 92-9002-216-7
*Problèmes d'intégration des enseignements
  supérieurs – Etude internationale de cas sur
  la Gesamthochschule*

1972. 87 pages
ISBN 92-9002-220-5
*La responsabilité sociale de l'Université dans
  les pays d'Asie – ses obligations et ses
  chances*
  1973. 130 pages.
  ISBN 92-9002-222-1
*Une approche critique de la coopération
  interuniversitaire*
  1974. 156 pages.

+ Peuvent être commandés chez: Kogan Page, 120 Pentonville Road, London, United Kingdom N1 9JN.
  Tel: +44(171) 278-0433. Fax: +44(171) 837-6348.(Dès 1996: Elsevier-Pergamon, voir ci-dessous).

* Peuvent être commandés chez: Macmillan Direct, Houndmills, Basingstoke, United Kingdom RG21
  6XS. Tel: +44(1256) 817-245. Fax: +44(1256) 28339, ou Stockton Press, 345 Park Avenue South, 10th
  Floor, New York, NY 10010–1707. Tel: +1(800) 221-2123. Fax: +1(212) 689-9711 (Orders from USA
  and Canada).

• Peuvent être commandés chez: Elsevier-Pergamon, The Boulevard, Langford Lane, Oxford, United
  Kingdom OX5 1GB. Tel: +44(1865) 794-141. Fax: +44(1865) 843-591.

ISBN 92-9002-230-6
Le droit à l'éducation et l'accès à l'enseign-
mement supérieur
1978. 112 pages.
ISBN 92-9002-232-9
Le rôle des universités dans les pays en voie de
développement: ses responsabilités envers
l'environnement naturel et culturel
1979. 94 pages.
ISBN 92-9002-233-7
Les mutations scientifiques et techniques

contemporaines: leurs répercussions sur les
sciences humaines dans la formation
universitaire
1983. 98 pages.
ISBN 92-9002-240-X
L'avenir de la formation universitaire
1983. 96 pages.
ISBN 92-9002-242-6
Les universités et leur développement régional
1984. 49 pages.
ISBN 92-9002-244-2

ETUDES ET RAPPORTS

Le recrutement du personnel d'enseignement
supérieur
1960. 170 pages.
ISBN 92-9002-206-X
Quelques aspects économiques du
développement de l'éducation en Europe
1961. 150 pages.
ISBN 92-9002-208-6
Programmes officiels de coopération
internationale entre institutions universitaires
1960. 41 pages in-4 (publié par l'Unesco).
Rapport de la réunion des chefs d'institutions
d'enseignement supérieur africains,
Khartoum, 16–19 septembre 1963
1964. 113 pages.
ISBN 92-9002-209-4
Rapport de la Conférence internationale des
Universités, Nice, décembre 1950
1951. 164 pages.
Rapport de la Deuxième Conférence générale de
l'Association internationale des Universités,
Istanboul, septembre 1955
1956. 240 pages.
ISBN 92-9002-201-9
Rapport de la Troisième Conférence générale de
l'Associaion internationale des Universités,
Mexico, septembre 1960.
1961. 232 pages.
ISBN 92-9002-207-8
Rapport de la Quatrième Conférence générale
de l'Association internationale des Universités,
Tokyo,31 août-6 septembre 1965
1966. 276 pages.
ISBN 92-9002-212-4
Rapport de la Cinquième Conférence générale
de l'Association internationale des Universités,
Montréal, 30 août–5 septembre 1970
1971. 309 pages.
ISBN 92-902-218-3
Rapport de la Sixième Conférence générale de
l'Association internationale des Universités,
Moscou, 19–25 août 1975
1977. 328 pages.
ISBN 92-9002-227-2
Rapport de la Septième Conférence générale de

l'Association internationale des Universités,
Manille, 25–30 août 1980
1981. 358 pages.
ISBN 92-9002-237-3
Rapport de la Huitième Conférence générale de
l'Association internationale des Universités,
Los Angeles, 12–17 août 1986
1986. 217 pages.
ISBN 92-9002-246-9
Rapport de la Neuvième Conférence générale de
l'Association internationale des Universités,
Helsinki, 5–11 août 1990
1991
ISBN 92-9002-255-8
Rapport de la Dixième Conférence générale
générale de l'Association internationale des
Universités, New Delhi, 6–9 février
(En cours de préparation)
Rapports administratifs de l'Association
internationale des Universités:
1951–1954
1955. 44 pages.
ISBN 92-9002-200-0
1955–1959
1960. 60 pages.
ISBN 92-9002-205-1
1960–1964
1965. 129 pages
ISBN 92-9002-211-6
1965–1969
1970. 121 pages.
ISBN 92-9002-217-5
1970–1974
1975. 119 pages.
ISBN 92-9002-225-6
1975–1979
1980. 109 pages.
ISBN 92-9002-236-1
1980–1984
1985. 82 pages.
ISBN 92-9002-245-0
1985–1989
1985. 87 pages.
ISBN 92-9002-257-3

PROGRAMME CONJOINT UNESCO-AIU D'ETUDES SUR L'ENSEIGNEMENT SU PERIEUR

(publiées conjointement par l'Unesco et l'IAU)

Etude internationale de l'admission à l'université:
Vol. I: *Accès à l'enseignement supérieur,*
par Frank Bowles.
1964. 233 pages.
Relié: ISBN 92-3-200574-3
Broché: ISBN 92-3-200575-1
Vol. II: National studies.
1965. 648 pages.
ISBN 92-3-100608-8
L'enseignement supérieur et le développement en
Asie du Sud-est:
Vol.I: *Rapport du Directeur,*
par Howard Hayden.
1969. 550 pages.
ISBN 92-3-200651-0
Vol. II: Country Profiles
1967. 615 pages.
ISBN 92-3-200650-9
Vol.III: 1ère partie. *Les cadres nécessaires au*
développement,
par Guy Hunter

1969. 204 pages.
ISBN 92-3-200649-9
2ème partie: *Politique linguistique et*
enseignement supérieur,
par Richard Noss
1969.235 pages.
ISBN 92-3-200648-0
Art d'enseigner et art d'apprendre: Introduction
aux méthodes et matériels nouveaux dans
l'enseignement supérieur
par N. MacKenzie, M. Eraut, H.C. Jones
1971. 236 pages.
ISBN 92-3-200789-3
Education permanente et potentiel universitaire
(huit études de cas)
1977. 202 pages.
ISBN 92-3-201397-5
Tendances et responsabilités nouvelles des
universités en Amérique latine
1980. 102 pages.
ISBN 92-3-201830-6

INDEX